OPTICAL RESOLUTION PROCEDURES
for
CHEMICAL COMPOUNDS

VOLUME 2
ACIDS
Part II

OPTICAL RESOLUTION PROCEDURES for CHEMICAL COMPOUNDS

VOLUME 2
ACIDS
Part II

Paul Newman
Manhattan College

The Section on Asymmetric Synthesis by

Spiro Alexandratos
University of Tennessee

A publication of the

OPTICAL RESOLUTION INFORMATION CENTER
Manhattan College
Riverdale, New York 10471

I S B N 0-9601918-2-8
I S B N Set 0-9601918-3-6

Library of Congress Catalog Card Number
78-61452

Distributed by: Optical Resolution Information Center
Manhattan College
Riverdale, New York 10471

CONTENTS

Permissions		v
List of Journals		vii
Acknowledgments		viii
Dedication		x
Introduction		1
Section 1.	RESOLVING AGENTS FOR ACIDS	5
Section 2.	CLASSICAL CHEMICAL METHODS FOR THE OPTICAL RESOLUTION OF ACIDS (including LACTONES)	23
	Addendum	819
Section 3.	OPTICAL RESOLUTION OF ACIDS BY CHROMATOGRAPHIC METHODS	873
	– Gas Liquid Chromatography on Chiral Phases – Gas Liquid Chromatography on Achiral Phases – Liquid Chromatography on Chiral Phases – Liquid Chromatography on Achiral Phases	
Section 4.	ADDITIONAL METHODS FOR THE OPTICAL RESOLUTION OF ACIDS (especially α-amino acids)	1057
	A. Preferential Crystallization Methods or Resolution by Entrainment	1058
	B. Enzymatic Methods	1065
Section 5.	METHODS FOR DETERMINING OPTICAL PURITY A Categorical List of References	1075
Section 6.	THE ASYMMETRIC SYNTHESIS OF CARBOXYLIC ACIDS	1080
Section 7.	REFERENCE LIST	1121

Aus der Mutterlauge schieden sich nach dem Einengen und Zusatz von Äther 11,3 g eines Gemisches ab, das zum größten Teil amorph war. Weiteres Einengen der Mutterlauge und Zusatz von Äther ergab eine braune ölige Fällung, die sich nicht kristallisieren ließ. Ausbeute etwa 6 g öliger Rückstand [N-Methyl-chininium-(+)-vinylbital].

2. Gewinnung der Vinylbital-Antipoden aus den diastereomeren N-Methyl-chininium-salzen

2.1. (—)-Vinylbital

6,0 g des Salzes vom Schmp. 218° wurden in wenig heißem Methanol gelöst und die Lösung mit 2 n H_2SO_4 und Wasser versetzt. Dabei fiel ein farbloses Öl aus, das innerhalb von 3 Tagen durchkristallisierte. Ausbeute: 1,1 g, Schmp. 94°.

$C_{11}H_{16}N_2O_3$ (224,3)	Ber.:	C 58,90	H 7,19
	Gef.:	C 58,76	H 7,01

Spezifische Drehung (s. Tab. 2)

a) Messung im Polarimeter mit visueller Ablesung:

α_D — 0,40°, c = 4,275, 1 dm Rohr, t = 20°, abs. Äthanol.

b) Messung im lichtelektrischen Präzisionspolarimeter:

c = 2,64, 1 dm Rohr, t = 20°, abs. Äthanol.

α_{578} — 0,265°, α_{546} — 0,300°, α_{436} — 0,485°, α_{405} — 0,570°, α_{365} — 0,750°.

2.2. (+)-Vinylbital

6 g des öligen diastereomeren Salzes wurden in wenig Methanol gelöst, mit 2 n H_2SO_4 und Wasser versetzt und anschließend die getrübte Lösung mehrmals mit Äther ausgeschüttelt. Die ätherische Phase wurde getrocknet und vom Lösungsmittel befreit. Es blieb ein farbloses Öl zurück, das nach 20 Tagen durchkristallisiert war. Ausbeute: 1,9 g, Schmp. 94°.

$C_{11}H_{16}N_2O_3$ (224,3)	Ber.:	C 58,90	H 7,19
	Gef.:	C 58,90	H 7,04

Spezifische Drehung (s. Tab. 2)

a) Messung im Polarimeter mit visueller Ablesung:

α_D + 0,32°, c = 3,460, 1 dm Rohr, t = 20°, abs. Äthanol.

b) Messung im lichtelektrischen Präzisionspolarimeter:

c = 2,62, 1 dm Rohr, t = 20°, abs. Äthanol.

α_{578} + 0,260°, α_{546} + 0,295°, α_{436} + 0,495°, α_{405} + 0,590°, α_{365} + 0,705°.

Tabelle 2

Spezifische Drehung der Pentobarbital- und der Vinylbital-Antipoden in abs. Äthanol

$[\alpha]^{20}_{nm}$	(—)-Vinylbital	(+)-Vinylbital
589*)	— 9,4°	+ 9,3°
589**)	— 9,6°	+ 9,6°
578	— 10,0°	+ 10,0°
546	— 11,4°	+ 11,3°
436	— 18,4°	+ 18,9°
405	— 21,6°	+ 22,5°
365	— 28,4°	+ 27,0°

*) Messung im Polarimeter mit visueller Ablesung.

**) Errechnet durch Extrapolation aus $[\alpha]^{20}_{578}$ und $[\alpha]^{20}_{546}$ (s. Versuchsteil V).

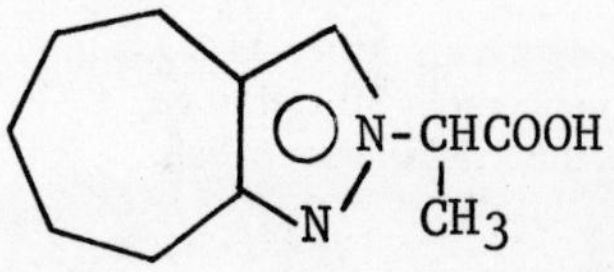

$C_{11}H_{16}N_2O_2$ Ref. 838

D(*R*) (−)*α-(Cycloheptapyrazolyl-2)propionic acid.* 12.5 g (0.060 mol) of Vc and 10.0 g (0.060 mol) (−)-ephedrine were dissolved in 780 ml of boiling ethyl acetate. After one night in a refrigerator the salt was filtered off and recrystallized several times from ethyl acetate. Acid was liberated from 0.10 g salt after each recrystallization and the optical activity was determined in chloroform. The results are given in Table 1.

Table 1.

Crystallization	Ethyl acetate (ml)	Salt obtained (g)	$[\alpha]_D^{25}$ of the acid (°)
1	780	12.5	−16
2	250	10.3	−27
3	180	8.8	−31
4	150	7.1	−37
5	130	6.0	−40
6	85	5.1	−45
7	65	4.3	−46
8	50	3.8	−45
9	50	3.2	−45

The acid was liberated from its (−)-ephedrine salt by adding 2 M sodium hydroxide. After extraction with chloroform the water phase was acidified to pH 3.5 with concentrated hydrochloric acid. The product was recrystallized from ethanol−water (2:1) and dried over phosphorus pentoxide in vacuum. 1.1 g of Vc was obtained with m.p. 177−178.5 °C. The optical activity of (−)Vc in some different solvents is given in Table 2.

L(+)*-α-(Cycloheptapyrazolyl-2) propionic acid.* The mother liquor from the first crystallization

Table 3.

Crystallization	Ethyl acetate (ml)	Salt obtained (g)	$[\alpha]_D^{25}$ of the acid (°)
1	130	7.8	+24
2	120	6.6	+28
3	120	5.8	+30
4	120	5.1	+35
5	160	4.4	+37
6	190	3.7	+41
7	120	2.7	+42
8	160	2.2	+43
9	210	1.3	+42

was evaporated to dryness. 10.5 g salt was isolated from which the acid was liberated as described earlier. 4.6 g acid with $[\alpha]_D^{25} = +17°$ was obtained. This acid (0.022 mol) and 3.77 g (0.022 mol) (−)-α-(*β*-naphthyl)ethylamine [19] were dissolved in 130 ml of boiling ethyl acetate and the salt allowed to crystallize in a refrigerator. After nine recrystallizations the optical activity remained constant. The course of the resolution is given in Table 3. The acid was then liberated and recrystallized from ethanol−water (2:1). 0.50 g acid in white glistening crystals was obtained with m.p. 178−180 °C. $[\alpha]_D^{25} = +46.9°$ (*c* 0.398).

19. Fredga, A., Sjöberg, B. and Sandberg, R. *Acta Chem. Scand. 11* (1957) 1609.

Table 2. The optical activity of (−)Vc in some different solvents. g = gram acid dissolved in the solvent to 10.0 ml

Solvent	$[\alpha]_D^{25}$ (°)	$[\alpha]_{365}^{25}$ (°)	g acid
Dimethyl formamide	+11.8	+33.8	0.0801
Glacial acetic acid	+1.5	+7.4	0.0830
Dimethyl sulphoxide	−0.4	−5.4	0.0790
Methanol	−7.5	−31.9	0.0800
Ethanol (abs.)	−11.8	−45.6	0.0811
Chloroform	−46.5	−156	0.0400

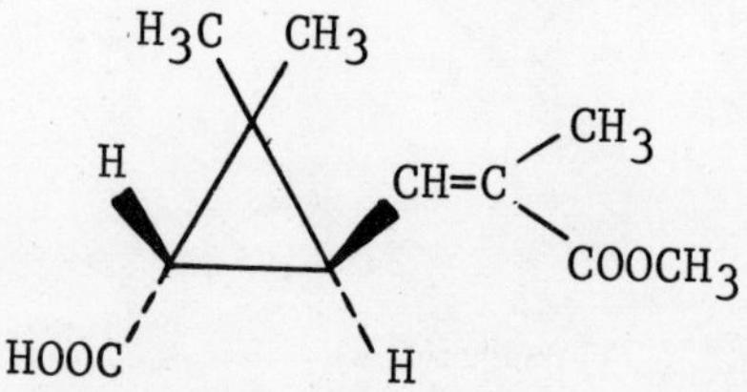

$C_{11}H_{16}O_4$ Ref. 839

10) Optical Resolution of (±)-*trans*-Pyrethric Acid.

Quinine (2.77 g) and water (2 ml) was added to (±)-*trans*-pyrethric acid (1.81 g) in acetone (13 ml). This solution was kept in a refrigerator for 15 hours and crystals of quinine salt were filtered. 2.1 g. M.p. 159∼169°C. Mother liquor was concentrated to 10 ml and 1.4 g of crystals was obtained. M.p. 157°C. The first crystals were recrystallized from acetone–water (8 : 2) and 0.8 g of crystals was obtained. M.p. 166∼167°C. The second crystals were recrystallized from acetone–water (5 : 1) and 0.3 g of crystals was obtained. M.p. 166∼167°C. These crystals were combined and recrystallized from acetone which contained 15% of water. Yield 0.35 g. M.p. 171°C. $[\alpha]_D^{24}$−92.1° (c, 1.78 in methanol). Recrystallization of this salt from acetone–water (5 : 1, 5 ml) afforded pure quinine salt of (+)-*trans*-pyrethric acid (0.24 g). M.p. 171°C. $[\alpha]_D^{24}$−92.4° (C, 1.58 in methanol). Decomposition of the quinine salt with diluted hydrochloric acid gave optically pure (+)-*trans*-pyrethric acid (0.1 g). λ_{max} 237 mμ. $[\alpha]_D^{24}$+89.3° (c, 1.90 in carbon tetrachloride).

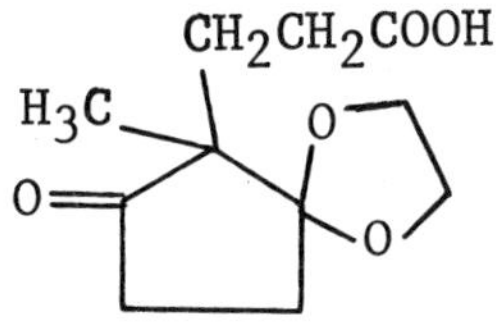

$C_{11}H_{16}O_5$ **Ref. 840**

a. *Formation du sel de cinchonine de l'acide 3-(1'-méthyl 2',2'-éthylènedioxy 5'-oxo cyclopentyl)propionique, V.*

Dans 180 cm³ d'éthanol, on introduit 11,6 g de cinchonine base, agite quinze minutes à température ambiante, puis porte au reflux sous agitation et introduit 10 g d'acide dl 3-(1'-méthyl 2',2'-éthylènedioxy 5'-oxo cyclopentyl)propionique. On agite dix minutes en maintenant au reflux, puis élimine 80 cm³ d'éthanol par distillation. On amène le mélange réactionnel à 20 °C, agite pendant une heure à cette température, puis abaisse la température du milieu réactionnel à une température comprise entre 0 et +5 °C et agite pendant deux heures à cette température. On laisse ensuite quinze heures au repos en maintenant cette température. On sépare le précipité formé par filtration, le lave à l'éthanol froid et obtient 15,4 g de sel de d-cinchonine brut $[\alpha]_D^{20} = +119°$ (c = 1 %, éthanol) qui est purifié par recristallisation dans l'éthanol. On obtient ainsi le sel dextrogyre de cinchonine de l'acide 3-(1'-méthyl 2',2'-éthylènedioxy 5'-oxo cyclopentyl)propionique, F = 186°, $[\alpha]^{20} = +127,5$ °C (c = 1 %, méthanol).

Dichroïsme circulaire (éthanol) :
à 295 mμ, $\Delta\varepsilon = +1,25$.

A la connaissance de la Société demanderesse, ce produit n'est pas décrit dans la littérature.

b. *Isolement de l'acide d-3-(1'-méthyl 2',2'-éthylènedioxy 5'-oxo cyclopentyl)propionique, VA.*

Dans 25 cm³ d'eau, on met en suspension 5 g de sel dextrogyre de cinchonine de l'acide 3-(1'-méthyl 2',2'-éthylènedioxy 5'-oxo cyclopentyl)-propionique, puis ajoute goutte à goutte sous agitation, 1,13 cm³ de solution aqueuse 10,7N d'ammoniaque. On agite trente minutes à température ambiante, élimine l'insoluble par filtration, sature le filtrat obtenu par du chlorure de sodium et acidifie à pH 4,0 par une solution aqueuse de sulfate acide de potassium. La phase aqueuse est extraite à l'éther, les solutions éthérées sont réunies, on lave la solution organique obtenue par une solution aqueuse saturée de chlorure de sodium, puis la sèche et la concentre à sec. Le résidu est purifié par cristallisation dans un mélange d'éther isopropylique et d'hexane et l'on obtient acide d 3-(1'-méthyl 2',2'-éthylènedioxy 5'-oxo cyclopentyl)propionique, F = 70-71 °C, $[\alpha]_D^{20} = +9,3$ (c = 1,1 %, dioxane).

Dichroïsme circulaire (éthanol) :
à 302 mμ, $\Delta\varepsilon = +0,58$.

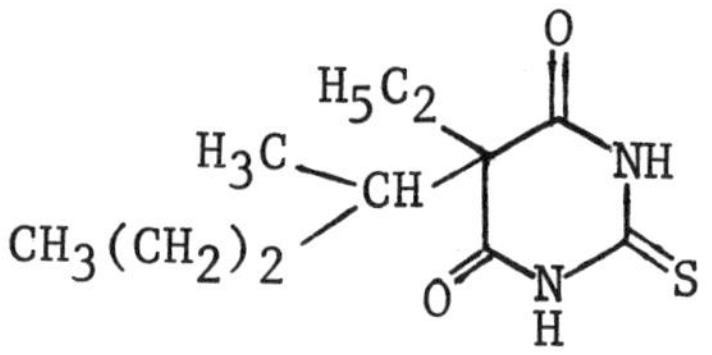

$C_{11}H_{18}N_2O_2S$ **Ref. 841**

Beschreibung der Versuche

1. Gewinnung von (+)-Thiopental (III)

14,85 g Thiopental wurden in 245,0 ml titrierter methanol. N-Methylchininiumhydroxid-lösung[2]) gelöst und etwa 1750 ml Äther allmählich zugegeben, wobei innerhalb 24 Std. 3,5 g Kristalle anfielen. Nach Zusatz von weiteren 1000 ml Äther fielen innerhalb 48 Std. nochmals 8 g Kristalle an. Nach Umkristallisation aus Methanol/Äther wurden 6,3 g N-Methyl-chininium-(+)-thiopental erhalten, Schmp. nach Trocknen i. Vak. 134°.

$C_{32}H_{44}N_4O_4S$ (580,7)	Ber.:	C 66,18	H 7,64
	Gef.:	C 66,02	H 7,62

6,3 g des Salzes vom Schmp. 134° wurden in Methanol gelöst, mit 2 n H_2SO_4 versetzt und die Lösung ausgeäthert. Nach Kristallisation aus wenig Methanol, das bis zur Trübung mit 2 n H_2SO_4 versetzt wurde, fielen 2,6 g (+)-Thiopental, Schmp. 152—153°, an. Ausbeute 35% d. Th. (ber. auf Thiopental).

$C_{11}H_{18}N_2O_2S$ (242,3)	Ber.:	C 54,53	H 7,49
	Gef.:	C 54,72	H 7,72

Spezifische Drehung

c = 5,10, 1 dm Rohr, t = 20°, abs. Äthanol.

$\alpha_{578} = +0,290°$	$[\alpha]_{578}^{20} = +5,69°$
$\alpha_{546} = +0,335°$	$[\alpha]_{546}^{20} = +6,57°$
$\alpha_{436} = +0,510°$	$[\alpha]_{436}^{20} = +10,00°$

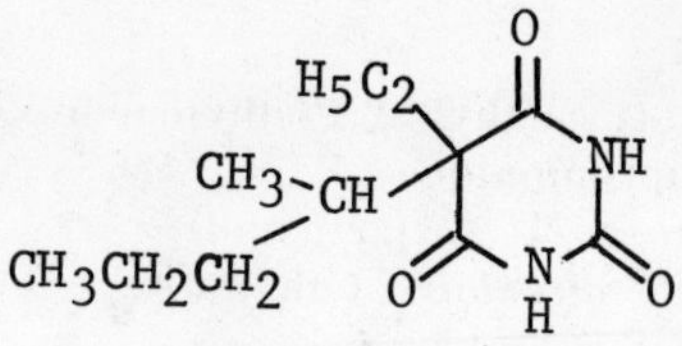

$C_{11}H_{18}N_2O_3$ Ref. 842

Resolution of *dl*-5-Ethyl-5(2′-pentyl)barbituric Acid (Pentobarbital).—*dl*-Pentobarbital (168 g, 0.74 mol) was converted to its N-methylquininium salt according to the method of Knabe and Philipson.[5] Twelve recrystallizations of this salt from a methanol and ethyl acetate mixture followed by regeneration of the acid from the separated N-methylquininium salt of (−)-pentobarbital gave 2.8 g (3%) of IIa purified by sublimation, mp 121–121.5°, $[\alpha]^{24}D$ −13.38° (*c* 2.38, absolute ethanol); lit.[5] mp 128°, $[\alpha]^{20}D$ −3.5° (*c* 1.83, absolute ethanol).

(5) J. Knabe and K. Philipson, Arch. Pharm. (Weinheim), 299, 231 (1966).

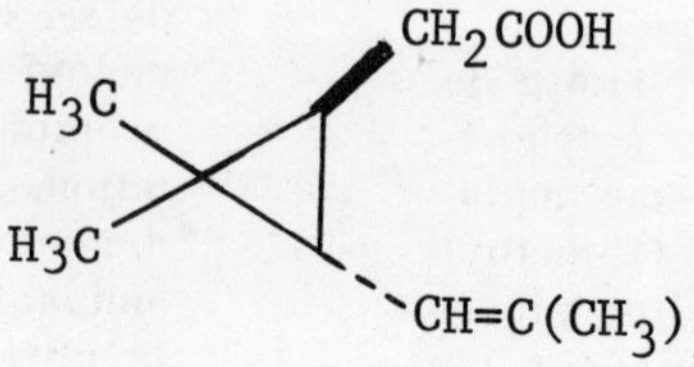

$C_{11}H_{18}O_2$ Ref. 843

Resolution of (±)-trans-*Homochrysanthemic Acid*.[11]—Quinine trihydrate (37·8 g.) in warm ethanol (40 ml.) was added to (±)-*trans*-homochrysanthemic acid (18 g.) in ethanol (25 ml.) and kept at 20° for 48 hr. Filtration gave the impure quinine salt of (−)-*trans*-homochrysanthemic acid and this, when crystallised seven times from aqueous ethanol (1 : 1), gave a salt, m. p. 106—107°, $[\alpha]_D^{20}$ −118° (*c* 1·98). On decomposition with hydrochloric acid this gave (−)-*trans*-homochrysanthemic acid (XIII) (1·5 g.), b. p. 91—96°/0·05 mm., n_D^{19} 1·4705, $[\alpha]_D^{18}$ −30·6° ± 0·6° (*c* 2·94).

Water (25 ml.) was added to the filtrate from which the (−)-*trans*-salt had initially crystallised. After 1 hr. at 0° an optically impure salt of the (+)-*trans*-acid (17·7 g.) separated {m. p. 69—87°, $[\alpha]_D^{20}$ −74·3° (*c* 3·55)}. Decomposition gave optically impure (+)-*trans*-homochrysanthemic acid (6·8 g.).

(−)-α-Methylbenzylamine (4·7 g.), b. p. 74°/15 mm., $[\alpha]_D^{20}$ −36·57°, was added to a suspension of this acid in water–ethanol (30 ml.; 3 : 2). On storage at 20° the impure (−)-base (+)-*trans*-acid salt (8·2 g.), m. p. 110—115°, $[\alpha]_D^{19}$ −12·0°, separated and was crystallised five times from water–ethanol (3 : 2) to give the pure salt, m. p. 123—124°, $[\alpha]_D^{21}$ +9·5° (*c* 0·22). On decomposition, (+)-*trans*-homochrysanthemic acid (XIV) (0·99 g.), b. p. 97—100°/0·05 mm., n_D^{19} 1·4710, $[\alpha]_D^{20}$ +30·0° ± 0·4° (*c* 2·15), was obtained. Equal weights of (+)- and (−)-*trans*-homochrysanthemic acid were mixed: the mixture solidified: one crystallisation from light petroleum gave the (±)-*trans* acid, m. p. and mixed m. p. 80—81° {lit.,[11] for (−)-*trans*-homochrysanthemic acid, b. p. 107°/3 mm., $[\alpha]_D^{16}$ −23·3° (*c* 3·00), n_D^{20} 1·4718, and for the (+)-*trans*-form, b. p. 114°/3·5 mm., $[\alpha]_D^{16}$ +23·8° (*c* 2·94), n_D^{20} 1·4718}. The less soluble quinine salt is reported [11] to give the (+)-acid.

[11] Katsuda and Chikamoto, *Bull. Agric. Chem. Soc. Japan*, 1958, **22**, 330.

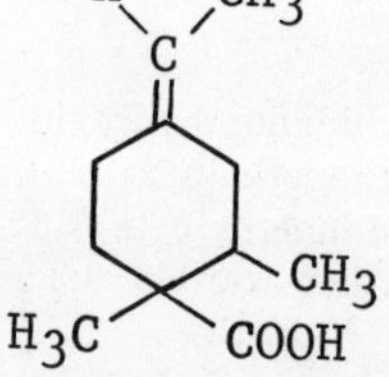

$C_{11}H_{18}O_2$ Ref. 844

Resolution of (±)-Integerrinecic Acid Lactone.—The racemate (198 mg.) and brucine (394 mg.) were dissolved in ethanol (5 ml.). Cooling gave crystals (307 mg.) which were filtered and recrystallized from ethanol to give essentially pure brucine salt of (+)-integerrinecic acid lactone (255 mg.) as needles, m.p. 233°. Further recrystallization raised the melting point to 236°.

Anal. Calcd. for $C_{10}H_{14}O_4 \cdot C_{23}H_{26}O_4N_2$: N, 4.7. Found: N, 4.7.

The mother liquors gave no additional crystals on concentration so the ethanol was removed and the residue taken up in acetone. Addition of ether precipitated a solid (273 mg.), m.p. 211–215°. Two recrystallizations from acetone gave the brucine salt of (−)-integerrinecic acid as prisms, m.p. 221–222°.

Anal. Calcd. for $C_{10}H_{14}O_4 \cdot C_{23}H_{26}O_4N_2$: C, 66.9; H, 6.8; N, 4.7. Found: C, 66.7; H, 6.8; N, 5.3.

The brucine salt of m.p. 236° was dissolved in dilute sulfuric acid and the solution extracted with ether. Evaporation of the extract and crystallization of the residue from benzene gave (+)-integerrinecic acid lactone as needles, m.p. 153°, $[\alpha]^{25}D$ + 40° (*c*, 0.94, ethanol).

Anal. Calcd. for $C_{10}H_{14}O_4$: C, 60.6; H, 7.1. Found: C, 60.8; H, 7.3.

The lactone derived from natural integerrinecic acid or senecic acid has m.p. 154°, $[\alpha]D$ + 39° (ethanol). A mixture of the lactone obtained from senecic acid and the synthetic (+)-lactone melted undepressed.

The second brucine salt, m.p. 221–222°, was treated similarly and the derived acid lactone crystallized from benzene to give (−)-integerrinecic acid lactone as fine needles, m.p. 153°, $[\alpha]^{25}D$ −40° (*c* 1.20, ethanol).

Anal. Calcd. for $C_{10}H_{14}O_4$: C, 60.6; H, 7.1. Found: C, 60.6; H, 7.1.

Equal weights of this compound and the (+)-lactone from senecic acid were dissolved in hot benzene and cooled to give needles of the racemic lactone, m.p. 142°, undepressed on admixture with the synthetic (±)-integerrinecic acid lactone.

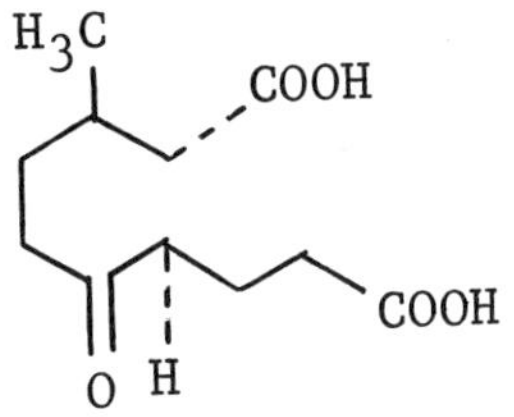

$C_{11}H_{18}O_5$ Ref. 845

B. *Optisch aktive Verbindungen*

Darstellung der beiden optisch aktiven 8-Methyl-trans-hydrindanol-(4)-one-(1) (X)

Racemattrennung mit 2 Mol Brucin und Isolierung der (+)-Säure: Die siedende Lösung von 10 g *racem. Ketodicarbonsäure Va* in 250 ccm Chloroform wurde mit einer Lösung von 18.92 g *Brucin-dihydrat* in 250 ccm Aceton versetzt. Man engte bis zur beginnenden Kristallisation ein (auf ca. 350 ccm) und ließ erkalten. Anschließend wurde das ausgefallene Brucinsalz, 12.32 g, abfiltriert. Durch weiteres Einengen konnten nochmals 1.74 g Salz abgetrennt werden. Somit waren insgesamt 14.06 g *Brucinsalz* gewonnen worden, Schmp. 218–219° (Kofler-Heizmikroskop).

Das Brucinsalz löste man in 200 ccm Chloroform und versetzte mit der gleichen Menge Aceton. Dann wurde bis zur beginnenden Kristallisation eingedampft und das nach dem Erkalten ausgefallene Produkt abfiltriert; 10.1 g Brucinsalz, Schmp. 220–222°. Eine kleine Probe kristallisierte man in dieser Weise noch zweimal um, Schmp. 222–224°.

$C_{34}H_{42}N_2O_9$ (622.7) Ber. C 65.58 H 6.80 N 4.50 Gef. C 65.85 H 6.77 N 4.57

Spaltung des krist. Brucinsalzes: Die Lösung von 10.1 g krist. Brucinsalz (Schmp. 220–222°), in 250 ccm $CHCl_3$ gelöst, wurde auf eine mit saurem Kieselgel (*n* HCl; 70 Min. bei 120° getrocknet) beschickte Säule (Höhe 42 cm, ⌀ 4.5 cm) gegeben; anschließend wurde mit etwa 3–4 *l* eines Gemisches aus 80 % Benzol (wasserhaltig) und 20 % Aceton eluiert. Nach dem Abdampfen des Lösungsmittels verblieb ein schwach bräunliches Öl, das man in 50–70 ccm Äther aufnahm und bis zur beginnenden Trübung mit Petroläther versetzte. Nach Reiben an der Gefäßwand mit einem Glasstab kristallisierte die Säure in weißen Nadeln, 2.98 g, Schmp. 101–103°, nach zweimaligem Umkristallisieren aus Äther/Petroläther: Schmp. 107–109°. $[\alpha]_D^{20}$: +16.0° (*c* = 1.01, in CH_2Cl_2).

$C_{11}H_{16}O_5$ (228.2) Ber. C 57.88 H 7.07 Gef. C 57.49 H 7.20

Racemattrennung mit 1 Mol Brucin und Isolierung der (–)-Säure: 20 g *racem. Ketodicarbonsäure Va* (Schmp. 129–131°) und 20.8 g *Brucin-dihydrat* löste man in je 250 ccm Aceton, vereinigte beide Lösungen und dampfte bis auf ca. 200 ccm ein. Dabei fiel bereits ein großer Teil des krist. Brucinsalzes aus. Nach dem Aufbewahren über Nacht im Tiefkühlschrank konnten 27.83 g (+)-Brucinsalz isoliert und abgetrennt werden. Um die letzten Reste des noch in Lösung befindlichen Brucinsalzes zu entfernen, wurde die Lösung bis zur starken Trübung mit Äther versetzt und unter Verschluß eine Weile kräftig durchgeschüttelt. Den ausfallenden Niederschlag filtrierte man ab. Das Filtrat mit der gewünschten (–)-Säure wurde eingeengt und über eine mit neutralem Kieselgel (3 Stdn. bei 140° getrocknet) beschickte Säule (⌀ 4.5 cm; Länge 12 cm) filtriert, wobei mit 1000 ccm eines Gemisches aus 80 % Benzol und 20 % Aceton eluiert wurde. Nach dem Eindampfen des Filtrats verblieben 9.1 g farbloses Öl, das man in Äther aufnahm und mit Petroläther bis zur beginnenden Trübung versetzte. Nach dem Reiben an der Gefäßwand und Animpfen kristallisierte das Produkt rasch durch.

Es konnten auf diese Weise 6.5 g *krist. (–)-Säure* gewonnen werden. $[\alpha]_D^{20}$: –15.8° (*c* = 1.01, in CH_2Cl_2).

Eine Probe wurde zweimal aus Äther/Petroläther umkristallisiert. $[\alpha]_D^{20}$: –16.0° (*c* = 1.0, in CH_2Cl_2), Schmp. 103–106°.

$C_{11}H_{16}O_5$ (228.2) Ber. C 57.88 H 7.07 Gef. C 57.64 H 6.95

```
           CN
           |
CH3(CH2)5-C-COOH
           |
           C2H5
```

$C_{11}H_{19}NO_2$ Ref. 846

Note:

The acid was resolved with quinine using methanol/H_2O as solvent, to obtain the (+)-enantiomer, b.p. 148-150/1.5 mm., $[\alpha]_D$ +2.5° and with codeine using methanol/H_2O as solvent, to obtain the (-)-enantiomer, b.p. 142-143/1.1 mm. $[\alpha]_D$ -2.6°.

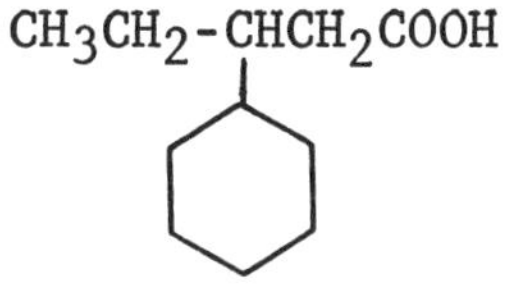

$C_{11}H_{20}O_2$ Ref. 847

Resolution of 3-Cyclohexylvaleric Acid-5—The inactive acid was prepared from ethylcyclohexylbromomethane and ethyl malonate.

The inactive acid was resolved by recrystallizing its quinine

salt from acetone as described for 2-cyclohexylbutyric acid-4. B. p. 148° at 4 mm. Yield 10 gm. $D^{27}_{4} = 0.996$.

$$[\alpha]^{27}_{D} = \frac{-1.37°}{1 \times 0.996} = -1.38°; [M]^{27}_{D} = -2.54° \text{ (homogeneous)}$$

4.689 mg. substance: 12.355 mg. CO_2 and 4.520 mg. H_2O

$C_{11}H_{20}O_2$.	Calculated.	C 71.7, H 11.0
184.16	Found.	" 71.8, " 10.8

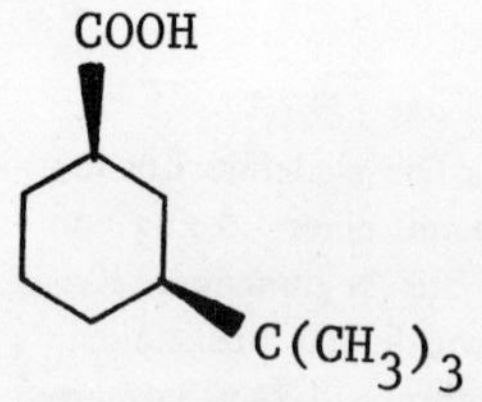

$C_{11}H_{20}O_2$ Ref. 848

Resolution of *dl-cis*-3-*t*-Butylcyclohexanecarboxylic Acid. Commercial *l*-menthol was converted[36] to *l*-menthylamine hydrochloride, $[\alpha]^{20}D$ −37.2° (*c* 2, water) (lit.[35] $[\alpha]^{15}D$ −35.8°), *via l*-menthone and its oxime. The salt formed by the reaction of 25.8 g of racemic acid with 26.85 g of *l*-menthylamine hydrochloride precipitated from aqueous solution. It was collected, dried, and fractionally crystallized from acetone until a less soluble salt of constant melting point and rotation (mp 168–170°, $[\alpha]^{25}D$ −13.3° (*c* 1.6, absolute ethanol)) and a more soluble salt (mp 125–128°, $[\alpha]^{25}D$ −29.7° (*c* 1.6, absolute ethanol)) were obtained. Neutralization of the former with hydrochloric acid gave an acid which was recrystallized from heptane, 1.9 g, mp 93–94°, $[\alpha]^{25}D$ +21.1° (*c* 1.6, $CHCl_3$). Two recrystallizations from heptane of the acid obtained by acidification of the lower melting salt gave 0.7 g of acid, mp 91–93°, $[\alpha]^{25}D$ −19.1° (*c* 1.6, $CHCl_3$).

(34) J. Sicher, F. Sipos, and M. Tichy, *Collection Czech. Chem. Commun.*, **26**, 847 (1961).
(35) M. Tichy, J. Jonas, and J. Sicher, *ibid.*, **24**, 3434 (1959).
(36) J. Read and G. J. Robertson, *J. Chem. Soc.*, 2209 (1926).

$CH_2{=}CH(CH_2)_6{-}CH_2{-}CH(OH){-}COOH$

$C_{11}H_{20}O_3$ Ref. 849

2L-Hydroxyundec-10-enoic acid (VIII). 32.5 g (0.16 mol) of (VI) was dissolved in 150 ml of dry ether and 19.7 g (0.16 mol) (−)-α-phenethylamine dissolved in 450 ml of light petroleum (b.p. 60–85°). The solutions were mixed and set for crystallization at +4° overnight. 21.6 g of salt crystals was obtained in the form of large colourless plates. A second crop of crystals (16.7 g) was obtained, when the mother liquor dissolved in 200 ml of an ether:light petroleum (7.5:92.5 v/v) mixture was allowed to crystallize at +4°. The course of resolution was followed by TLC of the corresponding amides after each crystallization, as previously described. The combined crops of crystals (38.3 g) were then recrystallized successively from 400 ml of ether:light petroleum (1:10 v/v), 560 ml of ether:light petroleum (1:1 v/v), 1000 ml of ether:light petroleum (3:1 v/v), 1000 ml of ether, 1100 ml of ether, and finally from 1400 ml of ether. After seven crystallizations, 7.9 g of salt (mother liquor 1.8 g) was obtained. The corresponding amides appeared optically pure when tested, using the TLC technique.

Decomposition of the salt with hydrochloric acid in water (1:3 v/v) followed by extraction with ether afforded 4.9 g of 2L-hydroxyundec-10-enoic acid. The acid isolated from the mother liquor (0.7 g) of m.p. 64.9–65.5° showed the same optical rotation. α_D^{25} −0.051° (pyridine, *l* 0.2, *c* 4.00); $[\alpha]_D^{25}$ $-6.3 \pm 0.3°$; $[M]_D^{25}$ -12.5 ± 0.5. α_D^{25} +0.033° (chloroform, *l* 0.2, *c* 4.00); $[\alpha]_D^{25}$ $+4.1 \pm 0.2°$; $[M]_D^{25}$ $+8.2 \pm 0.4$.

2D-Hydroxyundec-10-enoic acid (VII). The partially resolved, slightly dextrorotatory hydroxy acid (25.4 g) (0.13 mol), obtained from the decomposed mother liquors of the four first crystallizations, was dissolved in 205 ml of an ether:light petroleum (b.p. 60–85°) mixture, and added 15.5 g (0.13 mol) of (+)-α-phenethylamine. After standing overnight at +4°, 22.3 g of colourless crystals were isolated. These were successively recrystallized from 300 ml ether:light petroleum (1:10 v/v), 450 ml of ether:light petroleum (1:1 v/v), 1200 ml of ether:light petroleum (3:1 v/v), and twice from 1500 ml of ether. 8.4 g of optically pure salt was obtained as indicated by TLC. Decomposition of the salt yielded 5.1 g of (VII), m.p. 65.0–65.5°. α_D^{25} +0.051° (pyridine, *l* 0.2, *c* 4.00); $[\alpha]_D^{25}$ $+6.3 \pm 0.3°$; $[M]_D^{25}$ $+12.5 \pm 0.5$. α_D^{25} −0.033° (chloroform, *l* 0.2, *c* 4.00); $[\alpha]_D^{25}$ $-4.1 \pm 0.2°$; $[M]_D^{25}$ -8.2 ± 0.4.

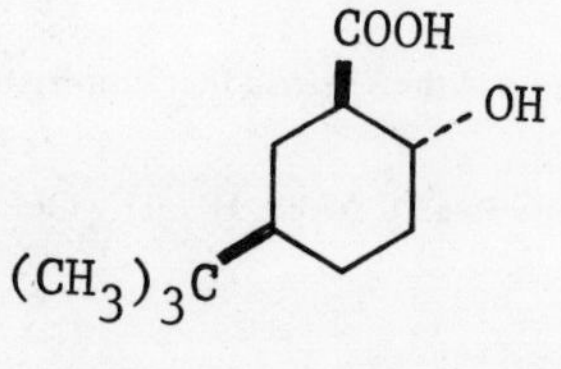

$C_{11}H_{20}O_3$ Ref. 850

Resolution of trans-2-*hydroxy*-cis-5-t-*butylcyclohexane-carboxylic acid*[11]

A hot solution of the acid (48 g, 0·24 mole) in acetone (250 cc) was treated with a hot solution of quinine (78 g, 0.24 mole) in acetone (900 cc), the solution allowed to cool, the crystals filtered off and recrystallized 6 times from methyl ethyl ketone to yield 27·0 g quinine salt as filtered needles, m.p. 173·5–174°, $[\alpha]^{23}_{D}$ −112° (*c*, 4·96, ethanol). (Found: N, 5·27, $C_{31}H_{44}N_2O_5$ requires: N, 5·34%). Treatment of the quinine salt with 1:1 aqueous hydrochloric acid afforded the (+)-antipode of the acid, m.p. 171–172° (ethyl acetate); $[\alpha]^{24}_{D}$ +22·7° (*c*, 6·00, ethanol); yield 8·05 g (Found: C, 65·89; H, 9·90. $C_{11}H_{20}O_3$ requires: C, 65·97; H, 10·07%).

The combined mother liquors from the crystallization of the quinine salt were taken to dryness, the liberated acid (20·6 g) taken up in acetone (140 cc) and treated with a solution of ephedrine (17·0 g) in acetone (20 cc). The ephedrine salt, after crystallization, alternately from acetonitrile and methyl ethyl ketone, afforded 8·0 g of material, m.p. 159–162°, $[\alpha]_D^{22}$ −32·4° (*c*, 4·01, ethanol). (Found: C, 69·97: H, 9·64. $C_{21}H_{33}O_4$ requires: C, 69·0; H, 9·65%). Decomposition of the salt afforded the (−) antipode of the acid, m.p. 171–172° (ethyl acetate), $[\alpha]_D^{23}$ −22·3° (*c*, 6·00, ethanol).

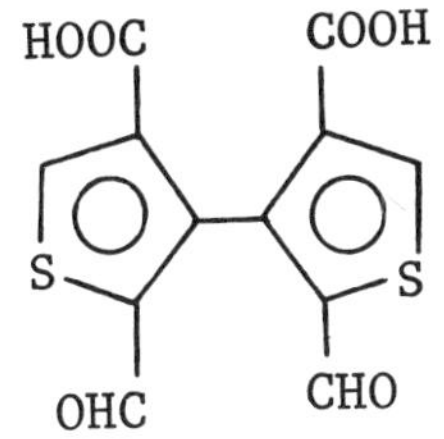

$C_{12}H_6O_6S_2$ Ref. 851

(*S*)-(+)-*4,4′-Dicarboxy-2,2′-diformyl-3,3′-bithienyl* (*XII*). Tests on the resolution with 0.5 mmol of racemic XII and 1.0 mmol of various bases are given below ($[\alpha]_D^{25}$ in ethanol):

Base	$[\alpha]_D^{25}$ of XII	Base	$[\alpha]_D^{25}$ of XII
Strychnine	− 4.6°	Quinidine	−79°
Brucine	−55°	Cinchonine	+79°
Quinine	−45°	Cinchonidine	+80°

9.3 g (30 mmol) of rac. XII and 17.7 g (60 mmol) of cinchonidine was dissolved in 550 ml of 96% hot ethanol and left at room temperature overnight. The precipitated crystals were filtered and the mother liquor stepwise evaporated by distilling off the solvent at atmospheric pressure. After each step the crystalline salt (a total of 26.0 g of the theoretical 27.0 g) obtained after cooling was collected, the acid liberated by treatment with hydrochloric acid, extracted with ether and the activity measured on ethanol solutions. The results are shown below.

Solvent, ml	g of salt	g of acid	$[\alpha]_D^{25}$ of acid
550	12.6	3.0	+87°
250	5.9	1.5	+85°
125	3.7	0.8	+80°
50	3.8	0.8	−17°

Obviously the laevorotatory form of XII is transformed into the dextrorotatory form in the resolution process. The ^{1}H-NMR and IR spectra and the m.p. of (*S*)-(+)-II, $[\alpha]_D^{25}$ = +87° were identical to those of racemic XII. [Found: C 46.5; H 2.05; S 20.1. Calc. for $C_{12}H_6O_6S_2$: C 46.4; H 1.96; S 20.6.] CD (CH_3CN): $[\theta]_{265}$ +3 500; $[\theta]_{351}$ +7 800; $[\theta]_{337}$ +8 100; $[\theta]_{325}$ +6 200; $[\theta]_{295}$ 14 700; $[\theta]_{263}$ −33 000; $[\theta]_{233}$ +83 000; $[\theta]_{212}$ −93 000. (0.01 N NaOH): $[\theta]_{345}$ − 9 000; $[\theta]_{302}$ + 62 000; $[\theta]_{272}$ −84 000; $[\theta]_{240}$ +8 000; $[\theta]_{220}$ −18 000. UV (CH_3CN): ε_{277} 15 500; ε_{223} 29 000. (0.01 N NaOH): ε_{290} 16 500; ε_{216} 24 500.

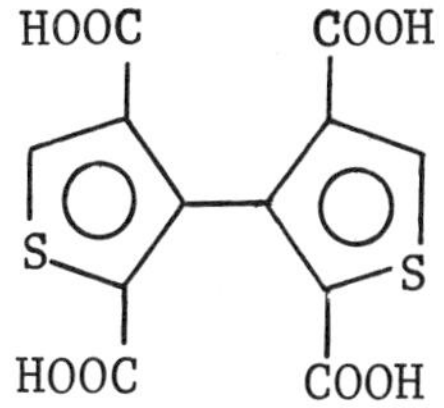

$C_{12}H_6O_8S_2$ Ref. 852

(*S*)-(+)-*2,2′,4,4′-Tetracarboxy-3,3′-bithienyl* (*II*). 4.10 g (12 mmol) of racemic II in 300 ml of hot 95% ethanol was added to 2.8 g (12 mmol) of brucine in 250 ml of hot ethanol and the solution kept at room temperature overnight. A plastic-looking film with a few crystals was obtained on the bottom of the vessel. On heating the solution the film dissolved and more crystals precipitated. (A second-order asymmetric transformation may have taken place.) After cooling, 6.3 g of salt was obtained. From 0.25 g of the salt an acid, $[\alpha]_D^{25}$ = +8.8°C (ethanol), was liberated. The residual salt was refluxed for 3 h in 800 ml of ethanol without dissolving. After cooling, 4.6 g of salt was obtained from which 0.7 g of II, m.p. 310°C (dec.), $[\alpha]_D^{25}$ = +12° (ethanol) was liberated by treating with hydrochloric acid and extracting the carboxylic acid with ether.

CD (CH_3CH): $[\theta]_{277}$ +19 000; $[\theta]_{250}$ −23 000; $[\theta]_{230}$ +38 000; $[\theta]_{207}$ −41 000.
(0.1 N NaOH): $[\theta]_{285}$ +32 000; $[\theta]_{255}$ −40 000; $[\theta]_{230}$ −28 000.
UV (CH_3CH): ε_{255} 9 500; ε_{222} 28 000. (0.01 N NaOH): ε_{265} 11 500; ε_{212} 32 500.

The CD spectra in Fig. 3 have been reflected through the wavelength axis to represent (*R*)-forms.

The mother liquor from the first crystallization was evaporated to 5–10 ml, and from the residual oil in dil. hydrochloric acid, 0.5 g of crystalline II, $[\alpha]_D^{25}$ = −7.5°C, was obtained after 2 days.

$C_{12}H_8Br_2O_4S_2$.

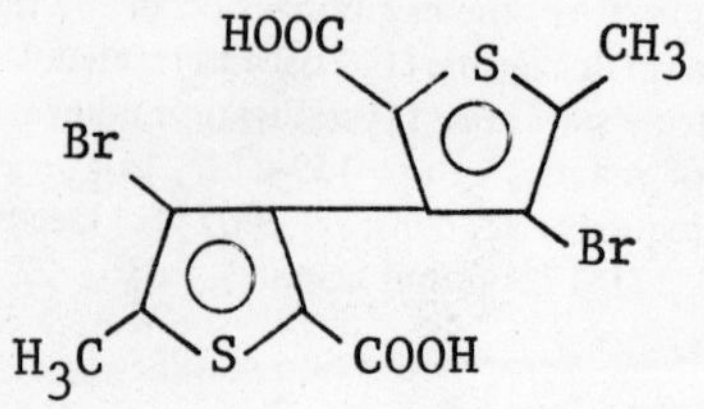

Ref. 853

Resolution of 2,2′-dicarboxy-4,4′-dibromo-5,5′-dimethyl-3,3′-bithienyl

Preliminary tests on resolution. 0.001 mole of optically inactive acid and 0.002 mole of optically active base were dissolved together in various solvents, *e.g.* water, aqueous ethanol, ethanol, ethyl acetate and acetone. Oils were obtained with cinchonidine, strychnine and quinidine. Phenyl isopropyl amine, α-phenyl ethylamine, brucine and quinine gave crystalline salts of inactive acid. Only cinchonine gave resolution.

Table 1.

Crystallisation	1	2	3
ml 50 % ethanol	1000	300	75
g, salt	6	2	0.6
$[\alpha]_D^{25}$ of acid	+ 42	+ 43	+ 43

7.0 g (0.017 mole) of 2,2′-dicarboxy-4,4′-dibromo-5,5′-dimethyl-3,3′-bithienyl and 10.2 g (0.035 mole) of cinchonine were dissolved in 1 l of hot aqueous ethanol (50 %) and allowed to stand over-night. The precipitate was filtered off and dried. About 0.3 g of the salt was set apart, the acid isolated and the optical activity measured in acetone. The remaining salt was recrystallised from 50 % ethanol. It appears from Table 1 that complete resolution had already been obtained after one crystallisation. The mother-liquors from the second and third crystallisations were therefore evaporated to dryness *in vacuo* and the salt used for the preparation of the (+)-acid *.
Since no base was found which gave a more insoluble salt with the (−)-form, the mother liquor from the first crystallisation of the cinchonine salt was concentrated step-wise *in vacuo*. The salt which separated was filtered off and the activity of the acid measured. The course of resolution is seen in Table 2.

Table 2.

Evaporation	1	2	3	4	5	6
Remaining mother-liquor	500	250	125	75	30	0
g, salt	6	3	1	0.6	0.4	0.11
$[\alpha]_D^{25}$	−10°	−35°	−39°	−41°	−43°	−43°

(+)-2,2′-Dicarboxy-4,4′-dibromo-5,5′-dimethyl-3,3′-bithienyl was obtained almost quantitatively by treating the cinchonine salt with 2 N hydrochloric acid and extracting with ether. The ether was evaporated and the residue recrystallised from acetic acid, yielding white crystals, m.p. 302−305° (decomp.) which had the same IR-spectrum as that of the active acids. R.D. in dioxane (*c* 0.725), temp. 26°: $[M]_{589}$ + 240°, $[M]_{400}$ + 690°, $[M]_{350}$ + 1000°, $[M]_{334}$ + 1300°, $[M]_{327}$ + 810°.

The rotations in some other solvents are given in Table 3.

(−)-2,2′-Dicarboxy-4,4′-dibromo-5,5′-dimethyl-3,3′-bithienyl was obtained by treating the last two fractions of the more soluble cinchonine salt in the same way as described for the (+)-form. M.p. 301−304° (decomp.) ($[\alpha]_D^{25}$ = −43°, *c*, 0.260, acetone).

Melting points of compounds which melted with decomposition were determined by placing the capillary tubes in the m.p. apparatus at a temperature of 10° below the melting point and heating with a rate of about 3°/min.

Racemization experiment. 0.0321 g of the (+)-acid was diluted to 5.00 ml with 0.100 N sodium hydroxide (α_D^{25} = −1.22). After heating in a closed vessel to 95° for 6 h the same rotation was obtained.

Table 3.

Solvent	conc.g acid/dl	α_D^{25}	$[\alpha]_D^{25}$	$[M]_D^{25}$
Acetone	0.836	+ 0.36°	+ 43°	+ 190°
Dimethyl sulphoxide	0.190	+ 0.10°	+ 53°	+ 230°
Ethanol	0.420	+ 0.23°	+ 55°	+ 240°
Chloroform	0.660	−0.38°	− 57.5°	−250°
0.1 N sodium hydroxide	0.642	−1.22°	−190°	−840°

* The antipode which is dextrorotatory in acetone will be designated the (+)-acid.

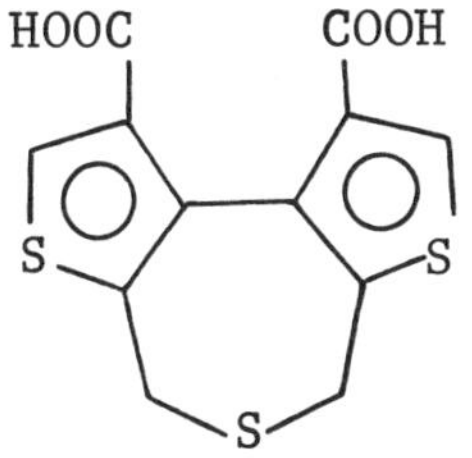

$C_{12}H_8O_4S_3$ **Ref. 854**

Resolution of 1,9-dicarboxy-4,6-dihydro-dithieno[2,3-c:3',2'-e]-thiepin (VI). Preliminary tests on resolution were carried out with 1 mmol of racemic acid VI and 2 mmol of optically active bases. The bases used were brucine, cinchonidine, cinchonine, quinidine, quinine and strychnine in ethanol and ethanol-water mixtures. Brucine gave a salt with the (−)-form of the acid and quinine gave a salt with the (+)-form.

3.5 g (11 mmol) of racemic VI and 7.3 g (22 mmol) of quinine were dissolved in 400 ml of hot ethanol (96%) and left at room temperature overnight. The precipitated crystals were filtered and the mother liquor left at room temperature for another 24 h. The precipitated crystals were filtered and the mother liquor was concentrated by evaporating the solvent at room temperature at reduced pressure. The crystalline salt obtained after each step was collected (a total of 10.4 g of the theoretical 10.8 g), the acid liberated by treatment with 5 N hydrochloric acid, extracted with ether and the activity measured on ethanol solutions. The progress of the resolution is shown below.

Crystallization	1	2	3	4	5
ml, 95% ethanol	400	400	350	200	50
g salt	0.7	3.9	1.3	3.0	1.5
g acid	0.2	1.1	0.4	0.7	0.4
$[\alpha]_D^{25}$ of acid	+113°	+112°	+113°	+111°	+101°

Obviously the levorotatory form of VI is transformed into the dextrorotatory form in the resolution process. M.p. of (+)-VI 310–313°C (dec.) $[\alpha]_D^{25}=+113°$, ethanol, $c=1.0$. [Found: C 45.5; H 2.55; S 30.3. Calc. for $C_{12}H_8O_4S_3$ (312.4): C 46.14; H 2.58; S 30.79]. $M^+=312$. IR: ν_{CO} 1670 cm^{-1} and 1710 cm^{-1}. The ^1H-NMR spectrum in DMSO-d_6 was identical to that of racemic VI.

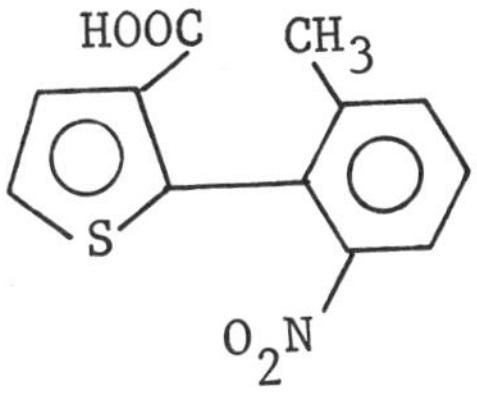

$C_{12}H_9NO_4S$ **Ref. 855**

Resolution of 2-(6-methyl-2-nitrophenyl)-3-thenoic acid. Brucine (3.63 g.) and 2-(6-methyl-2-nitrophenyl)-3-thenoic acid (2.27 g.) were dissolved in 150 cc. of hot absolute alcohol and water, 2:1. The solution was placed in the freezing compartment of the refrigerator (*ca* −15°) and at the end of four days, 2.2 g. of a light yellow solid had deposited, m.p. 122–126°.

Rotation. Hydrated L-salt: 0.2150 g. made to 50 cc. with chloroform at 20° gave an initial α_D +0.522°, l = 4; $[\alpha]_D^{20}$ +30.35° and a final α_D −0.491°, l = 4; $[\alpha]_D^{20}$ −28.55° after 2.5 hours.

Anal. Calc'd for $C_{35}H_{35}N_3O_8S \cdot H_2O$: C, 62.21; H, 5.52.
Found: C, 62.17; H, 5.32.

L-2-(6-Methyl-2-nitrophenyl)-3-thenoic acid. The above brucine salt (1 g.) was shaken at 0° with 50 cc. of hydrochloric acid. At the end of two hours, the hydrochloric acid was decanted and another 50-cc. portion was added. The mixture was then placed in the refrigerator overnight. After filtration, the solid was washed with dilute hydrochloric acid until the washings gave a negative test for brucine, and then with water. It amounted to 0.25 g., m.p. 185–187° with softening at 170°.

Rotation. 0.2001 g. made to 50 cc. with methanol at 20° gave an initial α_D −0.179°, l = 4; $[\alpha]_D^{20}$ −11.19° and a final α_D 0.000° after one hour.

Anal. Calc'd for $C_{12}H_9NO_4S$: C, 54.74; H, 3.45.
Found: C, 54.79; H, 3.25.

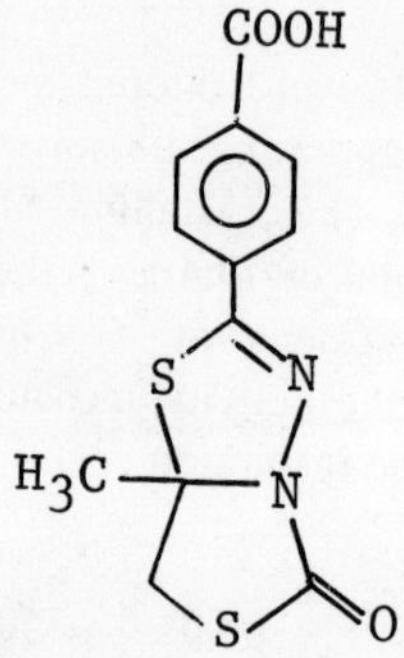

$C_{12}H_{10}N_2O_3S_2$

Ref. 856

The optical resolution of *(5b)* was carried out with brucine in methanol. After repeated recrystallization from methanol the brucine salt shows a specific rotation of $[\alpha]^{20}_{436} = -885°$ ($c = 0.5$; chloroform). Decomposition of this salt with dilute hydrochloric acid gave levorotatory *(5b)* having a specific rotation of $[\alpha]^{20}_{436} = -2250°$ ($c = 0.5$; acetone). The ORD curve exhibits the expected Cotton effect. Dextrorotatory *(5b)* was obtained by working up the mother liquor of the brucine salt.

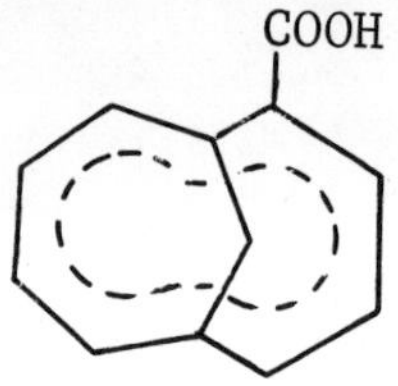

$C_{12}H_{10}O_2$

Ref. 857

Racematspaltung von 6

Eine Mischung der äthanolischen Lösungen von 600 mg (3.2 mMol) race. 6 und 400 mg (3.3 mMol) (-)-α-Phenäthylamin $[\alpha]_D = -39°$) wurde im Vak. eingedampft und der feste Rückstand aus 2 ml 96 %igem Äthanol umkristallisiert. Das so erhaltene Salz (410 mg, $[\alpha]_D = 39°$ in Äthanol, c = 1) wurde nochmals aus Äthanol umkristallisiert: 208 mg; $[\alpha]_D = +66°$, Schmp. 152°-154°C. Daraus wurde in Üblicher Weise (Äther, NaOH, H_3PO_4) die Saure freigesetzt: 90 mg vom Smp. 132°-134°C; $[\alpha]_D = +251°$ (Äthanol) c = 1.0).

Die aus den Mutterlaugen der Salz-Kristallisation gewonnene Säure wurde in analoger Weise mit (+)-α-Phenäthylamin ($[\alpha]_D = +35.5°$) behandelt, wobei ich 60 mg (-)-6 ($[\alpha]_D = -227°$) erhielt.

Bestimmung der optischen Reinheit von 6

50 mg (0.27 mMol) 6 ($[\alpha]_D = -135°$) wurden, wie unten beschrieben, in das Säurechlorid übergeführt, dieses in 5 ml trockenem Benzol gelöst und mit einer Lösung von 200 mg (1.6 mMol) (-)-α-Phenäthylamin in 5 ml Benzol 90 Min. bei Raumtemperatur geruhrt. Nach üblicher Aufarbeitung[37] wurde das NMR-Spektrum des Gemisches diastereomerer Phenäthylamide (60 mg, 77% d.Th) in $CDCl_3$ aufgenommen. Dabei zeigte sich eine deutliche Aufspaltung des Methylprotonensignals (Dubletts um 1.60 ppm). Weitere Signale im NMR-Spektrum (δ): um 7.5 (12H), um 6.5 (1H), um 5.4 (1H), -0.42 (s,2H). Das Intensitätenverhaltnis der Dubletts wurde durch mehrfache Integration und Mittelwertsbildung bestimmt. Daraus ergab sich fur die eingesetzte Säure eine optische Reinheit (p) von 54%: $[\alpha]^{max}_D = 250°$.

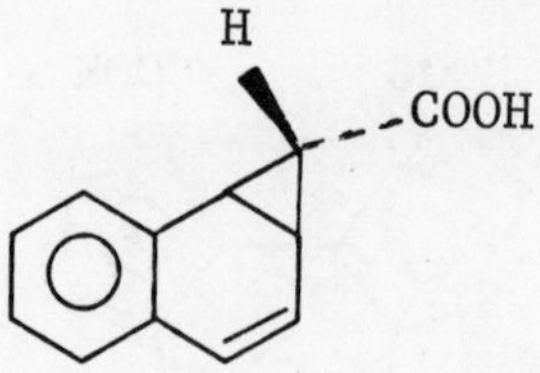

$C_{12}H_{10}O_2$

Ref. 858

Resolution of the racemic acid. Preliminary experiments with quinine and cinchonidine gave readily crystallising salts but very poor resolution. The salts of strychnine, brucine and cinchonine could not be obtained as crystals. Good resolution was obtained with α-phenyl-ethylamine and β-phenyl-*iso*propylamine, both yielding an acid with a direction of rotation opposite to that of the base used. Both bases were used in the final resolution and consistent values of the maximum rotation were obtained.

16.7 g acid (0.09 mole) and 12.1 g (0.09 mole) of (−)-β-phenyl-*iso*propylamine were dissolved in 70 ml methanol. The salt was filtered off after standing for 24 hours and recrystallised from the same solvent. The progress of the resolution was tested on small samples from each crystallisation, from which the acid was liberated and measured in acetone solution.

Crystallisation	1	2	3	4
ml methanol	70	85	65	45
g salt obtained	15.0	9.5	6.9	5.3
$[\alpha]^{25}_D$ of the acid	+ 65.5°	+ 120.5°	+ 122°	+ 123°

The mother liquors from the two first crystallisations were evaporated to dryness and the acid liberated; 11.2 g with $[\alpha]^{25}_D = -59°$ were obtained. This acid (0.06 mole) was dissolved with 7.2 g (0.06 mole) (+)-α-phenyl-ethylamine in 50 ml methanol + 35 ml water. The salt obtained on standing at room temperature for 24 hours was recrystallised and the course of the resolution tested as described above.

Crystallisation	1	2	3
ml methanol	50	50	40
ml water	35	20	20
g salt obtained	11.6	9.4	7.7
$[\alpha]^{25}_D$ of the acid	− 117°	− 122.5°	− 122.5°

(+)-Benznorcaradiene-carboxylic acid. The β-phenyl-*iso*propylamine salt (5.0 g) was decomposed with dilute sulphuric acid and the organic acid extracted with ether. After evaporation of the ether, 3.0 g of crude acid was obtained. It was recrystallised from formic acid, carbon tetrachloride + petroleum ether and once more from formic acid. 2.2 g of pure acid were obtained as fine colourless needles with m.p. 126.5–127.5°. The racemic acid has a quite different crystal habit, forming thin, glistening, rectangular plates or flakes.

0.2622 g acid: 12.41 ml 0.1134 *N* NaOH.
$C_{12}H_{10}O_2$ Equiv. wt. calc. 186.2, found 186.3.
0.1206 g dissolved in acetone to 10.00 ml: $\alpha^{25}_D = +2.925°$ (2 dm).
$[\alpha]^{25}_D = +121.3°$; $[M]^{25}_D = +226°$.

(−)-Benznorcaradiene-carboxylic acid. The α-phenyl-ethylamine salt (7.5 g) was decomposed and the acid recrystallised as described above, in all four times. 3.0 g of pure acid was obtained. M.p. 126.5–127.5°.

0.2725 g acid: 12.90 ml 0.1134 *N* NaOH.
$C_{12}H_{10}O_2$ Equiv. wt. calc. 186.2, found 186.3.

The activity data are given in Table 1.
The activity in acetone solution was also determined at a higher concentration:

0.2057 g dissolved in acetone to 10.00 ml: $\alpha^{25}_D = -4.96°$ (2 dm).
$[\alpha]^{25}_D = -120.6°$; $[M]^{25}_D = -224.5°$.

It is obvious that the rotatory power decreases with increasing concentration. This explains why somewhat higher values were obtained for the maximum activity in the course of the resolution; in these measurements the concentration was rather low.

Table 1. Rotatory power of (−)-benznorcaradiene-carboxylic acid. g = g acid; ml = ml solution.

	g	ml	α^{25}_D (2 dm)	$[\alpha]^{25}_D$	$[M]^{25}_D$
Water (ion)	0.1164	9.98	− 4.58°	− 196.3°	− 366.5°
Ethanol (abs.)	0.1103	10.00	− 3.24°	− 146.9°	− 273.5°
Acetic acid	0.1118	10.00	− 3.12°	− 139.5°	− 260°
Acetone	0.1073	10.00	− 2.61°	− 121.6°	− 226.5°
Chloroform	0.1055	10.00	− 2.40°	− 113.7°	− 212°
2.2.4-Trimethylpentane	0.1077	10.00	− 2.09°	− 97.0°	− 180.5°
Benzene	0.1118	9.98	− 1.83°	− 81.7°	− 152°

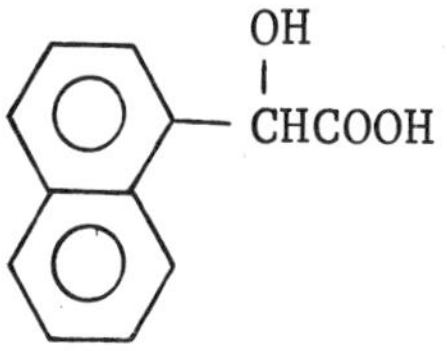

$C_{12}H_{10}O_3$ Ref. 859

Beschreibung der Versuche.

Spaltung der α-Naphthyl-glykolsäure in die optisch aktiven Komponenten.

Wir berichten zunächst über den typischen Verlauf einer solchen Spaltung: 20 g einer α-Naphthyl-glykolsäure (1 Mol.), die durch Einwirkung von Chloral auf α-Naphthyl-magnesiumbromid dargestellt worden war, lösten wir in 800 ccm rektifiziertem Alkohol, gaben dann zu der siedenden Lösung 15 g (1/2 Mol.) Cinchonin allmählich hinzu und kochten, bis die Gesamtmenge der Base in Lösung gegangen war. Beim Abkühlen setzte dann eine Krystallisation von Nadeln ein; nach dem Stehen über Nacht im Eiskasten hatten sich 17 g des Salzes abgeschieden. Das letztere wurde 3-mal aus rektifiziertem Spiritus umgelöst, wobei man das Fortschreiten der Spaltung durch eine polarimetrische Prüfung der Säuren kontrollierte, die sich bei der Zerlegung der Salze in den aufeinander folgenden Mutterlaugen ergaben; hierbei wurden in den etwa 2-proz. alkohol. Lösungen die Werte $[\alpha]_D = +175°$, $+179°$ und $+182°$ beobachtet. Obwohl dann das Alkaloid-Salz (12 g) noch nicht völlig rein war, wurde es mit verd. Schwefelsäure zerlegt und die Säure mit Äther extrahiert. Letztere wurde hiernach 3-mal aus Benzol umkrystallisiert, bis ein Wert für das spez. Drehungsvermögen erreicht war, der sich beim weiteren Umkrystallisieren nicht mehr änderte. Die Ausbeute an reiner Säure betrug 5.5 g.

Die *d*-α-Naphthyl-glykolsäure, $C_{10}H_7.CH(OH).COOH$, scheidet sich aus Benzol in Blättchen ab, aus Wasser dagegen in rhombischen Tafeln. Sie schmilzt bei 124—125°, während das *racem.* Isomere sich bei 98.5—99.5° verflüssigt.

$C_{12}H_{10}O_3$. Ber. C 71.3, H 5.0. Gef. C 71.5, H 5.0.

Trägt man eine Spur der Säure in konz. Schwefelsäure ein, so tritt eine blaue Färbung auf.

Die spez. Drehung wurde zunächst in Wasser bestimmt:

$$l = 2,\ c = 1.203,\ \alpha_D^{14} = +3.89°,\ [\alpha]_D^{14} = +162°.$$

In Äthylalkohol wurde beobachtet:

$$l = 2,\ c = 2.0416,\ \alpha_D^{14} = +7.92°,\ [\alpha]_D^{14} = +194°.$$

In äthylalkoholischer Lösung (bei $c = 2.028$ und $l = 2$) zeigt sich eine beträchtliche Rotationsdispersion:

λ	6563	5461	4861	4358
α^{13}	+ 5.92°	+ 9.31°	+ 12.51°	+ 15.78°
$[\alpha]^{13}$	+ 146°	+ 230°	+ 308°	+ 389°.

0.381 g der *d*-Säure wurden in 5 ccm wäßriger, 0.8754-*n*. Kalilauge gelöst und die Lösung dann durch Hinzufügen von Wasser zu 25 ccm aufgefüllt. Das α_D war hiernach (bei $l = 2$) $+3.45°$; dieser Wert änderte sich nicht, als die Lösung bei gewöhnlicher Temperatur 56 Stdn. stehen blieb.

Note: The above procedure was modified by A. McKenzie and E. R. L. Gow, J. Chem. Soc., 32 (1933), as follows:

The method of resolving *r*-α-naphthylglycollic acid (m. p. 98·5—99·5°) as described by McKenzie and Dennler (*loc. cit.*) was modified with advantage as follows. With the proportions formerly quoted, the cinchonine dissolves readily in the hot alc. solution of the acid, and the separation of the salt of the (+)acid takes place very quickly thereafter, even in the hot solution. It is not necessary to dissolve this deposit several times in more EtOH—an inconvenient procedure owing to the large quantities of solvent required—but the mixture is kept at 0° for about 4 hr. The mixture of alkaloidal salts (needles) is then decomposed with dil. H_2SO_4, and the acid after extraction with Et_2O gives the optically pure (+)acid after 2—4 crystns. from C_6H_6.

The prepn. of the (−)acid, which had not been previously carried out by McKenzie and Dennler, was conducted as follows. From the filtrate from which the crude salt of the (+)acid had been removed, crystals gradually separated containing a preponderance of the salt of the (−)acid. The latter was not removed, but the EtOH was expelled, and the residue decomposed by dil. H_2SO_4. The acid was extracted with Et_2O, and crystallised 4—6 times from C_6H_6 until optically pure.

(−)α-Naphthylglycollic acid crystallises from C_6H_6 in leaflets, m. p. 124—125°, identical with the m. p. for the (+)acid. The rotatory power in EtOH also agreed closely with that for the (+)enantiomorph.

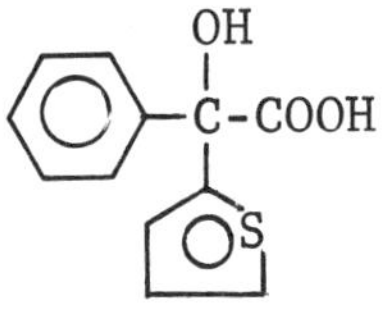

$C_{12}H_{10}O_3S$ Ref. 860

Note:

a) Amphetamine was used as resolving agent;

b) The following physical constants were reported by the authors for the active acid: m.p. 115-117°, $[\alpha]_D$ -7.4° (CH_3OH).

$C_{12}H_{10}O_3S$ Ref. 860a

Splitsing van fenyl-2-thienylglycolzuur in optische antipoden

(+)-*Fenyl-2-thienylglycolzuur*

15,00 g (0,064 mol) *rac.*-fenyl-2-thienylglycolzuur wordt opgelost in 270 ml hete ethylacetaat. Hieraan wordt 18,90 g (0,064 mol) cinchonine in porties toegevoegd. Er ontstaat een heldere oplossing, waarin na langzaam afkoelen een neerslag ontstaat. Door afzuigen wordt 25,30 g van het zout verkregen met smp. 188–194° (micr.). Het wordt aan herhaalde kristallisaties uit ethylacetaat onderworpen, waarbij de $[\alpha]_D$ en het smeltpunt veranderen zoals in de volgende tabel is aangegeven:

g zout	ml EtOAc	$[\alpha]_D$ (MeOH; c ± 1)	smp. (micr.)
25,30	360	+ 118,2°	188–194°
15,33	245	–	–
12,60	230	+ 124,8°	190–192°
9,71	200	+ 129,2°	–
7,58	170	+ 130,6°	–
6,50	160	+ 135,4°	192,5°
5,36	140	+ 146,7°	–
4,24	110	+ 145,2°	192°

De laatste kristallisatie levert 3,58 g witte kristallen. Uit ± 0,3 g hiervan wordt het zuur vrijgemaakt door opnemen in 2n H_2SO_4, uitschudden met ether, de ether uitschudden met water, drogen ($MgSO_4$) en indampen. Het zo verkregen zuur heeft een ontledingstemperatuur van 120–122° en $[\alpha]_D$ + 24,8° (MeOH, c = 1,00).

(−)-Fenyl-2-thienylglycolzuur

21,0 g Codeïne wordt toegevoegd aan een hete oplossing van een equimolaire hoeveelheid, 15,5 g, *rac.*-fenyl-2-thienylglycolzuur in 1400 ml ethanol 96%. Na enige uren wordt het gevormde zout, ± 36 g, afgezogen en als volgt gekristalliseerd:

g zout	ml EtOH 96%	$[\alpha]_D$ (DMF, c ± 1)	smp. (micr.)
± 36	700	− 88,1°	197–200°
22,00	620	–	–
18,05	620	− 89,8°	198–200°
16,38	600	− 90,8°	198–200°
14,81	520	− 89,8°	198–200°

De laatste kristallisatie levert 12,60 g witte, vlokkige kristallen. Het hieruit vrijgemaakte zuur wordt gekristalliseerd uit n-heptaan-benzeen (3 : 2); ontledingstemp. 120°, $[\alpha]_D$ — 23,9° (MeOH, c = 1,00).

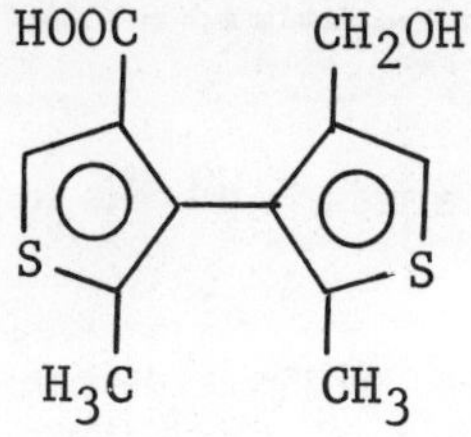

$C_{12}H_{10}O_4S_2$ Ref. 861

(S)-(+)-4,4′-Dicarboxy-2,2′-dimethyl-3,3′-bithienyl (VIa). 4.5 g (16 mmol) of racemic VI*a* and 5.2 g (16 mmol) of quinine were separately dissolved in 150 ml of hot ethanol. The solutions were combined, making a total volume of 300 ml. After standing at room temperature for 1 week, 4.7 g of salt was collected, from which 1.3 g (60%) of the title compound, $[\alpha]_D^{25} = +48°$, was liberated as described above. Recrystallization from ethanol–water raised the rotation to $[\alpha]_D^{25} = +49°$ (ethanol, C = 1.0 g/100 ml), m.p. ca. 210°C. (See the text; about 0.5 g of acid in 15 ml of cold ethanol and addition of 45 ml of cold water gave crystals from the milky solution after 2 days.) [Found: C 51.3; H 3.58; S 22.6. Calc. for $C_{12}H_{10}O_4S_2$ (282.3): C 51.05; H 3.57; S 22.7.] IR: ν_{CO} = 1 730 and 1 680 cm^{-1}.

(R)-(−)-4,4′-Dicarboxy-2,2′-dimethyl-3,3′-bithienyl (VIa). 3.0 g (10 mmol) of VI*a*, $[\alpha]_D^{25} = -25°$, obtained from the mother liquor of the crystallization of the quinine salt of (+)-VI*a*, was dissolved in 160 ml of hot 50% aq. ethanol, together with 8.1 g (20 mmol) of brucine. After standing overnight at room temperature, 5.5 g of salt was obtained, yielding 1.4 g (62%) of (R)-(−)-VI*a*, $[\alpha]_D^{25} = -47°$, which was recrystallized as described above for the dextrorotatory form; $[\alpha]_D^{25} = -49°$ (ethanol, *c* = 1.1) m.p. ca. 210°C (see the text).

Dimethyl ester of (R)-(−)-VIa: Oil. $[\alpha]_D^{25} = -78°$ (ethanol, *c* = 2.0).

Table II. *Resolution of 4,4′-dicarboxy-2,2′-dimethyl-3,3′-bithienyl (VIa)*

Crystallization	1	2	3	4	5
ml, 95% ethanol	300	150[b]	130	90	90
g, salt	5.8[a]	5.1	4.3	3.9	3.4
$[\alpha]_D^{25}$ of acid	+46°	+49°	+48°	+48°	+49°
ml, 50% aq. ethanol	160	100	100	100	80
g, salt	6.8[c]	5.4	4.0	3.3	0.8
$[\alpha]_D^{25}$ of acid	−47°	−48°	−48°	−49°	−48°

[a] From 5.0 g (18 mmol) of racemic VI*a* and 11.4 g (35 mmol) of quinine.
[b] Volume after evaporation The not easily soluble salt was dissolved in a larger amount of solvent.
[c] From 2.9 g (10 mmol) of VI*a*, $[\alpha]_D^{25} = -30°$, and 8.1 g (20 mmol) of brucine.

Note:

The enantiomers of dicarboxylic acid VI*a* ($[\alpha]_D^{25} = {}^{+}_{(-)}$ 49°, ethanol) were separated by fractional crystallization of the quinine and brucine salts. Optically pure dextrorotatory VI*a* was obtained after two crystallizations of the diquinine salt in ethanol. This salt is relatively difficult to dissolve on recrystallization. Later, it was shown that rapid resolution could also be obtained by using 1 mol of quinine per mol of racemic acid, (a disalt seems to have been formed also in this case), which gave optically pure (+)-VI*a* in good yields after one crystallization (see the Experimental section). The levorotatory form of VI*a* was optically pure after two crystallizations of the dibrucine salt in 50% aq. ethanol.

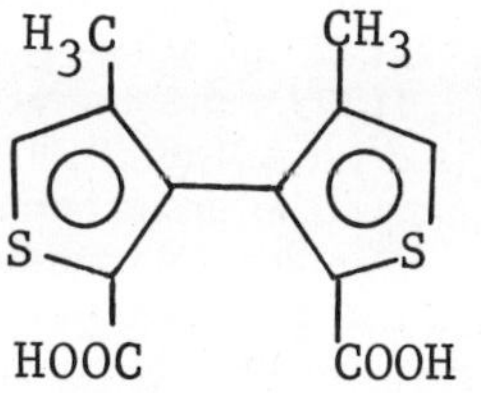

$C_{12}H_{10}O_4S_2$ Ref. 862

(R)-(+)-2,2′-Dicarboxy-4,4′-dimethyl-3,3′-bithienyl (VIb). 2.8 g (10 mmol) of racemic VI*b* and 2.8 g (10 mmol) of dehydroabiethylamine were dissolved in 100 ml of hot ethanol (95%). 40 ml of solvent was distilled off before the solution was allowed to cool to room temperature overnight. 2.2 g of salt was filtered off and decomposed with aq. sodium hydroxide (2 N), and the dehydroabiethylamine was extracted out twice with benzene and once with ether. The aqueous solution was acidified with conc. hydrochloric acid, and the precipitated acid was filtered off. After drying, the acid was dissolved in a small volume of hot ethyl acetate and the solution filtered, whereupon hot ligroin was added until the resulting opalescence remained. 1.0 g (71%) of (R)-(+)-VI*b*, $[\alpha]_D^{25} = +27°$ (ethanol, *c* = 1.4) was obtained; m.p. ca. 250°C see the text). The optically active forms of VI*b* could also be recrystallized from water. [Found: C 51.1; H 3.52; S 27.9. Calc. for $C_{12}H_{10}O_4S_2$ (282.3): C 51.05; H 3.57; S 22.71.] IR: ν_{CO} = 1 675 cm^{-1}.

Dimethyl ester of (R)-(+)-VIb ((R)-(−)-XIVb): m.p. 119.5–120.5°C (ligroin) $[\alpha]_D^{25} = -7°$ (ethanol, *c* = 1.1), (cf. Fig. 1). IR: ν_{CO} = 1 710 cm^{-1}.

(S)-(−)-2,2′-Dicarboxy-4,4′-dimethyl-3,3′-bithienyl (*VIb*). The mother liquor from the first crystallization of the dehydroabiethylamine salt was evaporated *in vacuo* to dryness. The acid ($[\alpha]_D^{25}$ = −16°) was liberated and recrystallized as above. Racemic VI*b* is not easily soluble in ethyl acetate, and could be filtered off after cooling. The solution was warmed again before hot ligroin was added until opalescence appeared and remained. 1.0 g (71%) of VI*b* was obtained; $[\alpha]_D^{25}$ = −27° (ethanol, *c* = 1.3); m.p. ca. 250°C (see the text).

Dimethyl ester of (S)-(−)-VIb ((S)-(+)-XIVb): m.p. 119.5–120.5°C (ligroin), $[\alpha]_D^{25}$ = +7° (ethanol, *c* = 1.1). (See Fig. 1.)

Table III. *Resolution of 2,2′-dicarboxy-4,4′-dimethyl-3,3′-bithienyl (VIb)*

Crystallization	1	2	3	4
ml, 95% ethanol	60	40	25	12
g, salt	1.5[a]	1.1	0.8	0.5
$[\alpha]_D^{25}$ of acid	+27°	+27°	+27°	+27°
ml, $CHCl_3/CCl_4$	25/50	15/30	10/20	
g, salt	1.2[b]	0.7	0.5	
$[\alpha]_D^{25}$ of acid	−27°	−27°	−27°	

[a] From 2.0 g (7.1 mmol) of racemic VI*b* and 2.1 g (7.2 mmol) of dehydroabiethylamine [29].
[b] From 1.1 g (3.9 mmol) of VI*b*, $[\alpha]_D^{25}$ = −19°, and 3.1 g (7.9 mmol) of brucine.

Note:

Except for dehydroabiethylamine, brucine was the only base investigated that gave a crystalline salt with racemic VI*b* (in 50% aq. ethanol). The acid liberated from this salt, however, was completely inactive. An attempt was made to use brucine as resolving base when the levorotatory form of VI*b* had been enriched, as for example in the acid obtained from the mother liquor after the first crystallization of racemic VI*b* with dehydroabiethylamine. When 95% or 50% aq. ethanol was used as solvent, no crystalline dibrucine salt separated, but the resolution could be completed with brucine in hot chloroform/carbon tetrachloride. In this way, the optically pure levorotatory form of VI*b* was afforded: $[\alpha]_D^{25}$ = −27° (ethanol). A more convenient way to obtain optically pure (−)-VI*b* involved treatment of the acid enriched in (−)-VI*b* (cf. above) with hot ethyl acetate. The racemic form of VI*b* is not easily soluble in this solvent, and can be filtered off. The optically pure levorotatory form of VI*b* crystallizes after addition of ligroin.

The optically active forms of dicarboxylic acids VI*a* and VI*b* showed no sharp melting points, probably due to racemization. They started to melt at about 210°C and 250°C, respectively, but crystallized successively again and remelted at the same temperatures as the racemic forms, 284–285°C dec. and 285–290°C dec., respectively.

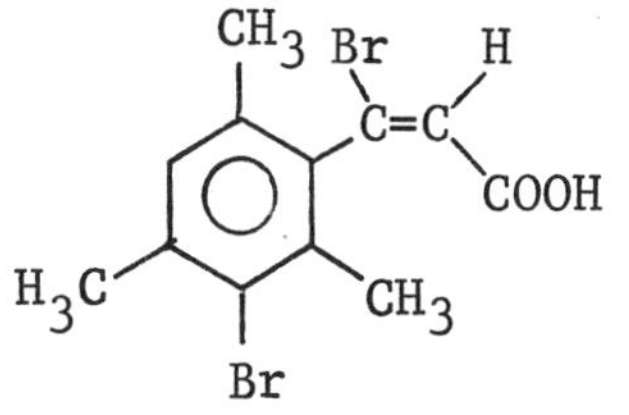

$C_{12}H_{12}Br_2O_2$ Ref. 863

Resolution of β-Bromo-β-(3-bromo-2,4,6-trimethylphenyl)-acrylic Acid.—A solution of 7 g. of β-bromo-β-(3-bromo-2,4,6-trimethylphenyl)-acrylic acid in 25 cc. of warm absolute ethanol was added to a solution of 6.524 g. of quinine in 50 cc. of absolute ethanol. The resulting solution was filtered, diluted to a total volume of 100 cc. of solvent, and cooled yielding 3.655 g. of salt (fraction A). Fractions B and C were removed after evaporation of the solvent to 40 cc. then 20 cc. and weighed 0.850 g. and 1.584 g., respectively. Fraction D (0.50 g.) was obtained by the addition of 20 cc. of petroleum ether (b. p. 30–60°) to the mother liquor from fraction C. Evaporation to dryness under reduced pressure yielded 5.860 g. of salt (fraction E)

Fraction A was twice recrystallized from absolute ethanol, after which a constant rotation had been reached; white plates m. p. 175° (cor.) with decomposition.

Anal. Calcd. for $C_{32}H_{36}N_2O_4Br_2$: C, 57.15; H, 5.40; N, 4.17. Found: C, 57.90; H, 5.81; N, 4.29.

Rotation. Less soluble salt (*l*B·*l*A) 0.0647 g. made up to 10 cc. with absolute ethano at 26° gave α_D −0.54; *l*, 1; $[\alpha]^{26}_D$ −83.2°.

Fraction E was purified by three recrystallizations from a mixture of equal volumes of benzene and petroleum ether (b. p. 90–110°) with no change in rotation after the last crystallization; sandy white granules m. p. 164–164.5° (cor.) with decomposition.

Anal. Calcd. for $C_{32}H_{36}N_2O_4Br_2$: C, 57.15; H, 5.40; N, 4.17. Found: C, 57.50; H, 5.49; N, 4.20.

Rotation. More soluble salt (*l*B·*d*A) 0.0260 g. made up to 5 cc. with absolute ethanol at 28° gave α_D −0.25; *l*, 1; $[\alpha]^{28}_D$ −48.1°.

***d*- and *l*-β-Bromo-β-(3-bromo-2,4,6-trimethylphenyl)-acrylic Acids.**—The salts were decomposed by stirring with an excess of aqueous acid containing 10 cc. of concentrated hydrochloric acid to 100 cc. of water. Decomposition of 1.700 g. of purified fraction A yielded 0.840 g. of *l*-acid crystallizing in thick white needles from petroleum ether; m. p. 155–155.5° (cor.).

Anal. Calcd. for $C_{12}H_{12}O_2Br_2$: C, 41.41; H, 3.47. Found: C, 41.48; H, 3.69.

Rotation. (*l*-acid) 0.0605 g. made up to 10 cc. with absolute ethanol at 25° gave α_D −0.225; *l*, 1; $[\alpha]^{25}_D$ −37.2°.

A 1.185-g. portion of the purified more soluble salt (fraction E) was similarly decomposed yielding 0.585 g. of *d*-acid. This *d*-acid was recrystallized three times from petroleum ether (b. p. 90–110°) with no change in rotation; m. p. 155–156° (cor.).

Rotation. (*d*-acid) 0.0298 g. made up to 5 cc. with absolute ethanol at 28° gave α_D +0.20; *l*, 1; $[\alpha]^{28}_D$ +33.6°.

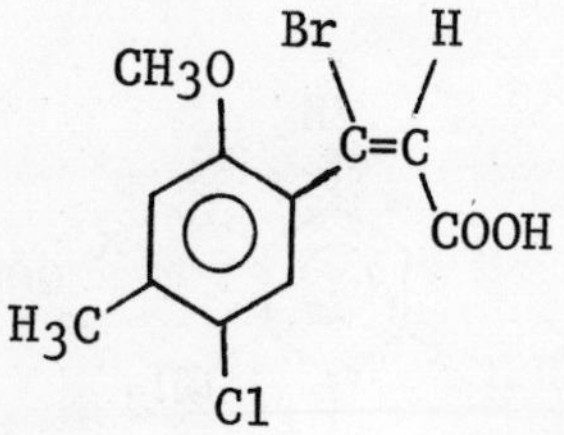

$C_{12}H_{12}BrClO_3$ Ref. 864

Resolution of β-Bromo-β-(2,4-dimethyl-3-chloro-6-methoxyphenyl)-acrylic Acid.—A solution of 1.1462 g. of the bromo acid in acetone was mixed with a solution of 1.1651 g. of quinine in acetone. The acetone was removed by evaporation and the oily residue was crystallized from ethyl acetate. All of the fractions had essentially the same rotation and the rotation did not change on recrystallization; 23.8 mg. made up to 5 cc. with absolute ethanol at 27° gave α_D −0.22; *l*, 1; $[\alpha]^{27}_D$ −46.2°.

d-β-Bromo-β-(2,4-dimethyl-3-chloro-6-methoxyphenyl)-acrylic Acid.—The quinine salt was decomposed by treating an aqueous suspension with ice-cold hydrochloric acid. The acid was separated by filtration and air-dried; 28.8 mg. made up to 5 cc. with absolute ethanol at 28° gave α_D +0.20; *l*, 1; $[\alpha]^{28}_D$ +34.7°.

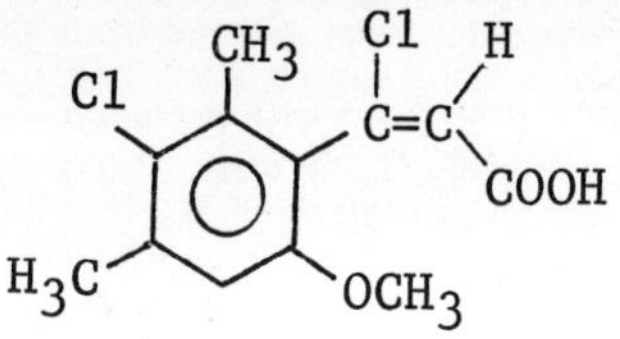

$C_{12}H_{12}Cl_2O_3$ Ref. 865

Resolution of β-Chloro-β-(2-methoxy-4,6-dimethyl-5-chlorophenyl)-acrylic Acid (VI).—A solution of 6.3 g. of β - chloro - β - (2 - methoxy - 4,6 - dimethyl - 5 - chlorophenyl)-acrylic acid in 50 cc. of ethyl acetate was added to a solution of 7.5 g. of quinine in 70 cc. of ethyl acetate. After filtration the solution was evaporated to 40 cc. and at two-day intervals the crystals were filtered and 5 cc. of solvent was removed. The rotations of the various fractions thus obtained were essentially the same and the same *d*-acid was obtained from all fractions, indicating the formation of only one salt. The various fractions were unchanged in rotation after recrystallization from ethyl acetate. No mutarotation was observed over a short period of time at room temperature.

Anal. Calcd. for $C_{32}H_{36}O_5N_2Cl_2$: C, 64.05; H, 6.05. Found: C, 64.15; H, 6.22. *Rotation.* (*l*BdA) 0.050 g. made up to 25 cc. with benzene at 20° gave α_D −0.10°; *l*, 2; $[\alpha]^{20}_D$ −25.00°.

d-β-Chloro-β-(2-methoxy-4,6-dimethyl-5-chlorophenyl)-acrylic Acid.—To a suspension of 2 g. of salt in 30 cc. of water was added 5 cc. of concentrated hydrochloric acid. After stirring at 5° for thirty minutes the product was filtered and washed with 5% hydrochloric acid and finally with water. The above was repeated until the product was quinine free; m. p. 180° (cor.).

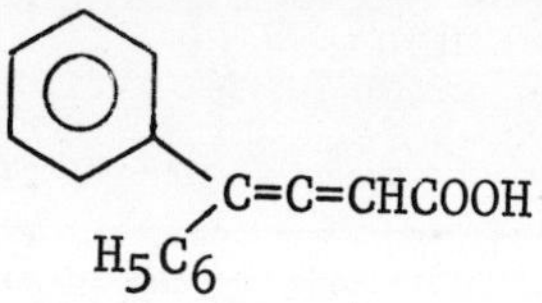

$C_{12}H_{12}O_2$ Ref. 866

Note:

The racemic acid was resolved via the cinchonidine salt. Reported physical constants obtained were m.p. 96-98° $[\alpha]_D$ -280° (methanol).

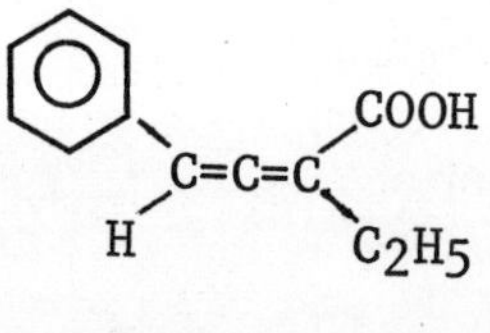

$C_{12}H_{12}O_2$ Ref. 867

*(+)- und (−)-***1m**: Nach der allgemeinen Vorschrift ergaben 5.108 g racem. **1m** und 4.082 g Cinchonidin nach fünf Umkristallisationen aus Aceton 2.252 g (40%) Komplex als farblose Nadeln mit Schmp. 151−152°C (Rotfärbung). $[\alpha]^{25}_{589}$ = +24.5°, $[\alpha]^{25}_{351}$ = +378° (*c'* = 0.006038, C_2H_5OH).

$C_{50}H_{60}N_4O_6$ (813.0) Ber. C 73.87 H 7.44 N 6.89 Gef. C 74.44 H 7.36 N 5.52

Aus dem Filtrat der ersten Kristallisationsfraktion wurden 1.529 g (30%) optisch sehr unreines (−)-**1m** gewonnen. Farblose Nadeln mit Schmp. 96−101°C (aus Petroläther). $[\alpha]^{25}_{589}$ = −7.8° (*c'* = 0.006213, C_2H_5OH). − Aus der Mutterlauge dieser Kristallisation erhielt man 0.471 g (9.2%) optisch nicht ganz reines (−)-**1m** als farblose Nadeln mit Schmp. 88−90°C (aus Petroläther). $[\alpha]^{25}_{589}$ = −73.4° (*c'* = 0.010453, C_2H_5OH). − Aus 3.803 g Cinchonidinkomplex wurden 0.810 g (92%) (+)-**1m** gewonnen. Farblose, lange Nadeln mit Schmp. 94−96°C (aus Petroläther). $[\alpha]^{25}_{589}$ = +83.5° (*c'* = 0.006293, C_2H_5OH). − CD (C_2H_5OH): λ_{max} (Δε) = 310 (−0.018), 295 (+0.11), 290 (+0.24), 285 (+0.37), 280 (+0.49), 271 (+1.0), 261 (+2.7), 254 (+4.1), 247 (+5.3), 242 (+6.3), 237 (+6.6), 234 (+6.6), 216 nm (−10.4),

$C_{12}H_{12}O_2$ (188.2) Ber. C 76.32 H 6.43 Gef. C 75.99 H 6.31

$C_{12}H_{12}O_2$

See Ref. 886 for a resolution of 1,3-dimethylindene-1-carboxylic acid which is inadvertently out of place.

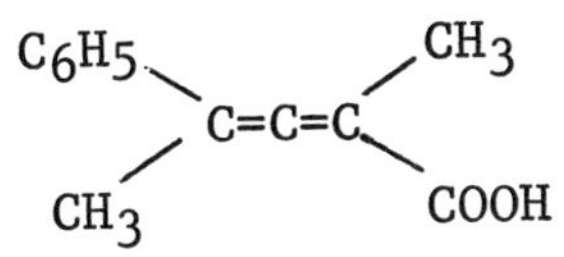

$C_{12}H_{12}O_2$ Ref. 868

*(+)- und (−)-***1d**. — 2.408 g *racem.* **1d** und 1.643 g *Cinchonidin* lieferten nach vier Umkristallisationen aus Essigester/Petroläther (7 : 6) 0.331 g (12%) Salz. Farblose Kristalle vom Schmp. 142—144° (aus Essigester/Petroläther = 7 : 6); $[\alpha]_D^{25}$ = +27.0° (*c* = 0.004062, C_2H_5OH).

$C_{31}H_{34}N_2O_3$ (482.6) Ber. C 77.15 H 7.10 N 5.81 Gef. C 75.98 H 7.01 N 5.90

Aus diesem Cinchonidinsalz wurden 0.087 g (3.6%) *(+)-***1d** gewonnen. Farblose Nadeln vom Schmp. 90—92° (aus Petroläther); $[\alpha]_D^{25}$ = +149° (*c* = 0.01444, C_2H_5OH). — *CD* (C_2H_5OH): λ_{max} ($\Delta\varepsilon$) = 278 (+1.1) sh, 250 (+7.0) sh, 240 nm (+11.5).

$C_{12}H_{12}O_2$ (188.2) Ber. C 76.57 H 6.43 Gef. C 76.56 H 6.55

Aus dem *Filtrat der ersten Fraktion* wurden 1.403 g (58%) *racem.* **1d** gewonnen. Farblose Rhomben vom Schmp. 101—103° (aus Petroläther). — Aus der *Mutterlauge* dieser Kristallisation konnten 0.110 g (4.6%) *(−)-***1d** isoliert werden. Farblose Kristalle vom Schmp. 90—93° (aus Petroläther); $[\alpha]_D^{25}$ = −128° (*c* = 0.02138, C_2H_5OH), −136° (*c* = 0.01100, $CHCl_3$).

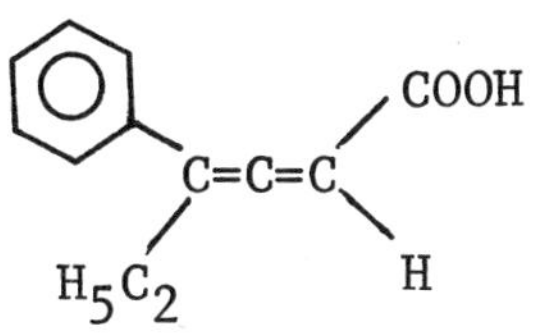

$C_{12}H_{12}O_2$ Ref. 869

*(+)- und (−)-***1k**: Nach der allgemeinen Vorschrift ergaben 2.980 g racem. **1k** und 2.356 g Cinchonidin nach fünf Umkristallisationen aus Aceton 0.262 g (8.0%) Addukt als kleine, farblose Nadeln mit Schmp. 137—139°C (Rotfärbung). $[\alpha]_{589}^{25}$ = +9.0, $[\alpha]_{350}^{25}$ = +184° (*c'* = 0.005388, C_2H_5OH).

$C_{50}H_{60}N_4O_6$ (813.0) Ber. C 73.87 H 7.44 N 6.89 Gef. C 74.37 H 7.41 N 5.60

Aus dem Filtrat der ersten Kristallisationsfraktion wurden 1.967 g (66%) racem. **1k** zurückgewonnen. Nach Umkristallisieren aus Petroläther farblose Kristalle mit Schmp. 98°C (Gelbfärbung). — Aus der Mutterlauge dieser Kristallisation erhielt man 0.340 g (11.4%) optisch unreines (−)-**1k** als farblose Kristalle (aus Petroläther). mit Schmp. 95—98°C (Gelbfärbung). $[\alpha]_{589}^{25}$ = −12.3° (*c'* = 0.009358, C_2H_5OH). — Aus 0.960 g Cinchonidinkomplex wurden 0.213 g (96%) (+)-**1k** gewonnen; kurze nach Umkristallisieren aus Petroläther farblose Nadeln mit Schmp. 95—97°C (Gelbfärbung; Lit.[25] 96—98°C). $[\alpha]_{589}^{25}$ = +63.0° (*c'* = 0.005864, C_2H_5OH), $[\alpha]_{589}^{25}$ = +66.9° (*c'* = 0.008904, CH_3OH) ⟨Lit.[25] $[\alpha]_{589}^{25}$ = +280° (CH_3OH)⟩. — CD(C_2H_5OH): λ_{max} ($\Delta\varepsilon$, umgerechnet auf optisch reines (+)-**1k**) = 313 (−0.040), 295 (−0.79), 271 (+0.40), 252 (+7.2), 247 (+9.3), 242 (+10.5), 232 nm (+12.5).

25) *K. Shingu, S. Hagishita* und *M. Nakagawa*, Tetrahedron Lett. **1967**, 4371.

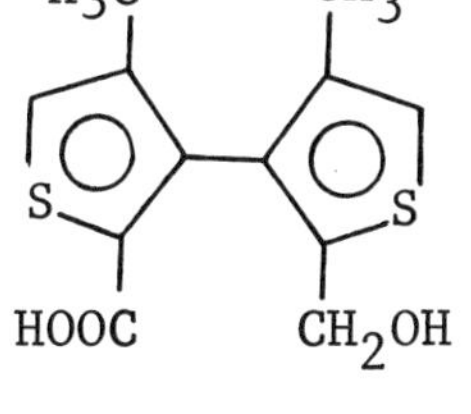

$C_{12}H_{12}O_3S_2$ Ref. 870

(R)-(−)-2-Carboxy-2'-hydroxymethyl-4,4'-dimethyl-3,3'-bithienyl (VIIb). 0.70 g (2.6 mmol) of inactive VII*b* and 0.75 g (2.6 mmol) of dehydroabiethylamine were dissolved in 30 ml of hot 50% aq. ethanol. After standing for 2 days at room temperature, a few needle-shaped crystals separated, together with a viscous oil. The needles could be swirled into the mother liquor and filtered off. After repeated warming and cooling of the remaining solution, a total of 0.3 g of solid salt was obtained, which was decomposed in the usual way. 0.12 g of crude product was obtained ($[\alpha]_D^{25}$ = −41°). Recrystallization from ethyl acetate/ligroin gave 0.10 g (29%) of (R)-(−)-VII*b* with the same optical activity; m.p. 138–142°C. IR: ν_{CO} = 1 670 cm^{-1}.

The mother liquor from the crystallization of the salt of (−)-VII*b* was evaporated to dryness and the residue combined with the viscous oil. The acid was liberated in the usual way ($[\alpha]_D^{25}$ = +14°, ethanol).

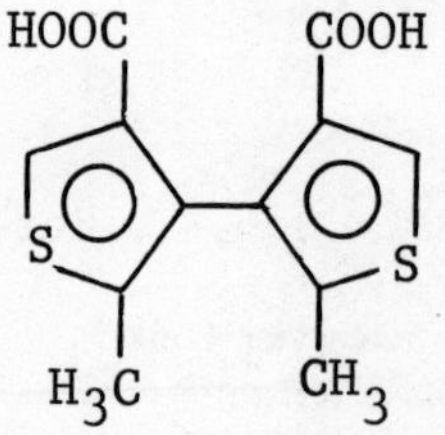

$C_{12}H_{12}O_3S_2$ Ref. 871

(S)-(+)-4-Carboxy-4'-hydroxymethyl-2,2'-dimethyl-3,3'-bithienyl (VIIa). 3.9 g of the brucine salt of VII*a* remaining after the fifth crystallization (Table IV) was decomposed in the usual way The carboxylic acid obtained ($[\alpha]_D^{25} = +29°$) was recrystallized by dissolving it in 10 ml of cold ethanol and adding cold water until the resulting opalescence remained. 1.2 g (44%) of (S)-(+)-VII*b* was obtained; m.p. 161–163°C; $[\alpha]_D^{25} = +29°$(ethanol $c = 2.1$); IR: $\nu_{CO} = 1\,690$ cm^{-1} and 1 670 cm^{-1} (cf. [6]).

Dimethyl ester of (S)-(+)-VIIa: Oil, $[\alpha]_D^{25} = +23°$ (ethanol, $c =$ 0.2).

(R)-(−)-4-Carboxy-4'-hydroxymethyl-2,2'-dimethyl-3,3'-bithienyl (VIIa). The mother liquor from the first crystallization of the dextrorotatory form with brucine (Table IV) was evaporated to dryness *in vacuo*. The hydroxy acid (1.9 g, $[\alpha]_D^{25} = -25°$) was isolated as described before. Recrystallization from ethanol–water, as for (S)-(+)-VII*a*, gave 1.1 g of (R)-(−)-VII*a* ($[\alpha]_D^{25} = -27°$). A second crystallization from water (insoluble material was filtered off) gave 0.7 g (26%) of optically pure (R)-(−)-VII*a*, $[\alpha]_D^{25} = -29°$ (ethanol, $c = 1.5$); m.p. 162–163°C.

Table IV. *Resolution of 4-carboxy-4'-hydroxymethyl-2,2'-dimethyl-3,3'-bithienyl (VIIa)*

Crystallization	1	2	3	4	5
ml, 95% ethanol	200	150	120	80	80
g, salt	6.5[a]	5.6	4.9	4.4	3.9
$[\alpha]_D^{25}$ of acid[b]	+21°	+25°	+29°	+29°	+29°

[a] From 5.4 g (20 mmol) of racemic VII*a* and 7.9 g (20 mmol) of brucine, after one week.
[b] The levorotatory form: see (R)-(−)-VII*a* below.

Note:

Hydroxy acid VII*a* was resolved into its enantiomers *via* the brucine salt, from which the dextrorotatory form ($[\alpha]_D^{25} = +29°$, ethanol), was obtained. (In the preliminary tests, this salt first crystallized from the solution after standing for 1.5 years. After that day crystals were formed soon after cooling of the solution even without seeding. This illustrates in a typical way the well known difficulties and elements of chance involved in resolution experiments. Under appropriate circumstances resolving bases may also be found in cases where we have failed to find them.) The levorotatory form was brought to the same activity ($[\alpha]_D^{25} = -29°$, ethanol) by recrystallization of the incompletely resolved acid obtained in the resolution process (Experimental section).

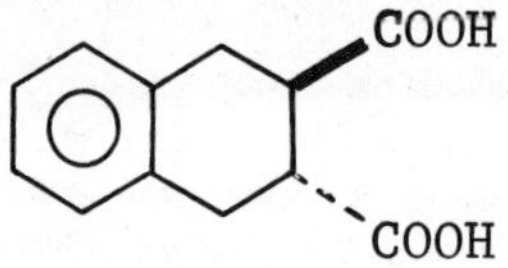

$C_{12}H_{12}O_4$ Ref. 872

Resolution of the trans-*Form of Acid* (I).—The *trans*-acid (0·75 g.), m. p. 226—227°, and strychnine (1·4 g.) were mixed in chloroform (20 c.c.), and the solution diluted with alcohol (70 c.c.) and concentrated until crystallisation commenced. The *strychnine* salt of the *l*-acid was collected and crystallised from alcohol–chloroform; slender needles (0·9 g.), m. p. 170—180° (Found: C, 69·3; H, 6·3. $C_{12}H_{12}O_4,C_{21}H_{22}O_2N_2,H_2O$ requires C, 69·2; H, 6·3%), were obtained, which were too sparingly soluble in cold solvents for the determination of α_D value. The combined mother-liquors gave on concentration first a small amount of unchanged strychnine and then the *strychnine* salt of the *d*-acid, which separated from alcohol in stout prisms (1·15 g.), m. p. 195—240° (Found: C, 71·2; H, 6·9. $C_{12}H_{12}O_4,C_{21}H_{22}O_2N_2$ requires C, 71·4; H, 6·1%). In alcohol (c, 2·00) it gave $[\alpha]_D^{16°} + 36{\cdot}5°$.

The strychnine salts, suspended or dissolved in chloroform, were decomposed by shaking with aqueous ammonia, and the acids liberated by acidification of the alkaline liquors. The d- and the l-*acid* separated from acetone–benzene in slender prisms, m. p. 182—183° (Found for the *d*-acid: C, 65·5; H, 5·0. Found for the *l*-acid: C, 65·5; H, 5·5. $C_{12}H_{12}O_4$ requires C, 65·5; H, 5·5%). An equimolecular mixture of the two melted at 215—220°. In chloroform solution (c, 1·00) they had $[\alpha]_D^{16°} + 85{\cdot}5°$ and $- 85{\cdot}0°$ respectively.

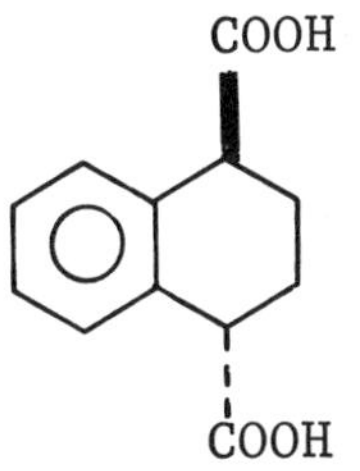

$C_{12}H_{12}O_4$ Ref. 873

(19) *Decomposition of trans-tetralindicarboxylic acid-1,4* (VIa) *in optically active components by the brucine salt method.*[9] *trans*-Tetralin acid VIa (11.2 g., 0.051 mole) and 47.5 g. (0.102 mole) of brucine were heated in 515 ml. of water. On cooling, 19.55 g. of salt crystallized, m.p. 149-152°, $[\alpha]_D$ −58° (*c*, 0.92 in chloroform). Recrystallization of 18.55 g. of above salt from 162 ml. of hot water gave 13.9 g. salt, $[\alpha]_D$ −61° (*c*, 1.05 in chloroform). Further crystallization of 12.9 g. of salt ($[\alpha]_D$ −61°) from 113 ml. of hot water gave 11.17 g. of salt, $[\alpha]_D$ −63° (*c*, 1.09 in chloroform). A final recrystallization of 10.2 g. of salt from 180 ml. of hot water gave 7.34 g. of salt of unchanged rotation $[\alpha]_D$ −63°. Brucine salt, 6.34 g. recrystallized four times, ($[\alpha]_D$ −63°), was dissolved in 300 ml. of hot water and an excess of ammonium hydroxide was added. The brucine was extracted with chloroform three times and with ether once, the ammonium salt solution of the dicarboxylic acid acidified, and extracted with diethyl ether. White crystals, 1.27 g. (93%), were formed; m.p. 236–238°, $[\alpha]_D$ −45° (*c*, 1.36 in ethanol), representing 1-*trans*-tetralindicarboxylic acid-1,4. The mother liquor of the first brucine salt crystallization was concentrated *in vacuo* to yield 16.15 g., 4.82 g., and finally 4.64 g. of brucine salt. From the fourth mother liquor, the solvent was completely removed and the residue (13.5 g.) treated with ammonium hydroxide as described above; yield: 1.35 g. of *d-trans*-tetralindicarboxylic acid-1,4, m.p. 200–210°. Recrystallization from water gave m.p. 228–230°, $[\alpha]_D$ +24.5°. The impure *d-trans*-acid was not further purified.

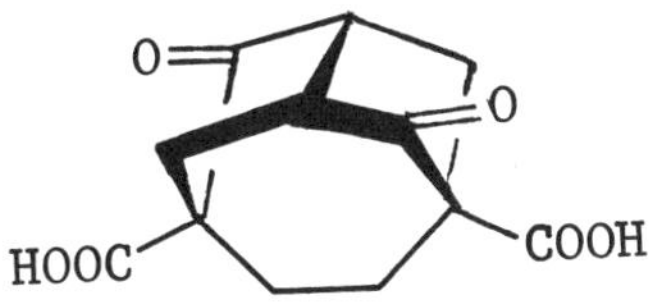

$C_{12}H_{12}O_6$ Ref. 874

Optical Resolution of (±)-18. A mixture of (±)-18 (21.3 g, 0.0845 mol) and cinchonidine (49.8 g, 0.169 mol) in 95% ethanol (500 mL) was refluxed for 8.5 h and allowed to stand overnight at room temperature. The deposited cinchonidine salt (44.7 g), $[\alpha]^{24}_D$ -92.9° (*c* 0.549, EtOH), was freed from the mother liquor which was reserved for isolation of the enantiomeric dicarboxylic acid 18. Five recrystallizations of the salt from ethanol furnished 6.44 g of the salt, $[\alpha]^{25}_D$ -97.0° (*c* 0.344, EtOH), which was stirred for 6 h with 5% HCl (80 mL) at room temperature. The acidic solution was extracted continuously for 3 days with ether, and removal of the solvent from the extract afforded 1.70 g of (+)-18, $[\alpha]^{27}_D$ +11.5° (*c* 0.738, EtOH), which was recrystallized three times from ethyl acetate to give 335 mg of (+)-18: $[\alpha]^{27}_D$ +13.2° (*c* 0.791, EtOH); mp 259 °C dec. The mother liquor containing the salt of (−)-18 was condensed to give a viscous oil which was diluted with 5% HCl. The same workup described for (+)-18 afforded 4.33 g of (−)-18, $[\alpha]^{26}_D$ -10.0° (*c* 0.720, EtOH), which was recrystallized four times from ethyl acetate to give (−)-18: $[\alpha]^{25}_D$ -12.9° (*c* 0.650, EtOH); mp 258 °C dec.

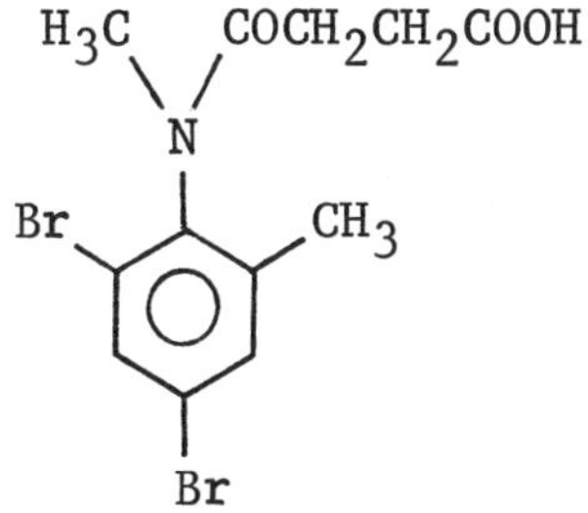

$C_{12}H_{13}Br_2NO_3$ Ref. 875

Resolution of N-Succinyl-1-methylamino-2-methyl-4,6-dibromobenzene.—A solution of 18 g. of N-succinyl-1-methylamino-2-methyl-4,6-dibromobenzene and 13.97 g. of cinchonidine in 200 ml. of 9:1 ethyl acetate–methanol by volume was filtered. This solution was concentrated by means of a gentle air stream to 170 ml. The crop of salt which had crystallized was collected. The dried product weighed 13.3 g. Concentration of the mother liquor to 130 ml. produced a second crop of 3.9 g. At 115 ml., 2.0 g. of salt crystallized; at 80 ml., 3.8 g.; and at 40 ml., 3.7 g. The first crop was recrystallized in the same manner to constant rotation. White feathery crystals were obtained; m. p. 161–163° (cor.); yield, 2.9 g.

Anal. (*l*B*d*A) Calcd. for $C_{12}H_{13}Br_2NO_3 \cdot C_{19}H_{22}N_2O$: C, 55.27; H, 5.20. Found: C, 55.63; H, 5.32. *Rotation.* (*l*B*d*A) 0.05 g. made up to 10 ml. with ethanol at 32° gave α_D −0.245°; *l*, 1; $[\alpha]^{32}_D$ −49°.

Recrystallization of the fifth crop failed to change its rotation.

Rotation. (*l*B*l*A) 0.05 g. made up to 10 ml. with ethanol at 30° gave α_D −0.285°; *l*, 1; $[\alpha]^{30}_D$ −57°.

d- **and** *l*-**N-Succinyl-1-methylamino-2-methyl-4,6-dibromobenzene.**—The salts were decomposed in the same manner as the salt of the 6-bromo compound. From the less-soluble salt the *d*-acid was obtained. The rotation was observed before the acid was crystallized from a carbon tetrachloride–petroleum ether (b. p. 60–110°) mixture.

Rotation. (*d*-acid) 0.10 g. made up to 10 ml. with *n*-butanol at 32° gave α_D +0.07°; *l*, 1; $[\alpha]^{32}_D$ +7°.

Crystallization of this acid produced white crystals; m. p. 118° (cor.).

Anal. (*d*-acid) Calcd. for $C_{12}H_{13}Br_2NO_3$: C, 38.00; H, 3.43. Found: C, 38.14; H, 3.52. *Rotation.* (*d*-acid) 0.51 g. made up to 15 ml. with *n*-butanol at 32° gave α_D +0.13°; *l*, 1; $[\alpha]^{32}_D$ +3.8°.

Decomposition of the more-soluble salt gave the *l*-acid, which was not entirely pure.

Rotation. (*l*-acid) 0.45 g. made up to 10 ml. with ethanol at 30° gave α_D −0.245°; *l*, 1; $[\alpha]^{30}_D$ −5.4°.

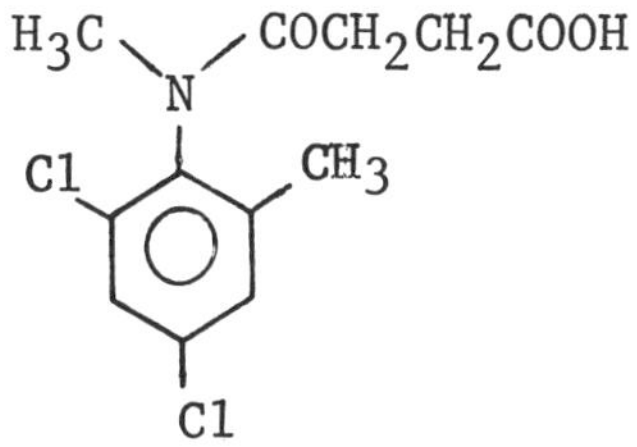

$C_{12}H_{13}Cl_2NO_3$ Ref. 876

Resolution of N-Succinyl-1-methylamino-2-methyl-4,6-dichlorobenzene.—A solution of 3.60 g. of N-succinyl-1-methylamino-2-methyl-4,6-dichlorobenzene and 3.64 g. of cinchonidine in 60 ml. of a mixture of 9:1 ethyl acetate and methanol by volume was filtered and placed in a refrigerator overnight. Crystals weighing 2.70 g. were collected. The mother liquor was taken down by means of a current of air and replaced in the refrigerator. Succeeding fractions were obtained as shown in the following table. The specific rotation readings were taken by making 0.10 g. of the salt up to 20 ml. with absolute ethanol and observing in a one-decimeter tube.

Crop	Wt., g.	α_D at 31°	$[\alpha]^{31}_D$	Vol. in ml.
I	2.70	−0.318	−64	60
II	1.57	− .316	−63	40
III	1.30	− .326	−65	20
IV	0.33	− .327	−65	5
V	0.50			0

Crop I, containing 37% of the total amount present, was recrystallized from a 9:1 ethyl acetate and methanol mixture. The following results were obtained.

Crop	Wt., g.	α_D 31°	$[\alpha]^{31}_D$	Vol. in ml.
A	0.97	−0.330	−66	30
B	1.40	− .331	−66	10
C	0.21			0

Crops A and B, having identical rotations, were accepted as the pure less-soluble salt (*lBlA*). It formed white, feathery crystals, m. p. 160° (cor.).

Rotation. 0.10 g. made up to 20 ml. with absolute ethanol at 31° gave α_D −0.330; *l*, 1; $[\alpha]^{31}_D$ −66.2°.

Anal. Calcd. for $C_{12}H_{13}NO_3Cl_2 \cdot C_{19}H_{11}N_2O$: C, 63.69; H, 6.01. Found: C, 62.97; H, 6.26.

d- and l-N-Succinyl-1-methylamino-2-methyl-4,6-dichlorobenzene.—The pure less-soluble salt, crops A and B, weighing 2.25 g., was decomposed in the usual way with 1:1 hydrochloric acid with the following improvement. After the decomposed salt turned from an oil to a crystalline mass, it was transferred to a sintered glass funnel. All washings were carried out in the funnel without removing the crystals. When the filtrate had given a negative Mayer's test and a negative chloride ion test, it was dried in a vacuum over phosphorus pentoxide. It formed white crystals, m. p. 157–158° (cor.). The yield was 1.03 g.

Rotation. 0.1110 g. made up to 2.0 ml. with absolute ethanol at 31° gave α_D −0.193°; *l*, 1; $[\alpha]^{31}_D$ −3°.

Anal. Calcd. for $C_{12}H_{13}NO_3Cl_2$: C, 49.65; H, 4.48. Found: C, 49.23; H, 4.91.

The more-soluble salt, crops III and IV, 1.43 g., which was decomposed in the usual manner produced white crystals, m. p. 157–158°. The yield was 0.54 g.

Rotation. 0.1140 g. made up to 2.0 ml. with absolute ethanol at 31° gave α_D +0.196°; *l*, 1; $[\alpha]^{31}_D$ +3°.

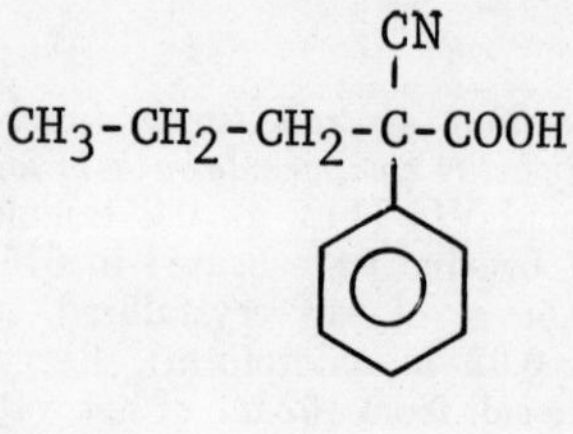

$C_{12}H_{13}NO_2$ **Ref. 877**

Note:

The acid was resolved with threo-1-[4-nitrophenyl]-2-aminopropanediol-(1,3) in acetone as solvent. The m.p. of the acids were 126-128° and the $[\alpha]_D$ were +13.7° and -14.6° for the enantiomers.

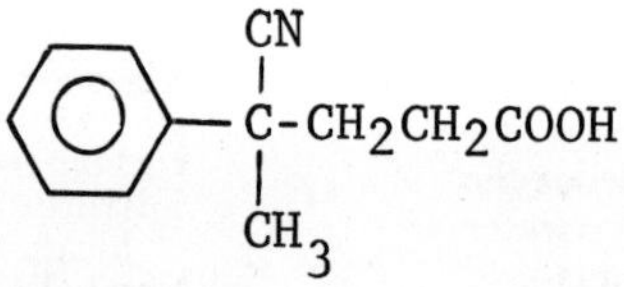

$C_{12}H_{13}NO_2$ **Ref. 878**

Resolution of 4-Cyano-4-phenylpentanoic Acid ((±)-IV)——Racemic 4-cyano-4-phenylpentanoic acid ((±)-IV) (10.3 g) and brucine (21.0 g) were dissolved in acetone (100 ml) by heating them, then water (20 ml) was added and the solution was allowed to stand. A white powder, mp 90—100° (foaming), $[\alpha]^{11}_D$ −20.8° (c=0.53, EtOH), precipitated and was filtered and dried. Twenty-six grams of powder was obtained. The powder was recrystallized two more times from acetone (100 ml) producing white small prisms, 6.8 g, mp 113—122°, $[\alpha]^{17}_D$ −31.0° (c=0.44, EtOH). Another recrystallization from acetone neither altered the melting point nor the optical rotation. *Anal. Calcd.* for $C_{25}H_{39}O_6N_3 \cdot \frac{1}{2}H_2O$: C, 67.30; H, 6.78; N, 6.73. Found: C, 67.30; H, 6.77; N, 7.09.

The brucine salt (6.8 g) was suspended in water and 10% hydrochloric acid was added to give pH 3. The acidified solution was extracted with ether, then the extract was washed with water, dried over sodium sulfate and evaporated. The residue was recrystallized from ether–hexane producing (−)-4-cyano-4-phenylpentanoic acid ((−)-IV), 2.1 g, as white prisms, mp 82—84°, $[\alpha]^{13}_D$ −20.7° (c=0.58, EtOH). Its IR spectrum in the solid state differed from that of the racemic compound, and in a chloroform solution IR spectra of the *levo* and racemic compounds were identical. ORD (c=0.45, MeOH) $[M]^{17}$ (mμ): −31° (700), −42° (589), −726° (230) (trough), −500° (200).

Mother liquors from the recrystallization of brucine salt were collected and evaporated, then the residue was recrystallized twice from acetone. Crystals, 6.3 g, mp 111—120°, $[\alpha]^{12}_D$ −30.6° (c=0.33, EtOH), were obtained from which free acid (2.0 g) was liberated. Recrystallization from ether–hexane gave crystals containing needles and prisms, mp 72—76°. Repeated recrystallization from acetone gave prisms, 1.10 g, mp 81—84°, $[\alpha]^{14}_D$ +20.7° (c=0.46, EtOH). The IR spectrum in the solid state was identical with that of the *levo* isomer. The ORD curve was antipodal to that of the *levo* isomer.

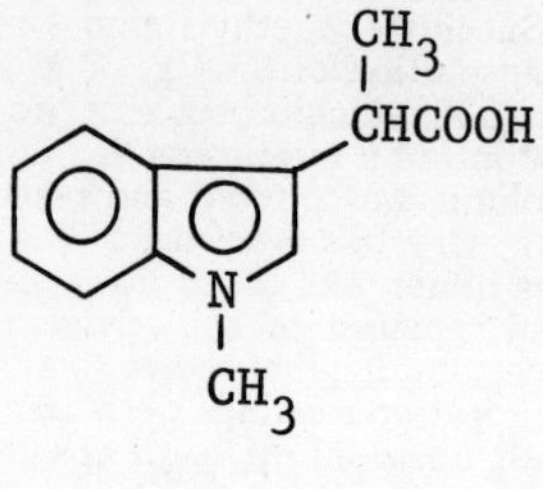

$C_{12}H_{13}NO_2$ **Ref. 879**

Preliminary experiments on resolution

The usual alkaloids were tried in dilute ethanol. Brucine and cinchonine gave dextrorotatory acid of high activity. The cinchonidine salt gave levorotatory acid while the acid from the quinine salt was quite inactive. The strychnine salt was only obtained as an oil.

An experiment on a preparative scale was started with brucine, which had formerly given the most promising results, but the activity obtained was much lower than in the preliminary experiments. The high resolution found in these experiments is probably due to supersaturation or a different rate of crystallisation. Cinchonine and cinchonidine were selected for the final resolution.

(+)-α-(1-Methyl-3-indolyl)-propionic acid

10.25 g (0.05 mole) of racemic acid and 15.4 g (0.05 mole) of cinchonine were dissolved in 75 ml ethanol + 25 ml water. The salt obtained was recrystallised twice from dilute ethanol; after each crystallisation a small sample of the acid was liberated and the activity measured in acetone solution:

Crystallisation	1	2	3
ml ethanol	75	30	20
ml water	25	10	7
g salt obtained	9.4	6.4	5.3
$[\alpha]_D^{25}$ of the acid	+44°	+84°	+84°

The acid was decomposed with dilute sulphuric acid and the organic acid isolated by extraction with ether. It was recrystallised from benzene + cyclohexane. The yield was 1.9 g. The acid forms plates or scales with the m.p. 114.5–116°.

93.65 mg acid: 9.180 ml 0.04999-*N* NaOH.
$C_{12}H_{13}O_2N$: Equiv.wt calc. 203.2, found 204.1.
0.2061 g acid dissolved in *acetone* to 10.00 ml: α_D^{25} = +3.53° (2 dm).
$[\alpha]_D^{25}$ = +85.6°; $[M]_D^{25}$ = +174.0°.

(−)-α-(1-Methyl-3-indolyl)-propionic acid

The mother liquor from the first crystallisation of the cinchonine salt was evaporated and the acid was isolated. 5.4 g having $[\alpha]_D^{25}$ = −24° were obtained. This acid (0.027 mole) and 8.1 g (0.026 mole) of cinchonidine were dissolved in 35 ml ethanol + 12 ml water. The salt was recrystallised until maximum activity of the acid was obtained as described above:

Crystallisation	1	2	3	4
ml ethanol	35	30	30	30
ml water	12	10	10	10
g salt obtained	8.7	8.1	7.5	7.3
$[\alpha]_D^{25}$ of the acid	−66°	−78°	−84°	−84°

The acid was isolated and recrystallised as described above. Its crystal form and IR-spectrum were quite similar to those of the (+)-form. Yield 2.5 g. M.p. 115–116°.

102.08 mg acid: 10.050 ml 0.04999-*N* NaOH.
$C_{12}H_{13}O_2N$: Equiv.wt calc. 203.2, found 203.2.
0.2028 g acid dissolved in *acetone* to 10.00 ml: α_D^{25} = −3.47° (2 dm).
$[\alpha]_D^{25}$ = −85.6°; $[M]_D^{25}$ = −173.9°.

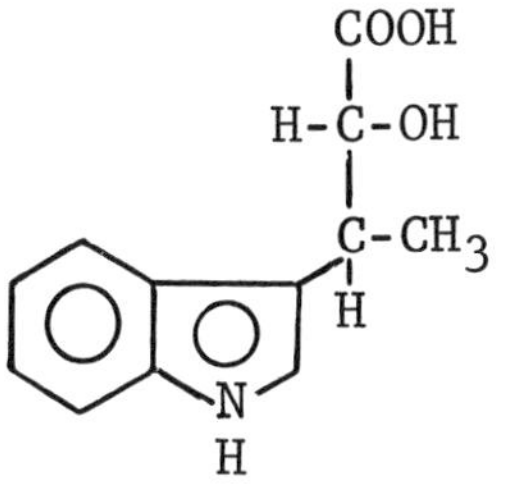

$C_{12}H_{13}NO_3$ **Ref. 880**

Resolution of (±)-α-*Indolmycenic Acid.*—To a solution of (±)-α-indolmycenic acid (33.8 g, 0.154 mol) in acetone (300 ml)–methylene chloride (300 ml), a solution of (−)-phenethylamine (18.7 g, 0.154 mol) in methylene chloride (75 ml) was added. The solvent was evaporated off, and the mixture of diastereoisomeric salts (47.7 g, 91%) washed with ethyl acetate (250 ml) and dissolved in hot acetone (1 l). On cooling, white crystals (18.96 g) separated. These were collected and after recrystallisation from acetone afforded pure (−)-α-*indolmycenic acid* (−)-*phenethylamine salt* (16.92 g, 64%), m.p. 173—175°, $[\alpha]_D^{20}$ −21.5° (*c* 10 in MeOH) (Found: C, 70.3; H, 7.0; N, 8.2. $C_{20}H_{24}N_2O_3$ requires C, 70.6; H, 7.1; N, 8.2%).

The filtrate from the first acetone crystallisation was concentrated to a gum, which was dissolved in ethyl acetate (1 l). The solution was washed with 0.1N-hydrochloric acid (100 ml) and then water (100 ml), dried ($MgSO_4$), and evaporated, yielding a gummy solid, which was dissolved in hot 1,2-dichloroethane (1.2 l). On cooling, crude (+)-α-indolmycenic acid separated as white crystals (14.06 g, 0.064 mol). These were dissolved in acetone (100 ml)–methylene chloride (100 ml) and a solution of (+)-phenethylamine (7.78 g, 0.064 mol) in methylene chloride (20 ml) was added. The solvent was evaporated off, and the residue (20.1 g) washed with ethyl acetate (150 ml) and dissolved in hot acetone (500 ml). On cooling, white crystals (15.11 g) separated. These were collected and on recrystallisation from acetone afforded pure (+)-α-*indolmycenic acid* (+)-*phenethylamine salt* (13.74 g, 52%), m.p. 174—176°, $[\alpha]_D^{20}$ +21.5° (*c* 10 in MeOH) (Found: C, 70.5; H, 7.0; N, 8.4. $C_{20}H_{24}N_2O_3$ requires C, 70.6; H, 7.1; N, 8.2%).

(−)- and (+)-α-indolmycenic acids were liberated from their phenethylamine salts in the following manner. The salt [(−),(−) 16.77 g; (+),(+) 13.52 g] was suspended in ethyl acetate (200 ml) and shaken with 0.5N-hydrochloric acid (100 ml). When all the solid had dissolved, the aqueous layer was separated and the ethyl acetate solution washed with water (100 ml), dried ($MgSO_4$), and evaporated. The solid thus obtained was triturated with 1,2-dichloroethane (50 ml), separated, and dried, yielding white crystals of (−)-α-*indolmycenic acid* (16) (10.08 g, 93%), m.p. 176—177°, $[\alpha]_D^{20}$ −9.3° (*c* 10 in MeOH) (Found: C, 65.7; H, 6.0; N, 6.4%), or (+)-α-*indolmycenic acid* (17) (7.98 g, 92%), m.p. 176—177°, $[\alpha]_D^{20}$ +9.3° (*c* 10 in MeOH) (Found: C, 65.9; H, 6.1; N, 6.5. $C_{12}H_{13}NO_3$ requires C, 65.7; H, 6.2; N, 6.4%). The i.r. and ^{1}H n.m.r. spectra of the α-indolmycenic acid enantiomers (16) and (17) were identical with those described previously[4] for (±)-α-indolmycenic acid.

[4] M. N. Preobrazhenskaya, E. G. Balashova, K. F. Turchin, E. N. Padeiskaya, N. V. Uvarova, G. N. Pershin, and N. N. Suvorov, *Tetrahedron*, 1968, **24**, 6131.

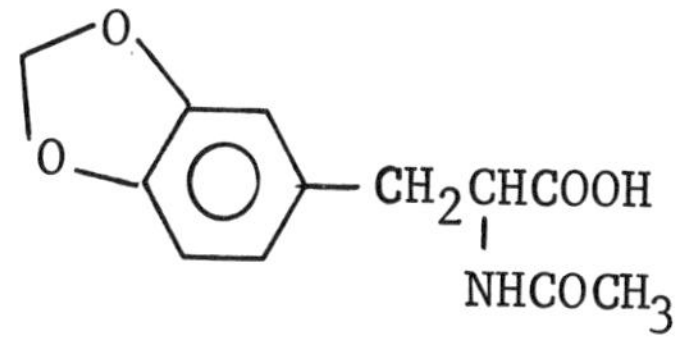

$C_{12}H_{13}NO_5$ **Ref. 881**

N-**Acetyl-3-(3,4-dimethoxyphenyl)-L-alanine-*d*-ephedrine Salt (*d*-Ephedrine-L-I Salt).**—*N*-Acetyl-3-(3,4-dimethoxyphenyl)-DL-alanine (DL-I) (53.4 g, 0.2 mole) and 33.0 g of *d*-ephedrine (0.2 mole) were dissd together in 130 ml of MeOH or in 200 ml of EtOH with warming at 55–60° for 1.0 hr, and the soln was kept in a refrigerator overnight. The colorless crystals that sepd were filtered off, washed with MeOH (*ca.* 30 ml), and dried, giving 37.9 g (87.8%) of the *d*-ephedrine-L-I salt: mp 147.5–149.5°, $[\alpha]^{20}D$ +49.8° (*c* 5, H_2O). After recrystn from 3 vol of MeOH, the mp and $[\alpha]D$ became constant: mp 152–153°; $[\alpha]^{20}D$ +54.5° (*c* 5, H_2O); yield, 28.4 g (68.1%). *Anal.* ($C_{23}H_{32}N_2O_6$) C, H, N.

N-**Acetyl-3-(3,4-dimethoxyphenyl)-L-alanine (L-I) from the *d*-Ephedrine-L-I Salt.**—*d*-Ephedrine-L-I (20 g was dissd in 50 ml of H_2O, then this soln was added dropwise with 30% HCl with cooling and stirring, giving colorless crystals. After standing in a refrigerator overnight they were filtered off, washed with H_2O (20 ml), and dried, affording 11.4 g (91.0%) of L-I: mp 149–150°; $[\alpha]^{20}D$ +46.2° (*c* 5, MeOH). *Anal.* ($C_{13}H_{17}NO_5$) C, H, N.

N-**Acetyl-3-(3,4-dimethoxyphenyl)-L-alanine (L-I) from the *d*-Ephedrine-L-I Salt.**—*d*-Ephedrine-L-I (20 g) was dissd in 50 ml of H_2O, then this soln was added dropwise with 20% HCl with cooling and stirring, giving colorless crystals. After standing in a refrigerator overnight they were filtered off, washed with H_2O (20 ml), and dried, affording 11.4 g (91.0%) of L-I: mp 149–150°; $[\alpha]^{20}D$ +46.2° (*c* 5, MeOH). *Anal.* ($C_{13}H_{17}NO_5$) H, C, N. From the filtrate and washings of the acid (L-I), *d*-ephedrine·HCl was nearly quant recovered as colorless crystals; mp 217–218°; $[\alpha]^{20}D$ +34.1° (*c* 1, H_2O).

$C_{12}H_{13}NO_5$ Ref. 881a

N-Acetyl-3-(3,4-methylenedioxyphenyl)-D-alanine Cinchonine Salt (Cinchonine·D-(IV) Salt)——N-Acetyl-3-(3,4-methylenedioxyphenyl)-DL-alanine (DL-(IV): 18.8 g.) and cinchonine (22.0 g.) were dissolved together in dehyd. EtOH (160 cc.) under warming and the solution was kept standing in a refrigerator for 3 days. The colorless prisms that separated were filtered off, washed with EtOH (ca. 20 cc.) and dried, giving 19.1 g. (93.6%) of the salt, m.p. 200~203°. The salt was recrystallized from EtOH (ca. 270 cc.) to form 15.2 g. (74.5%) of colorless prisms, m.p. 204~205°, $[\alpha]_D^{11}$ +68.7 (c=1.452, EtOH, l=1). After three recrystallizations from EtOH, m.p. and $[\alpha]_D$ of them became constant: m.p. 204~205°, $[\alpha]_D^{17}$ +68.1° (c=1.145, EtOH, l=1). Yield, 9.7 g. (47.6%). *Anal.* Calcd. for $C_{31}H_{35}O_6N_3$: C, 68.24; H, 6.47; N, 7.70. Found: C, 68.10; H, 6.71; N, 7.61.

The resolution was also effected by using MeOH as a solvent.

N-Acetyl-3-(3,4-methylenedioxyphenyl)-L-alanine Cinchonine Salt (Cinchonine·L-(IV) Salt)——The alcoholic mother liquor after removal of the crude insoluble cinchonine·D-(IV) salt was treated with charcoal and then concentrated under diminished pressure to a syrup. This was dissolved in Me_2CO (100 cc.) and the solution was kept standing at room temperature overnight. The colorless crystals, the salt of D-(IV), that separated was filtered, and the filtrate was evaporated *in vacuo* to give 18.5 g. (90%) of a slightly yellowish powder which sintered at ca. 120° and melted at 130~140°, $[\alpha]_D^{19}$ +134° (c=1.972, EtOH, l=1). The purification of this salt seemed so difficult that it was used directly in the next step.

N-Acetyl-3-(3,4-methylenedioxyphenyl)-D-, and -L-alanine (D- and L-(IV)) from the Corresponding Cinchonine Salts——D-(IV): To a suspension of 6.9 g. of the powdered cinchonine·D-(IV) salt (m.p. 204~205°, $[\alpha]_D^{17}$ +68.1°) in H_2O (5 cc.) was added dropwise *N* HCl (28 cc.) under cooling and shaking, resulting in a pale yellow, clear solution which soon separated out colorless crystals. After standing in a refrigerator overnight they were filtered off, washed with H_2O (20 cc.), and dried, affording 3.0 g. (93.8%) of D-)IV), m.p. 158~159°, $[\alpha]_D^{19}$ −53.3° (c=1.491, EtOH, l=1). Recrystallization from H_2O gave pure D-(IV) as colorless needles, m.p. 158~159°, $[\alpha]_D^{18}$ −53.4° (c=1.841, EtOH, l=1). *Anal.* Calcd. for $C_{12}H_{13}O_5N$: C, 57.37; H, 5.22; N, 5.58. Found: C, 57.31; H, 5.18; N, 5.48. IR ν_{max}^{Nujol} cm^{-1}: 3316 (NH), 1710 (COOH), 1610 (CONH). From the filtrate and washings of the acid (D-(IV)), cinchonine was nearly quantitatively recovered as colorless minute crystals, m.p. 260~262°, $[\alpha]_D^{11}$ +231° (c=0.614, EtOH, l=1).

L-(IV): When the crude cinchonine·L-(IV) salt (18.4 g.) was treated with *N* HCl (75 cc.) as in the case of the D-isomer, the crude L-acid was obtained as colorless crystals (7.5 g., 84.7%), m.p. 155~157°, $[\alpha]_D^{19}$ +47.1° (c=2.640, EtOH, l=1), which were recrystallized twice from H_2O to give L-(IV) as colorless needles, m.p. 158~159°, $[\alpha]_D^{13}$ +53.4° (c=2.262, EtOH, l=1). Yield, 3.9 g. *Anal.* Calcd. for $C_{12}H_{13}O_5N$: N, 5.58. Found: N, 5.39. The IR spectrum of this sample was superimposable with that of the D-acid. Mixed m.p. test with a sample of the D-isomer showed m.p. 178~180° sintering from 155°.

Cinchonine was also recovered in good yield.

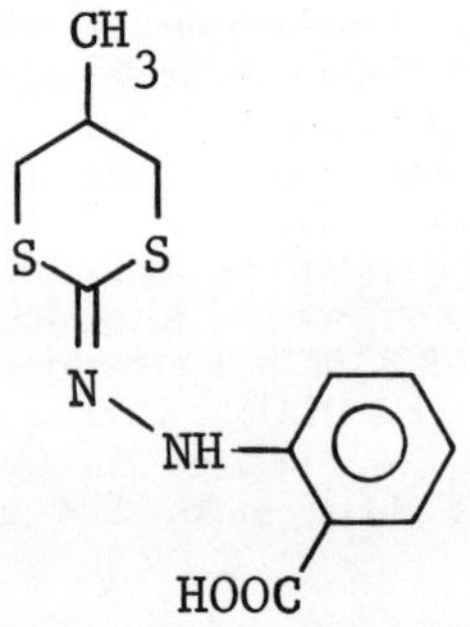

$C_{12}H_{14}N_2O_2S_2$ Ref. 882

Resolution of the o-*Carboxyphenylhydrazone of β-Methyltrimethylene Dithiolcarbonate.*—The *dl*-carboxyphenylhydrazone (5·64 g.) and quinine hydrate (7·56 g.) were dissolved in hot 90% alcohol (200 c.c.) and the filtered solution was kept; the *quinine* salt separated gradually in fine colourless needles. The weight of dried salt obtained was 6·2—6·7 g., a yield of 52—55%. It melted at 184—185°, and was very soluble in chloroform, slightly in cold alcohol, and practically insoluble in water (Found: C, 63·3; H, 6·4; N, 9·5. $C_{32}H_{38}O_4N_4S_2$ requires C, 63·4; H, 6·3; N, 9·2%).

After recrystallisation from 90% alcohol the salt showed a constant specific rotation. The following readings were made on a chloroform solution ($l = 2$; $c = 1·064$ g./100 c.c.) at 17°: $\alpha_{5461} = -5·44°$; $[\alpha]_{5461} = -255°$; $\alpha_{5780} = -4·60°$; $[\alpha]_{5780} = -216°$.

In chloroform solutions of similar concentration the quinine salt of the *dl*-compound, made by dissolving equivalent quantities of quinine and *dl*-hydrazone, had $[\alpha]_{5461}^{17°}$ − 300° and $[\alpha]_{5780}^{17°}$ − 242°.

The d-*acid*. The quinine salt (1·546 g.) was dissolved in chloroform (50 c.c.) and the quinine was removed by repeated extraction with dilute sulphuric acid. The greenish-yellow chloroform solution of the acid was examined polarimetrically after adjustment of the volume to 50 c.c. ($l = 4$; $c = 1·439$; $t = 17°$): $\alpha_{5461} = +0·72°$; $[\alpha]_{5461} = +12·5°$.

The acid was recovered from the chloroform solution by addition of light petroleum at 0° and crystallised in fine greenish-yellow needles, m. p. 199°. It was divided into two portions. The first was analysed (Found: C, 50·7; H, 5·0. Calc.: C, 51·1; H, 5·0%). The second was examined polarimetrically ($l = 4$; $c = 1·42$; $t = 17°$): $\alpha_{5461} = +0·70°$; $[\alpha]_{5461} = +12·3°$.

The sodium salt in aqueous solution has a somewhat smaller molecular rotation than the free acid. Quinine salt (0·0825 g.) was dissolved in chloroform (20 c.c.). After removal of the quinine and readjustment of the volume of the chloroform solution to 20 c.c., the solution gave $\alpha_{5461}^{17°}$ + 0·41° ($l = 2$), whence $[\alpha]_{5461} = +12·9°$. The chloroform was then extracted with *N*/5-sodium hydroxide solution, and the volume of the latter adjusted to 20 c.c. This colourless alkaline solution of the sodium salt had α_{5461} + 0·34°, giving $[\alpha]_{5461}$ + 10·7° calculated as for the acid. The acid recovered from the solution by acidification with dilute sulphuric gave, when dried and dissolved in chloroform, the following data ($l = 2$; $c = 1·406$; $t = 17°$): $\alpha_{5461} = +0·35°$; $[\alpha]_{5461} = +12·4°$.

A similar experiment in which the quinine salt was decomposed with *N*/5-sodium hydroxide and chloroform gave for the acid in alkaline solution $[\alpha]_{5461}$ + 10·5°.

On the other hand the piperidine salt has, in chloroform, a considerably higher molecular rotation than the free acid. In an experiment, made to look for possible mutarotation induced by piperidine in chloroform solution, a greenish-yellow solution of the acid ($c = 1·44$) showing α_{5461} + 0·74° ($l = 4$), corresponding with $[\alpha]_{5461}$ + 12·8°, gave on addition of a few drops of piperidine a colourless solution showing α_{5461} + 1·30° ($l = 4$), from which the *d*-acid was recovered unchanged after removal of the piperidine with dilute sulphuric acid.

The l-*acid*. The alcoholic mother-liquors obtained in the preparation of the quinine salt were mixed with chloroform and the quinine was completely removed by repeated extraction with dilute sul-

phuric acid. On the addition of light petroleum to the dried greenish-yellow solution the *l*-acid crystallised, m. p. 199° (Found: C, 50·6; H, 5·1. Calc.: C, 51·1; H, 5·0%). A solution in chloroform was examined polarimetrically with the following results ($l = 4$; $c = 1{\cdot}463$; $t = 17°$): $\alpha_{5461} = -0{\cdot}75°$, whence $[\alpha]_{5461} = -12{\cdot}8°$.

Racemisation. (i) *In chloroform solution.* In this solvent both the *d*- and the *l*-acid usually retained their optical activity unchanged over several days. In one case a solution (50 c.c.) of the *d*-acid (0·5708 g.), after being kept under observation for 3½ hours, was boiled for ½ hour (*), observed, boiled for 1½ hours (**), observed, and then left over-night. The readings were as follows.

Time (hours).	$\alpha^{17°}_{5461}$.	Time (hours).	$\alpha^{17°}_{5461}$.
0	+ 0·60°	4½	0·58°
2½	0·59	**	
3½	0·60	6½	0·59
*		7½	0·59
		24	0·01

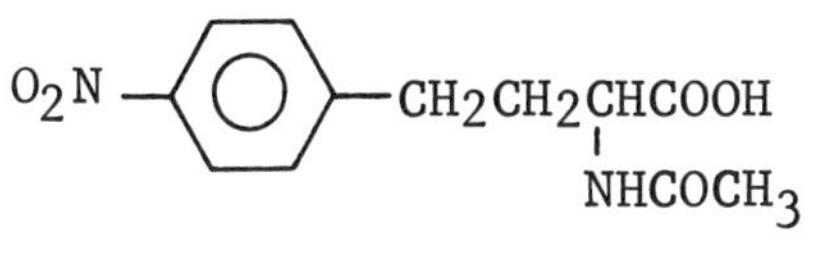

$C_{12}H_{14}N_2O_5$ Ref. 883

D-α-*Acetamido-γ-p-nitrophenylbutyric acid* (+)-α-*phenylethyleneamine salt.* To 18.8 g. of DL-α-acetamido-γ-*p*-nitrophenylbutyric acid (0.0707 mole) dissolved in 300 ml. of hot 95% ethanol was added 8.55 g. of (+)-α-phenylethylamine[14] (0.0707 mole) dissolved in 50 ml. of hot 95% ethanol and the mixture was allowed to cool slowly overnight at room temperature. On cooling light yellow plates were deposited and after filtration there was obtained 20.3 g. (70.5% of the total) of crystalline material with $[\alpha]^{27}_{D}$ +15 ± 1° (*c*, 1.17 in methanol). Two recrystallizations of this mixture from 300 ml. of 95% ethanol gave 8.5 g. of the D-α-acetamido-γ-*p*-nitrophenylbutyric acid (+)-α-phenylethylamine salt (62%) as light yellow plates with $[\alpha]^{21}_{D}$ +44 ± 2° (*c*, 0.96 in methanol) and m.p. 204–208° (dec.), the rotation of which was not altered by further recrystallization from ethanol. Reworking of the mother liquors produced an additional 0.8 g. of the salt with rotation and melting point identical with those above and this material was added to the main portion. The total yield was 68% for this diastereoisomer.

Anal. Calcd. for $C_{20}H_{25}N_3O_5$: C, 62.00; H, 6.50. Found: C, 62.12; H, 6.52.

L-α-*Acetamido-γ-p-nitrophenylbutyric acid* (+)-α-*phenylethylamine salt.* During the isolation of D-α-acetamido-γ-*p*-nitrophenylbutyric acid (+)-α-phenylethylamine salt from 18.8 g. of DL-α-acetamido-γ-*p*-nitrophenylbutyric acid (0.0707 mole) and 8.55 g. (+)-α-phenylethylamine (0.0707 mole) when the mother liquors were combined and evaporated to a small volume, two types of crystals were observed to form on cooling. One type was light yellow plates which were the D-α-acetamido-γ-*p*-nitrophenylbutyric acid (+)-α-phenylethylamine salt and very fine, long, almost colorless needles. By repeated recrystallizations from a minimum of 95% ethanol these two types of crystals were separated and there was obtained 1.4 g. of the L-α-acetamido-γ-*p*-nitrophenylbutyric acid (+)-α-phenylethylamine salt (10%) as fine, faintly yellow needles with $[\alpha]^{26}_{D}$ −38 ± 2° (*c*, 1.29 in methanol) and melting point 196–200° (dec.), the rotation of which was not changed by further recrystallization from ethanol.

Anal. Calcd. for $C_{20}H_{25}N_3O_5$: C, 62.00; H, 6.50. Found: C, 62.22; H, 6.63.

L-α-*Acetamido-γ-p-nitrophenylbutyric acid* (−)-α-*phenylethylamine salt.* The mother liquors from the isolation of 9.3 g. of the D-α-acetamido-γ-*p*-nitrophenylbutyric acid (+)-α-phenylethylamine salt and 1.4 g. of the L-α-acetamido-γ-*p*-nitrophenylbutyric acid (+)-α-phenylethylamine salt from 18.8 g. of the racemic acid (0.0707 mole) and 8.55 g. of the amine (0.0707 mole) were evaporated to dryness at reduced pressure (water pump) and there was obtained 16.3 g. of solid material. To this material suspended in 100 ml. of water was added concentrated aqueous sodium hydroxide until the solid was dissolved and the α-phenylethylamine was completely separated as an oil. The amine was removed from the aqueous solution by washing with three 60-ml. portions of ether. On acidification (*p*H 1) of the aqueous solution with concentrated hydrochloric acid, the partially resolved acid separated as a crystalline solid; and after cooling overnight at 0°, 10.8 g. (0.0406 mole) was collected by filtration. To the acid dissolved in 170 ml. of hot 95% ethanol was added 4.91 g. of (−)-α-phenylethylamine[13] (0.0406 mole) dissolved in 30 ml. of hot 95% ethanol, and the solution was allowed to cool slowly overnight at room temperature. On cooling light yellow plates were deposited and after filtration and one recrystallization from 95% ethanol, there was obtained 8.2 g. of the L-α-acetamido-γ-*p*-nitrophenylbutyric acid (−)-α-phenylethylamine salt (67% corrected for the L-α-acetamido-γ-*p*-nitrophenylbutyric acid (+)-α-phenylethylamine salt obtained above) as light yellow plates with $[\alpha]^{26}_{D}$ −44 ± 2° (*c*, 1.23 in methanol) and m.p. 203–207° (dec.), the rotation of which was not altered by further recrystallization from ethanol.

Anal. Calcd. for $C_{20}H_{25}N_3O_5$: C, 62.00; H, 6.50. Found: C, 62.10; H, 6.68.

D-α-*Acetamido-γ-p-nitrophenylbutyric acid* (IIIb). To 52.2 g. of the D-α-acetamido-γ-*p*-nitrophenylbutyric acid (+)-α-phenylethylamine salt (0.135 mole) suspended in 300 ml. of water was added concentrated aqueous sodium hydroxide until the solid was completely dissolved and the (+)-α-phenylethylamine was completely separated from the aqueous solution. The amine was removed by washing with three 200-ml. portions of ether and, on acidification (*p*H 1) of the aqueous solution with concentrated hydrochloric acid, the organic acid precipitated. After cooling the mixture overnight at 0°, filtration, and recrystallization, there was obtained 33.3 g. of D-α-acetamido-γ-*p*-nitrophenylbutyric acid (92.8%) with properties as shown in Table I.

L-α-*Acetamido-γ-p-nitrophenylbutyric acid* (IIIb). In the same way as with its enantiomorph, 26.5 g. of the L-α-acetamido-γ-*p*-nitrophenylbutyric acid (−)-α-phenylethylamine salt (0.0684 mole) was decomposed with aqueous sodium hydroxide to 14.2 g. of L-α-acetamido-γ-*p*-nitrophenylbutyric acid (78.9%) with properties as shown in Table I.

(12) O. Lutz and B. Jirgensons, *Ber.*, 63, 448 (1930).

(13) Melting points and elemental analyses were obtained as is indicated in Table I.

(14) A. W. Ingersoll, *Org. Syntheses*, Coll. Vol. II, 506 (1943).

TABLE I

Compound No. in Text	Isomer	M.P., °C.[b]	$[\alpha]_D$, ±2°[c]	Crystallization Solvent
IIIb	D	152–154	+36 (*c*, 1.23 in ethanol at 26°)	Water
IIIb	L	152–153	−34 (*c*, 1.03 in ethanol at 26°)	Water

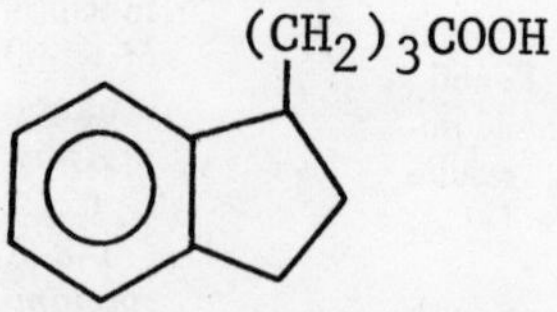

$C_{12}H_{14}O_2$

Ref. 884

Note:

Obtained an acid, m.p. 50-52°C. (hexane), $[\alpha]_D^{25}$ = +25.0°C. (c, 2.96, benzene), using (+)-α-phenylethylamine as resolving agent. Using (-)-α-phenylethylamine as resolving agent, obtained acid, m.p. 52-53.5°C. (hexane), $[\alpha]_D^{25}$ = -25.9° (c 2.63, benzene).

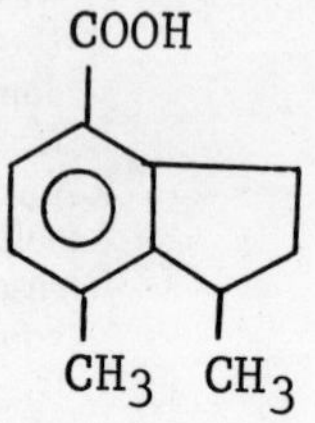

$C_{12}H_{14}O_2$

Ref. 885

Resolution of I. A solution containing 16.4 g. of racemic I and 28.1 g. of quinidine, m.p. 171.1–171.5° (purified by liberation from the sulfate and crystallization from methanol), was refluxed for one hour and treated with 150 cc. of ether. Crystallization began on cooling and seeding [the first crystal was obtained after ten days from an ether-petroleum ether (b.p. 65–70°, Skellysolve B) mixed solvent]. The first crop, m.p. 169–174°, $[\alpha]_D^{26}$ 155.2°, weighed 24.8 g. After six recrystallizations from chloroform-ether solutions, the last two of which yielded salt having the same rotation, 9.7 g. (44%) of salt, m.p. 181.4–182.8°, $[\alpha]_D^{28}$ 131.5° ± 0.4°, (*c*, 2.65% in chloroform, 2 dm. tube) was obtained.

Anal.[a] Calc'd for $C_{32}H_{36}N_2O_4$: C, 74.7; H, 7.4.

Found: C, 74.8; H, 7.7.

The free acid was liberated from the salt with hydrochloric acid and was crystallized from chloroform-Skellysolve B to yield the *l*-isomer, m.p. 136.2–137.0°, (racemic form, m.p. 177–178°), $[\alpha]_D^{27}$ −47.8° ± 0.2° (*c*, 2.6% in chloroform, 2 dm. tube). The over-all yield of resolved *l*-acid varied from 22 to 30% in several experiments.

When 0.4 g. of the optically active acid was sealed in a Pyrex ampoule and heated at 380–390° for twenty minutes it was partly racemized and partly decarboxylated. On recrystallization 230 mg. of acid, m.p. 155–170°, $[\alpha]_D^{23}$ −18°, was obtained.

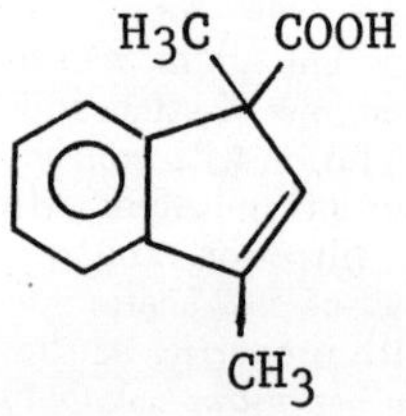

$C_{12}H_{12}O_2$

Ref. 886

Resolution of 1,3-Dimethylindene-1-carboxylic acid.

1,3-Dimethylindene-1-carboxylic acid (45 g) and quinine (78 g) were dissolved in ethanol and the volume reduced at 40°C under reduced pressure. On standing at 20°C the salt of the (+)-acid was deposited (52 g). After one recrystallisation from ethanol this gave the pure diasterioisomer (37.3 g), $[\alpha]_D^{20}$ = -32° (c = 1.97, $CHCl_3$), which on shaking with sulphuric acid (2N) and ether gave (+)-1,3-dimethylindene-1-carboxylic acid (13.3 g), $[\alpha]_D^{20}$ = +76° (c = 1.15 $CHCl_3$), m.p. 93-96° (from petroleum b.p. 60-80°).

Concentration of the mother liquor left after removal of the salt of the (+)-acid gave as a second crop the slowly crystallising and more soluble salt of the (-)-acid [38.79 g; $[\alpha]_D^{20}$ = -154.6° (c = 0.65; $CHCl_3$)]. After two recrystallisations from ethanol, this gave 12.98 g of the salt of the (-)-acid $[\alpha]_D^{20}$ = -180° (c = 0.56, $CHCl_3$). With dilute sulphuric acid this gave the (-)-acid (4.58 g), $[\alpha]_D^{20}$ = -68.6° (c = 2.2, $CHCl_3$).

A third crop (17.4 g) was obtained by addition of acetone to the original mother liquor. After two recrystallisations from ethanol this had $[\alpha]_D^{20}$ = -142° (c = 0.49, $CHCl_3$) (8.47 g), and was combined with material (8.3 g) from the mother liquors from recrystallisation of the second crop $[\alpha]_D^{20}$ -137° (c = 1.605, $CHCl_3$). Recrystallisation from ethanol failed to significantly change the rotation (12.08 g. $[\alpha]_D^{20}$ = -137.85° (c = 0.745, $CHCl_3$), and treatment with sulphuric acid gave acid $[\alpha]_D^{20}$ = -27.35° (c = 1.55, $CHCl_3$).

Note: I am indebted to Prof. D. W. Jones, Department of Organic Chemistry, University of Leeds, Great Britain, for this procedure.

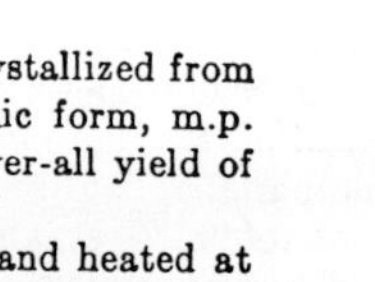

$C_{12}H_{14}O_2$

Ref. 887

Resolution of 1-Trishomobarrelene Carboxylic Acid

A hot solution of 3.5 g of racemic 1-trishomobarrelene carboxylic acid and 6.5 g of quinine in 30 ml of methanol was treated with 15 ml of water and allowed to stand at ambient temperature for 4 h and at 6°C over night. The precipitated salt was recrystallized five times from methanol/water (2:1) reducing

the amount of solvent each time to give 1.3 g of salt, m.p. 160-161°C. It was dissolved in a mixture of 20 ml 2 n hydrochloric acid and 20 ml ether. The organic layer was washed with 2 n hydrochloric acid and then extracted three times with 10 ml 10 % aqueous potassium carbonate solution. The combined extracts were acidified with hydrochloric acid to precipitate 420 mg of (-)-1-trishomobarrelene carboxylic acid, $[\alpha]^{20}_D$ = - 64.5° (c = 0.449, ethanol), enantiomeric purity: 52%.

The combined methanolic mother liquors were evaporated to dryness. From the residue 2.83 g of (+)-1-trishomobarrelene carboxylic acid, $[\alpha]^{20}_D$ = +10.5 (c= 0.895, ethanol), could be obtained by the procedure described above. A solution of 2.80 g of this carboxylic acid and 1.78 g D-(+)-α-phenylethylamine in 25 ml of methanol was treated with 50 ml of ether and allowed to stand over night at 6°C. The precipitated salt was recrystallized twice from methanol/ether (1:2) to give 1.02 g of salt, m.p. 190-193°C (phase changed between 120-130°C) which in turn gave 560 mg of (+)-trishomobarrelene carboxylic acid, $[\alpha]^{20}_D$ = +68.8° (c= 0.606, ethanol), enantiomeric purity: 55.0 %.

A D-(+)-α-phenyl-ethylamine salt with m.p. 230°C (phase changed between 155-160°C) yielded a carboxylic acid with $[\alpha]^{20}_D$ = +91.0° (c= 0.465, ethanol), enantiomeric purity: 72.8%.

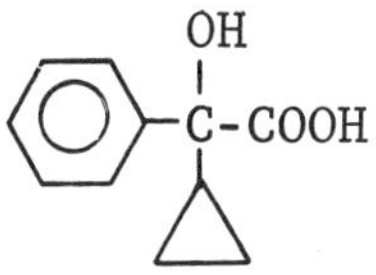

$C_{12}H_{14}O_3$ Ref. 888

Note:

a) Amphetamine was used as resolving agent.

b) The following physical constants were reported for the active acid: m.p. 75-81°, $[\alpha]_D$ -21.0° (CH_3OH).

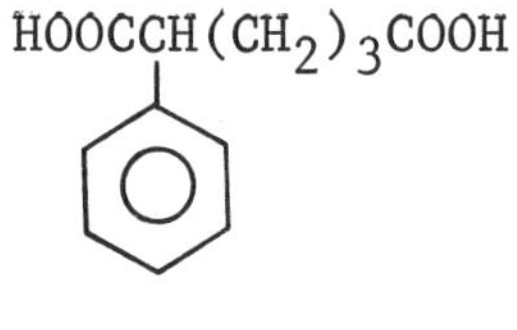

$C_{12}H_{14}O_4$ Ref. 889

Preliminary experiments on resolution.—0.22 g (0.001 moles) of racemic acid and 0.002 moles of the bases were dissolved in dilute ethanol or methanol. From the crystals formed the acid was isolated and the activity measured in abs. ethanol. The results are given in Table 1.

Resolution of the racemic acid

17.8 g (0.08 moles) of racemic α-phenyladipic acid and 53.5 g (0.16 moles) of strychnine were dissolved in 400 ml of hot 84 % ethanol. The solution was allowed to stand at room temperature and then in a refrigerator. After 24 hours the salt was collected (46.4 g) and from a sample the acid was isolated and the optical activity measured in absolute ethanol. The remaining salt was recrystallized from dilute ethanol (Table 2).

The first mother liquor was evaporated to dryness at room temperature and the remaining strychnine salt (24.9 g) was dissolved in 155 ml of boiling 77 % methanol. The recrystallization was carried out as described above (Table 3).

Table 1.

Base	$[\alpha]^{25}_D$ of acid, measured in abs. ethanol From ethanol + water	From methanol
Strychnine	+ 20°	− 19°
Cinchonine	oil	oil
Quinine	+ 8°	± 0°
Brucine	− 26°	+ 3°
Quinidine	oil	+ 15°
Cinchonidine	oil	oil
(+)-α-Phenylethylamine	− 13°	—

Table 2.

Cryst. No.	84 % ethanol (ml)	Weight of salt (g)	$[\alpha]^{25}_D$ of acid
1	400	46.4	+ 16.5°
2	400	31.2	+ 34.5°
3	225	22.0	+ 43°
4	200	16.6	+ 49.5°
5	100	12.9	+ 54.5°
6	100	10.5	+ 57.5°
7	100	7.4	+ 59.5°
8	67	5.4	+ 61.5°
9	33	4.2	+ 61.5°

Table 3.

Cryst. No.	77 % methanol (ml)	Weight of salt (g)	$[\alpha]^{25}_D$ of acid
1	155	14.1	− 38.5°
2	155	8.7	− 54.5°
3	105	6.0	− 58°
4	53	4.5	− 60°
5	31	3.1	− 61.5°
6	19	2.1	− 61.5°

(+)-α-Phenyladipic acid

The strychnine salt (4.2 g) was decomposed with 2-*N* sodium hydroxide and the strychnine extracted with chloroform. The remaining aqueous phase was acidified with dilute sulphuric acid and the active acid thoroughly extracted with ether. On evaporating the ether at room temperature 1.0 g of crude acid was obtained. This was recrystallized once from 85 % formic acid and once from water. Yield 0.80 g. The acid forms small rods melting at 153–155°.

0.0587 g acid: 10.33 ml 0.05127-*N* NaOH
Equiv. wt. calc. 111.1, found 110.8
0.1513 g acid dissolved in abs. ethanol to 10.00 ml: 2 α^{25}_D = + 1.93°, $[\alpha]^{25}_D$ = + 63.8°; $[M]^{25}_D$ = + 141.8°.

Weighed amounts of the acid were made up to 10.00 ml with different solvents and the optical activity measured (Table 4).

(−)-α-Phenyladipic acid

The acid was isolated from 2.1 g of strychnine salt and recrystallized in the same way as described for the (+)-acid. Yield 0.40 g. M.p. 153–155°.

0.0547 g acid: 9.62 ml 0.05127-*N* NaOH
Equiv. wt. calc. 111.1, found 110.9
0.1549 g acid dissolved in abs. ethanol to 10.00 ml: 2 α^{25}_D = − 1.97°, $[\alpha]^{25}_D$ = − 63.6°; $[M]^{25}_D$ = − 141.3°.

Table 4.

Solvent	mg acid	2 α^{25}_D	$[\alpha]^{25}_D$	$[M]^{25}_D$
Ethyl acetate	157.4	+ 2.61°	+ 82.9°	+ 184°
Acetone	153.1	+ 2.44°	+ 79.7°	+ 177°
Acetic acid	156.3	+ 2.41°	+ 77.1°	+ 171°
Ethanol (abs.)	151.3	+ 1.93°	+ 63.8°	+ 142°
Water (neutr.)	108.0	+ 0.34°	+ 15.7°	+ 35°

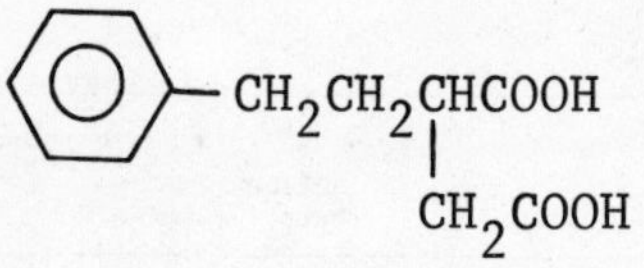

$C_{12}H_{14}O_4$ Ref. 890

Preliminary Experiments on Resolution.

Added brucine yielded crystalline salt, for the most part containing (—)-acid. Quinine and cinchonidine yielded voluminous precipitates of which the cinchonidine salt was suitable for isolating the (+)-acid. Cinchonine, strychnine, and quinidine did not give salts of good crystalline structure.

(—)-β-Phenylethylsuccinic acid.

33.3 g racemic acid and 139.6 g brucine were dissolved in 1400 ml boiling water On cooling the neutral salt crystallized in long white prisms. The salt was removed after two hours. Several recrystallizations were carried out. A sample was taken after each recrystallization, the acid was liberated and the rotatory power measured.

Crystallisation	1	2	3	4	5	6
Quantity of water used (ml)	1400	1400	700	700	700	700
g salt	92	63	56	42	26	22
$[\alpha]_D^{25}$ in ethanol solution	−16.2°	−31.2°	−33.0°	−36.9°	−38.6°	−38.1°

Analysis

0.1735 g air-dried salt was dried over P_2O_5. Weight reduction:

0.0265 g

0.2895 g salt: 12.03 ml N_2 (746 mm Hg, 19.9°).

$C_{12}H_{14}O_4$, $2C_{23}H_{26}N_2O_4$, $10H_2O$	calc.	H_2O 15.13	N 4.71
	found	» 15.12	» 4.75

20 g brucine salt yielded 3.65 g acid. The crude product was recrystallized from hot water. 3.50 g acid was collected as white needles (m.p. 124.5—125.0°).

0.1168 g (—)-acid: 10.38 ml 0.1012-N NaOH
E.W. calc. 111.1 found 111.2

0.2171 g (—)-acid in *ethanol*, made up to 10 ml: 2 $\alpha_D^{25} = -1.668°$; $[\alpha]_D^{25} = -38.4°$; $[M]_D^{25} = -85.4°$

0.1402 g (—)-acid in *acetic acid*, made up to 10 ml: 2 $\alpha_D^{25} = -1.13$; $[\alpha]_D^{25} = -40.3°$; $[M]_D^{25} = -89.5°$

0.1368 g (—)-acid in *ethyl acetate*, made up to 10 ml: 2 $\alpha_D^{25} = -1.355°$; $[\alpha]_D^{25} = -49.5°$; $[M]_D^{25} = -110.0°$

0.1102 g (—)-acid *neutralized* with sodium hydroxide and diluted with *water* to 10 ml: 2 $\alpha_D^{25} = -0.343°$; $[\alpha]_D^{25} = -15.5°$; $[M]_D^{25} = -34.5°$

(+)-β Phenylethylsuccinic acid.

The acid was liberated from the mother liquor of crystallization 1, above. The specific rotation was + 21.5°. 8.6 g of this acid and 22.8 g cinchonidine were dissolved in 300 ml hot alcohol. After 24 hours the salt had precipitated in the form of flocculations. A series of recrystallizations, each time from 300 ml alcohol, resulted in:

Crystallisation	1	2	3
g salt	9.7	7.1	5.8
$[\alpha]_D^{25}$ in ethanol solution	+32.5°	+37.5°	+38.0°

Analysis

0.2171 g salt: 14.89 ml N_2 (746 mm Hg, 18.9°)

$C_{12}H_{14}O_4 \cdot 2C_{19}H_{22}N_2O$ N calc. 6.91 found 6.97

5.5 g salt yielded 1.5 g acid. After recrystallization from hot water 1.35 g was obtained. The acid melted at 124.0—124.5° and appeared exactly like the (—)-acid.

0.1155 g (+)-acid: 10.25 ml 0.1012-N NaOH
E.W. calc. 111.1 found 111.5

0.2264 g (+)-acid in *ethanol*, made up to 100 ml: 2 $\alpha_D^{25} = +1.725°$; $[\alpha]_D^{25} = +38.1°$; $[M]_D^{25} = +84.6°$

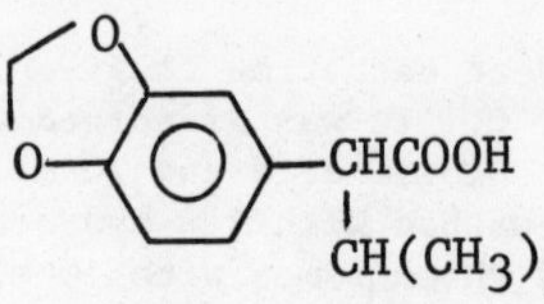

$C_{12}H_{14}O_4$ Ref. 891

For resolution procedure and physical constants for the above compound, see Ref. 905

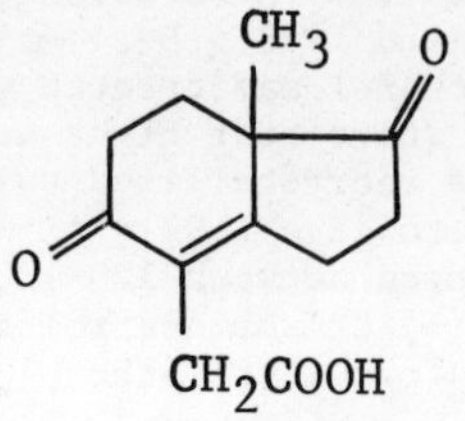

$C_{12}H_{14}O_4$ Ref. 892

Exemple 2. — Dédoublement de l'acide 1,5-dioxo 7a-méthyl 5,6,7,7a-tétrahydro indane 4-acétique, III.

a. Préparation du sel dextrogyre du D(—)-thréo 1-p-nitrophényl 2-N,N-diméthylamino propane 1,3-diol, I, avec l'acide 1,5-dioxo 7*a*-méthyl 5, 6, 7, 7*a*-tétrahydro indane 4-acétique, III*a*, dextrogyre.

On dissout au reflux 22,2 g d'acide 1,5-dioxo 7*a*-méthyl 5,6,7,7*a*-tétrahydro indane 4-acétique racémique et 24 g de D(—)thréo 1-p-nitrophényl 2-N,N-diméthylamino propane 1,3-diol, I, dans 100 cm³ d'acétate d'éthyle à 2 % d'eau et 7 cm³ d'éthanol. On amorce la cristallisation et laisse refroidir la solution jusqu'à température ambiante pendant deux heures environ, puis laisse au repos à froid pendant douze heures. On essore ensuite les cristaux formés, les lave à plusieurs reprises avec de l'acétate d'éthyle à 1 % d'eau et sèche.

On obtient 21,84 g du sel cherché, F. = environ 100 °C, $/\alpha/_D = + 78° \pm 1°$ ($c = 1$ %, eau).

Le produit est soluble dans l'eau et les alcools. Il est peu soluble dans l'acétate d'éthyle.

A la connaissance de la société demanderesse, ce composé n'est pas décrit dans la littérature.

b. Préparation de l'acide 1,5-dioxo 7*a*-méthyl 5,6,7,7*a*-tétrahydro indane 4-acétique, III*a*, dextrogyre.

On introduit, sous azote 24 g de sel dextrogyre du D(—)thréo 1-p-nitrophényl 2-N,N-diméthylamino propane 1,3-diol avec l'acide 1,5-dioxo 7*a*-méthyl 5,6,7,7*a*-tétrahydro indane 4-acétique dextrogyre dans 100 cm³ d'eau glacée. Puis, on ajoute lentement, sous agitation, 50 cm³ de soude N.

On filtre ensuite, recueille le filtrat, le lave à plusieurs reprises à l'acétate d'éthyle, puis l'acidifie avec de l'acide chlorhydrique concentré, ajoute du sulfate d'ammonium jusqu'à saturation et extrait à plusieurs reprises par le chlorure de méthylène. On réunit les extraits, les sèche sur sulfate de magnésium, traite au noir animal et évapore à sec sous vide.

On reprend le résidu par 20 cm³ de toluène, l'abandonne à la cristallisation, essore les cristaux formés, les lave au toluène glacé et sèche.

On obtient 10,5 g de l'acide 1,5-dioxo 7*a*-méthyl 5,6,7,7*a*-tétrahydro indane 4-acétique dextrogyre, III*a*, F. = 129 °C, $/\alpha/_D$ = + 225° ± 1° (*c* = 0,5 %, eau).

Le produit est peu soluble dans le toluène, assez soluble dans l'eau, soluble dans les alcools et le chloroforme.

A la connaissance de la société demanderesse, ce composé n'est pas décrit dans la littérature.

c. Préparation du sel lévogyre du L(+)-thréo 1-p-nitrophényl 2-N,N-diméthylamino propane 1,3-diol, II, avec l'acide 1,5-dioxo 7*a*-méthyl 5,6,7,7*a*-tétrahydro indane 4-acétique, III*b*, lévogyre.

On effectue selon le mode opératoire du paragraphe *a* ci-dessus le dédoublement de 61,5 g d'acide 1,5-dioxo 7*a*-méthyl 5,6,7,7*a*-tétrahydro indane 4-acétique, III, racémique au moyen de 68 g de D(—)thréo 1-p-nitrophényl 2-N,N-diméthylamino propane 1,3-diol, I, sépare le sel dextrogyre du D(—)thréo 1-p-nitrophényl 2-N,N-diméthylamino propane 1,3-diol avec l'acide 1,5-dioxo 7*a*-méthyl 5,6,7,7*a*-tétrahydro indane 4-acétique dextrogyre résultant, recueille les eaux mères, les évapore à sec sous vide, reprend le résidu huileux par l'eau, alcalinise la solution par la lessive de soude, filtre pour séparer les cristaux formés, les lave à l'eau à plusieurs reprises, réunit le filtrat et les eaux de lavage, lave par l'acétate d'éthyle, puis acidifie par l'acide chlorhydrique, ajoute du sulfate d'ammonium jusqu'à saturation, sépare l'acide racémique résiduel qui précipite alors, extrait à plusieurs reprises la solution saturée de sulfate d'ammonium par le chlorure de méthylène, réunit les extraits, les sèche sur sulfate de magnésium, traite au noir animal, filtre et évapore à sec sous vide.

Le résidu est dissous au reflux avec 30 g de L(+)-thréo 1-p-nitrophényl 2-N,N-diméthylamino propane 1,3-diol, II, dans 190 cm³ d'acétate d'éthyle à 2 % d'eau. On amorce la cristallisation et laisse reposer une nuit.

On essore ensuite les cristaux formés, les lave à l'acétate d'éthyle à 2 % d'eau, les sèche et obtient après purification 51,1 g du sel cherché, $/\alpha/^{20}_D$ = —78° ± 1° (*c* = 1 %, eau).

Le produit est peu soluble dans l'acétate d'éthyle, soluble dans l'eau et les alcools.

A la connaissance de la société demanderesse, ce composé n'est pas décrit dans la littérature.

d. Préparation de l'acide 1,5-dioxo 7*a*-méthyl 5,6,7,7*a*-tétrahydro indane 4-acétique, III*b*, lévogyre.

Par décomposition du sel obtenu ci-dessus et suivant la méthode décrite pour l'acide dextrogyre, on obtient l'acide 1,5-dioxo 7*a*-méthyl 5, 6, 7, 7*a*-tétrahydro indane 4-acétique, III*b*, lévogyre, F. = 129 °C, $/\alpha/^{20}_D$ = —225° ± 1° (*c* = 0,5 %, eau).

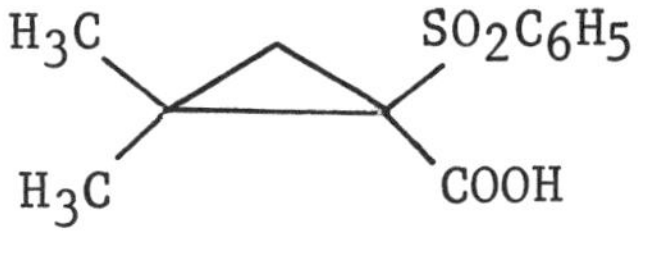

$C_{12}H_{14}O_4S$ Ref. 893

Acid V was resolved through its quinine salt from ethanol, and the (+)-V[5] obtained was brought to maximum rotation by fractional crystallization from benzene, mp 102–103°, $[\alpha]^{25}_{546}$ +20.7° (*c* 5, chloroform), 25% yield. From filtrates of the quinine salt crystallization, (−)-V[5] was recovered and brought to nearly maximum rotation by fractional crystallization from benzene, mp 100–102°, $[\alpha]^{25}_{546}$ −18.2° (*c* 5, chloroform), 10% yield.

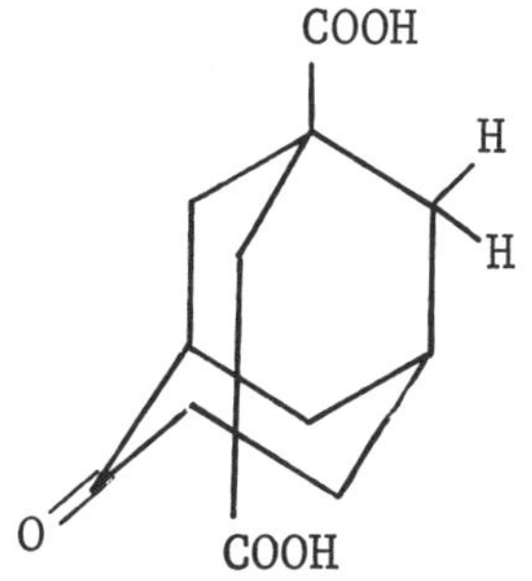

$C_{12}H_{14}O_5$ Ref. 894

Note:

Resolution of acid VI was accomplished through the di-dehydroabietylamine salt (7) (m.p. of racemic material 163-167°), which was fractionally crystallized from aqueous methanol and acetone to constant m.p. (176-180°) and maximum CD molecular ellipticity of the resulting acid (as determined in 2% aqueous sodium hydroxide solution). The optically active (-)-antipode of VI obtained by decomposition of the head fraction salt from the above recrystallization has m.p. 211-212° and CD $[\theta]_{293}$ = +248 ± 15 (c, 0.144 in 2% aqueous sodium hydroxide).

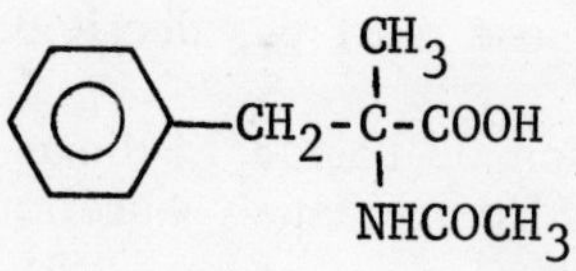

$C_{12}H_{15}NO_3$

Ref. 895

(+)- *and* (−)-N-*Acetyl-α-Methylphenylalanine.*—(A) Attempted resolution with Acylase I (Greenstein, 1957). To an aqueous suspension of 7 g of *N*-acetyl-DL-α-methylphenylalanine in 300 ml of water was added sufficient lithium hydroxide to bring the *p*H to 7.0; 0.2 g of Armour Acylase I, lot No. 945-40, was introduced and the solution maintained at 38°. At various time intervals 0.4-ml aliquots were withdrawn and analyzed for amino-nitrogen by the Van Slyke procedure (Archibald, 1957). The extent of hydrolysis was only 7.4% after 62 hours.

(B) Resolution with (+)-α-methylphenethylammonium sulfate. To an aqueous-ethanol solution containing equivalent amounts of (+)-α-methylphenethylammonium sulfate and *N*-acetyl-DL-α-methylphenylalanine was added one equivalent of 4 N aqueous sodium hydroxide. The precipitated sodium sulfate was removed, and the filtrate was concentrated until turbid and then stored at 4°. The crystalline precipitate was collected and fractionally recrystallized from aqueous-ethanol to give a series of dextrorotatory fractions, maximum $[\alpha]_D$ 17.9, minimum $[\alpha]_D$ 8.5°. Each fraction was dissolved in aqueous 4 N sodium hydroxide and the solutions (*p*H > 10) were extracted with ethyl ether, the aqueous phases acidified with concentrated hydrochloric acid, and the precipitated acylated amino acids collected. The end-fractions gave products $[\alpha]_D$ = 85.7° and $[\alpha]_D$ = −15° (*c*, 1% in water) respectively.

(C) Resolution with (+)- and (−)-α-phenethylamine. DL-α-Phenethylamine was resolved with D-tartaric acid (Theilacher and Winkler, 1954). The addition of one equivalent of (−)-α-phenethylamine in water, a mixture of isopropyl alcohol and isopropyl ether, ethyl acetate, or acetone, to one equivalent of the acylated DL-amino acid in the same solvent gave crystalline diastereoisomeric salts which were decomposed as described above to give acids of $[\alpha]_D$ −57°, −58°, −81°, and −85.6° (*c*, 0.3% in water) respectively. The acid $[\alpha]_D$ −85.6° (*c*, 0.3% in water), $[\alpha]_D$ −74.3° (*c*, 1% in methanol) was obtained in 55% yield. Reaction of (+)-α-phenethylamine with the acylated DL-amino acid in acetone, followed by decomposition of the crystalline salt, gave the other antipode of the acid, $[\alpha]_D$ 74.4° (*c*, 1% in methanol).

$C_{12}H_{15}NO_3$

Ref. 895a

N-Acetyl-α-methylphenylalanine 1-Menthyl Esters (VIa, VIb)——To the suspension of Na powder (5.8 g., 0.25 mole) in anhyd. benzene (200 ml.) was added 1-menthol*[6] (39.0 g., 0.25 mole). The reaction mixture was kept standing overnight at room temperature avoiding moisture and refluxed for 2 hr. Unreacted Na powder was decanted off and washed with anhyd. benzene (100 ml.). To the combined benzene solution of the supernatant and the washings was added a solution of DL-V (42.2 g., 0.208 mole) in anhyd. benzene (100 ml.). The reaction mixture was stirred at room temperature for 5 hr., and then kept standing overnight. The benzene solution was washed with 10% AcOH (300 ml. × 2), H_2O (300 ml. × 1), 2.5% Na_2CO_3 (300 ml. × 1), and H_2O (300 ml. × 2) successively, and then dried with anhyd. Na_2SO_4. Filtration and evaporation *in vacuo* of this benzene solution gave pale yellow oil, which solidified on standing. Recrystallization from iso-Pr_2O (700 ml.) afforded colorless plates (42.6 g.), m.p. 123～147°, $[\alpha]_D^{25}$ −28.8°(c=1.366, MeOH). Another twice recrystallizations from iso-Pr_2O gave crude VIa as colorless needles (18.6 g., 50%), m.p. 169.5～172°, $[\alpha]_D^{21}$ +35.0°(c=1.618, MeOH). Recrystallization of crude VIa from iso-Pr_2O–AcOEt (5:4) afforded pure VIa as colorless needles (15.1 g., 40%), m.p. 171～173°, $[\alpha]_D^{23}$ +37.5°(c=1.588, MeOH). Analytical sample obtained from further twice recrystallizations from the same solvent showed m.p. 171.5～172.5°, $[\alpha]_D^{22}$ +37.4°(c=1.112, MeOH). *Anal.* Calcd. for $C_{22}H_{33}O_3N$: C, 73.50; H, 9.25; N, 3.90. Found : C, 73.91; H, 9.16; N, 3.67. IR ν_{max}^{KBr} cm^{-1} : 3260, 1744, 1640, 1563, 1197, 735, 699. IR $\nu_{max}^{CHCl_3}$ cm^{-1} : 3440, 3400, 1730, 1677, 1505.

The combined mother liquor of the first two recrystallizations was evaporated *in vacuo* to give yellow solid, which was recrystallized from hexane (300 ml.) to afford pale yellow crystals (30.0 g.), m.p. 114～118°, $[\alpha]_D^{22}$ −71.5°(c=1.122, MeOH). Successive recrystallization from hexane, iso-Pr_2O, 70% aq. EtOH, and iso-Pr_2O (×2) gave crude partially resolved VIb*[7] as white crystals (3.7 g., 9.9%), m.p. 121.5～123°, $[\alpha]_D^{21}$ −87.6° (c=1.242, MeOH). Another twice recrystallizations from hexane gave partially resolved VIb as white crystals, m.p. 121.5～123.5°, $[\alpha]_D^{19}$ −80.9°(c=1.318, MeOH). *Anal.* Calcd. for $C_{22}H_{33}O_3N$: C, 73.50; H, 9.25; N, 3.90. Found : C, 72.95; H, 9.04; N, 4.14. IR ν_{max}^{KBr} cm^{-1} : 3360, 1727, 1672, 1535, 1122, 749, 709. IR $\nu_{max}^{CHCl_3}$ cm^{-1} : 3440, 3400, 1727, 1677, 1504.

(+)-N-Acetyl-*R*-α-methylphenylalanine (*R*(+)-III)——A mixture of (+)-VIa (m.p. 171～172.5°, $[\alpha]_D^{22}$ +37.4°(c=1.168, MeOH)) (11.0 g., 0.0307 mole) and KOH (17.2 g., 0.307 mole) in 50% aq. EtOH (200 ml.) was refluxed for 5 hr., condenced to ca. half volume and extracted with benzene (50 ml. × 3). Aqueous layer was acidified with dil. HCl and kept in an ice bath for 2 hr. to crystallize out the crude *R*(+)-III as white powdery crystals (5.5 g., 81%), m.p. 200～201.5°, $[\alpha]_D^{21}$ +78.2°(c=1.334, MeOH). Recrystallization from 50% aq. EtOH gave pure *R*(+)-III as colorless needles (5.0 g., 74%), m.p. 200.5～202°, $[\alpha]_D^{19}$ +80.3°(c=1.052, MeOH). Analytical sample was prepared by the repeated recrystallization from the same solvent, m.p. 200.5～202.5°, $[\alpha]_D^{20}$ +79.3°(c=1.082, MeOH) (lit.,[5] m.p. not described. $[\alpha]_D$ +74.4°(c=1, MeOH)). *Anal.* Calcd. for $C_{12}H_{15}O_3N$: C, 65.14; H, 6.83; N, 6.33. Found : C, 65.14; H, 6.76; N, 6.36. IR ν_{max}^{KBr} cm^{-1} : 3340, 1722, 1633, 1560, 752, 706. This IR spectrum was different from that of DL-III in solid state. Another hydrolysis using 70% aq. EtOH as a solvent raised the yield of the crude *R*(+)-III up to 97%.

5) H.R. Almond, Jr., D.T. Manning, C. Niemann : Biochem., 1, 243 (1962).

*6 $[\alpha]_D^{19}$ −51.1°(c=3.326, EtOH).

*7 Partial resolution of (−)-1-menthyl ester VIb was deduced from the fact that VIb showing $[\alpha]_D^{25}$ −83.5° (c=1.424, MeOH) gave *S*(−)-III whose optical purity was 59%.

(−)-**N-Acetyl-*S*-α-methylphenylalanine (*S*(−)-III)**——A mixture of (−)-VIIb (m.p. 120.5~122.5°, $[\alpha]_D^{25}$ −83.5°(c=1.424, MeOH)) (2.5 g., 0.00696 mole) and KOH (3.9 g., 0.0696 mole) in 50% aq. EtOH (45 ml.) was treated similarly to the case of *R*(+)-III to give crude partially resolved *S*(−)-III as white powdery crystals (1.5 g., 97%), m.p. 187~190°, $[\alpha]_D^{21}$ −46.8°(c=1.034, MeOH) (optical purity 59%).*8 Recrystallization from 50% aq. EtOH afforded colorless needles (1.1 g., 72%), m.p. 189.5~193.5°, $[\alpha]_D^{18}$ −55.6° (c=1.012, MeOH) (optical purity 70%).*8 Further recrystallization from the same solvent gave analytical sample as colorless needles, m.p. 196.5~200.5°, $[\alpha]_D^{19}$ −78.4° (c=1.036, MeOH) (optical purity 99%)*8 (lit.,[5]) m.p. not described, $[\alpha]_D$ −74.3°(c=1, MeOH)). *Anal.* Calcd. for $C_{12}H_{15}O_3N$: C, 65.14; H, 6.83; N, 6.33. Found: C, 65.18; H, 6.99; N, 6.37. IR ν_{max}^{KBr} cm^{-1}: 3440, 1721, 1633, 1577, 752, 706. This IR spectrum was identical with that of *R*(+)-III in solid state.

*8 Optical purity was calculated based on the assumption that *R*(+)-III showing $[\alpha]_D^{20}$ +79.3° (MeOH) was optically pure.

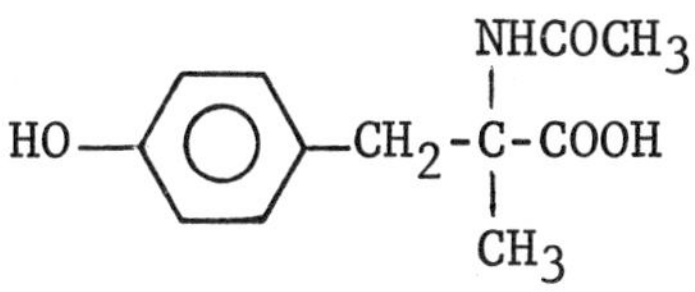

$C_{12}H_{15}NO_4$ **Ref. 896**

(−)-α-N-*Acetyl-α-methyltyrosine.*—To a solution of 1 g of α-*N*-acetyl-DL-α-methyltyrosine in 100 ml of acetone was added 0.75 equivalents of (−)-α-phenethylamine. The precipitated salt was collected and the filtrate evaporated to dryness. Both fractions were dissolved in 4 N aqueous sodium hydroxide, the solutions were extracted three times with ethyl ether, and the aqueous phases were acidified to *p*H 2 with concentrated hydrochloric acid. The precipitated acids were collected, washed with water, and dried, and their rotations were determined. The fractionation was repeated until products of constant rotation were obtained. Six successive fractionations of 20 g of the DL-acid gave 0.3 g of (−)-α-*N*-acetyl-α-methyltyrosine $[\alpha]_D$ −61.1° (*c*, 1–2% in methanol).

(+)-α-N-*Acetyl-α-methyltyrosine.*—Fractionation of 1 g of α-*N*-acetyl-DL-α-methyltryrosine with (+)-α-phenethylamine gave 0.2 g of (+)-α-*N*-acetyl-α-methyltyrosine, $[\alpha]_D$ 61.0° (*c*, 1–2% in methanol).

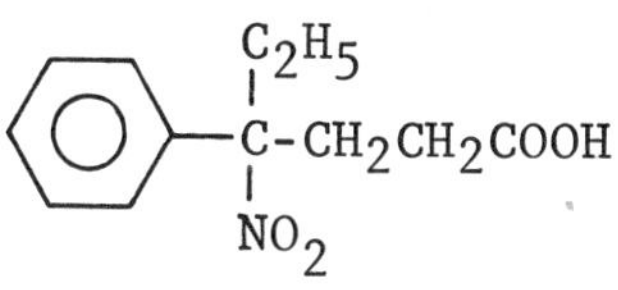

$C_{12}H_{15}NO_4$ **Ref. 897**

(+)-4-Nitro-4-phenylhexanoic Acid.—Cinchonidine (98.5 g., 0.33 mole) and the nitro acid (79.5 g., 0.33 mole) were dissolved in the minimum of hot ethanol. **Cinchonidine 4-nitro-4-phenylhexanoate** (69 g.) crystallized on cooling as long white needles, m.p. 147–148°.

Anal. Calcd. for $C_{31}H_{37}N_3O_5 \cdot H_2O$[26]: C, 67.74; H, 7.15; N, 7.65. Found: C, 68.14, 67.84; H, 7.02, 6.99; N, 7.67.

The acid, generated by shaking the salt with ether and dilute HCl, showed $[\alpha]^{22}D$ +14.6°, not increased by crystallization from benzene. The cinchonidine salt was recrystallized from ethanol five times and the progress of the resolution was followed by measuring $[\alpha]D$ for the acid rather than the sparingly soluble salt. The rotation was unchanged by the last two recrystallizations, giving for pure (+)-**nitro acid**, $[\alpha]^{22}D$ +23.4° (12.1 g., 62%).

Found: C, 61.24; 61.06; H, 6.42; 6.44; N, 5.73.

Cinchonidine (+)-4-nitro-4-phenylhexanoate showed $[\alpha]^{22}D$ +55.6° in ethanol.

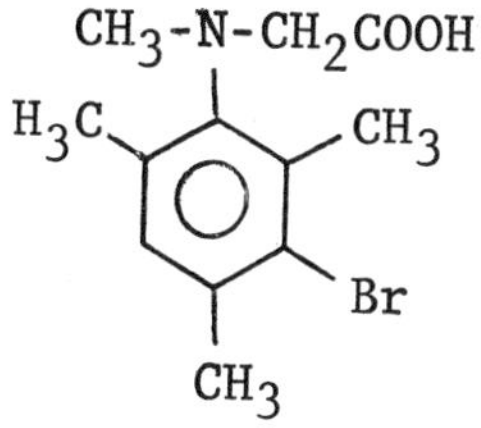

$C_{12}H_{16}BrNO_2$ **Ref. 898**

Resolution and Racemization of N-Carboxymethyl-N-methyl-3-bromomesidine.—A chloroform solution of 3.10 g. of N-carboxymethyl-N-methyl-3-bromomesidine and 3.20 g. of cinchonidine was evaporated *in vacuo* from 100 ml. to approximately 10 ml. The viscous residue was dissolved in 150 ml. of acetone by boiling under reflux for one hour. When the filtered acetone solution was allowed to stand overnight in a refrigerator, a colorless solid formed, which was removed by filtration and stored in a refrigerator. More solid crystallized out, as the solution stood at low temperature. Four crops were collected totaling in weight about 90% of the salt present; the melting point and rotation of each was essentially the same.

Crop	Time, days	Wt., g.	$[\alpha]^{33}D$	M.p., °C.
1	1	2.995	−56.3°	157–158
2	2	1.229	−58.0	158–158.5
3	3	0.403	−57.2	157–158
4	6	0.995	−57.5	156–158

Anal. Calcd. for $C_{12}H_{16}BrNO_2 \cdot C_{19}H_{22}N_2O$: C, 64.13; H, 6.60. Found: C, 64.11; H, 6.78.

By repeated extraction of combined crops 1 and 2 with 20% aqueous hydrochloric acid to which ice was added, 1.5 g. of *d*-acid was isolated, m.p. 104–104.5°.

From 1.25 g. of the *d*-acid, 20 ml. of a solution in methyl acetate was prepared, which was used in racemization experiments at the temperature of boiling methyl acetate (57°). The previously described technique with sealed tubes[22] was employed.

The results of one run, which were very closely duplicated in a second run, were as follows: 0.0 hr., αD +0.661°, $[\alpha]^{33}D$ +10.8°; 0.25 hr., αD +0.417°, $[\alpha]^{33}D$ +6.82°; 0.5 hr., αD +0.269°, $[\alpha]^{33}D$ +4.40°; 0.75 hr., αD +0.166°, $[\alpha]^{33}D$ +2.72°; 1.0 hr., αD +0.116°, $[\alpha]^{33}D$ +1.90°; 1.5 hr., αD +0.032°, $[\alpha]^{33}D$ +0.8°. From these data, $t_{1/2}$ = 0.47 hr.

(22) R. Adams and K. V. Y. Sundstrom, THIS JOURNAL, **76**, 5474 (1954).

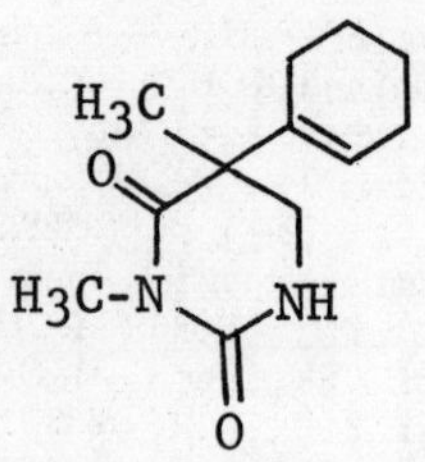

$C_{12}H_{16}N_2O_3$

Ref. 899

1. N-Methylchininiumhydroxid

N-Methylchininiumjodid wurde nach *Major* und *Finkelstein*[5]) dargestellt, indem zu einer gekühlten Lösung von 93 g Chinin in 100 ml Methanol 42 g Methyljodid zugefügt wurden. Das beim Stehen über Nacht ausgefallene Reaktionsprodukt wurde abgesaugt, mit Methanol/Äther (1 : 1) gewaschen und getrocknet. 30 g N-Methylchininiumjodid wurden in 100 ml Methanol aufgeschwemmt, mit 90 g hydroxidbeladenem stark basischem Anionenaustauscher *Merck* versetzt und 2 Std. geschüttelt. Danach wurde der Austauscher abgesaugt, mit Methanol nachgewaschen und das Filtrat in einem Meßkolben mit Methanol auf 250 ml aufgefüllt. 5,0 ml dieser Lösung wurden nach Verdünnen mit Wasser mit 0,1 n HCl titriert (Tashiro). Verbrauch 12,25 ml 0,1 n HCl. 1 ml 0,1 n HCl entspricht 23,63 mg Hexobarbital. 245 ml der Lösung des quartären N-Methylchininiumhydroxids sind 14,18 g Hexobarbital äquivalent. Aus 236,3 g (1 Mol) Hexobarbital können 574,5 g N-Methylchininium-Hexobarbital entstehen, aus 14,18 g Hexobarbital 34,48 g N-Methylchininium-Hexobarbital, bzw. je 17,24 g der diastereomeren Salze.

2. Gewinnung der diastereomeren N-Methylchininium-Hexobarbitale

14,18 g Hexobarbital wurden in 245,0 ml methanolischer N-Methylchininiumhydroxidlösung (s. o.) gelöst und das Lösungsmittel i. Vak. abgezogen. Das zurückbleibende Öl wurde in 150 ml Äthanol aufgenommen und die Lösung bis zur schwachen Trübung mit Äther versetzt. Es kristallisierten 12 g feine verfilzte Nadeln, die aus Äthanol/Äther umkristallisiert wurden. Ausbeute 10,8 g. Nach Trocknen i. Vak. über P_2O_5 Schmp. 148°.

$C_{33}H_{42}N_4O_5$ (574,7)	Ber.:	C 68,96	H 7,37
	Gef.:	C 68,51	H 7,26

Aus der Mutterlauge kristallisierten nach weiterem Ätherzusatz 8,1 g eines Gemisches von verfilzten Nadeln und derben Prismen. Nach Einengen der Lösung kristallisierten 11 g derbe Prismen, die aus Äthanol umkristallisiert wurden. Ausbeute 9,9 g. Schmp. 203° unter Braunfärbung.

$C_{33}H_{42}N_4O_5$ (574,7)	Ber.:	C 68,96	H 7,37
	Gef.:	C 68,89	H 7,05

3. Gewinnung der Hexobarbital-Antipoden aus den diastereomeren N-Methyl-chininium-salzen

a) (—)-Hexobarbital

10,8 g des Salzes vom Schmp. 148° wurden unter Erwärmen in Äthanol gelöst und die Lösung mit 2 n H_2SO_4 und Wasser versetzt. Es fielen derbe Nadeln aus, die aus Äthanol/Wasser umkristallisiert wurden. Ausbeute 3,8 g, Schmp. 153°.

$C_{12}H_{16}N_2O_3$ (236,3)	Ber.:	C 61,00	H 6,83
	Gef.:	C 61,08	H 6,72

Spezifische Drehung:

$$[\alpha]_D^{20} \; -11{,}94° \; (c = 2{,}388;\ \text{Äthanol})$$

$$[\alpha]_D^{18} \; -5{,}23° \; (c = 3{,}252;\ \text{Chloroform}).$$

b) (+)-Hexobarbital

9,9 g des Salzes vom Schmp. 203° wurden unter Erwärmen in Äthanol gelöst und die Lösung mit 2 n H_2SO_4 und Wasser versetzt. Es fielen derbe Nadeln aus, die aus Äthanol/Wasser umkristallisiert wurden. Ausbeute 3,1 g, Schmp. 153°.

$C_{12}H_{16}N_2O_3$ (236,3)	Ber.:	C 61,00	H 6,83
	Gef.:	C 61,39	H 6,82

Spezifische Drehung:

$$[\alpha]_D^{20} \; +12{,}17° \; (c = 3{,}452;\ \text{Äthanol})$$

$$[\alpha]_D^{18} \; +4{,}93° \; (c = 3{,}252;\ \text{Chloroform})$$

Die Schmp. wurden im Linström-Block bestimmt und sind unkorrigiert. Die Messung der IR-Spektren erfolgte im Beckman-Spektrophotometer IR 5 in KBr.

[5]) *R. T. Major* und *J. Finkelstein*, J. Amer. chem. Soc. *63*, 1368 (1941).

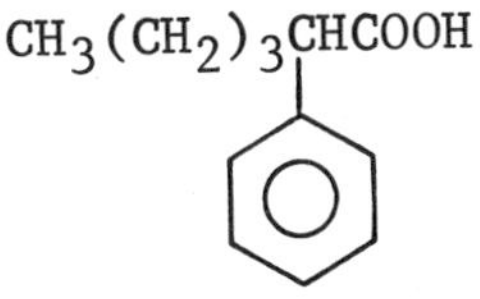

$C_{12}H_{16}O_2$ Ref. 900

Optical resolution of α-phenylcaproic acid

(−)-α-*Phenylethylamine* (+)-α-*phenylcaproate:* 19.2 g (0.1 mole) of racemic α-phenylcaproic acid and 12.1 g (0.1 mole) of (−)-α-phenylethylamine were dissolved in hot ethanol and the solution allowed to cool. The crystals obtained were recrystallised from ethanol and the resolution followed as described for the resolution of phenylvaleric acid. The optically pure salt formed long, colourless needles. The progress of the resolution is shown in Table 6.

Table 6.

Crystallisation number	(+)-(II) g of salt obtained	(+)-(II) $[\alpha]_D^{25}$	(−)-(II) g of salt obtained	(−)-(II) $[\alpha]_D^{25}$
1	12.5	+33°	8.0	−37°
2	10.5	+49°	6.2	−50°
3	9.6	+55°	5.0	−57°
4	8.9	+63°	4.2	−61°
5	8.5	+63°	3.5	−63°
6	8.2	+63°	3.3	−62°

(+)-α-*Phenylethylamine* (−)-α-*phenylcaproate:* The mother liquor from the first crystallisation of the (+)-acid salt was evaporated to dryness, the organic acid liberated with dilute sulfuric acid and extracted with ether. The ether was removed and the residual acid treated with an equivalent amount of (+)-phenylethylamine in ethanol. The resolution was carried out as described for phenylvaleric acid. The results are shown in Table 6.

(+)-α-*Phenylcaproic acid:* (−)-α-Phenylethylamine (+)-α-phenylcaproate was treated with dilute sulfuric acid and the liberated (+)-phenylcaproic acid isolated as described for the optically active phenylvaleric acids. Viscous almost colourless oil.

102.4 mg of the acid consumed 6.88 ml of 0.0776*N* NaOH.
$C_{12}H_{16}O_2$: Equiv. weight calc. 192.2 found 191.9.
96.7 mg of the acid was dissolved in absolute ethanol and made up to 10.00 ml.
$2\alpha_D^{25} = +1.207°$ $[\alpha]_D^{25} = +62.4°$ $[M]_D^{25} = +120.0°$.

(−)-α-*Phenylcaproic acid:* From the (+)-phenylethylamine salt as described for the (+)-acid. Almost colourless viscous oil.

111.2 mg of the acid consumed 7.66 ml of 0.0754*N* NaOH.
$C_{12}H_{16}O_2$: Equiv. weight calc. 192.2 found 192.5.
Optical activity in homogenous state: $[\alpha]_D^{20} = -72.9°$ $[M]_D^{20} = -150.8°$.
Optical activities in different solvents (*vide ante*) are given in Table 9.

Table 9.

Solvent	mg of acid	$2\alpha_D^{25}$	$[\alpha]_D^{25}$	$[M]_D^{25}$
Acetone	99.2	−1.629°	−82.1°	−157.8°
Benzene	166.8	−2.501°	−74.9°	−144.1°
Acetic acid	104.3	−1.502°	−72.0°	−138.4°
Ether	147.3	−1.916°	−65.0°	−125.0°
Ethanol	116.0	−1.430°	−61.6°	−118.5°
Water (ion)	115.1	−0.154°	− 6.7°	− 12.8°

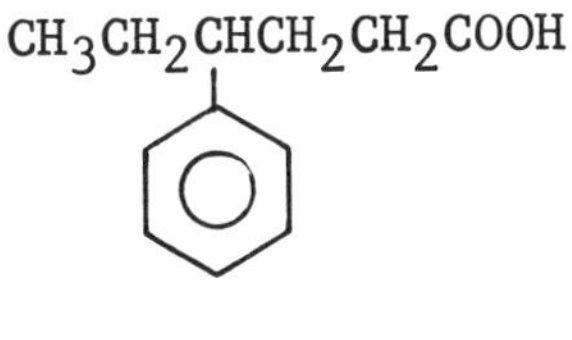

$C_{12}H_{16}O_2$ Ref. 901

Dextro-4-Phenylcaproic Acid (*6*)—The inactive acid was prepared from *n*-propylphenylbromomethane and ethyl malonate. 460 gm. of the inactive acid were dissolved in 6 liters of boiling acetone and 870 gm. of quinine were added. The solution was allowed to stand in the cold room overnight for crystallization. After six crystallizations the quinine salt was decomposed and the acid extracted as described for 3-methylphenylpropionic acid. B.p., 152° at 4 mm.; yield, 70 gm.; $n_D^{25} = 1.5078$; $D_4^{25} = 1.025$.

$$[\alpha]_D^{25} = \frac{+6.08°}{1 \times 1.025} = +5.93°. \quad [M]_D^{25} = +11.39° \text{ (homogeneous)}$$

4.395 mg. substance: 12.145 mg. CO_2 and 3.305 mg. H_2O.
$C_{12}H_{16}O_2$. Calculated. C 74.95, H 8.39
Found. " 75.35, " 8.41

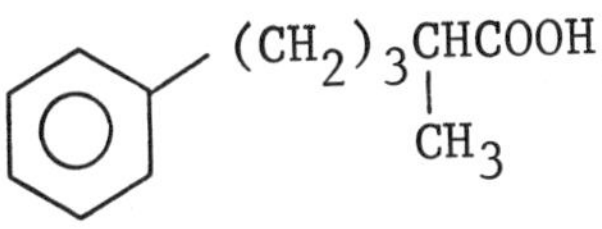

$C_{12}H_{16}O_2$ Ref. 902

The acid was resolved via salt formation with (+)- and (−)-α-phenylethylamine. The active acid obtained has $[\alpha]_D^{20}$ 20.2° (c 1.1, ethanol).

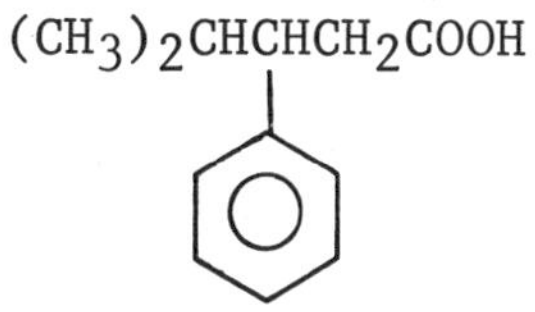

$C_{12}H_{16}O_2$ Ref. 903

(+)-*3-phenyl-4-methylpentanoic acid*

24.0 g (0.125 moles) of rac.-3-phenyl-4-methylpentanoic acid and 40.5 g (0.125 moles) of quinine were dissolved in 100 ml of hot ethanol and 60 ml of water were added. After standing for two days at room temperature, 49.6 g of salt had separated. It was recrystallized four times and each time measurements were made on small samples of liberated acid (Table 5).

(−)-*3-phenyl-4-methylpentanoic acid*

From combined mother liquors 21.6 g (0.112 moles) of (−)-3-phenyl-4-methylpentanoic acid ($[\alpha]_D = -7.8°$, in benzene) were liberated. It was dissolved in 150 ml of hot ethanol together with 32.9 g (0.112 moles) of cinchonidine and 50 ml of water were added. The salt was recrystallized four times (Table 6).

Table 6. Resolution of 3-phenyl-4-methylpentanoic acid with cinchonidine.

Crystallization	Ethanol (ml)	Water (ml)	Salt obtained (g)	m.p. of salt (degrees)	$[\alpha]_D^{25}$ of acid (in benzene) (degrees)
1	150	50	49.1	—	—
2	75	25	34.6	95–108.0	−17.8
3	40	20	27.4	96–109.0	−22.9
4	30	10	20.2	99–147.0	−35.0
5	20	10	16.9	146–148.0	−40.5

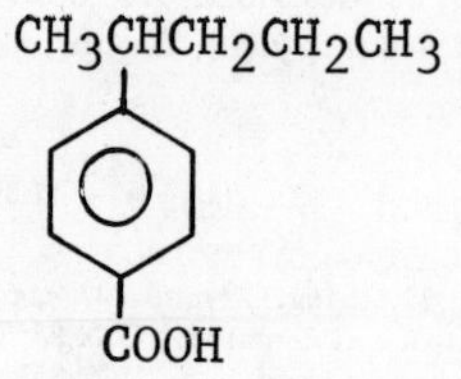

$C_{12}H_{16}O_2$ Ref. 904

Resolution of 4-(2′-Pentyl)-benzoic Acid.—To a boiling solution of 223 g. of quinine dissolved in 2 l. of 95% ethanol was added 223 g. of the acid. The salt that separated was recrystallized twenty-four times from 95% ethyl alcohol, in each case using enough solvent to just dissolve the salt at reflux temperature. Decomposition of the salt produced 21.5 g. of acid, m.p. 54–55°, $[\alpha]^{23}D$ −23.3° (3.3% solution in absolute ethanol). That optical purity was obtained is shown by the rotations of small samples of acid prepared from the salt at various stages of recrystallization: after sixteen recrystallizations, $[\alpha]^{23}D$ −19.5°; after eighteen, $[\alpha]^{23}D$ −22.5°; after twenty, $[\alpha]^{23}D$ −23.4°. Another 12.4 g. of material, m.p. 54–55°, $[\alpha]^{23}D$ −23.2° was recovered by fractional crystallization of second crops.

Fractional crystallization of the acid obtained from various filtrates gave 135 g. of racemic acid, m.p. 70–72°, and 31 g. of (+) acid, $[\alpha]^{23}D$ +12.3°, m.p. 50–58°.

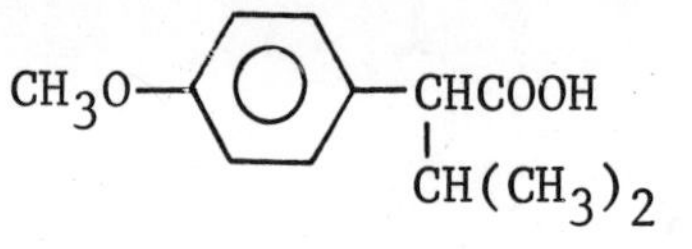

$C_{12}H_{16}O_2$ Ref. 905

Resolution of α-isopropyl-4-methylphenylacetic acid

dl-α-Isopropyl-4-methylphenylacetic acid (15.00 g), (−)-α-phenyl-β-4-tolylethylamine (16.48 g, $[\alpha]_D^{22°}$−12.1°, neat, l=1) and 60% aqueous ethanol (700 ml) were warmed and allowed to cool to room temperature for overnight. Upon filtration 14.80 g of the salt was separated and recrystallized 3 times from 60% aqueous ethanol (600, 400 and 350 ml) to give 10.2 g of the salt, $[\alpha]_D^{22°}$−69.0° (MeOH, c=0.49). The salt was decomposed with 10% H_2SO_4 *aq.*, extracted with ether, dried (Na_2SO_4) and concentrated to yield 4.80 g of (−)-α-isopropyl-4-methylphenylacetic acid, mp 88∼89°C, $[\alpha]_D^{20°}$ −61.6° ($CHCl_3$, c=0.42). The mother liquors were concentrated and the impure (+)-acid was recovered in the same way to give 5.20 g, $[\alpha]_D^{21°}$+19.3° ($CHCl_3$, c=1.65). The (+)-acid was purified by recrystallization of the (+)-α-phenyl-β-4-tolylethylamine salt. The pure (+)-acid was obtained by decomposition of the amine salt: yield: 3.18 g (42.4%), mp 89∼90°C, $[\alpha]_D^{20°}$+60.0° ($CHCl_3$, c=0.60).

Authors' comments:

Optical resolutions of the modified phenylacetic acids could be performed in high yields by recrystallizations of either the optically active α-phenyl-β-4-tolylethylamine (PTE) or α-phenylethylamine (PEA) salts: the (+)-acid salt with the (+)-PTE were preferentially recrystallized from aqueous ethanol. (+)-Isopropylphenylacetic acid and the (+)-4-bromo analog were obtainable by resolution with (−)-PEA. The (−)-optical isomers of the modified phenylacetic acids were also prepared by recrystallizations of either the (−)-PTE or (+)-PEA salts.

Optical purities of the resolved acids were determined by GLC analysis of the corresponding (−)-menthyl esters which were prepared from the acid chloride with (−)-menthol and pyridine. The esters of the (+)-acids gave on available data in Table II the larger retention times than those of the (−)-acids.[3]

3) B. Halpern and J. W. Westley, *Chem. Comm.*, **1967**, 237; C. J. W. Brooks and J. D. Gilbert, *ibid.*, **1973**, 194.

Table I. Properties of (S)-(+)-α-Isopropyl-4-substituted Phenylacetic Acids

(S)-(+)-form

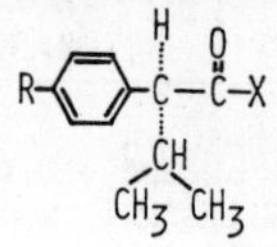

R	X=OH Acid mp (°C)	$[\alpha]_D$ deg	(°C)[a]	Amine salt confign. of amine[b]	$[\alpha]_D$ deg	(°C)[c]
-H	*dl* 61∼62[e] *d* 49.5∼50.5[e]	60.5	(25.0)	(−) PEA	+ 5.9	(23.0)
$-CH_3$	*dl* 95∼96 *d* 88∼89	60.0	(20.0)	(+) PTE	+69.0	(22.0)
$-OCH_3$	*dl* 131∼132 *d* 131∼132	52.8	(22.0)	(+) PTE	+61.9	(21.5)
-F	*dl* 64∼65 *d* 1.4838[f]	46.8	(23.5)	(+) PTE	+65.3	(23.0)
-Cl	*dl* 88∼89 *d* 104∼105	46.8	(21.0)	(+) PTE	+44.7	(21.0)
-Br	*dl* 96∼97 *d* 107∼108	39.2	(23.0)	(−) PEA	− 4.6	(21.5)
3,4<O O>CH_2	*dl* 90∼91 *d* 92∼93	42.6	(20.0)	(+) PTE	+44.4	(20.0)

a) Rotation in $CHCl_3$, concentration 1∼2 g/100 ml.
b) PEA: α-phenylethylamine (Aldrich chemicals), PTE: α-phenyl-β-4-tolylethylamine (K. Ueda *et al.*, Japan patent No. 46–20382 (1971)).
c) In MeOH, concentration 1∼2 g/100 ml.
d) In $CHCl_3$, concentration 1∼2 g/100 ml.
e) Ref. 4).
f) n_D value (21.5°C).

Table II. GLC Retentiontimes of (−)-Menthyl-(±)-α-isopropyl-4-substituted Phenylacetates

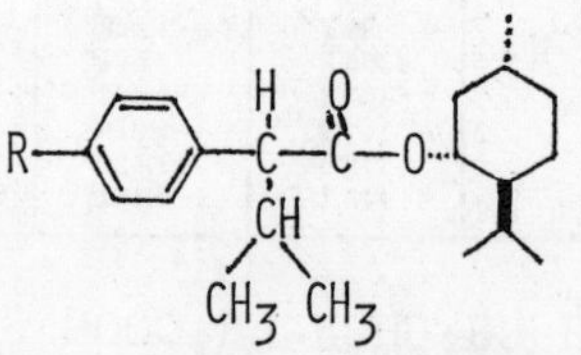

R	GLC column[a]	(+)-Phenyl acetate	(−)-Phenyl acetate	Ratio (+)/(−)
-H	A	8′40″	7′24″	1.169
$-CH_3$	B	6′48″	5′54″	1.153
$-OCH_3$	B	8′12″	7′05″	1.157
-F	A	10′55″	9′25″	1.159
-Cl	A	8′53″	7′40″	1.159
-Br	A	11′10″	9′50″	1.136
3,4<O O>CH_2	B	11′20″	9′50″	1.153

a) A: DGAP 5%, 1m, 120°C, carrier N_2 48ml/min.
B: DEGS 5%, 1.7m, 170°C, carrier N_2 50ml/min.

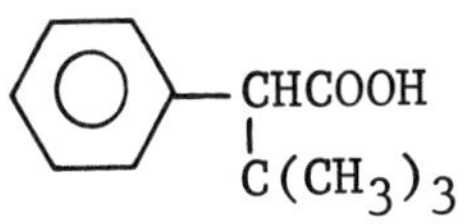

$C_{12}H_{16}O_2$ Ref. 906

Resoluton of α-t-Butylphenylacetic Acid.—*dl*-α-*t*-Butylphenyl-acid, 127.5 g, was heated with (+)-α-phenylethylamine, 80.7 g, α^{28}_D +37.6 (l = 1, neat), in 3 l. of 70% aqueous ethanol, and the solution was allowed to cool slowly to give 170 g of salt. Six successive crystallizations of this salt from 70% aqueous ethanol gave 31.5 g, mp 193–195°, $[\alpha]^{27}_D$ +21.2 (CH_3OH, c 3.5) which upon treatment with 25% sulfuric acid in the cold gave 17.2 g of acid, mp 141–142°, $[\alpha]^{27}_D$ +62.9 ($CHCl_3$, c 7). More dextrorotatory acid was recovered by fractional crystallization of the salts from the mother liquors. Regeneration of the non-crystalline mother liquors gave impure (−) acid, mp 103–110°, $[\alpha]^{24}_D$ −7.7 ($CHCl_3$, c 3). This was converted to the pure (−) acid, $[\alpha]^{25}_D$ −62.9 ($CHCl_3$, c 5), by fractional crystallization of the salt prepared from the enantiomeric (−)-α-phenylethylamine. It was determined in this portion of the resolution that methanol was superior to 70% ethanol as a solvent for the fractional crystallization.

$C_{12}H_{16}O_2$ Ref. 906a

Note:

Resolved using brucine. Obtained acid with $[\alpha]_{589}$ -48.2°, $[\alpha]_{405}$ -122° (c 2.315, ethanol).

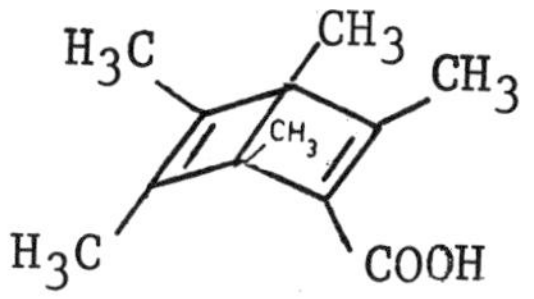

$C_{12}H_{16}O_2$ Ref. 907

Resolution of the above compound was achieved via the brucine salt. The highest observed specific rotation of the resolved acid was $[\alpha]^{20}_{578}$ -36.2° (c 0.29, ethanol) which corresponds with an optical purity of 40 ± 5%.

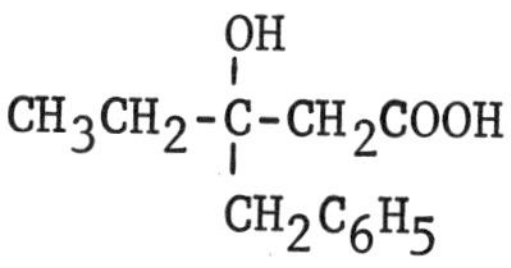

$C_{12}H_{16}O_3$ Ref. 908

Enantiomers of Sodium 3-Benzyl-3-hydroxyvalerate (+)-(VIII) and (−)-(VIII). The salt (VIII) was dissolved in water, and the solution was acidified to pH 2 with hydrochloric acid. The acid was extracted with ether, and to the extract we added an ethereal solution of (+)-DPPA. The mixture was stirred in the cold for 3 h. The precipitate was filtered off and fractionally crystallized from acetone. The less soluble salt (IX) was obtained fairly readily in 60% yield. The salt (X) was obtained by the evaporation of the acetone mother solutions and recrystallization of the residue from ether. Yield 40%. Each salt was decomposed with 5% NaOH, the amine was extracted with ether, and the solution of the sodium salt was saturated with carbon dioxide to lower the pH, vacuum-evaporated, and treated as described for the salts (IVa) and (IVb).

From the salt (IX) we obtained the salt (+)-(VIII), $[\alpha]_D^{18}$ +19° (c 2, water); from the salt (X) we obtained the salt (−)-(VIII) $[\alpha]_D^{18}$ −19°. The yield of the resolved enantiomers was about 50%.

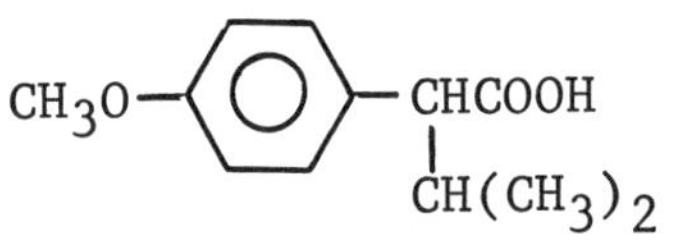

$C_{12}H_{16}O_3$ Ref. 909

For both the resolution procedure and physical constants for the above compound, see Ref. 905.

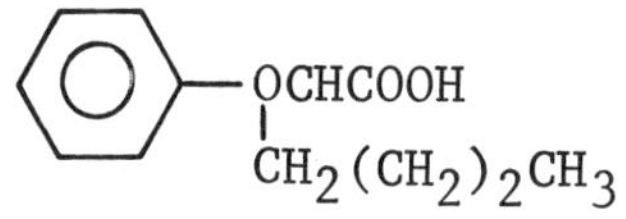

$C_{12}H_{16}O_3$ Ref. 910

(+)-α-*Phenoxy-n-caproic acid.* Racemic acid (11.5 g, 0.055 mole) and (−)-β-phenyl*iso*propylamine (7.4 g, 0.055 mole) were dissolved in a hot mixture of 85 ml alcohol and 195 ml water. The salt was allowed to crystallise in a cool place for some hours. The optical activity of the acid, liberated from a small sample, was measured in alcohol. The salt was recrystallised several times according to Table 2.

From the last salt fraction 1.78 g of the crude (+)-acid were obtained. Recrystallisation from 50% formic acid yielded 1.42 g of the pure (+)-form, m.p. 75–76.7°.

77.69 mg acid: 7.510 ml 0.04955-*N* NaOH
$C_{12}H_{16}O_3$ calc. equiv. wt. 208.3
found » » 208.8

0.1893 g dissolved in abs. *alcohol* to 20.06 ml: $2\alpha^{25}_D$ = +0.709°. $[\alpha]^{25}_D$ = +37.6°; $[M]^{25}_D$ = +78.2°.
0.1834 g » » *acetone* to 20.06 ml: $2\alpha^{25}_D$ = +0.877°. $[\alpha]^{25}_D$ = +48.0°; $[M]^{25}_D$ = +99.9°.
0.1710 g » » *chloroform* to 20.06 ml: $2\alpha^{25}_D$ = +0.418°. $[\alpha]^{25}_D$ = +24.5°; $[M]^{25}_D$ = +51.1°.
0.1835 g » » *benzene* to 20.06 ml: $2\alpha^{25}_D$ = +0.051°. $[\alpha]^{25}_D$ = + 2.8°; $[M]^{25}_D$ = + 5.8°.
0.1638 g neutralised with *aqueous NaOH* and made up to 20.06 ml: α^{25}_D = +0.132°. $[\alpha]^{25}_D$ = +16.2°; $[M]^{25}_D$ = +33.7°.

Table 2. Recrystallisation of the (−)-β-phenyl*iso*propylamine salt of α-phenoxy-*n*-caproic acid.

Cryst. No.	Solvent (ml)		Weight of salt (g)	$[\alpha]_D$ of the acid
	Alcohol	Water		
1	85	195	14.5	+ 6.0°
2	75	175	11.2	+14.8°
3	60	140	8.3	+26.3°
4	50	110	6.5	+33.7°
5	40	90	5.8	+36.0°
6	35	80	4.3	+36.8°
7	30	70	3.6	+37.3°
8	25	60	3.11	+37.3°

(−)-*α-Phenoxy-n-caproic acid.* From the mother liquors 1–3 (Table 2) a lævorotating acid ($[\alpha]_D = -19°$ in alcohol) was regenerated. This acid (6.15 g, 0.03 mole) and an equivalent quantity of (+)-β-phenyl*iso*propylamine (4.0 g) were dissolved in 70 ml of alcohol and 160 ml of water in the hot. The salt, which separated on cooling, was recrystallised as seen from Table 3. The rotatory power of the acid was measured in alcohol as usual.

Table 3. Recrystallisation of the (+)-β-phenyl*iso*propylamine salt of α-phenoxy-*n*-caproic acid.

Cryst. No.	Solvent (ml)		Weight of salt (g)	$[\alpha]_D$ of the acid
	Alcohol	Water		
1	75	160	7.3	−29.9°
2	60	130	6.1	−34.8°
3	50	105	5.1	−36.3°
4	40	90	4.2	−36.9°
5	30	70	3.52	−36.9°

Salt fraction 5 was decomposed and the organic acid isolated. The crude acid (2.0 g) was recrystallised from 50% formic acid. The pure (−)-acid melted at 75–76.4°.

73.54 mg acid: 7.095 ml 0.04955-*N* NaOH

$C_{12}H_{16}O_3$ calc. equiv. wt. 208.3

found » » 209.2

0.1731 g dissolved in abs. *alcohol* to 20.06 ml: $2\alpha^{25}_D = -0.648°$, $[\alpha]^{25}_D = -37.5°$; $[M]^{25}_D = -78.2°$.

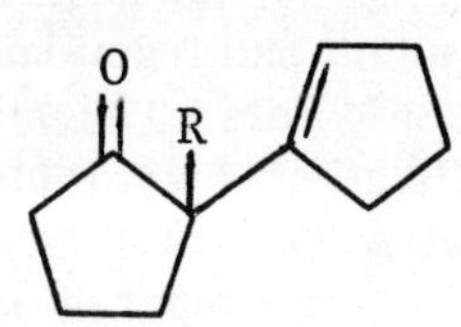

R=CH_2COOH

$C_{12}H_{16}O_3$ Ref. 911

Resolution of 2-Carboxymethyl-1-(1-cyclopentenyl)cyclopentanone (2c). Keto acid **2c** (10.30 g, 49.5 mmol) and 14.90 g (50.5 mmol) of cinchonidine were dissolved in 200 mL of boiling 95% ethanol and, on cooling, 26.45 g (105%) of solid was precipitated. Systematic recrystallization of this material from 95% ethanol, followed by acid hydrolysis of the salt, gave the following quantities of resolved and partially resolved acid **2c** (total recovery, 8.62 g, 84%) (Table III).

Table III

recovd keto acid, g	$[\alpha]^{28}_D$ (ethanol), deg
0.60	−139
0.94	−138
0.96	−131
0.83	−128
0.71	−30
2.97	+136
1.61	+105

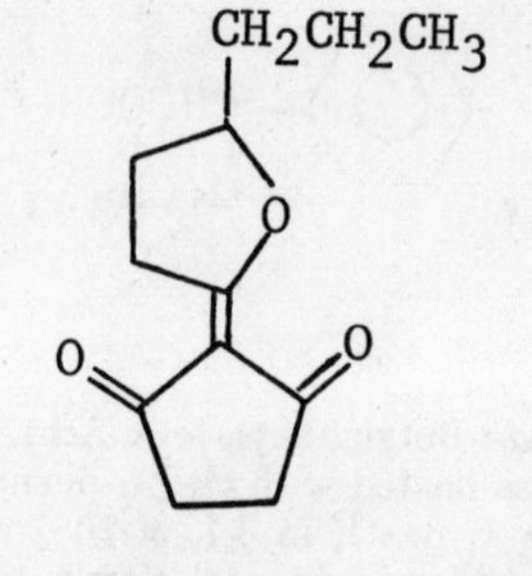

$C_{12}H_{16}O_3$ Ref. 912

EXAMPLE 4

Resolution of the synthetic Compound I

The Compound I synthesized (0.843 g.) from the process of Example 2 was dissolved in 30 cc. of ether and treated with brucine hydrate (1.741 g., 1.0 mol equivalent) dissolved in 12 cc. of tetrahydrofuran. The brucine salt of oudenone more easily precipitated was recrystallized from tetrahydrofuran seven times, showing M.P. 151–153° C. The melting point became constant at the temperature. It was treated with 2 N hydrochloric acid and extracted with a mixed solvent of ether and methylene chloride. The removal of the solvent afforded 182 mg. of d. form, showing $[\alpha]_D^{20} = +10.1$, 0.5% ethanol, M.P. 81–83° C. It showed the same spectra in IR, NMR, and UV as the natural oudenone.

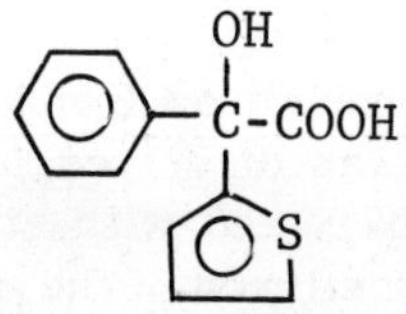

$C_{12}H_{16}O_3S$ Ref. 913

a) Amphetamine was used as resolving agent.
b) The following physical constants were reported for the active acid: m.p. 115-116°, $[\alpha]_D$ -10.0° (CH_3OH); m.p. 118-119°, $[\alpha]_D$ +10.5° (CH_3OH).

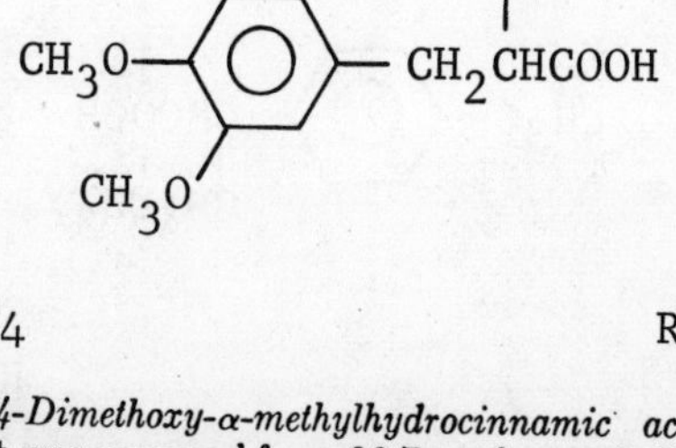

$C_{12}H_{16}O_4$ Ref. 914

L-(+)-*3,4-Dimethoxy-α-methylhydrocinnamic acid.*[10] The quinine salt was prepared from 96.7 g. of racemic IV and 140 g. of quinine in about 1800 ml. of ethanol and recrystallized thrice from the same solvent. It formed electrified needles, m.p. 163.7–164.3°, $[\alpha]^{20}_D$ −84.5° (*c* 1.98, chloroform). The yield, including pure material isolated from the mother liquors, was 90%.

Anal. Calc'd for $C_{12}H_{16}O_4 \cdot C_{20}H_{24}N_2O_2$: C, 70.05; H, 7.35; N, 5.11. Found: C, 69.71; H, 7.15; N, 5.00.

The free acid was isolated in the same way as (+)-I; evaporation of the ethereal solution gave a viscous oil which, dried in a high vacuum, was used directly for further reactions. A sample was distilled in a bulb tube: b.p. 130° (bath temperature)/0.01 mm., $[\alpha]^{21}_D$ +27.5° (*c* 4.01, chloroform).

Anal. Calc'd for $C_{12}H_{16}O_4$: C, 64.27; H, 7.19. Found: C, 63.84; H, 7.16.

The acid chloride, prepared from 1 g. of the acid with 1.15 ml. of oxalyl chloride in 97% yield, had b.p. 90° (bath temperature)/0.015 mm. and $[\alpha]_D^{20}$ +20.5° (*c* 5.73, benzene).

The amide was obtained from the acid chloride with concd. aqueous ammonia; it crystallized from water in colorless needles, m.p. 121.5–122.5°, $[\alpha]_D^{21}$ +60.5° (*c* 0.99, chloroform).

Anal. Calc'd for $C_{12}H_{17}NO_3$: C, 64.55; H, 7.68. Found: C, 64.44; H, 7.53.

D-(−)-*3,4-Dimethoxy-α-methylhydrocinnamic acid.*[10] Treating the impure (−)-IV, recovered from the quinine salt mother liquors, with (−)-III afforded the (−)-IV-(−)-III salt in 77% yield, based on the racemic IV used originally. The major portion was obtained pure after three recrystallizations from ethyl acetate; m.p. 107–109.3°, $[\alpha]_D^{20}$ −22.0° (*c* 2.01, chloroform).

Anal. Calc'd for $C_{12}H_{16}O_4 \cdot C_8H_{11}N$: C, 69.54; H, 7.88; N, 4.06. Found: C, 69.46; H, 7.68; N, 3.86.

The free acid had b.p. 120° (bath temperature)/0.005 mm., $[\alpha]_D^{21}$ −28.1° (*c* 4.16, chloroform).

Anal. Calc'd for $C_{12}H_{16}O_4$: C, 64.27; H, 7.19. Found: C, 63.80; H, 7.32.

The acid chloride had b.p. 95° (bath temperature)/0.01 mm., $[\alpha]_D^{21}$ −21.3° (*c* 4.89, benzene).

Anal. Calc'd for $C_{12}H_{15}ClO_3$: Cl, 14.61. Found: Cl, 14.01.

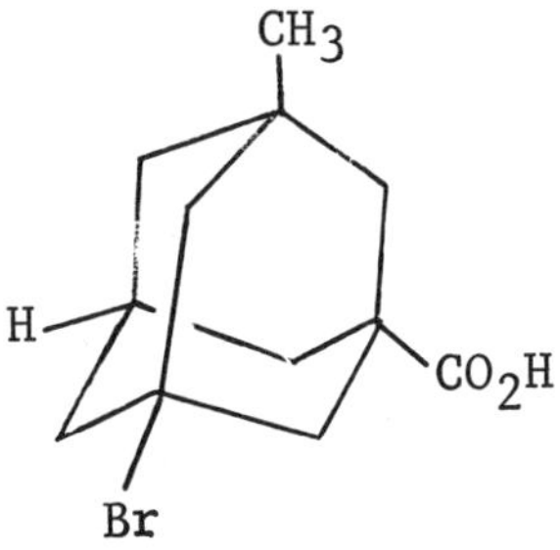

$C_{12}H_{17}BrO_2$ Ref. 915

The racemic acid was resolved via dehydroabietylamine in aqueous methanol. After 24 hrs., the crystalline salt isolated was fractionally crystallized from ethanol, affording material with m.p. 140.5-141°, $[\alpha]_D^{23}$ +18.9°. Decomposition of this salt with NaOH in water-ether gave, after acidification, the crystalline acid with m.p. 128-130° which had an immeasurably small optical rotation at the D-line of Na.

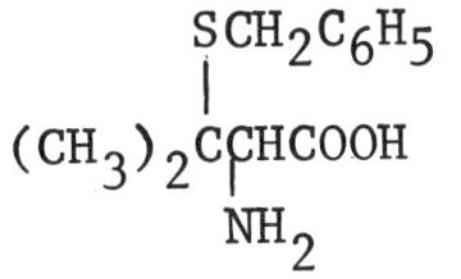

$C_{12}H_{17}NO_2S$ Ref. 916

l- bzw. *d*-S-Benzyl-*β*,*β*-dimethyl-cysteine (IV).

Wir lösten 49 g *d*,*l*-S-Benzyl-N-formyl-*β*,*β*-dimethyl-cystein in 140 cm³ absolutem Methanol und gaben eine Suspension von 72 g wasserfreiem Brucin in 100 cm³ absolutem Methanol zu. Dabei trat erst klare Lösung, nach kurzem Reiben mit dem Glasstab aber Krystallisation ein. Das ausgefallene Brucinsalz des *l*-S-Benzyl-N-formyl-*β*,*β*-dimethyl-cysteins (III) wurde in der Kälte abgenutscht und zweimal aus Methanol umkrystallisiert. Die getrocknete Substanz war äusserst hygroskopisch. Smp. 96—100°. $[\alpha]_D^{23}$ = −6 bis −10° (c = 1% in Methanol).

$C_{36}H_{43}O_7N_3S$	Ber.	C 65,33	H 6,55	N 6,35%
	Gef.	,, 64,95	,, 6,83	,, 6,23%

58 g krystallisiertes *l*-Brucinsalz III wurden in einem Scheidetrichter mit 150 cm³ Chloroform und 300 cm³ n. Ammoniak geschüttelt. Die ammoniakalische Lösung wurde mit Chloroform nachgewaschen und im Vakuum auf 250 cm³ eingeengt. Zum Rückstand setzten wir 20 cm³ konz. Salzsäure zu und erhitzten eine ½ Stunde unter Rückfluss zum Sieden, wobei die Fällung in Lösung ging. Nach Neutralisieren mit konz. Ammoniak krystallisierte das *l*-S-Benzyl-*β*,*β*-dimethyl-cystein (IV) aus. Nach Umkrystallisieren aus Methanol war sein Smp. 184—185° und die Drehung $[\alpha]_D^{21}$ = +97° (c = 1,085 in n. HCl).

$C_{12}H_{17}O_2NS$	Ber.	C 60,22	H 7,16	N 5,85%
	Gef.	,, 60,46	,, 7,47	,, 6,00%

Die Mutterlaugen des krystallisierten *l*-Brucinsalzes III, welche die *d*-Komponente enthalten, wurden im Vakuum eingeengt und wie oben mit Ammoniak und Chloroform gespalten. Durch Zusatz von 20 cm³ konz. Salzsäure und Kochen am Rückfluss wurde die Formylverbindung verseift und das *d*-S-Benzyl-*β*,*β*-dimethyl-cystein (IV) mit konz. Ammoniak gefällt. Es schmolz nach Umkrystallisieren aus Methanol bei 184—185°. $[\alpha]_D^{21}$ = −96° (c = 1,100 in n. HCl).

[1]) Alle Schmelzpunkte sind korrigiert.

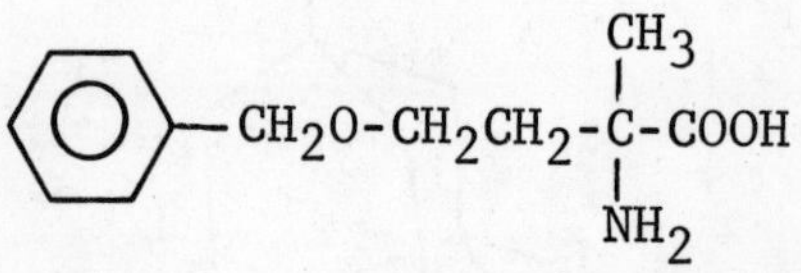

$C_{12}H_{17}NO_3$

Ref. 917

Exemple 1. — 21 parties en poids d'acide α-acétamino-γ-benzyloxy-α-méthyl-n-butyrique sont chauffées à reflux dans 210 parties en volume d'anhydride acétique pendant 6 heures. Après avoir retiré l'excès d'anhydride acétique et d'acide acétique par distillation, on a obtenu 17,2 parties en poids de 2,4-diméthyl-4-(β-benzyloxyéthyl)-oxazolone par distillation du résidu sous pression réduite. D'autre part, on a ajouté 14,2 parties en poids de 1-menthol ($[\alpha]^{12}_{D}$ = —51,3°(C = 3,06 CH_3CH) à une suspension de trois parties en poids de sodium métallique en poudre dans 100 parties en volume de benzène; le mélange a été laissé à reposer toute la nuit et puis chauffé à reflux pendant 2 heures. Le sodium métallique n'ayant pas réagi est retiré du mélange; on ajoute 30 parties en volume de benzène, puis une solution de 17,2 parties en poids de la 2,4-diméthyl-4-(β-benzyloxyéthyl)-oxazolone préalablement préparée dans 20 parties en volume de benzène. Le mélange réactionnel est agité pendant 4 heures à la température ambiante (20-30 °C) et on le laisse reposer toute la nuit. On ajoute alors 100 parties en volume de benzène et la couche benzénique du mélange est lavée avec une solution d'acide acétique dilué, une solution de carbonate alcalin dilué et finalement avec de l'eau.

Après avoir séché sur du sulfate de sodium anhydre, le benzène est enlevé par évaporation. Le résidu est distillé sous pression réduite. On obtient 23,5 parties en poids d'une fraction ayant un point d'ébullition de 198-220 °C sous 0,12 mm Hg.

Lorsque la fraction ainsi obtenue est dissoute dans 70 parties en volume de n-hexane et qu'on la laisse reposer un moment, on obtient 15,7 parties en poids de cristaux blancs (appelés ci-après « cristaux A_1 »). En laissant à nouveau reposer la solution mère pendant 48 heures, on obtient 2,8 parties en poids de cristaux blancs (appelés ci-après « cristaux B_1 »).

Lesdits « cristaux A_1 » et lesdits « cristaux B_1 » bruts, par recristallisation avec le n-hexane, donnent respectivement des « cristaux A'_1 » ayant un point de fusion de 98,5-100,5 °C, $[\alpha]^{18}_{D}$ = —49,5°(C = 0,92 CH_3OH) et des « cristaux B'_1 » ayant un point de fusion de 72,5-73,5 °C, $[\alpha]^{15}_{D}$ = —29,2°(C = 2,02 CH_3OH).

Deux parties en poids de « cristaux A'_1 » sont dissoutes dans un mélange de 30 parties en poids d'éthanol et de 30 parties en volume de solution aqueuse de NaOH contenant 30 parties en poids de NaOH et le mélange est chauffé à reflux pendant 5 heures.

Après avoir concentré le mélange jusqu'à environ un quart de son volume sous pression réduite et avoir extrait le menthol avec de l'éther, on règle le pH de la couche aqueuse à 1 avec HCl concentré et on rassemble les cristaux blancs séparés. Par recristallisation des cristaux blancs dans l'éthanol à 20 %, on obtient 1,3 partie en poids de cristaux blancs : c'est l'acide (—)-α-acétamino-γ-benzyloxy-α-méthyl-n-butyrique qui fond à 148,5-150,5 °C, $[\alpha]^{18}_{D}$ = —9,5° (C = 1,24 CH_3OH).

De la même manière, on obtient 1,2 partie en poids de cristaux blancs en aiguilles à partir des « cristaux B'_1 » ayant un point de fusion de 153,5-154,5 °C, $[\alpha]^{18}_{D}$ = + 10,9 ° (C = 1,84 CH_3OH).

Chacun des acides ainsi obtenus, c'est-à-dire l'acide (—)-α-acétamino-γ-benxyloxy-α-méthyl-n-butyrique et l'acide (+)-α-acétamino-γ-benzyloxy-α-méthyl-n-butyrique, est chauffé avec de l'acide chlorhydrique à 20 % pendant plusieurs heures. Le premier donne un isomère optiquement actif, l'acide (—)-α-amino-γ-benzyloxy-α-méthyl-n-butyrique et le dernier donne l'autre isomère optiquement actif (+)-α-amino-γ-benzyloxy-α-méthyl-n-butyrique.

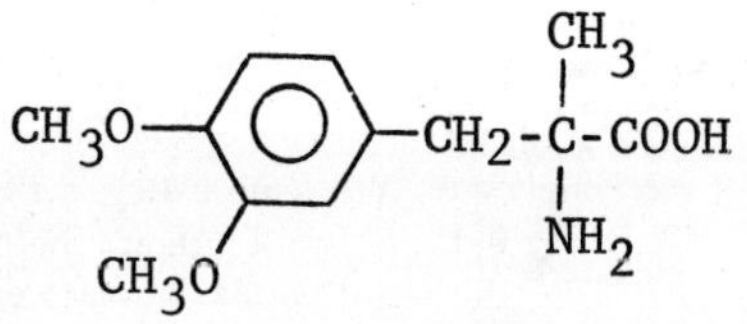

$C_{12}H_{17}NO_4$

Ref. 918

EXAMPLE 20.

L-N-acetyl-α-methyl-β-(3,4-dimethoxyphenyl)alanine-*L*-α-phenylethylamine salt.

To a slurry of 2.1 g. of *DL*-N-acetyl-α-methyl-β-(3,4-dimethoxyphenyl)alanine in 4 ml. of methanol is added a solution of 0.91 g. of *L*-α-phenylethylamine in 1 ml. of methanol. The mixture is heated to reflux, diluted with 10 ml. of methanol and refluxed until solution is complete. The solution is clarified by filtration through a filter containing a diatomaceous earth ("*Super-Cel*"). The filter cake is washed with 10 ml. of water. The filtrate is heated allowing the methanol to distil until the internal temperature is 95° C. The solution is cooled to 60° C., seeded with the product, *L*-N-acetyl-α-methyl-β-(3,4-dimethoxyphenyl)alanine *L*-α-phenylethylamine salt, and allowed to cool undisturbed to room temperature. The mixture is then aged at 8° C. in a refrigerator for an additional 18 hours. At the end of this aging period approximately half of the product, *L*-N-acetyl-α-methyl-β-(3,4-dimethoxyphenyl)alanine-*L*-α-phenylethylamine salt, has crystallized in the form of striated mounds. Seed crystals are formed by swirling the flask occasionally. The mixture is then allowed to stand for an additional 24 hours. The crude product *L*-N-acetyl-α-methyl-β-(3,4-dimethoxyphenyl)alanine *L*-α-phenylethylamine salt is filtered, washed with cold water and dried *in vacuo* at 56° C. The specific rotation is $[\alpha]_D$+55° (C=1 in methanol). The mother liquors are collected for recovery of impure *D*-N-acetyl-α-methyl-α-(3,4-dimethoxyphenyl)alanine.

To 1.38 g. of the crude product are added 10 ml. of water and 2 ml. of ethanol. The mixture is heated without a condenser with stirring until complete solution occurs and the internal temperature is 98° C. The solution is allowed to cool slowly to room temperature and then aged at 8° C. for two hours. The semi-solid mixture is filtered, washed with a small amount of cold water and dried at 56° C. *in vacuo*, yielding pure *L*-N-acetyl-α-methyl-β-(3,4-dimethoxyphenyl)alanine *L*-α-phenylethylamine salt. $[\alpha]_D$+69° (C=1 in methanol).

EXAMPLE 21

D-N-acetyl-α-methyl-β-(3,4-dimethoxyphenyl)alanine-*D*-α-phenylethylamine salt and the corresponding L-*L*-salt.

To a slurry of 77 g. of *DL*-N-acetyl-α-methyl-β-(3,4-dimethoxyphenyl)alanine in 200 ml. of methanol is added 33.2 g. of *D*-(+)-α-phenylethylamine in 50 ml. of methanol. One litre of water is added and the methanol stripped *in vacuo* at 50° to 60° C. The aqueous solution is heated to 90° and clarified by filtration through diatomaceous earth ("*Super-Cel*"). The filtrate is seeded with *D*-N-acetyl-α-methyl-β-(3,4-dimethoxyphenyl)alanine *D*-α-phenylethylamine salt and allowed to cool undisturbed to room temperature. The mixture is aged at about 8° C. for 18 hours and filtered, and the precipitate of *D*-N-acetyl-α-methyl-β-(3,4-dimethoxyphenyl)-

alanine *D*-α-phenylethylamine salt is washed with a small amount of cold water and dried over phosphorus pentoxide *in vacuo*. $[\alpha]_D - 59°$ (C=1 in methanol). This salt has a negative rotation and the product of Example 19 has a positive rotation. A second crop is obtained by concentration of the mother liquors to a volume of about 700 ml. and aging at 5°—10° C. for 18 hours. A third crop is obtained by further concentration of the mother liquors to 400 ml. and aging at room temperature for 2 hours.

The remaining mother liquors are made alkaline with 50 ml. of 2.5*N* sodium hydroxide and extracted with chloroform in two 100 ml. portions followed by two 50-ml. portions. To the basic aqueous solution is added 15 ml. of glacial acetic acid, and the solution is aged for 18 hours at about 8° C. The precipitate of impure *L*-N-acetyl-α-methyl-β-(3,4-dimethoxyphenyl)alanine is filtered, washed with cold water and dried *in vacuo* at 70° C. $[\alpha]_D - 23°$ (C=1 in methanol).

To a slurry of 30 g. of the *L*-N-acetyl-α-methyl-β-(3,4-dimethoxyphenyl)alanine obtained above in 200 ml. of methanol is added 13.0 g. of *L*-(−)-α-phenylethylamine. A thick precipitate forms. This precipitate is dissolved by addition of 200 g. more methanol and 100 ml. of water and heating to reflux. The hot solution is treated with decolorizing charcoal, filtered and allowed to cool to room temperature. The mixture is aged at 10° C. for one hour and filtered. The precipitate of *L*-N-acetyl-α-methyl-β-(3,4-dimethoxyphenyl)alanine L(−)-α-phenylethylamine salt is washed with cold water and dried over phosphorus pentoxide for about 18 hours. $[\alpha]_D + 68°$ (C=1 in methanol).

EXAMPLE 22.

L-N-acetyl-α-methyl-β-(3,4-dimethoxyphenyl)alanine

25 g. of *L*-N-acetyl-α-methyl-β-(3,4-dimethoxyphenyl)alanine *L*-α-phenylethylamine salt (the product of Examples 20 and 21) is dissolved in 100 ml. of water and 27.5 ml. of 2.5*N* sodium hydroxide. The solution is extracted with two 50-ml. portions followed by two 25-ml. portions of chloroform, and the extracts are saved for the recovery of *L*-α-phenylethylamine. The extracted aqueous solution is partially acidified with 6 ml. of 2.5*N* hydrochloric acid, heated to 70° C., transferred to a beaker and further acidified with 24 ml. of 2.5*N* hydrochloric acid. A precipitate of *L*-N-acetyl-α-methyl-β-(3,4-dimethoxyphenyl)alanine forms immediately. The precipitate is cooled to 10° C., filtered, washed with cold water and dried *in vacuo* at 70° C. $[\alpha]_D - 56°$ (c=1 in methanol).

EXAMPLE 23.

L-α-methyl-β-(3,4-dihydroxyphenyl)alanine.

A mixture of 10.0 g. of *L*-N-acetyl-α-methyl-β-(3,4-dimethoxyphenyl)alanine and 100 ml. of 48% by weight aqueous hydrobromic acid is purged with nitrogen and heated at reflux in a nitrogen atmosphere for 3—12 hours. The system is protected from air by a mercury trap. The mixture is concentrated to dryness under nitrogen. The residue is dissolved in 50 ml. of water and concentrated to dryness. The procedure is repeated successively with 50 ml. of *t*-butanol and 50 ml. of water. The residue is dissolved in 80 ml. of water, the pH adjusted to 6.4 with 6*N* ammonium hydroxide and the mixture is treated with 0.2 g. of decolorizing charcoal ("*Darco* G-60") and filtered while warm. The amber-coloured solution is cooled, saturated with sulphur dioxide and concentrated under nitrogen to a volume of 30 ml. The mixture is aged in an ice bath for one hour and filtered. The cake is washed with a minimum amount of cold water and dried at 56° C. *in vacuo*. The resulting product is *L*-α-methyl-β-(3,4-dihydroxyphenyl)alanine (V). $[\alpha]_D - 4° \pm 2°$ (C=1 in 1*N* hydrochloric acid).

A second crop of crystals weighing 0.6 g. and having a negative bromide test is obtained by aging the mother liquors for 3 days at 8° C.

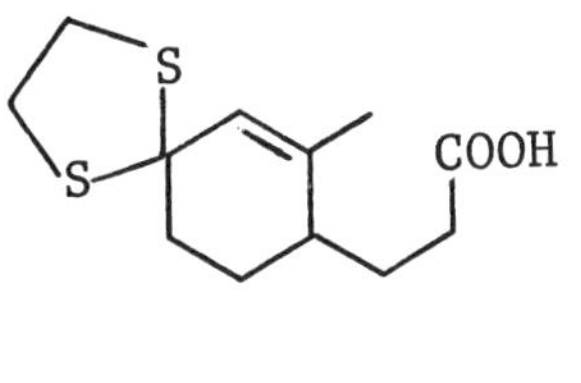

$C_{12}H_{18}O_2S_2$ Ref. 918.1

Resolution of 3-(2-Methyl-4-oxo-2-cyclohexenyl)propionic Acid Ethylene Thioketal (10). A solution of 25.2 g (0.21 mol) of *d*-α-methylbenzylamine in 100 mL of hot ethyl acetate was added to a solution of 53.2 g (0.21 mol) of the crude *dl*-thioketal acid **10** in 900 mL of hot ethyl acetate. The mixture was heated to boiling and then allowed to cool to room temperature to give 31.5 g (40% yield) of light tan needles. Two additional recrystallizations from ethyl acetate afforded 20.5 g (26% yield) of the *d* salt as colorless needles, mp 107–113 °C. Anal. ($C_{20}H_{29}NO_2S_2$): C, H, N, S.

The mother liquor from the first crystallization described above was concentrated to ca. 700 mL, cooled to 0 °C, and then treated with 10% aqueous hydrochloric acid. Ethyl acetate extraction[28] afforded the crude *l*-enriched acid. A solution of 15.3 g (0.13 mol) of *l*-α-methylbenzylamine in 100 mL of hot ethyl acetate was added to a solution of ca. 32 g (0.12 mol) of *l*-enriched acid **10** in 400 mL of hot ethyl acetate. The resulting solution was heated to boiling and then was allowed to cool to room temperature. Filtration afforded 29 g (37% yield) of *l* salt. Two additional recrystallizations from ethyl acetate gave 16.2 g (21% yield) of off-white needles, mp 107–112 °C. Anal. ($C_{20}H_{29}NO_2S_2$): C, H, N, S.

***d*-3-(2-Methyl-4-oxo-2-cyclohexenyl)propionic Acid Ethylene Thioketal (10).** A solution of 200 mL of 10% aqueous hydrochloric acid was added to a suspension of 19.8 g (0.052 mol) of *d* salt in 300 mL of ethyl acetate. The mixture was stirred at room temperature for 10 min, and then the layers were separated. Extraction with ethyl acetate[28] afforded 13.9 g (104% yield) of the *d*-thioketal acid **10** as a light tan oil, $[\alpha]_D$ +13.7°. The optical purity was estimated (see below) to be >94%. An analytical specimen was prepared by evaporative distillation at 169–173 °C (0.015 mm). Anal. ($C_{12}H_{18}O_2S_2$): C, H, S.

Similarly, hydrolysis of *l* salt afforded the *l*-thioketal acid **10** as a light tan oil, $[\alpha]_D$ −14.2°. The optical purity was estimated (see below) to be >94%.

3-(2-Methyl-4-oxo-2-cyclohexenyl)propanol Ethylene Thioketal (11). A solution of 35.7 g (0.13 mol) of the distilled thioketal ester **9** in 300 mL of dry THF was cooled to 0 °C; then 50 mL (0.18 mol) of a 3.54 M solution of Red-Al in benzene diluted with 60 mL of dry THF was added over a period of 15 min. The solution was stirred under nitrogen at 0 °C for 4 h; then a 5% aqueous sodium hydroxide solution was added in a dropwise manner until a granular precipitate formed. The supernatant was decanted and the salts were washed with ether. Ether extraction using a base wash[28] afforded 32.2 g (100% yield) of the thioketal alcohol **11** as a pale yellow oil.

An analytical specimen was obtained by preparative TLC (R_f 0.48, ethyl acetate) followed by evaporative distillation at 180 °C (0.05 mm): IR (film) 2.97 (OH), 6.08 μ (C=C), 7.85, 9.50, 11.80 μ; ^{1}H NMR 1.66 (s, 3, CH_3), 3.31 (s, 4, SCH_2CH_2S), 3.64 (m, 2, CH_2OH), 5.60 ppm (s, 1, vinyl proton). Anal. ($C_{12}H_{20}OS_2$): C, H, S.

***d*- and *l*-3-(2-Methyl-4-oxo-2-cyclohexenyl)propanol Ethylene Thioketal (11).** The *d*-thioketal acid **10** and *l*-thioketal acid **10** were reduced with Red-Al as described above for the *dl*-thioketal ester **9** to afford, after similar purification, the analogous *d* and *l* alcohols **11**, $[\alpha]_D$ +24.3°, −19.6°. Anal. ($C_{12}H_{20}OS_2$): (*d*) C, H, S; (*l*) C, H.

Estimation of the Optical Purity of the *d*- and *l*-Thioketal Acids (10). A published procedure[29] was employed. A solution of 29 mg (0.12 mmol) of alcohol **11** (from acid **10** with $[\alpha]_D$ −10.1°) in 0.3 mL of carbon tetrachloride was added to a solution of 0.35 mL (0.19 mmol) of (*R*)-(+)-α-methoxy-α-trifluoromethylphenylacetyl chloride[30] in 0.3 mL of dry pyridine. The mixture was stirred at room temperature for 5 min; then 0.15 mL (0.12 mmol) of 3-dimethylamino-1-aminopropane was added. After standing at room temperature for 5 min, ether was added. Extraction with ether using a wash with dilute aqueous hydrochloric acid, followed by a base wash,[28] afforded 49 mg (90% yield) of the ester as a clear oil: IR ($CHCl_3$) 5.70 (ester C=O), 7.9, 8.58 μ; ^{1}H NMR (CCl_4) 1.62 (s, 3, CH_3), 3.27 (s, 4, SCH_2CH_2S), 3.50 (s, 3, OCH_3), 4.28 (t, J = 7 Hz, 2, CO_2CH_2), 5.57 (s, 1 vinyl proton), 7.30 ppm (m, 5, aromatic protons). Upon addition of ca. 60 mg of Eu(fod)$_3$, the methoxyl absorption appeared as a doublet at 9.27 (0.867 H) and 9.43 ppm (0.133 H), corresponding to an 86.7:13.3 mixture of enantiomers in the acid **10**. The optical purity of this sample is 73.4 ± 3.7; thus a sample with an optical purity of 100% would show a rotation of 13.8 ± 0.7°.

(28) In cases where products were isolated by solvent extraction, the procedure generally followed was to extract the aqueous layer with several portions of the indicated solvent; then the organic layers were combined and washed with water followed by saturated brine. The organic layer was dried over anhydrous sodium sulfate or magnesium sulfate and filtered, and the solvent was evaporated under reduced pressure (water aspirator) using a rotary evaporator. The use of the term "wash" indicates washing the combined organic layers with saturated aqueous sodium bicarbonate solution ("base wash"), with dilute aqueous hydrochloric acid ("acid wash"), or with the indicated solution prior to the aforementioned washing with water.

(29) Dale, J. A.; Mosher, H. S. *J. Am. Chem. Soc.* **1973**, *95*, 512–519.

(30) We wish to thank Professor H. S. Mosher of Stanford University for providing us with this sample.

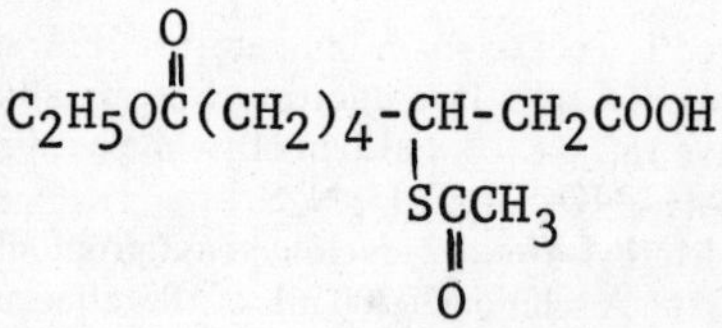

$C_{12}H_{20}O_5S$ Ref. 919

(−)-3-Acetylthio-7-carbethoxyheptanoic Acid *l*-Ephedrine Salt.—A solution of 5 g. (0.018 mole) of DL-3-acetylthio-7-carbethoxyheptanoic acid in 50 ml. of ether was mixed with a solution of 3 g. (0.018 mole) of *l*-ephedrine in 50 ml. of ether. After a short time, 4.4 g. of crystalline product, m.p. 125–128°, precipitated. The product was recrystallized once from 10 ml. of methanol to yield 3.5 g. of crystals, m.p. 129–131°. This material was recrystallized from 10 ml. of methanol to give 2.4 g. (30%) of (−)-3-acetylthio-7-carbethoxyheptanoic acid *l*-ephedrine salt, m.p. 129–131°.

Anal. Calcd. for $C_{22}H_{35}NO_6S$: C, 59.84; H, 7.99; N, 3.17; S, 7.26. Found: C, 60.14; H, 8.19; N, 3.49; S, 7.22.

(−)-3-Acetylthio-7-carbethoxyheptanoic Acid.—A 2.25-g. (0.0051 mole) portion of (−)-3-acetylthio-7-carbethoxyheptanoic acid *l*-ephedrine salt was suspended in about 50 ml. of water and 40 ml. of ether. The mixture was acidified and the ether extract was separated. The aqueous phase was extracted with a second 40-ml. portion of ether. The combined ether layers were dried and concentrated at reduced pressure to yield 1.2 g. (85%) of (−)-3-acetylthio-7-carbethoxyheptanoic acid, n^{25}_D 1.4840, $[\alpha]^{23}_D$ −6.8° (*c* 8.5, methanol).

Anal. Calcd. for $C_{12}H_{20}O_5S$: C, 52.15; H, 7.30; S, 11.60; neut. equiv., 276. Found: C, 52.07; H, 7.39; S, 11.69; neut. equiv., 277.

(+)-3-Acetylthio-7-carbethoxyheptanoic Acid Benzhydrylamine Salt.—The non-crystalline (+)-3-acetylthio-7-carbethoxyheptanoic acid *l*-ephedrine salt (remaining after the crystallization of the (−)-3-acetylthio-7-carbethoxyheptanoic acid *l*-ephedrine salt from 153 g. (0.554 mole) of DL-3-acetylthio-7-carbethoxyheptanoic acid) was acidified in a mixture of 600 ml. of ether and 500 ml. of water. The ether layer was separated and the aqueous layer was extracted with another portion of ether. The combined ether extracts were dried and concentrated at reduced pressure to yield 87 g. of crude (+)-3-acetylthio-7-carbethoxyheptanoic acid.

A 35-g. (0.146 mole) portion of crude (+)-3-acetylthio-7-carbethoxyheptanoic acid in 200 ml. of isopropyl ether was treated with a solution of benzhydrylamine (from 32 g. (0.146 mole) of benzhydrylamine hydrochloride) in 200 ml. of isopropyl ether. Crystals (35 g., m.p. 74–91°) of the benzhydrylamine salt separated. The product was recrystallized twice from about 500 ml. of isopropyl ether to yield finally 15 g. (22%) of (+)-3-acetylthio-7-carbethoxyheptanoic acid benzhydrylamine salt, m.p. 92–96°, $[\alpha]^{23}_D$ +1.3° (*c* 8.06, methanol).

Anal. Calcd. for $C_{25}H_{33}NO_5S$: C, 65.33; H, 7.24; N, 3.05; S, 6.98. Found: C, 65.33; H, 7.03; N, 2.90; S, 7.10.

(+)-3-Acetylthio-7-carbethoxyheptanoic Acid.—A 14.0-g. (0.030 mole) portion of (+)-3-acetylthio-7-carbethoxyheptanoic acid benzhydrylamine salt was dissolved in 100 ml. of chloroform and 100 ml. of water was added. The mixture was acidified with hydrochloric acid and the chloroform layer was separated. The chloroform layer was washed with water, with dilute hydrochloric acid and twice again with water. The chloroform layer was dried and concentrated at reduced pressure to yield 8.7 g. (97%) of (+)-3-acetylthio-7-carbethoxyheptanoic acid, $[\alpha]^{23}_D$ +6.8° (*c* 8.65, methanol), neut. equiv. 283.

In another experiment, 54 g. (0.120 mole) of (+)-3-acetylthio-7-carbethoxyheptanoic acid benzhydrylamine salt was suspended in 300 ml. of chloroform and 200 ml. of water and 60 ml. of 2.5 *N* hydrochloric acid was added. The chloroform extract was separated and washed with 20 ml. of 2.5 *N* hydrochloric acid and with two 20-ml. portions of water. The chloroform layer was dried, filtered and concentrated at reduced pressure to yield 31.8 g. of (+)-3-acetylthio-7-carbethoxyheptanoic acid, $[\alpha]^{25}_D$ +6.8° (*c* 5.93, methanol), neut. equiv. 285. The acid was dissolved in 200 ml. of ether and cooled to about 10° and washed with a cold solution of 20 g. of potassium bicarbonate in 200 ml. of water. The bicarbonate layer was acidified immediately and the product extracted into 200 ml. of ether. The ether layer was washed with water, dried and concentrated to yield 25 g. of (+)-3-acetylthio-7-carbethoxyheptanoic acid, $[\alpha]^{32}_D$ +6.7° (*c* 8.9, methanol), n^{25}_D 1.4840.

Anal. Calcd. for $C_{12}H_{20}O_5S$: C, 52.15; H, 7.30; S, 11.60; neut. equiv., 276. Found: C, 52.47; H, 7.12; S, 11.06; neut. equiv., 276.

(+)-3-Acetylthio-7-carbethoxyheptanoic Acid *d*-Ephedrine Salt.—A solution of *d*-ephedrine (from 2.2 g. of *d*-ephedrine hydrochloride) in 10 ml. of ether was added to a solution of 2.8 g. (0.01 mole) of DL-3-acetylthio-7-carbethoxyheptanoic acid in 5 ml. of ether. An additional 15 ml. of ether was added. A precipitate of 2.3 g. of crystalline salt, m.p. 119–126°, was obtained. The product was recrystallized from methanol–ether (1:2) to yield 1.55 g. (35%) of (+)-3-acetylthio-7-carbethoxyheptanoic acid *d*-ephedrine salt, m.p. 129–131°.

Anal. Calcd. for $C_{22}H_{35}NO_6S$: C, 59.84; H, 7.99; N, 3.17; S, 7.26. Found: C, 59.86; H, 7.63; N, 3.05; S, 7.62.

The *d*-ephedrine salt was suspended in 6 ml. of chloroform and 6 ml. of 1.3 *N* hydrochloric acid was added. The chloroform extract was separated and concentrated at reduced pressure to yield 1.1 g. of oil. A 0.66-g. portion of the oil was dissolved in chloroform and extracted into cold aqueous sodium bicarbonate solution. The bicarbonate extract was acidified with dilute hydrochloric acid and the product was extracted into chloroform. The chloroform solution was washed with water, dried over anhydrous magnesium sulfate and filtered. The filtrate was concentrated at reduced pressure to yield 0.3 g. of (+)-3-acetylthio-7-carbethoxyheptanoic acid, $[\alpha]^{25}_D$ +7.5° (*c* 7.5, methanol), n^{25}_D 1.4836.

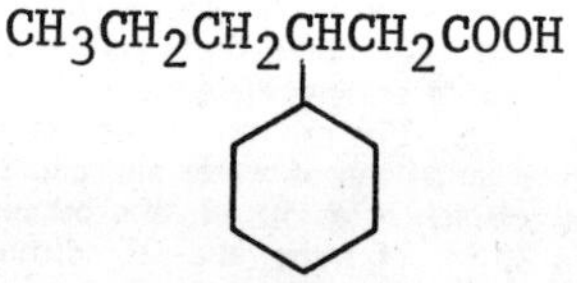

$C_{12}H_{22}O_2$ Ref. 920

Levo-4-Cyclohexylcaproic Acid-6—The inactive acid was prepared from *n*-propylcyclohexylbromomethane and ethyl malonate.

This was dissolved in 3 volumes of boiling acetone and 1 equivalent of quinine was added. To this was added 20 per cent water. The solution was cooled at −15° until crystallization was complete. The resolution was very difficult. B. p. 155° at 4 mm. Yield 65 gm. $D^{24}_4 = 0.982$.

$$[\alpha]^{24}_D = \frac{+2.00°}{1 \times 0.982} = +2.04°; [M]^{24}_D = +4.04° \text{ (homogeneous)}$$

5.216 mg. substance: 14.019 mg. CO_2 and 5.109 mg. H_2O

$C_{12}H_{22}O_2$. 198.18	Calculated.	C 72.7, H 11.2
	Found.	" 73.2, " 11.0

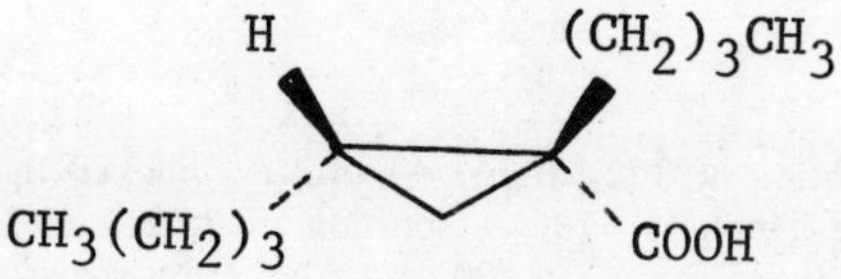

$C_{12}H_{22}O_2$ Ref. 921

Resolution of (±)-*trans*-2,3-Di-*n*-butylcyclopropanecarboxylic Acid. A mixture of 3.60 g (18.2 mmol) of (±)-*trans*-2,3-di-*n*-butylcyclopropanecarboxylic acid and 3.00 g (18.1 mmol) of ephedrine was dissolved in 100 ml of benzene and heated to 60° for 45 min. The mixture was then evaporated to a volume of 25 ml by passing a stream of dry nitrogen over the warm solution. Addition of 75 ml of hexane and cooling in the refrigerator overnight gave 0.90 g of the diastereomer as a solid white mass, mp 89–90°. Concentration and cooling of the filtrate yielded a second crop of the diastereomer, 2.20 g, to give a total 3.1 g (47%). This diastereomer

was then dissolved in 50 ml of a 2% sodium hydroxide in 50% methanol–water solution, and the mixture was heated at 40–50° for 2 hr. Approximately one-half of the solvent was removed, and the mixture was allowed to cool overnight. The precipitated ephedrine was then removed by filtration. The filtrate was washed with ether to remove the final traces of ephedrine. The water layer was acidified to pH 2 with 10% sulfuric acid and extracted with ether. Drying over magnesium sulfate and removal of the solvent yielded 1.52 g (89% from diastereomer) of the acid, $[\alpha]^{25}_D$ −2.78° (c 0.4005, 95% ethanol). Saponification of the filtrate in like manner yielded the enantiomeric acid, $[\alpha]^{25}_D$ +2.37° (c 0.1023, 95% ethanol).

$$\begin{array}{c} C(CH_3)_3 \\ | \\ HOOC-CH-CHCOOH \\ | \\ C(CH_3)_3 \end{array}$$

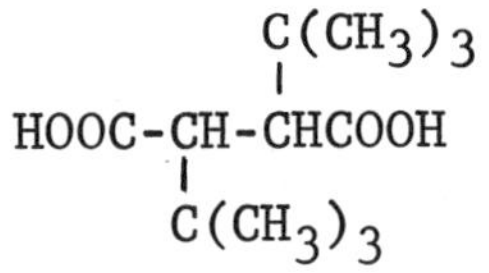

$C_{12}H_{22}O_4$ Ref. 922

Partial resolution of low-melting a,a′-di-(*tert.-butyl*)*-succinic acid.* Low-melting a,a′-di-(*tert.*-butyl)-succinic acid, 8.3 g, and brucine, 14.2 g, were dissolved in 200 ml of boiling water, filtered, and allowed to cool slowly. The salt (11.1 g) was collected and recrystallized once from water. The acid was liberated by treatment with dilute hydrochloric acid and showed after recrystallization from benzene $[a]^{20}_D = +6.1°$ in absolute ethanolic solution. In spite of further recrystallizations of the brucine salt higher rotations could not be achieved.

$$(CH_3)_3C-CH_2-\overset{\overset{\displaystyle CH_3}{|}}{\underset{\underset{\displaystyle C(CH_3)_3}{|}}{C}}-COOH$$

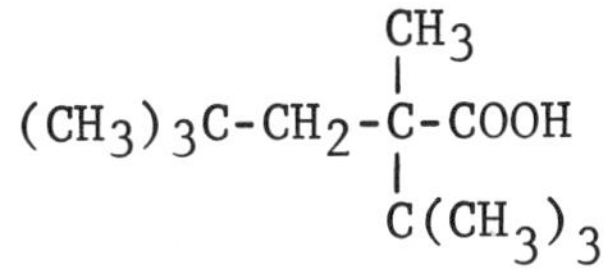

$C_{12}H_{24}O_2$ Ref. 923

(+)-*2 : 2 : 3 : 5 : 5-Pentamethylhexane-3-carboxylic Acid.* Ten recrystallisations of the brucine salt (m. p. 116—118°) from 75% aqueous acetone yielded a product which on decomposition afforded an optically inactive acid. The cinchonidine salt, m. p. 153°, was recrystallised four times from dilute alcohol and then decomposed with mineral acid, to yield a partially resolved acid, m. p. 135°, $[\alpha]^{18}_D$ +2·7°. The cinchonine salt, on the other hand, afforded an acid of $[\alpha]^{18}_D$ +3·1° after only three recrystallisations. Accordingly, cinchonine (112 g.) was gradually added to a boiling solution of the acid (75 g.) in ethanol (1 l.), and the liquid diluted with more ethanol until dissolution was complete, the total volume then being 4 l. On cooling, unchanged cinchonine (35 g.) was deposited. After filtration the solution was boiled and water added until crystallisation commenced. When cold, the liquid afforded a salt, m. p. 220—225°, $[\alpha]^{18}_D$ +143°. Eleven more recrystallisations from 50% aqueous ethanol yielded the pure *cinchonine 2 : 2 : 3 : 5 : 5-pentamethylhexane-3-carboxylate*, m. p. 215° (10 g.) (Found: C, 74·9; H, 9·3; N, 6·0. $C_{31}H_{46}O_3N_2$ requires C, 75·3; H, 9·4; N, 5·7%), whence was obtained a (+)-acid, m. p. 130°, $[\alpha]^{18}_D$ +23·8° (in ethanol).

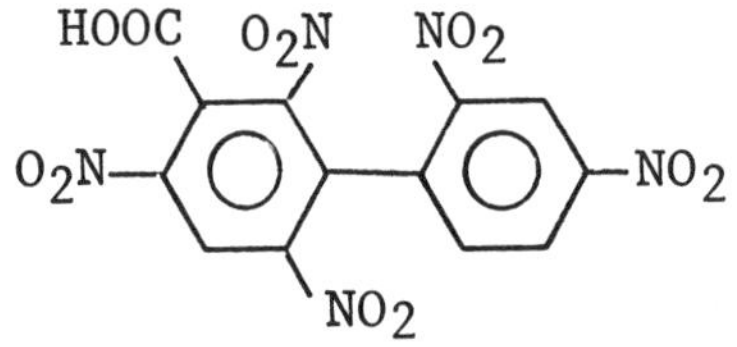

$C_{13}H_5N_5O_{12}$ Ref. 924

Resolution of 2,4,6,2′,4′-Pentanitro-3-carboxydiphenyl.—To a solution of 10.2 g. of 2,4,6,2′,4′-pentanitro-3-carboxydiphenyl in 700 cc. of methyl alcohol was added slowly and with stirring 800 cc. of a solution of 8.08 g. of strychnine in 2 liters of methyl alcohol. The solution was cooled to 0° and allowed to stand for one hour. A crop (7.5 g.) of pale yellow, needle-like crystals (A) was obtained. To the mother liquor from (A) was added an additional 300-cc. portion of the strychnine–methyl alcohol solution. The resulting mixture was evaporated to about 700 cc. under diminished pressure and a second crop (3 g.) of yellow crystals (B) was filtered off. To the mother liquor from (B) was added the remainder of the strychnine solution. This mixture was evaporated to a volume of about 300 cc., cooled overnight at 0°, and a third crop (7.8 g.) of orange-colored, granular crystals (C) obtained.

Crystals (A) were purified by dissolving them in a minimum of warm acetone and adding to this stirred solution petroleum ether until the solution was slightly opaque. Upon standing overnight at 0°, the salt separated as fine, pale yellow needles. The purified salt turns red at 265° and melts with decomposition at some point between 270 and 280°. Two successive recrystallizations of salt (A) sufficed to bring the salt to a constant rotation.

Rotation. 0.1373 g. of salt made up to 15 cc. with pyridine at 20° gave α_D −1.13°; $l = 1$, $[\alpha]^{20}_D$ −123.5°.

Anal. Calcd. for $C_{34}H_{27}O_{14}N_7$: C, 53.88; H, 3.59. Found: C, 53.75; H, 4.06.

Strychnine salt (C) was purified by dissolving it in boiling alcohol, evaporating this solution down to such a volume that crystals started to appear in the hot solution, then allowing the solution to stand at 0° overnight. Crystals of (C) were obtained as a light orange colored powder. This material turns red at 203–205° and apparently melts at 222–226°. Two successive recrystallizations brought the rotation to a constant value.

Rotation. 0.1319 g. made up to 15 cc. in pyridine at 20° gave α_D +0.74°, l = 1, $[\alpha]_D^{20}$ +84.4°.

Anal. Calcd. for $C_{34}H_{27}O_{14}N_7$: C, 53.88; H, 3.59. Found: C, 53.52; H, 4.35.

***l*-2,4,6,2′,4′-Pentanitro-3-carboxydiphenyl.**—To 2.19 g. of the pure strychnine salt (A) was added 20 cc. of acetone. Solution was not complete. The beaker was cooled with an ice-bath, and 50 cc. of concentrated hydrochloric acid added with stirring, at such a rate that the temperature of the mixture was always kept below 20°. The cooled mixture was permitted to stand for fifteen minutes so as to assure complete crystallization of the free acid, then filtered. The acid was completely redissolved in 10 cc. of acetone and again thrown out of solution by the addition of 50 cc. of concentrated hydrochloric acid in the manner just described. The acid was dried *in vacuo* at room temperature and then purified further by recrystallizing twice from benzene to a constant rotation and melting point. The pure acid was obtained as white, granular crystals of melting point 233°. The yield was 0.87 g. (71.3%).

Rotation. 0.1165 g. of acid made up to 15 cc. in acetone at 20° gave α_D −0.82°, l = 1, $[\alpha]_D^{20}$ −105.3°.

***d*-2,4,6,2′,4′-Pentanitro-3-carboxydiphenyl.**—To 1.19 g. of the strychnine salt (C) dissolved in 5 cc. of acetone and cooled with an ice-bath, slowly and with stirring was added 50 cc. of concentrated hydrochloric acid. The cooled mixture was permitted to stand for one-half hour so as to assure complete crystallization of the liberated acid, then filtered. The acid was redissolved in 9 cc. of acetone and reprecipitated by the addition of another 50-cc. portion of concentrated hydrochloric acid in the manner just described. It was recrystallized twice from benzene and formed a white, granular powder of melting point 229–231°. It gave a negative strychnine test when dissolved in sulfuric acid and treated with manganese dioxide. The yield of recrystallized acid was 0.4 g.

Rotation. 0.1116 g. of acid made up to 15 cc. in acetone at 20° gave α_D +0.73, l = 1, $[\alpha]_D^{20}$ +98.8°.

$C_{13}H_8O_8$

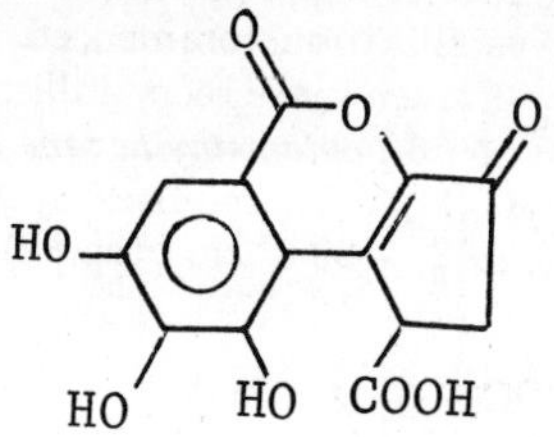

Ref. 925

Brevifolin-carbonsäure

Racematspaltung[18]: a) ***(−)-Brevifolin-carbonsäure.*** — 2.5 g lufttrockene racem. ***Brevifolin-carbonsäure*** werden in 1.5 *l* Wasser von 75° gelöst und mit einer warmen Lösung von 2.8 g *Chinidin* in 40 ccm Äthanol versetzt (Molverhältnis 1 : 1). Man erhitzt kurz auf 80° und filtriert. Beim Abkühlen scheiden sich das Chinidinsalz der (−)-Säure und etwa 50% des Chinidinsalzes der (+)-Säure kristallin aus. Nach 24 Stdn. wird abgesaugt (die Mutterlauge M 1 wird aufbewahrt), mit kaltem Wasser gewaschen und über $CaCl_2$ getrocknet. Ausbeute 3.5—3.8 g, Schmp. 164—165°, $[\alpha]_{578}^{25}$ = +122° (Methanol, c = 0.25). Das Rohkristallisat wird in 1.5 *l* Wasser von 80° gelöst, filtriert und langsam abgekühlt. Nach 24 Stdn. wird abgesaugt (Mutterlauge M 2). Ausbeute 2.25 g, Schmp. 165—167°, $[\alpha]_{578}^{25}$ = +120° (Methanol, c = 0.25). Nach 4 Umkristallisationen aus Wasser sind Schmp. 167—169° und Drehung $[\alpha]_{578}^{25}$ = +115° (Methanol, c = 0.22) konstant. Ausbeute 2.02 g (76%).

Chinidinsalz der (−)-Brevifolin-carbonsäure:

$C_{33}H_{32}N_2O_{10} \cdot 6H_2O$ (724.7)	Ber.	C 54.69	H 6.12	N 3.87	OCH_3 4.38	$6H_2O$ 14.92
	Gef.	54.96	6.25	4.02	4.38	14.99

Zur Zerlegung werden 2.9 g des *Chinidinsalzes* in 45 ccm 2*n HCl* aufgelöst, die Lösung filtriert. Im Kühlschrank scheiden sich nach Kratzen mit dem Glasstab bräunliche Kristalle ab. Nach einigen Tagen wird abgesaugt, mit kaltem Wasser gewaschen und getrocknet. 1.23 g (93%) (−)-Säure. $[\alpha]_{578}^{25}$ = −58.3° (Methanol, c = 0.2). Man kristallisiert aus wenig Wasser von 75—80° unter Zusatz einiger Tropfen verd. HCl um. Die Lösung soll langsam abkühlen und wird erst nach 24 Stdn. in den Kühlschrank gestellt. Nach 2—3 Tagen wird abgesaugt, mit kaltem Wasser gewaschen und getrocknet. Nach 4maligem Umkristallisieren ist die Drehung konstant: $[\alpha]_{578}^{25}$ = −72.9° (Methanol, c = 0.3). Reinausbeute 0.85 g (65%).

[18] Bearbeitet von *R. Eckert* und *E. Günther*; Frau *Inga-Maria Eckert* danken wir für ihre Mitarbeit.

Zur C,H-Analyse wurde bei 20°/760 Torr, zur Wasserbestimmung bei 60°/14 Torr über P_4O_{10} getrocknet.

(—)-Brevifolin-carbonsäure, $C_{13}H_8O_8 \cdot 2\,H_2O$ (328.2)	Ber. C 47.57	H 3.68	$2\,H_2O$ 10.98
	Gef. 47.60	3.84	11.85

b) *(+)-Brevifolin-carbonsäure.* — Die *Mutterlaugen* M 1 und M 2 und die Filtrate der Umkristallisationen des Chinidinsalzes der (—)-Säure werden gemeinsam i. Vak. eingedampft. 2.0 g, amorph. Die Zerlegung wird, wie beschrieben, mit *2n HCl* durchgeführt. Rohausbeute an kristallisierter (+)-Säure 0.9 g. Nach 3maligem Umkristallisieren wurden 0.62 g (+)-Säure der Drehung $[\alpha]_{578}^{25} = +65.0°$ (Methanol, $c = 0.2$) erhalten. Chromatogramme zeigten als Verunreinigung Brevifolin (in 2-proz. Essigsäure $R_F = 0.08$, in „Gemisch 10 2 4"[17] $R_F = 0.5$).

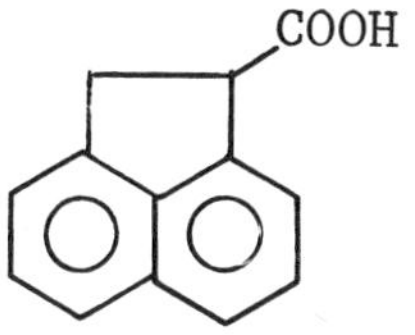

$C_{13}H_{10}O_2$ Ref. 926

Preliminary experiments on resolution

The salts of *cinchonine* and *quinine* gave (−)-acid of fairly high activity. Dextrorotatory acid was obtained via the salts of *brucine* and (+)-α-(*2-naphthyl)-ethylamine*. The *cinchonidine* salt gave dextrorotatory acid of very low activity and the *strychnine* salt failed to crystallise. Cinchonine and (+)-α-(2-naphthyl)-ethylamine were thus selected for the final resolution.

An attempt was also made to utilise brucine for resolution on a preparative scale. In this way the acid was easily brought to a rotation of about $[\alpha]_D = +100°$, but on further recrystallisation of the salt, the rotatory power increased very slowly and stopped at about +105°. This acid contains about 6 % (−)-form. The cause for this behaviour is not clear; it seems rather improbable that the salt obtained represents a defined double salt of (+)- and (−)-acid in this ratio.

(−)-Acenaphthene-1-carboxylic acid

Racemic acid (49.6 g, 0.25 mole) and cinchonine (73.6 g, 0.25 mole) were dissolved in 1 l of boiling methanol. The salt was filtered off after 24 h at −10° and recrystallised from the same solvent. After each crystallisation, a small sample of the salt was decomposed and the rotatory power of the acid determined in absolute ethanol.

Crystallisation	1	2	3
ml methanol	1000	950	900
g salt obtained	65.0	38.5	24.5
$[\alpha]_D^{25}$ of the acid	−93°	−118.5°	−118.5°

The acid was liberated from the salt by dilute sulphuric acid, extracted with ether, dried and recrystallised from ligroin. The salt obtained (24.5 g) yielded 8.5 g of pure acid, forming very long, slender needles with m.p. 158.5°.

$C_{13}H_{10}O_2$ (198.21)	calc.	C 78.77	H 5.09
	found	C 78.78, 78.73	H 5.06, 5.07

The rotatory power in various solvents is given in Table 1.

(+)-Acenaphthene-1-carboxylic acid

From the mother liquors after the crystallisations of the cinchonine salt, 34.8 g acid having $[\alpha]_D^{25} = +30°$ were obtained. 19.8 g (0.10 mole) of this acid and 17.3 g (0.10 mole) of (+)-α-(2-naphthyl)-ethylamine [11] were dissolved in 300 ml of boiling methanol. The salt was filtered off after 24 h at −10° and recrystallised to constant activity of the acid; the course of the resolution was followed as described above.

Table 1

g = g acid dissolved to 10.00 ml

Solvent	g	α_D^{25} (2 dm)	$[\alpha]_D^{25}$	$[M]_D^{25}$
Acetone	0.2045	−4.859°	−118.8°	−235.5°
Ethanol (abs.)	0.2013	−4.834°	−120.1°	−238.0°
Chloroform	0.2121	−6.234°	−147.0°	−291.3°
Water (neutr.)	0.2044	−5.867°	−143.5°	−284.5°
Benzene	0.2393	−9.633°	−201.3°	−398.9°

Crystallisation	1	2	3	4	5	6
ml methanol	300	275	275	250	200	200
g salt obtained	29.0	22.2	18.0	13.6	9.0	6.0
$[\alpha]_D^{25}$ of the acid	+75°	+93°	+102.5°	+110°	+118.5°	+118.5°

The acid was liberated and recrystallised from ligroin as described above for the (−)-form. 6.0 g salt yielded 2.6 g acid forming slender needles with m.p. 158.5°.

$C_{13}H_{10}O_2$ (198.21)	calc.	C 78.77	H 5.09
	found	C 78.67, 78.73	H 5.18, 5.18

0.2061 g dissolved in absolute *ethanol* to 10.00 ml: $\alpha_D^{25} = +4.949°$ (2 dm). $[\alpha]_D^{25} = +120.1°$; $[M]_D^{25} = +238.0°$.

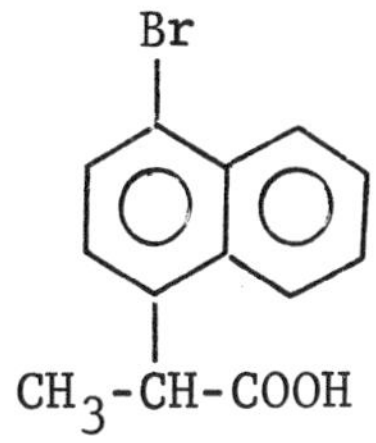

$C_{13}H_{11}BrO_2$ Ref. 927

L'acide bromoracémique a été dédoublé aux antipodes optiques par voie de la cristallisation fractionnée des sels neutres cinchonidinique et brucinique. La chinchonidine formait dans l'acétone dilué un sel moins soluble avec l'antimère dextrogyre. Après quelques cristallisations nous avons obtenu le sel cinchonidinique optiquement pur — aiguilles fines, F. 144—146°, $(\alpha)_D^{20} = +4{,}50°$ ($c = 0{,}333$, $d = 2$, $\alpha = +0{,}03°$) dans l'acétone (calc. pour: $C_{32}H_{33}BrO_3N_2$: N. 4,88; tr.: N. 4,60). La brucine se liait aussi le plus facilement avec l'acide racémique en proportion équimoléculaire dans l'acetone diluée. La cristallisation répétée plusieurs foir était suffisante pour obtenir un sel optiquement pur de l'enantiomère lévogyre. Ce sel formait des lamelles bien distinctes et régulières, F. 131—134°, $(\alpha)_D^{20} = -93{,}09°$ ($c = 0{,}333$, $d = 2$, $\alpha = -0{,}62°$) dans l'acétone (calc. pour: $C_{36}H_{37}BrO_6N_2$: N. 4,15; tr.: N. 3,95).

Les acides α-(1,4-bromonaphtyl)-propioniques antimériques, isolés de leurs sels alcaloïdiques de maniére ordinaire, après la purification du benzène et de l'éther de pétrole, accusaient les propriétés physiques suivantes; antimère dextrogyre — aiguilles F. 138—140°, $(\alpha)_D^{20} = +99{,}09°$ ($c = 0{,}333$, $d = 2$, $\alpha = +0{,}66°$) dans l'acétone (calc. pour: $C_{13}H_{11}BrO_2$: C. 55,93; H. 3,97; tr.: C. 55,83; H. 3,79), antimère lévogyre — aiguilles. F. 138—140°, $(\alpha)_D^{20} = -99{,}09°$ ($c = 0{,}333$, $d = 2$, $\alpha = -0{,}66°$) dans l'acétone (calc. pour: $C_{13}H_{11}BrO_2$: C. 55,93; H. 3,97; tr.: C. 55,62; H. 3,76).

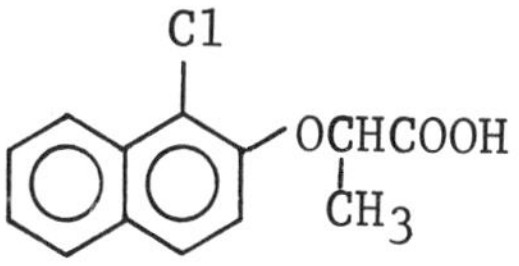

$C_{13}H_{11}ClO_3$ Ref. 928

Preliminary experiments on resolution

Cinchonidine and (+)-α-phenylethylamine yielded crystalline products from which a dextrorotatory acid could be isolated. The first base gave the best resolution and was used for the isolation of the (+)− form. With cinchonine, quinidine and (−)-phenylethylamine salts were obtained which on decomposition yielded products containing a slight excess of the (−)-acid. Better results were obtained with quinine and morphine, the latter being the most effective.

(+)-α-(1-Chloro-2-naphthoxy)-propionic acid

10.5 g (0.042 mole) of inactive acid and 12.3 g (0.042 mole) of cinchonidine were dissolved in a hot mixture of 200 ml alcohol and 240 ml water. After standing over night in a refrigerator the crystals were collected, a small sample was treated with dilute hydrochloric acid and extracted with ether. The ether was driven off and the rotatory power of the acid was determined in abs. alcohol. The salt was recrystallised several times according to Table 1.

The pure salt was treated with dilute hydrochloric acid and extracted with three portions of ether. On evaporation 3.05 g of crude acid were collected. After two recrystallisations from dilute alcohol (25–35 %) 2.95 g of pure (+)-acid were obtained as small, glistening needles with m.p. 162–162.8°.

Table 1

Recrystallisation of the cinchonidine salt of α-(1-chloro-2-naphthoxy)-propionic acid

Cryst. nr	Alcohol ml	Water ml	Yield of salt g	[α]D of the acid
1	200	240	16.4	+ 5.5°
2	200	240	11.0	+ 9.4°
3	120	150	8.7	+ 16.0°
4	100	120	8.3	+ 15.9°
5	100	120	7.8	+ 16.7°
6	100	120	7.2	+ 16.5°

0.1114 g acid: 9.20 ml 0.04824-*N* NaOH
$C_{13}H_{11}O_3Cl$ calc. equiv. wt. 250.7
found » » 251.0

0.0793 g dissolved in abs. *alcohol* to 9.98 ml: $\alpha_D^{55} = +0.151°$. $[\alpha]_D^{25} = +19.0°$; $[M]_D^{25} = +47.6°$.
0.0751 g dissolved in *acetone* to 9.98 ml: $\alpha_D^{25} = +0.087°$. $[\alpha]_D^{25} = +11.6°$; $[M]_D^{25} = +29.0°$.
0.0899 g dissolved in *chloroform* to 9.98 ml: $\alpha_D^{25} = +0.052°$. $[\alpha]_D^{25} = +\ 5.8°$; $[M]_D^{25} = +14.5°$.
0.0806 g dissolved in *benzene* to 9.98 ml: $\alpha_D^{25} = -0.304°$. $[\alpha]_D^{25} = -37.6°$; $[M]_D^{25} = -94.4°$.
0.0719 g neutralized with *aqueous sodium hydroxide* and made up to 9.98 ml: $\alpha_D^{25} = -\ 0.373°$. $[\alpha]_D^{25} = -51.8°$; $[M]_D^{25} = -129.8°$.

(−)-α-(1-Chloro-2-naphthoxy)-propionic acid

The acid was recovered from crystallisation 1 and 2 above; 5.2 g with $[\alpha]_D = -10°$ (in abs. alcohol) were obtained. This product (0.021 mole) and 6.3 g (0.021 mole) of morphine were dissolved in 225 ml of hot 30 % alcohol. The solution was set aside over night, the crystals were collected and the rotatory power of the acid was determined as described above. The purification of the salt was carried out according to Table 2.

Table 2

Recrystallisation of the morphine salt of α-(1-chloro-2-naphthoxy)-propionic acid

Cryst. nr	Alcohol ml	Water ml	Yield of salt g	[α]D of the acid
1	75	150	9.7	− 15.5°
2	75	150	7.7	− 18.2°
3	60	120	7.1	− 18.4°

From the last fraction 2.95 g of crude acid were obtained. Recrystallisation from 60 % ethanol yielded 2.4 g of pure (−)-acid with m.p. 162–162.8°.

0.0821 g acid: 6.77 ml 0.04824-*N* NaOH
$C_{13}H_{11}O_3Cl$ calc. equiv. wt. 250.7
found » » 251.4
0.0834 g dissolved in abs. *alcohol* to 9.98 ml: $\alpha_D^{25} = -0.156°$. $[\alpha]_D^{25} = -18.7°$; $[M]_D^{25} = -46.8°$.

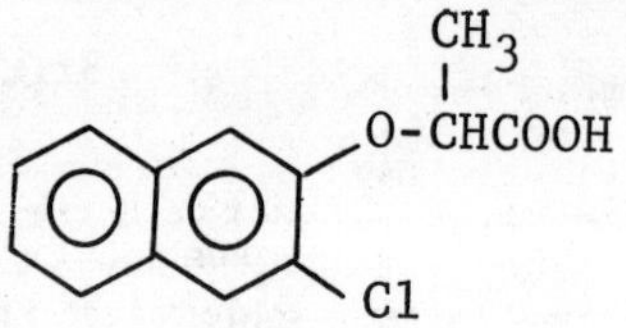

$C_{13}H_{11}ClO_3$ Ref. 929

Resolution of α-(3-chloro-2-naphthyloxy)propionic acid. A solution of the (±)-acid (5·0 g.) and cinchonine (5·8 g.) in boiling methanol (50 ml.) was diluted with hot water and allowed to cool. The *cinchonine salt* of the (−)-acid, which gradually separated, was twice recrystallised from aqueous methyl alcohol; monoclinic prismatic plates, which decomposed at 148—150° after softening *ca.* 125°, were obtained (Found: C, 68·2; H, 6·2; loss in vacuum at 110°, 3·2. $C_{13}H_{11}O_3Cl,C_{19}H_{22}ON_2,H_2O$ requires C, 68·2; H, 6·2; loss 3·2%); $[\alpha]_D^{21}$ +33·2° (*c*, 1·022 in MeOH). Concentration of the mother liquors yielded a little more of the same salt, and eventually the cinchonine salt of the (+)-acid was obtained as a gum. The two salts were separately dissolved in chloroform, the solutions shaken with dilute ammonia solution, and the acids recovered from the alkaline layers were crystallised twice from aqueous methanol. The (−)-*acid*, obtained as a matte of fine needles, m. p. 175—176° (Found: C, 62·5; H, 4·4; Cl, 13·8. $C_{13}H_{11}O_3Cl$ requires C, 62·3; H, 4·4; Cl, 14·2%), had $[\alpha]_D^{21}$ −56·8° (*c*, 1·012 in MeOH). The (+)-*acid* crystallised in fine needles, m. p. 175—176°, $[\alpha]_D^{20}$ +55·6° (*c*, 0·990 in MeOH) (Found: C, 62·3; H, 4·4; Cl, 14·1%). Crystallisation of equimolecular proportions of the (+)- and the (−)-acid from aqueous methanol yielded the (±)-acid, m. p. 175—176°.

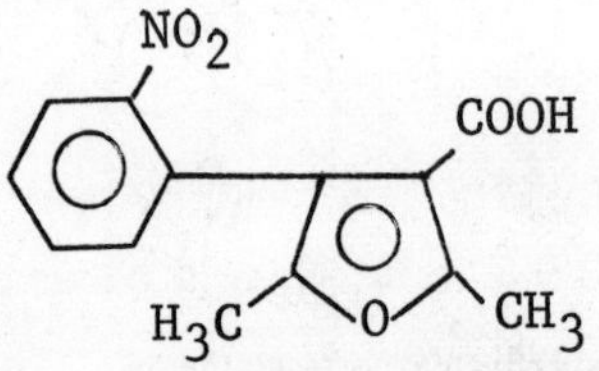

$C_{13}H_{11}NO_5$ Ref. 930

Resolution of 3-(2-Nitrophenyl)-2,5-dimethyl-4-furoic Acid.—The above acid (2.75 g.) was treated with an equimolar amount of quinine as in the previous cases in dilute alcohol. The solution was evaporated to dryness and the quinine salt was dissolved in 300 ml. of boiling acetone. After cooling for several days, a first crop of crystals (IIIa) was collected. After evaporation of the mother liquor *in vacuo*, a gum was left which solidified upon cooling (IIIb). The salt IIIa, m.p. 167–168°, had $[\alpha]^{25}D$ −38° (*c* 0.1924 g. in 10 ml. of $CHCl_3$). The salt IIIb, m.p. 183–185° had $[\alpha]^{25}D$ −52° (*c* 0.0906 g. in 10 ml. of $CHCl_3$). The salts were recrystallized from ethanol and dried over P_2O_5 at 70° for 24 hours.

Anal. Salt IIIa. Calcd. for $C_{33}H_{35}O_7N_3$: C, 67.69; H, 5.98. Found: C, 68.00; H, 5.87. Salt IIIb. Calcd. for $C_{33}H_{35}O_7N_3 \cdot {}^1/_2H_2O$: C, 66.66; H, 6.06. Found: C, 66.97; H, 6.00.

The rotation of both salts was −65 and −64°, respectively, after recrystallization, indicating racemization during this process.

The acid from salt IIIa had $[\alpha]^{25}D$ −7.8° (*c* 0.1533 g. in 10 ml. of $CHCl_3$) and melted at 170–171° with softening at 162–165°. The acid from salt IIIb had $[\alpha]^{25}D$ 12.3° (*c* 0.1216 g. in 10 ml. of $CHCl_3$) and melted at 168–169° with softening at 156°. The rotation of the chloroform solution fell to zero in three hours of standing at room temperature.

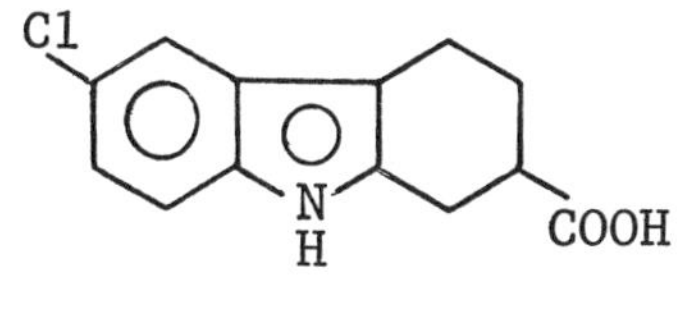

$C_{13}H_{12}ClNO_2$ Ref. 931

EXAMPLE 39

Preparation of (+) 6-chloro-1,2,3,4-tetrahydrocarbazole-2-carboxylic acid

A solution of 8.8 g. (0.0515 mole) of 1-α-(1-naphthyl)ethylamine in 50 ml. of acetone was carefully added to a warm solution of 12.7 g. (0.051 mole) of (±) 6-chloro-1,2,3,4-tetrahydrocarbazole-2-carboxylic acid. After standing at room temperature for 48 hours, the mixture was filtered and the filter cake was washed with cold acetone, yielding 11.7 g. of a colorless salt, m.p. 188°–191°; $[\alpha]_D^{25}$ + 2.4°, which upon recrystallization from 100 ml. of acetone returned 4.8 g. of salt, m.p. 192°–193°; $[\alpha]_D^{25}$ + 15.5°. Upon two subsequent recrystallizations from acetone, 1.20 g., m.p. 196°–197°; $[\alpha]_D^{25}$ + 31.1° was obtained. The salt (1.20 g.) was dissolved in warm acetone and after filtration, the solution was poured into a mixture of ice and hydrochloric acid. Following filtration and drying, 0.60 g. of product was obtained which gave, after crystallization from ethyl acetate, 0.45 g. of (+) 6-chloro-1,2,3,4-tetrahydrocarbazole-2-carboxylic acid, m.p. 249°–251°; $[\alpha]_D^{25}$ + 59.7°.

EXAMPLE 40

Preparation of (−) 6-chloro-1,2,3,4-tetrahydrocarbazole-2-carboxylic acid

A solution of 1.85 g. of d-α-(1-naphthyl)ethylamine in 30 ml. of acetone was carefully added to a solution of 2.7 g. of partially resolved 6-chloro-1,2,3,4-tetrahydrocarbazole-2-carboxylic acid ($[\alpha]_D^{25}$ −15.9°, recovered from the filtrate of a previous resolution of the racemate). After standing for 3 days at room temperature, the mixture was filtered and the filter cake was washed with cold acetone, yielding 2.3 g., m.p. 191°–193°; $[\alpha]_D^{25}$ −17.2°. Following two additional recrystallizations from acetone, 0.38 g. was obtained, m.p. 196°–197°; $[\alpha]_D^{25}$ −33.2°. The salt (0.38 g.) was dissolved in warm acetone, and the resulting solution was poured onto a mixture of ice and hydrochloric acid. Following filtration and drying, 0.17 g. of product was obtained, which upon crystallization from ethyl acetate gave 0.098 g. of (−) 6-chloro-1,2,3,4-tetrahydrocarbazole-2-carboxylic acid, m.p. 249°–250°; $[\alpha]_D^{25}$ −63.0°.

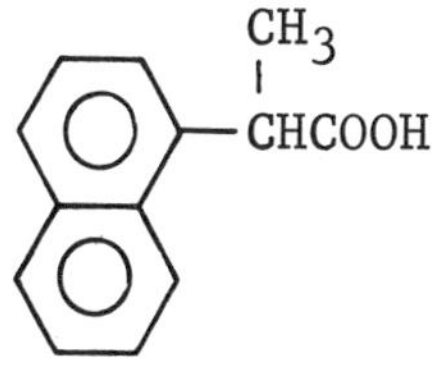

$C_{13}H_{12}O_2$ Ref. 932

Resolution of the racemic acid. Preliminary experiments were carried out with different alkaloids and solvents. Brucine gives in pure methanol a strongly dextrorotatory acid but in dilute methanol only poor resolution. Also the quinine salt gives a good excess of (+)-acid. The (−)-acid can be isolated using the cinchonidine salt in dilute acetone or methanol. Cinchonine and quinidine give levorotatory acid of low activity, optically active benzedrine (β-phenyl-*iso*-propylamine) acid of the same direction of rotation as the base but poor resolution. Strychnine and α-phenylethylamine gave no crystalline salts.

40 g (0.2 mole) of racemic acid were dissolved with 0.2 mole of brucine in 350 ml of hot methanol. The salt was filtered off after 24 hours and recrystallised several times from pure methanol. The progress of the resolution was tested on small samples from each crystallisation, from which the acid was liberated and examined in absolute ethanol:

Crystallisation	1	2	3	4	5	6
ml methanol	350	240	220	200	180	165
g salt obtained	68.9	58.9	54.4	50.6	47.8	45.1
$[\alpha]_D$ of the acid	+ 80.5°	+ 106.5°	+ 116.5°	+ 118.5°	+ 119.5°	+ 119.5°

The mother liquor from the first crystallisation was evaporated to dryness at room temperature and the acid liberated; 17.0 g having $[\alpha]_D$ = − 103° (absolute ethanol) were obtained. This acid (0.085 mole) was dissolved with 25 g (0.085 mole) of cinchonidine in 400 ml of boiling acetone and 300 ml of hot water were added. The salt obtained on standing was recrystallised from dilute acetone; as it is rather sparingly soluble, it is convenient to dissolve it in a small amount (*c.* 20 ml) of hot methanol, after which the acetone and the water are added. It is possible that a more favourable combination of solvents can be found on systematic investigation. The progress of the resolution was followed as described above:

Crystallisation	1	2	3	4	5	6	7
ml acetone	400	250	180	140	140	140	140
ml water	300	250	180	140	140	140	140
g salt obtained	38.4	34.9	32.5	30.5	28.9	27.6	25.9
$[\alpha]_D$ of the acid	− 111.5°	− 116°	− 117°	− 118.5°	− 119°	− 119.5°	− 119.5°

(+)-α-(1-Naphthyl)-propionic acid. The acid was liberated from the brucine salt with dilute sulphuric acid and extracted with ether. 44.2 g salt yielded 13.8 g of crude acid. After three recrystallisations from ligroin (b.p. 85–110°) there remained 10.5 g. The acid forms aggregates of small prisms or four-sided plates with m.p. 69–69.5°.

0.3153 g acid: 15.77 ml 0.0999-*N* NaOH.

$C_{13}H_{12}O_2$ Equiv. wt. calc. 200.2 found 200.1

0.2076 g dissolved in absolute *ethanol* to 10.00 ml: $2\alpha_D^{25}$ = + 4.995°. $[\alpha]_D^{25}$ = + 120.3°; $[M]_D^{25}$ = + 240.9°. — 0.2046 g dissolved in *acetone* to 10.00 ml: $2\alpha_D^{25}$ = + 5.97°. $[\alpha]_D^{25}$ = + 145.9°; $[M]_D^{25}$ = + 292.1°. — 0.2138 g dissolved in glacial *acetic acid* to 10.00 ml: $2\alpha_D^{25}$ = + 6.51°. $[\alpha]_D^{25}$ = + 152.2°; $[M]_D^{25}$ = + 304.8°. — 0.2025 g dissolved in *chloroform* to 10.00 ml: $2\alpha_D^{25}$ = + 5.425°: $[\alpha]_D^{25}$ = + 133.9°; $[M]_D^{25}$ = + 268.2°. — 0.2053 g dissolved in *benzene* to 9.99 ml: $2\alpha_D^{25}$ = + 7.42°. $[\alpha]_D^{25}$ = + 180.5°; $[M]_D^{25}$ = + 361.5°. — 0.2083 g dissolved in *2.2.4-trimethylpentane* to 10.00 ml: $2\alpha_D^{25}$ = + 7.125°. $[\alpha]_D^{25}$ = + 171.0°; $[M]_D^{25}$ = + 342.4°. — 0.2164 g *neutralised with aqueous NaOH* and made up with *water* to 10.00 ml: $2\alpha_D^{25}$ = + 1.49°. $[\alpha]_D^{25}$ = + 34.4°; $[M]_D^{25}$ = + 69.9°.

The *brucine salt* obtained in the course of the resolution forms short-prismatic crystals containing crystal solvent. It was not analysed.

(−)-α-(1-Naphthyl)-propionic acid. The acid was liberated from the cinchonidine salt with dilute sulphuric acid and extracted with ether. 25.9 g salt yielded 9.8 g of crude acid; after three recrystallisations from ligroin there remained 7.2 g with m.p. 69–69.5°.

0.3052 g acid: 17.48 ml 0.0999-*N* NaOH.

$C_{13}H_{12}O_2$ Equiv. wt. calc. 200.2 found 200.5

0.2021 g acid dissolved in absolute *ethanol* to 10.00 ml: $2\alpha_D^{25}$ = − 4.855°. $[\alpha]_D^{25}$ = − 120.1°; $[M]_D^{25}$ = − 240.5°.

Table 2. (−)-α-(1-Naphthyl)-propionic acid and (+)-hydratropic acid.

mole-% hydratropic acid	m.p.	mole-% hydratropic acid	m.p.
0.0	69.5°	60.3	61.1°
10.2	62.4°	65.0	59.8°
20.5	53.9°	70.1	58.2°
26.0	54.7°	80.3	50.3°
32.4	58.3°	90.0	35.5°
36.0	60.0°	97.0	28.9°
40.4	61.1°	100.0	31.0°
50.0	62.6°		

The *cinchonidine salt* obtained in the course of the resolution forms elongated prisms containing crystal solvent. It was not analysed.

Equivalent amounts of (+)- and (−)-acid were dissolved together in a little benzene and the racemic acid separating on cooling was recrystallised once from the same solvent. It had the m.p. 149–149.5°.

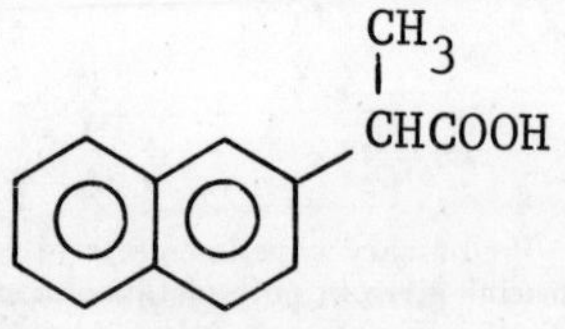

$C_{13}H_{12}O_2$ Ref. 933

Resolution of the racemic acid.—In preliminary tests, 0.001 mole of optically inactive acid and 0.001 mole of the base were dissolved in different solvents. The crystals formed were decomposed in the usual way. The acid was extracted with ether and the optical activity measured in abs. ethanol. The results are given in Table 1.

Equimolecular quantities of the racemic acid (20.02 g, 0.1 mole) and cinchonidine (29.44 g) were dissolved in 800 ml of hot methanol and the solution was left in a refrigerator for 24 hours. The salt was filtered off, washed with cold methanol and dried. From a sample (about 0.3 g) the acid was isolated and the optical activity measured in abs. alcohol. The remaining salt was recrystallized from methanol according to Table 2.

The mother liquors from the two first crystallizations were combined. After evaporating the methanol, 27.5 g of the cinchonidine salt was obtained. The salt was recrystallized from dilute ethanol. The progress of the resolution was followed as described above.

Table 1. Preliminary tests on the resolution of α-(2-naphthyl)-propionic acid.

Base	$[\alpha]_D^{25}$ of acid in abs. ethanol			
	From methanol	From ethanol	From acetone	From ethylacetate
Cinchonine	+ 7°	+ 19°	—	—
Cinchonidine	+ 50°	—27°	± 0°	—
Quinine	+ 19°	+ 14°	—	—
Chinidine	± 0°	oil	oil	oil
Brucine	oil	oil	oil	oil
Strychnine	oil	oil	oil	oil
(+)-Phenylethylamine	± 0°	± 0°	—	—
Morphine	oil	oil	—	oil

Table 2. Recrystallization of the cinchonidine salt of α-(2-naphthyl)-propionic acid.

Cryst. No.	Methanol (ml)	Weight of salt (g)	$[\alpha]_D^{25}$ of acid
1	800	27.9	+ 41.1°
2	600	21.8	+ 62.2°
3	500	18.3	+ 66.0°
4	500	16.6	—
5	500	14.8	+ 66.3°
6	500	12.6	+ 66.4°

Table 3. Recrystallization of the cinchonidine salt of α-(2-naphthyl)-propionic acid.

Cryst. No.	Solvent (ml)		Weight of salt (g)	$[\alpha]_D^{25}$ of acid
	Ethanol	Water		
0	—	—	27.5	− 47.2°
1	260	10	23.2	− 61.9°
2	220	8	18.6	− 66.4°
3	130	5	16.6	− 66.5°

Table 4. $[\alpha]_D^{25}$ and $[M]_D^{25}$ of (+)-α-(2-naphthyl)-propionic acid.

Solvent	mg of acid	$2\,\alpha_D^{25}$	$[\alpha]_D^{25}$	$[M]_D^{25}$
Benzene	114.0	+ 1.76°	+ 77.2°	+ 154.6°
2.2.4-Trimethylpentane	11.60	+ 0.19°	+ 82°	+ 164°
Acetic acid	116.8	+ 1.81°	+ 77.4°	+ 155.0°
Acetone	100.9	+ 1.98°	+ 98.1°	+ 196.4°
Chloroform	105.3	+ 1.50°	+ 71.2°	+ 142.5°
Ethanol	118.3	+ 1.63°	+ 68.8°	+ 137.7°
Water*	109.7	− 0.36°	− 16.4°	− 32.8°

* The acid neutralized with NaOH (pH 7)

(+)-α-(*2-Naphthyl*)-*propionic acid*.—The salt from cryst. No. 6 (Table 2) was decomposed with sulfuric acid and the organic acid extracted with ether. It was recrystallized once from cyclohexane and twice from ligroin (b.p. 85–110°). The yield of crude acid was 4.5 g; after the recrystallizations there remained 4.1 g. From the mother liquors No. 4 and 5 another 1.3 g of pure acid was obtained. The acid forms small needles with m.p. 139.5–141°.

0.1173 g acid: 7.71 ml 0.0754*N* NaOH
$C_{13}H_{12}O_2$ Equiv. wt. calc. 200.2 found 200.1

Weighed amounts of the acid were dissolved in different solvents, made up to 10.00 ml and the optical activity measured. The results are given in Table 4.

(—)-α-(*2-Naphthyl*)-*propionic acid*.—From the last fraction (Table 3) 6.6 g of crude acid was obtained. It was recrystallized once from cyclohexane and twice from ligroin (b.p. 85–110°). The yield of pure acid was 4.9 g. M.p. 139.5–141°.

0.1055 g acid: 7.02 ml 0,0754*N* NaOH
$C_{13}H_{12}O_2$ Equiv. wt. calc. 200.2 found 200.0
0.1080 g acid dissolved in abs. ethanol to 10.00 ml: $2\alpha_D^{25} = -1.48°$ $[\alpha]_D^{25} = -68.6°$; $[M]_D^{25} = -137.3°$.

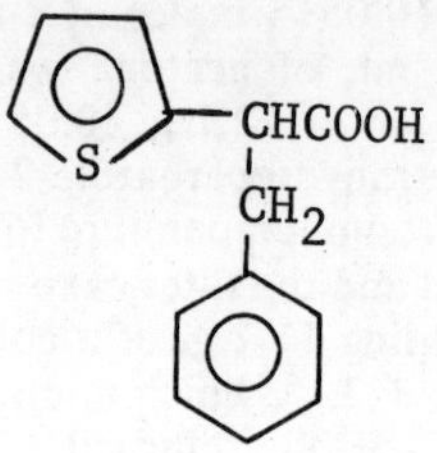

$C_{13}H_{12}O_2S$ Ref. 934

***Resolution** of α-(2-thienyl)hydrocinnamic acid:* 7.2 g (0.03 moles) of optically inactive benzyl-2-thienylacetic acid and 9.3 g (0.03 moles) of cinchonidine were dissolved in a hot mixture of 180 ml of ethanol and 150 ml of water. A few drops of the solution were set aside and allowed to crystallise and the principal part of the solution was seeded with the crystals formed. The solution was allowed to stand for 24 hours and the crystals were filtered off and dried. 0.5 g of the precipitate was set aside, the acid isolated and the optical activity measured in acetone. The remaining precipitate was recrystallised from dilute ethanol until the optical activity of the acid remained constant.

Crystallisation No.	1	2	3	4
ml of solvent (ethanol-water 6 : 5)	330	165	122	110
g of salt obtained	8.1	6.0	5.3	4.8
$[\alpha]_D^{25}$ of acid	+ 58°	+ 82°	+ 86°	+ 86°

Cinchonidine (+)-α-(*2-thienyl*)*hydrocinnamate* crystallises as colourless needles melting at 137°.

2.8 g (0.012 moles) of benzylthienylacetic acid ($[\alpha]_D^{25} = -58°$), isolated from the first mother liquor above, and 2.6 g of *l*-ephedrine dihydrate were dissolved in a hot mixture of 43 ml of ethanol and 129 ml of water. The mixture was allowed to stand for 24 hours and the precipitate recrystallised until the optical activity of the liberated acid remained constant.

Crystallisation No.	1	2	3	4	5	6
ml of solvent (ethanol-water 1 : 3)	172	128	112	72	60	52
g of salt obtained	4.3	3.8	2.6	2.2	1.9	1.7
$[\alpha]_D^{25}$ of acid	− 70°	− 77°	− 83°	− 85°	− 87°	− 87°

(+)-α-(*2-Thienyl*)*hydrocinnamic acid:* 4.8 g of the cinchonidine salt were decomposed with 2-*N* sulphuric acid and the liberated acid extracted with ether. After evaporation of the ether 2.0 g of crude acid remained. The acid was recrystallised several times from petrol (b.p. 60°–70°) and finally 1.6 g of pure acid was obtained as colourless needles. M.p. 71°–72°.

61.30 mg of acid, 5.88 ml of 0.04480–C NaOH.
$C_{13}H_{12}O_2S$. Equiv. wt. calc. 232.1, found 232.8.

97.3 mg in 10.01 ml of *acetone:* $2\,\alpha_D^{25} = +1.717°$, $[\alpha]_D^{25} = +88.3°$, $[M]_D^{25} = +205.0°$.
118.1 mg in 10.01 ml of *ethanol:* $2\,\alpha_D^{25} = +1.842°$, $[\alpha]_D^{25} = +78.1°$, $[M]_D^{25} = +181.2°$.
113.0 mg in 10.01 ml of glacial *acetic acid:* $2\,\alpha_D^{25} = +1.796°$, $[\alpha]_D^{25} = +79.6°$, $[M]_D^{25} = +184.6°$.
104.5 mg in 10.01 ml of *benzene:* $2\,\alpha_D^{25} = +1.567°$, $[\alpha]_D^{25} = +75.1°$, $[M]_D^{25} = +174.2°$.
114.3 mg of acid, dissolved in 2.0 ml of ethanol, were neutralised with 0.1–C NaOH and made up to 10.01 ml with *water:* $2\,\alpha_D^{25} = +1.531°$, $[\alpha]_D^{25} = +67.1°$, $[M]_D^{25} = +155.6°$.

(−)-α-(*2-Thienyl*)*hydrocinnamic acid:* 1.7 g of the *l*-ephedrine salt were decomposed with 2-*N* sulphuric acid and the liberated acid extracted with ether. From the ether layer 0.7 g of crude acid was obtained. After recrystallisation from petrol 0.5 g of acid remained. It resembles its optical antipode in all respects. M.p. 71°–72°.

51.09 mg of acid, 4.91 ml of 0.04480–C NaOH.
$C_{13}H_{12}O_2S$. Equiv. wt. calc. 232.1, found 232.5.

110.8 mg in 10.01 ml of *acetone:* $2\,\alpha_D^{25} = -1.942°$, $[\alpha]_D^{25} = -87.7°$, $[M]_D^{25} = -203.5°$.

Note:

The following refers to both the above resolution and the resolution that follows: Refs. 934 and 935. Compound I refers to the above compound and compound II refers to the compound in Ref. 935.

Preliminary tests on resolution: About 0.001 moles of the acids I and II and equivalent amounts of the bases were dissolved in 10 ml of the hot solvents. The mixtures were allowed to stand at room temperature and some water was added gradually until crystals or oils were formed. The crystals were filtered off, the acid liberated and the optical activity measured in absolute ethanol (Table 2).

In some cases the compounds remained in solution even when a large excess of water was added. In the table these are indicated by s.

Table 2.

Base	$[\alpha]_D^{25}$ of acid in ethanol					
	benzene		ethanol		acetone	
	I	II	I	II	I	II
l-Ephedrine	− 28°		− 28°			± 0°
Strychnine			− 22°	+ 16°	+ 35°	− 28°
Brucine			oil	oil	oil	oil
Quinine			− 8°	− 3°	− 20°	+ 41°
Cinchonine			oil		oil	s
Cinchonidine			+ 45°	− 19°		− 15°
Nicotine			s	s		s
Yohimbine				oil		oil
(+)-α-Phenylethylamine			± 0°	+ 61°		
(+)-Benzedrine	± 0°	± 0°	+ 17°	+ 70°		

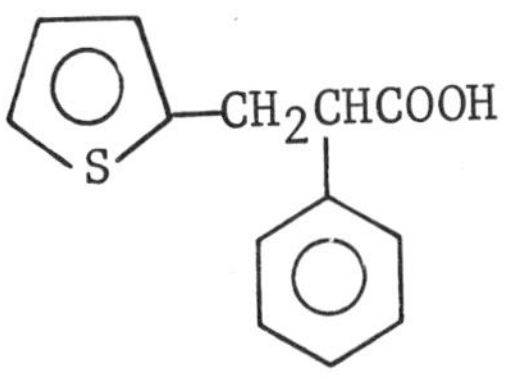

$C_{13}H_{12}O_2S$ Ref. 935

l-Ephedrine (−)-α-(2-thienyl)hydrocinnamate crystallises as colourless thread-like crystal aggregates melting at 149°.

Resolution of 2-thenylphenylacetic acid: 6.9 g (0.03 moles) of optically inactive 2-thenylphenylacetic acid and 4.1 g (0.03 moles) of (+)-benzedrine were dissolved in a hot mixture of 125 ml of ethanol and 125 ml of water. The mixture was allowed to stand for 24 hours and the precipitate then filtered off and dried. The salt was recrystallised from dilute ethanol until the optical activity of the liberated acid remained constant.

Crystallisation No.	1	2	3	4	5
ml of solvent (ethanol-water 1 : 1)	250	136	96	76	64
g of salt obtained	5.9	4.2	3.4	2.8	2.4
$[\alpha]_D^{25}$ of acid (acetone)	+ 56°	+ 100°	+ 122°	+ 125°	+ 125°

(+)-Benzedrine (+)-2-thenylphenylacetate crystallises as long, colourless, shining needles melting at 184°.

3.5 g (0.015 moles) of thenylphenylacetic acid ($[\alpha]_D^{25} = -65°$) and 1.8 g (0.015 moles) of (+)-α-phenylethylamine were dissolved in a hot mixture of 55 ml of ethanol and 20 ml of water. The mixture was allowed to stand for 24 hours. The crystals were filtered off, dried and recrystallised from dilute ethanol until the optical activity of the liberated acid remained constant.

Crystallisation No.	1	2	3	4
ml of solvent (ethanol-water 5.5 : 2)	75	60	49	40
g of salt obtained	4.2	3.5	2.9	2.4
$[\alpha]_D^{25}$ of acid (acetone)	− 112°	− 122°	− 128°	− 127°

(+)-α-Phenylethylamine (−)-2-thenylphenylacetate crystallises as colourless shining needles melting at 185°–187°.

(+)-2-Thenylphenylacetic acid: 2.4 g of the (+)-benzedrine salt were decomposed with 2-*N* sulphuric acid and the liberated acid was extracted and purified as described above. 1.0 g of pure (+)-acid were obtained as colourless needles, melting at 83°–85°.

40.14 mg of acid, 3.85 ml of 0.04480–C NaOH.
$C_{13}H_{12}O_2S$. Equiv. wt. calc. 232.1, found 233.0.

107.0 mg in 10.01 ml of *acetone:* $2\alpha_D^{25} = +2.714°$, $[\alpha]_D^{25} = +126.9°$, $[M]_D^{25} = +294.5°$.

(−)-2-Thenylphenylacetic acid: 2.4 g of the (+)-α-phenylethylamine salt were decomposed with 2-*N* sulphuric acid and the liberated acid extracted and purified as described for its optical antipode, which it resembles in all respects. M.p. 83.5°–85°.

53.40 mg of acid, 5.13 ml of 0.04480–C NaOH.
$C_{13}H_{12}O_2S$. Equiv. wt. calc. 232.1, found 232.6.

100.4 mg in 10.01 ml of *acetone:* $2\alpha_D^{25} = -2.565°$, $[\alpha]_D^{25} = -127.9°$, $[M]_D^{25} = -296.8°$.
96.5 mg in 10.01 ml of *ethanol:* $2\alpha_D^{25} = -2.198°$, $[\alpha]_D^{25} = -114.0°$, $[M]_D^{25} = -264.6°$.
98.0 mg in 10.01 ml of *benzene:* $2\alpha_D^{25} = -2.416°$, $[\alpha]_D^{25} = -123.4°$, $[M]_D^{25} = -286.4°$.
88.5 mg in 10.01 ml of glacial *acetic acid:* $2\alpha_D^{25} = -2.120°$, $[\alpha]_D^{25} = -119.9°$, $[M]_D^{25} = -278.3°$.
87.5 mg of acid, dissolved in 2.0 ml of ethanol, were neutralized with 0.1–C NaOH and made up to 10.01 ml with *water:* $2\alpha_D^{25} = -1.590°$, $[\alpha]_D^{25} = -91.0°$, $[M]_D^{25} = -211.2°$.

Note:

See note after Ref. 934.

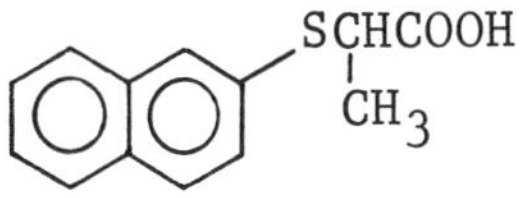

$C_{13}H_{12}O_2S$ Ref. 936

Preliminary experiments on resolution. Crystalline salts containing excess of the (+)-acid were obtained with quinine and (+)-α-phenylethylamine, the latter base being about twice as effective as the former. Cinchonine and (−)-α-phenylethylamine yielded salts from which a levorotatory acid was obtained. The latter base gave the best result.

(+)-α-(2-Naphthylsulphide)-propionic acid. 11.6 g (0.05 mole) inactive acid and 6.1 g (0.05 mole) (+)-α-phenylethylamine were dissolved in 500 ml of hot 50 % alcohol. On cooling, the salt separated and after standing overnight in a refrigerator the crystalline solid was collected, dried in the air and weighed. A small sample was treated with dilute hydrochloric acid and the organic acid extracted with ether which was evaporated. The optical rotation of the acid was measured in abs. alcohol. The salt was recrystallised several times and treated as above giving the following series of crystallisations:

Crystallisation nr	1	2	3	4	5	6
ml alcohol	250	100	60	30	25	25
ml water	250	100	60	30	25	25
Weight of salt (g)	9.6	7.8	7.2	6.9	6.6	6.3
$[\alpha]_D$ of the acid	+ 79.6°	+ 114.8°	—	+ 130.9°	+ 131.1°	+ 132.6°

The salt from crystallisation 6 above yielded 4.2 g crude acid, which was recrystallised alternately from formic acid and cyclohexane. 3.0 g pure (+)-acid were collected as small, white needles with m.p. 53-54°.

89.06 mg acid: 8.01 ml 0.04792-*N* NaOH
$C_{13}H_{12}O_2S$ calc. equiv. wt. 232.3
found " " 232.0

0.1069 g dissolved in abs. *alcohol* to 10.00 ml: $\alpha_D^{25} = +1.499°$. $[\alpha]_D^{25} = +140.2°$; $[M]_D^{25} = +325.7°$. — 0.1065 g dissolved in *acetone* to 10.00 ml: $\alpha_D^{25} = +1.654°$. $[\alpha]_D^{25} = +155.3°$; $[M]_D^{25} = +360.8°$. — 0.1004 g dissolved in *benzene* to 10.00 ml: $\alpha_D^{25} = +1.748°$. $[\alpha]_D^{25} = +174.1°$; $[M]_D^{25} = +404.4°$. — 0.1048 g dissolved in *chloroform* to 10.00 ml: $\alpha_D^{25} = +1.438°$. $[\alpha]_D^{25} = +137.2°$; $[M]_D^{25} = +318.7°$. — 0.1027 g neutralised with *aqueous sodium hydroxide* and made up to 10.00 ml: $\alpha_D^{25} = +0.983°$. $[\alpha]_D^{25} = +95.7°$; $[M]_D^{25} = +222.3°$.

(−)-α-(2-Naphthylsulphide)-propionic acid. From the mother liquor from crystallisation 1 above 5.1 g (0.022 mole) acid with $[\alpha]_D = -101°$ (c = 1 in abs. alcohol) were obtained. This acid was dissolved with 2.7 g (0.022 mole) (−)-α-phenylethylamine in 100 ml of hot 50 % alcohol. The crystallisations were carried out as described above. The following series of crystallisations was obtained:

Crystallisation nr	1	2	3	4	5
ml alcohol	50	50	30	25	25
ml water	50	50	30	25	25
Weight of salt (g)	6.2	5.6	5.4	5.1	4.9
$[\alpha]_D$ of the acid	− 111.6°	− 124.8°	− 133.1°	− 138.9°	− 137.0°

The pure salt on decomposition yielded 3.3 g crude (−)-acid. After recrystallisation 3 times from cyclohexane 2.1 g (−)-acid were collected. It closely resembled the (+)-form and melted at 52–53.5°.

87.62 mg acid: 7.84 ml 0.04792-*N* NaOH
$C_{13}H_{12}O_2S$ calc. equiv. wt. 232.3
found " " 233.2

0.0952 g dissolved in abs. *alcohol* to 10.00 ml: $\alpha_D^{25} = -1.323°$. $[\alpha]_D^{25} = -139.0°$; $[M]_D^{25} = -322.8°$. —

Ethyl α-cyano-β-(2-naphthyl)-*iso*-butyrate (IV). 4.6 g (0.2 g atom) sodium were dissolved in 80 ml abs. alcohol. To the solution were added 25.4 g (0.2 mole) ethyl α-cyanopropionate [prepared according to HOFFMAN and BARBIER (8) and WIDEQVIST (9)] and finally 48.6 g (0.22 mole) 2-bromomethylnaphthalene [prepared according to OLIVIER and WIT (10)] were added in portions while stirring. The reaction which started spontaneously was completed by boiling with reflux for 4 hours. The liquid was cooled down, water added and the alcohol distilled off. The oil which separated was washed with water, dilute sodium carbonate solution and water and was finally dried with anhydrous sodium sulphate. The product (45 g) was distilled *in vacuo* yielding 38.6 g (72 %) ethyl-α-cyano-β-(2-naphthyl)-*iso*-butyrate boiling at 218–224°/9 mm.

1-(2-Naphthyl)-propane-2,2-dicarboxylic acid (V). The ester was refluxed with 14.5 g sodium hydroxide in 50 ml water and enough alcohol to give a single phase system. After 55 hours no more ammonia was evolved. After the alcohol had been distilled off the alkaline residue was extracted with ether and acidified with dilute hydrochloric acid when an oil separated. This was taken up in ether, the water layer extracted with another portion of ether and the ether driven off from the combined extracts by a current of air. The remaining oil soon crystallised. The yield of 1-(2-naphthyl)-propane-2,2-dicarboxylic acid was 31.6 g (85 %). It melted under decarboxylation at 164° and was not further purified.

***rac.*-α-(2-Naphthylmethyl)-propionic acid (III).** The dicarboxylic acid was heated at 170° for 30 minutes when no more carbon dioxide was given off. The remaining oil crystallised in about one day. Yield 25.6 g (98 %). The acid was dissolved in dilute sodium hydroxide and the solution extracted with ether and benzene. The aqueous layer was again acidified with dilute hydrochloric acid when the organic acid was obtained in a crystalline state. The product was recrystallised once from 50 % alcohol, twice from formic acid and finally twice from petrol (b.p. 60–80°). 11.5 g pure acid were collected as irregular scales with m.p. 89.5–90.5°.

23.44 mg acid: 10.92 ml 0.1001-*N* NaOH.
43.52 mg acid: 124.42 mg CO_2 and 25.36 mg H_2O
$C_{14}H_{14}O_2$ calc. equiv. wt. 214.3, C 78.48, H 6.59
found " " 214.4, " 78.02, " 6.52

Preliminary experiments on resolution. From the salts of cinchonidine and (−)-α-phenylethylamine an acid containing excess of the (+)-form was obtained. Brucine, quinine and (+)-α-phenylethylamine yielded the (−)-form. Cinchonidine and α-phenylethylamine gave the best resolution.

(+)-α-(2-Naphthylmethyl)-propionic acid. 8.6 g (0.04 mole) racemic acid and 11.8 g (0.04 mole) cinchonidine were dissolved in 200 ml hot alcohol. 200 ml cold water were added and the solution set aside in a cool place after seeding with crystals from a preliminary run. The salt which separated was recrystallised according to the scheme below:

Crystallisation nr	1	2	3	4	5	6	7	8	9	10	11
ml alcohol	200	250	250	250	150	100	75	75	80	100	100
ml water	200	250	250	250	150	100	75	75	80	100	100
Weight of salt (g)	18.7	15.8	13.1	8.7	7.4	6.9	6.6	6.3	5.8	5.3	4.75
$[\alpha]_D$ of the acid	—	+3.9°	+5.9°	+16.8°	+20.6°	+21.6°	+21.6°	+22.7°	+23.4°	+23.7°	+23.2°

The pure salt from the last crystallisation yielded 1.9 g (+)-acid which was recrystallised from petrol (b.p. 60–80°). 1.4 g pure (+)-acid were collected as colourless, glistening plates with m.p. 84–85°. The compound is dimorphic and has a lower melting modification which can often be obtained when the melt is supercooled to room temperature. This unstable form crystallises in rectangular plates melting at 69°.

78.67 mg acid: 7.63 ml 0.04792-*N* NaOH
$C_{14}H_{14}O_2$ calc. equiv. wt. 214.3
found " " 215.2

0.0966 g dissolved in abs. *alcohol* to 10.00 ml: $\alpha_D^{25} = +0.233°$. $[\alpha]_D^{25} = +24.1°$; $[M]_D^{25} = +51.7°$. — 0.0990 g dissolved in *acetone* to 10.00 ml: $\alpha_D^{25} = +0.317°$. $[\alpha]_D^{25} = +32.0°$; $[M]_D^{25} = +68.6°$. — 0.0971 g dissolved in *benzene* to 10.00 ml: $\alpha_D^{25} = +0.237°$. $[\alpha]_D^{25} = +24.4°$; $[M]_D^{25} = +52.3°$. — 0.1042 g dissolved in *chloroform* to 10.00 ml: $\alpha_D^{25} = +0.253°$. $[\alpha]_D^{25} = +24.3°$; $[M]_D^{25} = +52.0°$. — 0.0908 g neutralised with *aqueous sodium hydroxide* and made up to 10.00 ml. $\alpha_D^{25} = +0.322°$. $[\alpha]_D^{25} = +35.5°$; $[M]_D^{25} = +76.0°$.

(−)-α-(2-Naphthylmethyl)-propionic acid. From the mother liquors from crystallisations 1–5 above, 5.1 g partially active (−)-acid were obtained. $[\alpha]_D = -11.2°$ (c = 1 in abs alcohol.) This acid (0.024 mole) and 2.9 g (0.024 mole) (+)-α-phenylethylamine were dissolved in a hot mixture of 95 ml alcohol and 190 ml water. The salt which had separated after standing over night in a refrigerator was recrystallised according to the following scheme:

Crystallisation nr	1	2	3	4	5	6
ml alcohol	95	90	75	65	60	50
ml water	190	180	150	130	120	100
Weight of salt (g)	6.1	5.1	4.4	4.8	3.2	2.7
$[\alpha]_D$ of the acid	−15.6°	−19.0°	−20.2°	−22.0°	−20.7°	−22.4°

From the last fraction 1.65 g crude (−)-acid could be isolated. After recrystallisation from petrol (b.p. 60–80°) 0.9 g pure (−)-acid was collected. It closely resembled the (+)-form and melted at 83–84.5°. The unstable modification melted at 69°.

66.82 mg acid: 6.50 ml 0.04792-*N* NaOH
$C_{14}H_{14}O_2$ calc. equiv. wt. 214.3
found " " 214.5

0.0980 g dissolved in abs. *alcohol* to 10.00 ml: $\alpha_D^{25} = -0.226°$. $[\alpha]_D^{25} = -23.1°$; $[M]_D^{25} = -49.4°$. —

8. **C. de Hoffmann** and **E. Barbier,** Bull. Soc. Chim. Belg. *45,* 565 (1936). — 9. **S. Wideqvist,** Ark. Kemi Min. Geol. *19 B,* No 9 (1945). 10. **S. Olivier** and **J. Wit,** Rec Trav. chim. Pays-Bas, *57,* 90 (1938).

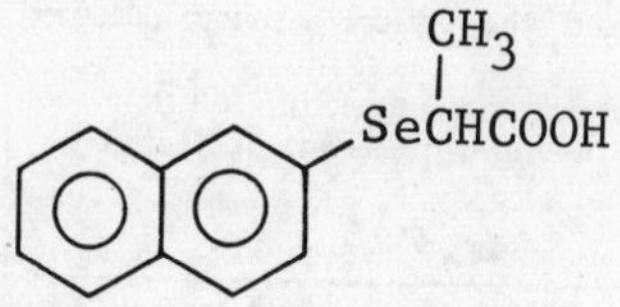

$C_{13}H_{12}O_3Se$ Ref. 937

Preliminary experiments on resolution were carried out with a number of the common bases in dilute ethanol. Cichonidine gave the most promising results: the acid isolated from the salt had $[\alpha]_D = -47°$ and that recovered from the mother liquor $[\alpha]_D = +45°$, As the yield of salt was not far from 50 % it could be concluded that a fairly good resolution had been obtained. The strychnine and dehydroabietylamine salts gave acid of much lower activity while the acid isolated from the quinine salt was quite inactive. The salts of brucine, quinidine and cinchonine failed to crystallise.

(−)-2-Methoxy-4,5-dichlorophenoxy-propionic acid. Racemic acid (26.5 g, 0.10 mole) and cinchonidine (29.4 g, 0.10 mole) were dissolved in a hot mixture of 270 ml ethanol and 180 ml water. The salt crystallised readily and was recrystallised as seen below. The progress of the resolution was tested on small samples of each crystallisation from which the acid was liberated and measured in acetone solution.

Crystallisation	1	2	3	4
ml ethanol	270	75	75	75
ml water	180	75	75	75
g salt obtained	25.5	24.3	22.9	22.1
$[\alpha]_D^{25}$ of the acid	−57°	−59.5°	−59°	−60°

The salt was decomposed with dilute sulphuric acid and the organic acid was extracted with ether. The crude product (10.0 g from 22.1 g salt) was recrystallised twice from dilute (30 %) formic acid yielding 9,1 g of pure acid as small needles with m.p. 101.5–102.5°.

Table 1

g = g acid in 10.00 ml solution.

	g	α_D^{25}(1 dm)	$[\alpha]_D^{25}$	$[M]_D^{25}$
Acetone	0.1243	−0.752°	−60.5°	−160.4°
Ethanol (abs.)	0.1206	−0.612°	−50.7°	−134.5°
Chloroform	0.1369	−0.391°	−28.6°	−75.7°
Water (neutr.)	0.1304	−0.185°	−14.2°	−37.6°
Benzene	0.1333	−0.226°	−17.0°	−44.9°

The acid was isolated and recrystallised twice as described for the enantiomer. The salt (13.7 g) yielded 6.5 g crude product and 5.4 g pure acid, quite similar to the (−)-form, m.p. 101.5–102.5°.

$C_{10}H_{10}O_4Cl_2$ (265.09)
Calc. C 45.31 H 3.80 Cl 26.75
Found C 45.17 H 3.77 Cl 26.63

0.1015 g acid, dissolved in *acetone* to 10.00 ml: $\alpha_D^{25} = +0.613°$ (1 dm). $[\alpha]_D^{25} = +60.4°$; $[M]_D^{25} = +160.1°$.

$C_{10}H_{10}O_4Cl_2$ (265.09)
Calc. C 45.31 H 3.80 Cl 26.75
Found C 45.32 H 3.77 Cl 26.75

The rotatory power in various solvents is given in Table 1.

(+)-2-Methoxy-4,5-dichlorophenoxy-propionic acid. The ethanolic mother liquor from the first crystallisation of the cinchonidine salt was evaporated, giving a mixture of oil and crystals. On addition of some acetone, the oil solidified at once to a crystalline product. The acid isolated from a small sample of this salt had $[\alpha]_D^{25} = +43.2°$. The rest of the salt (31.0 g) was recrystallised from dilute acetone.

Crystallisation	1	2
ml acetone	150	75
ml water	100	25
g salt obtained	18.4	13.7
$[\alpha]_D^{25}$ of the acid	+57°	+59.5°

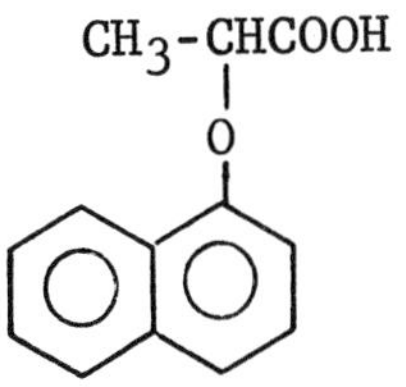

$C_{13}H_{12}O_3$ Ref. 938

On dissout 26gr,460 de cinchonine (cristallisée préalablement dans l'alcool) et 19gr,440 d'acide bien pulvérisé dans 900 centimètres cubes d'alcool a 96° (quantités moléculaires). On ajoute 2.400 centimètres cubes d'eau chaude et on porte a l'ébullition. On filtre â chaud et on abandonne à la température ordinaire. Après quelques minutes la cristallisation, très caractéristique, commence déjà. Aux aiguilles qui apparaissent sur quelques points de la surface du liquide, s'en ajoutent d'autres, formant ainsi des colonnes descendant jusqu'au fond, rappelant en quelque sorte les stalactites. Bientôt tout le liquide est envahi par une cristallisation abandante. Après 24 heures, on essore et on obtient après dessiccation à l'etuve 24gr,210 de sel bien cristallisé (rendemént théorique 45gr,900).

D'un échantillon de ce sel brut on isole l'acide par trituration avec de la soude normale. On filtre pour séparer la cinchonine, puis on met l'acide en liberté par de l'acide chlorhydrique dilué. Il se sépare sous forme d'aiguilles fines qu'on essore.

Lecture polarimétrique: 0,1 d'acide dans 20 centimètres cubes d'alcool absolu. Tube de 20 centimètres:

$$a = +0°,19 \quad \text{d'ou} \quad [\alpha]_D^{20} = +31°,66$$

calculé d'après la formule:

$$[\alpha]_D = \frac{\alpha \cdot 100}{1. \ c}$$

où α représente les degrés transformés en minutes centésimales, 1 = la longueur du tube exprimée en décimètres et c la concentration.

On fait cristalliser le sel brut dans l'alcool a 25%:

Sel de cinchonine........................20 gr.
Alcool a 25%........................... 4cc,500

On obtient apres 12 heures de repos a la glacière 17 grammes de sel, soit 85%.

Lecture polarimétrique. Conc. = 0,5 (dans l'alcool absolu). Tube 20 centimètres:

$$\alpha = +0°,28 \quad \text{d'ou} \quad [\alpha]_D^{20} = +46°,66$$

Une deuxième cristallisation du sel effectuée dans les mêmes conditions ne modifie plus le pouvoir rotatoire.

On met l'acide en liberté par la méthode ordinaire (trituration du sel avec de la soude normale, filtration et précipitation par l'acide chlorhydrique dilué).

Il est insoluble dans l'eau et l'éther de pétrole, soluble dans l'acétone, le benzène, l'éther, l'acide acétique, le chloroforme et le sulfure de carbone. On le fait cristalliser dans de l'alcool dilué. Comme il fond sous l'eau, il est preférable d'opérer à froid. Pour cela on le dissout dans un excès d'alcool, on ajoute ensuite de l'eau jusqu'à trouble persistant, et on amorce avec un cristal provenant d'une préparation antérieure. L'acide cristallise lentement sous forme de longues aiguilles blanches, soyeuses qui fondent a 126°.

Separation de l'acide a gauche. - Les eaux-mères qui contiennent l'isomère gauche sont traitées par du noir décolorant et filtrées.

On évapore dans le vide environ les neuf dixièmes du liquide. Le sel de l'acide gauche se sépare a l'état huileux, les essais de cristallisation que nous avons tentés n'ont pas donné de résultats. On met l'acide en liberté par trituration avec de la soude. Une lecture au polarimètre avant la cristallisation donne:

$$[\alpha]_D^{20} = -40°$$

Cristallisé dans les mêmes conditions que son isomère droit, cet acide possède l'activité optique de celui-ci avec le signe contraire.

L'acide α-naphtoxyméthylacetique racémique fond a 153-153°. Les isomères optiques fondent chacun vers 126°. En les melangeant intimement à sec, en parties égales on reproduit le racémique. En effet, on pareil mélange fond vers 152°; il est inactif à la lumière polarisée.

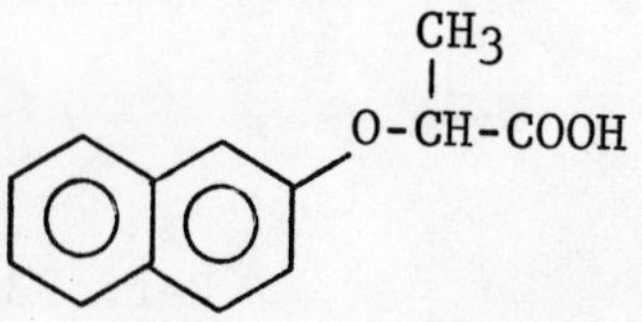

$C_{13}H_{12}O_3$

Ref. 939

13 g. α-(2-naphthoxy)propionic acid (m.p. 107 to 108·5° C), dissolved in 20 ml. ethanol, was added with vigorous stirring to the equivalent amount (17·7 g.) of (+)-cinchonine (twice recrystallized, m.p. 263 to 268° C) suspended in 1400 ml. of boiling 25% ethanol. The solution cleared completely and the salt began to separate within 10 min. On cooling the crystals were filtered and dried; yield 23·5 g. These crystals, rich in the salt of the (−)-acid, were recrystallized six times from 25% ethanol; yield 8·5 g.

The combined mother liquors from the original preparation and the first two recrystallizations of the (−)-acid salt when evaporated under reduced pressure gave 14 g. of salt rich in (+)-acid. This product was recrystallized six times from acetone to give 2·9 g. of crystals. Fractional crystallization of the mother liquors led to the separation of a further 1·9 g.

In each case the salt was decomposed with hydrochloric acid and the liberated acid taken into chloroform. The acid was then extracted from this solution with 2% sodium bicarbonate and reprecipitated with hydrochloric acid.

The (−)-acid was finally recrystallized twice from light petroleum giving white needles, m.p. 117·5 to 119° C; yield 2·9 g. (from 8·5 g. salt).

The (+)-acid when recrystallized twice from light petroleum gave white needles m.p. 118 to 119·5° C; yield 1·4 g. (from 4·8 g. salt).

Specific rotation

The specific rotation of each acid was determined in absolute ethanol solution. The following results were obtained:

(−)-*acid*. 664·3 mg. in 25 ml. alcohol; 2 dm.; $\alpha = -5{\cdot}03°$; $[\alpha]^{20}_{D} = -94{\cdot}6°$.

(+)-*acid*. 514·9 mg. in 25 ml. alcohol; 2 dm.; $\alpha = +3{\cdot}84°$; $[\alpha]^{20}_{D} = +93{\cdot}2°$.

These acids were used in the following series of tests.

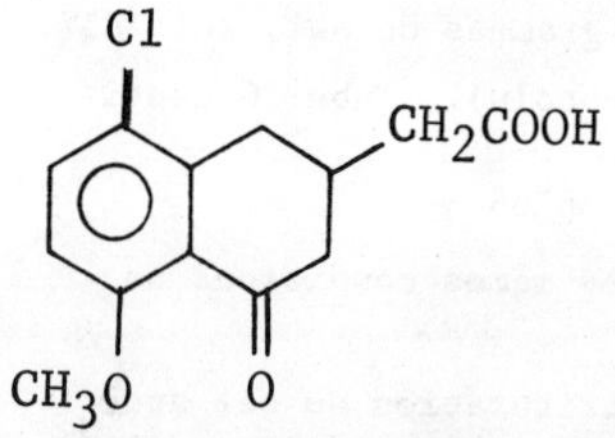

$C_{13}H_{13}ClO_4$

Ref. 940

Resolution of 8-chloro-1,2,3,4-tetrahydro-5-methoxy-4-oxo-2-naphthalene acetic acid (XV). To 1.60 g. (5.95 mmoles) of the acid in 50 ml. of absolute ethanol was added 1.95 g. of quinine base (6.0 mmoles). The mixture was warmed to get a clear solution which after being decolorized with charcoal was cooled in a refrigerator overnight. The long white needles which had formed were filtered off and washed with 20 ml. absolute ethanol. After drying, this solid weighed 2.78 g.; m.p., 180–182° and is called fraction A; $[\alpha]^{25}_{D}$ −65.7°. The ethanolic filtrate on concentration gave a gum which crystallized from acetone as white needles; yield, 1.03 g. of m.p. 172–174°, called fraction B; $[\alpha]^{25}_{D}$ −59.8°.

Fraction A on recrystallizing twice from ethanol yielded 1.57 g. m.p., 184.5–185.5°. When 1.0 g. of this was converted back to the acid and the acid recrystallized from methanol and water, a yield of 0.31 g. of white crystals was obtained, m.p. 194–196°; $[\alpha]^{25}_{D}$ −3.2° (methanol).

When fraction B (0.88 g.) was converted to the free acid, it also had a m.p. of 196–197° but a specific rotation of +3.1° in methanol.

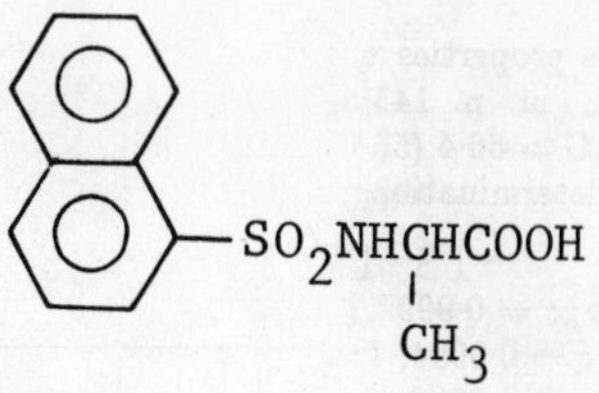

$C_{13}H_{13}NO_4S$

Ref. 941

Resolution of dl-*α-Naphthalenesulphonylalanine.*

This resolution was done twice and the same results were obtained in both cases. In the second experiment, 25·05 g. of the *dl*-acid, 19·3 g. of brucine (0·5 mol.), and 1·1793 g. of sodium hydroxide (0·5 mol.) in standard solution were boiled with 500 c.c. of water, when complete solution took place. The brucine salt of *d*-α-naphthalenesulphonylalanine separated in almost quantitative amount on cooling and was filtered from mother-liquor (*A*). The brucine salt was recrystallised twice, each time from 2 litres of water, but no alteration in rotatory power was observed after the first recrystallisation. It was finally recrystallised from ethyl alcohol (18·6 g. in 100 c.c.).

The *brucine salt of* d-*α-naphthalenesulphonylalanine*, $CHMe(NH{\cdot}SO_2{\cdot}C_{10}H_7){\cdot}CO_2H,C_{23}H_{26}O_4N_2,2\tfrac{1}{2}H_2O$, was obtained in soft, colourless needles, m. p. 145° [0·5256 lost at 125° 0·0329; H_2O = 6·26 (6·26)%. 0·1369 (anhydrous) gave 0·3206 CO_2 and 0·0776 H_2O; C = 63·9 (64·2), H = 6·30 (5·83)%]. Its rotatory power * in ethyl alcohol ($c = 0{\cdot}4886$, $l = 4$, $\alpha = -0{\cdot}24°$) was $[\alpha] = -12{\cdot}3°$.

The mother-liquor *A* was made alkaline with ammonia solution and extracted with chloroform until free from brucine. From the aqueous solution, after evaporation to about 50 c.c., the acid was precipitated by a slight excess of hydrochloric acid. The acid (12·3 g.) rapidly crystallised on cooling, and, from a determination of its rotatory power in a solution of sodium hydroxide, it contained 80·5% of the lævo-acid. This acid was mixed with another less pure specimen and finally 14·8 g. of acid containing 75·8% of the lævo-acid were mixed with strychnine (13·4 g., equivalent to the lævo-acid present) and sodium hydroxide (0·5162 g. in standard solution). This required 1500 c.c. of water for complete solution on boiling and the strychnine salt of *l*-α-naphthalenesulphonylalanine separated quantitatively on cooling. After one recrystallisation from 1450 c.c. of water, its rotatory power was constant and not changed by further recrystallisation from aqueous alcohol.

The *strychnine salt of* l-*α-naphthalenesulphonylalanine*, $CHMe(NH{\cdot}SO_2{\cdot}C_{10}H_7){\cdot}CO_2H,C_{21}H_{22}O_2N_2$, was obtained in colourless iridescent plates from water and colourless needles from aqueous alcohol. The air-dried salt has m. p. 132° [0·1446 (anhydrous) gave 0·3554 CO_2 and 0·0797 H_2O; C = 67·0 (66·5), H = 6·12 (5·75)%]. Its rotatory power in ethyl alcohol ($c = 0{\cdot}4204$, $l = 4$, $\alpha = -0{\cdot}33°$) was $[\alpha] = -19{\cdot}63°$.

The Optically Active α-Naphthalenesulphonylalanines.

d-*α-Naphthalenesulphonylalanine*, $CHMe(NH{\cdot}SO_2{\cdot}C_{10}H_7){\cdot}CO_2H$, was obtained from the pure brucine salt by adding an aqueous solution of ammonia, filtering off the precipitated brucine, and extracting the filtrate with chloroform until free from brucine. The aqueous solution was evaporated to small bulk and, on addition of a slight excess of hydrochloric acid, the acid separated as an oil which rapidly crystallised. After drying, it was recrystallised from benzene (6 g. in 350 c.c.) and obtained in small, colourless prisms, m. p. 141·5—142·5°. The acid is very sparingly soluble in water and readily soluble in ethyl alcohol, ethyl acetate, and acetone [0·1283 gave 0·2649 CO_2 and 0·0550 H_2O; C = 56·3 (55·9), H = 4·76 (4·69)%]. The following determinations of its rotatory power were made:

In the calculated quantity of N/10-NaOH and made up with water:

$$c = 0{\cdot}9976,\ l = 2,\ \alpha = +0{\cdot}69°;\ [\alpha] = +34{\cdot}58°.$$
$$c = 1{\cdot}9992,\ l = 2,\ \alpha = +1{\cdot}63°;\ [\alpha] = +40{\cdot}77°.$$

In ethyl alcohol: $c = 0{\cdot}9996$, $l = 4$, $\alpha = -0{\cdot}92°$; $[\alpha] = -23{\cdot}01°$.
In acetone: $c = 1{\cdot}0104$, $l = 4$, $\alpha = -0{\cdot}92°$; $[\alpha] = -22{\cdot}76°$.

l-*α-Naphthalenesulphonylalanine* was obtained from the pure strychnine salt in the usual manner. It was recrystallised from

* All rotatory powers were determined at 20° for the mercury-green (5461) line.

benzene and in its properties corresponded exactly with those of the above *d*-acid; m. p. 141·5—142·5° [0·2161 gave 0·4468 CO_2 and 0·0917 H_2O; C = 56·4 (55·9), H = 4·75 (4·69)%].

The following determinations of the rotatory power of the acid were made:

As Na salt in water; c = 0·9992, l = 2, α = − 0·69°; [α] = − 34·52°.
In ethyl alcohol; c = 0·9994, l = 4, α = + 0·92°; [α] = + 23·01°.
c = 4·0006, l = 4, α = + 3·58°; [α] = + 22·40°.

In spite of the inconclusive results of experiments undertaken with the object of throwing light on the above interesting reversal in sign of the optical rotatory powers, we hope to obtain further information in connexion with these and closely-related compounds.

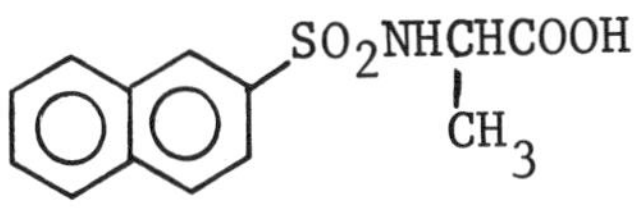

$C_{13}H_{13}NO_4S$ Ref. 942

Resolution of dl-β-*Naphthalenesulphonylalanine.*

As in the previous case, only the second resolution experiment will be described. The *dl*-acid (16 g.) was mixed with 1250 c.c. of water, strychnine (9·6 g.; 0·5 mol.), and sodium hydroxide (1·147 g.; 0·5 mol.). The whole dissolved on boiling and the strychnine salt of the dextro-acid (quantitative) was separated from the mother-liquor (*B*) after cooling. The strychnine salt was pure after one crystallisation from 450 c.c. of ethyl alcohol, but it was again recrystallised from 400 c.c. of the same solvent.

The *strychnine salt of* d-β-*naphthalenesulphonylalanine*,
$CHMe(NH{\cdot}SO_2{\cdot}C_{10}H_7){\cdot}CO_2H,C_{21}H_{22}O_2N_2,1\frac{1}{2}H_2O$,
was obtained in small, colourless needles, m. p. 197° [0·5210 lost 0·0215 at 125°; H_2O = 4·13 (4·2)%. 0·1078 (anhydrous) gave 0·2636 CO_2 and 0·0569 H_2O; C = 66·7 (66·5), H = 5·86 (5·75)%]. Its rotatory power in ethyl alcohol (c = 0·4540, l = 4, α = − 0·18°) was [α] = − 9·94°.

The acid was isolated from mother-liquor *B* in the usual manner (8·6 g.). A determination of its rotatory power in sodium hydroxide indicated that it contained 40% of the racemic acid. It was mixed with brucine (5·852 g., equivalent to the racemic acid present) and sodium hydroxide (0·7384 g.), and the whole was brought into solution in 900 c.c. of boiling water. The brucine salt of the racemic acid separated in almost quantitative amount on cooling. This was filtered from mother-liquor (*C*) and recrystallised from 800 c.c. of boiling water.

The *brucine salt of* dl-β-*naphthalenesulphonylalanine*,
$CHMe(NH{\cdot}SO_2{\cdot}C_{10}H_7){\cdot}CO_2H,C_{23}H_{26}O_4N_2,H_2O$,
was obtained in long, colourless needles, m. p. 188·5° [0·4566 lost 0·0136 at 125°; H_2O = 2·98 (2·60)%. 0·1215 (anhydrous) gave 0·2833 CO_2 and 0·0667 H_2O; C = 63·6 (64·2), H = 6·10 (5·83)%]. Its rotatory power in ethyl alcohol (c = 0·4906, l = 4, α = − 0·39°) was [α] = − 19·9°. The ammonium salt and also the free acid obtained from this brucine salt were optically inactive. The isolation of pure *l*-β-naphthalenesulphonylalanine from mother-liquor *C* is described below.

The Optically Active β-*Naphthalenesulphonylalanines.*

These substances have been previously described (Fischer and Bergell, Forster and Fierz, Abderhalden and Schittenhelm, *loc. cit.*), but they have not been obtained before by the resolution of the inactive acid and there is evidence to show that in some cases the substances as described were not optically pure.

d-β-*Naphthalenesulphonylalanine*,* $CHMe(NH{\cdot}SO_2{\cdot}C_{10}H_7){\cdot}CO_2H$, was isolated in the usual manner from the strychnine salt. The acid crystallised readily and was converted into the *ammonium* salt, which, after one crystallisation from ethyl alcohol, was found to be optically pure. The ammonium salt was obtained in long, colourless needles (0·2980 gave 0·01742 NH_3; NH_3 = 5·84. $C_{13}H_{16}O_4N_2S$ requires NH_3 = 5·74%). The rotatory power of the ammonium salt in aqueous solution (c = 0·8100, l = 4, α = + 1·43°) was [α] = + 44·13°. The pure acid was prepared from the pure ammonium salt by decomposing its dilute aqueous solution with standard acid and separated in long, colourless needles which were dried over phosphorus pentoxide for several days and then recrystallised from pure benzene. The melting point altered during the drying and this probably explains the low values obtained by previous workers. The final and constant melting point was 127—128°. Its rotatory power in solution in the calculated quantity of sodium hydroxide gave the following result: c = 2·5028, l = 2, α = + 2·59°, [α] = + 51·74°.

l-β-*Naphthalenesulphonylalanine* was obtained from mother-liquor *C*. The acid was converted into the *ammonium* salt, which had a constant rotatory power after one recrystallisation from ethyl alcohol (0·2032 gave 0·01174 NH_3; NH_3 = 5·78. $C_{13}H_{16}O_4N_2S$ requires NH_3 = 5·74%). The rotatory power of the ammonium salt in aqueous solution (c = 0·8064, l = 4, α = − 1·42°) was [α] = − 44·2°.

The acid, long, colourless needles, obtained from the pure ammonium salt was carefully dried as in the previous case. The melting point rose from 113—114° to a constant value of 127—128°, which was unchanged after the acid had been further recrystallised from pure benzene (1 g. in 30 c.c.) (0·1295 gave 0·2651 CO_2 and 0·0578 H_2O; C = 55·8, H = 4·96. $C_{13}H_{13}O_4NS$ requires C = 55·9, H = 4·69%). Its rotatory power in ethyl alcohol (c = 1·0010, l = 4, α = − 0·88°) was [α] = − 22·0°.

The rotatory power of the acid in the form of its salts in aqueous solution is of the same sign as that of the acid in ethyl alcohol and no reversal of sign takes place as in the case of the optically active α-acids.

* Described here as "*d*-" because it is dextrorotatory although it has been shown by Forster and Fierz (*loc. cit.*) that *d*-alanine gives rise to the laevo-isomeride.

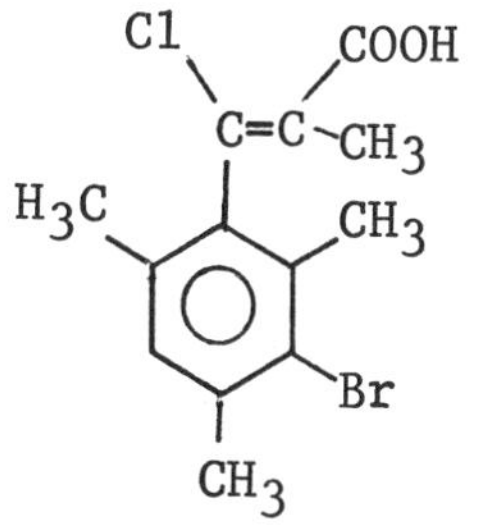

$C_{13}H_{14}BrClO_2$ Ref. 943

Resolution of β-Chloro-β-(2,4,6-trimethyl-3-bromophenyl)-α-methylacrylic Acid.—A solution of 10 g. of β-chloro-β-(2,4,6-trimethyl-3-bromophenyl)-α-methylacrylic acid in 75 cc. of warm absolute ethanol was added to a solution of 10 g. of quinine in 75 cc. of warm absolute ethanol. After filtration and cooling, 8.45 g. of salt (fraction A) crystallized. Evaporation of the filtrate to 100 cc. and cooling gave an additional 5.34 g. of salt (fraction B). The filtrate from the second fraction was diluted with 50 cc. of water whereupon 3.2 g. of oil separated (fraction C). Decantation of the solvent and slow evaporation yielded an additional crop of crystals (fraction D).

Fraction A was twice recrystallized from ethanol after which a constant rotation had been reached.

Rotation. Less soluble salt (*l*B·*d*A) 0.0995 g. made up to 25 cc. in absolute ethanol at 20° gave α_D −0.37; *l*, 2; $[\alpha]^{20}_D$ −46.8°.

Anal. Calcd. for $C_{33}H_{38}O_4N_2BrCl$: C, 61.73; H, 5.92. Found: C, 61.82; H, 6.05.

d-β-Chloro-β-(2,4,6-trimethyl-3-bromophenyl)-α-methylacrylic Acid.—To a suspension of 5.2 g. of the purified salt (fraction A) in 100 cc. of water was added 10 cc. of concentrated hydrochloric acid. After stirring for thirty minutes, the product was filtered and washed with 5% hydrochloric acid until quinine-free and then with water. The product (2.4 g.) was purified by recrystallization twice from petroleum ether (b. p. 60–110°). Its rotation was the same after each crystallization; white crystals, m. p. 155–156° (cor.).

Rotation. (*d*-acid) 0.0998 g. made up to 25 cc. with absolute ethanol at 20° gave α_D +0.42; *l*, 2; $[\alpha]^{20}_D$

+52.6°. 0.1008 g. made up to 25 cc. with glacial acetic acid at 20° gave αD +0.56; *l*, 2; $[\alpha]^{20}_D$ +69.4°.

Anal. Calcd. for $C_{13}H_{14}OBrCl$: C, 49.12; H, 4.42. Found: C, 49.04; H, 4.04.

Decomposition of the oily fraction C in a similar manner gave *l*-acid which after two crystallizations gave a constant rotation; white crystals, m. p. 155–156° (cor.).

Rotation. (*l*-acid) 0.0994 g. made up to 25 cc. with absolute ethanol at 20° gave αD −0.43; *l*, 2; $[\alpha]^{20}_D$ −54°.

Anal. Calcd. for $C_{13}H_{14}O_2BrCl$: C, 49.12; H, 4.42. Found: C, 49.62; H, 4.52.

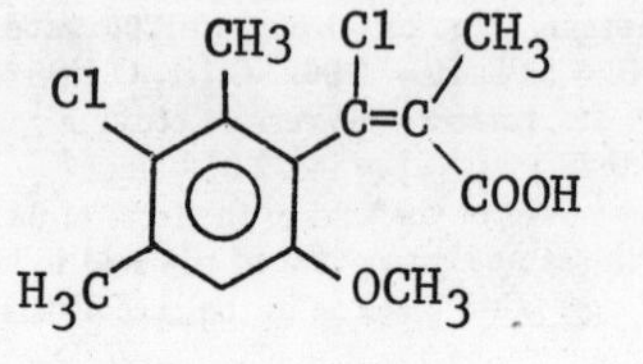

$C_{13}H_{14}Cl_2O_3$ Ref. 944

Resolution of β-Chloro-β-(2-methoxy-4,6-dimethyl-5-chlorophenyl)-α-methylacrylic Acid (V).—A solution of 2.7 g. of β-chloro-β-(2-methoxy-4,6-dimethyl-5-chlorophenyl)-α-methylacrylic acid in 40 cc. of warm acetone was added to a solution of 2.9 g. of quinine in 40 cc. of warm acetone. After filtration the solution was allowed to stand for five days after which fraction A (2.5 g.) was removed. This was unchanged in rotation after recrystallization from acetone. The filtrate was then evaporated to 60 cc. and after standing two days fraction B (0.55 g.) was collected. Evaporation of the filtrate to 25 cc. yielded fraction C (1.2 g.) after standing four days. Evaporation to dryness gave fraction D. The rotations of fractions B and C were essentially identical with those of fraction A from which it was deduced that only one salt was obtained. No mutarotation was observed over a short period of time at room temperature.

Anal. Calcd. for $C_{33}H_{38}O_5Cl_2N_2$: C, 64.57; H, 6.24. Found: C, 64.68; H, 6.46. *Rotation.* (*l*BdA) 0.050 g. made up to 25 cc. with benzene at 20° gave αD −0.12°; *l*, 2; $[\alpha]^{20}_D$ −30.0°.

d-β **Chl ro-β-(2-methoxy-4,6-dimethyl 5-chl repher α-methylacrylic Acid.**—To a suspension of 2 g. c (fraction A) in 30 cc. of water was added 5 cc. of trated hydrochloric acid. After stirring at 5° rty minutes the product was filtered, washed with ydrochloric acid and finally with water. The was repeated until the product was quinine f . p. 177° (cor.).

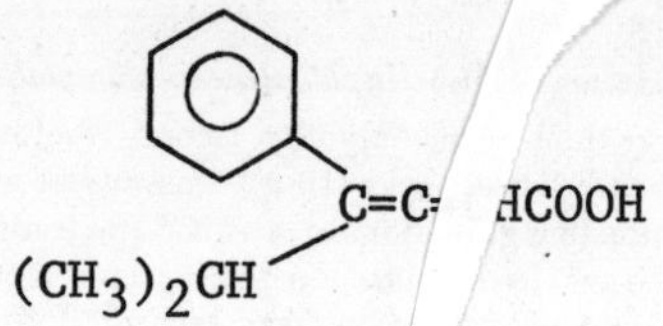

$C_{13}H_{14}O_2$ Ref. 945

Note:

The racemic acid was resolved via the cinchonidine salt. The m.p. and [α] obtained were: m.p. 88.5-89.5°C.; $[\alpha]_D$ = +205° methanol).

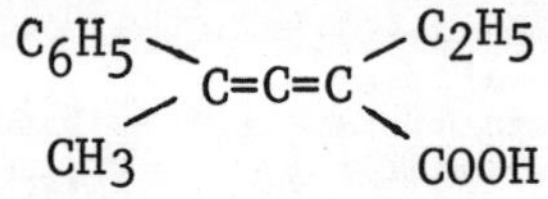

$C_{13}H_{14}O_2$ Ref. 946

Antipodenspaltung der Allencarbonsäuren (allgemeines Verfahren): 0.02 Mol *racem. Säure* **1** (außer **1e**) und 0.01 Mol *Cinchonidin* werden mit 5–10 ml Aceton in der Hitze gelöst. Falls nach zweitägigem Stehenlassen in der Kühltruhe die viskose Lösung nicht durchkristallisiert (bei **1c, 1d**) oder wenigstens Teile des Salzes auskristallisieren, so wird das Lösungsmittel abdestilliert und der sirupöse Rückstand in 5–10 ml Essigester aufgelöst. Erfolgt beim Kühlen auch hier keine Abscheidung, so verwendet man nach dem Abdestillieren des Essigesters Mischungen von Essigester und Petroläther als Lösungsmittel. Das aus einem dieser Lösungsmittel gewonnene Salz (erste Kristallfraktion) wird so oft fraktioniert umkristallisiert, bis der Schmelzpunkt und der optische Drehwinkel konstant bleiben (Tab. 3). — Das Salz dieser *letzten Fraktion* wird in wenig Methanol gelöst, die Lösung mit Äther und verd. *Schwefelsäure* (konz. Schwefelsäure/Wasser = 1 : 5) ausgeschüttelt, die Ätherphase über $MgSO_4$ getrocknet und eingedampft. Der zurückbleibende feste, *eine Antipode* der optimal gespaltenen Säure wird aus Petroläther umkristallisiert.

Aus dem *Filtrat der ersten Kristallfraktion* (s. o.) wird das jeweils eingesetzte **1** wie oben beschrieben in Freiheit gesetzt und umkristallisiert, wobei zunächst das Racemat ausfällt. Aus der Mutterlauge erhält man beim Einengen den *anderen Antipoden* mit fast gleichem, aber umgekehrten Drehwert und gleichem Schmelzpunkt wie beim zuvor gewonnenen Antipoden.

Die *Angaben der Ausbeuten* bei diesem Verfahren beziehen sich beim Salz auf die eingesetzte Menge Base, bei den optisch-aktiven Säuren auf die eingesetzte Menge racemischer Säure. — Die Schmelzpunkte und spezif. Drehungen der getrennten diastereomeren Salze vor der Freilegung der Antipoden enthält Tabelle 3 (S. 125).

*(+)- und (−)-***1b**. — Nach dem allgemeinen Trennverfahren ergaben 5.483 g *racem.*-**1b** und 3.993 g *Cinchonidin* nach fünf Umkristallisationen aus Aceton 3.331 g (49%) Salz als farblose Nadeln. $[\alpha]^{25}_D$ = −106° (*c* = 0.01260, C_2H_5OH); Schmp. 91–93° (aus Aceton), bei 99° Gasentwicklung, bei 110° klare Schmelze.

$C_{32}H_{36}N_2O_3$ (496.7) Ber. C 77.39 H 7.31 N 5.64 Gef. C 77.47 H 7.45 N 5.73

Aus diesem Cinchonidinsalz wurden 1.012 g (18.5%) *(−)*-**1b** gewonnen. Farblose Nadeln vom Schmp. 101−103° (aus Petroläther); $[\alpha]_D^{25} = -50.8°$ ($c = 0.01052$, C_2H_5OH), −66.8° ($c = 0.01360$, $CHCl_3$). — *CD* (C_2H_5OH): λ_{max} ($\Delta\varepsilon$) = 278 (−1.4) sh, 256 (−6.0) sh, 244 nm (−7.4).

$C_{13}H_{14}O_2$ (202.3) Ber. C 77.19 H 6.98 Gef. C 77.15 H 7.03

Aus dem *Filtrat der ersten Fraktion* wurden 1.940 g (36%) optisch unreines *(+)*-**1b** gewonnen. Farblose Kristalle vom Schmp. 106−107° (aus Petroläther); $[\alpha]_D^{25} = +13.6°$ ($c = 0.01950$, C_2H_5OH). — Aus der *Mutterlauge* dieser Kristallisation erhielt man 0.353 g (7%) reines *(+)*-**1b** als farblose Nadeln vom Schmp. 103−104° (aus Petroläther); $[\alpha]_D^{25} = +49.5°$ ($c = 0.01828$, C_2H_5OH).

Tabelle 3. Schmelzpunkte und spezifische Drehungen der diastereomeren Salze aus den letzten beiden Fraktionen der Antipodenspaltung von *racem.* **1b**−**e**

Säure	Base	Frakt.	Schmp. [°C]	$[\alpha]_{589}^{25}$	$[\alpha]_{500}^{25}$	$[\alpha]_{400}^{25}$	$[\alpha]_{333}^{25}$	c [g/ml]
(−)-**1b**	Cinchonidin	4	91−93[a)]	−105	—	−336	−752	0.00882
(−)-**1b**	Cinchonidin	5	91−93[a)]	−106	−164	−345	−771	0.01260
(−)-**1c**	Cinchonidin	4	141−143[b)]	−135	—	−446	−1030	0.00960
(−)-**1c**	Cinchonidin	5	142−144[b)]	−135	−214	−450	−1023	0.00842
(+)-**1d**	Cinchonidin	3	144−145[a)]	+27.1	—	+137	+449	0.00718
(+)-**1d**	Cinchonidin	4	142−144[c)]	+27.0	+49.8	+135	+439	0.00406
(+)-**1e**	Chinin	3	25[d,e)]	−44.5	−65.0	−132	—	0.01560
(+)-**1e**	Chinin	4	25[d)]	−42.5	−64.5	−129	—	0.01542

a−d) Umkristallisationen: a) Aus Aceton; b) aus Essigester; c) aus Essigester/Petroläther (7 : 6); d) aus Aceton.
e) Das Salz schmilzt bei 25° langsam, erstarrt wieder glasig und zeigt dann den Schmp. 65−69°. Diese Substanz liefert nach dem Trocknen bei 60° die angegebenen Analysenwerte.

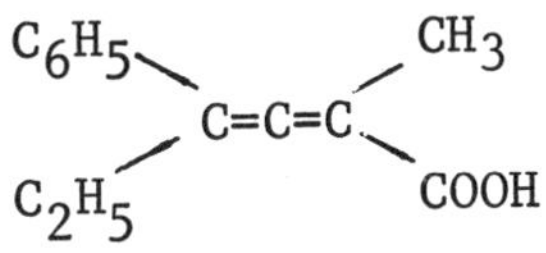

Ref. 947

$C_{13}H_{14}O_2$

(+)- und (−)-**1c**. — 5.593 g *racem.* **1c** und 4.099 g *Cinchonidin* ergaben nach fünf Umkristallisationen aus Essigester 2.350 g (34%) Salz. Farblose Nadeln vom Schmp. 142−144° (aus Essigester); $[\alpha]_D^{25} = -135°$ ($c = 0.00842$, C_2H_5OH).

$C_{32}H_{36}N_2O_3$ (496.7) Ber. C 77.39 H 7.31 N 5.64 Gef. C 77.38 H 7.63 N 5.81

Aus diesem Cinchonidinsalz wurden 0.692 g (12.4%) *(−)*-**1c** isoliert. Lange farblose Nadeln vom Schmp. 89−90° (aus Petroläther); $[\alpha]_D^{25} = -125°$ ($c = 0.00820$, C_2H_5OH), −128 ($c = 0.01114$, $CHCl_3$). — *CD* (C_2H_5OH): λ_{max} ($\Delta\varepsilon$) = 278 (−1.1) sh, 256 (−6.8) sh, 244 nm (−10.0).

$C_{13}H_{14}O_2$ (202.3) Ber. C 77.19 H 6.98 Gef. C 77.01 H 7.18

Aus dem *Filtrat der ersten Fraktion* wurden 2.330 g fast vollständig *racem.* **1c** gewonnen. Farblose Nadeln vom Schmp. 103−105° (aus Petroläther); $[\alpha]_D^{25} = +8.2°$ ($c = 0.01712$, C_2H_5OH). — Aus der *Mutterlauge* dieser Kristallisation erhielt man 0.592 g (10.5%) *(+)*-**1c**. Lange, farblose Nadeln vom Schmp. 89−90° (aus Petroläther); $[\alpha]_D^{25} = +119°$ ($c = 0.01800$, C_2H_5OH).

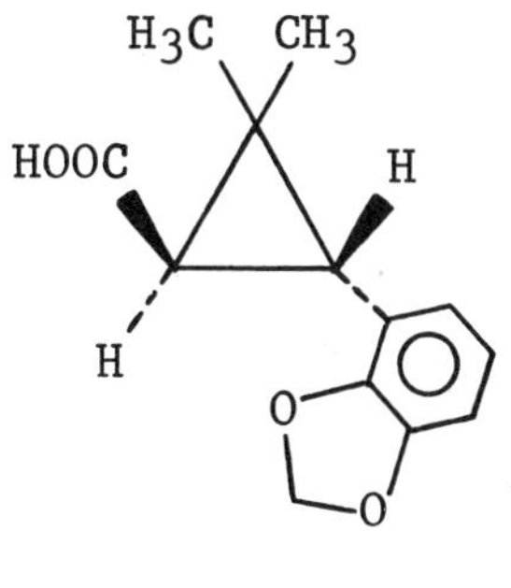

Ref. 948

$C_{13}H_{14}O_4$

Resolution of (±)-*trans*-2,2-Dimethyl-3-(3,′4′-methylenedioxyphenyl)-cyclopropane-1-carboxylic Acid (II).

To the solution of the (±)-*trans*-acid (II) (22.2 g) in 100 ml of methanol, was added (−)-α-phenylethylamine (11.5 g) having $[\alpha]_D^{20} -38.5°$, in 20 ml of methanol. The solution was kept overnight and the first crop of the salt was separated and the mother liquor evaporated; this procedure being repeated so that 15 g of the salt was obtained by successive reduction of the volume. After successive recrystallisations of these crops with approximately the same rotation and melting point to the first crop and recrystallising the combined salt many times from methanol, a pure (−)-α-phenylethylamine salt of the (−)-*trans*-acid was finally obtained, m.p. 165∼166°C, yield 9.1 g, $[\alpha]_D^{20} -22.94°$ (c, 2.31, ethanol). *Anal.* Found: C, 71.10; H, 7.18; N, 4.90. Calcd. for $C_{21}H_{25}O_4N$: C, 70.96; H, 7.18; N, 4.90%.

Further recrystallisation did not alter these values.

Subsequent decomposition of this salt (9.1 g) by dilute hydrochloric acid gave the pure crystalline (—)-*trans*-2,2-dimethyl-3-(3',4'-methylenedioxyphenyl)-cyclopropane-1-carboxylic acid (VI), m.p. 102~103°C, yield 3.2 g, $[\alpha]_D^{20}$—31.88° (c, 4.14, ethanol). *Anal.* Found: C, 66.69; H, 5.59. Calcd. for $C_{13}H_{14}O_4$: C, 66.65; H, 6.02%.

The combined filtrate from the salt of (—)-α-phenylethylamine and the (—)-*trans*-acid (VI) was evaporated, decomposed with dilute hydrochloric acid and recovered by extraction. To a solution of the recovered acid (16.3 g) in 80 ml of methanol, was added (+)-α-phenylethylamine (8.4 g) having $[\alpha]_D^{20}$ +37.7°, in 20 ml of methanol. The solution was kept overnight and the first crop of the salt was separated and the mother liquor concentrated, this procedure being repeated so that four crops were obtained. After successive recrystallisations of these crops with approximately the same rotation and melting point, and crystallising them as many times as before, a pure (+)-α-phenylethylamine salt of the (+)-*trans*-acid (V) was finally obtained, m.p. 165~166°C, yield 8.26 g, $[\alpha]_D^{20}$+22.81° (c, 1.14, ethanol). *Anal.* Found: C, 70.80; H, 7.19; N, 4.16. Calcd. for $C_{21}H_{25}O_4N$: C, 70.96; H, 7.09; N, 3.94%. Further recrystallisation did not alter these values.

The salt (8.2 g) was decomposed by dilute hydrochloric acid and gave the pure crystalline (+)-*trans*-2,2-dimethyl-3-(3',4'-methylenedioxyphenyl)-cyclopropane-1-carboxylic acid (V), m.p. 102~103°C, yield 1.7 g, $[\alpha]_D^{20}$+32.18° (c, 2.02, ethanol). *Anal.* Found: C, 66.88; H, 6.07. Calcd. for $C_{13}H_{14}O_4$: C, 66.65; H, 6.02%.

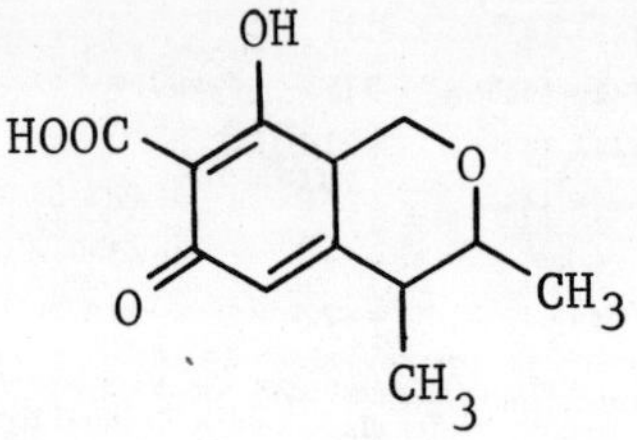

$C_{13}H_{14}O_5$ Ref. 949

Resolution of Optically Inactive Citrinin.—Brucine (1·9 g. of the tetrahydrate) dissolved in acetone–methanol (15 ml.; 1 : 3) was added to a warm solution of (±)-citrinin (Part VII, *loc. cit.*) (1 g.) in the same solvent (40 ml.), and the crystalline product (2·1 g.), m. p. 167—168° (decomp.), was collected 1 hour later. Recrystallisation of this solid from methanol gave 3 fractions, (*a*) (0·5 g.), m. p. 178° (decomp.), (*b*) (0·3 g.), m. p. 178° (decomp.), and (*c*) (0·3 g.), m. p. 176—178° (decomp.). Of these (*a*) and (*b*) were combined and recrystallised several times from much methanol, giving the brucine salt of (—)-citrinin as a *hydrate* in irregular hexagonal prisms, m. p. 182—183° (decomp.) (alone or on admixture with the salt from natural citrinin) (Found: C, 65·0; H, 6·3; N, 4·6. $C_{13}H_{14}O_5,C_{23}H_{26}O_4N_2,H_2O$ requires C, 65·3; H, 6·4; N, 4·2%. $C_{13}H_{14}O_5,C_{23}H_{26}O_4N_2$ requires C, 67·1; H, 6·2; N, 4·4%). Because of its low solubility in the usual organic solvents the rotation of this salt was not determined. Decomposition of the compound (0·5 g.) in acetone (15 ml.) with 2N-hydrochloric acid, followed by the addition of water (50 ml.), gave (—)-citrinin which was isolated with ether and crystallised from ethanol, forming characteristic long yellow prisms, m. p. 179° (decomp.) (alone or admixed with a natural specimen), $[\alpha]_D^{20}$ —34·5° (*c*, 0·600 in alcohol) (Found: C, 62·3; H, 5·4. Calc. for $C_{13}H_{14}O_5$: C, 62·4; H, 5·6%). A specimen of the hydrated brucine salt of natural citrinin was prepared by mixing warm solutions of (—)-brucine (1·9 g. of tetrahydrate) in acetone–methanol (20 ml. of 1 : 3) and the natural acid (1 g.) in the same solvent (25 ml.). Recrystallised from methanol this salt formed irregular hexagonal prisms, m. p. 182—183° (decomp.) (Found: C, 65·4; H, 6·7; N, 4·7%).

The combined mother-liquors left after the separation of the foregoing brucine salt of (—)-citrinin were concentrated in a vacuum and on being kept the residue deposited a crystalline solid (0·4 g.), m. p. 171° (decomp.), consisting mainly of the brucine salt of (—)-citrinin. Treatment of the residual liquor with dilute hydrochloric acid regenerated crude (+)-citrinin which was recrystallised from alcohol and then converted into a brucine salt. Recrystallised from much methanol, this product gave the *brucine* salt of (+)-citrinin in colourless needles, m. p. 167—168° (decomp.) (Found: C, 64·3; H, 6·5; N, 4·7%). Decomposition of this compound (0·4 g.) with 2N-hydrochloric acid furnished (+)-*citrinin* (0·15 g.) which separated from alcohol in long yellow needles, m. p. 179° (decomp.), $[\alpha]_D^{20}$ +33·0° (*c*, 0·600 in alcohol) (Found: C, 62·5; H, 5·6%). The chemical properties of (+)-citrinin were identical with those of natural (—)-isomeride.

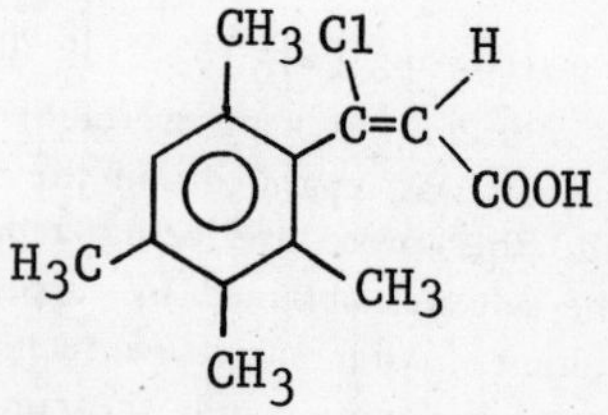

$C_{13}H_{15}ClO_2$ Ref. 950

Resolution of β-Chloro-β-(2,3,4,6-tetramethylphenyl)-acrylic Acid.[2]—A solution of 5 g. of β-chloro-β-(2,3,4,6-tetramethylphenyl)-acrylic acid in 50 cc. of hot ethyl acetate was added to a hot solution of 6.8 g. of quinine in 100 cc. of ethyl acetate and filtered. When cooled to room temperature this solution deposited 6.425 g. of salt (fraction 1) and an additional 0.160 g. when cooled to 0° (fraction 2). Fractions 3, 4, and 5 were removed at 75 cc., 35 cc. and by evaporation to dryness yielding 1.654 g., 1.272 g. and 2.158 g., respectively.

Fraction 1 was purified by recrystallization from ethyl acetate to which a small amount of ethanol had been added to increase the solubility of the salt. A constant rotation was reached after two crystallizations; large transparent cubes, m. p. 193–194° (cor.) with decomposition.

Anal. Calcd. for $C_{33}H_{39}N_2O_4Cl$: C, 70.38; H, 6.98; N, 4.98. Found: C, 70.79; H, 6.98; N, 5.06.

Rotation. Less soluble salt (*l*B·*l*A) 0.0530 g. made up to 10 cc. with absolute ethanol at 28° gave α_D —0.445; *l*, 1; $[\alpha]^{28}_D$ —84.0°.

Fraction 4 was purified by recrystallization from benzene–petroleum ether (b. p. 90–110°); long white needles, m. p. 163–165° (cor.) with decomposition.

Anal. Calcd. for $C_{33}H_{39}N_2O_4Cl$: C, 70.38; H, 6.98; N, 4.98. Found: C, 70.64; H, 7.15; N, 5.10.

Rotation. More soluble salt (*l*B·*d*A) 0.0508 g. made up to 10 cc. with absolute ethanol at 28° gave α_D —0.303; *l*, 1; $[\alpha]^{28}_D$ —59.6°.

***d*- and *l*-β-Chloro-β-(2,3,4,6-tetramethylphenyl)-acrylic Acid.**—Decomposition of 2.354 g. of purified less soluble salt (fraction 1) gave 0.945 g. of *l*-acid. Purification was effected by dissolving the acid in 10 cc. of ether, and 5 cc. of

petroleum ether (b. p. 90–110°) and allowing the solution to stand open to the air; clusters of long white prisms, m. p. 184–185° (cor.).

Anal. Calcd. for $C_{13}H_{16}O_2Cl$: C, 65.41; H, 6.33. Found: C, 65.64; H, 6.44.

Rotation. (*l*-Acid) 0.0273 g. made up to 5 cc. with absolute ethanol at 25° gave α_D −0.195; *l*, 1; $[\alpha]^{25}_D$ −35.7°.

Decomposition of purified fraction 4 in the same manner and similar recrystallization gave the *d*-acid; short, thick, white prisms, m. p. 184–185° (cor.).

Anal. Calcd. for $C_{13}H_{16}O_2Cl$: C, 65.41; H, 6.33. Found: C, 65.66; H, 6.37.

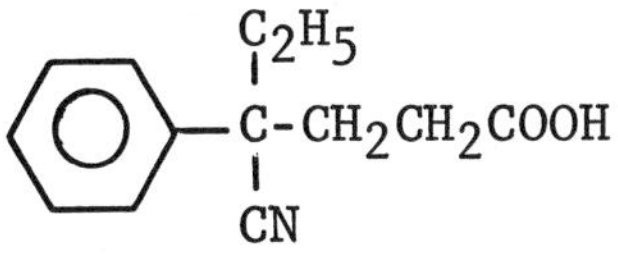

$C_{13}H_{15}NO_2$ Ref. 951

Preparazione e separazione dei sali di chinina degli antipodi dell'acido γ-fenil-γ-cianoesanoico.

G 13,7 di acido γ-fenil-γ-cianoesanoico (VI), p. f. 92-93°, vengono disciolti in 27,4 ml di acetone; a questa soluzione si aggiunge una soluzione ottenuta sciogliendo g 20,2 di chinina base anidra in 352 ml di acetone, contenenti 3,36 ml di acqua (3 moli di acqua per mole di chinina). La miscela viene addizionata di 100 ml di etere di petrolio ($T_{eb.}$ = 40-70°) e posta in termostato a 16°. Dopo riposo di una notte si aggiungono altri 150 ml di etere di petrolio e dopo altre 24 ore altri 50 ml. Ogni 24 ore si controlla l'andamento della cristallizzazione, prelevando una piccola porzione del precipitato cristallino ed esaminandone lo spettro a polvere ai raggi X con lo spettrogoniometro a contatore Geiger-Müller. Dopo 60 ore di riposo in termostato a 16°, la quantità del precipitato cristallino è abbondante, pesa g 21,30 e risulta costituita principalmente dal sale meno solubile, come si rivela dal rapporto tra le intensità dei riflessi caratteristici dei due sali a 6° e 6,5°.

Le acque madri vengono portate a secco sotto vuoto e il residuo cristallino risulta costituito principalmente dal sale più solubile (controllo con lo spettro a polvere ai raggi X). Le due porzioni si purificano per cristallizzazione frazionata da acetone puro.

I due sali puri sono stati da noi caratterizzati attraverso lo spettro a polvere ai raggi X (Figg. n. 1 e 2); i p. f. sono poco caratteristici e poco netti; sono compresi nell' intervallo tra 90-106° (determinati ai microscopio Kofler senza correzione). I due sali contengono acqua di cristallizzazione; essiccati nel vuoto a 60° presentano i seguenti poteri rotatori:

sale meno solubile: $[\alpha]^{25°}_D$ = −109° (1,0, C_2H_5OH assol.)

sale più solubile: $[\alpha]^{25°}_D$ = −91° (1,0, C_2H_5OH assol.)

Forme antipode dell'acido γ-fenil-γ-cianoesanoico (VII) *e* (VIII).

Dai sali di chinina si liberano le forme antipode dell'acido γ-fenil-γ-cianoesanoico (VI) per spostamento con acidi minerali, come nel seguente esempio: g 8,65 del sale di chinina meno solubile vengono disciolti in 156 ml di alcool etilico a 50° e addizionati di ac. cloridrico fino a pH = 2. Si estrae con etere; la soluzione eterea, seccata su solfato sodico anidro, viene evaporata nel vuoto fino a secchezza. Il residuo pesa g 3,26 e si rapprende in una massa semisolida per la presenza della forma racemica. La miscela viene disciolta in acetato di etile e addizionata di ligroina; per riposo in ghiacciaia si separa la maggior parte della forma racemica che pesa g 0,24, p. f. 94-96° (determinato al microscopio Kofler senza correzione). Le acque madri, tirate a secco nel vuoto, lasciano un residuo oleoso (VII) che pesa g 3 e mostra un $[\alpha]^{25°}_D$ = −24° (1,0, C_2H_5OH assol.). Tutti i tentativi per ottenere questo prodotto in forma solida cristallina non hanno avuto successo.

Analogamente da g 9,73 del sale più solubile si possono ottenere g 3,5 della forma destrogira (VIII) anch'essa liquido oleoso con $[\alpha]^{25°}_D$ = +24° (1,0, C_2H_5OH assol.).

Mg 50 di ciascuno dei due acidi oleosi (VII - VIII) vengono riuniti e disciolti in poco acetato di etile; per aggiunta di ligroina si ottengono cristalli aventi p. f. 94-96° (determinato al microscopio Kofler senza correzione).

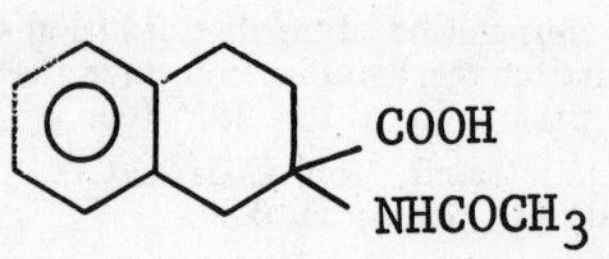

$C_{13}H_{15}NO_3$ Ref. 952

Resolution of Methyl 1,2,3,4-Tetrahydro-2-acetamido-2-naphthoate. To 3.0 g (12.2 mmol) of the methyl ester dissolved in 120 ml of methanol was added 480 ml of water and the pH was adjusted to 7.9 with 0.1 *M* sodium hydroxide. α-Chymotrypsin (400 mg) dissolved in 5 ml of water was added. During 12 hr 60 ml of base was consumed (98% of theoretical) and the reaction stopped. The reaction mixture was extracted with chloroform. The chloroform extracts were washed with water, dried over magnesium sulfate, filtered, and evaporated at reduced pressure to afford 1.5 g (100%) of (−) ester, mp 148–150°. Three recrystallizations from chloroform–hexane gave 1.4 g of (−)-methyl 2-acetamido-1,2,3,4-tetrahydro-2-naphthoate, mp 150.5–151°, $[\alpha]^{25}_D$ −59.6° (*c* 2.75, ethyl acetate).

The aqueous layer was adjusted to pH 2 with concentrated hydrochloric acid and refrigerated overnight. Isolation of the precipitate by filtration gave 900 mg of (+) acid which was recrystallized twice from water. The final yield of (+)-2-acetamido-1,2,3,4-tetrahydro-2-naphthoic acid, mp 259–261°, $[\alpha]^{25}_D$ +39.8° (*c* 2, dimethylformamide), was 400 mg.

(−)-2-Acetamido-1,2,3,4-tetrahydro-2-naphthoic acid was obtained by stirring 550 mg of the corresponding methyl ester overnight in 50 ml of 10% sodium hydroxide. The solution was acidified to pH 4 and the crystalline product was removed by filtration and dried at reduced pressure. The yield of (−) acid, mp 263–264°, $[\alpha]^{25}_D$ −45.5° (*c* 2, dimethylformamide), was 400 mg.

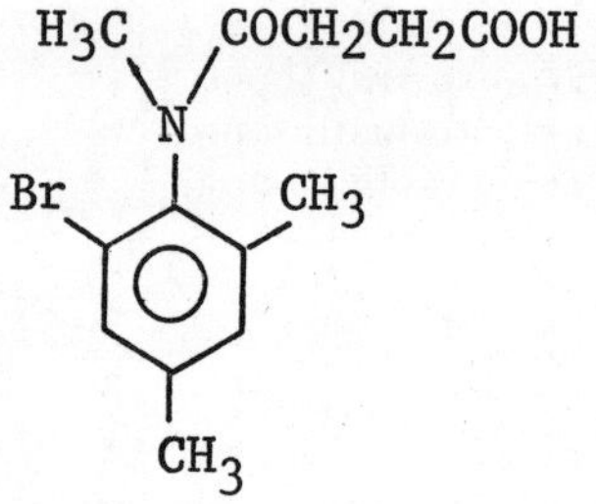

$C_{13}H_{16}BrNO_3$ Ref. 953

Resolution of N-Succinyl-1-methylamino-2,4-dimethyl-6-bromobenzene.—A solution of 5 g. of N-succinyl-1-methylamino-2,4-dimethyl-6-bromobenzene and 4.68 g. of cinchonidine in 180 ml. of 9:1 ethyl acetate–methanol by volume was filtered and evaporated to 145 ml. by directing a stream of air over its surface. After four days in the refrigerator, 3.1 g. of salt had crystallized. These crystals were collected and the filtrate evaporated to 137 ml. Refrigerated, it yielded a second crop of 1.4 g. At 125 ml., 1.3 g. of salt crystallized; at 110 ml., 0.1 g.; at 90 ml., 1.3 g. The first three fractions were combined and recrystallized in the same manner to constant rotation; this produced white feathery crystals m. p. 164–165° (cor.); yield, 1.8 g.

Anal. (*l*B*d*A) Calcd. for $C_{13}H_{16}BrNO_3 \cdot C_{19}H_{22}N_2O$: C, 63.36; H, 6.27. Found: C, 63.44; H, 6.60. *Rotation.* (*l*B*d*A) 0.03 g. made up to 10 ml. with absolute ethanol at 28° gave α_D −0.13°; *l*, 1; $[\alpha]^{28}_D$ −43°.

***d*-N-Succinyl-1-methylamino-2,4-dimethyl-6-bromobenzene.**—To 75 ml. of 1:1 hydrochloric acid at 0° was added 1.65 g. of the less-soluble salt. The mixture was stirred for fifteen minutes and then put in a refrigerator overnight. The next day the gummy material had solidified and it was broken up. The mixture was filtered and the solid material again stirred with cold 1:1 hydrochloric acid and put in a refrigerator overnight. This treatment was repeated until the filtrate gave a negative test with Folin's reagent.[9] The residue was dried in a vacuum desiccator; yield, 0.49 g. The acid was crystallized from a mixture of benzene and petroleum ether (b. p. 60–110°). The rotation was unchanged by the crystallization.

The *d*-acid was obtained from the less-soluble salt; white crystals, m. p. 118.5–120.5° (cor.).

Anal. (*d*-acid) Calcd. for $C_{13}H_{16}BrNO_3$: C, 49.68; H, 5.09. Found: C, 49.95; H, 5.18. *Rotation.* (*d*-acid) 0.05 g. made up to 10 ml. with absolute ethanol at 28° gave α_D +0.125°; *l*, 1; $[\alpha]^{28}_D$ +25°.

(9) Folin and Denis, *J. Biol. Chem.*, **12**, 239 (1912).

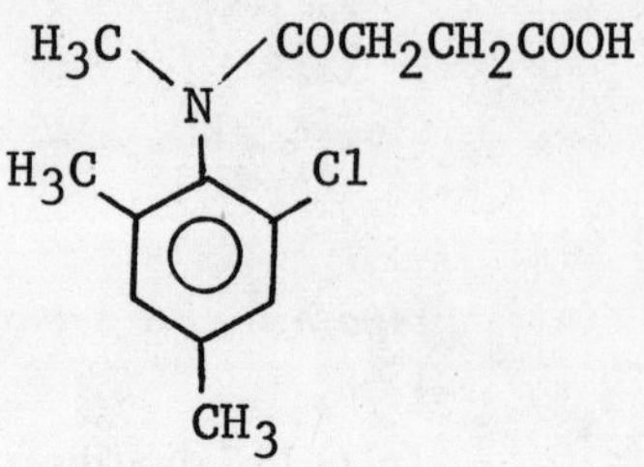

$C_{13}H_{16}ClNO_3$ Ref. 954

Resolution of N-Succinyl-1-methylamino-2,4-dimethyl-6-chlorobenzene.—A solution of 6.68 g. of N-succinyl-1-methylamino-2,4-dimethyl-6-chlorobenzene and 7.21 g. of cinchonidine in 200 ml. of a mixture of 9:1 ethyl acetate and methanol by volume was filtered and placed in a refrigerator overnight. No crystals formed. The solution was evaporated to 175 ml. by passing a current of air over its surface. After cooling overnight in the same manner, 5.35 g. of a salt had crystallized. These crystals were collected and the filtrate evaporated with a current of air to 125 ml. The solution was replaced in the refrigerator overnight and a second crop of 4.47 g. of crystals was collected. Succeeding fractions were collected as shown in the following table. The specific rotation readings were taken by making 0.10 g. of each crop up to 20 ml. with absolute ethanol. A one-decimeter tube was used.

Crop	Wt., g.	α_D at 29°	$[\alpha]^{29}_D$	Vol. in ml.
I	5.35	−0.315	−63	175
II	4.47	− .332	−67	125
III	0.91	− .344	−69	75
IV	0.245	− .331	−66	40
V	1.78	− .333	−67	20
VI	0.67			0

Of fraction I, 5.25 g. was recrystallized from 75 ml. of the ethyl acetate and methanol mixture. The results were

Crop	Wt., g.	α^{29}_D	$[\alpha]^{29}_D$	Vol. in ml.
A	3.40	−0.309	−61.8	75
B	0.70	− .313	−62.6	40
C	0.46	− .316	−63.2	20
D	0.51			0

Crops A and B had sufficiently similar rotations and were therefore taken as the pure less-soluble salt (*l*B*d*A). It formed white, feathery crystals, m. p. 166–167° (cor.).

Rotation. 0.10 g. made up to 20 ml. with absolute ethanol at 29° gave α_D −0.309°; *l*, 1; $[\alpha]^{29}_D$ −61.8°.

It has been found by experience that the alkaloidal salts of many acids are difficult to obtain in a strictly pure state so that the analyses will conform exactly to the theoretical. Since the acids have been analyzed before and after salt formation, the exact composition of the salts is irrelevant.

Anal. Calcd. for $C_{13}H_{16}NO_3Cl \cdot C_{19}H_{22}N_2O$: C, 68.02; H, 6.78. Found: C, 67.11; H, 6.99.

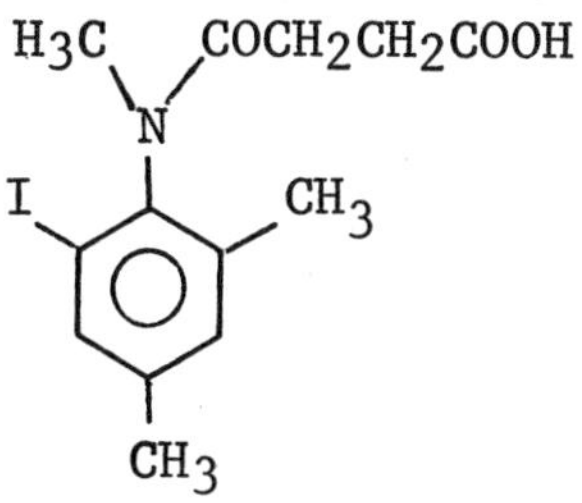

$C_{13}H_{16}INO_3$ Ref. 955

Resolution of N-Succinyl-1-methylamino-2,4-dimethyl-6-iodobenzene.—A solution of 5.6 g. of N-succinyl-1-methylamino-2,4-dimethyl-6-iodobenzene and 4.56 g. of cinchonidine in 55 ml. of 9:1 ethyl acetate-methanol by volume was filtered and evaporated to 45 ml. by directing a stream of air to the top of the flask. After four days in the refrigerator, 4 g. of salt had crystallized. Upon concentrating the mother liquor to 40 ml. and refrigerating, 1.5 g. of salt crystallized; at 30 ml., 1.6 g.; at 19 ml., 1.0 g.; at 4 ml., 0.5 g. It had been found while working with this salt previously that during recrystallization of the salt it dissociated, so the first crop was not recrystallized further; white crystals, m. p. 140–145° (cor.).

Anal. (*l*BdA) Calcd. for $C_{13}H_{16}INO_3 \cdot C_{19}H_{22}N_2O$: C, 58.62; H, 5.85. Found: C, 58.53; H, 5.97. *Rotation.* (*l*BdA) 0.05 g. made up to 10 ml. with ethanol at 26° gave α_D −0.23°; *l*, 1; $[\alpha]^{26}_D$ −46°.

The fourth and fifth fractions were combined and crystallized once; white crystals; yield, 1.1 g.

Rotation. (*l*B*l*A) 0.05 g. made up to 10 ml. with ethanol at 31° gave α_D −0.315°; *l*, 1; $[\alpha]^{31}_D$ −63°.

***d*- and *l*-N-Succinyl-1-methylamino-2,4-dimethyl-6-iodobenzene.**—The salts were decomposed in the same manner as the salt of the 6-bromo compound. From 4 g. of the less-soluble salt, 1.2 g. of the *d*-acid was obtained after one crystallization from a mixture of three volumes of carbon tetrachloride and one volume of petroleum ether (b. p. 60–110°); white crystals, m. p. 105–106° (cor.).

Anal. (*d*-acid) Calcd. for $C_{13}H_{16}INO_3$: C, 43.21; H, 4.43. Found: C, 43.22; H, 4.41. *Rotation.* (*d*-acid) 0.435 g. made up to 25 ml. with *n*-butanol at 33° gave α_D +0.21°; *l*, 1; $[\alpha]^{33}_D$ +12°.

This *d*-acid did not have the maximum specific rotation since it was found that recrystallizing the less-soluble salt of another resolution several times, in spite of the dissociation of the salt, and then decomposing gave an acid with a specific rotation of +43° and a m. p. of 108° (cor.).

The decomposition of the more-soluble fraction did not give the pure *l*-acid; white crystals, m. p. 105–106° (cor.).

Rotation. (*l*-acid) 0.05 g. made up to 10 ml. with ethanol at 31° gave α_D −0.09°; *l*, 1; $[\alpha]^{31}_D$ −18°.

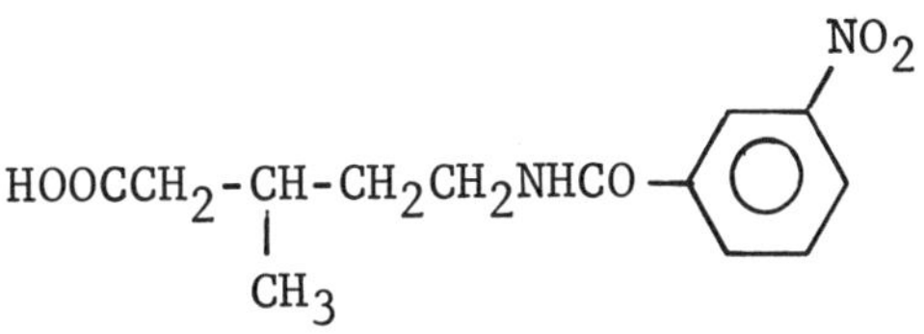

$C_{13}H_{16}N_2O_5$ Ref. 956

Resolution of *dl*-β-Methyl-δ-*m*-nitrobenzoylaminovaleric Acid.—A mixture of 100 g. of the *dl*-acid and 116 g. of anhydrous quinidine was dissolved in hot absolute ethanol, boiled with Darco and Norite and filtered. The ethanolic filtrate, which amounted to 450 cc., was diluted with 1300 cc. of anhydrous ether and allowed to stand at room temperature for several days. Rosets of colorless elongated prisms separated and these were isolated by filtration, washed with anhydrous ether and dried (Fraction 1); m. p., 125.0–126.5° (cor.); yield 77 g. (36% of total).

Rotation. 0.2286 g. made up to 5 cc. with absolute ethanol at 28° gave α_D +5.10°; *l*, 1; $[\alpha]^{28}_D$ +111.5° (±0.5°). Further recrystallization from absolute ethanol–anhydrous ether altered neither the melting point nor the rotation.

After removal of 77 g. of the most insoluble quinidine salt (Fraction 1), the filtrate was diluted further with anhydrous ether and allowed to stand in the cold. A further 48 g. (22%) of yellow, semicrystalline material separated, leaving approximately 42% of the total salt in solution (Fraction 2). The more soluble salt could not be obtained crystalline.

***l*-β-Methyl-δ-*m*-nitrobenzoylaminovaleric Acid.**—Fraction 1 (75 g.) was shaken thoroughly with 500 cc. of 2 *N* sulfuric acid and 200 cc. of ether, then separated. The mixture of dilute acid and undissolved quinidine salt was shaken with 200-cc. portions of ether until no more solid material remained. The ethereal extracts were combined, dried over anhydrous magnesium sulfate, and evaporated to give 30 g. of crystalline *l*-acid. This was purified by recrystallization from aqueous ethanol: colorless rods, m. p. 113–114°.

Anal. Calcd. for $C_{13}H_{16}N_2O_5$: C, 55.71; H, 5.75; N, 9.99. Found: C, 55.96; H, 6.02; N, 9.92.

Rotation. 0.2040 g. made up to 5 cc. with absolute ethanol at 30° gave α_D −0.205°; *l*, 1; $[\alpha]^{30}_D$ −5.0° (±0.2°).

***d*-β-Methyl-δ-*m*-nitrobenzoylaminovaleric Acid.**—The ethereal solution containing Fraction 2 was shaken with 2 *N* sulfuric acid, and 34 g. of the *d*-acid was obtained by the same procedure as that outlined above. Purification was accomplished by recrystallization from chloroform–ligroin (b. p. 90–110°): colorless elongated prisms, m. p., 113–114°.

Anal. Calcd. for $C_{13}H_{16}N_2O_5$: C, 55.71; H, 5.75; N, 9.99. Found: C, 55.94; H, 5.84; N, 10.09.

Rotation. 0.2164 g. made up to 5 cc. with absolute ethanol at 25° gave α_D +0.23°; *l*, 1; $[\alpha]^{25}_D$ +5.3° (±0.2°).

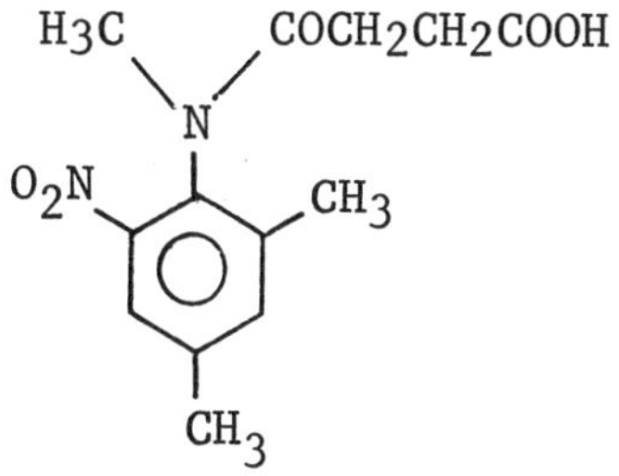

$C_{13}H_{16}N_2O_5$ Ref. 957

Resolution of N-Succinyl-1-methylamino-2,4-dimethyl-6-nitrobenzene.—A solution of 5.5 g. of N-succinyl-1-methylamino-2,4-dimethyl-6-nitrobenzene and 5.775 g. of cinchonidine in 100 ml. of 9:1 ethyl acetate-methanol by volume was filtered. The filtrate was evaporated to 65 ml. by directing a stream of air to the top of the flask. It was seeded with crystals obtained by allowing 1 ml. of the solution to evaporate slowly in a small test-tube. After five days in the refrigerator, 1.9 g. of salt had crystallized. Upon concentrating the mother liquor to 35 ml. and refrigerating, 4.7 g. of salt crystallized; at 20 ml., 1.8 g.; and at 5 ml., 0.25 g. The first two fractions were combined and recrystallized in the same manner to constant rotation. White feathery crystals were obtained; m. p. 141–143° (cor.); yield, 1.5 g.

Anal. (*l*BdA) Calcd. for $C_{13}H_{16}N_2O_5 \cdot C_{19}H_{22}N_2O$: C, 66.90; H, 6.67. Found: C, 66.32; H, 6.60. *Rotation.* (*l*BdA) 0.05 g. made up to 10 ml. with ethanol and 26° gave α_D −0.20°; *l*, 1; $[\alpha]^{26}_D$ −40°.

***d*-N-Succinyl-1-methylamino-2,4-dimethyl-6-nitrobenzene.**—The less-soluble salt was decomposed with 0.5% hydrochloric acid in the same manner as the salt of the 6-bromo compound. Before crystallization from benzene the specific rotation was determined.

Rotation. (*d*-acid) 0.05 g. made up to 10 ml. with ethanol at 25° gave α_D +0.125°; *l*, 1; $[\alpha]^{25}_D$ +25°.

Crystallization from benzene produced light yellow crystals; m. p. 130–131° (cor.).

Anal. (*d*-acid) Calcd. for $C_{13}H_{16}N_2O_5$: C, 55.71; H, 5.71; N, 10.00. Found: C, 56.22; H, 5.87; N, 10.07. *Rotation.* (*d*-acid) 0.05 g. made up to 10 ml. with ethanol at 25° gave α_D +0.05°; *l*, 1; $[\alpha]^{25}_D$ +10°.

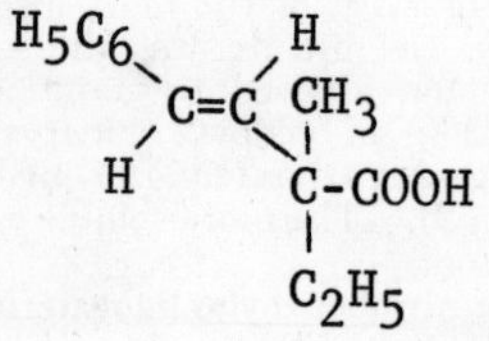

$C_{13}H_{16}O_2$ Ref. 958

To a solution of 7.286 g (35.7 mmol) of (±)-trans-2-ethyl-2-methyl-4-phenyl-3-butenoic acid (19) in 100 ml of hot ethyl acetate was added 4.403 g (36.2 mmol) of (+)-α-methylbenzylamine $[\alpha]^{25}_{578}$ 45.4, c 0.025 g/ml, hexane). Fine white needles began to precipitate almost immediately. The mixture was diluted with 50 ml of hot ethyl acetate and allowed to cool. This afforded 9.1 g of Fine colorless needles, mp 115-131°. A 128 mg portion of this salt was hydrolyzed with 6N hydrochloric acid to afford 79.7 mg of acid, $[\alpha]^{25}_{305}$ 10° (c 0.016 g/ml $CHCl_3$).

The remainder of the salt was recrystallized from ethyl acetate-chloroform to give 6.2 g of fine colorless needles mp 137-145°. Acid isolated from a portion of this salt had $[\alpha]^{25}_{365}$ 39° (c 0.013 g/ml, $CHCl_3$).

The remainder of this salt was recrystallized from ethyl acetate-chloroform. This afforded 4.3 g of salt of mp 139-145°. Acid from a portion of this had $[\alpha]^{25}_{365}$ 52 (c = 0.013 g/ml, chloroform). A fourth crystallization afforded 3.6 g of fine, colorless needles, mp 147-151°. This was hydrolyzed to give 2.38 g of acid, $[\alpha]^{25}_{365}$ 55 (c, 0.014 g/ml, chloroform). Recrystallization of this acid from hexane afforded 1.61 g (1.87 mmol, 22.1%) of (+)-trans-2-ethyl-2-methyl-4-phenyl-3-butenoic acid as colorless thick needles, mp 82.2-83.0°. The specific rotations at 25° were (λ in parentheses) 7.4 (578), 8.8 (546, 22 (436), 32 (405), 61.7 (365) (c, 0.017 g/ml, $CHCl_3$. This material was recrystallized from hexane to give 1.35 g of colorless thick needles, mp 82.5-83.5°, that had unchanged specific rotations.

The mother liquors from the first two crystallizations of the salt were combined, concentrated and hydrolyzed to give 3.75 g (1.83 mmol) of acid. This was resolved by recrystallization of its (-)-α-methylbenzylamine ($[\alpha]^{25}_{578}$ -45.1, c 0.027 g/ml, hexane) salt according to the procedure described above. This afforded 2.32 g (11.3 mmol, 31.8%) of the (-) acid as colorless thick needles, mp 81.0-82.7°. The specific rotations at 25° were (λ in parentheses) -7 (578), -8 (546), -22 (436), -32 (405), -62 (365) (c, 0.013 g/ml, $CHCl_3$.)

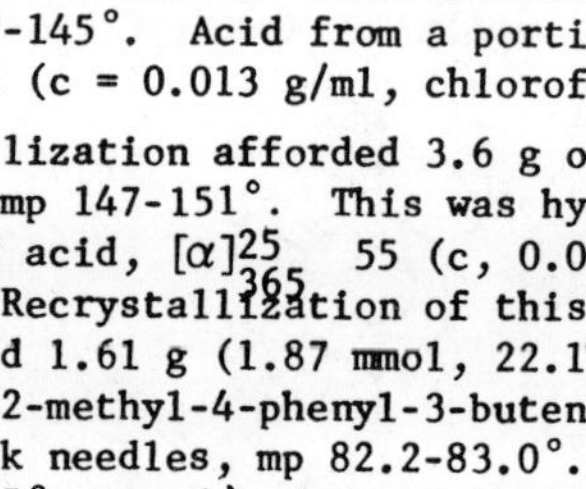

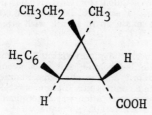

$C_{13}H_{16}O_2$ Ref. 959

Resolution of (+)-t-2-Ethyl-2-methyl-3-phenylcyclopropanecarboxylic Acid (31-t,t)

A solution of 1.623 g (7.94 mmol) of (±)-t- 2-ethyl-2-methyl-3-phenylcyclopropanecarboxylic acid and 1,090 g (8.04 mmol) of (-) N-methyl-α-phenethylamine (Roche division of Hoffman LaRoche) was dissolved in a boiling mixture of ca 5 ml of dichloromethane and ca 10 ml of hexane. The solution was allowed to cool and a seed (obtained by crystallization from ether) was added. White needles (869 mg, mp 107-113°) separated when the solvent was allowed to evaporate slowly.

Recrystallization of this material from hexane-dichloromethane gave 522 mg of white needles, mp 106-110°. Some (41 mg) of the salt was suspended in ether and hydrolyzed by shaking with 3N hydrochloric acid. This afforded 24 mg of acid that had the following specific rotations at 25°λ in parentheses): -75 (578), -86 (546), -172 (436), -220 (405), -324 (365) (c, 0.012 g/ml, $CHCl_3$).

Another recrystallization from hexane-dichloromethane gave 309 mg of colorless needles. This afforded acid that had the following specific rotations at 25° (λ in parentheses) -75 (578), -88 (546), -172 (436), -221 (405), -320 (365) (c, 0.012 g/ml, $CHCl_3$).

All of the salt from the second crystallization was hydrolyzed to give 290 mg (1.42 mmol, 35.4%) of acid. This was recrystallized from pentane to give 143 mg (17.4%) of colorless needles, mp 93.0-94.5, that had the following specific rotations at 25° (λ in parentheses) λ-83 ± 2 (578), -97 ± 2 (546), -190 ± 2 (436), -243 ± 2 (405), -358 ± 3 (365), (c, 0.012 g/ml, $CHCl_3$).

The nmr spectrum of the (-) acid was identical to that of the racemic acid.

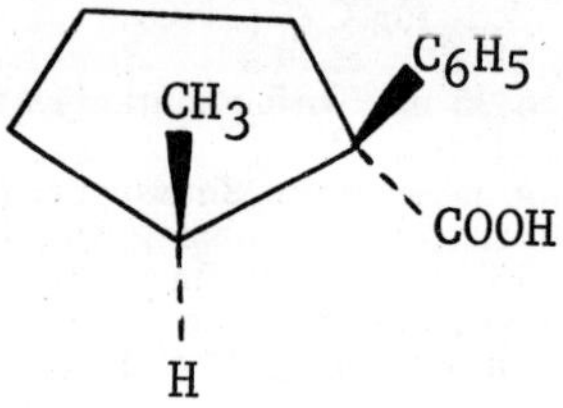

$C_{13}H_{16}O_2$ Ref. 960

Acide (±) *méthyl-2-t phényl-1 cyclopentane carboxylique-1-r* **3**.

20,4 g (0,1 mole) d'acide **3** racémique (5) et 25 g de cinchonidine optiquement pure, sont dissous à chaud dans le minimum d'alcool éthylique à 70 %. Après recristallisations, on isole un sel de point de fusion 135°. Traité à reflux pendant 2 h par 300 ml d'acide chlorhydrique 10 % et 200 ml d'éther, il conduit après extraction à l'éther et évaporation du solvant à 8 g d'acide (+) méthyl-2-*t* phényl-1 cyclopentane carboxylique-1-*r* de point de fusion 79°.

En traitant les eaux de cristallisation de la même façon on retire 10 g d'acide (—) **3**, F = 83°.

Les caractéristiques IR et RMN sont identiques à celles indiquées (5) pour l'acide racémique.

Analyse : $C_{13}H_{16}O_2$.

Mesures optiques :

DOR, t° = 27°, (c = 5,93.10⁻⁴ g/ml de méthanol), cellule = 0,1 dm

$[\varphi]_{600} = +440°$ $[\varphi]_{410} = +1\,172°$ $[\varphi]_{300} = +3\,223°$
$[\varphi]_{259} = +5\,860°$ $[\varphi]_{223} = 0°$ $[\varphi]_{220} = -4\,260°$

Rotation de l'échantillon utilisé pour la corrélation de configuration par voie chimique. t° = 27 °C, (c = 1,0 g/100 ml de méthanol), cellule = 1 dm.

$[\alpha]_D = +135°$, $[\varphi]_D = +275°$.

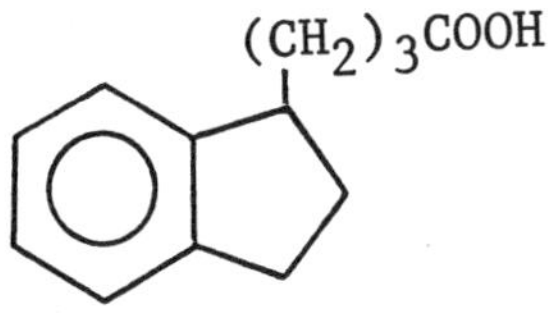

$C_{13}H_{16}O_2$ Ref. 961

Obtained an acid, m.p. 54-55°C. (hexane), $[\alpha]_D^{25}$ = +1.0°C. (c, 10.0, benzene), using (+)-α-phenylethylamine as resolving agent. Using (-)-α-phenylethylamine as resolving agent, obtained an acid m.p. 54-55°C., $[\alpha]_D^{25}$ = -1.0°C. (c 10.0, benzene).

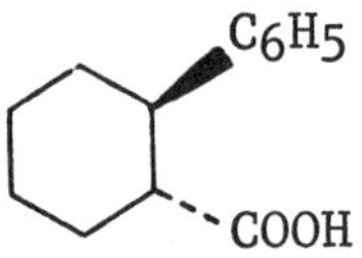

$C_{13}H_{16}O_2$ Ref. 962

Using N-benzyl-2-(hydroxymethyl)cyclohexylamine as resolving agent, obtained a less soluble diastereomeric salt after five recrystallizations from 2-propanol with $[\alpha]_{589}^{25}$ 33.4° (c 0.5 ethanol). (Melting point of authentic salt was found to be 149-150°.) The authentic more soluble salt had a m.p. 128-129° and $[\alpha]_{589}^{25}$ -24.2° (c 0.5, ethanol).

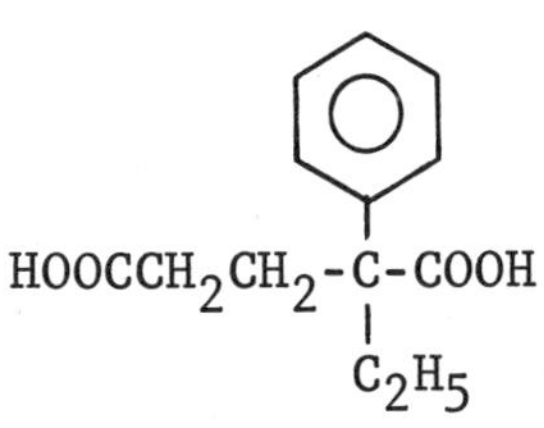

$C_{13}H_{16}O_4$ Ref. 963

1. *Trennung der racemischen Verbindung in den Antipoden:*

Die Trennung gelang auf folgendem Wege: α-Phenyl-α-äthyl-glutarimid wurde mit starker wässeriger Natronlauge zur racemischen α-Phenyl-α-äthyl-glutarsäure verseift. Diese Säure (Smp. 136–137°) wurde in Isopropanol gelöst und mit der äquimolekularen Menge (—) α-Phenäthylamin ($[\alpha]_D^{25°}$ = —38,5°) versetzt, wonach das bis-Phenäthylaminsalz kristallisierte. Letzteres wurde solange aus Isopropanol umkristallisiert, bis die Drehung der freien Säure nicht mehr zunahm. Auf diese Weise gewann man die optisch reine, links drehende α-Phenyl-α-äthyl-glutarsäure ($[\alpha]^{22°}$ = —15,1 ± 0,3 in Aethanol; Smp. 118–119°). Aus der Mutterlauge wurde die angereicherte rechtsdrehende Säure gewonnen und auf analoge Weise, diesmal über das bis-Salz mit (+) Phenäthylamin, optisch rein präpariert ($[\alpha]^{22°}$ = +15,2° ± 0,3 in Aethanol; Smp. 118–119°). In Abb. 2 ist das Misch-Smp.-Diagramm der zwei Antipoden aufgezeichnet.

Aus den enantiomeren Dicarbonsäuren liessen sich die optisch reinen Antipoden von α-Phenyl-α-äthyl-glutarimid ($[\alpha]_D^{25°}$ = (+) resp. (—) 183° ± 1° in Alkohol; Smp. 104°) herstellen, indem man die bis-Ammoniumsalze der Säuren im Ammoniakstrom auf 170° heizte. Es ist bemerkenswert, dass beim Ringschluss das Vorzeichen der Drehung wechselt, indem die (—) Säure zum (+)-, resp. die (+) Säure zum (—) Glutarimid führte. Die sedative Wirkung des rechtsdrehenden α-Phenyl-α-äthyl-glutarimids ist in verschiedenen pharmakologischen Testen 2–3 mal stärker als die der linksdrehende Form (1).

(1) Nachdem unsere Stoffwechselversuche sowie die pharmakologische Prüfung mit den optischen Antipoden von Doriden abgeschlossen waren und über die Resultate am Biochemie-Kongress in Zurück berichtet worden war (s. Anmerkung auf S. 1), erschien eine Arbeit von Branchini, R., Casini, G., Ferappi, M. und Gulinelli, S. in *Il Farmaco* (Ed. Sc.), 1960, *15*, 734. Darin wird die Herstellung der optischen Antipoden von α-Phenyl-α-äthyl-glutarimid auf einem anderen Wege und die pharmakologische Wirkung der Enantiomeren beschrieben. Die Angaben über chemische Eigenschaften und biologische Wirkung der Antipoden entsprechen unseren Befunden.

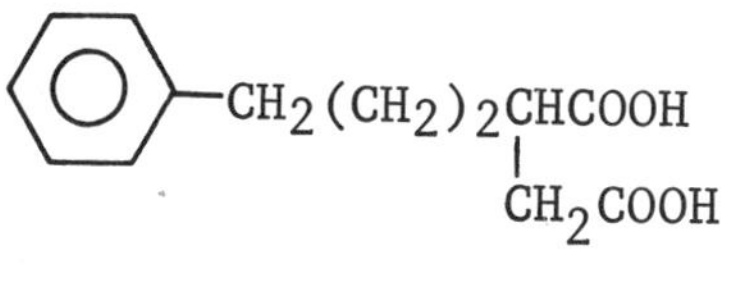

$C_{13}H_{16}O_4$ Ref. 964

Dehydroabietylamine acetate

Amine D (2.0 kg, from Hercules Powder Company) was dissolved in 3.3 l of toluene heated to 65–70°. To the solution was cautiously added with stirring acetic acid until the solution was acidic (460 g). The solution was allowed to cool first at room temperature and then in an ice-bath. The salt was filtered, washed with small portions of cold toluene and pressed as dry as possible on the filter. The filtrate was cooled to 0° and a second crop of crystals was filtered and combined with the main fraction. The combined crystal mass was recrystallised twice from toluene (3.2 l each time). The product was washed on the filter with cold toluene and finally with petroleum ether. After drying there was obtained 960 g of pure dehydroabietylamine acetate, m.p. 141–143°. Cheney reported m.p. 141–143.5° [5].

Dehydroabietylamine

The acetate was dissolved in water with slight warming and sodium hydroxide solution added. The amine was extracted with benzene. After evaporation of the benzene *in vacuo* the dehydroabietylamine remained as a viscous oil which slowly crystallised.

Racem. γ-phenylpropylsuccinic acid

To the alcoholate prepared from 7.5 g of sodium and 90 ml of absolute ethanol was added 74.2 g (0.30 mole) of ethyl ethane-1,1,2-tricarboxylate [8] and 60.0 g (0.30 mole) of γ-phenylpropyl bromide [9]. The reaction mixture was refluxed for 6 hours and the ester hydrolysed by the addition of 45 g of sodium hydroxide and 50 ml, of water followed by two hours of reflux boiling. The alkaline water solution was extracted with ether (discarded) and the water solution was then poured into concentrated hydrochloric acid. The product was extracted with ether, the ether solution washed with water and evaporated. The residue was heated at ca 150° until decarboxylation had ceased. At cooling the product crystallised. Yield 65 g (92 %). After two recrystallisations from ethanol-water there remained 48 g (68 %), m.p. 110°.

Calcd. for $C_{13}H_{16}O_4$: Equiv. wt. 118.2 C 66.07 H 6.83.
Found: Equiv. wt. 117.9 C 66.19 H 6.77.

(−)-γ-Phenylpropylsuccinic acid

To 132 g (0.382 mole) of dehydroabietylamine acetate was added excess of dilute sodium hydroxide and, the amine extracted with ether. The ether solution (1500 ml) was dried over potassium hydroxide and then combined with a solution of 44.2 g (0.187 mole) of racemic γ-phenylpropylsuccinic acid in 500 ml of ether. The salt that spontaneously crystallised from the solution was filtered off (97 g) and the acid was liberated from a small sample, $[\alpha]_D^{25}$ = −14.2° (abs. ethanol). The remaining salt was refluxed for one hour with 1500 ml of ether. The undissolved salt was filtered off (73.6 g) and the acid isolated from a small sample, $[\alpha]_D^{25}$ = −24.6°. The rest of the salt was recrystallised two times from chloroform-ethanol (1:1). The progress of the resolution is seen below.

Cryst. no.	Solvent (ml)	Salt obtained (g)	$[\alpha]_D^{25}$ of acid
1	140	44.2	−28.2°
2	100	27.9	−28.1°

The acid isolated from the last fraction was recrystallised twice from ethanol-water, m.p. 107°.

Equiv. wt.: Calc. 118.2. Found 118.0.
0.2054 g acid dissolved in absolute ethanol to 10.00 ml: 2 $\alpha_D^{25} = -1.16°$.
$[\alpha]_D^{25} = -28.2°$, $[M]_D^{25} = -66.6°$.

(+)-γ-Phenylpropylsuccinic acid

On evaporation of the first ether solution from the resolution of the (–)-acid there remained a sticky crystal mass, which was recrystallised twice from ethanol. The progress of the resolution is shown below.

Cryst. no.	Solvent (ml)	Salt obtained (g)	$[\alpha]_D^{25}$ of acid
1	300	25.7	+27.8°
2	120	16.3	+28.2°

The last salt fraction was treated with cold dilute sodium hydroxide solution and the dehydroabietylamine extracted with ether. The aqueous solution was acidified with hydrochloric acid and cooled in an ice-bath. The organic acid was filtered and recrystallised twice from ethanol-water, m.p. 107°.

Equiv. wt.: Calc. 118.2. Found 118.1.
0.2086 g acid dissolved in absolute ethanol to 10.00 ml: 2 $\alpha_D^{25} = +1.18°$.
$[\alpha]_D^{25} = +28.3°$, $[M]_D^{25} = +66.9°$.

5. Cheney, L. C., U.S. Pat. 2 787 637 (1957); C.A. *51*, 13926 (1957).
8. Bischoff, C. A., Ann. *214*, 38 (1882).
9. Aspinall, G. O., and Baker, W., J. Chem. Soc. *1*, 745 (1950).

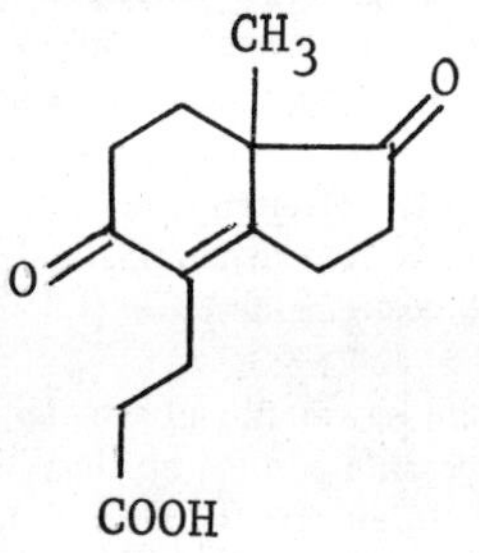

$C_{13}H_{16}O_4$

Ref. 965

Sel de (—)-éphédrine de l'acide (+) dioxo-1,5 méthyl-7aβ tétrahydro-5,6,7,7a indane-4 propionique.

On dissout au reflux 11,8 g d'acide racémique **2a** et 8,7 g de (—)-éphédrine dans 147 cm³ de benzène puis laisse cristalliser à température ambiante. On recueille après une nuit 15,5 g de sel qu'on recristallise 2 fois en benzène, puis en acétate de méthyle : 8 g. Rdt = 79 %, F = 150-151°, $[\alpha]_D = +108° \pm 1$ (1 %, eau).

Analyse $C_{23}H_{31}O_5N = 401{,}5$:

	C	H	O
Calc. % :	68,81	7,78	19,92
Tr. :	68,9	7,9	19,6.

Acide (+)-dioxo-1,5 méthyl-7aβ tétrahydro-5,6,7,7a indane-4 propionique, **2a.**

A la solution bouillante de 43 g du sel précédent dans 1 000 cm³ d'acétone, on ajoute, en agitant, la solution de 7,5 g d'acide oxalique dihydraté dans 75 cm³ d'acétone et chauffe pendant 1 h. On essore à chaud l'oxalate de (—)-éphédrine et le lave à l'acétone chaude : 22,3 g (99 % de la quantité théorique). La solution acétonique est concentrée à sec et le résidu cristallisé dans l'eau : 24 g. Rdt = 95 %, F = 143°, $[\alpha]_D = +242°$ (1 %, acétone).

Analyse $C_{13}H_{16}O_4 = 236{,}26$: Calc. % : C 66,08 H 6,83
Tr. : 65,9 6,7.

Sel de (+)-éphédrine de l'acide (—) dioxo-1,5 méthyl-7aα tétrahydro-5,6,7,7a indane-4 propionique.

On l'obtient comme précédemment à partir de l'acide racémique **2a** et de la (+)-éphédrine, F = 150°, $[\alpha]_D = -108°$ (1 %, eau).

Acide (—) dioxo-1,5 méthyl-7aα tétrahydro-5,6,7,7a indane-4 propionique, **2a.**

Obtenu comme l'énantiomère (+), F = 143°, $[\alpha]_D = -247°$ (1 %, acétone).

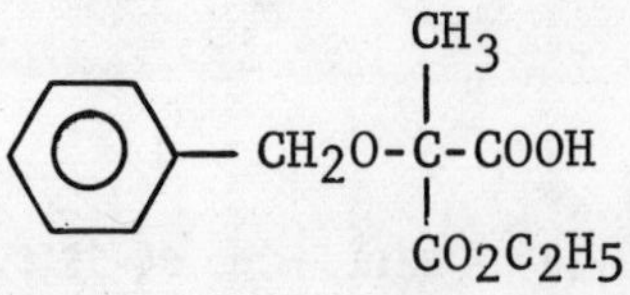

$C_{13}H_{16}O_5$

Ref. 966

EXAMPLE 6

Cinchonidine salts of (S)-(−)- and (R)-(+)-2-methyl-2-benzyloxymalonic acid monoethyl ester

541.5 g. (1.84 mols) of cinchonidine and 465.5 g. (1.84 mols) of racemic 2-methyl-2-benzyloxymalonic acid monoethyl ester (prepared as described in Example 5) are dissolved in 1.82 litres of hot absolute ethanol. The whole is allowed to cool slowly to 20° C., whereupon the bulk of the cinchonidine salt of the laevorotatary antipode crystallises out. The batch is kept for 3 hours at 20° C., thoroughly suction-filtered, and the filter cake is twice rinsed well with a mixture of 80% of ether and 20% of ethanol, to yield the optically pure cinchonidine salt of (S)-(−)-2-methyl-2-benzyloxymalonic acid monoethyl ester in colourless, long, slanting parallelepipeds melting at 155–156° C. with decomposition. Optical rotation $[\alpha]_D^{20} = -68.8°$ (c.=2, in ethanol). A specimen of the salt was further recrystallised twice from ethanol; no change in the melting point or in the rotation was observed. The semiester liberated from this salt after three recrystallisations displayed within the margins of error the identical rotation as the semiester that had been liberated from the bulk of the substance.

To purify the cinchonidine salt of the dextrorotatary semiester present in the mother liquor, the latter is evaporated to dryness, whereupon the residue crystallises. The crystalline residue is digested with enough hot ethyl acetate to dissolve the bulk of the readily soluble cinchonidine salt of the dextrorotatary semiester while leaving an insoluble residue, which is filtered off while hot, consisting predominantly of the cinchonidine salt (which is more sparingly soluble in ethyl acetate) of the laevorotatary semiester still present. On cooling, the solution furnishes a crystallisate which, after 3 further recrystallisations from ethyl acetate, yields the optically pure cinchonidine salt of (R)-(+)-2-methyl-2-benzyloxymalonic acid monoethyl ester in colourless, fine needles melting at 134° C. with decomposition. Optical rotation $[\alpha]_D^{20} = -64.4°$, $[\alpha]_{578}^{20} = -70.4°$, $[\alpha]_{546}^{20} = -82.4°$ (c.=1.6, in ethanol).

EXAMPLE 7

(S)-(−)-2-methyl-2-benzyloxymalonic acid monoethyl ester

190 g. (0.348 mol) of the cinchonidine salt of (S)-(−)-2-methyl-2-benzyloxymalonic acid monoethyl ester (melting at 155–156° C.) are agitated alternately with 1½ litres of ether and 600 ml. of 2 N-sulphuric acid until all has dissolved. The sulphuric acid solution is then extracted further with 2 x 1 litre of ether. To free the ether solutions completely from cinchonidine they are further agitated with 3 x 200 ml. of 2 N-sulphuric acid, and then washed with water until the washings run neutral and dried. After having cautiously expelled the solvent, the (S)-(−)-2-methyl-2-benzyloxymalonic acid monoethyl ester is obtained as a viscid, substantially colourless oil. Refractive index $n_D^{20} = 1.4990$. Optical rotation $[\alpha]_D^{20} = -10.3°$ (c.=4.3, in ethanol).

EXAMPLE 8

(R)-(+)-2-methyl-2-benzyloxymalonic acid monoethyl ester

90.0 g. (0.165 mol.) of the cinchonidine salt of (R)-(+)-2-methyl-2-benzyloxymalonic acid monoethyl ester (melting at 134° C.) are split with the use of ester and 2 N-sulphuric acid in the same manner as described for the cinchonidine salt of the laevorotatary semiester. There is obtained the (R)-(+)-2-methyl-2-benzyloxymalonic acid monoethyl ester as a viscous, substantially colourless oil. Refractive index n_D^{23}=1.5023. Optical rotation $[\alpha]_D^{20}=+10.1°$, $[\alpha]_{578}^{20}=+10.0°$,

$$[\alpha]_{546}^{20}=+11.4°$$

(c.=5.41, in ethanol).

$C_{13}H_{16}O_5$ Ref. 966a

1. (*R*)-Benzyloxy-methyl-malonsäure-monoäthylester ((*R*)-13). - 1.1. *(S)-1-Phenyläthylammoniumsalz des (R)-Benzyloxy-methyl-malonsäure-monoäthylesters.* Zu einer auf 50° erwärmten Lösung von 140.3 g (0,555 mol) rohem Halbester (*RS*)-**13** [10] in 600 ml Diisopropyläther und 200 ml trockenem Äthanol wurden 67 g (0,555 mol) (*S*)-1-Phenyläthylamin gefügt (unter N_2) und die so erhaltene Salzlösung bei RT. zum allmählichen Abkühlen stehengelassen. Nach Einsetzen der Kristallisation wurde 2 Std. bei 0° gerührt; dann das Kristallisat abfiltriert, 3mal mit 300 ml Äther gewaschen und bei 60°/11 Torr bis zur Gewichtskonstanz getrocknet. Auf diese Weise wurden 58,8 g (46,6%) des 1-Phenyläthylammoniumsalzes von (*R*)-**13** mit einer optischen Reinheit von 92,5% (bestimmt aus der spez. Drehung des freien Halbesters (siehe unten) erhalten. Durch Umkristallisation dieses Materials aus einem Gemisch von 120 ml Äthanol und 450 ml Diisopropyläther und Waschen der Kristalle mit Äther wurden 45 g optisch reines Salz vom Smp. 136-137° erhalten. $[\alpha]_D = +7,1°$ (c = 5,0; Chloroform) und 8,02° (c = 10,0; Chloroform); $[\alpha]_D = -2,6°$ (c = 2,0; Äthanol).

Aus einem zweiten Ansatz mit 49,5 g (196 mmol) (*RS*)-**13** wurden 21,5 g (57,5 mmol) des (*S*)-1-Phenyläthylammoniumsalzes von (*R*)-**13** erhalten (59%).

1.2. *Herstellung des freien Halbesters (*R*)-13.* Eine Suspension von 53,2 g des (*S*)-1-Phenyläthylammoniumsalzes von (*R*)-**13** in 300 ml Äther wurde in einem Scheidetrichter mit 200 ml 2N H_2SO_4 versetzt und der beim Schütteln freigesetzte Halbester in die Ätherphase aufgenommen. Die wässerige Phase wurde noch 2mal mit je 200 ml Äther extrahiert, die vereinigten Ätherphasen mit Wasser neutral gewaschen und über Natriumsulfat getrocknet. Nach Abdestillieren des Lösungsmittels und Trocknen des viskosen Rückstandes im Exsikkator (P_2O_5) zur Gewichtskonstanz wurden 34,2 g (95,2%) (*R*)-**13** als farbloses, hochviskoses Öl erhalten. - $[\alpha]_D = +9,65$ (c = 2,04; Äthanol) (Lit. [10]: $[\alpha]_D = +9,5°$ (c = 2,0; Äthanol)). - ^{1}H-NMR.: 1,30 (*t*, J = 7, CH_3CH_2); 1,76 (*s*, $CH_3C(2)$); 4,28 (*qa*, J = 7; CH_3CH_2O); 4,63 (*s*, $PhCH_2O$); 7,33 (*s*, Ph); 8,90 (*s*, COOH).

$C_{13}H_{16}O_5$ (252,27) Ber. C 61,91 H 7,29 N 3,75% Gef. C 61,62 H 7,35 N 3,70%.

$C_{13}H_{16}O_5$ Ref. 966b

Beispiel 2

Anhydropilosinsalz des (R)-(+)-2-Methyl-2-benzyloxymalonsäuremonoäthylesters

Zu einer heißen Lösung von 382 g (1,425 Mol) Anhydropilosin in 750 ml Isopropanol gibt man in einem Guß 359 g (1,425 Mol) racemischen 2-Methyl-2-benzyloxymalonsäuremonoäthylester in 150 ml Isopropanol zu, kühlt auf 30° ab, impft an und läßt über Nacht bei Zimmertemperatur auskristallisieren. Durch Abnutschen wird die Mutterlauge möglichst vollständig von den abgeschiedenen Kristallmassen entfernt und der Nutscheninhalt nachher noch mit einem Gemisch von Isopropanol und Heptan nachgewaschen. Dann wird nochmals aus einem Gemisch von 450 ml Isopropanol und 100 ml Heptan umkristallisiert, die Mutterlauge entfernt und die Kristalle wiederum mit einem Gemisch von 75 ml Isopropanol und 25 ml Heptan nachgewaschen. Man erhält so nach dem Trocknen am Hochvakuum das reine Anhydropilosinsalz des (R)-(+)-2-Methyl-2-benzyloxymalonsäuremonoäthylesters, verwitterte, farblose Stäbchen, Smp. 102–103°.

$[\alpha]_D^{20} = +24,5°$ (c = 2 in Äthanol).

Beispiel 3

(R)-(+)-2-Methyl-2-benzyloxymalonsäuremonoäthylester

200,5 g (0,385 Mol) (R)-(+)-2-Methyl-2-benzyloxymalonsäuremonoäthylester-anhydropilosinsalz (Smp. 102 bis 103°) werden zwischen 1½ l Äther und 600 ml 2n Schwefelsäure so lange geschüttelt, bis alles in Lösung gegangen ist. Anschließend wird die Schwefelsäurelösung weitere zweimal mit je 1½ l Äther extrahiert. Um das Anhydropilosin quantitativ vom Halbester abzutrennen, werden die drei Ätherlösungen weitere viermal mit je 100 ml 2n H_2SO_4 ausgeschüttelt. Anschließend werden die Ätherlösungen mit Wasser neutral gewaschen, gut mit Na_2SO_4 getrocknet und der Äther bei 50° entfernt. Man erhält den Halbester als schwach gelb gefärbtes Öl.

n_D^{20} = 1,5005, $[\alpha]_D^{20} = +9,5°$ (c = 2 in Äthanol).

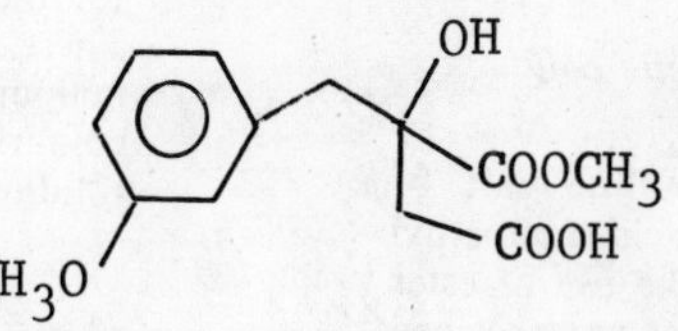

$C_{13}H_{16}O_6$

Ref. 967

23. (S)-(+)- *und* (R)-(−)-*2-(4'-Methoxybenzyl)-äpfelsäure-1-methylester* (**29**) *und* (**30**). Eine heisse Lösung von 400 mg (1,5 mmol) (±)-(4'-Methoxybenzyl)-äpfelsäure-1-methylester **27** und 570 mg (1,5 mmol) (−)-Chinin in 5 ml Aceton wurde langsam erkalten gelassen, dabei gelegentlich beimpft und 5 Std. nach Eintreten der Kristallisation die Mutterlauge abpipettiert.

a) Optisch reines **29**: 7maliges Umkristallisieren von 460 mg Erstkristallisat aus Aceton ergaben 115 mg **28** als farblosen Wollfilz vom Smp. 140–141°; $[\alpha]_D^{24} = -87° \pm 2°$ (*c* = 1,02, Methanol). – IR. (KBr): u.a. Banden bei 3400 (OH, NH; assoz., breit); 2950; 2840 (OCH_3); 1370 (C=O, Methylester); 1615 (arom.); 1590 (C=O, Carboxyl); 1510 (arom.); 1245; 1035 und 830 cm^{-1}.

$C_{33}H_{40}N_2O_8$ (592) Ber. C 66,87 H 6,80% Gef. C 68,35 H 7,07%

Lösen in Äther, Extraktion der Base mit 2N Salzsäure, Trocknen und Eindampfen lieferte nach 2maligem Umkristallisieren aus Benzol/Hexan 35 mg **28** in farblosen Nadeln vom Smp. 85–86°; $[\alpha]_D^{24} = +31° \pm 2°$ (*c* = 1,71, Chloroform) (vgl. auch unter *b*).

b) Angereicherte Präparate **29** und **30** am Beispiel von **30**: Aus einer Lösung von 510 mg Säure-Basen-Gemisch aus der Mutterlauge der Erstkristallisation in Äther resultierten nach Ausschütteln mit 2N Salzsäure, Neutralwaschen, Trocknen und Eindampfen 228 mg eines gelblichen Öls mit $[\alpha]_D^{24} = -14° \pm 2°$ (*c* = 2,30, Chloroform), was einer optischen Anreicherung von 45% entspricht. Umkristallisieren aus Benzol lieferte 115 mg farblose Kristalle mit $[\alpha]_D^{24} = -8° \pm 2°$ (*c* = 1,54, Chloroform) und 153 mg Mutterlauge mit $[\alpha]_D^{24} = -27° \pm 2°$ (*c* = 1,53, Chloroform), aus der durch Kristallisation keine weitere Anreicherung mehr möglich war. Umkristallisieren der Mutterlauge aus Benzol/Hexan ergab 114 mg **30** in farblosen Nadeln vom Smp. 85–86°; $[\alpha]_D^{24} = -27° \pm 2°$ (*c* = 1,32, Chloroform) (optische Reinheit *ca.* 85%). – IR. (KBr): u.a. Banden bei 3500 (OH); 3150 (OH, Carboxyl); 1735; 1720 (C=O); 1612, 1585, 1512 (arom.); 1210; 1115; 1025; 955 und 930 cm^{-1}.

$C_{13}H_{16}O_6$ (268) Ber. C 58,20 H 6,01% Gef. C 58,35 H 6,04% (**29**)
Gef. C 58,44 H 5,99% (**30**)

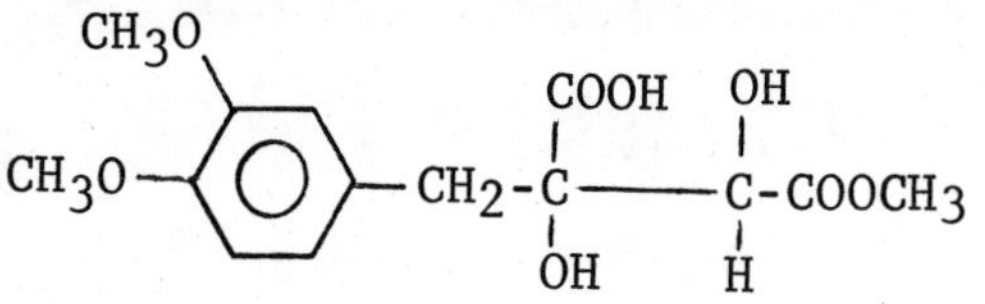

$C_{13}H_{16}O_8$

Ref. 968

Resolution of (±)-VIIb with Brucine. *a)*: Brucine dihydrate (595 mg) was dissolved in a hot solution of (±)-VIIb (433 mg) in methanol (8.0 m*l*), after which the solution was allowed to stand at room temperature. The precipitates were collected, washed with acetone, and then recrystallized from methanol to give colorless crystals; mp 185—186°C dec.; yield, 490 mg. A mixed-melting-point determination with (±)-VIIb (mp 185—186°C) showed 175—178°C.

Found: C, 61.15; H, 6.13; N, 3.81%. Calcd for $C_{37}H_{44}O_{12}N_2 \cdot H_2O$: C, 61.00; H, 6.38; N, 3.86%.

A suspension of the above brucine salt (255 mg) in dilute hydrochloric acid (2N: 5.0 m*l*) was extracted with ethyl acetate. The extract was washed with water, dried over sodium sulfate, and then evaporated under a vacuum. The residue (132 mg) was recrystallized from a mixture of acetone and petroleum ether to give (+)-VIIb as colorless crystals; mp 138—139°C, $[\alpha]_D^{25}+40.8°$ (*c* 1.25, methanol); yield, 114 mg.

Found: C, 50.82; H, 6.20%. Calcd for $C_{14}H_{18}O_8 \cdot H_2O$: C, 50.60; H, 6.07%.

b): The mother liquor in *a)*, after the separation of the brucine salt (490 mg: mp 185—186°C dec.), was evaporated under a vacuum. The residue was suspended in dilute hydrochloric acid (2N: 5.0 m*l*) and then treated by a method similar to that used for (+)-VIIb. The crude product was recrystallized from a mixture of acetone and petroleum ether to give (−)-VIIb as colorless crystals; mp 138—139°C, $[\alpha]_D^{25}-38.0°$ (*c* 0.72, methanol); yield, 104 mg.

Found: C, 50.68; H, 5.98%. Calcd for $C_{14}H_{18}O_8 \cdot H_2O$: C, 50.60; H, 6.07%.

Hydrolyses of (+)-VIIb and (−)-VIIb. *a)*: (+)-VIIb (245 mg) was hydrolyzed with aqueous potassium hydroxide (5%: 3.0 m*l*) by a method similar to that used for (±)-VIb. The crude product was recrystallized from a mixture of acetone and petroleum ether to give (+)-VIb as colorless crystals; mp 104—106°C, $[\alpha]_D^{25}+40.3°$ (*c* 0.72, methanol); yield, 124 mg.

Found: C, 49.18; H, 5.75%. Calcd for $C_{13}H_{16}O_8 \cdot H_2O$: C, 49.06; H, 5.70%.

b): Similarly, (−)-VIIb was also hydrolyzed to (−)-VIb; mp 104—106°C, $[\alpha]_D^{25}-40.5°$ (*c* 0.79, methanol).

Found: C, 49.27; H, 5.81%. Calcd for $C_{13}H_{16}O_8 \cdot H_2O$: C, 49.06; H, 5.70%.

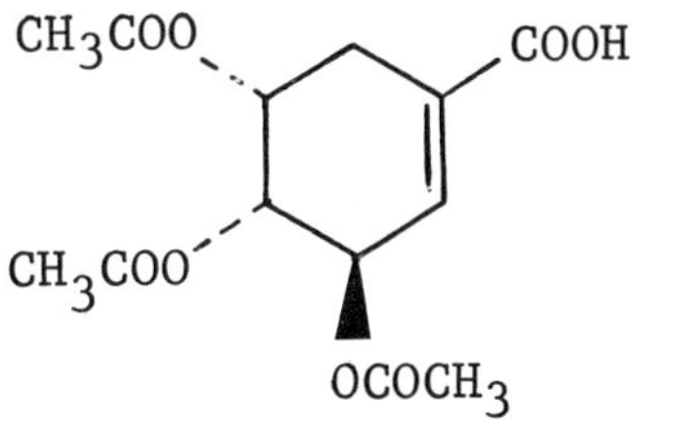

Ref. 969

$C_{13}H_{16}O_8$

(−)- bzw. (+)-Triacetyl-4-epishikimisäure-methylester (**2d**): Eine Lösung von 1.40 g *Triacetyl-4-epishikimisäure* (**2c**) in 100 ccm Äther wird mit der äquiv. Menge (0.56 g) *(−)-α-Phenyl-äthylamin* versetzt. Das abgeschiedene Salz wird mehrmals aus Essigester bis zum konstanten Drehwert umkristallisiert. Man erhält 0.5 g Substanz (50%) vom Schmp. 172 bis 173°; $[\alpha]_D^{20}$: −112° (*c* = 1, Methanol).

$C_8H_{12}N]C_{13}H_{15}O_8$ (421.4) Ber. C 59.85 H 6.46 N 3.32 Gef. C 60.04 H 6.35 N 3.37

Die Mutterlauge wird eingedampft, der Rückstand in wäßr. Methanol gelöst und über einen Kationenaustauscher (Amberlite IR 120) gegeben. Die zurückgewonnene Säure wird in gleicher Weise wie oben mit *(+)-α-Phenyl-äthylamin* umgesetzt. Man erhält 0.5 g Substanz (50%) vom Schmp. 172—173°; $[\alpha]_D^{20}$: +111° (*c* = 1, Methanol).

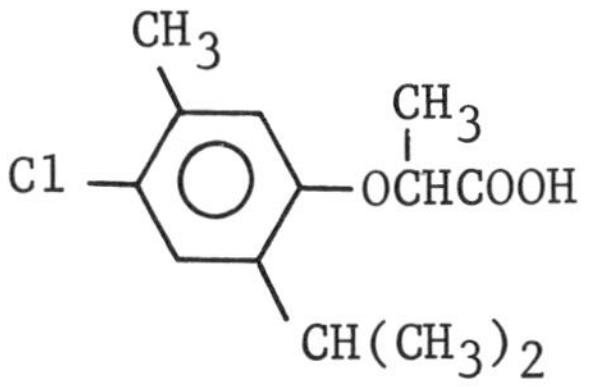

0.2102 g dissolved in abs. *ethanol* to 20.06 ml: $2\alpha_D^{25}$ = + 0.489°. $[\alpha]_D^{25}$ = + 23.3°; $[M]_D^{25}$ = + 59.9°.
0.2083 g dissolved in *acetone* to 20.06 ml: $2\alpha_D^{25}$ = + 0.622°. $[\alpha]_D^{25}$ = + 30.0°; $[M]_D^{25}$ = + 76.9°.
0.2188 g dissolved in *chloroform* to 20.06 ml: $2\alpha_D^{25}$ = + 0.440°. $[\alpha]_D^{25}$ = + 20.2°; $[M]_D^{25}$ = + 51.8°.
0.2146 g dissolved in *benzene* to 20.06 ml: $2\alpha_D^{25}$ = − 0.021°. $[\alpha]_D^{25}$ = − 1.0°; $[M]_D^{25}$ = − 2.5°.
0.2184 g neutralized with *aqueous NaOH* and made up to 20.06 ml: $2\alpha_D^{25}$ = + 0.133°. $[\alpha]_D^{25}$ = + 6.1°; $[M]_D^{25}$ = + 15.7°.

$C_{13}H_{17}ClO_3$ Ref. 970

(−)-α-(2-isoPropyl-4-chloro-5-methylphenoxy)propionic acid. — Equimolecular quantities of racemic acid (17.7 g, 0.69 mole) and cinchonidine (20.3 g) were dissolved in a hot mixture of 700 ml acetone and 850 ml water. After some hours the salt was collected and the activity of the acid determined in the usual way. The salt was recrystallized according to Table 3.

Table 3. Recrystallization of the cinchonidine salt of α-(2-*iso*propyl-4-chloro-5-methylphenoxy)propionic acid.

Cryst. no.	Solvent (ml)		Yield of salt (%)	$[\alpha]_D$ of the acid
	Acetone	Water		
1	700	850	47	−13.8°
2	300	100	32	−23.6°
3	200	50	29	−23.6°
4	150	25	23	−23.2°

From the salt fraction 4, 4.4 g crude (−)-acid were isolated. It was recrystallized from 85% formic acid. The pure acid (3.5 g) melted at 83–84.7°.

89.64 mg acid: 6.71_8 ml 0.0522_4N NaOH
$C_{13}H_{17}O_3Cl$ calc. equiv. wt. 256.7
found ,, ,, 255.5

0.2170 g dissolved in abs. *ethanol* to 20.06 ml: $2\alpha_D^{25}$ = − 0.496°. $[\alpha]_D^{25}$ = − 22.9°; $[M]_D^{25}$ = − 58.9°.

(+)-α-(2-isoPropyl-4-chloro-5-methylphenoxy)propionic acid.—8.9 g acid with $[\alpha]_D$ = + 17° and an equivalent quantity of .norphine (10.6 g) were dissolved in a hot mixture of 75 ml ethanol and 200 ml water. After cooling crystallization was initiated by seeding with crystals from a preliminary experiment and the salt was allowed to crystallize over night. The purification of the salt was performed as seen from Table 4.

Table 4. Recrystallization of the morphine salt of α-(2-*iso*propyl-4-chloro-5-methylphenoxy)propionic acid.

Cryst. no.	Solvent (ml)		Yield of salt %	$[\alpha]_D$ of the said
	Ethanol	Water		
1	75	200	88	+ 20.5°
2	50	200	79	+ 22.4°
3	30	100	75	+ 21.3°
4	40	125	72	+ 21.4°
5	50	130	66	+ 22.7°

The crude acid obtained from the last salt fraction was recrystallized from 85% formic acid yielding 4.5 g pure (+)-acid, m.p. 83–84.5°.

88.34 mg acid: 6.59_5 ml 0.0522_4N NaOH
$C_{13}H_{17}O_3Cl$ calc. equiv. wt. 256.7
found ,, ,, 256.4

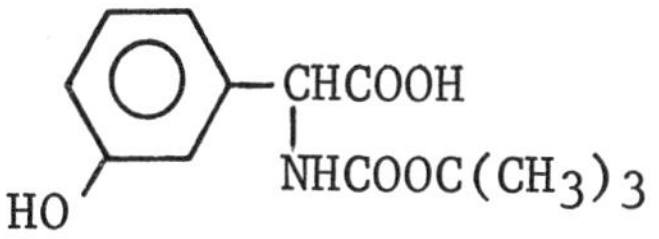

$C_{13}H_{17}NO_5$ Ref. 971

EXAMPLE

A solution of 10.5 g. (0.039 mole) of DL-2-t-butoxycarboxamido-2-(3-hydroxyphenyl)acetic acid and 11.6 g. (0.039 mole) of cinchonine was prepared in 100 ml. of warm ethyl acetate. After cooling overnight the crystalline solid was collected and washed with ethyl acetate. This solid was the cinchonine salt of the L isomer and had a melting point above 190° C. The filtrate, which contained the D isomer, was treated with dilute hydrochloric acid to obtain the free acid. After removal of solvent, 4.6 g. of noncrystalline oil was obtained. This partially resolved acid (0.017 mole) and 5.4 g. (0.017 mole) of quinine were dissolved in 150 ml. of ethyl acetate. After overnight cooling the crystalline quinine salt was collected and recrystallized from 125 ml. of ethyl acetate yielding 6.8 g. of D-2-t-butoxycarboxamido-2-(3-hydroxyphenyl) acetic acid quinine salt. The salt was treated with dilute hydrochloric acid and extracted with ethyl acetate yielding, after evaporation, 2.5 g. of the noncrystalline D isomer, [α]D=−129°.

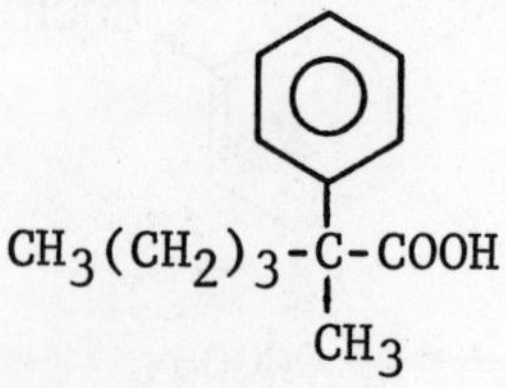

$C_{13}H_{18}O_2$ Ref. 972

d-α-Methyl-α-phenylcaproic Acid.—Ten grams of methylphenylcaproic acid and 16 g. of quinine were dissolved in 75 cc. of hot alcohol and filtered. The filtrate was diluted with water until turbid and sufficient alcohol then added until the solution became clear. After three crystallizations the salt was decomposed by dilute sulfuric acid. The free acid gave the following value for the specific rotation in alcohol solution

$$[\alpha]_{5461} = 13.65° = \frac{0.70° \times 100}{2 \times 2.559}$$

To determine whether the ease of resolution was greater with some other alkaloid, 10 g. of the acid and 14.3 g. of cinchonidine were dissolved in 100 cc. of hot alcohol and the solution filtered. The filtrate was diluted with water and set aside to crystallize. After three crystallizations the salt was decomposed with dilute hydrochloric acid. The free acid in this case gave a slightly lower specific rotation in alcohol solution.

$$[\alpha]_{5461} = 10.68° = \frac{0.26° \times 100}{2 \times 1.219}$$

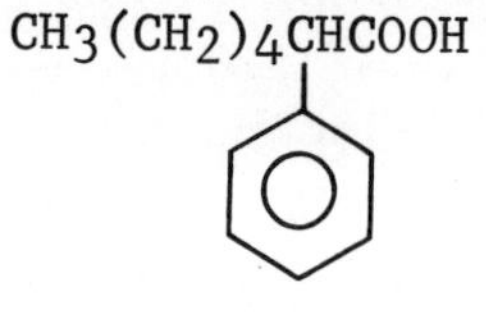

$C_{13}H_{18}O_2$ Ref. 973

(−)-α-*Phenylethylamine* (+)-α-*phenylheptanoate:* 20.6 g (0.1 mole) of racemic phenyloenantic acid and 12.1 g (0.1 mole) of (−)-α-phenylethylamine were dissolved in hot ethanol and the solution allowed to cool. The salt obtained was recrystallised from ethanol and the resolution followed as described for phenylvaleric acid. The optically pure salt was obtained as long, colourless needles. Table 10 shows the result of the resolution.

(+)-α-*Phenylethylamine* (−)-α-*phenylheptanoate:* The mother liquor from the first crystallisation of the (+)-acid salt was evaporated to dryness and the acid isolated and converted to the (+)-α-phenylethylamine salt as described for the (−)-phenylcaproic acid. The salt was recrystallised and the resolution followed in the usual manner. The results are collected in Table 10.

Table 10.

Crystallisation number	(+)-(III)		(−)-(III)	
	g of salt obtained	$[\alpha]_D^{25}$	g of salt obtained	$[\alpha]_D^{25}$
1	17	+33°	13	−34°
2	15	+43°	11	−53°
3	14	+55°	9.0	−58°
4	12	+59°	7.6	−59°
5	11	+60°	6.5	−60°
6	10	+60°	6.0	−59°

(+)-α-*Phenyloenantic acid:* From the (−)-phenylethylamine salt as described for the other antipodes. Colourless, highly viscous oil.

108.2 mg of the acid consumed 6.78 ml of 0.0776*N* NaOH.

$C_{13}H_{18}O_2$: Equiv. weight calc. 206.2 found 205.7.

96.7 mg of the acid was dissolved in absolute ethanol and made up to a volume of 10.00 ml. $2\alpha_D^{25} = +1.162°$ $[\alpha]_D^{25} = +60.2°$ $[M]_D^{25} = +124.1°$.

(−)-α-*Phenyloenantic acid:* Colourless, highly viscous oil, obtained from the (+)-α-phenylethylamine salt in the same manner as described for the other antipodes.

96.1 mg of the acid consumed 6.02 ml of 0.0776*N* NaOH.

$C_{14}H_{18}O_2$: Equiv. weight calc. 206.2 found 205.7.

Optical activity in homogenus state: $[\alpha]_D^{20} = -65.8°$ $[M]_D^{20} = -135.8°$.

Optical activities in different solvents (*vide ante*) are collected in Table 13.

Table 13.

Solvent	mg of acid	$2\alpha_D^{25}$	$[\alpha]_D^{25}$	$[M]_D^{25}$
Acetone	91.1	−1.416°	−77.7°	−160.3°
Benzene	80.3	−1.152°	−71.7°	−147.9°
Acetic acid	93.8	−1.218°	−64.9°	−133.9°
Ether	84.0	−1.007°	−59.9°	−123.6°
Ethanol	106.1	−1.253°	−59.1°	−121.8°
Water (ion)	96.1	−0.177°	− 9.2°	− 19.1°

Amide: Colourless waxy crystals. M.p. 106°–108°.

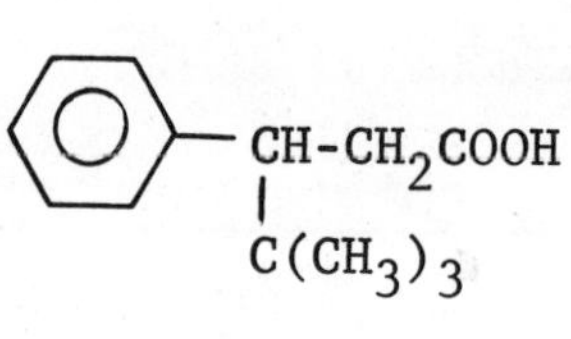

$C_{13}H_{18}O_2$ Ref. 974

Resolution of (+)- and (−)-3-*t*-Butylhydrocinnamic Acid ((+)- and (−)-V-*h*). The brucine salt of the acid was obtained by dissolving 18.5 g of racemic 3-*t*-butylhydrocinnamic acid[6] (mp 114–116°) and 42.0 g of brucine in 140 ml of hot methanol. The solution was cooled slowly to −20° for 48 hr and 17.0 g of salt was collected and recrystallized. The amounts of salt recovered at different stages of the resolution and the rotations of the corresponding acids were: first crystallization, 17 g, $[\alpha]^{25}_{546}$ +15.9°; third, 8.3 g, $[\alpha]^{25}_{546}$ +17.3°; fourth, 4.0 g, $[\alpha]^{25}_{546}$ +24.3°; fifth, 1.7 g, $[\alpha]^{25}_{546}$ +24.5° (*c* 2, $CHCl_3$, all rotations). A small amount of the fifth crop was again recrystallized from methanol, with no improvement in the rotation of the corresponding acid. The fifth crop was then hydrolyzed under the same procedure used for 3-phenylbutyric acid. The free acid was then recrystallized twice from cyclohexane to give the optically pure acid, $[\alpha]^{25}_{546}$ +26.0°, $[\alpha]^{25}_{589}$ +22.2° (*c* 2, $CHCl_3$), mp 94.5–95.0°. Further crystallization from cyclohexane failed to improve the rotation or the melting point.

The (−)-enantiomer of 3-*t*-butylhydrocinnamic acid, (−)-V-*h*, was obtained from its cinchonidine salt. Mother liquors from the brucine resolution were hydrolyzed, and the partially active (−)-acid was dissolved with an equimolar amount of cinchonidine. The progress of the resolution was followed as before. The fifth crystallization yielded a salt whose melting point (161–161.5°) was no higher than that of the fourth. The salt was then hydrolyzed, and the corresponding acid, $[\alpha]^{25}_{546}$ −24.1° (*c* 2, $CHCl_3$), was crystallized twice from cyclohexane, $[\alpha]^{25}_{546}$ −26.4° and $[\alpha]^{25}_{589}$ −22.4° (*c* 2, $CHCl_3$), mp 94.5–95.5°.

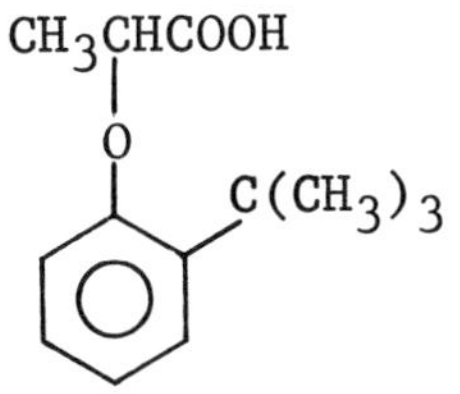

$C_{13}H_{18}O_3$ Ref. 975

Preliminary experiments on resolution were carried out with the common bases in various solvents (ethanol–water, methanol–water, acetone–water, ethyl acetate, benzene, benzene–ligroin). Strychnine in acetone–water and ephedrine in benzene gave (−)-acid of high activity. Dehydroabietylamine gave (+)-acid of very low activity. Cinchonidine in benzene–ligroine gave (+)-acid of moderate activity. The salts of brucine, quinine and phenyl-isopropylamine contained racemic acid. The salts of cinchonine, quinidine, α-phenyl-ethylamine and α-(2-naphthyl)-ethylamine failed to crystallise.

(−)-2-tert-Butylphenoxy-propionic acid. 22.2 g (0.1 mole) acid and 33.4 g (0.1 mole) strychnine were dissolved with gentle heating in 180 ml acetone + 180 ml water. After cooling, the solution was seeded with crystals from a preliminary experiment. The salt was filtered off after 2 days at room temperature and recrystallized from dilute acetone to constant activity of the acid (liberated from small samples of salt after each crystallization. See Table II).

Table II. *Recrystallization of the strychnine salt*

Crystallization	1	2	3	4
ml acetone	180	40	33	27
ml water	180	40	33	27
g salt obtained	16.6	13.5	11.6	9.4
$[\alpha]_D^{25}$ of the acid	−50.5°	−53.5°	−55.5°	−55.5°

The mother liquor from the first crystallisation was left to stand for 24 h at +5°C. The salt that separated was recrystallized once from dilute acetone and then from the successive mother liquors after the first series of crystallization yielding 3.0 g salt of maximum activity.

The salt was decomposed with sodium carbonate solution and the strychnine extracted with chloroform. Since it was found that part of the acid followed the strychnine, the chloroform phase was extracted several times with sodium carbonate solutions. The combined aqueous solutions were then acidified with excess sulphuric acid and the organic acid extracted with ether.

The strychnine salt (12.4 g) gave 4.1 g of crude acid. It was dissolved in petroleum ether at room temperature; on standing at −15°C the acid separated as short-prismatic crystals. The yield after two recrystallizations was 3.35 g. M.p. 70.5–71.5°C. [Found: equiv. wt. 222.5. Calc. for $C_{13}H_{18}O_3$: 222.27.] The rotatory power in different solvents is given in Table III.

Table III. *Optical activity data for the (−)-2-tert-butylphenoxy-propionic acid in different solvents*

g = g acid dissolved to 10.00 ml solution

Solvent	g	α_D^{25}(1 dm)	$[\alpha]_D^{25}$	$[M]_D^{25}$
Acetone	0.11532	−0.042°	−3.7°	−8.1°
Ethanol	0.10412	−0.061°	−5.9°	−13.0°
Methanol	0.07943	−0.057°	−7.2°	−15.9°
Chloroform	0.11892	+0.045°	+3.8°	+8.4°
Benzene	0.11948	−0.670°	−56.0°	−124.0°

(+)-2-tert-Butylphenoxy-propionic acid. On working up the mother liquors from the strychnine salt it was found that the diastereomeric salts had clearly different crystal habit: the salt of the (−)-acid forms needles, that of the (+)-form glistening scales or flakes. Fractionation using this criterion gave (+)-acid of rather high activity. It was also possible to utilise the different solubility of racemic and active acid in petroleum ether, where the active form is far more soluble, but none of these methods is practicable for preparing the optically pure (+)-acid in reasonable quantities. The best method was recrystallization of the cinchonidine salt from benzene + ligroine. 1.7 g (0.0077 mole) acid having $[\alpha]_D^{25} = +53°$ and 2.3 g (0.0077 mole) cinchonidine were dissolved with heating in 13 ml benzene + 9 ml ligroin. The salt was recrystallized twice (Table IV).

Table IV. *Recrystallization of the cinchonidine salt*

Crystallization	1	2	3
ml benzene	13	13	9.5
ml ligroin	9	9	6.5
g salt obtained	3.8	3.5	3.2
$[\alpha]_D^{25}$ of the acid	+53.8°	+54.5°	+54.5°

The salt (3.2 g) yielded 1.2 g crude acid: two recrystallizations from petroleum ether at −15°C gave 0.7 g pure acid, quite similar to the enantiomer. M.p. 70.5–71.5°C. [Found: equiv. wt. 222.2. Calc. for $C_{13}H_{18}O_3$: 222.27.] $[\alpha]_D^{25} = +56.0°$; $[M]_D^{25} = 124.0°$ (0.10986 g dissolved in benzene to 10.00 ml).

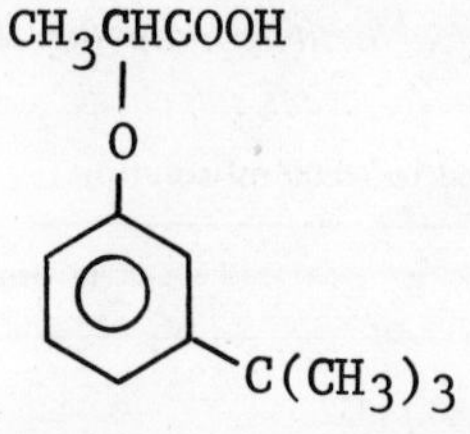

$C_{13}H_{18}O_3$ Ref. 976

In the preliminary experiments on resolution, several of the common alkaloids were tested. Brucine gave a good yield of a salt containing rather pure laevorotatory acid. From the cinchonidine salt, a dextrorotatory acid of somewhat lower activity was isolated. Other bases were less effective.

(−)-*3-tert.Butyl-phenoxypropionic acid*. 27.8 g (0.125 mole) racemic acid and 49.3 g (0.125 mole) anhydrous brucine were dissolved in 350 ml ethanol and 100 ml water. To the warm, clear solution 100 ml water was added. After seeding, the mixture was left at room temperature over night and then placed in a refrigerator for two hours. The salt was recrystallized to maximum activity of the acid, the rotatory power of which was determined on a small amount after each crystallization.

Crystallization	1	2	3	4	5
ml ethanol	350	150	130	115	100
ml water	200	90	75	55	55
g salt obtained	34.2	31.6	29.0	25.6	22.8
$[\alpha]_D^{25}$ of acid (in acetone)	−33°	−34°	—	−35.5°	−34.5°

The organic acid liberated by decomposing the brucine salt with dilute sulphuric acid was extracted with ether. After evaporation of the dried ethereal solution, 7.3 g of readily crystallizing oil was obtained. The enantiomorph is distinctly more soluble in ordinary solvents than the racemic acid and was recrystallized from 20 ml petroleum ether (b.p. 30–60°). Upon chilling the solution in an ice-salt mixture, the acid separated as colourless needles. The yield of product with m.p. 56.5–58° was 6.8 g (49 %).

0.09691 g acid: 8.92 ml 0.0489 *N* NaOH.
$C_{13}H_{18}O_3$ Equiv. wt calc. 222.3 found 222.2
0.19541 g dissolved in acetone to 10.00 ml:
$\alpha_D^{25} = -0.690°$ (1 dm); $[\alpha]_D^{25} = -35.3°$; $[M]_D^{25} = -78.5°$

(+)-*3-tert.Butyl-phenoxypropionic acid*. The mother liquor containing the brucine salt of the dextrorotatory acid was evaporated. From the remaining syrup, the acid was isolated as above giving 15.3 g of an oily product with the specific rotation $[\alpha]_D^{25} = +23°$ in acetone solution. This amount of crude acid (0.069 mole) and 20.2 g (0.069 mole) of cinchonidine were then dissolved in a mixture of 200 ml ethanol and 100 ml water. Upon cooling, the salt crystallized in extremely thin needles producing crystal aggregates not unlike cotton wool. The mixture was left at room temperature over night and placed in a refrigerator some hours before filtering. The salt obtained was recrystallized as above until constant rotatory power of the acid was attained.

Crystallization	1	2	3	4	5
ml ethanol	200	50	25	30	40
ml water	100	25	13	22	35
g salt obtained	28.8	25.0	23.9	23.5	23.2
$[\alpha]_D^{25}$ of acid (in acetone)	+32°	+34.5°	+35°	—	+34.5°

The acid is thus almost pure after only two crystallizations. The salt was decomposed with dilute sulphuric acid and the oily organic acid extracted with ether. After evaporation of the solvent, the remaining product was recrystallized from 25 ml petroleum ether, from which it was obtained as thin colourless needles with m.p. 56.5–58°. The yield was 8.7 g (63 %).

0.08370 g acid: 7.71 ml 0.0489 *N* NaOH.
$C_{13}H_{18}O_3$ Equiv. wt calc. 222.3 found 222.0
0.19845 g dissolved in acetone to 10.00 ml:
$\alpha_D^{25} = +0.701°$ (1 dm); $[\alpha]_D^{25} = +35.3°$; $[M]_D^{25} = +78.5°$

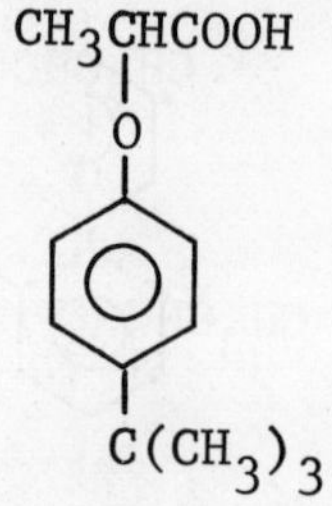

$C_{13}H_{18}O_3$ Ref. 977

In the preliminary experiments on resolution, strychnine and quinidine formed salts with laevorotatory acid of high activity, though the yield of the quinidine salt was rather low. Of the common bases tested, only dehydroabiethylamine in the form of its acetate was found to give a salt containing the dextrorotatory acid. An analogous experiment with the liberated amine however yielded a salt of nearly inactive acid.

(−)-*4-tert.Butyl-phenoxypropionic acid*. 33.4 g (0.15 mole) of racemic acid and 50.2 g (0.15 mole) of strychnine were dissolved in 400 ml ethanol and 300 ml water. After cooling, the solution was seeded and left at room temperature until next day. The mixture was then placed in a refrigerator some hours before filtering. Since the yield of salt was only about 70 % of the theoretical, the volume of the mother liquor was reduced to about three quarters, thus giving a further crop of crystals. The salt was recrystallized until optically pure as described above for the 3-tert.butyl acid.

Crystallization	1	2	3	4	5
ml ethanol	400	120	85	60	50
ml water	300	80	65	40	35
g salt obtained	34.5	30.3	28.5	26.8	25.8
$[\alpha]_D^{25}$ of acid (in acetone)	—	−49.5°	−50.5°	−50.5°	—

The salt was treated with sodium carbonate solution and the strychnine extracted with chloroform. The alkaline solution was acidified with dilute sulphuric acid, whereupon the organic acid separated as a colourless oil and was extracted with ether. Upon recrystallization from petroleum ether, the active acid formed large prismatic crystals of m.p. 57.5–58.5°. The yield was 8.7 g (52 %).

0.08446 g acid: 7.76 ml 0.0489 *N* NaOH.
$C_{13}H_{18}O_3$ Equiv. wt calc. 222.3 found 222.6
0.24461 g dissolved in acetone to 10.00 ml:
$\alpha_D^{25} = -1.220°$ (1 dm); $[\alpha]_D^{25} = -49.9°$; $[M]_D^{25} = -110.9°$

(+)-*4-tert.Butyl-phenoxypropionic acid*. The mother liquor remaining after filtration of the strychnine salt of laevorotatory acid was evaporated to dryness. From the salt obtained, 15.2 g of crude dextrorotatory acid was isolated ($[\alpha]_D^{25} = +28°$ in acetone). This acid (0.068 mole) was dissolved with 23.5 g (0.068 mole) of dehydroabiethylamine acetate in 300 ml ethanol and 150 ml water. The flask was insulated to attain very slow cooling, since the salt otherwise tended to crystallize too quickly to bring about a resolution. As before, the salt was recrystallized until constant optical activity of the acid was attained. However, as this increased rather slowly, polarimetric measurements were performed only after every second crystallization.

Crystallization	1	2	3	5	7
ml ethanol	300	250	265	150	150
ml water	150	90	80	30	30
g salt obtained	26.6	20.0	16.2	14.6	12.8
$[\alpha]_D^{25}$ of acid (in acetone)	—	—	+47°	+48°	+48.5°

The salt was decomposed in the same way as the strychnine salt of the (−)-acid. After recrystallization from petroleum ether, the acid was obtained as small colourless prisms of m.p. 57.5–58.5°. The yield of pure product was 4.9 g (29 %).

0.09490 g acid: 8.73 ml 0.0489 *N* NaOH.
$C_{13}H_{18}O_3$ Equiv. wt calc. 222.3 found 222.3
0.24132 g dissolved in acetone to 10.00 ml:
$\alpha_D^{25} = +1.207°$ (1 dm); $[\alpha]_D^{25} = +50.0°$; $[M]_D^{25} = +111.1°$

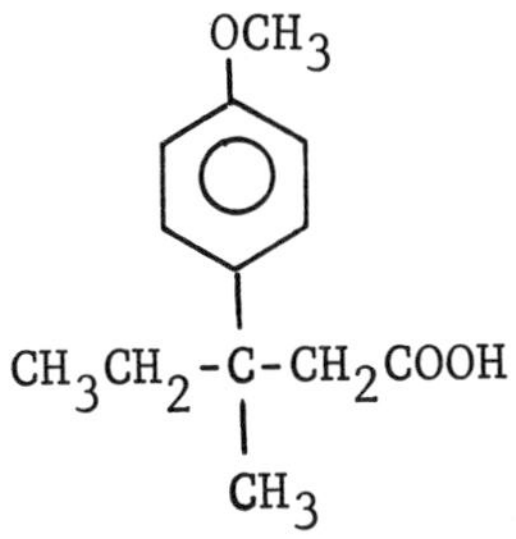

$C_{13}H_{18}O_3$ Ref. 978

Resolution of 3-(*p*-Methoxyphenyl)-3-methylpentanoic Acid. Racemic 3-(*p*-methoxyphenyl)-3-methylpentanoic acid (2.87 g, 12.9 mmol) was dissolved in 30 mL of hot hexane and a minimum amount of chloroform. To the warm solution was added 1.56 g (12.9 mmol) of (−)-1-phenylethylamine and a crystalline solid precipitated upon cooling. The solid was isolated by suction filtration and gave 1.92 g (8.6 mmol) of long colorless needles. Three successive recrystallizations from the same solvent system yielded 450 mg of this solid. The solid was treated with 3 N sodium hydroxide, and the resulting solution was washed with ether. The aqueous layer was then acidified to methyl orange end point with 6 N hydrocyloric acid and ether extracted. The extract was dried and the solvent removed in vacuo to afford 290 mg (1.29 mmol, 20%) of the (−)-3-(*p*-methoxyphenyl)-3-methylpentanoic acid, $[\alpha]_D^{25}$ −19.4° (*c* 0.0152, $CHCl_3$), mp 94–95 °C. Recrystallization of the acid from chloroform–hexane changed neither the specific rotation nor the melting point. The specific rotation was also not affected by formation of the amine salt (with (−)-1-phenylethylamine) and recrystallization. The specific rotations were (λ in parentheses): −19.4 ± 0.2° (589), −20.3 ± 0.2° (578), −23.7 ± 0.3° (546), −45.8 ± 0.5° (436), and −86.7 ± 0.9° (365) (*c* 0.0152, $CHCl_3$).

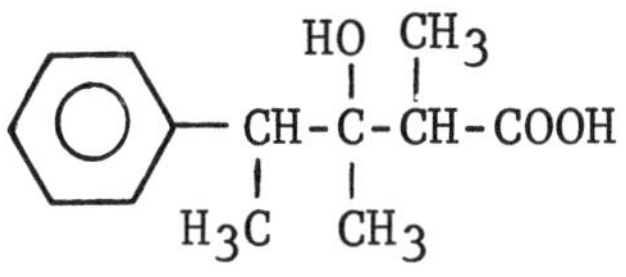

$C_{13}H_{18}O_3$ Ref. 979

Resolved by means of cinchonidine. The diastereomeric salt of m.p. 188-189°, $[\alpha]_D$ -81° (ethanol) was decomposed with dilute hydrochloric acid to give the acid $[\alpha]_D$ -41° ($CHCl_3$).

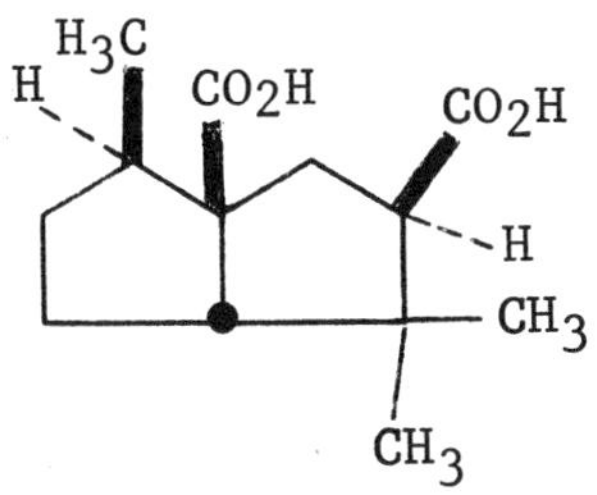

$C_{13}H_{20}O_4$ Ref. 980

Resolution of *dl*-Norcedrenedicarboxylic Acid.—To a hot solution of 410 mg. (1.0 equiv.) of quinine in acetone was added a solution of 300 mg. of *dl*-norcedrenedicarboxylic acid in acetone. No precipitate appeared when the stoppered flask was allowed to stand at room temperature for 24 hours, but when the flask was left open to permit slow evaporation of the solvent colorless crystals formed and were collected after one day. This first crop, m.p. 204–206°, weighed 156 mg. Concentration of the mother liquor and seeding with the first crop gave more crystals. There was obtained a total of 252 mg. (71% of theory) which melted above 204°. One recrystallization from chloroform–acetone gave 210 mg., m.p. 209–210°, $[\alpha]^{27}D$ −123° (*c* 1.04, chloroform). One more recrystallization from chloroform–acetone did not change the melting point or rotation and there was no depression of the melting point of the mixture with the quinine salt of natural norcedrenedicarboxylic acid, m.p. 209–210°, $[\alpha]^{27}D$ −122° (*c* 1.00, chloroform).

Anal. Calcd. for $C_{33}H_{44}O_6N_2$: C, 70.18; H, 7.85. Found: C, 70.13; H, 8.18.

To obtain the free acid, the quinine salt (121 mg.) was shaken for 15 minutes with 5 ml. of 6 *N* hydrochloric acid and the solid was collected and washed with 6 *N* hydrochloric acid. The free acid weighed 46 mg. (89% yield), m.p. 212–213°. One recrystallization from ether–pentane did not change the melting point and the mixture melting point with natural norcedrenedicarboxylic acid (m.p. 213–214°[14]) was not depressed. The optical rotation of the resolved diacid in acetone solution, $[\alpha]^{27}D$ −38.9 ± 1.5° (*c* 1.08), is the same as the rotation of the natural (−)-norcedrenedicarboxylic acid, $[\alpha]^{27}D$ −38.3 ± 1.0° (*c* 1.09), in acetone.[14]

(14) Norcedrenedicarboxylic acid from natural (+) cedrol is reported to have m.p. 209° and $[\alpha]^{14}D$ −39.4° (in $CHCl_3$); *cf.* ref. 16.

(16) Pl. A. Plattner, G. W. Kusserow and H. Kläui, *Helv. Chim. Acta*, **25**, 1345 (1942).

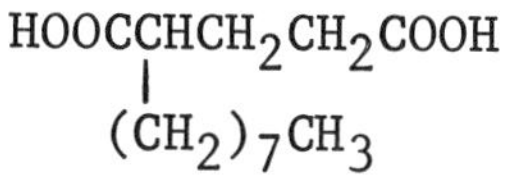

$C_{13}H_{24}O_4$ Ref. 981

Spaltung der racem. α-n-Octyl-glutarsäure. Vorproben mit Cinchonin, Brucin, Strychnin und Chinin ergaben, daß das Strychnin zur Spaltung der Octyl-glutarsäure am besten geeignet ist, da es ein gut krystallisierendes Salz mit der Säure bildet.

1,22 g der Octyl-glutarsäure wurde mit 1,67 g Strychnin gemischt und in 50 ccm heißem Alkohol gelöst. Da das entstandene Salz in Alkohol ziemlich gut löslich war, wurden durch jeweiligen Zusatz von Wasser in der Wärme bis zur deutlichen Trübung vier verschiedene Fraktionen ausgefällt, deren optische Drehung nur einen geringen Unterschied zeigte. Sie wurden deshalb vereinigt (A) und aus Benzol umkrystallisiert. Die wäßrig-alkoholische Mutterlauge dieser 4 Fraktionen wurde zur Trockne gedampft und der Rückstand aus einem Benzol–Chloroform–Ligroingemisch umkrystallisiert. Hierbei erhielt man eine Spitzenfraktion von fast derselben Drehung wie (A). Beide wurden vereinigt und noch einige Male aus Alkohol–Wasser bis zur konstanten Drehung ($[\alpha]_D^{20}$ = − 28°) umkrystallisiert.

Die Zerlegung des Strychninsalzes geschah mit verdünnter Schwefelsäure und lieferte die linksdrehende α-n-Octyl-glutarsäure vom Schmelzpunkt 48° und der Drehung $[\alpha]_D^{20}$ = − 9° in 1%iger alkoholischer Lösung.

Die rechtsdrehende Komponente wurde nicht isoliert.

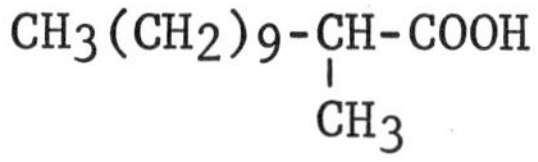

$C_{13}H_{26}O_2$ Ref. 982

Dextro-Methyl-n-Decylacetic Acid—The inactive acid was dissolved in boiling acetone and an equivalent weight of cinchonidine was added. It was allowed to crystallize in a refrigerator at −10°. After ten recrystallizations there was no change in the rotation of the free acid. The total was treated with hydrochloric acid, extracted with ether, purified through its sodium salt, then distilled. B.p. 150° at 1 mm. $D\frac{25}{4}$ = 0.884. n_D^{25} = 1.4395.

$$[\alpha]_D^{25} = \frac{+11.35°}{1 \times 0.884} = +12.85°; [M]_D^{25} = +27.5° \text{ (homogeneous)}$$

4.116 mg. substance: 11.085 mg. CO_2 and 4.555 mg. H_2O

$C_{13}H_{26}O_2$. Calculated. C 72.8, H 12.2

214.2 Found. " 73.4, " 12.4

0.137 gm. substance: 6.46 cc. 0.1 N NaOH (titration, phenolphthalein). Calculated, 6.40 cc.

$CH_3(CH_2)_9$-CHCH$_2$COOH
|
OH

$C_{13}H_{26}O_3$ Ref. 983

2. Resolution of DL-3-Hydroxytridecanoic Acid into Its Enantiomers. a) A solution of 6 g of (–)-α-methylbenzylamine [8] in 50 ml of ether was added slowly to a boiling solution of 11.5 g of DL-3-hydroxytridecanoic acid in 130 ml of ether. The mixture was cooled to –5° and left at this temperature for 10 h. The precipitated salt was filtered off and dissolved in 125 ml of chloroform, 250 ml of dry ether was added, and the solution was left for 3 h at –5°. The precipitate was filtered off and vacuum-dried; we obtained 4.5 g (51%) of the (–)-α-methylbenzylamine salt of (–)-3-hydroxytridecanoic acid (salt 1), mp 66–67° (mixture of chloroform and ether), $[\alpha]_D^{20}$ –17° (c 3, $CHCl_3$). Found %: C 71.53; H 10.63; N 3.85. $C_{21}H_{37}NO_3$. Calculated %: C 71.75; H 10.61; N 3.99.

b) 3.5 g of salt 1 was shaken with 20 ml of 2 N HCl and 30 ml of ether; the ethereal solution was dried with Na_2SO_4 and vacuum-evaporated. We obtained 2.28 g (99%) of (–)-3-hydroxytridecanoic acid, mp 79° (hexane), $[\alpha]_D^{20}$ –15° (c 2, $CHCl_3$). Found %: C 67.93; H 11.39. $C_{13}H_{26}O_3$. Calculated %: C 67.78; H 11.38.

c) The filtrate from the separation of salt 1 was vacuum-evaporated, and 50 ml of water, 10 ml of concentrated hydrochloric acid, and 50 ml of ether were added to the residue. The mixture was shaken, and the ether layer was separated, dried with Na_2SO_4, and evaporated. The residue (5 g), which was DL-3-hydroxytridecanoic acid enriched in the (+) form, was treated with 3 g of (+)-α-methylbenzylamine, and under the conditions of Expt. (a) we obtained 4 g (46%) of the (+)-α-methylbenzylamine salt of (+)-3-hydroxytridecanoic acid (salt 2), mp 66–67° (mixture of chloroform and ether) and $[\alpha]_D^{20}$ +18° (c 3, $CHCl_3$). Found %: C 71.64; H 10.59; N 4.02. $C_{21}H_{37}NO_3$. Calculated %: C 71.75; H 10.61; N 3.99.

d) From 3.5 g of salt 2 under the conditions of Expt. (b) we isolated 2.2 g (95%) of (+)-3-hydroxytridecanoic acid, mp 79° (hexane), $[\alpha]_D^{20}$ +16° (c 2, $CHCl_3$). Found %: C 67.74; H 11.41. $C_{13}H_{26}O_3$. Calculated %: C 67.78; H 11.38.

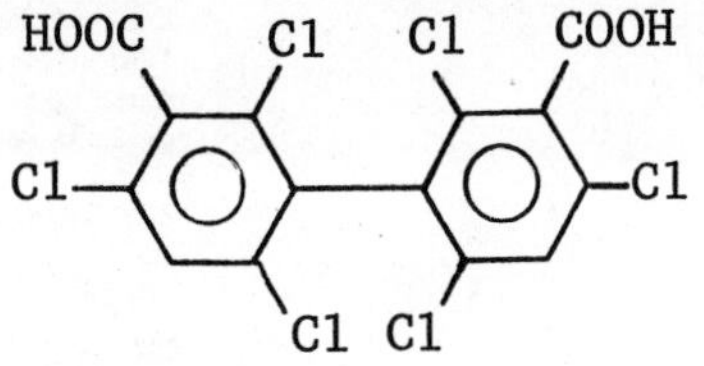

$C_{14}H_4Cl_6O_4$ Ref. 984

Resolution of 2,4,6,2′,4′,6′-Hexachloro-3,3′-dicarboxydiphenyl.—To 450 cc. of anhydrous ethyl acetate containing 5.384 g. (0.0136 mole) of anhydrous *l*-brucine was added 3.0675 g. (0.0068 mole) of hexachlorodicarboxydiphenyl dissolved in 350 cc. of anhydrous ethyl acetate. An immediate precipitate resulted. This was allowed to stand overnight. It was then filtered and washed with a small amount of anhydrous ethyl acetate. The weight of the salt was 3.4 g. melting at 209°.

Rotation. 0.2050 g. made up to 15 cc. with ethyl alcohol (95%) at 25° gave α_D –0.20°; l = 2; $[\alpha]_D^{25}$ –7.3°. The salt was purified by washing with boiling ethyl acetate but with no change in melting point or rotation.

Anal. Calcd. for $C_{60}H_{56}Cl_6N_4O_{12}$: C, 56.66; H, 4.53; Cl, 17.08; N, 4.49. Found: C, 56.93; H, 4.68; Cl, 16.79; N, 4.58.

The mother liquor was evaporated to 100 cc. and allowed to stand overnight. More salt separated. It weighed 1.2 g. The mother liquor was further concentrated *in vacuo* to 50 cc. and allowed to stand overnight. The weight of this last fraction of salt was 3.7 g., m. p. 206–210°.

Rotation. 0.2050 g. made up to 15 cc. with ethyl alcohol (95%) at 25° gave α_D –0.49°; l = 2; $[\alpha]_D^{25}$ –15.5°. The salt was recrystallized from a mixture of ethyl acetate and petroleum ether, melting again at 206–210° and with no change in rotation.

Anal. Calcd. for $C_{60}H_{56}Cl_6N_4O_{12}$: C, 56.66; H, 4.53. Found: C, 57.13; H, 4.74.

***d*-2,4,6,2′,4′,6′-Hexachloro-3,3′-dicarboxydiphenyl.**—The pure dibrucine salt was dissolved in chloroform and shaken with dilute hydrochloric acid several times. The chloroform layer was then separated and shaken with dilute sodium hydroxide. The

sodium hydroxide layer was separated and treated with dilute hydrochloric acid. The acid which precipitated out was filtered off and recrystallized from a mixture of ethyl acetate and petroleum ether. It was found to be brucine-free and melted at 293–294°. Further recrystallization did not change the melting point.

Rotation. 0.4442 g. made up to 15 cc. in ethyl alcohol (95%) at 25° gave α_D +0.10; $l = 2$; $[\alpha]_D^{25}$ +1.7°. The acid was again recrystallized and the rotation taken. 0.3234 g. made up to 15 cc. in ethyl alcohol (95%) at 25° gave α_D +0.08°; $l = 2$; $[\alpha]_D^{25}$ +1.8.

Further recrystallization did not alter the rotation.

Anal. Calcd. for $C_{14}H_4O_4Cl_6$: C, 38.4; H, 0.89. Found: C, 38.79; H, 1.08.

***l*-2,4,6,2',4',6'-Hexachloro-3,3'-dicarboxydiphenyl.**—The more soluble salt was hydrolyzed in a manner similar to the less soluble salt. The acid thus obtained was recrystallized from a mixture of ordinary ethyl acetate and petroleum ether, and melted at 292–293°.

Rotation. 0.4425 g. made up to 15 cc. in ethyl alcohol at 25° gave α_D −0.09°; l = 2; $[\alpha]_D^{25}$ −1.52°.

The acid was recrystallized and the rotation again taken.

0.4204 g. made up to 15 cc. in ethyl alcohol (95%) gave α_D 0.096°; $l = 2$; $[\alpha]_D^{25}$ −1.7°.

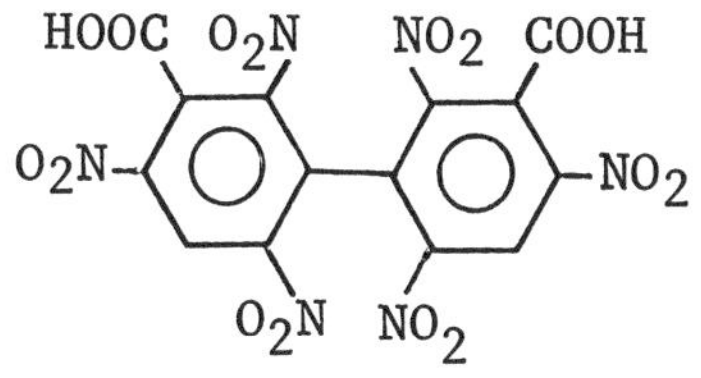

$C_{14}H_4N_6O_{16}$ Ref. 985

Resolution of 2,4,6,2',4',6'-Hexanitro-3,3'-dicarboxydiphenyl.—A solution of 10 g. of hexanitrodicarboxydiphenyl was dissolved in 500 cc. of methyl alcohol and added to 13.5 g. of strychnine dissolved in 3 liters of methyl alcohol. The solution was allowed to stand for several hours and the salt was filtered off. Concentration of the mother liquor showed that practically all of the salt had separated. The salt was dissolved in a mixture of one-third pyridine and two-thirds water by volume and crystallized slowly. The first fractions were recrystallized three times from the same solvent to obtain the maximum levo rotation. The soluble fraction separated as a gum on concentrating the mother liquors. By adding acetone to these mother liquors, the gum crystallized. Two recrystallizations yielded a salt of constant dextro rotation. The yields obtained were about 6 g. of *l*-salt and 4 g. of *d*-salt.

l-Salt. 0.1080 made up to 15 cc. with pyridine at 20° gave α_D − 0.54; $l = 1$, $[\alpha]_D^{20}$ −74.7°.

d-Salt. 0.1171 made up to 15 cc. with pyridine at 20° gave α_D 0.47, $l = 1$, $[\alpha]_D^{20}$ +60.0°.

No sharp melting point could be obtained for either salt as they decomposed above 250°, the *l*-salt decomposing at a slightly higher temperature.

Anal. Calcd. for $C_{56}H_{48}O_{20}N_{10}$: H, 4.1, C, 56.93. Found: *l*-salt—H, 4.0; C, 57.4. *d*-salt—H, 4.2; C, 58.04.

It was found impossible to resolve this compound either by means of brucine or quinine. Attempts to resolve by adding portions of strychnine to the acid and fractionally precipitating salt in this way gave variable results due, probably, to the separation of both normal and acid salt in the fractions.

***d*- and *l*-2,4,6,2',4',6'-Hexanitro-3,3'-dicarboxydiphenyls.**—The active acids were liberated from the active salts by treating with hydrochloric acid in alcohol. To a mixture of 150 cc. of 95% alcohol and 40 cc. of concentrated hydrochloric acid was added 4.5 g. of *l*-salt. The mixture was placed in a 500-cc. round-bottomed flask and stirred at 60° for two hours. The mixture was then cooled and 50 cc. of concentrated hydrochloric acid was added to insure the complete precipitation of the free acid. The mixture was then cooled to 0° and filtered. The solid obtained was redissolved in 95% alcohol, filtered to remove any undecomposed salt and again precipitated with hydrochloric acid. A yield of 2 g. of acid was obtained. The acid was recrystallized by dissolving in acetone and concentrating until crystals started to separate. An equal volume of benzene was then added and the solution allowed to stand until the acid had all crystallized. A pure acid was then readily obtained but the recovery was very poor. The product melts with decomposition at about 230–240°.

l-acid: 0.1143 g. made up to 15 cc. with acetone at 20° gave α_D −0.17°, $l = 1$, $[\alpha]_D^{20}$ −21.84°. 0.2230 g. made up to 25 cc. with acetic acid at 20° gave α_D −0.24°, $l = 1$, $[\alpha]_D^{20}$ −27.22°. 0.1034 g. made up to 15 cc. with 5% $NaHCO_3$ solution at 20°

gave α_D −0.55°, l = 1, $[\alpha]^{20}_D$ −80.5°. 0.1377 g. made up to 25 cc. with 5% $(NH_4)_2CO_3$ solution at 20° gave α_D −0.37°, l = 1, $[\alpha]^{20}_D$ −66.74°.

The *d*-acid was obtained from the *d*-salt by similar treatment. To a mixture of 15 cc. of 95% alcohol and 5 cc. of concentrated hydrochloric acid was added 0.6 g. of *d*-salt. On stirring, the salt completely dissolved, showing that it decomposed readily in the cold. An additional 5 cc. of concentrated hydrochloric acid was added to precipitate the free acid, and it was purified by the same method as used with the *l*-acid. About 0.2 g. of *d*-acid was obtained.

d-Acid. 0.0555 g. made up to 15 cc. with 5% $NaHCO_3$ solution at 20° gave α_D +0.29°, l = 1, $[\alpha]^{20}_D$ +79.67°.

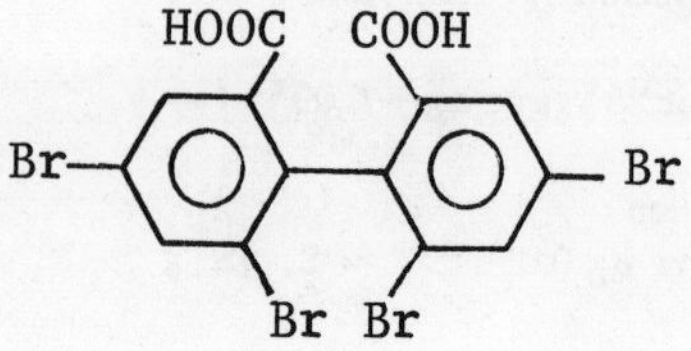

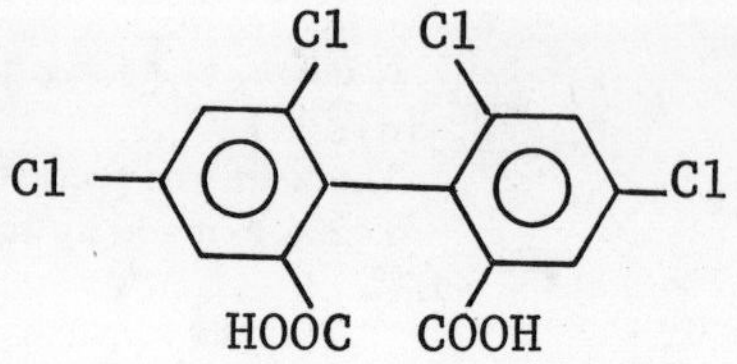

$C_{14}H_6Cl_4O_4$ Ref. 986

Resolution of *d,l*-4,6,4′,6′-Tetrabromodiphenic Acid.—Five grams (0.009 mole) of the acid in 70 cc. of hot ethyl acetate was added quickly to a solution of 8 g. (0.0203 mole) of anhydrous brucine in 200 cc. of boiling ethyl acetate. In a few minutes 6.2 g. of salt separated from the boiling solution. This less soluble salt (*l*A·*l*B) was leached with 400 cc. of boiling anhydrous ethyl alcohol. The residue and the first solid obtained on cooling the alcohol had about the same rotation and m. p. 259–260° decompn.

Rotation. 0.0350 g. made up to 1.95 cc. chloroform at 24° gave αD −0.19; *l*, 1; $[\alpha]^{24}$D −10.6°.

Anal. Calcd. for $C_{14}H_6O_4Br_4{\cdot}(C_{23}H_{26}O_4N_2)_2$: N, 4.16; Cl, 23.7. Found: N, 4.54; Cl, 23.2.

The more soluble salt (*d*A·*l*B) was obtained only when the original ethyl acetate solution had been concentrated to 50 cc.; 1.8 g. so obtained was crystalline but even after drying for five hours at 80° and 5 mm. it had m. p. 123–204° decompn.

Rotation. 0.0333 g. made up to 1.95 cc. in chloroform at 25° gave αD −0.55; *l*, 1; $[\alpha]^{25}$D −32.2°.

Anal. Calcd. for $C_{14}H_6O_4Br_4{\cdot}(C_{23}H_{26}O_4N_2)_2$: N, 4.16; Found: N, 4.10.

There was also a considerable amount of glassy residue which when decomposed gave the *d*-acid with a rotation slightly greater than that given by the acid from the crystalline fraction of the more soluble salt.

***l*-4,6,4′,6′-Tetrabromodiphenic Acid.**—The less soluble salt was decomposed with dilute sodium hydroxide giving an acid which upon recrystallization from ethyl acetate–ligroin had m. p. 282–283°.

Rotation. 0.1319 g. made up to 1.95 cc. in anhydrous ethyl alcohol[17] at 25° gave αD −0.52; *l*, 1; $[\alpha]^{25}$D −7.7°.

Anal. Calcd. for $C_{14}H_6O_4Br_4$: Br, 57.3. Found: Br, 57.1.

***d*-4,6,4′,6′-Tetrabromodiphenic Acid.**—The glassy residue was decomposed as above to give an acid which after recrystallization from ethyl acetate–ligroin had m. p. 279–282°.

Rotation. 0.0583 g. made up to 1.95 cc. in anhydrous ethyl alcohol at 25° gave αD +0.20; *l*, 1; $[\alpha]^{25}$D +6.7°.

(17) This solvent was used for the bromo acids because of their very low solubility in chloroform.

$C_{14}H_6Cl_4O_4$ Ref. 987

The amine salts described here were formed by neutralization of equimolar quantities of the amine and acid; impure samples of the normal brucine salts of (+) and (−)-tetrachlorodiphenic acid were described previously.[8] Chloroform used in this work was freshly purified anhydrous material that contained no ethyl alcohol stabilizer. The specific rotations of the acid isomers are unusually sensitive to the presence of alcohol; this phenomenon is being studied further. Specific rotations were measured in a 1 dm tube; the experimental error for all values was about ±1°.[10]

To a boiling solution of 50 g (0.132 mole) of 4,6,4′,6′-tetrachlorodiphenic acid[6,11] (mp. 265-270°) in 2 l. of boiling 95% ethyl alcohol there was added rapidly a boiling solution of 37.6 g (0.132 mole) of DHAA (Aldrich 10,519-8) in 630 ml of alcohol. The mixture was allowed to boil for a few minutes and then was stored in a covered beaker at room temperature to give needles, which were washed with 200 ml of alcohol to give 20 g of salt. An additional 5 g of product of equal optical purity was obtained by concentrating the filtrate to 600 ml. The 25 g obtained amounted to a 57% yield of the DHAA salt of (−)-4,6,4′,6′-tetrachlorodiphenic acid, mp. 271-272° decompn., $[\alpha]^{24}_D$ +39.5° (c, 0.7; MeOH). These constants were unchanged when a portion was recrystallized from ethyl alcohol (60 ml/g).

Anal. Calcd. for $C_{14}H_6Cl_4O_4{\cdot}C_{20}H_{31}N$: C, 61.36; H, 5.60; Cl, 21.31; N, 2.10. Found: C, 61.09; H, 5.48; Cl, 21.05; N, 2.17.

All washings and mother liquors from the above were combined and evaporated to dryness to give 59 g of impure DHAA salts, $[\alpha]^{27}_D$ +6° (c, 1; MeOH). Recrystallization of a small portion of this material from ethyl alcohol gave the DHAA salt of the (+)-acid with about 90% optical purity. No attempt was made to develop a practical procedure for the preparation of optically pure (+)-acid from the impure DHAA salt.

(−)-4,6,4′,6′-Tetrachlorodiphenic acid was prepared from its DHAA salt by adding solid Na_2CO_3 to a stirred suspension of 25 g of salt in a mixture of 200 ml of water and 100 ml of ether until the aqueous phase reached pH 10. The two clear layers were separated and the aqueous phase was washed with two 50-ml portions of ether. The aqueous phase was stirred at 60° until the odor of ether was absent and then was acidified carefully to pH 2 with 6N HCl. The colorless solid that precipitated was washed with water and dried at 65° to give 9 g (36% overall) of the (−)-acid, mp. 250-253°, $[\alpha]^{25}_D$ −140° (c, 1.3; $CHCl_3$). Recrystallization of a portion from benzene containing a little ethyl acetate raised the melting point to 253-258° but caused no significant change in the specific rotation.

Crude (+)-acid was obtained from the crude DHAA salts exactly as described above; 59 g gave 25 g, mp. 235-270°. To a solution of the 25 g (0.066 mole) of crude (+)-acid in 350 ml of boiling acetonitrile was added rapidly a hot dry (Na_2SO_4) solution of 30.8 g (0.066 mole) of brucine tetrahydrate in 350 ml of acetonitrile. The brucine salt precipitated within one minute. The suspension was refluxed for 24 hr,[12] the insoluble salt was washed on the filter with hot acetonitrile, and then was dried at 65° to give 39 g, $[\alpha]_D^{28}$ -29° (c, 1.4; $CHCl_3$). A suspension of this material in 1100 ml of fresh acetonitrile was refluxed vigorously for 24 hr and the insoluble salt was isolated and washed as before to give 22 g of

the brucine salt of (+)-4,6,4',6'-tetrachlorodiphenic acid, mp. 265-267° decompn., $[\alpha]_D^{28}$ -42° (c, 1.4; $CHCl_3$).[13]

Anal. Calcd. for $C_{14}H_6Cl_4O_4 \cdot C_{23}H_{26}N_2O_4$: C, 57.38; H, 4.16; Cl, 18.31; N, 3.62. Found: C, 57.41; H, 4.17; Cl, 17.61; N, 3.86.

All mother liquors from the above work were evaporated to dryness to give a recovery of 31 g of mixed brucine salts from which essentially racemic acid was subsequently isolated.

(+)-4,6,4',6'-Tetrachlorodiphenic acid was prepared from 22 g of its brucine salt by the same procedure used for the isolation of the (-)-acid; $CHCl_3$ was used, instead of ether, to extract brucine. We obtained 10 g (40% overall) of the (-)-acid, mp. 248-254°, $[\alpha]_D^{25}$ +144° (c, 1.2; $CHCl_3$). Recrystallization of a portion from benzene containing a little ethyl acetate raised the melting point to 255-260° but caused no significant change in the specific rotation.

The DHAA salt of (+)-4,6,4',6'-tetrachlorodiphenic acid was prepared by mixing a hot solution of 1 g (0.0026 mole) of the (+)-acid in 25 ml of absolute ethyl alcohol with a hot solution of 0.74 g (0.0026 mole) of DHAA in 25 ml of the same solvent. The mixture was allowed to stand at room temperature and deposited colorless needles which, after drying at 65°, had mp. 260-265° decompn., $[\alpha]_D^{30}$ -8.1° (c, 1.4; MeOH).

Anal. Calcd. for $C_{14}H_6Cl_4O_4 \cdot C_{20}H_{31}N$: C, 61.36; H, 5.60; Cl, 21.31; N, 2.10. Found: C, 60.79; H, 5.52; Cl, 20.73; N, 2.11.

The brucine salt of (-)-4,6,4',6'-tetrachlorodiphenic acid was prepared by mixing rapidly a hot solution of 1 g (0.0026 mole) of the (-)-acid in 25 ml of acetonitrile with a hot solution of 1.2 g (0.0026 mole) of brucine tetrahydrate in 25 ml of the same solvent. The mixture was boiled for a few minutes and deposited in the boiling solution a crystalline salt which, after drying at 65°, had mp. 261-264° decompn., $[\alpha]_D^{25}$ +41° (c, 1.3; $CHCl_3$).

Anal. Calcd. for $C_{14}H_6Cl_4O_4 \cdot C_{23}H_{26}N_2O_2$: C, 57.38; H, 4.16; Cl, 18.31; N, 3.62. Found: C, 57.23; H, 3.99; Cl, 18.33; N, 3.52.

When this salt was recrystallized from absolute ethyl alcohol, or when we attempted to prepare it from equimolar portions of brucine and the (-)-acid in ethyl alcohol solution, the salt that separated was found by analysis to be the very insoluble normal brucine salt, mp. 263-265° decompn., $[\alpha]_D^{20}$ -15.2° (c, 1.3; $CHCl_3$).[14]

References

6. E. R. Atkinson, D. M. Murphy and J. E. Lufkin, Org. Syntheses, Coll. Vol. 4, 872 (1963); the work was performed in 1950.

8. E. R. Atkinson and H. J. Lawler, J. Amer. Chem. Soc. 62, 704 (1940).

Note: This resolution procedure did not include references Nos. 11, 12 and 14 referred to in the body of this article.

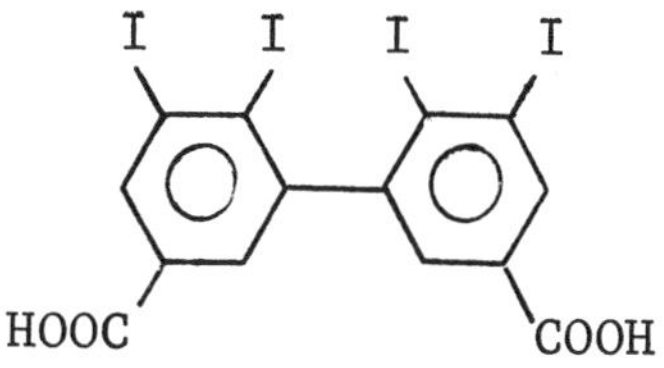

$C_{14}H_6I_4O_4$ Ref. 988

Resolution of 2,2',3,3'-Tetraiodo-5,5'-dicarboxybiphenyl.—The resolution of the tetraiodo acid was accomplished both through the monobrucine salt of the levo acid and through the dibrucine salt of the dextro acid. The two salts mentioned above are of comparable solubility in ethyl alcohol, and only from alcohol were successful resolutions accomplished. Numerous attempts at resolution were carried through before satisfactory seed crystals were obtained; subsequent resolutions were relatively easy. The resolution may be accomplished as follows:

1.5 g. of the tetraiodo acid was suspended in 25 cc. of 95% alcohol and exactly neutralized with a solution of potassium hydroxide in 95% alcohol. The solution of the salt was filtered, using filter-cell as a filtration aid. A solution of 1.58 g. of recrystallized brucine in 25 cc. of absolute alcohol was likewise filtered and added to the solution of the tetraiodo acid. The solution was heated to boiling, and an excess (above that needed to neutralize the potassium hydroxide) of a 95% alcoholic solution of acetic acid added to the hot, clear solution, which was then seeded with the monobrucine salt of the levo acid. The erlenmeyer containing the mixture was stoppered and placed in a dewar flask containing water at 80°. After fifteen hours, 0.3–0.4 g. of the monobrucine salt of the levo acid usually separated. If no crystals separated, absolute alcohol (in which the salts are much less soluble than they are in 95% alcohol) was added, and the attempt to crystallize repeated. The monobrucine salt consisted of hexagonal plates, which could be recrystallized from absolute alcohol. For analysis, the finely ground sample was dried at 145°.

Anal. Calcd. for $C_{14}H_6O_4I_4 \cdot C_{23}H_{26}O_4N_2$: N, 2.46; I, 44.52. Found: N, 2.48; I, 44.38, 44.84.

After the monobrucine salt of the levo acid had separated, the mother liquors were decanted and seeded with the dibrucine salt of the dextro acid. The latter crystallized as clusters of fine needles.

Anal. Calcd. for $C_{14}H_6O_4I_4 \cdot 2C_{23}H_{26}O_4N_2$: N, 3.65; I, 33.08. Found: N, 3.65; I, 32.98.

Not infrequently, despite all precautions, both salts crystallized together, and the recovered acid was either racemic or only slightly optically active. On one occasion, crystals were obtained which may have been an impure sample of the dibrucine salt of the levo acid.

The recovery of the free tetraiodo acid from the salts was carried out as follows: 1.3 g. of salt was dissolved in a mixture of 25 cc. of aqueous 5% sodium hydroxide and 25 cc. of ethyl alcohol. The resulting solution was filtered and warmed rapidly to the boiling point. Thirty cc. of a mixture of concentrated hydrochloric acid and ethyl alcohol was added, and the boiling continued until all the precipitated gel had coagulated into small particles. After cooling, the solid acid was filtered, washed with lukewarm 5% hydrochloric acid and then with warm water. The remaining solid was brucine-free (nitric acid test). Whenever the specific rotation of the sodium salt of the resolved acid was less than 65°, the resolution was repeated. The maximum specific rotation observed was $[\alpha]^{25}_D$ −112°.

The measurements of optical activity were made by dissolving the acid in an equivalent amount of aqueous sodium hydroxide and diluting to volume with a 1% solution of sodium bicarbonate (0.203 g. of levo acid in 10 cc. of NaOH–$NaHCO_3$ solution, 2-dm. tube, $\alpha_{obs.}$ $-4.58°$, $[\alpha]^{25}_D$ $-112°$; 0.1217 g. of dextro acid in 10 cc. of NaOH–$NaHCO_3$ solution, 2-dm. tube, $\alpha_{obs.}$ $+2.52°$, $[\alpha]^{25}_D$ $+104°$). The identity of the resolved acids was demonstrated by melting point and analysis. The melting points of the resolved acids were essentially identical with that of the racemic acid, presumably due to racemization during heating. A sample of the levo acid was specially purified for analysis; the dextro acid was analytically pure as recovered.

Dextro acid, $[\alpha]^{25}_D$ $+84°$. *Anal.* Calcd. for $C_{14}H_6O_4I_4$: C, 22.54; H, 0.85; neut. equiv., 373. Found: C, 22.74; H, 1.00; neut. equiv., 379.

Levo acid, $[\alpha]^{25}_D$ $-94°$. *Anal.* Calcd. for $C_{14}H_6O_4I_4$: C, 22.54; H, 0.85; I, 78.05; neut. equiv., 373. Found: C, 22.81; H, 0.81; I, 77.7; neut. equiv., 375.

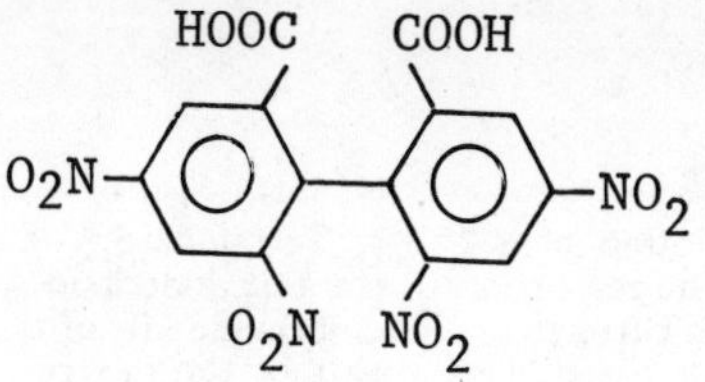

$C_{14}H_6N_4O_{12}$ Ref. 989

d- *and* l + dl-4 : 4′ : 6 : 6′-*Tetranitrodiphenic Acids.*—Boiling alcoholic solutions of tetranitrodiphenic acid (35·7 g. in 1 l.) and quinidine (30·5 g. in ½ l.) were mixed, and the precipitated salt was filtered off and boiled with alcohol until the residue attained constant rotatory power $[\alpha]_{5461}$ $+243·5°$ ($c = 2·15$ in 14·7*N*-acetic acid); m. p. 252° (decomp.). The alcoholic filtrates were evaporated, the residue was dissolved in acetic acid, and the resultant solution poured into dilute hydrochloric acid. The liberated tetranitrodiphenic acid was extracted with ether, and the well-washed extract dried with sodium sulphate and evaporated. The residue ($[\alpha]_{5461}$ *ca.* $-50°$) was boiled with benzene, and the more soluble material was repeatedly crystallised from benzene until it attained constant rotatory power. *l* + *dl*-Tetranitrodiphenic acid formed needles which, after being heated at 130° for ½ hour, melted at 224—226° and had $[\alpha]_{5461}$ $-138·5°$ ($c = 1·7$ in ethyl alcohol). The less soluble quinidine salt was decomposed (*a*) by dissolving it in acetic acid and pouring the solution into dilute hydrochloric acid, (*b*) by dissolving in pyridine and pouring the solution into dilute ammonia, (*c*) by grinding with concentrated hydrochloric acid. The acids, recovered as described above and dried at 140°, had almost the same rotatory power, showing that racemisation does not occur during the recovery process.

d-4 : 4′ : 6 : 6′-Tetranitrodiphenic acid, m. p. 226—227° (Found : equiv., 211. Calc. : 211) (0·3696 g. in 20 c.c. of ethyl alcohol in a 2 dm. tube) gave :

λ	4359	4602	5461	5790	6708
α	+16·70°	+11·64°	+5·26°	+4·12°	+2·58°

whence $[\alpha]_{5461}$ $+142·3°$.

0·4209 G. in 20 c.c. of 1·033*N*/10-NaOH in a 2 dm. tube gave :

λ	4359	4602	5106	5218	5461
α	+29—31°	+19·6—20·0°	+10·84°	+9·72°	+8·00°
λ	5790	5896	6104	6708	
α	+6·33°	+5·86°	+5·08°	+3·78°	

whence $[\alpha]_{5461}$ $+190·5°$.

$C_{14}H_6N_4O_{12}$ Ref. 989a

I. *Spaltung.*

Abweichend von dem Verfahren von G. H. Christie und J. Kenner[3]), die die Brucinsalze aus sehr großen Mengen Wasser krystallisierten, wurde die Spaltung in Aceton wie folgt bewerkstelligt. Die siedenden Lösungen von 2,533 g Tetranitrodiphensäure in 125 ccm Aceton und von 2,78 g kryst. Brucin (1 Mol) in 65 ccm Aceton wurden zusammengegossen und die gelbgefärbte Lösung, aus der das Brucinsalz allmählich auskrystallisierte, über Nacht in den Eisraum gestellt. Das ausgefallene Alkaloidsalz (3,35 g), entsprechend 93 Proc. der verwendeten Brucinmenge, berechnet auf sekundäres, wasserfreies Brucinsalz[2]), besteht z. T. aus kleinen, teilweise kugelig aggregierten Nädelchen, z. T. aus kleinen, undeutlich doppelbrechenden Tröpfchen und zeigte den Schmelzp. 255° unter Zersetzung (korr.). Die englischen Autoren[4]) geben für das aus Wasser erhaltene weniger lösliche Salz den Schmelzp. 252° unter Zersetzung an.

$[\alpha]^{20}_D = (+0{,}18° \cdot 100):(2 \cdot 1) = +9°$. (In 10,4 n-Essigsäure.)

G. H. Christie und J. Kenner[5]) fanden + 22,17° für gleiche Konzentration des Salzes im gleichen Lösungsmittel.

Beim Einengen der Mutterlauge des schwer löslichen Brucinsalzes im Vakuum wurden Gemenge von Salzen [0,1 g vom Schmelzp. 198° bis 199° (korr.) unter Zersetzung, 0,18 g vom Schmelzp. 202—203° (korr.) unter Zersetzung] erhalten. Eine Probe des letzteren Materials konnte nach dem Waschen mit einer größeren Menge 2 n-Schwefelsäure (200 ccm) nicht völlig brucinfrei gewonnen werden. Der getrocknete Rückstand schmolz bei 201—202° (korr.) unter Zersetzung. Nach dem vollständigen Verjagen des Lösungsmittels blieb ein rötliches Öl zurück, aus dessen Lösung in Aceton durch vorsichtigen Zusatz von wenig Äther 0,12 g fast farblose, doppelbrechende, aber schlecht ausgebildete Krystalle vom Schmelzp. 199—200° (korr.) unter Zersetzung abgeschieden wurden.

$[\alpha]^{20}_D = (-0{,}29° \cdot 100):(0{,}6892 \cdot 1) = -42{,}1°$. (In 10,4 n-Essigsäure.)

Die von diesen Krystallen abfiltrierte Mutterlauge hinterließ ein rotes Öl, das auch nach 6 Wochen nicht erstarrte.

Zerlegung des schwer löslichen Brucinsalzes. Nach dem Vorgange von K. Freudenberg[1]) wurden 2,62 g Alkaloidsalz allmählich mit einem Brei von 3,7 g Kaliumbisulfat in möglichst wenig Wasser verrieben und das Gemenge nach halbstündigem Stehen mit frisch geglühtem Natriumsulfat versetzt. Das scharf getrocknete und fein gemahlene Material wurde dann in einem Soxhletapparat einige Stunden mit absolutem Äther extrahiert. Beim Verdampfen des Extraktionsmittels fielen nur wenig gelbe Krystalle aus. Die Hauptmenge der freien Säure hinterblieb als gelbes Öl. In krystallisiertem Zustande konnte sie erhalten werden durch langsames Eintropfen der ammonialkalischen Lösung in etwa halbnormale Salzsäure unter starkem Kratzen mit einem Glasstab. Dabei trägt man zweckmäßig die Hauptmenge erst ein, nachdem sich reichlich Krystallkeime gebildet haben. Ölig kommt die Säure, wenn die anfängliche Tropfenfolge zu rasch ist. Die erhaltenen, schwach gelblichen Krystalle, die allerdings keine deutliche Form besitzen, aber deutlich doppelbrechend sind, schmelzen bei 258—259° (korr.) unter Zersetzung, nachdem die Substanz von 220° an unter Dunkelfärbung zusammengesintert ist. Das erhaltene Produkt war frei von Brucin und Sulfat. Ausbeute: 0,22 g.

$[\alpha]^{24}_D = (+0{,}66° \cdot 100):(0{,}6892 \cdot 1{,}02) = +93{,}9°$. (In 2 n-Soda.)

Durch weitere Extraktion während 4 Stunden wurden nochmals 0,32 g aktive Säure erhalten.

$[\alpha]^{22}_D = (+0{,}63° \cdot 100):(0{,}6892 \cdot 0{,}908) = +100{,}7°$. (In 2 n-Soda.)

Wiederholung der gleichen Operation lieferte nur noch einen geringen Rückstand. Gesamtausbeute: 0,60 g, entsprechend 66 Proc. d. Th., berechnet auf wasserfreies Brucinsalz. G. H. Christie und J. Kenner[1]) geben für die aus dem schwerer löslichen Brucinsalz mit Salzsäure freigemachte Säure den Schmelzp. 53—54° und dann 226—227° an, für $[\alpha]$ +115°, beides für nicht krystallisiertes, ölig ausgefallenes luftgetrocknetes Material.

[1]) B. 47, 2027 (1914), und zwar S. 2035. Vgl. auch R. Kuhn u. F. Ebel, B. 58, 919 (1925).

[2]) A. 366, 79 (1909), und zwar S. 89.

[3]) a. a. O., und zwar S. 619 ff.; Soc. 123, 779 (1923), und zwar S. 782.

[4]) G. H. Christie u. J. Kenner, a. a. O., erhielten dasselbe wasserfrei.

[5]) a. a. O., und zwar S. 619.

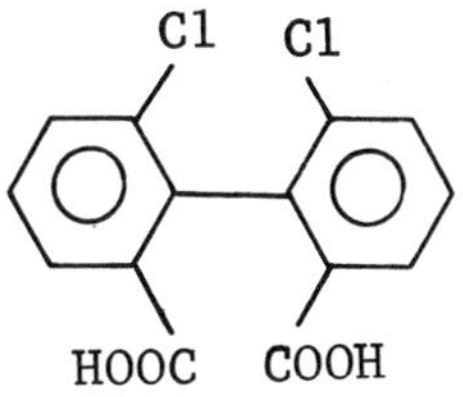

$C_{14}H_8Cl_2O_4$ Ref. 990

Resolution of r-6 : 6′-*Dichlorodiphenic Acid.*

By repeated fractional crystallisation of the mixture of salts prepared from 2 grams of the racemic acid and 6 grams of hydrated brucine, 2·3 grams of the pure, less soluble salt, and 1·35 grams of the pure, more soluble salt were separated with moderate ease.

Brucine l-6 : 6′-*dichlorodiphenate*, $C_{14}H_8O_4Cl_2,2C_{23}H_{26}O_4N_2,3H_2O$, consists of rectangular prisms, m. p. 235°, and is the less soluble of the two salts thus obtained. For a 1·23 per cent. solution in chloroform, $[\alpha]_D^{15°}$ + 1·97° (Found: H_2O = 4·66. $C_{60}H_{60}O_{12}N_4Cl_2,3H_2O$ requires H_2O = 4·68 per cent. Found: for the anhydrous material dried at 120°, N = 5·18. $C_{60}H_{60}O_{12}N_4Cl_2$ requires N = 5·09 per cent.).

Brucine d-6 : 6′-*dichlorodiphenate*, $C_{14}H_8O_4Cl_2,2C_{23}H_{26}O_4N_2,1\frac{1}{2}H_2O$, forms rectangular plates, m. p. 163° (decomp.). For a 1·16 per cent. solution in chloroform, $[\alpha]_D^{15°}$ − 58·62° (Found: H_2O = 2·43. $C_{60}H_{60}O_{12}N_4Cl_2,1\frac{1}{2}H_2O$ requires H_2O = 2·40 per cent. Found: for the anhydrous material dried at 120°, N = 5·17. $C_{60}H_{60}O_{12}N_4Cl_2$ requires N = 5·09 per cent.).

d-6 : 6′-*Dichlorodiphenic acid*, $C_{12}H_6Cl_2(CO_2H)_2$, from the brucine salt, forms rectangular plates, m. p. 259°. For a 0·69 per cent. solution of the sodium salt, $[\alpha]_D^{15°}$ − 20·18°. The acid recovered from this solution furnished a dextrorotatory solution in ether, which, however, was too dilute for anything more than qualitative observation.

l-6 : 6′-*Dichlorodiphenic acid*, $C_{12}H_6Cl_2(CO_2H)_2$, rectangular plates, m. p. 259°, furnished a sodium salt for which $[\alpha]_D^{15°}$ + 21·43° in a 1·01 per cent. aqueous solution.

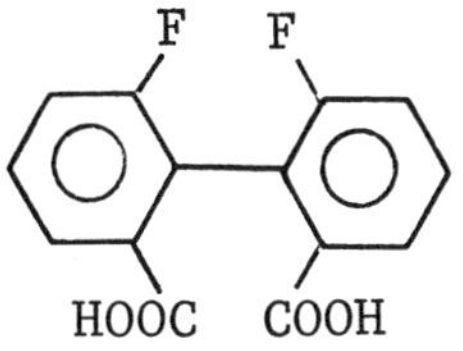

$C_{14}H_8F_2O_4$ Ref. 991

Resolution of 2,2′-Difluoro-6,6′-dicarboxydiphenyl.—To a hot solution of 2.5 g. of 2,2′-difluoro-6,6′-dicarboxydiphenyl in 75 cc. of 95% ethyl alcohol was added with stirring a hot solution of 3.0 g. of anhydrous quinine in 45 cc. of 95% ethyl alcohol. The solution was evaporated to 95 cc. and allowed to cool. A crop of white flaky crystals separated, which was essentially pure salt, as shown by rotation and melting point as compared with recrystallized material. The crystals of pure less soluble salt were removed by filtration with suction, washed with 95% alcohol and dried; weight 2.5 g. Recrystallization from 95% ethyl alcohol gave a pure product of melting point 221–222° (corr.).

Rotation. 0.1695 g. made up to 15 cc. with absolute ethyl alcohol at 20° gave α_D +0.44°; l = 1; $[\alpha]_D^{20}$ +38.9°. Recrystallization from 95% ethyl alcohol did not change the melting point or rotation.

Anal. Calcd. for $C_{34}H_{32}O_6F_2N_2$: N, 4.65. Found: N, 4.52.

The mother liquor from the first crop of crystals was further evaporated to 50 cc. Upon cooling, 0.32 g. of salt crystallized out, which was by rotation shown to be impure less soluble salt. The filtrate was evaporated to dryness and the residue of more soluble salt washed once with 25 cc. of a 10% solution of ethyl alcohol in water. After drying, the weight was 2.5 g. and the melting point was 159–160° (corr.).

Rotation. 0.1755 g. made up to 15 cc. with absolute ethyl alcohol at 20° gave α_D −1.18°; l = 1; $[\alpha]_D^{20}$ −101°. The more soluble salt was dissolved in ethyl alcohol and precipitated by the addition of water into two fractions. The melting point was unchanged and the rotation of the two fractions identical with that of the original material.

Anal. Calcd. for $C_{34}H_{36}O_6F_2N_2$: N, 4.65. Found: N, 4.32.

l-**2,2′-Difluoro-6,6′-dicarboxydiphenyl.**—The pure less soluble salt was hydrolyzed by two procedures, both giving practically the same results. The first procedure consisted in digesting 1.0 g. of salt three times for ten minutes each in the cold with 10 cc. of 2 *N* hydrochloric acid. The pasty mass which first formed changed to white flakes on continued stirring. The active *l*-acid so obtained was then washed on a filter with another 10-cc. portion of 2 *N* hydrochloric acid, then with water, and finally crystallized from 95% ethyl alcohol. The melting point was 305–306° (corr.), with a melting behavior similar to that of the racemic acid. A mixed melting point with the racemic acid gave 302–304° (corr.).

Rotation. (a) 0.1535 g. made up to 15 cc. with 95% ethyl alcohol at 20° gave α_D −0.23°; l = 1; $[\alpha]_D^{20}$ −22.5°. (b) 0.1008 g. made up to 15 cc. with 0.1 *N* sodium hydroxide at 20° gave α_D −0.835°; l = 1; $[\alpha]_D^{20}$ −124°.

The second procedure consisted in digesting 1.2 g. of pure less soluble salt with 10 cc. of cold 2 *N* hydrochloric acid for five minutes. The acid was decanted and the white flakes which were obtained from the pasty mass by stirring were washed with water and dissolved in 2 *N* sodium hydroxide solution. The solution was warmed to 80°, immediately cooled, and extracted three times with 4 cc. each of chloroform. The alkaline solution was then acidified with concentrated hydrochloric acid. The *l*-acid precipitated and was washed with water and dried. After crystallization from 95% ethyl

alcohol, the melting point was 305–306° (corr.).

Rotation. 0.0945 g. made up to 15 cc. with 0.1 *N* sodium hydroxide at 20° gave α_D −0.8°; l = 1; $[\alpha]^{20}_D$ −127.0°.

Anal. Neut. equiv., calcd., 278.1. Found: 280.

d-2,2′-Difluoro-6,6′-dicarboxydiphenyl.—The *d*-acid was obtained from 2.2 g. of the more soluble salt by the second procedure given above. After recrystallization from 95% ethyl alcohol the melting point was 305–306° (corr.).

Rotation. (a) 0.1387 g. made up to 15 cc. with 0.1 *N* sodium hydroxide at 20° gave α_D +0.94°; l = 1; $[\alpha]^{20}_D$ +101.8°. (b) 0.1071 g. made up to 15 cc. with 95% ethyl alcohol at 20° gave α_D +0.12°; l = 1; $[\alpha]^{20}_D$ +16.8°.

Synthesis of More Soluble Salt.—An alcohol solution of 0.1071 g. of *d*-acid having a rotation in alcohol of +16.8° was treated with 0.125 g. of quinine. The salt obtained upon evaporation of the alcohol to 2 cc. and precipitation with water was washed with water and dried. The melting point was 163–165° (corr.).

Rotation. 0.0860 g. made up to 15 cc. with absolute ethyl alcohol at 20° gave α_D −0.435°; l = 1; $[\alpha]^{20}_D$ −76.0°.

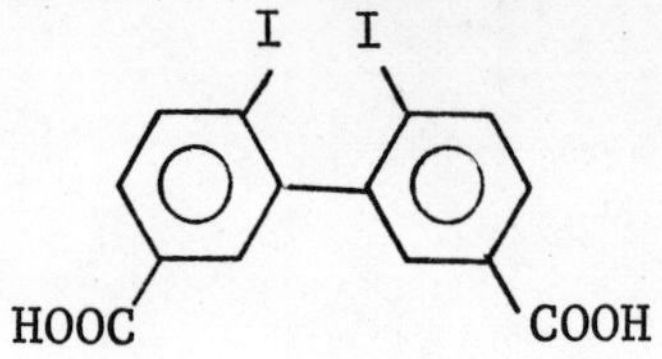

$C_{14}H_8I_2O_4$ Ref. 992

Resolution of 2,2′-Diiodo-5,5′-dicarboxybiphenyl.—The resolution of the diiodo acid was carried out through the monobrucine salt. Only levorotatory diiodo acid was isolated, and this enantiomorph was obtained in a yield considerably higher than 50% of the optically inactive starting material. Apparently an asymmetric transformation occurred. This is not surprising, since the half-life for the racemization of the diiodo acid at the boiling point of alcohol is of the order of one minute. Attempts to accomplish a resolution through the dibrucine salt failed; the monobrucine salt resulted when two moles of brucine was used for one mole of the acid. On the other hand, no crystals were obtained in attempts to prepare the monobrucine salt from one mole of acid and one mole of brucine.

The procedure followed is described below. Three grams (0.00608 mole) of 2,2′-diiodo-5,5′-dicarboxybiphenyl was added to 600 cc. of boiling 95% ethyl alcohol. To the resulting clear solution was added 4.8 g. (0.01216 mole) of brucine. Boiling was continued until the volume had been reduced to 200 cc. The hot solution was filtered rapidly into a flask which had previously been placed in a large Dewar filled with water at 80°. The solution was allowed to cool slowly. Best results were obtained if the solution was not disturbed at all during the cooling time. Usually some crystals appeared when the solution stopped boiling; fifteen hours later, when the mixture had cooled to 30–40°, the liquid contained clusters of needles. The yield was 3.4 g. of the monobrucine salt of the levorotatory acid; the salt melted with decomposition at 290–295°.

Anal. Calcd. for $C_{14}H_8O_4I_2{\cdot}C_{23}H_{26}O_4N_2$: N, 3.16; I, 28.57. Found: N, 3.23; I, 28.64.

To recover the free acid from the salt, 3 g. of the latter was dissolved in 30 cc. of 1% alcoholic sodium hydroxide, to which 30 g. of crushed ice had been added. The resulting solution was filtered and then poured slowly with rapid stirring into a mixture of 40 cc. of 95% ethyl alcohol, 30 g. of cracked ice, and 15 cc. of concentrated hydrochloric acid. If this operation was carried out properly, a white solid precipitated, and could be filtered easily. In some experiments the acid did not precipitate at all, and in others the acid precipitated as a gel. In the first instance the stirring was continued and more water was added; in the second the stirring was continued and more ethyl alcohol was added. The solid acid was filtered and washed with 500 cc. of cold 5% hydrochloric acid, followed by 500 cc. of cold water. The acid did not give a positive test for brucine with concentrated nitric acid, and did not have a bitter taste. After drying, the resolved acid weighed 1.5 g., and melted at 349–352°.

Anal. Calcd. for $C_{14}H_8O_4I_2$: C, 34.10; H, 1.66; neut. equiv., 247. Found: C, 34.42; H, 1.90; neut. equiv., 244.

No attempt was made to prepare an optically pure sample of this acid (0.1062 g. of diiodo acid, neutralized by sodium hydroxide in 38% alcohol, 2-dm. tube, $\alpha_{obs.}$ −0.518°, $[\alpha]^{25}$D −24.3°).

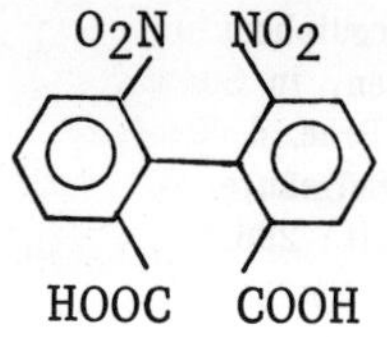

$C_{14}H_8N_2O_8$ Ref. 993

Resolution of β-Dinitrodiphenic Acid into Optically Active Components.—A solution of the acid (2 g.) and hydrated brucine (5·61 g.) in boiling water (1050 c.c.) deposited, on cooling, fern-shaped sprays of irregular plates (3·9 g.), m. p. 209° (decomp.). By successive concentration to 575 c.c., 200 c.c., and 50 c.c., further crops of 2·2 g., m. p. 206° (decomp.), 0·3 g., m. p. 209° (decomp.), and 0·4 g., m. p. 207° (decomp.), were respectively obtained. The salt was hydrated [Found: H_2O, 4·2. $C_{60}H_{60}O_{16}N_6,2\frac{1}{2}H_2O$ requires H_2O, 3·9%. Found, for the salt dried at 130°: N, 7·8. $C_{12}H_6(NO_2)_2(CO_2H)_2,2C_{23}H_{26}O_4N_2$ requires N, 7·5%]. For 1·5% solutions in 10*N*-acetic acid of the anhydrous salt from each of the first two fractions, $[\alpha]_D$ = − 13·29° and − 13·31°, respectively. It was therefore not surprising that a solution of the sodium salt of the acid prepared from the brucine salt was inactive.

But when boiling solutions of the acid (4 g.) in alcohol (100 c.c.) and of quinine hydrate (9·2 g.) in alcohol (80 c.c.) were mixed, colourless, rectangular plates (5·7 g.), m. p. 178—179° (decomp.), separated on cooling; no further crystallisation occurred on concentration. On evaporating the alcohol, an oil remained, which was obtained in a solid condition by precipitation with light petroleum from its solution in benzene. The melting point of the plates was unchanged after recrystallisation (Found: C_2H_6O, 2·45. $C_{54}H_{56}O_{12}N_6,\frac{1}{2}C_2H_6O$ requires C_2H_6O, 2·4. Found, for the salt dried at 130°: N, 8·6. $C_{54}H_{56}O_{12}N_6$ requires N, 8·6%). For a 1·43% solution of the dried salt in chloroform, $[\alpha]^{15°}_D$ = − 218·1°.

The more soluble salt melted at first at about 93°, but at 162—163° after being heated to constant weight at 120° (Found: N, 8·55. $C_{54}H_{56}O_{12}N_6$ requires N, 8·6%). For a 1·44% solution of the dried salt in chloroform, $[\alpha]^{15°}_D$ = − 62·10°.

d-β-*Dinitrodiphenic acid*, obtained from the less soluble quinine salt by treatment with hydrochloric acid, melted at 296°, whilst a mixture of the acid with the racemic acid melted over the range 285—293°.

For a 0·96% solution of the acid in ether, $[\alpha]^{15°}_D$ = + 26·90°, whilst for a 0·66% solution of the sodium salt in water, $[\alpha]^{15°}_D$ = − 186·4°.

l-β-*Dinitrodiphenic acid*, obtained from the more soluble quinine salt, also melted at 296°. For a 0·92% solution of the acid in ether, $[\alpha]^{15°}_D$ = − 26·46°, and for a 1·29% solution of the sodium salt in water, $[\alpha]^{15°}_D$ = + 179·4°.

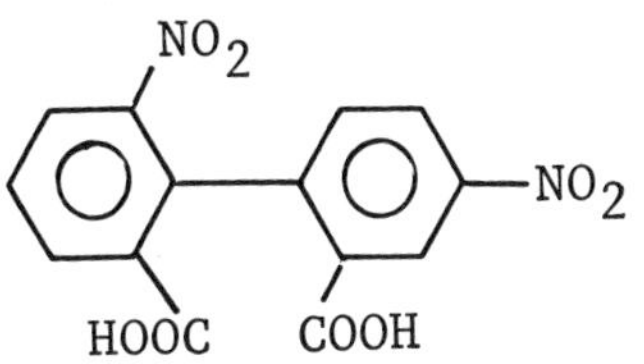

$C_{14}H_8N_2O_8$ Ref. 994

o-p'-Dinitrodiphensäure.

In Übereinstimmung mit G. H. Christie, A. Holderness und J. Kenner[1]) scheiterten Versuche zur Fraktionierung der Brucinsalze. Die Spaltung mit Chinin in 96-proc. Alkohol nach den Angaben derselben Autoren lieferte 40 Proc. schwer lösliches Chininsalz vom Schmelzpunkt 174—176° unter Zersetzung (unkorr.). Das leicht lösliche Salz wurde nach Verdampfen des Lösungsmittels aus benzolischer Lösung mit Petroläther gefällt. Ausbeute 3,6 g aus 2,0 g Dinitrodiphensäure + 4,6 g Chininhydrat (60 Proc. d. Th.).

2,6 g schwer lösliches Chininsalz wurden mit 50 ccm 2 n-Salzsäure kurze Zeit bei 40—50° digeriert. Die anfangs ölige d-o-p'-Dinitrodiphensäure erstarrt bald und zerfällt zu einem farblosen, in Soda klar löslichen Pulver. Ausbeute 0,6 g (70 Proc. d. Th.). Nach dem Umfällen mit Ammoniak und Salzsäure lag der Schmelzpunkt bei 303 bis 304° (korr., Lit.: 296°).

$$[\alpha]_D^{21} = (-2,96° \cdot 100) : (0,6892 \cdot 2,02) = -212,6°$$

(in 2 n-Soda). Die Entdecker[1]) geben für die wäßrige Lösung des sekundären Natriumsalzes $[\alpha]_D^{5} = -186,4°$ an. Da die freie Säure, in Äther gelöst, rechtsdrehend ist, wird sie als d-Verbindung bezeichnet.

Das leichter lösliche Chininsalz, in gleicher Weise mit Salzsäure zerlegt, lieferte l-o-p'-Dinitrodiphensäure von

$$[\alpha]_D^{7} = (+1,64° \cdot 100) : (0,5 \cdot 1,864) = +176°$$

(in 2 n-Soda).

3,901 mg Subst.: 0,300 ccm N (korr., 22°, 729 mm).
$C_{14}H_8O_8N_2$ Ber. N 8,48 Gef. N 8,54.

[1]) In dieser Weise ist G. H. Christie, A. Holderness und J. Kenner, Soc. 129, 671 (1926) der Abbau der β-Dinitrodiphensäure zu o-p'-Dinitrodiphenyl geglückt.

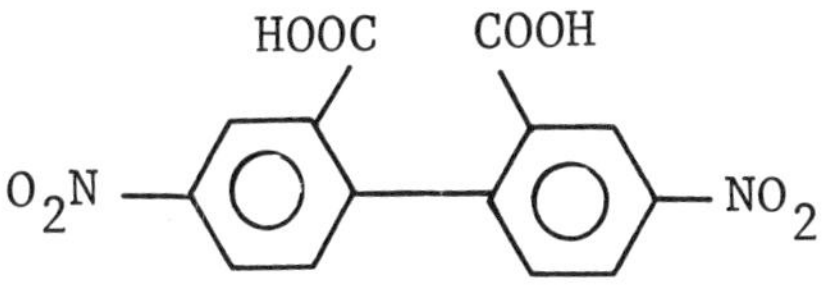

$C_{14}H_8N_2O_8$ Ref. 995

p-p'-Dinitrodiphensäure.

Die siedenden Lösungen von 1 g Säure in 25 ccm 96-proc. Alkohol und von 2,3 g (2 Mole) Chininhydrat in 20 ccm 96-proc. Alkohol wurden vermischt. Beim Stehen in der Kälte fielen im Laufe von einigen Stunden 1,75 g Chininsalz aus, von dem abfiltriert wurde (Fraktion I). Die Mutterlauge davon setzte bei längerem Stehen ohne eingeengt zu werden, 0,8 g schöne, vierseitige Doppelpyramiden ab (Fraktion II). Beim Eindunsten des alkoholischen Filtrates auf dem Wasserbade hinterblieb ein Öl, das in der Kälte erstarrte (Fraktion III).

Fraktion I. Schmelzp. 207—208° unter Zersetzung:

$$[\alpha]_D^{23} = (+1,12° \cdot 100) : (0,6892 \cdot 1,5) = +108,4°$$
(in Chloroform.)

3,572 mg Subst.: 0,259 ccm N (korr., 22°, 718 mm).
Ber. N 7,72 Gef. N 7,87.

Fraktion II. Schmelzp. 207—208° unter Zersetzung.

$$[\alpha]_D^{23} = (+1,52° \cdot 100) : (0,6892 \cdot 2,0) = +110,3°$$
(in Chloroform).

4,022 mg Subst.: 0,281 ccm N (korr., 21°, 731 mm).
$C_{54}H_{56}O_{12}N_6$ Ber. N 7,72 Gef. N 7,80.

Fraktion III. Schmelzp. 84—88°.

$$[\alpha]_D^{23} = (-0,30° \cdot 100) : (0,6892 \cdot 1,00) = -43,5°$$
(in Chloroform).

Das Drehungsvermögen des Chinins in Chloroformlösung beträgt

$$[\alpha]_D = -117°.$$

In einem zweiten gleichartig ausgeführten Versuch fielen zunächst 2,0 g schwer lösliches Chininsalz in rechtwinklig abgeschnittenen Prismen vom Schmelzp. 218—219° (unkorr., unter Zersetzung) aus. Dann folgten etwa 0,3 g eines Gemisches von Stäbchen und ganz kleinen Kryställchen, die bei 181—182° (unkorr., unter Zersetzung) schmolzen. Der Rest erstarrte nach dem Verjagen des Alkohols und längerem Stehen glasig. Schmelzp. 164—165° (unkorr., unter Zersetzung).

Die Mittelfraktion besaß

$$[\alpha]_D^{21} = (+0,08° \cdot 100) : (0,6892 \cdot 0,946) = +12,3°$$
(in E_{18}),

die Endfraktion

$$[\alpha]_D^{21} = (-1,15° \cdot 100) : (0,6892 \cdot 0,825) = -202,3°$$
(in absolutem Alkohol).

Vermischt man die alkoholischen Lösungen von p-p'-Dinitrodiphensäure und der berechneten Menge Chininhydrat in der Kälte, so hängt das spezifische Drehungsvermögen der erhaltenen Lösung stark ab vom Grade der Verdünnung.

Wir fanden für 0,230 g Chininhydrat in 3 ccm 96-proc. Alkohol und 0,100 g p-p'-Dinitrodiphensäure in 3,5 ccm 96-proc. Alkohol unmittelbar nach dem Zusammengießen

$$[\alpha]_D^{8} = (+1,32° \cdot 100) : (0,5 \cdot 5,07) = +52,2°$$
(berechnet auf Chininsalz).

Der Drehungswinkel muß sofort abgelesen werden, da in der Polarisationsflüssigkeit rasch Krystalle von Chininsalz anschießen.

Die aufs doppelte Volum verdünnte und schwach erwärmte Lösung drehte nach Erkalten

$$[\alpha]_D^{8} = (+0,28° \cdot 100) : (0,6892 \cdot 2,54) = +16,0°.$$

Nachdem das Volum der bereits einmal verdünnten Lösung auf 45 ccm gebracht worden war, ergab die Polarisation im 4-dm-Rohr

$$[\alpha]_D^{8} = (+0,06° \cdot 100) : (4 \cdot 0,73) = +2,06°.$$

Die Aktivität verminderte sich weiter nach Zusatz von 2 ccm 2 n-Natronlauge. Nach Abfiltrieren von einer geringen Trübung war

$$[\alpha]_D^{8} = (-1,0° \cdot 100) : (4 \cdot 0,70) = -35,6°.$$

Bemerkenswerterweise verändert das Chininhydrat bei Salzbildung mit m-Nitro-benzoesäure und mit Phtalsäure sein spezifisches Drehungsvermögen nur unwesentlich.

Nach Vermischen von 0,127 g m-Nitro-benzoesäure in 4 ccm 96-proc. Alkohol und 0,287 g Chininhydrat in 2 ccm 96-proc. Alkohol fanden wir

$$[\alpha]_D^{8} = (-5,39° \cdot 100) : (0,6892 \cdot 4,78) = -163,5°$$
(berechnet auf Chininhydrat).

Für eine Lösung, bereitet durch Zusammengießen von 0,1014 g Phtalsäure in 3 ccm 96-proc. Alkohol und 0,4625 g Chininhydrat in 3 ccm 96-proc. Alkohol war

$$[\alpha]_D^{8} = (-8,94° \cdot 100) : (0,6892 \cdot 7,71) = -168,2°$$
(berechnet auf Chininhydrat).

Wie weit die Aktivität einer gemeinsamen Lösung von p-p'-Dinitrodiphensäure und Chininhydrat in absolutem Alkohol–Chloroform bei konstant gehaltener Menge der Säure von der Konzentration des Alkaloids abhängt, zeigen die folgenden Versuche.

Es wurden jeweils die in Spalte 1 der nachstehenden Tabelle angegebenen Mengen als 20-proc. absolut alkoholische Chininhydratlösung mit 0,128 g p-p'-Dinitrodiphensäure in 2 ccm absolutem Alkohol und mit 2 ccm Chloroform vermischt. Nach Auffüllen auf 6 ccm mit absolutem Alkohol fanden wir im 0,5-dm-Rohr die in Spalte 4 verzeichneten Drehungswinkel. Die Werte in Spalte 5 geben den dem Chininhydrat in der gleichen Menge Lösungsmittel zukommenden Drehungswinkel an, der nach jedem Versuch im gleichen Rohr be-

stimmt wurde. Die Differenz Δ = Drehungswinkel des Gemisches (Chinin + Säure) − Drehungswinkel der entsprechenden Chininlösung findet sich in Spalte 6.

Optische Aktivität von p-p'-Dinitrodiphensäure-Chininhydratlösungen (4 ccm absoluter Alkohol + 2 ccm Chloroform) bei 18°:

1	2	3	4	5	6
g Chininhydrat	g Säure	Mol Chinin / 1 Mol Säure	Drehung Gemisch	Drehung Chininhydrat	Δ
0,452	0,128	3,1	+0,53°	−4,87°	5,40°
0,286	0,128	1,96	+2,25	−3,28	5,53
0,226	0,128	1,55	+1,77	−2,54	4,31
0,100	0,128	0,69	+0,81	−1,42	2,23
0,045	0,128	0,31	+0,23	−0,61	0,84

Es scheint bei der Salzbildung von Chinin mit p-p'-Dinitrodiphensäure ein anomaler Effekt vorzuliegen.

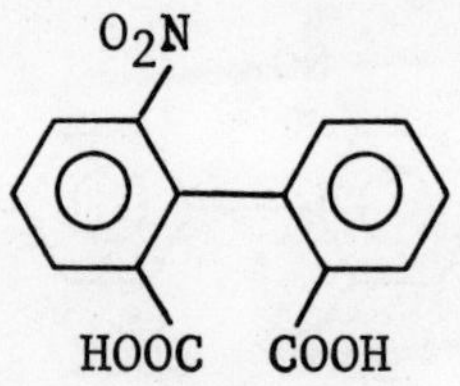

$C_{14}H_9NO_6$ Ref. 996

d- *and* l-6-*Nitrodiphenic Acids*.—The normal quinine salt of 6-nitrodiphenic acid was systematically crystallised from alcohol until it was separated into a slightly less soluble salt, $[\alpha]_{5461}$ + 286·6° (c = 2·5 in chloroform), and a slightly more soluble salt, $[\alpha]_{5461}$ − 122·4° (c = 2·5 in chloroform). The former on decomposition gave the *d*-acid with $[\alpha]_{5461}$ + 65·2° (c = 3·01 in ethyl alcohol), whilst the latter gave the *l*-acid with $[\alpha]_{5461}$ − 66·4° (c = 4·91 in ethyl alcohol). The *l*-acid had $[\alpha]_{5461}$ + 433° (c = 4·69 in 0·261*N*-sodium hydroxide), whilst the *d*-acid, obtained from its morphine salt, had $[\alpha]_{5461}$ − 434° (c = 4·73 in 0·426*N*-sodium hydroxide).

The solution of the sodium salt was kept at room temperature, and the following observations were made:

Time (days)	0	2	9	23	36·5	51
α_{5461}	−20·51°	−18·61°	−14·42°	−8·23°	−4·00°	−1·50°

$C_{14}H_9NO_6$ Ref. 996a

6-Nitro-2,2'-dicarboxybiphenyl and its resolution. 4-Nitrophenanthrenequinone was oxidized to 6-nitro-2,2'-dicarboxybiphenyl by the method of Schmidt [8] and the product then recrystallized from water. M.p. 250−253°C (decomp); lit.[8] m.p. 248−250°C (decomp). The acid was resolved with morphine in ethanol according to Bell and Robinson [9] except that the hydrolysis of the morphine salt was performed in the following way. The salt was ground with 10 equivalents of 2 N K_2CO_3 at room temperature. After 5 min the morphine was filtered off and the optically active acid was precipitated by carefully acidifying the filtrate with dilute HCl. The mixture was allowed to stand in the refrigerator for a few hours before filtering off the acid. This procedure was repeated twice to ensure complete separation of morphine and (−)-6-nitro-2,2'-dicarboxybiphenyl. The specific rotation of the acid was $[\alpha]_{436}^{50} = -792°$ (c=4.70 in 2 N K_2CO_3).

8. Schmidt, J. and Austin, P. C. *Ber.* 36 (1903) 3731.
9. Bell, F. and Robinson, P. H. *J. Chem. Soc.* 1927 1696.

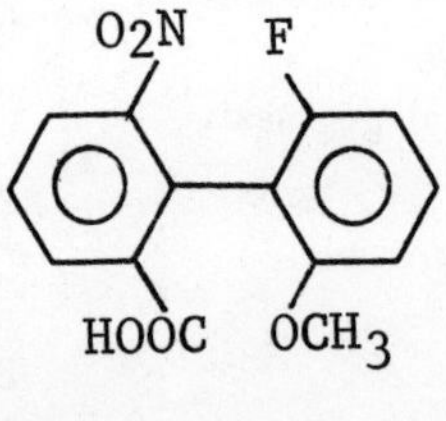

$C_{14}H_{10}FNO_5$ Ref. 997

Resolution of 2-Nitro-6-carboxy-2'-fluoro-6'-methoxydiphenyl.—The monobrucine salt was made in alcohol and the two diastereoisomers were obtained by fractionation. Both the less soluble and the more soluble salts were purified by recrystallization from alcohol. The salts were decomposed to the active acids by shaking for one hour with 5 cc. of concentrated hydrochloric acid, a little ice and a few drops of chloroform. The free acids precipitated and were recrystallized from 50% alcohol.

Constants of Salts and Acids

	M. p., °C.	Wt. made up to 15 cc. in $CHCl_3$	l = 2 α_D	$[\alpha]_D^{23}$
1 Less sol. brucine salt	215	0.0388	+0.538°	+103.9°
2 More sol. brucine salt	207	.047	− .657°	−104.8
3 *d*-Acid	157	.0146 (alc.)	+ .12	+ 61.6
4 *l*-Acid	157	.0120 (alc.)	− .105	− 65.6

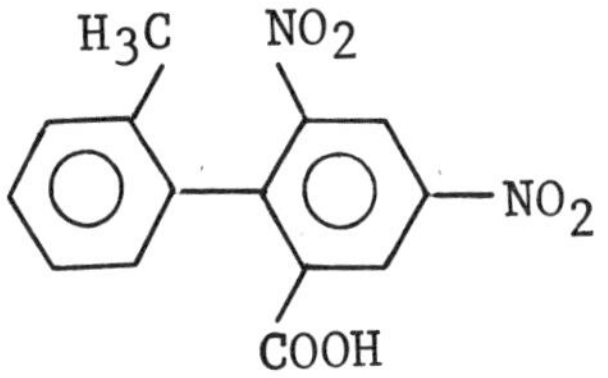

$C_{14}H_{10}N_2O_6$ Ref. 998

Resolution of 2 : 4-Dinitro-2'-methyldiphenyl-6-carboxylic Acid.— When a mixture of equivalent quantities of brucine and the acid was caused to crystallise from alcoholic solution, no resolution occurred. Repeated crystallisation of the salt from acetone failed to effect any change in rotation.

A similar result was obtained when the brucine salt was prepared by treating an aqueous solution of the ammonium salt with brucine hydrochloride. Resolution was, however, effected by the following process.

A solution of 12 g. of the acid in acetone was treated with a half-equivalent of brucine (7·8 g.) and the resulting solution (400 c.c.) was allowed to crystallise. Clusters of rectangular needles separated (8 g.), having $[\alpha]_{5791}$ −7·2° in chloroform ($l = 2$, $c = 2·002$). To the mother-liquor were added a further 7·8 g. of brucine, and 9 g. of salt were obtained, consisting mainly of rectangular plates and having $[\alpha]_{5791}$ −5·8° in chloroform ($l = 2$, $c = 2·052$). On removal of some of the acetone from the mother-liquor, a further 5 g. of salt separated in rectangular needles, having $[\alpha]_{5791}$ −2·4° in chloroform ($l = 2$, $c = 2·04$).

After five crystallisations of the three salts from acetone, these had respectively $[\alpha]_{5791}$ −11·7°, −7·3°, and −2·2° in chloroform, and when decomposed gave three fractions of acid having respectively $[\alpha]_{5791}$ −17·5°, 0·0°, and +16·8° in alcoholic solution. Decomposition of the salts was effected as follows : A chloroform solution of the salt was shaken with approximately the calculated amount of aqueous ammonia, and the alkaline solution then extracted thrice with chloroform. Acidification of the solution, followed by extraction with ether, afforded the free acid.

By employing the fractional crystallisation method, using brucine hydrochloride and the ammonium salt of the acid in aqueous solution, the same salts were obtained, and they crystallised from the aqueous solution in the same order.

l-2 : 4-*Dinitro-2'-methyldiphenyl-6-carboxylic acid* crystallised from aqueous solution in pale yellow, hexagonal prisms, m. p. 158—159°, and had $[\alpha]_{5791}$ −18·6° in ethyl-alcoholic solution (Found : C, 55·5; H, 3·2. $C_{14}H_{10}O_6N_2$ requires C, 55·6; H, 3·3%). It is sparingly soluble in water or light petroleum, readily soluble in acetone and in alcohol, but less so in benzene. It crystallises from benzene in clumps of hexagonal plates, m. p. 158—159° (with previous softening at 140°), and then has $[\alpha]_{5791}$ −7·8° in ethyl-alcoholic solution. From an equivalent-weight determination it was found that 0·5 mol. of benzene of crystallisation was present. After being heated for 2 days at 100°, the compound still had the same composition and rotation. An alcoholic solution of the compound was evaporated and the process was twice repeated. The compound remained unchanged. It was dissolved in aqueous sodium hydroxide and the solution was boiled until free from benzene. The acid recovered by acidification, etc., had $[\alpha]_{5791}$ −18·6° in ethyl-alcoholic solution.

The benzene-free acid had $[\alpha]_{5791}$ −19·5° in acetone (c, 1·382) and − 11·2° in benzene (c, 1·318).

d-2 : 4-*Dinitro-2'-methyldiphenyl-6-carboxylic acid* has properties similar to those of its *l*-isomeride. It has $[\alpha]_{5791}$ −18·8° in ethyl alcohol (c, 1·462), and after crystallisation from benzene contains 0·5 mol. of benzene, then having $[\alpha]_{5791}$ +7·8° in ethyl alcohol (c, 1·772) (Found : C, 55·6; H, 3·5. $C_{14}H_{10}O_6N_2$ requires C, 55·6; H, 3·3%).

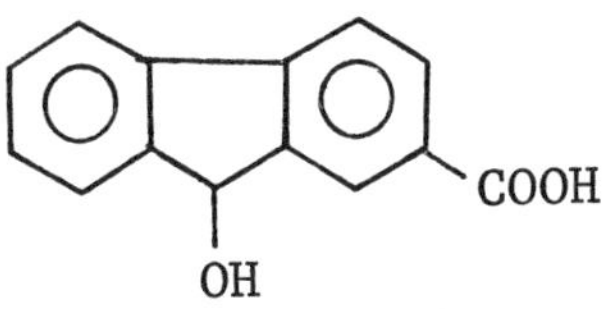

$C_{14}H_{10}O_3$ Ref. 999

Resolution of 9-Hydroxyfluorene-2-carboxylic Acid.— To 11.3 g. (0.05 mole) of 9-hydroxyfluorene-2-carboxylic acid in 125 cc. of 95% ethanol there was added 16.7 g. (0.05 mole) of strychnine in 125 cc. of chloroform. Distillation removed the greater part of the chloroform. The next day, crystals in the form of rosets, weighing 13.2 g., were obtained. These, recrystallized from 700 cc. of ethanol, sintered at 190° and melted at 203°. This strychnine salt was dissolved in a mixture of 100 cc. of ethanol and 100 cc. of 2% sodium hydroxide. This was poured into a liter of water containing 20 cc. of 6 *N* hydrochloric acid. The white fluffy precipitate was recrystallized from 60 cc. of ethanol and fine needles melting at 263° (block) were obtained. The rotations obtained are shown in Table I.

The mother liquor from the precipitation of the insoluble *d*-acid salt was boiled with Darco and filtered. The levo acid was isolated from this solution similarly to the dextro form and recrystallized from 75 cc. of ethanol. The acid had a light yellow color which a second recrystallization did not remove. The purified acid melted at 260° (block).

Table I

9-Hydroxyfluorene-2-carboxylic Acid

Actual and Specific Rotations of Isomers

Wave length of light, Å.	Actual rotation Dextro[a]	Levo[a]	Specific rotation Dextro	Levo
6563	α^{27} +0.82°	α^{27} −0.83°	$[\alpha]^{27}$ +29.3°	$[\alpha]^{27}$ −27.6°
5893	α^{27} +1.11°	α^{27} −1.09°	$[\alpha]^{27}$ +39.6°	$[\alpha]^{27}$ −36.3°
5463	α^{27} +1.39°	α^{27} −1.35°	$[\alpha]^{27}$ +49.6°	$[\alpha]^{27}$ −45.0°

[a] The actual rotation for the dextro compound was found using 0.7000 g. of the acid in 50 cc. of ethanol in a 2-dm. tube. The actual rotation for the *levo* compound was found using 0.7500 g. of the acid in 50 cc. of ethanol in a 2-dm. tube.

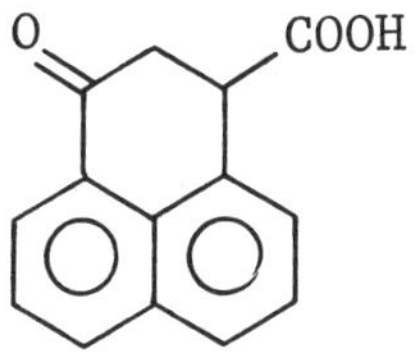

$C_{14}H_{10}O_3$ Ref. 1000

Preliminary experiments on resolution. The salts of *brucine* and *cinchonidine* gave (+)-acid of very high activity. Levorotatory acid of high activity was obtained via the salt of *dehydroabietylamine*. The salt, and even the alkaloid, were soluble in dilute methanol or ethanol only with great difficulty, and the salt crystallised suddenly as big lumps in moderate yield. The progress of the resolution was very rapid, but a better solvent can perhaps be found. *Cinchonine, quinine, quinidine* and *strychnine* gave no crystalline salts from various solvents. The racemic acid can also be resolved by using optically active α-(2-*naphthyl*)-*ethylamine* as the base. This synthetic amine [15] has some disadvantages in price and preparation and must be resolved. The optically active base gave acid of high activity and of the same direction of rotation as the base. An attempt was also made to utilise (−)-α-(2-naphthyl)-ethylamine for resolution on a preparative scale, but much solvent and many recrystallisations were needed to get levorotatory acid with maximum activity. For the final resolution cinchonidine and dehydroabietylamine were selected.

(+)-*3-Perinaphthanone-1-carboxylic acid.* 98.0 g (0.43 mole) of racemic acid were dissolved with 127.6 g (0.43 mole) of cinchonidine in 1.7 l of boiling dilute methanol. The salt was filtered off after 24 hours at +4° and recrystallised from the same solvent. The progress of the resolution was tested on small samples from each crystallisation, from which the acid was liberated and the rotatory power determined in absolute ethanol.

Crystallisation	1	2	3	4	5
ml methanol	1325	1200	900	700	500
ml water	375	350	300	250	150
g salt obtained	110.0	85.5	70.0	56.0	46.0
$[\alpha]_D^{25}$ of the acid	+195.3°	+240.0°	+262.0°	+278.8°	+278.8°

The cinchonidine salt obtained in the course of the resolution forms long, colourless needles.

The acid was liberated from the salt with dilute hydrochloric acid, extracted rapidly with ether and recrystallised twice with charcoal from dilute acetic acid (1:1). 46 g salt yielded 13.5 g of pure acid forming short, colourless needles melting at 198.0°.

$C_{14}H_{10}O_3$(226.23) calc. C 74.33 H 4.46
found C 74.21 H 4.41

0.2043 g acid dissolved in absolute ethanol to 10.00 ml:
$\alpha_D^{25} = +5.696°$ (1 dm); $[\alpha]_D^{25} = +278.8°$; $[M]_D^{25} = +630.7°$.

(−)-*3-Perinaphthanone-1-carboxylic acid.* The mother liquor from the first crystallisation of the cinchonidine salt was evaporated to dryness, and the acid liberated as described above; 51.0 g having $[\alpha]_D^{25} = -208°$ (absolute ethanol) were obtained. 45.2 g (0.20 mole) of this acid and 57.0 g (0.20 mole) of dehydroabietylamine were dissolved in 10 l hot dilute methanol. The salt was filtered off after 24 hours at −10° and recrystallised from the same solvent. The course of the resolution was followed as described above.

Crystallisation	1	2
ml methanol	9000	4500
ml water	1000	500
g salt obtained	64.0	45.0
$[\alpha]_D^{25}$ of the acid	−279.0°	−279.0°

The acid was liberated by decomposing the salt with sodium hydroxide solution and the dehydroabietylamine was extracted with ether. Acidifying of the remaining aqueous solution with conc. hydrochloric acid yielded, after recrystallised twice with charcoal from dilute acetic acid (1:1), 11.0 g of pure acid forming short, colourless needles melting at 198.0°.

$C_{14}H_{10}O_3$(226.23) calc. C 74.33 H 4.46
found C 74.22 H 4.47

Table 1.

g = gram acid dissolved to 10.00 ml.

Solvent	g	α_D^{25} (1 dm)	$[\alpha]_D^{25}$	$[M]_D^{25}$
Ethanol (abs.)	0.2043	−5.700°	−279.0°	−631.4°
Ethanol (abs.)	0.1005	−2.804°	−279.0°	−631.4°
Acetone	0.2024	−5.272°	−260.5°	−589.5°
Ethyl acetate	0.2027	−5.147°	−253.9°	−574.6°
Acetic acid	0.2051	−6.544°	−319.1°	−722.0°
Chloroform	0.2050	−6.216°	−303.2°	−686.2°

The rotatory power was determined in various solvents using a Perkin-Elmer 141 polarimeter, and the results are given in Table 1. The activity in absolute ethanol solution was also determined at different concentrations, which showed that the rotatory power was independent of the concentration.

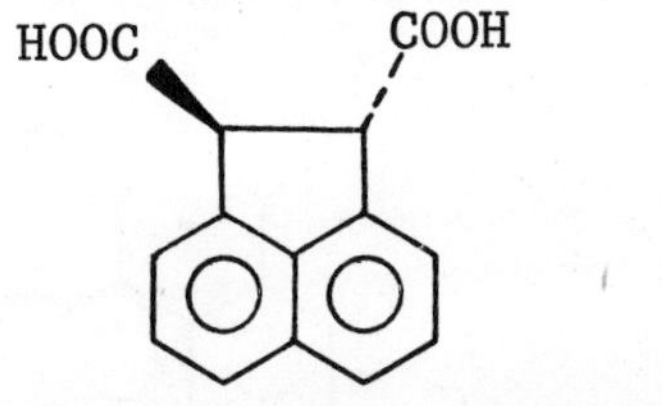

$C_{14}H_{10}O_4$ Ref. 1001

Dédoublement de l'acide acénaphtène-dicarboxylique-1,2 trans.

4 g de diacide et 16 g de brucine sont dissous à chaud dans 100 cm³ d'éthanol. Après refroidissement, on recueille 12 g de précipité qui après 2 recristallisations dans l'éthanol donnent 4,2 g de sel. Par décomposition par l'acide chlorhydrique N, on obtient 970 mg d'acide $[\alpha]_{578}^{52} = +170°$ (EtOH, $c = 0{,}4$). Après recristallisation dans un mélange benzène (90 %)-acide acétique (10 %), on obtient 550 mg d'acide $[\alpha]_{578}^{25} = +209°$ (EtOH, $c = 0{,}2$).

Ester méthylique (par le diazométhane). Après recristallisation dans l'éther, on obtient 410 mg d'ester optiquement pur (> 98 %), $[\alpha]_{578}^{25} = +179°$ (EtOH, $c = 0{,}67$), F = 115,5°. *Analyse.*

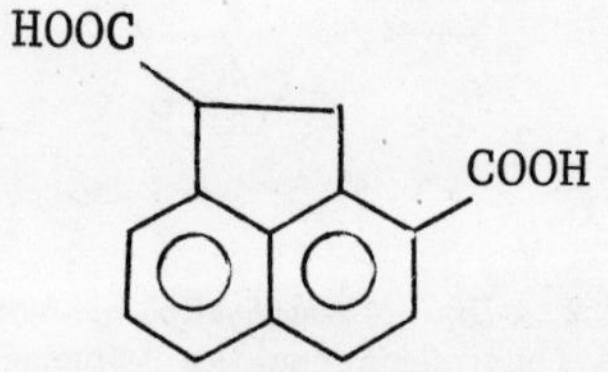

$C_{14}H_{10}O_4$ Ref. 1002

Dédoublement de l'acide acénaphtène-dicarboxylique-1,3.

On traite 2,97 g de diacide-1,3 par 8,1 g de quinine dans l'éthanol. Après 2 recristallisations dans l'éthanol (il est nécessaire de le dissoudre dans un excès puis de concentrer), on recueille 5 g de sel. En décomposant par l'acide chlorhydrique N, on obtient 0,95 g d'acide $[\alpha]_{578} = -180°$ (EtOH).

Cet acide étant difficile à recristalliser et correspondant à un racémique très stable, il est avantageux de le transformer en ester, qui se recristallise aisément et correspond à un racémique ayant un faible domaine d'existence. On obtient ainsi rapidement les deux antipodes pratiquement purs. 1 g d'ester $[\alpha]_{578} = -127°$ (EtOH), recristallisé dans l'éthanol donne 800 mg $[\alpha]_{578} = -176°$ dont la pureté optique est supérieure à 98 %. F = 100°. *Analyse.*

$C_{14}H_{10}O_4$ Ref. 1003

Dédoublement de l'acide acénaphtène-dicarboxylique-1,5.

2 g d'acide et 8 g de brucine dissous à chaud dans 100 cm³ d'éthanol donnent au refroidissement 6,8 g de sel. Après 5 recristallisations dans 50 cm³ d'éthanol (à chaque fois), on recueille 1,7 g de sel, qui, décomposé par l'acide chlorhydrique N, donne 345 mg d'acide $[\alpha]_{578}^{25} = -67°$ (EtOH, $c = 0{,}7$).

Cet acide étant très difficile à recristalliser on le transforme en ester méthylique par le diazométhane. Après recristallisation dans le méthanol, on obtient 250 mg d'ester $[\alpha]_{578}^{25} = -53°$ (EtOH, $c = 0{,}7$) de pureté optique supérieure à 98 %, F = 113,5°. *Analyse.*

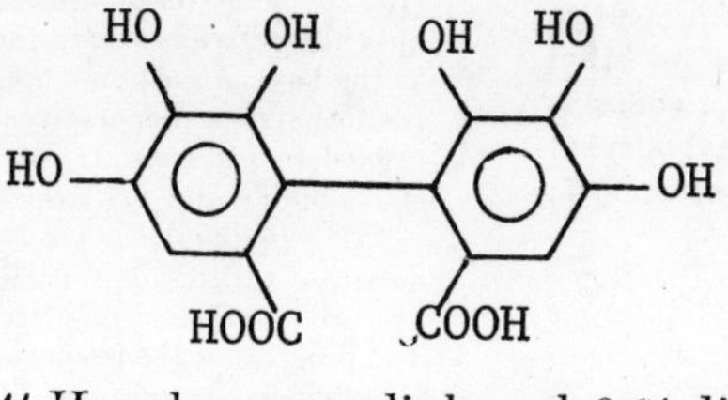

$C_{14}H_{10}O_{10}$ Ref. 1004

I. 2,3,4,2′,3′,4′-Hexabenzoxy-diphenyl-6,6′-dicarbonsäure

a) Racematspaltung mit Cinchonin

1. *Dicinchonin-salz.* 20 g D,L-Hexabenzoxy-diphensäure[12]) und 13,4 g Cinchonin wurden in 350 ccm abs. Äthanol in der Wärme gelöst. Beim Stehen im Eisschrank bildeten sich farblose, prismatische Kristalle (12,8 g = 76,6% d. Th., bezogen auf Dicinchonin-salz eines Antipoden), deren Schmp. und Drehung sich

[12]) Liebigs Ann. Chem. **586**, 165 (1954).

nach 2maligem Umkristallisieren aus abs. Äthanol nicht mehr änderte. Das Salz schmilzt bei 195° und ist unlöslich in Wasser, Äther, Dipropyläther und Cyclohexan. Es löst sich in Chloroform, Benzol, Toluol, Tetrachlorkohlenstoff, Essigester und Eisessig, besser in Aceton und kann aus abs. Methanol oder Äthanol (1 ccm löst bei 20° 4,2 mg) umkristallisiert werden. Zur Analyse und Drehung wurde bei 55°/5 über P_2O_5 getrocknet.

$C_{56}H_{46}O_{10}$, 2 $C_{19}H_{22}N_2O$ (1467,65)	Ber.	C 76,92	H 6,18	N 3,82
	Gef.	» 76,85	» 6,23	» 3,85

$[\alpha]_D^{20}$ = —8,5 ± 1° (Chloroform, c = 2).

2. *D(—)-Hexabenzoxy-diphensäure*

Zur Zerlegung wurden 19,3 g des Salzes in 100 ccm Chloroform gelöst und mit 100 ccm n-H_2SO_4 auf der Maschine geschüttelt. Die chloroformische Schicht wurde abgetrennt und noch 2mal mit je 60 ccm 0,5n-H_2SO_4, dann mit 50 ccm Wasser ausgeschüttelt und über Na_2SO_4 getrocknet. Darauf wurde das Chloroform, zuletzt i. V., abdestilliert und der Rückstand in 40 ccm Essigester gelöst. Durch langsamen Zusatz von Petroläther wurde die Säure zur Kristallisation gebracht. Bei wiederholtem Umkristallisieren änderten sich Schmp. und Drehung nicht. Ausbeute 5,9 g, 88% d. Th. D(—)-Hexabenzoxy-diphensäure bildet farblose Prismen, die bei 147° schmelzen. Sie löst sich in der Kälte in Aceton, Chloroform, Benzol, Butylacetat, Essigester und Eisessig, in der Hitze in Äthanol, Dioxan und Dipropyläther, schwer in Äther und ist unlöslich in Wasser und Cyclohexan. Zum Umkristallisieren eignet sich Eisessig mit einer Spur Wasser, wobei allerdings die Säure zuerst als Sirup ausfällt, der dann kristallisiert, ferner Butylacetat oder Essigester durch Zugabe von Cyclohexan oder Petroläther. Zur Analyse wurde bei 78°/3 über P_2O_5 getrocknet.

$C_{56}H_{46}O_{10}$ (878,93)	Ber.	C 76,52	H 5,28
	Gef.	» 76,71	» 5,43

Zur Drehung wurde bei 55°/4 über P_2O_5 getrocknet.

$[\alpha]_D^{20}$	= —63,6 ± 1°	(Chloroform, c = 1)	$[M]_D$	= —559°
»	= —43,4 ± 2°	(abs. Äthanol, c = 1,6)	»	= —381°
»	= —31,7 ± 2°	(Eisessig, c = 0,6)	»	= —279°
»	= —48,1 ± 3°	(abs. Methanol, c = 1,3)	»	= —423°

3. *Dicinchonin-salz der L(+)-Hexabenzoxy-diphensäure*

Die alkoholische Mutterlauge von 1. wurde i. V. zur Trockene gebracht und der Rückstand aus 180 ccm abs. Aceton umkristallisiert. Nach nochmaligem Umkristallisieren aus Aceton und aus Äthanol änderten sich Schmp. und Drehung nicht mehr. Ausbeute 11,2 g, 67% d. Th.[13]). Das Salz schmilzt unscharf bei 112—118°. Im Gegensatz zum Salz der D-Säure bildet es farblose, sechseckige Plättchen. Im allgemeinen besitzt das Salz der L-Säure ähnliche Löslichkeiten wie das der D-Säure. Auffallend ist die viel geringere Löslichkeit des ersten in Aceton und größere Löslichkeit in Äthanol. Zur Analyse wurde bei 100°/5 über P_2O_5 zur Drehung bei 55° getrocknet.

$C_{56}H_{46}O_{10}$, 2 $C_{19}H_{22}ON_2$ (1467,65)				
	Ber.	C 76,92	H 6,18	N 3,82
	Gef.	» 77,05	» 6,42	» 3,68

$[\alpha]_D^{20}$ = +54,4 ± 1° (Chloroform, c = 0,9).

4. *L(+)-Hexabenzoxy-diphensäure*

12,25 g des L-Salzes wurden, wie bei der D-Verbindung beschrieben, zerlegt. Schmp. 147—148°, Ausbeute nach einmaligem Umkristallisieren 6,55 g, 90% d. Th. Zur Analyse wurde wie vorstehend getrocknet.

$C_{56}H_{46}O_{10}$ (878,93)	Ber.	C 76,52	H 5,28
	Gef.	» 76,49	» 5,46

$[\alpha]_D^{20}$	= +66,2 ± 3°	(Chloroform, c = 0,9)	$[M]_D$	= +582°
»	= +44,6 ± 1°	(abs. Äthanol, c = 1,1)	»	= +392°
»	= +50,0 ± 3°	(abs. Methanol, c = 1,1)	»	= +439°
»	= +31,6 ± 2°	(Eisessig, c = 0,6)	»	= +278°

---

[13]) Durch abwechselndes Umkristallisieren der eingedampften Mutterlauge aus Äthanol und Aceton konnten noch weitere Mengen an reinem D- und L-Salz gewonnen werden.

b) Racematspaltung mit Chinidin

1. Dichinidin-salz der D(—)-Hexabenzoxy-diphensäure

1,0121 g D,L-Hexabenzoxy-diphensäure und 0,7475 g Chinidin wurden in 25 ccm abs. Äthanol in der Wärme gelöst. Beim Stehenlassen bildeten sich farblose, prismatische Kristalle, die nach dem Umkristallisieren aus Äthanol konstant bei 196° schmolzen. Ausbeute 0,330 g, 37,4% d. Th. Zur Analyse wurde bei 120°/5 über P_2O_5 getrocknet.

$C_{56}H_{46}O_{10}$, 2 $C_{20}H_{24}O_2N_2$ (1527,68)

Ber.	C 75,47	H 6,22	N 3,67	OCH_3 4,06
Gef.	» 75,21	» 6,38	» 3,75	» 4,06

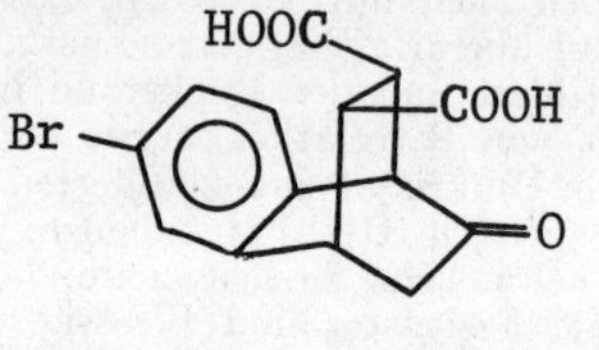

IXe

$C_{14}H_{11}BrO_5$

Ref. 1005

Optical resolution of trans-*diacid* VIIIa, b, d, IX c, e, *and* XVb *with cinchonidine*

General procedure. A soln of *trans*-diacid (0·5 g) and cinchonidine (0·5 g) in EtOH (15 ml) was heated under reflux for 1 hr. The soln was evaporated and the residue was dissolved in AcOEt. After standing overnight the precipitated salt was recrystallized from MeOH until the optical rotation ($[\alpha]_D$) of the salt became constant. The purified salt (molecular ratio, 1:1, as shown by elemental analyses) was suspended in ether and decomposed by shaking with dil HCl. The free active acid was purified by recrystallization.

M.ps and solvents for recrystallization of the active acids were as follows: (+)-VIIIa·1/2H_2O, 168–169° (MeOH-H_2O); (+)-IXc·1/2H_2O, 112–114° (MeOH-H_2O); (+)-VIIId, 230–231° (AcOEt-$CHCl_3$); (+)-IXe, 166–167·5° (AcOEt-C_6H_6); (−)-IXe, 166–167·5° (AcOEt-C_6H_6). Satisfactory elemental analyses were obtained for these active acids. Attempted crystallizations of the active acid VIIIb and its dimethyl ester were unsuccessful. However, when the diacid was chromatographed on silica gel (Merck, 0·2–0·5 mm) and developed with MeOH-AcOEt (1:19), crystals of the Na salt-dihydrate were accidentally obtained: IR ν_{max}^{KBr} (cm^{-1}) 3390, 1720, 1615, 1575. (Found: C, 48·37; H, 4·36. Calc. for $C_{15}H_{12}Na_2O_6 \cdot 2H_2O$: C, 48·65; H, 4·62%); $[\alpha]_D$ of the pure salts and active acids thus obtained are shown in Table 3.

TABLE 3. OPTICAL ROTATION OF CINCHONIDINE SALTS OF TRANS-ACIDS

	$[\alpha]_D$ (MeOH) Salt	Free compd.
E* XVIII		+ 356·2[d]
XVa	+ 50·3[b]	+ 208·1[c]
VIIId	+ 31·0	+ 209·5
IXc	+ 44·6	+ 249·8
IXe	+ 52·0 (− 176·0)†	+ 192·3 (− 193·3)†
VIIIb	+ 24·5	+ 152·7[a]
IXa	+ 19·1	+ 207·0
E* XIX		+ 140·4[d]
XVI		+ 12·4[e]

[a] sodium salt [b] in EtOH [c] methyl ester

[d] in $CHCl_3$ [e] in *iso*-octane

* The letter E is used to indicate "enantiomer of."

† The value for (−)-IXe.

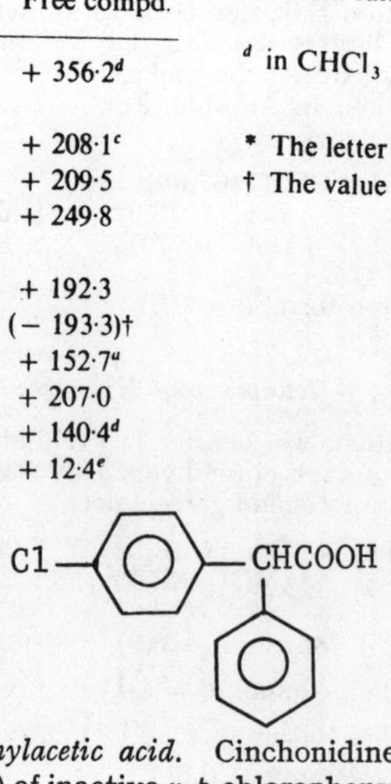

$C_{14}H_{11}ClO_2$

Ref. 1006

(+)-α-p-*Chlorophenyl-α-phenylacetic acid.* Cinchonidine (98 g.) was gradually added to a boiling ethanolic solution (1·5 l.) of inactive α-*p*-chlorophenyl-α-phenylacetic acid [4] (82 g.). The liquid was boiled under reflux for 30 min. and sufficient water was added to produce cloudiness. The cooled solution deposited *cinchonidine* α-p-*chlorophenyl-α-phenylacetate*, m. p. 160° (74 g.) (Found: C, 73·7; H, 6·3; N, 5·1; Cl, 6·7. $C_{33}H_{33}O_3N_2Cl$ requires C, 73·3; H, 6·1; N, 5·2; Cl, 6·7%). Eight recrystallisations of the cinchonidine salt from 60% aqueous acetone afforded the optically pure salt (12 g.). This was decomposed by dilute sulphuric acid, and the precipitated (+)-α-*p*-chlorophenyl-α-phenylacetic acid recrystallised from dilute acetic acid. It had m. p. 112° and $[\alpha]_D^{18}$ 15·3° (in ethanol).

[4] Grundy, Hsü, and Rothstein, unpublished work.

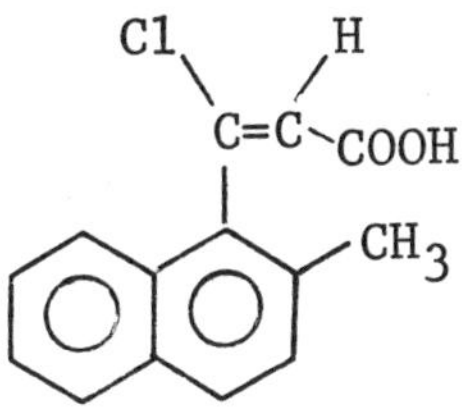

$C_{14}H_{11}ClO_2$ Ref. 1007

Resolution of β-Chloro-β-(2-methyl-1-naphthyl)-α-methylacrylic Acid.—To a solution of 1.5 g. of β-chloro-β-(2-methyl-1-naphthyl)-α-methylacrylic acid in 60 cc. of hot ethyl acetate was added 2 g. of quinine. Upon cooling 1.5 g. of salt crystallized, and by evaporation of the solvent nearly to dryness, an additional 1.7 g. of salt was obtained. These fractions were purified separately by recrystallization from ethyl acetate to constant rotation; less-soluble salt, white crystals, m. p. 194° (cor.) with decomposition; more-soluble salt, white crystals, m. p. 132° (cor.) with decomposition.

Anal. Calcd. for $C_{15}H_{13}O_2Cl \cdot C_{20}H_{24}O_2N_2$: C, 71.82; H, 6.38. Found: less-soluble salt: C, 71.54; H, 6.59; more-soluble salt: C, 71.98; H, 6.46.

Rotations. Less-soluble salt: 0.018 g. made up to 10 cc. with ethanol at 26° gave αD −0.140°; *l*, 1; $[\alpha]^{26}_D$ −72°. More-soluble salt: 0.017 g. made up to 10 cc. with ethanol at 26° gave αD −0.23°; *l*, 1; $[\alpha]^{26}_D$ −136°.

d- and l-β-Chloro-β-(2-methyl-1-naphthyl)-α-methylacrylic Acids.—The acids were obtained from their salts in the manner described for the β-chloro-β-(2-methyl-1-naphthyl)-acrylic acids except that it was not necessary to extract aqueous solutions of their sodium salts with chloroform. Recrystallized from petroleum ether (b. p. 60–110°); *d*-acid, white crystals, m. p. 123° (cor.); *l*-acid, white crystals, m. p. 123° (cor.).

Anal. Calcd. for $C_{15}H_{13}O_2Cl$: C, 69.06; H, 5.03. Found: *d*-acid: C, 69.02; H, 5.19; *l*-acid: C, 69.41; H, 5.15.

Rotations. *d*-Acid: 0.020 g. made up to 10 cc. with ethanol at 26° gave αD +0.11°; *l*, 1; $[\alpha]^{26}_D$ +55°. *l*-Acid: 0.024 g. made up to 10 cc. with ethanol at 26° gave αD −0.14°; *l*, 1; $[\alpha]^{26}_D$ −58°.

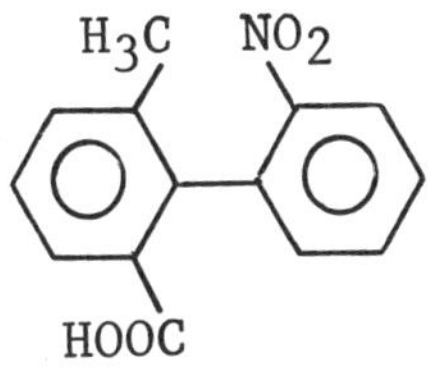

$C_{14}H_{11}NO_4$ Ref. 1008

Resolution of 2-Methyl-6-carboxy-2′-nitrobiphenyl.—A solution of 3 g. of 2-methyl-6-carboxy-2′-nitrobiphenyl in 20 cc. of boiling methanol was mixed with a boiling solution of 5.43 g. of anhydrous brucine in 50 cc. of methanol. After standing for three hours, 5 g. of salt deposited. After three recrystallizations from 50 cc. of methanol a constant rotation was obtained: white crystals, m. p. 165–167°.

Rotation. 0.05 g. made up to 15 cc. in chloroform at 25°. αD +0.32; *l* = 2; $[\alpha]^{25}_D$ +48°.

Anal. Calcd. for $C_{37}H_{37}N_3O_8$: N, 6.97. Found: N, 7.02.

Upon cooling the mother liquor, 2.4 g. of salt separated. This was dissolved in 40 cc. of methanol and cooled slowly. The first portion of crystals was discarded and finally 1.6 g. of salt was collected. Recrystallization of this from methanol did not change the melting point or the rotation: white crystals, m. p. 153–160°.

Rotation. 0.05 g. made up to 15 cc. in chloroform at 25°. αD −0.34; *l* = 2; $[\alpha]^{25}_D$ −51°.

Anal. Calcd. for $C_{37}H_{37}N_3O_8$: N, 6.97. Found: N, 6.86.

d- and l-2-Methyl-6-carboxy-2′-nitrobiphenyl.—The active acids were formed as previously described for the active 2-carboxy-6-nitro-2′-nitrobiphenyls. The active acids were purified by recrystallization from dilute ethanol, *d*-acid m. p. 179–181°, *l*-acid m. p. 175–179°.

Rotation. (*d*-acid) 0.05 g. made up to 15 cc. in chloroform, αD +0.49; *l* = 2; $[\alpha]^{25}_D$ +73.5°. (*l*-acid) 0.0485 g. made up to 15 cc. in chloroform. αD −0.47; *l* = 2; $[\alpha]^{25}_D$ −72.6°.

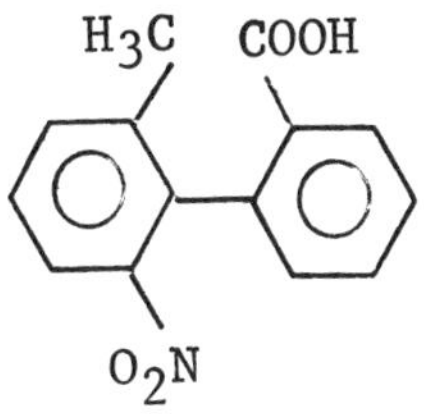

$C_{14}H_{11}NO_4$ Ref. 1009

d- and l-2-Methyl-6-nitrobiphenyl-2′-carboxylic Acid.—The *dl*-acid was resolved by crystallization of the quinidine salt from ethanol; the recrystallized salt had $[\alpha]^{20}_D$ +217° in 1.5% solution in acetic acid. Other salt samples had $[\alpha]_D$ +217°, +221°, +233° and +218°. The *d*-2-methyl-6-nitrobiphenyl-2′-carboxylic acid was obtained (4.5 g. from 15.3 g. *dl*-acid) by stirring the salt with 6 *N* hydrochloric acid; it had $[\alpha]^{23}_D$ +65° in 1.5% solution in methanol. Other preparations of the acid had $[\alpha]_D$ +69°, +71°, m.p. 170–173°.

The 8 g. of recovered crude *l*-acid was converted to the brucine salt, which was recrystallized from acetone. This salt had $[\alpha]^{20}_D$ −23° in 1% solution in acetic acid. Crude *l*-acid (5.78) obtained on treatment with hydrochloric acid had $[\alpha]^{20}_D$ −57° in 1.3% solution in methanol; recrystallization from methanol gave 3.20 g. of almost colorless crystals, m.p. 172–175°, $[\alpha]^{25}_D$ −69° in 2% solution in methanol.

$C_{14}H_{11}NO_4$ Ref. 1009a

Resolution of 2-Methyl-6-nitro-2′-carboxybiphenyl.—To a boiling solution of 3.28 g. of 2-nitro-6-carboxy-2′-methylbiphenyl in 500 cc. of 60% ethanol was added 4.13 g. of quinine. After standing overnight 3.8 g. of crystals separated which were purified by crystallization three times from 200 cc. of hot 50% ethanol. The salt thus obtained gave a constant rotation and weighed 1.7 g. Before drying, the product had a melting point of 135–140° and after drying, 168–171°.

Rotation (dry *l* salt). 0.05 g. made up to 15 cc. in chloroform at 25°. αD −0.89°; *l* = 2; $[\alpha]^{25}_D$ −133.5°.

Anal. Calcd. for $C_{34}H_{35}O_6N_3$: N, 7.22. Found: N, 7.53.

Rotation (solvated *l* salt) 0.05 g. made up to 15 cc. in chloroform at 25°. αD −0.83°; *l* = 2; $[\alpha]^{25}_D$ −124.2°.

On cooling the original mother liquor from the less soluble salt, a small crop of crystals separated which were discarded. The alcohol solution was then allowed to evaporate until the more soluble salt separated. This was purified by three crystallizations from 100 cc. of hot 30% ethanol. The precaution was taken during the first two crystallizations to discard the first third of the salt

which separated. The final product gave a constant rotation, m. p. 118–123° before drying and 128–131° after drying.

Anal. (dry *d*-salt) Calcd. for $C_{34}H_{35}O_8N_3$: N, 7.22. Found: N, 7.12.

Rotation (solvated *d*-salt) 0.10 g. made up to 15 cc. in chloroform at 25°. αD −1.40°; *l* = 2; $[\alpha]^{25}D$ −105°.

The solvation of these salts appeared not to be constant so that the rotations of the solvated salts are not significant.

d- and l-2-Nitro-6-carboxy-2′-methylbiphenyl.—A suspension of 2 g. of the less soluble salt in 10 cc. of water was cooled in an ice-bath and treated with 10 cc. of cold dilute hydrochloric acid. After stirring for a few minutes the mixture was extracted with ether and the ether extracts washed several times with dilute hydrochloric acid and then with water. The ether solution was then treated with 10 cc. of dilute sodium hydroxide and the aqueous alkaline extract acidified in the cold with hydrochloric acid. The *l*-form of the product separated and was recrystallized from dilute ethanol: white crystals, m. p. 153–155°.

Rotation. (*l*-acid) 0.10 g. made up to 25 cc. in ethanol at 25°. αD −0.52; *l* = 2; $[\alpha]^{25}D$ −65°.

The *d*-acid was obtained in a similar manner and had a melting point of 153–156°.

Rotation. (*d*-acid) 0.0464 g. made up to 15 cc. in ethanol at 25°. αD +0.38°; *l* = 2; $[\alpha]^{25}D$ +61.5°.

$C_{14}H_{11}NO_4$

Ref. 1009b

Resolution of 2-Methyl-6-nitro-2′-carboxydiphenyl.—To a boiling solution of 2 g. of 2-methyl-6-nitro-2′-carboxydiphenyl in 1500 cc. of water was added 3.07 g. of anhydrous brucine. As soon as solution was complete, it was filtered and at the end of one-half hour 2.1 g. of flaky white crystals had deposited. These were collected and after three recrystallizations from water yielded one gram of salt of constant rotation melting from 169–175°. This salt was found to contain water which corresponds to one molecule of water of crystallization. The analytical sample was dried over phosphorus pentoxide in a vacuum at 117° for twenty-four hours. The melting point of the anhydrous form is 173–175°.

Rotation. Hydrated *l*-salt: 0.1368 g. made up to 25 cc. with chloroform at 20° gave αD = +0.33°; *l* = 2; $[\alpha]^{20}_D$ +30.4°.

Anal. 0.3304 g. lost 0.0086 g. on drying. Calcd. for $C_{37}H_{37}N_3O_8 \cdot H_2O$: H_2O, 2.69. Found: H_2O, 2.60. Calcd. for $C_{37}H_{37}N_3O_8$: C, 68.17; H, 5.73. Found: C, 67.67; H, 5.75.

Upon concentrating the mother liquors to 100 cc., 1.8 g. of impure *d*-salt was obtained. This was recrystallized from water and on each crystallization the very first crystals that separated were discarded. Five recrystallizations in this manner yielded 0.5 g. of salt with a constant rotation melting from 145–155°. This salt appears to contain water equivalent to one and one-half molecules of water of crystallization. The anhydrous form which was used for analysis melts at 172° with softening beginning at 145°.

Rotation. Hydrated *d*-salt. 0.0850 g. made up to 15 cc. with chloroform at 20° gave αD = −0.65°; *l* = 2; $[\alpha]^{20}_D$ −57.3°.

Anal. 0.1780 g. lost 0.0070 g. on drying. Calcd. for $C_{37}H_{37}N_3O_8 \cdot 1.5\ H_2O$; H_2O, 3.98. Found: H_2O, 3.93. Calcd. for $C_{37}H_{37}N_3O_8$: C, 68.17; H, 5.73. Found: C, 67.86; H, 5.93.

l and d-2-Methyl-6-nitro-2′-carboxydiphenyl.—The active acids were liberated from their salts by treatment with hydrochloric acid in the cold. The organic acid was obtained as a fine cream-colored powder when 0.77 g. of the *l*-salt (less soluble) was shaken with 6 *N* hydrochloric acid for one hour. This was filtered, washed with dilute hydrochloric acid and finally with water. After two recrystallizations from dilute methyl alcohol, 0.21 g. remained melting at 174–175° with slight softening at 168°.

Rotation. *l*-acid. 0.2052 g. made up to 25 cc. with methyl alcohol at 20° gave αD = −1.11°; *l* = 2; $[\alpha]^{20}_D$ −67.7°.

The *d*-acid was obtained in exactly the same way; melting point 171–173° with slight softening at 167°.

Rotation. *d*-acid. 0.0309 g. made up to 15 cc. with methyl alcohol at 20° gave αD = +0.26°; *l* = 2; $[\alpha]^{20}_D$ +63.1°.

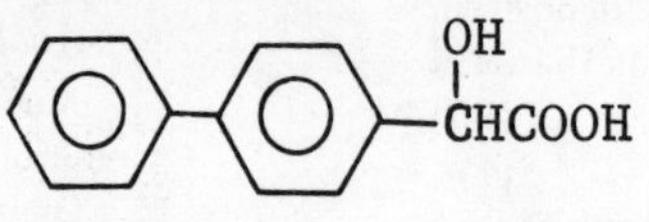

$C_{14}H_{12}O_3$

Ref. 1010

Antipodo (IV) (+): 10,6 g di acido racemo (IV) sono sciolti in 250 ml di metanolo contenente la quantità stechiometrica di chinina (15 g), scaldando a ricadere. Per raffreddamento in frigorifero cristallizza il diastereoisomero (+) (—), dal quale si hanno 5,1 g di antipodo destrogiro. P.f. 203-5° (acido acetico glaciale); $[\alpha]_D$ = +30° (c 6; tetraidrofurano).

	trov. % :	C 74,05;	H 5,67
per $C_{14}H_{12}O_3$	calc. :	73,67;	5,30

Antipodo (IV) (—): il filtrato metanolico dà 5,4 g di antipodo levogiro che fonde a 203-5° (acido acetico glaciale); $[\alpha]_D$ = —36° (c 6; tetraidrofurano).

trov. % : C 73,90; H 5,26

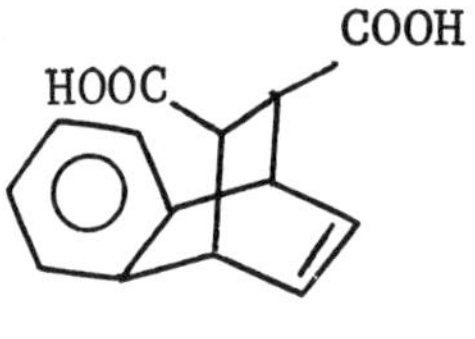

$C_{14}H_{12}O_4$ Ref. 1011

Dédoublement de l'acide dihydro-1,4 éthano-1,4 naphtalène dicarboxylique-9,10 trans **8***a*.

18 g d'acide racémique préparé selon Takeda et coll. (8) et 42 g de déhydroabiétylamine sont dissous dans 200 cm^3 d'éthanol. Après 2 jours de repos, on essore 43,7 g de sel qu'on recristallise dans 300 cm^3 d'éthanol, laisse refroidir 2 h et essore 24,3 g qu'on recristallise 2 fois dans 200 cm^3 d'éthanol. On obtient ainsi 16,35 g de sel qui est décomposé par la soude ~ N. L'acidification des fractions alcalines et l'extraction à l'éther fournit 4,9 g d'acide **8***a* $[\alpha]_{578}^{25} = + 54,1°$ (éthanol, $c = 1,8$), résine qui cristallise lentement.

Les premières eaux-mères du sel, après évaporation à sec et décomposition, fournissent 5,3 g d'acide énantiomère $[\alpha]_{578}^{25} = — 38,8°$.

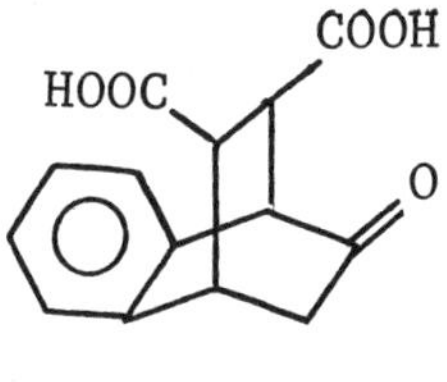

$C_{14}H_{12}O_5$ Ref. 1012

Dédoublement de l'acide oxo-2 dihydro-1,4 éthano-1,4 naphtalènedicarboxylique-9,10 **12***a*.

On dissout à chaud 50 g de cétoacide **12***a* racémique (solvaté), préparé selon Takeda et coll. (4), et 100 g de cinchonidine dans 650 cm^3 d'éthanol et 1 500 cm^3 d'eau. Le sel obtenu (76,5 g) est recristallisé 2 fois dans 500 cm^3 d'éthanol et 1 250 cm^3 d'eau et fournit 56 g de sel qu'on décompose par l'acide chlorhydrique dilué. On extrait à l'éther l'acide (résine) $[\alpha]_{578}^{25} = — 247,5°$ (éthanol, $c = 1$).

Les premières eaux-mères du dédoublement après décomposition fournissent 20 g d'acide **12***a* $[\alpha]_{578}^{25} = + 201,5°$.

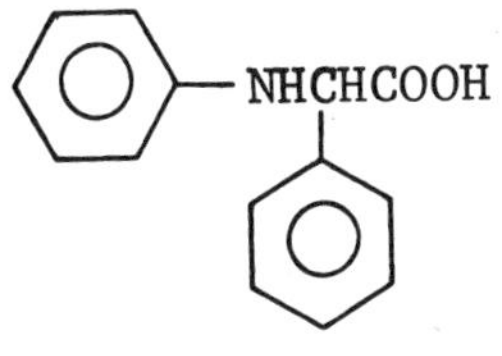

$C_{14}H_{13}NO_2$ Ref. 1013

Forty grams of cinchonine (1 mol.) were added to 1600 c.c. of ethyl alcohol, and the mixture boiled until the alkaloid dissolved. Thirty-one grams of the *r*-acid (1 mol.) were then added, and glassy needles grouped in rosettes began to separate after the solution had been kept for several hours in the ice-chest. The liquid was then stirred vigorously, and, on the following day, 38·1 grams of the salt were collected. This was crystallised from 2700 c.c. of alcohol, and the resulting 25·2 grams were then crystallised twice from as little alcohol as possible. The crystals obtained after this treatment amounted to 15·3 grams, and it was found advisable to decompose them at this stage, although they were not yet homogeneous. They were rubbed in a mortar with concentrated aqueous ammonia, which dissolved the liberated acid, whilst the cinchonine was collected and washed with dilute ammonia. The acid (6·1 grams), obtained from the ammoniacal solution by precipitation with dilute sulphuric acid, had $[\alpha]_D$ −107·7° in acetone solution. It was dissolved in the minimum quantity of hot alcohol, and boiling water was added until cloudiness appeared. On cooling, 5·4 grams of the pure *l*-acid separated.

l-*Phenylanilinoacetic acid* melts at 188°. It is very readily soluble in acetone, ethyl acetate, or ether; it can be crystallised from benzene, toluene, ethyl alcohol, or methyl alcohol, and it is almost insoluble in carbon disulphide or in water. For analysis, it was dried in a vacuum over sulphuric acid:

0·2200 gave 0·5943 CO_2 and 0·1122 H_2O. C=73·7; H=5·7.
0·2712 „ 15·2 c.c. N_2 (moist) at 14·2° and 732 mm. N=6·3.
$C_{14}H_{13}O_2N$ requires C=74·0; H=5·8; N=6·2 per cent.

The following polarimetric values were obtained:

In acetone:
$l=2$, $c=1·467$, α_D −3·46°, α_{5461} −4·21°; whence $[\alpha]_D$ −117·9° and $[\alpha]_{5461}$ −143·5°.

In ethyl alcohol:
$l=2$, $c=1·021$, α_D −2·28°, $[\alpha]_D$ −111·7°.

In ethyl acetate:
$l=2$, $c=2·06$, α_D −4·40°, $[\alpha]_D$ −106·8°.

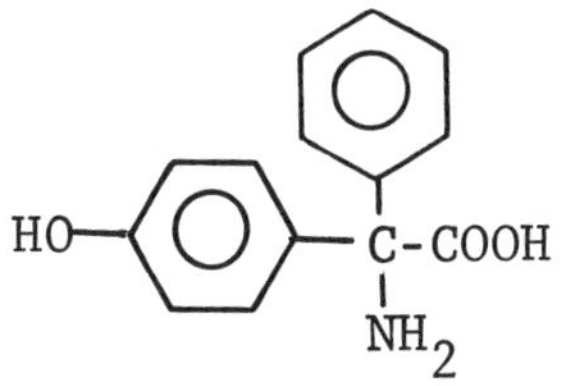

$C_{14}H_{13}NO_3$ Ref. 1014

Example 1

Acetoxymethyl 6-[(−)N-(1-methoxycarbonylpropen-2-yl) α-amino-α (p-hydroxyphenyl)acetamido] penicillanate.

(a) Resolution of α-benzyloxycarbonylamino-α-(p-hydroxyphenyl)acetic acid

A solution of the title acid (224 g) and quinine trihydrate (285 g) in boiling ethanol (2.5 l.) was allowed to cool. The crystals which separated were collected and recrystallised twice from ethanol to give a 76% yield of the quinine salt of the laevorotatory acid $[\alpha]_D^{20}$ −158.5° (C, 1 in MeOH). Treatment of the quinine salt (68 g) with dilute sodium hydroxide, removal of quinine by ether-extraction, and acidification of the aqueous solution gave the laevorotatory acid. This was crystallised twice from aqueous ethanol to give 28 g. (85%) of (−) α-benzyloxycarbonylamino-

α-(p-hydroxyphenyl) acetic acid m.p. 159—161° C, $[\alpha]_D^{18}$ −120.0° (C, 1 in MeOH). (Found: C, 64.1; H, 5.2; N, 4.7. $C_{24}H_{21}NO_7$ requires C, 63.9; H, 4.9; N, 4.7%).

The mother liquor from the crude quinine salt was evaporated to dryness *in vacuo* to leave a syrup which was treated with aqueous sodium hydroxide and the quinine removed by ether-extraction. Acidification of the aqueous layer gave the crude dextrorotatory acid (108 g.) which was collected, dried, and treated with ephedrine (63 g.) in boiling ethanol (450 ml.). On cooling the solution the ephedrine salt of the dextrorotatory acid separated, and was collected and recrystallised from ethanol. Yield 111 g., $[\alpha]_D^{21}$ +46.8° (C, 1 in H_2O). The acid was recovered from this salt in the usual way to give (+)α-benzyloxycarbonylamino-p-hydroxyphenylacetic acid (96%) which, after recrystallisation from 50% aqueous ethanol, had m.p. 158—161° C, $[\alpha]_D^{21}$ +120.2° (C, 1 in MeOH). (Found: C, 64.1; H, 5.3; N, 4.8. $C_{24}H_{21}NO_7$ requires C, 63.9; H, 4.9; N, 4.7%).

(b) Preparation of (−)α-amino-α-(p-hydroxyphenyl)acetic acid

A suspension of (−)-α-benzyloxycarbonylamino-α-(p-hydroxyphenyl) acetic acid (21.8 g.) in water (180 ml.) was treated with dilute sodium hydroxide solution to give a clear solution of pH 8.7. 5% Palladium on calcium carbonate catalyst (2.2 g.) was added, and the mixture was shaken in hydrogen at atmospheric pressure until no more gas was absorbed. The catalyst was filtered off through a pad of kieselguhr and washed with water. The combined filtrate and washings were adjusted to pH 5.0 and the solution was evaporated *in vacuo* to small bulk. The crude product separated as a gelatinous precipitate which redissolved when the mixture was boiled. Colourless, crystalline (−)-α-amino-α-(p-hydroxyphenyl)acetic acid separated when the solution was cooled. It was collected, washed with a little cold water, and dried *in vacuo* over phosphorous pentoxide. The yield was 10.1 g. (83%), m.p. 225—226° $[\alpha]_D^{22}$ −108° (*c*, 1 in H_2O). (Found: C, 57.2; H, 5.4; N, 8.3%. $C_8H_9NO_3$ requires: C, 57.5; H, 5.4; N, 8.4%). N.M.R. (D_2O+NaOD): multiplet centred on 3.15 (4H, aromatic), singlet 5.8 (1H N—CH).

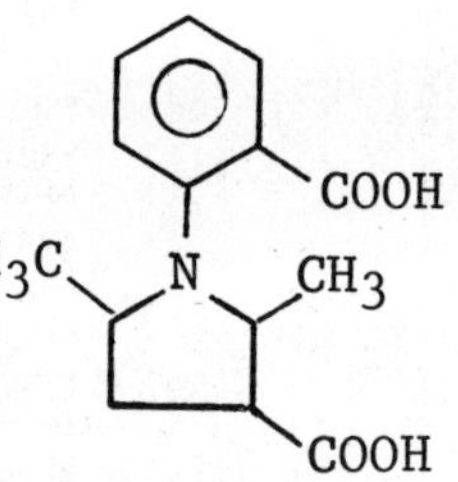

$C_{14}H_{13}NO_4$ Ref. 1015

3-Carbethoxy-2,5-hexadione.—This compound was previously prepared by Weltner[3] from monochloroacetone and acetoacetic ester. In a 1-liter, three-necked flask equipped with a mercury-sealed stirrer, reflux condenser and dropping funnel were placed 260 g. of acetoacetic ester and 25 g. of sodium. The mixture was stirred at room temperature until all of the sodium had dissolved. This required about twenty-four hours. Then 250 cc. of dry ether was added and 99 g. of monochloroacetone was slowly added. Stirring was continued for eighteen hours. The reaction mixture was filtered, washed with water and extracted with ether. The product distilled at 95–105° (3 mm.). The yield was 96 g. (48% of the theoretical amount).

N-2-Carboxyphenyl-2,5-dimethyl-3-carboxypyrrole.—A solution of 18.6 g. of 3-carbethoxy-2,5-hexadione and 13.7 g. of anthranilic acid in 100 cc. of absolute ethyl alcohol was refluxed for one hour. The reaction mixture was then refluxed for fifteen minutes with alcoholic sodium hydroxide, filtered, cooled and acidified with dilute hydrochloric acid. Eight grams of crude product precipitated. It was purified by crystallization from one liter of ethyl acetate containing a little alcohol; m. p. 224.5–225.5°. It is soluble in alcohol, ether and acetic acid but only slightly soluble in ethyl acetate and chloroform.

Anal. Calcd. neut. equiv.: 129.6. Found: 128.6. Calcd. for $C_{14}H_{13}O_4N$: C, 64.84; H, 5.0. Found: C, 65.33; H, 5.1.

Resolution of N-2-Carboxyphenyl-2,5-dimethyl-3-carboxypyrrole.—A solution of 15.5 g. of brucine in 400 cc. of dry ethyl acetate was added hot to a suspension of 10 g. of N-2-carboxyphenyl-2,5-dimethyl-3-carboxypyrrole in 400 cc. of hot ethyl acetate. A clear solution resulted from which the brucine salt precipitated when the side of the beaker was rubbed with a stirring rod. The mixture was cooled and filtered, yielding 12.8 g. of salt which gave $[\alpha]_D$ −37°. On concentrating the filtrate, 10 g. of salt of $[\alpha]_D$ +12° was obtained. The first fraction was recrystallized from 200 cc. of absolute alcohol to constant rotation. The more soluble fraction was recrystallized from ethyl acetate.

l-Salt.—0.1137 g. made up to 15 cc. with chloroform at 20° gave α_D −0.68°; l = 2; $[\alpha]_D^{20}$ −44.9°; m. p. 231–232° (dec.).

[3] Weltner, *Ber.*, **17**, 67 (1884).

Anal. Calcd. for $C_{37}H_{39}O_8N_3$ (monobrucine salt): C, 67.96; H, 6.0. Found: C, 67.74; H, 6.1.

d-**Salt.**—0.1551 g. made up to 15 cc. with chloroform at 20° gave α_D +0.28°; l = 2; $[\alpha]^{20}_D$ +13.5°; m. p. 175–180° (dec.).

Anal. Calcd. for $C_{37}H_{39}O_8N_3$: C, 67.96; H, 6.0. Found: C, 67.71; H, 6.1.

d- **and** *l*-**N-2-Carboxyphenyl-2,5-dimethyl-3-carboxypyrroles.**—The salts were decomposed by shaking in a separatory funnel with dilute hydrochloric acid and ether. The acid went into the ether layer and was obtained by evaporating to dryness. The acids were crystallized from ethyl acetate to constant rotation.

l-**Acid.**—0.1349 g. made up to 15 cc. with absolute alcohol at 20° gave α_D −0.49°; l = 2; $[\alpha]^{20}_D$ −27.2°; m. p. 203–204°.

d-Acid.—0.1753 g. made up to 15 cc. with absolute alcohol at 20° gave α_D + 0.63; l = 2; $[\alpha]^{20}_D$ + 27.0°; m. p. 202–204°.

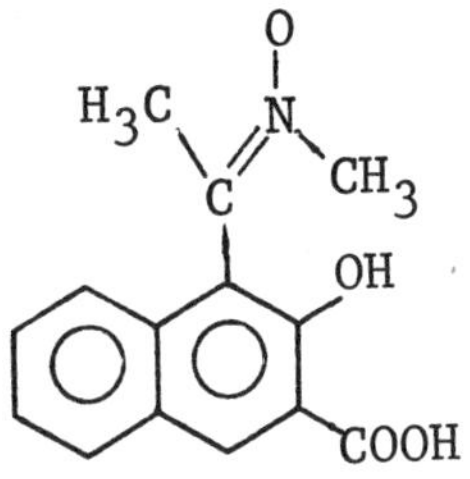

$C_{14}H_{13}NO_4$ Ref. 1016

Zerlegung der N-Methyläthersäure XVI in optische Antipoden.

Äquimolekulare Mengen getrocknete N-Äthersäure (7,1 g) und *Cinchonin* (8,05 g) werden in 10 ccm heißem Methylalkohol gelöst. Binnen 2 Tagen krystallisieren etwa 7,5 g in großen gelben Prismen aus. Der Schmelzpunkt liegt sehr unscharf zwischen 165 und 175° und ändert sich durch vielfaches Umkrystallisieren nur unwesentlich. Auch das Drehungsvermögen erfährt durch wiederholtes Umlösen nur noch eine geringe Erhöhung; es ist also bereits die erste Krystallisation nahezu einheitlich.

0,1220 g 4-mal aus Methylalkohol umkrystallisierte, lufttrockene Substanz, in absolutem Alkohol zu 10 ccm gelöst[1]): α^{21}_D = + 2,91°, $[\alpha]^{21}_D$ = + 119°. — 0,3017 g lufttrockene Substanz verloren i. V. bei 100° in 2½ Stunden 0,0095 g an Gewicht = 3,1 Proc.

0,1306 g getrockn. Subst.: 0,3416 g CO_2, 0,0765 g H_2O. — 0,1342 g Subst.: 9,0 ccm trockn. N (741 mm, 20°).

$C_{14}H_{13}O_4N.C_{19}H_{22}ON_2$ (553,5).	Ber.	C 71,58	H 6,37	N 7,59
	Gef.	„ 71,36	„ 6,55	„ 7,62.

Die Mutterlauge obiger 7,5 g scheidet allmählich bei sehr langem Stehen weitere Krystalle ab, und zwar von der gleichen Art, wie die erste Krystallisation. Die nachträglichen Ausscheidungen sind offenbar auf langsame Racemisation zurückzuführen. Isoliert man aus der Mutterlauge die darin enthaltene Säure, so zeigt diese das entgegengesetzte Drehungsvermögen, wie die dem auskrystallisierten Cinchoninsalz entsprechende Säure; der höchste beobachtete Wert war $[\alpha]^{20}_D$ = − 47° in 0,1 n-Natronlauge.

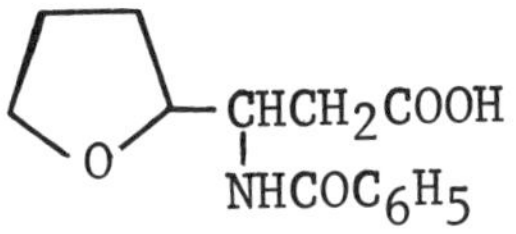

$C_{14}H_{13}NO_4$ Ref. 1017

Resolution of N-benzoyl β-furyl-β-alanine (I). A hot solution of 145 g. of *dl*-I and 263 g. of anhydrous brucine in 1450 cc. of absolute alcohol was allowed to cool to room temperature After being seeded, the mixture was allowed to stand overnight. The brucine salt was collected and washed with 145 cc. of absolute alcohol; wt. 164 g., $[\alpha]^{28}_D$ −46° (1% in acetone). The rotation of a similar preparation was the same and was unchanged after recrystallization from absolute alchol.

A hot solution of 71 g. of brucine salt in 100 cc. of absolute alcohol was poured into a mixture of 500 cc. of water and 25 cc. of 12 *N* hydrochloric acid with stirring. The mixture was cooled to 0°, filtered, and the white crystals were washed with water; yield, 26.8 g.

(75% over-all), m.p. 191–192°. Another preparation, m.p. 193°, gave $[\alpha]_D^{24}$ −44° (1% in acetone) and $[\alpha]_D^{24}$ −66° (0.8% in 0.1 *N* NaOH).

Anal. Calc'd for $C_{14}H_{13}NO_4$: C, 64.9; H, 5.02; N, 5.41.
Found: C, 64.9; H, 5.39; N, 5.41.

The filtrate from the brucine salt deposited additional crystals after standing several weeks. One recrystallization from absolute alcohol gave the optically pure salt of the *l*-acid and brought the yield of resolution to near quantitative.

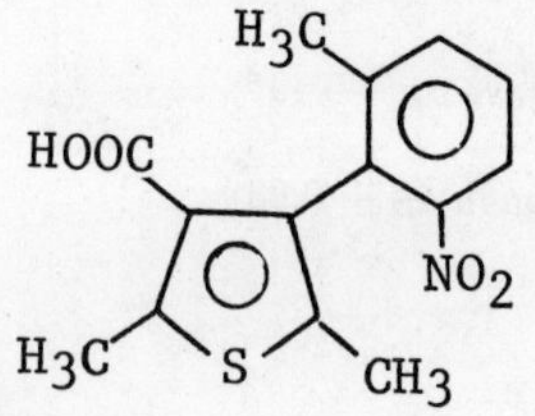

$C_{14}H_{13}NO_4S$ Ref. 1018

Resolution. *dl*-2,5-Dimethyl-4-(6′-methyl-2′-nitrophenyl)-3-thenoic acid (0.437 g., 0.0015 *M*) and anhydrous *l*-brucine (0.591 g., 0.0015 *M*) were dissolved in 100 ml. of 50% aqueous ethanol which had been brought to a gentle boil. The resulting solution was stirred continuously for 10 minutes and then was allowed to cool to room temperature and was placed in the refrigerator. At the end of three days a gum-like material had precipitated. After suction filtration it was washed with cold ethanol and air-dried. The salt then was placed in a vacuum desiccator over silica-gel for 24 hours. The hardened material now could be powdered to a crystalline form and it weighed 0.484 g. After two recrystallizations from ethanol, the melting point was constant, 115–117° (after first softening at 109°), as was the rotation; the latter was determined after the salt had been dried *in vacuo* at room temperature for 24 hours. The microanalytical sample was recrystallized again from ethanol and then from acetone and finally was dried *in vacuo* over P_2O_5 at 100° for 8 hours.

Rotation. Less soluble salt (*l*-brucine, *l*-acid): 0.0986 g. made up to 10 ml. with chloroform at 25° gave α_D −0.301°, l = 1; $[\alpha]_D^{25°}$ −30.56°.

Anal. Calc'd for $C_{37}H_{39}N_3O_8S$: N, 6.13. Found: (Micro Dumas) N, 6.21.

The filtrate was evaporated *in vacuo* almost to dryness and then was cooled in an ice-bath. There was obtained a gum-like material which appeared to be slightly more crystalline than the precipitate of the less soluble salt. After suction filtration and drying *in vacuo* over silica-gel the material could be powdered to a crystalline form; it weighed 0.263 g. It is of interest to note that this fraction appeared to be distinctly less yellow in color than its diastereoisomer. After two recrystallizations from ethanol it gave a constant melting point, 114–116° (after first softening at 109°), and rotation. The same procedure was followed for the preparation of the microanalytical sample as in the case of its diastereoisomer.

Rotation. More soluble salt (*l*-brucine, *d*-acid): 0.0735 g. made up to 10 ml. with chloroform at 25° gave α_D −0.403°, l = 1; $[\alpha]_D^{25°}$ −54.86°.

Anal. Calc'd for $C_{37}H_{39}N_3O_8S$: N, 6.13. Found: (Micro Dumas) N, 6.34.

Both brucine salts were found to be stable inasmuch as they could be recrystallized, their color did not change on standing in the sunlight, and their solutions did not mutarotate.

l-2,5-Dimethyl-4-(6′-methyl-2′-nitrophenyl)-3-thenoic acid. The less-soluble brucine salt (0.300 g.) was treated with 15 ml. of ice-cold 6 *N* HCl at 0° with vigorous stirring. After 30 minutes the precipitated acid was filtered, washed with a small amount of 2 *N* HCl, until the washings gave a negative test for brucine, and then with sufficient ice-cold water to remove any trace of inorganic acid. After drying in a vacuum desiccator the product amounted to 0.112 g. and melted at 208–210° with softening at 203°. A depression in the melting point of the racemic acid (m.p. 211–212°) could be observed on admixture with an equal amount of the *l*-acid (mixture m.p. 202–204° after first softening at 194°).

Rotation. 0.0895 g. of the *l*-acid made up to 10 ml. with methanol at 25° gave α_D −0.035°, l = 1; $[\alpha]_D^{25°}$ −3.91°.

The optical rotation remained essentially the same after standing at room temperature, but attempts to recrystallize the material from boiling methanol caused partial racemization to occur. The *l*-acid therefore was dissolved in dry acetone at room temperature, and an excess of petroleum ether (b.p. 20–40°) was added; after standing in the refrigerator overnight, a small amount of the acid crystallized out as a flaky material. However, the melting point and rotation were unchanged by this treatment.

d-2,5-Dimethyl-4-(6′-methyl-2′-nitrophenyl)-3-thenoic acid. The more-soluble brucine salt (0.120 g.) was decomposed in the usual manner with ice-cold 6 *N* HCl to afford 0.041 g. of the *d*-acid, m.p. 209–211° with softening at 204°. A depression in the melting point of the racemic acid (m.p. 211–212°) could be observed on admixture with an equal amount of the *d*-acid (mixture m.p. 203–205° with softening at 196°).

Rotation. 0.0332 g. of the *d*-acid made up to 10 ml. with methanol at 25° gave α_D +0.11°, l = 1; $[\alpha]_D^{25°}$ +3.31°.

A mixture of equal amounts (0.010 g.) of the *d*- and *l*-acids was prepared; it melted at 210–211° with softening at 204°. Its chloroform solution was optically inactive.

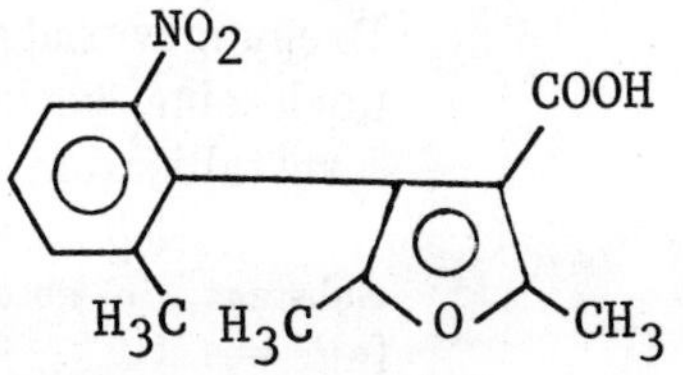

$C_{14}H_{13}NO_5$ Ref. 1019

Resolution of 3-(2-Methyl-3-nitrophenyl)-2,5-dimethyl-4-furoic Acid.—To 800 mg. of the above acid dissolved in 300 ml. of boiling 40% ethanol, 1.05 g. of quinine was added, the solution was boiled for a few minutes with 0.5 g. of charcoal, filtered and left in an ice-box. A few pieces of ice were added daily for three days until a gummy material precipitated. After standing several more days in an ice-box, the gum solidified, was separated, pressed dry on a porcelain plate and dried two days *in vacuo*. The first crop of 835 mg. was collected in this way. After evaporation of the mother liquor to 150 ml. another 200 mg. of the quinine salt was separated giving a total of 1.035 g. of quinine salt Ia, m.p. 110–115° with previous softening at 100°. The filtrate was evaporated to dryness *in vacuo* and 525 mg. of salt Ib was collected, m.p. 110–114°. Salt Ia had $[\alpha]^{25}D$ −30.3° (*c* 0.1745 g. in 10 ml. of $CHCl_3$[9]). Salt Ib had $[\alpha]^{25}D$ −128.3° (*c* 0.0653 g. in 10 ml. of $CHCl_3$).

The salts were recrystallized from ethanol and dried over P_2O_5 at 70° for 24 hours.

Anal. Salt Ia. Calcd. for $C_{34}H_{37}O_7N_3\cdot{}^1/_2H_2O$: C, 67.10; H, 6.25. Found: C, 67.11; H, 6.10. Salt Ib. Calcd. for $C_{34}H_{37}O_7N_3$: C, 68.11; H, 6.17. Found: C, 67.85; H, 5.88.

The two salts were decomposed by 6 *N* HCl in the cold, washed with 2 *N* HCl and an excess of water, then dried *in vacuo*. The acid from salt Ia (*l*-form) had $[\alpha]^{25}D$ −22.8° (*c* 0.1290 g. in 10 ml. of $CHCl_3$) and melted at 220–222°. The acid from salt Ib (*d*-form) had $[\alpha]^{25}D$ 22.1 (*c* 0.0760 g. in 10 ml. of $CHCl_3$) and melted at 223–224°. The chloroform solution of the acid did not change in rotation on standing one week at room temperature. Attempts to recrystallize the acid from hot ethanol cause complete loss of activity.

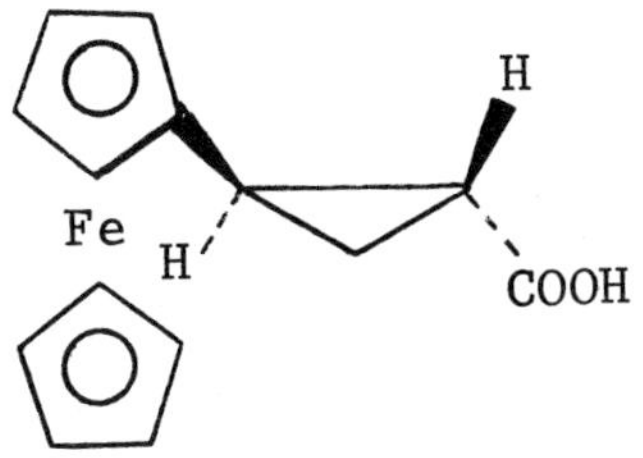

$C_{14}H_{14}FeO_2$

Ref. 1020

Racematspaltung von **1a**

Zur Darstellung des *Phenäthylaminsalzes* wurden äther. Lösungen von **1a** (1,5 g, 5,56 mMol; in 45 ml) und (—)-α-Phenäthylamin (0,71 g, 5,86 mMol; in 5 ml; $[\alpha]_D$ — 37,5°) unter Eiskühlung vereinigt. Dabei fielen 2,0 g (92% d. Th.) des Salzes aus. Schmp. 162—170°, subl. ab 130°.

$C_{14}H_{14}FeO_2 \cdot C_8H_{11}N$. Ber. N 3,58. Gef. N 3,50.

Dieses Salz wurde — wie in der folgenden Tabelle angegeben — mehrfach aus Äthanol—Methanol (1 : 1) umkristallisiert.

g Salz	aus ml	auskrist. Salz g	auskrist. Salz Schmp., °C	auskrist. Salz $[\alpha]_D^{20}$ (c=1—1,5; Äthanol)	Säure 1a* $[\alpha]_D^{20}$ (c=1—1,3; Äthanol)
1,9	18	1,1	150—166	— 8,4 ± 1°	—
1,1	12	0,85	165—170	— 7,3°	—
0,85	11	0,50	161—167	— 10,6 ± 1,2°	—
0,50	8	0,20	168—176	+ 6,7 ± 1°	+ 11,5 ± 1,5°
0,15	3,5	0,05	165—180	+ 12,8°	+ 20,0 ± 2°
0,05	1,1	0,016	170—180	+ 11,0 ± 1,6°	+ 19,8 ± 0,2°**

* Aus dem Salz wurde die Säure in üblicher Weise (Suspendieren in Äther und mehrfaches Ausschütteln mit verd. H_3PO_4) in Freiheit gesetzt.

** Gemessen auf dem Perkin-Elmer-Polarimeter 141; für die Möglichkeit zur Messung danken wir Herrn Prof. Dr. *H. Tuppy*, Biochem. Institut der Universität Wien. Die spezif. Drehung $[\alpha]_D$ in Benzol (c=0,91) betrug + 26,7 ± 0,2°. Diese Säure schmilzt unscharf von 105—120°.

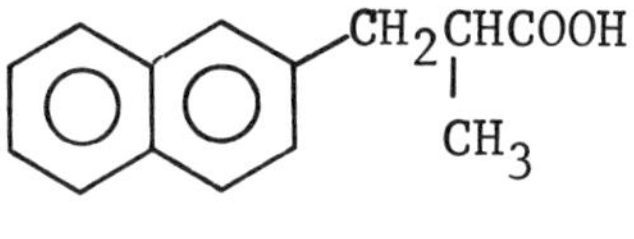

Ref. 1021

$C_{14}H_{14}O_2$

(+)-α-(2-Naphthylmethyl)-propionic acid. 8.6 g (0.04 mole) racemic acid and 11.8 g (0.04 mole) cinchonidine were dissolved in 200 ml hot alcohol. 200 ml cold water were added and the solution set aside in a cool place after seeding with crystals from a preliminary run. The salt which separated was recrystallised according to the scheme below:

Crystallisation nr	1	2	3	4	5	6	7	8	9	10	11
ml alcohol	200	250	250	250	150	100	75	75	80	100	100
ml water	200	250	250	250	150	100	75	75	80	100	100
Weight of salt (g)	18.7	15.8	13.1	8.7	7.4	6.9	6.6	6.3	5.8	5.3	4.75
$[\alpha]_D$ of the acid	—	+3.9°	+5.9°	+16.8°	+20.6°	+21.6°	+21.6°	+22.7°	+23.4°	+23.7°	+23.2°

The pure salt from the last crystallisation yielded 1.9 g (+)-acid which was recrystallised from petrol (b.p. 60–80°). 1.4 g pure (+)-acid were collected as colourless, glistening plates with m.p. 84–85°. The compound is dimorphic and has a lower melting modification which can often be obtained when the melt is supercooled to room temperature. This unstable form crystallises in rectangular plates melting at 69°.

78.67 mg acid: 7.63 ml 0.04792-*N* NaOH

$C_{14}H_{14}O_2$ calc. equiv. wt. 214.3
found " " 215.2

0.0966 g dissolved in abs. *alcohol* to 10.00 ml: $\alpha_D^{25} = +0.233°$. $[\alpha]_D^{25} = +24.1°$; $[M]_D^{25} = +51.7°$. — 0.0990 g dissolved in *acetone* to 10.00 ml: $\alpha_D^{25} = +0.317°$. $[\alpha]_D^{25} = +32.0°$; $[M]_D^{25} = +68.6°$. —0.0971 g dissolved in *benzene* to 10.00 ml: $\alpha_D^{25} = +0.237°$. $[\alpha]_D^{25} = +24.4°$; $[M]_D^{25} = +52.3°$. — 0.1042 g dissolved in *chloroform* to 10.00 ml: $\alpha_D^{25} = +0.253°$. $[\alpha]_D^{25} = +24.3°$; $[M]_D^{25} = +52.0°$. — 0.0908 g neutralised with *aqueous sodium hydroxide* and made up to 10.00 ml. $\alpha_D^{25} = +0.322°$. $[\alpha]_D^{25} = +35.5°$; $[M]_D^{25} = +76.0°$.

(−)-α-(2-Naphthylmethyl)-propionic acid. From the mother liquors from crystallisations 1–5 above, 5.1 g partially active (−)-acid were obtained. $[\alpha]_D = -11.2°$ (c=1 in abs alcohol.) This acid (0.024 mole) and 2.9 g (0.024 mole) (+)-α-phenylethylamine were dissolved in a hot mixture of 95 ml alcohol and 190 ml water. The salt which had separated after standing over night in a refrigerator was recrystallised according to the following scheme:

Crystallisation nr	1	2	3	4	5	6
ml alcohol	95	90	75	65	60	50
ml water	190	180	150	130	120	100
Weight of salt (g)	6.1	5.1	4.4	4.8	3.2	2.7
$[\alpha]_D$ of the acid	−15.6°	−19.0°	−20.2°	−22.0°	−20.7°	−22.4°

From the last fraction 1.65 g crude (−)-acid could be isolated. After recrystallisation from petrol (b.p. 60–80°) 0.9 g pure (−)-acid was collected. It closely resembled the (+)-form and melted at 83–84.5°. The unstable modification melted at 69°.

66.82 mg acid: 6.50 ml 0.04792-*N* NaOH

$C_{14}H_{14}O_2$ calc. equiv. wt. 214.3
found " " 214.5

0.0980 g dissolved in abs. *alcohol* to 10.00 ml: $\alpha_D^{25} = -0.226°$. $[\alpha]_D^{25} = -23.1°$; $[M]_D^{25} = -49.4°$. —

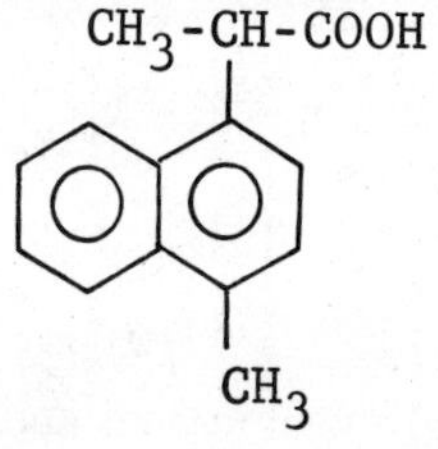

$C_{14}H_{14}O_2$

Ref. 1022

Table 2. Preliminary tests on the resolution of α-(4-methyl-1-naphthyl)-propionic acid.

Base	$[\alpha]_D^{25}$ of acid in abs. ethanol: From methanol	From ethanol	From acetone	From ethyl acetate
Cinchonine	± 0°	± 0°	+17°	oil
Chinconidine	−18°	−28°	−47°	−18°
Quinine	oil	oil	oil	+37°
Quinidine	oil	oil	oil	oil
Brucine	+12°	− 3°	− 4°	− 9°
Strychnine	oil	oil °	oil	oil
Morphine	oil	+ 2	oil	oil
(+)-α-Phenylethylamine	oil	oil	oil	oil

Table 3. Recrystallization of the quinine salt of α-(4-methyl-1-naphthyl)-propionic acid.

Cryst. no.	Ethyl acetate (ml)	Weight of salt (g)	$[\alpha]_D^{25}$ of acid
1	100	15.6	69°
2	80	12.5	90°
3	60	10.6	102°
4	50	9.3	106.5°
5	50	8.0	108°
6	50	7.0	108°

Resolution of the racemic acid

Preliminary experiments were carried out with 0.001 mole of the racemic acid and 0.001 mole of the bases in different solvents. As can be seen in Table 2 the best results were obtained from quinine and cinchonidine.

In a hot solution of 100 ml of ethyl acetate were dissolved 12.8 g (0.06 mole) of racemic acid and 19.5 g (0.06 mole) of quinine. The salt was allowed to crystallize at room temperature and then in a refrigerator. The salt was filtered off after 24 hours and recrystallized from ethyl acetate. The progress of the resolution was tested on small samples from each crystallization, from which the acid was isolated and the optical activity measured in absolute ethanol (Table 3).

The mother liquors from the three first crystallizations were evaporated to dryness and 8.4 g of acid was isolated with $[\alpha]_D^{25} = -29°$ (absolute ethanol). This acid was dissolved with 11.4 g of cinchonidine in a boiling mixture of 180 ml of acetone and 18 ml of water. The salt was recrystallized from dilute acetone until the optical activity of the acid remained constant (Table 4).

(+)-α-(4-Methyl-1-naphthyl)-propionic acid

The acid was liberated from 6.5 g of the salt with dilute sulphuric acid and extracted with ether. The yield of the crude acid was 2.5 g and after two recrystallizations from formic acid there remained 2.0 g with m.p. 77–78°.

Table 4. Recrystallization of the cinchonidine salt of α-(4-methyl-1-naphthyl)-propionic acid.

Cryst. no.	Solvent (ml): Acetone	Water	Weight of salt (g)	$[\alpha]_D^{25}$ of acid
1	180	18	13.5	− 83°
2	100	10	10.3	−102°
3	100	10	8.5	−106°
4	100	10	6.8	−108°
5	100	10	5.9	−108°

Table 5. Optical activity of (−)-α-(4-methyl-1-naphthyl)-propionic acid.

Solvent	mg of acid	$2\ \alpha_D^{25}$	$[\alpha]_D^{25}$	$[M]_D^{25}$
2,2,4-Trimethylpentane	64.6	−2.04°	−157.1°	−336.7°
Benzene	67.5	−2.09°	−154.8°	−331.7°
Acetic acid	69.6	−1.93°	−138.6°	−297.0°
Acetone	66.4	−1.72°	−129.5°	−277.5°
Chloroform	74.8	−1.73°	−115.6°	−247.7°
Ethanol	76.1	−1.66°	−109.0°	−233.6°
Water (ion)	72.4	−0.32°	− 22.1°	− 47.4°

Anal. $C_{14}H_{14}O_2$: Equiv. wt. calc. 214.3; found 214.5.

0.0643 g acid dissolved in absolute ethanol to 10.00 ml: $2\alpha_D^{25} = +1.39°$, $[\alpha]_D^{25} = +108.5°$, $[M]_D^{25} = +232.4°$.

(−)-α-(*4-Methyl-1-naphthyl*)-*propionic acid*

From 5.6 g of the cinchonidine salt 2.3 g of acid was isolated. It was recrystallized twice from formic acid. Yield 1.8 g, m.p. 77–78°.

Anal. $C_{14}H_{14}O_2$: Equiv. wt. calc. 214.3; found 214.4.

Optical activity in different solvents

Weighed amounts of the acid were dissolved in different solvents, made up to a volume of 10.00 ml and the rotatory power determined. In the case of water the acid was neutralized with dilute sodium hydroxide to pH 7 (Table 5.)

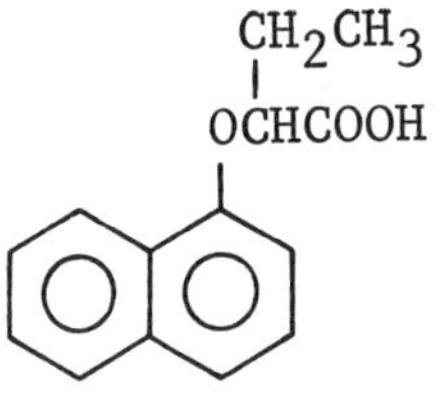

$C_{14}H_{14}O_3$ Ref. 1023

Optically active α-(*1-naphthoxy*)-*n-butyric acid* (*II*). With cinchonine, cinchonidine and strychnine crystalline salts were obtained, which on decomposition yielded products containing excess of the (+)-acid. The best resolution was obtained with cinchonine.

α-(1-Naphthoxy)-*n*-butyric acid (19.8 g, 0.086 mole) and cinchonine (25.4 g, 0.086 mole) were dissolved in hot alcohol (300 ml), water (350 ml) was added and the solution left to crystallise at + 4° C till next day when the solid was collected. The purification of the salt was carried out as seen from Table 5; $[\alpha]_D$ of the acid, liberated from small samples of each salt fraction, was determined in benzene.

Table 5. Recrystallisation of the cinchonine salt of α-(1-nahpthoxy)-*n*-butyric acid.

Cryst. No.	Solvent (ml)		Weight of salt (g)	$[\alpha]_D$ of the acid
	Water	Ethanol		
1	350	300		
2	260	320	25.6	+50.4°
3	250	350	18.0	
4	175	175	14.2	+86.7°
5	135	135	13.0	+94.2°
6	135	135	11.2	+94.0°
7	125	125	7.75	+94.1°

The crude acid liberated from the last fraction was brownish red; yield 3.4 g. It was recrystallised four times alternately from 85 % formic acid and cyclohexane. 2.05 g of the pure (+)-acid were collected as small colourless needles. M.p. 100.8–101.8°.

91.48 mg acid: 8.21 ml 0.04823-*N* NaOH
$C_{14}H_{14}O_3$ calc. equiv. wt. 230.3
found » » 231.0

0.1827 g dissolved in abs. *alcohol* to 20.03 ml: $2\alpha_D^{25} = +0.120°$. $[\alpha]_D^{25} = +6.6°$; $[M]_D^{25} = +15.1°$.
0.1733 g dissolved in *acetone* to 20.03 ml: $2\alpha_D^{25} = +0.087°$. $[\alpha]_D^{25} = +5.0°$; $[M]_D^{25} = +11.6°$.
0.2141 g dissolved in *chloroform* to 20.03 ml: $2\alpha_D^{25} = +0.206°$. $[\alpha]_D^{25} = +9.6°$; $[M]_D^{25} = +22.2°$.
0.1042 g dissolved in *benzene* to 10.00 ml: $\alpha_D^{25} = +0.982°$. $[\alpha]_D^{25} = +94.2°$; $[M]_D^{25} = +217.0°$.
0.2200 g neutralised with *aqueous sodium hydroxide* and made up to 20.03 ml: $\alpha_D^{19} = +0.514°$. $[\alpha]_D^{19} = +46.8°$; $[M]_D^{19} = +107.8°$.

As none of the common alkaloids used for resolution gave a crystalline salt containing excess of the (−)-acid, an attempt was made to isolate the (−)-form by recrystallisation from different solvents of an acid containing about 85 % of the (−)-form but without success.

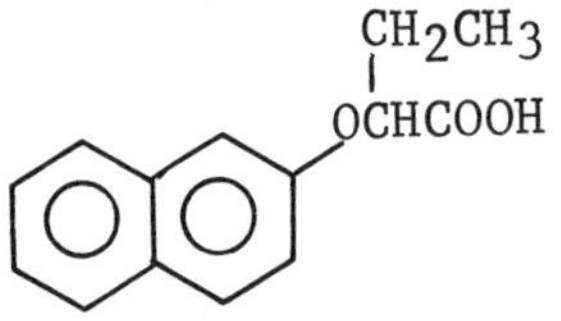

$C_{14}H_{14}O_3$ Ref. 1024

Optically active α-(*2-naphthoxy*)-*n-butyric acid* (*III*). A dextrorotatory acid could be isolated over the cinchonidine salt but the best result was obtained with quinine. Also α-phenylethylamine gave a crystalline salt and the (+)-amin salt was used for the preparation of the (−)-acid.

α-(2-Naphthoxy)-*n*-butyric acid (17.3 g, 0.075 mole) and quinine (28.4 g, 0.075 mole) were dissolved in hot 50 % ethanol (750 ml). After standing over night the crystals were collected and the rotatory power of the acid liberated from a small sample was measured in abs. alcohol. The salt was recrystallised several times as shown by Table 6.

Table 6. Recrystallisation of the quinine salt of α-(2-naphthoxy)-*n*-butyric acid.

Cryst. No.	50 % ethanol ml	Weight of salt (g)	$[\alpha]_D$ of the acid
1	750	29.8	+27.0°
2	700	19.5	+81.2°
3	500	16.4	+88.2°
4	400	15.5	+90.7°
5	350	14.8	+91.0°

The acid was isolated from the last salt fraction and recrystallised twice from petroleum (b.p. 60–80°). 5.5 g of the pure (+)-acid were collected as a colourless wadlike mass, m.p. 134.5–135.6°.

79.52 mg acid: 7.23 ml 0.04792-*N* NaOH
$C_{14}H_{14}O_3$ calc. equiv. wt. 230.3
found » » 229.5

0.1012 g dissolved in abs. *alcohol* to 10.00 ml: $\alpha_D^{25} = +0.929°$. $[\alpha]_D^{25} = +91.8°$; $[M]_D^{25} = +211.4°$.
0.1006 g dissolved in *acetone* to 10.00 ml: $\alpha_D^{25} = +0.982°$. $[\alpha]_D^{25} = +97.6°$; $[M]_D^{25} = +224.8°$.
0.1006 g dissolved in *chloroform* to 10.00 ml: $\alpha_D^{25} = +0.620°$. $[\alpha]_D^{25} = +61.6°$; $[M]_D^{25} = +141.9°$.
0.1018 g dissolved in *benzene* to 10.00 ml: $\alpha_D^{25} = +0.856°$. $[\alpha]_D^{25} = +84.1°$; $[M]_D^{25} = +193.7°$.
0.1020 g neutralised with *aqueous sodium hydroxide* and made up to 10.00 ml: $\alpha_D^{25} = +0.686°$. $[\alpha]_D^{25} = +67.3°$; $[M]_D^{25} = +154.9°$.

From the mother liquors an acid with $[\alpha]_D = -55°$ (in ethanol) was regenerated. This acid (7.6 g, 0.033 mole) and an equimolecular quantity of (+)-α-phenylethylamine (4.0 g) were dissolved in hot alcohol (150 ml) and water (200 ml) was added. After some hours the crystals were collected and the optical activity of the acid determined in the usual manner. As seen from Table 7 only three recrystallisations were necessary to accomplish the resolution.

Table 7. Recrystallisation of the (+)-phenethylamine salt of α-(2-naphthoxy)-*n*-butyric acid.

Cryst. No.	Solvent (ml)		Weight of salt (g)	$[\alpha]_D$ of the acid
	Water	Ethanol		
1	200	150	8.3	−87.5°
2	135	100	7.4	−89.7°
3	135	100	6.4	−89.8°

From the (−)-acid salt 4.0 g of crude acid were obtained. It was recrystallised from petroleum (p.b. 60–80°), cyclohexane and 25 % alcohol. Yield of pure (−)-acid 3.7 g with m.p. 134.5–135.4°.

95.38 mg acid: 8.61 ml 0.04792-*N* NaOH
$C_{14}H_{14}O_3$ calc. equiv. wt. 230.3
found » » 231.2

0.1045 g dissolved in abs. *alcohol* to 10.00 ml: $\alpha_D^{25} = -0.949°$. $[\alpha]_D^{25} = -90.8°$; $[M]_D^{25} = -209.1°$.

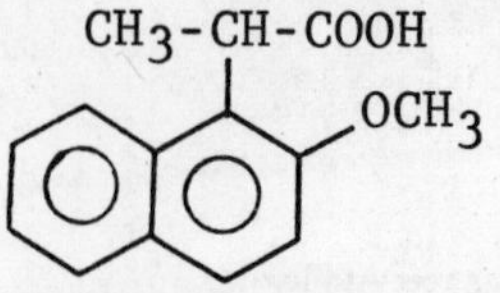

$C_{14}H_{14}O_3$ Ref. 1025

L'acide racémique α-(2-méthoxy-1-naphtyl)-propionique a été dédoublé aux antipodes optiques par voie de la cristallisation fractionnée des sels quininique et hydroquinidinique. Le sel de quinine de l'antimère dextrogyre formait, dans l'acétone diluée, des aiguilles (F 170—171°, $(\alpha)_D^{20} = -56{,}25°$, dans l'éthanol 96%). Le sel hydroquinidinique de l'enantiomère lévogyre se cristallisait de l'acétone en aiguilles (F 140° avec déc., $(\alpha)_D^{20} = +81{,}25°$, dans l'éthanol 96%). Les acides enantiomériques α-(2-méthoxy-1-naphtyl)-propioniques, isolés de leurs sels alcaloidiques après cristallisation du méthanol, avaient les constantes physiques suivantes: F 175°, $(\alpha)_D^{20} = \pm 100{,}00°$, dans l'éthanol 96%.

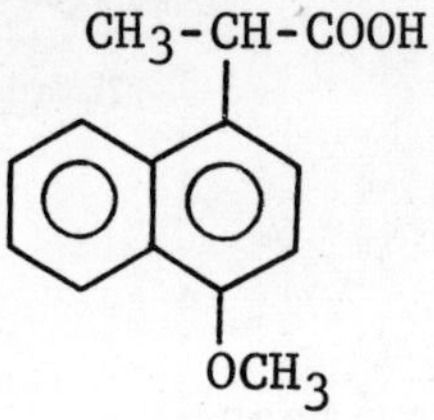

$C_{14}H_{14}O_3$ Ref. 1026

Des résultats positifs ont été obtenus aussi dans les essais de séparer les antimères de l'acide racémique α-(4-méthoxy-1-naphtyl)-propionique. La cristallisation fractionnée des sels brucinique et quininique nous a satisfait le plus vite. Le sel de brucine de l'antimère dextrogyre formait, dans l'acétone, des lamelles rectangulaires (F 123—124°, $(\alpha)_D^{20} = -15{,}00°$, dans l'éthanol 96%). Le sel quininique (aiguilles du méthanol) de l'enantiomère levogyre accusait les propriétés suivantes: F 199—202°, $(\alpha)_D^{20} = -125{,}00°$, dans l'éthanol 96%. Les acides enantiomériques α-(4--méthoxy-1-naphtyl)-propioniques (F 117—118°), isolés de leurs sels alcaloidiques, après la cristallisation de l'éthanol 50%, avaient les pouvoirs rotatoires spécifiques siuvants, mesurés dans l'éthanol 96%: acide dextrogyre $(\alpha)_D^{20} = +77{,}50°$ et acide lévogyre $(\alpha)_D^{20} = -82{,}50°$.

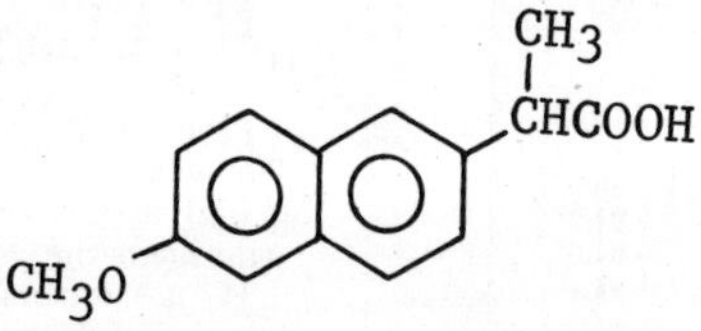

$C_{14}H_{14}O_3$ Ref. 1027

B e i s p i e l 1

Es wurde eine Mischung hergestellt, indem man in einen 1-l-Kolben 70 g (0,305 g/Mol) dl-2-(6-Methoxy-2-naphthyl)-propionsäure, 44 g (0,150 g-Mol) Cinchonidin 8,67 g (0,155 g-Mol) Kaliumhydroxid und 220 ccm Methanol einführte. Diese Bestandteile wurden gerührt, und die Mischung wurde 4 Stunden zum Rückfluß erhitzt. Dann wurde die Mischung allmählich innerhalb von 12 Stunden auf 25°C. abgekühlt und weitere 12 Stunden auf dieser Temperatur gehalten. Die erhaltene Suspension wurde filtriert und die Feststoffe mit 100 ccm Methanol gewaschen und bei 50-55°C. getrocknet. Die Ausbeute an Cinchonidinsalz der d-2-(6-Methoxy-2-naphthyl)-propionsäure betrug etwa 90 % (Gew./Gew.); $[\alpha]_D = 57\text{-}58°$ (der freigesetzten Säure).

Beispiel 4

Ein 65-g-Anteil des Cinchonidinsalzes der d-2-(6-Methoxy-2-naphthyl)-propionsäure ($[\alpha]_D$ = 58,8°; der freigesetzten Säure) wurde mit 195 ccm Methanol gemischt und die Mischung 4 Stunden unter Rühren zum Rückfluß erhitzt. Die Lösung wurde innerhalb von 5 Stunden auf 25°C. abgekühlt und filtriert. Das Filtrat wurde mit 30 ccm Methanol einer Temperatur von 25°C. gewaschen und bei 45-50°C. getrocknet. Die Ausbeute an Cinchonidinsalz der d-2-(6-Methoxy-2-naphthyl)-propionsäure betrug etwa 95,2 % (Gew./Gew.); $[\alpha]_D$ = 66,1° (der freigesetzten Säure).

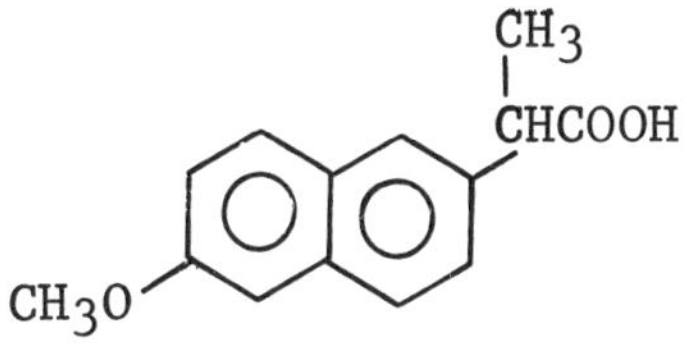

$C_{14}H_{14}O_3$ Ref. 1028

EXAMPLE I

100 milliliters of water and 23 grams (0.1 mole) of racemic 2-(6-methoxy-2-naphthyl)-propionic acid are added to a one-liter flask. The mixture is agitated and neutralized to a pH of 9.5 by the addition of a 50% (weight/weight) aqueous solution of sodium hydroxide, to give a solution of the sodium salt of d, 1 2-(6-methoxy-2-naphthyl)propionic acid. After 200 grams of toluene are added to the solution, the reaction mixture is heated to 80°C. and an aqueous solution of 21.1 grams (0.06 mole) of dehydrobietylamine acetate in 100 ml. of water is added with vigorous stirring during a 30 minute period while the temperature of 80°C. is maintained. After the addition of the dehydroabietylamine acetate is completed, the reaction mixture is held at 80°C for one hour and then cooled to ambient temperature over a period of 2 hours. The crystalline precipitate consisting of the dehydroabietylamine salt of the 1 2-(6-methoxy-2-naphthyl)propionic acid is removed by filtration and washed with 25 milliliters of water. The washings are combined with the original filtrate and transferred to a 1-liter separatory funnel. The aqueous phase is adjusted to a pH of 10 with dilute sodium hydroxide solution. The aqueous phase is separated from the upper toluene layer, and washed twice with 50 milliliter portions of toluene which are combined with the original toluene layer. 15 grams of sodium chloride are added to the aqueous layer which is then warmed to 35°C. The aqueous layer is cooled slowly over a 2 hour period. When the temperature reaches 30°C the aqueous layer is seeded with a pure crystal of the sodium salt of d 2-(6-methoxy-2-naphthyl)-propionic acid, after which cooling is continued with agitation to a temperature of 13°C. The solution is stirred at this temperature for 15 minutes. The crystalline solid which results is removed by filtration and redissolved in 200 milliliters of water. The resulting solution is acidified with hydrochloric acid to a pH of 2. The white crystalline precipitate which results is separated by filtration, washed with water at 0°C. until the washings are essentially neutral, and dried *in vacuo* at 50°C. for 2 hours to yield 4 grams of d 2-(6-methoxy-2-naphthyl)propionic acid [m.pt. 154°-155°C; $[\alpha]^{25}_D$=64.6 (1% in chloroform)]. This optical rotation represents a purity of about 98.9%.

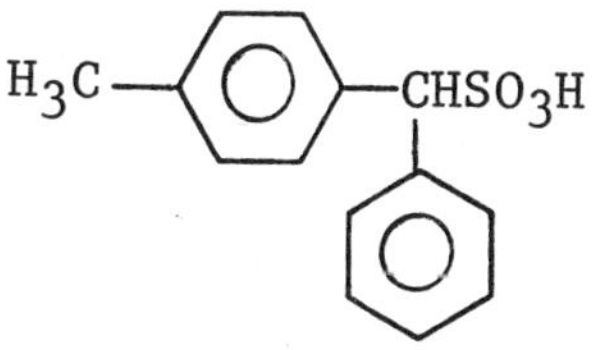

$C_{14}H_{14}O_3S$ Ref. 1029

Resolution of the sulphonic acid into optically active components

The cinchonine and brucine salts of the acid crystallised poorly. Recrystallisations of the *l*-menthylammonium salts from water and ethanol and of the *l*-α-phenethylammonium salts from water, ethanol, methanol, chloroform and dioxane did in no case lead to any resolution.

The resolution was effected, however, through the strychnine salts. Strychnine (40.9 g = 0.12 mole) was dissolved in 127 ml of 1 *N* sulfuric acid plus 1 liter of water. The solution was heated to 100° and, under stirring, dropped into a solution of 78 g of sodium *p*-methylbenzhydrylsulphonate (0.24 mole) in 1 liter of water, heated to 80°. The mixture was cooled, and the precipitate (75 g) was filtered off. The mother liquor was heated again to 80°, and 0.12 mole of strychnine sulphate was added dropwise. After cooling 54 g of strychnine salt was filtered off. The first fraction (75 g) was boiled for 1.5 hours with 1800 ml of ethanol, which dissolved only part of the salt. The mixture was cooled and filtered, and the precipitate was reboiled 8 times in the same way, namely with 1450, 1250, 1100 and 5 times 1000 ml of alcohol respectively. At this stage 49.6 g of strychnine salt remained. The second fraction of strychnine salt (54 g) was boiled three times with 900 ml of alcohol each time; 40.6 g remained.

The sulphonic acid was liberated in the following way: 12 g of the strychnine salt from the first crop was shaken in a separatory funnel with 100 ml of 0.2160 *N* barium hydroxide, 600 ml of CO_2-free water and 150 ml of chloroform. By this treatment the chloroform dissolved the strychnine, while the barium salt of the sulphonic acid remained in the aqueous solution. The aqueous layer was extracted twice with 50 ml of chloroform. The chloroform remaining in the aqueous layer was removed by evaporation under reduced pressure. A little excess of 1 *N* sulphuric acid was added, and the mixture was left overnight. The barium sulphate was filtered off and the filtrate concentrated to 50 ml under reduced pressure at 40°. In the same way the acid was liberated from two other 12 g-portions of strychnine salt, and to the combined fractions of sulphonic acid 500 ml of conc. hydrochloric acid were added. The sulphonic acid was filtered off and dried in the air, then it was put in a desiccator and the last trace of hydrogen chloride removed by repeated evacuation; finally it was dried over potassium hydroxide. Yield 16.2 g or 90 % of the theoretical amount. M. p. 115.0°—119.5°. $[\alpha]_D = +7.7°$.

$C_{14}H_{14}O_3S \cdot 2H_2O$ Calc. Equiv. wt. 298.3 Found Equiv. wt. 297.1

The second fraction of strychnine salt yielded the levorotatory acid with $[\alpha]_D = -7.1°$.

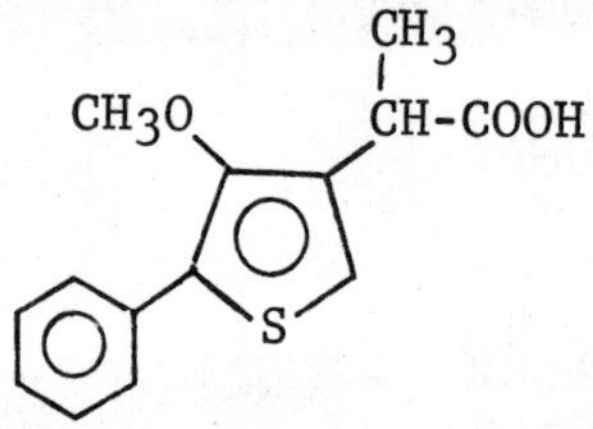

$C_{14}H_{14}O_3S$ Ref. 1030

8. *Antipodentrennung von* **1**. 262 g (1,0 mol) 2-(4-Methoxy-5-phenyl-3-thienyl)propionsäure (**1**) und 294 g (1,0 mol) Cinchonidin werden in 8 l Aceton heiss gelöst. Man kühlt ab, filtriert nach 2 Std. (Kühlschrank), und wäscht mit 2 l Aceton.

(+)-*Antipode*: Die Mutterlaugen werden weitgehend eingeengt und anschliessend in Äther/2 N Schwefelsäure verteilt. Der eingedampfte, glasartige Ätherextrakt [141 g (0,54 mol)] wird in 430 ml Äthanol gelöst und mit 65 g (0,54 mol (−)-1-Phenyläthylamin versetzt. Man lässt 2 Std. im Kühlschrank auskristallisieren, filtriert und wäscht mit wenig Äthanol nach. Dieses Salz wird noch 6mal aus jeweils 5facher Menge Äthanol umkristallisiert. Smp. 157°, $[\alpha]_D^{20} = +26{,}0°$ ($c = 1{,}0$, $CHCl_3$); Ausbeute: 28,6 g Phenyläthylamin-Salz (15% der Theorie). Reine Säure[3]): $[\alpha]_D^{20} = +76°$ ($c = 1{,}0$, $CHCl_3$).

Natriumsalz: Zu einer Lösung von 4,2 g (0,05 mol) Natriumhydrogencarbonat in 50 ml Wasser werden 13,1 g (0,05 mol) (+)-2-(4-Methoxy-5-phenyl-3-thienyl)propionsäure gegeben. Man verdampft zur Trockne und hält den glasigen Eindampfrückstand 3 Std. im Hochvakuum bei 80°. Nun kocht man mit Aceton auf, worauf das Salz farblos kristallisiert: Smp. 199–201°, $[\alpha]_D^{20} = +19{,}3°$ ($c = 1{,}0$, H_2O). $C_{14}H_{13}NaO_3S$ (284,3).

(−)-*Antipode*: Das oben abgetrennte Cinchonindinsalz, welches den (−)-drehenden Antipoden stark angereichert enthält, wird noch 5mal aus jeweils 20facher Menge Aceton umkristallisiert; Smp. 136°, $[\alpha]_D^{20} = -96°$ ($c = 1{,}0$, C_2H_5OH). Ausbeute: 121 g Cinchonidinsalz (43,4% der Theorie). Reine Säure[3]): $[\alpha]_D^{20} = -78°$ ($c = 1{,}0$, $CHCl_3$).

Natriumsalz: Herstellung gleich wie beim (+)-drehenden Antipoden. Smp. 201–203°, $[\alpha]_D^{20} = -19{,}5°$ ($c = 1{,}0$, H_2O).

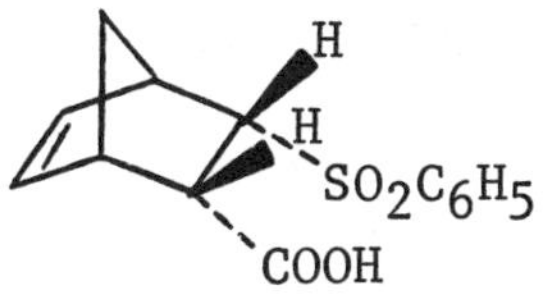

$C_{14}H_{14}O_4S$ Ref. 1031

(3R)-(+)-2-endo-*Phenylsulphonylbicyclo*[2,2,1]*heptane*-3-endo-*carboxylic Acid* (XIIa).—2-*endo*-Phenylsulphonylbicyclo[2,2,1]hept-5-ene-3-*endo*-carboxylic acid [46] (20 g.) was partially resolved by crystallisation of its quinine salt from absolute ethanol. After three crystallisations the salt (10 g.) afforded the (−)-acid (4·5 g.), m.p. 178—180°, $[\alpha]_D^{20}$ −14·7° (*c* 3·1 in ethanol). By working up the more soluble fraction of the salt the (+)-acid was isolated (2·3 g.), $[\alpha]_D^{20}$ +13·0° (*c* 3·8 in ethanol).

[46] D. Albera, G. Luciani, and F. Montanari, *Boll. sci. Fac. Chim. ind. Bologna*, 1960, **18**, 52.

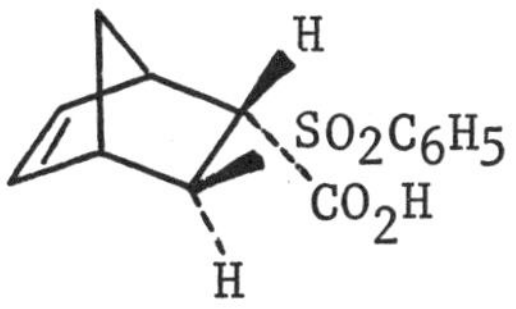

$C_{14}H_{14}O_4S$ Ref. 1032

(3S)-(−)-2-endo-*Phenylsulphonylbicyclo*[2,2,1]*heptane*-3-exo-*carboxylic Acid* (XIIIa).—2-*endo*-Phenylsulphonylbicyclo[2,2,1]hept-5-ene-3-*exo*-carboxylic acid [46] was partially resolved by crystallisation of the quinine salt from absolute ethanol. Five crystallisations afforded a salt, m.p. 213—214° (5 g. from 15 g. of racemic acid), from which a (−)-acid, m.p. 161—163°, $[\alpha]_D^{20}$ −75·4° (*c* 3·3 in ethanol) (2 g.) was isolated. By working up the more soluble fraction of the salt a (+)-acid (2·2 g.), m.p. 158—173°, $[\alpha]_D^{20}$ +30·0° (*c* 3·1 in ethanol) was isolated.

[46] **D. Albera, G. Luciani, and F. Montanari, *Boll. sci. Fac. Chim. ind. Bologna*, 1960, 18, 52.**

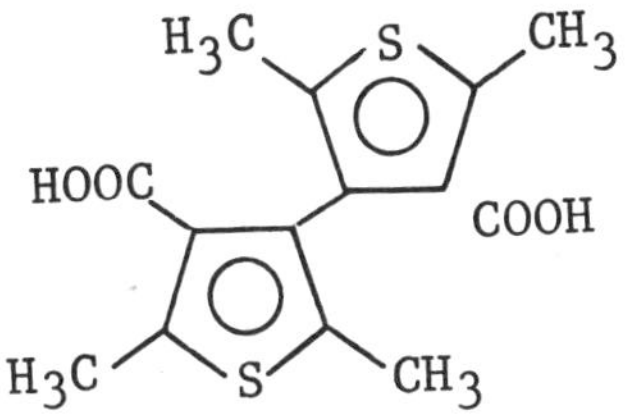

$C_{14}H_{14}O_4S_2$ Ref. 1033

Preliminary tests on resolution were made with 0.001 moles of inactive acid and 0.002 moles of optically active bases in different solvents such as water, ethanol, methanol, aceton and ethyl acetate, and in mixtures of these solvents. Many bases such as strychnine, cinchonine and (−)-α-phenyl ethylamine gave oily salts. An almost inactive acid was obtained from the quinidine salt. An acid was obtained from the quinine salt in aqueous ethanol $[\alpha]_D^{25} = +46°$ and, from the cinchonidine salt in aqueous acetone, $[\alpha]_D^{25} - +32°$, and, from the brucine salt in alcohol, $[\alpha]_D^{25} = -45°$. Quinine and brucine were therefore used for the resolution.

Optical resolution of 4,4′-dicarboxy-2,2′,5,5′-tetramethyl-3,3′-bithienyl. 21 g (0.068 moles) of 4,4′-dicarboxy-2,2′,5,5′-tetramethyl-3,3′-bithienyl and 44 g (0.136 moles) of quinine were dissolved by heating in 1250 ml of 50 % aqueous ethanol and the solution left over night at room temperature. The quinine salt crystallized in flakes and was filtered off and dried. From 0.5 g of salt the acid was liberated by macerating with 2 *N* hydrochloric acid followed by careful washing of the liberated acid with 2 *N* hydrochloric acid and water on the filter. The optical activity of the dried acid was then measured in dioxane solution. The remaining salt was recrystallized from 50 % aqueous ethanol[1] and the process repeated until the optical activity of the acid remained constant. The course of resolution is seen below.

Crystallization	1	2	3	4	5
ml, 50 % ethanol	1250	500	300	250	220
g, salt	26	17	15	13	11
$[\alpha]_D^{25}$ of acid	+56°	+58°	+61°	+61°	+61°

The mother liquor from the first crystallization with quinine was evaporated *in vacuo* and the residue decomposed with hydrochloric acid to give 10 g of acid having $[\alpha]_D^{25} = -49°$. 10 g (0.032 moles) of acid and 28 g (0.065 moles) of brucine dihydrate were dissolved in 900 ml of 95 % alcohol and the salt allowed to crystallize at −15°. The progress of the resolution is seen below.

Crystallization	1	2	3
ml, 95 % ethanol	900	500	200
g, salt	26	12	9
$[\alpha]_D^{25}$ of acid	−54°	−61°	−61°

(+)-*4,4′-Dicarboxy-2,2′,5,5′-tetramethyl-3,3′-bithienyl.* 10.5 g of pulverized quinine salt was macerated with 6 *N* hydrochloric acid and precipitate carefully washed with dilute hydrochloric acid and water, yielding 3.5 g of the (+)-acid, which was recrystallized from methanol–water (1:3), containing some hydrochloric acid. 2.5 g of pure (+)-acid, m.p. 295–305°, dec. (IR-spectrum, Fig. 3) was obtained. Additional amounts of pure acid were obtained from the last three crystallizations of the quinine salt. R.D. in 0.1 *N* NaOH (c. 0.381), temp. 26°, $[M]_{700}$ −160°, $[M]_{600}$ −200°, $[M]_{589}$ −220°, $[M]_{500}$ −350°, $[M]_{400}$ −725°. The rotations in different solvents are given below.

Solvent	conc./g acid/dl	$2\alpha_D^{25}$	$[\alpha]_D^{25}$	$[M]_D^{25}$
Chloroform	0.473	+1.42°	+150°	+465°
Dioxane	0.453	+0.55°	+61°	+190°
Ethanol	0.424	+0.45°	+53°	+165°
Dimethyl sulphoxide	0.565	+0.48°	+42°	+130°
Acetone	0.478	+0.33°	+35°	+105°
0.1 *N* NaOH	0.491	−0.71°	−72°	−225°

Anal. $C_{14}H_{14}O_4S_2$ (310.4)
Calc. C 54.18 H 4.54 S 20.65
Found C 54.19 H 4.54 S 20.67

(−)-*4,4′-Dicarboxy-2,2′5,5′-tetramethyl-3,3′-bithienyl.* 8.5 g of the brucine salt were decomposed with 6 *N* hydrochloric acid and the (−)-*acid* isolated as described above, yielding 2.1 g of acid which was recrystallized twice from methanol–water (1:3), m.p. 295–305°, dec. Its IR-spectrum was identical to that of the (+)-acid. R.D. in dioxane (c. 0.027–0.270), temp. 26°. $[M]_{700}$ −140°, $[M]_{600}$ −200°, $[M]_{589}$ −205°, $[M]_{500}$ −300°, $[M]_{400}$ −545°, $[M]_{300}$ −2050°.

[1] For the last three recrystallizations it was found most convenient to dissolve the salt in hot ethanol and then carefully add an equal volume of hot water. The salt was then allowed to crystallize at −15°.

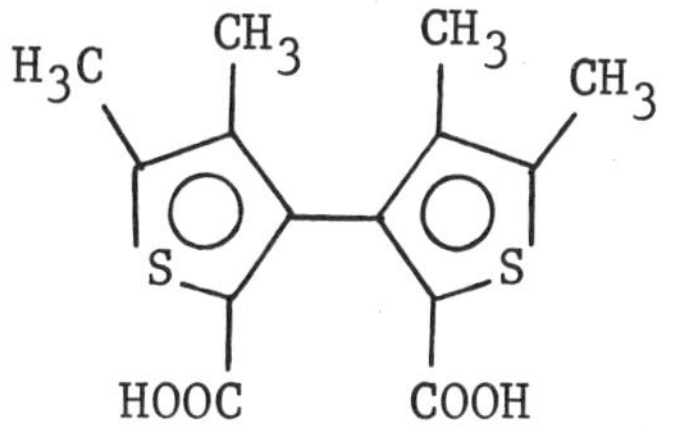

$C_{14}H_{14}O_4S_2$ Ref. 1034

Resolution of 2,2′-dicarboxy-4,4′,5,5′-tetramethyl-3,3′-bithienyl (*Ia*) [1]. Preliminary tests showed that crystalline salts of levorotatory I*a* (EtOH) could be obtained with strychnine and quinine in ethanol and ethanol–water respectively. Brucine yielded salt of inactive I*a* and quinidine, cinchonine, and cinchonidine gave oils in alcohol–water. A salt of the dextrorotatory form of I*a* was obtained with cinchonine in acetone–water. Quinine and cinchonine were used for the resolution.

3.10 g (10 mmol) of dicarboxylic acid I*a* and 6.5 g (20 mmol) of anhydrous quinine were dissolved in 100 ml of hot ethanol (95 %) and 100 ml of water was added. After standing at room temperature overnight, 3.8 g of salt was filtered from the solution, and 0.2 g of salt was set aside. The acid was liberated from the 0.2 g sample with dilute hydrochloric acid and taken up in ether, the solvent was evaporated and the residue dried at 70° (except for the substance obtained in the first crystallization). The activity was measured on ethanol solutions. The remaining salt was recrystallized from ethanol–water. After evaporation of the

mother liquor of the first crystallization, 1.5 g of acid $[\alpha]_D^{25} = +44°$ was liberated from the remaining salt. 1.3 g of this dicarboxylic acid and 2.5 g of cinchonine were dissolved in 50 ml of hot acetone and 50 ml of water was added. The salt obtained was treated as described above and recrystallized from 50% aq. acetone. The progress of the resolution is shown below.

Crystallization	1	2	3	4	1′	2′
ml, solvent	200	70	70	65	100	80
g, salt	3.8	3.3	2.6	1.9	2.8	2.2
$[\alpha]_D^{25}$ of acid	−72°	−79°	−78°	−78°	+78°	+78°

(S)-(−)-2,2′-Dicarboxy-4,4′,5,5′-tetramethyl-3,3′-bithienyl. 12.1 g (39 mmol) of racemic I*a* and 25.3 g (78 mmol) of anhydrous quinine dissolved in 350 ml of hot 95% ethanol and 350 ml of water gave, after cooling to room temperature, 12.8 g of a salt from which 4.1 g (68%) of levoratatory I*a* was liberated. Recrystallization from 200 ml of ethanol–water 1:2 yielded 3.9 g of I*a* $[\alpha]_D^{25} = -73°$, m.p. 265–270°, dec. in the form of long, white rods containing water as solvent of crystallization. [Found: C 50.7; H 4.99; S 19.3. Calc. for $C_{14}H_{14}O_4S_2 \cdot H_2O$ (328.4): C 51.20; H 4.91; S 19.53]. After dissolution of the crystals in acetone, evaporation of the solvent and drying of the residue at 100° the anhydrous crystalline form was obtained, $[\alpha]_D^{25} = -79°$. [Found: C 54.1; H 4.46; S 20.6. Calc. for $C_{14}H_{14}O_4S_2$ (310.4): C 54.17; H 4.55; S 20.66].

(R)-(+)-2,2′-Dicarboxy-4,4′,5,5′-tetramethyl-3,3′-bithienyl. The mother liquor from the crystallization of the levorotatory form was evaporated. 7.8 g (25 mmol) of acid $[\alpha]_D^{25} = +37°$ was liberated from the remaining salt and dissolved in 600 ml of hot acetone–water 1:1 together with 15 g (50 mmol) of cinchonine. After cooling to room temperature, 13.1 g of salt was isolated yielding 4.5 g (74%) of dextrorotatory I*a*. Recrystallization from ethanol-water as above gave 4.2 g of the hydrate $[\alpha]_D^{25} = +73°$, from which the anhydrous form could be obtained as above; m.p. 270–273°, dec., $[\alpha]_D^{25} = +79°$ (EtOH); +82° (dioxane); +143° (0.1 N NaOH).

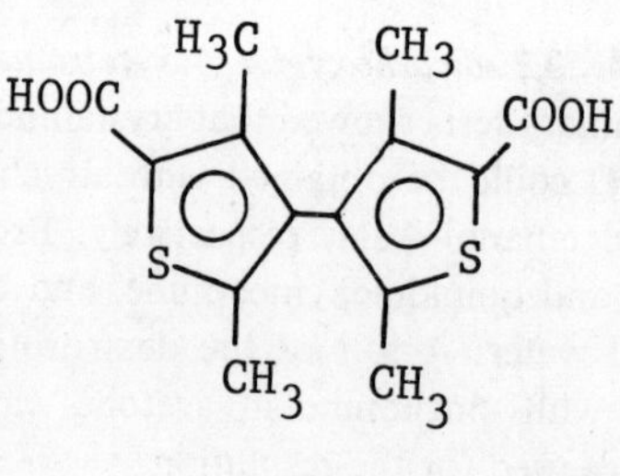

$C_{14}H_{14}O_4S_2$ Ref. 1035

Resolution of 5,5′-dicarboxy-2,2′,4,4′-tetramethyl-3,3′-bithienyl (Ib)

0.1 mmol of racemic dicarboxylic acid I*b* and 0.1 or 0.2 mmol of an optically active base such as strychnine, brucine, quinine, quinidine, cinchonine, or cinchonidine were dissolved together in various solvents, e.g. water, ethanol, aq. ethanol, acetone, aq. acetone or ethyl acetate. Only strychnine and brucine in ethanol gave crystalline salts, the former base with inactive acid. The brucine salts were discussed in the text above.

Two hot ethanolic solutions of 15.5 g (0.050 mol) of racemic I*b* and 39.5 g (0.100 mol) of brucine, respectively, were combined, the total volume being 1 200 ml. After standing for three weeks, 22.3 g of salt was filtered off. The acid was liberated from 0.3 g of salt as described for (S)-(+)-I*b* below, and the activity measured on acetone solution. The remaining salt was recrystallized from ethanol, yielding 18.9 g of salt. The resolution experiment was continued with 3.0 g of these crystals and the activity of the acid tested as above after each crystallization. The progress of the resolution is shown below.

Evidently the resolution

Crystallization	1	2	3	4	5
Solvent, ml	1 200	650	75	50	40
Salt, g	22.3	18.9	2.4	1.7	1.1
$[\alpha]_D^{25}$ of acid	+6.5°	+7.6°	+7.6°	+7.6°	+7.6°

was complete after the second crystallization. Since it was difficult to dissolve the salts obtained in ethanol, a 50% excess of solvent was used and the volume then reduced by distillation. For complete crystallization the solutions had to stand for at least 3–4 days.

The mother liquor from the first crystallization of the salt of the dextrorotatory form was evaporated *in vacuo* and the residue decomposed by 5 N hydrochloric acid to yield 6.5 g (0.021 mol) of I*b*, which was dissolved in 300 ml of ethanol together with 8.2 g (0.021 mol) of brucine. 3.0 g of the salt obtained was further recrystallized as above. The progress of the resolution is shown below. It was evidently complete after the first crystallization.

Crystallization	1	2	3	4
Solvent, ml	300	60	50	40
Salt, g	10.6	2.5	2.0	1.5
$[\alpha]_D^{25}$ of acid	−7.6°	−7.6°	−7.6°	−7.6°

(S)-(+)-5,5′-Dicarboxy-2,2′,4,4′-tetramethyl-3,3′-bithienyl (Ib)

The mother liquors of crystallizations 3–5 of the salt of the dextrorotatory form of I*b* were combined and evaporated and the residual salt added to that left after crystallizations 2 and 5 (a total of 17.5 g). The salt was treated with 5 N hydrochloric acid, and the acid extracted out with ether. The combined ether phases were washed with water, dried and evaporated and the residue was recrystallized from ethyl acetate-petroleum ether (b.p. 40–60°). 3.2 g (41% of the theoretical 7.75 g) was obtained; m.p. 214–216°. $[\alpha]_D^{25} = +7.6°$ (acetone, $c = 1.9$ g/100 ml); +5.5° (EtOH, $c = 1.6$). [Found: C 54.3; H 4.6; S 20.5. Calc. for $C_{14}H_{14}O_4S_2$ (310.4): C 54.18; H 4.55; S 20.66.]

(R)-(−)-5,5′-Dicarboxy-2,2′,4,4′-tetramethyl-3,3′-bithienyl (Ib)

The mother liquors of crystallizations 2–4 of the salt of the levorotatory form of I*b* were evaporated and the residue added to the salt left after crystallizations 1 and 4 (a total of 9.0 g). The acid was liberated and recrystallized as described for (S)-I*b*, yielding 2.7 g (35%) of the title compound, m.p. 214–216°, $[\alpha]_D^{25} = -7.6°$ (acetone, $c = 2.4$); −5.5° (EtOH, $c = 1.4$).

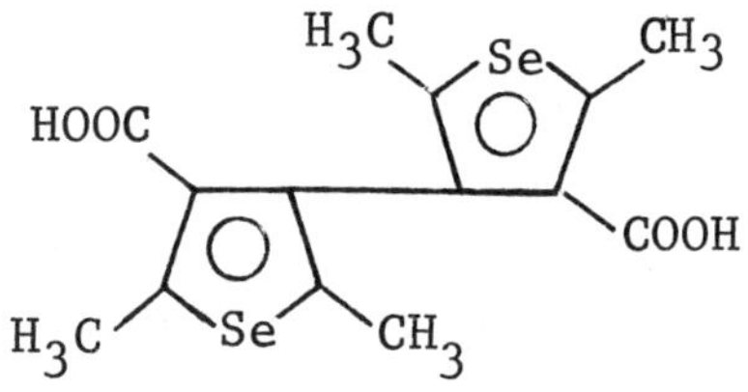

$C_{14}H_{14}O_4Se_2$ Ref. 1036

Optical resolution of 4,4'dicarboxy-2,2',5,5'-tetramethyl-3,3'-biselenienyl. 6.00 g (0.0148 mol) of racemic acid and 9.65 g (0.0297 mol) of quinine were dissolved in 55 ml of boiling ethanol, and 55 ml of hot water was added. After filtration, the solution was allowed to stand at room temperature for 48 h. The quinine salt was filtered off and recrystallized from 50 % aqueous ethanol. The progress of the resolution is shown below. Additional recrystallizations did not increase the rotation and the resolution has been repeated successfully several times.

Crystallization	1	2	3
ml 50 % ethanol	110	80	70
g, salt	7.10	6.53	5.55
$[\alpha]_D^{25}$ of acid [dioxane]	+20°	+24°	+24°

The mother liquor from the first recrystallization was evaporated *in vacuo* and the residue (8.3 g) decomposed with acid to give 2.22 g (0.00549 mol) of acid having $[\alpha]_D^{25} = -23°$. This acid and 4.34 g (0.0110 mol) of brucine were dissolved in 170 ml of absolute ethanol and allowed to stand at room temperature for 48 h. The progress of the resolution is shown below.

Crystallization	1	2
ml ethanol	170	150
g, salt	6.02	5.50
$[\alpha]_D^{25}$ of acid (dioxane)	−24°	−24°

(+)-*4,4'-Dicarboxy-2,2',5,5'-tetramethyl-3,3'biselenienyl.* 5.40 g of the quinine salt was decomposed with 2 N hydrochloric acid and the aqueous phase extracted with ether, yielding after recrystallization from a mixture of ethyl acetate−petroleum ether (40−60°C) 1.9 g of the title compound, m.p. 203−204°C. $[\alpha]_D^{25}$ (dioxane) = +24°. $[\alpha]_D^{25} = -10°$ (0.1 N NaOH). [Found: C 41.75; H 3.64; O 15.58. Calc. for $C_{14}H_{14}O_4Se_2$ (404.2): C 41.60; H 3.49; O 15.83.]

(−)-*4,4'-Dicarboxy-2,2',5,5'-tetramethyl-3,3'-biselenienyl.* 5.5 g of the brucine salt was decomposed with 2 N hydrochloric acid and the acid purified as described above, yielding a product (1.78 g) with the same IR spectrum as the (+)-form; m.p. 203−204°C. $[\alpha]_D^{25} = -24°$ (dioxane). $[\alpha]_D^{25} = +10°$ (0.1 N NaOH).

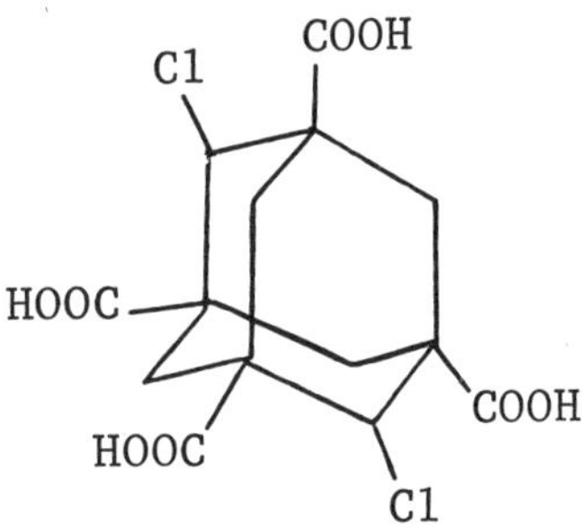

$C_{14}H_{16}Cl_2O_8$ Ref. 1037

S p a l t u n g d e r S ä u r e VI ü b e r d i e S a l z b i l d u n g m i t C i n c h o n i n: 9.8 g der Säure VI wurden mit der ber. Menge 0.5*n* NaOH neutralisiert und heiß zu einer heißen Lösung von 37.7 g C i n c h o n i n - h y d r o c h l o r i d - d i h y d r a t in 1000 ccm Wasser gegeben. Nach dem langsamen Erkalten kristallisierte man das ausgeschiedene Salz aus 3000 ccm Wasser um und erhielt 15.7 g des Salzes. Erneutes Umkristallisieren aus 1500 ccm Wasser lieferte 10 g des Salzes, die nochmals aus 1000 ccm Wasser umkristallisiert wurden. Weiteres Umkristallisieren ließ den Drehwert $[\alpha]_D^{20}$: 159.0 unverändert. Die Zusammensetzung entspricht einem Verhältnis von Säure zu Cinchonin = 1:4. Ber. N 7.19 Gef. N 6.98. Durch Zersetzen mit Salzsäure und Ausäthern erhielt man 1.25 g der rechtsdrehenden Säure. 0.3 g dieser Säure, in 20 ccm Wasser gelöst, zeigten im 2-dm-Rohr einen Drehwert von +0.21°, entspr. $[\alpha]_D^{20}$: +7.00°. Durch erneute Salzbildung mit Cinchonin und einmaliges Umkristallisieren ließ sich die spezif. Drehung auf $[\alpha]_D^{20}$: +7.67° steigern (0.300 g der Säure in 20 ccm Wasser, 2-dm-Rohr, Drehung +0.23°). Da auch bei Wiederholung der Trennungsoperation niemals eine höhere spezif. Drehung gefunden wurde, nehmen wir an, daß es sich hier um die reine r e c h t s d r e h e n d e Komponente der Säure handelt.

Das Filtrat der ersten Kristallisation wurde auf die Hälfte eingeengt. Die dabei erhaltenen 3 g Salz wurden verworfen. Aus dem Filtrat wurden durch Ansäuern und Ausäthern 1.6 g l i n k s d r e h e n d e S ä u r e erhalten. Die Drehung einer Lösung von 0.4 g in 20 ccm Wasser betrug im 2-dm-Rohr −0.11°, entspr. $[\alpha]_D^{20}$: −2.75°.

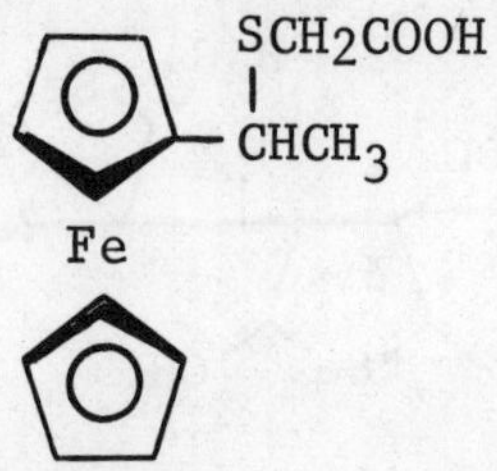

$C_{14}H_{16}FeO_2$

Ref. 1038

Resolution of (±)-S-(1-ferrocenylethyl)thioglycolic acid into enantiomers

3.32 g (0.2 mol) of ephedrine was dissolved in 100 ml of methanol at room temperature and a solution of 5.6 g (0.0184 mol) of (±)-I acid in 50 ml of methanol was added.

The flask was allowed to stand in the dark for 2 days at room temperature, after which 3 g of yellow-orange salt, m.p. 174-176° (dec.) was found to have crystallized. The salt was finely-powdered, crystallized from 70 ml of methanol, and the sample was allowed to stand at room temperature for 1 day. A crystalline precipitate in the form of compact orange plates was filtered off, 2.1 g, m.p. 172-174°C (dec.). The filtrate was concentrated to 20 ml and after 2 h an orange precipitate (0.6 g, m.p. 173-175° (dec.)) had separated. Both portions of the precipitate (2.7 g) were recrystallized together from 55 ml of methanol and allowed to stand overnight at room temperature. A salt (1.88 g) of m.p. 170-172° (dec.) was obtained. The solution was concentrated to 20 ml and after 3 h 0.390 g of the salt (m.p. 172-173° (dec.)) was filtered off. Both portions (2.27 g) were finely powdered together, 20 ml of ether and 20 ml of 10% phosphoric acid were added and the slurry was shaken in a separatory funnel till dissolution of the solid was complete. The aqueous layer was separated and the ether layer washed with 5% phosphoric acid (2 × 10 ml) and water (3 × 5 ml). The mixture was dried and the ether distilled off leaving 1.44 g (99%) of (+)-*S*-(1-ferrocenylethyl)-thioglycolic acid $[\alpha]^{24}_{546}$ + 22.5°, (*c*, 10; methanol; *l*, 0.1), in form of a dark-red oil.

The mother liquor was concentrated to 75 ml and allowed to stand in a refrigerator at 0° for 24 h. Fine crystals precipitated (0.130 g, m.p. 160-162° (dec.)) and were then filtered off. The solution was again concentrated to 36 ml and a further portion of fine crystals (0.250 g, m.p. 162-164° (dec.)) was obtained. After complete evaporation of the methanol, 20 ml of acetone was added and the solution allowed to stand for 6 days at 0° when a yellow precipitate (0.120 g, m.p. 170-172° (dec.)) separated. The acetone was then removed by evaporation leaving an oily salt from which the free acid I was isolated by the procedure described previously. Moreover, the acid was converted into its sodium salt by extraction with 10% sodium hydroxide solution the impurities being left in the ether layer. The free acid was obtained after acidifying the aqueous layer with 10% phosphoric acid and subsequently extracting with ether. After the extract had been dried and the ether had been evaporated, 2.24 g of the (—)-*S*-(1-ferrocenylethyl)thioglycolic acid in the form of a dark-red oil, was obtained ($[\alpha]^{22}_{546}$ —20° *c*, 10; methanol; *l*, 0.1).

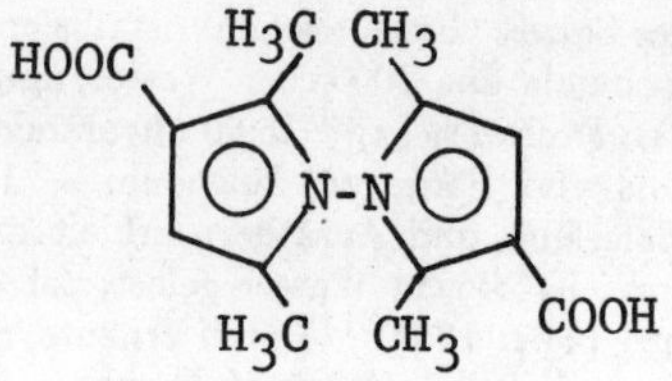

$C_{14}H_{16}N_2O_4$

Ref. 1039

Experimental

N,N',2,5,2',5'-Tetramethyl-3,3'-dicarboethoxydipyrryl.—A solution of 15 g. of N-amino-2,5-dimethyl 3-carboethoxypyrrole (Korschun)[3] in 200 cc. of absolute methyl alcohol was heated with 15 g. of 3-carboethoxy-2,5-dimethylhexadione in a 500-cc. flask fitted with a reflux condenser for four hours on a steam-bath. The solvent was then evaporated from the reaction mixture. A thick oily substance was obtained; yield 26 g. (94% of the theoretical).

N,N',2,5,2',5'-Tetramethyl-3,3'dicarboxydipyrryl.—A mixture of 26 g. of N,N',2,-5,2',5'-tetramethyl-3,3'-dicarboethoxydipyrryl with 70 cc. of 10% alcoholic potassium hydroxide was heated for two hours on a steam-bath. Upon acidifying the resulting solution with a little hydrochloric acid, a brownish precipitate was obtained. The product was filtered and washed with water. This was then dissolved in about 400 cc. of absolute methyl alcohol and refluxed for half an hour with 6 g. of decolorizing charcoal. After filtration, sufficient water was added until a precipitate just appeared. Upon standing the dipyrryl separated as a white precipitate which upon drying amounted to 18 g. (84% of the theoretical). It was purified by crystallizing from absolute methyl alcohol until it had a constant melting point of 278–280°.

It is slightly soluble in ethyl acetate, ethyl alcohol, benzene and chloroform and somewhat more soluble in absolute methyl alcohol and acetone.

Anal. Calcd. for $C_{14}H_{16}O_4N_2$: mol. wt., 276; N, 10.11. Found: mol. wt., 279; N, 9.96.

Resolution of N,N',2,5,2',5'-Tetramethyl-3,3'-dicarboxydipyrryl.—A solution of 20 g. of brucine in 400 cc. of absolute methyl alcohol was heated to its boiling point and 7 g. of powdered N,N',2,5,2',5'-tetramethyl-3,3'-dicarboxydipyrryl was added slowly with stirring. After standing for several hours at 0°, the salt which separated was filtered. The first fraction thus obtained which amounted to 12.7 g. was crystallized from absolute methyl alcohol three times until a constant rotation was obtained; melting point 153–157°.

Rotation. *d*-Salt, 0.1024 g. made up to 25 cc. with pyridine at 20° gave α_D −0.60; $l = 2$; $[\alpha]^{20}_D$ −73.2.

Anal. Calcd. for $C_{60}H_{68}N_6O_{12}$: N, 7.87. Found: N, 7.76.

The more soluble fraction obtained in solution as a filtrate from the less soluble salt was evaporated part way to dryness and again allowed to cool. Any crystalline material which separated was filtered and consisted of a mixture of the two salts, though primarily of the less soluble. It was necessary to concentrate to dryness before the more soluble salt was obtained. It then separated from the methyl alcohol as a gum which on long standing in a desiccator solidified. It was found impossible to recrystallize this material so that in the crude form a sample was weighed out and a rotation taken. The rotation undoubtedly is not the maximum one for the salt.

Rotation. *l*-Salt, 0.1550 g. made up to 50 cc. with pyridine at 20° gave α_D −0.51; $l = 2$; $[\alpha]^{20}_D$ −82.3°.

The *l*-salt in this crude form melted at 293–304°. It turned dark at 241°.

***d*- and *l*-N,N',2,5,2',5-Tetramethyl-3,3'-dicarboxydipyrryl.**—The active acids were liberated from the individual salts by suspending in water and treating with hydrochloric acid. A suspension of 4 g. of the less soluble salt in 100 cc. of water was treated with 4 cc. of concentrated hydrochloric acid and thoroughly stirred. The solid acid which precipitated was filtered and recrystallized to a constant melting point from absolute methyl alcohol. Melting point, 218–219°.

Rotation. *d*-Acid, 0.1817 g. made up to 25 cc. with pyridine at 20° gave α_D +0.40; $l = 2$; $[\alpha]^{20}_D$ +27.5.

Anal. Calcd. for $C_{14}H_{16}O_4H_2$: C, 60.87; H, 5.85. Found: C, 61.03; H, 6.10.

The *l*-acid was obtained in a similar manner from the crude soluble salt. The free acid was recrystallized from absolute methyl alcohol; melting point 220–221°.

Rotation. *l*-Acid, 0.1544 g. made up to 25 cc. with pyridine at 20° gave α_D −0.31; $l = 2$; $[\alpha]^{20}_D$ −25.1.

Racemization Experiments.—A solution of 0.1817 g. of *d*-acid made up to 25 cc. with pyridine at 20°, α_D +0.40, $l = 2$, $[\alpha]^{20}_D$ +27.5, was refluxed for twenty-four hours. No change in initial rotation was observed.

A solution of 0.1990 g. of *d*-acid in 50 cc. of 0.1 *N* sodium hydroxide gave an initial rotation of α_D +0.19; $l = 2$; $[\alpha]^{20}_D$ +23.9; upon boiling for eighty-four hours the rotations were as follows: nine hours, α_D +0.14, $l = 2$, $[\alpha]^{20}_D$ +17.6; forty-eight hours, α_D +0.12, $l = 2$, $[\alpha]^{20}_D$ +15.1; seventy-two hours, α_D +0.07, $l = 2$, $[\alpha]^{20}_D$ +8.8; eighty-four hours, α_D +0.06, $l = 2$, $[\alpha]^{20}_D$ +7.5.

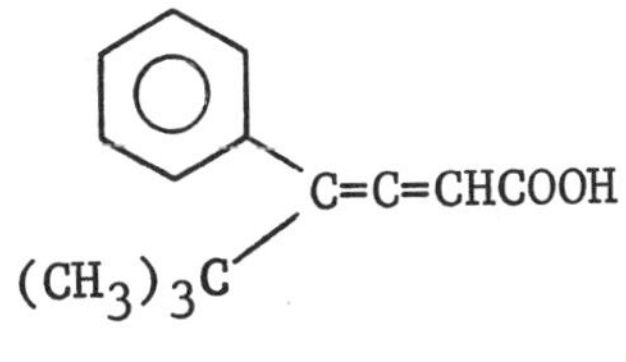

$C_{14}H_{16}O_2$ Ref. 1040

The racemic acid was resolved via the cinchonidine salt. The melting point and [α] obtained for the active acid were: m.p. 125°C; $[\alpha]_D$ = +177° (methanol).

$C_{14}H_{16}O_2$

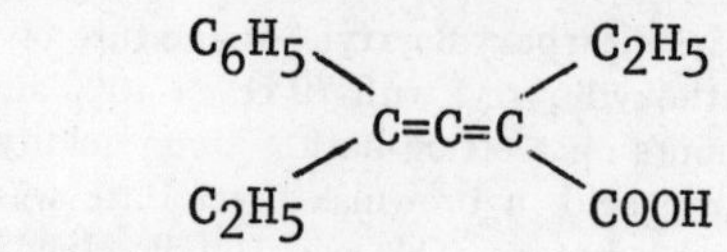

Ref. 1041

Verfahren zur Trennung von (+)- und (−)- **1e**: Da Spaltungsversuche von *racem.* **1e** nach der allgemeinen Vorschrift (S. 123) auch bei Verwendung von Äther als Lösungsmittel nicht zum Erfolg führten, wurde die Spaltung mit Chinin als Hilfsbase wie folgt ausgeführt: 6.151 g *racem.* **1e** und 4.618 g *Chinin* ergaben nach vier Umkristallisationen aus Aceton 1.550 g (20%) Salz, das mittels einer vorgekühlten Filtrieranordnung isoliert wird. Farblose Nadeln vom Schmp. 25° (aus Aceton); $[\alpha]_D^{25} = -42.5$ ($c = 0.01542$, C_2H_5OH). – Über das zur Elementaranalyse benutzte Präparat vgl. Tabelle 3 (dort Fußnote[e]).

$C_{34}H_{40}N_2O_4$ (540.7) Ber. C 75.53 H 7.46 N 5.18 Gef. C 75.13 H 7.65 N 5.27

Aus diesem Chininsalz wurden 0.305 g (5%) *(+)*-**1e** gewonnen. Farblose Nadeln vom Schmp. 77–79° (aus Petroläther); $[\alpha]_D^{25} = +41.1°$ ($c = 0.00974$, C_2H_5OH), $+54.0°$ ($c = 0.01228$, $CHCl_3$). – *CD* (C_2H_5OH): λ_{max} ($\Delta\varepsilon$) = 278 (+1.4) sh, 256 (+4.6) sh, 244 nm (+6.6).

$C_{14}H_{16}O_2$ (216.3) Ber. C 77.75 H 7.46 Gef. C 77.57 H 7.44

Aus dem *Filtrat der ersten Fraktion* wurden 3.133 g (51%) *racem.* **1e** zurückgewonnen. Farblose Kristalle vom Schmp. 83–86°. – Aus der *Mutterlauge* konnten 0.443 g (7.2%) *(−)*-**1e** isoliert werden. Farblose Nadeln vom Schmp. 74–77° (aus Petroläther); $[\alpha]_D^{25} = -39.5°$ ($c = 0.01670$, C_2H_5OH).

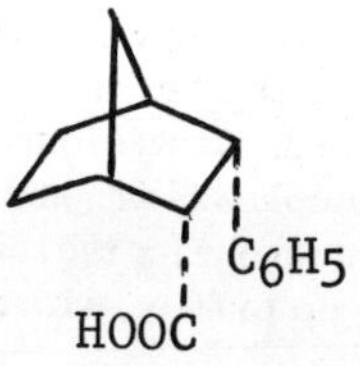

$C_{14}H_{16}O_2$

Ref. 1042

(2R)-endo-3-*Phenyl*-endo-2-*norbornanecarboxylic acid* [(2*R*)-**14**]. A hot soln of 54·3 g (0·251 mole) of (±)-**14**, white prisms, m.p. 157–158° (sealed tube) (lit.[21] m.p. 157–158°), prepared by catalytic reduction of 3-phenyl-2,5-norbornadiene-2-carboxylic acid,[21] in 1 l. of abs EtOH was added to a boiling soln of 74·0 g (0·251 mole) of cinchonidine in 1 l. of abs EtOH, and the mixture allowed to cool to room temp. The resulting ppt was recrystallized from 1·25 l. of abs EtOH, and there was obtained 36·1 g of the cinchonidine salt of (2*R*)-**14** (56%), m.p. 185–186°, $[\alpha]_D^{24}$ −65° (*c* 1·0, abs EtOH). A 35·1 g portion of this salt was decomposed with dil HCl aq. The carboxylic acid was extracted into ether, the ether soln was washed with dil HCl aq and then dried (Na_2SO_4). Evaporation of the ether gave 14·6 g of (2*R*)-**14** (98%) as a viscous, yellow oil, $[\alpha]_D^{25}$ −19° (*c* 4·3, abs EtOH).

(2S)-endo-3-*Phenyl*-endo-2-*norbornanecarboxylic acid* [(2*S*)-**14**]. A hot soln of 2·59 g (12·0 mmoles) of (±)-**14**, characterized above, in 20 ml of abs EtOH was added to a boiling soln of 1·46 g (12·0 mmoles) of (+)-α-phenylethylamine in 50 ml of abs EtOH, and the mixture was allowed to cool to room temp. The resulting ppt was recrystallized from abs EtOH and there was obtained 0·743 g of the (+)-α-phenylethylamine salt of (2*S*)-**14** (37%), $[\alpha]_D^{25}$ +11° (*c* 1·0, abs EtOH). As outlined above, 0·642 g of this salt (1·90 mmoles) was decomposed, and there was obtained 0·412 g of (2*S*)-**14** (100%) as a viscous, yellow oil, $[\alpha]_D^{25}$ +16° (*c* 4·2, abs EtOH).

[21] G. I. Poos, J. Kleis, R. R. Wittekind and J. D. Rosenau, *J. Org. Chem.* **26**, 4898 (1961).

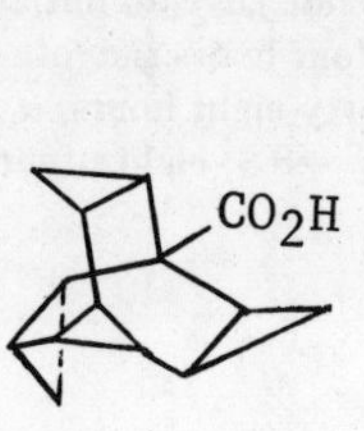

$C_{14}H_{16}O_2$

Ref. 1043

Resolution of 1-Trishomobullvalene Carboxylic Acid

The salt obtained from 3.43 g racemic 1-trishomobullvalene carboxylic acid and 5.15 g of quinine was recrystallized four times from methanol/water (2:1) as described above for trishomobarrelene carboxylic acid to give 540 mg of a salt with m.p. 210-211°C and in turn 215 mg (-)-1-trishomobullvalene carboxylic acid, $[\alpha]_D^{20}$ = -230°C (c= 0.474, ethanol), enantiomeric purity: 98.7%.

2.65 g of (+)-1-trishomobullvalene carboxylic acid, $[\alpha]_D^{20}$ = +17.6° (c= 0.511, ethanol), were obtained from the mother liquors. The salt from 2.64 g of this carboxylic acid and 1.49 g of D-(+)-α-phenyl-ethylamine was recrystallized three times from methanol/ether (1:2) as described above to give 940 mg of (-)-1-trishomobullvalene carboxylic acid, $[\alpha]_D^{20}$ = -166° (c= 0.560, ethanol).

The combined mother liquors yielded 1.6 g of (+)-1-trishomobullvalene carboxylic acid, $[\alpha]_D^{20}$ = +130° (c= 0.503, ethanol), enantiomeric purity: 55.8%.

The salt of 1.5 g of this carboxylic acid and 0.84 g of L-(-)-α-phenyl-ethylamine was crystallized once from methanol/ether (1:2) to give after acidification 520 mg of (+)-1-trishomobullvalene carboxylic acid, $[\alpha]^{20}_{D}$ = +200° (c= 0.422, ethanol), enantiomeric purity: 85.8%.

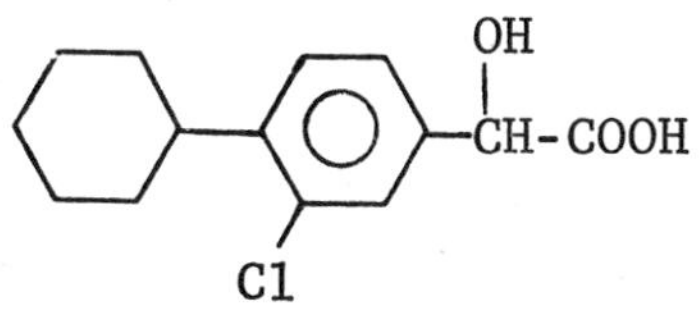

$C_{14}H_{17}ClO_3$ Ref. 1044

EXAMPLE 31

l 3-Chloro-4-cyclohexylphenylglycolic acid

To a boiling solution of 29.4 g. (0.10 mole) of cinchonidine in 1 liter of absolute ethanol is added a boiling solution of 26.9 g. (0.10 mole) of dl 3-chloro-4-cyclohexylphenylglycolic acid in 500 ml. of absolute ethanol. The solution is stirred briefly then allowed to cool to room temperature overnight. The precipitate is collected and washed with 2 × 25 ml. of ethanol and air dried. Recrystallization from isopropanol gives white needle crystals. This material is hydrolyzed with 200 ml. of 1.2 N-HCl. The white solid is collected, washed with 3 × 50 ml. water and dried at 55°C overnight. Recrystallization from benzene = cyclohexane 3:2 gives l 3-chloro-4-cyclohexylphenylglycolic acid. (m.p. 158°-60°C) $[\alpha]_D$ - 86.5° (C=1%, EtOH).

EXAMPLE 32

d 3-Chloro-4-cyclohexylphenylglycolic acid

The combined ethanol and isopropanol filtrates from Example 27 are evaporated to dryness. This material is triturated with 1 liter of boiling acetone. The material which does not go into solution is filtered off. The filtrate is evaporated to dryness and hydrolyzed with 100 ml. of 1.2 N-HCl. The precipitate is collected, washed with 3 × 25 ml. of water, and dried at 55°C. Recrystallization from benzene-cyclohexane 3:2 gives d 3-chloro-4-cyclohexylphenylglycolic acid. (m.p. 158–60°C) $[\alpha]_D$ + 86.5° (C = 1%, CH_3OH)

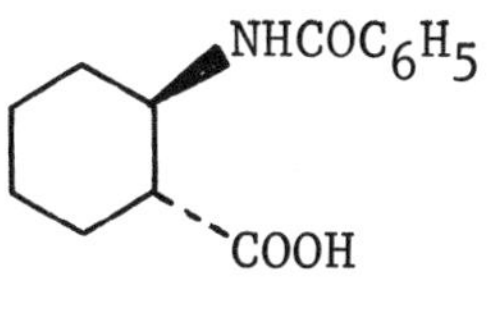

$C_{14}H_{17}NO_3$ Ref. 1045

An improved method for the optical resolution of (±)-N-benzoyl-trans-2-aminocyclohexanecarboxylic acid.

A mixture of 20.0g (0.08mol) of (±)-N-benzoyl-trans-2-aminocyclohexanecarboxylic acid [1] and 6.05g (0.08 mol) of (±)-1-amino-2-propanol* was dissolved in 200ml of 40vol% of aqueous methanol. To this solution was added 5.0g of (±)-[1], and dissolved at an elevated temperature. In the resulting hot solution was scattered the seed-crystals of 0.1g of (+)-[1], and allowed to stand for 1hr. The precipitated crystals were collected by filtration, washed with a small amount of 70% methanol and dried. The crude crystals of (+)-[1] weighed 3.3g. Subsequently, to the mother liquor was added 5.0g of (±)-[1], and dissolved at an elevated temperature. The mixture was seeded with 0.1g of pure crystals of (-)-[1], and allowed to stand for 1hr, giving 5.05g of crude (-)-[1].

The process was repeated analogously. Crystals with the same sign of optical rotation were put together and recrystallized from 95% ethanol to give a pair of the pure active acids, mp 257-258°C, $[\alpha]^{18}_{D}$ + and - 45° (c=0.50, 95% ethanol).

*Such aminoalcohols as 2-aminoethanol and 2-amino-1-butanol are also applicable.

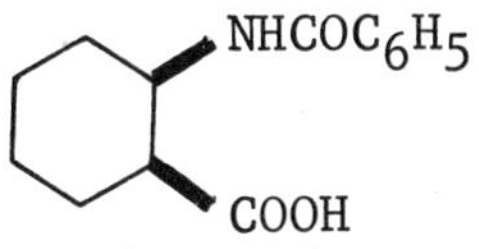

$C_{14}H_{17}NO_3$ Ref. 1046

Optical Resolution of cis-2-*Benzamidocyclohexanecarboxylic Acid*.—The acid [2] (7·5 g., 1 mol.) and cinchonidine (9·0 g., 1 mol.) in ethanol (100 ml.) were warmed at 60° for 15 min. The solution was concentrated to 70 ml. and cooled to give needles, which (from 95% ethanol) yielded the *cinchonidine salt* (A), m.p. 209—210° (decomp.) (7·0 g., 85% based on half of the racemate), $[\alpha]_{578}$ −53°, $[\alpha]_{364}$ −213° (*c* 0·33) (Found: C, 73·2; H, 7·0; N, 7·75. $C_{33}H_{39}N_3O_4$ requires C, 73·2; H, 7·3; N, 7·8%). The mother liquor was diluted with water and the solid obtained was recrystallised twice from aqueous ethanol (50%) to give the diastereomeric *cinchonidine salt* (B), m.p. 167—168° (6·0 g., 73% based on half of the racemate), $[\alpha]_{578}$ −73·6°, $[\alpha]_{364}$ −320° (*c* 0·55) (Found: C, 73·35; H, 7·1; N, 7·8. $C_{33}H_{39}N_3O_4$ requires C, 73·2; H, 7·3; N, 7·8%). Salt (A) was decomposed with 4N-hydrochloric acid to give (1S,2R)-*cis-2-benzamidocyclohexanecarboxylic acid*, m.p. 206·5—207° (97%), $[\alpha]_{578}$ +41·9°, $[\alpha]_{364}$ +132° (*c* 0·31) (Found: C, 67·8; H, 6·8; N, 5·6. $C_{14}H_{17}NO_3$ requires C, 68·0; H, 6·9; N, 5·7%). Similarly salt (B) gave (1R,2S)-*cis-2-benzamidocyclohexanecarboxylic acid*, m.p. 205—206·5°, $[\alpha]_{578}$ −40·4°, $[\alpha]_{364}$ −129° (*c* 0·26) (Found: C, 67·9; H, 6·8; N, 5·7. $C_{14}H_{17}NO_3$ requires C, 68·0; H, 6·9; N, 5·7%).

(1R,2R)-trans-(−)-2-*Aminocyclohexanecarboxylic Acid*.—(1*S*,2*R*)-*cis*-(+)-2-Benzamidocyclohexanecarboxylic acid was epimerised and hydrolysed with concentrated hydrochloric acid as already described to the *trans*-amino-acid hydrochloride (95%), which gave (1R,2R)-trans-(−)-2-*aminocyclohexanecarboxylic acid*, m.p. 239—240° (decomp.), $[\alpha]_{578}$ −51·9°, $[\alpha]_{364}$ −151° (*c* 0·53), after passage through a Dowex-50W column and elution with 3N-ammonium hydroxide followed by recrystallisation from ethanol and sublimation at 190°/1 mm. (Found: C, 58·5; H, 9·1; N, 9·4. $C_7H_{13}NO_2$ requires C, 58·7; H, 9·15; N, 9·8%).

[2] S. Hünig and H. Kahanek, *Chem. Ber.*, 1953, **86**, 518; L. Bauer and S. V. Miarka, *J. Org. Chem.*, 1959, **24**, 1293.

Note: See also Ref. 328.

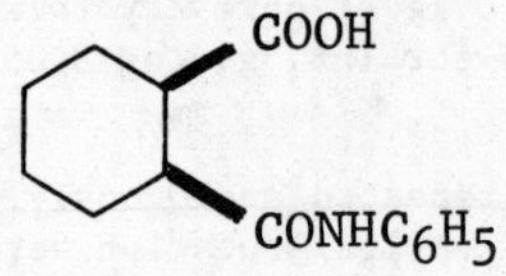

$C_{14}H_{17}NO_3$ Ref. 1047

Spaltung der *cis*-Hexahydro-phthalanilidsäure.

Löst man *cis*-Anilidsäure und Cinchonin (1:1 Mol.) in Methylal (auf 1 g Säure 100 ccm Methylal) in der Wärme, so krystallisiert nach dem Erkalten ein neutrales, schwer lösliches Salz aus, das durch öfteres Umkrystallisieren aus Methylal, aber nicht ohne erhebliche Verluste, gereinigt werden kann.

0.1099 g Sbst.: 7.5 ccm N (24°, 765 mm).
$C_{33}H_{39}O_4N_3$ (541.5). Ber. N 7.76. Gef. N 7.89.

Das Salz schmilzt unter Bräunung bei 205°, im vorgeheizten Bade aber schon bei etwa 152° nach vorherigem Sintern. Es wurde mit Ammoniak in der Kälte zersetzt und die Anilidsäure unter guter Kühlung mit Salzsäure in Freiheit gesetzt und durch Kochsalz ausgesalzen. Die so gewonnene Säure zeigt den Schmp. der Racemsäure (170°), schmilzt aber im vorgewärmten Bade schon bei 142°, erstarrt dann wieder und schmilzt erneut bei 170°. Der Schmelzpunkt der optisch aktiven Form dürfte daher bei etwa 142° liegen.

0.6768 g, in Aceton zu 10 ccm gelöst, zeigten im 1-dm Rohr bei 24°: α = +0.97°; $[\alpha]_D^{24}$ = +14.32°.

Eine Eisessig-Lösung der optisch aktiven Säure, ganz kurze Zeit auf 55° erwärmt, ließ keine optische Aktivität mehr erkennen, doch behielt die nicht erwärmte Aceton-Lösung nach Stunden noch ihre Drehung bei.

Die linksdrehende Anilidsäure konnte nicht rein erhalten werden, da das Cinchoninsalz der Mutterlauge ölig war und ziemlich viel der Antipoden-Säure zurückhielt. Der niedrigste Schmelzpunkt der *l*-Form wurde bei etwa 138° beobachtet.

0.2022 g, in Aceton zu 10 ccm gelöst, zeigten im 1-dm-Rohr bei 17°: α = —0.14°; $[\alpha]_D^{17}$ = —6.93°.

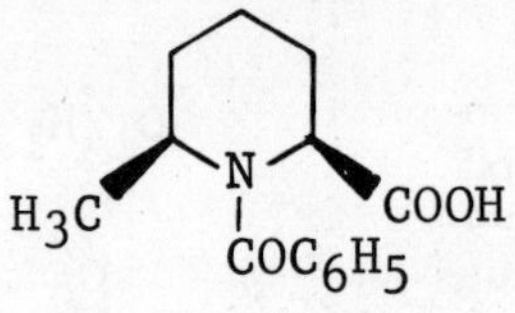

$C_{14}H_{17}NO_3$ Ref. 1048

Resolution of D,L-III. A mixture of 4·94 g D,L-III and 6·69 g strychnine was dissolved in a boiling solution of 40 ml ethanol and 10 ml water. To the cooled solution 200 ml ether was added. The precipitate obtained after 1 day standing weighed 5·4 g. It was recrystallized repeatedly from CCl_4 and pet. ether to give 2·0 g salt, m.p. 148–149°, $[\alpha]_D^{20}$ −51·7°. An aqueous solution of 1·5 g of this salt was made alkaline to liberate the strychnine (0·82 g), and the aqueous solution acidified to give 0·25 g levorotatory acid. After one crystallization from $CHCl_3$–pet. ether, it melted at 122–123°, $[\alpha]_D^{20}$ −180° ($CHCl_3$).

To obtain the enantiomer, the filtrate from the original separation was evaporated to dryness, taken up in hot 50% ethanol, and the acid regenerated as described above. The acid obtained (2·5 g) had $[\alpha]_D^{20}$ +119°. Four recrystallizations from $CHCl_3$–pet. ether gave material with constant m.p. (128–129°) and rotation ($[\alpha]_D^{20}$ +185°). No depression of the m.p. was observed on admixture with (+) III from the pinidine degradation, and the IR spectra of the two were identical.

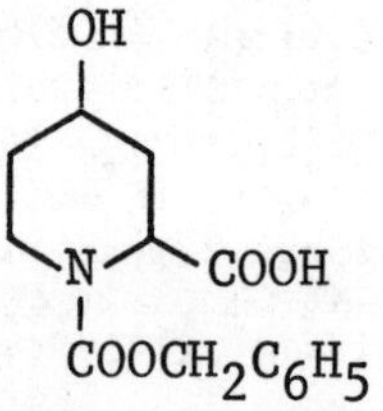

$C_{14}H_{17}NO_5$ Ref. 1049

Acides D et L N-carbobenzoxy hydroxy-4 allopipécolique 5.

La résolution de 4 est effectuée au moyen de quinine. 4,05 g de 4 sont mis en solution dans 70 ml d'éthanol. On ajoute 4,7 g de quinine. On filtre un léger insoluble et évapore le filtrat à siccité sous 10 mm de mercure à 30°. L'huile obtenue est reprise par 25 ml d'acétate d'éthyle; on chauffe jusqu'à dissolution puis laisse cristalliser. Après filtration et séchage, on obtient 4,54 g de sel de quinine enrichi en isomère L : $[\alpha]_D^{23}$ = — 112° (*c* = 1, éthanol). Par évaporation des liqueurs-mères, on obtient 3,95 g de sel de quinine enrichi en isomère D : $[\alpha]_D^{24}$ = — 89° (*c* = 1, éthanol).

Le sel de quinine enrichi en isomère L est recristallisé dans l'acétate d'éthyle jusqu'à pouvoir rotatoire constant : trois recristallisations sont nécessaires. On obtient 2,65 g de sel de quinine de l'acide L N-carbobenzoxy hydroxy-4 allopipécolique : $[\alpha]_D^{26}$ = — 128° (*c* = 1, éthanol).

Le sel de quinine enrichi en isomère D est recristallisé dans l'eau jusqu'à pouvoir rotatoire constant : trois recristallisations sont nécessaires. On obtient 1,80 g de sel de quinine de l'acide D N-carbobenzoxy hydroxy-4 allopipécolique : $[\alpha]_D^{24}$ = — 80° (*c* = 1, éthanol).

Le déplacement des sels de quinine est effectué dans l'eau bouillante en présence d'ammoniaque.

On obtient ainsi respectivement 1,21 g d'acide L N-carbobenzoxy hydroxy-4 allopipécolique et 0,79 g d'isomère D correspondant.

Isomère L $[\alpha]_D^{25}$ = — 62° (*c*=1, éthanol); R_F^1=0,62; R_F^2=0,81; R_F^3 = 0,63.

Isomère D $[\alpha]_D^{25}$ = + 62° (*c*=1, éthanol); R_F^1=0,62; R_F^2=0,81; R_F^3 = 0,63.

$HOOCCH(CH_2)_3COOH$
|
$NHCO_2CH_2CH_2C_6H_5$

$C_{14}H_{17}NO_6$ Ref. 1050

1. L-Isomer

DL-2-Carbobenzyloxyaminoadipic acid (80 g, 0.27 mole) and D(—) threo-1-*p*-nitrophenyl-2-aminopropane-1,3-diol were dissolved in 750 ml of hot absolute ethanol. The solution was slowly cooled, and a crystalline precipitate (58 g) was formed. By keeping the solution at room temperature for one day, another 44 g was obtained. The first crop of salt was recrystallized in hot absolute ethanol according to the scheme given below, and the progress of the resolution of the isomers was examined by determination of the rotation of the acid obtained from 0.5 g of salt.

Number of crystallizations	1	2	3	4
g of salt	102	74.8	56	49
$[\alpha]_D^{25}$ (*c* 2, in EtOH-2 *N* NaOH, 9:1) of the acid	+10	+13	+16	+18

The salt obtained in the last recrystallization was dissolved in 180 ml of water, and the solution was extracted four times with 100 ml of ethyl acetate after acidification with 5 *N* HCl to pH 2.0. The organic layer was washed with 2.5 *N* HCl and with water, and dried on Na_2SO_4. The residue obtained by evaporation of the organic solvent, was recrystallized in an acetone-cyclohexane mixture and 15.8 g of L-carbobenzyloxyaminoadipic acid mp 136-137° and $[\alpha]_D^{25}$ +17±1 (*c* 2, in EtOH-2 *N* NaOH, 9:1) was obtained.

2. D-Isomer

2-Carbobenzyloxyaminoadipic acid (42 g, 0.145 mole), obtained from the mother liquors of the preceding operation, and L(+) threo-1-*p*-nitrophenyl-2-aminopropane-1,3-diol were dissolved in 450 ml of hot absolute ethanol. The solution was slowly cooled and a first crop of 66.5 g of salt was obtained. After the filtrate was kept for one day at room temperature an additional 16.5 g of product was isolated. The amine salt was recrystallized in absolute ethanol according to the following scheme:

Number of crystallizations	1	2	3	4
g of salt	83	64	49	37
$[\alpha]_D^{25}$ (*c* 2, in EtOH-2 *N* NaOH, 9:1) of the acid	−7	−10	−13	−15

The acid was isolated from the salt obtained in the last crystallization, according to the method described for the L-isomer. An amount of 9.6 g of D-carbobenzyloxyaminoadipic acid mp 135-136° and $[\alpha]_D^{25}$ −15 (*c* 2, in EtOH-2 *N* NaOH, 9:1) was obtained.

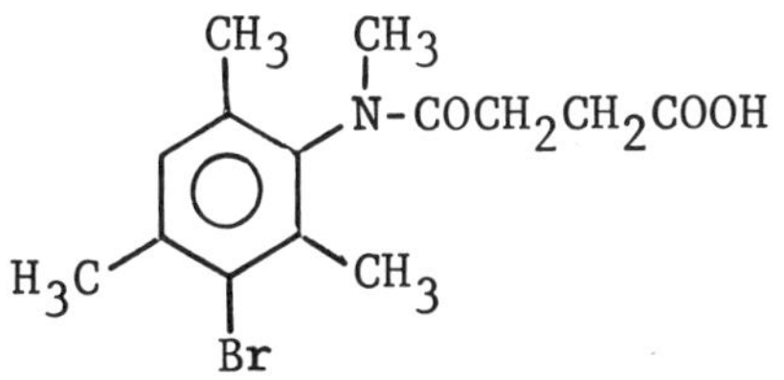

$C_{14}H_{18}BrNO_3$ Ref. 1051

Resolution of N-Succinyl-N-methylbromomesidine.—A solution of 5 g. of N-succinyl-N-methylbromomesidine in 15 cc. of chloroform was added to a solution of 7.1 g. of brucine tetrahydrate in 20 cc. of chloroform. The mixture was filtered, concentrated to 15 cc. and allowed to stand for two days during which time crystals separated. Fraction A, weighing 5 g., was filtered and recrystallized twice from chloroform. The original material and each successive crystallization gave the same rotation. The salt contains chloroform of crystallization as shown by analysis and by the tendency of the crystals to effloresce if treated with petroleum ether (b. p. 30–60°).

Anal. Calcd. for $C_{14}H_{18}O_3NBr{\cdot}C_{23}H_{26}O_4N_2{\cdot}CHCl_3$: C, 54.6; H, 5.21. Found: C, 54.50; H, 5.21. *Rotation.* 0.05 g. made up to 25 cc. with ethanol at 27° gave α_D −0.15°; *l*, 2; $[\alpha]^{27}_D$ −37.5°.

The filtrate from fraction A was concentrated to 7 cc. and allowed to stand. Fraction B, weighing 3 g., was thus obtained. Further evaporation of the filtrate from fraction B to 3 cc. was allowed to stand and fraction C (1 g.) separated. These were not used, but the filtrate from fraction C was evaporated to dryness. An amorphous residue (D) weighing 2.5 g. was primarily the diastereoisomeric salt.

Fraction A was decomposed by digesting six times with 12% aqueous hydrochloric acid at 0° or until no test for brucine was obtained in the filtrates. From 1 g. of salt was obtained 0.4 g. of acid. It was purified by crystallization from petroleum ether (b. p. 60–110°); white crystals, m. p. 132° (cor.).

Anal. (*l*-form) Calcd. for $C_{14}H_{18}O_3NBr$: C, 51.26; H, 5.53. Found: C, 51.39; H, 5.62. *Rotation.* 0.050 g. made up to 25 cc. with ethanol at 27° gave α_D −0.115°; *l*, 2; $[\alpha]^{27}_D$ −29°.

Fraction D was decomposed in a similar manner. The free acid was recrystallized from petroleum ether (b. p. 60–110°); white crystals, m. p. 132° (cor.).

Rotation. 0.050 g. made up to 25 cc. with ethanol at 27° gave α_D +0.11°; *l*, 2; $[\alpha]^{27}_D$ +27°.

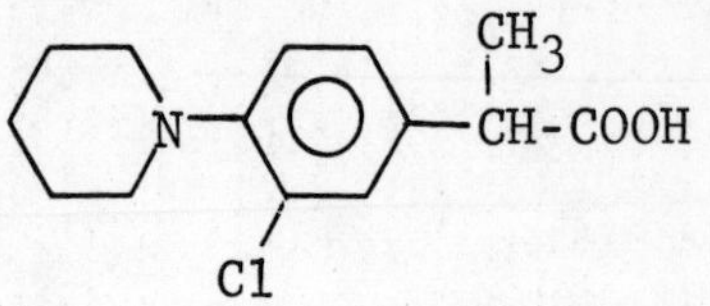

$C_{14}H_{18}ClNO_2$ Ref. 1052

EXAMPLE 41

53.5 g. of 3-chloro-4-piperidino-α-methyl-phenylacetic acid and 18.2 g. of L-ephedrine are allowed to stand in 200 ml. of ether for 2 days at room temperature. The thus-precipitated salt is vacuum filtered, then recrystallized three times from ethyl acetate and thereafter twice from acetone, m.p. 125°–126°; (α) −26.8°.

Six g. of this salt is dissolved in a mixture of 150 ml. of methanol and 150 ml. of ethanol. The solution is conducted over a weakly acidic cation exchanger and eluted with methanol/ethanol (1:1). The eluates are evaporated at 40°. The oily residue (3.12 g.; (α) +35.5°) is dissolved in 50 ml. of ether, filtered over charcoal, and mixed with a solution of 1.15 g. of cyclohexylamine in 10 ml. of ether. The thus-precipitated cyclohexylammonium-3-chloro-4-piperidino-α-methyl-phenylacetate is vacuum filtered, m.p. 197°–198° (methanol); (α) −7.2°.

Two grams of this salt is dissolved in 100 ml. of methanol/ethanol (1:1) under heating, passed over a weakly acidic cation exchanger, and eluted with methanol/ethanol (1:1). The eluates are concentrated by evaporation, thus obtaining 1.2 g. of (+)-3-chloro-4-piperidino-α-methyl-phenylacetic acid, (α) +37.4°.

EXAMPLE 42

26.7 g. of 3-chloro-4-piperidino-α-methyl-phenylacetic acid is allowed to stand in 100 ml. of acetonitrile with 9.1 g. of L-ephedrine for 48 hours at 0°–6°. The thus-precipitated salt is recrystallized twice from ethyl acetate, m.p. 124°–126°; (α) −15.6°. 5 g. of this salt is dissolved in 250 ml. of methanol/ethanol (1:1), passed over a weakly acidic cation exchanger and eluted with methanol/ethanol (1:1). The eluates are concentrated by evaporation. The residue (2 g. of oil, (α) −37.2°) is dissolved in 40 ml. of ether and mixed with a solution of 0.73 g. of cyclohexylamine in 10 ml. of ether. The thus-precipitated cyclohexylamine salt (m.p. 197°–198°; (α) +8.1°) is vacuum filtered, dissolved in 100 ml. of methanol/ethanol (1:1), passed over a weakly acidic cation exchanger, and eluted with methanol/ethanol (1:1). The eluates are concentrated by evaporation, thus obtaining 1.1 g. of (-)-3-chloro-4-piperidino-α-methyl-phenylacetic acid, (α) −41.1°.

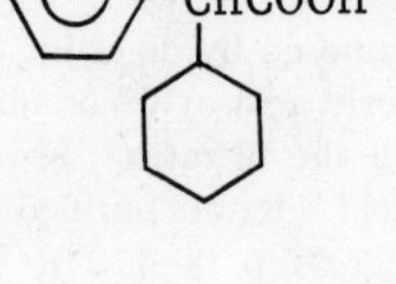

$C_{14}H_{18}O_3$ Ref. 1053

(+)- and (−)-Cyclohexylphenylacetic Acids. The racemic acid[9] (170 g) was added to quinine (252 g) dissolved in boiling ethanol and left at +4° for 2 hr. The salt which crystallized was filtered off, and after eight recrystallizations from ethanol had a constant mp 170.8–171.4° and rotation α^{25}D +11.05° (*c* 20, chloroform). This was treated with excess sulfuric acid (0.5 *M*) and extracted with ether. The extract was dried with anhydrous magnesium sulfate, and the crude (+)-acid recrystallized from petroleum ether: mp 100–102°; α^{25}D +38.7° (*c* 20, chloroform).

The mother liquors, left after filtration of the quinine salt, were combined, concentrated, converted back to the acid, and added to quinidine, dissolved in boiling ethyl acetate. The hot solution was filtered and left at +4° overnight. The salt which crystallized was filtered off and after four crystallizations had a constant mp 133.4–134.4° and rotation α^{25}D +48.10° (*c* 20, chloroform). This was converted to the (−)-acid which had mp 100–101°, α^{25}D −38.8° (*c* 20, chloroform). The rotations of the quinine and quinidine salts were very temperature-sensitive; αD varied as much as 1°/°C.

(9) E. M. Hancock and A. C. Cope, *Org. Syn.*, **25**, 25 (1945).

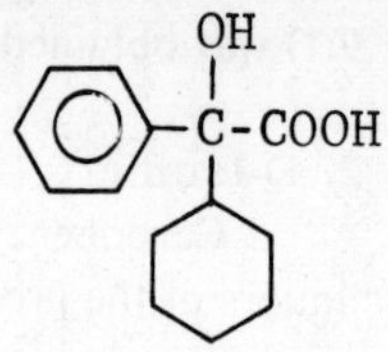

$C_{14}H_{18}O_3$ Ref. 1054

(*R*)- and (*S*)-Cyclohexylphenylglycolic Acids. The racemic acid[10] was resolved with quinine;[11] after six recrystallizations from ethanol the quinine salt of the (*S*)-(+)-acid had constant mp 222.4–222.6° dec and rotation α^{25}D −76.0° (*c* 4.0, chloroform) and when converted to the acid this had mp 140.6–141.1°, α^{25}D +24.8° (*c* 4.5, ethanol). The mother liquors were combined, concentrated, converted back to the acid, dissolved in ethanol, added to (−)-ephedrine dissolved in aqueous ethanol, and left at +4° overnight. The salt which crystallized was filtered off, and after four recrystallizations from aqueous ethanol had constant mp 170.8–171.6° and rotation α^{25}D −43.5° (*c* 2, ethanol). When converted to the acid this had mp 141.9–142.3°, α^{25}D −24.9° (*c* 4.5, ethanol). The values in the literature[11] for the (+)- and (−)-acids respectively are mp 142–143 and 145°; αD +25.8 ± 1 and −25.2 ± 1° (*c* 4.48, ethanol). This acid has also been resolved with (+)- and (−)-amphetamine by Ellenbroek.[12] The assignment of the *R* configuration to the (−)-acid follows from its synthesis by a stereospecific route.[13]

(10) K. Hoffman and H. Schellenberg, *Helv. Chim. Acta*, **30**, 292 (1947).
(11) C. H. Boehringer Sohn, British Patent 708,370 (1954); *Chem. Abstr.*, 49, 11031 (1955).
(12) B. W. J. Ellenbroek, Ph.D. Thesis, Catholic University of Nijmegen, Rotterdam, Bronder Offset, 1964.
(13) T. D. Inch, R. V. Ley, and P. Rich, *J. Chem. Soc. C*, 1693 (1968).
(14) A. Vecchi and G. Melone, *J. Org. Chem.*, 24, 109 (1959).

$C_{14}H_{18}O_3$ Ref. 1054a

Exemple. — A une solution bouillante de 42,1 g (0,13 mol/g) de quinine anhydre $[\alpha]_D = -162°$, dans 250 cm³ d'alcool absolu, on ajoute peu à peu 30,4 g (0,13 mol/g) d'acide α-phényl-α-cyclohexyl-glycolique racémique. On filtre à chaud, et on abandonne le filtrat 22 heures à la glacière. On essore le sel de quinine précipité, concentre le filtrat alcoolique au 1/4 de son volume, y ajoute de l'acide sulfurique N pour décomposer le sel. On essore l'acide α-phényl-α-cyclohexylglycolique, le lave à l'eau et le sèche dans le vide sur de l'anydride phosphorique : $[\alpha]_D = -19{,}5° \pm 1{,}5$ (alcool, c = 3,030).

On recristallise le sel de quinine, précédemment essoré, 7 fois successivement dans l'alcool absolu, les $[\alpha]_D$ des acides α-phényl-α-cyclohexyl-glyco-liques récupérés dans les filtrats des deux dernières recristallisations étant pratiquement identiques.

Dans le tableau ci-dessous, est résumé le progrès de la résolution du sel de quinine, au fur et à mesure des recristallisations successives, recristallsations qui aboutissent finalement au sel optiquement pur.

Recristallisation	D	c
1	$- 14,2^o \pm 1,2^o$ (alcool)	3,847
2	$+ 3^o \pm 1,5^o$ (alcool)	3,021
3	$+ 14,1^o \pm 2,3^o$ (alcool)	1,93
4	$+ 19,7^o \pm 3,6^o$ (alcool)	1,273
5	$+ 24,5^o \pm 2,2^o$ (alcool)	2,041
6	$+ 26^o \pm 1,5^o$ (alcool)	2,878
7	$+ 25,4^o \pm 3,3^o$ (alcool)	1,43

On met en suspension finalement les 10 g du sel de quinine, provenant de la dernière recristallisation dans 80 cm³ d'alcool absolu, acidifie par l'acide sulfurique N, ajoute de l'eau jusqu'à la fin de précipitation, essore l'acide précipité, le lave à l'eau et le sèche dans le vide sur de l'anhydride phosphorique.

On recueille 3,5 g de l'acide α-phényl-α-cyclohexyl-glycolique dextrogyre qui, recristallisé dans 110 cm³ de cyclohexane, fond à 142-143°; $[\alpha]_D = + 25,2^o \pm 1^o$ (alcool c = 4,483).

Pour séparer l'acide α-phényl-α-cyclohexyl-glycolique lévogyre, on réunit les acides $[\alpha]_D = - 19,5^o \pm 1,5^o$ et $[\alpha]_D = - 14,2^o \pm 1,2^o$ provenant

des deux premiers filtrats alcooliques, et salifie les 12,5 g d'acide ainsi réunis par 17 g de quinine anhydre dans 110 cm³ d'alcool bouillant. Après un repos d'une nuit à la glacière, on essore le sel précipité et le décompose par l'acide sulfurique N : $[\alpha]_D = - 23,7^o \pm 2^o$ (alcool c = 2,305).

On libère finalement l'acide du filtrat alcoolique en l'acidifiant par SO_4H_2 N, on l'essore, le lave copieusement à l'eau et le sèche dans le vide sur de l'anydride phosphorique. On recueille 2,7 g d'acide α-phényl-α-cyclohexyl-glycolique lévogyre, P.F. 145 °C $[\alpha]_D = - 25,2^o \pm 1^o$.

$C_{14}H_{18}O_3$ Ref. 1054b

Optical Resolution of Glycolic Acids. In a typical resolution procedure a solution of 40 g (0.182 mol) of racemic cyclopentylphenylglycolic acid in 500 mL of EtOAc was neutralized at the boil with a solution of 25 g (0.185 mol) of (+)-amphetamine in 200 mL of EtOAc. The (+)-acid (+)-amphetamine salt was collected after standing overnight at room temperature. The 34 g so obtained was recrystallized to constant optical rotation from EtOH (12 mL/g) to give 13.7 g, which was then suspended in 100 mL of H₂O and treated with 6 N NaOH to decompose it. The basic solution was extracted with ether to recover (+)-amphetamine and then acidified with 6 N HCl to precipitate the (+)-cyclopentylphenylglycolic acid.

The mother liquors from the preparation of the (+)-acid (+)-amphetamine salt were evaporated to dryness and the crude (-)-acid (+)-amphetamine salt so obtained was decomposed as above to give crude (-)-acid. This was in turn converted to the (-)-acid (-)-amphetamine salt by neutralization with (-)-amphetamine; the salt was recrystallized to constant rotation and then was decomposed to give optically pure (-)-acid.

Note:
    The following physical constants were reported by the authors for the active acids: m.p. 140-142°, $[\alpha]_D$ -23.3° (c 5%, ethanol) and m.p. 139-142° $[\alpha]_D$ +24.6° (c 5% ethanol).

$$C_2H_5OOC-\underset{\underset{OCH_2C_6H_5}{|}}{\overset{\overset{C_2H_5}{|}}{C}}-COOH$$

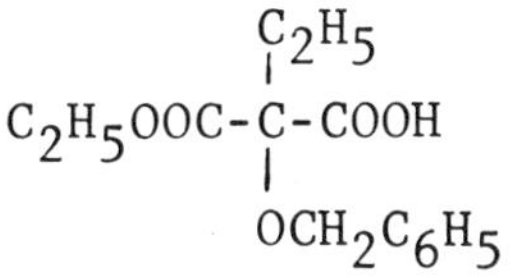

$C_{14}H_{18}O_5$ Ref. 1055

Spaltung des rac. *Äthyl-benzyloxy-malonsäure-monoäthylesters 4 in die optischen Antipoden 5 und 6.* 532 g (2,13 Mol) roher, rac. Äthyl-benzyloxy-malonsäure-monoäthylester 4 und 630 g Cinchonidin (2,13 Mol) wurden in möglichst wenig Essigester warm gelöst und beim Erkalten mit 700 ml Heptan verdünnt, wobei langsam Kristallisation einsetzte. Man liess einen Tag bei +5° stehen, wobei ein dicker Kristallbrei des Cinchonidinsalzes von (−)-Äthyl-benzyloxy-malonsäure-monoäthylester entstand. Die Kristalle wurden nochmals aus Essigester umkristallisiert. Das Cinchonidinsalz des (−)-Äthyl-benzyloxy-malonsäure-monoäthylesters fiel dabei bereits optisch rein an: 277 g farblose Nadeln, Smp. 147–148°, $[\alpha]_D^{20} = - 66^o$ (c = 1 in Äthanol).

$C_{33}H_{40}O_6N_2$ Ber. C 70,7   H 7,2   O 17,1   N 5,0%
(560,7)   Gef. „ 70,5   „ 7,1   „ 17,4   „ 5,1%

Die erste Mutterlauge, die das angereicherte Cinchonidinsalz des (+)-Äthyl-benzyloxy-malon-säure-monoäthylesters enthielt, wurde, da Kristallisationsversuche misslangen, durch Verteilen zwischen Äther und 10-proz. wässeriger Phosphorsäure zu Cinchonidin und angereichertem (+)-Äthyl benzyloxy-malonsäure-monoäthylester 6 aufgespalten. Man erhielt so 337 g rohen, angerei-cherten (+)-Äthyl-benzyloxy-malonsäure-monoäthylester 6 als braunes Öl, $[\alpha]_D^{20} = + 2,3^o$ (c = 4 in Äthanol), $n_D^{22} = 1,4965$, Äqu.-Gew.: gef. 255, ber. 266.

Die in gleicher Weise durchgeführte Aufspaltung des optisch reinen Cinchonidinsalzes des (−)-Äthyl-benzyloxy-malonsäure-monoäthylesters lieferte quantitativ den optisch homogenen Monoäthylester 5: farbloses Öl, $n_D^{21} = 1,4973$, $[\alpha]_D^{20} = - 6,9^o$ (c = 3 in Äthanol).

$C_{14}H_{18}O_5$ (266,3)   Ber. C 63,1   H 6,8   O 30,0%   Gef. C 62,0   H 6,6   O 30,3%

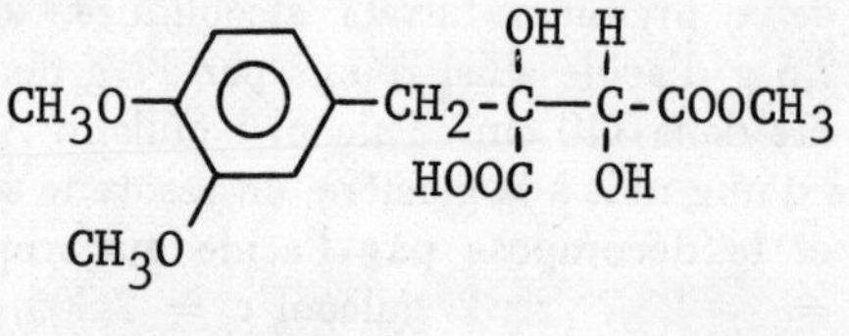

$C_{14}H_{18}O_8$ Ref. 1056

The (±)-VIIb acid in methanol was successfully resolved by means of brucine and one of the diastereomeric salt (mp 185-186°C dec.) was decomposed with dilute hydrochloric acid to give (+)-VIIb, mp 138-139°C, $[\alpha]_D$ +40.8° (methanol). The mother liquor, after the separation of the above brucine salt, was also treated with dilute hydrochloric acid to give (-)-VIIb, mp 138-139°C, $[\alpha]_D$ -38.0° (methanol). The alkaline hydrolyses of (+)-VIIb and (-)-VIIb gave (+)-VIb, mp 104-106°C, $[\alpha]_D$ +40.3° (methanol) and (-)-VIb, mp 104-106°C, $[\alpha]_D$ -40.5° (methanol) respectively.

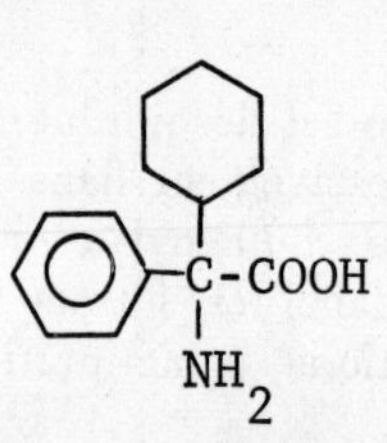

$C_{14}H_{19}NO_2$ Ref. 1057

(*R*)-(−)- and (*S*)-(+)-*N*-Formyl-2-cyclohexyl-2-phenylglycine (6b and 6c). The *N*-formylamino acid **6a** (10 g, 38.4 mmol) and brucine·4H_2O (23 g, 49.4 mmol) were dissolved in boiling water (1200 ml). By successive concentration to around 200 ml, 9.2 g of the brucine salt of the dextrorotatory acid was obtained. The specific rotation of each fraction was measured on a sample obtained by treatment of a small amount of the salt with 0.5 *N* NaOH, extraction of brucine with $CHCl_3$, and precipitation of the acid with 0.5 *N* HCl. Three crystallizations from water and decomposition of the salt afforded **6c:** $[\alpha]^{25}_{546}$ +68.4° (*c* 0.4, 0.5 *N* NaOH). By subsequent concentration of the above mother liquor (200 ml), 8 g of the salt of the levorotatory acid was isolated. Two crystallizations from water and decomposition of the salt afforded **6b:** $[\alpha]^{25}_{546}$ −69.3° (*c* 0.4, 0.5 *N* NaOH).

(*R,S*)- and (*R*)-(−)-2-Cyclohexyl-2-phenylglycine (5a and 5b). A suspension of **6b** (1.5 g, 5.7 mmol), $[\alpha]^{25}_{546}$ −68.4° (*c* 0.4, 0.5 *N* NaOH), in 10% sulfuric acid (25 ml) was refluxed for 6 hr. The hot solution was cooled, filtered, and brought to pH 1.3 with 20% sodium hydroxide yielding 0.566 g. Further neutralization to pH 4 afforded 0.503 g of additional material (80.5%): R_f 0.72 (II); mp 274–276° dec; $[\alpha]^{25}_{546}$ −26.25° (*c* 0.1295, H_2O); $[\alpha]^{25}_{546}$ −23.7° (*c* 0.135, 2 *N* HCl). In the same way, **6a** gave **5a** (0.984 g, 74%): mp 270–271° dec.

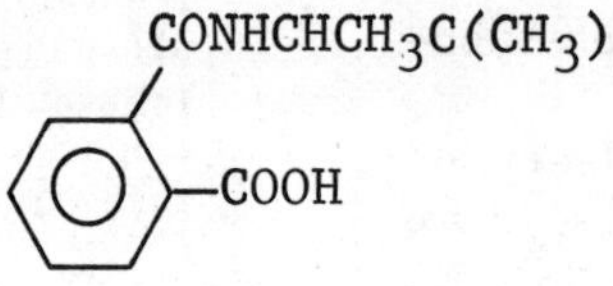

$C_{14}H_{19}NO_3$ Ref. 1058

Racematspaltung von X: 101.2 g (0.405 Mol) *X* wurden in 1.3 *l* absol. Aceton gelöst und zu einer filtrierten Lösung von 190.5 g (0.408 Mol) *Brucin* (Tetrahydrat) in 2.9 *l* Aceton gegeben. Nach einem Tag bei 0° waren 132.8 g des Salzes auskristallisiert, welches aus 4.5 *l* Aceton umkristallisiert wurde. Ausb. 90.2 g *Brucinsalz von (S)(+)-X*, Schmp. 193−197° (1. Schmp. bereits bei ca. 131−143°, Rekristallisation bei 160°), welches in warmem Wasser gelöst und mit einem kleinen Überschuß an verd. Salzsäure in die Komponenten zerlegt wurde. Beim Abkühlen auf 0° kristallisierten aus dieser Lösung 19.1 g *(S)-X*, Schmp. 142−147°, $[\alpha]^{25}_D$: +19.1° (*c* = 2, in Essigester). Die Mutterlauge lieferte bei der Extraktion mit Essigester weitere 4.5 g *(S)*-X in etwa der gleichen Reinheit.

Die erste Acetonmutterlauge wurde auf ca. 500 ccm eingeengt und durch Kühlen auf 0° eine fast *racem.* Brucinsalz-Mittelfraktion abgeschieden. Die Endmutterlauge wurde zur Trockne eingedampft und mit verd. Salzsäure zerlegt, wobei 22.8 g *(R)(−)-X*, Schmp. 144−157°, $[\alpha]^{25}_D$: −19.8° (*c* = 2, in Essigester) isoliert wurden.

Der Drehwert von *(S)*(+)-X ließ sich durch einmaliges Umkristallisieren aus Benzol oder Benzol/Cyclohexan auf $[\alpha]^{25}_D$: +22 bis +23° steigern, während häufigeres Umkristallisieren die Reinheit nicht mehr veränderte.

Eine Probe wurde zur weiteren Reinigung erneut, wie oben beschrieben, in das Brucinsalz übergeführt und nach Umkristallisieren aus diesem regeneriert. Schmp. 142−145°, $[\alpha]^{25}_D$: +26.3° (*c* = 2, in Essigester).

$C_{14}H_{19}NO_3$ (249.3) Ber. N 5.62 Gef. N 6.04 Äquiv.-Gew. 251 (gegen NaOH)

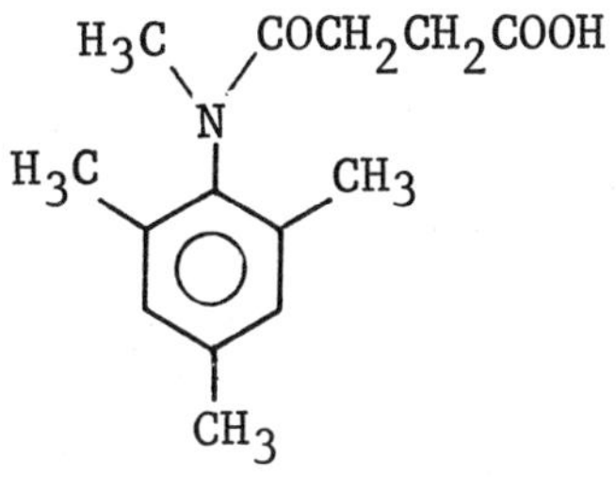

$C_{14}H_{19}NO_4$ Ref. 1059

Resolution of N-Succinyl-N-ethyl-3-bromomesidine.—Of the various alkaloids and solvents studied, only cinchonidine in ethyl acetate proved satisfactory. The presence of a small amount of methanol was desirable to prevent separation of alkaloid during crystallization of the salt. Heating a concentrated solution and cooling led to precipitation of some alkaloid which made purification of the salt difficult. Consequently crystallizations were performed by concentration of solutions at room temperature.

A boiling solution of 5 g. of N-succinyl-N-ethyl-3-bromomesidine and 4.3 g. of cinchonidine in 130 cc. of ethyl acetate and 10 cc. of methanol was filtered and allowed to cool to room temperature. The solution was then concentrated to 90 cc. by directing a gentle stream of air at the top of the flask and frequently rinsing the walls of the flask. At 90 cc., 2.83 g. of salt had crystallized; at 75 cc. another 1.56 g. of salt. These two fractions were combined and dissolved in 110 cc. of boiling ethyl acetate and 10 cc. of methanol. After concentration at room temperature to 90 cc., 1.14 g. of salt crystallized, at 70 cc., 1.15 g. and at 40 cc., 0.84 g. The residual fraction was discarded. All three fractions gave a rotation of $[\alpha]^{30}D$ −41°. From another crystallization of the combined three fractions in a similar manner just two fractions were isolated both of which were identical in rotation with each other and with the product from the previous crystallization; white crystals, m. p. 117–118° (cor.).

Rotation. 0.025 g. made up to 5 cc. with absolute ethanol at 30° gave αD −0.205; *l*, 1; $[\alpha]^{30}D$ −41°.

Upon evaporating further the original solution of the salt, 1.33 g. of product was obtained at 60 cc., 1.0 g. at 40 cc., 0.72 g. at 25 cc. and a residue at dryness of 1.90 g. This residue was dissolved in a mixture of 15 cc. of ethyl acetate and 1.5 cc. of methanol, the solution filtered and evaporated to 10 cc.; 0.47 g. of salt separated. At dryness a residue of 1.37 g. was left. Both gave identical rotations; white crystals, m. p. 112.5–114.5° (cor.).

Rotation. 0.025 g. made up to 5 cc. with absolute ethanol at 30° gave αD −0.33; *l*, 1; $[\alpha]^{30}D$ −66°.

***d*- and *l*-N-Succinyl-N-ethyl-3-bromomesidine.**—About 1 g. of less-soluble salt, $[\alpha]^{30}D$ −41°, was decomposed by stirring with 100 cc. of 12% aqueous hydrochloric acid at 0° for about three hours or longer. The salt turned to a gum on treatment with the hydrochloric acid and was allowed to remain with the acid until the product again appeared crystalline. The material was filtered and treated four times for one-half hour each in a similar manner. Cinchonidine was shown to be absent from the filtrate by Folin's reagent.[7] It was necessary also to remove a small amount of occluded salt in the crystals. This was done by dissolving in 2% aqueous sodium carbonate, filtering and precipitating with 1:2 hydrochloric acid. This treatment had to be repeated once before the crystals were free of cinchonidine. The acid thus obtained was decolorized in carbon tetrachloride solution with Darco and recrystallized from a mixture of three volumes of carbon tetrachloride and two volumes of petroleum ether (b. p. 80–92°); white crystals, m. p. 104.5° (cor.).

Anal. Calcd. for $C_{15}H_{20}O_3NBr$: C, 52.62; H, 5.89. Found: C, 52.22; H, 5.91.

Rotation. (*d*-Acid) 0.05 g. made up to 5 cc. with absolute ethanol at 30° gave αD +0.25; *l*, 1; $[\alpha]^{30}D$ +25°.

Decomposition of the more-soluble salt, $[\alpha]^{30}D$ −66°, in a similar manner gave white crystals, m. p. 104.5° (cor.).

Anal. Calcd. for $C_{15}H_{20}O_3NBr$: C, 52.62; H, 5.89. Found: C, 52.28; H, 6.02.

Rotation. (*l*-Acid) 0.05 g. made up to 5 cc. with absolute ethanol at 30° gave αD −0.25; *l*, 1; $[\alpha]^{30}D$ −25°.

(7) Folin and Denis, *J. Biol. Chem.*, **12**, 239 (1912)

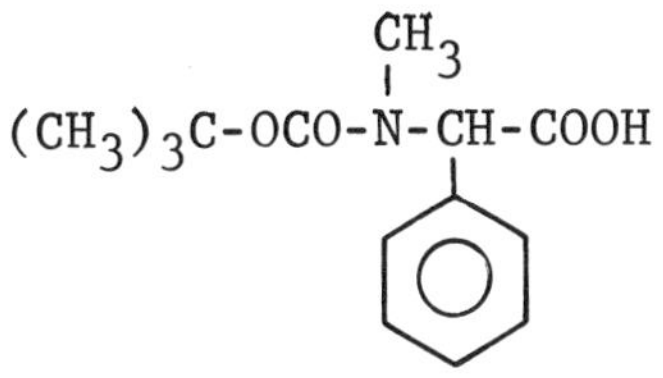

$C_{14}H_{19}NO_4$ Ref. 1060

All the melting points are uncorrected. The optical rotation values were measured with a Jasco DIP-SL-type polarimeter.

t-*Butyloxycarbonyl*-DL-*α-phenylsarcosine (I).* A stock solution of *t*-butyl chloroformate was added to a solution of 7.59 g (0.03 mol) of DL-α-phenylsarcosine in ethanol containing 3.89 g of potassium hydroxide, and then 10 m*l* of dimethylformamide was added with stirring at 0—−3°C. The reaction mixture was agitated vigorously during the addition over a period of about half an hour. The stirring was continued for a further 2 hr at 0°C, and then for an additional hour at room temperature. The reaction mixture was subsequently adjusted to pH 2—3 with N hydrochloric acid, and the product was extracted with ethyl acetate. The ethyl acetate layer was washed with a saturated solution of sodium chloride and dried over anhydrous sodium sulfate. The ethyl acetate was evaporated to dryness to afford 4.4 g of *t*-butyloxycarbonyl-DL-α-phenylsarcosine (55.3%). Recrystallization from benzene-petroleum ether gave 4.0 g of I with a melting point of 122—123°C (50.2%).

Found: C, 63.30; H, 7.35; N, 5.26%. Calcd for $C_{14}H_{19}O_4N$: C, 63.38; H, 7.22; N, 5.28%.

t-*Butyloxycarbonyl*-L-*α-phenylsarcosine*·(−)-*Ephedrine Salt (II) and* t-*Butyloxycarbonyl*-D-*α-phenylsarcosine*·(+)-*Ephedrine Salt (III).* 1.060 g (0.004 mol) of I and (−)-ephedrine hemihydrate (750 mg, 0.0043 mol) were dissolved in 2 m*l* of hot benzene, and then 7 m*l* of hexane were added. The mixture was then allowed to stand for 24 hr at room temperature. The deposited crystals were filtered off and washed with 4 m*l* of benzene-hexane (1 : 3) to afford 830 mg (92.6%) of II, mp 84—88°C. Two recrystallizations from ethyl acetate-petroleum ether gave 680 mg (75.9%) of the pure material with a melting point of 91—93°C. $[\alpha]^{27}_D$ +65.2° (*c* 0.951; absolute ethanol).

Found: C, 64.23; H, 8.10; N, 6.37%. Calcd for $C_{24}H_{34}O_5N_2 \cdot H_2O$: C, 64.26; H, 8.09; N, 6.25%.

The mother liquor obtained after the removal of II was evaporated to dryness to give an oily material. This oily material was dissolved in 6 m*l* of ethyl acetate, and the ethyl acetate layer was washed with 3 m*l* of N hydrochloric acid and water. The organic layer was dried over anhydrous sodium

sulfate and then evaporated to dryness to give 530 mg of an oily product. This product and (+)-ephedrine hemihydrate (375 mg, 0.0022 mol) were dissolved in 1.3 m*l* of hot benzene, and then 7 m*l* of hexane were added. The deposited crystals were filtered off to afford 560 mg (65.2%, mp 84—89°C) of III. Two recrystallizations from ethyl acetate-petroleum ether gave 500 mg (55.8%) of an optically pure material with a melting point of 91—93°C. $[\alpha]^{28}_{D}$ −65.2° (*c* 0.605; absolute ethanol).

Found: C, 63.85; H, 8.17; N, 5.93%. Calcd for $C_{24}H_{34}O_5N_2 \cdot H_2O$: C, 64.26; H, 8.09; N, 6.25%. A mixed-melting-point determination of (−) and (+) salt was depressed to 80—85°C.

t-*Butyloxycarbonyl-*L*-α-phenylsarcosine (IV).* To a suspension of 600 mg (0.0014 mol) of II in 7 m*l* of ethyl acetate, there were added 2.3 m*l* of N hydrochloric acid; the mixture was then shaken effectively in a separatory funnel. After washing with water (three 1-m*l* portions), the ethyl acetate layer was dried over anhydrous sodium sulfate. The ethyl acetate was evaporated to dryness to give 370 mg of crude crystals (quantitative, mp 110—112°C). Recrystallization from benzene-petroleum ether gave 312 mg (84.3%) of pure crystals with a melting point of 111.5—112.5°C. $[\alpha]^{24}_{D}$ +134.8° (*c* 0.804, absolute ethanol).

Found: C, 63.73; H, 7.23; N, 5.60%. Calcd for $C_{14}H_{19}O_4N$: C, 63.38; H, 7.22; N, 5.28%.

t-*Butyloxycarbonyl-*D*-α-phenylsarcosine (V).* Following the method used for the preparation of IV, from 600 mg (0.0014 mol) of III, 340 mg of crude crystals were obtained (91.9%, mp 110—111°C). Recrystallization from benzene-petroleum ether gave 300 mg (80.1%) of pure crystals with a melting point of 112—112.5°C. $[\alpha]^{29}_{D}$ −134.1° (*c* 0.682, absolute ethanol).

Found: C, 63.25; H, 7.32; N, 5.18%. Calcd for $C_{14}H_{19}O_4N$: C, 63.38; H, 7.22; N, 5.28%.

L*-α-Phenylsarcosine (VI).* 150 mg (0.566 mmol) of IV were dissolved in 7.5 m*l* of formic acid, and the mixture was allowed to stand for 1.5 hr at 22°C. The formic acid was evaporated to dryness at 22°C to afford 87 mg of VI (93.7%). Recrystallization from water - acetone gave 80 mg of a pure material (86.2%). $[\alpha]^{24}_{D}$ +169.3° (*c* 0.655, N hydrochloric acid), mp 245° (sublime).

Found: C, 65.45; H, 6.72; N, 8.18%. Calcd for $C_9H_{11}O_2N$: C, 65.44; H, 6.71; N, 8.43%.

D*-α-Phenylsarcosine (VII).* Following the method used for the preparation of L-α-phenylsarcosine, 88 mg of VII was obtained from 150 mg of V (94.8%). Recrystallization from water - acetone gave 80 mg of a pure material (86.2%). $[\alpha]^{24}_{D}$ −170.7° (*c* 0.571, N hydrochloric acid), mp 244°C (sublime).

Found: C, 65.68; H, 6.84; N, 8.34%. Calcd for $C_9H_{11}O_2N$: C, 65.44; H, 6.71; N, 8.43%.

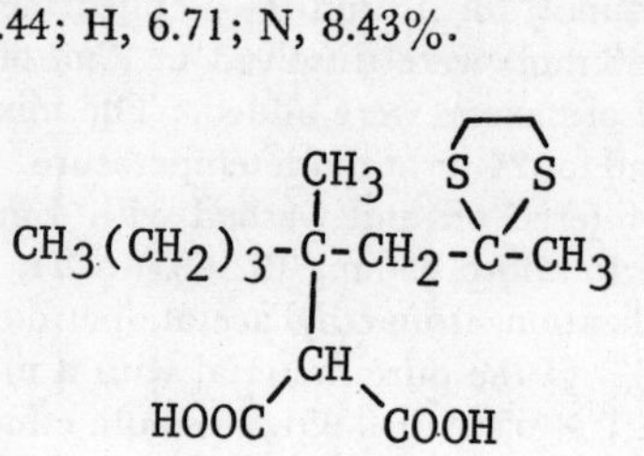

$C_{14}H_{24}O_4S_2$ Ref. 1061

(-)-Cinchonidine Salt of 34. To one portion of crude diacid **34** (ca. 82 g) in warm ethyl acetate (300 mL) was added 78 g of (-)-cinchonidine suspended in warm ethyl acetate (ca. 200 mL) (a solution of (-)-cinchonidine in 200 mL of methanol can be used as well). Immediate salt formation occurred. After the mixture was heated under slight reflux for 5 min, it was cooled to room temperature. The salt was filtered off and washed with methanol (to give ca. 70 g of salt). The filtrate was evaporated, heated under reflux with methanol (200 mL), and evaporated again, and then ethyl acetate was added to give a solid. This solid was filtered off and washed with methanol to give another 7 g of salt. The filtrate was evaporated and dissociated (see below) to afford a residue (ca. 30 g) which consisted mostly of the decarboxylated acid, **38**. This was distilled to give 20.0 g of acid **38**, bp 180–184 °C (0.1 mm). From the other portion of crude **34** (ca. 69 g) there was obtained in the same way ca. 93.5 g of (-)-cinchonidine salt and 8.0 g of acid **38**: total yield ca. 170 g of the (-)-cinchonidine salt (0.277 mol, 63% based on the diester **32**); 28.0 g of acid **38** (0.101 mol, 23% based on the diester **32**).

Resolution of the (-)-Cinchonidine Salt of 34. A 77-g sample of (-)-cinchonidine salt (salt of the first portion described above) was dissolved by heating with 5 L of methanol. The solution was cooled overnight at about 0 °C, and the crystals were filtered and washed with methanol. This gave 41.9 g of salt, mp 172.5–173 °C. The filtrate was concentrated to about 1.5 L, heated until a clear solution was obtained, and cooled again at 0 °C for 3 days. This gave another 2.94 g of salt, mp 171.5–172 °C. The two portions of salt were combined and stirred with ca. 20% sulfuric acid and benzene until two clear layers were obtained. The two layers were separated, and the benzene layer was washed with ca. 20% sulfuric acid and with water, dried, and evaporated to give 26.6 g of (+)-**34** as a viscous oil: $[\alpha]_{578}$ +4.81°, $[\alpha]_{546}$ +5.43° (*c* 9.30, chloroform).

Both diacid enantiomers, obtained in this way, presumably contained some solvent and/or other impurities which could not be removed; hence the specific rotations will be somewhat too low. Anal. Calcd for $C_{33}H_{46}N_2O_5S_2$ [(-)-cinchonidine salt with (+)-**34**]: C, 64.46; H, 7.54; N, 4.56; S, 10.43. Found: C, 64.10, 64.14; H, 7.70, 7.62; N, 4.62, 4.55; S, 10.24, 10.25.

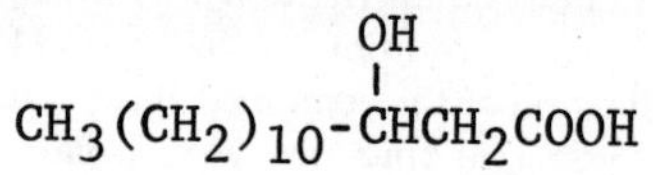

$C_{14}H_{28}O_3$ Ref. 1062

Resolution of DL-β-Hydroxymyristic Acid.—To 0.5 g. of D-α-methyl-β-phenylethylamine sulfate (Dexedrine Sulfate)[20] was added 5 ml. of *N* aqueous sodium hydroxide, the mixture extracted with 5 ml. of ether and the ethereal solution of the amine added to a solution of 0.345 g. of the DL-acid in 30 ml. of dry ether. The solid that formed was suspended in boiling ether and sufficient absolute ethanol added to effect solution. The more insoluble salt, m.p. 123–125°, crystallized in fine silky threads. The more soluble salt, m.p. 85–86°, was obtained from the mother liquors in the form of glistening needles. The salts were suspended in dilute aqueous hydrochloric acid, extracted with ether, the ethereal extracts freed of solvent and the residues recrystallized from 60–70° ligroin to give the respective acids. A mixture of the *l*-acid, m.p. 73–74°, $[\alpha]^{25}_{D}$ −9.4° (*c* 1.9% in pyridine) obtained from the less soluble salt and the *l*-acid isolated from the phosphatide had a m.p. of 73–74°. The benzylamine salt, m.p. 84–86°, and the *p*-bromophenacyl ester, m.p. 111–112°, of the synthetic *l*-acid caused no depression in the m.p. of the corresponding derivatives prepared from the naturally occurring *l*-acid. The *d*-acid, m.p., 71–73°, $[\alpha]^{25}_{D}$ +6.5° (*c* 1.5% in pyridine) isolated from the more soluble salt appeared to contain *ca.* 15% of the *l*-acid.

(20) Trade Mark of Smith, Kline and French Laboratories.

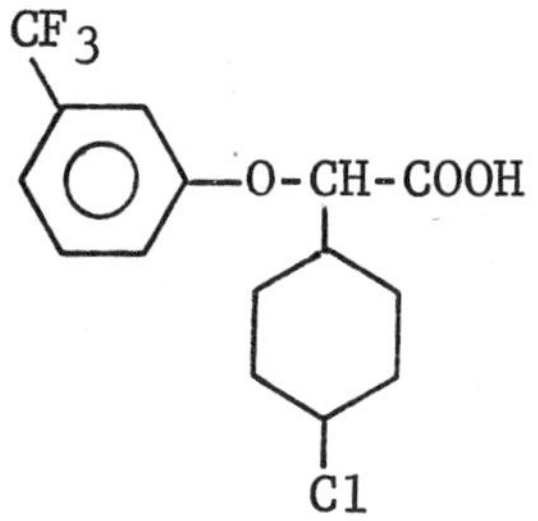

$C_{15}H_{10}ClF_3O_3$ Ref. 1063

Exemple 1 — Acide d-(3-trifluorométhylphénoxy) (4-chlorophényl) acétique.

Opération A : sel de cinchonidine de l'acide *d* - (3 - trifluorométhylphénoxy) (4 - chlorophényl) acétique.

A 2 000 cm³ d'alcool isopropylique à la température ambiante, on ajoute 100 g (0,303 mole) d'acide *dl* - (3 - trifluorométhylphénoxy) (4 - chlorophényl) - acétique et 89,3 g (0,303 mole) d'alcaloïde cinchonidine. La cristallisation du sel commence au bout de quelques minutes. On élève alors la température au niveau de reflux (83 °C) et on refroidit le mélange à 55 °C dans les conditions ambiantes, puis on le laisse vieillir 2 heures. On recueille la matière cristalline formée, on la lave avec 200 cm³ d'alcool isopropylique chaud et on sèche; on obtient 110 g de sel brut de cinchonidine, point de fusion : 204-206 °C (la liqueur-mère ainsi obtenue est utilisée dans l'opération A de l'exemple 2 pour préparer l'acide lévogyre). On délaie le sel brut de cinchonidine avec 2 000 cm³ d'alcool éthylique et 400 cm³ d'alcool méthylique au reflux, puis on agite et on refroidit une nuit dans les conditions ambiantes. On filtre le produit, on le lave avec 200 cm³ d'alcool éthylique, puis on le sèche à l'air à 60 °C jusqu'à un poids constant de 69,2 g, point de fusion (avec décomposition) : 213-214 °C, [α]D —-30,2° (à 0,5 % dans l'alcool méthylique). En faisant recristalliser 58 g dans 1 800 cm³ d'alcool éthylique, on obtient 43,1 g de sel de cinchonidine pur de l'acide *d* - (3 - trifluorométhylphénoxy) (4 - chlorophényl) - acétique, point de fusion (décomposition) 216-217 °C, [α]D — 29,8° (à 0,5 % dans l'alcool méthylique).

Opération B : acide *d* - (3 - trifluorométhylphénoxy) (4 - chlorophényl) acétique.

On ajoute 7,1 g du sel obtenu dans l'opération A à un mélange comprenant 200 cm³ d'éther, 200 cm³ d'eau et 4 cm³ d'acide sulfurique concentré. On sépare les couches et on lave à trois reprises la solution éthérée avec 200 cm³ d'eau. Après séchage, on évapore la solution éthérée, on fait cristalliser l'huile dans 25 cm³ de méthylcyclohexane et on obtient 2,95 g de l'acide *d* - (3 - trifluorométhylphénoxy) (4 - chlorophényl) acétique, point de fusion 98-100,5 °C, [α]D + 95,3° (à 0,5 % dans l'alcool méthylique).

Exemple 2 – Acide 1-(3-trifluorométhylphénoxy) (4chlorophényl) acétique.

Opération A : sel de cinchonidine de l'acide *1* -(3 - trifluorométhylphénoxy) (4 - chlorophényl) - acétique.

On prend la liqueur-mère provenant du sel brut de cinchonidine de l'acide *d* - (3 - trifluorométhylphénoxy) (4 - chlorophényl) acétique isolé dans l'opération A de l'exemple 1 et on la chauffe pour obtenir une dissolution complète puis on la refroidit dans les conditions ambiantes. On retire par filtration la petite quantité de solide présente à 30 °C, on agite le filtrat limpide à la température ambiante pendant une nuit, on recueille par filtration le précipité cristallin obtenu, on le lave avec 200 cm³ d'alcool isopropylique et on obtient 58,8 g de sel de cinchonidine de l'acide *1* - (3 - trifluorométhylphénoxy) (4 - chlorophényl) - acétique, point de fusion (décomposition) 200-201 °C, [α]D — 94,7° (à 0,5 % dans l'alcool méthylique). On fait recristalliser 43,8 g du produit dans 800 cm³ d'alcool isopropylique et on obtient 37,3 g de sel de cinchonidine pur, point de fusion (décomposition) 200,5-201,5 °C, [α]D — 95,5° (0,5 % dans l'alcool méthylique).

Opération B : acide *1* - (3 - trifluorométhylphénoxy) (4 - chlorophényl) acétique.

Essentiellement de la même façon que pour l'acide *d* correspondant (opération B de l'exemple 1), on convertit en acide 5,9 g du sel pur de cinchonidine d'acide lévogyre, obtenu dans l'opération A ci-dessus; on obtient 2,7 g d'acide *1* - (3 - trifluorométhylphénoxy) (4 - chlorophényl) - acétique pur; point de fusion : 98-100 °C, [α]D — 99° (à 0,5 % dans l'alcool méthylique).

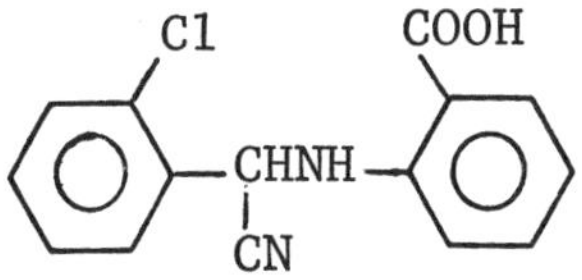

$C_{15}H_{11}ClN_2O_2$ Ref. 1064

(c) *Resolution of* (±) *α-(o-Carboxyphenylamino)-o-chlorobenzylnitrile* : (—)-Brucine (7.45 g.) was added to (±) α-(*o*-Carboxyphenylamino)-*o*-chlorobenzylnitrile (5.38 g.) in hot acetone (150 ml.). The less soluble brucine salt (6.1 g.) m.p. 186°–87° was separated after 24 hr., part of which on decomposition gave (—)-nitrile $[\alpha]_D^{32}$ —29.85 (l, 1, c, 0.67 in acetone).

This on further four crystallisations from acetone-chloroform gave a specimen (1.12 g.), m.p. 189°–90°, which on decomposition gave fully active (—)-nitrile m.p. 176°–77°, $[\alpha]_D^{32}$ —85.82 (l, 1; c, 1.34 in acetone). There is no increase in optical rotation on further crystallisation.

The more soluble brucine salt on concentration gave a solid (6.4 g.) m.p. 184°–85°, part of which on decomposition gave (+)-nitrile $[\alpha]_D^{32}$ +27.79 (l, 1; c, 0.72 in acetone). This on further two crystallisations from acetone-chloroform afforded a specimen (1.14 g.) m.p. 160°–61°, which on decomposition gave (+)-nitrile m.p. 176°, $[\alpha]_D^{32}$ +86.0 (l, 1; c, 1.16 in acetone). The optical rotation does not increase on further crystallisation.

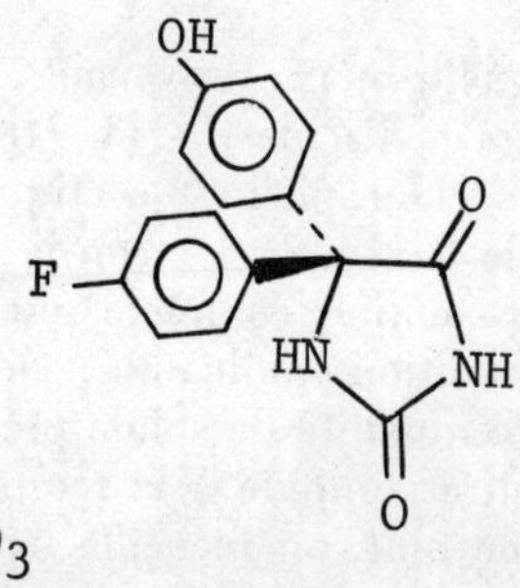

$C_{15}H_{11}FN_2O_3$ Ref. 1065

(R)-(-)-5-(4'-Fluorophenyl)-5-(4'-hydroxyphenyl)hydantoin [(-)-4] and (S)-(+)-5-(4'-Fluorophenyl)-5-(4'-hydroxyphenyl)hydantoin [(+)-4]. Anhydrous brucine (34.8 g, 88.3 mmol) was added to a stirred boiling solution of (±)-4 (11 g, 38.4 mmol) in methanol (1.2 L). After stirring the solution for 24 h at room temperature and for 24 h in a refrigerator, a white precipitate was collected (16 g). Decomposition of a sample with 2 N HCl afforded partially resolved (-)-4 ($[\alpha]^{25}_{546}$ -91°). An additional crystallization of the salt and two crystallizations of the free hydantoin from ethanol-water gave 850 mg of (-)-4: $[\alpha]^{25}_{546}$ -120°; mp 319-321 °C. Further crystallizations did not modify the molecular rotation. The dextrorotatory mother liquors were evaporated to dryness. The salt was treated with 2 N HCl and the resulting partially enriched (+)-4 was recrystallized twice from ethanol-water to give a first crop of 500 mg of (+)-4: $[\alpha]^{25}_{546}$ +120°.

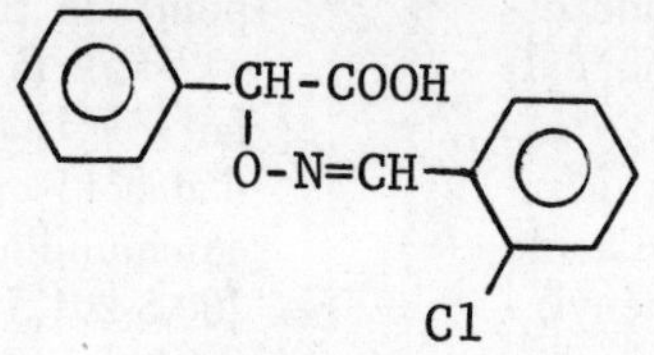

$C_{15}H_{12}ClNO_3$ Ref. 1066

Resolution of α-(2-Chlorobenzylideneimino-oxy) phenylacetic acid (Vd, Table 3). To 35 g of α-(2-chlorobenzylideneimino-oxy)phenylacetic acid (Vd) in 150 ml of dry ether was added (−)-ephedrine (22 g) in 150 ml of dry ether. The precipitated salt was filtered and crystallized six times from acetone containing a little methanol until the rotation of the acid isolated from the salt as described below remained constant. Yield of pure acid, 1.5 g (9 %), $[\alpha]_D^{20}$ −95.5° (ethanol), m.p. 131—133°. The ephedrine salt was decomposed with 2 N HCl, the acid extracted with ether, the extract washed several times with 2 N HCl and saturated NaCl-solution, and the acid isolated as usual.

The mother liquors from the first two crystallizations were evaporated to dryness and from the residual salt 22.3 g of acid were isolated. This was dissolved in 150 ml of dry ether to which were added 10.4 g of (+)-benzylisopropylamine in 150 ml of dry ether. The precipitated salt was recrystallized four times from methanol until its free acid had a constant rotation; yield of pure acid, 3.5 g (20 %), $[\alpha]_D^{20}$ + 96° (ethanol), m.p. 131—133°.

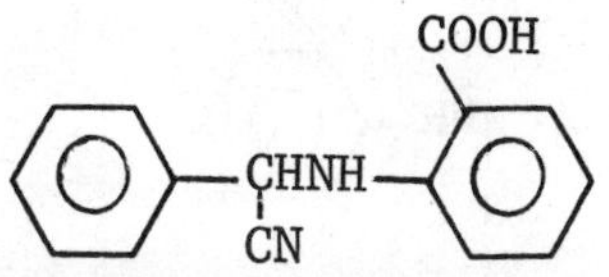

$C_{15}H_{12}N_2O_2$ Ref. 1067

(b) *Resolution of* (±) *α-(o-Carboxyphenylamino)-benzylnitrile*: (−)-Brucine (15.16 g.) was added to (±) α-(o-Carboxyphenylamino) benzylnitrile (10.12 g.) in hot acetone (400 ml.). The less soluble brucine salt (11.65 g.) m.p. 142°-143° was separated after 96 hr., part of which on decomposition gave (+)-nitrile $[\alpha]_D^{34}$ +54.19 (l, 1; c, 2.03 in ethanol). This on further four crystallisations from acetone and chloroform gave crop E (1.2 g.) m.p. 155° which on decomposition gave fully active (+)-nitrile m.p. 167°, $[\alpha]_D^{34}$ +64.73 (l, 1; c, 1.70 in ethanol) and $[\alpha]_D^{34}$ +65.48 (l, 1, c, 0.96 in acetone). No increase in optical rotation was observed on further crystallisation.

The mother liquor on concentration gave a solid (12.0 g.) m.p. 128°-129°, which on decomposition gave (−)-nitrile $[\alpha]_D^{34}$ −14.29 (l, 1, c, 2.1 in ethanol). This on three more crystallisations from dioxane gave a sample (1.09 g.), m.p. 140° which on decomposition gave (−)-nitrile m.p. 166°; $[\alpha]_D^{34}$ −61.22 (l, 1, c, 0.49 in ethanol) and $[\alpha]_D^{34}$ −62.00 (l, 1; c, 0.50 in acetone). The rotation did not increase on further crystallisation.

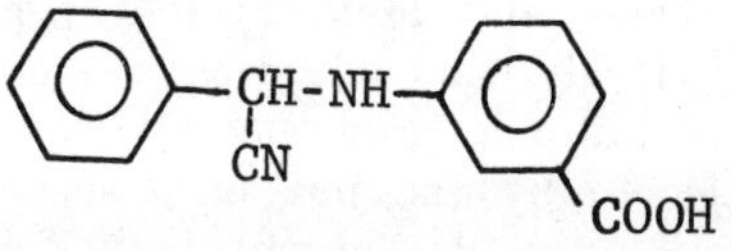

$C_{15}H_{12}N_2O_2$ Ref. 1068

(b) *Preparation of (+) and (−) α-(m-carboxyphenylamino) phenyl-aceto nitrile :—*

(—) Brucine (13 86 g.) was added to (±) α-(m-carboxyphenyl-amino) phenyl aceto nitrile (8.82 g.) dissolved in ethyl acetate (100 ml.). Less soluble brucine salt crop-A (12.4 g.) m.p. 131-32°C was separated after 2 hours, part of which on decomposition gave (—) nitrile $[\alpha]^{32}_D$ -45.4 (1, 1, c, 0.55 in ethylacetate). This crop-A on further three crystallisations from acetone and ethylacetate gave crop-D (1.02 g.) m.p. 136-37°C which on decomposition gave fully active (—) nitrile m.p. 150-51°C, $[\alpha]_D^{32}$ −100 (1,1,c, 0.75 in ethylacetate). There is no increase in optical rotation on further crystallisation. (Found N=11.12%, $C_{15}H_{12}O_2N_2$ requires N=11.11%.).

More soluble brucine salt on concentration gave crop-A' (10.0 g) m.p. 128-30°C, part of which on decomposition gave (+) nitrile, $[\alpha]_D^{32}$ +50.00 (1,1,c, 0.80 in ethylacetate). This crop on further crystallisation from ethyl acetate gave crop B'' (6.0 g.) m.p. 135-38°C, part of which on decomposition gave partially active (+) nitrile m.p. 151-52°C, $[\alpha]_D^{32}$ + 54.54 (1,1,c, 0.55 in ethylacetate). There is no change in optical rotation on further crystallisation.

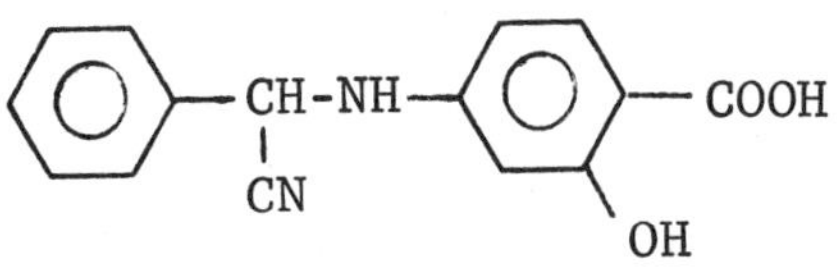

$C_{15}H_{12}N_2O_3$ Ref. 1069

(d) *Preparation of (+) and (−) α-(p-carboxy-m-hydroxyphenyl amino) phenyl aceto nitrile :—*

(−) Brucine (11.88) g.) was added to (±) α-(p-carboxy-m-hydroxyphenyl amino) phenyl aceto nitrile (8.04 g.) dissolved in hot acetone (120 ml.). The less soluble brucine salt—crop-A (10.0 g.) m.p. 190-91°C. was separated after 48 hours, part of which on decomposition gave (+) nitrile $[\alpha]_d^{32}$ +50.00 (1,1,c, 10.00 in acetone). This crop-A on further two crystallisations from dioxane and acetone chloroform gave crop-C (2.0 g.) m.p. 199-200°C, which on decomposition gave fully active (+) nitrile m.p. 163-64°C, $[\alpha]_D^{32}$ +80.00 (1,1,c, 0.75 in acetone). There is no increase in optical rotation on further crystallisation. (Found N = 10.48%, $C_{15}H_{12}O_3N_2$ requires 10.45%).

The more soluble brucine salt on concentration gave crop-A′ (9.0 g.) m.p. 181-82°C, part of which on decomposition gave (−) nitrile $[\alpha]_D^{32}$ −37.50 (1,1,c, 0.80 in acetone). Attempts to crystallise this crop-A′ in different solvents were not successful.

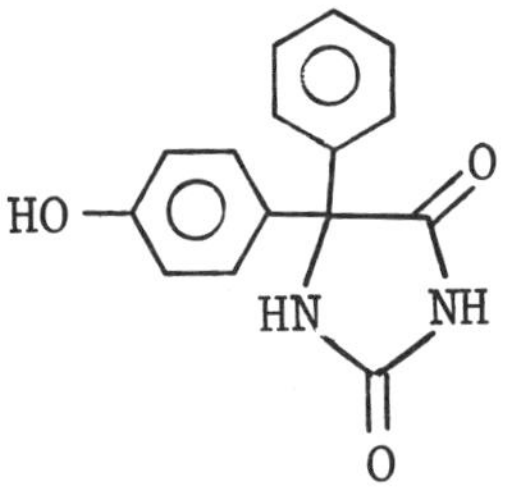

$C_{15}H_{12}N_2O_3$ Ref. 1070

(*R*)-(+)- and (*S*)-(−)-5-(4′-Hydroxyphenyl)-5-phenylhydantoin (1b and 1c). Anhydrous brucine (225 g) was added to a stirred hot solution of **1a** (100 g) in absolute ethanol (4 l.). After 24 hr at room temperature and 24 hr in a refrigerator, pellets of the resulting salt were collected (230 g). Decomposition of a sample of this salt with 2 *N* hydrochloric acid afforded **1c**, $[\alpha]^{25}_{546}$ −27° (*c* 1, 0.5 *N* NaOH). After five further crystallizations from absolute ethanol and decomposition of the brucine salt, 24 g of **1c** was recovered; $[\alpha]^{25}_{546}$ −71.5°. Three crystallizations of the free hydantoin furnished 9 g of **1c**: $[\alpha]^{25}_{546}$ −107.3 ± 0.8° (*c* 1, 0.5 *N* NaOH); $[\alpha]^{25}_{546}$ −25.7° (*c* 0.43, CH_3OH). The dextrorotatory mother liquors were concentrated and additional amounts of **1c** were isolated until the filtrate had a specific rotation of approximately +60°. The filtrate was evaporated to dryness and treatment with 2 *N* HCl afforded 28 g of **1b**: $[\alpha]^{25}_{546}$ +60°. Three crystallizations from ethanol yielded 9.5 g of **1b**, $[\alpha]^{25}_{546}$ +107 ± 0.8° (*c* 1, 0.5 *N* NaOH).

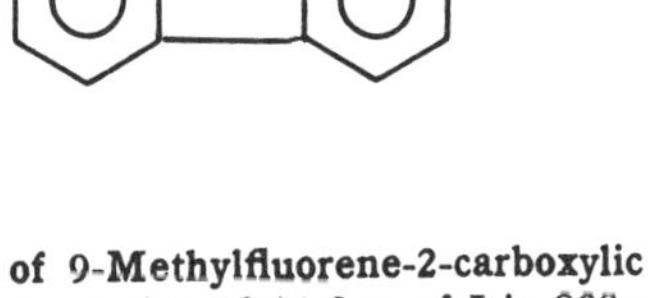

$C_{15}H_{12}O_2$ Ref. 1071

Resolution of 9-Methylfluorene-2-carboxylic Acid ((+)- and (−)-I).—A hot solution of 14.6 g. of I in 360 ml. of acetone was combined with a hot solution of 21.2 g. of quinine in 72 ml. of chloroform. The resulting solution was filtered, seeded, and allowed to cool to 25°. After 48 hr., 19 g. of salt was collected and recrystallized 9 times from chloroform to give 1.4 g. of salt. The progress of the resolution was followed by converting small amounts of salt to the free acid as follows. The salt was shaken with 6 *N* hydrochloric acid and ether. The ether solution was washed with 2 *N* hydrochloric acid and with water, dried, and evaporated to give a white powder. The amounts of salt recovered at different stages of the resolution and the rotations of the corresponding acids were: 1st crystallization, 19 g., $[\alpha]^{25}_{546}$ −7.5°; 2nd, 14 g., $[\alpha]^{25}_{546}$ −17.3°; 4th, 8.8 g., $[\alpha]^{25}_{546}$ −33.6°; 6th, 6.7 g., $[\alpha]^{25}_{546}$ −36.4°; 7th, 5.5 g., $[\alpha]^{25}_{546}$ −39.6°; 8th, 3.8 g., $[\alpha]^{25}_{546}$ −40.1°; 9th, 1.4 g., $[\alpha]^{25}_{546}$ −39.4°; *c* 1.0 to 6.2 in dioxane for all rotation (see below). This acid was crystallized from acetone to give fine white needles of (−)-I, m.p. 215–216°.

Partially active acid ($[\alpha]^{25}_{546}$ +8°), 14.9 g., obtained from quinine mother liquors was dissolved in 136 ml. of acetone, and the solution was combined with a solution of 19.5 g. of cinchonidine in 246 ml. of chloroform. The resulting solution was seeded and left at 25° for 20 hr. The salt (14.4 g.) was collected and recrystallized 8 times from chlofororm–acetone. The amounts of salt recovered at different stages and the rotations of the corresponding acids were: 1st recrystallization, 10 g., $[\alpha]^{25}_{546}$ +23.0°; 3rd recrystallization, 7 g., $[\alpha]^{25}_{546}$ +37.0°; 5th recrystallization, 5.1 g., $[\alpha]^{25}_{546}$ + 40.0°; 8th recrystallization, 2.9 g., $[\alpha]^{25}_{546}$ +39.6°; *c* 1.0 to 6.2 in dioxane for all rotations (see below). Recrystallization of this acid from acetone gave (+)-I as white needles, m.p. 215–216°.

In a subsequent large-scale resolution, 82 g. of a much recrystallized cinchonidine salt was converted to 31.5 g. of acid, $[\alpha]^{26}_{546}$ + 40.2°, *c* 2.84 in dioxane, m.p. 210.5–212.5°. Three recrystallizations of this material from acetone gave material, m.p. 216–216.5°, $[\alpha]^{25}_{546}$ + 43.1°, *c* 6.65 in dioxane, whose properties did not change with further purification.

Anal. Calcd. for $C_{15}H_{12}O_2$: C, 80.33; H, 5.40. Found: C, 80.15; H, 5.39.

The rotation of a sample of partially optically active acid was measured at different concentrations in dioxane; *c* 1.00, $[\alpha]^{25}_{546}$ −33.8°; *c* 3.2, $[\alpha]^{25}_{546}$ −33.4°; *c* 6.19, $[\alpha]^{25}_{546}$ −34.2°.

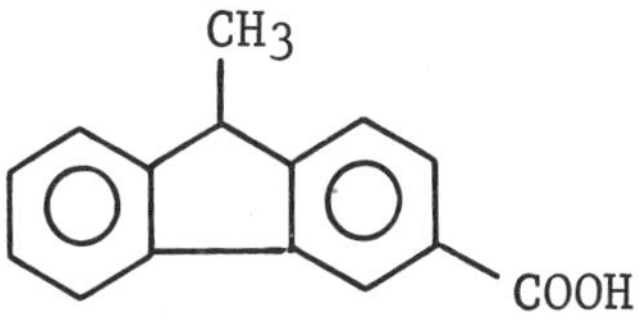

$C_{15}H_{12}O_2$ Ref. 1072

Resolution of 9-Methylfluorene-3-carboxylic Acid (X). Hot solutions of 2.87 g (10.0 mmol) of dehydroabietylamine in 20 ml of methanol and 2.26 g (10.1 mmol) of X in 15 ml of methanol were combined and reduced to 20 ml. The solution was cooled to 25°. After 5 days, 1.30 g (25%) of salts was collected, washed with water, and dried. The progress of the resolution was followed by converting 50-mg portions of the salt back to the free acid using the following procedure. The salt was shaken with 10 ml of 1 *N* formic acid and 5 ml of ether. The acidic solution was washed with another 5 ml of ether. The combined ether solutions were washed twice with 10 ml of 1 *N* formic acid and twice with 10 ml of water, dried, and evaporated. Attempts to perform this conversion with mineral acids resulted in troublesome emulsions of the corresponding dehydroabietylammonium salts. Optical rotation of the recovered acid was measured at *c* 0.91–1.3, dioxane. Acid recovered in this manner from once-crystallized salt had $[\alpha]^{25}_{546}$ −6.0°, $[\alpha]^{25}_{436}$ −13.6°.

Subsequent recrystallizations of the salt were carried out as follows. The salt was dissolved in 10–15 ml of methanol per gram of salt. Enough hot water to make the solution 10% water by volume was added and thoroughly mixed. The salt crystallized at 25° and its solubility decreased as its optical purity increased. Second crystallization gave 825 mg (66%), $[\alpha]^{25}_{546}$ −7.7°, $[\alpha]^{25}_{436}$ −16.7°; third crystallization gave 546 mg (70%), $[\alpha]^{25}_{546}$ −9.9°, −22.1°; fourth crystallization gave 390 mg (71%), $[\alpha]^{25}_{546}$ −9.8°, $[\alpha]^{25}_{436}$ −21.4°, mp 184–185°. After four crystallizations the salt was converted to free carboxylic acid X which was recrystallized from methanol to give white needles having $[\alpha]^{25}_{546}$ −13.5°, $[\alpha]^{25}_{436}$ −27.0°, mp 186.5–187.5°.

The resolution was also performed on a larger scale starting with 34.7 g of X and 44.1 g of dehydroabietylamine. The procedure was the same as above except that 90% aqueous methanol was used for the first crystallization as well as all succeeding ones. However,

once the free acid reached an optical rotation in the range $[\alpha]^{25}_{546}$ −9 to −12°, it did not fractionate further. All attempts at fractional crystallization of this material from methanol, acetone, toluene, and chloroform resulted in recovery of material in the same range of rotations, even when white needles of (−)-X-*h* with $[\alpha]^{25}_{546}$ −13.5° were used as seed crystals.

The salt recovered from the mother liquors of the first three crystallizations of the large-scale resolution was converted to free acid and recrystallized from methanol to obtain material with mp 175–178°, $[\alpha]^{25}_{546}$ +10.8°, $[\alpha]^{25}_{436}$ +23.1°.

$C_{15}H_{12}O_3S$

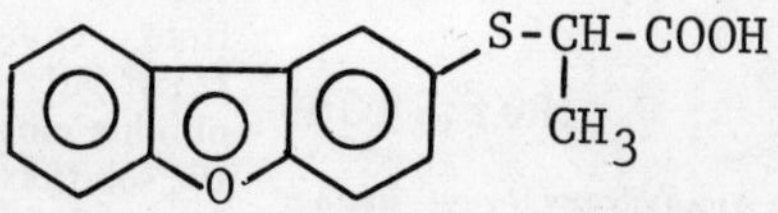

Ref. 1073

8. Hydrocinchonidine salt of dextrorotatory α-(2-dibenzofuryl-mercapto)-propionic acid (8)

Powdered acid **2** (25 g, 0.092 mole) was mixed with 27.2 g (0.092 mole) of hydrocinchonidine and was dissolved in 1.25 dm^3 of boiling ethyl acetate. The hot solution was filtered and was left for crystallization at room temperature. After 24 hrs the first fraction of the salt was filtered. Rods, m.p. 178—179°C, $[\alpha]^{20}_D = -33°$ ($c = 0.5$, $d = 2$, $\alpha = -0.33°$) in 96% ethanol. After three crystallizations of the first fraction from ethyl acetate the product had the properties which did not change during attempted further purification. Rods, m.p. 191—192°C, $[\alpha]^{20}_D = -17°$ ($c = 0.5$, $d = 2$, $\alpha = -0.17$) in 96% ethanol. Yield 8.5 g. The salt is very readily soluble in dioxane, chloroform, methanol and 96% ethanol, and is readily soluble in benzene and acetone. It is sparingly soluble in carbon tetrachloride.

Analysis:
$C_{34}H_{36}N_2O_4S$ (568.7) — Calcd.: 4.9% N;
found: 4.9% N.

9. Dextrorotatory α-(2-dibenzofuryl-mercapto)-propionic acid (9)

Powdered salt **8** (6.1 g) (m.p. 191—192°C, $[\alpha]^{20}_D = -17°$) was suspended in 60 ccm of water and after stirring it was added to 100 ccm of 3% NaOH solution. The mixture was stirred at room temperature for 20 minutes. The liberated alkaloid was filtered. The filtrate was extracted with chloroform (5×15 ccm). The chloroform dissolved in alkaline solution was evaporated under reduced pressure (12 mm Hg, water bath) and the residue was acidified to Congo red with 3% HCl. A colorless oil was separated and was soon solidified. It was filtered and, after washing with water (3×20 ccm), it was dried in a vacuum desiccator over anhydrous $CaCl_2$. Dextrorotatory acid (2.7 g) was crystallized from a mixture of chloroform (15 ccm) and petroleum ether (40 ccm). Rods, m.p. 115.5—116°C, $[\alpha]^{20}_D = +101°$ ($c = 0.5$, $d = 2$, $\alpha = +1.01°$) in 96% ethanol. Yield 1.8 g. The compound is very readily soluble in benzene, dioxane, chloroform, acetone, methanol, 96% ethanol, and is readily soluble in carbon tetrachloride.

Table 2

The course of fractional crystallization of hydrocinchonidine salt of dextrorotatory α-(2-dibenzofuryl-mercapto)-propionic acid. Crystallization time = 24 hrs

Fraction No	Volume of solvent in ccm	Quantity of salt obtained in g	Specific rotation in 96% ethanol $[\alpha]^{20}_D$	M.p. of the salt °C
1	1250	23.1	−33°	178—180
1.1	1250	14.9	−20°	185—187
1.1.1	1050	11.1	−19°	188—190
1.1.1.1	850	8.5	−17°	191—192
1.1.1.1.1	850	6.2	−17°	191—192

Analysis:
For $C_{15}H_{12}O_3S$ (272.31) — Calcd.: 66.2% C, 4.4% H;
found: 65.9% C, 4.4% H.

IR (cm^{-1}): 690 (ν C—S); 760 (δ C_{Ar}—H, subst. 1, 2); 820, 870, 1140 (δ C_{Ar}—H, subst. 1, 2, 4); 1020, 1050, 1100, 1178 (δ C_{Ar}—H, subst. 1, 2, and 1, 2, 4); 1460, 1580 (ν C_{Ar}=C_{Ar}); 1250 (ν C_{Ar}—O); 940 (δ OH(COOH)); 1190, 1220, 1330 (δ OH and ν C—O(COOH)); 1690 and 1705 (db. ν C=C(COOH)).

10. Hydrocinchonine salt of laevorotatory α-(2-dibenzofuryl-mercapto)-propionic acid (10)

The mother liquors remaining after filtration of the first fraction of hydrocinchonidine salt of dextrorotatory acid **9** were allowed to stand at room temperature. A fine crystalline precipitate was soon separated. It was filtered after 24 hrs. Fine crystals (22.2 g), m.p. 163—165°C, $[\alpha]_D^{20} = -63°$ ($c = 0.5$ $d = 2$, $\alpha = -0.63°$), in 96% ethanol. The salt was powdered and was suspended in 200 ccm of water. The suspension was stirred, and 300 ccm of 3% NaOH was added. The liberated alkaloid was filtered off and free acid was isolated from the filtrate by the method described in section 8. Yield 10 g, m.p. 109—111°C, $[\alpha]_D^{20} = -51°$ ($c = 0.5$, $d = 2$, $\alpha = -0.51°$) in 96% ethanol.

A sample of 8.9 g (0.33 mole) of powdered acid, having $[\alpha]_D^{20} = -51°$, was mixed with 9.68 g (0.33 mole) of hydrocinchonine and the mixture was dissolved in 300 ccm of boiling acetone diluted with 30 ccm of water. The solution was filtered while still hot and was allowed to stand at room temperature. After 24 hrs 165 ccm of the solvent was distilled off under reduced pressure (12 mm Hg, water bath). The concentrated solution, on standing at room temperature, soon deposited a fine crystalline precipitate. After 24 hrs it was filtered. Plates (10.4 g), m.p. 195—200°C, $[\alpha]_D^{20} = +63°$ (in 96% ethanol). After recrystallization from a mixture of acetone (120 ccm) and water (60 ccm) the product had physical properties which remained unchanged by further purification. Plates, m.p. 201—203°C, $[\alpha]_D^{20} = +60°$ ($c = 0.5$, $d = 2$, $\alpha = +0.60°$) in 96% ethanol. Yield 6.1 g. The salt is very readily soluble in chloroform, methanol and 96% ethanol, and is readily soluble in benzene, carbon tetrachloride and dioxane.

Analysis:
For $C_{34}H_{36}N_2O_4S$ (568.7) — Calcd.: 4.4% N;
found: 4.4% N.

11. Laevorotatory α-(2-dibenzofuryl-mercapto)-propionic acid (11)

A sample of 3.1 g of powdered salt **10** (m.p. 200—203°C, $[\alpha]_D^{20} = +60°$) was suspended in 30 ccm of water and, after stirring, it was treated with 50 ccm of 3% NaOH. The suspension was stirred at room temperature for 20 min. The liberated alkaloid was filtered off and the filtrate was extracted with chloroform (5×10 ccm). The chloroform dissolved in the aqueous phase was distilled off under reduced pressure (12 mm Hg, water bath at 40—50°C) and the residue was acidified to Congo red with 3% HCl. A colorless oil was separated and was soon solidified. Free acid was filtered and, after washing with water (2×15 ccm), it was dried in a vacuum desiccator over anhydrous $CaCl_2$. The product (1.43 g) was crystallized from a mixture of chloroform (12 ccm) and petroleum ether (23 ccm). Rods, m.p. 115—116°C, $[\alpha]_D^{20} = -99°$ ($c = 0.5$, $d = 2$, $\alpha = -0.99°$) in 96% ethanol. Yield 0.98 g. The laevorotatory acid is very readily soluble in benzene, dioxane, chloroform, acetone, methanol and 96% ethanol, and is readily soluble in carbon tetrachloride. It is sparingly soluble in petroleum ether.

Analysis:
For $C_{15}H_{12}O_3S$ (272.31) — Calcd.: 66.2% C, 4.4% H;
found: 65.9% C, 4.2% H.

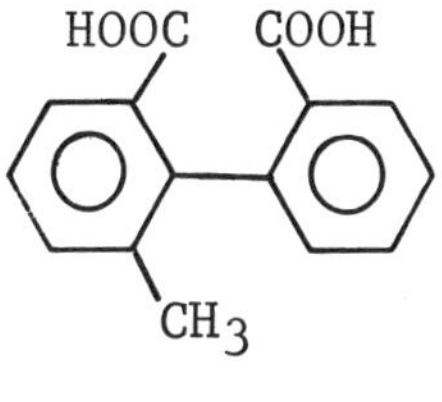

$C_{15}H_{12}O_4$ Ref. 1074

The resolution of the diacid was carried out as follows: 2.72 gm. (0.1 mole) of the diacid and 0.1 mole morphine hydrate were dissolved in 50 ml. hot ethanol, and on cooling the solution a yield of 2.5 gm. white crystals, m.p. 208°C., was obtained. Calc. for $C_{32}H_{31}O_7N.H_2O$: C, 68.7; H, 5.94; N, 2.50%. Found: C, 69.2, 68.9; H, 5.90, 5.89; N, 2.60%. In glacial acetic acid ($c = 1$), $[\alpha]_{5461}^{23} = -78.5°$, $[\alpha]_{5780}^{23} = -69.4°$. On decomposition of the morphine salt with cold dilute hydrochloric acid, the laevo-form of the diacid was obtained, with m.p. 228°C. after softening at 192°C. and resolidifying. In methanol ($c = 1$), $[\alpha]_{5461}^{25} = -7.73°$, $[\alpha]_{5780}^{25} = -6.95°$.

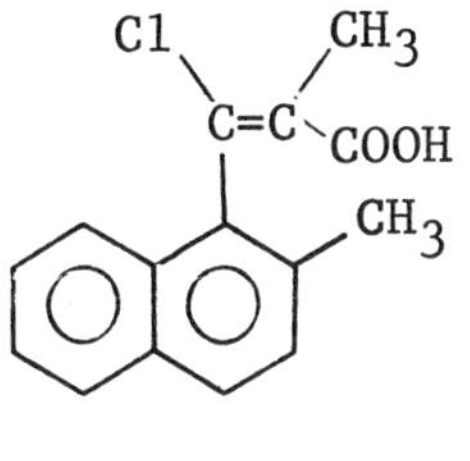

$C_{15}H_{13}ClO_2$ Ref. 1075

Resolution of β-Chloro-β-(2-methyl-1-naphthyl)-acrylic Acid.—A solution of 2 g. of β-chloro-β-(2-methyl-1-naphthyl)-acrylic acid in 75 cc. of warm ethyl acetate and 1 g. of *d*-α-phenylethylamine on cooling resulted in a voluminous precipitate of fine white needles. These were allowed to stand in the liquor overnight to complete precipitation. The salt weighed 1.3 g. This was dissolved in ethyl acetate and the solution allowed to evaporate. Four successive fractions gave identical rotations; white crystals, m. p. 158–160° (cor.) with decomposition.

Anal. Calcd. for $C_{14}H_{11}O_2Cl{\cdot}C_8H_{11}N$: C, 71.82; H, 6.03. Found: C, 71.98; H, 6.23.

Rotation. Less-soluble salt: 0.048 g. made up to 25 cc. with ethanol at 32° gave α_D +0.16°; *l*, 2; $[\alpha]^{32}_D$ +42°.

The filtrate from the original precipitation of the less-soluble salt was evaporated partially but no more salt separated. The solvent was removed completely, leaving an oil which after twenty-four hours solidified. Attempts to find a solvent for recrystallization failed.

Rotation. Crude more-soluble salt: 0.051 g. made up to 25 cc. with ethanol at 32° gave α_D −0.16°; *l*, 2; $[\alpha]^{32}_D$ −39°.

***d*- and *l*-β-Chloro-β-(2-methyl-1-naphthyl)-acrylic Acids.**—The salts were decomposed by stirring with successive portions of 10% hydrochloric acid which were removed by filtration. The product which still contained unchanged salt was dissolved in 10% aqueous sodium hydroxide, the solution extracted with chloroform and then acidified. The *d*-acid thus obtained was recrystallized from petroleum ether (b. p. 60–90°); white crystals, m. p. 191° (cor.). the *l*-acid recrystallized from petroleum ether (b. p. 60–110°); white crystals, m. p. 186° (cor.)

Anal. Calcd. for $C_{14}H_{11}O_2Cl$: C, 68.15; H, 4.50. Found: *d*-acid: C, 68.05; H, 4.75; *l*-acid: C, 68.05; H, 4.67.

Rotation. *d*-Acid: 0.019 g. made up to 10 cc. with ethanol at 32° gave α_D +0.125°; *l*, 1; $[\alpha]^{36}_D$ +66°.

Rotation. (*l*-Acid) 0.019 g. made up to 10 cc. with ethanol at 32° gave α_D −0.12°; *l*, 1; $[\alpha]^{26}_D$ −63°.

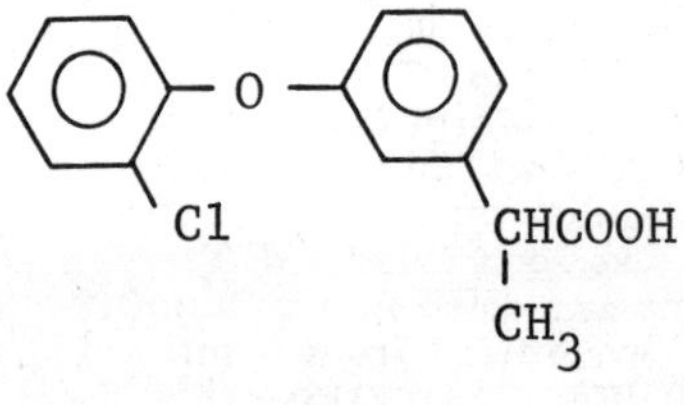

$C_{15}H_{13}ClO_3$

Ref. 1076

Resolution of d- and l-enantiomer of CPA

To a solution of 27.6 g of dl-CPA in 360 ml of ethyl acetate, 12.1 g of R-(+)-phenylethylamine was added at room temperature and the mixture was heated to a clear solution, which was allowed to reflux for 10 min.. After cooling, the resultant drystals were filtered and recrystallized from ethyl acetate. After five recrystallizations, the crystals were dissolved in 173 ml of water and 60 ml ethyl ether, the solution was acidified with 6N-HCl and the aqueous layer was extracted twice with 30 ml of ethyl ether. The extracts were washed with water, dried with $MgSO_4$ and evaporated to dryness. The residue was recrystallized five times from ethyl acetate to afford pure d-CPA. (m.p. 81.0 - 82.0 °C, $[\alpha]^{20}_D$ + 43.61.).

The same procedure was repeated using S-(-)-phenylethylamine as the resolving agent to afford pure l-CPA. m.p. 81.5 - 82.5 °C, $[\alpha]^{20}_D$ - 43.07.

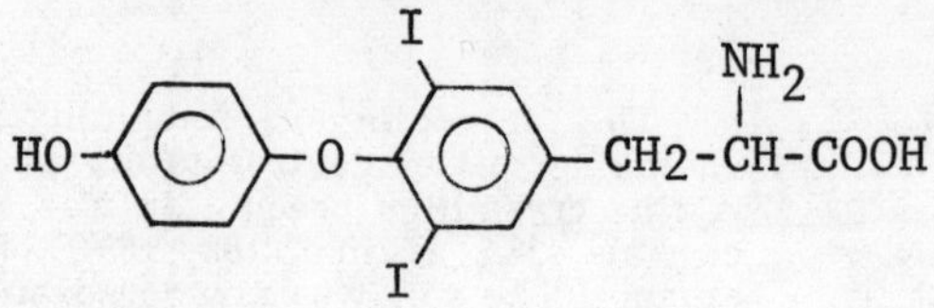

$C_{15}H_{13}I_2NO_4$

Ref. 1077

A preliminary experiment was carried out as follows: 11.06 g. dl-formyl-3:5-diiodothyronine were suspended in 1100 cc. of boiling water and treated with 2.42 g, l-α-phenylethylamine dissolved in 200 cc. of warm water; after boiling for a minute the acid had passed into solution, a trace of impurity was removed by filtration and the solution allowed to cool slowly and stand for 24 hours at the ordinary temperature; the salt which separated was crystalline but evidently not homogeneous, appearing under the microscope as clumps of stout needles mixed with a felt of fine ones. It was filtered off, washed with water and dried; it amounted to 8.35 g. (theoretical 6.74 g.). On concentrating the mother liquor under diminished pressure to about 100 cc. the more soluble salt separated at first as an oil, which, however, soon crystallised to an apparently homogeneous felted mass of fine colourless needles (3.7 g.). The latter salt was fairly soluble in alcohol, whilst the first fraction seemed to be much less so; the 8.35 g. were therefore ground up with cold alcohol, filtered off and washed with alcohol; it was then recrystallised by dissolving in dilute alcohol and boiling until the alcohol was removed; it still, however, did not appear homogeneous. The two fractions were then decomposed and the optical rotations of the acids observed; that from the soluble salt had $[\alpha]^{23°}_{5461}$ +21.3°; that from the insoluble salt $[\alpha]^{23°}_{5461}$ -16.9°.

In the light of the above results the following series of experiments were carried through; repetition of the resolution has given essentially similar results.

A. l-Thyroxine.

6.1 g. formyl-dl-3:5-diiodothyronine were converted into the salt with l-phenylethylamine under the conditions described above; the insoluble salt amounted to 4.6 g. and the soluble salt to 2.5 g.; the latter had $[\alpha]^{22°}_{5461}$ +22.0° (c = 5 in 50% alcohol); after two recrystallisations from water it had $[\alpha]^{22°}_{5461}$ +23.8° under the same conditions; it crystallised in masses of fine colourless needles which were anhydrous and melted at 188-189°.

Formyl-l-3:5-diiodothyronine. The above salt was dissolved in dilute alcohol and decomposed by the addition of slightly more than the theoretical amount of dilute hydrochloric acid. Precipitation of the acid was completed by cautious dilution with water. The formyl-l-3:5-diiodothyronine formed colourless plates, darkening at 195° and melting at 214° (decomp.). In 5% solution of alcohol in a 2 dm. tube α = 2.78°, whence $[\alpha]^{21°}_{5461}$ = +27.8°.

l-3:5-Diiodothyronine. The formyl derivative was boiled for 1 hour under a reflux condenser with 15% hydrobromic acid; the solution was evaporated to dryness under diminished pressure and the residual hydrobromide dissolved in warm aqueous alco-

hol; the solution was then cautiously neutralised with ammonia whereupon the amino-acid separated in glistening colourless plates, M.P. 256° (decomp.).

In 5.4% solution in 0.880 ammonia it has $[\alpha]^{20}_{5461}$ -1.3°.

11.06 g. formyl-dl-3:5-diiodothyronine were converted into the salts with d-α-phenylethylamine. The soluble fraction amounted to 3.6 g. and, on recrystallisation, formed colourless needles, melting at 187-188°, and having $[\alpha]^{19.5°}_{5461}$ -21.9 in 5% solution of 50% alcohol.

Formyl-d-diiodothyronine. On decomposition the above salt gave formyl-d-3:5-diiodothyronine, which formed colourless plates melting at 210°, and having, in 5% solution in alcohol $[\alpha]^{21°}_{5461}$ -26.9°.

d-3:5-Diiodothyronine. The formyl derivative, on hydrolysis, yielded d-3:5-diiodothyronine, M.P. 256° with decomposition. In 4.35% solution of 0.880 ammonia this had $[\alpha]^{18°}_{5461}$ + 1.15°.

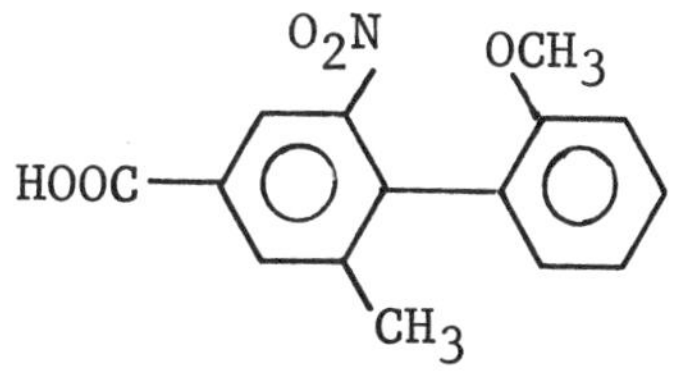

$C_{15}H_{13}NO_5$ Ref. 1078

Resolution of 2-Methyl-4-carboxy-6-nitro-2′-methoxybiphenyl.—A mixture of 1.0 g. of *dl*-acid in 30 cc. of absolute ethanol and 1.372 g. of brucine in 30 cc. of absolute ethanol was evaporated to half its volume and allowed to stand in a refrigerator. After twelve hours 1.88 g. of yellow prisms separated, m. p. 145–147° (cor.). Obviously it contained ethanol of crystallization.

Anal. Calcd. for $C_{38}H_{39}O_9N_3 \cdot C_2H_5OH$: N, 5.78. Found: N, 5.77. *Rotation.* 0.1001 g. made up to 10 cc. with chloroform at 25° gave α_D −0.156; *l*, 2; $[\alpha]^{25}_D$ −7.8°.

The rotation did not change on recrystallization of the salt from ethanol.

A second crop obtained from the mother liquor of the original salt preparation weighed 0.3417 g. and gave the same melting point and rotation. Recrystallization of this salt gave no change in rotation.

No mutarotation at room temperature was observed for any of the salt fractions and only very minor differences occurred in the rotation of the salt fractions.

***l*-2-Methyl-4-carboxy-6-nitro-2′-methoxybiphenyl.**—The different samples of salt were decomposed at 0° with iced hydrochloric acid until free from brucine; white crystals, m. p. 227–228° (cor.). This acid racemized gradually in solution. Several duplicate experiments gave consistent results. A typical experiment follows. *Rotation.* 0.0768 g. of *l*-acid made up to 10 cc. with glacial acetic acid at 25° after 5 minutes gave α_D −0.114°; *l*, 2; $[\alpha]^{25}_D$ −7.43°: 44 min., −6.51°; 84 min., −5.87°; 129 min., −4.95°; 199 min., −4.04°; 309 min., −2.74°; 459 min., −1.82°. Calculated half-life, 215 min.; $[\alpha]^{25}_D$ (calcd. to 0 time) −7.55°. At the temperature of boiling glacial acetic acid the half-life approximated eleven minutes.

Anal. Calcd. for $C_{15}H_{13}O_5N$: C, 62.72; H, 4.53. Found: C, 63.03; H, 4.86.

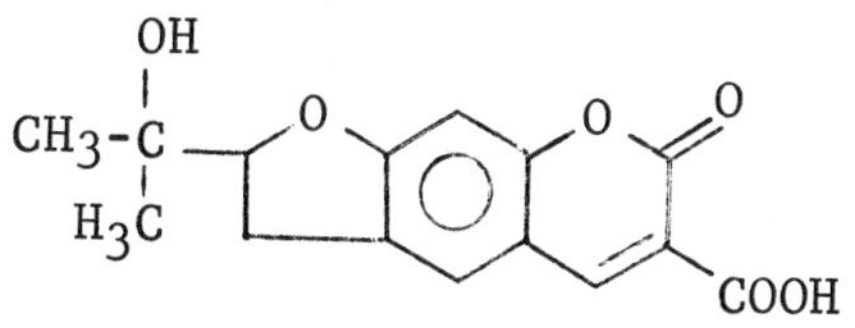

$C_{15}H_{13}O_6$ Ref. 1079

(−)-Nodakenetin and (+)-Marmesin. A mixture of the carboxylic acid (VIe) (1.1 g) and brucine (1.7 g) in methanol (20 ml) was boiled for two minutes and allowed to stand over night at room temperature. After removal of methanol, the residue was dissolved in water, boiled for two minutes and allowed to stand over night at room temperature. The product (m.p. 158°C, decomp.) was filtered off and decomposed with 2 N-hydrochloric acid. The acid was recrystalliezd three times from methanol to give yellow needles, 240 mg (m.p. 236∼7°C, $[\alpha]^{17}_D$ +91° (in chloroform)). *Anal.* Found: C, 61.92; H, 4.86. Calcd. for $C_{15}H_{14}O_6$: C, 62.06; H, 4.86%. On the other hand, the filtrate was treated with 2 N hydrochloric acid in the same way as above to give 280 mg of colorless needles, m.p. 241°C (from methanol), $[\alpha]^{17}_D$ −94° (in chloroform). *Anal.* Found: C, 61.75; H, 5.04. Calcd. for $C_{15}H_{14}O_6$: C, 62.06; H, 4.86%.

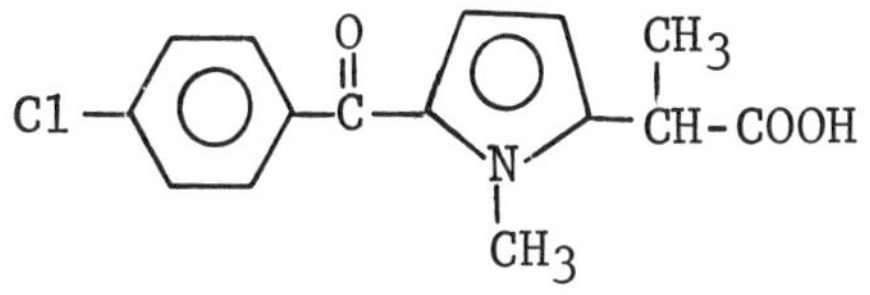

$C_{15}H_{14}ClNO_3$ Ref. 1080

EXAMPLE CXXI

(−)-5-(p-chlorobenzoyl)-1,α-dimethylpyrrole-2-acetic acid

A solution of 16.5 g. (0.057 mole) of racemic 5-(p-chlorobenzoyl)-α-methyl-1-methylpyrrole - 2 - acetic acid and 6.8 g. (0.057 mole) of (+)-α-methylbenzylamine in 95% ethanol deposits crystals on standing. The solid is collected and recrystallized twice from 2-propanol to give 4.4 g. of salt, M.P. 181–182° C., the mother liquors being set aside for use as shown in Example CXXII. The salt is partitioned between ether and 3 N hydrochloric acid. The ether layer is washed with dilute hydrochloric acid and brine and dried over magnesium sulfate. The solvent is evaporated in vacuo. The solid residue is dissolved in hot ether and methylcyclohexane is added. The ether is allowed to evaporate and the precipitated solid, (−) - 5 - (p-chlorobenzoyl)-1,α-dimethylpyrrole-2-acetic acid, is collected by filtration: (13% yield), M.P. 106–107° C.

EXAMPLE CXXII

(+)-5-(p-chlorobenzoyl)-1,α-dimethylpyrrole-2-acetic acid

The mother liquors set aside in Example CXXI are evaporated to dryness. The residue is acidified with 3 N hydrochloric acid and the precipitated acid is extracted into ether. The ether solution is then extracted with saturated sodium bicarbonate solution. The latter is acidified with dilute HCl and the precipitated solid is extracted into ether. The ether solution is washed with brine, dried over anhydrous magnesium sulfate and evaporated to

dryness to yield 5-(p-chlorobenzoyl)-α-methyl-1-methylpyrrole-2-acetic acid [presumably rich in the (+)-enantiomorph] as a yellow solid. A 14.8 g. sample is dissolved in ethanol. To the solution is added 6.15 g. (.051 mole) of (−)-α-methylbenzylamine. A crystalline salt precipitates on standing which is collected and recrystallized three times from 2-propanol to give about 6.6 g. of white crystals, M.P. 175–177° C. The salt is partitioned between ether and 3 N HCl solution. The ether layer is washed with dilute HCl and brine and dried over magnesium sulfate. The solvent is partially evaporated in vacuo and methylcyclohexane is added. The ether is allowed to evaporate at room temperature and the precipitate is collected. It is recrystallized once more in the same manner to give about 3.1 g. (21% yield) of (+)-5-(p-chlorobenzoyl)-1,α-dimethylpyrrole-2-acetic acid as a white solid, M.P. 105.5–106.5° C.

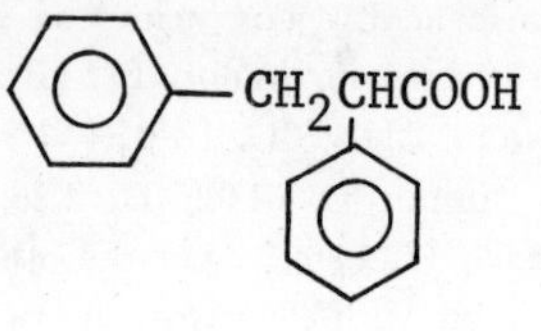

$C_{15}H_{14}O_2$ Ref. 1081

Optical resolution of phenylhydrocinnamic acid: 9.5 g (0.04 moles) of optically inactive phenylhydrocinnamic acid and 9.0 g of *l*-ephedrine dihydrate were dissolved in 150 ml of hot acetone. The solution was allowed to cool and crystallise for 12 hours in a refrigerator. The precipitate was filtered off, dried and weighed. About 0.5 g was set apart, the acid was liberated and the optical activity measured in acetone. The remaining part of the precipitate was recrystallised from acetone, until the optical activity of the liberated acid remained constant. The precipitate is rather difficult to dissolve in the appropiate amounts of the solvent, and it is necessary to reflux for a few minutes. The course of the resolution was as follows:

Crystallisation No.	1	2	3	4	5
ml of acetone	150	50	22	12	8
g of salt obtained	4.6	2.0	1.2	0.8	0.5
$[\alpha]_D^{25}$ of acid (acetone)	− 81°	− 116°	− 122°	− 132°	− 132°

The mother liquor from the first crystallisation was evaporated to dryness at room temperature and the residue recrystallised from the successive mother liquors in the first series of crystallisations. In this way a further 2.0 g of salt was obtained. The liberated acid showed an optical activity of − 132°. The total yield of salt was thus 2.5 g.

The mother liquor from the first crystallisation of the second series was evaporated to dryness at room temperature and the acid was liberated from the residue. 2.5 g (0.011 moles) of the acid ($[\alpha]_D^{25} = +75°$ in ethanol) and 1.4 g (0.011 moles) of (−)-α-phenylethylamine were dissolved in a warm mixture of 13 ml of ethanol, 13 ml of acetone and 26 ml of water. The salt obtained was recrystallised until the optical activity of the acid (measured in ethanol) remained constant.

Crystallisation No.	1	2	3	4
ml of ethanol	13	13	10	10
ml of acetone	13	20	16	16
ml of water	26	23	18	18
g of salt obtained	3.6	2.8	2.4	1.9
$[\alpha]_D^{25}$ of acid (ethanol)	+ 89°	+ 114°	+ 122°	+ 122°

(−)-α-*Phenylhydrocinnamic acid:* 2.5 g of the *l*-ephedrine salt were decomposed with 2-*N* sulphuric acid and the liberated acid was extracted with ether. After removal of the ether by distillation 1.4 g of crude acid remained. It was recrystallised from petrol (b.p. 60°–80°) from which it was obtained as a colourless powder, melting at 82.5°–84°.

47.59 mg of acid, 4.68 ml of 0.04475-C NaOH

$C_{15}H_{14}O_2$. Equiv. wt. calc. 226.1, found 227.2.

Weighed amounts of acid were made up to 10.01 ml with different solvents and the optical activity measured. In the case of water the acid was dissolved in 2.0 ml of ethanol, neutralised with 0.1-C NaOH and finally made up to 10.01 ml with water.

Solvent	mg of acid	$2\alpha_D^{25}$	$[\alpha]_D^{25}$	$[M]_D^{25}$
Acetone	49.1	− 1.318°	− 134.3°	− 303.7°
Ethanol	51.3	− 1.258°	− 122.7°	− 277.4°
Benzene	50.5	− 1.350°	− 133.8°	− 302.5°
Glacial acetic acid	62.2	− 1.582°	− 127.3°	− 287.8°
Water (ion)	51.1	− 1.065°	− 104.3°	− 235.8°

(+)-α-*Phenylhydrocinnamic acid:* 1.9 g of the (−)-α-phenylethylamine salt were decomposed with 2-*N* sulphuric acid and the liberated acid was extracted with ether and purified as described for its optical antipode, which it resembles in all respects. M.p. 82.5°–84°.

60.76 mg of acid, 6.00 ml of 0.04475-C NaOH

$C_{15}H_{14}O_2$. Equiv. wt. calc. 226.1, found 226.4

55.4 mg of the acid in 10.01 ml of acetone: $2\alpha_D^{25} = +1.483°$, $[\alpha]_D^{25} = +133.8°$, $[M]_D^{25} = +302.5°$.

$C_{15}H_{14}O_2$ Ref. 1081a

(+)-2,3-*Diphenylpropanoic Acid* (VII). The (±)-acid (59·4 g.) in 80% ethanol (750 ml.) was warmed to near boiling and (−)-α-phenethylamine (29 g.) was added. The salt (65 g., dry), deposited overnight, after recrystallisation (×11) from 75% ethanol melted 176—177° and had $[\alpha]_D^{20}$ +55·30° (*c* 2·016 in MeOH). Decomposition of the salt gave the (+)-acid (8 g.) from light petroleum (b. p. 60—80°), m. p. 83—84°, $[\alpha]_D^{20}$ +140·8° (*c* 2·030 in C_6H_6), +133·7° (*c* 0·535 in acetone) [lit.,[25] $[\alpha]_D^{18}$ +133·8° (*c* 0·505 in acetone)].

[25] K. Pettersson, *Arkiv Kemi*, **1954**, **7**, 339.

$C_{15}H_{14}O_2$ Ref. 1081b

47 g α-Phenyl-hydrozimtsäure[2]) wurden mit 50 g Thionylchlorid zunächst vorsichtig erwärmt, dann, nach dem Nachlassen der ziemlich kräftigen Reaktion, noch eine halbe Stunde unter Rückfluß gekocht. Bei möglichst niedriger Temperatur wurde dann das überschüssige Thionylchlorid im Vakuum abdestilliert. Es wurden 51 g Säurechlorid erhalten[3]), das ohne weitere Reinigung zu einem Gemische von 45 g Menthol, 45 g Pyridin und 50 g Benzol hinzugefügt wurde. Schließlich kochte man noch eine Stunde auf dem Wasserbade am Rückflußkühler. Nachdem dann überschüssiges Menthol, Pyridin und Benzol mit Wasserdampf abgetrieben worden waren, nahm man den festen Kolbenrückstand in Äther auf, schüttelte mehrmals mit Sodalösung durch und destillierte den Äther nach dem Trocknen über geglühtem Magnesiumsulfat ab.

Es zeigte sich jetzt, daß zwei Ester entstanden waren, die durch Umkrystallisieren aus Alkohol getrennt werden konnten. Das rohe Gemisch der beiden Körper wurde in der doppelten oder dreifachen der zur Lösung nötigen Menge heißen Alkohols gelöst; nach dem Erkalten schied sich eine reichliche Menge feiner, weißer Nadeln von schönem Seidenglanze aus, nach ein- bis zweimaligem Umkrystallisieren zeigten sie den konstanten Schmelzpunkt 100—101°. Zur Gewinnung des zweiten, leichter löslichen Esters, verfährt man so, daß man das Filtrat vom ersten Körper stehen läßt, bis einige Gramm Substanz sich ausgeschieden haben; man filtriert ab, läßt wieder stehen und wiederholt diese Operation so oft, bis das Auskrystallisierte einen konstanten Schmelzpunkt besitzt. Der Schmelzpunkt der ebenfalls in schönen, weißen Nadeln krystallisierenden Substanz ist nicht ganz scharf, 58—62°.

Dieser zweite Ester ist identisch mit dem schon von Busolt beschriebenen, er gibt zwar den Schmelzpunkt 67—68° an, wenn man indessen bei der Bestimmung sehr langsam erwärmt, so erhält man immer den richtigen, niedrigeren Schmelzpunkt. Öfters wiederholtes Umkrystallisieren ändert an diesem, sowie an der optischen Drehung nichts mehr.

[2]) Die α-Phenyl-zimtsäure wurde nach dem von Posner (J. pr. [2] 82, 437 [1910]) verbesserten Verfahren von Oglialoro (G. 27, II, 49; 31, II, 77) dargestellt, die Hydrierung zur Hydrozimtsäure wurde mit Natriumamalgam unter beständigem Rühren und Einleiten von Kohlensäure mit guter Ausbeute durchgeführt.

[3]) Das Chlorid läßt sich ebensogut mit Phosphortrichlorid darstellen. Doch enthält dann der Menthylester immer etwas Phosphor- oder Phosphorigsäure-Ester, der sehr schwer zu entfernen ist.

Der hochschmelzende Ester dagegen ist neu.

0.1850 g Sbst.: 0.5584 g CO_2, 0.1501 g H_2O.

$C_{25}H_{32}O_2$. Ber. C 82.36, H 8.86.
Gef. » 82.32, » 9.07[1]).

Polarisationen (ausgeführt in Benzollösung im 1-dm-Rohr):

Ester vom Schmp.

100–101° p = 9.75, d_4^{20} = 0.8914, α_{20}^{D} = –1.91°, $[\alpha]_D^{20}$ = –21.97°.

58–62° p = 10.05, d_4^{20} = 0.8904, α_{20}^{D} = –7.54°, $[\alpha]_D^{20}$ = –84.28°.

58–62° p = 9.95, d_4^{20} = 0.8901, α_{20}^{D} = –7.53°, $[\alpha]_D^{20}$ = –84.99°.

Die zweite Polarisation des niedrig schmelzenden Esters war mit einer Substanz ausgeführt worden, die schon den richtigen Schmelzpunkt hatte und dann noch sechs Mal umkrystallisiert wurde. Merkwürdigerweise fanden wir das spezifische Gewicht der Lösung des niedrig schmelzenden Esters immer etwas kleiner als das des höher schmelzenden. Zur Bestimmung der Löslichkeit der beiden Körper ließen wir genau abgewogene Mengen Ester und Alkohol 2½ Stunden gleichzeitig auf der Maschine schütteln, das Gewicht des ungelösten Teiles sowie des aus dem Filtrate zurückgewonnenen konnte dann genau festgestellt werden. Bei Zimmertemperatur löst sich ein Gewichtsteil des Esters vom Schmp. 100–101° in 166 Tln., ein Teil des Esters vom Schmp. 58–62° in 32 Tln. Alkohol von 95 %.

Es ist uns ein Rätsel, weshalb Busolt seinerzeit den höher schmelzenden Ester nicht erhalten hat. Man kann ihn unmöglich übersehen, da er viel leichter rein zu gewinnen ist, als der andere. Busolt hat offenbar den niedrig schmelzenden Ester ganz rein und einheitlich in Händen gehabt, denn die von ihm gefundene Drehung ist um ein weniges höher als die von uns beobachtete: $[\alpha]_D$ = –86.04°.

Bei der Verseifung dieser Ester mit 15-proz. methylalkoholischer Kalilauge wurden entweder völlig optisch-inaktive oder aber nur sehr schwach drehende Säuren erhalten. Wählte man eine verdünntere Lauge, so nahmen die Drehungen etwas zu (bei Verwendung von 10-proz. alkoholischer Kalilauge erhielten wir eine Säure von der spezifischen Drehung ca. 1°), die Ausbeuten an Säure wurden aber dementsprechend schlechter, auch nach längerem Kochen fand sich viel unveränderter Ester vor. Die stärkste Drehung wurde erhalten, als 3 g Ester vom Schmp. 100–101° in alkoholischer Lösung mit 3 g Bariumhydroxyd, das in heißem Wasser gelöst war, 4 Stunden gekocht wurden. Wir erhielten hierbei 0.25 g Säure, welche eine spezifische Drehung von ca. 17° besaß. Die Drehungen der Natriumsalze der verseiften Säuren waren immer etwas kleiner als die der freien Säuren. Mit Säuren läßt sich eine Verseifung überhaupt nicht erzielen.

Da es aber für uns von prinzipieller Bedeutung war, zu zeigen, daß die beiden Menthylester der α-Phenyl-hydrozimtsäure tatsächlich den beiden optisch-aktiven Säuren entsprechen, daß also durch die Menthol-Veresterung eine sterische Spaltung auch in diesem Falle erzielt worden ist, so versuchten wir, die Säure durch Alkaloide in die optischen Antipoden zu spalten, um diese dann in die Menthylester zu verwandeln. Diese Spaltung gelang einzig mit dem neutralen Strychninsalze; mit Brucin, Cinchonin, Cinchonidin und Chinin konnten keine krystallisierenden Salze gewonnen werden.

20 g der reinen Hydrosäure vom Schmp. 91–92° löst man in einem Gemische von 90 ccm Alkohol (95 %) und 90 ccm Wasser unter Kochen, und trägt sodann rasch 28.6 g fein gepulvertes Strychnin unter Umschütteln in die kochende Lösung ein. Man kühlt ab und setzt noch soviel Alkohol hinzu, daß die Lösung bei Zimmertemperatur eben noch klar bleibt; durch kräftiges Reiben mit einem Glasstabe – am besten wirken natürlich Impfkrystalle – wird die Krystallisation eingeleitet. Man läßt über Nacht im Eisschranke stehen, saugt ab und krystallisiert aus Alkohol um, was dergestalt ausgeführt wird, daß das rohe Strychninsalz durch Schütteln mit 100 ccm kaltem Alkohol in Lösung gebracht wird, worauf man filtriert und noch soviel Alkohol zugibt, daß in der Kälte zunächst keine Ausscheidung stattfindet, auf Reiben oder Animpfen erfolgt dann die Krystallisation.

Da diese Strychninsalze keinen richtigen Schmelzpunkt besitzen sie zersetzen sich allmählich unter Kohlensäure-Entwicklung schon unter 100°, so wurde bis zur konstanten optischen Drehung umkrystallisiert.

Nach der ersten Krystallisation drehten 0.5 g in genau 10 ccm Alkohol –1.25°, nach der zweiten –1.58°, nach der dritten –1.59°. Man konnte also annehmen, das Salz sei einheitlich; als es aber durch Schütteln mit verdünnter Natronlauge zerlegt wurde, erhielten wir eine Säure von der schwachen Linksdrehung $[\alpha]_D^{20}$ = –6.91°.

Aus den weiteren Fraktionen der Strychninsalze konnten etwas stärker rechtsdrehende Säuren gewonnen werden; man erhielt aber den Eindruck, daß die Spaltung eine unvollkommene und nicht geglückt sei; die Drehung der Linkssäure war zweifellos eine viel zu geringe.

[1]) Die Analyse wurde von Hrn. E. Lenziger ausgeführt.

Eine genauere Untersuchung zeigte, daß das zuerst ausgeschiedene Strychninsalz der Linkssäure noch sehr viel Rechts-Salz enthält, auch wenn die optische Drehung anscheinend schon konstant ist.

Deshalb krystallisierten wir das erste Salz so lange um, bis die Säure aus der Mutterlauge eine starke, konstante Drehung aufwies. Die Krystallisations-Mutterlaugen wurden im Vakuum auf dem Wasserbade eingedunstet, bis die Lösung sich stark trübte; schied sich dann beim Erkalten das Salz harzig aus, so wurde es in Alkohol gelöst; beim allmählichen Verdunsten des letzteren kam das Salz krystallinisch heraus. Es wurde abgesogen, getrocknet und nun, da wir den Einfluß der Natronlauge auf das Drehungsvermögen, wohl mit Grund, fürchteten, mit Magnesiumoxyd innig zerrieben und mit Wasser auf der Maschine einige Stunden geschüttelt. Die Säure ging dabei vollständig in das Magnesiumsalz über. Man filtrierte vom Strychnin ab, säuerte das Filtrat mit Salzsäure an, extrahierte die Phenyl-hydrozimtsäure mit Äther und schüttelte den Äther mehrmals mit verdünnter Salzsäure aus, um die letzten Reste Strychnin sicher zu entfernen. Die nach dem Verdunsten des Äthers hinterbleibende Säure wurde nach dem Trocknen untersucht; genau 0.8 g lösten wir in 12.8 g Benzol und polarisierten. Aus der Mutterlauge von der dritten Krystallisation erhielten wir so eine Säure von der Drehung α_D = + 1.05°; erst nach der fünften Krystallisation drehte die Mutterlaugen-Säure links: α_D = –1.12°, und nach der siebenten Krystallisation betrug die Drehung α_D = –3.66°. Da bei einem Vorversuche in kleinerem Maßstabe diese Drehung nicht mehr zugenommen hatte, so hielten wir das Salz nunmehr für einheitlich, obgleich das offenbar nicht ganz richtig war, indem die daraus erhaltene Säure noch nicht die maximale Drehung besaß.

0.1711 g Sbst.: 7.7 ccm N (15°, 738.5 mm).

$C_{36}H_{36}O_4N_2$. Ber. N 5.15. Gef. N 5.09.

Die Darstellung der Säure aus dem Strychninsalze geschah, wie oben beschrieben; nach dem Umkrystallisieren aus verdünntem Alkohol bildete sie feine, weiße Nadeln. Der Schmelzpunkt war nicht ganz scharf; das Schmelzen beginnt bei 83°, klar geschmolzen bei 89° (die racemische Säure schmilzt bei 91–92°). Polarisation in Benzollösung im 1-dm-Rohr:

p = 9.93, d_4^{20} = 0.8996, α_D^{20} = –7.60°, $[\alpha]_D^{20}$ = –85.08°.

Zur Gewinnung der Rechts-Säure gingen wir von einer sechsten und letzten Ausscheidung des Strychninsalzes aus, wie sie bei der Spaltung einer größeren Menge Säure erhalten worden war. Eine vorläufige Untersuchung der aus dem Salze abgesonderten, nicht umkrystallisierten Säure ergab eine spezifische Drehung von ca. + 35°. Die Säure wurde zum Umkrystallisieren in kochendem Wasser suspendiert mit soviel Alkohol versetzt, daß beim Abkühlen auf Zimmertemperatur die Lösung eben noch klar blieb; nach dem Stehen über Nacht wurde vom Auskrystallisierten abfiltriert. Aus dem Filtrate schied sich beim freiwilligen Verdunsten eine Säure ab, deren Drehung sich bei weiterem Umkrystallisieren nicht mehr änderte; sie zeigte den gleichen unscharfen Schmelzpunkt, wie die Links-Säure (83–89°). Die Polarisation ergab:

p = 10.01, d_4^{20} = 0.8997, α_D^{20} = + 8.47°, $[\alpha]_D^{20}$ = + 94.04°.

Nun verwandelten wir die beiden aktiven Säuren in die Menthylester (Darstellung der Säurechloride mit Thionylchlorid). Der aus der linksdrehenden Säure entstandene Ester zeigte nach dem Umkrystallisieren aus Alkohol den Schmelzpunkt 58–62°, also genau den Schmelzpunkt des früher direkt erhaltenen (Ester von Busolt); auch der Mischschmelzpunkt mit diesem war derselbe. Die Polarisation in Benzol ergab:

p = 10.02, d_4^{20} = 0.8997, α_D^{20} = –7.95°, $[\alpha]_D^{20}$ = – 89.06°.

Die Drehung ist also noch etwas höher, als die von Busolt gefundene (– 86.04°), während wir selbst als höchste Drehung $[\alpha]_D$ = –84.99° erhalten hatten. Es ist wohl möglich, daß die direkt aus der racemischen Säure dargestellten Ester der Links-Säure hartnäckig etwas Rechts-Ester enthielten, der auch durch häufiges Umkrystallisieren nicht ganz entfernt werden konnte; die Zahl $[\alpha]_D^{20}$ = – 89.06° dürfte deshalb als die maximale Drehung des Menthylesters der Links-α-Phenyl-hydrozimtsäure betrachtet werden.

Aus der rechtsdrehenden Säure erhielten wir sogleich den schön krystallisierenden Menthylester vom richtigen Schmelzpunkt 100–101°; auch der Schmelzpunkt eines Gemisches mit dem direkt aus der racemischen Säure dargestellten Präparate war der nämliche. Polarisation in Benzol:

p = 9.97, d_4^{20} = 9.8914, α_D^{20} = –1.95°, $[\alpha]_D^{20}$ = –21.97°.

Die optischen Drehungen des direkt aus der inaktiven Säure dargestellten Menthylesters und des aus der Rechts-Säure erhaltenen stimmen also vollkommen überein.

Die kleine Untersuchung zeigt also, daß die beiden durch Veresterung der α-Phenyl-hydrozimtsäure gebildeten Menthylester tatsächlich den optisch-aktiven Antipoden dieser Säure entsprechen, so-

daß hier ein neuer Fall einer **vollständigen sterischen Spaltung einer inaktiven Säure mittels Menthol-Veresterung** vorliegt. Wir haben es hier ferner mit einer äußerst rasch verlaufenden Racemisierung zu tun, indem die beiden optisch-aktiven α-Phenyl-hydrozimtsäuren durch alkoholisches Kali nach kurzer Zeit schon vollständig inaktiviert werden.

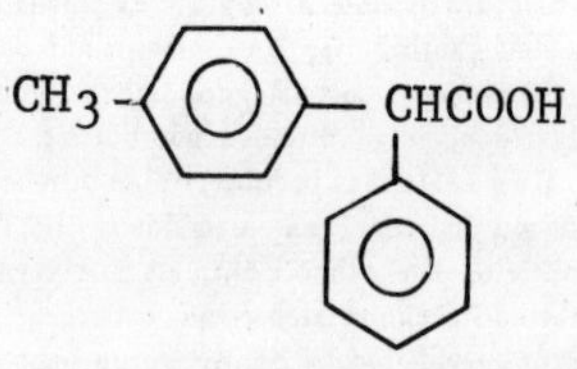

$C_{15}H_{14}O_2$ Ref. 1082

Cinchonidine was found to be a suitable alkaloid for this purpose. When 6·5 grams of the alkaloid (1 mol.) were dissolved in a solution of 5 grams of the acid (1 mol.) in 160 c.c. of ethyl alcohol, 8·5 grams of crystals separated; these were crystallised twice from ethyl alcohol, and the resulting 4 grams gave 1·5 grams of acid with $[\alpha]_D + 10°$ in acetone. On the other hand, when 5 grams of the *r*-acid were dissolved in 90 c.c. of alcohol and combined with 3·25 grams of the alkaloid (½ mol.), the crystals, which separated, amounted to 4 grams, and gave 1·7 grams of acid with $[\alpha]_D + 7·9°$ in acetone. It was, therefore, advantageous to employ the acid and the alkaloid in molecular quantities.

Fifty grams of the *r*-acid (1 mol.) were dissolved in 2 litres of boiling ethyl alcohol, and 65 grams of cinchonidine (1 mol.) were added. Crystallisation proceeded during two days in an ice-chest. The 54 grams of salt which separated were crystallised as before from 900 c.c. of alcohol, and, after five additional crystallisations, the salt (24 grams), which separated in needles, was homogeneous. It melted and decomposed at 204—205°, and, after being dried at the ordinary temperature, it gave the following values when dissolved in chloroform; $l = 2$, $c = 3·025$, $\alpha_D^{16} - 2·12°$, $[\alpha]_D^{16} - 35°$. It was decomposed by shaking with an excess of dilute sulphuric acid, and the organic acid was then extracted with ether. Yield of acid, 9·2 grams.

d-*Phenyl*-p-*tolylacetic acid*, $C_7H_7·CHPh·CO_2H$, separates from aqueous alcohol or from dilute acetic acid as an oil, which solidifies gradually to form feathery needles. It is very soluble in ethyl alcohol, acetone, benzene, chloroform, and acetic acid. It melts at 83—84° with slight preliminary softening. For analysis, it was dried in a vacuum over sulphuric acid:

0·175 gave 0·5096 CO_2 and 0·0982 H_2O. C = 79·4; H = 6·2.
$C_{15}H_{14}O_2$ requires C = 79·6; H = 6·2 per cent.

Its specific rotation was determined in acetone:

$$l = 2,\ c = 4·214,\ \alpha_D^{19·4} + 1·23°,\ [\alpha]_D^{19·4} + 14·6°.$$

Owing to the small rotatory power of the acid both in acetone and in other solvents, polarimetric measurements of the cinchonidine salts obtained from each separate crystallisation are of little value as an indication of the progress of the resolution. In order to establish the purity of the acid as prepared by the method just described, the filtrate from each crop in another resolution was decomposed by mineral acid, and the resulting organic acid examined. Thirty-nine grams of cinchonidine were dissolved in a solution of 30 grams of the *r*-acid in 1200 c.c. of ethyl alcohol, the progress of the separation being shown as follows:

	Cinchonidine salt.	Alcohol.	Acid from filtrate.	$[\alpha]_D'$ in Acetone.*
1	36 grams	600 c.c. }	14·0 grams	−4·3°
2	29 ,,	500 }		
3	23 ,,	380	1·3 ,,	+1·6
4	21 ,,	345	0·8 ,,	7·1
5	18 ,,	300	0·6 ,,	9·9
6	16 ,,	250	0·5 ,,	11·7
7	14 ,,	230	0·5 ,,	14·6
8	12·5 ,,	225	0·3 ,,	not examined.
9	11·0 ,,	210	0·3 ,,	14·4
10	10·5 ,,	190	0·3 ,,	14·2
11	9·0 ,,	170	0·4 ,,	14·6
12	7·0 ,,	(gave an acid with $[\alpha]_D + 14·5°$).		

* The influence of temperature on the rotatory power between 12° and 33° was found to be very slight.

A portion of the acid with $[\alpha]_D + 14·5°$ was converted into the calcium salt, from the aqueous solution of which two separate fractions of crystals were withdrawn; the acids obtained from these fractions gave in each case the value $[\alpha]_D + 14·4°$.

Since the pure acid does not have a sharp melting point, tends to separate as an oil from aqueous alcohol, and does not crystallise readily from other solvents, some such proof of its homogeneity as that just given was rendered necessary. It may also be added that the separation of the pure *d*-acid by crystallising a mixture of it and the *r*-acid from aqueous alcohol is not practical, even when the proportion of the *r*-acid present is small.

For the preparation of the *l*-acid, the various amounts of the lævorotatory acid mixture, obtained from the mother liquors of the first crystallisations during the isolation of the *d*-acid by cinchonidine, were united, dissolved in alcohol, and combined with quinine. The separation of the pure quinine *l*-salt is not, however, accomplished readily. Thus 34·8 grams of the lævorotatory acid mixture were dissolved in 170 c.c. of ethyl alcohol and combined with 24·7 grams of quinine. Fine needles (35 grams) separated on cooling, and a portion on decomposition with mineral acid gave an acid with $[\alpha]_D - 8·3°$ in acetone. Nevertheless, even after ten crystallisations the pure quinine *l*-salt was not obtained, since the acid resulting from the crystals (10 grams) had only $[\alpha]_D - 11·5°$, a value which is about 3° too low. A better result was obtained in another experiment, where 121 grams of a lævorotatory acid mixture were combined with 86 grams of quinine. After seven crystallisations from alcohol, the salt amounted to 47 grams, whilst the acid obtained from it had $[\alpha]_D - 13·9°$ in acetone, and was therefore almost pure.

The difficulty in preparing the *l*-acid is to be attributed in all probability to the formation of mixed crystals of the quinine salts of the enantiomorphously related acids. The separation of such a product must necessarily be tedious; compare, for example, Schütz and Marckwald (*Ber.*, 1896, **29**, 52) on the resolution of *dl*-valeric acid, and Perkin, Pope, and Wallach (T., 1909, **95**, 1789) on the resolution of 1-methyl*cyclo*hexylidene-4-acetic acid.

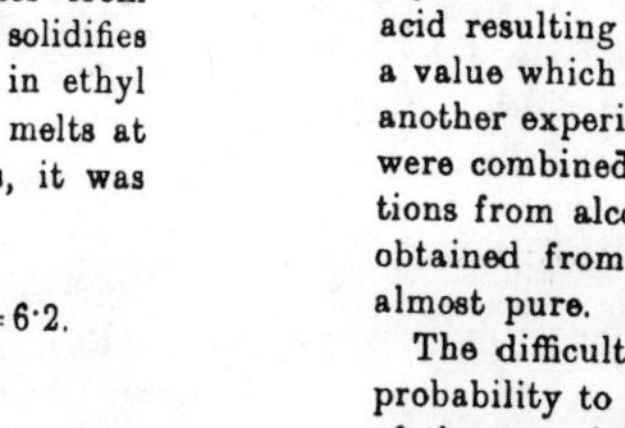

$C_{15}H_{14}O_2$ Ref. 1083

L'acide racémique α-(3-acénaphtyl)-propionique a été dédoublé aux antipodes optiques par voie de cristallisation fractionnée des sels neutres de quinine et de cynchonidine. La quinine formait dans l'éthanol un sel difficilement soluble avec l'enantiomère dextrogyre, tandis que la cynchonidine séparait, dans les fractions frontales de l'acétone, l'antimère lévogyre. Les sels alcaloïdiques optiquement purs avaient les constantes physiques suivantes: (a) sel quininique, f. 207°; $[\alpha]_D^{20} = -40{,}00°$ ($c = 0{,}2$, $d = 2$, $\alpha = -0{,}16°$) dans l'éthanol 96%; et (b) sel cinchonidinique, f. 125°; $[\alpha]_D^{20} = -140{,}00°$ ($c = 0{,}2$, $d = 2$, $\alpha = -0{,}56°$) dans l'éthanol 96%. Les acides α-(3-acénaphtyl)-propioniques optiquement actifs fondaient à 137° et possédaient le pouvoir rotatoire spécifique $[\alpha]_D^{20} = \pm 175{,}00°$ ($c = 0{,}2$, $d = 2$, $\alpha = \pm 0{,}70°$) dans l'éthanol 96%.

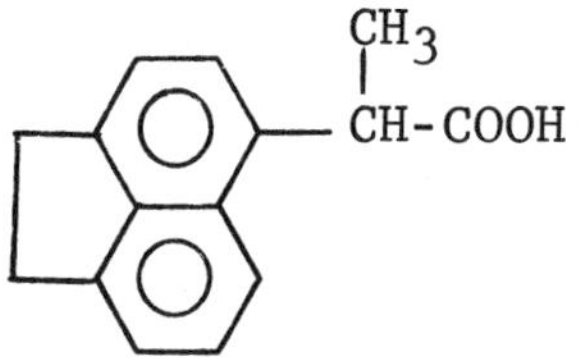

$C_{15}H_{14}O_2$ Ref. 1084

Die razemische α-(5-Acenaphthyl)-propionsäure teilten wir in optische Antipoden durch fraktionierte Kristallisation des Cinchonidinsalzes aus feuchtem Aceton. Cinchonidin bildete ein mit linksdrehender Säure schwerer lösliches Salz. Das optisch reine Alkaloidsalz der linksdrehenden Form stellte dar gut ausgebildete Nadeln mit Drehungsvermögen $[\alpha]_D^{20} = -112°$ in 96%-igem Äthanol ($c = 0{,}4$, $d = 2$, $\alpha = -0{,}09)°$, Schmp. 142° (bei 132° erweicht die Substanz). Die aus Cinchonidinsalz ausgeschiedene freie linksdrehende Säure zeigte nach dem Kristallisieren aus Äthanol (Blättchen, Schmp. 96°) ein Drehungsvermögen $[\alpha]_D^{20} = -125°$ in 96%-igem Äthanol ($c = 0{,}4$, $d = 2$, $\alpha = -1°$). Aus den Mutterlaugen, die wir nach Ausscheiden des Cinchonidinsalzes der linksdrehenden Form erhalten hatten, sonderten wir die rechtsdrehende Form ab, nach der in einer früheren Arbeit beschriebenen Methode [2].

Die rechtsdrehende α-(5-Acenaphthyl)-propionsäure kristallisierte aus Äthanol in Form von rechteckigen Plättchen, Schmp. 96—97°, Drehungsvermögen $[\alpha]_D^{20} = +118{,}7°$ in 96%-igem Äthanol ($c = 0{,}4$, $d = 2$, $\alpha = +0{,}95°$).

2. Janczewski M., Podkościelny W., *Roczniki Chem.*, **33**, **605** (**1959**).

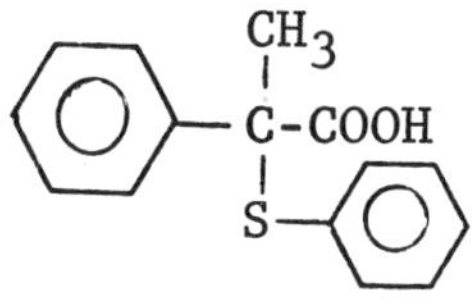

$C_{15}H_{14}O_2S$ Ref. 1085

Resolution of 2-Phenyl-2-phenylmercaptopropionic Acid.—The acid (25.8 g.) in ethanol (35 ml.) was treated with a solution of (+)-1-phenylethylamine[15] (12.1 g.) in ethanol (35 ml.). The mixture was boiled, treated with hot water (70 ml.), and the salt allowed to crystallize at 0°, filtered, dried and weighed (33.5 g.). The salt was then repeatedly recrystallized by dissolving in hot alcohol and adding one-third its volume of hot water. The quantity of this solvent used in each recrystallization was 4.2 ml. per gram of salt. Crystallization was allowed to proceed at room temperature. The specific rotation of the dried salt was determined after each recrystallization. After eight recrystallizations 4.7 g. of (+)-1-phenylethylammonium (+)-2-phenyl-2-phenylmercaptopropionate resulted as long needles, m.p. 154–155°, $[\alpha]^{25}D$ 196.2° (*c* 0.621, ethanol).

Anal. Calcd. for $C_{23}H_{25}O_2NS$: C, 72.90; H, 6.66. Found: C, 72.38, 72.42; H, 6.53, 6.60.

These were treated with dilute (1:3) hydrochloric acid, and the mixture shaken with ether until the solid was dissolved. The ether extract was washed with water, dried and evaporated to produce 3.15 g. of the dextro acid which crystallized spontaneously. It was recrystallized from benzene (1.5 ml.) to which hot ligroin (10 ml.) had been added, giving 2.30 g. of (+)-2-phenyl-2-phenylmercaptopropionic acid, m.p. 88°, $[\alpha]^{30}D$ 162.0° (*c* 1.92 ethanol).

Anal. Calcd. for $C_{15}H_{14}O_2S$: C, 69.79; H, 5.46; S, 12.43. Found: C, 69.81, 69.93; H, 5.43, 5.49; S, 12.19, 12.29.

The mother liquors from the above resolution were acidified with concentrated hydrochloric acid, extracted twice with benzene, and the organic acid (21.1 g.) is isolated as before. The total acid recovery was 96%.

The recovered acid (21.1 g.) was dissolved in ethanol (29 ml.) and treated with a solution of (−)-1-phenylethylamine[14] (10.1 g.) in ethanol (29 ml.). Hot water (80 ml.) was added, and the salt collected as before. Seven recrystallizations of this salt in the manner previously described led to pure (−)-1-phenylethylammonium (−)-2-phenyl-2-phenylmercaptopropionate, 6.3 g., m. p. 154–155°, $[\alpha]^{25}D$ −204.3° (*c* 0.881 ethanol).

Anal. Calcd. for $C_{23}H_{25}O_2NS$: C, 72.90; H, 6.66. Found: C, 72.82, 72.93; H, 6.65, 6.78.

This was decomposed with hydrochloric acid in the previously described manner to produce 3.2 g. of pure (−)-2-phenyl-2-phenylmercaptopropionic acid, m.p. 87.5–88°, $[\alpha]^{26}D$ −165.3° (*c* 1.903, ethanol).

Anal. Calcd. for $C_{15}H_{14}O_2S$: C, 69.79; H, 5.46; S, 12.43. Found: C, 69.67, 69.78; H, 5.51, 5.59; S, 12.22.

(15) A. W. Ingersoll, "Organic Syntheses," Coll. Vol. II, John Wiley and Sons, Inc., New York, N. Y., 1943, p. 506.

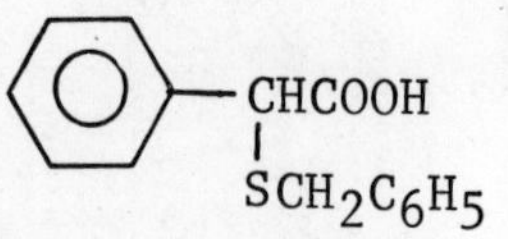

$C_{15}H_{14}O_2S$ Ref. 1086

Resolution of α-Benzylmercaptophenylacetic Acid.—The above crude acid (33.54 g) was dissolved in hot ethanol (100 ml) and treated with (−)-α-phenylethylamine (15.76 g). After 2 hr, 24.37 g of salt crystallized, $[\alpha]^{25}D$ + 59° (*c* 1.43, EtOH). This material was recrystallized from hot ethanol (75 ml), cooling slowly for 1.5 hr, to yield 17.48 g of salt, $[\alpha]^{25}D$ +111° (*c* 1.32, EtOH). Another recrystallization from ethanol (80 ml) afforded 13.30 g, $[\alpha]^{25}D$ +136° (*c* 1.47, EtOH). Two additional recrystallizations produced what appeared to be optically pure (−)-α-phenylethylammonium (+)-α-benzylmercaptophenylacetate, long needles, 9.76 g, mp 156.5–157.5°, $[\alpha]^{25}D$ +144° (*c* 1.88, EtOH).

Anal. Calcd for $C_{23}H_{25}NO_2S$: C, 72.78; H, 6.64. Found: C, 72.57; H, 6.58.

The above pure salt (9.40 g) was decomposed with dilute sulfuric acid, followed by extraction with ether. Customary processing afforded 6.47 g (101%) of thick colorless oil which crystallized on standing, $[\alpha]^{25}D$ +161° (*c* 0.97, EtOH). The product was recrystallized from a mixture of benzene (12 ml) and hexane (30 ml) to yield 5.70 g of pure (*S*)(+)-α-benzylmercaptophenylacetic acid [(*S*)(+)-IIa], mp 91–91.5°, $[\alpha]^{25}D$ +161° (*c* 0.89, EtOH).

Anal. Calcd for $C_{15}H_{14}O_2S$: C, 69.74; H, 5.46; S, 12.41. Found: C, 69.77; H, 5.48; S, 12.28.

From the mother liquors the unresolved acid was recovered in a similar manner, 30.49 g (91%). A portion of this (24.02 g) was dissolved in hot ethanol (70 ml) and treated with (+)-α-phenylethylamine (11.26 g). On standing at room temperature for 4 hr, 19.02 g of salt crystallized, $[\alpha]^{25}D$ −122.5° (*c* 1.23, EtOH). Another recrystallization from ethaol (80 ml) afforded 15.90 g of salt having $[\alpha]^{25}D$ −141.8° (*c* 1.42, EtOH). A third recrystallization from ethanol yielded 13.51 g of (+)-α-phenylethylammonium (−)-α-benzylmercaptophenylacetate, mp 156–156.5°, $[\alpha]^{25}D$ −142° (*c* 1.30, EtOH).

Anal. Calcd for $C_{23}H_{25}NO_2S$: C, 72.78; H, 6.64. Found: C, 72.52; H, 6.65.

The above salt (13.05 g) was decomposed as before and the crude syrupy product (8.90 g, 100%), which quickly crystallized, was recrystallized from benzene (16 ml) and hexane (40 ml), yielding pure (*R*)(−)-α-benzylmercaptophenylacetic acid [(*R*)-(−)-IIa], mp 91.5–92°, $[\alpha]^{25}D$ −161° (*c* 1.65, EtOH).

Anal. Calcd for $C_{15}H_{14}O_2S$: C, 69.74; H, 5.46; S, 12.41. Found: C, 69.89; H, 5.34; S, 12.40.

(*S*)(+)- and (*R*)(−)-α-Benzylmercaptophenylacetamide.—The above (*S*)(+) acid was converted to its amide using thionyl chloride as described for the conversion of the above racemic acid. The crude product (92.4%) had mp 164.5–166° and was recrystallized (Norit) from a mixture of acetone and hexane. The pure product had mp 170–170.5° and $[\alpha]^{25}D$ +160° (*c* 0.78, acetone).

Anal. Calcd for $C_{15}H_{15}NOS$: C, 70.00; H, 5.87. Found: C, 69.98; H, 6.01.

In exactly the same manner, the above (*R*)(−)-α-benzylmercaptophenylacetic acid was converted into its amide, mp 169–170°, $[\alpha]^{25}D$ −156° (*c* 0.53, acetone).

Anal. Calcd for $C_{15}H_{15}NOS$: C, 70.00; H, 5.87. Found: C, 70.35; H, 6.00.

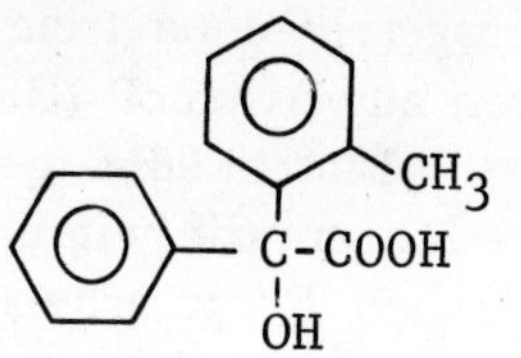

$C_{15}H_{14}O_3$ Ref. 1087

Resolution of 2-Methylbenzilic Acid.—Attempts were made to resolve the acid by the fractional crystallization of one of its alkaloidal salts. Of the several alkaloidal salts which were employed for this purpose, among them those of morphine, strychnine and brucine, the cinchonine salt was found to be the most suitable.

To a solution of 60.0 g. (0.247 mole) of 2-methylbenzilic acid in 350 ml. of hot 95% ethanol was added 73.0 g. (0.247 mole) of cinchonine. On cooling, the solution deposited 68 g. of salt,[8] $[\alpha]^{26}D$ +106° (*c* 0.63, methanol).

Seven recrystallizations from 95% ethanol gave 13.3 g. of salt, $[\alpha]^{26}D$ +117° (*c* 1.47, methanol), whose rotation remained unchanged upon further recrystallization. This salt was hydrolyzed with dilute sulfuric acid and the desired acid extracted with ether. Evaporation of the ether yielded 5.0 g. of a residue, m.p. 93–98°. Seven recrystallizations, from ligroin–ether, in which the more soluble tail fractions proved to concentrate the optically active component, yielded needle rosettes of constant m.p. 93–95°, and constant rotation $[\alpha]^{26}D$ +11.4° (*c* 6.87, ethanol).

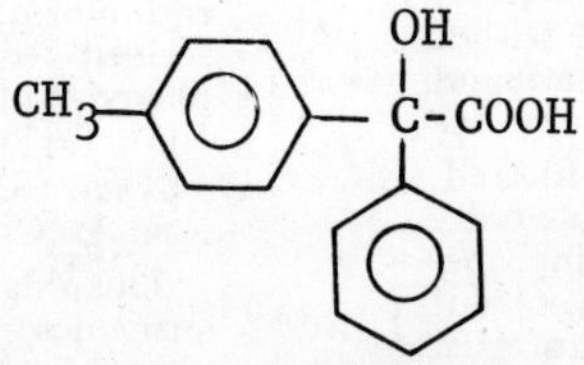

$C_{15}H_{14}O_3$ Ref. 1088

Resolution of r-*Phenyl*-p-*tolylglycollic Acid.*—Hydrated quinine (45 g.) was dissolved in a boiling solution of 34 g. of *r*-phenyl-*p*-tolylglycollic acid (McKenzie and Christie, J., 1934, 1070) in ethyl alcohol (1100 c.c.), the amount calculated for quinine trihydrate being 53 g. After 5 hours at the ordinary temperature, the bulky crystals (27 g.) were collected, and recrystallised four times from ethyl alcohol; the homogeneous quinine salt (12 g.) of the (+)acid was then obtained as rosettes of needles. The progress of the resolution was noted by decomposing the filtrates from successive crystallisations by means of dilute sulphuric acid and determining the rotatory power of the acids so obtained. The quinine salt was acidified by dilute sulphuric acid, the organic acid being then extracted with ether.

(+)*Phenyl*-p-*tolylglycollic acid* crystallised from acetone–light petroleum (b. p. 80—100°) in long prisms, m. p. 125—127° (Found: C, 74·8; H, 6·0. $C_{15}H_{14}O_3$ requires C, 74·4; H, 5·8%), whereas the *r*-acid has m. p. 133—134°. A trace gave a cherry-red coloration with concentrated sulphuric acid. In ethyl alcohol: $l = 2$, $c = 5{\cdot}2965$, $\alpha^{20°}_{5461} + 0{\cdot}26°$, $[\alpha]^{20°}_{5461} + 2{\cdot}5°$, the rotatory power being unchanged after the acid had been crystallised.

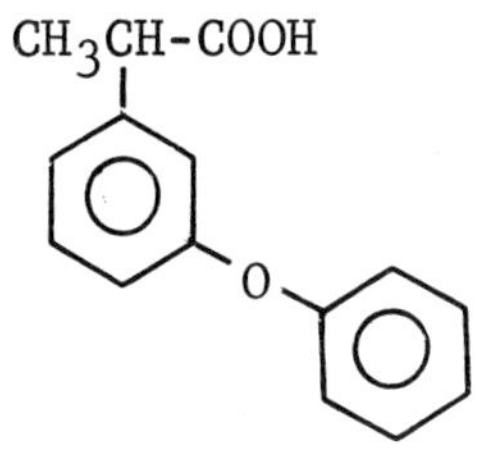

$C_{15}H_{14}O_3$ Ref. 1089

EXAMPLE 38

Resolution of α-dl-2-(3-phenoxyphenyl)propionic acid

Two hundred grams of dl-2-(3-phenoxyphenyl)propionic acid, prepared according to Example 25, were dissolved in 3000 ml. of hot ethyl acetate and 100 g of d-(+)-α-methylbenzylamine were added to the solution. A crystalline mass separated upon cooling. This was filtered to yield 229 g. of dl-2-(3-phenoxyphenyl)propionic acid, d-(+)-α-methylbenzylamine salt, M.P., 115–126° C. Five successive recrystallizations from hot ethyl acetate yielded 63.5 g. of d-(+)-2-(3-phenoxyphenyl)propionic acid, d-(+)-α-methylbenzylamine salt, M.P. 142–144° C., $[\alpha]_D^{25}$ +14.5° (C=1 percent, $CHCl_3$), $[\alpha]_D^{25}$ +3.74 (C=1 percent, CH_3OH).

Analysis.—Calc. for $C_{23}H_{25}NO_3$ (percent): C, 76.00; H, 6.93; N, 3.85. Found (percent): C, 75.72; H, 6.80; N, 3.63.

In a similar manner, l-(−)-2-(3-phenoxyphenyl)propionic acid, l-(−)-α-methylbenzylamine salt was prepared, M.P., 141–142° C., $[\alpha]_D^{25}$ −3.63 (C=1 percent, CH_3OH).

Fifty-two grams of d-(+)-2-(3-phenoxyphenyl)propionic acid, d-(+)-α-methylbenzylamine salt were suspended between 1.5 l. H_2O and 0.5 l. Et_2O and acidified by the addition of 6 N HCl. The ether layer was washed with water, dried over sodium sulfate, and evaporated in vacuo to yield d-(+)-2-(3-phenoxyphenyl)propionic acid, $[\alpha]_D^{25}$ +46.0 (C=1 percent, $CHCl_3$).

In a similar manner, l-(−)-2-(3-phenoxyphenyl)propionic acid, $[\alpha]_D^{25}$ −45.7 (C=1 percent, $CHCl_3$) was prepared from l-(−)-2-(3-phenoxyphenyl)propionic acid, l-(−)-α-methylbenzylamine salt.

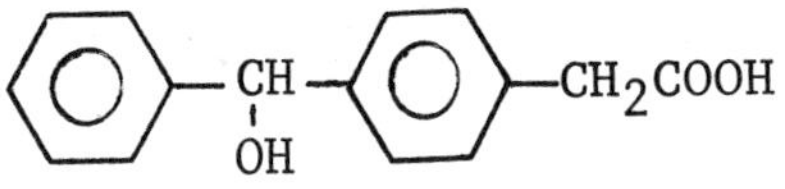

$C_{15}H_{14}O_3$ Ref. 1090

d-p-(α-**Hydroxybenzyl)-phenylacetic Acid** (**XI**).—A solution of 2.8 g. of strychnine in 70 ml. of hot dioxane was added to 2.0 g. of VII in 10 ml. of dioxane and the whole was evaporated on a steam-bath to a volume of 25 ml. Dilution with 25 ml. of water and chilling overnight yielded 0.05 g. of crystals, m.p. 119–126°. The mother liquor was concentrated to a volume of 30 ml. and, after addition of 5 ml. of water and chilling, produced an additional 0.65 g. of solid. The 0.70 g. of strychnine salts was recrystallized from 50% dioxane to yield 0.24 g. of material, m.p. 120–127°, $[\alpha]^{25}D$ −26° (methanol, *c* 0.25). Dilution of the mother liquor with another 10 ml. of water precipitated an additional 2.0 g. of salts which, after three recrystallizations, yielded 0.56 g. of strychnine salt having physical constants identical with those of the first two crops. Further dilution of the mother liquor with 25 ml. of water gave 0.34 g. of material, m.p. 112–127°, which was not subsequently employed. After combination of the first three crops, the constants were m.p. 120–127°, $[\alpha]^{25}D$ −27° (methanol, *c* 0.60). Recrystallization from 8 ml. of 50% dioxane finally yielded 0.66 g. of the pure strychnine salt (VIII) of *d-p-*(α-hydroxybenzyl)-phenylacetic acid, m.p. 120–127°, $[\alpha]^{25}D$ −27° (methanol, *c* 0.60).

Anal. Calcd. for $C_{36}H_{36}O_5N_2$: C, 74.99; H, 6.28; N, 4.86. Found: C, 74.95; H, 6.40; N, 4.99.

The strychnine salt (VIII) was treated with 10% sodium hydroxide, the mixture was filtered and the mother liquor was acidified. Recrystallization of the acid from 10 ml. of benzene gave 0.18 g. of *d-p-*(α-hydroxybenzyl)-phenylacetic acid (XI), m.p. 121.5–123°, $[\alpha]^{25}D$ +2.8° (dioxane, *c* 5.9).

Attempted Resolutions with Other Amines. *l*-α-**Phenylethylamine Salt** (**IX**).—A solution containing 3.0 g. of VII and 1.6 g. of *l*-α-phenylethylamine in 180 ml. of ethyl acetate slowly deposited 3.8 g. of IX, the *l*-α-phenylethylamine salt of VII. Recrystallization from ethyl acetate, butanone or isopropyl alcohol failed to alter the physical constants of IX, m.p. 140–142°, $[\alpha]^{25}D$ −5.9° (ethanol, *c* 5).

Anal. Calcd. for $C_{23}H_{25}O_3N$: C, 76.01; H, 6.93; N, 3.85. Found: C, 76.24; H, 7.27; N, 3.74.

When IX was treated with alkali, VII was recovered unchanged.

Quinine Salt (**X**).—Upon cooling a solution of 1.0 g. of VII and 1.3 g. of quinine in 40 ml. of ethanol, 1.9 g. of X, the quinine salt of VII, crystallized. Three recrystallizations from ethanol failed to change the physical constants, m.p. 204–206°, $[\alpha]^{25}D$ −114 (methanol, *c* 0.4).

Anal. Calcd. for $C_{35}H_{38}O_5N_2$: C, 74.18; H, 6.76; N, 4.94. Found: C, 74.71; H, 7.06; N, 5.18.

When X was treated with alkali, VII was recovered unchanged.

Attempts to prepare salts of VII with brucine, D-desoxyephedrine, quinidine and cinchonine produced only oils which could not be crystallized.

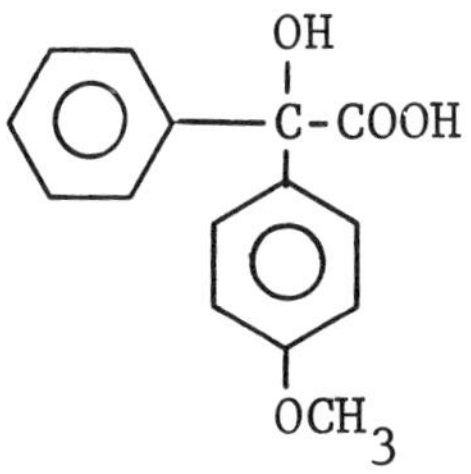

$C_{15}H_{14}O_4$ Ref. 1091

(+)-4-*Methoxybenzilic Acid.*—A solution of the (±)-acid (79 g.) and cinchonine (90 g.) in hot acetone (300 c.c.) after 2 hr. had deposited the cinchonine salt (100 g.) in compact cubes, m. p. 105—106°. The acid liberated from this salt showed no optical rotation in 5% solution in dioxan, ethanol, or pyridine, but the amount of salt which separated, and its great decrease in solubility in acetone, indicated that resolution was taking place. Accordingly the salt was recrystallised eight times from ethanol; it was then optically pure: cubes, m. p. 93—95°, unchanged by further recrystallisation. By decomposition with dilute hydrochloric acid it yielded (+)-4-methoxybenzilic acid (16 g.; m. p. 147·5—149°) which separated from benzene as needles, m. p. 148—149°, $[\alpha]_D^{19}$ +1·2°, $[\alpha]_{5461}^{19}$ +1·7° (*l* 2; *c* 5·76 in dioxan). These low rotatory

powers were not raised when dioxan was replaced by ethanol or pyridine.

(−)-4-*Methoxybenzilic Acid.*—The cinchonine salt from the first mother-liquor yielded 4-methoxybenzilic acid (33 g.), m. p. 147—148°, $[\alpha]_{5461} \not> 0{\cdot}02°$ (in dioxan). A solution of this acid (1·8 g.) and brucine (2·75 g.) in acetone (6 c.c.) rapidly deposited the brucine salt, needles (3·4 g.), m. p. 195—198°. Decomposition of this salt with hydrochloric acid–acetone yielded (−)-4-methoxybenzilic acid (1·2 g.) which by recrystallisation from benzene was obtained optically pure, as the less soluble fraction, m. p. 147—148°, $[\alpha]_D^{18}$ −1·2°, $[\alpha]_{5461}^{18}$ −1·35° (*l* 2; *c* 2·52 in dioxan).

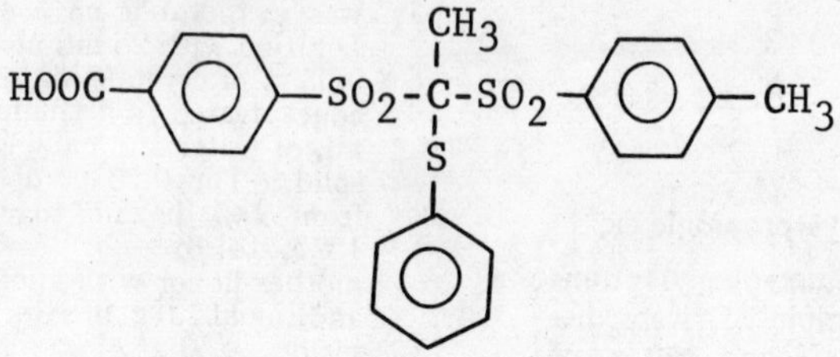

$C_{15}H_{14}O_4S_2$

Ref. 1092

dl-α-p-*Carboxyphenylsulphonyl-α-phenylthioethane* (XII) crystallised from acetic acid in prisms, m. p. 167—168° (Found: C, 55·6; H, 4·5. $C_{15}H_{14}O_4S_2$ requires C, 55·8; H, 4·35%). The methyl ester, prepared by the hydrogen chloride method, crystallised from methyl alcohol in prisms, m. p. 72°. No sodium salt of this ester could be obtained. The ester was dissolved in methyl alcohol containing sodium methoxide (1 equiv.), and ether was added: on standing over-night, the sodium salt of the acid was isolated.

Resolution of dl-α-p-*Carboxyphenylsulphonyl-α-phenylthioethane.*—The *quinine* salt of the acid was first obtained crystalline from a mixture of absolute alcohol and petroleum (b. p. 60—80°) and was afterwards fractionated from alcohol, from which it separated in needles. The acid (33 g.) and quinine (33 g.) in alcohol (200 c.c.) deposited 40 g. of the quinine salt, m. p. 122—126°. $[\alpha]_{5461}$—128° in chloroform (*c* = 1). After six crystallisations from alcohol, 20 g. of product were obtained, m. p. 136—138°. $[\alpha]_{5461}$—97° in chloroform (*c* = 1·06). These values were unchanged by further crystallisation and refer to specimens dried at 80° in a vacuum [Found: H_2O, 2·4, 2·9. $C_{15}H_{14}O_4S_2,C_{20}H_{24}O_2N_2,H_2O$ requires H_2O, 2·7%. Found: N (after drying at 80°), 4·4. Required, 4·3%]. The *d*-acid was obtained from the final fraction by dissolving the salt in acetic acid and adding water. It had m. p. 164—165° (Found: C, 56·0; H, 4·7%), $[\alpha]_{5780}$ + 113°, $[\alpha]_{5461}$ + 134° in chloroform (*c* = 0·75).

The acid recovered from the initial mother-liquors was dissolved in alcohol, and 1 equiv. of *l*-menthylamine hydrochloride and sodium hydroxide added successively. A menthylamine salt was precipitated which, after crystallisation from alcohol, was finally obtained in fine needles, m. p. 182—183°, $[\alpha]_{5461}$ − 95° in chloroform (*c* = 0·5). The acid from this had $[\alpha]_{5461}$ − 134° in chloroform.

The following weights of acid were dissolved in 5 c.c. of alcohol, the specified quantity of sodium hydroxide (*N*/10-solution) added, and the solution made up to 20 c.c. with water and examined at once in a 2 dcm. polarimeter tube. The values of [α] are calculated on the weight of acid taken.

Wt. of acid, g.	Equivs. of sodium hydroxide.	$[\alpha]_{5461}$.	Approximate time from addition of alkali.
0·1177	0·99	+123°	2 mins. and 12 hrs.
0·1032	0·997	+120	" " "
0·1612	1·035	+100	1·5 mins.
		+ 80	13 mins.
		+ 27	86 mins.
		0	18 hrs.
0·2450	1·39	+ 20	1 min.
		+ 10	2 mins.
		0	3 mins.

The acid was stable in pyridine solution, showing $[\alpha]_{5461}$ + 122·5°.

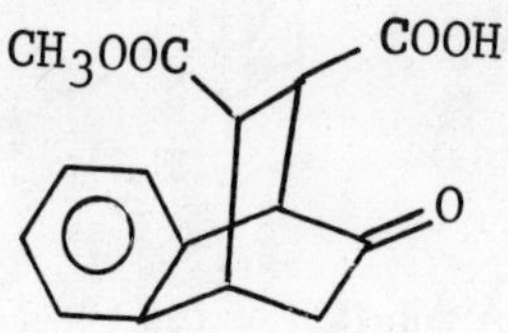

$C_{15}H_{14}O_5$

Ref. 1093

Resolution of XVb *and preparation of* (+)-XVa. A soln of XVb (10·045 g) and cinchonidine (5·412 g, 0·5 molar equiv) in abs MeOH (200 ml) was refluxed for 1 hr. After evaporation, the crystalline residue was recrystallized several times from acetone and then from $CHCl_3$-ether. Finally, recrystallization from MeOH was repeated until the $[\alpha]_D$ became constant; needles (0·682 g), m.p. 208–209° (dec), $[\alpha]_D^{24.5}$ + 50·3° (±0·7) (EtOH, *c* = 1·067). (Found: C, 71·55; H, 6·50; N, 5·04. Calc. for $C_{34}H_{36}N_2O_6$: C, 71·81; H, 6·38; N, 4·93%). The pure salt (370 mg) in CH_2Cl_2 (15 ml) was shaken with cold 5% $NaHCO_3$aq, and aqueous

layer was washed with ether, acidified with 5% H_2SO_4 and extracted with ether. Evaporation of the ether gave an oil (159 mg, active XVb). The dimethyl ester obtained by methylation of the active XVa was also an oily substance and purified by preparative TLC to give (+)-XVa. The IR in CCl_4 was identical with that of racemic XVa; $[\alpha]_D^{24}$ +208·1° (±4·6) (MeOH, c = 0·571). (Found: C, 66·49; H, 5·82. Calc. for $C_{16}H_{16}O_5$: C, 66·66; H, 5·59%).

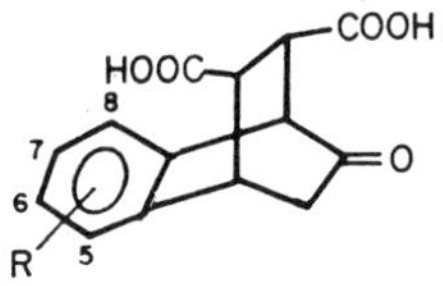

VIII a : 8-OMe
b : 7-OMe
d : 5-OMe

$C_{15}H_{14}O_6$ Ref. 1094

Optical resolution of trans-*diacid* VIIIa, b, d, IX c, e, *and* XVb *with cinchonidine*

General procedure. A soln of *trans*-diacid (0·5 g) and cinchonidine (0·5 g) in EtOH (15 ml) was heated under reflux for 1 hr. The soln was evaporated and the residue was dissolved in AcOEt. After standing overnight the precipitated salt was recrystallized from MeOH until the optical rotation ($[\alpha]_D$) of the salt became constant. The purified salt (molecular ratio, 1:1, as shown by elemental analyses) was suspended in ether and decomposed by shaking with dil HCl. The free active acid was purified by recrystallization.

M.ps and solvents for recrystallization of the active acids were as follows: (+)-VIIIa·1/2H_2O, 168–169° (MeOH-H_2O); (+)-IXc·1/2H_2O, 112–114° (MeOH-H_2O); (+)-VIIId, 230–231° (AcOEt-$CHCl_3$); (+)-IXe, 166–167·5° (AcOEt-C_6H_6); (−)-IXe, 166–167·5° (AcOEt-C_6H_6). Satisfactory elemental analyses were obtained for these active acids. Attempted crystallizations of the active acid VIIIb and its dimethyl ester were unsuccessful. However, when the diacid was chromatographed on silica gel (Merck, 0·2–0·5 mm) and developed with MeOH-AcOEt (1:19), crystals of the Na salt-dihydrate were accidentally obtained: IR ν_{max}^{KBr} (cm^{-1}) 3390, 1720, 1615, 1575. (Found: C, 48·37; H, 4·36. Calc. for $C_{15}H_{12}Na_2O_6 \cdot 2H_2O$: C, 48·65; H, 4·62%); $[\alpha]_D$ of the pure salts and active acids thus obtained are shown in Table 3.

TABLE 3. OPTICAL ROTATION OF CINCHONIDINE SALTS OF TRANS-ACIDS

	$[\alpha]_D$ (MeOH) Salt	Free compd.
E* XVIII		+ 356·2[d]
XVa	+ 50·3[b]	+ 208·1[c]
VIIId	+ 31·0	+ 209·5
IXc	+ 44·6	+ 249·8
IXe	+ 52·0 (− 176·0)†	+ 192·3 (− 193·3)†
VIIIb	+ 24·5	+ 152·7[a]
IXa	+ 19·1	+ 207·0

[a] sodium salt [b] in EtOH

[c] methyl ester [d] in $CHCl_3$ [e] in *iso*-octane

* The letter E is used to indicate "enantiomer of."
† The value for (−)-IXe.

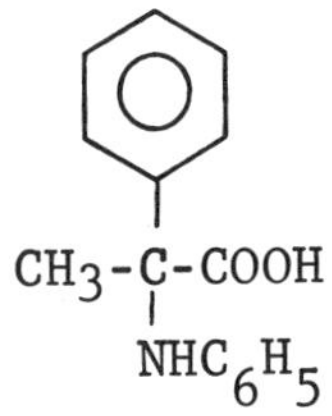

Ref. 1095

$C_{15}H_{15}NO_2$

R(−)-*2-Anilino-2-phenyl-propionsäure* (R(−)-II)[5]. 3,37 g (14,0 mMol) RS-II in 35 ml Methanol wurden mit 5,04 g (14,0 mMol) Chinin in 35 ml Methanol versetzt; nach Kristallisationsbeginn wurden noch 35 ml Methanol zugegeben. Nach 30 Min. Stehen bei 0° wurde das Chininsalz abfiltriert und dreimal aus Methanol umkristallisiert: 1,69 g (40%) vom Smp. 210–211° (Zers.): $[\alpha]_D^{28}$ = −127° ± 1° (c = 1,00 in $CHCl_3$). Lit. [9]: Smp. 200°; $[\alpha]_D^{6}$ = −89,0 (c = 1,07 in $CHCl_3$).

$C_{35}H_{39}N_3O_4$ (565,7) Ber. C 74,04 H 6,95 N 7,61% Gef. C 74,31 H 6,95 N 7,43%

Das Chininsalz wurde durch Verteilen zwischen 1N NaOH und Äther zersetzt und die wässerige Phase angesäuert und mit Benzol extrahiert. Die Benzollösung wurde eingeengt und mit Petroläther versetzt: 0,46 g (67%) R(−)-II vom Smp. 146–147°; $[\alpha]_D^{28}$ = −29,0° ± 2,0° (c = 0,50 in $CHCl_3$). Lit. [9]: Smp. 147–148°; $[\alpha]_D^{8}$ = 50,0° (c = 5,0 in 99-proz. Alkohol). $[\alpha]_{650}$ = −21°; $[\alpha]_{600}$ = −26°; $[\alpha]_{550}$ = −32°; $[\alpha]_{500}$ = −42°; $[\alpha]_{400}$ = −85°; $[\alpha]_{324}$ = −157°; $[\alpha]_{306}$ = −100°;

[5]) Versuch von *R. Mauli*.

[9] *S. Mitsui & E. Sato*, Nippon Kagaku Zasshi *86*, 416 (1965) [Chem. Abstr. *63*, 8149 (1965)].

$[\alpha]_{300} = -500°$; $[\alpha]_{260-240} = -3000°$; $[\alpha]_{230} = 0°$; $[\alpha]_{220} = +4500°$ ($c = 0,9$ in Methanol bei 25°). IR.-Spektrum: identisch mit *RS*-II. UV.-Spektrum: Maxima bei 293,5 und 247,6 nm. NMR.-Spektrum (CF_3COOH): 2,21 ppm, Singulett, 3 H (CH_3); 6,8-8,0 ppm, Multiplet, 11 H (2 Phenyl + NH).

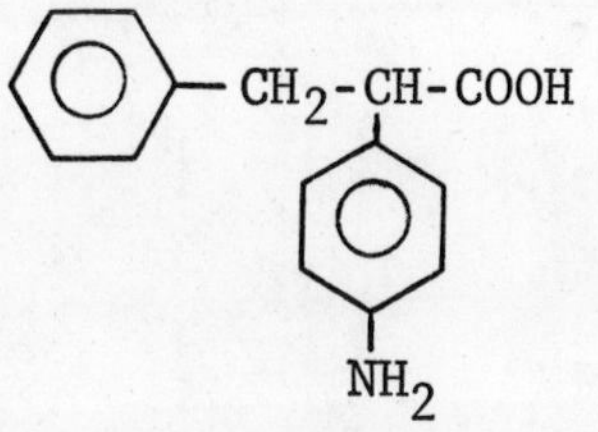

$C_{15}H_{15}NO_2$ Ref. 1096

Resolution of *dl*-α-(4-Aminophenyl)-β-phenylpropionic Acid.—A solution of 240 g. of the *dl*-amino acid and 160 g. of *d*-desoxyephedrine in 2500 ml. of ethyl acetate was allowed to stand at 25° for one hour. The crystals were filtered and recrystallized from ethyl acetate. In this way 129 g. of a pure diastereomeric salt, m. p. 148–150°, was secured. A 120-g. sample was dissolved in 2500 ml. of boiling water and slowly acidified with 50 ml. of acetic acid. On cooling, 70 g. of pure *d*-α-(4-aminophenyl)-β-phenylpropionic acid deposited. The acid melted at 186–188°; $[\alpha]^{25}D$ (5% in H_2O) +102°.

Anal. Calcd. for $C_{15}H_{15}NO_2$: neutral equivalent, 241.1. Found: neutral equivalent, 240.2.

The ethyl acetate filtrate from the original crystallization was concentrated to dryness *in vacuo*. The residue was dissolved in water and made strongly basic. The desoxyephedrine was gathered with ether. In this way 100 g. of the resolving agent was recovered. The aqueous solution was acidified and the crude *l*-amino acid was filtered off.

The product was dissolved in 1600 ml. of boiling ethyl acetate and 104 g. of *l*-desoxyephedrine added. On cooling a salt separated which was recrystallized from the same solvent. It weighed 115 g. and melted at 148–150°. Thirty three grams of this salt was converted to 19 g. of the *l*-amino acid, which melted at 186–188°, $[\alpha]^{25}D$ (5% in water) −103°.

Anal. Calcd. for $C_{15}H_{15}NO_2$: neutral equivalent, 241.1. Found: neutral equivalent, 239.5.

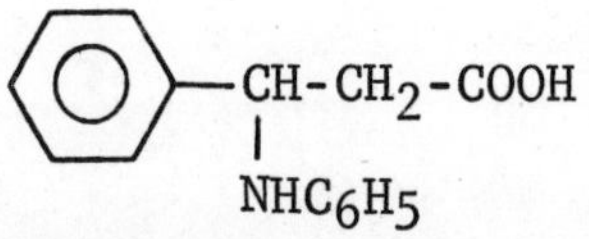

$C_{15}H_{15}NO_2$ Ref. 1097

Preparation of the Quinine Salt of β-Anilinohydrocinnamic Acid and Its Subsequent Resolution.

To a slurry of 400 g. of quinine sulfate and 3 liters of chloroform in a 5 l. separatory funnel was added a solution of 52 g. of sodium hydroxide in 1.5 liters of water. After shaking, the water layer was separated and discarded. The remaining chloroform solution of quinine was washed with three 1-liter portions of water. The chloroform solution was evaporated to dryness in vacuo and the quinine thus obtained was dissolved in 1400 ml. of hot absolute ethanol. To the alcoholic solution was added 235 g. of β-anilinohydrocinnamic acid and the mixture was heated to effect solution. The solution was cooled to room temperature and was allowed to stand for 12 hours. The salt obtained was recrystallized from absolute ethanol until a constant rotation of the salt was obtained with a yield of 246 g., $[\alpha]^{27.5°}_D = -188°$ (c. 1.0, 5% HCl). The original mother liquor was diluted with an equal volume of water and the salt was allowed to crystallize at room temperature. This one crystallization from the diluted mother liquor yielded 246 g. of product which showed no additional change in rotation on further recrystallization $[\alpha]^{25°}_D = -88°$ (c. 1.0, 5% HCl). A total yield of 492 g. of the separated diastereoisomers was obtained which corresponds to 87% of the salt originally present. In addition, 67 g. of unresolved salt corresponding to 12% of the original salt was recovered.

Recovery of the Resolved β-Anilinohydrocinnamic Acid From Its Quinine Salt.

In 2 liters of chloroform was dissolved 243 g. of the quinine salt of β-anilinohydrocinnamic acid, $[\alpha]^{25°}_D = -88°$ (c. 1.0, 5% HCl). The chloroform solution was extracted with 700 ml. of water containing 340 ml. of concentrated ammonium hydroxide solution*. The alkaline layer was separated and the chloroform layer was further extracted three times with 350 ml. portions of 5% ammonium hydroxide solution. The combined ammonium hydroxide solutions were extracted with 800 ml. of ether. The ammonium hydroxide layer was concentrated in vacuo to three-fourths of its original volume, filtered and the filtrate was acidified with concentrated hydrochloric acid to maimum turbidity.

The β-anilinohydrocinnamic acid which separated was extracted with 400 ml. of ether. The pH of the water layer was alternately adjusted with 5% hydrochloric acid solution or 5% ammonium hydroxide solution to maximum turbidity and re-extracted with 100 ml. portions of ether. This procedure was repeated until all of the β-anilinohydrocinnamic acid was removed. The combined ether extracts were dried over anhydrous magnesium sulfate. The magnesium sulfate was removed by filtration and washed with dry ether. The ether solutions were combined and concentrated to a volume of about 400 ml. and dry Skelly Solve A was added to incipient turbidity. Successive crops yielded 82 g. (91% of theory) of d-β-anilinohydrocinnamic acid, $[\alpha]^{22.5°}_D = +110°$ (c. 1.0, 5% HCl). Recrystallization of a small amount of this enantiomorph from a mixture of benzene and Skelly Solve C yielded crystals having a melting point of 105-6° and $[\alpha]^{24°}_D = +111°$ (c. 0.8, 5% HCl).

The same procedure was used to recover the other enantiomorph, $[\alpha]^{25°}_D = -188°$ (c. 0.8, 5% HCl). Recrystallization of this enantiomorph from a mixture of benzene and Skelly Solve C yields crystals of m.p. 103-105°, $[\alpha]^{25°}_D = -109°$ (c. 8, 5% HCl).

*The use of sodium hydroxide solution in place of ammonium hydroxide solution resulted in a yellow-oily product which is difficult to recrystallize.

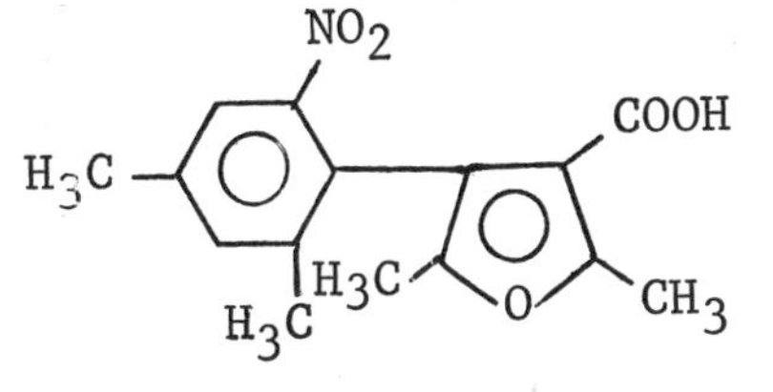

$C_{15}H_{15}O_5$ Ref. 1098

Resolution of 3-(2,4-Dimethyl-6-nitrophenyl)-2,5-dimethyl-4-furoic Acid.—The above acid (2.65 g.) was dissolved in 1 l. of boiling 45% ethanol, 3.30 g. of quinine was added and the solution filtered. After the addition of a few pieces of ice, the solution was left in the ice-box for several days. A first crop of 2.75 g. of a salt (IIa), m.p. 114–115°, was collected. The solution was evaporated to 750 ml. and left in the ice-box for three days when 2.10 g. of salt IIb, m.p. 112–114°, was collected. Salt IIa had $[\alpha]^{25}D$ 52.6° (*c* 0.1705 g. in 10 ml. of $CHCl_3$). Salt IIb, had $[\alpha]^{25}D$ −53.5° (*c* 0.1710 g. in 10 ml. of $CHCl_3$).

The salts were recrystallized from ethanol and dried over P_2O_5 at 70° for 24 hours.

Anal. Salt IIa. Calcd. for $C_{35}H_{39}O_7N_3 \cdot H_2O$: C, 66.56; H, 6.4. Found: C, 66.70; H, 6.24. Salt IIb. Found: C, 66.54; H, 6.02.

After decomposition of the salts in the usual manner, the acid from salt IIa had $[\alpha]^{25}D$ −33.6° (*c* 0.1540 g. in 10 ml. of $CHCl_3$) and melted at 206–208° with softening at 205° and the acid from salt IIb had $[\alpha]^{25}D$ +26.2° (0.1378 g. in 10 ml. of $CHCl_3$) and melted at 203–206° with softening at 198°. The chloroform solution of the acid did not change in rotation on standing one week at room temperature. Attempts to recrystallize the acid from hot ethanol caused complete loss of activity.

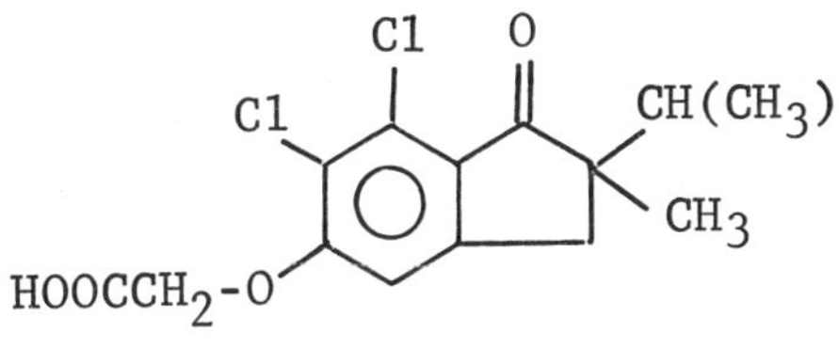

$C_{15}H_{16}Cl_2O_3$ Ref. 1099

The racemic acid was resolved via cinchonine in CH_3CN. The reported $[\alpha]^{25}_D$ for the active acid was +48.4° (c 3, acetone).

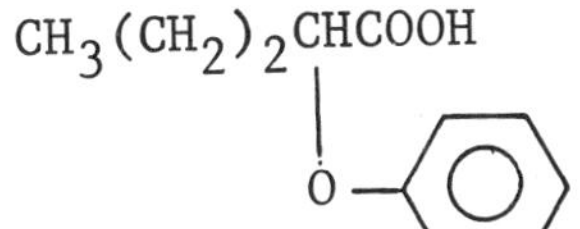

$C_{15}H_{16}O_3$ Ref. 1100

(+)- *and* (−)-*α-(2-naphthoxy)-n-valeric acids.*—Preliminary experiments on resolution were carried out with 9 optically active bases. Of these only brucine and β-phenyl*iso*propylamine gave good resolution. Due to accidental lack of the (−)-form of the latter base brucine was first tried. The first recrystallization from 30% ethanol gave a salt from which an acid with $[\alpha]_D$ = +25° (in ethanol) could be isolated. On further recrystallizations this value did not change. The rotatory power of the pure (+)-acid is +73.6° (in ethanol) and the salt should thus contain about 67% of the (+)-acid and 33% of the (−)-acid. A possible explanation is thus that the (+)-acid-brucine salt forms a molecular compound with the (−)-acid-brucine salt in the relation 2 : 1. Another explanation is that the salts are isomorphic, forming a phase system with a maximum at about 67% in which case the relation 2 : 1 between (+)- and (−)-acid is a mere chance.

The acid regenerated from the brucine salt (10.9 g) and an equivalent quantity of (−)-β-phenyl*iso*propylamine (6.0 g) were dissolved in 360 ml of hot 70% ethanol. After crystallization the salt was collected and recrystallized several times from 70–80 % ethanol. The rotatory power of the acids isolated from the salt fractions were: +66.4°, +72.2°, +74.7° and +74.2°. From the last fraction 4.6 g of the crude (+)-acid were collected, m.p. 140–141.2°. It was recrystallized from petroleum (b.p. 60–80°). It forms colourless, thread-like crystals with m.p. 140.8–141.7°.

62.90 g (+)-acid: 5.59_5 ml 0.0464-*N* NaOH
$C_{15}H_{16}O_3$ calc. equiv. wt. 244.3
found ,, ,, 242.2

0.1998 g dissolved in *ethanol* to 20.06 ml: $2\alpha^{25}_D$ = +1.467°. $[\alpha]^{25}_D$ = +73.6°; $[M]^{25}_D$ = +179.9°.
0.1966 g dissolved in *acetone* to 20.06 ml: $2\alpha^{25}_D$ = +1.748°. $[\alpha]^{25}_D$ = +89.2°; $[M]^{25}_D$ = +217.8°.
0.2117 g dissolved in *benzene* to 20.06 ml: $2\alpha^{25}_D$ = +1.650°. $[\alpha]^{25}_D$ = +78.2°; $[M]^{25}_D$ = +191.0°.
0.1939 g dissolved in *chloroform* to 20.06 ml: $2\alpha^{25}_D$ = +0.954°. $[\alpha]^{25}_D$ = +49.3°; $[M]^{25}_D$ = +120.6°.
0.1972 g neutralized with *aqueous NaOH* and made up to 20.06 ml: $2\alpha^{25}_D$ = +1.048°. $[\alpha]^{25}_D$ = +53.3°; $[M]^{25}_D$ = +130.2°.

The acid from the first three mother liquours was dissolved with an equimolecular quantity of (+)-β-phenyl*iso*propylamine in hot 75 % ethanol. The salt which separated on standing was recrystallized several times from 75 % ethanol. The optical activity of the acid (in alcohol) increased in the following series: −65.3°, −71.9°, −72.5°, −72.5° and −72.6°. 7.05 g of the pure (−)-acid-(+)-amine salt yielded 4.65 g (−)-acid. Recrystallization from 50 % ethanol yielded 4.1 g of the pure (−)-acid, m.p. 140.8–141.8°.

68.40 mg (−)-acid: 6.01_5 ml 0.0464-*N* NaOH
$C_{15}H_{16}O_3$ calc. equiv. wt. 244.3
found ,, ,, 245.0

0.2110 g dissolved in abs. *ethanol* to 20.06 ml: $2\alpha^{25}_D$ = −1.541°. $[\alpha]^{25}_D$ = −73.3°. $[M]^{25}_D$ = −178.9°.

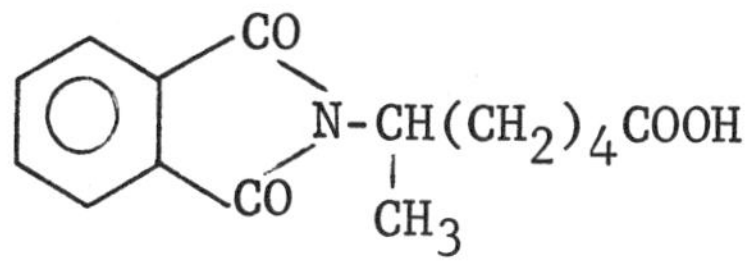

$C_{15}H_{17}NO_4$ Ref. 1101

(−)-6-Phthalimido-6-methylhexanoic Acid (XXII)

Racemic 6-phthalimido-6-methylhexanoic acid (XX), 103 g. (0.374 mole), were dissolved in 5 liters of ethyl acetate, and to this solution was added 121.6 g. (0.374 mole) of quinine. Before the quinine salt would crystallize from solution, it was necessary to reduce the volume of the solution to 2 liters and cool it to 0°. The yield was 141.3 g. (63%); m.p., 111 to 114°. Thirty recrystallizations from ethyl acetate gave 28.3 g. (25.2%) of the resolved diastereoisomer; m.p., 117 to 119°.

This quinine salt, 28.0 g. (0.047 mole), was dissolved in 350 ml. of hot benzene and shaken with 300 ml. of 12% aqueous hydrochloric acid in a separatory funnel. The aqueous layer was separated and twice extracted with 100 ml. portions of benzene. The combined benzene extracts were evaporated to dryness, and the residue was dissolved in 100 ml. of hot benzene and filtered. Addition of a large excess of hexane (b.p., 66 to 69°) to the filtered solution yielded a white, flocculant precipitate of (−)-6-phthalimido-6-methylhexanoic acid. The yield was 11.85 g. (93%); m.p., 78 to 80°; $[\alpha]^{25}_D$ = −18.91° (c 4.50, chloroform). The infrared spectrum of this isomer was essentially the same as its racemic counterpart.

(+)-6-Amino-6-methylhexanoic Acid (XXIII)

The procedure used was that of Adams and Fles[3] for the preparation of 4-amino-2-methylbutyric acid, and was the same as reported in our preparation of (+)-6-amino-2-methylhexanoic acid (VII).

From 11.85 g. (0.043 mole) of (−)-6-phthalimido-6-methylhexanoic acid (XXII) and 2.85 g. (0.057 mole) of hydrazine hydrate was obtained 4.74 g. (76%) of a white crystalline precipitate of (+)-6-amino-6-methylhexanoic acid; m.p., 206 to 207.5°; $[\alpha]^{25}_D$ = +2.03° (c 5.1, water). The infrared spectrum of this material differed from that of racemic 6-amino-6-methylhexanoic acid in the region from 1500 to 840 cm.$^{-1}$.

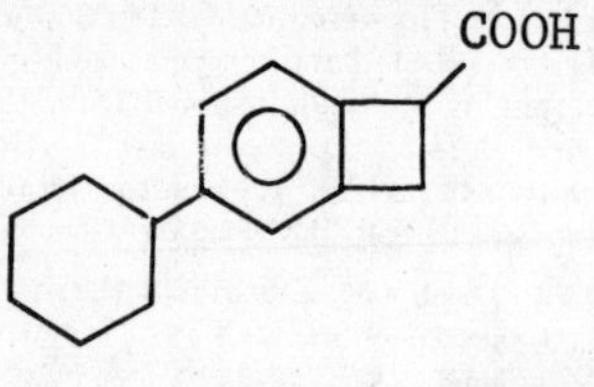

$C_{15}H_{18}O_2$

Ref. 1102

A solution of (±)-4-cyclohexylbenzocyclobutene-1-carboxylic acid (5.77 g., 0.025 mole) and cinchonidine (7.35 g., 0.025 mole) in ethanol (175 ml.) was boiled down to a volume of about 110 ml. The hot solution was allowed to stand three hours at 25°. The colorless crystalline material was collected and washed with cold ethanol to give the cinchonidine salt (7.76 g.), m.p. 193°–196° with prior softening. The salt was recrystallized twice from ethanol to give colorless crystals (4.4 g.), m.p. 199°–202°° with slight prior softening.

The combined mother liquors from the cinchonidine salt formation and the first ethanol recrystallization were saved for eventual isolation of (+)-4-cyclohexylbenzocyclobutene-1-carboxylic acid.

The cinchonidine salt (4.4 g.) was partitioned between diethyl ether (50 ml.) and 0.5 N HCl (30 ml.). The ethereal layer was washed with water (20 ml.) followed by two washings with water saturated with sodium chloride and dried (sodium sulfate). Removal of the ether left colorless crystals (1.77 g.) of (−)-4-cyclohexylbenzocyclobutene-1-carboxylic acid: m.p. 91°–93; $[\alpha]^{25}_D - 9.54°$ (c. 2.173, ethanol). The acid was recrystallized twice from n-pentane to give colorless crystals; m.p. 93°–95°; $[\alpha]^{25}_D$–9.0° (c. 2.00, ethanol).

Boiling Skellysolve B (10 ml.) was added to a boiling solution of the (−)-acid (1.19 g., 0.00516 mole) with m.p. 93°–95° and (+)-α-(1-naphthyl)ethylamine (0.884 g., 0.00516 mole) in benzene (10 ml.). The hot solution was allowed to stand at 25° for 2 hours with an occasional scratching of the inside of the beaker with a glass stirring rod. The colorless crystals (1.87 g., m.p. 158°–160°) were collected and recrystallized from acetonitrile to give the salt (1.69 g.) of (+)-α-(1-naphthyl)ethylamine with (−)-4-cyclohexylbenzocyclobutene-1-carboxylic acid, m.p. 161°–163° with slight prior softening. The salt was decomposed with hydrochloric acid and the product extracted into ether as previously described. The ether was removed and the residue (0.908 g., m.p. 101°–102°) recrystallized from n-pentane to give 0.775 g. of (−)-4-cyclohexylbenzocyclobutene-1-carboxylic acid: m.p. 101°–102°; $[\alpha]^{25}_D$ −12.2° (c. 1.54, ethanol).

Anal. calc'd. for $C_{15}H_{18}O_3$: C, 78.23; H, 7.88.
Found: C, 78.03; H, 7.97.

EXAMPLE 7

(+)-4-Cyclohexylbenzocyclobutene-1-carboxylic Acid

The mother liquors which were retained in Example 6 were reduced to dryness and the resulting mixture of salt decomposed with hydrochloric acid and the liberated acids extracted into ether. Removal of the ether left a mixture of acids (2.54 g.) enriched in the (+)-isomer.

Hot Skellysolve B (20 ml.) was added to a boiling solution of the enriched acid (2.54 g., 0.011 mole) and (−)-α-(1-naphthyl)-ethylamine (1.89 g., 0.011 mole) in benzene (19 ml.). The hot solution was allowed to stand at 25° C. for 2 hours with occasional scratching of the inside of the beaker with a glass stirring rod. The off white crystalline material was collected, washed with cold benzene-Skellysolve B and dried to give the salt (2.44 g.) of (−)-α-1-naphthyl)ethylamine with (+)-4-cyclohexylbenzocyclobutene-1-carboxylic acid, m.p. 155°–157° with slight prior softening. The salt was recrystallized from acetonitrile to give off white needles (2.28 g.), m.p. 158.5°–16.5°.

This salt (2.28 g.) was partitioned between ether (30 ml.) and 0.5 N HCl (20 ml.). The ethereal layer was washed with water followed by water saturated with sodium chloride (2X) and dried (sodium sulfate). Removal of the ether left 1.22 g. of (+)-4-cyclohexylbenzocyclobutene-1-carboxylic acid; m.p. 97°–100° C. with prior softening; $[\alpha]^{25}_D$+11.61° (c. 2.041, ethanol). The acid was recrystallized twice from n-pentane to give 0.763 g. of the product; m.p. 101.5°–102.5° C. with slight prior softening; $[\alpha]^{25}_D$ +12.6° (c. 1.39, ethanol).

Anal. calc'd. for $C_{15}H_{18}O_2$: C, 78.23; H, 7.88.
Found: C, 78.21; H, 8.00.

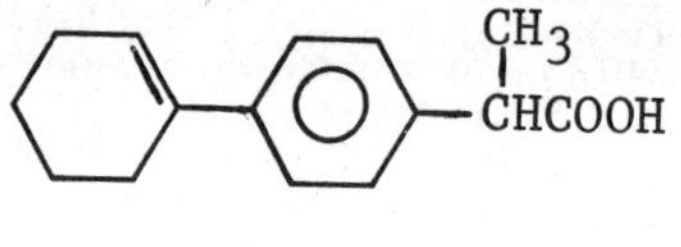

$C_{15}H_{18}O_2$

Ref. 1103

EXAMPLE 2

A hot solution of 50 g of α - [para - (1 - cyclohexenyl) - phenyl] - propionic acid in 1850 ml of ethanol is mixed with a hot solution of 63.9 g of cinchonidine in 1850 ml of ethanol. The mixture is allowed to cool slowly and after 16 hours, the crystals of the cinchonidine salt of the enriched (+) - α - [para - (1 - cyclohexenyl) - phenyl] - propionic acid that have precipitated are filtered off. Repeated fractional crystallization according to the usual scheme yields the cinchonidine salt of the dextro-rotary acid. In each case the crystals are recrystallized from a 4% ethanolic solution, while the mother liquors which contain mainly the cinchonidine salt of the levo-rotating acid are caused to crystallize by evaporation to two-thirds of their volumes. The middle fractions are separated by dissolution with the application of heat, and slow cooling.

The cinchonidine salt of the dextro-rotating acid is suspended in ether and agitated with 2N-hydrochloric acid until both phases are clear. The ethereal layer is washed with water, dried over sodium sulfate, and evaporated to obtain (+) - α - [para - (1 - cyclohexenyl) - phenyl] - propionic acid melting at 101—102°C; $[\alpha]_D^{20}$=+53°C. (ethanol, c=1).

In an analogous manner the dextro-rotating acid can be obtained with (−) - α - phenylethylamine instead of cinchonidine.

The fractions which contain the cinchonidine salt of the levo-rotating acid are suspended in ether and agitated with 2N-hydrochloric acid until both phases are clear. The ethereal solution is washed with water, dried over sodium sulfate, and evaporated. The

residue is reacted in hot ethanol with the calculated quantity of (+) - α - phenylethylamine and the resulting salt subjected to fractional crystallization. From the pure fraction, (−) - α - [para - (1 - cyclohexenyl) - phenyl] - propionic acid melting at 101—102°C, $[\alpha]_D^{20} = -53°$, can be isolated.

By heating a 1% solution of an antipode in 2N-sodium hydroxide solution at 100°C for 16 hours, partial racemization is achieved. The optical rotation of the (−) antipode thus drops from −53° to −24°.

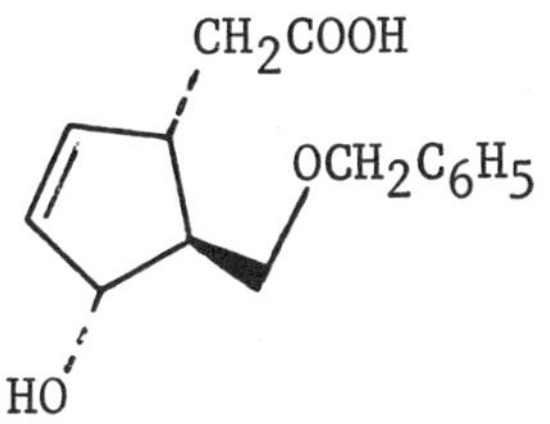

$C_{15}H_{18}O_4$ Ref. 1104

Note:

Obtained acid m.p. 112.5°-113.5° $[\alpha]_D^{25}$ = +17° (c 1.5 methanol) by recrystallizing amphetamine salt followed by liberation of acid.

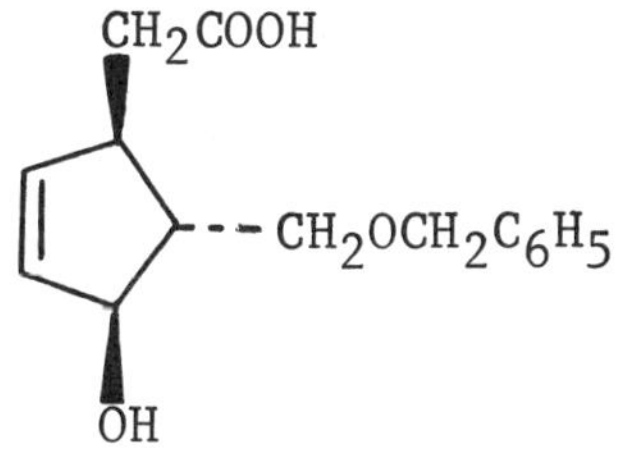

$C_{15}H_{18}O_4$ Ref. 1105

Beispiel 2

215,0 g Dehydroabietylammoniumsalz der Säure I werden einer fraktionierten Kristallisation aus Äthanol-Äther unterworfen. Dabei werden 69,0 g (64.2%) des diastereomeren Salzes von Ib, Fp.: 140-142°C, $[\alpha]_D^{23}$ = +10,4° (c = 1,5, CH_3OH) sowie 30,0 g (29,9%) des Salzes von Ia, Fp: 143-145°C, α_D^{23} = +26,9° (c = 1,5, CH_3OH) erhalten. Aus den Mischfraktionen lassen sich weitere 23,5 g (21,9%) Dehydroabietylammoniumsalz von Ib gewinnen, wodurch sich die Gesamtausbeute an diesem Diastereomeren auf 86,1% belauft. Die Mutterlaugen werden in das Amphetaminiumsalz überführt. Daraus werden weitere 37,8 g (48,4%) Amphetaminiumsalz von Ia erhalten.

Beispiel 3

Die wässrige Lösung von 80,0 g Ammoniumsalz von I wird bei 0°C mit verdünnter H_2SO_4 angesäuert (pH = 4); die freie Säure I wird durch Extraktion in Äther überführt. Die getrocknete (Na_2SO_4) Ätherlösung wird mit einer ätherischen (+)-Amphetaminlösung (aus 55,5 g (+)-Amphetaminiumsulfat) versetzt. Das ausgefallene Salz wird umkristallisiert. Die nach Abtrennung von 32,9 g (57,8%) optisch reinem Amphetaminium-Salz von Ia verbleibenden Mutterlaugen (74,9 g) werden mit einer wässrigen Lösung von 8,3 g NaOH bei 0°C gerührt. Nach Ausathern des freien Amphetamin wird die wässrige Phase auf pH = 4 gebracht. Die freie Säure wird mit Äther extrahiert, die Ätherphase wird getrocknet (Na_2SO_4) und mit 54 g Dehydroabietylamin in Ather versetzt. Aus den 93,2 g Dehydroabietylammoniumsalz, $[\alpha]_D^{23}$ = +15,3° (c = 1.5, CH_3OH) werden durch fraktionierte Kristallisation 56,8 g (72,5%) des diastereomeren Salzes von Ib gewonnen. Aus den sich ergebenden Mutterlaugen wird erneut das Amphetaminsalz von I hergestellt, durch dessen Kristallisation man weitere 15,0 g (26,3%) Amphetaminiumsalz von Ia erhält.

Beispiel 4

5,3 g Dehydroabietylammoniumsalz von Ib mit $[\alpha]_D^{23}$ = +10,4° (c = 1.5, CH_3OH) werden bei 0°C mit einer Lösung von 2,3 g Na_2CO_3 in 80 ml Wasser eine Stunde lang gerührt. Nach Extraktion mit Äther wird die Wasserphase bei 0°C mit CO_2 neutralisiert und mit einer Lösung von 6,1 g Jod und 16,0 g KJ in 60 ml Wasser versetzt und uber Nacht bei 0°C belassen. Nach Extraktion mit Äther wird die organische Phase mit einer wässrigen $Na_2S_2O_3$ x 5 H_2O-Lösung und Wasser gewaschen und mit $MgSO_4$ getrocknet. Nach Abziehen des Äthers verbleiben 3,5 g (97% d.Th.) Kristalle, die nach Umkristallisation aus Methylenchlorid/Hexan 3,4 g (94% d.Th.) Jodlacton, Fp.: 120-122°C $[\alpha]_D^{23}$ = +36,1° (C = 1,1, $CHCl_3$) ergeben.

Beispiel 5

2,3 g Dehydroabietylammoniumsalz von Ia mit $[\alpha]_D^{23}$ = +26,9° (c = 1,5, CH_3OH) werden wie in Beispiel 4 umgesetzt. Man erhalt 1,5 g (96% d.Th.) Jodlacton vom Fp.: 120-122°C und $[\alpha]_D^{23}$ = -36,3° (c = 1,1, $CHCl_3$).

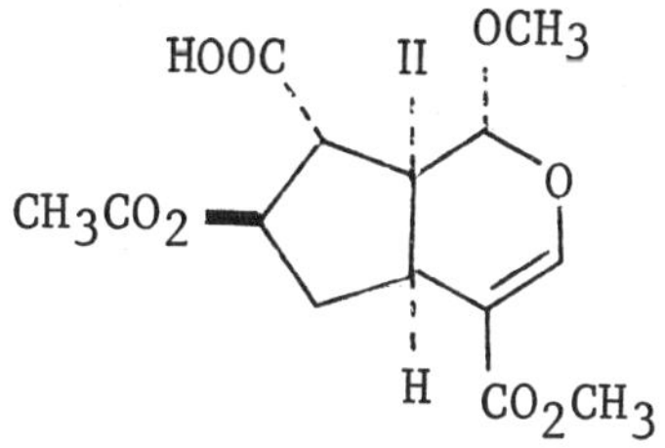

$C_{15}H_{18}O_7$ Ref. 1106

Note:

Upon resolution using (-)- and (+)-α-methylbenzylamine acids having m.p. 165-166° $[\alpha]_D^{25}$ -68° and m.p. 164-165° $[\alpha]_D^{25}$ +67° were obtained.

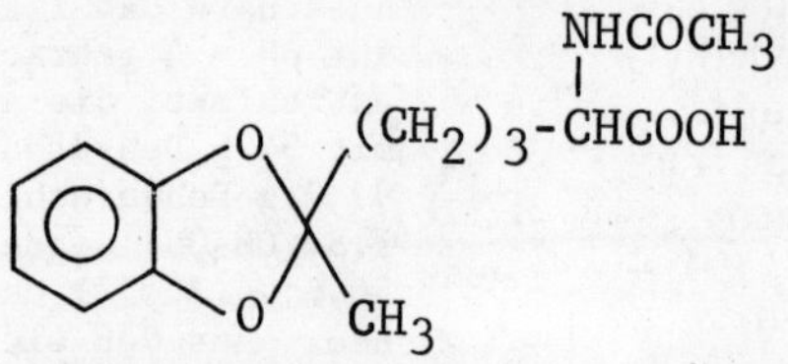

$C_{15}H_{19}NO_5$ Ref. 1107

6,6-o-Phenylenedioxy-2(R)*-acetamido-heptanoic acid* (**22**). The free acid **21** (R′ = H) (15.4 g) was dissolved in hot methyl ethyl ketone (2 l), mixed with (*S*)-α-methylbenzylamine (7.5 ml), seeded with the desired isomer (from previous separations) and left at room temperature for 18 h. The solids were filtered off (7.205 g; $[\alpha]_D^{25} = -21.2°$, $c = 1$, methanol) and recrystallized from methyl ethyl ketone to give the pure *salt* (6.4 g): m.p. 180–181°; $[\alpha]_D^{25} = -23°$ ($c = 1.37$, methanol).

Partitioning of this salt between dichloromethane and sulfuric acid (6 N) yielded the *free acid*, crystallization from ether gave the pure **22** (*e.g.* 280 mg from 590 mg of salt): m.p. 129–130°, $[\alpha]_D^{25} = -13.8°$ ($c = 1.8493$, methanol).

$C_{15}H_{19}NO_5$ (293) Calc. C 61.42 H 6.53 N 4.78% Found C 61.38 H 6.69 N 4.70%

6,6-o-Phenylenedioxy-2(S)*-acetamido-heptanoic acid.* The enantiomeric acid of **22** could be isolated from the mother liquors of the salts, but was more conveniently obtained by using (*R*)-α-methylbenzylamine in the resolution. This then yielded 6,6-*o*-phenylenedioxy-2(*S*)-acetamido-heptanoic acid: m.p. 129–130°, $[\alpha]_D^{25} = +13.43°$ ($c = 1$, methanol).

$C_{15}H_{19}NO_5$ (293) Calc. C 61.42 H 6.53 N 4.78% Found C 61.17 H 6.73 N 4.66%

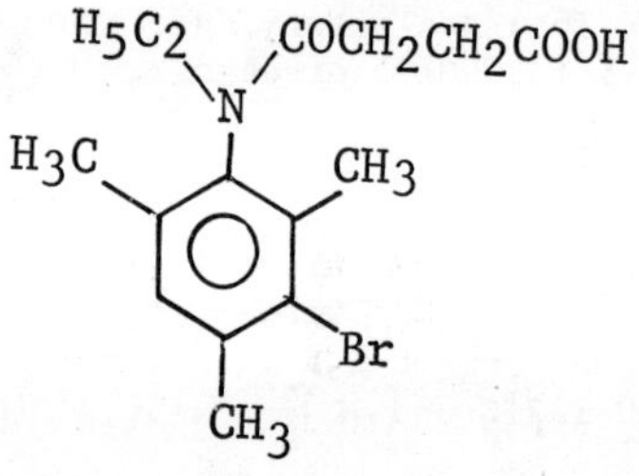

$C_{15}H_{20}BrNO_3$ Ref. 1108

Resolution of 5-Methoxy-4-N-succinyl-4-methylamino-1,3-dimethylbenzene.—The same precautions in this resolution were observed as were described for the resolution of N-succinyl-N-ethyl-3-bromomesidine.

A boiling solution of 5 g. of 5-methoxy-4-N-succinyl-4-methylamino-1,3-dimethylbenzene and 5.55 g. of cinchonidine in 200 cc. of ethyl acetate and 10 cc. of ethanol was filtered and allowed to cool to room temperature. Concentration at room temperature to 120 cc. resulted in the crystallization of 2.62 g. of salt; at 60 cc., 0.54 g.; at 35 cc., 1.77 g.; at 20 cc., 0.64 g. These all gave the same rotation so they were combined (5.47 g.) and dissolved at room temperature in 300 cc. of ethyl acetate and 5 cc. of ethanol. Upon concentration at room temperature, four fractions were isolated at various concentrations. All gave the same rotation; white crystals, m. p. 133–136° (cor.).

Rotation. (Less-soluble salt) 0.025 g. made up to 5 cc. with absolute ethanol at 30° gave α_D −0.28; *l*, 1; $[\alpha]^{30}_D$ −56°.

From the original solution of the salt, after separation of the four fractions just described, 2 cc. of petroleum ether (b. p. 80–92°) was added and the crystals which separated were filtered. Evaporation to 15 cc. and addition of 7 cc. of petroleum ether gave another salt fraction. Both of these were discarded. The remaining solution was evaporated to dryness. No method was found for purifying this amorphous material (2.88 g.).

Rotation. (More-soluble salt) 0.025 g. made up to 5 cc. with absolute ethanol at 30° gave α_D −0.23; *l*, 1; $[\alpha]^{30}_D$ −46°.

d- and *l*-**5-Methoxy-4-N-succinyl-4-methylamino-1,3-dimethylbenzene.**—About 3 g. of less-soluble salt was stirred at 0° with 25 cc. of 0.5% hydrochloric acid. The salt became gummy at first and gradually crystals formed. After one hour the product was filtered and washed. This procedure was repeated several times until all the cinchonidine was removed; white crystals, m. p. 152–153° (cor.). By decomposition of the crude more-soluble salt, the *l*-form of the acid resulted, m. p. 152–153° (cor.).

Anal. Calcd. for $C_{14}H_{19}O_4N$: C, 63.37; H, 7.22. Found: (*d*-acid) C, 63.37; H, 6.98. (*l*Acid) C, 63.76; H, 7.41.

Rotation. (*d*-Acid) 0.025 g. made up to 5 cc. with absolute ethanol at 30° gave α_D +0.065; *l*, 1; $[\alpha]^{30}_D$ +13°. (*l*-Acid) 0.025 g. made up to 5 cc. with absolute ethanol at 30° gave α_D −0.065; *l*, 1; $[\alpha]^{30}_D$ −13°.

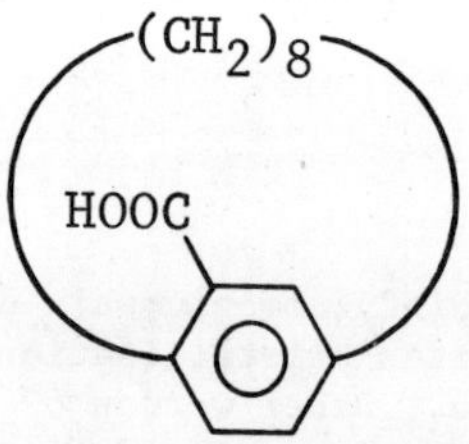

$C_{15}H_{20}O_2$ Ref. 1109

Resolution of the Acid 6d. A mixture of **6d** (18 g, 0.077 mol) and (+)-1-(β-naphthyl)ethylamine (13.3 g, 0.077 mol) ($[\alpha]^{18}_D$ +17.5°) in 95% ethanol (100 mL) was warmed to give a clear solution. After standing at room temperature for 24 h, the mixture yielded 3.8 g of a crystalline solid, mp 115–121°. The filtrate was reduced in volume to 50 mL and was kept at room temperature for another 24 h to give 3.6 g of a crystalline solid, mp 112–118 °C. Recrystallization of the combined crops from 95% ethanol afforded the salt, 6.4 g (20%): mp 141–143 °C; $[\alpha]^{23}_D$ −14.7° (c 0.68, $CHCl_3$). The purified salt was dissolved in chloroform (10 mL), and 5% hydrochloric acid (30 mL) was added with vigorous shaking. The chloroform extract was washed with water and then dried. Evaporation of the solvent afforded a white solid which was recrystallized from methanol–water to give (+)-**6d** (3.5 g): mp 139–140 °C; $[\alpha]^{18}_D$ +18.1° (c 0.52, $CHCl_3$); CD (CH_3OH), $[\theta] \times 10^{-4}$ (nm), −6.38 (212), 0 (228), +4.97 (248), +0.24 (290), +0.41 (305), 0 (327).

Anal. Calcd for $C_{15}H_{20}O_2$: C, 77.55; H, 8.68. Found: C, 77.48; H, 8.65.

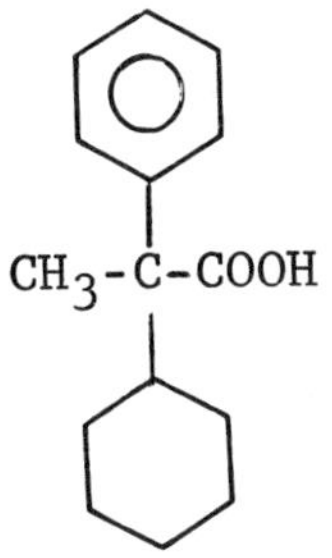

$C_{15}H_{20}O_2$ Ref. 1110

Acide S(+) *phényl-2 cyclohexyl-2 propanoïque* **5**.

100 g d'acide phényl-2 cyclohexyl-2 propanoïque racémique sont traités par une solution chaude de 120 g de quinine dans un litre d'alcool absolu. Par retour à la température ambiante, le sel de quinine précipite. Ce sel est essoré et recristallisé six fois dans l'alcool absolu. Traité par l'acide chlorhydrique à 10 %, il donne 10 g d'acide S(+) **5**.

$[\alpha]_D^{21*} = +3{,}5^\circ$ (0,42, méthanol).

$[\alpha]_D^{21*} = +2{,}7^\circ$ (2,1, hexane).

Les eaux de cristallisation sont ensuite évaporées à sec. Le résidu obtenu est traité par une solution d'acide chlorhydrique à 10 %. On régénère ainsi l'acide phényl-2 propanoique enrichi en isomère lévogyre qui est à nouveau dédoublé à l'aide de quinine. On obtient 9 g d'acide optiquement actif.

$[\alpha]_D^{20*} = +2{,}7^\circ$ (1,9, hexane).

DOR (0,42, méthanol), $[\varphi]_{600}^{21} = +24{,}5$, $[\varphi]_{560} = +32{,}5$, $[\varphi]_{430} = +49$, $[\varphi]_{430} = +49$, $[\varphi]_{375} = +56{,}5$, $[\varphi]_{360} = +65$, $[\varphi]_{355} = +73$, $[\varphi]_{317} = +81$, $[\varphi]_{300} = +89$, $[\varphi]_{290} = +97$, $[\varphi]_{287} = +105$.

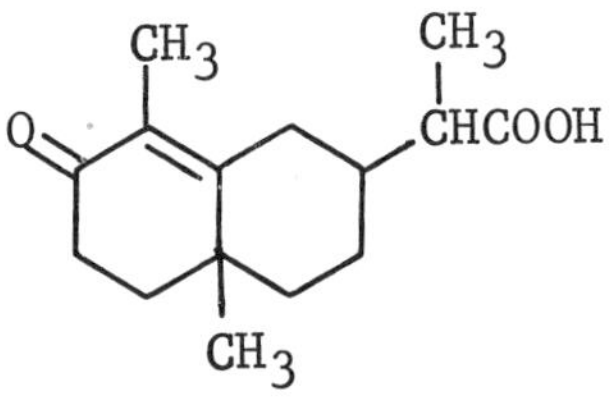

$C_{15}H_{22}O_3$ Ref. 1111

Example 32

Twelve grams of α-(2-keto-1,10-dimethyl-2,3,4,5,6,7,8,10-octahydronaphthyl-7)-propionic acid-A, M. P. 181° C., was dissolved in a warm solution of 22 g. of brucine in 30 cc. of alcohol and allowed to stand at room temperature for several hours. The separated crystals were filtered and washed several times with cold methanol to yield 15 g. of the brucine salt. The washings were combined with the mother liquors and concentrated to give 0.6 g. of the additional crop. The combined products were recrystallized from methanol into colorless needles, M. P. 125° C.

Fifteen grams of the brucine salt was decomposed with 5% sodium hydroxide solution, the liberated brucine was removed by shaking with chloroform, and the alkaline solution was acidified with hydrochloric acid to separate 5.5 g. of the dextrorotatory acid. Recrystallization from dilute methanol of the product gave colorless prisms of dextrorotatory α-(2-keto-1,10-dimethyl-2,3,4,5,6,7,8,10-octahydronaphthyl-7)-propionic acid-A, M. P. 121–122° C., $[\alpha]_D^{16}+91.0^\circ$ (in alcohol).

When the mother liquors of the brucine salt was evaporated to dryness, and the residue was treated with sodium hydroxide solution, the crude laevorotatory acid was obtained. Five and one-tenth grams of the crude acid and 3.3 g. of d-ephedrine were dissolved in 25 cc. of warm ethyl acetate, and the solution was left standing to separate 8.2 g. of the ephedrine salt. Repeated recrystallizations of the product from ethyl acetate gave 4.5 g. of colorless needles, M. P. 123° C. The pure salt was decomposed and treated as in the case of the brucine salt, and the resulting acid (2.8 g.) was recrystallized from dilute methanol to yield colorless prisms of laevorotatory α-(2-keto-1,10-dimethyl-2,3,4,5,6,7,8,10-octahydronaphthyl-7)-propionic acid-A, M. P. 121–122° C., $[\alpha]_D^{15}-90.0^\circ$ (in alcohol).

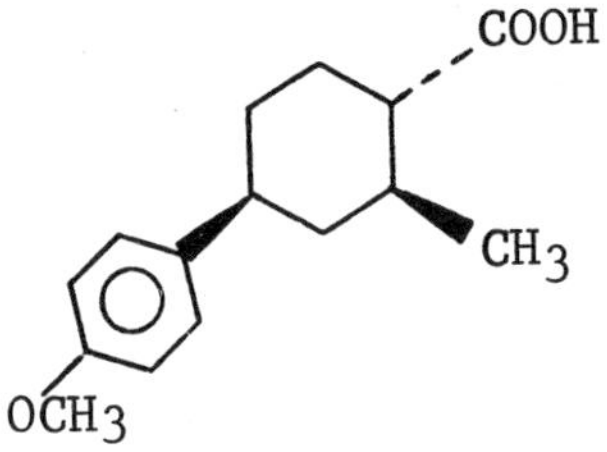

$C_{15}H_{20}O_3$ Ref. 1112

B. From Resolution. A solution of oxalyl chloride (25 ml) and (±)-1 (12.0 g, 0.048 mol) in benzene (250 ml) was stirred at 20° for 2.5 hr. The solvent was evaporated and to the residual acid chloride was added toluene (180 ml) and testosterone (13.8 g, 0.048 mol). The mixture was heated at reflux for 17 hr and then was worked up to yield an oil; chromatography on silica gel (elution with 95:5 toluene–Et_2O) yielded 22.3 g (90%) of diastereoisomeric testosteronyl esters of (±)-**1**. Successive recrystallizations from MeCN, EtOAc, MeCN (twice), and EtOH gave 3.02 g of white needles: mp 150–151°; $[\alpha]_D$ +85°; melting point and rotation unchanged with subsequent recrystallization.

A mixture of this ester (2.80 g, 0.005 mol) in EtOH (40 ml) and H_2O (5 ml) containing KOH (0.50 g, 0.009 mol) was stirred at reflux for 20 hr. Usual work-up gave (−)-1 (0.49 g, 38%); recrystallized (MeCN) to $[\alpha]_D$ −13.2°. The unhydrolyzed ester was recovered and treated similarly using 1.6 g of KOH in refluxing aqueous EtOH for 16 hr. The acid obtained (0.67 g, 51%) was recrystallized twice (MeCN) to yield (−)-**1**: $[\alpha]_D$ −17.7°; mp 122–123.5 ° (turbid melt as above, clearing at 153°).

Optical Purity Assay of (−)-1. The acid (−)-1 (25.3 mg, 0.10 mmol) from part B above was converted with oxalyl chloride to the acid chloride which then was heated with methyl (−)-mandelate (33.7 mg, 0.20 mmol) at 160° for 2.5 hr. The product was dissolved in toluene and the solution was filtered through alumina. The solvent was evaporated and the residue was examined by nmr: nmr ($CDCl_3$) δ 5.96 ppm [s, 1, $CO_2CH(Ph)CO_2CH_3$]. The racemic acid (±)-1 and methyl (−)-mandelate were treated in an identical procedure and the resultant product was analyzed: nmr ($CDCl_3$) δ 5.96 and 5.99 ppm [s, ½, s, ½, $CO_2CH(Ph)CO_2CH_3$ diastereomers].

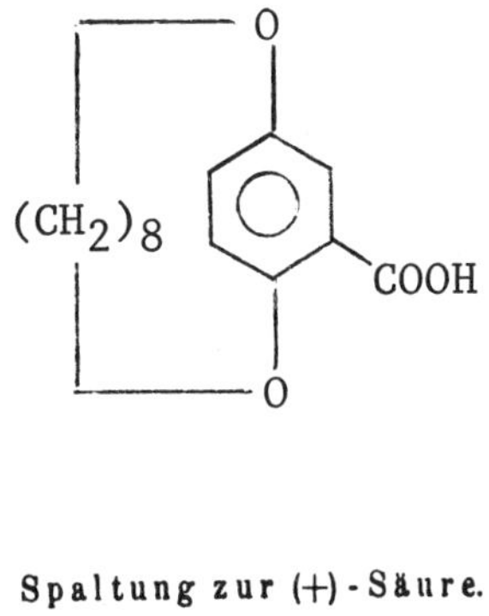

$C_{15}H_{20}O_4$ Ref. 1113

Spaltung zur (+)-Säure.

2,85 g racem. Säure brachte man mit 3 g Cinchonidin durch Kochen in 20 ccm Alkohol zur Lösung. Das beim Abkühlen abgeschiedene Salz (2,6 g) wurde mit eiskaltem Alkohol gewaschen und aus Alkohol umkrystallisiert.

$C_{34}H_{42}O_5N_2$	Ber. C 73,06	H 7,58
	Gef. C 73,20	H 7,53.

$[\alpha]_D^{21} = +12{,}4^\circ$ $[\alpha]_{Hg}^{21} = +19{,}4^\circ$ (1,3 % in Chloroform).

Die Drehung blieb nach weiterem Umkrystallisieren konstant.

Zerlegung: Die Chloroformlösung des Cinchonidinsalzes schüttelte man sechsmal mit verd. Schwefelsäure und mit Wasser, destillierte das Chloroform ab und erhielt aus Cyclohexan 1,15 g

der aktiven Säure VI vom Schmp. 94,5°.

$C_{15}H_{20}O_4$ Ber. C 68,16 H 7,63
Gef. C 68,22 H 7,61.

85 6 mg Subst.: 3,27 ccm n/10 NaOH; ber. 3,24 ccm.

Spez. Drehung: 30,4 mg in 3,1 ccm *Alkohol*:

$a_C = +0{,}73°$ $a_D = +1{,}02°$ $a_{Hg} = +1{,}31°$

$[a]^{21}_{6563} = +74{,}5°$ $[a]^{21}_D = +104°$ $[a]^{21}_{5461} = +133{,}5°$

38 mg Subst. in 3,1 ccm *Aceton*:

$a_C = +0{,}51°$ $a_D = +0{,}73°$ $a_{Hg} = +0{,}95°$

$[a]^{21}_{6563} = +41{,}6°$ $[a]^{21}_D = +59{,}6°$ $[a]^{21}_{5461} = +77{,}6°$

42 mg in 3,1 ccm *Benzol*:

$a_C = +0{,}31°$ $a_D = +0{,}48°$ $a_{Hg} = +0{,}64°$

$[a]^{21}_{6563} = +22{,}5°$ $[a]^{21}_D = +35{,}4°$ $[a]^{21}_{5461} = +47{,}2°$

43,1 mg in 3,1 ccm *Chloroform*:

$a_C = -0{,}10°$ $a_D = 0°$ $a_{Hg} = +0{,}08°$

$[a]^{21}_{6563} = -7{,}2°$ $[a]^{21}_D = 0°$ $[a]^{21}_{5461} = +5{,}7°$

Linksdrehende Säure VI: Der Mutterlaugen-Rückstand vom Cinchonidinsalz wurde, in Chloroform gelöst, mit verd. Schwefelsäure zerlegt, der Rückstand der Chloroformschicht (1,45 g) mit 2,5 g Brucin in 20 ccm Alkohol heiß gelöst. Erst nach starkem Einengen erschienen langsam Krystalle, wegen ihrer Leichtlöslichkeit nur durch Zusatz von etwas Äther umkrystallisierbar und nicht ganz einheitlich zu erhalten.

$[a]^{20}_D = -58{,}3°$.

Durch Zerlegung dieses Salzes mit verd. Schwefelsäure wie oben wurde die (—) Form von VI nicht ganz rein erhalten. Schmp. 85—93°,

$[a]^{20}_D = -40{,}5°$, $[a]^{20}_{5461} = -56°$ (1,3% in Aceton).

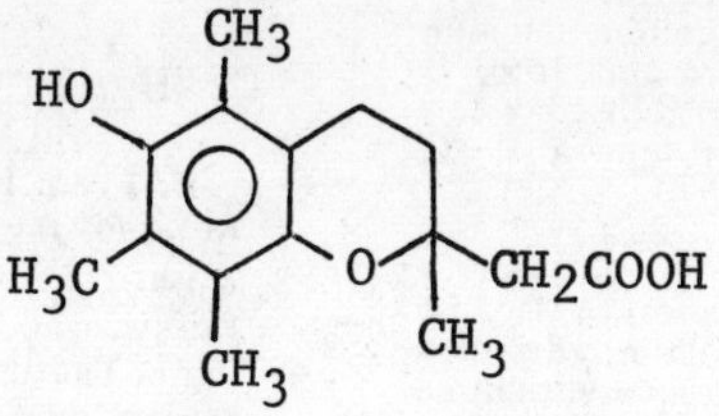

$C_{15}H_{20}O_4$ **Ref. 1114**

(S)-*(6-Hydroxy-2,5,7,8-tetramethyl-chroman-2-yl)acetic Acid* (**14**). To a solution of 26.43 g (0.10 mol) of *rac.*-acid **13** in 500 ml of tetrahydrofuran were added 15 ml (ca. 115 mmol) of (*S*)-α-methyl-benzylamine (*Aldrich*). The mixture was stirred at 25° under N_2 for 1 h, filtered and stripped of solvent to give a brownish resin. Two crystallizations from methanol/ether gave 13.65 g of α-methyl-benzylamine salt as shiny, cream-white prisms, sintering at 162°, m.p. 164–166°, $[\alpha]^{25}_D = -15.20°$ ($c = 1.04$, C_2H_5OH). A similarly prepared sample was crystallized again to give analytically pure (*S*)-(6-hydroxy-2,5,7,8-tetramethyl-chroman-2-yl)acetic acid (*S*)-α-methyl-benzylamine salt as colorless prisms: m.p. 164–166.5°, $[\alpha]^{25}_D = -15.66°$ ($c = 1.0088$, C_2H_5OH). – IR. (KBr): 3600–2000 (OH, acid salt). – UV.: 225 (9400), 291.5 (3350).

$C_{23}H_{31}N_1O_4$ (385.49) Calc. C 71.66 H 8.11 N 3.63% Found C 71.80 H 8.34 N 3.54%

A suspension of the α-methyl-benzylamine salt in 200 ml of ether and 200 ml of 2N HCl was stirred at 23° for 1 h and worked-up as usual to give a cream-white solid. Crystallization from ethanol/H_2O gave 9.20 g (35%) of acid **14** as a white granular solid, m.p. 145.5–148.5°, $[\alpha]^{25}_D = -14.8°$ ($c = 0.915$, C_2H_5OH). A similarly prepared sample was recrystallized to give analytically pure material as fine, white prisms: m.p. 124–127°[14]; $[\alpha]^{25}_D = -15.39°$ ($c = 0.9878$, C_2H_5OH). – IR., UV., NMR. and MS. identical with those of racemic acid **13**.

$C_{15}H_{20}O_4$ (264.31) Calc. C 68.16 H 7.63% Found C 68.33 H 7.62%

(S)-*(6-Hydroxy-2,5,7,8-tetramethylchroman-2-yl)acetic Acid* (**14**) *with racemization of the* (R)-*enantiomer* **15**. A suspension of 13.22 g (50 mmol) of *rac.*-acid **13** in 30 ml of methanol and 170 ml of ether was stirred at 20° as 7.5 ml (*ca.* 62.5 mmol) of (*S*)-α-methyl-benzylamine (*Aldrich*) were added. The solution was immediately seeded with the (*S*)-acid (*S*)-salt. Stirring and cooling, finally to – 20°, gave 7.80 g of white powder. Crystallization from 25 ml of methanol and 175 ml of ether gave 6.78 g of (*S*)-acid (*S*)-salt as a white powder, m.p. 162.5–165°, $[\alpha]^{25}_D = -13.68°$ ($c = 0.9942$, C_2H_5OH). Conversion of this salt to the free acid **14** and crystallization as above gave 4.50 g (34%) of white powder: m.p. 146–149°[14], $[\alpha]^{25}_D = -16.89°$ ($c = 1.2147$, C_2H_5OH). The mother liquors from the preparation and crystallization of the (*S*)-acid (*S*)-salt were stripped of solvent to give 19.3 g of orange-brown resin which was converted as above to free acid, giving 8.70 g of tan solid. This acid, enriched in the (*R*)-enantiomer **15**, was suspended in 480 ml of 12N H_2SO_4, degassed, placed under N_2, and heated at reflux for 30 h. Work-up of the red-orange suspension with ethyl acetate in the usual manner gave 8.40 g of brown solid. This material was triturated with 60 ml of hot ether, cooled to – 20°, and filtered. The resulting 7.1 g of tan powder were crystallized from 25 ml each of ethanol and H_2O to give 6.88 g (52%) of *rac.*-acid **13** as a light tan powder: m.p. 173.5–175°, mixed m.p. with authentic acid undepressed, $[\alpha]^{25}_D = \pm 0°$ ($c = 0.9463$, C_2H_5OH). The effective yield of (*S*)-acid **14** was thus 71%, based on a conversion of 48%. – NMR., IR., UV., and MS. identical with those of authentic *rac.*-acid.

---

14) Apparently polymorphic forms of this compound exist. Our first samples had this lower m.p., (124–127°) while later preparations had the higher m.p. (146–149°).

$CH(CH_3)_2$
|
$C_2H_5OCO-C-OCH_2C_6H_5$
|
COOH

$C_{15}H_{20}O_5$ Ref. 1115

1.4. R-(+)-*Isopropyl-benzyloxy-malonsäure-monoäthylester* (**7**): 2330 g (8,32 Mol) *rac.*-Isopropyl-benzyloxy-malonsäure-monoäthylester (**6**) wurden in 15 l abs. Äther gelöst und unter heftigem Rühren und Feuchtigkeitsausschluss mit 1460 g (8,83 Mol) (–)-Pseudoephedrin (wasserfrei, getrocknet im Hochvakuum bei 50°) versetzt, wobei sich dieses schnell löste. Zur Entfernung des Hauptteils des negativ drehenden Isomeren wurde mit 1 g *S*-(–)-Isopropyl-benzyloxy-malonsäure-monoäthylester-(–)-pseudoephedrinsalz angeimpft und 2 Tage bei 0° stehengelassen. Es bildete sich eine Kruste des obgenannten Salzes, von welcher abdekantiert wurde und die mit 1 l abs. Äther nachgewaschen wurde. Man erhielt so nach dem Trocknen 731 g (–)-Pseudoephedrinsalz des negativ drehenden Halbesters. Dessen Reinigung erfolgte durch Kristallisation aus abs. Essigester/Äther: Farblose, lange Rechtecke bis Nadeln, Smp. 113–114°, $[\alpha]_D^{20} = -28°$ ($c = 2$, Äthanol).

$C_{25}H_{35}NO_6$	Ber.	C 67,4	H 7,9	N 3,1	O 21,5%
(445,6)	Gef.	,, 67,3	,, 7,8	,, 3,3	,, 21,8%

Die ätherische Mutterlauge, den angereicherten *R*-(+)-Isopropyl-benzyloxy-malonsäure-monoäthylester als (–)-Pseudoephedrinsalz enthaltend, wurde mit 3 kg Eis versetzt und unter Rühren mit 1130 ml konz. Phosphorsäure angesäuert. Nach der Trennung der Phasen wurde der wässerige Teil noch dreimal mit 1 l Äther nachextrahiert, die Ätherlösungen mit Kochsalzlösung und Wasser gewaschen, mit Natriumsulfat getrocknet und das Lösungsmittel schonend entfernt. Der zähflüssige, ölige Rückstand wurde bei 30° im Hochvakuum bis zur Gewichtskonstanz getrocknet, wobei 1870 g angereicherter *R*-(+)-Halbester anfielen. Dieser Rückstand wurde in 12 l abs. Äther gelöst und mit 1127 g (6,81 Mol) wasserfreies (+)-Pseudoephedrin versetzt.

Die Lösung wurde mit 1 g *R*-(+)-Isopropyl-benzyloxy-malonsäure-monoäthylester-(+)-pseudoephedrinsalz angeimpft und bei 0° 2 Tage stehengelassen. Dann wurde von der Kristallkruste abdekantiert, 5 l abs., auf 0° abgekühlter Äther zugegeben, die Kristallkruste pulverisiert und filtriert. Eine kleine Probe dieses rohen Salzes, $[\alpha]_D^{20} = +27,5°$ ($c = 2$, Äthanol), wurde aus wenig abs. Essigester/Äther bis zur Konstanz der physikalischen Daten umkristallisiert: Kleine, verfilzte Rechtecke bis Nadeln, Smp. 112–113°, $[\alpha]_D^{20} = +28°$ ($c = 2$, Äthanol).

$C_{25}H_{35}NO_6$	Ber.	C 67,4	H 7,9	N 3,1	O 21,5%
(445,6)	Gef.	,, 67,4	,, 8,1	,, 3,4	,, 21,6%

Da die Drehung des rohen *R*-(+)-Isopropyl-benzyloxy-malonsäure-monoäthylester-(+)-pseudoephedrinsalzes sich von der des umkristallisierten Musters praktisch nicht unterschied, wurde das Rohkristallisat direkt in die Komponenten aufgespalten. Dazu wurde es in 5 l Äther suspendiert, mit 3 kg Eis und dann unter intensivem Rühren mit 685 ml konz. Phosphorsäure versetzt. Die wässerig-saure Phase wurde dreimal mit je 1 l Äther nachextrahiert, der Ätherextrakt mit Wasser neutral gewaschen, getrocknet und das Lösungsmittel im Vakuum entfernt. Man erhielt 1096 g (94%) *R*-(+)-Isopropyl-benzyloxy-malonsäure-monoäthylester (**7**) als zähes Öl, homogen im Dünnschichtchromatogramm (Kieselgelplatte mit Chloroform/Methanol 7:3). $[\alpha]_D^{20} = +8,2°$ ($c = 5$, Äthanol); $n_D^{22} = 1,4988$; IR.: $\tilde{\nu}$CO 1715, 1740 cm^{-1}.

$C_{15}H_{20}O_5$	Ber.	C 64,3	H 7,2	O 28,5	C_2H_5O 16,0%
(280,3)	Gef.	,, 64,3	,, 7,0	,, 29,0	,, 15,8%

$C_6H_5CH_2OCH_2-CHCOOH$
|
$NHCOOC(CH_3)_3$

$C_{15}H_{21}NO_5$ Ref. 1116

***N-tert*-Butyloxycarbonyl-*O*-benzyl-L-serine Dicyclohexylammonium Salt.** *N-tert*-butyloxycarbonyl-*O*-benzyl-DL-serine (mp 90–91 °C, from ether/*n*-hexane) (5.9 g, 20 mmol) prepared from *O*-benzyl-DL-serine was dissolved in ether (100 mL). The ethereal solution of diazomethane[7] was dropped in until the solution remained pale yellow. The mixture was then washed twice with 20-mL portions of 1 N $NaHCO_3$, dried over anhydrous sodium sulfate, and evaporated under reduced pressure to dryness. The oily ester (6.0 g, 98%) obtained was dissolved in 10 mL of dimethylformamide and then added to a phosphate buffer solution (0.05 M, pH 6.0) containing 5 mmol of β-mercaptoethanol, 5 mmol of EDTA and 500 mg of crude papain. The mixture was kept at 35 °C with stirring and the pH was maintained at 6.0 by addition of 1 N NaOH. After 4 h and with no decrease in pH, the mixture was extracted twice with 50-mL portions of ether to recover the unreacted ester. The aqueous solution was then acidified to pH 3.0 with 3 N HCl and extracted three times with 50-mL portions of ethyl acetate. The combined ethyl acetate was washed with water, dried over anhydrous sodium sulfate, and then evaporated under reduced pressure to give a colorless oil. The oil was dissolved in 30 mL of ether/*n*-hexane (1:1 v/v) followed by addition of dicylcohexylamine (1.6 mL). The precipitates formed after cooling were collected by filtration to give the title compound (3.4 g, 72%): mp 135–136 °C; R_f 0.78 (system A), 0.20 (system B); $[\alpha]^{25}_D$ +25.0 (*c* 2, MeOH) [lit.[7] mp 135.5–136 °C, $[\alpha]^{25}_D$ +24.3 (*c* 2.94, MeOH)].

Anal. Calcd for $C_{15}H_{21}NO_5 \cdot C_{12}H_{23}N$: C, 68.03; H, 9.24; N, 5.88. Found: C, 67.90; H, 8.92; N, 6.03.

***N-tert*-Butyloxycarbonyl-*O*-benzyl-D-serine Dicyclohexylammonium Salt.** The unreacted ester obtained above in ether was washed with water, dried, and evaporated to give an oil (3.4 g, 11 mmol), which was further digested with papain (50 mg) in the same way as described above (in 100 mL of solution) for 4 h and the unreacted ester was isolated again (2.5 g, 8.1 mmol): R_f 0.88 (system B); $[\alpha]^{25}_D$ +2.5 (C 2, MeOH). It was hydrolyzed by stirring in a mixture of dioxane–1 N NaOH (1:1 v/v) (30 mL) with 1.5 equiv of alkali for 20 min. The solution was then acidified and followed by extraction to prepare the dicyclohexylammonium salt of *N-tert*-butyloxycarbonyl-*O*-benzyl-D-serine (3.8 g, 8 mmol): mp 133–134 °C; $[\alpha]^{25}_D$ −24.2 (*c* 2, MeOH) [lit.[7] mp 130–131 °C; $[\alpha]^{25}_D$ −23.6 (*c* 2.28, MeOH)]; TLC data were the same as for the L isomer.

Anal. Calcd for $C_{15}H_{21}NO_5{\cdot}C_{12}H_{23}N$: C, 68.03; H, 9.24; N, 5.88. Found: C, 67.90; H, 9.11; N, 6.06.

The Steric Purity. An aliquot of *N-tert*-butyloxycarbonyl-*O*-benzyl-L-serine and its antipode obtained by the above procedure were dissolved in 5 mL of 2 N HCl–AcOH, respectively. After 1 h at room temperature, the reaction mixture was evaporated under reduced pressure at 25 °C to yield a residue which was then diluted to 5 mL with 1 N HCl for optical rotation determination. The samples showed the same optical rotation in absolute value, respectively, as a sample of *O*-benzyl-L-serine[1] similarly treated, $[\alpha]^{25}_D = 7.4$ (*c* 2, 1 N HCl).

(7) H. Otsuka, K. Inouye, F. Shinokazi, and M. Kanayma, *Bull. Chem. Soc. Jpn.*, **39**, 1171 (1966).

Authors' comments:

O-Benzyl-L-serine derivatives are useful in peptide synthesis. The currently available methods for preparing these compounds are laborious and not convenient for large-scale preparation. Okawa[1] prepared *O*-benzyl-L-serine via bromination of methyl acrylate and resolved the racemate of the *N*-acetyl derivative by acylase. The other method is benzylation of N-*tert*-butyloxycarbonyl-L-serine in sodium–liquid ammonia[2] or in sodium hydride–dimethylformamide.[3] The acylase method can obtain optically pure *O*-benzyl-L-serine but the amino-protecting group should be introduced again for peptide synthesis. The enzyme, however, is not cheap and is hard to obtain. The second method, benzylation of *N-tert*-butyloxycarbonyl-L-serine, is only around 50% in yield and racemization might occur in the benzylation process.

The direct resolution of *N-tert*-butyloxycarbonyl derivatives of racemic amino acids would be a better way of preparing optically pure protected amino acids rather than incorporating the protecting group onto optically active amino acids or derivatives.

We present here a new method for the preparation of *N-tert*-butyloxycarbonyl-*O*-benzyl-L-serine and its antipode. Both enantiomers appeared optically pure and the yields are higher than the published values.

Starting from methyl acrylate, *O*-benzyl-DL-serine obtained[1] was converted to *N-tert*-butyloxycarbonyl derivative[4] and then methylated by diazomethane.[5] The butyloxycarbonyl group might be introduced to the amino acid methyl ester prepared by thionyl chloride in methanol. The racemic acyl amino acid methyl ester was then hydrolyzed under papain catalysis to afford the L acid in 72% yield; its antipode was recovered in 81% yield from the unreacted D ester by mild alkaline treatment.

The same approach to other amino acids including threonine derivative, which has two optical centers, is under investigation.

(1) K. Okawa, *Bull. Chem. Soc. Jpn.*, **30**, 110 (1957); K. Okawa, *ibid.*, **29**, 486 (1956).
(2) V. J. Hruby and K. W. Ehler, *J. Org. Chem.*, **35**, 1690 (1970).
(3) H. Sugano and M. Niyoshi, *J. Org. Chem.*, **41**, 2352 (1976).
(4) E. Schnabel, *Justus Liebigs Ann. Chem.*, **702**, 188 (1967).
(5) D. B. Backer, "Organic Synthesis", Collect. Vol. II, Wiley, New York, 1963, p 250.
(6) Melting points were determined in capillaries on a Büchi melting point apparatus and are uncorrected. Optical rotation was measured with Jasco Dip 180 automatic digital polarimeter. TLC was run on silica gel plate using chloroform–methanol–acetic acid (9:1:0.5 v/v/v), system A, and chloroform–ethyl acetate (7:3 v/v), system B. Crude papain (1900 milk-clotting units/mg) from papaya latex stem was purchased from Tree Co., Ltd., Taiwan and was used without further purification.

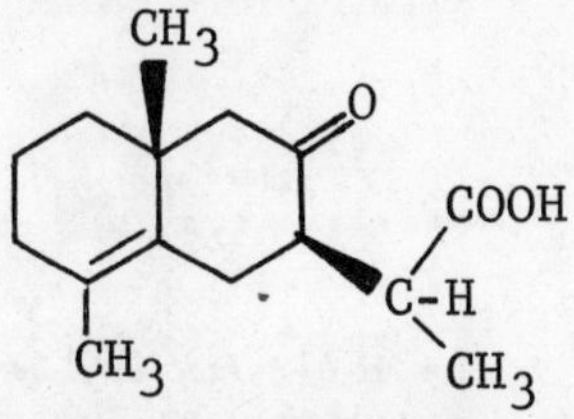

$C_{15}H_{22}O_3$ Ref. 1117

Crystallization of brucine salt of acid from methanol-water gave a salt $[\alpha]^{22}_D$ -15.7° (c 0.5, ethanol). The acid regenerated from the salt was esterified with CH_2N_2 to give a methyl ester b.p. 118-121°/0.1 mm Hg., $[\alpha]^{22}_D$ +42.9° (c 0.3, ethanol).

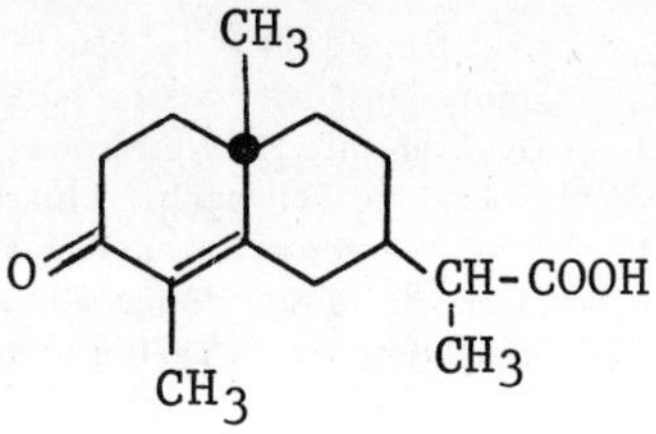

$C_{15}H_{22}O_3$ Ref. 1118

Resolution of α-(3-Keto-4,9-dimethyl-1,2,3,5,6,7,8,9-octahydro-6-naphthyl)-propionic Acid A (XXIV). (a) (+)-A-Acid.—A solution of 12 g. of A-acid XXIV[3] and 2.2 g. of brucine in 30 ml. of methanol was heated, and allowed to stand at room temperature. After several hours the separating crystals were collected by suction and washed with methanol. There was obtained 15 g. of the brucine salt of (+)-A-acid. Recrystallization from methanol gave colorless needles, m.p. 123–125°, $[\alpha]^{15}_D$ 0° (*c* 1.0).

Anal. Calcd. for $C_{38}H_{47}O_7N_2{\cdot}2H_2O$: C, 67.13; H, 7.56; N, 4.12. Found: C, 66.99; H, 7.84; N, 4.06.

Three grams of the salt was shaken with 5% sodium hydroxide and chloroform to complete its decomposition. The alkaline solution was then acidified with hydrochloric acid, and 1.1 g. of (+)-A-acid was obtained. This was recrystallized from dilute methanol or petroleum ether as colorless prisms, m.p. 122°, $[\alpha]^{16}_D$ +91° (*c* 1.0).

(b) **(−)-A-Acid.**—After removal of the less soluble brucine salt described in the preceding experiment, the mother liquor was concentrated and treated with aqueous alkali to give crude (−)-A-acid. A solution of 5.1 g. of the crude acid and 3.3 g. of *d*-ephedrine in 25 ml. of ethyl acetate was warmed and then allowed to stand at room temperature. The separated crystalline salt was filtered (8.2 g.). Several recrystallizations from ethyl acetate afforded colorless needles, m.p. 123°, $[\alpha]^{15}_D$ −37.0° (*c* 0.5).

This was treated in the same way as for (+)-A-acid to yield 2.8 g. of (−)-A-acid, recrystallized from dilute methanol as colorless prisms, m.p. 122°, $[\alpha]^{15}_D$ −91.0° (*c* 0.5).

Anal. Calcd. for $C_{15}H_{22}O_3$: C, 71.97; H, 8.86. Found: C, 71.76; H, 8.80.

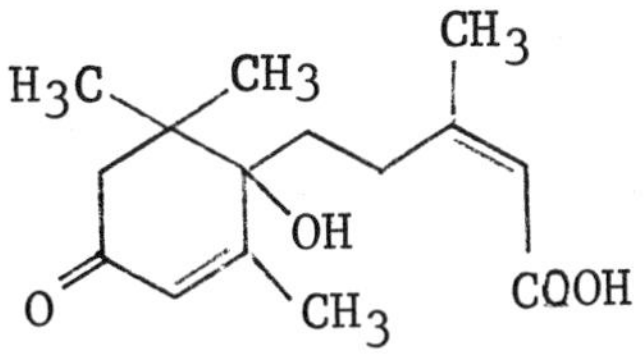

$C_{15}H_{22}O_4$ Ref. 1119

<u>Résolution optique du t-ABA</u>

La séparation des énantiomères du t-ABA s'effectue par l'intermédiaire du sel de brucine du mélange racémique que l'cn soumet à des recristallisations dans l'acétone anhydre. C'est le sel de brucine du (-) t-ABA qui cristallise le premier ($|\alpha|_D = - 162°$). Après l'élimination de ces fractions, du sel de composition sensiblement racémique cristallise ($|\alpha|_D = - 30°$). Enfin cristallisent des fractions de sel de (+) t-ABA ($|\alpha|_D = + 87°$).

Les sels de brucine possédant les rotations extrêmes de - 162° et + 87° conduisent, après hydrolyse par la potasse aqueuse, à des échantillons de t-ABA optiquement actifs, de pouvoirs rotatoires respectifs :

$|\alpha|_D = - 330°$ et $|\alpha|_D = + 320°$ (Solvant éthanol, concentration 2 mg/ml)

Malgré des essais de recristallisation, les sels de brucine possédant les rotations extrêmes n'ont pu être enrichis en l'énantiomère correspondant.

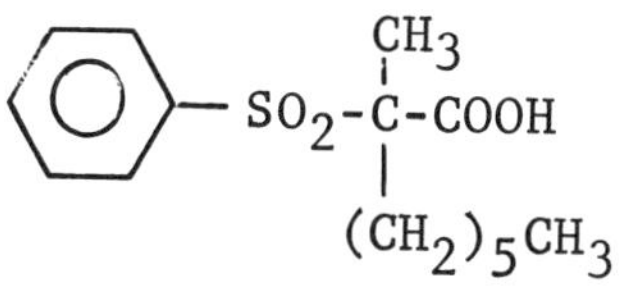

$C_{15}H_{22}O_4S$ Ref. 1120

(+)-2-Methyl-2-benzenesulfonyloctanoic Acid ((+)-I).—A solution of 86.5 g. of I and 94 g. of quinine in 200 ml. of absolute ethanol was prepared, and after 30 min. the salt separated. The mixture was heated to reflux, and sufficient absolute ethanol was added to effect solution (2100 ml.). The solution was cooled to 25°, and after 3 days white needles separated. A small portion of this salt was converted to acid, which exhibited $[\alpha]^{29}_{546}$ +12.1° (*c* 8.4, chloroform). Five additional recrystallizations of the salt gave acid, $[\alpha]^{29}_{546}$ +15.6° (*c* 8.4, chloroform). Two additional recrystallizations of the salt provided no change in rotation of the derived acid. After the four crystallizations, 35 g. (19%) of the quinine salt was obtained. An additional 7 g. was obtained by fractional recrystallizations of salt from the mother liquors. Thus 42 g. (23%) of optically pure salt was obtained. This material was shaken with 300 ml. of 6 *N* sulfuric acid and 500 ml. of ether, and the aqueous layer was extracted with ether. The combined ether extracts were washed with water, dried, and evaporated to give 19.8 g. of optically pure acid as an oil, $[\alpha]^{29}_{546}$ +15.6° (*c* 8.4, chloroform).

Attempts to obtain (−)-I from the mother liquors failed. Use of cinchonidine gave salt whose acid became more positive on successive recrystallizations.

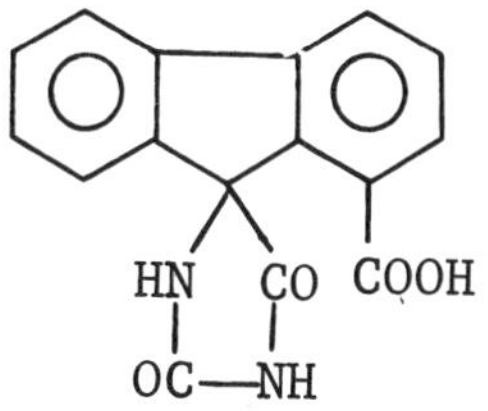

$C_{16}H_{10}N_2O_4$ Ref. 1121

Zerlegung in die Antipoden: 3 g reines _Hydantoin II_ werden zusammen mit 1.9 g _l-Ephedrin·H_2O_ in 220 ccm Wasser heiß gelöst. Bei sehr langsamem Abkühlen beginnt unterhalb von 50° die Abscheidung des _rechtsdrehenden Salzes_ in cm-langen schmalen Blättchen. Nach dem Abkühlen auf Raumtemperatur wird abgesaugt und an der Luft getrocknet (ca. 2.0 g). $[\alpha]^{20}_D$: +124.6°, nach zweimaligem Umkristallisieren aus wenig Wasser unverändert $[\alpha]^{20}_D$. +124.1° (beides in Methanol, $c = 0.5$).

Aus der Mutterlauge des rechtsdrehenden Salzes scheidet sich das _linksdrehende Salz_ bei 8–14tägigem Stehenlassen, viel rascher nach Animpfen im Kühlschrank, in Nadelbüscheln ab (0.8 g). $[\alpha]^{20}_D$: −171.5°, nach zweimaligem Umkristallisieren aus wenig Wasser −173.0° (beides in Methanol, $c = 0.5$).

Die reinen Ephedrinsalze wurden in wenig Wasser gelöst und mit 2*n* NaOH versetzt. Nach Ausäthern des Ephedrins fielen beim Ansäuern die _optisch aktiven Carbonsäuren_ aus, die beim Umkristallisieren aus Wasser/Äthanol farnkrautähnliche Kristalle bildeten. Aus dem rechtsdrehenden Ephedrinsalz wurde die rechtsdrehende Säure, $[\alpha]^{20}_D$: +155 ± 2°, aus dem linksdrehenden die linksdrehende Säure, $[\alpha]^{20}_D$: −155 ± 2° (beides in Methanol, $c = 0.5$) erhalten.

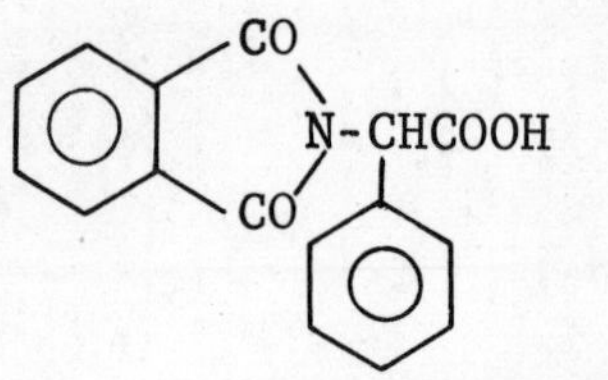

$C_{16}H_{11}NO_4$ Ref. 1122

Resolution of r-α-*Phthalimidophenylacetic Acid.*—Morphine (30·7 g.) was dissolved by heating with ethyl alcohol (2850 c.c.), the solution cooled to 30°, and the *r*-acid (28·5 g.) added. The acid dissolved readily. The morphine salt (36·5 g.), which had separated overnight, was crystallised once from ethyl alcohol (2900 c.c.), and the resulting needles were dissolved in boiling water (2500 c.c.), and decomposed, while the solution was still warm, by concentrated hydrochloric acid. The acid precipitated was crystallised once from aqueous acetone, washed with ice-cold water, and dried in a vacuum over sulphuric acid. It was then optically pure, repeated crystallisation failing to raise the value of its specific rotation. Yield: 10 g.

l-α-*Phthalimidophenylacetic acid*, $C_8H_4O_2$:N·CHPh·CO_2H, forms glassy needles, m. p. 192—193° (Found: C, 68·3; H, 4·0; N, 5·1. $C_{16}H_{11}O_4N$ requires C, 68·3; H, 3·9; N, 5·0%). In acetone: $l = 2$, $c = 3·5385$, $\alpha_D^{14·8°}$ −3·67°, $[\alpha]_D^{14·8°}$ −51·9°. In methyl alcohol: $l = 2$, $c = 4·588$, $\alpha_D^{17·8°}$ −1·86°, $[\alpha]_D^{17·8°}$ −20·3°; $l = 2$, $c = 2·251$, $\alpha_{5461}^{12·8°}$ −1·11°, $[\alpha]_{5461}^{12·8°}$ −24·7°.

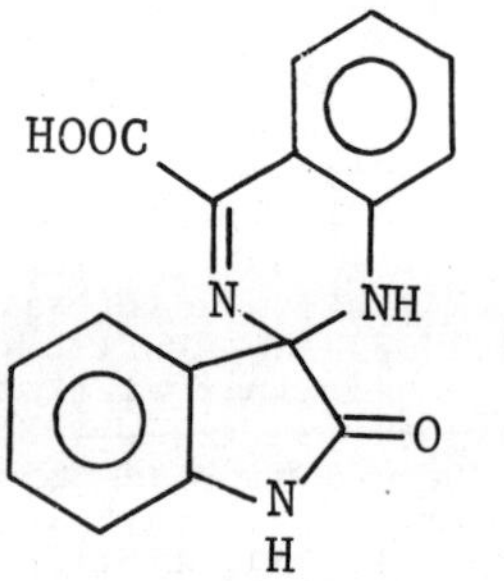

$C_{16}H_{11}N_3O_3$ Ref. 1123

Resolution of Isamic Acid.—Isamic acid (6.22 g) was suspended in propan-2-ol and added to a solution of brucine (from 10.13 g of brucine sulphate by shaking with ammonia and chloroform) in propan-2-ol, a total of 135 ml of the alcohol being used. The yellow slurry was heated to boiling and water (37 ml) was added gradually. From the resulting solution three crops of crystals (total 11.6 g) were obtained. On recrystallization of this material from 80% propan-2-ol it was noted that yellow, well-formed, sparingly soluble prisms tended to separate first (or to remain undissolved on warming) and that the needle-like crystals which sometimes separated were always contaminated by prisms, even after recrystallization of mechanically separated needles. Eventually it was recognized that interconversion of diastereoisomers must be occurring on recrystallization and the strategy finally adopted was to heat mother liquors in 80% propan-2-ol on a steam-bath during the day and to collect the prisms that separated overnight. In this way, despite handling losses, a total of 9.35 g of prisms, m.p. 193—196° (decomp.), was obtained. These all showed $[\alpha]_D^{20}$ −0.5° (*c* 1.43 in 80% methanol) and may be substantially pure *brucine* (+)-*isamate* (Found: C, 64.05; H, 5.8; N, 9.9. $C_{23}H_{26}N_2O_4$,$C_{16}H_{11}N_3O_3$,$3H_2O$ requires C, 64.0; H, 5.9; N, 9.55%).

The salt (3.15 g) was decomposed by prolonged shaking with chloroform and aqueous ammonia (1.7N; 50 ml) until the layers separated clean and clear. The aqueous layer was extracted several times with chloroform and the excess of ammonia was removed at low pressure with slight warming. A sample (10 ml) of this solution (60 ml) was reserved; the remainder was carefully acidified with hydrochloric acid (2N) to pH 2. The red crystalline precipitate was collected, dried (1.1 g), and recrystallized rapidly without heating by dissolving it in methanol, concentrating the filtered solution, and carefully adding water. The fine red needles (0.85 g) of (+)-*isamic acid*, m.p. 159—165° (decomp.) had an i.r. spectrum almost identical with that of (±)-isamic acid (Found: C, 61.9; H, 3.85; N, 13.65. $C_{16}H_{11}N_3O_3$,H_2O requires C, 61.75; H, 4.2; N, 13.5%). In methanol (*c* 0.235) it showed $[\alpha]_D^{20}$ +90° when fresh; after 3 days at 20 °C the specific rotation had sunk to +68° and it was +54° after 6 days.

The aqueous solution of the ammonium salt initially showed $[\alpha]_D^{20}$ −6.6° (*c* 2.23; reckoned on anhydrous ammonium isamate). An aliquot portion diluted with 4 volumes of methanol was dextrorotatory: $[\alpha]_D^{20}$ +1.8°. The rotatory power of the aqueous solution fell steadily at 20 °C. After 8 weeks, when the rotation was *ca.* 6% of the initial value, the solution was concentrated somewhat at low pressure and acidified. The red crystalline precipitate was identified as (±)-isamic acid by its i.r. spectrum and its negligible optical rotation. The ammonium salt in 80% methanol appeared to undergo racemization more slowly.

To test whether the violet cation from (+)-isamic acid retained chirality, (+)-isamic acid (20 mg in 2 ml of methanol) was added to concentrated hydrochloric acid (1.652 ml). After 30 s the deep violet solution was poured into ice-cold potassium hydroxide (20% in methanol) equivalent to the hydrochloric acid. A control solution was made by mixing the acid and the alkali before adding the (+)-isamic acid. The filtered solutions were examined: the control showed α_D +0.351° and the test solution α_D +0.285°.

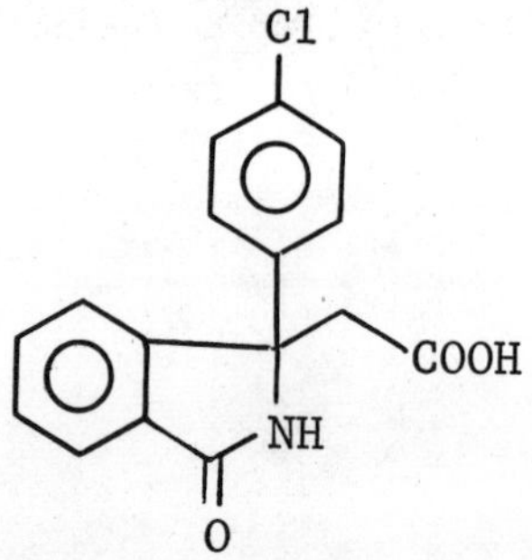

$C_{16}H_{12}ClNO_3$ Ref. 1124

(*S*)-(+)-3-(4-Chlorophenyl)-3-phthalimidineacetic Acid (8b). Separation of Racemic 8a. A solution of 222.0 g (0.74 mol) of the racemic acid **8a** in 2.5 L of hot methanol was treated with 295.0 g (0.75 mol) of brucine in 0.8 L of methanol. A solid formed immediately and was filtered from the cold solution, washed with methanol/ether, and dried to give 260 g of the complex. This was suspended in 500 mL of methanol and acidified with 160 mL of 2 N HCl solution. The mixture was cooled and the solid acid removed by filtration. The crude acid was dissolved in hot methanol and precipitated by the addition of 20 mL of concentrated HCl followed by the addition of 150 mL of water. The acid was recrystallized from hot methanol: yield 76.0 g (69%); mp 215–217 °C; mass spectrum, *m/e* 301 (M^+); $[\alpha]_D$ +236.5° (*c* 0.95); NMR (Me_2SO-d_6) δ 3.35 (q, 2, *J* = 16 Hz, Δν = 13.6 Hz, CH_2), 7.2–7.8 (m, 8, 2 C_6H_4); IR (Nujol) 3350, 3440 (NH, COOH), 1725, 1710 (COOH), 1665 cm^{-1} (lactam). Anal. Calcd for $C_{16}H_{12}ClNO_3$ (mol wt 301.7): C, 63.7; H, 4.0; N, 4.6; Cl, 11.7. Found: C, 63.3; H, 4.2; N, 4.6; Cl, 11.8.

(*R*)-(−)-3-(4-Chlorophenyl)-3-phthalimidineacetic Acid

(8c). The filtrate containing the soluble brucine complex was evaporated to dryness, acidified with concentrated HCl, and diluted with water. The acid was collected by filtration and recrystallized from hot methanol: yield 49.5 g (44.6%); mp 215–216 °C; $[\alpha]_D$ −244.5° (*c* 0.89); second crop yield 20.5 g (18.5%); mp 213–215 °C; $[\alpha]_D$ −221.9° (*c* 0.92).

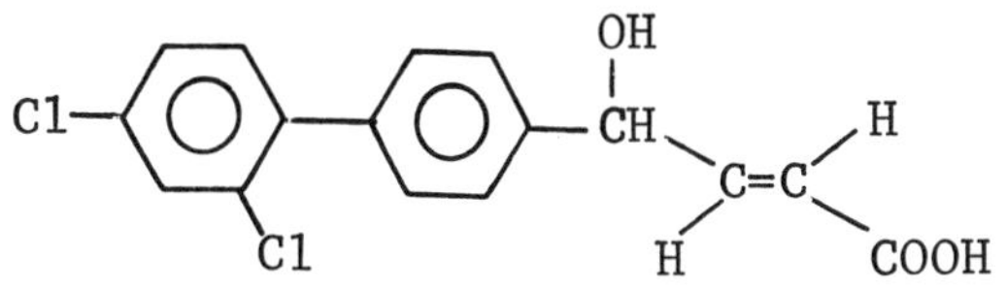

$C_{16}H_{12}Cl_2O_3$ Ref. 1125

Note:
Obtained acids with $[\alpha]_D^{23}$ +45.1° (c 0.5, CH_3OH) and $[\alpha]_D^{23}$ -24.7° (c 0.5, CH_3OH) in a manner analogous to procedure in Ref. 1133

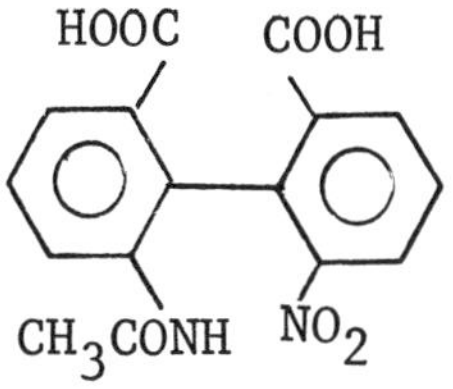

$C_{16}H_{12}N_2O_7$ Ref. 1126

(B) Resolution of *dl*-6-Nitro-6′-acetamidodiphenic acid (VI), and its Conversion into 5-Nitrophenanthridone-4-carboxylic Acid (XI). Attempts to resolve *dl*-6-nitro-6′-acetamidodiphenic acid with brucine have not been successful. An easy resolution, however, has been accomplished through the strychnine salts.

Acid Strychnine l-6-nitro-6′-acetamidodiphenate. A hot solution of strychnine (6.68 g.) in chloroform (40 c.c.) was added to a boiling solution of *dl*-6-nitro-6′-acetamidodiphenic acid (6.88 g.) in methanol (280 c.c.) and the resulting solution was heated under reflux for 1.0 to 1.5 hours. The acid strychnine *l*-6-nitro-6′-acetamidodiphenate usually began to appear as yellow needles after 20 to 40 minutes' heating. Most of the salt separated while heating, but it was allowed to stand overnight to complete crystallization. As the yellow needles are very difficultly soluble in cold methanol, the *l*-acid present could be separated almost completely in this form, which, after being filtered, could be thoroughly washed with the solvent. (The mother liquor obtained here was used for the separation of the strychnine salts of the *d*-acid as described later.) The yellow needles obtained in this way were found to be so pure that further purification was unnecessary. No change was observed in the melting point (273° with decomposition), in the analytical results, and in the rotation before and after recrystallization from methanol (Found: C, 66.1; H, 5.8; N, 8.4. Calculated for $C_{16}H_{12}O_7N_2 \cdot C_{21}H_{22}O_2N_2$: C, 65.5; H, 5.0; N, 8.3%. Rotation: 0.0226 g. of the substance made up to 15 c.c. with methanol gave $\alpha_D^{20} = -0.22°$ for $l = 2$, hence $[\alpha]_D^{20} = -73.0°$). To dissolve one gram of the acid strychnine salt of the *l*-acid, it is necessary to boil it with 300 c.c. of methanol for a considerable time. The yellow needles dried in the desiccator somewhat gain weight on exposure to the moist air.

Acid Strychnine d-6-Nitro-6′-acetamidodiphenate. This salt was obtained by concentrating the mother liquor separated from the yellow needles of the acid strychnine salt of the *l*-acid described above. It was often found necessary to inoculate or to scratch the wall of the vessel to start crystallization. It separated usually as crystals free from methanol, but occasionally it happened that crystals containing one molecule of the solvent was formed, which almost completely melted at 175°, where the other showed no change. Both were decomposed, however, at the same temperature, 263°C. They were both nearly colourless, a property in which they differ from the distinctly yellow salt of the *l*-acid. The separation of the acid strychnine salt of the *d*-acid from a methyl alcoholic solution was so sluggish that it was not complete even after leaving overnight, but by evaporation of the solvent on the water bath a greatly supersaturated solution could be obtained, from which the major part of the salt separated fairly quickly on cooling. Crystallized in this way, it formed clusters of almost colourless plates containing no methanol. (The methanol containing substance lost 4.7 per cent. in weight at 80°. Calculated for $C_{28}H_{34}O_9N_4 \cdot CH_3OH$: CH_3OH, 4.5%. Found for methanol-free substance: C, 65.8; H, 5.6. Calculated for $C_{28}H_{34}O_9N_4$: C, 65.5; H, 5.4%. Rotation: 0.0678 g. of substance not containing methanol made up to 15 c.c. with methanol gave $\alpha_D^{20} = +0.33°$ for $l = 2$; hence $[\alpha]_D^{20} = +36.5°$.)

Neutral Strychnine d-6-Nitro-6′-acetamidodiphenate. As stated above, the crystallization of the acid strychnine salt of the *d*-acid from the methyl alcoholic mother liquor is very sluggish and, moreover, incomplete, a rather large loss of the material being caused. On the other hand, the neutral strychnine salt of the *d*-acid separates from methanol more completely and more quickly, and, therefore, it is better to isolate the *d*-acid in this form. For this purpose, the boiling methyl alcoholic solution (the filtrate separated from the *l*-acid salt) containing the acid strychnine salt of the *d*-acid was treated with a solution of the required quantity of strychnine in chloroform, and the resulting solution concentrated into one-third the original bulk. On cooling, the neutral salt of the *d*-acid appeared in colourless, voluminous needles. In this way, from 6.88 g. of the *dl*-acid, 9.0 g. of neutral strychnine salt was obtained. One recrystallization from methanol (90 c.c.) sufficed to obtain the salt in pure state. It melted at 175° almost completely and decomposed slowly at 207°. It had two molecules of methanol removable by heating at 80°C. (The substance lost 6.2 per cent. in weight at 80°C. Calculated for $C_{58}H_{56}O_{11}N_6 \cdot 2CH_3OH$: CH_3OH, 6.0%. Found for methanol-free substance: C, 68.3; H, 6.1. Calculated for $C_{58}H_{56}O_{11}N_6$: C, 68.8; H, 5.5%. Rotation: 0.1012 g. of substance freed from methanol made up to 15 c.c. with methanol gave $\alpha_D^{20} = +0.16°$ for $l = 2$; hence $[\alpha]_D^{20} = +11.9°$.)

d- and l-6-Nitro-6′-acetamidodiphenic acids. A mixture of 0.1695 g. of the acid strychnine *d*(or *l*)-6-nitro-6′-acetamidodiphenate (corresponding to 0.0860 g. of the free acid) and a slight excess of ammonia was shaken repeatedly with chloroform until the solution was free from strychnine, and the solution was diluted up to 15 c.c. with water. It had $\alpha_D = \pm 1.40°$ for $l = 2$; hence $[\alpha]_D = \pm 122.1°$. The neutral strychnine salt of the *d*-acid (0.1012 g. which contain 0.0344 g. of the free acid) was treated in the same way with aqueous ammonia and chloroform. The solution made up to 15 c.c. gave $\alpha_D = +0.56°$ for $l = 2$; hence $[\alpha]_D = +122.1°$.

The rotation of the active acids had to be examined in the way described above because of the difficulty in isolating the active forms in pure crystalline state. Unlike the *dl*-form, the active forms are very soluble in water and, moreover, when forced to separate from a solution, they tend to form an oil which crystallizes with difficulty. These properties rendered the isolation of the active acids in pure state impossible. Thus, for instance, when a concentrated aqueous solution of the ammonium salt of the active acid, obtained by shaking the strychnine salt with ammonia and chloroform, was acidified with a large quantity of sulphuric acid, only a small portion of the active acid crystallized, which, for the above-mentioned reasons, could not be purified by crystallization.

The decomposition of the ammonium salt of the *l*-acid, obtained by drying its aqueous solution in vacuo, with the calculated amount of oxalic acid in acetone met with rather better success. On mixing an acetone solution of oxalic acid with that of the ammonium salt of the *l*-acid, ammonium oxalate separated, which was filtered off. The filtrate, on concentration followed by addition of chloroform, deposited a small quantity of an oil which, on being left overnight, formed light yellow thin needles (resembling the *dl*-acid in colour) melting at 93°C. with slight decomposition after softening at 85°C. It was readily soluble in acetone and methanol and insoluble in chloroform. It was not quite pure as indicated by the rotation (0.0344 g. of substance made up to 15 c.c. with methanol gave $\alpha_D = -0.33°$ for $l = 2$, while α_D for the *l*-acid, calculated from those of the three strychnine salts obtained under the same conditions as already described, is −0.50°). The yield of the crystals, 17 per cent. of the theoretical, proved, however, to be too small for purification, and the matter was no further pursued.

The active acid appeared to racemize easily in concentrated hydrochloric acid at low temperatures. When a solution of the ammonium salt of the *d*-acid in 5 c.c. of water, obtained from the neutral strychnine salt (3.0 g.), was saturated with hydrogen chloride in a freezing mixture bath, ammonium chloride (0.2 g.) separated first. On filtration, the hitherto yellow solution suddenly turned brown in colour, a small quantity of brownish crystals separating. The brown colour, however, disappeared after a time. Evidently, this must have been the indication that at least a part of the substance had racemized, for the crystals (0.30 g.) collected after some time had α_D in methanol about one-fourth the value expected. The aqueous solution of the ammonium salt of the active acid is stable to heat, no change in optical activity being observed by heating on the water bath for a long time.

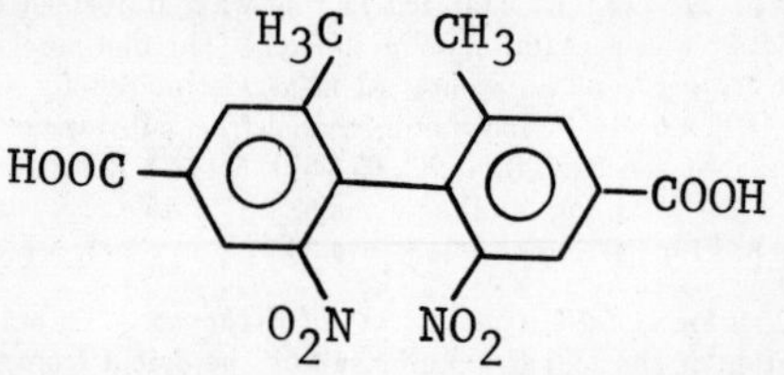

$C_{16}H_{12}N_2O_8$ Ref. 1127

Optical Activation of 2,2'-Dimethyl-6,6'-dinitro-4,4'-diphenic Acid (4).[8]—A solution of racemic 2,2'-dimethyl-6,6'-dinitro-4,4'-diphenic acid (40.2 g., m.p. 335–343° dec., lit.[8] m.p. above 340° dec.) in 800 ml. of boiling acetone was mixed with a solution of brucine (43.8 g.) in 1 l. of boiling acetone. The resulting crystals were recrystallized six times from 80% aqueous ethanol to give 14.3 g. of diastereomeric salt, $[\alpha]^{25}D$ −13° (*c* 0.795, dioxane). A slurry of the brucine salt (14.0 g.) in 100 ml. of water was warmed on the steam bath and 25 ml. of a 7 *M* solution of aqueous ammonia was added. The resulting yellow solution slowly deposited crystals of brucine upon standing in the refrigerator. The cold solution was filtered and the clear filtrate was acidified with 20% aqueous hydrochloric acid. The white precipitate was collected by filtration and was purified by dissolution in dilute Na_2CO_3 solution, followed by filtration and acidification of the filtrate with dilute aqueous hydrochloric acid. The resulting product after drying consisted of 6.0 g. of a white powder: m.p. 330–332° dec. (with some evidence of decomposition beforehand), $[\alpha]^{28.5}D$ −16.3° (*c* 1.23, 95% ethanol), lit.[8] $[\alpha]^{20}D$ −20° (ethanol). The infrared spectrum of a sample of (−)-**4** was superimposable on that of the racemic modification. The spectrum was dominated by a strong band at 5.88 μ, corresponding to the carbonyl stretching vibration, and by two bands at 6.50 and 7.45 μ, corresponding to the asymmetric and symmetric vibrations, respectively, of the nitro group.

A second resolution of racemic **4** gave 13.4 g. of optically active acid: m.p. 321–335° dec., $[\alpha]^{24}D$ −7.0 (ethanol). This was the sample of (−)-**4** which was subsequently used as the starting material in the synthesis described in Chart I.

Anal. Calcd. for $C_{16}H_{12}N_2O_8$: C, 53.34; H, 3.36; N, 7.78. Found: C, 53.87; H, 3.75; N, 7.62.

(8) H. Mix, *Ann.*, **592**, 146 (1955).

$C_{16}H_{12}N_2O_8$ Ref. 1127a

Spaltung der Dicarbonsäure (II) in die optischen Antipoden

9 g Dicarbonsäure (II) und 9,8 g Brucin wurden in der Hitze in 285 ccm Äthanol gelöst. Nach kurzem Sieden begannen wasserklare Kristalle von saurem Brucinsalz der rac. Dicarbonsäure auszufallen. Das nach 24 Stunden abgetrennte Salz (etwa 16 g vom Zersp. um 275°) wurde nun durch längeres Kochen in 250 ccm 80-proc. Äthanol erneut gelöst und mindestens 12 Stunden möglichst erschütterungsfrei stehengelassen. Danach waren 12 g Salz in Form strahliger, gelber Nädelchen auskrist., in denen sich jetzt die (—)-Dicarbonsäure erheblich angereichert hatte. Das Umkristallisieren wurde aus der jeweils 15-fachen Menge 80-proc. Äthanol so lange fortgesetzt (4—5-mal), bis das Salz in Dioxan eine spez. Drehung $[\alpha]_D^{20} = -11{,}5°$ zeigte. Blaßgelbe, verfilzte Nädelchen, unscharfer Schmp. 220—222°, nach Sintern > 200°.

$C_{39}H_{38}O_{12}N_4$ (754,73) Ber. N 7,43 Gef. N 7,52

Durch vorsichtiges Unterkühlen und Animpfen konnte es gelingen, daß schon am Anfang ein opt. akt. Produkt herauskam. Im allgemeinen waren aber die ersten Fraktionen auch äußerlich mehr oder weniger stark von dem partiellen Racemat begleitet.

Zur Zerlegung wurde das Spaltungsprodukt in der Wärme mit verd. Ammoniak behandelt. Das in der Kälte auskristallisierte Brucin wurde abfiltriert und die opt. akt. Dicarbonsäure (II) aus der Mutterlauge ausgefällt. Ihre spez. Drehung betrug in Alkohol $[\alpha]_D^{20} = -20°$. Aus 9 g rac. (II) wurden durchschnittlich 3 g des opt. reinen (—)-Antipoden erhalten.

Da die Mutterlaugen besonders der zweiten und dritten Kristallfraktion das Brucinsalz des (+)-Antipoden in bedeutendem Überschuß enthielten, wurden diese Lösungen vereinigt, eingedampft und der Rückstand wie oben zerlegt. Es wurden etwa 3,5 g Dicarbonsäure (II) mit einer spez. Drehung $[\alpha]_D^{20} = +12°$ bis +14° (Alk., c = 1) erhalten. Dieses Produkt wurde 3-mal aus Eisessig umkristallisiert: 1,5 g Dicarbonsäure, welche nur noch schwach optisch aktiv war. Aus den Eisessigmutterlaugen konnte die opt. fast reine (+)-Verbindung isoliert werden. 2 g, $[\alpha]_D^{20} = +19{,}5°$ (Alk., c = 1).

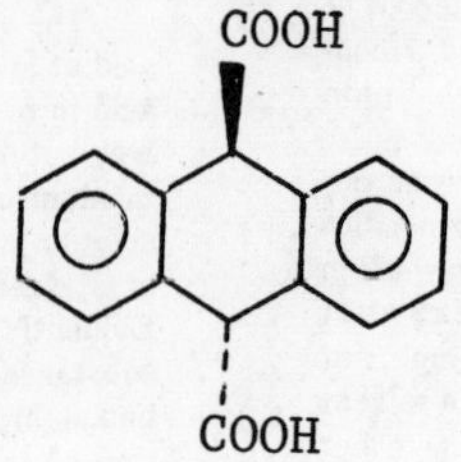

$C_{16}H_{12}O_4$ Ref. 1128

L'acide *trans* a été dédoublé aux antipodes optiques par la méthode de cristallisation fractionnée des sels diastéréomériques avec les bases alcaloïdiques. La séparation de l'acide racémique de l'énantiomère lévogyre a été réalisée à l'usage du sel brucinique. Le sel optiquement pur présentait des aiguilles (de l'éthanol), F. 167—173° avec déc. et $(\alpha)_D^{20} = -26{,}25°$ (méthanol). Libéré de cette base, l'antimère lévogyre, après cristallisation dans le méthanol,

fondait à 174—175° avec déc. et avait $(\alpha)_D^{20}$ = −20,00° (méthanol). Pendant l'élimination du second antimère, le meilleur résultat a été obtenu avec la quinine. Le sel (F. 197—198°) de cette base (aiguilles), après quelques cristallisations de l'acétone diluée avait un pouv. rot. spéc. $(\alpha)_D^{20}$ = −122,50° (méthanol), inchangeable dans la suite de la purification. L'antimère dextrogyre obtenu du sel quininique accusait les mêmes propriétés physiques que l'antimère lévogyre, différant seulement par la direction de la rotation (F. 274—275° avec déc., $(\alpha)_D^0$ = +19,60°, méthanol).

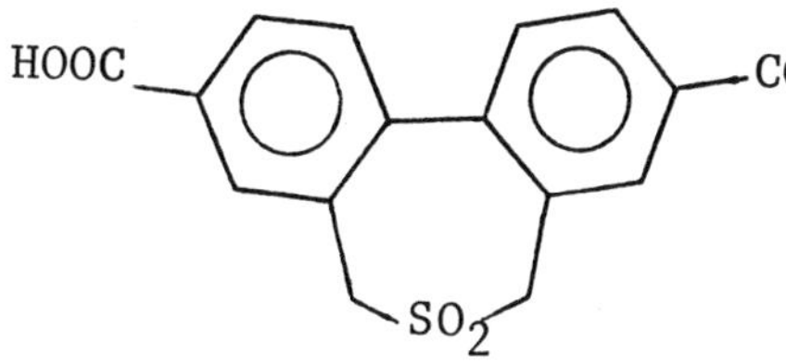

$C_{16}H_{12}O_6S$ Ref. 1129

Resolution of 2,7-Dihydro-3,4-5,6-dibenzothiepin-1-dioxide-2′,3″-dicarboxylic Acid *via* its Hydrogen *d*-Cinchonine Salt.—In about 150 ml. of ethanol 1.380 g. of 2,7-dihydro-3,4-5,6-dibenzothiepin-1-dioxide-2′,3″-dicarboxylic acid and 1.221 g. of *d*-cinchonine were dissolved and the resulting solution was evaporated down to about 70 ml. About 80 ml. of hot water was added and the mixture was allowed to cool slowly and crystallize spontaneously for a period of 48 hours. Fine crystalline masses were deposited. The initially deposited crystals were filtered off and the mother liquors were allowed to crystallize spontaneously for 48 hours at room conditions to give a second fraction of crystals. In like manner, third and fourth fractions of crystals were obtained. These four fractions had the following respective specific rotations: (1) $[\alpha]^{23}D$ +90.0° (l = 2 dm.; c 1.510 g., ethanol); [2] $[\alpha]^{30}D$ +93.7° (l = 2 dm.; c 0.7652 g., ethanol); (3) $[\alpha]^{29}D$ +98.8° (l = 2 dm.; c 0.7748 g., ethanol); (4) $[\alpha]^{25}D$ +121° (l = 4 dm.; c 0.1832 g., ethanol). By recrystallization and consolidation of these fractions from 20–30% ethanol (in water) fractions were obtained, which were subjected to decomposition with hydrochloric acid. For a period of 75 minutes a pulverized sample (0.830 g.) of the less dextrorotatory sample of the cinchonine hydrogen salt was stirred and intimately mixed with 90 ml. of cold 2 N hydrochloric acid at −5 to −10°. The mixture was filtered (sintered glass funnel) and the residual dicarboxylic acid was macerated with an additional 100 ml. of cold 2 N hydrochloric acid at −5° for a period of 15–20 minutes. Filtration was followed by washing the cold residue with an additional 100 ml. of cold 3 N hydrochloric acid and then with three successive 100-ml. portions of cold water (0°). The residual cold dicarboxylic acid was then dissolved in 25 ml. of cold (−5 to 0°) 0.5 N ammonia in 5% aqueous urea solution and filtered. The resulting solution of the ammonium salt of 2,7-dihydro-3,4-5,6-dibenzothiepin-1-dioxide-2′,3″-dicarboxylic acid when examined in a 2 dm. polarimeter tube, had $\alpha^{29}D$ +0.14°; this corresponds to $[\alpha]^{29}D$ +1.81° (l 4 cm.; c 1.936 g., diammonium salt, 0.5 N ammonia in 5% aqueous urea) for the diammonium salt of the acid.

In exactly the same manner as that just described, the more dextrorotatory fraction (0.860 g.) gave a diammonium salt in 25 ml. of 0.5 N ammonia and 5% urea having $\alpha^{25}D$ +0.225° when examined in a 4 dm. macro polarimeter tube; this corresponds to $[\alpha]^{25}D$ +3.1° (l 4 dm.; c 1.828 g., 0.5 N ammonia in 5% aqueous urea) for the acid, or expressed in respect to the diammonium salt, $[\alpha]^{25}D$ +2.85° (l = 4 dm.; c 1.98 g., diammonium salt; 0.5 N ammonia in 5% aqueous urea).

Since there is abundant evidence that in most simple cinchonine salts optical activity is relatively additive,[23] it would appear that the material is extensively racemized during the conversion of the cinchonine acid salt to the ammonium salt. This is confirmed by the difficulty in obtaining an active acid from the brucine salt (see above), by the fact that, effectively, only one (the dextrorotary) antipode can be isolated from recrystallization of the acid cinchonine salt.

Anal. Calcd. for $C_{19}H_{22}N_2O \cdot C_{16}H_{12}SO_6 \cdot 2H_2O$: C, 63.42; H, 5.78; N, 4.23. Found: C, 63.70; H, 5.50; N, 4.28; $[\alpha]^{23}D$ +90°.

(23) H. Landolt, ref. 21, p. 681; A. C. Oudemans, *Ann.*, **182**, 55 (1876). Anomalous activities are sometimes observed with alkaloid salts, especially salts, of unsaturated acids, *cf.* T. P. Hilditch, *J. Chem. Soc.*, **93**, 1388 (1908); **95**, 335, 1570 (1909); **99**, 224 (1911).

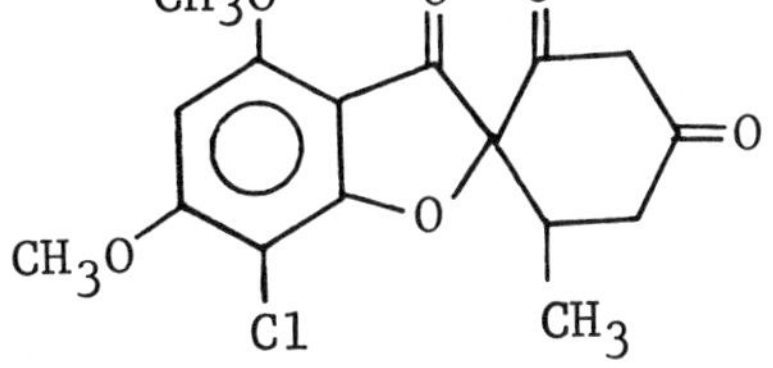

$C_{16}H_{13}ClO_6$ Ref. 1130

Resolution of (±) griseofulvic acid

A solution of 390 mg (±) griseofulvic acid in 10 ml methanol was treated with 10·65 ml 0·108 N cinchonine N-methohydroxide[39] and the solution subsequently evaporated to dryness *in vacuo* and flushed several times with ethanol followed by benzene. The amorphous mixed salts were dissolved in a small volume methanol and the latter displaced with acetone in the hot to the point of near turbidity. The solution was seeded at this point with N-methyl cinchonine salt prepared from (+) griseofulvic acid and allowed to crystallize for 3–4 days. The deposited N-methylcinchonine salt of (+) griseofulvic acid was filtered and washed with acetone; 305 mg, m.p. 228–230°. Recrystallization afforded 230 mg, m.p. 230–232·5°. Further crystallization did not raise the m.p. further. A mixed m.p. with a sample of N-methylcinchonine salt prepared from (+) griseofulvic acid showed no depression and the IR spectra of the two samples were the same. $[\alpha]_D^{24°}$ +314 (c = 1·02, CH_3OH). (Found: C, 66·87; H, 6·10; N, 4·05; Cl, 5·36; Calc. for $C_{36}H_{39}N_2O_7Cl$: C, 66·77; H, 6·03; N, 4·33; Cl, 5·49%).

A second resolution with 430 mg ± griseofulvic acid in 20 ml ethanol and 11·8 ml 0·10 N cinchonine N-methohydroxide yielded 290 mg recrystallized (+) salt, m.p. 228–230°.

(+) *Griseofulvic acid* XXI *from its N-Methyl cinchonine salt*

A 400 mg sample of the N-methyl cinchonine salt of (+) griseofulvic acid was dissolved in 25 ml hot water and acidified with 2·5 N HCl. The precipitated (+) griseofulvic acid was crystallized from methanol (160 mg), m.p. 259–261°, $[\alpha]_D^{24°}$ +201° (*c* = 0·99 pyridine). (Found: C, 56·86; H, 4·30; Cl, 10·30; Calc. for $C_{16}H_{15}O_6Cl$: C, 56·73; H, 4·47; Cl, 10·47%).

(−) *Griseofulvic acid* (XXI)

The mother liquors from the resolutions after separation of all possible (+) salt, remained amorphous despite attempts to induce crystallization of a (−) salt. These mother liquors were decomposed with excess 2·5 N HCl and the precipitated material extracted with ethyl acetate, which was evaporated and the residue crystallized from methanol, m.p. 252–256°. Recrystallization from methanol gave material with m.p. 261·5–263°; (80 mg) $[\alpha]_D^{24}$ −201 (*c* = 0·093, pyridine). The IR spectrum was identical with that of (+) griseofulvic acid in pyridine solution. (Found: C, 56·76; H, 4·34; Cl, 10·47; Calc. for $C_{16}H_{15}O_6Cl$: C, 56·73; H, 4·47; Cl, 10·47%).

[39] Prepared by a modification of the method of R. Major and J. Finkelstein (*J. Amer. Chem. Soc.* 63, 1368 (1947) wherein the N-methiodide of cinchonine is prepared in tetrahydrofuran solution. Care must be exercised that the cinchonine methochloride precursor of the hydroxide base does not contain sodium chloride since otherwise it will provide sodium hydroxide in the silver oxide reaction and precipitate the sodium salt of griseofulvic acid in the resolution step.

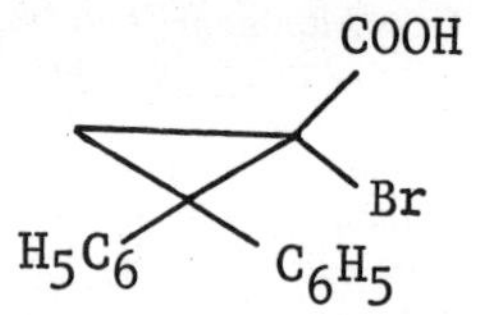

$C_{16}H_{13}BrO_2$ Ref. 1131

Note:

Resolved using brucine. Acid obtained had following physical constants: m.p. 184-185.5° $[\alpha]_D^{23}$ +112.2° ± 2.5° (c 1.061, $CHCl_3$). Mother liquors treated with quinine. Acid finally obtained had m.p. 185-186°, $[\alpha]_D^{22}$ -109° ± 2.5° (c 1.104, $CHCl_3$).

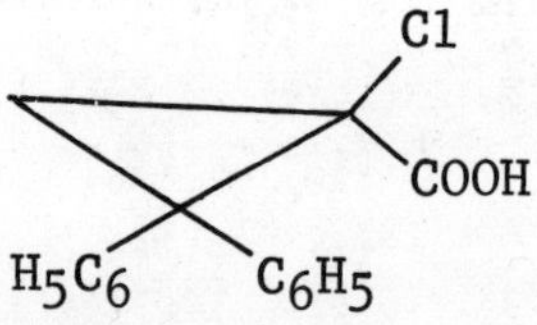

$C_{16}H_{13}ClO_2$ Ref. 1132

(−)-1-Chloro-2,2-diphenylcyclopropanecarboxylic Acid.—The (−)-enantiomer was obtained from its quinine salt by fractional recrystallization from N,N-dimethylformamide, after obtaining the salt from a methanol solution. The analytical sample had m.p. 193–194°, $[\alpha]^{21.5}{}_D$ −77.6 ± 2.1° (*c* 1.074).

Anal. Calcd. for $C_{16}H_{13}ClO_2$: C, 70.46; H, 4.80; Cl, 13.00. Found: C, 70.21; H, 4.90; Cl, 12.78.

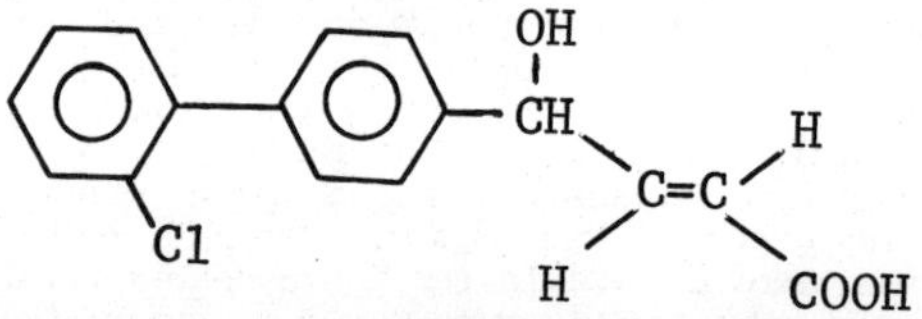

$C_{16}H_{13}ClO_3$ Ref. 1133

EXAMPLE 54

(+)- and (−)-4-[2″-chloro-biphenyl-(4′)]-4-hydroxy-crotonic acid

45.1 gm. of (±)-4-[2″-chloro-biphenylyl-(4′)]-4-hydroxy-crotonic acid were precipitated from 250 ml. of acetone as its salt with (−)-α-phenyl-ethyl-amine. The raw salt (46.0 gm., M.P. 166–168° C.) was recrystallized once from 5 liters and twice from 2 liters of boiling water; during the third recrystallization the precipitated salt was collected by vacuum filtration at 52° C. 15 gm. of the sparsely soluble diastereomeric salt, M.P. 165–166° C., were thus obtained. The free (+)-4-[2″-chloro-biphenylyl-(4′)]-4-hydroxy-crotonic acid liberated therefrom with acetic acid had a specific rotation $[\alpha]_D^{23}$=+6.6° (c.=0.5 in methanol). Its morpholine salt had a melting point of 152–153° C. and a specific rotation $[\alpha]_D^{23}$=+3.52° (c.=0.5 in methanol).

The aqueous mother liquors from the racemate separation were evaporated, and the residue was again fractionally crystallized. The free (−)-4-[2″-chloro-biphenylyl-(4′)]-4-hydroxy-crotonic acid (3.4 gm.) liberated from the salt thus obtained with acetic acid had a specific rotation $[\alpha]_D^{23}$=−8.0° (c.=0.5 in methanol); its morpholine salt had a melting point of 152–154° C. and a specific rotation $[\alpha]_D^{23}$=−3.13° (c.=0.5 in methanol).

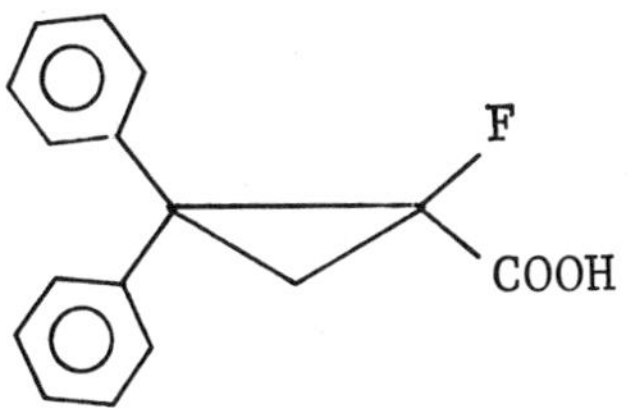

$C_{16}H_{13}FO_2$ Ref. 1134

(+)-(*R*)- and (−)-(*S*)-1-Fluoro-2,2-diphenylcyclopropanecarboxylic Acid.—The salt obtained by adding 52.6 g (0.212 mol) of the above racemic acid to 99.0 g (0.212 mol) of brucine in acetone was crystallized from acetone to constant rotation (six times). Hydrolysis with hydrochloric acid yielded acid, $[\alpha]^{25}_{Hg}$ −155 ± 1° (*c* 1.2, acetone), and an additional crystallization of the acid from dimethylformamide did not change the rotation.

The mother liquors from the first two of the above crystallizations yielded on hydrolysis 39.7 g of acid, $[\alpha]^{25}_{Hg}$ +13°, which was combined with 52 g (0.16 mol) of quinine in acetone. One crystallization of the salt afforded on hydrolysis acid of the above maximum, but opposite, rotation. A second crystallization of the acid from acetone and another from ethanol produced no change in rotation.

The resolved acid crystallized from chloroform as cubes: mp 181–183°; $[\alpha]^{25}_{Hg}$ +155° (*c* 1.0, acetone); ir (KBr) 3235 (ν, OH), 1741, 1708 (d, C=O), 1226 (β, COH), and 821 cm⁻¹ (γ, C=OH–); the nmr ($CDCl_3$) was identical with that of the racemic acid.

Anal. Calcd for $C_{16}H_{13}FO_2$: C, 74.99; H, 5.11. Found: C, 75.12; H, 5.25.

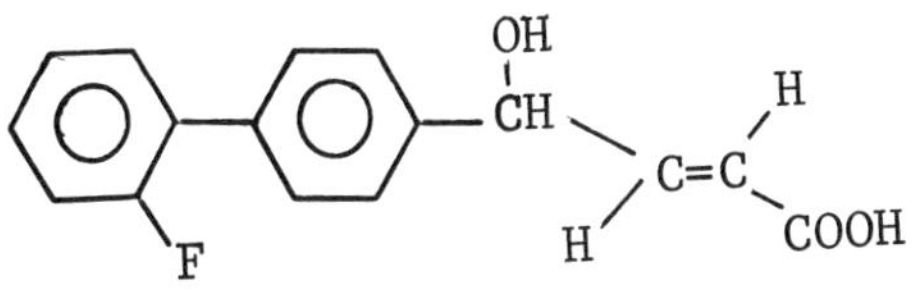

$C_{16}H_{13}FO_3$ Ref. 1135

Note:
Obtained acids with $[\alpha]^{23}_{D}$ +34.0° (c 0.5, CH_3OH) and $[\alpha]^{23}_{D}$ -29.1° (c 0.5 CH_3OH) in a manner analogous to procedure in Ref. 1133

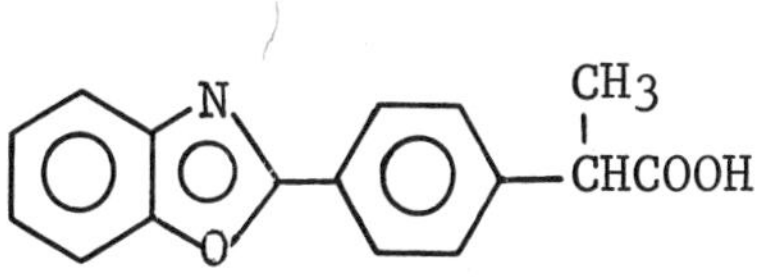

$C_{16}H_{13}NO_3$ Ref. 1136

EXAMPLE 5

Resolution of 2-(4-[Benzoxazol-2-yl]phenyl)propionic Acid

A. 1-isomer

To a solution of 3.0 gm. of 2-(4-[benzoxazol-2-yl]phenyl)propionic acid in 200 cc. of ether-methylene chloride (1:1) is added 3.0 ml. of (-)-α-methylbenzylamine. The resulting salt precipitates and is collected by filtration to give 4.0 gm. of the amine salt of the acid. Repeated recrystallization from acetone (5 times from 100–150cc. acetone) gives 0.666 gm. of salt which when dissolved in methanol-water and treated with concentrated hydrochloric acid gives 1-2-(4-[benzoxazol-2-yl]phenyl)propionic acid, m.p. 175°–177°C. $[\alpha]_D = -45.1 \pm 0.8°$.

B. d-isomer

A mixture of 2.0 gm. of d-enriched 2-(4-[benzoxazol-2-yl]phenyl)propionic acid recovered from the mother liquors of the above recrystallizations and 2.5 gm. of cinchonidine is heated in 500 cc. of chloroform until solution occurs and is then concentrated in vacuo to give a yellow white solid. Repeated recrystallization from acetone (5X) gives 1.6 gm. of salt which when taken up between benzene-ether and dilute hydrochloric acid yields from the organic layer d-2-(4-[benzoxazol-2-yl]phenyl) propionic acid. Recrystallization from methanol-water gives the pure product, m.p. 175°–178°C. $[\alpha]_D = +44.2 \pm 0°$.

Note: Solvent in which rotation was taken was methanol.

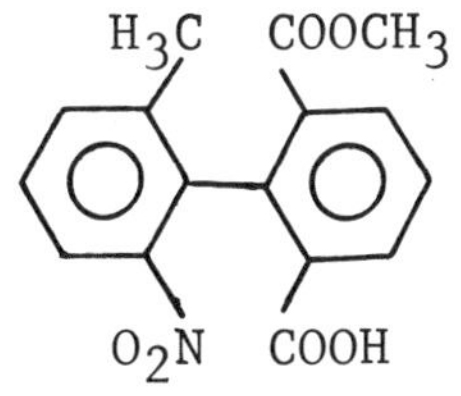

$C_{16}H_{13}NO_6$ Ref. 1137

Trennung des racemischen Gemisches von V über die Dehydroabietylamide in Enantiomeren. 1,000 g (3,17 mMol) des Dicarbonsäuremonomethylesters V wurden mit 3,0 ml Thionylchlorid 1,5 Std. zum Sieden erhitzt. Das überschüssige Reagens wurde abgedampft; nach Zusatz von je 5 ml trockenem Benzol wurde noch 2mal eingedampft. Die Lösung des rohen öligen Säurechlorids in 10 ml wasserfreiem Dioxan kühlte man bis nahe an den Gefrierpunkt und tropfte unter Rühren während 10 Min. eine Lösung von 2,0 g (7,0 mMol) (aus einer stöchiometrischen Menge des Acetats nach den Angaben von *W. J. Gottstein & L. C. Cheney* [10] hergestelltes) Dehydroabietylamin in 10 ml Dioxan hinzu. Es entstand eine Gallerte, welche mit 10 ml Dioxan und 2,0 ml Triäthylamin versetzt wurde. Nach 3 Std. Stehen bei Raumtemperatur war die Umsetzung beendet (Kontrolle mittels Dünnschichtchromatographie, Benzol/Äthylacetat/Eisessig 4:1:0,1, Rf (+)-Dehydroabietylamid 0,84, (−)-Dehydroabietylamid 0,76, Dehydroabietylamin 0,0).

Zur Entfernung des überschüssigen Dehydroabietylamins verfuhr man folgendermassen: Zufügen von 5 ml Eisessig zum Reaktionsgemisch, Filtration durch Kieselgel und Nachwaschen mit Benzol, Wiederholung dieser Operation, Eindampfen, Verteilung zwischen Äther und 1N Salzsäure sowie 5proz. Natriumhydrogencarbonat-Lösung, Waschen, Trocknen und Eindampfen der ätherischen Auszüge. Das zurückgebliebene gelbe Öl (2,5 g) wurde an 200 g Kieselgel mit Benzol/Äthylacetat 4:1 als Elutionsmittel chromatographiert. Man sammelte Fraktionen von je

10 ml und analysierte sie dünnschichtchromatographisch. Die Fraktionen 35–40 enthielten 574 mg (+)-, die Fraktionen 41–51 1053 mg eines Gemisches und die Fraktionen 52–60 138 mg (−)-Dehydroabietylamid. In einer zweiten Chromatographie gelang die Abtrennung von weiteren 268 mg des unreinen (−)-Dehydroabietylamids. Der Rest des Gemisches wurde aus Hexan fraktioniert umkristallisiert. Dabei schied sich stets aus der gesättigten Lösung des 1:1-Gemisches das (−)-, aus der auf die Hälfte eingeengten Mutterlauge das (+)-Dehydroabietylamid ab. Eine nochmalige Umkristallisation dieser Anteile ergab dünnschichtchromatographisch einheitliche Diastereomere. Die Vereinigung sämtlicher Mutterlaugen enthielt wieder 1:1-Gemisch, welches durch mehrmalige Wiederholung der oben beschriebenen Operationen vollständig zerlegt werden konnte. Die zum Schluss erhaltenen Diastereomeren wurden nochmals am Kieselgel chromatographiert.

(+)-(aS)-*6-Methoxycarbonyl-2'-methyl-6'-nitro-biphenyl-2-carbonsäure-dehydroabietylamid.* Die Ausbeute betrug 824 mg (89%), blassgelbe Rhomben, Smp. 169,5–170,5°. Zur Analyse wurde im Hochvakuum (150°/0,005 Torr) sublimiert. $[\alpha]_{578}^{23} = +152°$, $[\alpha]_{546}^{23} = +188°$, $[\alpha]_{436}^{23} = +625°$, ($c = 6{,}01$, Benzol). IR. (KBr): Banden u.a. bei 3385 (m), 1725 (s), 1660 (s), 1535 (m), 1515 (m), 1345 (m), 1280 (m), 1210 (w) mit Schulter 1200 (w), 1135 (m) cm^{-1}. NMR. ($CDCl_3$): δ 0,6–2,3 (*Sh*, 9H), 0,82 (*s*, 3H), 1,14 (*s*, 3H), 1,28 (*d*, $J = 7$, 6H), 1,90 (*s*, 3H), 2,3–3,0 (*Sh*, 4H), 3,4–3,7 (*Sh*, 1H), 3,53 (*s*, 3H), 6,38 (*t*, $J = 8$, 1H), 6,8–7,7 (*Sh*, 7H), 7,77 (*dd*, $J_1 = 7{,}5$, $J_2 = 1{,}5$, 1H), 7,98 (*dd*, $J_1 = 8$, $J_2 = 1{,}5$, 1H). MS.: M^+ 583.

$C_{36}H_{42}N_2O_5$ Ber. C 74,19 H 7,27 N 4,81% Gef. C 74,10 H 7,34 N 4,84%

(−)-(aR)-*6-Methoxycarbonyl-2'-methyl-6'-nitro-biphenyl-2-carbonsäure-dehydroabietylamid.* Man gewann 854 mg (92%) farblose Kristalle, Smp. 169–171°. Zur Analyse wurde im Hochvakuum (150°/0,005 Torr) sublimiert. $[\alpha]_{578}^{22} = -185°$, $[\alpha]_{546}^{22} = -227°$, $[\alpha]_{436}^{22} = -719°$, ($c = 6{,}00$, Benzol). IR. (KBr): Banden u.a. bei 3400 (m), 1730 (s), 1665 (s), 1525 (s), 1520 (s), 1355 (m), 1285 (m), 1200 (m) mit Schulter 1210 (w), 1130 (m) cm^{-1}. NMR. ($CDCl_3$): δ 0,6–1,8 (*Sh*, 8H), 0,71 (*s*, 3H), 1,13 (*s*, 3H), 1,27 (*d*, $J = 7$, 6H), 2,00 (*s*, 3H), 2,0–2,4 (*Sh*, 1H), 2,4–3,05 (*Sh*, 3H), 2,89 (*dd*, $J_1 = 13{,}5$, $J_2 = 8$, 1H), 3,24 (*dd*, $J_1 = 13{,}5$, $J_2 = 8$, 1H), 3,53 (*s*, 3H), 6,38 (*t*, $J = 8$, 1H), 6,85–7,65 (*Sh*, 7H), 7,74 (*dd*, $J_1 = 7{,}5$, $J_2 = 1{,}5$, 1H), 7,98 (*dd*, $J_1 = 8$, $J_2 = 1{,}5$, 1H). MS.: M^+ 583.

$C_{36}H_{42}N_2O_5$ Ber. C 74,19 H 7,27 N 4,81% Gef. C 74,24 H 7,38 N 4,83%

(−)-(aR)-*6-Methoxycarbonyl-2'-methyl-6'-nitro-biphenyl-2-carbonsäure* (*V*). Zu 5,7 g wasserfreiem Natriumacetat, welches mit Trockeneis gekühlt war, gab man 114,5 ml einer 0,15 M Lösung von Distickstofftetroxid in Tetrachlorkohlenstoff. Nach Erwärmen auf 0° und Zufügen von 1,807 g (3,10 mMol) des (−)-Dehydroabietylamids ($[\alpha]_{578}^{22,5} = -178°$, $c = 5{,}97$, Benzol) in 25 ml Tetrachlorkohlenstoff liess man die Mischung während 20 Std. bei 4° stehen. Die Isolierung des Nitrosamids erfolgte durch Verdünnen mit 200 ml eiskaltem Äther, Extraktion 3mal mit je 100 ml 5proz. Natriumhydrogencarbonat-Lösung (Eiszusatz), Waschen mit Eiswasser, Trocknen und Eindampfen bei Raumtemperatur. Das zurückgebliebene gelbe Öl (dünnschichtchromatographisch einheitlich, Ausbeute quantitativ) wurde im Hochvakuum bis zur Gewichtskonstanz getrocknet.

Zur Umlagerung wurde das rohe Nitrosamid in 60 ml Tetrachlorkohlenstoff während $5^1/_2$ Std. zum Sieden erhitzt, wobei peinlichst auf Feuchtigkeitsausschluss geachtet wurde. Man arbeitete auf, indem man die auf ein kleines Volumen eingeengte Lösung zwischen 200 ml Äther und 4mal je 75 ml 5proz. Natriumhydrogencarbonat-Lösung verteilte. Die organische Phase hinterliess nach Waschen, Trocknen und Eindampfen ein rotgelbes Öl, aus welchem die farbigen Anteile mittels Filtration der Lösung in Hexan/Benzol 4:1 durch 10 g Kieselgel weitgehend entfernt werden konnten. Zweimalige Destillation im Kugelrohr (140–150°/0,005 Torr) lieferte schliesslich 607 mg (73%) eines schwach gelben Öls. Es handelte sich hier, wie aus Spektren (IR., NMR.), Gas-Chromatogramm (Apiezon L, Kapillarkolonne) und Dünnschichtchromatogramm (Kieselgel, mit Silbernitrat imprägniert) ersichtlich war, um ein Kohlenwasserstoff-Gemisch, welches aus mindestens fünf Komponenten bestand. $[\alpha]_{578}^{23,5} = +204°$, $[\alpha]_{405}^{23,5} = +502°$ ($c = 1{,}66$, Chloroform). MS.: M^+ 268.

$C_{20}H_{28}$ Ber. C 89,49 H 10,51% Gef. C 89,78 H 10,51%

Aus den vereinigten wässerigen Phasen wurden durch vorsichtiges Ansäuern (pH 3–4), Extraktion mit Methylenchlorid und Waschen, Trocknen und Eindampfen der organischen Phasen 692 mg roher kristalliner (−)-Dicarbonsäure-monomethylester V erhalten, die durch Umkristallisation aus Benzol/Hexan 665 mg (68%) schöne blassgelbe Nadeln, Smp. 162,5–164°, ergaben. In einem anderen Versuch wurde zur Nitrosamidumlagerung 14 Std. gekocht, wodurch sich die Ausbeute (84%) merklich besserte. $[\alpha]_{578}^{23,5} = -86{,}9°$, $[\alpha]_{546}^{23,5} = -103°$, $[\alpha]_{436}^{23,5} = -268°$ ($c = 1{,}26$, Benzol). Das IR. (KBr) war deckungsgleich dem des racemischen Gemisches.

$C_{16}H_{13}NO_6$ Ber. C 60,95 H 4,16 N 4,44% Gef. C 61,20 H 4,24 N 4,36%

(+)-(aS)-*6-Methoxycarbonyl-2'-methyl-6'-nitro-biphenyl-2-carbonsäure* (*V*). Die Herstellung erfolgte analog zu derjenigen des Enantiomeren. Zur Nitrosamidumlagerung wurde 11 Std. gekocht, die Neutralteile wurden nicht untersucht. Ausgehend von 401 mg (+)-Dehydroabietylamid ($[\alpha]_{578}^{23,5} = +152°$, $c = 6{,}01$, Benzol) erhielt man 183 mg (84%) der Verbindung, die zur Analyse nochmals aus Benzol/Hexan umkristallisiert und im Hochvakuum (145°/0,05 Torr) sublimiert wurde, Smp. 163,5–165°. $[\alpha]_{578}^{23,5} = +89{,}4°$, $[\alpha]_{546}^{23,5} = +107°$, $[\alpha]_{436}^{23,5} = +276°$, ($c = 1{,}29$, Benzol).

$C_{16}H_{13}NO_6$ Ber. C 60,95 H 4,16 N 4,44% Gef. C 60,85 H 4,19 N 4,38%

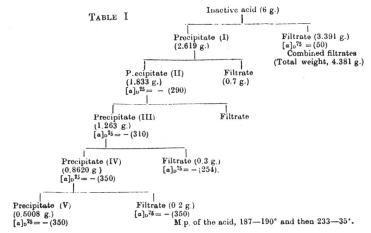

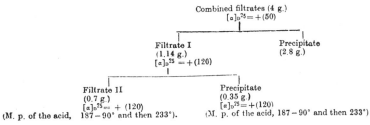

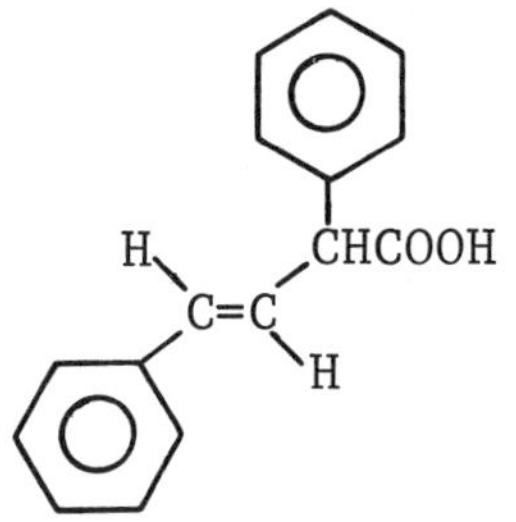

$C_{16}H_{14}O_2$ Ref. 1138

αγ-Diphenylglutaconic acid was prepared according to the method of Phalnikar and Nargund (*loc. cit*).

The method followed for resolving the acid was similar to the one used by McCombs *et al.* (*loc. cit.*) in resolving αγ-dimethylglutaconic acid. Strychnine (½ equivalent) was dissolved in chloroform and was added to a cold solution of the acid (4 equivalents) in ether. The precipitated strychnine salt was filtered after half an hour and the precipitate and filtrates were collected separately. The precipitated salt was washed with a mixture of chloroform and ether, and then decomposed by shaking with *N*-ammonia and the solution extracted with chloroform four times to remove all the strychnine. The ammoniacal salt solution of the acid was then decomposed with *N*-hydrochloric acid and the precipitated acid was taken up in ether. The ether layer was washed, dried and ether removed as usual. The residual acid was taken in a beaker and was dried in a vacuum desiccator, weighed and its rotation was found from the 1% solution of the acid in ethyl alcohol. This acid obtained in the first precipitation was fractionally reprecipitated a number of times till the final precipitated acid showed a constant rotation.

A Stanley-Belingham precision type polarimeter with an accuracy of 0.01 degree in sodium light was used The determinations were carried out in all the cases with a 2 dcm. tube at 25°. Absolute alcohol was used for preparing the solutions. Concentration of the solution was 1% (vol.) in each case. Table I summarises the results.

TABLE I

Inactive acid (6 g.)

- Precipitate (I) (2.619 g.)
  - Precipitate (II) (1.833 g.) $[\alpha]_D^{25}$ = − (290)
    - Precipitate (III) (1.263 g.) $[\alpha]_D^{25}$ = − (310)
      - Precipitate (IV) (0.8620 g) $[\alpha]_D^{25}$ = − (350)
        - Precipitate (V) (0.5008 g.) $[\alpha]_D^{25}$ = − (350)
        - Filtrate (0 2 g.) $[\alpha]_D^{25}$ = − (350) M.p. of the acid, 187—190° and then 233—35°.
      - Filtrate (0.3 g.) $[\alpha]_D^{25}$ = − (254).
    - Filtrate
  - Filtrate (0.7 g.)
- Filtrate (3.391 g.) $[\alpha]_D^{25}$ = (50) Combined filtrates (Total weight, 4.381 g.)

M.p of strychnine salt, 177°—180° ;
M.p. of acid, 187—90° and then 233—35°

After the fifth precipitation the specific rotation of the acid from the filtrate and of the acid from the precipitated strychnine salt was identical (−350). This shows that the substance was obtained as a pure *laevo*-form.

The filtrate was also subjected to the same treatment in order to obtain the pure *d*-form of the acid, but after the third precipitation it was found that the acid had a rotation which could not be increased by further fractional precipitation. Thus the *d*-form obtained was optically impure. Table II summarises the results.

TABLE II

Combined filtrates (4 g.) $[\alpha]_D^{25}$ = + (50)

- Filtrate I (1.14 g.) $[\alpha]_D^{25}$ = + (120)
  - Filtrate II (0.7 g.) $[\alpha]_D^{25}$ = + (120) (M. p. of the acid, 187 − 90° and then 233°).
  - Precipitate (0.35 g.) $[\alpha]_D^{25}$ = + (120) (M. p. of the acid, 187 − 90° and then 233°)
- Precipitate (2.8 g.)

As after the second precipitation, the specific rotation of the acid from the precipitate was the same + (120) as that from the filtrate, no further separation was assumed to be possible.

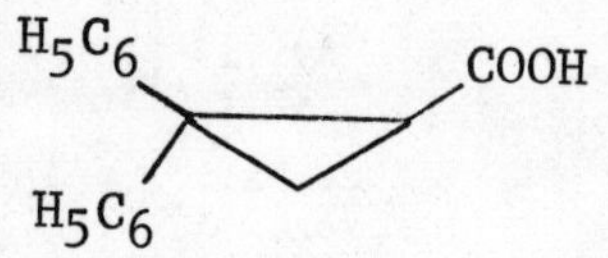

$C_{16}H_{14}O_2$ Ref. 1139

Resolution of I.—Thirty-one grams (0.13 mole) of acid was dissolved in 200 ml. of acetone with gentle warming. When solution was complete, 52 g. (0.13 mole) of anhydrous brucine alkaloid was added and the mixture again warmed and stirred to form a clear solution. On cooling in an ice-box overnight a crop of crystals was obtained. The crop was recrystallized from acetone by allowing the solution to undergo a slow evaporation at room temperature. In this way crops of brucine salt crystals weighing 3–5 g. were separated and their specific rotations taken. A negative specific rotation, $[\alpha]^{23}D$ $-112°$, was the maximum value obtainable. In like manner the mother liquor from the original crop was subjected to a slow evaporation and crops were obtained which had specific rotations, $[\alpha]^{23}D$ as high as $+30°$.

To hydrolyze the brucine salt the following procedure was found advantageous. The brucine salt was dissolved in a minimum amount of acetone and the solution cooled in an ice-bath. Concentrated hydrochloric acid was then added slowly with stirring until a precipitate formed and the mixture was acid to litmus. On addition of water the precipitate dissolved. The acetone was partially removed *in vacuo* and cold dilute hydrochloric acid added to make the mixture distinctly acid during which a second precipitate appeared. (The first precipitate was probably brucine hydrochloride.) The acid was fully precipitated by addition of water and filtered. After thorough washing with water and drying, 2,2-diphenylcyclopropanecarboxylic acid was obtained. The brucine salts having $[\alpha]^{23}D$ $-112°$ and $[\alpha]^{23}D$ $+30°$, gave the levorotatory and dextrorotatory acids, respectively, having $[\alpha]^{24}D$ $-216 \pm 6°$ and $[\alpha]^{24}D$ $+212 \pm 6°$ and melting at 150–151°. The brucine salt having $[\alpha]^{23}D$ $-40°$ afforded the racemic acid.

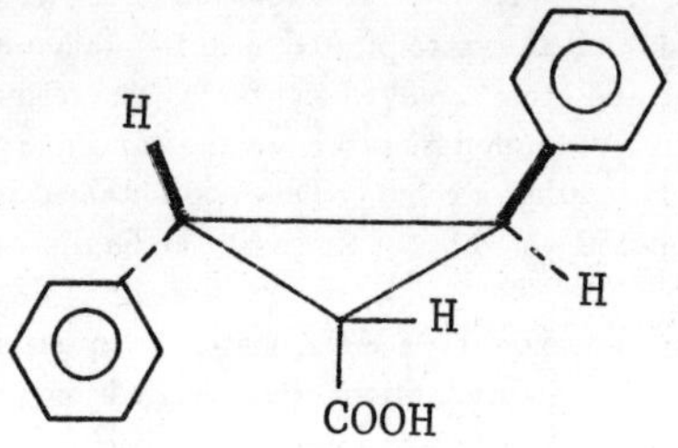

$C_{16}H_{14}O_2$ Ref. 1140

3. Trans-(+)-1,2-diphenylcyclopropane-3-carboxylic acid (IIa). A hot solution of 10.7 g of the trans-(+)-acid (II) in 100 ml of 95% alcohol was added to a hot solution of 14.5 g of (+)-quinine (free base) in 100 ml of alcohol. The voluminous precipitate which formed (22.4 g), consisting of a mixture of the quinine salts of the (+)-and (-)-acids (m. p. 208-212°), was placed in the thimble of a Soxhlet apparatus and extracted with alcohol. Extraction was continued until the melting point of the salt extracted from the thimble did not change when the operation was repeated. A yield of 10.7 g (85%) was obtained of a salt with m. p. 222-223°, very sparingly soluble in alcohol, which, as further investigation showed, was the quinine salt of the (+)-acid.

Found %: C 76.73, 76.75; H 6.91, 6.81; N 4.97. $C_{36}H_{38}O_4N_2$. Calculated %: C 76.88; H 6.76; N 4.98.

The salt obtained (10.7 g) was suspended in water and 2% alcoholic caustic soda was added to the suspension until it had gone completely into solution. The alcohol was distilled off, the residue of quinine was filtered off with suction and washed with water. The free (+)-acid was isolated by adding 10% sulfuric acid to the filtrate. Yield 3.5 g (76.9); m.p. 136-137°.

Found %: C 80.88, 80.40; H 5.97, 6.05. $C_{16}H_{14}O_2$. Calculated %: C 80.61; H 5.96.

$[\alpha_D]^{20}$	Solvent	Concentration (in g/l.)
+9.04	Chloroform	0.31
+9.12	Ditto	0.88
-23.52	Alcohol	0.21
-23.87	Ditto	0.23

It can be seen from the data given that the acid is dextrorotary in chloroform and levorotary in alcohol. It is called provisionally the (+)-acid.

From the combined alcoholic extracts taken from the Soxhlet apparatus after removing the salt of the (+)-acid from it, 11.2 g of the crude quinine salt of the (-)-acid, melting over a wide temperature range (205-212°) was obtained. Experiments to obtain pure material by additional crystallization of the crude salt from alcohol and other organic solvents gave no positive result. After decomposing the salt with alkali and then acidifying with mineral acid, an organic acid melting over the range 130-145° and showing only weak levorotation in chloroform was obtained. Apparently the (-)-acid was highly contaminated with the racemate. Attempts to purify the material were unsuccessful.

4. Trans-(-)-1,2-diphenylcyclopropane-3-carboxylic acid (IIb). A solution of 10.50 g of the racemic acid (II) in 100 ml of chloroform was added to a solution of 4.05 g of (-)-ephedrine in 20 ml of chloroform and the combined solutions were kept at 0° for 5 hours. The crystals of the crude ephedrine salt of the (+)-acid which separated (6.8 g, 73.1%), with m. p. 189-212°, were filtered off and washed with chloroform, but were not subjected to further purifica-

tion and subsequent decomposition in order to isolate the free (+)-acid. The mother liquors remaining after removal of the salt, were poured into a fresh portion of a solution of 4.05 g of (-)-ephedrine in 20 ml of chloroform and 50 ml of ether was added to the solution obtained. The colorless crystals of the (-)-ephedrine salt of the (-)-acid which separated melted at 145° (from ethyl acetate). Yield 4.0 g (54.3%).

Found %: C 73.71, 73.61; H 7.59, 7.63; N 3.38. $C_{26}H_{31}O_4N$. Calculated %: C 74.08; H 7.41; N 3.32.

To isolate the free acid (IIb), 4 g of the salt was treated with 50 ml of 2% caustic soda and the solution of the sodium salt of the acid (IIb)* obtained was acidified with 10% sulfuric acid. The acid (IIb) which separated was filtered off and dried. M. p. 136-137°. Yield 2 g (85%).

Found %: C 80.50, 80.36; H 6.06, 6.01. $C_{16}H_{14}O_2$. Calculated %: C 80.61; H 5.96.

$[\alpha_D]^{20}$	Solvent	Concentration (in g/liter)
- 9.04	Chloroform	0.52
- 9.11	Ditto	0.30
+23.49	Alcohol	0.23
+23.70	Ditto	0.21

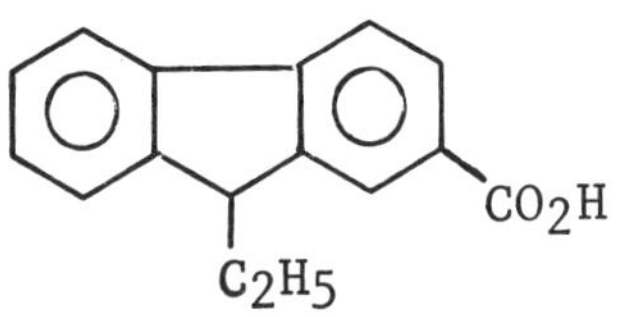

$C_{16}H_{14}O_2$ Ref. 1141

The authors reported that brucine was used to separate the (-) enantiomer (from either CH_3OH, acetone or an 8:2 mixture of acetone and chloroform). The physical constants of the brucine salt was found to be m.p. 103° (dec.) (CH_3OH); $[\alpha]_D^{20}$ -35.00° (CH_3OH). The liberated acid was found to have the following physical constants: m.p. 148-149° (CH_3OH), $[\alpha]_D^{20}$ -50.00° (CH_3OH). Cinchonidine was used to obtain the (+)-enantiomer (from either CH_3OH, acetone or 8:2 acetone/chloroform). The cinchonidine salt had the following physical constants: m.p. 178-180° (acetone:chloroform), $[\alpha]_D^{20}$ -52.00° (CH_3OH). The liberated acid was found to have the following physical constants: m.p. 148-149° (CH_3OH), $[\alpha]_D^{20}$ +53.00° (CH_3OH).

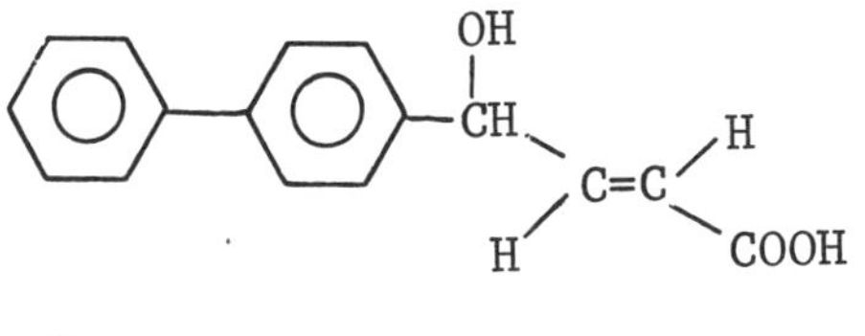

$C_{16}H_{14}O_3$ Ref. 1142

EXAMPLE 53

(+)-4-(biphenylyl-4')-4-hydroxy-crotonic acid

25.4 gm. (0.1 mol) of (±)-4-(biphenylyl-4')-4-hydroxy-crotonic acid were dissolved in a hot mixture of 200 ml. of chloroform and 40 ml. of methanol, the resulting solution was admixed with a solution of 14.7 gm. (0.05 mol) of (−)-cinchonidine in 150 ml. of chloroform, and the mixture was allowed to stand for 30 minutes. Thereafter, the clear solution was evaporated in vacuo, leaving a glassy residue which was treated with boiling acetone. Upon cooling, 24.8 gm. of a crystalline substance, M.P. 183–186° C., were obtained, which was recrystallized twice from isopropanol, yielding 12.4 gm. of (+)-4- biphenylyl-4')-4-hydroxy-crotonic acid, M.P. 188–189° C., specific rotation $[\alpha]_D^{25}$=+60.25° (c.=0.7 in methanol).

Its morpholine salt had a melting point of 172–173° C. and a specific rotation $[\alpha]_D^{25}$=+18.8° (c.=0.64 in methanol).

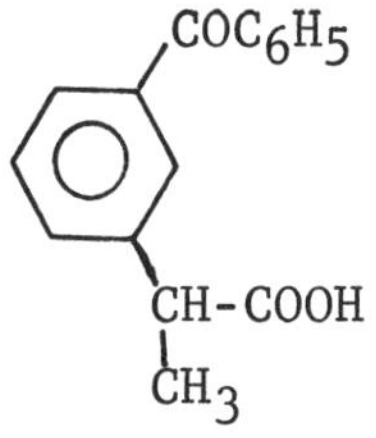

$C_{16}H_{14}O_3$ Ref. 1143

Note:

Obtained acids with $[\alpha]_D^{23}$ +49.6° (c 1.15, CH_2Cl_2) and $[\alpha]_D^{23}$ -52.4° (c 1.05, CH_2Cl_2) by preparing the diastereomeric amides with (R)-(+)-α-phenylethylamine and separating these products by column chromatography on silica as described in Chimia (Aarau) 29, 170 (1975).

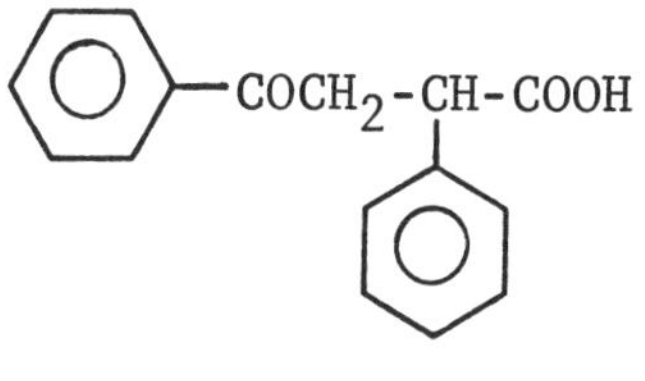

$C_{16}H_{14}O_3$ Ref. 1144

Resolution of the *dl*-Acid, I.—Hahn and Lapworth first resolved β-benzoyl-α-phenylpropionic acid using quinine as the active base and ethyl acetate as the solvent. The same active base and the same solvent were used in this problem but the procedure has been standardized so much that it seems wise to give it in detail.

A boiling solution of 57 g. of quinine in 500 cc. of ethyl acetate is mixed with a boiling solution of 45 g. of the *dl*-acid in 300 cc. of ethyl acetate and the combined solution heated on the steam-bath for thirty minutes. During this period a solid begins to separate. The mixture is allowed to stand for one and one-half hours with frequent stirring by means of a stout glass rod. At the end of this period the separated solid has produced a very thick paste.

The solid (a) is filtered off and washed with 100 cc. of

ethyl acetate.

The combined filtrates are allowed to stand overnight and any solid filtered off. This can be called solid (b).

The filtrate from solid (b) is concentrated to a very small volume, the ethyl acetate being recovered, and allowed to solidify. This is solid (c).

Each fraction of solid is worked up in the following way. The solid is shaken in a separatory funnel with ether and dilute sulfuric acid. The sulfuric acid takes up the quinine, leaving the acid in the ether. The acid is extracted from the ether by dilute sodium hydroxide solution and recovered by acidification of the alkaline solution. The quinine is recovered by pouring the sulfuric acid solution, with vigorous stirring, into a large excess of sodium hydroxide solution. Quinine precipitates out and can be collected.

The acid from each fraction of solid is fractionally crystallized from acetone.

Solid (a) gives about 12 g. of dextro acid, melting at 181° and having a molecular rotation in methyl alcohol of $[\alpha]^{26}_D$ +148°.

Solid (b) is small and gives inactive acid.

Solid (c) gives about 12 g. of levo acid, melting at 181° and having a molecular rotation in methyl alcohol of $[\alpha]^{26}_D$ −148°.

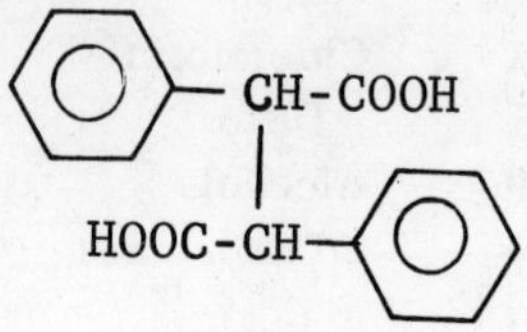

$C_{16}H_{14}O_4$

Ref. 1145

Resolution of r-*Diphenylsuccinic Acid into its Optical Antipodes*.—The resolution by brucine in aqueous solution (Wren and Still, J., 1915, **107**, 444) involves the use of very large volumes of solvent. The substitution of 50% aqueous alcohol for water gives better yields of the active acids and is much more economical of time and labour. The following experiment is typical. *r*-Diphenylsuccinic acid (50 g.) and brucine (162 g.) were dissolved in a warm mixture of water (530 c.c.) and rectified spirit (530 c.c.). The solution was filtered, seeded with brucine *d*-diphenylsuccinate, and kept at rest at room temperature for 24 hours. Prolongation of the time of contact of crystals and solution leads to separation of brucine *l*-diphenylsuccinate. The crystalline crop (110 g.), recrystallised from 50% alcohol (5 c.c. of solvent per g. of salt), gave 90 g. of salt which, when decomposed with acid and extracted with ether, yielded 20 g. of *d*-diphenylsuccinic acid having $[\alpha]_{5461}$ + 390° in acetone. One crystallisation from water (160 c.c. per g.) yielded 13 g. of homogeneous *d*-acid. In acetone ($l = 2, c = 0{\cdot}7490$), $\alpha^{21°}_{5461} + 7{\cdot}09°$, $[\alpha]^{21°}_{5461} + 473{\cdot}3°$; $\alpha^{20°}_{5780} + 6{\cdot}21°$, $[\alpha]^{20°}_{5780} + 414{\cdot}7°$.

The mother-liquor from the first crop of brucine salt yielded 18 g. of *l*-acid with $[\alpha]_{5461}$ − 310° in acetone; two crystallisations from water yielded 9 g. of the homogeneous *l*-acid. In acetone ($l = 2, c = 0{\cdot}6160$), $\alpha^{20°}_{5461} - 5{\cdot}80°$, $[\alpha]^{20°}_{5461} - 471{\cdot}5°$; $\alpha^{20°}_{5780} - 5{\cdot}08°$, $[\alpha]^{20°}_{5780} - 412{\cdot}2°$.

Less satisfactory results were obtained with solvents composed of alcohol and water in the volume ratios 1 : 3 and 3 : 1.

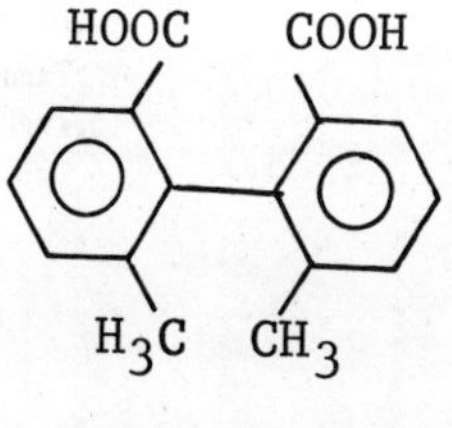

$C_{16}H_{14}O_4$

Ref. 1146

Resolution.—The quinidine salt was not obtained crystalline and the brucine salt gave no indication of separation, but both the quinine and the morphine salt proved suitable, the latter appearing the better of the two. Morphine (5·6 g.) was added to 6 : 6′-dimethyldiphenic acid (5·0 g.) in alcohol (75 c.c.). On cooling, 4·8 g. of salt, m. p. 196°, $[\alpha]_{5461}$ − 65·5° in acetic acid ($c = 2$), were obtained and the properties were little altered after thorough extraction with alcohol, $[\alpha]_{5461}$ changing only to 64·7° ($c = 2$ in acetic acid). On decomposition this salt gave the *d*-acid, $[\alpha]_D$ + 15° in methyl alcohol ($c = 2$). The alcoholic mother-liquor would not give a further crop of the morphine salt and therefore the whole was decomposed. The *l* + *dl* acid so obtained had $[\alpha]_D$ − 11·5° in methyl alcohol ($c = 2$).

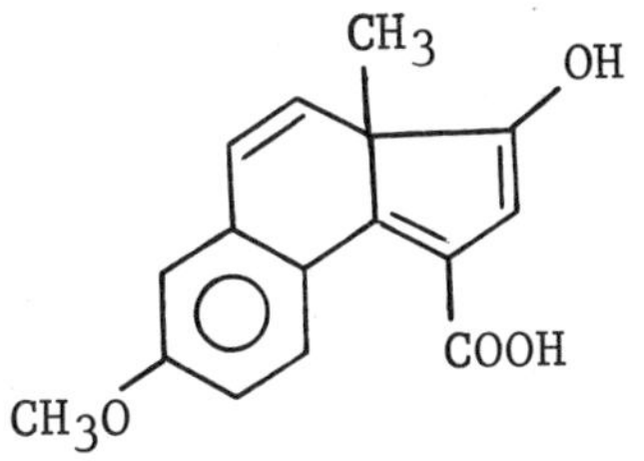

$C_{16}H_{14}O_4$ Ref. 1147

EXAMPLE

Isolation of the Dextro-Rotary and Levo-Rotary Enantiomorphs of 1β - Hydroxy-3-Carboxy-6-Methoxy-9aβ-Methyl-1,2,3a,8,9,9a-Hexahydro-Δ3(3a)Benzo[e]indene

(A) FORMATION OF THE COMPLEX WITH L-(+)-THREO-1-(p-NITROPHENYL)-2-AMINO-PROPANE-1,3-DIOL

7.31 gm. (0.0345 mol.) of L-(+)-threo-1-(p-nitrophenyl)-2-aminopropane-1,3-diol and 60 cc. of methanol are added to 9 gm. (0.0328) of racemic 1β-hydroxy-3-carboxy-6-methoxy-9aβ-methyl-1,2,3a, 8,9,9a-hexahydro-Δ3(3a)-benzo[e]indene, prepared according to D. K. Banerjee, J. Am. Chem. Soc., 78, 3769 (1956), the container is closed and the contents are agitated for about one-half hour until complete solution has taken place. The amino-propanediol is in a slightly molar excess with respect to the racemic benzo[e]indene. The resulting yellow solution is allowed to stand at room temperature for one-half hour and then 210 cc. of isopropyl ether are slowly added, accompanied by agitation. After all the ether has been added, crystallization is initiated by scratching and the mixture is allowed to stand for one hour in the dark. The crystals of the salt formed by the dextro-rotary base with the levo-rotary acid are filtered off at room temperature and are then triturated successively with 20 cc. and 15 cc. of a mixture of methanol and isopropyl ether in a ratio of 1:3.5. The wet crystals are then dried in a vacuum over P_2O_5. 7.9 gm. of yellowish-green crystals are obtained. M.P.=120–122° C., $[\alpha]_D^{20}=-31.5°\pm1$(c.=1% in methanol). For analysis, the product is recrystallized from water, whereby a product solvated with one-half molecule of water is obtained which is in the form of pale yellow prisms or platelets which are soluble in water, methyl or ethyl alcohol and acetone, poorly soluble in benzene or chloroform, insoluble in isopropyl ether, and decompose in dilute aqueous acids. M.P.=145–149° C., $[\alpha]_D^{20}=-35°$ (c.=1% in methanol). Recrystallization yield: 64%.

Analysis.—$C_{25}H_{30}O_8N_2$, ½ H_2O, mol. wt. 495.52. Calculated: C, 60.59%; H, 6.3%; N, 5.65%. Found: C, 60.4%; H, 6.2%; N, 5.7%.

Loss of weight at 110° C.=1.8% (calculated 1.82%).

This compound is not described in the literature and is the hemihydrate of the acid addition salt of levo-rotary 1β-hydroxy-3-carboxy-6-methoxy-9aβ-methyl - 1,2,3a,8,9,-9a-hexahydro-Δ3(3a)-benzo[e]indene and L-(+)-threo-1-(p-nitrophenyl)-2-amino-propane-1,3-diol.

(B) ISOLATION OF LEVO-ROTARY 1β-HYDROXY-3-CARBOXY-6-METHOXY-9aβ-METHYL-1,2,3a,8,9,9a-HEXAHYDRO-Δ3(3a)-BENZO[E]INDENE

7 gm. of the salt obtained in A above are dissolved at 40–50° C. in 250 cc. of water, and 22.5 cc. of 1 N hydrochloric acid are then added to the solution while stirring. The levo-rotary acid begins to precipitate. The solution is allowed to stand for one hour at room temperature and is then filtered. The precipitate is filtered off and triturated twice in 25 cc. of water. The preciptate is then dried in a vacuum over P_2O_5. 3.71 gm. of the raw levo-rotary acid are obtained which are then recrystallized from 60 cc. methanol containing 20% water. The yield is 86% based on the amount of racemic acid. The novel compound, levo-rotary 1β-hydroxy-3-carboxy-6-methoxy-9aβ-methyl-1,2,3a,8,9,9a-hexahydro - Δ3(3a) - benzo[e]indene substantially free from its optical antipode, which is not described in the literature, is obtained in the form of white needles and is soluble in dilute alkaline solutions, alcohol, ethyl ether and acetone, poorly soluble in benzene and chloroform, and very slightly soluble in water, dilute acidic solutions and isopropyl ether. M.P.=223–225° C., $[\alpha]_D^{20}=-120°$ (c.=1% in methanol).

Analysis.—$C_{16}H_{18}O_4$, mol. wt. 274.30. Calculated: C, 70.05%; H, 6.61%. Found: C, 70.0%; H, 6.6%.

By rendering the mother liquor from the acidification step alkaline, the resolving reagent can be recovered. The yield from this recovery procedure is about 90% of the starting L-(+)-threo-1-(p-nitrophenyl)-2-amino-propane-1,3-diol.

(C) ISOLATION OF DEXTRO-ROTARY-1β-HYDROXY-3-CARBOXY-6-METHOXY-9aβ-METHYL-1,2,3a,8,9,9a-HEXAHYDRO-Δ3(3a)-BENZO[E]INDENE

The solvents in the mother liquor from the filtration step in the preparation of the salt of the levo-rotary enantiomorph described under A above are distilled off in vacuo on the water bath. The yellow gummy residue, the acid addition salt of dextro-rotary 1β-hydroxy-3-carboxy-6-methoxy-9aβ-methyl - 1,2,3a,8,9,9a-hexahydro-Δ3(3a)-benzo[e]indene and L-(+) - threo - 1 - (p-nitrophenyl)-2-amino-propane-1,3-diol, is then dissolved in 60 cc. water and 20 cc. 1 N hydrochloric acid are added dropwise to the solution while stirring. The dextro-rotary 1β-hydroxy-3-carboxy-6-methoxy-9aβ-methyl - 1,2,3a,8,9,-9a-hexahydro-Δ3(3a)-benzo[e]indene precipitates out in finely divided form. The mixture is allowed to stand for a few minutes, the preciptate is filtered off, triturated three times with 25 cc. water and dried in vacuo. 4.61 gm. of the raw product having a M.P. of 214° C. are obtained. By recrystallization from 80% methanol, 3.98 gm. (representing a yield of 88.5% of the dextro-rotary 1β-hydroxy-3-carboxy-6-methoxy-9aβ- methyl - 1,2,3a,8,9,9a-hexahydro-Δ3(3a)-benzo[e]indene substantially free from its optical antipode are obtained, having a M.P. of 223–225° C., $[\alpha]_D^{20}=+118°$ (c.=1% in methanol). The dextro-rotary compound, like its levo-rotary enantiomorph, is obtained in the form of white needles and has the same solubility properties. The resolving reagent is recovered in the manner described under B above.

$C_{16}H_{14}O_4$ Ref. 1147a

STAGE A:

Isolation of the dextro-rotatory enantimorph:

1 kg. of racemic 1β - hydroxy - 3 - carboxy-6 - methoxy - 9aβ - methyl - 1,2,3a,8,9,9a-hexahydro - Δ3(3a) - benzo - [e] - indene is suspended in 4.634 litres of water, and the suspension is heated with agitation to 80°C. Then 0.366 litres of 36°Bé, sodium hydroxide solution is added, followed by 735 g. of ephedrine hydrochloride. Ten minutes after admixture has been completed the mixture is cooled, and crystallization of the ephedrine salt of the dextra-rotatory enantiomorph commences. The mixture is agitated then left at room temperature overnight. On the following day the precipitate is filtered off from the mother liquors with suction.

The ephedrine salt of the dextro-rotatory enantiomorph has never previously been described. A sample taken for purposes of analysis shows the following constants: m.p = 131°C, $[\alpha]_D^{20} = +33.5°$ (c = 1%, water).

The precipitate obtained as described above is pasted with one litre of water. The paste is heated to 80°C, then three litres of N hydrochloric acid are added, and the mixture is agitated for half an hour, filtered with suction, washed with water and dried in an oven. A yield of 450 g. of the dextro-rotatory enantiomorph is thus obtained, identical with that described in our aforesaid Application No. 18432/59 (Serial No. 914,731).

STAGE B:
Isolation of the laevo-rotatory enantiomorph:

For purposes of analysis a sample of the ephedrine salt of the laevo-rotatory enantiomorph is first recovered from the mother liquors obtained as described in Stage A above, by concentration thereof. This salt, which has never previously been described, shows rotatory power of $[\alpha]_D{}^{20} = -67°$ ($c = 1\%$, water).

To isolated the laevo-rotatory enantiomorph itself however the following procedure is adopted:—

The mother-liquors obtained as described in Stage A above are treated with activated charcoal, then filtered and heated to 80°C. Then 850 c.c. of 2.5 N hydrochloric acid are added, and the mixture is cooled to 20°C and filtered with suction. The product thus obtained is washed with water, dried in an oven and recrystallized from methanol. A yield of 455 g. of the laevo-rotatory enantiomorph is thus obtained, m.p. = 228°C, $[\alpha]_D{}^{20} = -125°$ ($c = 1\%$, methanol).

EXAMPLE 2:
Recovery of the ephedrine

The mother-liquors of the suction-filtering of the laevo-rotatory enantiomorph secured from Stage B of Example 1 are combined with the various washings. To these are then added 2.3 kg. of sodium hydroxide flakes, and the mixture is cooled to 20°C, then extracted with benzene. The benzene solution is evaporated to dryness *in vacuo*. 1.14 litres of acetone are added to the residue followed, very slowly, by 165 c.c. of 22°Be hydrochloric acid. The mixture is then agitated for one hour at room temperature and filtered with suction. After drying, a yield of 344 g. of ephedrine hydrochloride is obtained.

$$C_6H_5-CH-COOH$$
$$|$$
$$Se$$
$$|$$
$$C_6H_5-CH-COOH$$

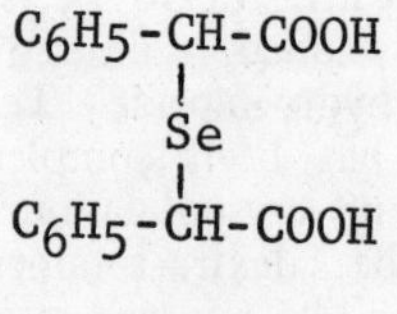

$C_{16}H_{14}O_4Se$ **Ref. 1148**

10.6 g (0.025 Mol) *racem*-Säure (mit Kristallbenzol) wurden in 850 ml Methylalkohol gelöst und mit 19 g (0.05 Mol) Chinin versetzt. Das beim Erkalten kristallisierende Salz wurde aus 50-prozentigem Äthylalkohol auf konstante Drehung umkristallisiert. Es bereitete anfänglich gewisse Schwierigkeiten, eine praktische Methode zur Verfolgung des Verlaufes der Spaltung zu finden; das durch Ausschütteln der schwefelsauren Lösung des Salzes mit Äther und Verdampfen des Äthers im Vakuumex-

sickator erhaltene Produkt war nicht hinreichend wohldefiniert, um das Einwägen mit nötiger Genauigkeit zu erlauben. Es war auch nicht daran zu denken, die Konzentration einer Lösung, an der die Drehung bestimmt worden war, durch alkalimetrische Titration zu bestimmen, da die Löslichkeit der Säure in Wasser zu gering ist und die möglicherweise in Betracht kommenden organischen Lösungsmittel zufolge ihrer Flüchtigkeit für genaue Messungen wenig geeignet sind. Ich bestimmte mich schliesslich dafür, die Drehung von Lösungen des Chininsalzes in Eisessig zu bestimmen. Zu diesem Zwecke wurde von jeder Salzfraktion eine geringe Menge (etwa 0.25 g) abgetrennt, über P_2O_5 auf Gewichtskonstanz getrocknet, eingewogen, in Eisessig gelöst und auf ein bekanntes Volumen (etwa 10 ml) aufgefüllt.

Kristallisation	1	2	3	4
Ausbeute in g	11.9	10.3	8.4	7.4
$[\alpha]_D^{25}$	$-247.2°$	$-257.4°$	$-258.8°$	$-258.9°$

Die Mutterlauge nach der ersten Kristallisation des Chininsalzes wurde zur Trockne eingedampft und aus dem Rückstand die Säure isoliert. Dabei wurden 4.5 g stark rechtsdrehendes Produkt erhalten, das zusammen mit 8 g Strychnin in warmem 50-prozentigem Alkohol gelöst wurde. Das aus der filtrierten Lösung erhaltene Salz wurde aus einer möglichst geringen Menge desselben Lösungsmittels umkristallisiert. Der Verlauf der Spaltung wurde in derselben Weise wie beim Chininsalz verfolgt; zur vollständigen Entfernung des Kristallwassers musste in diesem Falle verhältnismässig lange über P_2O_5 getrocknet werden. Da bekanntlich Strychnin linksdrehend ist, zeigt das Salz keine besonders grosse Rechtsdrehung.

Kristallisation	1	2	3	4
Ausbeute in g	9.3	8.0	6.6	5.7
$[\alpha]_D^{25}$	—	$+71.4°$	$+71.6°$	$+71.6°$

Zwecks Isolierung der aktiven Säuren wurden die betreffenden Salze in verdünnter Sodalösung aufgeschlämmt und das Alkaloid durch wiederholtes Ausschütteln mit Chloroform entfernt. Dann wurde mit Schwefelsäure angesäuert und mit Äther ausgeschüttelt; die bei Verdampfen des Äthers spontan kristallisierende Säure wurde einmal aus Benzol und einmal aus Wasser umkristallisiert.

(−)-Selen-di-phenylessigsäure.

Die Säure wird aus Wasser in kleinen feinen Nadeln mit gerader Auslöschung erhalten. Auch aus Benzol erhält man feine Nadeln, die wie die *racem*-Form Kristallbenzol zu enthalten scheinen, das an der Luft leicht abgegeben wird. Es konnte kein zuverlässlicher Benzolwert erhalten werden. Aus Toluol kristallisiert die Säure in kompakten Kristallen oder Kristallaggregaten. Hinsichtlich ihrer Löslichkeit ist die Säure der *racem*-Form ähnlich aber ausnahmslos etwas leichter löslich. Der Schmelzpunkt scheint etwas von der Erhitzungsgeschwindigkeit abzuhängen; er wurde zu 144—145° bestimmt.

0.2420 g Subst. : 12.50 ml 0.1107-n NaOH;

$C_{16}H_{14}O_4Se$ (349.1) Äqu.-Gew. ber. 174.6 gef. 174.9.

0.1041 g Subst. in 0.2-n Sodalösung auf 10.03 ml gelöst : $2\alpha = -11.09°$.

$$[\alpha]_D^{25} = -534.5°; \quad [M]_D^{25} = -1865°.$$

Das bei der Spaltung erhaltene *Chininsalz* kristallisiert aus wasserhaltigem Alkohol in feinen Nadeln mit einem Molekül Kristallwasser, das ziemlich leicht abgegeben wird.

0.6100 g wasserfreie Subst. : 0.0482 g. Se.

$C_{16}H_{14}O_4Se$, 2 $(C_{21}H_{24}O_4N_2)$ (997.5) Se ber. 7.92 % gef. 7.90 %.

0.3611 g kristallwasserhaltige Subst. : 0.0101 g H_2O.

1 H_2O ber. 1.77 % gef. 1.80 %.

0.2755 g wasserfreie Subst. in Eisessig auf 10.03 ml gelöst : $2\alpha = -14.22°$.

$$[\alpha]_D^{25} = -258.9°; \quad [M]_D^{25} = -2583°.$$

Das *Strychninsalz* wurde aus Säure und Strychnin in verdünntem Alkohol dargestellt. Es bildet flache, scharf abgeschnittene Nadeln mit gerader Auslöschung. Das lufttrockene Salz enthält ein Molekül Kristallwasser.

0.4667 g Subst. : 0.0083 g H_2O; 0.3263 g Subst. : 0.0248 g Se.

$C_{16}H_{14}O_4Se$, 2 $(C_{21}H_{22}O_2N_2)$, H_2O (1035.5) ber. H_2O 1.74 % Se 7.63 %.

gef. » 1.78 » » 7.60 ».

(+)-Selen-di-phenylessigsäure.

Die Säure gleicht in ihrem Aussehen vollständig der optischen Antipode. Schmelzpunkt 144—145°.

0.2338 g Subst. : 12.08 ml 0.1107-n NaOH.

$C_{16}H_{14}O_4Se$ (349.1) Äqu.-Gew. ber. 174.6 gef. 174.8.

0.1109 g Subst. in 0.2-n Sodalösung auf 10.03 ml gelöst : 2 α = +11.80°.

$[\alpha]_D^{25} = +533.5°$; $[M]_D^{25} = +1863°$.

Das *Strychninsalz* wurde bei der Spaltung erhalten. Es bildet dünne, glänzende, sechsseitige Tafeln oder Schuppen mit diagonaler Auslöschung. Es enthält 3¹/₂ Moleküle Kristallwasser oder möglicherweise 1 Molekül Wasser + 1 Molekül Alkohol. Die Selenbestimmung wurde an über P_2O_5 auf Gewichtskonstanz getrocknetem Produkt ausgeführt.

0.5438 g Subst. : 0.0425 g Se.

$C_{16}H_{14}O_4Se$, 2 $(C_{21}H_{22}O_2N_2)$ (1017.5) Se ber. 7.76 % gef. 7.82 %.

Analyse an kristallwasserhaltiger Subst. :

0.3111 g, 0.3145 g Subst. : Gewichtsverlust über P_2O_5 : 0.0183 g, 0.0185 g.

3¹/₂ H_2O ber. 5.83 %

1 H_2O + 1 C_2H_5OH » 5.92 » gef. 5.89, 5.89 %.

0.2800 g Subst. in Eisessig auf 10.03 ml gelöst : 2 α = +4.00°.

$[\alpha]_D^{25} = +71.6°$; $[M]_D^{25} = +729°$.

Wenn gleiche Teile (+)- und (—)-Säure in Benzollösung zusammengebracht werden, kristallisiert ein Produkt, dessen Eigenschaften vollständig mit denen der oben beschriebenen *racem*-Form übereinstimmen.

$$C_6H_5-CH-COOH$$
$$|$$
$$Se$$
$$|$$
$$Se$$
$$|$$
$$C_6H_5-CH-COOH$$

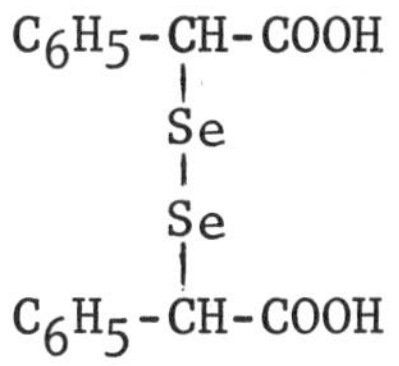

$C_{16}H_{14}O_4Se_2$ Ref. 1149

Die rechtsdrehende Antipode wurde sehr leicht mit Hilfe des gut kristallisierenden Strychninsalzes erhalten. Das Brucinsalz gibt ebenfalls rechtsdrehende Säure, allerdings von wesentlich geringerer Aktivität. Die übrigen untersuchten Alkaloide und organischen Basen (Chinin, Chinidin, Cinchonin, Morphin und α-Phenäthylamin) gaben amorphe gummiartige Salze, die zwar in einigen Fällen nach längerem Stehen teilweise kristallisierten, ohne sich aber umkristallisieren zu lassen. Es gelang mir daher nicht, die linksdrehende Antipode darzustellen, die sonst aus mehreren Gründen von Interesse gewesen wäre.

15 g Säure wurden mit der äquivalenten Menge (23.5 g) Strychnin in einem Liter warmen 50-prozentigen Alkohol gelöst. Das ziemlich langsam kristallisierende Salz wurde nach drei Tagen abgesaugt und dann aus demselben Medium umkristallisiert, bis konstante Drehung der im Salz enthaltenen Säure gefunden wurde. Dabei wurde auf 1 g Salz 12 bis 15 ml Lösungsmittel genommen. Zwecks Bestimmung der Aktivität der in Wasser unlöslichen Säure wurde von jeder Salzfraktion etwa 0.3 g (entsprechend etwa 0.12 g Säure) abgetrennt und in verdünnter Soda-

lösung suspendiert. Das Strychnin wurde dann durch wiederholtes Ausschütteln mit Chloroform entfernt. Die Lösung wurde mit Salzsäure angesäuert, wobei die Säure in kleinen Nadeln ausfiel, die nach 12 Stunden abgesaugt, gewaschen und über P_2O_5 getrocknet wurden. Zur Drehungsbestimmung wurde schliesslich etwa 0.1 g des Präparats eingewogen, in verdünnter Sodalösung auf bekanntes Volumen gelöst und im Polarimeter untersucht. Wie sich aus der folgenden Zusammenstellung ergibt, erfolgt die Spaltung sehr rasch.

Kristallisation	1	2	3	4
Ausbeute in g	10.4	8.7	8.0	7.2
$[\alpha]_D^{25}$	+435.5°	+445.5°	+446.5°	+446°

Die Ausbeute ist bei dieser Spaltung weniger zufriedenstellend und entspricht (wenn wir schon die Säure der zweiten Kristallisation als sterisch rein betrachten) nur etwa 45 % der theoretisch möglichen. Versuche die Mutterlauge aufzuarbeiten, waren aussichtslos: das Salz scheidet sich aus dieser nur als Öl ab.

Die Säure wurde in der oben angegebenen Weise aus dem Strychninsalz in Freiheit gesetzt und zweimal durch Lösen in Bikarbonatlösung und Fällung mit Salzsäure umkristallisiert.

(+)-Diselen-di-phenylessigsäure.

Aus 7 g Strychninsalz wurden 2.4 g Säure erhalten. Bei Fällung aus wässriger Lösung erhält man sie in sehr schwach gelblichen, feinen Nadeln mit gerader Auslöschung. Aus organischen Lösungsmitteln kristallisiert die Säure bei langsamem Verdampfen bisweilen in grossen, gelben, viereckigen Kristallen, deren Aussehen sehr an Kochsalzkristalle erinnert. Sie sind stark doppelbrechend und können daher nicht dem kubischen System angehören.

Die Säure ist sehr schwerlöslich in Wasser, Benzol und Petroleumäther, leichter in Chloroform, sehr leichtlöslich in Äther, Alkohol und Aceton. Sie schmilzt zwischen 160 und 165°. Der Schmelzpunkt ist an sich sehr scharf, aber nicht vollständig reproduzierbar, sondern von der Erhitzungsgeschwindigkeit abhängig. Unmittelbar nach dem Schmelzen tritt Zersetzung ein.

0.2998 g Subst. in methylalkoholischer Lösung : 12.79 ml 0.1098-n NaOH.

0.1261 g Subst. : 0.0466 g Se.

$C_{16}H_{14}O_4Se_2$ (428.0) ber. Äqu.-Gew. 214.0 Se 36.91 %

gef. 213.5 36.96 .

0.1018 g Subst. in 0.2-n Sodalösung auf 10.03 ml gelöst : 2 α = + 9.055°.

$[\alpha]_D^{25} = + 446.1°$; $[M]_D^{25} = + 1910°$.

50.0 ml bei 25° gesättigte wässrige Lösung : 0.24 ml 0.1393-n NaOH.

Löslichkeit bei 25° : 0.14 g je Liter = 0.00033 Mol je Liter.

Das *Strychninsalz*, dessen Darstellung oben beschrieben wurde, bildet kleine, glänzende, schwach gelbliche Kristalle von würfeloder oktaederähnlichem Habitus. In der ersten Kristallisation, wo es noch nicht vollständig rein ist, tritt es in spitzigen Pyramiden oder Nadeln auf. Bisweilen sind die Kristalle wie Salmiakkristalle zu farnkraut- oder federartigen Aggregaten vereinigt. Das Salz enthält 4 Moleküle Kristallwasser.

0.6412 g Subst. : 0.0861 g Se und 0.0409 g H_2O. — 0.5877 g Subst. : 0.0800 g Se.

$C_{16}H_{14}O_4Se_2$, 2 $(C_{21}H_{22}O_2N_2)$, 4 H_2O (1168.5) ber. H_2O 6.16 % Se 13.52 %

gef. H_2O 6.36 % Se 13.43, 13.61 %.

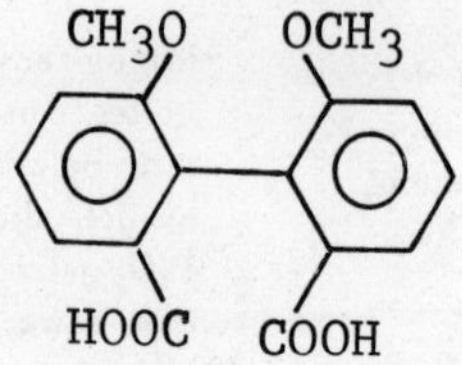

$C_{16}H_{14}O_6$ Ref. 1150

Resolution of 2,2′-Dimethoxy-6,6′-dicarboxydiphenyl

Monobrucine Salt.—To a hot solution of 1.305 g. of anhydrous brucine in 30 cc. of dry ethyl acetate was added a hot solution of 0.500 g. of 2,2′-dimethoxy-6,6′-dicarboxydiphenyl in 25 cc. of absolute methyl alcohol. Upon cooling for five hours a crop of fine white crystals weighing 0.96 g. separated. After recrystallization from absolute methyl alcohol the salt melted at 198–199° (corr.).

Rotation. 0.2000 g. made up to 20 cc. in chloroform at 20° gave α_D +0.235°; l = 2; $[\alpha]^{20}_D$ +11.7°. Recrystallization from absolute methyl alcohol did not raise the melting point or change the rotation.

Kenner and Turner[9] report the preparation of this compound and give a melting point of 268° but do not report its rotation.

Anal. Calcd. for $C_{39}H_{40}O_{10}N_2$: N, 4.02. Found: N, 4 02.

The remaining material which separated upon further evaporation of the solvent was found to be a mixture of the salt with unchanged brucine.

Diquinine Salt.—To a hot solution of 12.88 g. of anhydrous quinine in 80 cc. of absolute methyl alcohol was added a hot solution of 6 g. of 2,2′-dimethoxy-6,6′-dicarboxydiphenyl in 170 cc. of absolute methyl alcohol. Upon evaporation *in vacuo* at room temperature a dry residue was obtained which was heated to boiling with 200 cc. of dry acetone. Upon cooling, 9.79 g. of white crystals separated. After recrystallization from dry acetone, the salt melted at 178–179° (corr.).

Rotation. 0.2045 g. made up to 20 cc. in chloroform at 20° gave α_D +2.27°; l = 2; $[\alpha]^{20}_D$ +111.0°. The salt, upon recrystallization from dry acetone, was not changed in melting point or rotation. Kenner and Turner[9] report a melting point of 172–173° and an $[\alpha]_D$ in chloroform of +126°.

Anal. Calcd. for $C_{56}H_{62}O_{10}N_4$: N, 5.90. Found: N, 5.80.

The mother liquor from the first crop of crystals was evaporated to 50 cc. by bubbling nitrogen through the solution. Upon cooling, 0.30 g. of salt separated. This was removed by filtration. The mother liquor was evaporated to dryness. The residue consisted of a resin which, when the last traces of solvent were removed, formed a white powder. The salt could be dissolved in acetone or ethyl acetate and precipitated as a white, flocculent mass by addition of petroleum ether (b. p. 20–40°). Upon filtration, however, this solid turned to a gummy mass which reverted to a white powder when all traces of the solvent were removed. The salt melted at 98–100° (corr.). The weight of salt thus obtained was 8.5 g.

Rotation. 0.1550 g. made up to 20 cc. in chloroform at 20° gave α_D −0.93°; l = 2; $[\alpha]^{20}_D$ −60°.

Anal. Calcd. for $C_{56}H_{62}O_{10}N_4$: N, 5.90. Found: N, 5.93.

Kenner and Turner[9] report that the more soluble salt melts at about 60° with decomposition and has an $[\alpha]_D$ in chloroform of −68°.

***l*-2,2′-Dimethoxy-6,6′-dicarboxydiphenyl.**—A mixture of 3 g. of the less soluble salt and 40 cc. of 5% sodium hydroxide solution was ground in a mortar. This mixture was extracted with four 15-cc. portions of cold chloroform. The alkaline solution was then acidified with 6 *N* hydrochloric acid. The *l*-acid precipitated as a white spongy mass which was filtered and dried. After drying, the compound was crystalline and melted at 291–292°.

Rotation. 0.0766 g. made up to 20 cc. in dry acetone at 20° gave α_D −0.88°; l = 2; $[\alpha]^{20}_D$ −114.9°.

Kenner and Turner[9] report a melting point of 294–295° and an $[\alpha]_D$ −115°.

The active acid was recrystallized from boiling chloroform, but apparently racemized somewhat during the procedure.

Rotation. 0.0785 g. made up to 20 cc. in dry acetone at 20° gave α_D −0.70°; l = 2; $[\alpha]^{20}_D$ −89.5°.

If the *l*-acid was dissolved in dry acetone and excess petroleum ether (b. p. 20–40°) was added, feathery crystals separated after standing in the cold for two hours. The melting point and rotation were unchanged by this treatment.

(9) Kenner and Turner, *J. Chem. Soc.*, 2340 (1928).

Anal. Calcd. for $C_{16}H_{14}O_6$: C, 63.6; H, 4.64. Found: C, 63.7; H, 4.57.

d-2,2'-Dimethoxy-6,6'-dicarboxydiphenyl.—Three grams of the more soluble salt was decomposed by the procedure used for the less soluble salt. The *d*-acid obtained in this way melted at 291–292°.

Rotation. 0.0737 g. made up to 20 cc. in dry acetone at 20° gave α_D +0.80°; l = 2; $[\alpha]^{20}_D$ +108.5°.

The *d*-acid was recrystallized from boiling chloroform. Partial racemization took place.

Rotation. 0.0717 g. made up to 20 cc. in dry acetone at 20° gave α_D +0.62°; l = 2; $[\alpha]^{20}_D$ +86.5°.

The *d*-acid was then purified by dissolving in dry acetone and adding excess petroleum ether. The product had the same melting point and rotation.

Anal. Calcd. for $C_{16}H_{14}O_6$: C, 63.6; H, 4.64. Found: C, 63.61; H, 4.77.

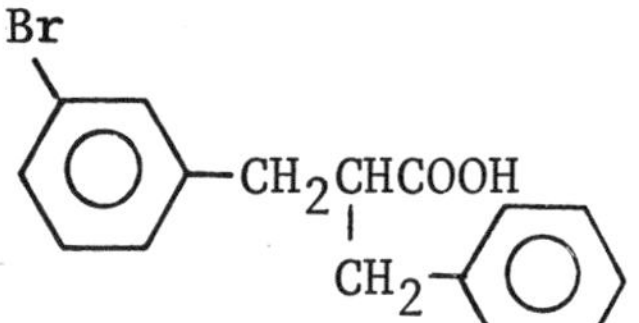

$C_{16}H_{15}BrO_2$ Ref. 1151

dl-a-m-*brombenzyl-β-phenyl propionic acid.*—(Acid I, X=*m*-Br). Meta bromtoluene could not be brominated in the side chain on exposure to sunlight but only at the boiling point. The meta acid was prepared similarly to the para acid; yield 72%, m.p. 81°C. (Found: E, by silver salt, 319·6; Br, 24·77; $C_{16}H_{15}O_2Br$ requires E, 319·0; Br, 25·08%).

l-a-m-*brombenzyl-β-phenyl propionic acid.*—The acid was resolved by crystallising the quinine salt from alcohol, resolution was complete after four crystallisations. The quinine salt, m.p. 161°C. had $[a]^{30}_D$ −96·3°, $[M]^{30}_D$ −619·2°. (Found: N, 4·6; $C_{36}H_{39}N_2O_4Br$ requires N, 4·36%). The free acid was isolated in the usual way. Yield 8·5 gms.; m.p. 89·5°. (Found: E, by titration 319·3; required 319). The acid had $[a]^{29.5}_D$ in benzene solution (c=4·5396) −10·46°; $[M]^{29.5}_D$ −33·4°.

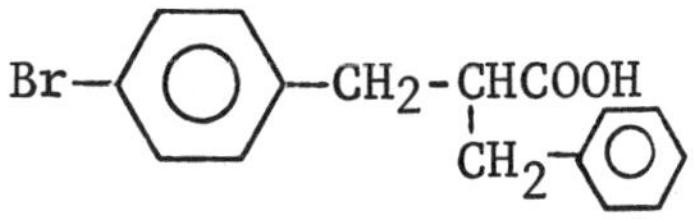

$C_{16}H_{15}BrO_2$ Ref. 1152

d-a-p-*brombenzyl-β-phenyl propionic acid.*—The *dl* acid was resolved by means of the quinine salt. Resolution was complete after four crystallisations from alcohol; m.p. 175°C., $[a]^{30}_D$ −89·8°, $[M]^{30}_D$ −576·4°. (Found: N, 4·76; $C_{36}H_{39}N_2O_4Br$ requires N, 4·36%). The yield of active acid was 7·5 gms.; m.p. 90°C. (Found: E, 314·3; Calculated, 319·0). $[a]^{29.5}_D$ in benzene solution (c=3·2644) + 16·1°, $[M]^{29.5}_D$ +51·35°.

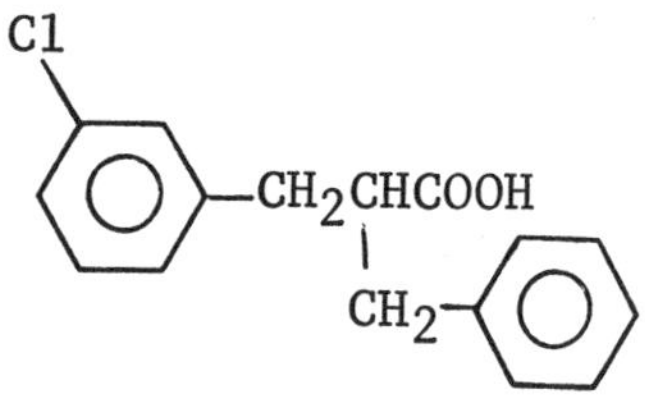

$C_{16}H_{15}ClO_2$ Ref. 1153

d-a-m-*chlorbenzyl-β-phenyl propionic acid.*—The *dl* acid I (X=*m*-Cl) was resolved by means of the quinine salt. Resolution was complete after four crystallisations from alcohol; m.p. 173°C., $[a]^{30}_D$ −90·5°, $[M]^{30}_D$ −541·6°. (Found: N, 4·45; $C_{36}H_{39}N_2O_4Cl$ requires N, 4·68%). The free acid weighed 2·5 gms.; m.p. 73·5°C. (Found: E, 267·7; Calculated 274·5). $[a]^{29.5}_D$ in benzene solution (c=3·788) +8·18°, $[M]^{29.5}_D$ +22·45°.

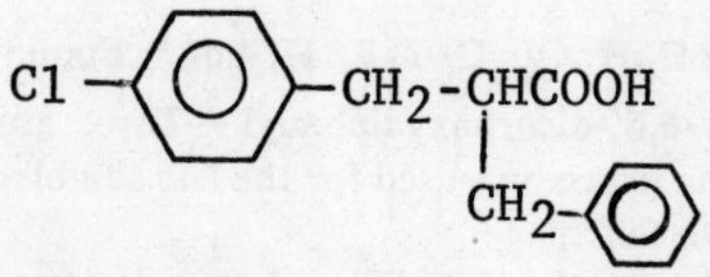

$C_{16}H_{15}ClO_2$ Ref. 1154

d-α-p-*chlorbenzyl-β-phenyl propionic acid.*—Quinine (24·3 gms.) and the acid I (X=*p*-Cl; 20·1 gms.) were dissolved in hot ethyl alcohol and the solutions mixed. After 24 hours the first crop of crystals, weight 35 gms., m.p. 172°C. was filtered off and crystallised. The product from the second crystallisation had m.p. 178°C., $[\alpha]_D^{29}$ −95·8°, fourth crystallisation m.p. 182°C., $[\alpha]_D^{29}$ −91·1°, sixth crystallisation, m.p. 183°C., $[\alpha]_D^{29}$ −91·5°. All rotations were measured in absolute alcohol. (Found: C, 72·5; H, 6·8; $C_{36}H_{39}N_2O_4Cl$ requires C, 72·1; H, 6·5%). The molecular rotation of the salt was −547·6°; for quinine hydrochloride in absolute alcohol $[M]_D^{29}$ is −601·9°. Therefore the acid was dextrorotatory. The quinine salt was decomposed by dilute sulphuric acid, the crude acid dissolved in ammonia, filtered and reprecipitated; yield 3 gms., m.p. 74°C. (Found: E, by titration with caustic soda, 276·2; calculated, 274·5). $[\alpha]_D^{30.5}$ in absolute alcohol (c = 2·528), + 5·93°, $[M]_D^{30.5}$ + 16·7°. In benzene $[\alpha]_D^{29.5}$ (c = 4·3660), +10·19°, $[M]_D^{29.5}$ + 27·97°.

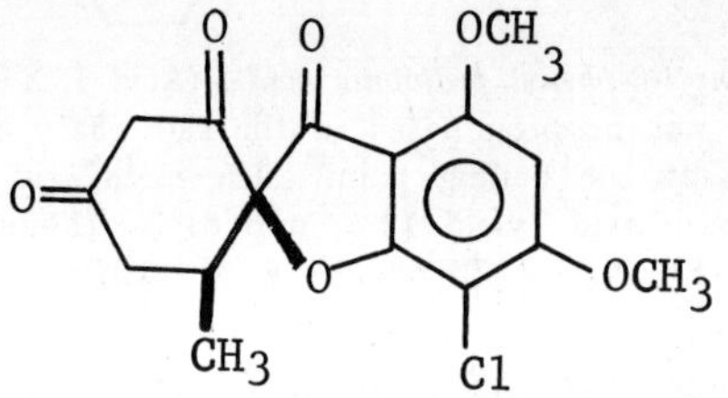

$C_{16}H_{15}ClO_6$ Ref. 1155

Experimenteller Teil[9])

Synthese von (−)-Griseofulvin (I). – (+)-*Epigriseofulvinsäure* (*II*): Die Suspension von 20 g rac. Epigriseofulvinsäure[3a]) in 44 ml Wasser wird mit 9 g (+)-α-Phenyl-äthylamin[10]) versetzt. Aus der nach leichtem Erwärmen entstandenen klaren Lösung scheiden sich nach dem Animpfen und Abkühlen 10,7 g eines Aminsalzes ab. Nach Umlösen aus wenig Wasser erhält man 8,3 g des (+)-α-Phenyl-äthylaminsalzes der (+)-Epigriseofulvinsäure (II) vom Smp. 186–188°, $[\alpha]_D^{22}$ = +164° (in Methanol).

$C_{16}H_{15}O_6Cl,C_8H_{11}N$ (459,91) Ber. C 62,67 H 5,69% Gef. C 62,49 H 5,72%

8,3 g des optisch reinen Salzes liefern nach dem Lösen in Eisessig, Zugeben von Wasser bis zur Trübung, Filtrieren und Umlösen aus Eisessig 4,7 g (+)-Epigriseofulvinsäure (II) vom Smp. 221–222°, $[\alpha]_D^{22}$ = +102° (in DMF). UV.-Maxima bei 233 (Schulter), 290 und 326 mμ, ε = 17900, 29100 und 5440. Das UV.-Spektrum in 0,01N alkoholischer NaOH zeigt Maxima bei 232 (Schulter), 290 und 330 mμ, ε = 18600, 45100 und 5440.

$C_{16}H_{15}O_6Cl$ (338,74) Ber. C 56,73 H 4,46 Cl 10,47% Gef. C 56,37 H 4,53 Cl 10,34%

(−)-*Epigriseofulvinsäure* (*II*): Die nach dem Abfiltrieren des (+)-α-Phenyl-äthylaminsalzes von (+)-II erhaltene Mutterlauge wird mit verdünnter Salzsäure kongosauer gestellt, die ausgefallene Rohsäure abgetrennt, in wässeriger Natriumhydrogencarbonatlösung gelöst, die Lösung mit Äther gewaschen und anschliessend mit Salzsäure angesäuert. Man erhält nach dem Filtrieren und Trocknen 9,5 g einer optisch unreinen (−)-Epigriseofulvinsäure vom Smp. 205–207°, $[\alpha]_D^{22}$ = −58° (in DMF). Zur Gewinnung eines optisch reinen Präparates löst man durch Erwärmen und unter Zugabe von 5 g (−)-α-Phenyläthylamin[10]) in 36 ml Wasser. Beim Abkühlen kristallisieren 10 g eines Aminsalzes aus. Nach Umlösen aus Wasser und Methanol-Äther erhält man 7,5 g des (−)-α-Phenyl-äthylaminsalzes der (−)-Epigriseofulvinsäure (II) vom Smp. 184–185°, $[\alpha]_D^{22}$ = −159° (in Methanol).

$C_{16}H_{15}O_6Cl,C_8H_{11}N$ (459,91) Ber. C 62,67 H 5,69% Gef. C 62,65 H 5,76%

Zur Gewinnung von (−)-II löst man 7,5 g des oben beschriebenen (−)-Aminsalzes in wenig Eisessig, versetzt mit Wasser bis zur Trübung, filtriert und löst aus Eisessig um. Man erhält so 5,5 g (−)-Epigriseofulvinsäure (II) vom Smp. 221–223°, $[\alpha]_D^{22}$ = −104° (in DMF). UV.-Maxima bei 232 (Schulter), 290 und 330 mμ, ε = 18700, 30000 und 5750. Das UV.-Spektrum in 0,01N

[3]) a) A. Brossi, M. Baumann, M. Gerecke & E. Kyburz, Helv. *43*, 1444, 2071 (1960).

[10]) Organic Syntheses, Coll. Vol. *II*, S. 506 (1946).

alkoholischer NaOH zeigt Maxima bei 232 (Schulter), 290 und 330 mμ, ε = 20000, 45500 und 6100.

$C_{16}H_{15}O_6Cl$ (338,74) Ber. C 56,73 H 4,46 Cl 10,47% Gef. C 56,47 H 4,38 Cl 10,20%

---

[9]) Alle Smp. sind unkorrigiert. Die UV.-Spektren wurden, sofern nicht anders vermerkt, in alkoholischer Lösung aufgenommen. Die Rotationsdispersion (RD) wurde auf einem photoelektrischen, selbstabgleichenden Polarimeter kontinuierlich aufgenommen. Als Lösungsmittel wurde Chloroform verwendet. Die Messlösung wurde soweit verdünnt, dass ihre Transmission immer mindestens 2% betrug. Gemessen wurde bei 25°. Die Genauigkeit der spezifischen Drehungen beträgt ± 0,5°/c. Die $[\alpha]_D$-Werte wurden bei einer Konzentration c = 1 und, sofern nicht anders vermerkt (DMF = Dimethylformamid), in Aceton aufgenommen.

[10]) Organic Syntheses, Coll. Vol. *II*, S. 506 (1946).

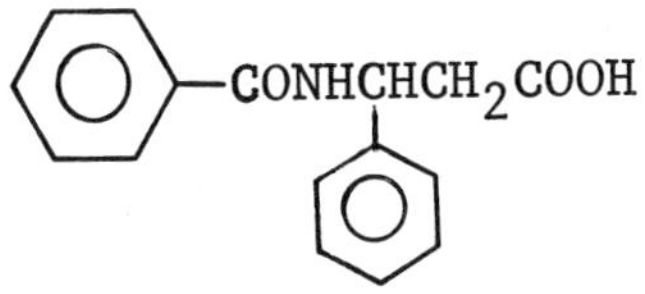

$C_{16}H_{15}NO_3$ Ref. 1156

(−)β-Benzoylamino-β-phenyl-propionsäure (XIII):

Zwecks Benzoylierung der (+)β-Amino-β-phenyl-propionsäure war es nicht erforderlich, diese im freien Zustand zu isolieren. Man kann folgendermaßen arbeiten: Die Lösung, die aus 19,2 g Chinidinsalz der (+)Formylaminosäure nach dem Ausfällen des Chinidins mit Ammoniakwasser erhalten wurde, behandelt man mit konz. Salzsäure 1 Std. auf dem Wasserbade. Dann wurde neutralisiert und mit 15 ccm Benzoylchlorid und 20%iger Natronlauge nach *Schotten-Baumann* benzoyliert. Die (−)β-Benzoylamino-β-phenyl-propionsäure zeigte nach dem Umkristallisieren den Schmp. 191° (aus Methanol) und eine Drehung $[\alpha]_D^{17}$ = −3,1° ± 0,7° (α_D^{17} = −0,08° ± 0,02°, c = 1,2995 in Methanol, l = 2).

$C_{16}H_{15}O_3N$ (269,3) Ber.: N 5,19. Gef.: N 5,01.

12 g rac. β-Benzoylamino-β-phenyl-propionsäure wurden mit 22 g Brucin in 50 ccm Methanol gelöst und mit 100 ccm Äther versetzt. Das ausgefallene Salz wurde dreimal aus Methanol/Äther umkristallisiert. 9,3 g des erhaltenen Salzes wurden durch Erwärmen in verdünnter Salzsäure gelöst. Nach kurzer Zeit kristallisierten 3,4 g (+)β-Benzoylamino-β-phenyl-propionsäure aus, Schmp. 191° (aus Methanol); $[\alpha]_D^{17}$ = + 2,9 ± 0,4° (α_D^{17} = +0,15° ± 0,02°, c = 2,6045 in Methanol, l = 2).

Aus den eingeengten Mutterlaugen wurde durch Ansäuern mit Salzsäure die (−)β-Benzoylamino-β-phenyl-propionsäure ausgefällt; $[\alpha]_D^{17}$ = −2,2° ± 0,5° (α_D^{17} = −0,13° ± 0,03°, c = 2,9135 in Methanol, l = 2).

10 g rac. β-Benzoylamino-β-phenyl-propionsäure wurden mit 11 g Cinchonidin in 50 ccm Methanol warm gelöst und mit 125 ccm Äther versetzt. Das auskristallisierte Salz wurde dreimal aus Methanol umkristallisiert und mit verdünnter Salzsäure daraus die (+)β-Benzoylamino-β-phenyl-propionsäure gefällt, Schmp. 191°; $[\alpha]_D^{17}$ = +2,7° ± 0,3° (α_D^{17} = + 0,02°, c = 2,8160 in Methanol, l = 2).

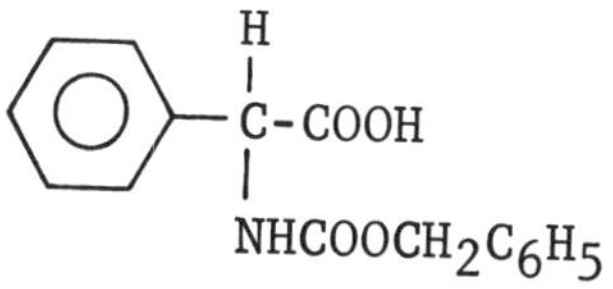

$C_{16}H_{15}NO_4$ Ref. 1157

Dehydroabietylammonium D-(−)-α-Benzyloxycarbonylaminophenylacetate.—To a solution of 163 g. (0.57 mole) of racemic α-benzyloxycarbonylaminophenylacetic acid dissolved in 3.7 l. of methanol was added 163 g. (0.57 mole) of dehydroabietylamine. The solution was diluted with 550 ml. of water and stored at 10° for 3 hr. The salt was collected and dried to obtain 203 g., m.p. 170–190°. Recrystallization from a mixture of 6 l. of methanol and 1.5 l. of water gave 103 g. of dry salt. A final recrystallization from a mixture of 4 l. of methanol and 700 ml. of water afforded 75 g. of colorless crystals, m.p. 199–200°, $[\alpha]^{25}D$ −93.2° (c 0.8, alcohol).

D-(−)-α-Benzyloxycarbonylaminophenylacetic Acid.—The aforementioned diastereomeric salt (75 g., 0.131 mole) was treated with 1 l. of saturated sodium carbonate solution and 2 l. of ether as described for the isolation of (+)-α-phenoxypropionic acid. The acid was isolated by extraction of the aqueous layer at pH 2 with three 500-ml. portions of ether. The ether extracts were combined, washed with water, and dried over anhydrous sodium sulfate. The ether was evaporated to one-fifth its original volume and 1 l. of Skellysolve B (petroleum ether, b.p. 60–71°) was added. The crystals weighed 30 g. after drying *in vacuo* over P_2O_5: m.p. 128–129°, $[\alpha]^{25}D$ −116.5° (c 1, absolute alcohol), lit.[6] m.p. 130–130.5°, $[\alpha]^{21}D$ −119° (c 4, alcohol).

(6) F. P. Doyle, *et al.*, *J. Chem. Soc.*, 1440 (1962).

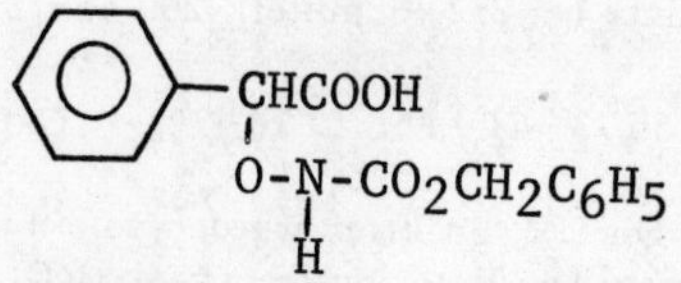

$C_{16}H_{15}NO_5$

Ref. 1158

Resolution of α-(N-benzyloxycarbonylamino-oxy)phenylacetic acid (VI). To VI (30.1 g) in 150 ml of dry ether was added (+)-benzylisopropylamine (13.5 g) in 100 ml of ether. The salt was isolated and recrystallized from methanol until the acid VI showed constant rotation; yield of pure acid, 7.3 g (48 %). $[\alpha]_D^{20}$ −67.7° (ethanol), m.p. 116−117°.

(−)-α-Amino-oxyphenylacetic acid hydrochloride from (−)-α-(N-benzyloxycarbonylamino-oxy)phenylacetic acid (VI). (−)-α-(N-Benzyloxycarbonylamino-oxy)phenylacetic acid (4.0 g) was heated in 6 N HCl (50 ml) for 45 min and the (−)-α-amino-oxyphenylacetic acid hydrochloride (2.0 g, 74 %) was isolated as previously described for racemic IV; $[\alpha]_D^{20}$−85.5° (water), m.p. 143−145°.

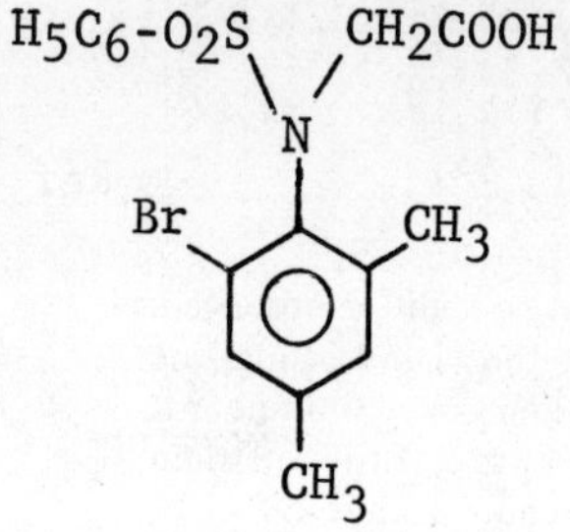

$C_{16}H_{16}BrNO_4S$

Ref. 1159

N-Benzenesulfonyl-N-carboxymethyl-2,4-dimethyl-6-bromobenzene.—The oil which was assumed to be N-benzenesulfonyl-N-carbomethoxymethyl-1-amino-2,4-dimethyl-6-bromobenzene was added to a solution of 50 ml. of glacial acetic acid, 5 ml. of concentrated sulfuric acid and 20 ml. of water. The mixture was refluxed for eight hours and cooled. Then 200 ml. of water was added and the aqueous ammonia until neutralized. The mixture was filtered and the filtrate acidified with hydrochloric acid. An oil separated which crystallized on standing. The product was recrystallized from ethanol as white crystals, m. p. 196–197° (cor.). The yield was 10.4 g. (78%). Yuan[4] reports m. p. 196–197°.

Resolution of N-Benzenesulfonyl-N-carboxymethyl-1-amino-2,4-dimethyl-6-bromobenzene.—A solution of 4.28 g. of N-benzenesulfonyl-N-carboxymethyl-1-amino-2,4-dimethyl-6-bromobenzene and 3.08 g. of cinchonidine in 85 ml. of a mixture of 9:1 ethyl acetate and methanol by volume was filtered and placed in a refrigerator overnight. Crystals weighing 2.28 g. were collected. Succeeding fractions were obtained as shown in the following table. The specific rotation readings were taken by making 0.06 g. of the salt up to 20 ml. with absolute ethanol. A one-decimeter tube was used.

Crop	Wt., g.	α_D at 24°	$[\alpha]^{24}D$	Vol. in ml.
I	2.28	−0.225°	−75.1°	85
II	0.86	− .220	−73.2	50
III	0.74	− .224	−74.8	30
IV	2.40	− .228	−76.0	0

Crops I and II containing 43% of the total amount present were recrystallized from a 9:1 ethyl acetate and methanol solution. From this solution 2.05 g. of salt was collected. This fraction was the pure less-soluble salt (*l*B*l*A). It formed white feathery crystals, m. p. 180–180.5° (cor.).

Rotation. 0.06 g. made up to 20 ml. with absolute ethanol at 24° gave α_D −0.208°; *l*, 1; $[\alpha]^{24}D$ −69.3°.

Anal. Calcd. for $C_{16}H_{16}NO_4BrS \cdot C_{14}H_{22}N_2O$: C, 60.69; H, 5.53. Found: C, 60.50; H, 5.70.

***d*- and *l*-N-Benzenesulfonyl-N-carboxymethyl-1-amino-2,4-dimethyl-6-bromobenzene.**—The pure less-soluble salt (1.90 g.) was decomposed with cold 1:1 hydrochloric acid in the manner previously described. It formed white crystals, m. p. 196–198° (cor.). The yield was 1.20 g.

Rotation. 0.196 g. made up to 20 ml. with absolute ethanol at 28° gave α_D −0.296°; *l*, 2; $[\alpha]^{28}D$ −15°.

Anal. Calcd. for $C_{16}H_{16}NO_4SBr$: C, 48.13; H, 4.04. Found: C, 48.01; H, 4.32.

The more-soluble salt (crop IV, 2.30 g.) was decomposed with cold 1:1 hydrochloric acid in the usual manner, m. p. 196–198° (cor.). The yield was 1.02 g.

Rotation. 0.2035 g. made up to 20 ml. with absolute ethanol at 28° gave α_D +0.297°; *l*, 2; $[\alpha]^{28}D$ +15°.

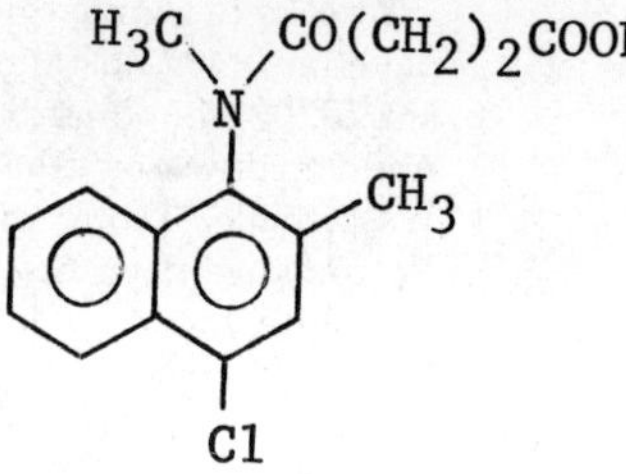

$C_{16}H_{16}ClNO_3$

Ref. 1160

Resolution of N-Succinyl-1-methylamino-4-chloro-2-methylnaphthalene.—A solution of 6.1 g. of N-succinyl-1-methylamino-4-chloro-2-methylnaphthalene and 6.7 g. of quinine in 100 cc. of boiling ethyl acetate was filtered, cooled to room temperature, and concentrated to 35 cc. by means of a gentle air stream. The salts in this resolution showed the same crystallization characteristics as did those of N-succinyl-1-methylamino-2-methylnaphthalene and the same procedure was followed. At 35 cc., 0.59 g. of salt crystallized out; at 30 cc., 0.90 g.; at 25 cc., 1.15 g.; at 20 cc., two successive crops of 0.33 g. and 1.14 g. These five fractions were combined (4.11 g.) and recrystallized from ethyl acetate to constant rotation. White feathery crystals were obtained; m. p. 117–119° (cor.).

Anal. (*l*B*d*A) Calcd. for $C_{16}H_{16}ClNO_3 \cdot C_{20}H_{24}N_2O_2 \cdot {}^1/_2\ C_4H_8O_2$: C, 67.68; H, 6.58; N, 6.23. Found: C, 67.66; H, 6.59; N, 6.45. *Rotation.* (*l*B*d*A) 0.047 g. made up to 25 cc. with absolute ethanol at 30° gave α_D −0.21°; *l*, 2; $[\alpha]^{30}D$ −56°.

Upon concentration of the original solution to 15 cc., 3.67 g. of crystalline salt was obtained and at 12 cc., another crop of 1.39 g. crystallized. These two fractions were discarded. At 10 cc., 0.75 g. of salt crystallized and by allowing the mother liquor to remain in a refrigerator for several days, another 0.53 g. of salt was obtained. These two crops were combined (1.28 g.). Recrystallization failed to change the rotation of this fraction; white crystals; m. p. 111–113° (cor.).

Rotation. (*l*B*l*A) 0.052 g. made up to 25 cc. with absolute ethanol at 30° gave α_D −0.38°; *l*, 2; $[\alpha]^{30}D$ −91°.

No additional crystalline material could be obtained from the original solution; weight of dry residue, 1.96 g.

d- and *l*-**N-Succinyl-1-methylamino-4-chloro-2-methylnaphthalene.**—The salts were decomposed by digestion with 20% hydrochloric acid as in the previous case. The *d*-acid was recrystallized from benzene–petroleum ether (b. p. 60–110°) mixture without effecting any change in

rotation; white crystals; m. p., 115.5–116° (cor.).

Anal. (*d*-acid) Calcd. for $C_{16}H_{16}ClNO_3$: C, 62.83; H, 5.28. Found: C, 63.09; H, 5.40. *Rotation.* (*d*-acid) 0.067 g. made up to 25 cc. with absolute ethanol at 30° gave α_D +0.30°; *l*, 2; $[\alpha]^{30}_D$ +56°.

The *l*-acid obtained from the more-soluble salt was apparently not entirely pure; white crystals, softening at 116° (cor.) but not melting completely until a temperature of 163–167° was reached.

Rotation. (*l*-acid) 0.045 g. made up to 25 cc. with absolute ethanol at 30° gave α_D −0.13°; *l*, 2; $[\alpha]^{30}_D$ −36°.

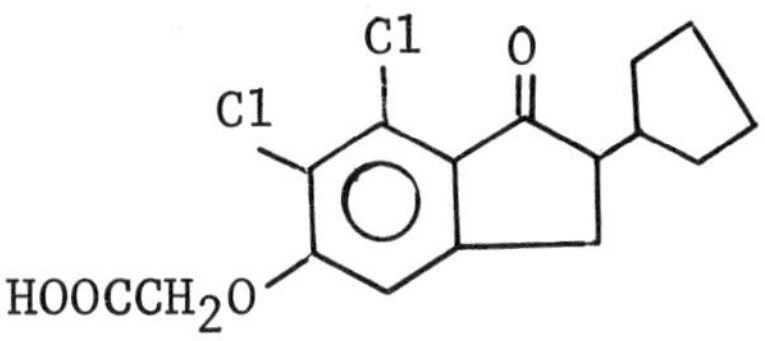

$C_{16}H_{16}Cl_2O_4$ Ref. 1161

Note:
The racemic acid was resolved via cinchonine in ethanol. The reported $[\alpha]^{25}_D$ for the active acid was -38.2 (c 3, acetone).

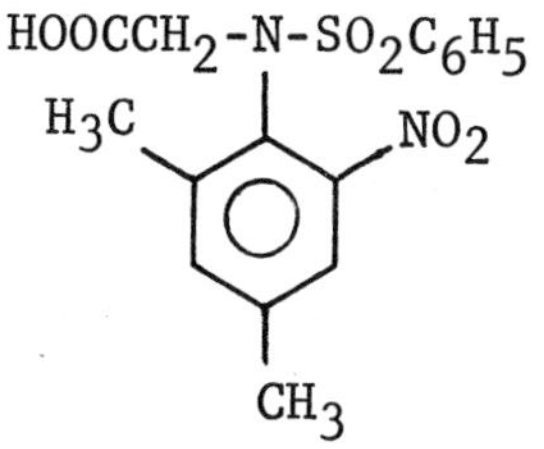

$C_{16}H_{16}N_2O_6S$ Ref. 1162

Resolution of N-Benzenesulfonyl-N-carboxymethyl-1-amino-2,4-dimethyl-6-nitrobenzene.—A solution of 2.34 g. of N-benzenesulfonyl-N-carboxymethyl-1-amino-2,4-dimethyl-6-nitrobenzene in 50 ml. of ethyl acetate was added to a solution of 1.87 g. of cinchonine in 125 ml. of boiling ethanol. The mixture was evaporated to 65 ml. with the aid of a suction pump and then placed in a refrigerator overnight. From this solution 1.04 g. of crystals was collected. Solvent was removed from the mother liquor until the volume was 50 ml. and another 0.98 g. of crystals was collected. Solvent was again evaporated until the mother liquor was 15 ml., when 30 ml. of ethyl acetate was added. A third fraction of 0.25 g. of crystals was collected. The specific rotation readings were taken by making 0.05 g. up to 50 ml. with absolute ethanol. A two-decimeter tube was used.

Crop	Wt., g.	α_D at 30°	$[\alpha]^{30}_D$
I	1.04	0.259°	130
II	0.98	.265	132
III	0.25	.268	134

Several small fractions, averaging about 0.2 g. each, were then separated from the mother liquor. Their specific rotations were similar to the above fractions. Crystals were collected even at dryness.

A sample of crop I was recrystallized from ethyl acetate and an almost quantitative yield obtained. No oil was found when the residue was evaporated to dryness. No change in specific rotation of the recrystallized salt was noted. Only the *d*B*d*A salt could be isolated. The product formed white crystals, m. p. 193–195° (cor.).

Rotation. 0.05 g. made up to 50 ml. with absolute ethanol at 30° gave α_D +0.259°; *l*, 2; $[\alpha]^{30}_D$ +130°.

Anal. Calcd. for $C_{16}H_{16}N_2O_6S{\cdot}C_{19}H_{22}N_2O$: C, 63.95; H, 5.83. Found: C, 63.23; H, 5.74.

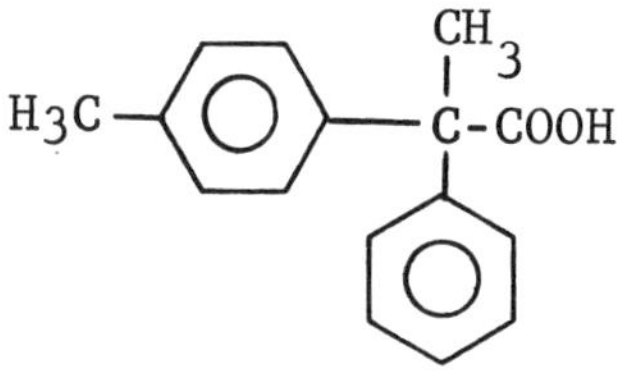

$C_{16}H_{16}O_2$ Ref. 1163

The quinine salt was recrystallised eleven times from 50% aqueous acetone and on decomposition afforded (−)-*α-phenyl-α-*p*-tolylpropionic acid,* m. p. 96°, $[\alpha]^{18}_D$ −11·0° (7%) (Found: C, 80·2; H, 6·7. $C_{16}H_{16}O_2$ requires C, 80·0; H, 6·7%).

Note: Rotation taken in chloroform.

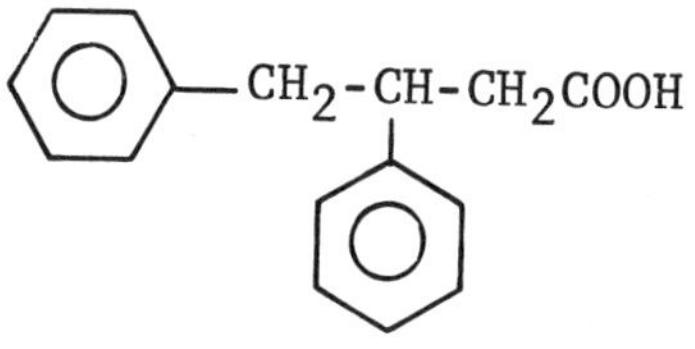

$C_{16}H_{16}O_2$ Ref. 1164

The Resolution of 3, 4-Diphenylbutyric Acid (VI).—A mixture of 4.8 g. (0.02 mol.) of VI, m. p. 89—95°C, $[\alpha]^{28}_D$ −9° (*c* 2.25, benzene) which had been obtained by the above asymmetric synthesis, 6.5 g. (0.02 mol.) of quinine, and 70 ml. of ethanol was boiled until dissolution was complete. After the mixture had stood overnight at 0°C, the crystalline product was separated and washed with small quantities of ethanol. Weight of the dried product, 4.0 g.; $[\alpha]^{25}_D$ −95° (*c* 1.82, chloroform), m. p. 160—162°C. Three further recrystallizations from the same solvent gave 1.8 g. of quinine salt as needles, m. p. 165—166°C, $[\alpha]^{25}_D$ −101° (*c* 1.72, chloroform), as was indicated by its constant rotation when subjected to further recrystallization.

Found: C, 76.61; H, 7.07; N, 4.96. Calcd. for $C_{36}H_{40}N_2O_4$: C, 76.56; H, 7.14; N, 4.96%.
Decomposition in the usual manner gave a specimen of (−)-acid (VI) with a m. p. of 84—86°C, $[\alpha]^{28}_D$ −67° (*c* 0.81, chloroform), which after four recrystallizations from ligroin, had a m. p. of 87—88°C, $[\alpha]^{28}_D$ −60°

(c 1.92, benzene). Yield, 280 mg. Further recrystallization led to no change in the optical rotation.

Found: C, 80.03; H, 6.50. Calcd. for $C_{16}H_{16}O_2$: C, 79.97; H, 6.71%.

The mother liquors containing the (+)-acid were concentrated and allowed to stand overnight at room temperature. After the precipitate had been filtered out, the filtrate was concentrated to dryness. The reresulting solid (4.0 g.), which had a m. p. of 65—100°C, $[\alpha]_D^{25}$ −57° (c 1.63, chloroform), was recrystallized three times from 50% aqueous ethanol to give quinine salt of (+)-acid (VI) as needles, m. p. 110—111°C, $[\alpha]_D^{25}$ −66° (c 1.47 chloroform).

Found: C, 75.13; H, 7.14; N, 4.75. Calcd. for $C_{36}H_{40}N_2O_4 \cdot 1/2H_2O$: C, 75.36; H, 7.20; N, 4.88%. Decomposition gave (+)-acid (VI) with a m. p. of 82—88°C, $[\alpha]_D^{27}$ +46° (c 1.24, benzene), which, after three recrystallizations from ligroin, had a m. p. of 86—88°C, $[\alpha]_D^{28}$ +59° (c 1.85, benzene). Yield, 200 mg. Further recrystallization led to no change in the optical rotation.

Found: C, 80.25; H, 6.64. Calcd. for $C_{16}H_{16}O_2$: C, 79.97; H, 6.71%.

IR_{max}^{KBr}: 3023, 2914, 1711, 1659, 1407, 1279 cm⁻¹. Its infrared spectrum (in chloroform) was identified with that of racemic acid (VI).

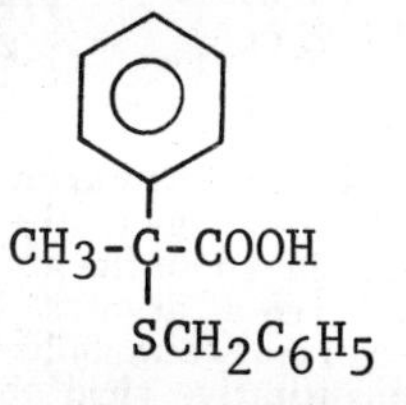

$C_{16}H_{16}O_2S$ Ref. 1165

Resolution of 2-Phenyl-2-benzylmercaptopropanoic Acid.— The above acid (28.6 g) in ethanol (35 ml) was converted to its (+)-α-phenylethylammonium salt by reaction with (+)-α-phenylethylamine (12.7 g) in ethanol (35 ml) and water (70 ml). Coarse crystals (16.3 g) formed and were recrystallized from ethanol (100 ml)–water (16 ml) and from ethanol (75 ml), resulting in 10.8 g of (+)-α-phenylethylammonium (−)-2-phenyl-2-benzylmercaptopropanoate, mp 174–174.5°, $[\alpha]^{27}_D$ −54.4° (c 1.33, EtOH), unchanged on further recrystallization. The salt was shaken with dilute hydrochloric acid and extracted with benzene. The extract was dried and stripped of solvent, yielding 7.2 g of (R)-(−)-2-phenyl-2-benzylmercaptopropanoic acid ((−)-IVa), a thick oil, $[\alpha]^{24}_D$ −46.5° (c 2.2, EtOH), which was characterized below as its crystalline amide.

Unresolved acid (20.7 g), similarly obtained, was recovered from the mother liquors of the above resolution, then converted to its (−)-α-phenylethylammonium salt with (−)-α-phenylethylamine (9.3 g) in hot ethanol (60 ml) and water (100 ml). The resulting salt was recrystallized three times as above, affording 10.6 g of (−)-α-phenylethylammonium (+)-2-phenyl-2-benzylmercaptopropanoate, mp 174–175°, $[\alpha]^{27}_D$ +53.8° (c 1.24, EtOH). This was converted, as above, into free (S)-(+)-2-phenyl-2-benzylmercaptopropanoic acid ((+)-IVa), a viscous oil, $[\alpha]^{24}_D$ +46.6° (c 2.3, EtOH).

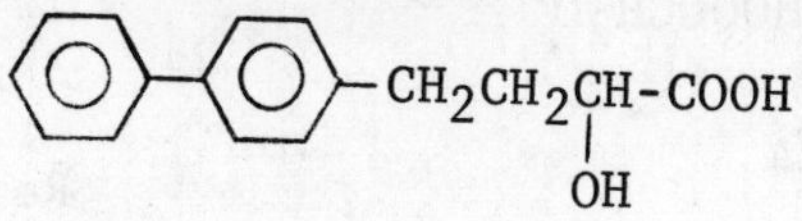

$C_{16}H_{16}O_3$ Ref. 1166

Antipodo (II) (+): 7,03 g di acido (±)4-(4-bifenilil)-2-ossibutirrico (2,74 x 10^{-2} moli) e la quantità stechiometrica di (—)α-feniletilamina (3,3 g) sono sciolti in 60 ml di etanolo scaldando a ricadere. Alla soluzione calda si aggiungono 180 ml di acqua e si lascia quindi a sè per 2 giorni. Cristallizza così il diastereoisomero (+) (—), dal quale si ottengono 3,5 g di antipodo destrogiro. P.f. 184-6° (etanolo); $[\alpha]_D$ = +75° (c 2; metanolo).

	trov. % :	C 75,01;	H 6,11
per $C_{16}H_{16}O_3$	calc. :	74,98;	6,29

Antipodo (II) (—): dalle acque madri idroalcooliche, si ottengono 3 g di antipodo levogiro. P.f. 184-6° (etanolo); $[\alpha]_D$ = —7° (c 2; metanolo).

trov. % : C 75,31; H 6,17

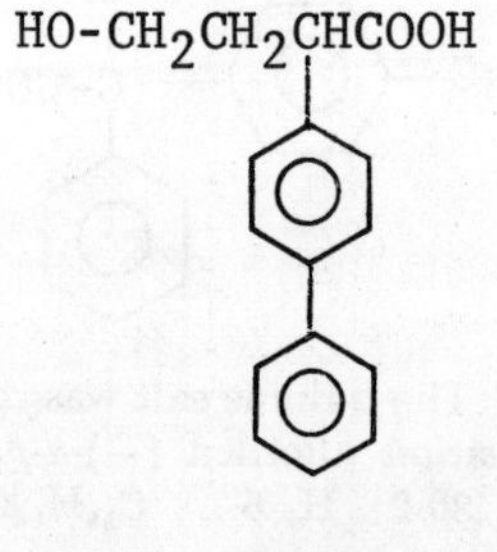

$C_{16}H_{16}O_3$ Ref. 1167

Antipodo (I) (+): 9,22 g di ossiacido racemo (I) (3,59 x 10^{-2} moli) e la quantità stechiometrica di chinina (15,09 g) vengono sciolti a caldo in 200 ml di etanolo e la soluzione tenuta in frigorifero per una notte. Cristallizza così il diastereoisomero (+) (—), dal quale per acidificazione con acido solforico diluito ed estrazione con etere, si ottengono 4,9 g di antipodo destrogiro, che cristallizza da acetato di etile e fonde a 160-1°; $[\alpha]_D$ = +7,5° (c 2; etanolo).

trov. % : C 75,19; H 6,07

Antipodo (I) (—): il filtrato etanolico precedente è evaporato; dal residuo, per acidificazione ed estrazione, si ottengono 4,65 g di antipodo levogiro, che cristallizza da acetato di etile e fonde a 154-5°; $[\alpha]_D$ = —6,5° (c 2; acetone).

trov. % : C 75,22; H 6,18

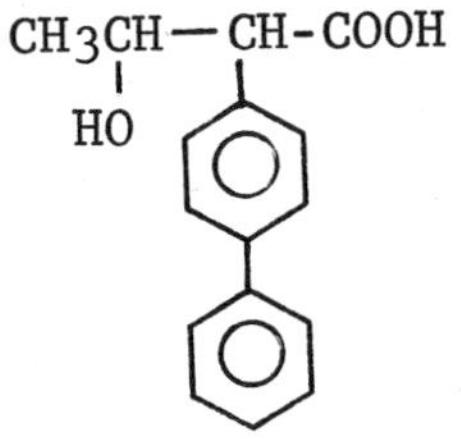

$C_{16}H_{16}O_3$ Ref. 1168

Acidi (+)- (V) *e* (—)eritro-2-(4-*bifenilil*)-3-*ossibutirrico* (VI)

3,85 g di acido (±)*eritro*-2-(4-bifenilil)-3-ossibutirrico (I) e la quantità stechiometrica di chinina (4,9 g) vengono sciolti in ml 50 di etanolo bollente. Dopo riposo di una notte a temperatura ambiente, cristallizza il diastereoisomero (+)(—) che è filtrato e trattato con acido solforico diluito; dopo estrazione con etere, lavaggio, essiccamento ed evaporazione del solvente, si ottengono g 2,1 di antipodo destrogiro (V), che cristallizza da cloroformio e fonde a 163-64°; $[\alpha]_D$ = +77° (c 4; acetone).

Il filtrato etanolico è evaporato ed il residuo è trattato con acido solforico diluito. Dopo estrazione con etere, lavaggio, essiccamento ed evaporazione del solvente, si ottengono g 1,8 di antipodo levogiro (VI), che, cristallizzato da benzene, fonde a 163-64°; $[\alpha]_D$ = —77,5° (c 4; acetone).

	Comp. (V)	trov. % :	C 74,93;	H 6,32
	Comp. (VI)	trov. % :	C 74,79;	H 6,31
per $C_{16}H_{16}O_3$		calc. :	74,98;	6,29

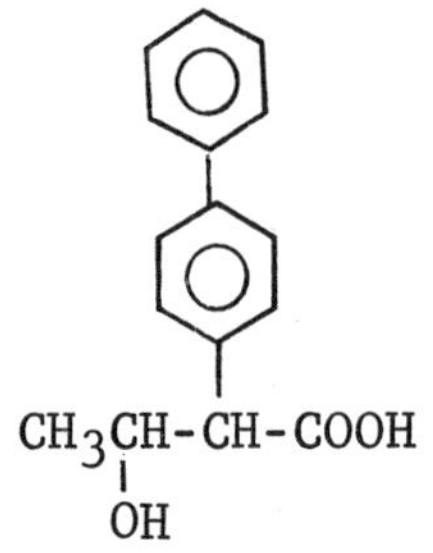

$C_{16}H_{16}O_3$ Ref. 1169

Acidi (+)- (VII) *e* (—)treo-2-(4-*bifenilil*)-3-*ossibutirrico* (VIII)

3,4 g di acido (±)*treo*-2-(4-bifenilil)-3-ossibutirrico (II) sono trattati come descritto per il corrispondente acido racemo *eritro*. Dalla soluzione etanolica cristallizza il diastereoisomero (+)(—), dal quale si ottengono g 1,65 di antipodo destrogiro (VII), che cristallizza da etanolo e fonde a 223-24°; $[\alpha]_D$ = +55,5° (c 2; diossano). Dal filtrato etanolico si ottengono g 1,75 di antipodo levogiro (VIII) che, cristallizzato da etanolo, fonde a 226-27°; $[\alpha]_D$ = —55° (c 2; diossano).

	Comp. (VII)	trov. % :	C 75,13;	H 6,30
	Comp. (VIII)	trov. % :	C 74,88;	H 6,35
per $C_{16}H_{16}O_3$		calc. :	74,98;	6,29

Gli AA. desiderano ringraziare il Prof. M. Amorosa *per gli utili suggerimenti forniti.*

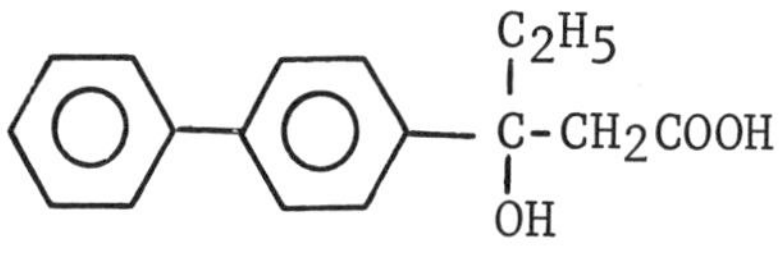

Ref. 1170

$C_{16}H_{16}O_3$

Risoluzione ottica degli ossiacidi racemi

Si aggiunge l'ossiacido racemo alla soluzione calda preparata sciogliendo la quantità stechiometrica di chinina nel solvente appropriato; si scalda a ricadere sino a solubilizzazione completa e poi si lascia a temperatura ambiente o in frigorifero per uno o più giorni. Si filtra alla pompa il prodotto che è cristallizzato e si evapora a secco il filtrato. I cristalli ed il residuo che si ottiene dal filtrato per evaporazione del solvente, vengono separatamente acidificati con acido solforico diluito ed estratti con etere.

Dai due estratti eterei, lavati e seccati, per evaporazione si ottengono i singoli antipodi, che vengono cristallizzati.

TABELLA I

R	R'	Risoluz. ottica (*)	P.f.°	Solvente di cristall.	Rf	$[\alpha]_D$	Formula	ν_{IR} cm^{-1} CO	ν_{IR} cm^{-1} OH
	C_2H_5		50-2	etanolo	0,18		$C_{18}H_{20}O_3$	1700	3450
	H (±)	3,5%	132-4	etan./acqua	0,23		$C_{16}H_{16}O_3$	1690	3520 e 3560
CH_3	H (+)	benzene	155-6	clorof.		+ 11,33°	$C_{16}H_{16}O_3$		
	H (—)		142-4	clorof.		— 10,00°	$C_{16}H_{16}O_3$		
	C_2H_5		83-4	etanolo	0,27		$C_{19}H_{22}O_3$	1720	3460 e 3540
	H (±)	6%	171-1,5	clorof.	0,25		$C_{17}H_{18}O_3$	1680	3500 e 3550
C_2H_5	H (—)	acetone	183	clorof.		— 3,6°	$C_{17}H_{18}O_3$		
	H (+)		184-6	clorof.		+ 3,6°	$C_{17}H_{18}O_3$		
	C_2H_5		70-1	etanolo	0,30		$C_{20}H_{24}O_3$	1710	3500
	H (±)	6%	165-6	clorof.	0,27		$C_{18}H_{20}O_3$	1675	3495
n—C_3H_7	H (+)	acetone	165-7	clorof.		+ 2°	$C_{18}H_{20}O_3$		
	H (—)		166-7	clorof.		— 1,2°	$C_{18}H_{20}O_3$		
	C_2H_5		76-7	etanolo	0,35		$C_{20}H_{24}O_3$	1700	3495
	H (±)	5,5%	164-5	clorof.	0,28		$C_{18}H_{20}O_3$	1685	3495 e 3560
i—C_3H_7	H (—)	etanolo	192-4,5	clorof.		— 6°	$C_{18}H_{20}O_3$		
	H (+)		192	clorof.		+ 7°	$C_{18}H_{20}O_3$		

(*) Le percentuali esprimono la concentrazione del racemo nel solvente sotto indicato; è citato per primo l'antipodo ottenuto dal diastereoisomero che si separa cristallino dalla soluzione.

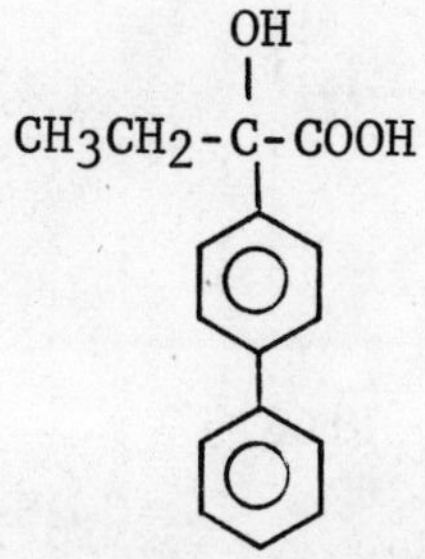

$C_{16}H_{16}O_3$ **Ref. 1171**

Acido (—) *e* (+) 2-(4-*bifenilil*)-2-*ossibutirrico* (III) (—) *e* (III) (+)

Antipodo (III) (—): 12,30 g di acido (±)2-(4-bifenilil)-2-ossibutirrico (III) (6, 7) e la quantità stechiometrica di chinina (15,5 g) sono sciolti scaldando a ricadere in 370 ml di benzene e la soluzione lasciata a sè a temperatura ambiente per alcuni giorni. Cristallizza così il diastereoisomero (—) (—) dal quale si hanno 6,5 g di antipodo levogiro. P.f. 184-6° (etile acetato); $[\alpha]_D$ = —13° (c 6; acetone).

	trov. % :	C 75,39;	H 6,65
per $C_{16}H_{16}O_3$	calc. :	74,98;	6,29

Antipodo (III) (+): il filtrato benzenico dà 5,8 g di antipodo destrogiro. P.f. 184-6° (etile acetato); $[\alpha]_D$ = +11° (c 6; acetone).

trov. % : C 75,10; H 6,59

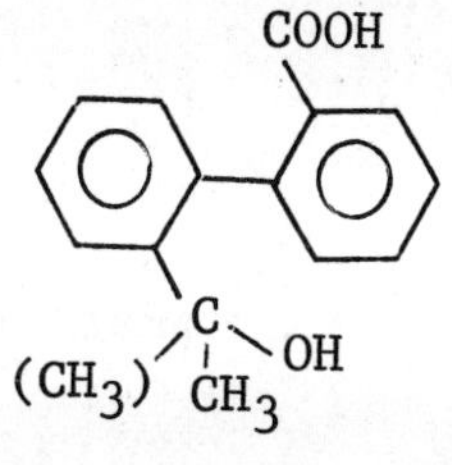

$C_{16}H_{16}O_3$ **Ref. 1172**

Scissione dell'acido. Ad una soluzione di 6.15 (1 mol.) di brucina anidra in 50 cmc. di alcool si aggiungono 4 gr. (1 mol.) di acido 2[bis-metil–ossimetil]-2'–difenilcarbossilico. Si bolle per breve tempo e si filtra la soluzione.

Per raffreddamento si separa la prima frazione del sale di brucina (gr. 8.45; p. f. 217°); evaporando a secco l'alcool madre in essicatore a vuoto su acido solforico si ottiene una seconda frazione (gr. 1.33 p. f. 214°).

La microdeterminazione dell'azoto nelle due frazioni ha fornito:

I frazione	trovato	%	4.38
II »	»	%	4.15
per $C_{39}H_{42}O_7N_2$	calcolato	%	4.31;

ed il loro potere rotatorio in soluzione cloroformica misurato appena fatta la soluzione risulta:

I frazione $[\alpha]_D^{24°} = (-0°, 59.100) : (1,6680.1) = -35°.35$

II » $[\alpha]_D^{24°} = (-0°, 64.100) : (1,9112.1) = -33°.49.$

Il potere rotatorio delle due soluzioni va diminuendo con il tempo; dopo 64 ore vennero osservati i seguenti valori:

I frazione $[\alpha]_D^{23°} = (-0°,04.100) : (1,6688.1) = -2°.39$

II » $[\alpha]_D^{25°} = (-0°,04.100) : (1,9112.1) = -2°.09.$

Essi tendono evidentemente al valore del potere rotatorio del sale di brucina della miscela racemica che dalla misura di una soluzione di 0.2420 gr. di brucina anidra e 0.1575 di acido in 24 cmc. di cloroformio risulta essere:

$$[\alpha]_D^{25°} = (-0°,03.100) : (1,5980.1) = -1.88°.$$

La racemizzazione della prima frazione è praticamente completa riscaldando la sua soluzione cloroformica per circa tre ore all'ebollizione. Infatti il suo potere rotatorio è diminuito a

$$[\alpha]_D^{24°} = (-0°,03.100) : (1,6000.1) = -1.87°.$$

La scissione del sale di brucina si effettua sciogliendolo a temperatura ordinaria nella minore quantità possibile di anilina e trattando la soluzione con acido cloridrico diluito ghiacciato. La parte insolubile costituita dall'acido attivo viene lavata parecchie volte prima con acido cloridrico diluito poi con acqua e si asciuga in essicatore.

L'acido attivo proveniente dalla prima frazione (gr. 0.20 da gr. 1 di sale; p. f. 126°) in soluzione cloroformica ha il seguente potere rotatorio:

$$[\alpha]_D^{24°} = (-0°,24.100) : (0,5656.2) = -21°.21.$$

Esso va diminuendo con il tempo e dopo circa tre giorni si annulla.

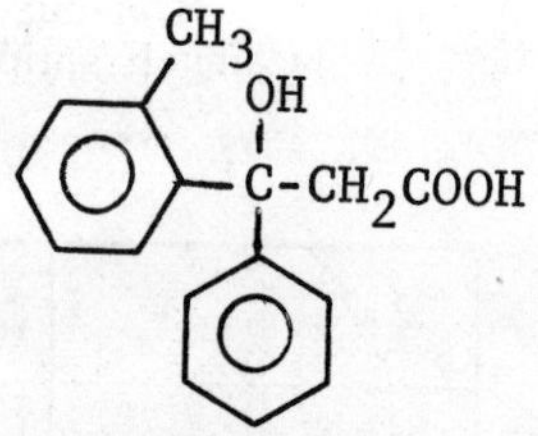

$C_{16}H_{16}O_3$ **Ref. 1173**

Resolution of 3-Phenyl-3-(*o*-tolyl)-hydracrylic Acid.—When 7.1 g. (one equivalent) of brucine tetrahydrate was added to a solution 3.9 g. of the racemic acid dissolved in 450 ml. of hot ethanol, 5.4 g. of the salt deposited. Since the partially racemic acid having $[\alpha]$D −90°, which was regenerated from this salt, showed rotation similar to that of the product in run 7 (Table I), 3.6 g. of the product in run 7 and 6.6 g. of brucine tetrahydrate was added to the crop. After three recrystallizations from ethanol, a salt having $[\alpha]^{12}$D −90° (*c* 1.49, chloroform) was obtained. Decomposition in the usual manner gave a specimen of acid having $[\alpha]^{10}$D −159°: repeated recrystallizations from methanol afforded the (−)-acid, $[\alpha]^{13}$D −168° (*c* 4.63, acetone), m.p. 153.5–154° (with foaming). Further recrystallization led to no change in optical rotation.

Anal. Calcd. for $C_{16}H_{16}O_3$: C, 74.98; H, 6.29. Found: C, 75.22; H, 6.20.

The original mother liquor was concentrated and, after two cycles of fractional recrystallization, decomposed. The acid obtained from the more soluble salt had $[\alpha]^{8}$D +129°: recrystallizations from methanol gave (+)-acid which was not quite optically pure, $[\alpha]^{13}$D +151° (*c* 2.44, acetone), m.p. 154–154.5° (with foaming).

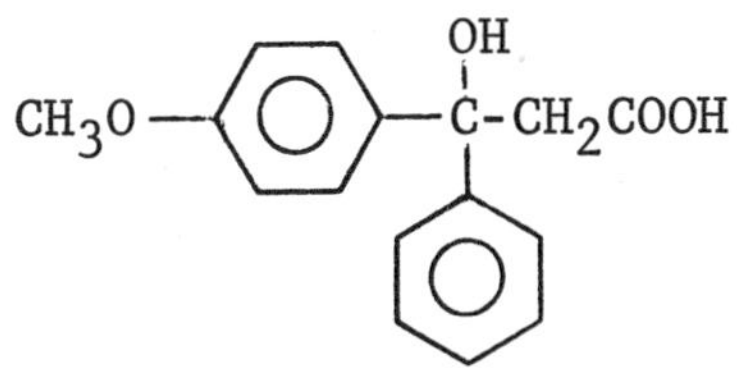

$C_{16}H_{16}O_4$ Ref. 1174

Resolution of 3-(*p*-Anisyl)-3-phenylhydracrylic Acid.—When 9.1 g. (one equivalent) of *d*-cinchonine was added to a solution of 8.4 g. of the racemic acid dissolved in 200 ml. of hot ethanol, 10.6 g. of the salt separated out. Four recrystallizations from ethanol gave a material, $[\alpha]^{18}_D$ +104° (*c* 2.01, chloroform), which was dissolved in chloroform and decomposed with dilute hydrochloric acid followed by extractions with sodium bicarbonate solution. The combined alkaline layers were extracted with chloroform and acidified. The resulting acid showed $[\alpha]^{14}_D$ +12.3°: after recrystallizations from methanol (+)-acid having $[\alpha]^{14}_D$ +14.2° (*c* 1.46, dioxane) and m.p. 153.5–154° (with foaming) was obtained. Further recrystallization led to no change in rotation.

Anal. Calcd. for $C_{16}H_{16}O_4$: C, 70.57; H, 5.97. Found: C, 70.59; H, 5.88.

The original mother liquor was concentrated and subjected to three cycles of fractional recrystallization from ethanol. The more soluble salt was decomposed as above and the resulted acid was recrystallized from methanol. The (−)-acid was obtained in less optical purity: $[\alpha]^{12}_D$ −11.4° (*c* 5.04, dioxane), m.p. 153.5° (with foaming).

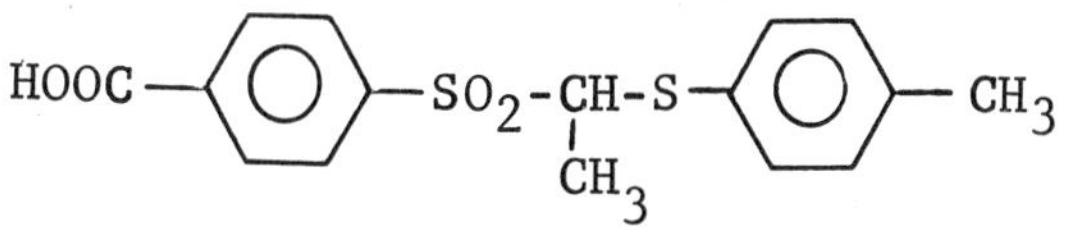

$C_{16}H_{16}O_4S_2$ Ref. 1175

Resolution of dl-α-p-*Carboxyphenylsulphonyl*-α-p-*tolylthioethane* (IX).—The l-*menthylamine* salt was precipitated when aqueous solutions of equivalent proportions of the sodium salt of the acid and the hydrochloride of the base were mixed. After one recrystallisation from 50% alcohol, it had m. p. 175—185° (Found: C, 63·7, 63·9; H, 6·5, 7·1. $C_{16}H_{16}O_4S_2,C_{10}H_{21}N$ requires C, 63·7; H, 7·5%). $[\alpha]_{5461}$ − 2·21° in chloroform (*c* = 0·9). The salt was then crystallised five times from aqueous alcohol and four times from alcohol, from which it finally separated in long fine needles, m. p. 199—202° (Found: C, 63·8, 64·2; H, 7·3, 7·5%). $[\alpha]_{5461}$ + 57·0° in chloroform (*c* = 1·2).

The acid liberated from the last fraction by solution of the salt in acetic acid and addition of water had m. p. 160°, and $[\alpha]_{5461}$ + 130° in chloroform (*c* = 0·55).

The resolution can be simplified by dissolving *l*-menthylamine hydrochloride (1 equiv.) and the sodium salt of the acid (2 equivs.) in 50% aqueous alcohol and seeding the solution with the pure *l*B*d*A salt described above. When crystallisation is complete, the deposit is recrystallised once from alcohol, and the acid isolated from it. The crude *d*-acid is dissolved in acetic acid, the solution seeded with the *dl*-acid and kept until no further crystallisation occurs. After filtration, the filtrate is precipitated with water, and the *d*-acid collected, $[\alpha]_{5461}$ = + 130°. From the original mother-liquor the crude *l*-acid is liberated, and purified with acetic acid, $[\alpha]_{5461}$ = − 126°. The *dl*-acid is practically insoluble in cold acetic acid, but the active isomerides are moderately readily soluble.

The active acid racemises in faintly alkaline solution: a sample ($[\alpha]_{5461}$ + 122° in chloroform), dissolved in sodium hydroxide solution (1 equiv.), showed a half-life period of about 10 hours, whereas a similar sample in aqueous ammonia had a half-life period of about 60 hours at the ordinary temperature. The acid can also be resolved with the aid of its quinine salt, which after repeated crystallisation from alcohol finally separates in prisms, m. p. 180—181°, $[\alpha]_{5461}$ − 100° in chloroform (*c* = 0·6). The acid from this salt gave $[\alpha]_{5461}$ + 112° in chloroform.

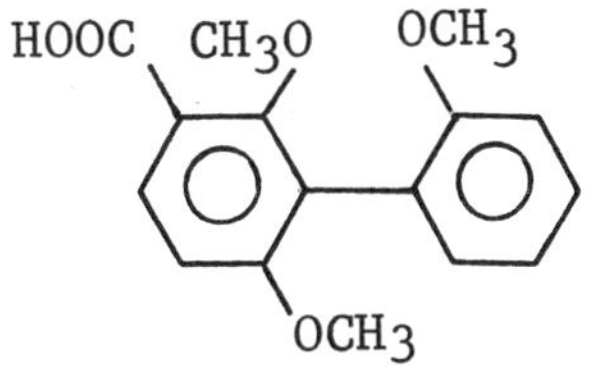

$C_{16}H_{16}O_5$ Ref. 1176

The resolution of the racemic acid was achieved through a brucine salt from acetone to give an optically active acid, m.p. 151-153°, $[\alpha]^{15}_D$ = -12.3°, and $[\alpha]^{15}_{400}$ = -58.5° (c, 1.3, $CHCl_3$).

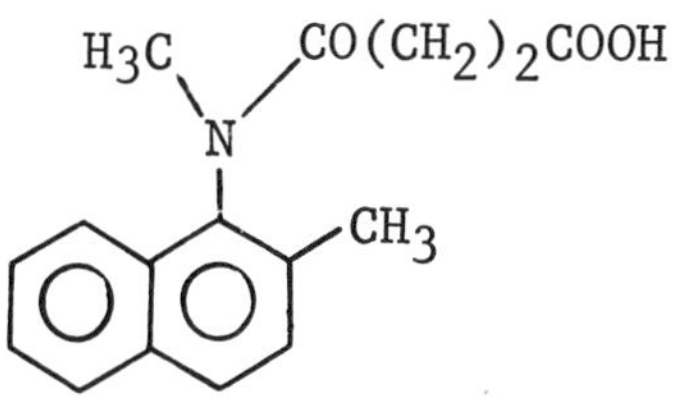

$C_{16}H_{17}NO_3$ Ref. 1177

Resolution of N-Succinyl-1-methylamino-2-methylnaphthalene.—A solution of 5.0 g. of N-succinyl-1-methylamino-2-methylnaphthalene and 6.0 g. of quinine in 50 cc. of boiling ethyl acetate was filtered, cooled to room temperature, and concentrated to 30 cc. by means of a gentle air stream. After standing at room temperature in a loosely stoppered flask for several days, the solution had concentrated to 25 cc. and a small crop of salt had crystallized. The crystals were collected and washed free of the sirupy mother liquor with ethyl acetate. The dry product weighed 1.81 g. The combined mother liquor and washings were concentrated to 20 cc. by air stream. After

standing for several days, it yielded a second crop of salt amounting to 0.82 g. A third crop, 2.11 g., was obtained by repetition of this procedure. These three fractions were combined (4.74 g.), dissolved in ethyl acetate, and the solvent allowed to evaporate slowly. Recrystallization in this manner to constant rotation gave white feathery crystals, m. p. 129.5° (cor.).

Anal. (*l*B*l*A) Calcd. for $C_{16}H_{17}NO_3 \cdot C_{20}H_{24}N_2O_2 \cdot {}^1/_2C_4H_8O_2$: C, 71.32; H, 7.10; N, 6.57. Found: C, 70.91; H, 7.20; N, 6.93.

Rotation. (*l*B*l*A) 0.050 g. made up to 25 cc. with absolute ethanol at 27° gave α_D −0.51°; *l*, 2; $[\alpha]^{27}_D$ −128°.

By continuing to allow the original solution to stand for several days at a volume of about 20 cc., two more successive crops of salt were obtained weighing 1.36 g. and 1.08 g., respectively. These were discarded. The mother liquor was concentrated to 15 cc. in an air stream and placed in a refrigerator; 0.73 g. of salt was obtained. Concentration of the mother liquor to 10 cc. and refrigeration yielded an additional 0.81 g. of salt. These two fractions were combined (1.54 g.), and dissolved in ethyl acetate. An equal volume of petroleum ether (b. p. 60–110°) was added and the solvent allowed to evaporate. Recrystallization thrice in this manner gave white crystals, m. p. 99–100° (cor.).

Rotation. (*l*B*d*A salt) 0.057 g. made up to 25 cc. with absolute ethanol at 27° gave α_D −0.26; *l*, 2; $[\alpha]^{27}_D$ −57°.

No additional crystalline material could be obtained from the original solution. The dry residue amounted to 2.10 g.; $[\alpha]^{27}_D$ −69°.

***d*- and *l*-N-Succinyl-1-methylamino-2-methylnaphthalene.**—The salts were decomposed by stirring with 20% hydrochloric acid at 0° for several hours until the product, which at first was a gum, appeared crystalline. The material was filtered and the digestion with hydrochloric acid repeated as many times as was necessary to give a filtrate free of alkaloid as shown by Folin's reagent. The acids were recrystallized from benzene–petroleum ether (b. p. 60–110°) mixture. The rotations were unchanged by the recrystallization.

The *l*-acid was obtained from the less-soluble salt in white crystals, m. p. 108° (cor.).

Anal. (*l*-acid) Calcd. for $C_{16}H_{17}NO_3$: C, 70.82; H, 6.31. Found: C, 70.78; H, 6.30. *Rotation.* (*l*-acid) 0.050 g. made up to 25 cc. with absolute ethanol at 27° gave α_D −0.30°; *l*, 2; $[\alpha]^{27}_D$ −75°.

Decomposition of the more-soluble salt gave white crystals, m. p. 107–108° (cor.).

Rotation. (*d*-acid) 0.023 g. made up to 10 cc. with absolute ethanol at 27° gave α_D +0.17°; *l*, 1; $[\alpha]^{27}_D$ +74°.

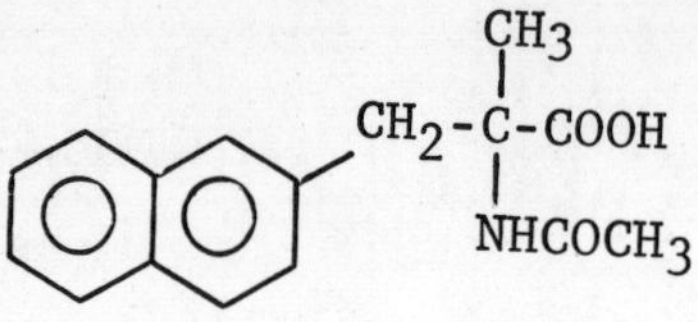

$C_{16}H_{17}NO_3$ Ref. 1178

(+)- *and* (−)-N-*Acetyl-α-methyl-β-(2-naphthyl)-alanine* —The DL-compound was resolved with (+)- and (−)-α-phenethylamine, as described for the analogous α-methyltyrosine derivative, to give after five fractional precipitations (−)-*N*-acetyl-α-methyl-β-(2-naphthyl)alanine, $[\alpha]_D$ −160° (*c*, 1% in methanol). The (+) enantiomer, $[\alpha]_D$ 140° (*c*, 1% in methanol), was only partially resolved after seven fractional precipitations.

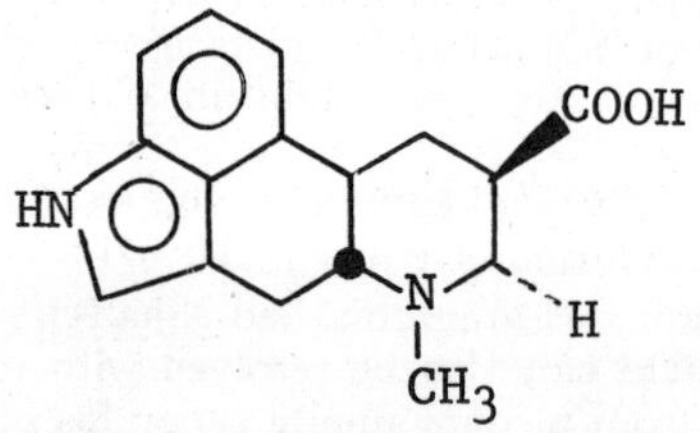

$C_{16}H_{18}N_2O_2$ Ref. 1179

b) D-Dihydro-lysergsäure-L-norephedrid und L-Dihydro-lysergsäure-L-norephedrid. 930 mg rac. Dihydro-lysergsäure-hydrazid wurden auf bekannte Weise[1]) mit salpetriger Säure umgesetzt und das Azid aus der mit Natriumhydrogencarbonat alkalisch gemachten Lösung ausgeäthert. Man engte die ätherischen Lösungen ohne Erwärmen im Vakuum etwas ein und vereinigte sie mit einer Lösung von 1,2 g L-Norephedrin in Äther. Im Verlauf von einigen Stunden bildete sich ein harziger Niederschlag. Die Lösung blieb über Nacht im Eisschrank stehen und wurde dann im Vakuum zur Trockne eingedampft. Der in Chloroform gelöste Rückstand wurde wiederholt mit Wasser und etwas Natriumhydrogencarbonat-Lösung ausgeschüttelt, die Chloroformlösung mit Natriumsulfat getrocknet und zur Trockne verdampft. Man erhielt 1,18 g eines gelblichen Harzes, das in Essigester aufgenommen und zur Trennung in seine Komponenten an einer Säule von 250 g Aluminiumoxyd chromatographiert wurde. Die durchlaufende Lösung fing man in Fraktionen von je 150 cm³ auf. Die Eindampfrückstände der ersten sechs Fraktionen kristallisierten beim Erwärmen mit einigen Tropfen Aceton und wurden gemeinsam aus diesem Lösungsmittel umkristallisiert. Man erhielt 350 mg D-Dihydro-lysergsäure-L-norephedrid in Form massiver Prismen und Polyeder. Für die Bestimmung der spez. Drehung und die Analyse wurde das Präparat noch dreimal aus Aceton umkristallisiert. Smp. 240—241°. Die Mischprobe mit einem Vergleichspräparat, das aus kristallisiertem D-Dihydro-lysergsäure-azid natürlicher Herkunft hergestellt worden war und die gleichen Eigenschaften aufwies, zeigte keine Depression.

$C_{25}H_{29}O_2N_3$	Ber.	C 74,41	H 7,24	N 10,42%
	Gef.	,, 74,36	,, 7,04	,, 10,47%

$[\alpha]^{20}_D = -114°$ (c = 0,3 in Pyridin)

Die weiteren Fraktionen, die durch Waschen des Chromatogramms mit Essigester und dann mit Aceton erhalten wurden, kristallisierten aus Essigester. Sie wurden gemein-

sam aus diesem Lösungsmittel umkristallisiert und ergaben 230 mg rohes L-Dihydro-lysergsäure-L-norephedrid. Das aus feinen Nadeln bestehende Produkt wurde noch mehrmals aus Essigester umkristallisiert, bis der Smp. bei 252—253° konstant blieb. Zur Analyse wurde die Verbindung im Hochvakuum bei 100° getrocknet.

$C_{25}H_{29}O_2N_3$ Ber. C 74,41 H 7,24 N 10,42%
Gef. ,, 73,99 ,, 7,26 ,, 10,28%

$[\alpha]_D^{20} = +107°$ (c = 0,3 in Pyridin)

c) D(–)-Dihydro-lysergsäure. 130 mg D-Dihydro-lysergsäure-L-norephedrid wurde mit 3 cm³ 25-proz. Kalilauge und 3 cm³ Äthanol 9 Stunden am Rückfluss gekocht. Die Verseifung war nach dieser Zeit noch nicht vollständig; es musste deshalb das unveränderte Ausgangsmaterial durch Ausschütteln der mit etwas Wasser verdünnten Lösung mit Chloroform abgetrennt werden. Die wässerig-alkalische Lösung wurde darauf mit 15-proz. Salzsäure vorsichtig neutralisiert und durch Zusatz von Eisessig auf pH 6 eingestellt. Beim Einengen kristallisierte die D(–)-Dihydro-lysergsäure aus. Nach dem Umkristallisieren aus reinem Wasser zeigte sie die richtige spez. Drehung und zersetzte sich beim Erhitzen von 300° an ohne richtig zu schmelzen. Die Kristalle hatten die charakteristische Form rhombischer oder sechseckiger Blättchen.

$[\alpha]_D^{20} = -120°$ (c = 0,2 in Pyridin)

d) L(+)-Dihydro-lysergsäure. 90 mg L-Dihydro-lysergsäure-L-norephedrid wurde durch Kochen mit je 3 cm³ 25-proz. Kalilauge und Äthanol verseift und die L-Dihydro-lysergsäure auf die gleiche Art isoliert, wie die D-Form. Die Säure zeigte dieselben Eigenschaften wie ihr Antipode, indessen natürlich das entgegengesetzte spez. Drehvermögen.

$[\alpha]_D^{20} = +120°$ (c = 0,2 in Pyridin)

[1]) *A. Stoll, A. Hofmann & Th. Petrzilka*, Helv. **29**, 650 (1946).

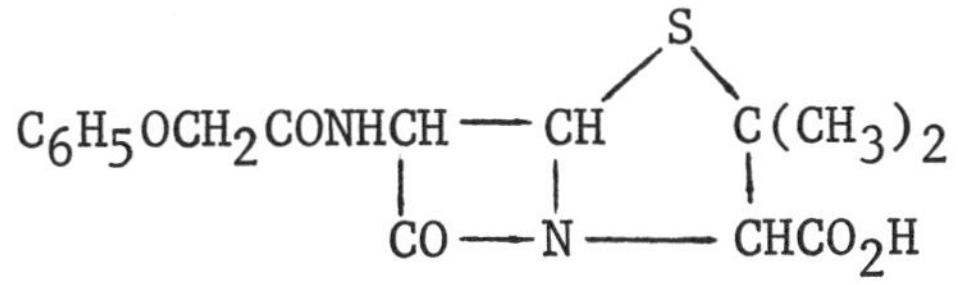

Ref. 1180

$C_{16}H_{18}N_2O_5S$

The Resolution of Potassium DL-Phenoxymethylpenicillinate (VIII).—To a solution of 78 mg. (0.2 mmole) of DL-VIII in 2.5 ml. of water was added a solution of 43 mg. (0.16 mmole) of *levo-erythro*-IX·HCl[24,25] in 2 ml. of water. Seeding the solution with traces of X failed to induce crystallization, but storage at 5° for 9 days afforded 46 mg. (70%) of crystalline product of m.p. 168° dec. Part of this solid (16 mg., 0.02 mmole) was purified further by shaking with 1.5 ml. of *n*-butyl acetate and 1.5 ml. of 0.7% phosphoric acid until two clear layers resulted. The aqueous layer was discarded, and the organic layer was washed with two 1-ml. portions of water. To this solution was added a solution of 4.6 mg. (0.02 mmole) of *levo-erythro*-IX in 0.4 ml. of *n*-butyl acetate. Storage at 5° overnight afforded 10 mg. (44%) of a crystalline salt, m.p. 175° dec., $\alpha^{25}D$ +92° (*c* 0.2 in N-methyl-2-pyrrolidone). Comparison of infrared spectra (potassium bromide) showed this compound to be identical with X. This compound showed 95 ± 10% (576 μ/mg.) of the theoretical bioactivity expected for the salt.[16]

The aqueous filtrate containing L-penicillin V was covered with 6 ml. of *n*-butyl acetate, and 3.5 ml. of 1% phosphoric acid was added; shaking caused the solid which precipitated to redissolve. The organic layer was washed with two 5-ml. portions of water. To the organic layer was added a solution of 46 mg. (0.2 mmole) of *dextro-erythro*-IX[24,25] in 3 ml. of *n*-butyl acetate. Scratching initiated crystallization and storage for 3 days at 5° afforded 35 mg. of crystals, m.p. 177° dec. A second crop was obtained from the filtrate, m.p. 175° dec. The total yield was 41 mg. (66%). Recrystallization from dioxane–ether gave an analytical sample of the *dextro-erythro*-IX salt of L-VIII, m.p. 175° dec., $\alpha^{25}D$ −86° (*c* 0.4 in N-methyl-2-pyrrolidone). The infrared spectrum (potassium bromide) was identical to that of X. This salt of L-penicillin V showed, 0.7% (4μ/mg.) of the theoretical bioactivity (606 μ/mg.) expected for the salt of natural penicillin V.[16]

Anal. Calcd. for $C_{31}H_{35}N_3O_6S$: C, 64.46; H, 6.11. Found: C, 64.09; H, 6.41.

(16) The synthetic samples were compared to standard natural penicillin V in a plate diffusion assay carried out under the supervision of Dr. J. Lein, Bristol Laboratories, Syracuse, N. Y. Bioassays of crude samples of synthetic penicillin V tend to decrease on storage, even at 5°, which may account for the discrepancy between chemical and microbiological assay.

(24) V. V. Young, *J. Am. Pharm. Assoc., Sci. Ed.*, **40**, 261 (1951); W. B. Wheatley, W. E. Fitzgibbon and L. C. Cheney, *J. Org. Chem.*, **18**, 1564 (1953).

(25) Samples of *levo-* and *dextro-erythro*-1,2-diphenyl-2-methylaminoethanol hydrochlorides were kindly supplied by Dr. L. C. Cheney, Bristol Laboratories, Syracuse, N. Y.

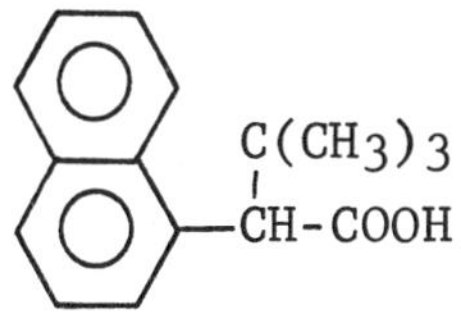

$C_{16}H_{18}O_2$ Ref. 1181

Note:

Resolved using brucine. Obtained acid with $[\alpha]_{589}$ +119°, $[\alpha]_{405}$ +330° (c 0.295, ethanol).

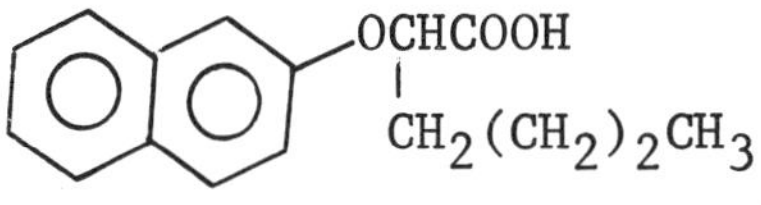

$C_{16}H_{18}O_3$ Ref. 1182

(+)-*α-(2-Naphthoxy)-n-caproic acid.* Racemic acid (15.5 g, 0.06 mole) and β-phenyl*iso*propylamine (8.1 g, 0.06 mole) were dissolved in a hot mixture of alcohol (300 ml) and water (120 ml). The solution was set aside in a refrigerator over night. The crystalline salt was collected and the organic acid was liberated from a small sample. The rotatory power of this acid was measured in abs. alcohol. The salt was recrystallised according to Table 4.

Table 4. Recrystallisation of the (–)-β-phenyl*iso*propylamine salt of α-(2-naphthoxy)-*n*-caproic acid.

Cryst. No.	Solvent (ml)		Weight of salt (g)	$[\alpha]_D$ of the acid
	Alcohol	Water		
1	300	120	11.9	+39.7°
2	150	60	9.6	+56.4°
3	100	40	8.5	+58.2°
4	85	45	7.7	+57.5°
5	80	40	7.1	+58.8°

From the last salt fraction 4.5 g of the crude (+)-acid were obtained. It was recrystallised from petroleum (b.p. 60–80°). The pure acid melted at 134.5–135.2°.

100.10 mg acid: 7.800 ml 0.04955-*N* NaOH
$C_{16}H_{18}O_3$ calc. equiv. wt. 258.3
found » » 259.0

0.1885 g dissolved in abs. *alcohol* to 20.06 ml: $2\alpha_D^{25} = +1.102°$. $[\alpha]_D^{25} = +58.6°$; $[M]_D^{25} = +151.5°$.
0.1818 g » » *acetone* to 20.06 ml: $2\alpha_D^{25} = +1.324°$. $[\alpha]_D^{25} = +73.0°$; $[M]_D^{25} = +188.7°$.
0.1968 g » » *chloroform* to 20.06 ml: $2\alpha_D^{25} = +0.736°$. $[\alpha]_D^{25} = +37.5°$; $[M]_D^{25} = +96.9°$.
0.1943 g » » *benzene* to 20.06 ml: $2\alpha_D^{25} = +1.197°$. $[\alpha]_D^{25} = +61.8°$; $[M]_D^{25} = +159.6°$.
0.1669 g neutralised with *aqueous NaOH* and made up to 20.06 ml: $2\alpha_D^{25} = +0.661°$. $[\alpha]_D^{25} = +39.7°$; $[M]_D^{25} = +102.6°$.

(−)-α-(2-*Naphthoxy)-n-caproic acid*. The organic acid was regenerated from mother liquor 1 (Table 4). This acid (7.75 g, 0.03 mole, $[\alpha]_D = -35°$ in alcohol) and an equimolecular quantity of β-phenyl*iso*propylamine (4.05 g) were dissolved in a hot mixture of alcohol (150 ml) and water (60 ml). The salt, which separated on cooling, was recrystallised according to Table 5: $[\alpha]_D$ refers to the optical activity of the acid measured in alcohol.

The crude acid, which was isolated from the last salt fraction, was recrystallised from petroleum (b.p. 60–80°). 3.12 g of the pure (−)-acid were collected. M.p. 134.5–135.2°.

Table 5.

Recrystallisation of the (+)-β-phenyl*iso*propylamine salt of α-(2-naphthoxy)-*n*-caproic acid.

Cryst. No.	Solvent (ml)		Weight of salt (g)	$[\alpha]_D$ of the acid
	Alcohol	Water		
1	150	60	8.8	−51.1°
2	120	50	6.9	−56.3°
3	95	40	5.9	−57.4°
4	80	35	5.15	−57.0°

104.86 mg acid: 8.185 ml 0.04955-*N* NaOH
$C_{16}H_{18}O_3$ calc. equiv. wt. 258.3
found » » 258.5

0.1948 g dissolved in abs. *alcohol* to 20.06 ml: $2\alpha_D^{25} = -1.136°$. $[\alpha]_D^{25} = -58.5°$; $[M]_D^{25} = -151.1°$

$C_{16}H_{18}O_6S_2$

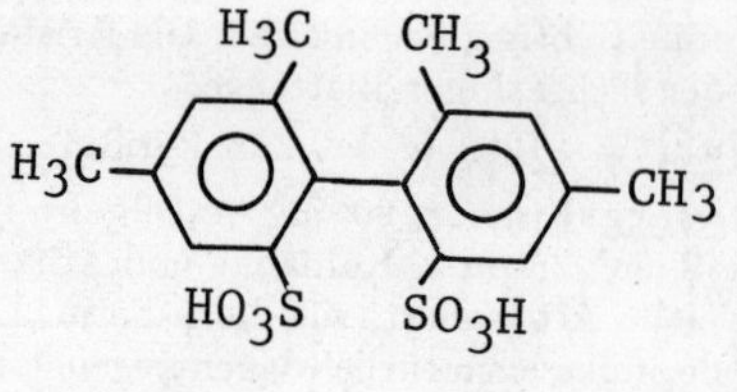

Ref. 1183

Optical Resolution of Strychnine 4 : 6 : 4′ : 6′-Tetramethyldiphenyl-2 : 2′-disulphonate.—Strychnine (66·88 g., 2 mol.) was dissolved in water (2 l.) containing concentrated hydrochloric acid (7·3 g., 2 mol.) by boiling. Anhydrous sodium 4 : 6 : 4′ : 6′-tetramethyldiphenyl-2 : 2′-disulphonate (41·4 g., 1 mol.), dissolved in water (400 c.c.), was added to the hot solution. A precipitate suddenly separated. The mixture was kept overnight and then filtered. The solid was dried in a vacuum at 67° and crystallised from methanol (10 l.) as rhombs (25 g.), m. p. 340° (decomp.), $[\alpha]_{5461}^{19\cdot2}$ −100·0° (±0·5°), $[\alpha]_{5791}^{19\cdot2}$ −96·0° (±0·5°) (*c* 1·0310 in $CHCl_3$). Recrystallisation of this (−)-*base* (−)-*acid salt* from a large volume of methanol did not affect the specific rotation (Found: C, 65·2; H, 6·3. $C_{58}H_{62}O_{10}N_4S_2,2CH_3{\cdot}OH$ requires C, 65·3; H, 6·4%).

The first aqueous filtrate was concentrated to 400 c.c. An oil separated. This was isolated by decanting off the mother-liquor and washing the residue twice with a little water. The washings were added to the mother-liquor, and the solution was concentrated to 200 c.c. More oil separated. The combined oils, after being washed, were then dried in a vacuum. The almost pure solid (−)-*base* (+)-*acid salt* so obtained was very soluble in water and in cold methanol {yield 25 g.; m. p. 270° (decomp.; softening at 250°), $[\alpha]_{5461}^{18\cdot2}$ −70·5° (±0·5°), $[\alpha]_{5791}^{18\cdot2}$ −61·0° (±0·5°) (*c* 1·0905 in $CHCl_3$)} (Found: C, 61·2; H, 6·4. $C_{58}H_{62}O_{10}N_4S_2,6H_2O$ requires C, 61·2; H, 6·2%).

Sodium (−)-*4 : 6 : 4′ : 6′-Tetramethyldiphenyl-2 : 2′-disulphonate.*—A chloroform solution of the (−)-base (−)-acid salt (22 g.) was thrice extracted with 10% aqueous sodium hydroxide (in all about 400 c.c.). The combined alkaline solutions were extracted with chloroform until the latter had no optical activity. The alkaline solution was neutralised with concentrated hydrochloric acid and evaporated in a vacuum on a water-bath. The residual solid was dried at 120—130° for 2 hr. and then extracted with hot absolute ethanol until the extract ceased to possess optical activity. The ethanol solution (about 1 l.) was filtered and concentrated to about 150 c.c. On cooling, the disodium (−)-salt separated as needles (8·5 g.). After being dried in a vacuum it had $[\alpha]_{5461}^{18}$ −39·0° (±0·5°), $[\alpha]_{5791}^{20}$ −35·0° (±0·5°) (*c* 1·1015 in H_2O), and $[\alpha]_{5461}^{18}$ +9·5° (±0·5°), $[\alpha]_{5791}^{20}$ +8·0° (±0·5°) (*c* 0·968 in absolute EtOH). Evaporation of the ethanolic mother-liquor gave 3·0 g. of almost pure (−)-salt.

Sodium (+)-*4 : 6 : 4′ : 6′-Tetramethyldiphenyl-2 : 2′-disulphonate.*—From the (−)-base (+)-acid salt (22 g.), sodium (+)-salt was obtained, having $[\alpha]_{5461}^{20}$ +40·5° (±0·5°), $[\alpha]_{5791}^{20}$ +35·0° (±0·5°) (*c* 1·0870 in H_2O), and $[\alpha]_{5461}^{18}$ −9·5° (±0·5°), $[\alpha]_{5791}^{18}$ −9·0° (±0·5°) (*c* 0·9680 in EtOH).

Rotations in aqueous ethanol are tabulated.

A solution of the sodium salt in water, with α_{5461} +0·56° and α_{5791} +0·49° ($l = 2$), was heated for 26 hr. in a sealed tube at 180—200° and although the resulting solution was slightly turbid the rotation was unchanged.

Effect of adding water to absolute ethanol solutions (20 *ml.*; *c* 0·968; $l = 2$) *of sodium* 4 : 6 : 4′ : 6′-*tetramethyldiphenyl*-2 : 2′-*disulphonates.*

Added water (ml.)	(−)-Salt α_{5461}^{20}	(−)-Salt α_{5791}^{20}	(+)-Salt α_{5461}^{18}	(+)-Salt α_{5791}^{18}	Added water (ml.)	(−)-Salt α_{5461}^{20}	(−)-Salt α_{5791}^{20}	(+)-Salt α_{5461}^{18}	(+)-Salt α_{5791}^{18}
0·0	+0·18°	+0·15°	−0·19°	−0·17°	2·5	−0·41°	−0·39°	+0·40°	+0·35°
0·1	+0·13	+0·10	−0·12	−0·12	3·0	−0·42	−0·40	+0·41	+0·36
0·3	+0·02	0·00	—	—	3·5	−0·43	−0·41	—	—
0·5	−0·07	−0·06	0·00	+0·01	4·0	−0·44	−0·41	+0·43	+0·39
0·7	−0·13	−0·13	+0·09	+0·06	5·0	−0·42	−0·39	+0·40	+0·35
1·0	−0·22	−0·21	+0·19	+0·15	7·0	−0·39	−0·37	+0·37	+0·32
1·5	−0·32	−0·31	+0·30	+0·25	9·0	−0·36	−0·34	+0·34	+0·31
2·0	−0·39	−0·37	+0·36	+0·31	11·0	−0·32	−0·31	+0·32	+0·29

Error ± 0·01°.

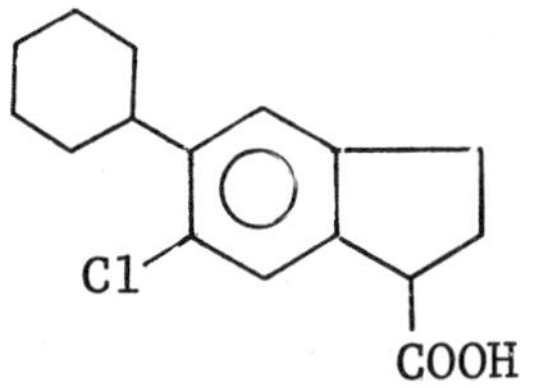

$C_{16}H_{19}ClO_2$ Ref. 1184

(1*S*)-(+)-6-Chloro-5-cyclohexylindan-1-carboxylic Acid (50). A soln of 17 (20.0 g, 0.0719 mole) and dehydroabietylamine (10.22 g, 0.03595 mole) in EtOH (700 ml) was boiled down to about 380 ml. The mixt was allowed to cool slowly and left for 20 hr at 25°. The solid (16.3 g), mp 188–190°, was collected and recrystallized from MeOH-H_2O (20:1) to give the salt (11.0 g), mp 192–194°. Recrystallization from MeOH gave colorless crystals (7.4 g), mp 194–195.5°. The salt was partitioned between Et_2O and 1 *N* HCl. The Et_2O layer was washed (1 *N* HCl, H_2O, saturated aqueous NaCl), dried (Na_2SO_4), and concentrated to give 50 (3.5 g) as colorless crystals, mp 133–134°. Recrystallization from Skellysolve B gave colorless needles (3.0 g): mp 135–136°; $[\alpha]^{25}D$ +28.7° (*c* 2, EtOH) and $[\alpha]^{25}_{365}$ + 87.7° (*c* 2, EtOH).

$C_{16}H_{19}ClO_2$ Ref. 1184a

Optical Resolution of TAI-284 (1)——a) (*R*)-(−)-6-Chloro-5-cyclohexylindan-1-carboxylic Acid: A suspension of 9.8 g of TAI-284 (1) and 5.6 g of quinine in 105 ml of acetone was warmed to give a clear solution. The solution was allowed to stand overnight at room temperature. The precipitate was collected, washed with acetone, and recrystallized from 600 ml of CH_3CN to give the quinine salt of (−)-TAI-284 as colorless crystals, mp 124—129°. This salt was dissolved in $CHCl_3$. The solution was washed with dilute HCl and water, dried over anhydrous Na_2SO_4, and concentrated to dryness under reduced pressure. The residual solid was recrystallized from 70 ml of hexane to give (*R*)-(−)-TAI-284 as colorless needles, mp 130—135° (1.4 g, 29%). *Anal.* Calcd. for $C_{16}H_{19}O_2Cl$: C, 68.94; H, 6.87; Cl, 12.72. Found: C, 68.73; H, 6.89; Cl, 12.84. $[\alpha]^{25}_D$: −28.3° (*c*=1, MeOH). IR $\nu^{\text{Nujol}}_{\text{max}}$ cm^{-1}: 1700 (C=O).

b) (*S*)-(+)-6-Chloro-5-cyclohexylindan-1-carboxylic Acid: The mother liquor of the first isolation of the quinine salt of (−)-TAI-284 was concentrated to dryness under reduced pressure. The residual solid was dissolved in $CHCl_3$. The solution was washed with dilute HCl and water, dried over anhydrous Na_2SO_4, and concentrated to dryness under reduced pressure. The residual solid was recrystallized from hexane. The first crystals thus obtained were those of (±)-TAI-284. The second mother liquor was concentrated to dryness under reduced pressure. The residual solid also gave (±)-TAI-284 by recrystallization. The third mother liquor was worked up similarly, and this time (+)-TAI-284 was obtained as colorless crystals, mp 130—135° (1.3 g, 27%). *Anal.* Calcd. for $C_{16}H_{19}O_2Cl$: C, 68.94; H, 6.87; Cl, 12.72. Found: C, 68.87; H, 6.97; Cl, 12.93. $[\alpha]^{25}_D$: +28.1° (*c*=1, MeOH). IR $\nu^{\text{Nujol}}_{\text{max}}$ cm^{-1}: 1700 (C=O).

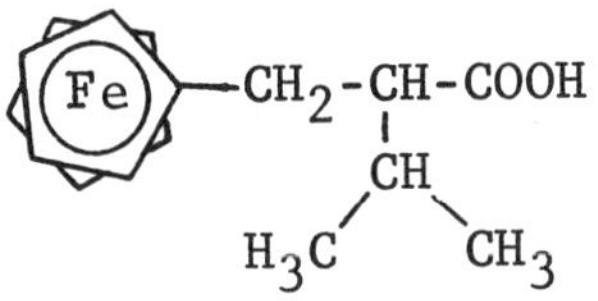

$C_{16}H_{20}FeO_2$ Ref. 1185

Cyclisation des acides α-isopropyl β-ferrocénylpropioniques actifs.

Dédoublement de l'acide racémique **3***a*.

Une solution de 0,05 M d'acide **3***a* (15 g) dans 400 cm³ d'éther anhydre est traitée par 0,05 M (6,05 g) de (+) α-phényléthylamine diluée dans 20 cm³ d'éther anhydre. Le sel précipite immédiatement sous forme de cristaux jaunes: $[\alpha]_D = +14°$ (C = 4,1). Des recristallisations successives dans l'acétate d'éthyle conduisent à un sel de pouvoir rotatoire maximum observé: $[\alpha]_D = +20°$ dont la coupure par HCl dilué donne l'acide α-isopropyl β-ferrocénylpropionique **9***a*: $[\alpha]_D = +8 \pm 1°$ (C = 5), F = 103°.

Les eaux-mères des recristallisations précédentes fournissent 9 g d'acide partiellement dédoublé $[\alpha]_D = -3°$ que l'on traite, en solution dans 350 cm³ d'éther anhydre par 2,8 g de (—) α-phényléthylamine. Le sel obtenu ($[\alpha]_D = -15°$) présente après trois recristallisations dans l'acétonitrile un pouvoir rotatoire maximum $[\alpha]_D = -20°$ et conduit à l'acide **9'***a*: $[\alpha]_D = -8 \pm 1°$ (C = 5), F = 104°, énantiomère de **9***a*.

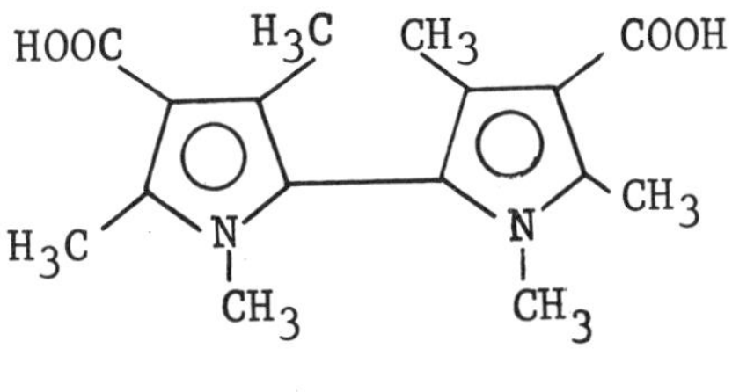

$C_{16}H_{20}N_2O_4$ Ref. 1186

Resolution of 4,4'-dicarboxy-1,1',3,3',5,5'-hexamethyl-2,2'-bipyrryl (V). A solution of 8.97 g. (0.023 mole) of brucine in 200 cc. absolute methanol was brought to a gentle boil and with stirring a suspension of 3.45 g. (0.011 mole) of 4,4'-dicarboxy-1,1',3,3',5,5'-hexamethyl-2,2'-bipyrryl (V) in 100 cc. of absolute methanol was added slowly with continuous stirring. The mixture was boiled for ten minutes, allowed to cool to room temperature, and then placed in an ice-bath for four hours. After suction filtration and drying in a vacuum desiccator over silica gel the crystalline material weighed 8.0 g. After three recrystallizations from absolute methanol the material weighed 2.79 g. and the melting point was constant, 217–218° (bath pre-heated to 210°), as was the rotation.

Rotation. Dibrucine salt of D-acid: 0.1000 g. made up to 10.00 cc. in pyridine gave $[\alpha]^{25}_D$ −82.00°.

D-*4,4'-Dicarboxy-1,1',3,3',5,5'-hexamethyl-2,2'-bipyrryl* (V). To a suspension of 2.634 g. of the above dibrucine salt in 60 cc. of water 2.7 cc. of conc'd hydrochloric acid was added slowly with vigorous stirring. After 30 minutes the precipitated dicarboxylic acid was fil-

tered, washed with a small amount of cold water, and dried in a vacuum desiccator. The dried acid, weighing 0.775 g., was recrystallized three times from dioxane and dried under an oil-pump vacuum at 50° for two hours. This material sublimed at 289–290° in a bath pre-heated to 280°.

Rotation. D-acid: 0.1000 g. made up to 10.00 cc. in pyridine gave $[\alpha]_D^{25}$ +37.00°. No muta-rotation was observed on heating to 50° in pyridine solution. Infrared absorption indicated racemization on melting.

The filtrate containing the brucine•HCl from the regeneration of the above D-acid was made basic with sodium hydroxide and the precipitated brucine was filtered, water-washed, and dried under an oil-pump vacuum at 50° for two hours. This material melted 173–174° and weighed 1.885 g. (Theory for dibrucine salt of D-acid, 1.898 g.).

L-*4,4'-Dicarboxy-1,1',3,3',5,5'-hexamethyl-2,2'-bipyrryl* (V). (*a*) All of the filtrates from the dibrucine salt of the D-acid were combined, evaporated under a water-pump vacuum to 20 cc., and cooled in ice. The crystals thus obtained, which melted 191–193° with decomposition, after three recrystallizations from absolute methanol weighed 2.68 g. and had the constant m.p. 196–197° with decomposition when put in a bath pre-heated to 190°.

Rotation. Monobrucine salt of impure L-acid: 0.1000 g. made up to 10.00 cc. in pyridine gave $[\alpha]_D^{25}$ −82.5°.

To a suspension of 2.116 g. of the above monobrucine salt in 40 cc. of water 2.0 cc. of conc'd hydrochloric acid was added slowly with stirring. After one-half hour the precipitated dicarboxylic acid was filtered, washed with a small amount of dilute hydrochloric acid, then with water, and dried in a vacuum desiccator. The acid, recrystallized twice from dioxane and dried in a vacuum desiccator, weighed 0.355 g. and melted with decomposition and sublimation at 289–290° when put in a bath pre-heated to 280°.

Rotation. Impure L-acid: 0.1000 g. made up to 10.00 cc. in pyridine gave $[\alpha]_D^{25}$ −5.0°.

The filtrate from the above impure L-acid containing brucine·HCl was neutralized with vigorous stirring; the precipitated brucine was filtered, washed with water, and dried in an oil-pump vacuum at 50° weighed 1.190 g. (Theory for monobrucine salt of the diacid, 1.194 g.).

(*b*) In a second attempt to obtain the pure L-acid the filtrates from the above brucine salts were acidified and the diacid thus obtained was combined with that above. A solution of 1.902 g. (0.00482 mole) of brucine in dioxane was added to 0.733 g. (0.00241 mole) of the diacid dissolved in 40 cc. of dioxane. The solution was evaporated to dryness under a water-pump vacuum on the steam-bath and the syrupy residue was taken up in absolute methanol. After a few minutes crystals began to form which on filtration weighed 1.180 g. (the dibrucine salt of the D-acid).

The filtrate from the above, concentrated and cooled in ice, yielded 0.568 g. of crystalline material. Extraction of these crystals once with boiling absolute ethyl acetate failed to dissolve an appreciable amount of material. After three recrystallizations from absolute methanol the melting point was 216–217° in a bath pre-heated to 210°.

Rotation. Dibrucine salt of impure L-acid: 0.1000 g. made up to 10.00 cc. in pyridine gave $[\alpha]_D^{25}$ −75.0°.

The free diacid was isolated from the dibrucine salt as described above and after two recrystallizations from absolute methanol melted 288–290° with decomposition when put in a bath pre-heated to 280°.

Rotation. Impure L-acid: 0.1000 g. made up to 10.00 cc. in pyridine gave $[\alpha]_D^{25}$ −12.0°.

The samples for infrared absorption were prepared as a solid suspension in mineral oil.

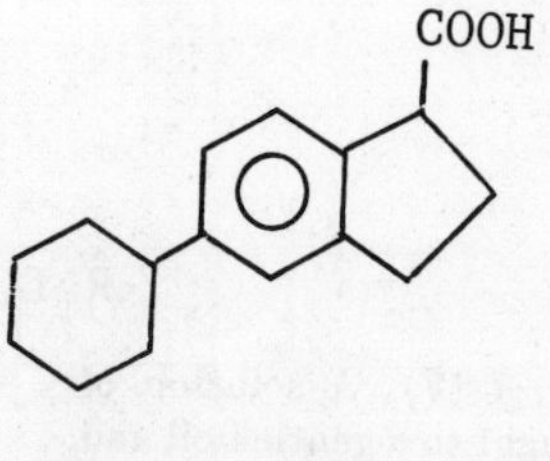

$C_{16}H_{20}O_2$ Ref. 1187

A. (±)-5-cyclohexyl-1-indancarboxylic acid: A solution of (±)-5-cyclohexyl-1-indancarboxylic acid (15.0 grams, 0.0614 mole) and cinchonidine (9.05 grams, 0.037 mole) in absolute ethanol (700 ml.) was boiled down to a volume of about 300 ml. The mixture was allowed to cool slowly and was left for 20 hours at 25° C. The colorless crystals were collected and washed with cold ethanol to give the cinchonidine salt of (+)-5-cyclohexyl-1-indancarboxylic acid (13.0 grams), m.p. 212°–212.5° C. Additional cinchonidine (1.0 gram, 0.0034 mole) was added to the mother liquors and their volume reduced to about 165 ml. by boiling. The hot solution was seeded with the salt of the (+) acid and stored at 5° C. for 65 hours, when an additional crop (2.4 grams) of the cinchonidine salt of the (+) acid, m.p. 211°–215° C. was obtained. The mother liquors were retained for isolation of the (−) isomer.

The salt with m.p. 212°–212.5° C. was recrystallized from ethanol to give colorless crystals (11.8 grams), m.p. 217.5°–219° C. The product was partitioned between ether (500 ml). and 10 percent aqueous hydrochloric acid (250 ml). and water saturated with sodium chloride (250 ml.). The ethereal solution was dried (Na_2SO_4), filtered, and the filtrate reduced to dryness to give (+)-5-cyclohexyl-1-indancarboxylic acid (5.5 grams), m.p. 108°–110° C. Two recrystallizations from petroleum ether (b.p. 39°–50° C.), gave colorless needles, m.p. 108°–109.5° C.,

$[\alpha]_D^{25}$ +9.60° (ethanol) and $[\alpha]_{365}^{25}$ +44.8° (ethanol).

Anal. calc'd. for $C_{16}H_{20}O_2$ (percent): C, 78.65; H, 8.25.

Found: C, 78.40; H, 8.27.

B. (−)-5-cyclohexyl-1-indancarboxylic acid: The mother liquors from the salt formation in part A.) were reduced to dryness and the residue treated with ether and 10 percent aqueous hydrochloric acid as previously described for the salt of the (+) isomer and from the ethereal layer was obtained a partially resolved mixture of acids (7.6 grams), enriched in the (−) isomer,

$[\alpha]_D^{25}$ −7.69° (ethanol) and $[\alpha]_{365}^{25}$ −35.4° (ethanol).

This mixture was extracted with boiling petroleum ether (b.p. 39°–50° C., 3 × 35 ml.) and the combined extracts were reduced in volume (50 ml.) and cooled in an ice bath. The crystalline solid (5.1 grams), m.p. 105°–108° C.,

$[\alpha]_D^{25}$ −8.91° (ethanol) and $[\alpha]_{365}^{25}$ −41.5° (ethanol) was collected.

The solution of this acid (5.02 grams, 0.0205 mole) and dehydroabietylamine (5.85 grams, 0.0205 mole) in ethanol (500 ml.) was boiled down to a volume of about 175 ml. and cooled to 25° C. during 2 hours. The dehydroabietylamine salt of (−)-5-cyclohexyl-1-indancarboxylic acid (8.7 grams), m.p. 179°–181° C., was collected and recrystallized from ethanol to give colorless crystals (8.0 grams), m.p. 184°–185° C. The mother liquors from the product with M.P. 179°–181° C., were reduced in volume and an additional crop of salt (0.95 gram), m.p. 178.5°–180.5° C., was isolated. This latter material was recrystallized from ethanol and the product (0.78 gram), m.p. 182°–183° C., was combined with the main crop. The dehydroabietylamine salt (8.78 grams) was partitioned between ether (400 ml.) and 10 percent aqueous hydrochloric acid. The ethereal solution was washed with water (3 × 150 ml.) followed by water saturated with sodium chloride (2 × 100 ml.), dried (Na_2SO_4), and reduced to dryness to leave the (−) isomer (4.0 grams). Recrystallization from petroleum ether (B.P. 39°–50° C.) gave colorless needles (3.41 grams) of (−)-5-cyclohexyl-1-indancarboxylic acid: m.p. 108°–109.5° C.,

$[\alpha]_D^{25}$ −9.66° (ethanol) and $[\alpha]_{365}^{25}$ −44.7° (ethanol).

Anal. calc'd. for $C_{16}H_{20}O_2$ (percent): C, 78.65; H, 8.25.

Found: C, 78.85; H, 8.31.

$C_{16}H_{20}O_2$ Ref. 1187a

(1*S*)-(−)-5-Cyclohexylindan-1-carboxylic Acid (47). A soln of (−)-α-(1-naphthyl)ethylamine (1.76 g, 0.0103 mole) in MeCN (2 ml) was added to a boiling soln of **12e** (5.0 g, 0.0205 mole) in MeCN (250 ml). The soln was allowed to cool slowly and stand at 25° for 3 hr. The crystalline product was collected and recrystallized twice from MeCN to give the salt (3.0 g), mp 163–164.5°. The salt was partitioned between EtOAc (20 ml) and 0.5 *N* HCl (20 ml). The EtOAc layer was washed (1 *N* HCl, H_2O, saturated aqueous NaCl), dried (Na_2SO_4), and concentrated. The residue (1.68 g), mp 108–110°, was recrystallized from petr ether (bp 39–50°) to give **47** (1.51 g) as colorless crystals: mp 108–110°; $[\alpha]^{25}D$ −9.69° (*c* 2, EtOH) and $[\alpha]^{25}_{365}$ −44.76° (*c* 2, EtOH); ORD (*c* 0.4, MeOH), 24°, $[\alpha]_{450}$ −30°, $[\alpha]_{350}$ −70°, $[\alpha]_{310}$ −120°, $[\alpha]_{276}$ −280° (trough), $[\alpha]_{268}$ −100° (peak), $[\alpha]_{257}$ −380° (shoulder), and $[\alpha]_{250}$ −590°.

(1*R*)-(+)-5-Cyclohexylindan-1-carboxylic Acid (48). A soln of **12e** (15.0 g, 0.0614 mole) and cinchonidine (9.05 g, 0.0307 mole) in EtOH (700 ml) was boiled down to a vol of 300 ml. The mixt was allowed to cool slowly and was left for 20 hr at 25°. The mixt was filtered to yield the salt (13.0 g), mp 212–212.5°. The salt was recrystallized from EtOH to give a product (11.8 g), mp 217.5–219°, which was partitioned between Et_2O (500 ml) and 10% HCl (250 ml). The Et_2O layer was washed (10% HCl, H_2O, satd aqueous NaCl), dried (Na_2SO_4), and concentrated to give **48** (5.0 g), mp 108–110°. Two recrystallizations from petr ether (bp 39–50°) gave colorless needles: mp 108–109.5°; $[\alpha]^{25}D$ +9.60° (*c* 2, EtOH) and $[\alpha]^{25}_{365}$ + 44.8° (*c* 2, EtOH).

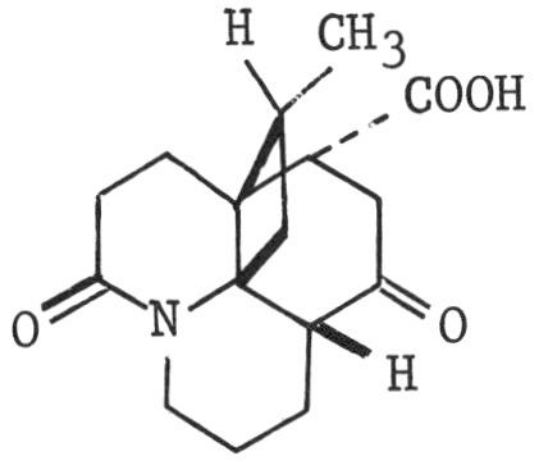

$C_{16}H_{21}NO_4$ Ref. 1188

Preparation of the Synthetic Optically Active Acid (23)

The racemic acid (**23**) (145 mg) was dissolved in acetone (10 ml) and a few drops of methanol were added. To this solution brucine (200 mg) in acetone (10 ml) was added and the volume of the solvent was reduced to 5 ml. Crystals appeared after standing for 2 h and they were recrystallized several times from methanol–acetone until the constant m.p. of 158–160 °C was reached. The yield of the pure constant melting brucine salt was 100 mg. This material was dissolved in a small volume of methanol and 10% sulfuric acid (30 ml) was added to the solution. Continuous extraction of the mixture with ether yielded 45 mg of the optically active acid (**23**). It was recrystallized from methanol to a m.p. of 240–242 °C. Its mass and infrared (KBr) spectra were identical with the spectra of the racemic acid (**23**).

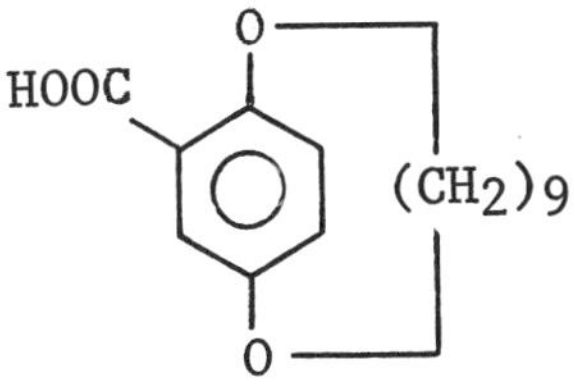

$C_{16}H_{22}O_4$ Ref. 1189

Strychninsalz der (+)-Säure VII. 5 g racemische Säure VII (0.018 Mol) und 5.4 g Strychnin (kleiner Unterschuß) werden in 50 ccm Äthanol durch Erwärmen auf dem Wasserbad gelöst und nach dem Erkalten durch Absaugen i. Vak. bei höchstens 25° auf 15 ccm eingeengt. Die abgeschiedenen Nadeln werden bis zur Drehungskonstanz aus Alkohol (unter kurzem Erhitzen) umkristallisiert. Im allgemeinen genügt dreimaliges Umkristallisieren. Es ergeben sich 2.7 g Salz vom Schmp. 204—206° (unter Braunfärbung). $[\alpha]_D^{20}$ = + 10.6° (Chloroform, *c* = 4.05).

$C_{37}H_{44}O_6N_2$ (612.7) Ber. C 72.52 H 7.24 N 4.57 Gef. C 72.75 H 7.60 N 4.82

(+)-Säure VII. 2.7 g Strychninsalz werden in 40 ccm $CHCl_3$ gelöst, 3mal mit verd. Essigsäure und 3mal mit 10-proz. Schwefelsäure ausgeschüttelt, dann mit Wasser bis zur neutralen Reaktion gewaschen. Die Chloroformlösung trocknet man mit Na_2SO_4 und saugt anschließend das $CHCl_3$ i. Vak. bei höchstens 25° weg. Das hinterbleibende Öl kristallisiert auf Anreiben nach Tagen. Man kristallisiert aus Eisessig unter Wasserzusatz um.

Durchkristallisation erfolgt wiederum erst nach Tagen. Schmp. 83°. $[\alpha]_D^{20} = +16.68°$ (Chloroform, $c = 4$).

$C_{16}H_{22}O_4$ (278.3) Ber. C 69.04 H 7.97 Gef. C 68.75 H 7.58

Chininsalz der (−)-Säure VII. Der vom Lösungsmittel befreite Rückstand aus den Mutterlaugen des Strychninsalzes wird in $CHCl_3$ gelöst und durch Ausschütteln wie oben vom Strychnin befreit. Die Substanz wird mit 3.5 g feingepulvertem Chinin in 50 ccm Alkohol bei 50° gelöst und bei 25° auf 20 ccm eingeengt. Durch weiteres Einengen auf 10 ccm erhält man eine zweite Fraktion. Beide werden vereinigt und bis zur Drehungskonstanz aus Alkohol (unter kurzem Erhitzen) umkristallisiert. Weiße Nadeln vom Schmp. 124–126° (unter Gelbfärbung). $[\alpha]_D^{20} = -123°$ (Chloroform, $c = 3.95$).

Die bei ~20° getrocknete Substanz gibt leidlich stimmende Analysenwerte bei Annahme von 1½ Moll. Kristallalkohol:

$C_{36}H_{46}O_6N_2 \cdot 1^1/_2C_2H_6O$ (671.8) Ber. C 69.72 H 8.25 N 4.17 Gef. C 69.52 H 7.96 N 4.14

(−)-Säure VII. Die Zerlegung des Chininsalzes erfolgte in Chloroform wie beim Strychninsalz. Beim Umkristallisieren aus Essigsäure-Wasser fiel die linksdrehende Säure, wie der Antipode und das Racemat, immer erst als Öl an, was die Reinigung sehr erschwerte. Farblose Kristalle vom Schmp. 82–83°. $[\alpha]_D^{20} = -16.73°$ (Chloroform, $c = 4.06$); $[\alpha]_D^{20} = -55.5°$ (*m-Xylol*, $c = 8$).

Die Werte für die spezif. Drehung in anderen Lösungsmitteln und bei verschiedenen Wellenlängen sind der Abbildung 1 zu entnehmen[24]. Sie sind durchweg in rund 4-proz. Lösung gemessen.

[24] Genauere Werte: Diplomarbeit G. EYRING, Univ. Freiburg i. Br. 1956.

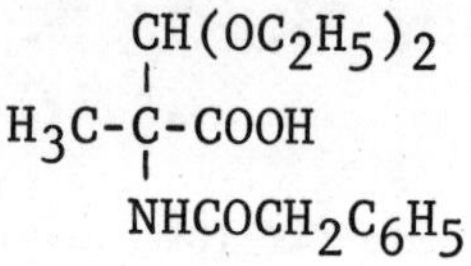

$C_{16}H_{23}NO_5$ Ref. 1190

Resolution of DL-α-Methylbenzylpenaldic Acid Diethyl Acetal.—The racemic acid (9.3 g.) and 12.1 g. of anhydrous brucine were suspended in 300 ml. of water and heated to boiling. When the solid material had all dissolved the solution was filtered and left in the refrigerator for two days. The brucine salt which had crystallized out, 10.8 g., was filtered. Concentration of the mother liquor to about half-volume afforded a further small crop. The combined salts were recrystallized from water containing a little ethanol, until the specific rotation became constant (−33°).

The salt was suspended in 50 ml. of *N* sodium hydroxide, and stirred for 30 minutes. After removal of the brucine by filtration the filtrate was cooled in an ice-bath and acidified to *p*H 2 with concd. hydrochloric acid. The precipitated acid was filtered and recrystallized from aqueous alcohol, 2.2 g., m.p. 148–150° (dec.); $[\alpha]^{25}D$ −10.5 ± 1.0° (*c*, 1.08 in chloroform); $[\alpha]^{25}D$ +9.6 ± 1.0° (*c*, 1.06 in *N* sodium hydroxide).

Anal. Calcd. for $C_{16}H_{23}O_5N$: C, 62.12; H, 7.49; N, 4.53. Found: C, 62.39; H, 7.44; N, 4.49.

To the mother liquor from the first crystallization of the brucine salts was added 40 ml. of *N* sodium hydroxide, with stirring. The brucine was filtered, the filtrate cooled in an ice-bath, and acidified to *p*H 2 with concentrated hydrochloric acid. The precipitated acid was removed by filtration and was twice recrystallized from aqueous ethanol, 2.4 g., m.p. 148–149.5°; $[\alpha]^{25}D$ +8.8 ± 1.0° (*c*, 126 in chloroform); $[\alpha]^{25}D$ −8.3 ± 1.0° (*c*, 1.17 in *N* sodium hydroxide).

Anal. Calcd. for $C_{16}H_{23}O_5N$: N, 4.53. Found: N, 4.44.

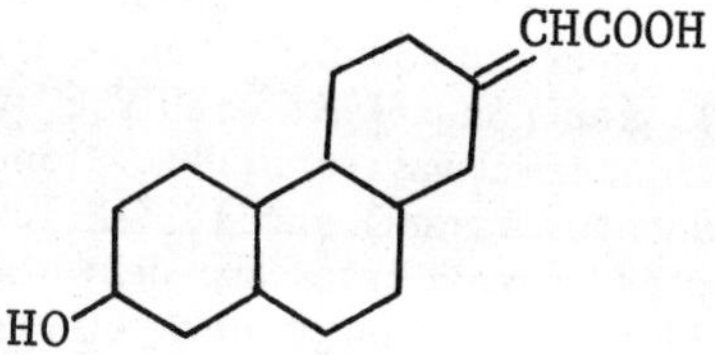

$C_{16}H_{24}O_3$ Ref. 1191

Resolution of (±)-*trans*-3,4,4aα,4bβ,5,6,7,8,8aα,9,10,10aβ-Dodecahydro-7β-hydroxy-Δ^2(1H),α^-phenanthreneacetic Acid (3).—A solution of 3.70 g (0.014 mol) of the (±)-*trans* acid **3** in 50 ml of hot MeOH was treated with a solution of 4.00 g (0.014 mol) of dehydroabietylamine in 10 ml of hot MeOH. A crystalline salt precipitated immediately. The mixture was cooled and filtered to give 5.19 g of solid. The filtrate will be referred to below as the *original filtrate.*

Recrystallization of this salt twice from absolute EtOH with cooling only to room temperature produced 2.83 g of needles of the (−)-*trans* acid dehydroabietylamine salt, mp 232–234° dec (evac tube). A third recrystallization gave 2.40 g of this salt which decomposed at 232.5–234.5° (evac tube); $[\alpha]^{25}D$ −19.7° (1% in HOAc). *Anal.* ($C_{36}H_{55}NO_3$) C, H, N.

The mother liquor from the recrystallization of the 5.19 g of solid was concentrated to half volume and 0.47 g of needles was obtained showing $[\alpha]^{25}D$ −3° (1% in HOAc). Concentration of the filtrate to dryness yielded 1.27 g of solid, $[\alpha]^{25}D$ +36° (1% in HOAc). This dextrorotatory residue was combined with the residue from the original filtrate and this solid was shaken with 85 ml of H_2O, 15 ml of 2 *N* NaOH, and 100 ml of Et_2O. The Et_2O layer was separated and washed with two 15-ml portions of H_2O. Acidification of the combined H_2O layer and washings gave a crystalline precipitate which was washed well with H_2O and air dried; 1.57 g, $[\alpha]^{25}D$ +40.3° (1% in EtOH). Multiple recrystallization of this enriched (+)-*trans* acid **3** from MeCN failed to raise the melting point above 212–216°; $[\alpha]^{25}D$ +43.0° (1% in EtOH). Isolation of pure (+)-*trans* acid from this mixture is described later in this experiment.

The (−)-*trans* acid dehydroabietylamine salt described earlier in this experiment (2.25 g) was shaken with 85 ml of H_2O, 15

ml of 2 N NaOH, and 100 ml of Et₂O and the layers were separated. The Et₂O layer was washed with H₂O and the combined aqueous layers were acidified with 2 N HCl. The precipitated (−)-trans acid **3** was collected, washed with H₂O, and dried; 1.03 g.

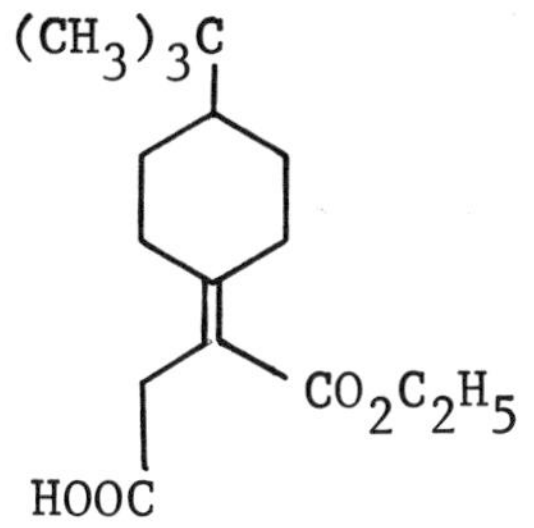

$C_{16}H_{26}O_4$ Ref. 1192

2 g der reinen Säure werden in 50 ml Cyclohexan unter Erwärmen gelöst und in der Siedehitze mit 0,9 g Phenyläthylamin versetzt. Man lässt die Mischung langsam abkühlen *) und filtriert nach etwa 15 Stunden das feine, nadelartig ausgefallene Salz ab. Man erhält so

1,9 g Salz mit α_D = +4,08° (Methanol).

Umkristallisieren dieser Fraktion aus Cyclohexan liefert

1,3 g Salz mit α_D = +9,38° (Methanol).

Zweimalige Wiederholung dieser Reinigungsoperation ergibt schliesslich

0,79 g Salz mit α_D = +14,4° (Methanol).

Zur Regenerierung der Säure wird dieses Salz in Äther aufgenommen, zweimal mit verdünnter Salzsäure extrahiert, mit Wasser neutral gewaschen und wieder vom Lösungsmittel befreit. Auf diese Weise ergibt sich 0,5 g optisch reine Säure mit α_D^{20} = +44,2° (Methanol).

Die gesammelten Mutterlaugen werden in weiteren Reinigungsoperationen wiederverwendet, so dass die optische Ausbeute schliesslich einen Wert von etwa 50% erreicht.

*) Die Zugabe von wenig optisch reinem Salz bewirkt eine bessere Enantiomerenanreicherung.

$$CH_3(CH_2)_5\overset{\overset{\textstyle OH}{|}}{CH}-\overset{\overset{}{}}{CH}\underset{\underset{\textstyle OH}{|}}{}(CH_2)_7COOH$$

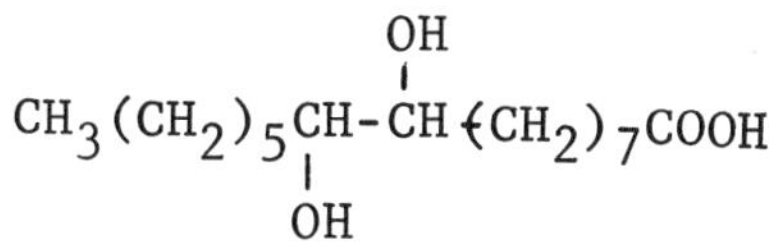

$C_{16}H_{32}O_4$ Ref. 1193

The dihydroxy acid (16 g) and (−)-brucine (28 g) were dissolved by gentle heating in a mixture of acetone (50 ml) and water (100 ml). The solution was allowed to stand for 2 days at 0°, and the precipitated salt (33 g) was collected and crystallized three times from acetone–water (1:2 by volume), yielding 15 g of the brucine salt, m.p. 51°, [α]$_D$ −22.2° (c, 1.1 in EtOH). It was decomposed by boiling with 2 N hydrochloric acid (25 ml), and the resulting solid was crystallized from aqueous acetone to yield (+)-threo-9,10-dihydroxypalmitic acid (2.3 g), m.p. 87–88°, [α]$_D$ +23.2° (c, 0.9 in MeOH).
Anal. Calcd. for C₁₆H₃₂O₄: C, 66.63; H, 11.18. Found: C, 66.45; H, 10.89.
The mother liquors from the crystallization of the brucine salt were combined and cooled to give a second crop of the salt, [α]$_D$ −40° (c, 1.0 in EtOH); this was discarded. The filtrate was evaporated to

dryness, leaving an oil which solidified after 2 days. This solid was dissolved in acetone and cooled. The small crop of crystals that formed was discarded. Evaporation of the filtrate gave an oil that did not crystallize, [α]$_D$ −55° (c, 1.3 in EtOH). It was decomposed by hydrochloric acid in the same way as the dextro isomer. The solid product was dissolved in ethyl acetate and a little unchanged brucine salt was removed. The levo acid crystallized when the filtrate was cooled. It was crystallized once more from ethyl acetate, giving (−)-threo-9,10-dihydroxy-palmitic acid (1.1 g), m.p. 87°, [α]$_D$ −22.2° (c, 1.0 in MeOH).
Anal. Found: C, 66.94; H, 11.34.

$$HOOC(CH_2)_7\overset{\overset{\textstyle OH}{|}}{CH}-\underset{\underset{\textstyle OH}{|}}{CH}(CH_2)_5CH_2OH$$

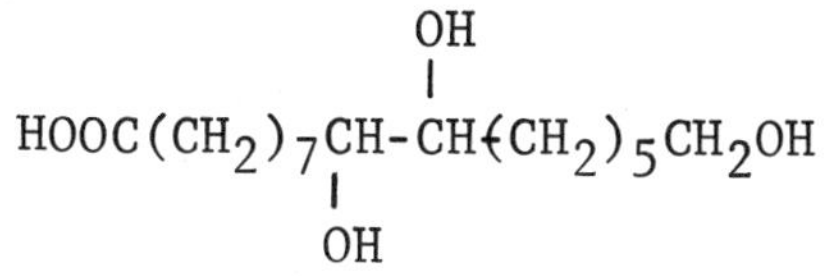

$C_{16}H_{32}O_5$ Ref. 1194

Fractional crystallisation of the (−)-ephedrine salt of compound (I) afforded the pure alkaloidal salt, mp 124–125°C, [α]$_D$ −34.06°. On decomposition this salt gave (−)-threo-9,10,16-trihydroxy-decanoic acid (I, R=H), mp 103–104°C, [α]$_D$ −24.45°; the (−)-methyl ester (I, R=Me) had mp 72–73°C, [α]$_D$ −23.45°. The alkaloidal salt mother liquors, upon decomposition and repeated recrystallisation, yielded (+)-threo-9,10,16-trihydroxyhexadecanoic acid (I, R=H), mp 102·5–103·5°C, [α]$_D$ +24.6°; the (+)-methyl ester (I, R=Me) had mp 71–72°C, [α]$_D$ +23.45°.

$$HOCH_2(CH_2)_5-\overset{\overset{\textstyle OH}{|}}{CH}-\underset{\underset{\textstyle OH}{|}}{CH}(CH_2)_7COOH$$

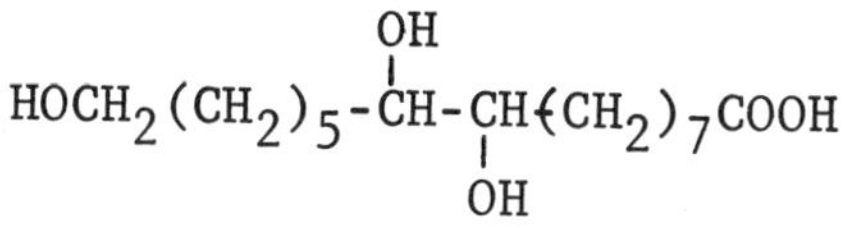

$C_{16}H_{32}O_5$ Ref. 1195

It is noteworthy to record the resolution of threo-7,8,16-trihydroxyhexadecanoic (iso-aleuritic)-acid (XIV).[6] The (−)-ephedrine salt had mp 82-83°C, [α]$_D$ −32·7°. This on decomposition afforded (−)-threo-7,8,16-trihydroxyhexadecanoic acid, mp 97-98°C, [α]$_D$ −24·16°, (−)-methyl ester, mp 69·0°C, [α]$_D$ −23·19°. The alkaloidal mother liquors on decomposition afforded (+)-threo-7,8,16-trihydroxyhexadecanoic acid, mp 95-96°C, [α]$_D$ +23·9°, (+)-methyl ester, mp 67-69°C, [α]$_D$ +22·98°. The alkaloidal salts were much more difficult to crystallise than in the case of the isomeric (−)-threo-9,10,16-trihydroxyhexadecanoic acid.

[6] Sabris, S. D., Mathur, H. H. & Bhattacharyya, J. chem. Soc., 1963, 2477

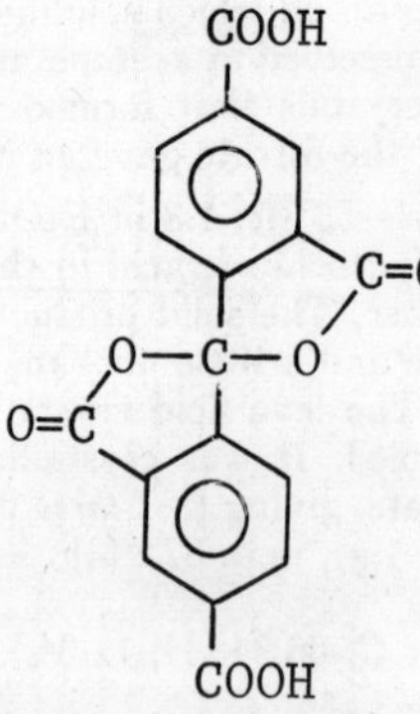

$C_{17}H_8O_8$ Ref. 1196

The l-*Keto-dilactonic Acid.*—The following experiment is described as an example of several which have been carried out with similar results. The keto-dilactonic acid (5·75 grams) was suspended in methyl alcohol (100 c.c.), and a solution of *d*-α-phenylethylamine (4·09 grams), having $[\alpha]_D^{21}$ 39·64°, in methyl alcohol (12 c.c.) was added drop by drop. The temperature rose from 22° to 26°, and a clear solution was obtained after the addition of about two-thirds of the base. After all the base had been introduced, dry ether (110 c.c.) was added. The salt rapidly crystallised, crystallisation being assisted by rubbing with a glass rod. The crop thus obtained (about 7 grams) was recrystallised from a mixture of methyl alcohol (210 c.c.) and ether (330 c.c.). The recrystallised salt (about 2 grams) was decomposed by treatment with hydrochloric acid (D 1·08), and the liberated keto-dilactonic acid carefully washed with water and dried. It was dissolved in methyl ethyl ketone, in which it is more readily soluble than in the other common solvents, and polarimetrically examined; 1·0375 grams in 30 c.c. gave α_D^{20} −2·25° (l=4), whence $[\alpha]_D^{20}$ −16·3°.

Of this product, 0·943 gram was combined, as before, with 0·671 gram of *d*-base. About 1 gram of salt was obtained, which, on decomposition, gave 0·6127 gram of acid. This was polarimetrically examined: 0·6127 in 13·1 c.c. gave $\alpha_D^{22.5}$ −1·58° (l=2), whence $[\alpha]_D^{22.5}$ −16·9°. The *l*-keto-dilactonic acid was recovered from solution and analysed (Found: C=59·4; H=2·44. $C_{17}H_8O_8$ requires C=59·99; H=2·37 per cent.).

The highest specific rotation which we have observed for the *l*-acid in the experiments which we have carried out up to the present is $[\alpha]_D^{20}$ −17·4° in methyl ethyl ketone solution.

The d-*Keto-lactonic Acid.*—The filtrate from which, as described above, the first crop of *d*-base–*l*-acid salt had been deposited gave, on acidification, 1·3 grams of an acid, which proved to be dextrorotatory; 0·679 gram in 30 c.c. of methyl ethyl ketone gave α_D^{21} 0·71° (l=4), whence $[\alpha]_D^{21}$ 7·9°. This acid was then combined with *l*-α-phenylethylamine, having $[\alpha]_D^{21}$ −38·5°, in the following manner. The acid (1·23 grams) was suspended in methyl alcohol (10 c.c.), *l*-base (0·87 gram) dissolved in methyl alcohol (2 c.c.) was added, and the salt precipitated with dry ether (6 c.c.). The acid (0·6585 gram) liberated from this salt was again combined with *l*-base (0·47 gram). The salt thus obtained gave, on decomposition, 0·559 gram of acid, which was polarimetrically examined; 0·559 gram in 13·1 c.c. gave α_D^{19} 1·50° (l=2), whence $[\alpha]_D^{19}$ 17·5°. From this acid, by repeating the above process, 0·426 gram of acid was obtained, on which the following observation was made: 0·426 gram in 13·1 c.c. of methyl ethyl ketone gave α_D^{19} 1·11°, whence $[\alpha]_D^{19}$ 17·1°. This acid was then recovered from solution and analysed (Found: C=59·70; H=2·38. $C_{17}H_8O_8$ requires C=59·99; H=2·37 per cent.).

The optically active forms of the keto-dilactonic acid are considerably more readily soluble than the racemic form in all solvents examined. When saturated solutions of the *d*- and *l*-modifications in methyl ethyl ketone are mixed, an immediate, copious precipitate of the racemic form is produced.

To show the dependence of the optical activity on the lactonic structure of the compound, a solution of the *d*-acid in approximately 1 per cent. sodium hydrogen carbonate was examined in the polarimeter. The rotation was observed to diminish gradually, sinking to the half value in about twenty-four hours, and disappearing completely in about four days.

Further experiments on larger quantities of material are in progress in order to extend these observations, and particularly to determine the specific rotation of the optically pure acids.

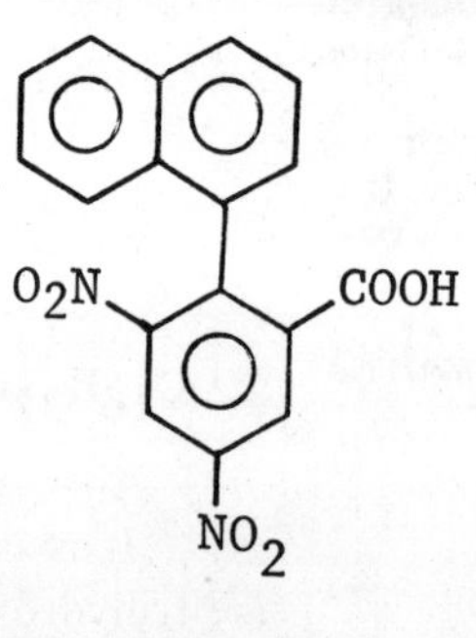

$C_{17}H_{10}N_2O_6$ Ref. 1197

Resolution of 3,5-Dinitro-6-α-naphthylbenzoic Acid.—The acid was prepared by the hydrolysis of the pure ester according to the directions of Lesslie and Turner. The melting point of the acid was 185–187°. The brucine salt was obtained by precipitation from ethyl alcohol. The *dl*-brucine salt was found to be much more insoluble in methyl alcohol (synthetic) than reported by Lesslie and Turner, and inconveniently large volumes of methanol were required for resolution using this solvent. Methyl alcohol containing acetone or chloroform, or acetone itself effected separation of the salts after repeated crystallizations. From a solution of 31 g. of the *dl*-brucine salts in 1500 cc. of boiling acetone there separated on standing 14.1 g. of orange-yellow square prisms; 0.1005 g. dissolved in chloroform and made up to a volume of 15 cc. gave α_D^{20} +0.33° in a 1-dc. tube; $[\alpha_D^{20}]$ +49.3°. Two more recrystallizations from acetone gave 8 g. of crystals; 0.1016 g. in a total volume of 15 cc. of chloroform gave α_D^{20} +0.58° in a 1-dc. tube; $[\alpha]_D^{20}$ +85.6°. A final recrystallization from 1300 cc. of methanol containing a small amount of acetone gave the pure brucine salt of the *d*-acid; 0.1006 g. in a total volume of 15 cc. of chloroform gave α_D^{20} +0.80° in a 1-dc. tube; $[\alpha]_D^{20}$ +119.4°. Lesslie and Turner reported $[\alpha]_{5791}^{20}$ +120.1°. The brucine salt of the *l*-acid in various degrees of resolution was obtained by concentration of the first acetone mother liquor. The corresponding free acids were prepared from their brucine salts in the usual manner, and were converted into the corresponding amides by the method previously described by Lesslie and Turner. The pure *d*-amide used in these experiments melted at 168°;

(10) Lesslie and Turner, *J. Chem. Soc.*, 1189 (1931).

0.1273 g. dissolved in benzene and the solution made up to a volume of 25 cc. gave the following rotations in a 2-dc. tube: α^{20}_{6563} +0.25°; α^{20}_{5893} +0.31°; α^{20}_{5463} +0.38°; α^{20}_{4861} +0.48°; $[\alpha]^{20}_{6563}$ +24.5°; $[\alpha]^{20}_{5893}$ +30.4°; $[\alpha]^{20}_{5463}$ +37.3°; $[\alpha]^{20}_{4861}$ +47.1°. The incompletely resolved *l*-amide melted at 172–176°; 0.1260 g. in a total volume of 25 cc. of benzene gave α^{20}_{5893} −0.14° in a 2-dc. tube; $[\alpha]^{20}_{5893}$ −13.8°. The racemic amide melted sharply at 192°.[11]

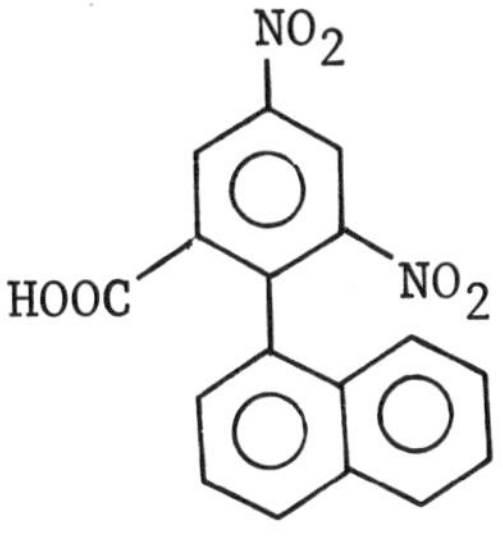

$C_{17}H_{10}N_2O_6$ Ref. 1198

Resolution of 3 : 5-*Dinitro*-6-α-*naphthylbenzoic Acid.*—Preliminary experiments showed that brucine was more satisfactory for this purpose than quinine or strychnine. Recrystallisation of the *dl*-brucine salt from water or ethyl alcohol effected no separation into the diastereoisomerides. Attempted resolution starting with the ammonium salt of the *dl*-acid and brucine sulphate in aqueous solution met with no success. The following method was finally adopted (all rotations were measured in chloroform solutions). When an ethyl-alcoholic solution of the *dl*-acid (7 g.) was added to a solution of brucine (8·5 g.) in the same solvent, almost quantitative precipitation of the brucine *dl*-salt of the acid occurred. It was dissolved in hot methyl alcohol (700 c.c.). The cold solution deposited 7 g. of deep yellow, glassy, square plates which had $[\alpha]^{20°}_{5791}$ + 96·0° (*c* = 1·000). From the mother-liquor were obtained 2 g. having $[\alpha]^{20°}_{5791}$ + 45·8° (*c* = 1·09), and after removal of most of the solvent a third fraction (6 g.) was obtained having $[\alpha]^{20°}_{5791}$ − 99·1° (*c* = 7·22).

Repeated recrystallisations of the first crop from methyl alcohol gave the brucine salt of the *d*-acid (4 g.), having $[\alpha]^{20°}_{5791}$ + 120·1° (*c* = 0·6310). It crystallised in clumps of small, square, bright yellow plates, and was very sparingly soluble in most solvents, but readily soluble in chloroform.

The pure brucine salt of the *l*-acid (2·3 g.) was similarly obtained by recrystallisation of the third crop from methyl alcohol and had $[\alpha]^{20°}_{5791}$ − 114·0° (*c* = 0·5220).

On recrystallising from methyl alcohol the middle fraction having $[\alpha]^{20°}_{5791}$ + 45·8°, a small amount of the racemic acid salt was obtained as small yellow needles having $[\alpha]^{20°}_{5791}$ + 3·8° (*c* = 0·5280).

The free acids were obtained from their brucine salts by adding the calculated amount of *N*-ammonium hydroxide to an aqueous suspension of the salt, together with a little chloroform. The chloroform solution of brucine was then removed, and after two or three extractions of the aqueous layer with chloroform, the free acid was precipitated with dilute hydrochloric acid.

d-3 : 5-*Dinitro*-6-α-*naphthylbenzoic acid* crystallised from aqueous ethyl alcohol in very fine, yellow needles, m. p. 179—180°, and had $[\alpha]^{20°}_{5791}$ + 63·4° in acetone (*l* = 2; *c* = 0·615; $\alpha^{20°}_{5791}$ = + 0·78°) (Found: C, 60·2; H, 3·2. $C_{17}H_{10}O_6N_2$ requires C, 60·3; H, 3·0%). It is sparingly soluble in water and in light petroleum, but readily dissolves in alcohol, acetone or benzene.

The sodium salt had $[\alpha]^{20°}_{5791}$ + 67·6° in water (*l* = 2; *c* = 0·629; $\alpha^{20°}_{5791}$ + 0·85°), unchanged after 48 hours. When the solution was decomposed with dilute hydrochloric acid, the free acid obtained had $[\alpha]^{20°}_{5791}$ + 63·0° for *c* = 0·167 in acetone, showing that no racemisation had occurred.

l-3 : 5-*Dinitro*-6-α-*naphthylbenzoic acid* was similar to its *d*-isomeride. It had $[\alpha]^{20°}_{5791}$ − 63·3° for *c* = 0·560 in acetone (Found: C, 60·1; H, 3·2%).

$C_{17}H_{10}N_2O_6$ Ref. 1198a

Resolution of 3 : 5-*Dinitro*-6-α-*naphthylbenzoic Acid.*—Lesslie and Turner (*J.*, 1931, 1189) and Wallis and Moyer (*J. Amer. Chem. Soc.*, 1933, **55**, 2598) have described the resolution using brucine and, owing to the low solubility of the salt, relatively large volumes of solvent are required. It was decided to examine other alkaloidal salts. Morphine in alcohol gave as crop a salt, $[\alpha]_{5461}$ −37° (*c*, 0·59 in chloroform), which on decomposition gave an acid, $[\alpha]_{5461}$ +33·3° (*c*, 0·60 in chloroform). The (−)-acid obtained from the original mother-liquor had $[\alpha]_{5461}$ −39·0° (*c*, 0·54 in chloroform). A trial experiment with quinidine again furnished as the first crop a salt of the (+)-acid and the result appeared more favourable than that with morphine. A larger-scale experiment led to an altogether less advantageous result. The acid (30 g.) was dissolved in boiling ethanol (475 c.c.), and quinidine (29·5 g.) added. The slightly cloudy solution was filtered and left overnight. The crop consisted of two types of crystal—pale yellow feathery needles (18 g.) and deep yellow clusters of square prisms (20 g.) of relatively high specific gravity. The crystals were separated roughly by hand picking, and a further mechanical separation was effected by shaking them with a small bulk of mother-liquor and decanting, to carry away the feathery needles, leaving the heavy crystal clusters. The pale yellow needles were recrystallised until of constant rotatory power, $[\alpha]_{5461}$ −25·1° (*c*, 0·64 in chloroform), and this salt on decomposition gave 6·9 g. of acid of $[\alpha]_{5791}$ −57·7° (*c*, 0·61 in acetone). This on recrystallisation from alcohol gave 5·6 g. of acid, m. p. 177—179°, $[\alpha]_{5791}$ −60° (*c*, 0·60 in acetone). The other quinidine salt on recrystallisation from alcohol gave 7·5 g. of salt of $[\alpha]_{5461}$ +295°, which on decomposition gave 3·5 g. of acid, $[\alpha]_{5791}$ +50° (*c*, 0·54 in acetone). This could be purified by further recrystallisation, for it was strikingly evident that the optically active forms were less soluble and crystallised more readily and in much more compact crystals than the inactive acid.

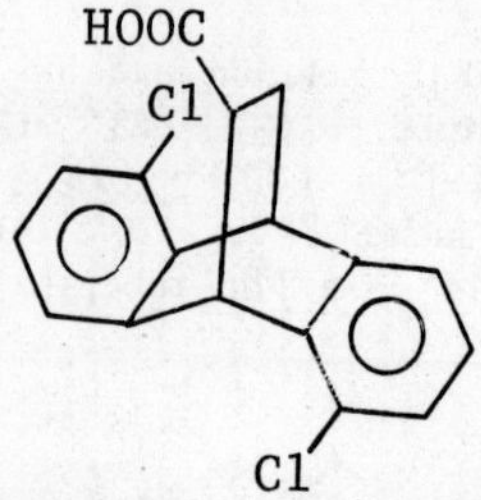

$C_{17}H_{12}Cl_2O_2$ Ref. 1199

Resolution of the mixture of carboxylic acids ((−)-**18**). To the mixture of carboxylic acids (**17**, 8·57 g) dissolved in EtOAc (100 ml) and EtOH (100 ml), (−)-phenethylamine (3·35 g) in EtOAc (5 ml) was added in one portion. The solution was warmed at 60° for 1 hr and evaporated to *ca.* 40 ml. To this residue, EtOAc (150 ml) was added. The crystals, $[\alpha]_D$ −30·6° (MeOH, *c* 0·466), were collected and recrystallized from acetone (5 ×) to give the pure diastereomer (1·348 g), m.p. 218–223°. $[\alpha]_D$ −127·6° (MeOH, *c* 0·261). The mother liquors of the recrystallizations were collected and concentrated to dryness. The residue was recrystallized from acetone (5 ×) to give another product (1·20 g), m.p. 267–269°. $[\alpha]_D$ −1·9° (MeOH, *c* 0·467). The salt (1·34 g, $[\alpha]_D$ −127·6°) was suspended in ether (20 ml) and decomposed by addition of dil. HCl. After usual treatment, the product was recrystallized from methanolic water to give colourless plates (88·3 mg), m.p. 225–227°. $[\alpha]_D$ −159·1° (MeOH, *c* 0·132); IR ν_{max}^{Nujol} cm^{-1}: 1705, 788.

The other salt (1·20 g, $[\alpha]_D$ −1·9°) was treated in a similar manner, but the product (816 mg) did not show optical activity, m.p. 270–271°.

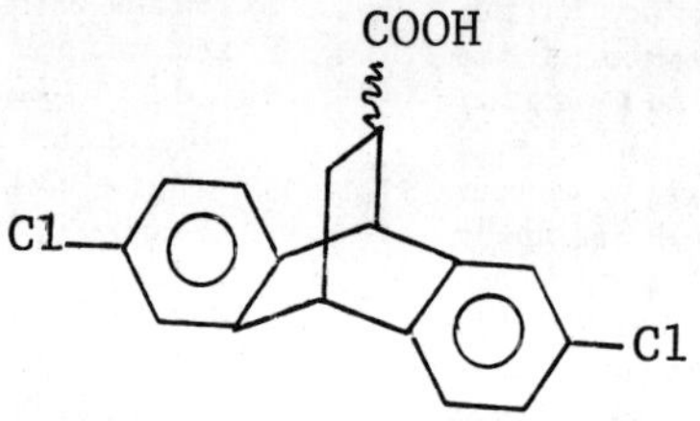

$C_{17}H_{12}Cl_2O_2$ Ref. 1200

Resolution of 2,6-*dichloro*-9,10-*ethano anthracene* 11(endo *or* exo)-*carboxylic acid.* (a) A mixture of 2,6-dichloro acid **32** (2·6 g), cinchonidine (2·4 g) and MeOH (50 ml) was warmed to 70° (bath temp.). Crystals soon appeared and were recrystallized (10 ×) from MeOH to give pure diastereomer (1·079 g). $[\alpha]_D$ −116·8° (MeOH, *c* 0·155). This compound (1·66 g) was warmed for 15 min with 6N HCl (30 ml) and the crystals which formed were collected, washed with water, and dried *in vacuo* (0·842 g). Purification was unsuccessful, therefore the crude acid was esterified as for the preparation of (−)-**3**. Crystallization from MeOH gave the pure ester, m.p. 116–117°. $[\alpha]_D$ −91·6° (dioxane, *c* 0·297); IR ν_{max}^{Nujol} cm^{-1}: 1738. NMR τ: 8·02 (1H, dd, *J* = 5·5, 2·5 Hz), 7·88 (1H, dd, *J* = 2·5, 1·5 Hz), 7·16 (1H, td, *J* = 10·0, 5·5, 2·5 Hz), 6·39 (3H, s), 5·73 (1H, t, *J* = 2·5 Hz), 5·38 (1H, d, *J* = 2·5 Hz), 2·7 ~ 2·9 (6H, m). (Found: C, 65·20; H, 4·39; Cl, 22·29. $C_{18}H_{14}O_2Cl_2$ requires: C, 64·91; H, 4·23; Cl, 21·28 %).

(b) Partially resolved (+)-acids (1·25 g), recovered from the mother liquor described above, (+)-phenethyl amine (494 mg), and acetone (20 ml) were mixed and allowed to stand at room temp. overnight. Crystals were collected and recrystallized (3 ×) from MeOH to give pure diastereomer (440 mg). $[\alpha]_D$ +78·7° (MeOH, *c* 0·313). The salt (440 mg) and dil. HCl (5 ml) were shaken at 70° for 10 min, solid was collected, washed with water, and dried *in vacuo*. Recrystallization from MeOH–H_2O gave the pure isomer (314 mg), m.p. 192–194°. $[\alpha]_D$ +92·3° (MeOH, *c* 0·116); IR ν_{max}^{Nujol} cm^{-1}: 1716, 822. (Found: C, 64·07; H, 3·80; Cl, 22·17. $C_{17}H_{12}Cl_2O_2$ requires: C, 63·97; H, 3·79; Cl, 22·22 %). Though the (−)-acid was difficult to crystallize the (+)-acid was easy to purify and was esterified according to the above procedure, but crystallization failed. These two compounds have an epimeric relation to each other, one being 11(*endo*)- and the other 11(*exo*)-.

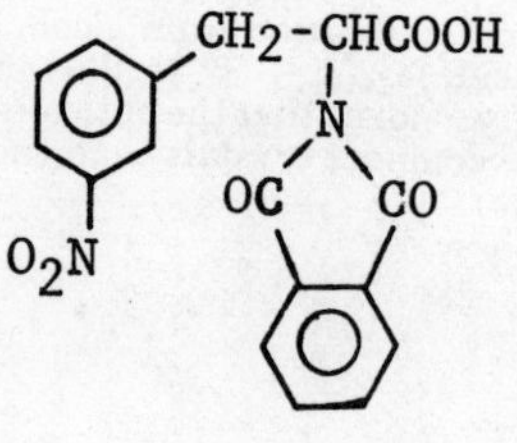

$C_{17}H_{12}N_2O_6$ Ref. 1201

Experimental[11]

Chemical Resolution. (1) 3-(*m*-Nitrophenyl)-N-phthalyl-L-alanine (L-I) Brucine Salt.—Hot solutions of 18.8 g. (0.0550 mole) of the racemic acid I in 95% ethanol (420 ml.) and of 23.8 g. (0.0600 mole) of brucine in 95% ethanol (185 ml.) were combined and allowed to cool slowly to room temperature. After 20 hr., the yellow salt that separated was collected on a filter, washed with two 50-ml. portions of ethanol (the filtrates were saved for (2) below), and recrystallized from 1200 ml. of boiling 95% ethanol. The product weighed 20.3 g. (99% yield), m.p. 158–161° dec., $[\alpha]^{25}D$ −107.1 ± 2.5° (50% water–dioxane), and included a second crop (0.9 g.) obtained by concentrating the mother liquor (from the recrystallization) to 400 ml. Easy solubility in methanol was characteristic.

Anal. Calcd. for $C_{40}H_{38}N_4O_{10}$: C, 65.4; H, 5.21; N, 7.62. Found: C, 65.7; H, 5.24; N, 7.47.

(2) 3-(*m*-Nitrophenyl)-N-phthalyl-D-alanine (D-I) Brucine Salt.—The combined filtrate after removal of the yellow salt above was concentrated *in vacuo*. The semisolid residue was dissolved in 200 ml. of hot methanol and the solution allowed to cool slowly to room temperature. After 20 hr., 18.9 g. (92%) of the white salt was collected, m.p. 142–145°. Recrystallization from boiling methanol (200 ml.) afforded 16.8 g. (82%), m.p. 142–146°, $[\alpha]^{25}D$ +83.9 ± 2.0° (50% water–dioxane). This salt was characteristically a white powder, contained methanol of crystallization, and was easily soluble in 95% ethanol.

Anal. Calcd. for $C_{40}H_{38}N_4O_{10}\cdot CH_3OH$: C, 64.2; H, 5.52; N, 7.37. Found: C, 64.0; H, 5.69; N, 7.07.

3-(*m*-Nitrophenyl)-N-phthalyl-L-alanine (L-I).—The yellow brucine salt of L-I (1.5 g., 2.0 mmoles) was suspended in 20 ml. of 4 *M* hydrochloric acid. The resultant gum, when broken up and stirred intermittently, gradually formed a white solid (0.68 g., 100%), m.p. 159–164°. Recrystallization from a chloroform-Skellysolve C[12] mixture (1:1) afforded 0.50 g. (73%), m.p. 162–165°, $[\alpha]^{28}D$ −212.6 ± 3.2° (absolute ethanol).

Anal. Calcd. for $C_{17}H_{12}N_2O_6$: C, 60.0; H, 3.56; N, 8.23. Found: C, 59.7; H, 3.73; N, 8.06.

3-(*m*-Nitrophenyl)-N-phthalyl-D-alanine (D-I) was obtained in 66% yield, m.p. 160–163°, $[\alpha]^{25}D$ +209.7 ± 3.0° (absolute ethanol). A sample recrystallized for analysis melted at 163–165°, $[\alpha]^{15}D$ +212.4 ± 3.0°

Anal. Found: C, 59.6; H, 3.86; N, 8.45.

(11) Melting points were observed on a Fisher–Johns apparatus and are uncorrected. Optical rotations were taken in 1% solutions at 1 dcm. path length. Paper chromatograms were run by the descending technique on Schleicher and Schuell No. 2496 acetylated paper in benzene–methanol–water (2:6:1), except as noted with D- and L-VI. Spots were detected visually under ultraviolet light.

(12) A hydrocarbon fraction, b.p. 88–109°.

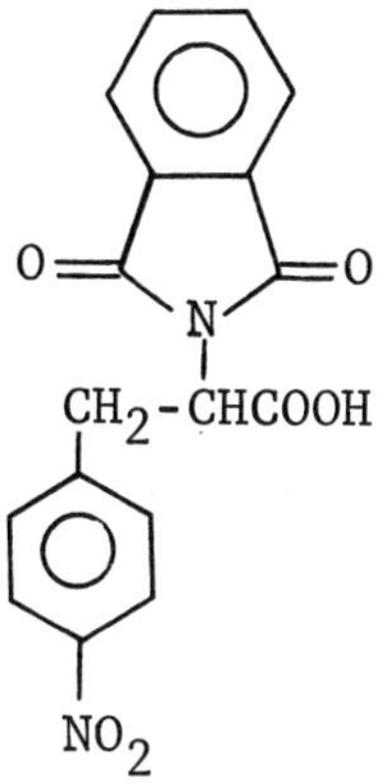

$C_{17}H_{12}N_2O_6$ Ref. 1202

Resolution. Solutions of *p*-nitro-*N*-phthaloyl-DL-phenylalanine (1·0 g.) in methanol (25 ml.) and of cinchonidine (0·865 g., 1·00 mol.) in methanol (30 ml.) were mixed. Crystallisation soon set in. The mixture was left overnight, and the colourless needles (0·97 g.), m. p. 209—210°, were collected. After two recrystallisations from methanol the *cinchonidine salt* of the D-acid had m. p. 211° and $[\alpha]^{21}_D$ +82° ± 1° (*c*, 0.84 in dioxan) (Found, after drying at 100° in a high vacuum: C, 67·0; H, 5·8; N, 8·8. $C_{36}H_{34}O_7N_4$,MeOH requires C, 66·7; H, 5·7; N, 8·4%).

To the salt (2·9 g.) in warm ethanol (50 ml.) was added water (50 ml.) and a slight excess (*ca.* 10 ml.) of N-aqueous sodium hydroxide. The mixture was diluted with water, cooled, and filtered from the precipitated base, and the filtrate acidified with hydrochloric acid. The tiny needles of p-*nitro*-N-*phthaloyl*-D-*phenylalanine* (1·05 g.) had, after recrystallisation from ethanol, m. p. 207—208°, $[\alpha]^{20}_D$ +240° ± 2° (*c*, 1·01 in EtOH) (Found: C, 60·1; H, 3·7; N, 8·2. $C_{17}H_{12}O_6N_2$ requires C, 60·0; H, 3·55; N, 8·2%). Refluxing with 2N-ethanolic hydrogen chloride yielded *p*-nitro-*N*-phthaloyl-D-phenylalanine ethyl ester, m. p. 82—83°, $[\alpha]^{20}_D$ +206° ± 1° (cf. Part I).

Evaporation of the mother-liquors from the original cinchonidine experiment gave a gum which crystallised readily from aqueous ethanol in almost colourless needles (0·73 g.), m. p. 191—192·5°. Two recrystallisations from aqueous ethanol gave the L-acid cinchonidine *salt*, m. p. 192·5—194°, $[\alpha]^{20}_D$ −170° ± 1° (*c*, 1·32 in EtOH) (Found, after drying at 100° in a high vacuum: C, 66·2; H, 5·6; N, 8·6. $C_{36}H_{34}O_7N_4,H_2O$ requires C, 66·3; H, 5·5; N, 8·6%).

The acid was isolated as for the D-isomer. The recrystallised p-*nitro*-N-*phthaloyl*-L-*phenylalanine* had m. p. 209—211° and $[\alpha]^{21}_D$ −233° ± 2° (Found: C, 60·3; H, 3·8; N, 8·4%).

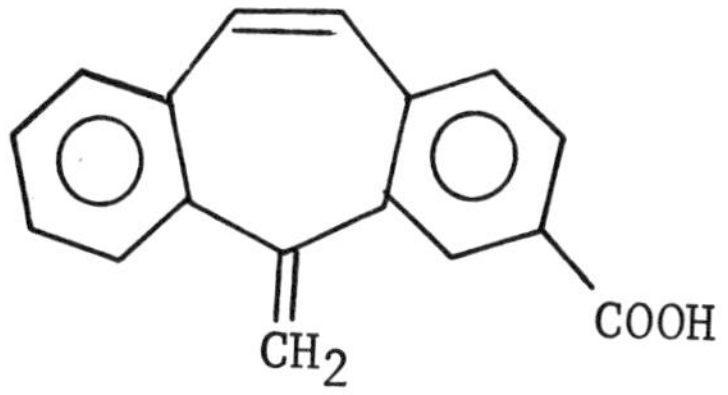

$C_{17}H_{12}O_2$ Ref. 1203

l-*Ephedrinsalz von V.* 1 g V und 665 mg *l*-Ephedrin wurden in 15 ml Aceton gelöst. Nach zweistündigem Stehen im Eisschrank wurde abfiltriert. Der Rückstand wurde bei 50° in 3 ml Äthanol gelöst, die Lösung filtriert und mit 3 ml Äthanol nachgewaschen. Dann gab man 4 ml Wasser zu und impfte an. Nach 1/2 Std. bei −5° wurde abfiltriert und im Exsikkator bei Zimmertemperatur getrocknet. 800 mg; sint. ~95°, Smp. 100–110° unter Aufschäumen. $[\alpha]^{20}_{436}$ = −42,5°, *c* = 3 (CH_3OH). Keine Mutarotation.

$C_{17}H_{12}O_2,C_{10}H_{15}ON,1^1/_2H_2O$	Ber.	C 73,6	H 6,9	O 16,3	N 3,2%
(440,54)	Gef.	,, 73,6	,, 6,7	,, 16,2	,, 3,1%

Die Lösung von 250 mg Ephedrinsalz in Methanol wurde mit einigen Tropfen 5N-Salzsäure versetzt. Die ausgefallene *Säure* wurde abfiltriert, mit Methanol und Wasser gewaschen und im Exsikkator getrocknet. $[\alpha]^{20}_{436}$ = 0°, *c* = 2 (Dimethylsulfoxid).

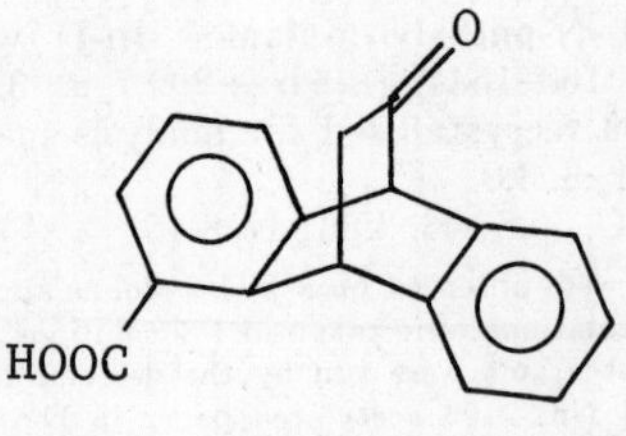

$C_{17}H_{12}O_3$ Ref. 1204

Optical Resolution of the Carboxylic Acid (8a).—(−)-Pseudoephedrine (4.03 g) was added to a suspension of the carboxylic acid (8a) (6.6 g) in ethyl acetate (30 ml). The mixture was briefly warmed to give a clear solution and allowed to stand at room temperature overnight. The crystals were collected by filtration, washed with ethyl acetate, and dried. Recrystallization from methanol three times gave the pure diastereomer, $[\alpha]_D^{26}$ +65.9 ± 2.4° (MeOH; *c* 0.443).

The salt (4.32 g) was shaken with a mixture of dilute HCl and ethyl acetate. After the usual treatment, the oily residue was crystallized from benzene to give a powder, (2.56 g), m.p. 188—188.5°, $[\alpha]_D^{25}$ +121.3 ± 2.3° (MeOH; *c* 0.700), $\nu_{max.}$ (Nujol) 1 690 cm^{-1}.

Note:

Cinchonidine, dehydroabietylamine, (+)-phenethylamine, brucine, ephedrine and quinine were also tried as resolving agent but pseudoephedrine turned out to be the most effective. (Author's comments)

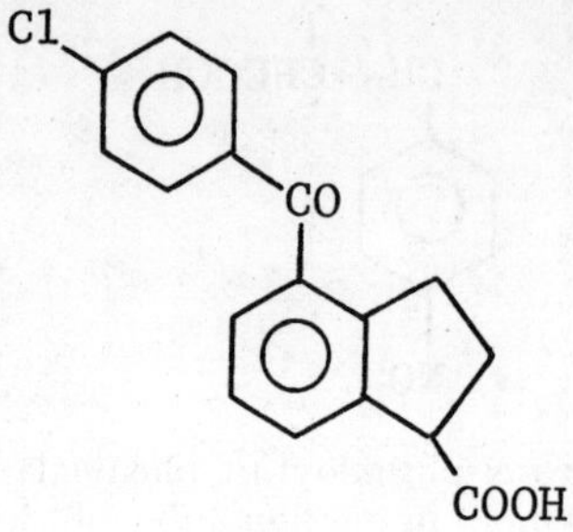

$C_{17}H_{13}ClO_3$ Ref. 1205

Optical Resolution of 4-(4-Chlorobenzoyl)-1-indancarboxylic Acid (Ic)——a) (*S*)-*l*-Ic: A suspension of 3.1 g of Ic and 1.5 g of cinchonine in 100 ml of acetone was warmed to give a clear solution. The solution was allowed to stand overnight in a refrigerator. The resulting precipitate was collected by filtration and recrystallized from CH_3CN to give 1.7 g (56%) of the cinchonine salt of (*S*)-*l*-Ic as colorless crystals, mp 190.0—192.0°. *Anal.* Calcd. for $C_{36}H_{34}ClN_2O_4$: C, 72.78; H, 5.77; N, 4.72. Found: C, 72.51; H, 5.92; N, 4.72. $[\alpha]_D^{23}$ +32.9° (*c*=1, $CHCl_3$). This salt was dissolved in 170 ml of $CHCl_3$. The solution was washed with 1 N HCl and water, dried over anhydrous $MgSO_4$ and concentrated under reduced pressure. The residue was recrystallized from a mixture of benzene and cyclohexane (1:4) to give 0.60 g (70%) of (*S*)-*l*-Ic, mp 121—122°. *Anal.* Calcd. for $C_{17}H_{13}ClO_3$: C, 67.89; H, 4.36. Found: C, 67.96; H, 4.09. $[\alpha]_D^{24}$ −66.9° (*c*=1, MeOH). The NMR spectrum was identical with that of the racemic compound.[4)]

b) (*R*)-*d*-Ic: The mother liquor of the crude cinchonine salt of *l*-Ic in a) was concentrated to dryness under reduced pressure. The residue was dissolved in 50 ml of CH_3CN. The solution was allowed to stand for 10 days and the resulting precipitate was removed by filtration. The filtrate was concentrated under reduced pressure and the residue was dissolved in 150 ml of $CHCl_3$. The solution was washed with 1 N HCl and water, dried over anhydrous $MgSO_4$ and concentrated under reduced pressure. The residue was dissolved with 0.6 g of *l*-α-phenylethylamine in 80 ml of CH_3CN and the solution was allowed to stand overnight. The resulting precipitate was collected and recrystallized five times from CH_3CN to give 0.78 g (37%) of the *l*-α-phenylethylamine salt of (*R*)-*d*-Ic as colorless crystals, mp 148—150°. *Anal.* Calcd. for $C_{25}H_{24}ClNO_3$: C, 71.17; H, 5.73; N, 3.32. Found: C, 71.24; H, 5.67; N, 3.50. $[\alpha]_D^{24}$ +62.2° (*c*=1, $CHCl_3$). From this salt (*R*)-*d*-Ic was obtained by the similar procedures to that described in a), mp 121—122° [32%, recrystallized from a mixture of benzene and cyclohexane (1:4)]. *Anal.* Calcd. for $C_{17}H_{13}ClO_3$: C, 67.89; H, 4.36. Found: C, 68.08; H, 4.17. $[\alpha]_D^{24}$ +65.0° (*c*=1, MeOH).

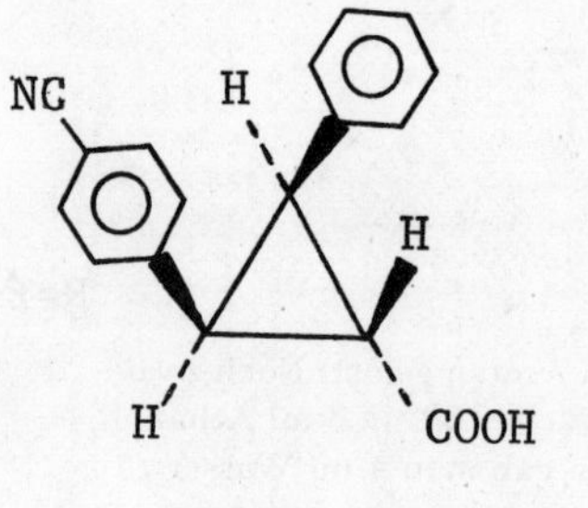

$C_{17}H_{13}NO_2$ Ref. 1206

Resolution of *trans*-2-*p*-Cyanophenyl-*trans*-3-phenylcyclopropanecarboxylic Acid. To 13.27 g (0.0504 mol) of racemic *trans*-2-*p*-cyanophenyl-*trans*-3-phenylcyclopropanecarboxylic acid was added 14.85 g (0.0504 mol) of (−)-cinchonidine alkaloid and 133 ml of ethyl acetate. The mixture was heated until solution occurred and then filtered and let stand overnight at room temperature, yielding 12.61 g of cinchonidine salt, mp 155–160°, $[\alpha]^{25}_{436}$ −192° (*c* 0.00240, $CHCl_3$). This salt was recrystallized three times from hot ethyl acetate to give 4.121 g of salt, $[\alpha]^{25}_{436}$ −63° (*c* 0.00350, $CHCl_3$). A total of 73.59 g (0.279 mol) of acid and 84.32 g (0.286 mol) of cinchonidine was carried through this procedure to give a total of 25.31 g of salt with a constant $[\alpha]^{25}_{436}$ −53 ± 10°, mp 202° dec.

The 25.31 g of resolved salt thus obtained was hydrolyzed with 10% HCl to give 11.59 g of the resolved acid, mp 154–156°, $[\alpha]^{25}_{436}$ +215 ± 2° (*c* 0.00300, $CHCl_3$). Recrystallization of the acid from methylene chloride–hexane yielded 9.901 g (13% based on racemic acid used) of optically active *trans*-2-*p*-cyanophenyl-*trans*-3-phenylcyclopropanecarboxylic acid, mp 154–156°, $[\alpha]^{25}_{436}$ +217 ± 2° (*c* 0.00300, $CHCl_3$). The nmr ($CDCl_3$) and ir ($CHCl_3$) spectra of the optically active acid were identical with those of the racemic material.

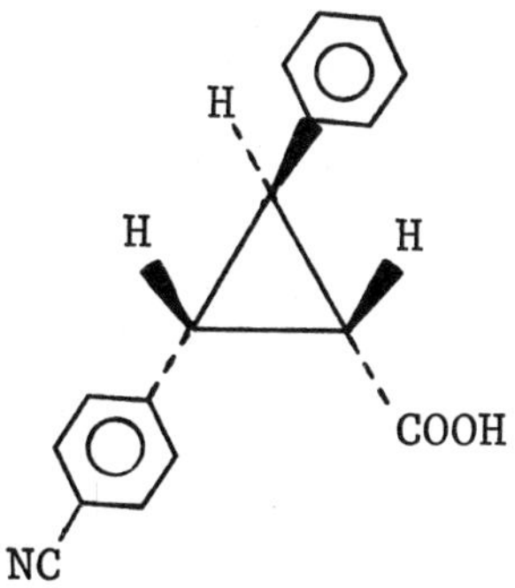

$C_{17}H_{13}NO_2$ Ref. 1207

Resolution of *cis*-2-*p*-Cyanophenyl-*trans*-3-phenylcyclopropanecarboxylic Acid. A mixture of 15.98 g (0.0607 mol) of racemic *cis*-2-*p*-cyanophenyl-*trans*-3-phenylcyclopropanecarboxylic acid, 17.90 g (0.0607 mol) of (−)-cinchonidine, and 3.5 l. of 50% ethyl acetate–chloroform was heated until solution occurred, then filtered and let stand 18 hr at room temperature, yielding 12.79 g of white crystalline salt, mp 191° dec. A portion of the salt on hydrolysis (10% HCl) gave acid with $[\alpha]^{25}_{436}$ +142° (*c* 0.00228, $CHCl_3$). Two more crystallizations of the salt produced 9.493 g, hydrolyzed to 4.445 g of acid, mp 103–106°, $[\alpha]^{25}_{436}$ +158° (*c* 0.00236, $CHCl_3$). Four crystallizations of the acid from ether–hexane yielded 1.837 g (11%) of *cis*-2-*p*-cyanophenyl-*trans*-3-phenylcyclopropanecarboxylic acid, $[\alpha]^{25}_{436}$ +165 ± 1° (*c* 0.00317, $CHCl_3$), mp 103–105°, with no further change in rotation on crystallization.

Concentration of the mother liquor of the first crop of the salt followed by cooling at 0° gave 11.10 g of the salt of acid, $[\alpha]^{25}_{436}$ −123° (*c* 0.00856, $CHCl_3$). Three more crystallizations of the salt from ethyl acetate–chloroform yielded 5.246 g which gave acid with $[\alpha]^{25}_{436}$ −141 ± 1° (*c* 0.00584, $CHCl_3$). This solvent system would not resolve the salt further. Recrystallization from 50% methanol–acetone gave 4.477 g of salt with acid $[\alpha]^{25}_{436}$ −145° (*c* 0.00378, $CHCl_3$). The acid, regenerated from the salt with 10% HCl and recrystallized four times from ether–hexane, gave 0.981 g of *cis*-2-*p*-cyanophenyl-*trans*-3-phenylcyclopropanecarboxylic acid with constant $[\alpha]^{25}_{436}$ −164° (*c* 0.00532, $CHCl_3$), mp 101.5–104.5° (6%). The nmr ($CDCl_3$) and ir ($CHCl_3$) spectra of both enantiomers were identical with those of the racemic acid.

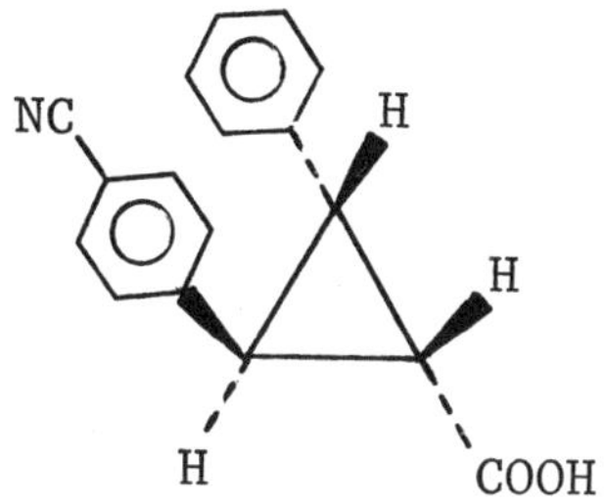

$C_{17}H_{13}NO_2$ Ref. 1208

Resolution of *trans*-2-*p*-Cyanophenyl-*cis*-3-phenylcyclopropanecarboxylic Acid. To 15.78 g (0.0595 mol) of racemic *trans*-2-*p*-cyanophenyl-*cis*-3-phenylcyclopropanecarboxylic acid was added 17.53 g (0.0595 mol) of (−)-cinchonidine and 3.6 l. of ethyl acetate; solution occurred upon refluxing. After filtration and standing 18 hr at room temperature, 9.829 g of salt, mp 189° dec, crystallized, corresponding to acid with $[\alpha]^{25}_{436}$ −47° (*c* 0.00253, $CHCl_3$). Two recrystallizations from ethyl acetate yielded 4.173 g of salt with acid $[\alpha]^{25}_{436}$ −70° (*c* 0.00257, $CHCl_3$). Hydrolysis with 10% HCl gave an oil which crystallized (4 weeks) from benzene, yielding 1.921 g of acid, $[\alpha]^{25}_{436}$ −78° (*c* 0.00310, $CHCl_3$). This was recrystallized three times from benzene to give 1.063 g of acid with a constant $[\alpha]^{25}_{436}$ −85 ± 1° (*c* 0.00291, $CHCl_3$), mp 155.5–158.5°. The mother liquor of the salt of the −70° acid, after concentration, gave on standing 1.210 g of salt, acid $[\alpha]^{25}_{436}$ −86° (*c* 0.00151, $CHCl_3$). Recrystallization from ethyl acetate provided 0.824 g of salt which gave 0.379 g more *trans*-2-*p*-cyanophenyl-*cis*-3-phenylcyclopropanecarboxylic acid with a constant $[\alpha]^{25}_{436}$ −85 ± 1° (*c* 0.00254, $CHCl_3$) on hydrolysis; total 9% of this enantiomer.

The mother liquor of the original salt of the −47° acid, after standing at 0° for 2 days, gave 7.240 g of salt, mp 190° dec, acid $[\alpha]^{25}_{436}$ +57° (*c* 0.00258). This salt was crystallized four times from ethyl acetate to give 1.376 g of salt corresponding to acid of constant $[\alpha]^{25}_{436}$ +85 ± 2° (*c* 0.00304, $CHCl_3$). Hydrolysis gave 0.637 g (4%) of this enantiomer of *trans*-2-*p*-cyanophenyl-*cis*-3-phenylcyclopropanecarboxylic acid, mp 155.5–158.5°. The nmr ($CDCl_3$) and ir ($CHCl_3$) spectra of both enantiomers were identical with those of the racemic acid.

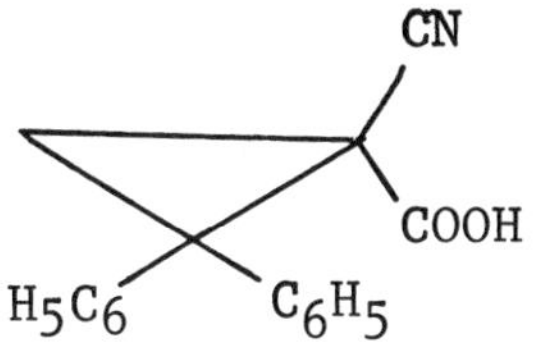

$C_{17}H_{13}NO_2$ Ref. 1209

Resolution of 1-Cyano-2,2-diphenylcyclopropanecarboxylic Acid. A solution of 10.5 g (26.2 mmol) of brucine (recrystallized from acetone) in 105 ml of methanol was added to a hot solution of 7.0 g (26 mmol) of 1-cyano-2,2-diphenylcyclopropanecarboxylic acid in 105 ml of methanol. Crystallization began almost immediately. The solution was cooled slowly to 5° to give 9.0 g (51%) of nicely formed prisms, $[\alpha]_{546}^{25}$ +34.8° (*c* 0.342, $CHCl_3$). The rotation of the highly insoluble salt was raised to $[\alpha]_{546}^{25}$ +49.8° (*c* 0.540, $CHCl_3$), by four additional recrystallizations. The free acid was obtained by shaking 3.9 g of salt, $[\alpha]_{546}^{25}$ +34.8°, with 100 ml of ethyl acetate and 50 ml of 1 *M* hydrochloric acid. The aqueous layer was extracted three times more with ethyl acetate; the combined organic washings were extracted once with brine, dried, and evaporated to give 1.5 g of a white solid, $[\alpha]_{546}^{25}$ +128° (*c* 0.710, ethyl acetate). One recrystallization of this material from chloroform–ethyl acetate (minimum) gave 1.3 g of white crystals, $[\alpha]_{546}^{25}$ +147° (*c* 0.560, ethyl acetate), mp 183–185°. Optically pure acid was not prepared. The nmr and ir spectra of this partially optically pure acid were identical with those of racemic acid. *Anal.* Calcd for $C_{17}H_{13}NO_2$: C, 77.56; H, 4.98; N, 5.32. Found: C, 77.41; H, 4.85; N, 5.14.

From the brucine salt mother liquor, the negative enantiomer was obtained as follows: the filtrate from crystallization of the first crop of the original brucine salt was evaporated to give an oily resin. Treatment of the resin with hydrochloric acid and ethyl acetate as above gave 3.9 g (56%) of a yellow-white powder, $[\alpha]_{546}^{25}$ −121° (*c* 0.530, ethyl acetate). The crude acid was esterified (see below) without further purification.

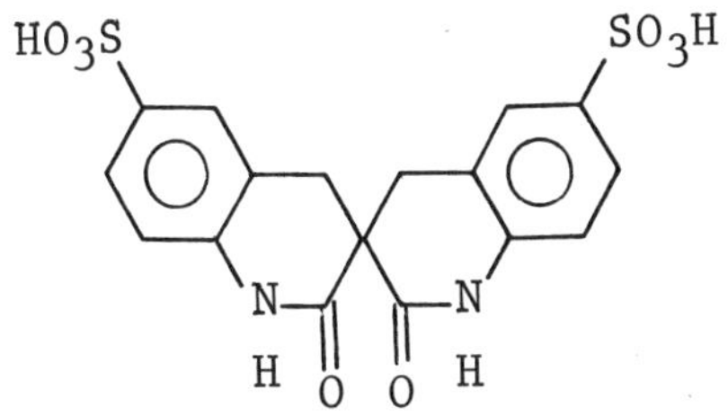

$C_{17}H_{14}N_2O_8S_2$ Ref. 1210

Spaltung der Bis-dihydrocarbostyril-3.3′-spiran-6.6′-disulfonsäure in die *l*- und *d*-Form

3.5 g der inaktiven Sulfonsäure, die bei 100° getrocknet waren, wurden in 390 ccm Methylalkohol gelöst und zu einer siedenden Lösung von 3.0 g Chinin + 3 H_2O (1 Mol.) in 1200 ccm des gleichen Mittels gegeben. Beim Abkühlen schied sich das Chinin-Salz amorph aus. Nach 24 Stdn. löste man durch Erhitzen auf dem Wasserbade wieder, worauf nun bei langsamem Erkalten feine Nadeln und etwas derbere Krystalle ausfielen. Man unterbrach die Krystallisation, sobald sich etwa 1/4 des Salzes abgeschieden hatte,

was nach 18—24 Stdn. der Fall war.

Bei einem Versuch wurden so 1.57 g Salz gewonnen, das ziemlich fest an den Wandungen haftete. Diese Menge löste man in 78 ccm heißem Wasser, worauf man 78 ccm Methylalkohol zufügte. Aus dieser Mischung krystallisierten im Laufe von 9 Tagen bei 10—15° lange, feine Nadeln, deren Gewicht nach dem Waschen mit Methylalkohol 0.39 g war. Das Filtrat gab weder durch Abkühlen, noch durch Einengen eine zweite Fraktion davon.

Auch das alkoholische Filtrat von den 1.57 g Salz lieferte nur Krystallfraktionen, die, in gleicher Weise behandelt, keine Nadeln abschieden, deren nochmaliges Umlösen aus reinem Methylalkohol aber nicht mehr möglich war, da sie davon kaum mehr aufgenommen wurden.

Zur Zerlegung des Chininsalzes und Prüfung auf optische Aktivität löste man die 0.39 g Salz in je 20 ccm Wasser und Ammoniak und entfernte das ausgefallene Chinin, das 1 Mol. entsprach, durch öfteres Ausschütteln mit Chloroform. Nach dem Absaugen des gelösten Chloroforms und des überschüssigen Ammoniaks im Vakuum ergab sich für das in Lösung befindliche Di-ammoniumsalz, Proz.-Geh. etwa 1.77, eine Drehung von

$$[\alpha]_D^{20} = -\frac{1.61^0 \times 200}{1.77 \times d} = -\frac{182^0}{d}.$$

Zur Überführung in das Bariumsalz dampfte man die Lösung mit einem kleinen Überschuß von Baryt bei 40—50° im Vakuum zur Trockne. Nach Austreibung des Ammoniaks nahm man in Wasser auf, leitete Kohlendioxyd ein, um den freien Baryt zu fällen, filtrierte vom Carbonat ab und engte im Exsiccator über Schwefelsäure ein. Dabei krystallisierten schöne, schief vier- oder sechsseitige Täfelchen des Bariumsalzes aus.

Die Menge der ersten Fraktion war nach dem Trocknen auf Ton 0.198 g. Ihr Krystallwassergehalt war 15.92 %; ihre Drehung in Wasser:

$$[\alpha]_D^{17} = -\frac{2.16^0 \times 100 \times 2}{2.26 \times 1.008} = -189.6^0.$$

Für die Analyse trocknete man das Salz bei 100° und 15 mm über P_2O_5.

0.1432 g lufttr. Sbst.: 0.0228 g H_2O. — 0.1178 g getr. Sbst.: 0.0475 g $BaSO_4$.

$C_{17}H_{12}O_8N_2S_2Ba + 6\,H_2O$ (681.4). Ber. H_2O 15.85. Gef. H_2O 15.92.

$C_{17}H_{12}O_8N_2S_2Ba$ (573.4). Ber. Ba 23.96. Gef. Ba 23.74.

Als zweite und dritte Fraktion wurden noch 0.06 g Salz erhalten, so daß die Gesamtausbeute 0.26 g statt 0.35 g betrug.

Zur Prüfung auf optische Reinheit löste man 0.34 g Salz mit $\alpha = -189.6^0$ aus je 4—6 Tln. heißem Wasser dreimal um. Die gebliebenen 0.16 g schiefen Täfelchen zeigten unverändert

$$[\alpha]_D^{17} = -190^0.$$

Die freie *l*-Säure blieb nach Fällung des Bariums als in Wasser sehr leicht löslicher Sirup zurück, der beim Anreiben mit einigen Tropfen 5-*n*. Salzsäure in Nadeln krystallisierte, die in Wasser ebenfalls sehr leicht löslich waren..

Auf Ton an der Luft getrocknet, enthielten sie Wasser:

0.0414 g Sbst. verloren 0.0081 g bei 95°, 15 mm, über P_2O_5.

$C_{17}H_{14}O_8N_2S_2 + 6\,H_2O$ (546). Ber. H_2O 19.78. Gef. H_2O 19.57.

Ihre Drehung in Wasser war:

$$[\alpha]_D^{14} = -\frac{1.04^0 \times 100 \times 2}{0.887 \times 1.003} = -233.8^0.$$

Die Säure sinterte über 200° schwach und schmolz bei 230—235° unter Aufblähen.

d-Bariumsalz.

Die nachträglich aus dem Methylalkohol fallenden Krystallisationen des Chininsalzes enthielten einen Überschuß der *d*-Säure. Zu ihrer Isolierung wurden 9.55 g des Salzes aus einigen Versuchen wie zuvor in das Bariumsalz verwandelt. Nach dem Einengen seiner wäßrigen Lösung auf 50 ccm fielen 7.5 g des inaktiven Salzes aus. Das Filtrat enthielt nach seiner Drehung 0.43 g wasserfreies *d*-Bariumsalz. Man behandelte mit Tierkohle und engte, zuletzt im Exsiccator auf 4 g ein. Dabei erhielt man noch 0.3 g Krystalle, die nur $[\alpha]_D = +53^0$ zeigten und in heißem Wasser schwer löslich waren. Die Mutterlauge dieser 0.3 g von 6 ccm gab nun beim Anreiben 0.25 g schiefe Tafeln, die, auf Ton abgepreßt, 16 % Wasser enthielten und

$$[\alpha]_D^{17.5} = +\frac{1.51^0 \times 2 \times 100}{1.563 \times 1.005} = +192.2^0 \ (\pm 2.6^0)$$

hatten.

Ihre Analyse ergab:

0.0862 g getr. Sbst.: 0.0353 g $BaSO_4$.

$C_{17}H_{12}O_8N_2S_2Ba$ (573.4). Ber. Ba 23.96. Gef Ba 24.10.

Eine zweite Fraktion des *d*-Salzes hatte:

$$[\alpha]_D^{19} = +\frac{1.55^0 \times 200}{1.628 \times 1.005} = +189.5^0$$

und eine dritte, auch dem Aussehen nach, unreine $+171^0$.

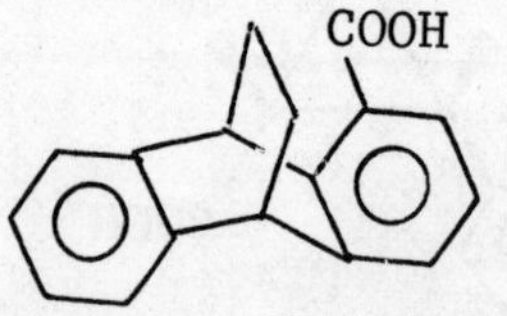

$C_{17}H_{14}O_2$ Ref. 1211

Racematspaltung der 9,10-Dihydro-9,10-äthanoanthracen-carbonsäuren* **(2)**

2 a: Lösungen von 3,8 g (15,2 mMol) racem. **2 a**[8] und 7,1 g (15,2 mMol) Brucinhydrat in insgesamt 20 ml Äthanol wurden vereinigt und in der Hitze mit 10 ml Wasser versetzt. Die klare Lösung ließ man langsam abkühlen und filtrierte das Salz nach zwei Tagen ab. Vor der Kristallisation wurde eine CH_2Cl_2-Lösung im Vak. abgedampft und das schaumige Salz, wie in der Tab. 3 angegeben, umkristallisiert. Nach drei Kristallisationen waren die $[\alpha]_D$-Werte des Salzes und der (mit H_3PO_4) freigesetzten Säure konstant.

Tabelle 3. Racematspaltung von „Äthanoanthracenen"

g Salz	umkristall. aus (ml)	erhalten (g Salz)	$[\alpha]_D^{20}$ ($c \sim 1,0$) Salz (in $CHCl_3$)	Säure (in Äthanol)
Carbonsäure **2 a** (Brucinsalz aus Äthanol—H_2O, 2 : 1)				
9,8	30	5,2	— 82,1°	— 137,5°
5,2	9	4,2	— 113,3°	— 182,0°
4,0	9	3,5	— 108,3°	— 185,0°[a]
Carbonsäure **2 b** (wie bei **2 a**)				
5,4	15	2,4	+ 8,8°	+ 35,6°
2,4	12	2,0	+ 19,9°	+ 42,0°
1,9	12	1,4	+ 38,6°	+ 74,7°
1,4	9	1,1	+ 39,0°	+ 76,0°[a]
Ketosäure **8 b** (Cinchonidinsalz, wie bei **2 a**)				
3,0	24	1,5	— 100,8°	— 56,1°
1,5	15	1,3	— 104,5°	— 68,0°
1,2	12	1,0	— 110,5°	— 79,3°
0,9	10	0,88	— 109,6°	— 82,0°[a]

[a] Schmp.: 200—201° (**2 a**); 229° (**2 b**); 102° (**8 b**).

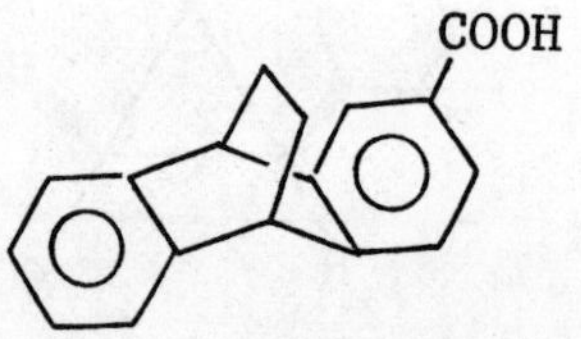

$C_{17}H_{14}O_2$ Ref. 1212

2 b: Die Salze wurden aus 2,1 g (8,4 mMol) racem. **2 b**[8] und 3,32 g (8,4 mMol) wasserfr. Brucin durch kurzes Erhitzen und Kühlen einer Lösung in 10 ml 96proz. Äthanol und 5 ml Wasser erhalten. Nach 10 Tagen wurde abfiltriert und weiter wie bei **2 a** behandelt. Die Kristallisation erfolgte, wie in Tab. 3 angegeben.

For Tabelle 3, see Ref. 1211.

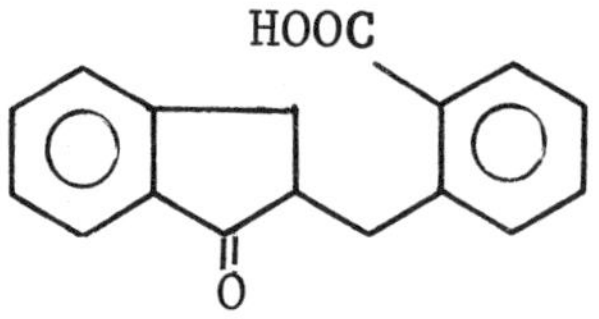

$C_{17}H_{14}O_3$ Ref. 1213

1,13 g de brucine et 756 mg de **5a** racémique sont dissous dans 10 cm³ d'acétone en présence de traces d'eau. On obtient 1,75 g de sel cristallisé. L'acide est libéré de son sel dans $CHCl_3$ par SO_4H_2 2,5 N : $+ 60° < [\alpha]_J^{21} < + 73°$. Si on fait le sel de brucine en solution 2 fois plus diluée, le rendement en sel est de 50 % mais le pouvoir rotatoire de **5a** est alors $[\alpha]_J^{22} = + 84°$, $[\alpha]_{546}^{22} = +93°$, $[\alpha]_{436}^{22} = + 160°$ (C = 2,8, $CHCl_3$).

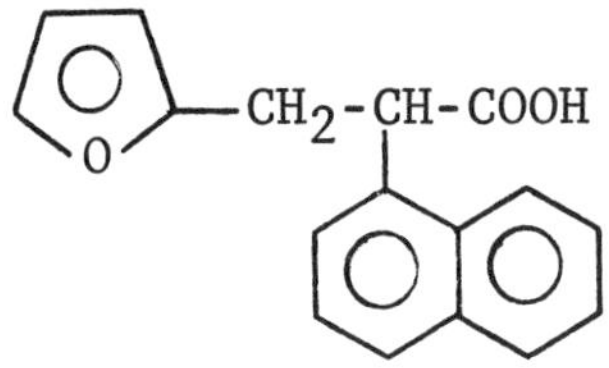

$C_{17}H_{14}O_3$ Ref. 1214

Sel d'éphédrine de l'acide (—) *α-(naphtyl-1) furylpropionique* (n° 24) :

$C_{27}H_{29}NO_4$ P.M. = 431,50

On place dans un ballon muni d'un réfrigérant à reflux :

200 cm³ de potasse alcoolique N/2 $\left(\text{contenant } 5{,}6\,g = \frac{\text{mol}}{10}\ KOH\right)$

22 g $\left(\frac{\text{mol}}{10}\right)$ de chlorhydrate d'éphédrine.

La solution est portée à l'ébullition et on y introduit, à l'aide d'une ampoule à brome : 26,7 g $\left(\frac{\text{mol}}{10}\right)$ acide (±) α-(naphtyl-1) furylpropionique en solution dans 100 cm³ d'alcool.

Le mélange, contenant un dépôt solide, est chauffé à reflux pendant 15 mn. Essorage à chaud dans un ballon, sur un büchner chauffé par circulation d'eau chaude.

Le chlorure de potassium formé (7 g; quantité théorique : 7,45 g) reste sur le büchner. On le lave avec 50 cm³ d'alcool.

Le filtrat est concentré sous vide à un volume de 100 cm³. On le transvase dans un bécher et on l'abandonne à la température ambiante, en grattant les parois du récipient avec une baguette de verre de temps en temps. Au bout de 2 h, déjà la masse se solidifie. On laisse le produit brun à la température du laboratoire pendant la nuit, puis on l'essore. Lavage à l'acétate d'éthyle glacé. Séchage sous vide.

Rdt = 14 g = 65 % (Rdt th. = 21,5 g).

Cristaux blancs. F = 132-134° (tube capillaire).

$[\alpha]_D^{28} = - 75{,}6°$ ($\alpha = - 1{,}11°$; l = 2 dm; c = 0,734; solvant = alcool).

Après deux à trois recristallisations dans de l'acétate d'éthyle (100 cm³ ≠ pour 10 g de produit), le sel est analytiquement pur.

F = 146,5-147° (tube capillaire).

Cristaux blancs. $[\alpha]_D^{27} = - 96{,}4° \pm 1{,}5°$.

($\alpha = - 1{,}5°$; l = 2 dm; c = 0,778; solvant = alcool).

Acide (—) *α-(naphtyl-1) furylpropionique* (n° 3) :

$C_{17}H_{14}O_3$ P.M. = 266,28

On place dans un ballon muni d'un agitateur mécanique et d'un réfrigérant à reflux :

32 g $\left(\frac{\text{mol}}{13{,}5}\right)$ de sel d'éphédrine de l'acide (—) α-(naphtyl-1) furylpropionique,

500 cm³ d'eau, et 200 cm³ HCl conc.

On chauffe au bain-marie bouillant, sous bonne agitation, pendant 1 h. Dès le début du chauffage, l'acide lévogyre se sépare, sous forme d'une huile jaune.

La réaction terminée, la couche aqueuse contenant du chlorhydrate d'éphédrine est décantée, l'huile restant est lavée plusieurs fois à l'eau dans le ballon même. Puis on l'extrait au benzène. Séchage sur SO_4Na_2. Le benzène est évaporé sous vide, sans chauffage. Le produit reste sous vide jusqu'à poids constant.

On obtient :

17 g de produit solide jaune. F = 48-52°.

Rdt = 86,5 % (Rdt th. = 19,7 g).

$[\alpha]_D^{28} = - 148°$ ($\alpha = - 3{,}224°$; l = 2 dm; c = 1,089 2; solvant = alcool).

Ce produit peut être purifié par dissolution dans une lessive de carbonate de soude, suivie de précipitation à l'HCl. En subissant ce traitement, le point de fusion du produit s'élève de quelques degrés, mais sa pureté optique ne s'améliore plus.

Purification :

On dissout 5 g $\left(\frac{\text{mol}}{53}\right)$ acide (—) α-(naphtyl-1) furylpropionique obtenu ci-dessus, dans une lessive contenant 2 g $\left(\frac{\text{mol}}{53}\right)$ CO_3Na_2 dans une centaine de cm³ d'eau.

La dissolution est lente. En employant la quantité stœchiométrique de CO_3Na_2, elle est incomplète. Le mélange est agité doucement, à l'aide d'un agitateur mécanique.

La solution orange filtrée est additionnée de quelques morceaux de glace. On y ajoute, goutte à goutte, à l'aide d'une ampoule à brome, de l'HCl 1/2, jusqu'à acidité au papier rouge Congo (10 cm³).

Dès la première goutte d'acide, des cristaux précipitent. Au bout de 10 mn environ, le solide est essoré, lavé abondamment à l'eau et est séché sous vide, sur P_2O_5.

5 g de solide ocre. Rdt = quantitatif. F = 50-52°.

$[\alpha]_D^{21} = - 150{,}8° \pm 2°$ ($\alpha = - 3{,}02°$; c = 1,006; l = 2 dm; solvant = alcool).

En répétant cette opération, le produit purifié possède les constantes ci-dessous :

F = 57-59°.

$[\alpha]_D^{22} = - 150° \pm 2°$ ($\alpha = - 2{,}1°$; l = 2 dm; c = 0,698; solvant = alcool).

Le résultat d'une troisième purification ne se répercute que très légèrement sur le point de fusion : F = 58-59°, le pouvoir rotatoire demeure inchangé. Le produit s'obtient donc, dès le premier traitement, optiquement pur.

Le chlorhydrate d'éphédrine peut être récupéré, pour ainsi dire quantitativement, par évaporation sous vide des eaux chlorhydriques ayant servi à décomposer le sel d'éphédrine de l'acide (—) α-(naphtyl-1) furylpropionique et peut être réutilisé pour une nouvelle opération.

Il est à noter, pour la caractérisation de ce produit, que l'on peut distiller sous racémisation partielle.

$Eb_{1,5}$ = 193-195° (72 % de pureté optique, $[\alpha]_D^{26} = - 108°$).

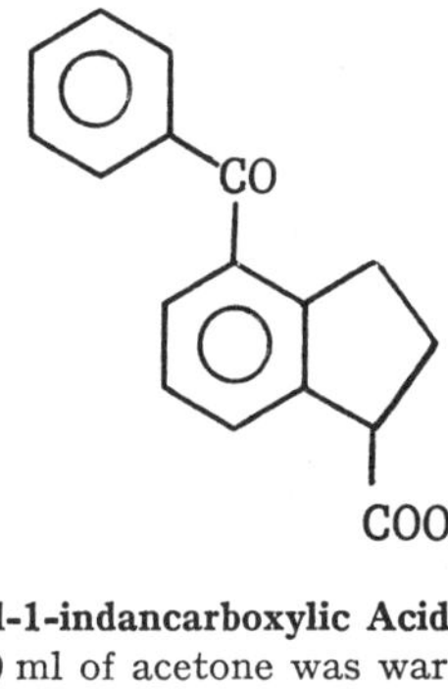

$C_{17}H_{14}O_3$ Ref. 1215

Optical Resolution of 4-Benzoyl-1-indancarboxylic Acid (Ia)——a) (*S*)-*l*-Ia: A suspension of 3.20 g of Ia and 1.76 g of cinchonidine in 60 ml of acetone was warmed to give a clear solution. The solution was allowed to stand overnight at room temperature. The resulting precipitate was collected by filtration and recrystallized twice from acetone to give 1.17 g (34%) of the cinchonidine salt of (*S*)-*l*-Ia as colorless crystals,

mp 189—192°. *Anal.* Calcd. for $C_{36}H_{36}N_2O_4$: C, 77.12; H, 6.47; N, 5.00. Found: C, 77.18; H, 6.28; N, 4.91. $[\alpha]_D^{22}$ −132.2° (*c*=1, $CHCl_3$). This salt (1.15 g) was dissolved in 115 ml of $CHCl_3$. The solution was washed twice with 50 ml of 1 N HCl and water, dried over anhydrous $MgSO_4$ and concentrated under reduced pressure to give (*S*)-*l*-Ia as an oil in a quantitative yield. *Anal.* Calcd. for $C_{17}H_{14}O_3$: C, 76.67; H, 5.30. Found: C, 76.45; H, 5.37. $[\alpha]_D^{22}$ −66.4° (*c*=1, MeOH). The NMR spectrum was identical with that of the racemic compound.[4]

b) (*R*)-*d*-Ia: The mother liquor of the crude cinchonidine salt of *l*-Ia in a) was concentrated under reduced pressure. The residue and 1.70 g of cinchonidine were dissolved in 120 ml of CH_3CN by warming. The clear solution was allowed to stand overnight at room temperature. The precipitate was collected and recrystallized three times from CH_3CN to give 1.23 g (35%) of the cinchonidine salt of (*R*)-*d*-Ia as colorless crystals, mp 179—182°. *Anal.* Calcd. for $C_{36}H_{36}N_2O_4$: C, 77.12; H, 6.47; N, 5.00. Found: C, 77.15; H, 6.42; N, 4.72. $[\alpha]_D^{22}$ +11.2° (*c*=1, $CHCl_3$). Treatment of this salt with 1 N HCl in the similar manner to a) gave (*R*)-*d*-Ia as an oil in a quantitative yield. *Anal.* Calcd. for $C_{17}H_{14}O_3$: C, 76.67; H, 5.30. Found: C, 76.53; H, 5.30. $[\alpha]_D^{22}$ +66.4° (*c*=1, MeOH). The NMR spectrum was identical with that of the racemic compound.[4]

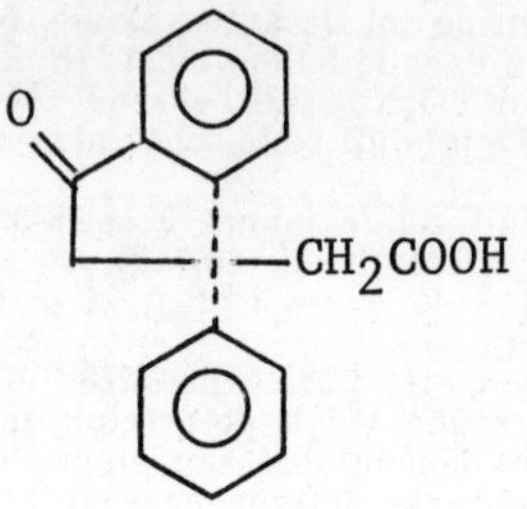

$C_{17}H_{14}O_3$ Ref. 1216

Resolution of 3-Carboxymethyl-3-phenyl-1-indanone (3a and 3b). A solution of 6.1 g (18.8 mmol) of quinine in 150 ml of dry methyl ethyl ketone (MEK) was heated to reflux and treated with 5.0 g (18.8 mmol) of 3-carboxymethyl-3-phenyl-1-indanone. The salt which crystallized after 48 hr at 24° was collected, mp 187.5–192.0°, $[\alpha]^{25}D$ −79.8° (*c* 2.3396, $CHCl_3$). An ether suspension of 0.2 g of this salt was extracted with 10% hydrochloric acid. The ether solution was dried (Na_2SO_4) and concentrated under reduced pressure to yield 0.062 g of acid, mp 164.0–164.3°, $[\alpha]^{25}D$ +69.8° (*c* 0.6188, $CHCl_3$). The rest of the salt was repeatedly recrystallized from 75 ml of fresh MEK. While the melting point of the salt gradually rose to 196.0–196.5°, its specific rotation varied erratically between −70.9 and −87.1°. A portion of each crop of salt was cleaved and the acid recovered. After three recrystallizations of the salt, the melting point of the recovered acid had risen to 165.5–166.0° and the specific rotation had risen to +80.7° (*c* 1.3410, $CHCl_3$). After a total of eight recrystallizations, the salt was cleaved and the resulting acid recrystallized from $CHCl_3$ to yield 1.07 g (21.4%) of (*R*)-(+)-3-carboxymethyl-3-phenyl-1-indanone (**3b**), mp 165.5–166.0°, $[\alpha]^{25}D$ +80.5° (*c* 0.6390, $CHCl_3$).

Subsequently, 23.3 g (87.6 mmol) of racemic acid and 28.4 g (87.6 mmol) of quinine were mixed in 600 ml of MEK which was heated at reflux. The crystals that formed after 48 hr were collected, cleaved, and recrystallized from $CHCl_3$–CCl_4 to yield 5.47 g (20.6 mmol, 23.4%) of acid, $[\alpha]^{26}D$ +79.8° (*c* 1.2886, $CHCl_3$) which rose to +80.7° after a single recrystallization of the partially resolved acid from $CHCl_3$–CCl_4. The crystalline salt which formed in the original mother liquor after a total of 6 days at 24° was similarly collected, cleaved, and recrystallized to yield 3.23 g (1.21 mmol, 13.9%) of (*S*)-(−)-3-carboxymethyl-3-phenyl-1-indanone (**3a**), $[\alpha]^{26}D$ −80.4° (*c* 1.1422, $CHCl_3$) which similarly rose to 80.7° after a single recrystallization. The ir and nmr spectra of (*R*)-(+)-3-carboxymethyl-3-phenyl-1-indanone were identical with those for racemic material. Uv, see Table II; $[\alpha]^{26}D$ +77.4° (*c* 0.6948, CH_3OH); ORD (*c* 1.92 × 10^{-3}, CH_3OH) [M] (nm) +970 (400), 0 (357), +20,620 (305), 0 (290), −8310 (277), −5540 (272.5), −7630 (296), −4850 (265), −6690 (262), −5960 (258), −5540 (252.5), −7070 (245), −47,100 (227), 0 (218), +37,380 (214), 0 (209); CD (*c* 1.92 × 10^{-3}, CH_3OH) [θ] (nm) 0 (400), −2830 (338), −5870 (327), 0 (310), +23,100 (295), +7400 (275), +9360 (270), +6310 (267), +9360 (263), +6970 (259), +12,390 (235), 0 (228), −54,400 (220), 0 (213), +40,900 (212).

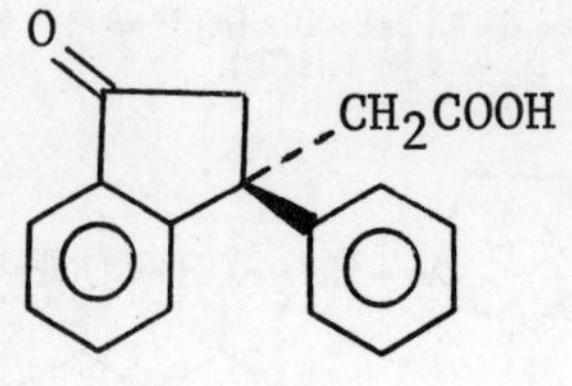

$C_{17}H_{14}O_3$ Ref. 1217

Resolution of 3-Carboxymethyl-3-phenyl-1-indanone. A mixture of 30.0 g of 3-carboxymethyl-3-phenyl-1-indanone and 44.6 g of brucine was dissolved in 800 ml of boiling methanol. On allowing to stand overnight the solution deposited 31.1 g of fine colorless leaflets. Three recrystallizations of this salt gave material of constant melting point (117–118°) and constant rotation, $[\alpha]^{25}D$ −23.2° (*c* 1.1, $CHCl_3$).

The brucine salt was stirred into excess 5% sodium hydroxide solution and the recovered brucine extracted into chloroform. The remaining aqueous solution was acidified and extracted with ether. Concentration of the dried extracts and crystallization of the residue from benzene–pentane afforded 10.2 g (68% of one enantiomer) of (*R*)-(+)-3-carboxymethyl-3-phenyl-1-indanone (**12**), mp 160°, $[\alpha]^{25}D$ +85.3° (*c* 1.6, $CHCl_3$).

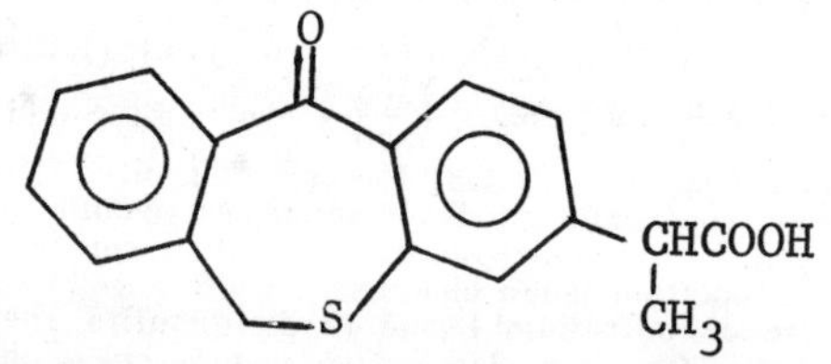

$C_{17}H_{14}O_3S$ Ref. 1218

Resolution of *dl*-2-(6,11-Dihydro-11-oxodibenzo[*b,e*]thiepin-3-yl)propionic Acid. Thionyl chloride (5 mL) and dimethylformamide (3 drops) were added in succession to a solution of the racemic acid (5 g, 0.016 mol) in benzene (50 mL). After 1.5 h at room temperature, the solution was evaporated; the residue was dissolved in benzene (50 mL) and concentrated in vacuo once again. The residual oily acid chloride was dissolved in acetonitrile (250 mL) and *l*-1-phenylethylamine (10 mL) and triethylamine (6.5 mL) were added. After 2 h at room temperature the solution was diluted with water (750 mL) and extracted with ethyl acetate (400 mL). The extract was washed with water, dried, and evaporated in vacuo. The residue was subjected to column chromatography on silica gel (400 g) using benzene–ethyl acetate (10:1) as the eluting solvent. The less polar *l*-2-(6,11-dihydro-11-oxodibenzo[*b,e*]thiepin-3-yl)propionic acid *l*-1-phenylethylamide A (3.3 g) had mp 162–163 °C (ethyl acetate) and $[\alpha]_D$ +16.4° (0.01 g/mL, $CHCl_3$), while the more polar *dl*-amide B (2.8 g) had mp 170–171 °C [ethyl acetate–hexane (1:2)] and $[\alpha]_D$ −1.4° (0.01 g/mL, $CHCl_3$).

A solution of amide A (3.0 g) in acetic acid (62 mL) and concentrated hydrochloric acid (9.3 mL) was heated at 87 °C for

8 h. The cooled solution was diluted with water and extracted with ethyl acetate (250 mL). The extract was washed with water and then extracted with aqueous sodium carbonate solution (250 mL, 0.5 M). The organic phase on evaporation gave the starting amide (1.06 g) which was subjected to the hydrolysis conditions described above (85 °C, 14 h). The aqueous sodium carbonate extracts were made acidic with hydrochloric acid and the product was taken up in ethyl acetate. The dried extract on evaporation gave an oil (2.2 g) which was dissolved in 2-propanol (10 mL). *l*-Amphetamine (0.95 g) was added and the solution was cooled to −10 °C to give the crystalline amphetamine salt. The salt was collected by filtration and then shaken with aqueous hydrochloric acid (100 mL, 2 M) and ethyl acetate (100 mL). The organic layer was separated, washed with water, dried, and evaporated. The crystallization of the *l*-amphetamine salt and regeneration of the acid was repeated a further three times to give *d*-2-(6,11-dihydro-11-oxodibenzo[*b,e*]thiepin-3-yl)propionic acid (**56**) as a gum (1.65 g): $[\alpha]_D$ +37.2° (0.005 g/mL, $CHCl_3$).

The more polar amide B (2.64 g) was dissolved in acetic anhydride (111 mL) and acetic acid (21 mL) and the solution was cooled to 0 °C. Sodium nitrite (9.25 g) was added in four portions over a 1-h period. After 5 h at 0 °C and 17 h at room temperature, the mixture was stirred vigorously with water (250 mL) and ethyl acetate (100 mL) for 1.5 h. Additional water (500 mL) was added and the reaction mixture was extracted with ethyl acetate (400 mL). The extract was washed with water, dried, and evaporated to give a residue which was heated at reflux temperature in benzene (50 mL) for 1 h. The solution was cooled, washed with aqueous potassium carbonate solution (100 mL, 0.5 M), dried, and evaporated. The residue was purified by column chromatography on silica gel (100 g) using benzene as the eluent. Evaporation of the eluate gave 1-phenylethyl *l*-2-(6,11-dihydro-11-oxodibenzo[*b,e*]thiepin-3-yl)propionate (0.75 g) as an oil with NMR δ 1.29–1.52 (m, 6 H), 3.68 (q, 1 H), 4.02 (s, 2 H), 7.00–7.60 (m, 11 H), 8.16 (m, 1 H). A solution of the above ester (0.74 g) in benzene (10 mL) and trifluoroacetic acid (10 mL) was stirred at room temperature for 2 h. The solution was diluted with water (200 mL) and the product was extracted into ethyl acetate (200 mL). The extract was washed with water, dried, and evaporated to give the *l* acid **55** (0.51 g) as a gum with $[\alpha]_D$ −37.8° (0.005 g/mL, $CHCl_3$).

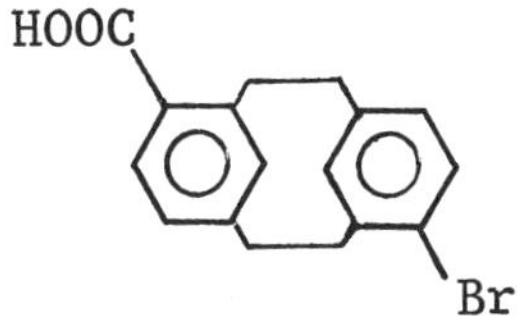

$C_{17}H_{15}BrO_2$ Ref. 1219

(−)- und (+)-12-Brom[2.2]metacyclophan-4-carbonsäure [(−)-**5a**] *und* [(+)-**5a**]: 265 mg (0.8 mmol) **5a** und 260 mg (0.8 mmol) Chinin wurden in Chloroform gelöst, vereinigt und dann zur Trockene eingeengt. Kristallisation aus Methanol ergab 200 mg des Chininsalzes mit Schmp. 140−145°C. Daraus wurde (−)-**5a** (80 mg) in üblicher Weise freigesetzt; $[\alpha]_D^{20}$ = −6.9° (c = 0.51%), $\Delta\varepsilon_{295}$ = −1.90, das entspricht einer optischen Reinheit von p = 100% [zur Korrelation mit (+)-**2h** s. unten]. — Das aus der Mutterlauge erhaltene (+)-**5a** (120 mg) zeigte $[\alpha]_D^{20}$ = +3.1° (c = 0.62%), $\Delta\varepsilon_{295}$ = +0.86, das entspricht p = 45%. — IR, MS und H-NMR identisch mit **5a**.

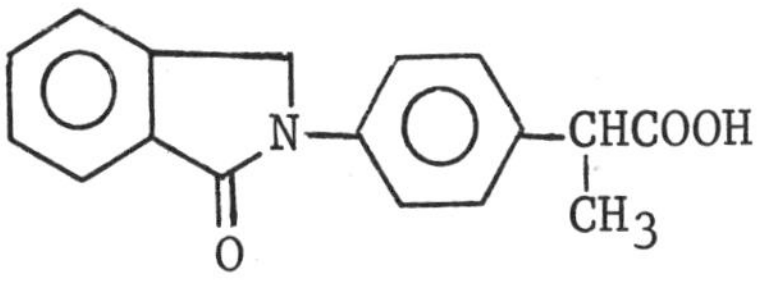

$C_{17}H_{15}NO_3$ Ref. 1220

A mixture of (±)-**1** (2.97 g.) and cinchonidine (3.11 g.) was dissolved in ethanol (70 ml.) by warming and the mixture was allowed to stand overnight. The resulting crystals were collected by filtration and recrystallized from ethanol to afford cinchonidine salt of (+)-**1** (2.45 g., 81%) as colorless scales, m.p. 205-207°.

Anal. Calcd. for $C_{36}H_{37}N_3O_4$: C, 75.10; H, 6.48; N, 7.30. Found: C, 75.28; H, 6.70; N, 7.01.

The ethanolic mother liquor during recrystallization was evaporated to give a solid, which was recrystallized from isopropanol to afford cinchonidine salt of (-)-**1** (1.2 g., 39%) as colorless scales, m.p. 176-177°.

Anal. Calcd. for $C_{36}H_{37}N_3O_4 \cdot H_2O$: C, 72.82; H, 6.62; N, 7.08. Found: C, 73.19; H, 6.65; N, 6.94.

(+)-2-[4-(1-Oxo-2-isoindolinyl)phenyl]propanoic Acid.

A suspension of cinchonidine salt of (+)-**1** (2.05 g.) in ethyl acetate (100 ml.) was washed with diluted hydrochloric acid and water. The organic layer was dried over sodium sulfate and evaporated to give a solid, which was recrystallized from isopropanol to afford (+)-**1** (0.78 g., 78%) as colorless scales, m.p. 205-207°, showing the nmr spectrum consistent with racemic **1**: $[\alpha]_D^{20}$ = +48° (c = 0.05, dimethyl sulfoxide, l = 0.1 dm).

Anal. Calcd. for $C_{17}H_{15}NO_3 \cdot 0.25\ H_2O$: C, 71.44; H, 5.47; N, 4.90. Found: C, 71.81; H, 5.30; N, 4.76.

(-)-2-[4-(1-Oxo-2-isoindolinyl)phenyl]propanoic Acid.

Under the same conditions as above, cinchonidine salt of (-)-**1** (1.2 g.) afforded (-)-**1** (0.5 g., 85%) as colorless scales, m.p. 205-207° (from 2-propanol), showing the nmr spectrum consistent with racemic **1**: $[\alpha]_D^{20}$ = -48° (c = 0.05, dimethylsulfoxide, l = 0.1 dm).

Anal. Calcd. for $C_{17}H_{15}NO_3$: C, 72.58; H, 5.37; N, 4.98. Found: C, 72.44; H, 5.36; N, 4.68.

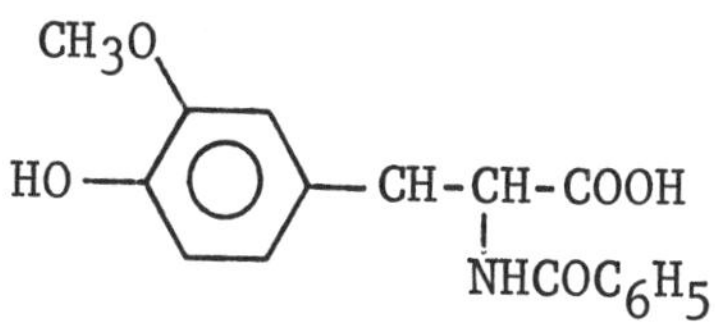

$C_{17}H_{16}NO_5$ Ref. 1221

EXAMPLE 4

31.5 g. of D,L-N-benzoyl-3-(4-hydroxy-3-methoxyphenyl)-alanine are dissolved in 50 ml. of methanol at 50° C. At the same time, likewise at 50° C., 14.2 g. of dehydroabietylamine (0.05 mole) are dissolved in 20 ml. of methanol. The methanolic dehydroabietylamine solution is poured into the acid solution and the flask rinsed with 5 ml. of methanol. After seeding, crystal-

lization of the dehydroabietylamine salt of the L-antipode occurs. The mixture is allowed to stand overnight at room temperature and the crystals are filtered off on the following morning. After rinsing with 50 ml. of methanol at 0° C. and drying in vacuum at 60°–70° C., there are obtained 18.8 g. of dehydroabietylamine salt of the L-antipode with the specific rotation $[\alpha]_D^{20}$ = +49.9° (c = 1 in methanol).

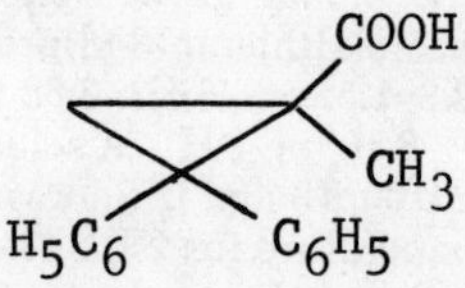

$C_{17}H_{16}O_2$ Ref. 1222

Note:

Resolved using brucine. Acid obtained had following physical constants: m.p. 190-191°, $[\alpha]_D^{23}$ +34° ± 1° (c 1.025, $CHCl_3$).

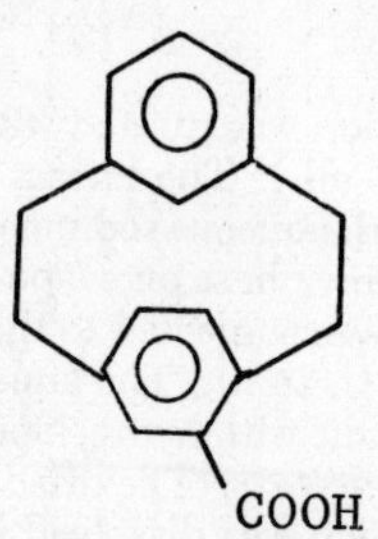

$C_{17}H_{16}O_2$ Ref. 1223

Resolution of 12-Carboxy[2.2]metaparacyclophane ((+)-IIb and (−)-IIb). Attempts to form a crystalline salt of the acid with quinine using either methanol or acetone were unsuccessful. A mixture of 2.0 g (7.95 mmol) of 12-carboxy[2.2]metaparacyclophane, 3.2 g (8.10 mmol) of brucine (mp 178–182°, recrystallized from acetone), and 200 ml of acetone was stirred to give solution. The solvent was then evaporated to give a glass. Addition of 10 ml of methanol to this glass forced most of the salt out of solution as button-shaped crystals. This salt was fractionally crystallized four times from methanol to give 1.5 g of salt, $[\alpha]^{25}_{546}$ −32.7°, $[\alpha]^{25}_{436}$ −61.7° (c, 1.07, $CHCl_3$). Since the rotation of the salt remained constant upon further recrystallization, it was converted to the free acid with 6 N hydrochloric acid (weaker acid was later found to give better yield) and ether. The aqueous phase was again extracted with ether. The ether extracts were combined, washed with water, dried ($MgSO_4$), and concentrated, and the acid crystallized from ether–pentane to give 450 mg (23%) of (+)-IIb: mp 167.7–169.7°; $[\alpha]^{25}_{546}$ 34.2°, $[\alpha]^{25}_{436}$ 116° (c 1.01, $CHCl_3$, unchanged by further recrystallization). A sample of less optically pure salt, $[\alpha]^{25}_{546}$ −34.8°, gave partially optically pure (+)-IIb, $[\alpha]^{25}_{546}$ 33.3° (c 1.02, $CHCl_3$), which had a low and broad melting point, mp 161–167°. *Anal.* Calcd for $C_{17}H_{16}O_2$: C, 80.92; H, 6.39. Found: C, 81.01; H, 6.31.

Crystals (0.78 g) of brucine salt formed in the mother liquor, which had a different shape, gave rotation $[\alpha]^{25}_{546}$ −34.5°, $[\alpha]^{25}_{436}$ −87.2° (c 1.09, $CHCl_3$). Recovery of acid with 1 N hydrochloric acid and ether as above gave 251 mg of (−)-IIb: $[\alpha]^{25}_{546}$ −31.7°, $[\alpha]^{25}_{436}$ −107° (c 0.99, $CHCl_3$); mp 158–168.8°. Crystallation gave fractionation yielding 70 mg of (−)-IIb: $[\alpha]^{25}_{546}$ −33.1°, $[\alpha]^{25}_{436}$ −112°, $[\alpha]^{25}_{365}$ −520° (c 1.04, $CHCl_3$); mp 165–167.5°. *Anal.* Calcd for $C_{17}H_{16}O_2$: C, 80.92; H, 6.39. Found: C, 80.70; H, 6.20.

$C_{17}H_{16}O_2$ Ref. 1223a

Racematspaltung von **6a**. — Eine Lösung von 600 mg (2.36 mMol) *racem.* **6a** in 5 ml Methanol wurde mit 290 mg (2.4 mMol) (+)-α-Phenäthylamin ($[\alpha]_D^{20}$ = +38°; p = 90%) versetzt. Die Mischung wurde i. Vak. eingedampft und der Rückstand mehrmals mit Wasser abgedampft. Man erhielt 800 mg Salz (Frakt. A), welches wie folgt umkristallisiert wurde:

Frakt.	mg	Salz Schmp.	$[\alpha]_D^{20}$	$[\alpha]_D^{20}$	Säure 6a $[\alpha]_{500}^{20}$	$\Delta\varepsilon_{295}$	p [%]	Salz umkrist. aus Methanol/ H_2O (ml)	erhalten Frakt.
A	800	135–161°	—	—	—	—		4 : 6 (10)	B
B	360	144–167°	+7.2°	−2.2° (A) −4.9° (C)	−6.2° (A) −10° (C)	+1.0	59	3 : 1 (4)	C
C	210	161–174°	+6.4°	—	—	+1.3	71.5	2 : 1 (3)	D
D	160	159–175°	+4.6°	—	—	+1.45	85	2 : 1 (2)	E
E	90	166–174°	+4.6°	—	—	+1.43	84	4 : 1 (1.6)	F

Aus der Fraktion F haben wir die Säure freigesetzt und aus Methanol umkristallisiert. Ausb. 60 mg (−)-**6a**; Schmp. 195°, $[\alpha]_D^{20}$ = −8°, $[\alpha]_{500}^{20}$ = −20° (c = 0.5, Chloroform), $\Delta\varepsilon_{295}$ = +1.53 (optische Ausbeute p = 90%).

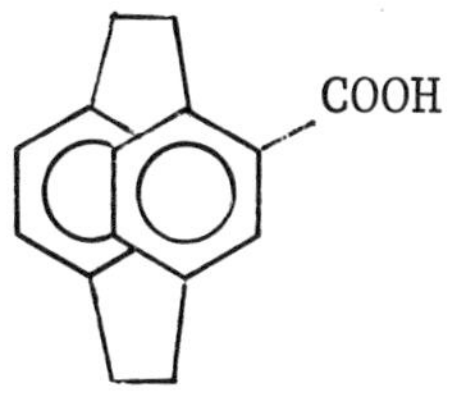

$C_{17}H_{16}O_2$ Ref. 1224

[2.2]*Paracyclophan-carbonsäure* (**1**). (Die Darstellung erfolgte nach[9]).

Phenäthylaminsalz. 1·01 g **1** (4·0 mMol) wurde zusammen mit 0·50 g (−)-α-Phenäthylamin (4·1 mMol) in 50 ml $CHCl_3$ gelöst. Der Abdampfrückstand kristallisierte nach Verreiben mit Äther: 1·450 g (98% d.Th.); Schmp. 134–155°; $[\alpha]_D$ +10·9° (*c* = 0·8; $CHCl_3$); (Gef: N, 3·70. Ber: für $C_{25}H_{27}NO_2$; N, 3·75%).

Racematspaltung von **1**:

mg Salz	aus ml Äthanol	mg Salz	$[\alpha]_D$	$[\alpha]_D$ der Säure **1**
1450	20	680	+87°	+140°
680	11	350	+97°	+164°
350	5	180	+97°	+164°
180	3	70	+97°	+164°

[9] D. J. Cram and N. L. Allinger, *J. Am. Chem. Soc.* 77, 6289 (1955).

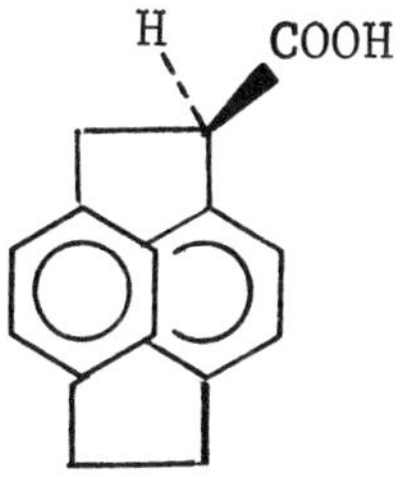

$C_{17}H_{16}O_2$ Ref. 1225

Note:

Resolved via its α-phenylethylamine salts to give acids, m.p. 187-188°, $[\alpha]^{25}_{546}$ -44.1° (c 0.54 $CHCl_3$) and m.p. 187-188°, $[\alpha]^{25}_{546}$ +42.0° (c 0.56 $CHCl_3$).

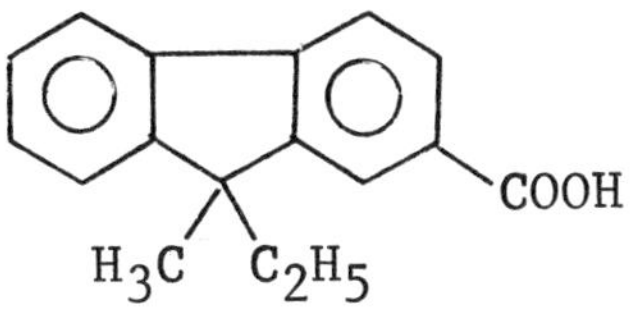

$C_{17}H_{16}O_2$ Ref. 1226

Dans le cas de l'acide 9,9-méthyléthyle-fluorènecarboxylique-2, les meilleurs résultats ont été obtenus lors de l'emploi de la cinchonidine et de la brucine pour séparer des énantiomères. La première de ces bases séparait l'énantiomère lévogyre, la seconde cependant — l'antimère dextrogyre. Les sels optiquement purs avait les propriétés physiques suivantes: le sel cinchonidinique — aiguilles, F. 115—117°, $(\alpha)^{20}_D$ = −77,77° (méthanol) et le sel brucinique — aiguilles, F. 121—122°, $(\alpha)^{20}_D$ = −9,16° (méthanol). Pour le dédoublement de l'acide 9,9-méthylepropyle-fluorènecarboxylique-2 on préférait également les sels avec la brucine et la cinchonidine. Le premier de ces sels, pendant la cristallisation de l'étanol dilué, dans les fractions moins solubles, séparait l'antimère lévogyre, tandis que le second dans l'acétone dilué isolait d'abord l'énantiomère dextrogyre. Les composès optiquement purs avaient les constants physiques suivantes: sel brucinique — aiguilles, F. 104—106°, $(\alpha)^{20}_D$ = −25,83° (méthanol); sel cinchonidinique — aiguilles, F. 169—170°, $(\alpha)^{20}_D$ = −47,50° (méthanol).'

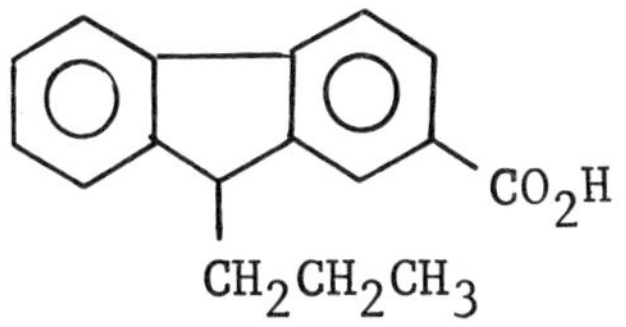

$C_{17}H_{16}O_2$ Ref. 1227

The authors reported that brucine was used to separate the (-) enantiomer (from either CH_3OH, acetone or an 8:2 mixture of acetone and chloroform. The physical constants of the brucine salt were found to be: m.p. 107° (dec.) (acetone), $[\alpha]^{20}_D$ -39.00° (CH_3OH). The liberated acid was found to have the following physical constants: m.p. 137-138° (ethanol), $[\alpha]^{20}_D$ -60.00° (CH_3OH). Cinchonidine was used to obtain the (+)-enantiomer (from either CH_3OH, acetone or 8:2 acetone/$CHCl_3$). The cinchonidine salt had the following physical constants: m.p. 183-184°, $[\alpha]^{20}_D$ -42.00° (CH_3OH). The liberated acid was found to have the following physical constants: m.p. 133-134°, $[\alpha]^{20}_D$ +57.70° (CH_3OH).

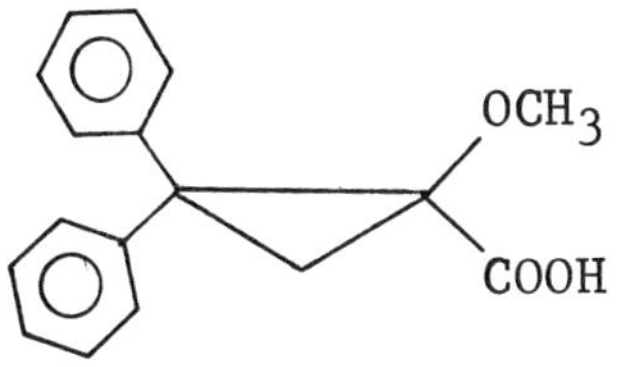

$C_{17}H_{16}O_3$ Ref. 1228

(+)-(*R*) and (−)-(*S*)-1-Methoxy-2,2-diphenylcyclopropanecarboxylic Acid. A.—A mixture of 13.4 g (0.05 mol) of (±) acid and 19.7 g of brucine was added to 500 ml of acetone and the mixture was refluxed for 1 hr. The hot solution was filtered and evaporated to one-half its volume, and water was added until the solution became slightly cloudy. The solution was allowed to remain overnight at ambient temperature. The first crop of crystals (15 g) was dried in a vacuum oven at 50° (12 mm). The dried crystals (12.1 g) were recrystallized twice from acetone to yield 8.1 g of brucine salt.

The brucine salt was dissolved in acetone, acidified with 30 ml

of concentrated hydrochloric acid, and diluted with water. The solid was filtered and recrystallized from chloroform–hexane (1:1) to yield 3.3 g of acid: mp 179°; $[\alpha]^{25}_{Hg}$ −84° (c 1.0, $CHCl_3$); ir and nmr were identical with those of (±) acid.

Anal. Calcd for $C_{17}H_{16}O_3$: 76.10; H, 7.31. Found: C, 75.81; H, 6.95.

B.—The combined filtrates from the above resolution were acidified with 30 ml of concentrated hydrochloric acid and diluted with water to yield 9.8 g of acid, $[\alpha]^{25}_{Hg}$ +12°. The partially resolved acid was added to 11.8 g of quinine dissolved in 500 ml of acetone. The solution was filtered and concentrated to one-half its volume, and water was added until the solution was slightly cloudy. After the solution had remained overnight at ambient temperatures, 10.4 g of quinine salt was obtained which after two recrystallizations from acetone and hydrolysis with hydrochloric acid gave 4.3 g of (+)-(*R*)-1-methoxy-2,2-diphenylcyclopropanecarboxylic acid. A further crystallization from chloroform–hexane (1:1) gave mp 179°, $[\alpha]^{25}_{Hg}$ +84.5° (c 1.0, $CHCl_3$).

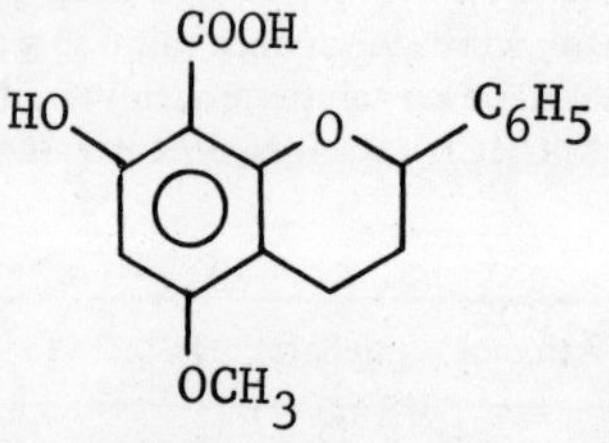

$C_{17}H_{16}O_5$ Ref. 1229

(−)-7-*Hydroxy-5-methoxyflavan-8-carboxylic Acid* (IV; R = H).—A solution of (±)-7-hydroxy-5-methoxyflavan-8-carboxylic acid (250 mg.) and brucine tetrahydrate (400 mg.) in a mixture of acetone (2 ml.) and methanol (15 ml.) was inoculated with a small crystal of the brucine salt of dracoic acid. 4 Hours later the product, which had separated in rosettes of colourless prisms (100 mg.), m. p. 134° (decomp.), $[\alpha]^{20}_{D}$ −46·3° (c, 0·95 in acetone), was collected and washed with methanol. Decomposition of this salt in acetone (5 ml.) with 2N-hydrochloric acid followed by the addition of water (5 ml.) gave (−)-7-hydroxy-5-methoxyflavan-8-carboxylic acid, m. p. 165°, which was esterified by diazomethane. Purified from methanol, this ester formed long, slender, colourless needles, m. p. 140°, alone or mixed with a specimen of methyl dracoate, $[\alpha]^{25}_{D}$ −74·0° (c, 0·19 in chloroform).

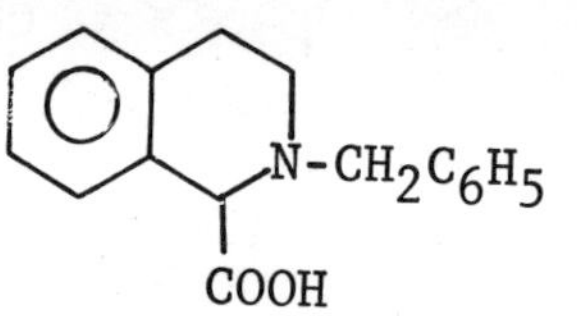

$C_{17}H_{17}NO_2$ Ref. 1230

EXAMPLE VII

Preparation of 1 - (−) - *N* - benzyl - 1,2,3,4 - tetrahydro - *iso*quinaldic acid.

Stage A:

Preparation of 1 - (−) - α - phenylethylamine salt.

5 g. of dl - *N* - benzyl - 1,2,3,4 - tetrahydro - *iso*quinaldic acid were introduced into 35 ccs. of ethanol, the resultant suspension was then taken to reflux, and 5 ccs. of 1 - (−) - α - phenylethylamine were added. The resulting solution was left to stand for about two hours, and the precipitate thus formed was filtered off under vacuum, washed with ethanol and then dried. The product thus obtained was purified by recrystallization from ethanol in the presence of 1 - (−) - α - phenylethylamine.

The 1 - (−) - α phenylethylamine salt of 1 - (−) - *N* - benzyl - 1,2,3,4 - tetrahydro - *iso*quinaldic acid thus obtained has a rotatory power of $[\alpha]_D^{20}$ = −92° ± 3° (c= 0.5%, pyridine).

To the best of our knowledge this compound has never previously been described.

Stage B:

Isolation of 1 - (−) - *N* - benzyl - 1,2,3,4 - tetrahydro - *iso*quinaldic acid.

The salt secured in Stage A above was dissolved in 10 volumes of an aqueous Normal solution of sodium hydroxide. The resulting solution was extracted with methylene chloride, then the aqueous phase was acidified by passing in sulphur dioxide. The precipitate thus formed was filtered off with suction, and after washing with water and drying, a yield of 0.5 g. of 1 - (−) - *N* - benzyl - 1,2,3,4 - tetrahydro - *iso*quinaldic acid, m.p.=218°C, $[\alpha]_D^{20}$ = −130° (c=0.5% pyridine), was obtained .

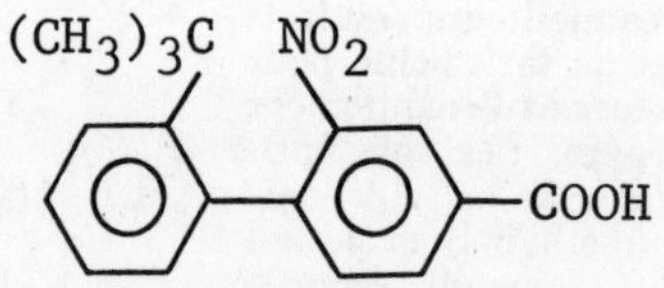

$C_{17}H_{17}NO_4$ Ref. 1231

Strychnine 6-Nitro-2′-t-butylbiphenyl-4-carboxylate.—All rotations were measured in chloroform at room temperature (c ~1·0) in 2 dm. tubes unless otherwise stated. The acid (4·5 g.) and strychnine (5·0 g.) were dissolved in boiling ethanol (250 c.c.) and kept overnight at +4°. The first fraction of salt separated (4·5 g.) in rectangular plates, $[\alpha]_{5791}$ +14·6°. Evaporation of the mother-liquor gave successive crops which had approximately the same specific rotation. A portion of salt, on decomposition, gave an acid of $[\alpha]_{5791}$ +33·4°. On one occasion only, a small amount of salt separated as fine needles from the (+)-acid salt mother-liquor. It had $[\alpha]_{5791}$ −19·1° and gave a (−)-acid. The (+)-acid salt was recrystallised three times from ethanol. *Strychnine* (+)-*6-nitro-2′-t-butylbiphenyl-4-carboxylate* crystallised in pale yellow

rectangular plates, m. p. 234—236°, $[\alpha]_{5791}$ +15·2°, $[\alpha]_{5461}$ +19·5° (Found: C, 71·7; H, 6·0. $C_{17}H_{17}NO_4,C_{21}H_{22}N_2O_2$ requires C, 72·0; H, 6·2%). In chloroform solution it racemised slowly at room temperature (14 days); the "partial racemate" had $[\alpha]_{5791}$ −2·8°, $[\alpha]_{5461}$ −4·1°. When the chloroform solution was boiled under reflux for 2 hr. racemisation was complete.

(+)6-*Nitro-2′-t-butylbiphenyl-4-carboxylic acid*, obtained by decomposition at 0° of the above strychnine salt, had m. p. 148—149°, $[\alpha]_{5791}$ +33·4°, $[\alpha]_{5461}$ +40·5° (Found: C, 68·4; H, 5·8. $C_{17}H_{17}NO_4$ requires C, 68·2; H, 5·7%).

Racemisation of (+)-*Acid*.—Racemisation of the (+)-acid in toluene was followed in a water-jacketed polarimeter tube thermostatically controlled, with the following results:

Temp.	51·0°	55·8°	60·5°	64·2°	70·1°	75·2°
10^3k (min.$^{-1}$)	3·47	6·31	9·49	15·2	28·1	47·8
Half-life (min.)	200	110	73·0	45·5	24·6	14·5

The activation energy was found to be 25·4 kcal. mole^{-1}.

$C_6H_5CH_2OCONHCHCOOH$
　　　　　　　|
　　　　　$SCH_2C_6H_5$

$C_{17}H_{17}NO_4S$ Ref. 1232

Trennung von rac. N-Benzyloxycarbonyl-thiobenzylglycin (**6b**). 1,90 g (6,5 mmol) Cinchonidin wurden in 12 ml heissem 2-Propanol gelöst. 2,10 g (6,5 mmol) rac. Säure **6b** wurden in 3 ml 2-Propanol gelöst, der Cinchonidinlösung zugegeben, auf Raumtemp. gebracht, mit 3 ml Wasser versetzt und über Nacht stehengelassen. Die Kristalle des Cinchonidinsalzes wurden abgenutscht und mit genau einem Äquivalent Natronlauge versetzt: durch Extraktion mit Methylenchlorid erhielt man Cinchonidin zurück, durch Ansäuern der wässerigen Phase mit Salzsäure und 2maliger Extraktion mit Methylenchlorid erhielt man die optisch aktive Säure.

2,10 g rac. Säure **6b**, 1,835 g (−)-Salz (Krist.), 1,90 g Cinchonidin, 2,113 g (+)-Salz (Mutterlauge).

816 mg (−)-*Säure* **6b**:

(−)-Säure: Smp. 112–118°. $[\alpha]_D^{25}$: −26° (c = 0,72, EtOH); 604 mg Cinchonidin (Smp. 192–198°).

878 mg (+)-*Säure* **6b**.

(+)-Säure: Smp. 112–118°; $[\alpha]_D^{25}$: +19° (c = 0,80, EtOH); 857 mg Cinchonidin (Smp. 192–198°).

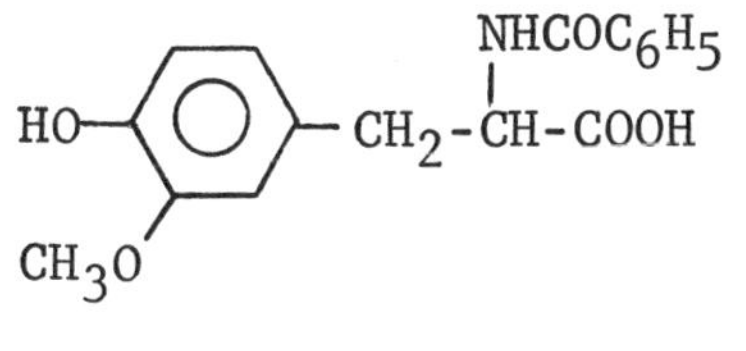

$C_{17}H_{17}NO_5$ Ref. 1233

Resolution of *d,l*-α-Benzamido-4-hydroxy-3-methoxydihydrocinnamic Acid (III)—Dehydroabietylamine (IV) (57 g., 0.20 mole) was dissolved in 450 ml. boiling methanol, and a small amount of mechanical impurity was removed by filtration. The solution was heated to boiling, and a solution of III (3) (63 g., 0.20 mole) in 160 ml. boiling methanol was added. The solution was boiled, and 113 ml. of boiling water was added (to turbidity). The mixture was allowed to cool gradually to room temperature and was stored at room temperature for 18 hr. The product was washed with two 125-ml. portions of methanol–water (4:1), air dried, and then dried at 60° to give 51 g. (83%) of the product, m.p. 223–224°; $[\alpha]_D^{25}$ +50.30° (concentration 1.91%, methanol). The analytical sample was obtained after three recrystallizations from methanol–water (4:1); $[\alpha]_D^{25°}$ +53.50° (concentration 1.97%, methanol).

Anal.—Calc. for $C_{17}H_{17}NO_5 \cdot C_{20}H_{31}N$: C, 73.87; H, 8.44; N, 4.66. Found: C, 73.97; H, 8.05; N, 4.66.

***l*-3,4-Dihydroxyphenylalanine (I)**—A 3-ml. portion of concentrated hydrochloric acid was added to a mixture of 3.85 g. (0.0064 mole) of the resolved salt of IV and III, 40 ml. water, and 40 ml. ethyl acetate. The organic layer was separated, and the aqueous layer was extracted with two 40-ml. portions of ethyl acetate. The combined organic layers were washed with 50 ml. water, dried (magnesium sulfate), and concentrated to dryness *in vacuo* to give 3.10 g. of the acid. To the acid was added 50 ml. 48% HBr. The mixture was stirred and refluxed for 2.25 hr. and then allowed to stand at room temperature for 15 hr. The solid was filtered and washed with two 5-ml. portions of 48% HBr. The fitrate and washings were combined and concentrated to dryness *in vacuo*. To the residue was added 10 ml. water and a few drops of sulfur dioxide–water. The solution was warmed, decolorized, and filtered. The filtrate was cooled, adjusted to pH 5 (pH paper) with concentrated ammonium hydroxide, and stored in the refrigerator for 2 days. The solid was filtered, washed with two 10-ml. portions of absolute ethanol, and air dried to give 0.52 g. (40%) of I; $[\alpha]_D^{25°}$ −11.15° (concentration 2%, 1 N HCl). An analytically pure sample of I was isolated from velvet bean extract by the literature method (4); $[\alpha]_D^{25°}$ (obs.): −11.62° (concentration 2%, 1 N HCl), (lit.): −12.0° (concentration 1%, 4% HCl). The product exhibited an IR spectrum identical to that of an authentic sample of I. Amino acid analysis indicated the purity of the product to be 97%.

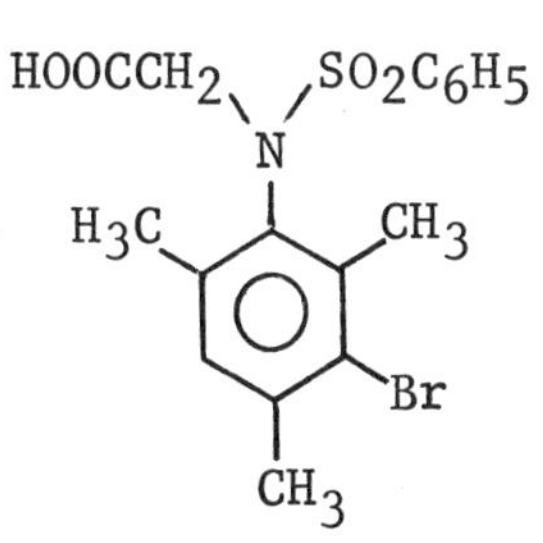

$C_{17}H_{18}BrNO_4S$ Ref. 1234

Resolution of N-Benzenesulfonyl-N-carboxymethyl-3-bromomesidine.—A solution of 5.0 g. of N-benzenesulfonyl-N-carboxymethyl-3-bromomesidine and 3.58 g. of cinchonidine in 80 ml. of ethyl acetate was filtered and then placed in a refrigerator overnight. Crystals weighing 2.00 g. were collected. Succeeding fractions were obtained as shown in the following table. The specific rota-

tion readings were taken by making 0.06 g. of the salt up to 20 ml. with absolute ethanol. A one-decimeter tube was used.

Crop, g.		α_D at 23°	$[\alpha]^{23}_D$	Vol. in ml.
I	2.00	−0.146°	−49°	80
II	1.31	− .137	−46	70
III	1.99	− .159	−53	25
IV	0.76	− .165	−55	15
V	0.77	− .171	−57	5
VI	0.21			0

Crops I and II containing 39% of the total amount present were recrystallized from 50 ml. of ethyl acetate. The following results were obtained.

Crop	Wt., g.	α_D at 23°	$[\alpha]^{23}_D$	Vol. in ml.
A	1.92	−0.147°	−49°	50
B	0.23	− .156	−50	40
C	.19	− .148	−49	20
D	.18			0

Crops A, B and C, having identical rotations, were accepted as the pure less-soluble salt (*l*B*l*A). It formed white feathery crystals, m. p. 136–137° (cor.).

Rotation. 0.06 g. made up to 20 ml. with absolute ethanol at 23° gave α_D −0.147°; *l*, 1; $[\alpha]^{23}_D$ −49°.

Anal. Calcd. for $C_{17}H_{18}NO_4SBr \cdot C_{19}H_{22}N_2O$: C, 61.19; H, 5.71. Found: C, 60.27; H, 6.17.

***d*- and *l*-N-Benzenesulfonyl-N-carboxymethyl-3-bromomesidine.**—The pure less-soluble salt (2.28 g.) was decomposed with cold 1:1 hydrochloric acid in the manner previously described. The product formed white crystals, m. p. 212–214° (cor.). The yield was 0.94 g.

Rotation. 0.203 g. made up to 20 ml. with absolute ethanol at 25° gave α_D −0.117°; *l*, 2; $[\alpha]^{25}_D$ −6°.

Anal. Calcd. for $C_{17}H_{18}NO_4SBr$: C, 49.53; H, 4.41. Found: C, 49.63; H, 4.22.

The more-soluble salt, crops IV and V, 1.34 g., was decomposed with cold 1:1 hydrochloric acid in the usual manner. The product melted at 211–214°. The yield was 0.54 g.

Rotation. 0.198 g. made up to 20 ml. with absolute ethanol at 27° gave α_D +0.111°; *l*, 2; $[\alpha]^{27}_D$ +6°.

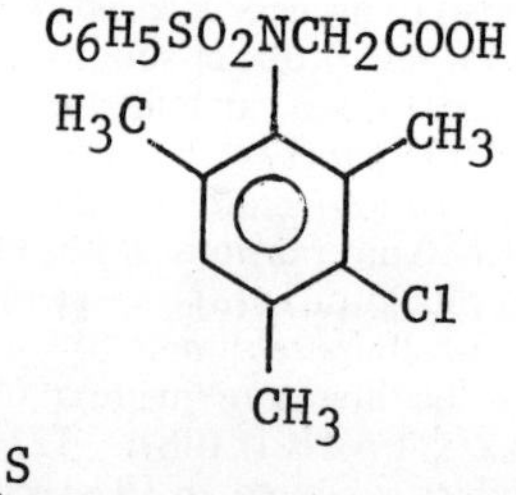

$C_{17}H_{18}ClNO_4S$ Ref. 1235

Note:

See Ref. 1239 for resolution procedure and physical constants.

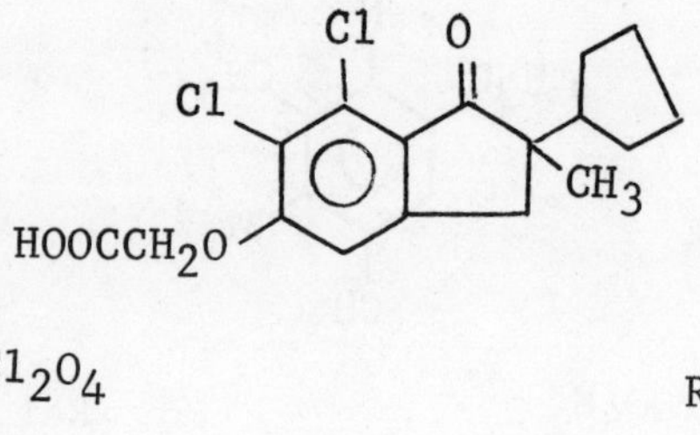

$C_{17}H_{18}Cl_2O_4$ Ref. 1236

Note:

The racemic acid was resolved via (-)-cinchonidine in ethanol-H_2O. The reported $[\alpha]^{25}_D$ for the active acid was +34° (c 3, acetone).

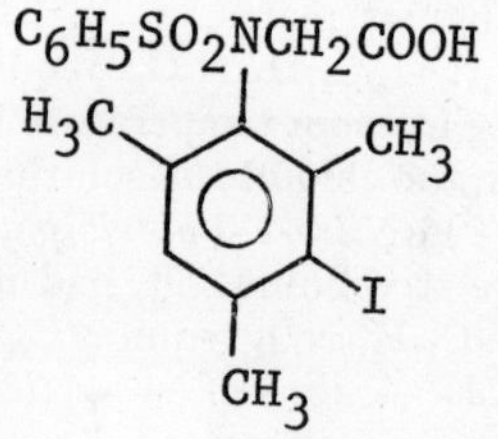

$C_{17}H_{18}INO_4S$ Ref. 1237

Note:

See Ref. 1239 for resolution procedure and physical constants.

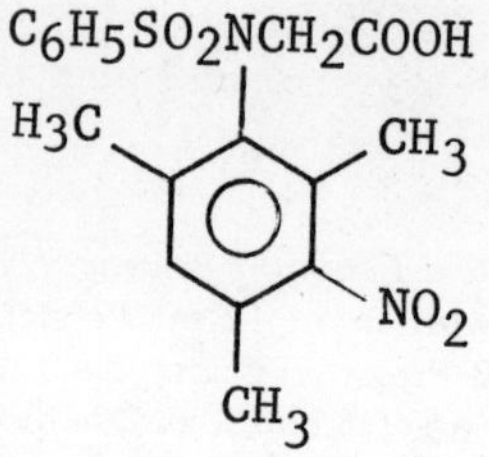

$C_{17}H_{18}N_2O_6S$ Ref. 1238

Resolution of N-Benzenesulfonyl-N-carboxymethyl-3-nitromesidine.—A solution of 5.0 g. of N-benzenesulfonyl-N-carboxymethyl-3-nitromesidine, 3.89 g. of cinchonine and 110 ml. of ethyl acetate was prepared by heating the mixture and filtering the hot solution. The solution was cooled for several days in a refrigerator, and large, pale green, rectangular prisms were deposited; 3.47 g., m.p. 207–209°, $[\alpha]^{24}_D$ +109.0° (ethanol). The filtrate was concentrated to 75 ml., seeded with the first crop, cooled for several days and a second fraction obtained; 3.62 g., m.p. 203–205°, $[\alpha]^{24}_D$ +98.7° (ethanol). The first fraction, $[\alpha]^{24}_D$ +109.0°, was recrystallized repeatedly from a mixture of ethyl acetate and methanol (3:1), with seeding of the solution each time with the immediately preceding crop until a constant rotation in the salt was achieved. The pure less-soluble salt amounted to 1.33 g., m.p. 215–216°, $[\alpha]^{24}_D$ +115.0° (ethanol).

The (+)-3-nitro acid was regenerated from the pure, less-soluble cinchonine salt in a manner described previously.[17] From 1.21 g. of the pulverized salt was obtained 0.61 g. (90%) of (+)-N-benzenesulfonyl-N-carboxymethyl-3-nitromesidine, m.p. 196–198° (resolidified and melted again at 224–225°); rotation: 0.0769 g. made up to 5 ml. with ethanol at 31° gave α_D +0.21°, *l* 1; $[\alpha]^{31}_D$ +13.7°; 0.1122 g. made up to 5 ml. with DMF at 31° gave α_D −0.15°, *l* 1; $[\alpha]^{31}_D$ −6.7°.

In a similar manner, recrystallization of the second fraction (3.62 g.) of the more soluble cinchonine salt, $[\alpha]^{24}_D$ +98.7° in ethanol, from an ethyl acetate–methanol mixture afforded 1.67 g. of the pure, more-soluble, feather-like crystalline salt, $[\alpha]^{24}_D$ +93.3° (ethanol). Regeneration of the acid in a manner just described afforded a comparable yield of (−)-N-benzenesulfonyl-N-carboxymethyl-3-nitromesidine, m.p. 199–200° (resolidified and melted again at 223–225°); rotation: 0.1225 g. made up to 10 ml. with ethanol at 25° gave α_D −0.14°, *l* 1; $[\alpha]^{25}_D$ −11.4°.

The resolutions of the other compounds in this investigation were carried out in a manner similar to that of the nitro compound just described; however, only the less-soluble salts were used. Details are summarized in Table V.

Racemization of (+)-N-Benzenesulfonyl-N-carboxymethyl-3-nitromesidine.—A dimethylformamide solution of 0.9756 g. of the (+)-3-nitro acid was made up to 10 ml. and the racemization carried out at 118° (boiling point of *n*-butyl alcohol) in a manner described previously.[2] The following results were obtained: 0.0 hr., α^{30}_D +0.23°; 0.5 hr., α^{30}_D +0.17°; 1.0 hr., α^{30}_D +0.14°; 1.5 hr., α^{30}_D +0.12°; 2.5 hr., α^{30}_D +0.09°; 3.5 hr., α^{30}_D +0.04°.[18]

A plot of α *vs.* time on semi-logarithmic paper afforded a straight line typical of a first-order rate equation from whose slope was derived the rate constant, $k = 2.4 \times 10^{-1}$ hr.$^{-1}$ and the half-life, $t_{1/2}$ = 1.5 hr.

TABLE V

RESOLUTION OF N-BENZENESULFONYL-N-CARBOXYMETHYL-3-SUBSTITUTED MESIDINES[a]

Sub-stituent	Alkaloid	Resolving solvent	Ml. of solv. per g. acid	Purif. solvent	Pure less-sol. salt m.p., °C.	Rotation in EtOH[b] Wt., g.	Vol., ml.	$[\alpha]_D$, l 1	t, °C.
NO_2	Cinchonine	AcOEt	22	AcOEt–MeOH (3:1)	215–216	.0557	20	+115.0	23
F[c]	Cinchonidine	AcOEt	20	AcOEt	125–138	.0387	5	− 60.7	27
	Cinchonine	AcOEt	23	AcOEt–MeOH (10:1)	201–202	.0579	5	+ 94.1	29
Cl	Cinchonine	AcOEt–MeOH (11:1)	22	AcOEt–MeOH (6:1)	198–200	.0596	5	+106.5	26
Br	Cinchonine	AcOEt	16	AcOEt–MeOH (15:1)	200–203	.0720	20	+100.0	23
I	Cinchonine	AcOEt–MeOH (7:1)	24	AcOEt–MeOH (2:1)	204–205	.0683	5	+114.2	28
NH_2	Optically active compound prepared by reduction of optically active nitro compound.								

[a] Only the less-soluble salts are described. [b] A 1-dm. tube was used in all cases. [c] Resolution of the 3-fluoro acid was attempted with both cinchonine and cinchonidine, but the regenerated acid showed no optical rotation, and all the salt fractions exhibited similar rotation. A check for mutarotation in the cinchonidine salt was negative. Cinchonidine salt: *Anal.* Calcd. for $C_{36}H_{40}FN_3O_5S$: C, 66.95; H, 6.24. Found: C, 66.75; H, 6.15.

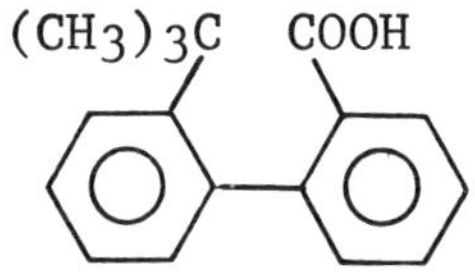

$C_{17}H_{18}O_2$ Ref. 1239

Strychnine salt. To a boiling solution of (±)-acid (5 g.) in ethanol (100 c.c.) strychnine (6·6 g.) was added. The salt which separated overnight at room temperature (8·0 g.) had $[\alpha]_{5791}$ −45·6°. Evaporation of the mother-liquor gave successive crops whose specific rotations were approximately the same as above. A portion of salt on decomposition gave an acid, $[\alpha]_{5791}$ −19·9°. When prepared in more concentrated solutions of ethanol the specific rotations of the salts were lower and acids were recovered whose specific rotations varied from $[\alpha]_{5791}$ −13·5° to −18·2°. Recrystallising the salt from ethanol gave erratic results because of dissociation into free acid and base; methanol was therefore preferred and recrystallisation from this solvent was continued until the specific rotation of the salt remained constant.

Strychnine (−)-2′-t-butylbiphenyl-2-carboxylate crystallised from methanol in sheaves of rectangular prisms, m. p. 208—212°, $[\alpha]_{5791}$ −49·9°, $[\alpha]_{5461}$ −58·6° (Found: C, 77·3; H, 6·8. $C_{17}H_{18}O_2,C_{21}H_{22}N_2O_2$ requires C, 77·5; H, 6·8%). When it was boiled under reflux in chloroform solution for 15 min. its specific rotation fell to $[\alpha]_{5791}$ −38·2° and $[\alpha]_{5461}$ −44·8°. This salt, the "partial racemate," was always recovered from rotation solutions when the chloroform was removed by heat or by slow evaporation. When the methanol mother-liquor from recrystallisations was allowed to evaporate slowly to dryness at room temperature the residual salt yielded acid of low rotation ($[\alpha]_{5791}$ −6·3°). All salts were decomposed in the usual manner with ice-cold sodium hydroxide solution. Addition of ice-cold acid to the alkaline solution (after extraction with chloroform) gave the free acid. The purest strychnine salt gave acid, m. p. 185—187°, $[\alpha]_{5791}$ −24·3°, $[\alpha]_{5461}$ −29·8°. Crystallisation from ethanol caused complete racemisation of the acid.

Brucine salt. The (±)-acid (1 g.) and brucine (1·44 g.) were dissolved in boiling ethanol (14 c.c.). After 2 days at 4° the first crop of salt separated (1·2 g.), having $[\alpha]_{5791}$ −23·9° and $[\alpha]_{5461}$ −29·7°. From the reduced mother-liquor a second crop separated with the same rotation. After recrystallisation from ethanol the rotation was unchanged. The acid recovered from the salt had $[\alpha]_{5791}$ +7·7°. The preparation of brucine salt was repeated twice, the rotation of the recovered acids being +3·3° and +5·1°.

Racemisation of (−)-acid. The rate of racemisation in boiling ethanol was measured for a solution (20 c.c.) containing 0·2268 g. of (−)-acid. The temperature was rapidly raised to the b. p. (79°) and after a suitable interval the solution was rapidly cooled to room temperature. Polarimetric readings were taken at 20°. The heating and cooling processes were repeated until racemisation was complete; α_{5791} (l = 2) fell from −0·39° to 0°. From a logarithmic plot, k was found to be 0·00207 sec.$^{-1}$ and the half-life 5·6 min. The racemisation of the (−)-acid in ethanol was also followed at 57° and 67° in a well-lagged water-jacketed polarimeter tube (l = 2) thermostatically controlled. The rate constants were found to be 0·00033 and 0·00082 sec.$^{-1}$, and the half-life periods 35 and 14·1 min. respectively. From these data the activation energy was found to be 24 kcal. mole^{-1}.

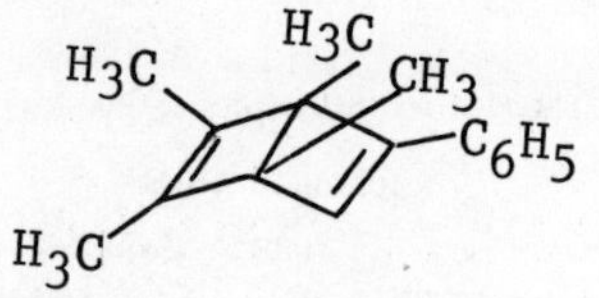

$C_{17}H_{18}O_2$ Ref. 1240

A solution of **1** (298 mg) in absolute alcohol (9 cm^3) was treated with a solution of 334 mg of (+)-dehydroabietylamine[7] ($[\alpha]^{20}_{405}$ +139.2°, *c* 9.7 in pyridine) in absolute alcohol (4 cm^3) and refluxed for 30 min. Water (4 cm^3) was added and the solution cooled overnight at −20° furnishing 290 mg of a white crystalline solid ($[\alpha]^{20}_{405}$ +47.5°), mp 93-101°. A further crystallization from 70% ethyl alcohol gave 149 mg of the diastereomeric salt ($[\alpha]^{20}_{405}$ +29.4°), which was decomposed by treatment with 2*N* hydrochloric acid, yielding 70 mg of (−)-**1**. The free optically active acid **1**[8] (with a superimposible ir spectrum with that of racemic **1**) showed an $[\alpha]^{20}_{405}$ of −61.5° (*c* 0.26 in absolute alcohol).

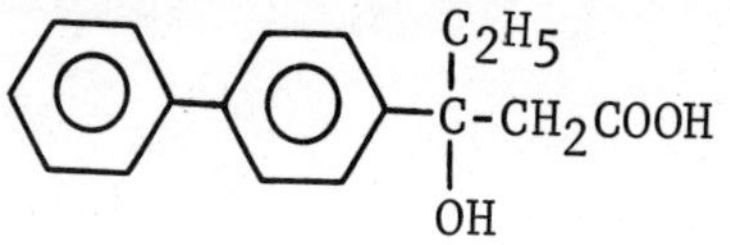

$C_{17}H_{18}O_3$

Ref. 1241

Note:

For resolution procedure and physical constants, see Ref. 1170.

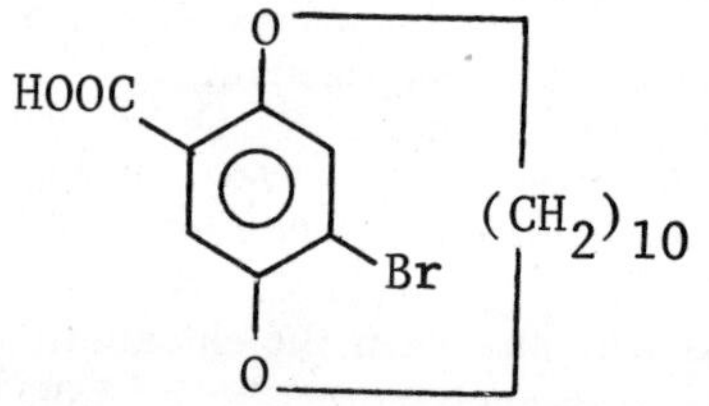

$C_{17}H_{23}BrO_4$ Ref. 1242

Spaltungsversuche über das Brucinsalz.

5,1 g rac. Säure kocht man mit 6,25 g Brucin in 25 ccm Alkohol bis zur Lösung. Die nach 2-tägigem Stehen ausgefallenen Krystalle schmelzen nach 2-maligem Umkrystallisieren aus Alkohol bei 103—105°.

Spec. Drehung: 34,0 mg Salz in 3 ccm Aceton,

$\alpha = -0{,}61°$, $[\alpha]^{17}_{D} = -55°$.

Weiteres Umkrystallisieren aus Alkohol veränderte die Drehung nicht. Die Analysenwerte des bei 77° i. V. über P_2O_5 getrockneten Salzes stimmen leidlich nur bei Annahme von je 1 Mol Krystallwasser und -alkohol.

4,543 mg Subst.: 10,035 mg CO_2, 2,71 mg H_2O. — 3,892 mg Subst.: 0,120 ccm N_2 (24°, 739 mm).

$C_{40}H_{49}O_8N_2Br + H_2O + C_2H_5OH$	Ber.	C 60,7	H 6,92	N 3,38
	Gef.	„ 60,27	„ 6,68	„ 3,44.

Die Zerlegung des Salzes durch Ausschütteln seiner Chloroformlösung mit verdünnter Schwefelsäure bis zum Ausbleiben der Brucinreaktion ergab eine Säure, die nach Umkrystallisieren aus Essigester-Petroläther und aus Eisessig sehr unscharf bei 113—145° schmolz und ihrer spec. Drehung nach noch optisch sehr unrein war.

Spec. Drehung: 348,0 mg in 3 ccm Aceton,

$\alpha = -2{,}71°$, $[\alpha]^{17}_{D} = -23{,}4°$.

Wiederverwandlung in das Brucinsalz, dessen weitere Umkrystallisation und Wiederzerlegung führte zu einer ebenfalls optisch noch sehr unreinen Säure mit $[\alpha]^{17}_{D} = -27°$ (1,2 Proc. in Aceton). Dagegen ließ sich die Säure über das Strychninsalz sofort in die scharfschmelzende, optisch reine (−)-Säure verwandeln. Ebenso ließ sich aus der ursprünglichen Mutterlauge des Brucinsalzes über das Cinchoninsalz leicht die reine (+)-Säure gewinnen.

Strychninsalz der (−)-Säure.

5,6 g der rac. Säure XIX kocht man mit 4,8 g (kleiner Unterschuß) feinst gepulvertem Strychnin in 60 ccm abs. Alkohol bis zur Lösung und engt auf etwa 20 ccm ein. Nach $1^1/_2$-tägigem Stehen beginnt die Krystallisation an angekratzten Wandstellen, um von da ab stets leicht zu erfolgen. Am zweiten Tag saugt man 4,5 g Salz ab; nach 2-maligem Umkrystallisieren aus Alkohol schmilzt es bei 138—140° und verändert bei weiterem Umkrystallisieren weder Drehung noch Schmelzpunkt.

Spec. Drehung: 34,6 mg Salz in 3 ccm Chloroform,

$\alpha = -0{,}67°$, $[\alpha]^{17}_{D} = -58°$.

5,28 mg Subst.: 12,425 mg CO_2, 3,17 mg H_2O. — 4,065 mg Subst.: 0.138 ccm N_2 (23°, 754 mm).

$C_{38}H_{45}O_6N_2Br$	Ber.	C 64,64	H 6,43	N 3,97
	Gef.	„ 64,19	„ 6,72	„ 3,88.

(−)-4-Bromgentisinsäure-dekamethylenäther.

Die Lösung von 4 g Strychninsalz in Chloroform wird mit verdünnter Essigsäure, zuletzt mit verdünnter Schwefelsäure und Wasser erschöpfend ausgeschüttelt. Man trocknet über Natriumsulfat, engt stark ein, gibt Ligroin zu und destilliert das restliche Chloroform heraus. Die nach Erkalten abfiltrierten Krystalle schmelzen, aus verdünntem Eisessig umkrystallisiert, bei 154°. Die Löslichkeitseigenschaften ähneln denen der rac. Säure.

Spec. Drehung: 32,3 mg Säure in 3 ccm Aceton,

$\alpha = -0{,}40°$, $[\alpha]^{17}_{D} = -37{,}2°$.

Die Drehungen bei anderen Wellenlängen sowie in anderen Lösungsmitteln bei gleicher Temperatur und einer Konzentration von etwa 3,5 Proc. gemessen, sind aus dem Diagramm im theoretischen Teil zu entnehmen.

4.73 mg Subst.: 9,53 mg CO_2, 2,65 mg H_2O. — 6,332 mg Subst.: 3,21 mg AgBr. — 7,6 mg Subst., in 115,7 mg Campher: $\Delta = 7{,}2°$.

$C_{17}H_{23}O_4Br$	Ber.	C 54,97	H 6,24	Br 21,54	Mol.-Gew. 371,1
	Gef.	„ 54,98	„ 6,27	„ 21,58	„ 365.

Cinchoninsalz der (+)-Säure.

Die Mutterlauge vom Strychninsalz wird nach dem Vertreiben des Alkohols in Chloroform gelöst und wie beschrieben zerlegt. Den krystallisierenden Rückstand der Chloroformschicht (2,3 g) bringt man durch Kochen mit 1,7 g (geringer Unterschuß) Cinchonin in 10 ccm Alkohol zur Lösung. Beim Abkühlen erfolgt rasch Krystallisation. Man beläßt über Nacht im Eisschrank und krystallisiert das Salz aus Alkohol und aus Chloroform–Essigester. Weiteres Umkrystallisieren verändert weder den etwas unscharfen Schmelzpunkt von 205—209°, noch die Rotation.

Spec. Drehung: 39 mg in 3 ccm Chloroform,

$\alpha = +1{,}92$, $[\alpha]^{17}_{D} = +147{,}6°$.

5,253 mg Subst.: 12,505 mg CO_2, 3,24 mg H_2O. — 4,248 mg Subst.: 0,167 ccm N_2 (24°, 754 mm).

$C_{36}H_{45}O_5N_2Br$	Ber.	C 64,93	H 6,82	N 4,21
	Gef.	„ 64,95	„ 6,90	„ 4,48.

(+)-4-Bromgentisinsäure-dekamethylenäther.

Das in Chloroform gelöste Cinchoninsalz wird durch Ausschütteln mit verdünnter Schwefelsäure zerlegt. Nach Verjagen des Chloroforms krystallisiert man aus Äther–Cyclohexan und aus verdünntem Eisessig um. Schmelzp. 154°, wie bei der antilogen Form.

Spec. Drehung: 37,6 mg Säure in 3 ccm Aceton,

$\alpha = +0{,}47°$, $[\alpha]^{17}_{D} = +37{,}5°$.

5,92 mg Subst.: 2,99 mg AgBr.

$C_{17}H_{23}O_4Br$ Ber. Br 21,54 Gef. Br 21,48.

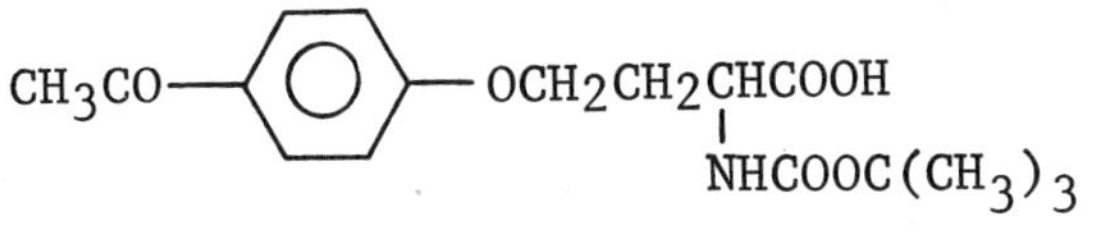

$C_{17}H_{23}NO_6$ Ref. 1243

Resolution of **18**. *dl*-Acid **18** (25.66 g, 0.076 mole) and cinchonidine (22.40 g, 0.076 mole) were dissolved in hot acetonitrile (600 ml) and the soln was allowed to stand overnight. The resulting crystals were filtered and further recrystallized four times from acetonitrile to give 13.6 g (56.7%) of L-acid **20** cinchonidine salt: m.p. 144–7° (dec); $[\alpha]_D$ −64.1° (c = 2.2, MeOH). The mother liquor was concentrated to about 300 ml and allowed to stand overnight. The crystals were filtered off and further recrystallized three times from acetonitrile to give 11.2 g (46.7%) of D-acid **19** cinchonidine salt: m.p. 130–3° (dec); $[\alpha]_D$ −77.5° (c = 2.0, MeOH).

D-Acid **19** cinchonidine salt (10.0 g) was dissolved in $CHCl_3$ and washed twice with 5% HCl aq. The organic layer was dried ($MgSO_4$) and evaporated to an oil, which was crystallized from ether-isopropyl ether to give 4.60 g (43% from *dl*-acid **18**) of D-acid **19**: m.p. 90–2°; $[\alpha]_D$ + 18.1° (c = 2.0, MeOH). (Found: C, 60.30; H, 6.97; N, 4.14. $C_{17}H_{23}O_6N$ requires: C, 60.52; H, 6.87; N, 4.15%).

L-Acid **20** cinchonidine salt (11.0 g) was treated as for D-acid **19** to give 5.70 g (51% from *dl*-acid **18**) of L-acid **20**: m.p. 90–2°; $[\alpha]_D$ −8.1° (c = 2.0, MeOH). (Found: C, 60.59; H, 7.03; N, 4.19. $C_{17}H_{23}O_6N$ requires: C, 60.52; H, 6.87; N, 4.15%).

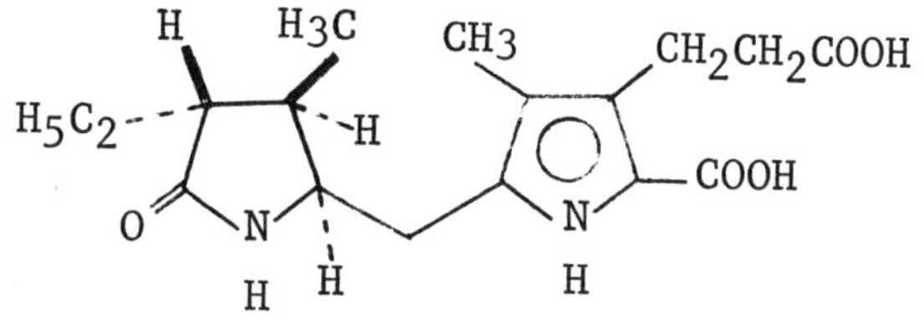

Ref. 1244

$C_{17}H_{24}N_2O_5$

(+)- und (−)-5'-Oxo-5-carboxy-4-[2-carboxyäthyl]-3.3'-dimethyl-4'-äthyl-2'.3'.4'.5'-tetrahydro-dipyrromethan-(2.2') [(+)- und (−)-**16**]. — Man löst 4.3 g (0.01 Mol) *Brucin*·$2H_2O$ in etwa 50 ccm Methanol und gibt unter Erwärmung 3.36 g (0.01 Mol) **16** portionsweise hinzu. Nach dem Lösen wird heiß filtriert und langsam abgekühlt. Es setzt allmählich Kristallisation ein unter Bildung von feinen, langen, verfilzten Nadeln. Nach 3 Stdn. bei 20° saugt man ab und trocknet über P_2O_5/Paraffin i. Hochvak.; Ausbeute 3.08 g (39%) *Brucinsalz*·$3H_2O$. Nach dreimaliger Umkristallisation des rohen Brucinsalzes aus Methanol ist ein konstanter Drehwert erreicht, der sich nach weiterer Umkristallisation aus Methanol, Äthanol oder Aceton nicht mehr verändert. Ausbeute 2.15 g (28%), Schmp. 149—150°. — *Spezif. Drehung* des Brucinsalzes in Methanol:

λ =	589,	578,	546,	436,	365
$[\alpha]^{20}_{\lambda}$ =	+57,	+58,	+67,	+120,	+216

$C_{40}H_{50}N_4O_9 \cdot 3H_2O$ (784.9)	Ber.	C 61.21	H 7.19	N 7.13	OCH_3 7.91
	Gef.	61.33	7.20	7.13	7.95

Man löst 2.15 g *Brucinsalz* in 20 ccm $CHCl_3$ und schüttelt zweimal mit insgesamt 30 ccm *2n NaOH* aus. Die alkalisch-wäßrige Phase wird nochmals mit $CHCl_3$ sowie zweimal mit Äther extrahiert und dann vorsichtig unter Eiskühlung mit *2n* H_2SO_4 angesäuert. Die positiv drehende *Dicarbonsäure* (+)-**16** fällt als farbloses Kristallpulver aus, das abgesaugt und gut mit Wasser gewaschen wird. Nach dem Trocknen über P_2O_5 erhält man 874 mg (26%, bez. auf eingesetzte racemische Säure) (+)-**16** vom Zers.-P. 182—183°. — Die Verbindung besitzt in Methanol bei 20° folgende *spezif. Drehwerte:*

λ =	589,	578,	546,	436,	365
$[\alpha]^{20}_{\lambda}$ =	+179,	+187,	+218,	+416,	+802

Die *Mutterlauge der Brucinsalz-Darstellung* wird i. Vak. eingedampft, der Rückstand mit Chloroform (30 ccm) aufgenommen und mit *2n NaOH* ausgeschüttelt. Die alkalische Phase wird nochmals mit $CHCl_3$ und zweimal mit Äther gewaschen und dann unter Eiskühlung mit *2n* H_2SO_4 vorsichtig angesäuert. Man erhält 1.03 g (31%, bez. auf eingesetzte racem. Säure) negativ drehende *Dicarbonsäure* (−)-**16** vom Zers.-P. 180—182°. — Die Verbindung besitzt in Methanol bei 20° folgende *spezif. Drehwerte:*

λ =	589,	578,	546,	436,	365
$[\alpha]^{20}_{\lambda}$ =	−103,	−109,	−125,	−234,	−450

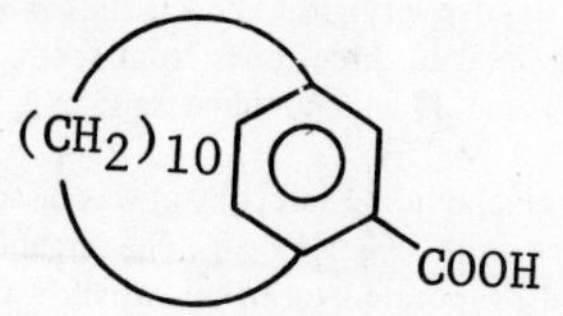

$C_{17}H_{24}O_2$

Ref. 1245

Resolution of the acid VI. A mixture of 0.2500 g. (0.00096 mole) of the acid VI and 0.2826 g. (0.0096 mole) of cinchonidine (Merck) in 30 ml. of acetone was warmed until solution was complete. The warm solution was filtered and reduced in volume to 15 ml. After standing at room temperature for 84 hr., 0.069 g. of a white solid, m.p. 147–151°, was filtered. The filtrate was reduced in volume to 5 ml. and, after standing at room temperature for 24 hr., 0.080 g. of a solid, m.p. 143–147°, was filtered. The two crops of solids were combined and after three recrystallizations from acetone showed constant m.p. 154–155° and unchanged optical rotation, $[\alpha]^{27}_{D}$ +22 ± 2° (*c* = 10 in chloroform).

Anal. Calcd. for $C_{36}H_{46}N_2O_3$: C, 77.93; H, 8.36; N, 5.06. Found: C, 78.15; H, 8.20; N, 5.03.

This solid salt was dissolved in 2 ml. of chloroform and 15 ml. of 5% hydrochloric acid added with vigorous shaking. The layers were separated and the chloroform solution dried with magnesium sulfate. The dried solution was evaporated at room temperature under a stream of nitrogen to give a white solid, m.p. 152–165°. After two recrystallizations from ethanol-water this solid gave (+) VI as fine white needles; m.p. 160–161°, $[\alpha]^{24}_{D}$ + 80.5 ± 2° (*c* = 0.77 in chloroform). Further crystallization did not change either the melting point or the optical rotation. The infrared spectrum of this (+) VI was identical with that of (±) VI.

Anal. Found: C, 78.50; H, 9.25.

The original mother liquor and filtrates from the recrystallization of the (+) acid (−) base salt were combined and evaporated to give a glassy residue. This residue was dissolved in 5 ml. of chloroform and treated with 20 ml. of 5% hydrochloric acid (vigorous shaking). From the separated and dried chloroform solution there was obtained a white solid, m.p. 150–188°, after evaporation of the solvent. This solid was dissolved in warm ethanol, water was added to the cloud point, and the solution then allowed to stand at room temperature until cool. The solid which separated was filtered and dried *in vacuo*. It showed m.p. 192–193° and $[\alpha]^{28}_{D}$ 0° in chloroform. The filtrate was cooled to 0° for 30 min., the crystalline solid filtered and recrystallized twice from ethanol-water. There was thus obtained (−) VI; m.p. 159–160°, $[\alpha]^{28}_{D}$ −82.3 ± 2° (*c* = 0.96 in chloroform). Another recrystallization of this (−) VI effected no further change in either the melting point or optical rotation. The infrared spectrum of this (−) VI was identical with that of (±) VI.

Anal. Found: C, 78.39; H, 9.31.

$C_{17}H_{24}O_2$

Ref. 1245a

*Racematspaltung zu (+)- und (−)-***5**: Eine Lösung von 1.0 g (3.84 mMol) *racem.* **5** in 20 ml Äther wurde mit 10 ml einer äther. Lösung von 0.50 g (4.13 mMol) (−)-α-Phenäthylamin ($[\alpha]^{20}_{D}$ = −39.3°) versetzt. Nach 15 Stdn. bei Raumtemperatur wurde das Salz abgesaugt, mit etwas Äther gewaschen und getrocknet. Ausbeute 1.46 g (100%); Schmp. 110–140°.

$C_{25}H_{35}NO_2$ (381.6) Ber. N 3.67 Gef. N 3.80

Dieses Salz wurde zweimal aus Äthanol umkristallisiert, wobei sich folgende Drehwertänderung ergab:

Salz [mg]	umkrist. aus ml	erhalten mg Salz	$[\alpha]^{20}_{D}$ für Salz (Äthanol)	Säure (−)-**5** ($CHCl_3$)
1460	10	899	−24°	−18°
899	5	549	−64°	−63°

Die aus der Mutterlauge mit verd. Phosphorsäure freigesetzte Säure wurde mit (+)-α-Phenäthylamin ($[\alpha]^{20}_{D}$ = +39°) in Äther in das Salz übergeführt und dieses aus Äthanol umkristallisiert, wobei sich folgende Drehwertänderungen ergaben:

Salz [mg]	umkrist. aus ml	erhalten mg Salz	$[\alpha]^{20}_{D}$ für Salz (Äthanol)	Säure (+)-**5** ($CHCl_3$)
500	3	434	+57°	+54°
434	3	374	+59°	+60°
374	2	337	+61°	+67°

Aus 1.0 g *racem.* **5** wurden dabei 353 mg (−)-**5** und 220 mg (+)-**5** erhalten. Die optische Reinheit (bezogen auf den Drehwert 80°)[9] betrug 79 bzw. 84%. — Die Massenspektren der aktiven Säuren **5** waren mit jenem von *racem.* **5** identisch.

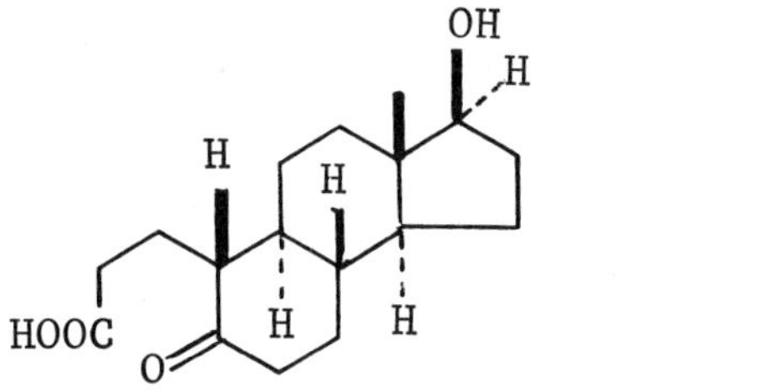

$C_{17}H_{26}O_4$ Ref. 1246

Resolution of (±) *17β-hydroxy-5-keto-3,5-seco-4-norestran-3-oic acid* (XIIIa) with (+) *amphetamine.* To a warm solution of 0.898 g. (0.00305 mole) of (±) XIIIa in 15 ml. of ethyl acetate was added a solution of 0.182 g. (0.00135 mole) of (+) amphetamine in 1 ml. of ethyl acetate. On cooling to room temperature, the reaction mixture deposited an oil. The solution was decanted, and on further standing at room temperature it afforded a colorless crystalline product. The product was collected, yield 0.109 g. (18.8% based on amphetamine used), m.p. 114.5–119°. Repeated crystallizations from ethyl acetate gave the (+) *amphetamine·*(−) *acid salt,* m.p. 124–127°; $[\alpha]_D$ + 0.5 ± 1.0° (1% water), peak, λ 308 mμ, $[M]_{308}$ + 3,800, trough, λ 270 mμ, $[M]_{270}$ −5,300, *a* +9,100 (methanol); infrared (potassium bromide) 3.02, 5.84, 6.08 μ. Its infrared spectrum was identical with that of the (−) amphetamine·(+) acid salt and differed considerably from that of the (+) amphetamine·(+) acid salt.

Anal. Calcd. for $C_{26}H_{39}O_4N$: C, 72.69; H, 9.15. Found: C, 72.65; H, 8.78.

A sample of the (+) amphetamine·(−) acid salt, m.p. 116–119°, was acidified with 6*N* hydrochloric acid. The mixture was extracted with ethyl acetate, and the combined ethyl acetate extracts were washed with water and a saturated solution of sodium chloride, dried over anhydrous sodium sulfate and evaporated to dryness to afford a brown oil. The oil was crystallized from acetone-ether-hexane to afford colorless dense crystals, m.p. 147–152°; peak, λ 310 mμ, $[M]_{310}$ + 3,500, trough, λ 265 mμ, $[M]_{265}$ −6,500, *a* +10,000 (methanol); infrared (potassium bromide) 2.93, 2.98, *ca.* 5.78, 5.88 μ. The infrared spectrum was found to be identical with the corresponding spectrum, determined in potassium bromide, of (+) XIIIa.

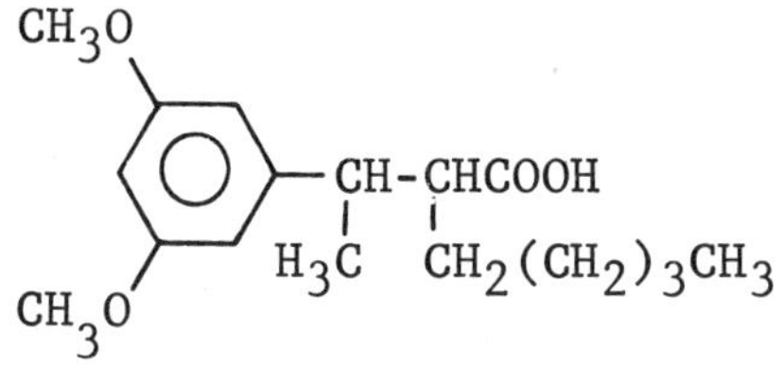

$C_{17}H_{26}O_4$ Ref. 1247

Resolution of *erythro* 12.—The (±)-*erythro* **12** was resolved with (−)- and (+)-α-methylbenzylamine.[15] The initial salt was prepared in ether (2–5 ml/1 g of salt), then recrystallized once or twice from ether (10 ml/g). The tail crop fractions were shaken with aqueous base and then acidified to obtain the free acid, which was resolved as above using the enantiomorphic amine. This process, twice repeated on an initial 35 g of (±)-*erythro* **12**, gave 9 g of the (+)-α-methylbenzylamine salt of (−)-*erythro* **12**, mp 96–98°, $[\alpha]^{28}D$ −21.8° (methanol, *c* 2), and 9 g of the (−)-α-methylbenzylamine salt of (+)-*erythro* **12**, mp 96–98°, $[\alpha]^{26}D$ +22.0° (methanol, *c* 2).

The resolved amine salts were dissolved in 2 *N* aqueous sodium hydroxide (10 ml/g), washed with ether and then petroleum ether, acidified, and cooled to give the free acids in essentially quantitative yield (see Table I).

Anal. Calcd for $C_{17}H_{26}O_4$: C, 69.36; H, 8.90; O, 21.73; neut equiv, 294.4. Found, (+)-*erythro* **12**: C, 69.0; H, 9.0; O, 21.5; neut equiv, 295.

(15) W. Theilacker and H. Winkler, *Chem. Ber.*, **87**, 690 (1954); A. Ault, *J. Chem. Educ.*, **42**, 269 (1965).

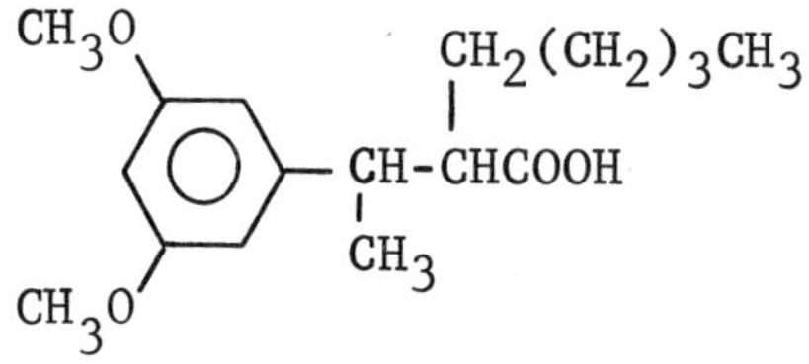

$C_{17}H_{26}O_4$ Ref. 1248

Resolution of *threo* 12.—The resolution of this acid with (−)- and (+)-α-methylbenzylamine proved to be difficult and tedious, and only a partial resolution was achieved. Ether was most conveniently used as the initial solvent. After a point, however, ethyl acetate had to be used to obtain further resolution. Thus, the (±)-*threo*-(+)-amine salt, obtained as the head crop in 75% yield, melted at 75° and had a specific rotation of about +3° (methanol). It was recrystallized five times from ether (15 ml/g), and then four times from ethyl acetate (5 ml/g). The melting point showed little or no change during this process, but the specific rotation changed by about 1° with each recrystallization, decreasing at first, then increasing with a negative sign. About a 60% recovery of head crop was obtained on cooling at each step. The filtrates were concentrated, and successive new crops were combined on the basis of their rotations, recrystallized as above, and eventually added to the head crops of the resolution. The final filtrates of the tail crops were converted to *threo* **12** (as in the *erythro* series) and treated with the (−)-amine, and the process was repeated.

By this procedure, from 200 g of (±)-*threo* **12**, there was obtained 12 g of the (+)-*threo* **12** salt of (−)-α-methylbenzylamine, $[\alpha]_D$ +5.0° (methanol, *c* 3.5), and 11 g of the (−)-*threo* **12** salt of the (+)-amine, $[\alpha]_D$ −5.0° (*c* 4.3). The optical purity of these salts is uncertain, since a known optically pure product was not obtained, even upon several additional recrystallizations of another, comparably resolved, sample.

The partially resolved amine salts were each converted (as in the *erythro* series) in quantitative yield to (−)- and (+)-*threo* **12** (Table I).

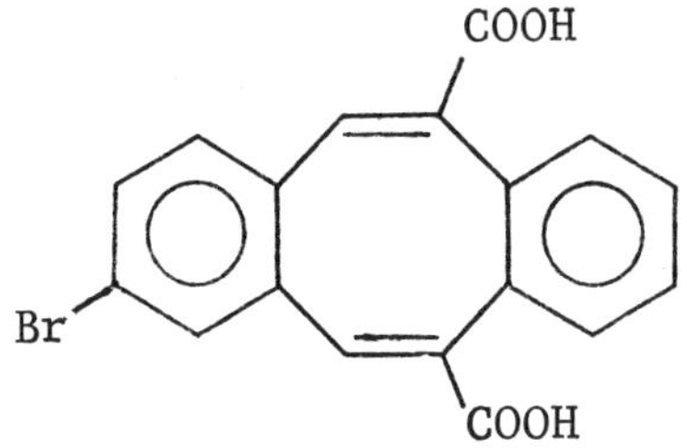

$C_{18}H_{11}BrO_4$ Ref. 1249

Note:

Resolved using brucine. The obtained acids had $[\alpha]_D^{21}$ +71.2° and $[\alpha]_D^{26}$ -61.6° (c 0.9, ethanol).

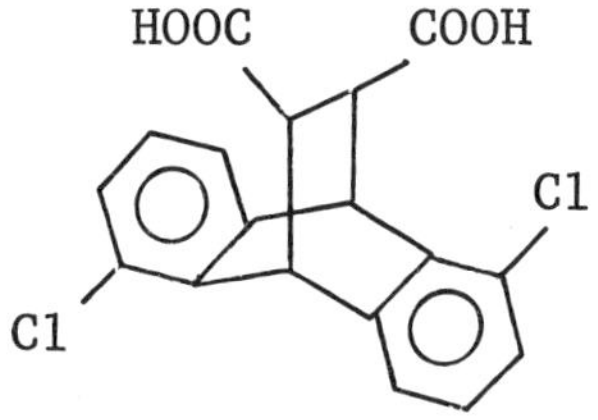

$C_{18}H_{12}Cl_2O_4$ Ref. 1250

On dissout 5,5 g d'acide *B* et 9,1 g de cinchonidine dans 110 cm³ d'éthanol et laisse cristalliser. Le sel obtenu (3,3 g) est recristallisé deux fois dans 350 cm³ d'éthanol. On obtient 1,62 g de sel acide d'après l'*analyse* ($C_{37}H_{34}Cl_2N_2O_5$).

La décomposition de ce sel par l'acide chlorhydrique dilué conduit à 850 mg d'acide *B*, $[\alpha]_{578}^{22}$ = −114,3° (dioxanne, *c* = 1) qui a le même pouvoir rotatoire, après recristallisation dans le méthanol aqueux.

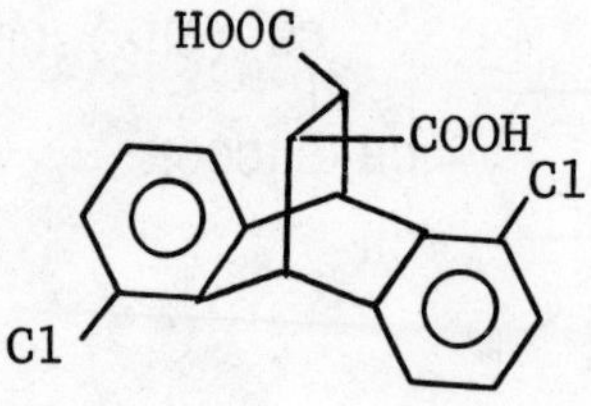

$C_{18}H_{12}Cl_2O_4$ Ref. 1251

On dissout 4 g d'acide **11***a* et 8,8 g de brucine dans 100 cm³ d'éthanol. On laisse cristalliser pendant 4 h et essore 3,9 g de sel qu'on recristallise trois fois dans 400 cm³ d'éthanol, on obtient 1,83 g de sel, constitué d'une mole de brucine pour une mole d'acide d'après l'*analyse* ($C_{41}H_{38}Cl_2N_2O_8$).

On décompose de la façon habituelle par l'acide chlorhydrique dilué, on obtient l'acide *A*, $[\alpha]_{578}^{22} = +176,2°$ (dioxanne, *c* = 1). On recristallise dans l'acide acétique aqueux, F = > 260°. Les premières eaux-mères du dédoublement, concentrées à moitié, fournissent 1,3 g de sel et des eaux-mères qui, après décomposition, conduisent à 1,5 g d'acide $[\alpha]_{578}^{22} = -101,1°$. Cet acide, recristallisé dans 35 cm³ d'acide acétique, fournit 500 mg d'acide $[\alpha]_{578} = -8,2°$ et des eaux-mères qu'on évapore à sec et recristallise dans 5 cm³ d'acide acétique et 5 cm³ d'eau. On essore 450 mg d'acide $[\alpha]_{578}^{22} = -176,0°$.

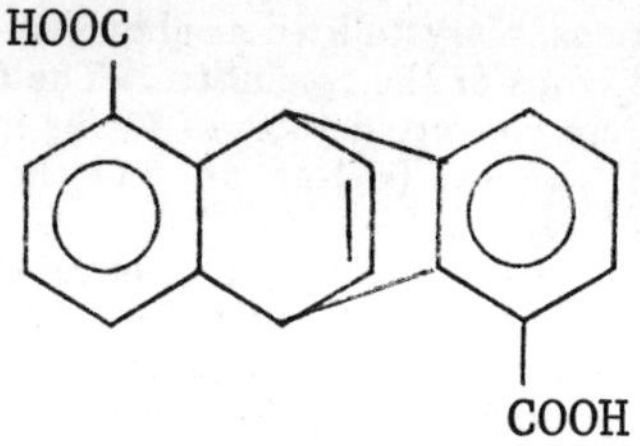

$C_{18}H_{12}O_4$ Ref. 1252

Optical Resolution of (±)-1,5-Dicarboxy-9,10-dihydro-9,10-ethenoanthracene (X). A solution of equimolar strychnine (4.58 g, 0.0137 mol) in 99% ethanol (600 ml) was added to a solution of (±)-X (4.00 g, 0.0137 mol) in the same solvent (3500 ml). After being refluxed for 3 hr, the mixture was concentrated to *ca.* 1000 ml and allowed to stand overnight. Crystalline salt deposited (3.43 g) was recrystallized 4 times from 99% ethanol to give optically pure salt, mp 322—326°C (decomp.), 1.43 g.

Found: C, 74.41; H, 5.45; N, 4.43%. Calcd for $C_{39}H_{34}N_2O_6$: C, 74.74; H, 5.47; N, 4.47%.

Since the measurement of rotation of the strychnine salt was difficult owing to its poor solubility in organic solvents, the increase in optical purity of the salt was followed by measurements of rotation of dicarboxylic acids obtained from the mother liquors of recrystallization on acidification with acetic acid.

Optically pure salt thus obtained was decomposed with aqueous 50% acetic acid to yield optically pure (−)-X, mp 315—322°C (decomp.), 0.65 g.

Found: C, 73.45; H, 4.24%. Calcd for $C_{18}H_{12}O_4$: C, 73.96; H, 4.14%.

The mother liquor of the first recrystallization was concentrated to give crystalline salt (5.05 g). Decomposition of the salt with aqueous 50% acetic acid afforded (+)-enantiomer, 2.35 g, $[\alpha]_D$ +291.2° (*c*, 0.215, dioxane), optical purity, 87.3%.

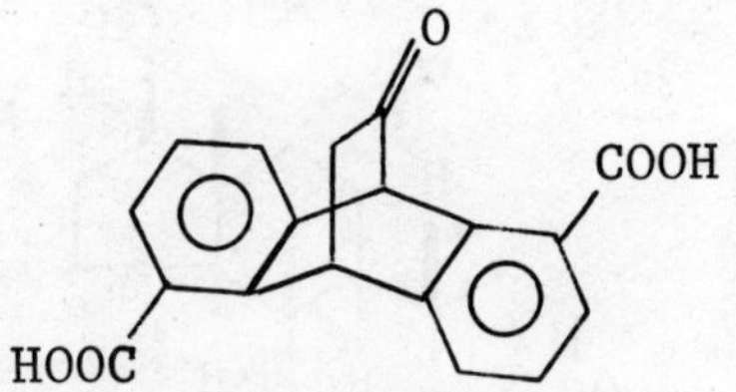

$C_{18}H_{12}O_5$ Ref. 1253

Optical Resolution of the Carboxylic Acid (9a).—A mixture of the carboxylic acid (9a) (846 mg), ephedrine (967 mg), and ethanol (5 ml) was briefly heated. Ethyl acetate was added dropwise, until the solution became slightly cloudy. The mixture was allowed to stand for 2 days. The crystals were collected by filtration, washed with ethanol–ethyl acetate, and dried. Recrystallization three times from ethanol gave the diastereomer, $[\alpha]_D^{22}$ +80.7 ± 4.4° (MeOH; *c* 0.274).

The salt (81.4 mg) was shaken with dilute HCl at 60° for 10 min. The crystals were collected by filtration, washed with water, dried, and recrystallized from methanol to give a powder (29.4 mg), m.p. 310°, $[\alpha]_D^{20}$ +233.0 ± 12.9 (MeOH; *c* 0.212).

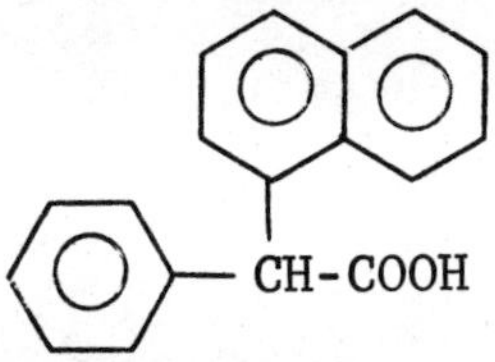

$C_{18}H_{14}O_2$ Ref. 1254

α-Benzylnaphthalene[8] was metalated with *n*-butyllithium in ether–hexane and the resulting purple-red solution was carbonated to give α-naphthylphenylacetic acid, m.p. 139–141°, lit.[9] 140–141°, in 65% yield. After conversion to the acid chloride with thionyl chloride the crude acid chloride was treated directly with one equivalent of (−)-menthol in pyridine–benzene. The crude ester was crystallized from ethanol to give 79% of a diastereomeric mixture of menthyl esters, m.p. 59–68°, $[\alpha]^{23}$D −61.5° (cyclohexane, *c* 5).[10] The ester was crystallized from methanol (about 20 ml./g.) several times, finally yielding large needles. During this process the rotation increased to $[\alpha]^{23}$D −68.7° and the m.p. rose to 95–96°. The filtrates from these crystallizations were concentrated and the residue was recrystallized from methanol, two fractions of solid being removed. The filtrate was concentrated, yielding material melting at 74–80° with $[\alpha]^{23}$D −55.4°. After two recrystallizations from hexane (5 ml./g.) and one from heptane (2 ml./g.) the solid, m.p. 77–83°, $[\alpha]^{23}$D −52.0°, was crystallized from methanol (3 ml./g.) containing a trace of hexane to give the second diastereomeric ester, m.p. 84.5–85.5°, $[\alpha]^{23}$D −51.1°, as fine needle clusters.

(8) E. Koike and M. Okawa, *J. Chem. Soc. Japan, Pure Chem. Sect.*, **74**, 971 (1953).

(9) C. J. Collins, L. S. Ciereszko, and J. G. Burr, *J. Am. Chem. Soc.*, **75**, 405 (1953).

(10) All rotations unless otherwise indicated were determined in $CHCl_3$, *c* 10.0–10.3.

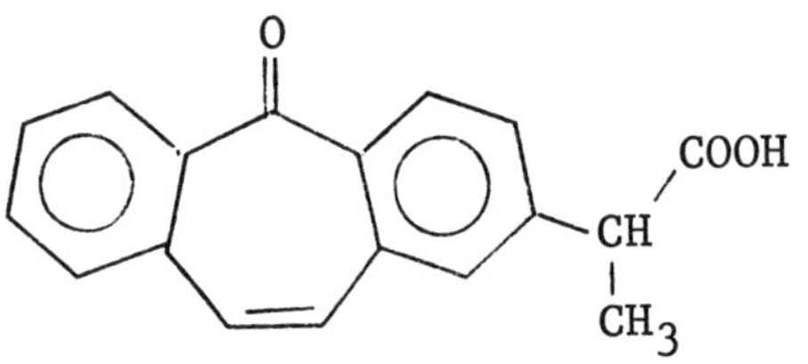

$C_{18}H_{14}O_3$ Ref. 1255

Resolution of 14a. The racemic acid *dl*-**14a** (3.6 g, 0.013 mol) and *l*-amphetamine (1.75 g, 0.013 mol) were mixed in hot *i*-PrOH (150 mL). The solution was cooled slowly and then filtered, and the residue was recrystallized four times from *i*-PrOH. The melting points of successive crops of the salt showed no systematic variation. The isolated salt (1.87 g, 35%) was shaken with dilute HCl–Et_2O, the Et_2O solution was dried and evaporated, and the residue was recrystallized from $CHCl_3$–hexane to afford *d*-**14a** (1.1 g, 30%): mp 104–107 °C; $[\alpha]_D$ +46° (10 mg/mL, $CHCl_3$). Anal. ($C_{18}H_{14}O_3$) C, H. This material was shown to contain 99% *d* and 1% *l* isomers as follows.[11] About 0.5 mg was dissolved in C_6H_6 (0.5 mL), and *d*-2-octanol (50 μL) and H_2SO_4 (5 μL) were added. The mixture was heated to 80 °C for 2 h, then cooled, and washed with aqueous $NaHCO_3$. The dried solution was then injected onto a GLC column (1.75 m, 10% OV 101, 260 °C) and the ratio of the areas of the peaks due to the diastereomeric 2-octyl esters was determined by integration. After correcting for the optical purity of the 2-octanol, the optical purity of *d*-**14a** was calculated. Resolution of *dl*-**14a**, as described above, using *d*-amphetamine, gave *l*-**14a**: mp 105–107 °C; $[\alpha]_D$ −47° (1 mg/mL, $CHCl_3$). Anal. ($C_{18}H_{14}O_3$) C, H. GLC analysis as described above indicated 98% *l* and 2% *d* isomers.

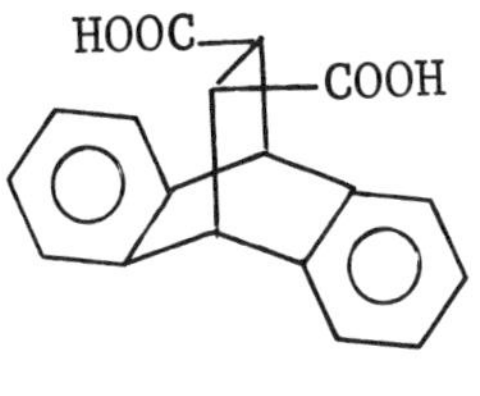

$C_{18}H_{14}O_4$ Ref. 1256

On dissout 7,5 g d'acide **8a** et 24 g de brucine dans 150 cm³ d'éthanol et 240 cm³ d'eau. Une recristallisation dans 90 cm³ d'éthanol et 150 cm³ d'eau du sel brut fournit 11,5 g de sel qu'on décompose par l'acide chlorhydrique dilué. On obtient 3,1 g d'acide $[\alpha]_{578}^{25}$ = — 13,5° (dioxanne, *c* = 2) qu'on recristallise dans l'éther-hexane. Après désolvatation (à 120° pendant quelques heures) : 2,5 g, F = 220,5°, $[\alpha]_{578}^{25}$ = — 15,3° (dioxanne, *c* = 2).

Les premières eaux-mères alcooliques sont évaporées à sec et le sel décomposé comme précédemment fournit 4 g d'acide $[\alpha]_{578}^{25}$ = + 4,4° (éthanol, *c* = 5) ; $[\alpha]_{578}^{25}$ = + 11,7° (dioxanne, *c*=5).

$C_{18}H_{14}O_4$ Ref. 1256a

Resolution of DEA-11,12-trans-*dicarboxylic acid* ((+)-**12**). DEA-11,12-*trans*-dicarboxylic acid[29] and cinchonidine (4·0 g) were dissolved in warm MeOH (70 ml). Solvent was evaporated to dryness, acetone (100 ml) added to the residue and the mixture allowed to stand overnight. Crystals were collected and recrystallized from methanolic acetone (1 : 1) three times to give a pure diastereomer (1·174 g), $[\alpha]_D$ −79·7° (MeOH, *c* 0·402). This salt was suspended in ether and 6N HCl (20 ml) was added. The mixture was shaken for 10 min and the ether layer separated, washed with water and dried (Na_2SO_4). Ether was stripped off and the residue crystallized from benzene to give a powder (325 mg), m.p. 226–227°, $[\alpha]_D$ +7·9° (MeOH, *c* 0·795).

[29] W. E. Bachmann and L. B. Scott, *J. Am. Chem. Soc.* **70**, 1458 (1948)

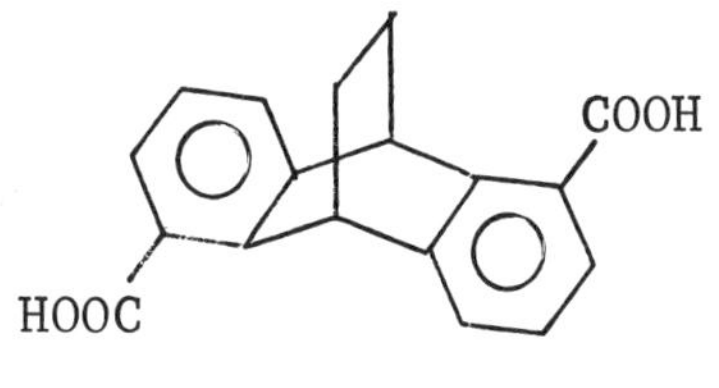

$C_{18}H_{14}O_4$ Ref. 1257

Resolution of DEA-1,5-*dicarboxylic acid.* To a suspension of dicarboxylic acid (+)-**20** (1·49 g) in MeOH, a solution of brucine tetrahydrate (5·18 g) in MeOH (25 ml) was added in one portion. The mixture was warmed for one hr at 70° (bath temp.). Solids were collected by filtration from the hot solution and recrystallized (3 ×) from $CHCl_3$ and MeOH (2·45 g), m.p. 185–186° (dec.), $[\alpha]_D$ +90·2° ($CHCl_3$, *c* 1·112).

The mother liquor of the mixture was allowed to stand overnight and crystals were collected, washed with MeOH and dried. Recrystallization from $CHCl_3$ and MeOH four times gave needles (1·25 g), m.p. 173–176°, $[\alpha]_D$ −152·4° ($CHCl_3$, *c* 0·681).

(+)-Salt (2·45 g) was shaken with dil. HCl (30 ml) at 50° for 20 min. The free acid was collected by filtration, washed with water and dried. Recrystallization from MeOH gave a colourless powder (0·617 g), m.p. 325° (dec.), $[\alpha]_D$ +340·0° (dioxane, *c* 0·861).

The (−)-salt (1·02 g) was similarly decomposed to give the (−)-isomer (277 mg).

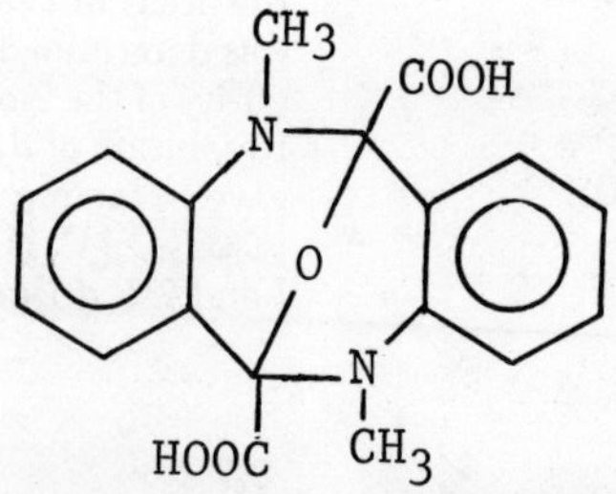

$C_{18}H_{16}N_2O_5$ Ref. 1258

Resolution of DL-N:N′-*dimethylanhydrobiisatic acid* (IVc) *into optically active components*

(a) *Diastereoisomeric brucine salts of* IVc. N:N′-Dimethylanhydrobiisatic acid (18·8 g; 0·05 mole), m.p. 118°, was dissolved in 700 ml ethanol and mixed with a solution of 19·7 g (0·05 mole) brucine in 700 ml ethanol. After 4 hr at room temp., the precipitate was filtered (20·8 g) and triturated 5 times with ethanol (5 × 200 ml) to give 18·2 g of *brucine salt of* (−)-N:N′-*dimethylanhydrobiisatic acid*, m.p. 154°. $[\alpha]^{D}_{20} = -38{\cdot}3°$ ($c = 0{\cdot}60$, water). Further washing with ethanol did not raise the melting point of the product nor change the rotation. Crystallization from ethanol was not possible because the acidic salt, like the acid itself, decomposed readily on heating in ethanol.

The ethanolic filtrate, obtained on filtration of the crude salt (but not the washings), was concentrated to 200 ml, under reduced pressure and at temp. below 40°. After standing at 0°, 8·6 g of *brucine salt of* (+)-N:N′-*dimethylanhydrobiisatic acid*, m.p. 171–172°, was obtained. $[\alpha]^{D}_{20} = +20{\cdot}8°$ ($c = 1{\cdot}92$, ethanol).

(b) *Isolation of* (−)- *and* (+)-N:N′-*dimethylanhydrobiisatic acids*. The diastereoisomer insoluble in ethanol (9·175 g; 0·0125 mole), m.p. 154°, was dissolved in 27·5 ml of N aqueous KOH and the resulting solution was diluted with water to 100 ml. After removal of brucine by chloroform extraction (5 × 50 ml), the aqueous layer was cooled to 5° and acidified with a slight excess of 5% HCl. Crystallization of the precipitate from ethanol–water afforded 2·87 g (62·4%) of (−)-N:N′-*dimethylanhydrobiisatic acid* (IVc), m.p. 115–116°. $[\alpha]^{D}_{20} = -50{\cdot}6°$ ($c = 3{\cdot}00$, ethanol). (Found: C, 57·18; H, 5·33; N, 7·28; $C_{18}H_{16}O_5N_2{\cdot}2H_2O$ requires: C, 57·44; H, 5·36; N, 7·44%).

The diastereoisomer soluble in ethanol (3·67 g; 0·005 mole), m.p. 171–172°, was dissolved in 11·0 ml of N aqueous KOH. Treatment as above gave 1·08 g (60·4%) of (+)-N:N′-*dimethylanhydrobiisatic acid* (IVc), m.p. 114°. $[\alpha]^{D}_{20} = +51{\cdot}3°$ ($c = 3{\cdot}00$, ethanol). (Found: C, 57·07; H, 5·24; N, 7·46. $C_{18}H_{16}O_5N_2{\cdot}2H_2O$ requires: C, 57·44; H, 5·36; N, 7·44%).

Both acids crystallized with two molecules of water. They were soluble in 3% aqueous sodium bicarbonate, and could be reprecipitated unchanged from such solutions with dilute acids. By heating their aqueous solution, both acids were converted quantitatively to N-methylisatin.

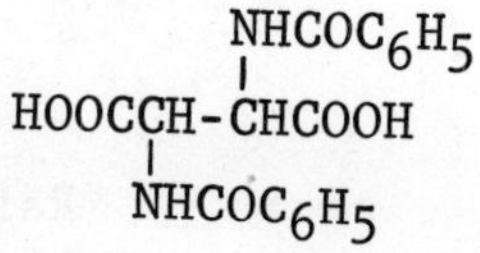

$C_{18}H_{16}N_2O_6$ Ref. 1259

12 g ***d, l-N, N′***-Dibenzoyl-α, β-diaminobernsteinsäure und 10.4 g Morphin wersden fein gepulvert und in 1060 ccm siedendem Wasser gelöst. Nach 18-tdg. Stehen bei 0° sind etwa 15 g Morphinsalz der rechtsdrehenden Säure, das noch viel ungespaltene *d, l*-Säure enthält, ausgefallen. Aus dem Filtrat entfernen wir durch Zugabe von Ammoniak-Ammoniumcarbonat das Alkaloid, dessen Abscheidung bei 0° nach 4—6 Stdn. beendet ist. Die ammoniakalische Lösung wird mit verd. Schwefelsäure angesäuert, wobei die linksdrehende Dibenzoyl-diaminosäure (4 g) in feinen, farblosen Prismen auskrystallisiert. Schmp. 163—164° (unt. Zers.).

$[\alpha]^{20}_{D} = (-2.87° \times 100)/(1.455 \times 1.894) = -104.2°$ (in $n/_{10}$-NH_3).

Das Morphinsalz der rechtsdrehenden Säure wird mit Alkohol ausgekocht, wobei *racem*. Dibenzoylverbindung in Lösung geht. Es wird dann noch 3-mal aus heißem Wasser umkrystallisiert. Zers.-Pkt. 198—201° (unkorr.) nach vorangegangener Braunfärbung. Das Salz krystallisiert mit 4 Mol. Krystallwasser, von denen 3 im Vakuum bei 130—140° entweichen.

7.370 mg Sbst. (über P_2O_5 getr.): 0.402 ccm N (korr., 17°, 713 mm). — 47.0 mg Sbst. verlieren in 5 Stdn. bei 130—140° unter 15 mm Druck 3.6 mg.

$C_{35}H_{33}O_8N_3$, $H_2O + 3H_2O$. Ber. N 6.04, H_2O 7.76. Gef. N 6.02, H_2O 7.66.

7.502 mg Sbst. (bei 130—140° getr.): 18.12 mg CO_2, 3.67 mg H_2O.

$C_{35}H_{33}O_8N_3 + H_2O$. Ber. C 65.48, H 5.46. Gef. C 65.89, H 5.47.

Die Zerlegung des Morphinsalzes mit Ammoniak-Ammoniumcarbonat liefert rechtsdrehende Dibenzoyl-diaminobernsteinsäure vom Schmp. 163—164°. Die schmalen, glänzenden Prismen enthalten 1 Mol. Krystallwasser, das im Vakuum bei 130° abgegeben wird.

6.95 mg Sbst.: 0.473 ccm N (korr., 19°, 714 mm).

$C_{18}H_{16}O_6N_2 + H_2O$. Ber. N 7.49. Gef. N 7.47.

6.165 mg Sbst. (bei 130—140° getr.): 13.77 mg CO_2, 2.37 mg H_2O.

$C_{18}H_{16}O_6N_2$. Ber. C 60.66, H 4.55. Gef. C 60.93, H 4.30.

Die krystallwasser-haltige Substanz zeigt

$[\alpha]^{20}_{D} = (+2.84° \times 100)/(1.408 \times 1.894) = +106.5°$ (in $n/_{10}$-NH_3).

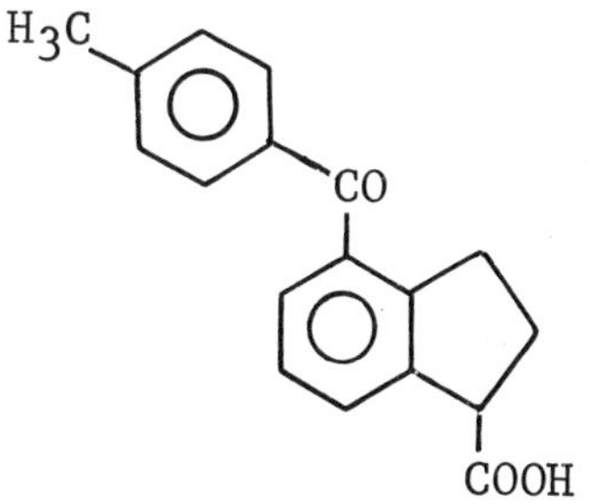

$C_{18}H_{16}O_3$ Ref. 1260

Optical Resolution of 4-(4-Methylbenzoyl)-1-indancarboxylic Acid (Ib)——a) (*S*)-*l*-Ib: A suspension of 14.0 g of Ib and 7.4 g of cinchonine in 500 ml of CH_3CN was warmed to give a clear solution. The resulting solution was allowed to stand overnight at room temperature. The precipitate was collected by filtration and recrystallized from 2.2 l of CH_3CN to give 10.5 g (73%) of the cinchonine salt of (*S*)-*l*-Ib as colorless crystals, mp 195.0—197.0°. *Anal.* Calcd. for $C_{37}H_{38}N_2O_4$: C, 77.32; H, 6.67; N, 4.87. Found: C, 77.28; H, 6.62; N, 4.94. $[\alpha]_D^{23}$ +31.7° (*c*=1, $CHCl_3$). This salt (10.0 g) was dissolved in 200 ml of benzene. The solution was washed twice with 100 ml of 1 N HCl and water, dried over anhydrous $MgSO_4$ and concentrated under reduced pressure. The residue was recrystallized from a mixture of benzene and cyclohexane (3: 8) to give 4.25 g (87%) of (*S*)-*l*-Ib, mp 113.5—115.5°. *Anal.* Calcd. for $C_{18}H_{16}O_3$: C, 77.12; H, 5.75. Found: C, 77.08; H, 5.65. $[\alpha]_D^{23}$ −70.8° (*c*=1, MeOH). The NMR spectrum was identical with that of the racemic compound.[4]

b) (*R*)-*d*-Ib: The mother liquor of the crude cinchonine salt of *l*-Ib in a) was concentrated to dryness under reduced pressure. The residue was dissolved in $CHCl_3$. The solution was washed with 1 N HCl and water, dried over anhydrous $MgSO_4$ and concentrated under reduced pressure. The residue was dissolved with 3.0 g of *l*-α-phenylethylamine in 400 ml of CH_3CN by warming. The solution was allowed to stand overnight. The resulting precipitate was collected by filtration and recrystallized twice from CH_3CN to give 5.6 g (56%) of the *l*-α-phenylethylamine salt of (*R*)-*d*-Ib as colorless needles, mp 149.0—150.0°. *Anal.* Calcd. for $C_{26}H_{27}NO_3$: C, 77.78; H, 6.78; N, 3.49. Found: C, 77.82; H, 6.68; N, 3.56. $[\alpha]_D^{23}$ +65.8° (*c*=1, $CHCl_3$). From this salt (*R*)-*d*-Ib was obtained by the similar procedures to that described in a), mp 110.5—114.0° [79%, recrystallized from a mixture of benzene and cyclohexane (3: 8)]. *Anal.* Calcd. for $C_{18}H_{16}O_3$: C, 77.12; H, 5.75. Found: C, 77.20; H, 5.66. $[\alpha]_D^{23}$ +64.3° (*c*=1, MeOH). The NMR spectrum was identical with that of the racemic compound.[4]

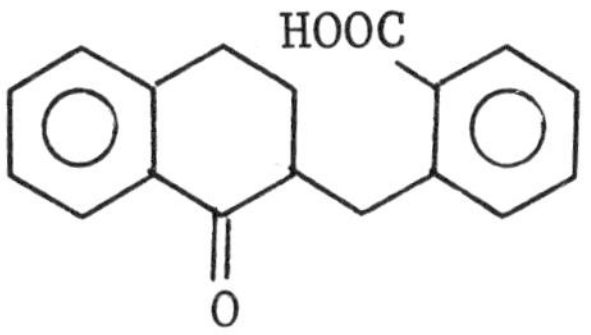

$C_{18}H_{16}O_3$ Ref. 1261

Dédoublement de **11a**.

3,4 g de céto-acide et 5 g de brucine sont dissous à chaud dans 135 cm³ d'acétone en présence de traces d'eau. On obtient 6,7 g de sel (Rdt = 82 %). L'acide optiquement actif est libéré de son sel, dans le chloroforme, par SO_4H_2 2,5 N. Le pouvoir rotatoire de l'acide varie suivant les essais entre $-20° < [\alpha]_J^{22} < -26°$, $[\alpha]_J^{22} = -26°$, $[\alpha]^{22}_{546} = -30{,}5°$, $[\alpha]^{22}_{436} = -62°$ (C = 2,41, $CHCl_3$).

Analyse $C_{18}H_{16}O_3$ (280,31) : Calc. % : C 77,1 H 5,75
Tr. : 77,1 5,85.

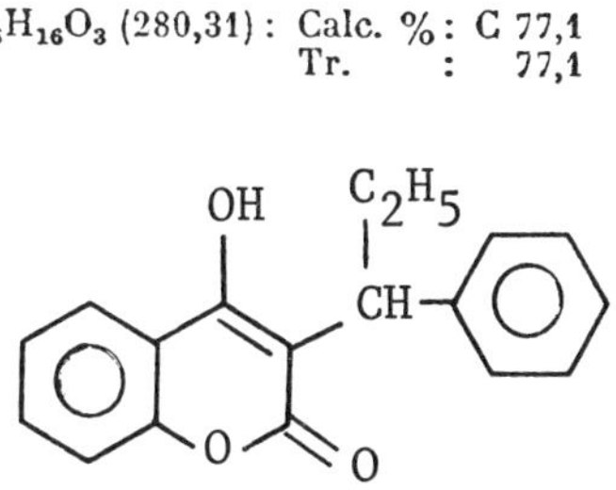

$C_{18}H_{16}O_3$ Ref. 1262

(-)(S)-Marcumar.

rac-Marcumar was prepared by the method of Schroeder *et al.*, (10). Quinidine (52 g , 0.16 mole) and 89.5 g. (0.32 mole) of *rac*-Marcumar were dissolved in a warmed mixture of 250 ml. of chloroform and 500 ml. of acetone. A first crop (51 g.) of Marcumar-quinidine salt was collected after crystallization had proceeded for 24 hours at 25°. The filtrate was concentrated to a syrup. Acetone (250 ml.) was added and the solution was held at -10° for 24 hours, yielding an additional 23 g. of the salt. The first crop was recrystallized once and the second crop twice, then the head fractions were combined and crystallized again. The solvent in each case was 45 ml. per g. of 1:4 (V:V) absolute ethanol - chloroform. Yield 42 g. $[\alpha]_D^{23}$ + 75°±1° (*C* 1, butanone-2). Further recrystallization did not change this rotation (11). The (-)(S)-Marcumar was recovered by stirring the salt with 200 ml. each of chloroform and 5% sodium hydroxide and acidifying the separated aqueous layer with hydrochloric acid. One crystallization from ethanol-water yielded 18 g. of (-)(S)-Marcumar, $[\alpha]_D^{28}$ -122.6°±0.5° (*C* 2, 95% ethanol), m.p. 170-171°.

(+)(R)-Marcumar.

All the filtrates from the Marcumar-quinidine salt were concentrated to a glassy residue which was decomposed by chloroform-alkali partition as above to yield 57 g. of partially resolved (+)(R)-Marcumar; $[\alpha]_D^{25}$ + 39° (*C* 2, 95% ethanol). This product (0.205 mole) and 62.5 g. (0.205 mole) of quinine were dissolved in 950 ml. of ethanol and 360 ml. of warm water was added. Cooling to -10° gave a crystalline product which was recrystallized four times from 11 ml. per g. of 70% (by vol.) ethanol. The terminal rotation was $[\alpha]_D^{24}$ -64±1°, (*C* 1, butanone-2), which did not change on further crystallization. Partition of the salt, acid precipitation and crystallization from ethanol-water yielded 8.5 g. of (+)(R)-Marcumar; $[\alpha]_D^{27}$ +122.8°±0.5° (*C* 2, 95% ethanol), m.p. 170-170.5°. The infrared spectra of chloroform solutions of (+)-, (-)- and *rac*-Marcumar were indistinguishable; λ max ($CHCl_3$): 2.89, 3.37, 5.97, 6.20 μ.

(10) C. H. Schroeder, E. D. Titus and K. P. Link, *ibid.*, 79, 3291 (1957).

(11) **All Marcumar-alkaloid salt samples were dried at least 12 hours at 0.1 mm and 25°. Rotations were measured in a Schmidt and Haensch model 82-B polarimeter with monochromater; 1=4 dm (solutions) and 1=1 dm (neat).**

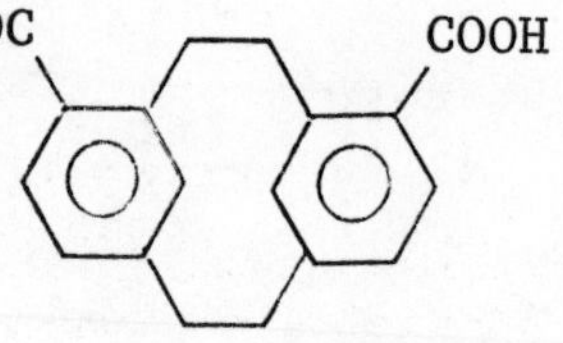

$C_{18}H_{16}O_4$ Ref. 1263

b) A solution of 330 mg (1.1 mmol) of IV and 730 mg (2.3 mmol) of quinine, which had been liberated from the hydrochloride, in 9 m*l* of hot ethanol was left to stand at room temperature for one day. Filtration then afforded 280 mg of a crystalline salt, which was recrystallized from ethanol, mp 150—160°C. Dicarboxylic acid was freed from the salt by shaking it with 20 m*l* of benzene and 10 m*l* of dilute hydrochloric acid. By the evaporation of the benzene solution, there were obtained 45 mg of a colorless powder, mp >300°C, with $[\alpha]_D^{22}=+5°$ (*c* 1.8, ethanol). It had IR spectra identical with those of the racemic compound.

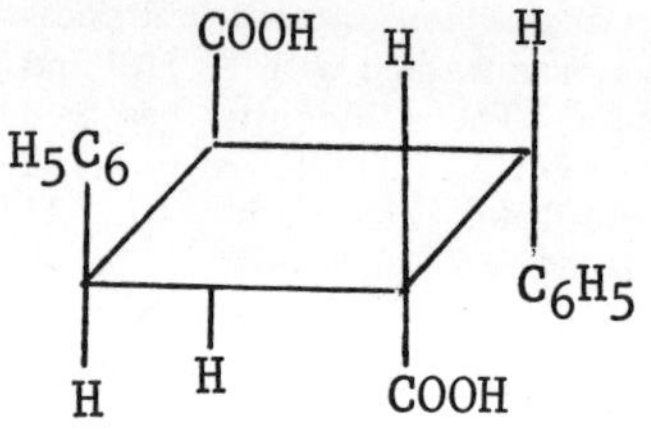

$C_{18}H_{16}O_4$ Ref. 1264

Die Spaltung der α-Truxillanilidsäure in ihre optischen Antipoden gelang nach zahlreichen vergeblichen Versuchen auf folgendem Wege. 2 g der Säure vom Schmp. 235° wurden mit 0.9 g Strychnin (2:1) in 150 ccm Methylal bis zur Lösung gekocht, was nach ca. 2 Stdn. der Fall war. Nach Abdestillieren von 25 ccm des Lösungsmittels wurde die Lösung in einem mit einem Uhrglase lose bedeckten Kolben drei Tage sich selbst überlassen, wonach 1.3 g des Salzes der *l*-Säure auskrystallisiert waren, das aus Methylal (50 ccm) umkrystallisiert, zu Drusen vereinigte Nadeln vom Schmp. 162° (unter Zersetzung) bildet. Das reine Salz, mit Ammoniak in der Wärme zerlegt, liefert die **l-α-Truxillanilidsäure**, die nach dem Umkrystallisieren aus verd. Alkohol feine Nadeln vom Schmp. 205° bildet.

0.5002 g, in Aceton zu 10 ccm gelöst, zeigten im 1-dm-Rohr bei 19° $\alpha = -1.151°$.

$$[\alpha]_D^{19} = -23.0°.$$

Löst man 1 g *racem.* α-Anilidsäure und 0.9 g Strychnin (1:1) unter Kochen in 50 ccm 80-proz. Alkohol und überläßt die Lösung langsamer Verdunstung, so ist nach 4 Tagen ebenfalls das Salz der linksdrehenden Säure, etwa zur Hälfte, ausgefallen, woraus die reine Säure vom Schmp. 205° darstellbar ist.

Das nach beiden Verfahren aus den Mutterlaugen gewonnene Salz der Antipodensäure wurde mit Ammoniak zerlegt und das in überwiegender Menge die *d*-α-Anilidsäure enthaltende Säuregemisch zur Gewinnung der reinen *d*-Säure benutzt. 2 g dieses Säuregemisches wurden mit 0.7 g Brucin (2:1) und 50 ccm Methylal unter Erhitzen in Lösung gebracht, schon dabei aber begann sich das Brucinsalz teilweise auszuscheiden, das dann am nächsten Tage abgesogen und aus Methylal umkrystallisiert wurde, Schmp. 159° (unter Zersetzung). Durch Zerlegung des Salzes mit Ammoniak wurde daraus die **d-α-Truxillanilidsäure** gewonnen, die aus verd. Alkohol in feinen Nadeln vom Schm. 205° herauskam, aber optisch nicht ganz so rein war wie die *l*-Säure.

0.3338 g, in Aceton zu 10 ccm gelöst, zeigten im 1-dm-Rohr bei 20° $\alpha = +0.738°$.

$$[\alpha]_D^{20} = +21.8°.$$

Beim Mischen gleicher Teile der *d*- und *l*-Form stieg der Schmelzpunkt auf den der racemischen Säure, 235°; der der letzteren sank durch Zusatz der *d*-Säure auf 224°. Die Antipodensäuren zeigen erheblich größere Löslichkeit als die Racemform.

Löslichkeitsbestimmung. Bei 20° lösen 100 g Eisessig 0.558 g der *racem.* α-Anilidsäure, dagegen 2.538 g der optisch aktiven Säure, so daß letztere rund 4.5-mal so löslich ist als erstere.

Gegen Racemisierungsmittel zeigen sich die drehenden Formen außerordentlich widerstandsfähig, sie können 1 Stde. lang (wahrscheinlich noch länger) selbst mit konz. Ammoniak oder konz. Salzsäure auf dem Wasserbade erhitzt werden, ohne daß der Schmelzpunkt sich irgendwie ändert, was zugleich auch zeigt, wie schwer die Anilidgruppe wieder abgespalten wird (vergl. unten).

Der **Methyl-** und **Äthylester** der optisch aktiven Säure wurde genau wie bei der Racemform dargestellt. Der *l*-Methylester schmilzt nach dem Umkrystallisieren aus verd. Alkohol bei 176°, feine Nadeln.

0.3348 g, in Aceton zu 10 ccm gelöst, zeigten im 1-dm-Rohr bei 20° $\alpha = -0.75°$.

$$[\alpha]_D^{20} = -22.4°.$$

Der *d*-Äthylester schmilzt bei 153°.

0.4478 g, in Aceton zu 10 ccm gelöst, zeigten im 1-dm-Rohr bei 20° $\alpha = +0.84°$.

$$[\alpha]_D^{20} = +18.75°.$$

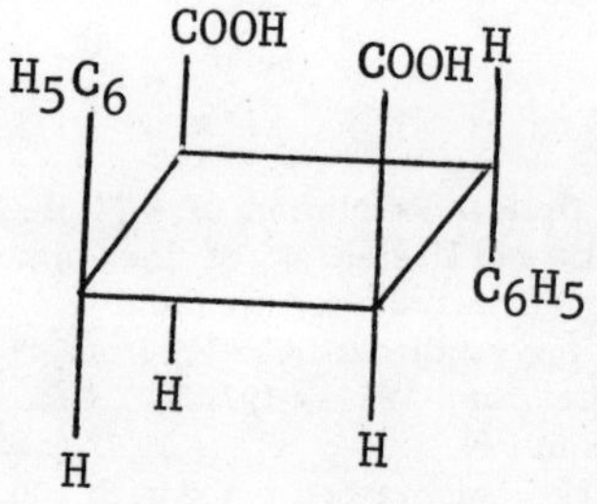

$C_{18}H_{16}O_4$ Ref. 1265

Spaltung der γ-Truxillanilidsäure.

Nach verschiedenen vergeblichen Versuchen wurde gefunden, daß die Spaltung der γ-Anilidsäure durch **Cinchonin** überraschend leicht gelingt, wenn Säure und Base (1:1) in **absolutem** Alkohol zur Lösung gebracht werden. 5 g der Säure werden in 150 ccm absol. Alkohol gelöst und mit einer Lösung von 4 g Cinchonin, ebenfalls in 150 ccm absol. Alkohol gelöst, kurze Zeit erhitzt. Schon dabei beginnt die Ausscheidung des ungemein schwer löslichen Salzes der *d*-Säure, das am andern Tage die Gefäßwandungen mit dichten Drusen überzogen hat (4.4 g). Es wird mit Alkohol ausgekocht und ist dann rein (das Salz der Antipodensäure ist außerordentlich leicht löslich). Aus viel Alkohol oder Aceton umkrystallisiert, bildet es feine Nadeln vom Schmp. 247° unter Zersetzung. Man zerlegt das Cinchoninsalz durch längeres Kochen mit Ammoniak und gewinnt aus der ammoniakalischen Lösung durch Salzsäure die **d-γ-Truxillanilidsäure**, die, aus verd. Alkohol oder besser noch aus Äther + Ligroin umkrystallisiert, feine, watteartig zusammengeballte Nadeln vom Schmp. 228° bildet. Die Säure, die denselben Schmp. hat wie die Racemform, ist in Lösungsmitteln sehr viel leichter löslich als diese, so vor allem in Aceton und Alkohol, gut löslich ist sie auch in Äther und Chloroform, merklich in heißem Wasser, wenig in Eisessig, nicht in Benzol und Ligroin. Die Mischprobe mit der Racemform schmolz bei 215°.

0.3145 g, in Aceton zu 10 ccm gelöst, zeigten im 1-dm-Rohr bei 21° $\alpha = +1.54°$.

$$[\alpha]_D^{21} = +48.73°.$$

Aus der Mutterlauge des *d*-Säuresalzes gewann man den optischen Antipoden, indem man sie mit noch etwas Cinchonin aufkochte, dann stark einengte und einige Tage stehen ließ, filtrierte, und dies Verfahren noch einige Male wiederholte, bis keine Abscheidung mehr erfolgte. Eine Krystallisation des Salzes der *l*-Säure war erst bei völligem Verdunsten des Lösungsmittels zu beobachten; es wurde nach Behandeln mit Tierkohle in Alkohol als fast weiße, krystalline Masse erhalten, die bei 112° unter Aufschäumen schmolz. Die *l*-Säure bildete nach dem Umkrystallisieren aus Äther + Ligroin feine Nadeln vom Schmp. 228°. Gleiche Teile der *d*- und *l*-Form schmolzen ebenfalls bei 228°, dagegen schmolz die Mischprobe der *l*-Säure mit der Racemform bei 217—219°.

Charakteristisch ist das **Natriumsalz** der optisch aktiven γ-Truxillanilidsäure. Löst man sie in heißer, gesättigter Sodalösung, so krystallisiert das Salz nicht wie bei der Racemform aus, sondern gesteht beim Erkalten zu einer durchsichtigen, gallertartigen Masse. Auch das **Kaliumsalz** gelatiniert in ähnlicher Weise.

Löslichkeitsbestimmung: 100 g Eisessig lösten von der Racemform bei 17° 0.6278 g, von der optisch aktiven Form 1.1811 g. Die Löslichkeiten verhalten sich demnach wie 1 : 1.88.

0.4476 g, in Aceton zu 10 ccm gelöst, zeigten bei 23° im 1-dm-Rohr $\alpha = -2.22°$.

$$[\alpha]_D^{23} = -49.54°.$$

Gegen Umlagerungsmittel ist die optisch aktive Säure recht widerstandsfähig. Durch längeres Kochen mit konz. Ammoniak oder konz. Salzsäure tritt durchaus keine Veränderung im Schmelzpunkt ein. Der **l-γ-Truxillanilidsäure-methylester**, dargestellt wie der racemische Ester, bildet, aus Methylalkohol umkrystallisiert, glänzende, wollige Nadeln vom Schmp. 202°. *d*- und *l*-Ester, zu gleichen Teilen gemischt, zeigen den Schmp. 184° des racemischen Esters.

0.5006 g, in Aceton zu 10 ccm gelöst, zeigten im 1-dm-Rohr bei 18° $\alpha = -1.93°$.

$$[\alpha]_D^{18} = -38.55°.$$

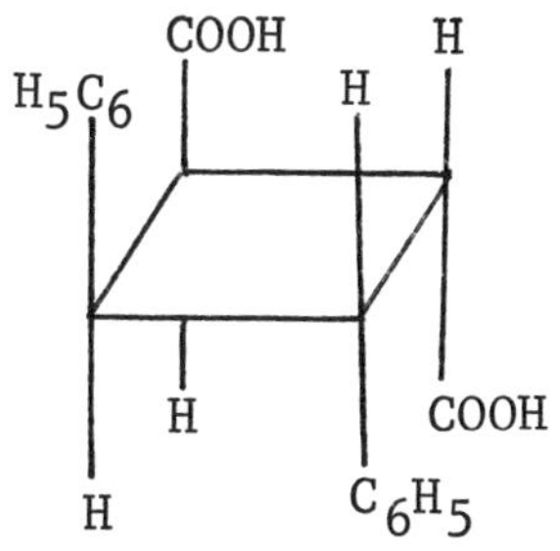

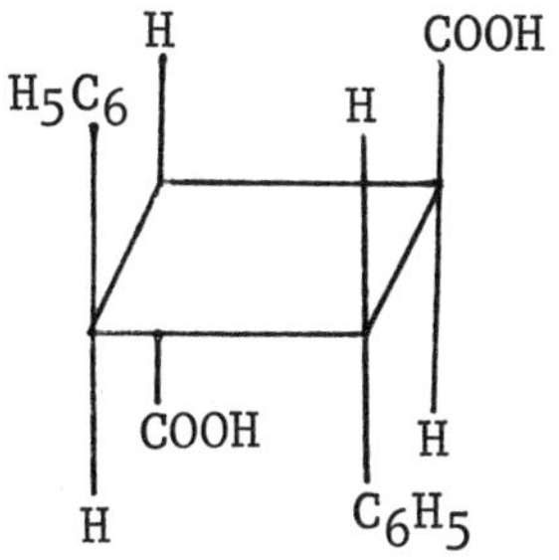

$C_{18}H_{16}O_4$ Ref. 1266

Die Spaltung der Säure in die optischen Antipoden wurde folgendermaßen bewerkstelligt: 2.5 g Neosäure wurden in 43 ccm Alkohol gelöst und hierin 5 g Cinchonin durch Aufkochen in Lösung gebracht. Nach Zugabe von 20 g Wasser trat langsam Krystallisation ein und die nach 24 Stdn. ausgeschiedenen Krystalle (2 g) wurden durch Umlösen aus Alkohol gereinigt. Das Salz schmolz bei 211—212° unter Zersetzung. Nach Zerlegen mit Ammoniak zeigte die aus verdünntem Alkohol umkrystallisierte rechtsdrehende Säure den Schmp. 233—234°.

In Aceton gelöst, ergab die Polarisation im 1-dm-Rohr für 0.2793 g Substanz in 10 ccm Lösung $\alpha = +1.3°$ und somit

$$[\alpha]_D^{20} = +46.5°.$$

Aus dem Filtrat des ausgeschiedenen Cinchonin-Salzes konnte, wie zu erwarten, die linksdrehende Form nicht in reinem Zustand erhalten werden. Hrn. stud. chem. Hagge ist es indessen auf folgendem Wege geglückt, die beiden Antipoden in noch reinerer Form darzustellen: 2.5 g Neosäure wurden in 42 ccm Alkohol gelöst und 2.5 g Cinchonin (1:1) darin durch Aufkochen in Lösung gebracht. Beim Erkalten scheidet sich sofort die Hälfte des gesamten Salzes als reines *d*-Säure-Salz vom Schmp. 216—217° aus. Die daraus gewonnene Säure, aus verd. Alkohol umkrystallisiert, bildete feine Nadeln vom Schmp. 236—237°.

Polarisation in Aceton: 0.2558 g Säure in 10 ccm Lösung im 1-dm-Rohr, $\alpha = +1.346°$.

$$[\alpha]_D^{18} = +52.63°.$$

Die aus der Mutterlauge gewonnene *l*-Neo-truxinsäure schmolz ebenfalls bei 236—237° und zeigte fast genau die gleiche spezif. Drehung in Aceton (H.).

0.2156 g in 10 ccm Lösung, $\alpha = -1.140°$.

$$[\alpha]_D^{18} = -52.87°.$$

Die aus der Mutterlauge nach dem ersten Verfahren gewonnene, unreine *l*-Säure hat Hr. Hagge mit Hilfe von Chinin in eine sehr reine *l*-Säure überführen können. 1 g dieser Säure wurde mit 2.1 g wasserfreiem Chinin in 20 ccm Alkohol heiß in Lösung gebracht und der erkalteten Lösung allmählich 13 ccm Wasser zugesetzt. Nach mehreren Stunden schieden sich 2.6 g des Chinin-Salzes aus, das aus Alkohol umkrystallisiert, strahlenförmige, verfilzte Krystalle vom Schmp. 138° bildete.

Die daraus in Freiheit gesetzte Säure ergab bei Polarisation in Aceton, 0.1770 g in 10 ccm Lösung, 1-dm-Rohr, $\alpha = -0.955°$.

$$[\alpha]_D^{20} = -53.95°.$$

$C_{18}H_{16}O_4$ Ref. 1267

Die Spaltung der δ-Truxinsäure in optische Antipoden ist uns auf folgendem Wege gelungen: Man löst 3 g Deltruxinsäure und 6 g Cinchonin in 50 ccm Alkohol in der Siedehitze und versetzt die event. klar filtrierte Lösung mit 22 ccm Wasser. Die Krystallisation des *l*-δ-Truxinsäure-Salzes gelingt nur schwer, leicht dagegen beim Impfen mit einem vorhandenen Krystall des Salzes. Schmp. 192°.

Nach 24 Stdn. wurde abgesaugt und so etwa 4 g des Cinchonin-Salzes gewonnen; zur Reinigung wurde es aus etwa 60-proz. Alkohol umkrystallisiert, wobei nur etwa 3 g des reinen Salzes vom Schmp. 192° erhalten wurden, der Rest war ein dickes Öl. Das Salz wurde durch Ammoniak auf dem Wasserbade zersetzt und das Filtrat vom Cinchonin durch Salzsäure gefällt.

Die *l*-δ-Truxinsäure zeigt eine von der inaktiven Säure vollkommen abweichende Krystallform, indem sie sich in zentimeterlangen, kreuz und quer gelagerten, haarfeinen Nadeln abscheidet und getrocknet einem Asbestpolster ähnlich sieht. Sie schmilzt bei 158—159°. (Die [*d,l*]-Säure hat den Schmp. 175°.)

1.9662 g Sbst. in 9.9568 g Aceton zeigten im 1-dm-Rohr eine Drehung von $-1.15°$, $d^{20} = 0.8374$.

$$[\alpha]_D^{20} = \frac{-1.15 \times 11.9230}{1 \times 1.9662 \times 0.8374} = -8.8°.$$

Die Löslichkeit dieser Säure ist noch erheblich größer als die der inaktiven Form: 100 g Eisessig lösen bei 20° 17.89 g *l*-Deltruxinsäure, während die Racemform sich zu 10.38% löst.

7.123 mg Sbst.: 18.976 mg CO_2, 3.618 mg H_2O.

$C_{18}H_{16}O_4$. Ber. C 72.90, H 5.40.

Gef. » 72.70, » 5.68.

Die Gewinnung der *d*-Form der Deltruxinsäure war mit Hilfe des Cinchonin-Salzes nicht zu erreichen, sie gelang mit Chinin. 1 g der aus der Mutterlauge der *l*-Form abgeschiedenen, unreinen Antipodensäure wurde mit 2 Mol. Chinin in 100 g Aceton gelöst; bei langsamem Verdunsten des Lösungsmittels setzt die Krystallisation von selbst und ohne Impfen in büschelförmigen Nadeln ein, und man hat nur darauf zu achten, daß das Lösungsmittel sich nicht zu stark verflüchtigt. Das Chinin-Salz, nochmals aus Aceton umkrystallisiert, schmilzt bei 135° unter Zersetzung; bei seiner Zersetzung wurde *d*-Deltruxinsäure vom Schmp. 157—158° gewonnen.

0.6944 g Sbst. in 10 ccm Aceton zeigten im 1-dm-Rohr $\alpha = +0.56°$, woraus

$$[\alpha]_D^{20} = +8.06°.$$

Eine Mischprobe von *d*- und *l*-Säure ergab fast genau den Schmp. der Racemform. Die optisch aktiven Formen werden bei 1-stündigem Erhitzen mit konz. Salzsäure nicht racemisiert, doch ergibt die Kalischmelze die Racemform.

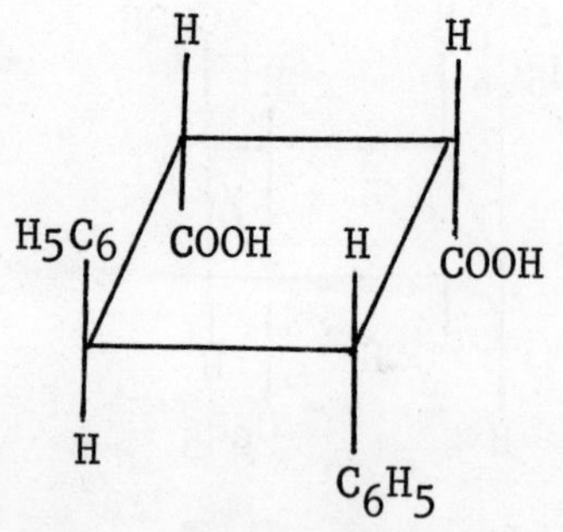

$C_{18}H_{16}O_4$ Ref. 1268

Spaltung der ζ-Truxinsäure in ihre optisch-aktiven Komponenten

2 g ζ-Truxinsäure und 4 g Cinchonin wurden in 90 ccm etwa 75-proz. Alkohols unter Erwärmen gelöst und die Lösung sich selbst überlassen. Über Nacht krystallisierte das neutrale Salz der l-Säure in schönen Nadeln vom Schmp. 192° aus; es wurde abgenutscht, mit Alkohol nachgewaschen und getrocknet. Seine Menge betrug fast genau die Hälfte des zu erwartenden Salzes. Es wurde mit Wasser und überschussigem Ammoniak verrührt, kurz aufgekocht und nach dem Erkalten aus dem Filtrat die Säure durch Salzsäure ausgefällt. Nach dem Absaugen wurde die wässrige Flüssigkeit noch einmal mit Äther ausgeschüttelt, der noch eine kleine Menge der l-Säure aufnahm, ein Zeichen, dass diese in Wasser etwas löslicher ist als die inaktive Säure. Die das Salz der d-Säure enthaltende Mutterlauge wurde genau so wie das feste Salz behandelt und ergab die nicht ganz so reine d-Säure. Beide Säuren wurden wiederholt aus Aceton und aus Methylalkohol umkrystallisiert und zeigten beide den gleichen Schmp. 222°. Eine Mischung gleicher Teile der beiden Säuren zeigte sofort den Schmelzpunkt der racemischen Säure 239°.

Mangels genügender Mengen der Säuren konnten die Löslichkeiten nicht genau bestimmt werden, doch loste sich etwa viermal so viel der l-Säure in Eisessig auf als von der racemischen Säure.

Dehungsvermogen der l-Säure in Alkohol (von 96%):

0.400 g l-Säure in 14.600 g Alkohol zeigten bei 20° eine Drehung von -1.72° im 1-dm-Rohr mit D-Licht, d_4^{20} = 0.823, p = 2.66%.

$$[\alpha]_D^{20} = \frac{-1.72 \times 15.000}{1 \times 0.400 \times 0.823} = -78.37°.$$

Drehnungsvermogen der d-Säure in Alkohol (von 96%):

0.4376 g d-Säure in 16.410 g Alkohol zeigten bei 20% eine Drehung von +1.39° im 1-dm-Rohr mit D-Licht. d_4^{20} =0.818, p = 2.598%.

$$[\alpha]_D^{20} = \frac{+1.39 \times 16.8476}{1 \times 0.4376 \times 0.818} = +65.42°.$$

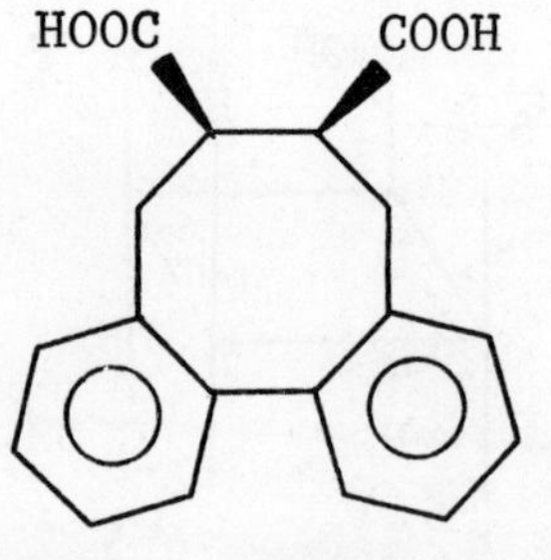

$C_{18}H_{16}O_4$ Ref. 1269

Preparation and Resolution of α-1,2,3,4-Dibenz-1,3-cyclooöctadiene-6,7-dicarboxylic Acid (α-Ie).—A mixture of ethyl 1,2,3,4-dibenz-1,3-cyclooöctadiene-6,6,7,7-tetracarboxylate (Ib, 4.0 g.), potassium hydroxide (15.0 g.) and ethylene glycol (100 ml.) was refluxed for two hours. The solution was poured into 400 ml. of water; acidification with 6 *N* hydrochloric acid yielded the desired product, 1.95 g. (82%), m.p. 216–218° dec. Several recrystallizations from acetic acid yielded microcrystalline aggregates of α-Ie, m.p.[11] 219–220° dec.

Anal. Calcd. for $C_{18}H_{16}O_4$: C, 73.0; H, 5.4; neut. equiv., 148. Found: C, 73.1, 72.6; H, 5.2, 5.5; neut. equiv., 144.

Difficulties were experienced in preparing the derived **methyl ester** (α-If) by the usual route (with methanol/HCl). Treatment of α-Ie with diazomethane in ether at 5° gave a 99% yield of the desired product, m.p. 127–128° after recrystallization from benzene–petroleum ether or ethanol; λ_{max}^{MeOH} 236 mμ (ε, 12,000).

Anal. Calcd. for $C_{20}H_{20}O_4$: C, 74.0; H, 6.2. Found: C, 74.1, 74.0; H, 6.4, 6.1.

A solution of 30.0 g. of α-Ie in 500 ml. of acetone was added to a solution of 44.4 g. of anhydrous brucine in 600 ml. of acetone. The mixture was concentrated to 500 ml. and left to crystallize in the refrigerator for 48 hours. The precipitated solid (59.4 g.) was refluxed with 200 ml. of acetone for two hours and the mixture was filtered hot. The residue (47.8 g.) was similarly leached, in succession, with 100 ml. of acetone for one hour, 100 ml. of acetone for two hours, and 300 ml. of acetone for three hours. The residual **brucine salt** (18.8 g.) had m.p. 227–229° dec., $[\alpha]^{31}D$ +71.5° (*c* 1.3, chloroform). No mutarotation could be observed.

Anal. Calcd. for $C_{41}H_{42}N_2O_8$: C, 71.3; H, 6.1. Found: C, 71.4; H, 5.9.

The (+)-α-Ie was liberated by treating 0.5 g. of brucine salt with concd. aqueous ammonia. The resulting suspension was filtered and the filtrate made acid with 6 *N* hydrochloric acid. The precipitate was collected and recrystallized from acetic acid to give product, m.p. 221–222° dec., $[\alpha]^{31.5}D$ +159° (*c* 5.0, ethanol; equil. value).

Anal. Calcd. for $C_{18}H_{16}O_4$: C, 73.0; H, 5.4. Found: C, 73.0; H, 5.3.

Further leachings of the brucine salt with acetone did not increase the rotation of liberated α-Ie.

The combined mother liquors and leachings from the resolution were reduced to a volume of 30 ml. The solid thus obtained (24.7 g., m.p. 190–225° dec.) was decomposed with concd. aqueous ammonia to give acid, 8.2 g., which was recrystallized from acetic acid. The (−)-α-Ie (3.4 g.) which crystallized had m.p. 223–225° dec., $[\alpha]^{31.5}D$ −158° (*c* 5.9, ethanol; equil. value).

Anal. Calcd. for $C_{18}H_{16}O_4$: C, 73.0; H, 5.4. Found: C, 72.7; H, 5.5.

The mother liquors from the acetic acid crystallization after removal of solvent yielded 3.1 g. of acid, $[\alpha]^{31.5}D$ −0.3° (*c* 5.0, ethanol). This procedure thus leads to clean-cut separation of optically pure and racemic fractions of α-Ie from optically impure samples.

The methyl esters were prepared from the respective acids by reaction with diazomethane. (+)-α-Ie afforded (+)-α-If, m.p. 159–160° after four recrystallizations from ethanol, $[\alpha]^{31.5}D$ +178° (*c* 2.0 diglyme; equil. value).

Anal. Calcd. for $C_{20}H_{20}O_4$: C, 74.0; H, 6.2. Found:

C, 74.2; H, 6.3.

Similarly, (−)-α-Ie gave (−)-α-If, m.p. 159–160°, $[\alpha]^{31.5}D$ −178° (c 2.0, diglyme; equil. value).

Anal. Calcd. for $C_{20}H_{20}O_4$: C, 74.0; H, 6.2. Found: C, 74.2; H, 6.5.

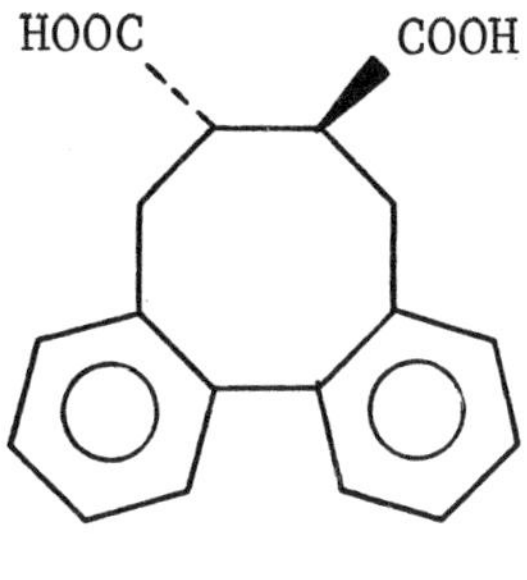

$C_{18}H_{16}O_4$ Ref. 1270

Synthesis and Optical Activation of β-1,2,3,4-Dibenz-1,3-cycloöctadiene-6,7-dicarboxylic Acid (β-Ie).—A solution of the anhydride (10.0 g.) and potassium hydroxide (8 g.) in 90 ml. of 50% aqueous ethanol was refluxed for one hour (or allowed to stand for several days at room temperature). The solution was diluted to one liter with water and made acid. The resulting product (9.2 g., 82%) after recrystallization from acetic acid had m.p. 196–198° dec. (variable, depending on rate of heating).

Anal. Calcd. for $C_{18}H_{16}O_4$: C, 73.0; H, 5.4. Found: C, 72.5; H, 5.6.

The corresponding **methyl ester** (β-If), prepared from the acid by reaction with diazomethane, had m.p. 139–140° after recrystallization from methanol or benzene–petroleum ether; λ_{max}^{MeOH} 236 mμ (ε 13,000). A mixture of α-If and β-If melted at 110–124°.

Anal. Calcd. for $C_{20}H_{20}O_4$: C, 74.0; H, 6.2. Found: C, 74.0, 74.2; H, 6.3, 6.3.

The ethyl ester, prepared from the acid by reaction with diazoethane,[36] had m.p. 91–92° after recrystallization from petroleum ether (lit.[5a] m.p. 77–79°).

Anal. Calcd. for $C_{22}H_{24}O_4$: C, 75.0; H, 6.9. Found: C, 74.9; H, 7.0.

A solution of β-Ie (4.8 g.) in 50 ml. of acetone was added to a solution of morphine (4.9 g.) in 750 ml. of acetone. The mixture was placed in the refrigerator and allowed to stand for three weeks. The resulting precipitate of **morphine salt** (6.0 g.) was collected, washed with cold acetone and air-dried, m.p. 195–203° dec., $[\alpha]^{27}D$ −11.3° (c 2.5, ethylene glycol monomethyl ether; equil. value), mutarotation with k_1^{27} 1.2 × 10^{-4} sec.$^{-1}$. The sample was not obtained in a state of analytical purity.

Anal. Calcd. for $C_{35}H_{35}NO_7$: C, 72.3; H, 6.1. Found: C, 71.2; H, 6.4.

The (−)-**β-Ie**, liberated from the morphine salt by addition of concd. aqueous ammonia in the cold (*ca.* 5°), filtration, acidification of filtrate in the cold, and collection of resulting precipitate, was dried *in vacuo* over sulfuric acid. The product (2.3 g.) had m.p. 189–210° and variable specific rotation (see text).

Anal. Calcd. for $C_{18}H_{16}O_4$: C, 73.0; H, 5.4. Found: C, 72.8; H, 5.6.

The derived **methyl ester** ((−)-β-If) was prepared by addition of ethereal diazomethane at −10° over a period of one min. to (−)-β-Ie slurried with ether at −10°. The solution was dried under vacuum; no attempt was made to purify the residue, m.p. 125–135°, $[\alpha]^{31.5}D$ −77.2° (c 1.6, diglyme; initial value), owing to its rapid racemization in solution ($k_1 \times 10^4$ sec.$^{-1}$ = 0.31 (16.5°), 2.40 (31.5°), 19.3 (50.0°); $k = 6.31 \times 10^{12}$, exp $(-22.8/RT)$). The analysis indicated gross impurities.

Anal. Calcd. for $C_{20}H_{20}O_4$: C, 74.0; H, 6.2. Found: C, 67.8; H, 6.0.

A solution of β-Ie (4.0 g.) in 50 ml. of acetone was added to a solution of brucine (5.32 g.) in 100 ml. of acetone. The mixture was concentrated to 75 ml. and allowed to stand at room temperature for 24 hours. The precipitated **brucine salt** (4.2 g., m.p. 160–164°) was not obtained in a state of analytical purity.

Anal. Calcd. for $C_{41}H_{42}N_2O_8$: C, 71.3; H, 6.1. Found: C, 68.9; H, 6.4.

The (+)-**β-Ie**, liberated as described for the morphine salt, had variable specific rotation (see text), m.p. 185–200°.

Anal. Calcd. for $C_{18}H_{16}O_4$: C, 73.0; H, 5.4. Found: C, 72.5; H, 5.6.

In five similar optical activations, only three attempts led to optically active **β-Ie**. Slow precipitation of the salt seems to be an essential requirement.

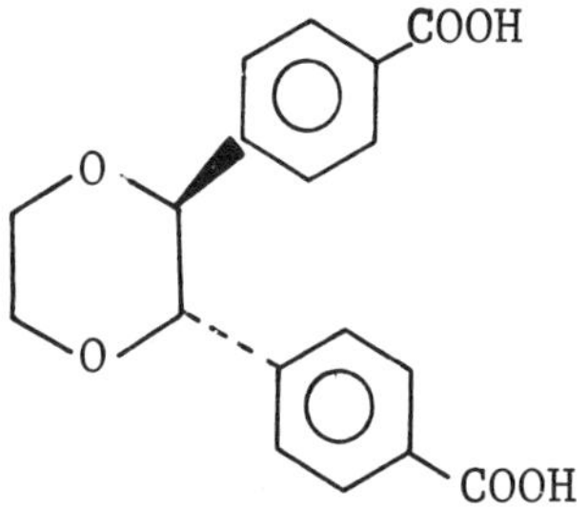

$C_{18}H_{16}O_6$ Ref. 1271

Resolution of ***trans*****-2,3-Bis(4-carboxyphenyl)-1,4-dioxane** (6).—A solution of 2.00 g (6.1 mmoles) of racemic 6 and 6.00 g (15.2 mmoles) of anhydrous brucine in 500 ml of ethyl alcohol was allowed to stand uncovered overnight in a 1-l. erlenmeyer flask. The salt which was deposited weighed 0.59 g (8.7%). Treatment of this salt with 20% sodium hydroxide, filtration of the insoluble brucine, and acidification with concentrated hydrochloric acid furnished 0.16 g (8.0%) of (+)-6: mp 302–306° (no depression), neut equiv 166, and$[\alpha]^{25}D$ +94° (α +1.17°; c 0.155, 25.0 ml of ethyl alcohol; l = 2 dm).

A second crop of crystals deposited on continued slow evaporation weighed 3.2 g (47%). The (+)-6 recovered as above amounted to 0.90 g (45%) and exhibited $[\alpha]^{25}D$ +50° (α 0.80°, c 0.200, 25 ml of ethyl alcohol; l = 2 dm).

A third crop of brucine salt weighing 1.5 g (22%) gave 0.40 g (20%) of (−)-6 having $[\alpha]^{25}D$ −37° (α 0.48°; c 0.160, 25.0 ml of ethyl alcohol; l = 2 dm).

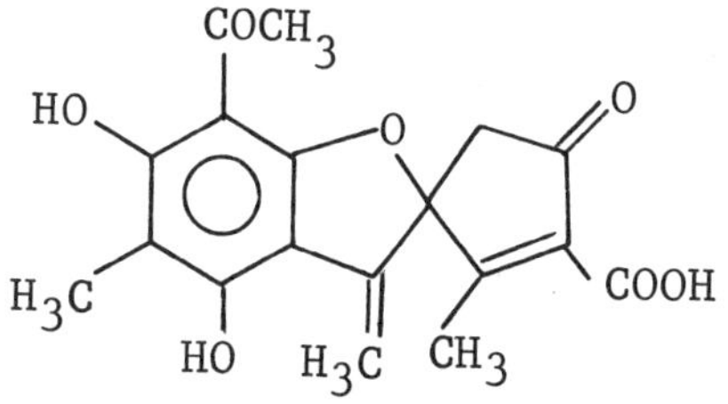

$C_{18}H_{16}O_7$ Ref. 1272

Attempted Resolution of Usnolic Acid.—A solution of the acid (2 g.) in the minimum amount of hot acetone was mixed with (−)-brucine (2·3 g.), dissolved in acetone (20 ml.), and the mixture concentrated; the *brucine* salt of usnolic acid separated in irregular fawn-coloured prisms (4·2 g.), m. p. 190°, $[\alpha]_D^{20}$ −10° (c, 4·0 in $CHCl_3$) (Found: N, 4·1. $C_{41}H_{42}O_{11}N_2$ requires N, 3·8%). This salt (4 g.) was digested with hot methanol (50 ml.) for 2 min. and the insoluble residue then repeatedly extracted with boiling methanol (100 ml.) until the weight was reduced to about 1·5 g. This residual solid (0·5 g.), m. p. 209° (decomp.), $[\alpha]_D^{20}$ −30° (c, 2·0 in $CHCl_3$),

was decomposed with 2N-hydrochloric acid (2 ml.) in methanol (10 ml.), and the precipitated usnolic acid twice recrystallised from dilute methanol containing a drop of dilute hydrochloric acid, forming plates (0·2 g.), m. p. 233°, $[\alpha]_D^{20}$ −19° (*c*, 1·0 in MeOH). Treatment of this product (0·25 g.) with sulphuric acid monohydrate (5 ml.) at 50° for 1 hour gave usnolic acid, m. p. 233°, after purification which had a zero rotation and gave a brucine salt, m. p. 190°, $[\alpha]_D^{20}$ −10° (*c*, 0·25 in $CHCl_3$).

On dilution with water followed by acidification with 2N-hydrochloric acid the initial extract (50 ml.) of the brucine salt gave usnolic acid, m. p. 233°, $[\alpha]_D^{20}$ +31° (*c*, 1·0 in MeOH), after being twice recrystallised from dilute methanol. The brucine salt of this product had m. p. 203° $[\alpha]_D^{20}$ −3·3° (*c*, 0·3 in $CHCl_3$).

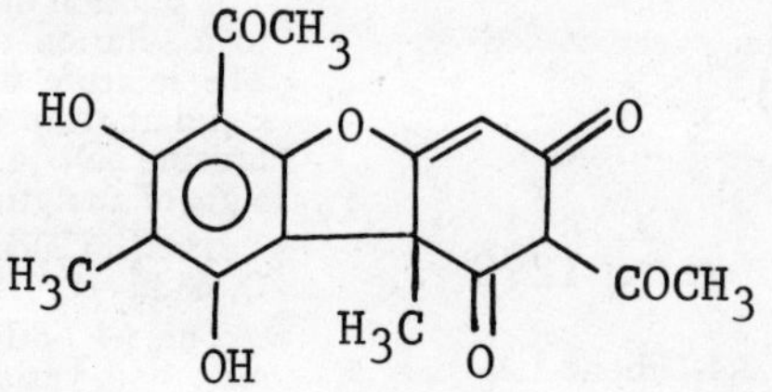

$C_{18}H_{16}O_7$ Ref. 1273

Resolution of Optically Inactive Usnic Acid.—(+)-Usnic acid, m. p. 204°, $[\alpha]_D^{20}$ +495° (*c*, 0·5 in $CHCl_3$) was isolated from *Usnea florida* (Web), *U. florida* (Ach), and *Usnea hirta* (Ach) which had been collected in Wales. (+)-Usnic acid (0·5 g.), dissolved in 8% aqueous sodium hydroxide (20 ml.), was treated with methyl sulphate (1·5 c.c.), added in 3 portions, the solution was acidified, and the precipitate was well washed with water and heated with 75% methanol (20 ml.). On cooling, the filtered solution deposited (+)-O-*methylusnic acid* which crystallised from acetone in bright yellow prisms (0·25 g.), m. p. 136°, $[\alpha]_D^{20}$ +355° (*c*, 2·0 in $CHCl_3$) (Found : C, 63·1; H, 5·0; OMe, 8·6. $C_{18}H_{15}O_6$·OMe requires C, 63·7; H, 5·0; OMe, 9·0%).

A solution of (±)-usnic acid (2 g.) (Schöpf and Heuck, *Annalen*, 1927, **459**, 233) in the minimum amount of acetone was treated with (−)-brucine (2·35 g.), dissolved in methanol (10 ml.), and the greater part of the acetone evaporated on the steam-bath. On cooling, the mixture deposited (−)-brucine (±)-usnate in small colourless plates, m. p. 213° (decomp.) $[\alpha]_D^{20}$ −10° (*c*, 5·0 in $CHCl_3$). This salt (4 g.) was boiled with methanol (100 ml.) for 2 minutes and filtered, giving solid (A) and solution (B). Solid (A) was then extracted with boiling methanol (100 ml.) for 5 min., yielding solid (A_1) and solution (B_1). Repetition of this process with (A_1) and methanol (50 ml.) gave solid (A_2) and solution (B_2). The solutions (B), (B_1), and (B_2) were combined and diluted with water (1 l.), and 24 hours later the solid (C) was collected, leaving the filtrate (D).

The almost colourless residue (A_2) had m. p. 226° (decomp.), $[\alpha]_D^{20}$ +212° (*c*, 2·5 in $CHCl_3$) and was indistinguishable from a specimen of the (−)-brucine salt of authentic (+)-usnic acid which had m. p. 227° (decomp.), $[\alpha]_D^{20}$ +222° (*c*, 5·0 in $CHCl_3$). Decomposition of this salt (A_2) with 2N-sodium hydroxide followed by acidification with 2N-hydrochloric acid gave (+)-usnic acid which was purified from chloroform and alcohol, forming long yellow prisms, m. p. 204°, $[\alpha]_D^{20}$ +467° (*c*, 5·0 in $CHCl_3$), identical with a natural specimen.

Treatment of the filtrate (D) with 2N-hydrochloric acid gave (−)-usnic acid which on purification from chloroform and alcohol had m. p. 203°, $[\alpha]_D^{20}$ −367° (*c*, 5·0 in $CHCl_3$), identical with an authentic specimen. The (−)-brucine salt was prepared from this (−)-acid and had m. p. 222° (decomp.), $[\alpha]_D^{20}$ −240° (*c*, 0·3 g. in $CHCl_3$), whilst the (−)-brucine salt of authentic (−)-usnic acid had m. p. 224° (decomp.), $[\alpha]_D^{20}$ −254° (*c*, 5·0 in $CHCl_3$).

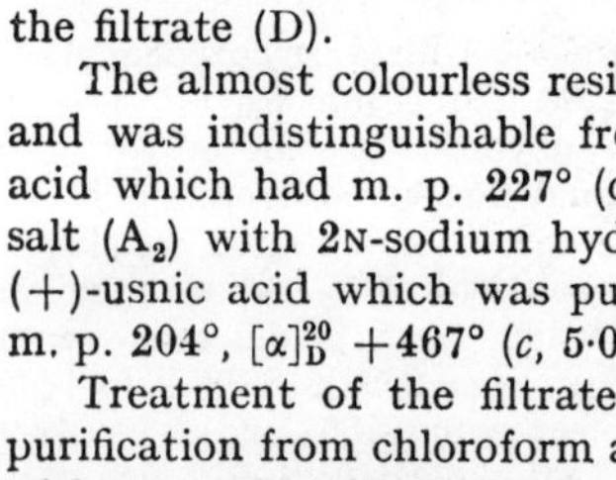

$C_{18}H_{17}ClO_3$ Ref. 1274

C. *Resolution of a racemic 5-oxohexanoic acid. 4-(o-Chlorophenyl)-4-phenyl-5-oxohexanoic acid. Levo form.* Racemic 4-(*o*-chlorophenyl)-4-phenyl-5-oxohexanoic acid (50 g., 0.158 mole) and cinchonine (46.5 g., 0.158 mole) were dissolved in 95% ethanol (250 ml.). The solution was seeded with a few crystals of previously isolated product and refrigerated for 24 hr. The solid that separated (33.1 g.) was filtered off and dried. The mother liquor was concentrated (to 200 ml.) and refrigerated for a week. Another 6.7 g. separated, bringing the total to 39.8 g. The filtrate was concentrated (to 150 ml.), seeded, and refrigerated for a month. Another 2 g. of solid separated. This material was removed by filtration and discarded. The mother liquor was preserved for isolation of the dextro-acid. (This will be referred to as mother liquor I).

The 39.8 g. of combined products were recrystallized from 95% ethanol (250 ml.). After refrigerating for 16 hr. the yield was 28.8 g. After three more recrystallizations from ethanol, 16.1 g. remained, m.p. 171–172°.

Anal. Calcd. for $C_{18}H_{17}ClO_3 \cdot C_{19}H_{22}N_2O$: C, 72.71; H, 6.43; N, 4.58. Found: C, 73.01; H, 6.49; N, 4.54.

The above cinchonine salt (15.85 g., 0.026 mole) was suspended in water and acidified with excess hydrochloric acid. The liberated carboxylic acid was twice extracted with benzene. The combined benzene extracts were washed with water and then twice extracted with an excess of 5% sodium hydroxide solution. The aqueous solution was acidified with hydrochloric acid and extracted with benzene. The

benzene solution was washed with water and dried over sodium sulfate.

Evaporation of the benzene gave 8.2 g. of the *levo*-acid. After three recrystallizations from a mixture of benzene (6 ml.) and cyclohexane (75 ml.), 6.93 g. remained; m.p. 125.5–126.5° (corr.). The $[\alpha]^{25}_{D}$ for a 1% solution in 95% ethanol was −59°.

Dextro form: Mother liquor I, containing the dextro acid–cinchonine salt, was evaporated at reduced pressure. The glasslike product was dissolved in acetonitrile and the insoluble material removed by filtration and discarded. The filtrate was evaporated at reduced pressure and the residue was treated with water and an excess of dilute hydrochloric acid added. The liberated carboxylic acid that separated was extracted twice with benzene. After washing with water, the benzene extract was dried over sodium sulfate.

Evaporation of the benzene gave 28.3 g. of product *A*. Recrystallization of this material from a mixture of cyclohexane (275 ml.) and benzene (60 ml.) gave 16.7 g. of product *B* which is rich in the racemic acid. Recrystallization of *B* from acetonitrile (50 ml.) gave 9.8 g. of nearly pure racemic acid *C*, m.p. 131–132°.

Concentrating and cooling the mother liquors from *B* gave 8.7 g. of *dextro* acid, m.p. 121–122°. Evaporation of the mother liquors from *C* gave 5.2 g. of the same isomer, m.p. 120–122°. These products were combined and twice recrystallized from a mixture of cyclohexane (125 ml.) and benzene (15 ml.). The final yield of *dextro* acid was 11 g., m.p. 124.5–125.5° (corr.). The $[\alpha]^{25}_{D}$ of a 1% solution in 95% ethanol was +59°.

$C_{18}H_{17}NO_2$

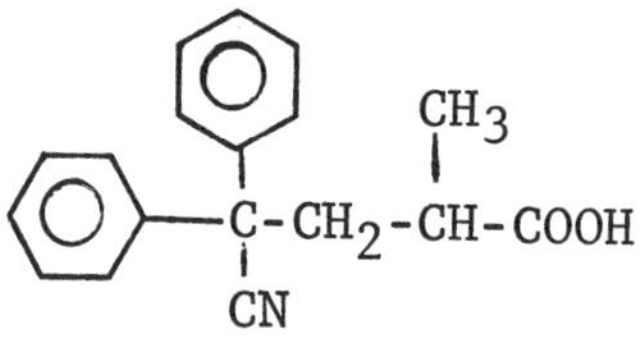

Ref. 1275

Versuch 5: Umwandlung von aktivem Thiuroniumchlorid in das Acetat und Rückverwandlung

2 g (+)-α-Phenyläthyl-thiuroniumchlorid werden in 5 ccm warmem Wasser gelöst und mit 4 g kristall. Natriumacetat in 10 ccm Wasser versetzt. Die sofort entstehende Kristallisation beträgt nach dem Trocknen 2,2 g (quantitativ), Zersp. 152 bis 154°, $[\alpha]^{20}_{D} = +160°$, $c = 2{,}5$ in Alkohol (96%), $l = 1$ dm, $\alpha^{20}_{D} = +4{,}0°$.

Durch Lösen von 1,2 g dieses Acetats in 3 ccm Wasser, enthaltend 0,5 ccm konz. Salzsäure, unter leichtem Erwärmen und Versetzen der abgekühlten Lösung mit 2 ccm eiskalter konz. Salzsäure, lassen sich nach längerem Stehen auf Eis 0,87 g (80% d. Th.) des unveränderten (+)-α-Phenyläthyl-thiuronium-chlorides zurückgewinnen.

In der gleichen Weise ist auch der im Vers. 3 beschriebene (—)-Antipode in das essigsaure Salz und in der weiteren Folge wieder in das Chlorid verwandelbar.

Versuch 6: Spaltung der racem. 3,3-Diphenyl-3-cyan-1-methyl-propan-carbonsäure-(1),(—)-Antipode

38 g camphersaures α-Phenyläthyl-thiuroniumsalz, $[\alpha]^{20}_{D} = -90{,}0°$, Schmp. 190 bis 191°, werden in 220 ccm 96%igem Alkohol suspendiert und auf zirka 50° erwärmt. Die Suspension wird mit 27,8 g 3,3-Diphenyl-3-cyan-1-methyl-propancarbonsäure[6] (Schmp. 135°) in 80 ccm heißem Alkohol versetzt. Dann wird bis zur fast vollständigen Lösung erwärmt und rasch durch eine vorbereitete Porzellannutsche filtriert.

Nach 18stünd. Stehen erhält man so 21,4 g (93%) eines Salzes aus (—)-Phenyläthyl-thiuroniumbase und der (—)-Nitrilocarbonsäure (Mutterlauge siehe unten). Zersp. 182 bis 184° (ab 175° Tröpfchen). $[\alpha]^{20}_{D} = -95{,}0°$ (Methanol). Nach Umkristallisieren aus Methanol zeigte das Salz folgende Konstanten: Zersp. 184 bis 186°, $[\alpha]^{20}_{D} = -105°$; $c = 1$ in Methanol, $l = 2$ dm, $\alpha^{20}_{D} = -2{,}1°$.

$C_{27}H_{29}O_2N_3S$ (459,58). Ber. N 9,14. Gef. N 9,33.

18,3 g des reinen Salzes werden in 60 ccm Äther suspendiert und mit 40 ccm 5%iger Salzsäure bis zur vollständigen Lösung geschüttelt. Die äther. Schicht wird nochmals mit 10 ccm 5%iger Salzsäure nachgeschüttelt und die wäßrigsauren Lösungen vereinigt. Beim Versetzen der salzsauren Lösung mit 25 g kristall. Natriumacetat in 25 ccm warmem Wasser kristallisieren 11 g (—)-α-Phenyläthyl-thiuroniumacetat, $[\alpha]^{20}_{D} = -158°$, Zersp. 152 bis 153°. Die äther. Schicht hinterläßt nach dem Trocknen und Abdestillieren 10,5 g (75% d. Th., bezogen auf eingesetztes Racemat) (—)-3,3-Diphenyl-3-cyano-1-methyl-propancarbonsäure, Schmp. 83 bis 86°. $[\alpha]^{20}_{D} = -58°$; $c = 5$ in Pyridin, $l = 1$ dm, $\alpha^{20}_{D} = -2{,}9$.

$C_{18}H_{17}O_2N$ (279,14). Ber. N 5,02. Gef. N 4,99.

Die obengenannte, alkohol. Mutterlauge der Kristallisation des rohen, (—)-drehenden Salzes vom Zersp. 182 bis 184° wird bei 40° Badtemp. im Vak. zur Trockene verdampft. Der Trockenrest wird im Scheidetrichter zwischen 200 ccm Äther und 50 ccm 5% Salzsäure verteilt. Die saure, wäßr. Schicht gibt nach nochmaligem Ausschütteln mit Äther (Äther verworfen) und Versetzen mit einer konz. Lösung von 30 g Natriumacetat in 30 ccm Wasser, 9,6 g (—)-α-Phenyläthyl-thiuroniumacetat, $[\alpha]_D^{20} = -136°$ (Alkohol) (natriumacetathaltig).

Die äther. Schicht (200 ccm) enthält racem. Nitrilocarbonsäure, (+)-Nitrilocarbonsäure und d-Camphersäure. Zur Trennung wird die äther. Lösung mit 18 g Kaliumbicarbonat (1,8 Mol, bezogen auf Camphersäure) in 100 ccm Wasser 3 bis 4 Stdn. geschüttelt. Beim Ansäuern der $KHCO_3$-Lösung mit konz. Salzsäure erhält man 17,5 g Camphersäure (88% d. Th.). Die äther. Lösung hinterläßt nach dem Trocknen und Eindampfen als Rückstand (14,8 g) größtenteils (+)-Nitrilocarbonsäure.

Versuch 7: (+)-3,3-Diphenyl-3-cyano-1-methyl-propancarbonsäure-1

18 g rohe (+)-3,3-Diphenyl-3-cyan-1-methyl-propancarbonsäure (aus Vers. 6) werden in 30 ccm Methanol bei 40° gelöst und tropfenweise Wasser bis zur bleibenden Trübung zugegeben. Dann wird mit racem. Nitrilocarbonsäure angeimpft und langsam abkühlen gelassen. Dabei tritt Kristallisation der schwerer löslichen, racem. Verbindung ein, während sich die überstehende Lösung trübt. Nach 30 Min. Stehen wird durch Zusatz von einigen Tropfen Methanol die Trübung beseitigt und filtriert. Man erhält so 4,5 g größtenteils racem. Nitrilocarbonsäure, Schmp. 120 bis 130°. Das Filtrat wird im Vak. zur Trockene eingeengt. Der Rückstand, 13,0 g (stark angereicherte (+)-Nitrilocarbonsäure) wird in 30 ccm heißem Alkohol gelöst und mit einer warmen Lösung von 11 g (+)-α-Phenyläthyl-thiuroniumacetat (Vers. 5, $[\alpha]_D^{20} = +160°$ in Alkohol) in 70 ccm Alkohol versetzt. Nach mehrstünd. Stehen erhält man 20 g des Salzes aus (+)-α-Phenyläthyl-thiuroniumbase und d-Nitrilocarbonsäure, Zersp. 182 bis 186°.

Zur Analyse wird aus Methanol umkristallisiert, Zersp. 184 bis 186°. $[\alpha]_D^{20} = +105$; $c = 1$ in Methanol, $l = 2$ dm, $\alpha_D^{20} = +2{,}1°$.

$C_{27}H_{29}O_2N_3S$ (459,58). Ber. N 9,14. Gef. N 9,07.

Die bereits am diastereomeren Salz der (—)-Base mit der (—)-Säure beschriebene Zerlegung (Vers. 6) ergab in fast quantitativer Ausbeute neben dem (+)-α-Phenyläthyl-thiuroniumacetat die (+)-3,3-Diphenyl-3-cyano-1-methyl-propancarbonsäure, Schmp. 83 bis 86°. $[\alpha]_D^{20} = +58°$; $c = 5$ in Pyridin, $l = 1$ dm, $\alpha_D^{20} = +5{,}8°$.

Annähernd gleiche Teile dieses Antipoden mit dem im Vers. 6 erhaltenen (—)-Antipoden der Nitrilocarbonsäure ergaben bei der Mischprobe eine Schmelzpunktserhöhung auf 130°.

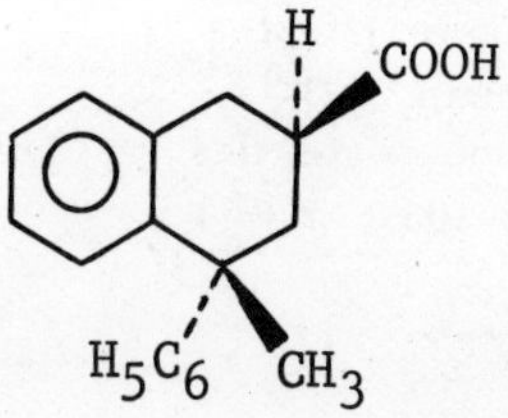

$C_{18}H_{18}O_2$

Ref. 1276

(−)-1-Methyl-*trans*-1-phenyl-1,2,3,4-tetrahydro-3-naphthoic Acid [(−)-II*b*]—To a solution of 2.50 g (9 mmoles) of (+)-dehydroabietylamine (19) dissolved in 210 ml of boiling ethanol was added 2.40 g (9 mmoles) of II*b*. The solution was chilled, and the precipitate was collected and dried to give 4.8 g of a mixture of the diastereomeric salts. Fractional recrystallization from 95% ethanol yielded 2.0 g of white needles, mp 186.5–187°.

The dehydroabietylamine salt was shaken gently with a mixture of 40 ml of 10% sodium carbonate and 100 ml of ether until the solid had dissolved. The aqueous layer was separated and extracted twice with small portions of ether. After acidification, the aqueous phase was extracted twice with ether; the combined ether extracts were washed once with water and dried over anhydrous sodium sulfate. Solvent removal gave crystals of (−)-II*b*, which were recrystallized from 95% ethanol, mp 177.5–178.5°, $[\alpha]_D^{26}$ −100° (c 5, carbon tetrachloride).

(+)-1-Methyl-*trans*-1-phenyl-1,2,3,4-tetrahydro-3-naphthoic Acid [(+)-II*b*]—The mother liquors remaining from the isolation of the dehydroabietylamine salt of (−)-II*b* were diluted intermittently with water over several days; each addition generated the formation of crystals. When a sufficient quantity accumulated, it was isolated and recrystallized from 95% ethanol to give 1.5 g of white crystals, mp 162°. The free acid was recovered in the same manner as described for the (−)-isomer, producing 0.7 g of white needles, mp 175–176°, $[\alpha]_D^{27}$ +96° (c 5, carbon tetrachloride).

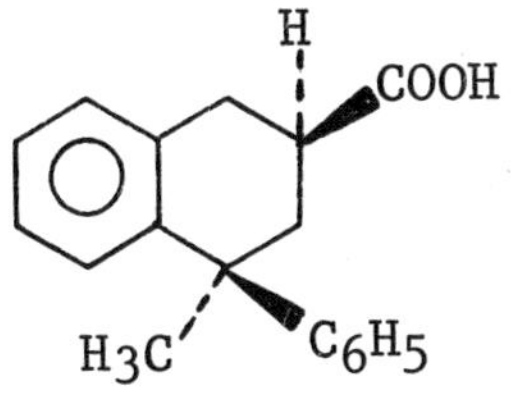

$C_{18}H_{18}O_2$ Ref. 1277

(−)-1-Methyl-*cis*-1-phenyl-1,2,3,4-tetrahydro-3-naphthoic Acid [(−)-IIa]—A mixture of diastereomeric dehydroabietylamine salts of IIa was obtained and resolved in the same manner as described for IIb. The first salt isolated and purified had a melting point of 184–186° and yielded (−)-IIa as an amorphous powder, mp 94–105°, $[\alpha]^{25}_{D}$ −33° (c 3, carbon tetrachloride).

(+)-1-Methyl-*cis*-1-phenyl-1,2,3,4-tetrahydro-3-naphthoic Acid [(+)-IIa]—The second salt obtained from the mother liquors of the isolation of (−)-IIa was purified by recrystallization (ethanol) to yield white needles, mp 167–168°. Liberation of the free acid gave (+)-IIa as an amorphous powder, mp 95–105°, $[\alpha]^{27}_{D}$ +30° (c 3, carbon tetrachloride).

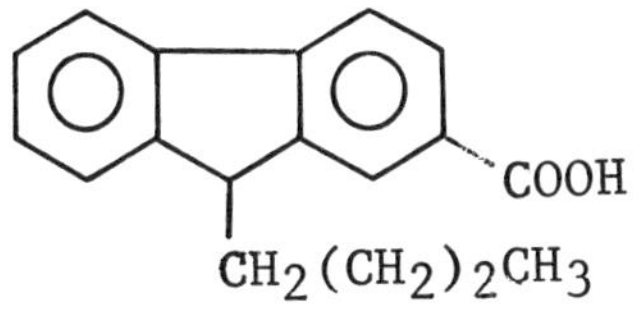

$C_{18}H_{18}O_2$ Ref. 1278

Note:

The authors reported that brucine was used to separate the (-)-enantiomer (from either CH_3OH, acetone or an 8:2 mixture of acetone and $CHCl_3$). The physical constants of the brucine salt were found to be: m.p. 225° (acetone-dilute) $[\alpha]^{20}_{D}$ -40.00° (CH_3OH). The liberated acid was found to have the following physical constants: m.p. 134-135° (CH_3OH), $[\alpha]^{20}_{D}$ -71.60° (CH_3OH). Cinchonidine was used to obtain the (+)-enantiomer (from either CH_3OH, acetone or an 8:2 acetone/$CHCl_3$). The cinchonidine salt had the following physical constants: m.p. 197-198° (acetone-dilute), $[\alpha]^{20}_{D}$ -45.00° (CH_3OH). The liberated acid was found to have the following physical constants: m.p. 135° (CH_3OH), $[\alpha]^{20}_{D}$ +69.00° (CH_3OH).

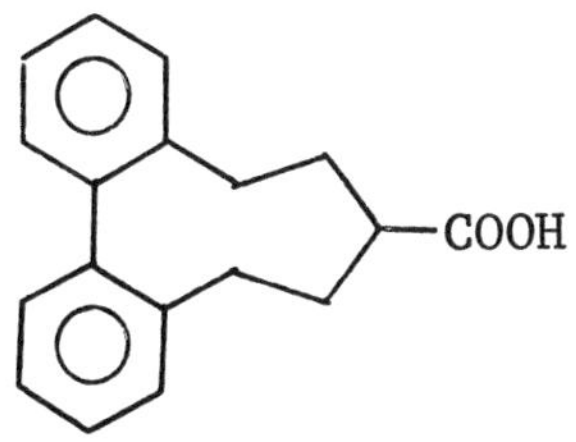

$C_{18}H_{18}O_2$ Ref. 1279

(−)-1,2,3,4-Dibenzcyclonona-1,3-diene-7-carboxylic Acid (I).—A solution of 0.500 g. of (±)-I and 0.548 g. of quinidine in 15 ml. of acetone was heated under reflux for 1 hour. **The quinidine salt** (0.842 g., 84%) which crystallized during that period and on standing overnight had m.p. 188–192°, $[\alpha]^{25}D$ + 129° (*c* 1.0, chf.).

Anal. Calcd. for $C_{38}H_{42}N_2O_4$: C, 77.26; H, 7.17; N, 4.74. Found: C, 77.47; H, 7.34; N, 4.75.

A solution of quinidine salt in a minimum volume of chloroform was shaken with ice-cold dil. hydrochloric acid. The mixture was extracted with ether. The combined ethereal extracts were washed with water and dried. The solvent was evaporated under reduced pressure. The residue crystallized on standing overnight at −20°. The product (88%) had m.p. 135–139°, undepressed by admixture of (±)-I. The infrared spectrum was identical with that of (±)-I; optical rotation: $[\alpha]^{28}D$ − 48.4° (*c* 1.0, benzene), $[\alpha]^{28}D$ − 42.3° (*c* 1.0, chloroform); ORD in dioxane (*c* 1.02–0.0045, 31°): $[\alpha]_{589}$ − 15°, $[\alpha]_{236}$ − 8840°, $[\alpha]_{226}$ − 2810° (using an automatically recording Rudolph spectropolarimeter).

Anal. Calcd. for $C_{18}H_{18}O_2$: C, 81.17; H, 6.81. Found: C, 81.44; H, 6.94.

The (+)-isomer ($[\alpha]^{25}D$ + 25° (*c* 0.9, chloroform)) was obtained by decomposition of the salt ($[\alpha]^{28}D$ − 68° (*c* 1.0, chf.)) which precipitated from (±)-I and *quinine* in acetone. The product was not further investigated.

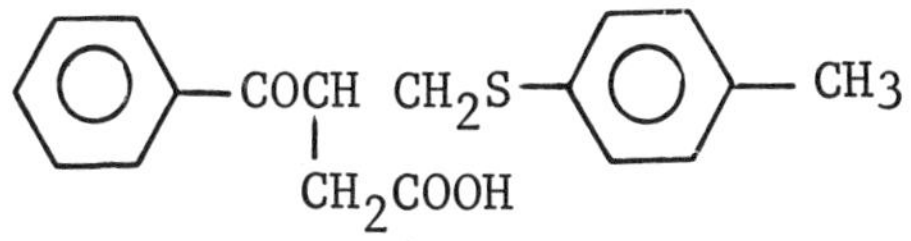

$C_{18}H_{18}O_3S$ Ref. 1280

(+)-α-*Carboxymethyl*-β-(p-*tolylthio*)*propiophenone*. α-Carboxymethyl-β-(*p*-tolylthio)propiophenone (VII) (*ca.* 14 g.) and (−)-brucine (18 g.) were dissolved in acetone (80 ml.). After 1 hr., the brucine salt (9 g.) precipitated, m. p. 138—139° (from acetone), $[\alpha]_D$ +42° (*c* 1 in chloroform) (Found: C, 70·05; H, 5·95; N, 4·1. $C_{41}H_{44}N_2O_7S$ requires C, 69·45; H, 6·25; N, 3·95%). Crystallisation of the residue from evaporation of the acetone mother-liquor from ethyl acetate, yielded more dextro-rotatory salt, $[\alpha]_D$ +25—30°.

The (−)-brucine salt of (+)-α-carboxymethyl-β-(*p*-tolylthio)propiophenone (5 g., finely powdered) was suspended in ether and shaken with dilute hydrochloric acid. The ether layer was washed with acid and water, dried, and evaporated to give the sulphide (XV) as a thick oil (2·1 g.), $[\alpha]_D$ +43° (*c* 1 in methanol), characterised by oxidation to the corresponding sulphone.

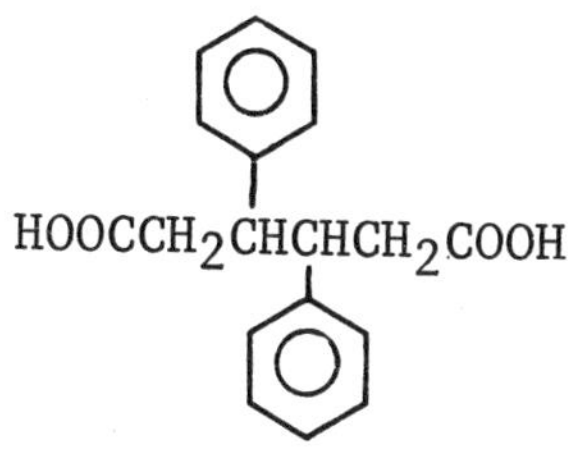

$C_{18}H_{18}O_4$ Ref. 1281

Note:

Acid resolved via brucine. The more insoluble salt had a m.p. of 200-201° and $[\alpha]^{20}_{D}$ 14.36° (c 3.09, ethanol).

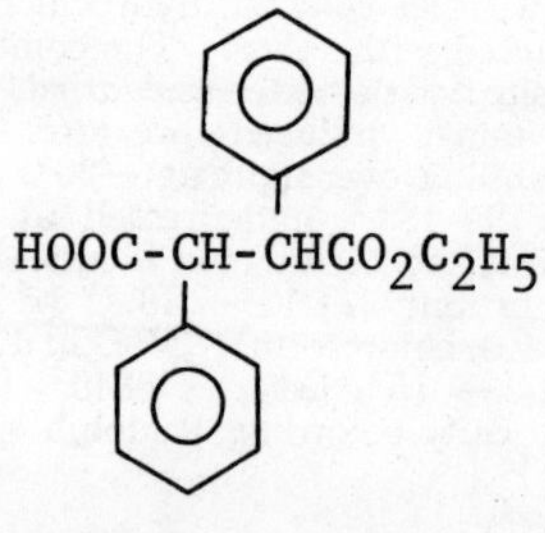

$C_{18}H_{18}O_4$ Ref. 1282

(+)-*Ethyl Hydrogen αα′-Diphenylsuccinate* (II).—The (±)-half-ester (35 g.) [prepared from the (±)-anhydride and ethanol] and (−)-ephedrine (20 g.) were dissolved in hot aqueous ethanol (35%; 3·75 l.). The salt (50 g.) was deposited overnight, and recrystallised (five times) to constant rotation, $[\alpha]_D^{20}$ +164° (*c* 0·780 in ethanol). The (+)-half-ester [from the salt (9 g.)], after one recrystallisation from light petroleum (b.p. 80—100°) had m.p. 118—119°, $[\alpha]_D^{20}$ +336° (*c* 1·40 in acetone), $\nu_{max.}$ (Nujol) 942, 1207, 1250, 1401, 1696, and 1733 cm.$^{-1}$.

The salt recovered from the mother liquors of the above resolution, after five recrystallisations from absolute ethanol gave, when decomposed, the (−)-half-ester (15 g.), m.p. 118—119°, $[\alpha]_D^{20}$ −335·6 (*c* 2·436 in acetone) {lit.,[7] m.p. 113·5—114·5°, $[\alpha]_D^{20}$ −328·7° (*c* 1·4496 in acetone)}.

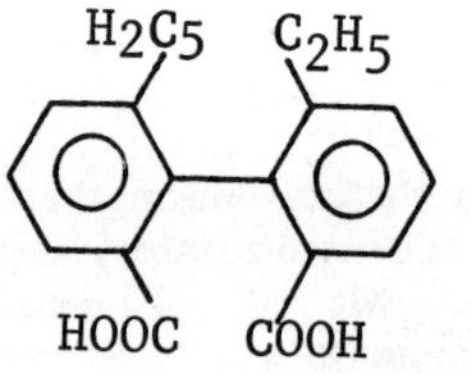

$C_{18}H_{18}O_4$ Ref. 1283

Resolution of 6,6′-Diethyl-2,2′-diphenic Acid. A mixture of 29.837 g (0.1 mol) of racemic 6,6′-diethyl-2,2′-diphenic acid, 37.921 g (0.1 mol) of (−)-quinine, and 150 ml of 95% ethanol was heated on a steam bath until solution occurred and then filtered and allowed to stand overnight, yielding 23.009 g of white crystalline salt, mp 155–158°, $[\alpha]^{30}_{589}$ −123°[24] (*c* 0.66, MeOH). An additional crystallization gave 18.431 g, mp 158–159°, $[\alpha]^{30}_{589}$ −137° (*c* 0.77, MeOH). A portion of this salt on hydrolysis (6 *N* HCl) gave acid with mp 170–172°, $[\alpha]^{30}_{589}$ +6.9° (*c* 1.85, MeOH). Further recrystallization of the salt did not improve these values. A 14.49-g sample of salt, hydrolyzed to 5.243 g of acid, mp 170–172°, $[\alpha]^{30}_{589}$ +7.1° (*c* 0.70, MeOH). Two crystallizations from ether–hexane gave 4.535 g (15.2%) of 6,6′-diethyl-2,2′-diphenic acid, mp 170–172°, $[\alpha]^{30}_{589}$ +7.1° (*c* 0.70, MeOH), with no further change in rotation on crystallization. The ir and nmr spectra were identical with those of racemic material; ORD max at 300 nm, intercept at 260 nm, $[\alpha]^{30}_{300}$ +460° (*c* 0.05, MeOH). Treatment of the resolution mother liquors with acetone at 0° and removing three crops of crystals gave a fourth crop of 1.3760 g of salt, mp 140–150°, $[\alpha]^{30}_{589}$ −76° (*c* 0.67, MeOH). A portion of this salt on hydrolysis (6 *N* HCl) gave acid with mp 178–180°, $[\alpha]^{30}_{589}$ −6.7° (*c* 0.47, MeOH), with no further change in rotation on recrystallization.

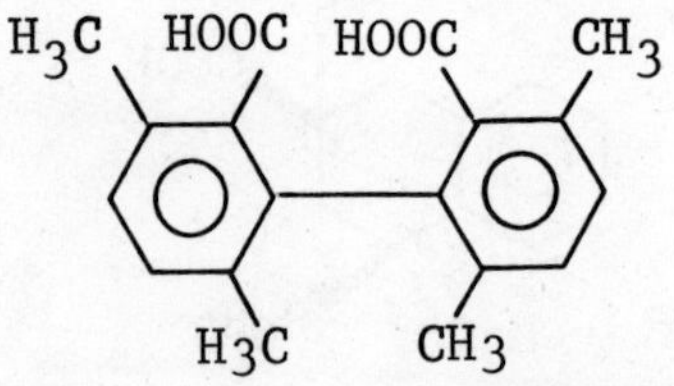

$C_{18}H_{18}O_4$ Ref. 1284

Optical resolution of 3,3′,6,6′-tetramethyldiphenic acid. Preliminary tests were carried out as described for 4,4′-dicarboxy-2,2′,5,5′-tetraethyl-3,3′-bithienyl. With brucine, an oily salt was obtained. The acid derived from the cinchonidine salt was almost inactive. However, quinine in 50% ethanol gave a crystalline salt from which an acid $[\alpha]_D^{20}$ = −70 (chloroform) was obtained, while the salt with cinchonine gave an acid having $[\alpha]_D^{20}$ = +60° (chloroform). These two alkaloids were chosen for the resolution of 3,3′,6,6′-tetramethyldiphenic acid.

A mixture of 17 g (0.057 mole) of 3,3′,6,6′-tetramethyldiphenic acid [2] and 43.1 g (0.114 mole) of quinine trihydrate was dissolved in 1600 ml of hot 50% ethanol.

The filtered solution was allowed to stand overnight at room temperature and the salt which separated was filtered off. The resolution was then carried out as described for 4,4′-dicarboxy-2,2′,5,5′-tetraethyl-3,3′-bithienyl. The course of the resolution is given below:

Crystallization	1	2	3	4	5
ml, 50% ethanol	1600	800	450	300	250
g, salt	22.6	19.3	17.3	15.2	13.1
$[\alpha]_D^{20}$ of acid ($CHCl_3$)	−67°	−69°	−66°	−67°	−67°

The mother liquor from the first crystallization of the quinine salt was evaporated and the residue decomposed to give 7.4 g (0.0248 mole) of acid which was dissolved together with 14.6 g (0.0497 mole) of cinchonine in 600 ml of boiling 96% ethanol and allowed to stand overnight at room temperature. The salt formed was filtered off, it's activity measured, and the salt recrystallized. The progress of resolution is given below:

Crystallization	1	2	3	4	5
ml, 96% ethanol	600	450	300	250	250
g, salt	21.5	14.4	9.0	5.4	4.5
$[\alpha]_D^{20}$ of acid ($CHCl_3$)	+55°	+64°	+68°	+67°	+68°

(+)-*3,3′,6,6′-Tetramethyldiphenic acid.* 12.0 g of cinchonine salt (from the last three crystallizations) was decomposed with 6-*N* hydrochloric acid and the active acid extracted with ether. The combined ether phases was washed with dilute hydrochloric acid and water, dried and the ether evaporated *in vacuo* giving 3.8 g of (+)-acid, m.p. 265–270°C dec, after recrystallization from ether-ligroin.

The rotations (sodium line) in different solvents are given below:

Solvent	Conc. (g acid/dl)	α_D^{20}	$[\alpha]_D^{20}$	$[M]_D^{20}$
Chloroform (with 1% ethanol)	0.001	+0.007°	+67°	+200°
	0.982	+0.567°	+67°	+200°
Methylene chloride	0.062	+0.035°	+56°	+165°
0.1-*N* sodium hydroxide	0.273	−0.218°	−80°	−240°

Anal. $C_{18}H_{18}O_4$ (298.3)
Calc. C 72.47 H 6.08
Found C 72.21 H 6.20

(−)-*3,3′,6,6′-Tetramethyldiphenic acid.* 13.1 g of the quinine salt was treated with 6-*N* hydrochloric acid and worked up as described above, giving 4.1 g of (−)-acid, m.p. 265–270°C dec after recrystallization from ether-ligroin. The IR-spectrum was identical to that of the (+)-acid. The rotations (sodium line in different solvents) are given below:

Solvent	Conc. (g acid/dl)	α_D^{20}	$[\alpha]_D^{20}$	$[M]_D^{20}$
Ethanol	0.046	−0.037°	−80°	−240°
Chloroform (with 1% ethanol)	0.521	−0.349°	−67°	−200°
Methylene chloride	0.081	−0.045°	−56°	−165°
Dioxane	0.365	+0.185°	+51°	+150°
0.1-*N* sodium hydroxide	0.324	+0.260°	+80°	+240°

Anal. $C_{18}H_{18}O_4$ (298.3)
Calc. C 72.47 H 6.08
Found C 72.23 H 6.19

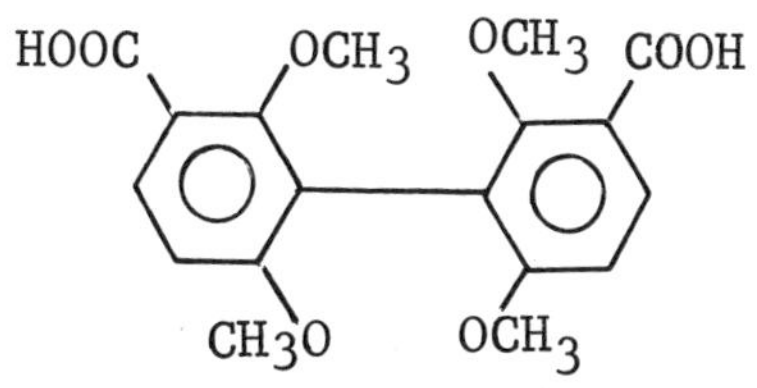

$C_{18}H_{18}O_8$ Ref. 1285

Note: A brucine salt of I was easily obtained and showed m.p. 203-204° (decomp.) after three time recrystallizations from ethanol. Decomposition of the salt with acid gave an optically active acid, m.p. 183-184° (uncor.) (from ethyl acetate), $[\alpha]^{22}_D$ = -18.5° and $[\alpha]^{22}_{400}$ = -31.5° (c, 5, $CHCl_3$).

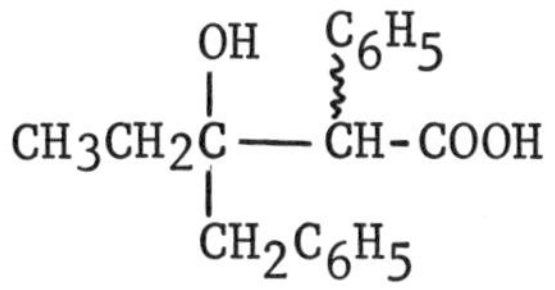

$C_{18}H_{20}O_3$ Ref. 1286

Enantiomers of the Predominant Diastereoisomer of 3-Benzyl-3-hydroxy-2-phenylvaleric Acid (–)-(Ia) and (+)-(Ia) and Their Salts with (+)-1,3-Diphenylpropylamine (V) and (VI). The acid (Ia) was dissolved in a small amount of a 4:1 mixture of ether and methanol, and with stirring an ethereal solution of (+)-DPPA was added. After stirring and cooling a precipitate separated; it was filtered off, washed well with ether, and fractionally crystallized from acetone. The less soluble salt with mp 184-186° (V) and the more soluble salt with mp 165-166° (VI) were isolated fairly readily. The unseparated salt was obtained in 93.5% yield, and the separation was effected in about 80% yield. The two salts were decomposed with 5% KOH. The amine was extracted with ether. Aqueous solutions of the potassium salts were acidified to Congo Red with hydrochloric acid, and the mixtures were cooled. The two acids were recrystallized from alcohol. From the salt (V) we obtained the levorotatory acid (–)-(Ia), $[\alpha]_D^{18}$ –66.7° (c 1.5, alcohol).* From the salt (VI) we obtained the dextrorotatory acid (+)-(Ia), $[\alpha]_D^{18}$ +66.7° (c 1.5, alcohol). Yield of separated acids 76%.

*Angles of rotation were measured with an A-1-EPL automatic polarimeter.

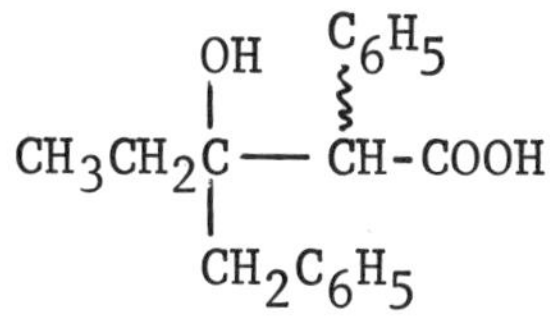

$C_{18}H_{20}O_3$ Ref. 1287

Enantiomers of the Second Diastereoisomer of 3-Benzyl-3-hydroxy-2-phenylvaleric Acid (+)-(Ib) and (–)-(Ib). Ethereal solutions of equimolecular amounts of (Ib) and (+)-DPPA were mixed with stirring, and the crystalline precipitate that separated in the cold was filtered off. The filtrate was evaporated, and a thick noncrystallizing oil was obtained. The crystalline precipitate, after three crystallizations from acetone, melted at 155-157°. From this salt, by the method described for (+)-(Ia) and (–)-(Ia), we prepared the acid (+)-(Ib), except that aqueous alcohol was used for its crystallization; $[\alpha]_D^{18}$ +117° (c 0.7, alcohol). By the same method, from the noncrystallizing salt we obtained the acid (–)-(Ib), $[\alpha]_D^{18}$ –117° (c 0.7, alcohol). Yield 50%.

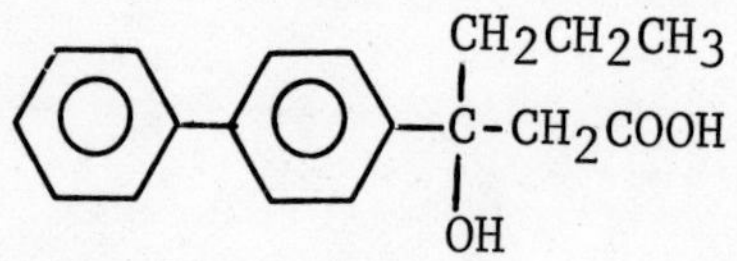

$C_{18}H_{20}O_3$ Ref. 1288

Note:

For resolution procedure and physical constants, see Ref. 1170.

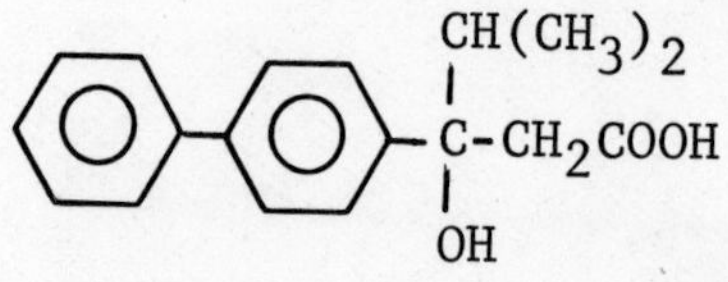

$C_{18}H_{20}O_3$ Ref. 1289

Note:

For resolution procedure and physical constants, see Ref. 1170.

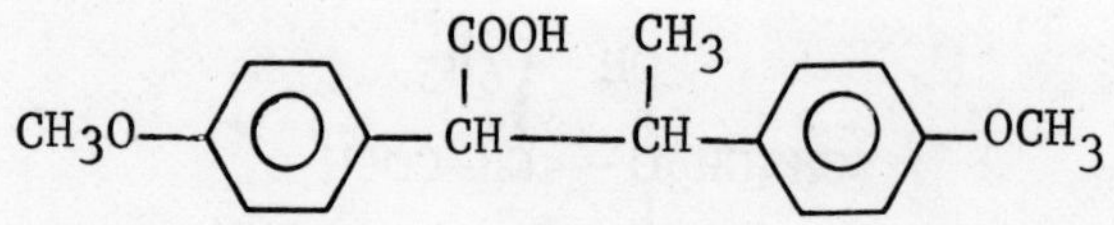

$C_{18}H_{20}O_4$ Ref. 1290

(x) *Resolution of* erythro-*2,3-Bis*(p-*methoxyphenyl*)*butyric Acid* (*10c*)

(i) *Dextro.*—The acid (13·5 g) and (−)-quinine (17·1 g) were dissolved in hot absolute ethanol (750 ml), and the solution allowed to cool slowly. After 3 hr the crude salt (20·6 g), m.p. 179–184°, was collected. Ten recrystallizations from ethanol, and fractional crystallization of the mother liquors, gave pure (+)-erythro-*2,3-bis*(p-*methoxyphenyl*)*butyric acid* (−)-*quinine salt* (3·3 g), m.p. 202–203·5°, $[\alpha]_D$ −60·1° (*c*, 1·05 in dioxan) (Found: C, 72·8; H, 7·2; N, 4·5. $C_{18}H_{20}O_4,C_{20}H_{24}N_2O_2$ requires C, 73·1; H, 7·1; N, 4·5%).

The acid was recovered from the salt in the usual way. Two recrystallizations from methanol afforded (+)-erythro-*2,3-bis*(p-*methoxyphenyl*)*butyric acid* (1·3 g), m.p. 206–207·5°, $[\alpha]_D$ +29·9° (*c*, 1·13 in dioxan) (Found: C, 71·9; H, 6·8. $C_{18}H_{20}O_4$ requires C, 72·0; H, 6·7%).

Esterification with diazomethane gave the (+)-*methyl ester*, m.p. 124–125·5°, $[\alpha]_D$ +23·9° (*c*, 1·13 in dioxan) (Found: C, 72·8; H, 6·9. $C_{19}H_{22}O_4$ requires C, 72·6; H, 7·1%).

(ii) *Laevo.*—Mother liquor enriched in the soluble (−)-acid quinine salt was evaporated. The recovered acid (1·4 g) had m.p. 202–205°, $[\alpha]_D$ −19·7° (*c*, 1·01 in dioxan). This was dissolved in ethanol (45 ml) containing (−)-ephedrine (0·77 g). Three recrystallizations of the product gave (−)-erythro-*2,3-bis*(p-*methoxyphenyl*)*butyric acid* (−)-*ephedrine salt* (830 mg), m.p. 185–186°, $[\alpha]_D$ −37·0° (*c*, 0·81 in dioxan) (Found: C, 71·9; H, 7·6. $C_{18}H_{20}O_4,C_{10}H_{15}NO$ requires C, 72·2; H, 7·6%).

Two recrystallizations of the recovered acid from ethanol gave (−)-erythro-*2,3-bis*-(p-*methoxyphenyl*)*butyric acid*, m.p. 205–207°, $[\alpha]_D$ −28·1° (*c*, 1·21 in dioxan) (Found: C, 71·9; H, 6·7. $C_{18}H_{20}O_4$ requires C, 72·0; H, 6·7%).

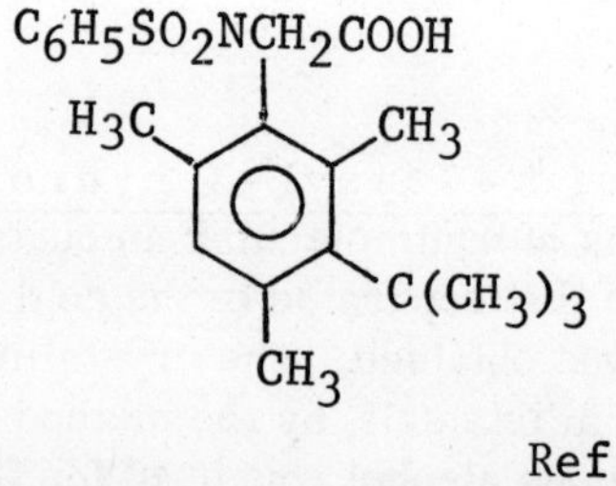

$C_{18}H_{21}NO_4S$ Ref. 1291

Resolution of N-Benzenesulfonyl-N-carboxymethylisoduridine.—A solution of 4.20 g. of N-benzenesulfonyl-N-carboxymethylisoduridine, 3.54 g. of cinchonine and 325 ml. of ethyl acetate was prepared by warming the mixture and filtering the hot solution. The volume was reduced to 200 ml. by passing an air stream over the solution at room temperature. The solution was cooled in a refrigerator for several days, and 2.85 g. of colorless prisms was collected, m.p. 185–188°. After recrystallization from ethyl acetate the melting point was 186–188°, and the specific rotation unchanged; rotation: 0.0508 g. made up to 10 ml. at 30° with ethanol gave α_D +0.50°, *l* 1; $[\alpha]^{30}_D$ +98.5°.

The optically active acid was regenerated from the pure salt in a manner previously described.[11] From 1.48 g. of the pulverized salt was obtained 0.75 g. (94%) of (+)-N-benzenesulfonyl-N-carboxymethylisoduridine, m.p. 184–186°; rotation: 0.0185 g. made up to 1.607 ml. with ethanol at 29° gave α_D +0.08°, *l* 1; $[\alpha]^{29}_D$ + 6.9°.

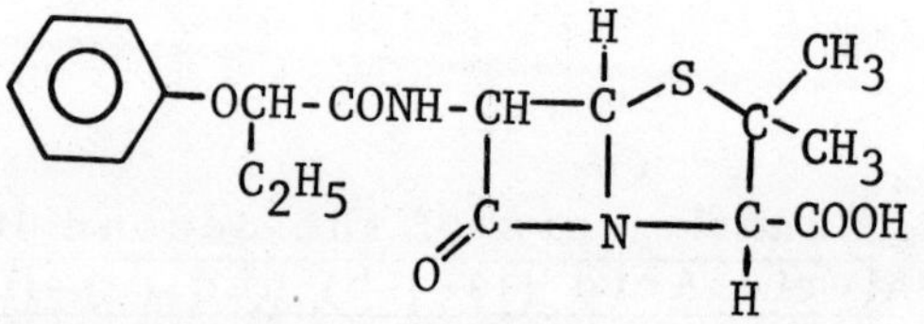

$C_{18}H_{22}N_2O_5S$ Ref. 1292

Beispiel

10 Teile D,L-α-Phenoxypropylpenicillinkalium werden in 400 Teilen Wasser bei 0°C mit 100 Teilen n-Phosphorsäure versetzt. Die Suspension wird dreimal mit je 80 Teilen Essigester extrahiert. Die gewaschenen und getrockneten vereinigten Extrakte werden mit 5,2 Teilen D-threo-1-p-Nitrophenyl-2-amino-1,3-dihydroxypropan in 70 Teilen warmem n-Butanol versetzt. Nach einigen Minuten fällt ein kristalliner Niederschlag aus. Nach 2 Stunden Stehen bei 0°C wird der Niederschlag abgesaugt, mit Äther gewaschen und getrocknet. Die Ausbeute beträgt 6,6 Teile. Das Salz entspricht der Zusammensetzung $C_{27}H_{34}N_4O_9S$, hat den Schmelzpunkt 155 bis

157°C (Zersetzung) und $[\alpha]_D^{22} = +112°$ (in Dioxan—Methanol—Wasser = 6 : 2 : 2). Säuert man eine Suspension von 5,5 g dieses Salzes in 500 ml Wasser auf einen p_H-Wert von 2 an, extrahiert mit 120 ml Essigester und versetzt mit 15 ml 1molarer acetonischer Kaliumcaprylatlösung, so erhält man 2,19 g des L-α-Phenoxypropylpenicillin-Kaliums mit $[\alpha]_D^{20} = +193°$C, das sich im mikrobiologischen Test wie das aus reiner L-α-Phenoxybuttersäure hergestellte verhält.

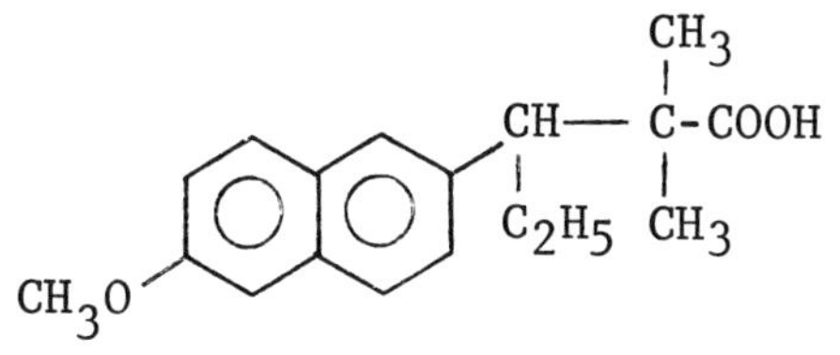

$C_{18}H_{22}O_3$ Ref. 1293

I. - Obtention de l'acide levogyre

20 g d'éther methylique de l'acide α,α-diméthyl-β-éthyl allénolique (F:137-138°) et 22 g de quinine anhydre sont dissous dans 300 cm³ de méthanol. On récolte, après une nuit, 23,8 g de sel A: $[\alpha]_D$ = -101°. Cette fraction, recristallisée dans 430 cm³ de méthanol, donne 16,3 g de B: $[\alpha]_D$ = -108°. Ceux-ci, après recristallisation dans 350 cm³, fournissent 12 g (C), lesquels, dans 300 cm³ de méthanol, donnent 9,1 g (D, avec $[\alpha]_D$ = -111°,5±1°,5). Finalement une derniere cristallisation dans 250 cm³ de méthanol, donne 6,3 g de E: $[\alpha]_D$ = -112° ± 1°,5.

Les eaux-mères de B, C, D sont évaporées à moitié de leur volume: on récolte respectivement les fractions B_1(2,5 g), C_1(2 g) et D_1(1,4 g). Les eaux-mères de C_1 et D_1 sont à nouveau évaporées à moitié et l'on obtient C_2(1 g) et D_2(0,7 g).

B_1 et C_2 sont recristallisés dans les eaux-mères de D_2 (complétées à 90 cm³): on récolte 2,8 g de F.

C_1, D_2 et F song recristallisés dans 250 cm³ de méthanol et donnent 3,7 g de H.

Les eaux-mères de E, par évaporation, fournissent, E_1. Les fractions D_1, E_1 et H pour lesquelles $[\alpha]_D$ = -111°,5 sont jointes et traitées de meme que E, pour regénérer l'acide.

A cet effet on agite les sels de quinine avec un excès d'acide chlorhydrique N, en presence d'ether. Lorsque tout le solide est dissous, on décante la couche éthérée lave à l'eau, séche et évaporé. On récolte 2,9 g d'acide a partir de E et 3,5 g à partir de E_1, D_1 et H.

Sel de quinine de l'acide lévogyre.

Fines aiguilles feutrées, fondant vers 194°-195° (bloc, instantané). Solubilité dans le méthanol à 16°: 1,1 g dans 100 cm³.

$[\alpha]_D$ = -112° ± 1°,5 (0,206 g dans 10 cm³ d'ether monoéthylique du glycol).

Sel d'éphedrine gauche de l'acide levogyre

A partir de 1,4 g d'acide α_D = -23° et 0,9 g d-éphédrine gauche, dans 10 cm³ de méthanol, on obtient 1,75 g de sel: $[\alpha]_D$ = -42° ± 0°,5 (0,2214 g dans 10 cm³ d'ethylglycol). Après une seconde crystallisation dans le méthanol, on a encore $[\alpha]_D$ = -42°.

Sel d'ephedrine droite de l'acide lévogyre.

1 g d'acide $[\alpha]_D$ = -23° est traité par 0,7 g de base droite dans 5 cm³ de méthanol. On recueille 1,1 g de sel qu'on recristallise dans le méthanol $[\alpha]_D$ = -12°,5 ± 0°,5 (dans l'éthylglycol).

Solubilité dans le méthanol à 16°: 8,8 g dans 100 cm³.

Acide 2-méthyl α,α-diméthyl β-éthyl allénolique lévogyre.

5,5 g d'acide provenant de l'hydrolyse précédemment décrite sont recristallisés dans 27,5 cm³ d'ethanol et 13,5 cm³ d'eau. On récolte 4,8 g d'acide F : 142°-143°. Fines aiguilles très differentes des cristaux trapus de l'acide racémique. $[\alpha]_D$ = -24° ± 0°,5 (0,2078 g dans 5 cm³ d'alcool absolu).

Acide α,α-diméthyl β-éthyl allénolique lévogyre.

La déméthylation de l'acide précédent a été effectuée par le chlorhydrate de pyridine suivant le mode operatoire décrit pour le racémique (3). L'acide est recristallisé dans l'éthanol aqueux ou dans le benzene. F: 187°-188° $[\alpha]_D$ = -24° ± 1° (0,222 g dans 10 cm³ d'alcool absolu).

II. - Obtention de l'acide dextrogyre.

Les eaux-mères de précipitation du sel de quinine A sont évaporées a sec et le résidu est hydrolysé comme précédemment par l'acide chlorhydrique dilué. On obtient ainse 8,4 g d'acide brut: $[\alpha]_D$ = +20°. Celui-ci est traité par 6 g d'éphédrine droite cristallisee (hydrate), dans 80 cm³ de méthanol. Après une nuit de repos, on essore 10,1 g de sel. Avec deux recristallisations dans 50 cm³ de méthanol, on récolte 8,2 g, puis 6,2 g de sel pure.

Sel d'éphédrine droite de l'acide dextrogyre.

$[\alpha]_D^{18}$ = +42°,5 ± 0°,5 (0,216 g dans 10 cm³ d'éthyl glycol). Fines aiguilles brillantes. Solubilité dans le méthanol a 16°: 3,3 g dans 100 cm³.

Acide 2-méthyl α,α-diméthyl β-éthyl allénolique dextrogyre.

Le sel d'éphédrine précédent est décomposé suivant le procédé utilisé pour l'obtention de l'isomère gauche. 5,5 g de sel ont donné 3,4 g d'acide qu'on recristallise deux fois dans l'éthanol aqueux. Fines aiguilles F: 142°-143°. $[\alpha]_D$ = +23° ± 0°,5 (0,397 g dans 10 cm³ d'alcool absolu).

Sel de quinine de l'acide dextrogyre.

A partir de 0,7 g d'acide $[\alpha]_D = + 23°$ et 0,8 g de quinine dans 10 cm³ de méthanol, on obtient 1,2 g de sel $[\alpha]_D = - 75°,5$.

F : 182°-183° (bloc instantané). Le mélange avec le sel de quinine de l'acide lévogyre fond vers 177°.

Acide α.α-diméthyl β-éthyl allénolique dextrogyre.

Obtenu en traitant à 190° pendant une heure 0,5 g d'acide méthoxylé dextrogyre par 2,5 g de chlorhydrate de pyridine. Le produit brut de la réaction (rendement sensiblement quantitatif) est recristallisé dans le benzène avec décoloration par le noir animal.

F : 185°-187°,5. $[\alpha]_D^{18} = + 25°,5 \pm 0°,5$ (0,274 g dans 10 cm³ d'alcool absolu).

(*) Les sels d'éphédrine droite ou gauche des deux acides stéréoisomères ne présentent pas de points de fusion nets. Posés sur le bloc, ils se décomposent après des temps variables, à partir de 135° environ; les points de fusion instantanés se situent aux environs de 150°-160°, mais ils sont trop imprécis pour qu'on puisse en tenir compte comme critère de pureté. Seul le pouvoir rotatoire a un sens à cet égard.

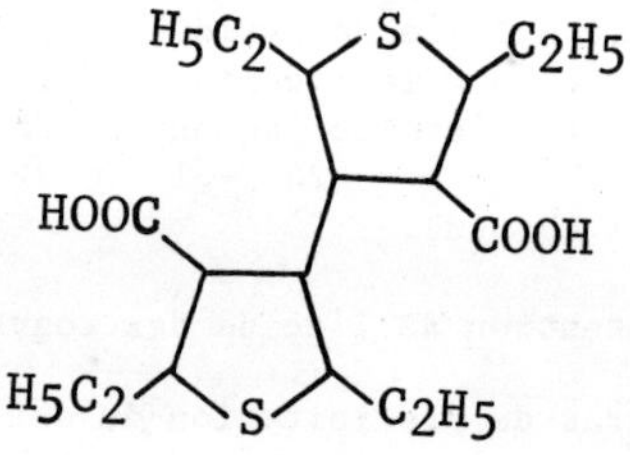

$C_{18}H_{22}O_4S_2$ Ref. 1294

Optical resolution of 4,4'-dicarboxy-2,2',5,5'-tetraethyl-3,3'-bithienyl. Preliminary resolution experiments were made with 0.001 mole of inactive acid and 0.002 mole of optically active base in 96 % ethanol and in 50 % aqueous ethanol. With brucine, strychnine and cinchonine, difficultly crystallizable salts which gave acid of low activity were obtained. Quinine in 50 % ethanol gave a crystalline salt from which an acid $[\alpha]_D^{20} = -65°$ (chloroform) was obtained, and from the same solvent cinchonidine gave an acid $[\alpha]_D^{20} = +64°$ (chloroform); these two alkaloids were therefore chosen for the resolution.

A mixture of 18.0 g (0.049 mole) of 4,4'-dicarboxy-2,2',5,5'-tetraethyl-3,3'-bithienyl and 29.0 g (0.098 mole) of cinchonidine was dissolved in 1400 ml of hot 50 % aqueous ethanol and the solution left standing over night at room temperature. The crystalline salt thus obtained was filtered off and dried. The acid was liberated from 0.5 g of salt by treating with 2-*N* hydrochloric acid and extracting with ether. The ether phase was washed with 2-*N* hydrochloric acid and water, dried over magenesium sulphate and the ether evaporated *in vacuo*. The optical activity of the dried acid was first measured in chloroform solution, but when it was found that the specific rotation in this solvent was concentration dependent, the optical activity was measured in 0.1-*N* sodium hydroxide solution. The remaining salt was recrystallized from 50 % aqueous ethanol and the process repeated until the optical activity of the acid remained constant. The course of the resolution is given below:

Crystallization	1	2	3	4	5
ml, 50 % ethanol	1400	700	300	250	250
g, salt	23.3	22.0	19.7	17.4	16.8
$[\alpha]_D^{20}$ of acid (chloroform)	+78°	+62°			
$[\alpha]_D^{20}$ of acid (NaOH)			−76°	−75°	−75°

The mother liquor from the first crystallization of the cinchonidine salt was evaporated *in vacuo* and the residue decomposed, giving 8,7 g (0.024 mole) of acid which was dissolved together with 18.2 g (0.048 mole) of quinine trihydrate in 700 ml of hot 50 % aqueous ethanol and allowed to stand overnight at room temperature. The progress of the resolution is given below:

Crystallization	1	2	3	4	5
ml, 50 % ethanol	700	350	300	250	250
g, salt	22.6	20.6	18.7	15.9	12.2
$[\alpha]_D^{20}$ of acid (chloroform)	−86°	−76°			
$[\alpha]_D^{20}$ of acid (NaOH)			+75°	+75°	+75°

(+)-4,4'-Dicarboxy-2,2',5,5'-tetraethyl-3,3'-bithienyl. 16.0 g of the cinchonidine salt was decomposed with 6-*N* hydrochloric acid and the active acid extracted with ether. The ethereal phase was washed with dilute hydrochloric acid and water, dried and the ether evaporated *in vacuo*. The (+)-acid (5.1 g) was obtained in the form of a petrified foam which filled the whole flask. The acid was recrystallized from an ether-ligroin mixture, but even after seven recrystallizations from different solvents, it showed a peculiar melting behaviour. At 70°C the crystals collapsed to a glassy mass, which became completely liquefied only after 80°C. During this process the mass was homogeneous and showed no signs of decomposition.

The rotations (sodium line) in different solvents are given below.

Solvent	Conc. (g acid/dl)	α_D^{20}	$[\alpha]_D^{20}$	$[M]_D^{20}$
Benzene	0.173	+0.492°	+284°	+1040°
Chlorobenzene	0.249	+0.708°	+284°	+1040°
Carbon tetrachloride	0.061	+0.133°	+218°	+800°
	0.302	+0.657°	+218°	+800°
Methylene chloride	0.348	+0.480°	+138°	+505°
Dioxane	0.258	+0.040°	+16°	+58°
Methanol	0.041	+0.001°	+3°	+11°
	0.433	+0.013°	+3°	+11°
Ethanol	0.059	−0.002°	−3°	−11°
	0.199	−0.006°	−3°	−11°
0.1-*N* sodium hydroxide	0.170	−0.128°	−75°	−275°
	0.609	−0.456°	−75°	−275°

Anal. $C_{18}H_{22}O_4S_2$ (366.5)

Calc.	C 59.02	H 6.01	S 17.50
Found	C 58.34	H 5.87	S 17.96

(−)-4,4'-Dicarboxy-2,2',5,5'-tetraethyl-3,3'-bithienyl. 11.3 g of the quinine salt was decomposed with 6-*N* hydrochloric acid and the (−)-acid isolated as described above, yielding 3.5 g of acid which was recrystallized from an ether-ligroin mixture. The product showed the same melting behaviour between 70–80°C as the (+)-acid and had the same IR-spectrum.

The rotations in different solvents are given below.

Solvent	Conc. (g acid/dl)	α_D^{20}	$[\alpha]_D^{20}$	$[M]_D^{20}$
Benzene	0.262	−0.735°	−281°	−1030°
Methylene chloride	0.276	−0.378°	−137°	−500°
0.1-*N* sodium hydroxide	0.341	+0.256°	+75°	+275°

Anal. $C_{18}H_{22}O_4S_2$ (366.5)

Calc.	C 59.02	H 6.01	S 17.50
Found	C 58.35	H 6.01	S 17.29

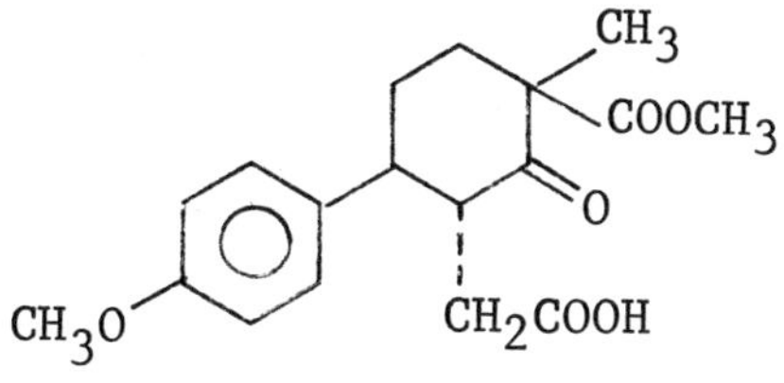

$C_{18}H_{22}O_6$ Ref. 1295

Diastereoisomeric Ephedrine Salts of 3α-(Methoxycarbonyl)-6β-p-methoxyphenyl-3β-methyl-2-oxocyclohexaneacetic (α) Acid (I). 33.4 g of (I) was dissolved with heating in 565 ml of ethyl acetate. The solution was cooled to 35-40°, and a solution of 19.0 g of ephedrine in 35 ml of ethyl acetate was added. There quickly set in the separation of an ephedrine salt in the form of very fine needles, which were distributed throughout the whole volume of the solution. After two hours the crystals (salt A) were filtered off; weight 11.0 g; m. p. 160-162°. The mother solution was warmed until the remaining crystals were completely dissolved, cooled to room temperature, and seeded with the second diastereoisomeric salt (salt B). After two hours the large clear crystals of salt B which had collected on the bottom of the flask were filtered off; they amounted to 4.8 g; m. p. 144-146°. The mother solution was evaporated down to 180-200 ml and seeded with salt A, and after two hours a further 5.5 g of salt A of m. p. 158-161° was isolated. This solution was warmed up, and by seeding with salt B a further 7.9 g of salt B, m. p. 144-146°, was isolated. Further evaporation and successive crystallizations gave 6.4 g more of salt A, m. p. 159-161°, and 6.9 g of salt B, m. p. 144-146°. The total yield of salt A was 22.9 g (92 %), and the total yield of salt B was 19.6 g (79%). These ephedrine salts are sparingly soluble in ether and water, better in acetone, and appreciably soluble in methanol (particularly salt B). After salt A had been heated with ethyl acetate (1 : 8) its melting point had risen to 162-163°, $[\alpha]_D^{23}$ −49.6° (c 1, alcohol). Found %: N 2.45, 2.61. $C_{28}H_{37}NO_7$. Calculated %: N 2.81.

Crystallization of salt B from ethyl acetate (1 : 5) gave a product of m. p. 145-146°; $[\alpha]_D^{23}$ + 20.2° (c 1, alcohol). Found %: N 2.68, 2.54. $C_{28}H_{37}NO_7$. Calculated %: N 2.81.

Decomposition of the Ephedrine Salts and the Isolation of the Enantiomers A and B of 3α-(Methoxycarbonyl)-6β-p-methoxyphenyl-3β-methyl-2-oxocyclohexaneacetic (α) Acid (I). A mixture of 20.9 g of the salt A (m. p. 162-163°), 250 ml of ether, and 40 ml of water was prepared in a separating funnel. On shaking no appreciable dissolution of the salt was observed. 40 ml of 10% hydrochloric acid was added, and with shaking the salt gradually dissolved. The ether layer was separated, washed with water and with saturated NaCl solution, and dried with anhydrous Na_2SO_4; ether was evaporated to leave a small volume of solution, and this was left at room temperature. The clear colorless needles that separated contained ether of crystallization, so that on being dried in air they rapidly effloresced and became opaque. The yield was quantitative; m. p. 97-100°, $[\alpha]_D^{23}$ −60.5° (c 1, alcohol). Under similar conditions from salt B we obtained the crystalline enantiomer B, m. p. $[\alpha]_D^{23}$ + 59.2° (c 1, alcohol). The enantiomers A and B of (I) are readily soluble in organic solvents (except ether), but they cannot be crystallized from them. A mixture of these enantiomers melted at 174-179° and melted without depression in admixture with the racemate of (I).

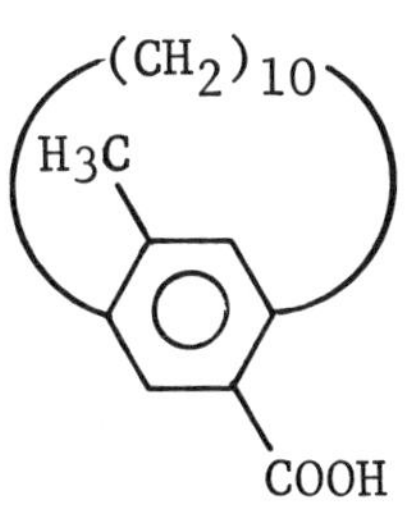

$C_{18}H_{26}O_2$ Ref. 1296

Note:

Resolved using brucine as resolving agent. There was obtained optically active acid, m.p. 134-135°, $[\alpha]_D^{21}$ -28° ($CHCl_3$).

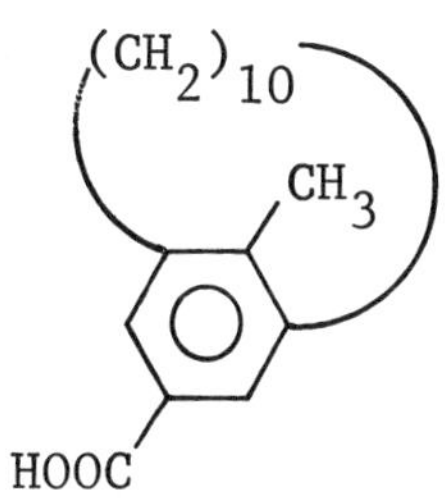

$C_{18}H_{26}O_2$ Ref. 1297

Resolution of the Acid 14c. A mixture of **14c** (7.9 g, 0.029 mol) and brucine (12.5 g, 0.029 mol) in methanol (200 mL) was warmed until solution was complete. After standing at room temperature for 48 h, the mixture yielded 11.7 g of a solid, mp 93–99 °C; $[\alpha]^{25}_D$ −38.6° (*c* 0.58, CH_3OH), which was recrystallized from methanol three times to yield 6.4 g of white needles: mp 118–124 °C; $[\alpha]^{26}_D$ −41.4° (*c* 0.79, CH_3OH). This salt was dissolved in chloroform (80 mL), and 5% hydrochloric acid (70 mL) was added with vigorous shaking. The separated chloroform layer was washed with water and then dried. After evaporation of the solvent, the crude (−)-acid obtained was recrystallized from ethanol–water to give (−)-**14c** (2.9 g): mp 134–135 °C; $[\alpha]^{21}_D$ −28° (*c* 0.94, CH_3OH); CD (CH_3OH), $[\alpha] \times 10^{-4}$ (nm), +6.82

(213), 0 (224), −3.84 (245), −0.33 (380), −0.43 (294), 0 (315).

Anal. Calcd for $C_{18}H_{26}O_2$: C, 78.79; H, 9.55. Found: C, 78.88; H, 9.51.

$CH_3(CH_2)_{15}CH(OH)COOH$

$C_{18}H_{36}O_3$ Ref. 1298

A. 2L-hydroxyoctadecanoic acid: resolution as (−) phenylethylamine salt

10.0 g of racemic acid were dissolved in 500 ml of diethyl ether and added to a solution of 4.25 g (−) PA in 1000 ml of light petroleum (bp. 60–70°C). A minor precipitate was dissolved by warming and the clear solution left for crystallization at room temperature. After 2 days the crystals were collected, washed with light petroleum and dried. For recrystallization the salt was dissolved by warming in light petroleum–diethyl ether 2 : 1, v/v (200 ml/g salt), and crystallized as above. The degree of resolution was checked by TLC for each step as described below (II, F,1). 6–7 crystallizations were needed for complete resolution. The salt (3.42 g) was decomposed with 0.2 M HCl and the free acid extracted with diethyl ether. The ether layer was washed, dried ($MgSO_4$) and evaporated. The residue was dissolved in 15 ml of chloroform and crystallized by addition of 500 ml of warm hexane.

Yield 2.2 g (44%): cottonlike fibres. M.p. 96.6–97.0°C. $[\alpha]_D^{24}$ − 4.32° ± 0.1 (*c* = 4 in pyridine). $[M]_D^{24}$ − 12.9° ± 0.3.

B. 2D-hydroxyoctadecanoic acid: resolution as (+) phenylethylamine salt

7.5 g of partially resolved acid recovered from the mother liquors above and 3.2 g (+) PA were treated essentially as described for the L isomer.

Yield after 7 crystallizations 2.4 g (48%). M.p. 96.2–97.0 C. $[\alpha]_D^{24}$ + 4.26° ± 0.1 (*c* = 4 in pyridine) $[M]_D^{24}$ + 12.8° ± 0.3.

$HOOC(CH_2)_7$-CH(OH)-CH(OH)$(CH_2)_7CH_2OH$

$C_{18}H_{36}O_5$ Ref. 1299

Fractional crystallisation of the (−)-ephedrine salt of compound (II, R=H) afforded the pure salt, mp 93-95°C, $[\alpha]_D$ −32·72°, which on decomposition gave (−)-*threo*-9,10,18-trihydroxyoctadecanoic acid, represented as (III, R=H) from evidence to be presented later, mp 105-106°C, $[\alpha]_D$ −22·63°, (−)-methyl ester (III, R=Me), mp 79-80°C, $[\alpha]_D$ −21·40°. Decomposition of the mother liquors of the alkaloidal salt yielded (+)-*threo*-9,10,18-trihydroxyoctadecanoic acid (IV, R=H), mp 104-105°C, $[\alpha]_D$ +22·65°, (+)-methyl ester (IV, R=Me), mp 79-80°C, $[\alpha]_D$ +21·52°. This acid was more conveniently isolated if (+)-ephedrine was employed in the resolution of compound (II, R=H), when the salt, mp 92-93°C, $[\alpha]_D$ +32·33°, was obtained, which yielded (IV, R=H) upon decomposition, mp 104-105°C, $[\alpha]_D$ +22·47°, (+)-methyl ester, mp 79-80·5°C, $[\alpha]_D$ +21·52°.

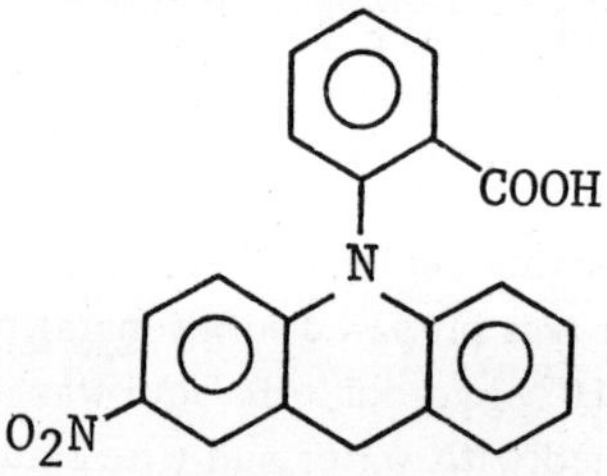

$C_{19}H_{12}N_2O_4$ Ref. 1300

A hot solution of 2.2 g. of *o*-(3-nitrocarbazyl)-benzoic acid in 20 cc. of anhydrous ethyl acetate was added to a hot solution of 2.6 g. of anhydrous brucine in 60 cc. of anhydrous ethyl acetate. After standing for twenty-four hours at room temperature, a crystalline precipitate weighing 2.5 g. resulted. This fraction was purified by dissolving in chloroform and adding an excess of absolute alcohol. After twenty-four hours at room temperature the product had separated as large lemon colored crystals, m. p. 246–247°.

Rotation. 1.2574 g. made up to 25 cc. with chloroform at 20° gave α_D −1.05°; *l* = 2; $[\alpha]_D^{20}$ −10.44°.

Anal. Calcd. for $C_{42}H_{38}O_8N_4$: N, 7.71; C, 69.39; H, 5.27. Found: N, 7.78; C, 69.29; H, 5.33.

The filtrate from the 2.5 g. fraction was allowed to evaporate to half its volume and a small amount of crystalline material which separated was filtered and consisted primarily of the less soluble salt. The more soluble salt remained as a resin after all the solvent had been evaporated from the filtrate. All attempts to crystallize the salt failed. The rotation of the crude material varied from $[\alpha]_D^{20}$ +21.7 to +46.7°. It decomposed at 160–180°.

Rotation. 0.3104 g. made up to 25 cc. with chloroform at 20° gave α_D +0.90°; *l* = 2; $[\alpha]_D^{20}$ +21.7°.

***d*- and *l*-*o*-(3-nitrocarbazyl)-benzoic Acid.**—The active acids were liberated from the individual salts by shaking with ether and 6 *N* hydrochloric acid in a separatory funnel until complete solution of the solid matter occurred. Regardless of the rate of evaporation of the ether solution, either moist or dry, an oil, sometimes containing a small amount of crystalline material, was always obtained when the evaporation was carried out at room temperature.[7] Alcohol and chloroform gave similar results. After long standing in a desiccator the oil gradually changed to a glassy solid which, on powdering, melted at 225–226°, and gave a negative test for brucine with concentrated nitric acid. The rotation of the acid thus obtained from different samples of the less soluble salt varied from $[\alpha]_D^{20}$ −56° to $[\alpha]_D^{20}$ −62°.

(7) After the alcoholic solution of the oil had been boiled for a few minutes, dilution with water until a permanent clouding occurred, followed by cooling, gave a crystalline acid which melted at 226–227°. This crystalline acid always possessed optical activity, provided that the heating was not continued too long.

Rotation. *l*-Acid, 0.2924 g. made up to 25 cc. with chloroform at 20° gave α_D −1.45°; *l* = 2; $[\alpha]^{20}_D$ −62°.

Anal. Calcd. for $C_{19}H_{12}O_4N_2$: N, 8.44. Found: N, 8.36.

The *d*-acid obtained similarly from the crude more soluble salt was also an oil which gradually solidified. A rotation was taken on the crude acid melting at 224–225°. Different samples of the salt produced acids with widely variable rotations, but the rotation was always positive.

Rotation. *d*-Acid, 0.2497 g. made up to 16.1 cc. with chloroform at 20° gave α_D +1.26°; *l* = 2; $[\alpha]^{20}_D$ +40.57°.

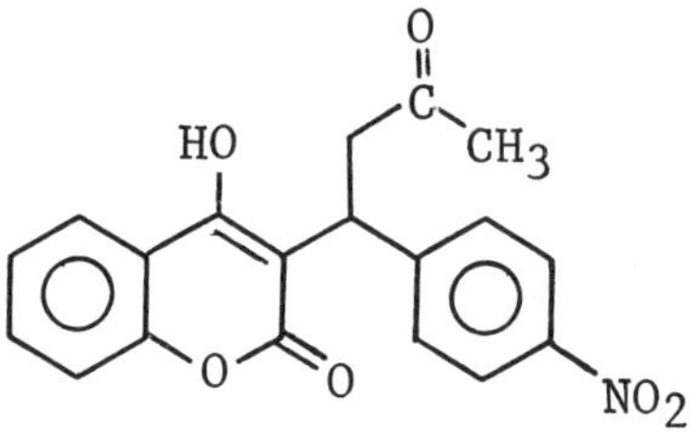

$C_{19}H_{15}NO_6$ Ref. 1301

Resolution of Acenocoumarin. Quinidine (13.77 g, 42.4 mmol) and (±)-**2** (15 g, 42.4 mmol) were dissolved in a warmed mixture of Me_2CO (125 mL) and $CHCl_3$ (85 mL).[13] The resulting solution was allowed to stand overnight at room temperature. The following day, the mixture was kept at 4 °C for 12 h prior to collecting a first crop (15.7 g): $[\alpha]^{25}_D$ +39.0 ± 0.2 (*c* 1, 95% EtOH). This material was dissolved in a boiling mixture of Me_2CO (400 mL) and EtOH (300 mL). Crystallization proceeded at 4 °C for 15 h, to yield a second crop (9.2 g) of the salt: $[\alpha]^{25}_D$ +26.7 ± 0.2 (*c* 1, 95% EtOH). A final recrystallization from Me_2CO (300 mL) and EtOH (300 mL) yielded 2.3 g of the salt: $[\alpha]^{25}_D$ +26.0 ± 0.5 (*c* 1, 95% EtOH). Acenocoumarin was recovered by partitioning the salt from the last recrystallization between $CHCl_3$ (50 mL) and NaOH (1 N, 100 mL) and acidifying (HCl) the separated aqueous layer. The precipitate was recovered by filtration and recrystallized from EtOH–H_2O to yield 0.8 g of white material. Recrystallization from EtOH–H_2O led to problems with spontaneous ethyl ketal formation. To remove the ethyl ketal, the entire 0.8 g was dissolved in 1 N base and the insoluble ketal removed by filtration. The basic solution was acidified (HCl) to give a white precipitate (0.65 g): $[\alpha]^{25}_D$ −224.2 ± 0.4 [*c* 0.62, 0.5 N NaOH, lit.[14] −225 (1% in 0.5 N NaOH)]; mp 191–192 °C; CD (×10^{-3}; 42.6 μg/mL of MeOH) $[\theta]_{410}$ 0, $[\theta]_{315}$ −12.1, $[\theta]_{290}$ 0, $[\theta]_{281}$ +33.7, $[\theta]_{267}$ −8.6, $[\theta]_{244}$ −16, $[\theta]_{220}$ −33.7, $[\theta]_{200}$ 0.

(14) T. Meinertz, W. Kasper, C. Kahl, and E. Jähnchen, *Br. J. Clin. Pharmacol.*, 5, 187 (1978).

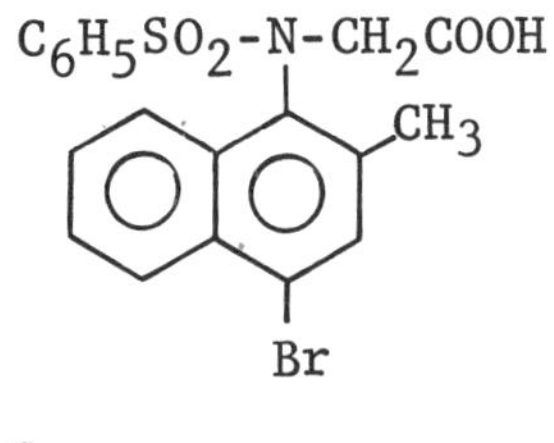

$C_{19}H_{16}BrNO_4S$ Ref. 1302

Resolution of *dl*-N-Benzenesulfonyl-N-carboxymethyl-1-amino-4-bromo-2-methylnaphthalene.—Resolution was effected by fractional crystallization of the cinchonine salt of the *dl*-acid in the manner described above for the resolution of *dl*-N-benzenesulfonyl-N-carboxymethyl-1-amino-4-chloro-2-methylnaphthalene. Although two attempts were made using 2.000 g. of *dl*-N-benzenesulfonyl-N-carboxymethyl-1-amino-4-bromo-2-methylnaphthalene and 1.356 g. of cinchonine, successive fractions of the salt could not be obtained for which the specific rotations described a regular pattern. Crops of similar rotation melted over the same temperature ranges and no depression of this range was observed when an intimate mixture of two such crops was melted. Consequently, five fractions, obtained from both attempts at fractional crystallization, weighing 0.223, 0.206, 0.207, 0.318 and 0.283 g. with specific rotations of 128, 118, 125, 120 and 123°, respectively, were combined and dissolved in excess hot 9:1 ethyl acetate–methanol. The solution was filtered and concentrated to 115 ml. when crystals began to appear. The mixture was placed in a refrigerator overnight. There was obtained 0.586 g. of white granular crystals, m.p. 227–228° dec. in a rapidly heated bath. This was taken as the less soluble salt.

Rotation.—(*dBdA*) 0.040 g. made up to 20 ml. with absolute ethanol at 27° gave α_D +0.50°; *l* 2, $[\alpha]^{27}_D$ +125°.

Anal. Calcd. for $C_{19}H_{16}BrNO_4S{\cdot}C_{19}H_{22}N_2O$: C, 62.63; H, 5.26. Found: C, 62.84; H, 5.35.

Similarly, three fractions weighing 0.366, 0.280 and 0.375 g. with specific rotations of 10, 8 and 8°, respectively, were combined and dissolved in an excess of hot 9:1 ethyl acetate–methanol and filtered. The filtrate was concentrated to 35 ml. and allowed to stand for 3 days. There was obtained 0.923 g. of white granular crystals, m.p. 221–223° dec. in a rapidly heated bath. This was taken as the more soluble salt.

Rotation.—(*dBdA*) 0.041 g. made up to 20 ml. with absolute ethanol at 28° gave α_D +0.03°; *l* 2, $[\alpha]^{27}_D$ +7.3°.

***d*- and *l*-N-benzenesulfonyl-N-carboxymethyl-1-amino-4-bromo-2-methylnaphthalene.**—The procedure described above for *d*- and *l*-N-benzenesulfonyl-N-carboxymethyl-1-amino-4-chloro-2-methylnaphthalene was followed. From 0.500 g. of the less soluble salt was obtained 0.213 g. (71.5%) of the *d*-acid. A sample recrystallized from 2:1 benzene–cyclohexane gave fine white crystals, m.p. 212–213°.

Rotation.—(*d*-acid) 0.040 g. made up to 20 ml. with absolute ethanol at 27° gave α_D +0.23°; *l* 2, $[\alpha]^{27}_D$ +58°.

Anal. Calcd. for $C_{19}H_{16}BrNO_4S$: C, 52.54; H, 3.71. Found: C, 52.30; H, 3.92.

In the same manner, from 0.500 g. of the more-soluble salt was obtained, after one recrystallization from 2:1 benzene–cyclohexane, 0.104 g. (35%) of fine white crystals, m.p. 211–212°. No attempt was made to collect additional product from the mother liquor.

Rotation.—(*l*-acid) 0.40 g. made up to 20 ml. with absolute ethanol at 28° gave α_D −0.24°; *l* 2, $[\alpha]^{28}_D$ −60°.

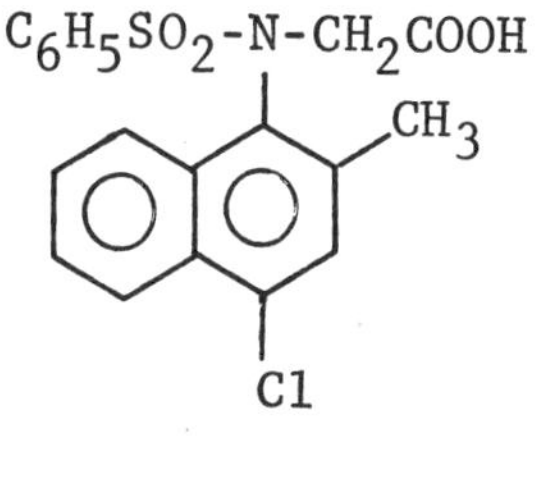

$C_{19}H_{16}ClNO_4S$ Ref. 1303

Resolution of *dl*-N-Benzenesulfonyl-N-carboxymethyl-1-amino-4-chloro-2-methylnaphthalene.—A solution of 3.00 g. of *dl*-N-benzenesulfonyl-N-carboxymethyl-1-amino-4-chloro-2-methylnaphthalene and 2.266 g. of cinchonine in 130 ml. of 9:1 ethyl acetate–methanol was prepared and filtered. The solution was concentrated to 100 ml. by warming under a current of air. The flask was placed in a refrigerator and after two days the first crop of white granular crystals, 1.565 g., $[\alpha]^{27}_D$ +130°, was collected on a filter. Continued fractional crystallization gave another 5 crops of crystals of the following weights and specific rotations: 0.315 g., 128°; 1.226 g., 15°; 0.526 g., 130°; 0.166 g., 13°; and 0.285 g., 22°. All rotations were determined in a 2-decimeter tube using 20-ml. absolute ethanol solutions containing

0.040 g. of the salt. The first two crops were combined and dissolved in an excess of hot 9:1 ethyl acetate–methanol. Fractional crystallization gave two crops, 1.122 and 0.316 g., which showed the same rotation. This was taken as the less soluble salt (*d*B*d*A), m.p. 218–219° dec.

Rotation.—0.040 g. made up to 20 ml. with absolute ethanol at 26° gave α_D +0.54°; *l* 2, $[\alpha]^{26}_D$ +135°.

Anal. Calcd. for $C_{19}H_{16}ClNO_4S \cdot C_{19}H_{22}N_2O$: C, 66.70; H, 5.60. Found: C, 66.69; H, 5.82.

In view of the erratic nature of the rotations of the successive fractions, the last four crops of crystals from the original fractionation were combined and dissolved in excess hot 9:1 ethyl acetate–methanol. In spite of seeding the initial solution with crystals of the less-soluble salt, fractional crystallization gave three crops of crystals as erratic as those from which they were derived. The weights and specific rotations were, respectively, 1.082 g., 25°; 0.167 g., 130°; 0.473 g., 20°. The first and last of these crops were recrystallized from 9:1 ethyl acetate–methanol to give 1.107 g. of white crystals, m.p. 199–201° dec. This was taken as the more soluble salt.

Rotation.—(*d*B*l*A) 0.040 g. made up to 20 ml. with absolute ethanol at 28° gave α_D +0.03°; *l* 2, $[\alpha]^{28}_D$ +7.5°.

***d*- and *l*-N-Benzenesulfonyl-N-carboxymethyl-1-amino-4-chloro-2-methylnaphthalene.**—The procedure of earlier workers[2a,c,d] for decomposing the alkaloid salts was improved and consequently is described here in detail. A slurry of 0.500 g. of the less soluble salt in 40 ml. of ethanol-free ether was cooled in an ice-bath and to this was added slowly with rapid stirring 20 ml. of 18% hydrochloric acid. The mixture was stirred for about 20 minutes to give two clear layers. About 20 ml. more ethanol-free ether was added to facilitate handling and the aqueous layer separated. The ether solution was washed 3 times with 5% hydrochloric acid and a test with Mayer reagent showed the last wash to be free of cinchonine. (Since the washes are saturated with ether, it is necessary to remove the latter by warming before performing the test for alkaloid in order to avoid a misleading cloudiness caused by dissolved ether.) The ether solution was evaporated to dryness under a current of air. The residue was dissolved in hot glacial acetic acid, the solution filtered, and water added to precipitate the optically active acid. There was obtained 0.247 g. (87%) of the *d*-acid, m.p. 204–205°. A sample recrystallized from 2:1 benzene–cyclohexane gave fine white crystals of the same melting point.

Rotation.—(*d*-acid) 0.040 g. made up to 20 ml. with absolute ethanol at 26° gave α_D +0.28°; *l* 2, $[\alpha]^{26}_D$ +70°.

Anal. Calcd. for $C_{19}H_{16}ClNO_4S$: C, 58.53; H, 4.14. Found: C, 58.69; H, 4.35.

In the same manner, decomposition of 0.509 g. of the more soluble salt gave, after one recrystallization from 2:1 benzene–cyclohexane, 0.230 g. (79%) of the *l*-acid, m.p. 206–207°.

Rotation.—(*l*-acid) 0.041 g. made up to 20 ml. with absolute ethanol at 28° gave α_D −0.29°; *l* 2, $[\alpha]^{28}_D$ −72°.

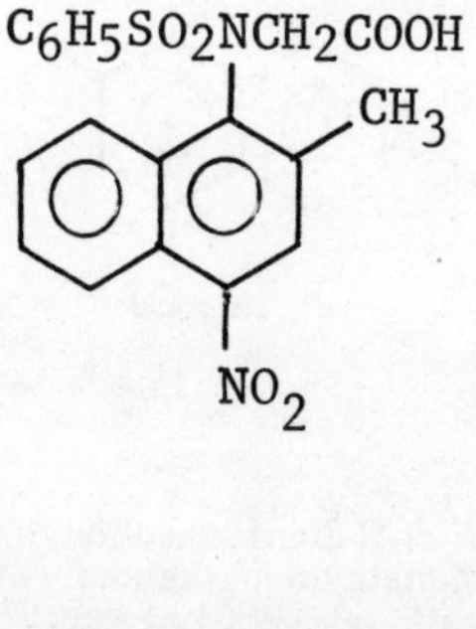

$C_{19}H_{16}N_2O_6S$ Ref. 1304

Resolution and Racemization of N-Benzenesulfonyl-N-carboxymethyl-1-amino-2-methyl-4-nitronaphthalene.—When a filtered solution of 10.00 g. of N-benzenesulfonyl-N-carboxymethyl-1-amino-2-methyl-4-nitronaphthalene and 7.35 g. of cinchonine in 3 l. of ethyl acetate was kept in a refrigerator for 10 days, a solid formed gradually; weight 6.27 g., m.p. 213–214°, $[\alpha]^{30}_D$ +108.0° in dimethylformamide. The solution was concentrated *in vacuo* to 1.9 l. and 7 days later a second crop was collected; weight 2.93 g., m.p. 213–214°, $[\alpha]^{30}_D$ +107.0° in dimethylformamide. The two crops were combined and recrystallized from ethyl acetate, yielding 8.3 g. of purified salt, m.p. 214–214.5°.

Rotation.—0.0868 g. made up to 20 ml. with dimethylformamide at 30° gave α_D +0.9361; *l* 1, $[\alpha]^{30}_D$ +108.0°.

Anal. Calcd. for $C_{38}H_{38}N_4O_7S$: C, 65.61; H, 5.53. Found: C, 65.88; H, 5.46.

To isolate the *d*-acid, 4.0 g. of the purified less-soluble salt was introduced into a 500-ml. separatory funnel containing 150 ml. of diethyl ether, 50 ml. of 20% aqueous hydrochloric acid and ice. The funnel was shaken until all the solid had dissolved. The aqueous layer was removed, and the ether layer was extracted with fresh portions of hydrochloric acid, until the extract gave a negative test for alkaloid with Mayer reagent. The ether layer was then washed with water, the ether evaporated under an air jet and the product dried over sulfuric acid. The yield was 2.0 g. (87%), m.p. 216–217°.

A solution of 0.568 g. of the *d*-acid was made up quantitatively to 20 ml. with dimethylformamide and transferred in 2-ml. portions to glass tubes (15 cm. long, 8 mm. diameter). These were sealed and immersed in boiling *n*-butyl alcohol at the intervals indicated below. At the end of the heating, the tubes were all quenched at the same time in ice-water. They were then allowed to come to room temperature, opened and the contents of each transferred to a 1-dm. polarimeter tube. The unheated sample had α_D +0.853°, $[\alpha]^{33}_D$ +30.0°; one-quarter hour of heating α_D +0.538°, $[\alpha]^{33}_D$ +18.9°; one-half hour α_D +0.325°, $[\alpha]^{33}_D$ +11.8°; three-fourths hour α_D +0.247°, $[\alpha]^{33}_D$ +8.20°; one hour α_D +0.149°, $[\alpha]^{33}_D$ +5.27°; two hours α_D +0.031°, $[\alpha]^{33}_D$ +1.10°.

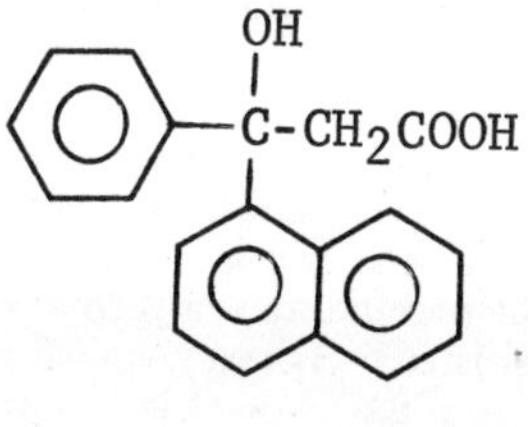

$C_{19}H_{16}O_3$ Ref. 1305

When a mixture of 6.4 g. of the acid and 10.2 g. (1 equiv.) of brucine tetrahydrate was dissolved in 60 ml. of ethyl acetate, 14.8 g. of the salt separated out. Repeated digestions of this salt with ethanol followed by three recrystallizations gave the salt, $[\alpha]^{25}_D$ −129° (*c* 3.30, chloroform), m.p. 234° dec. This was decomposed in the usual manner. The resulting acid had $[\alpha]^{19}_D$ −159°: after recrystallizations from benzene it had $[\alpha]^{16}_D$ −205° (*c* 1.56, acetone), m.p. 142.5–143.5° (with foaming).

Anal. Calcd. for $C_{19}H_{16}O_3$: C, 78.06; H, 5.52. Found: C, 77.94; H, 5.69.

The first, second and third mother liquors of digestion on concentration to dryness yielded the residues: 4.1 g., $[\alpha]_D$ +96°; 3.0 g., +80°; and 0.7 g., +73°, respectively. These crops were combined and recrystallized from methanol until further recrystallization led to no change in optical rotation and melting point: $[\alpha]^{15}_D$ +115° (*c* 3.09, chloroform), m.p. 154–157°. Decomposition as above gave the acid having $[\alpha]^{17}_D$ +194°; after recrystallizations it had $[\alpha]^{15}_D$ +207° (*c* 1.69, acetone), m.p. 143.5–144° (with foaming).

Attempted resolution by means of *d*-cinchonine was not successful. The cinchonine salt of the (−)-acid was also less soluble than that of the (+)-acid.

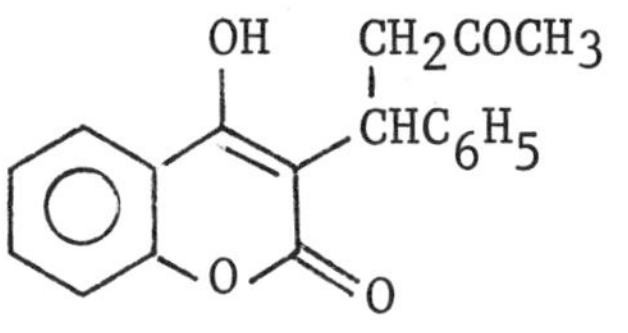

$C_{19}H_{16}O_4$ Ref. 1306

Quinidine-(S)-warfarin Salt and (S)-Warfarin [(−)(S)-I]. —A mixture of 2 l. of chloroform and 3 l. of acetone containing 324 g. (1.0 mole) of quinidine and 308 g. (1.0 mole) of *rac*-warfarin was warmed to effect solution. A crystalline product separated and the solution was held at −10° overnight. The quinidine-warfarin salt, filtered from the solution (filtrate A), weighed 241 g., $[\alpha]^{24}D$ + 92° (*c* 1.8, 95% ethanol). A second crystallization from 3.5 l. of acetone yielded 153 g. of pure quinidine-(S)-warfarin salt, $[\alpha]^{25}D$ + 87° (*c* 1.7, 95% ethanol). The quinidine-(S)-warfarin salt was soluble in acetone to the extent of 5 mg./ml. at −10° and 16 mg./ml. at 25°. There was no change in rotation upon recrystallization from acetone or tetrahydrofuran.

Anal. Calcd. for $C_{39}H_{40}N_2O_6 \cdot H_2O$: C, 71.98; H, 6.55; N, 4.36. Found: C, 72.4; H, 6.6; N, 4.1.

The salt was decomposed by partition between 1 l. of 0.5*N* sodium hydroxide and 0.5 l. of chloroform. The aqueous layer was added to excess hydrochloric acid and 70 g. of (S)-warfarin was collected.

Crystallization at room temperature from 600 ml. of warmed 80% aqueous acetone yielded 25 g. of (S)-warfarin, m.p. 172–173°, $[\alpha]^{25}D$ −148.0 ± 0.5° (*c* 1.2, 0.5 *N* sodium hydroxide), −25.5 ± 1° (*c* 2, acetic acid), −15.5 ± 1° (*c* 3, acetonitrile), + 15.7 ± 1° (*c* 3.7, butanone-2) and +19.1 ± 1° (*c* 1.1, propanol-2). Addition of 100 ml. of water to the filtrate and cooling resulted in a second crop of 32 g. of (S)-warfarin, m.p. 171–173°, $[\alpha]^{25}D$ −148.0 ± 0.5° (*c* 1.2, 0.5 *N* sodium hydroxide).

(S)-Warfarin Sodium.—An excess of (S)-warfarin was stirred with 7 ml. of 0.5 *N* sodium hydroxide solution. Lyophilization of the filtrate yielded 1.1 g. (S)-warfarin sodium, $[\alpha]^{24}D$ −95.8 ± 0.5° (*c* 3.2, 95% ethanol).

(R)-Warfarin [(+)(R)-I].—The filtrate A from above was concentrated to 1 l. and diluted with 1 l. of acetone. Upon cooling, 96 g. of quinidine-warfarin salt, $[\alpha]^{25}D$ +105° (*c* 2.0, 95% ethanol), separated. The filtrate was concentrated *in vacuo* to a glass. The glass was taken up in 1 l. of chloroform and extracted with 2 l. of 5% sodium hydroxide. Addition of the aqueous layer to excess hydrochloric acid yielded 124 g. (0.405 mole) of partially (*ca.* 65%) resolved (R)-warfarin, $[\alpha]^{24}D$ + 95 ± 2° (*c* 1.0, 0.5 *N* sodium hydroxide). The warfarin was dissolved in a boiling solution of 132.5 g. (0.405 mole) of quinine in 850 ml. of absolute ethanol. The solution was cooled to room temperature and 3350 ml. of dry ether was added. The solution then was held at −10° for 24 hr. Quinine-warfarin salt (201 g.) was collected by filtration in a cold room, $[\alpha]^{23}D$ −72.0 ±0.3° (*c* 2.5, 95% ethanol). This product was recrystallized twice by dissolving it in 3 ml. per g. of hot absolute ethanol, adding 12 ml. per g. of dry ether and cooling to −10°. A final recrystallization from 2.5 ml. of absolute ethanol per g. of salt (cooling to room temperature) yielded 88 g. of pure quinine-(R)-warfarin salt, $[\alpha]^{23}D$ −71.0 ± 0.3° (*c* 1.7, 95% ethanol). This salt was partitioned between 1 l. of chloroform and 1 l. of 5% sodium hydroxide and the warfarin was precipitated by the addition of the aqueous phase to excess hydrochloric acid. One crystallization from acetone–water yielded 37 g. of (R)-warfarin, m.p. 170–171°, $[\alpha]^{25}D$ +149.0 ± 0.5° (*c* 2, 0.5 *N* sodium hydroxide), +24.8 ± 1° (*c* 2, acetic acid), +15.5 ± 1° (*c* 3, acetonitrile), −16.6 ± 1° (*c* 3, dioxane), −14.8 ±1° (*c* 3.7, butanone-2) and −20.1 ± 1° (*c* 2, propanol-2).

Large prismatic crystals of the pure enantiomers were obtained by slow crystallization from acetone or acetic acid. The solubilities of the pure enantiomers at 25° were 112 mg./ml. of acetone and 26 mg./ml. of acetic acid. The solubilities of *rac*-warfarin were 65 mg./ml. of acetone and 20 mg./ml. of acetic acid. The infrared spectra of optically pure and *rac*-warfarin were identical; $\lambda_{max}^{chloroform}$ 2.78(w), 5.88, 6.16 and 6.38 μ.

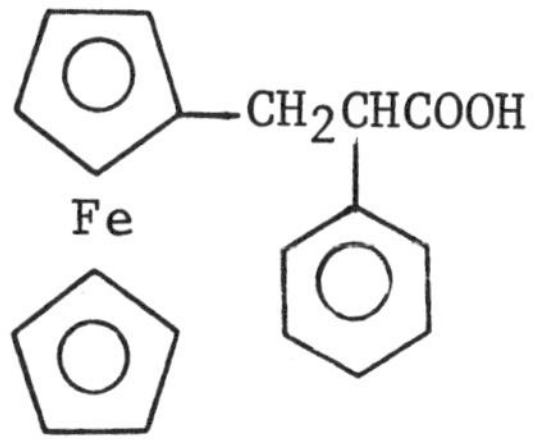

$C_{19}H_{18}FeO_2$ Ref. 1307

Racematspaltung mit (—)-α-Phenäthylamin: (—)-**22**

Äther. Lösungen von 0,5 g (1,5 mMol) **22** und 0,184 g (1,5 mMol) (—)-α-Phenäthylamin ($[\alpha]_D$ — 36°) wurden vereinigt, wobei das Salz sofort kristallin ausfiel. 0,666 g (97% d. Th.), orangegelbe Nadeln, Schmp. 155—165°. $[\alpha]_D$ — 8,3 ± 1,0° (c = 0,36).

$C_{27}H_{29}FeNO_2$. Ber. N 3,08. Gef. N 3,02.

Dieses Salz wurde wie folgt umkristallisiert:

Salz (g)	umkrist. aus (ml Äthanol)	Kristallisat (g)	(Schmp.)	$[\alpha]_D$**	Freie Säure* $[\alpha]_D$†
0,451	70	0,276	163—173°	— 16°	— 0,86°
0,250	37	0,175	166—176°	— 17,6°	— 1,07°
0,100	13	0,073	178—188°	— 29,1°	— 1,19°
0,044	6,5	0,031	180—188°	—	— 1,43°
0,030	5	0,023	185—190°	—	— 1,48°

* Die Säure wurde in üblicher Weise in Freiheit gesetzt. $C_{19}H_{18}FeO_2$. Schmp. 123—130°.

** ± 2°, c = 0,2—0,5.

† ± 0,10°, c = 1,4—1,6.

ERRATA: Ref. 1307 should have followed Ref. 1308.

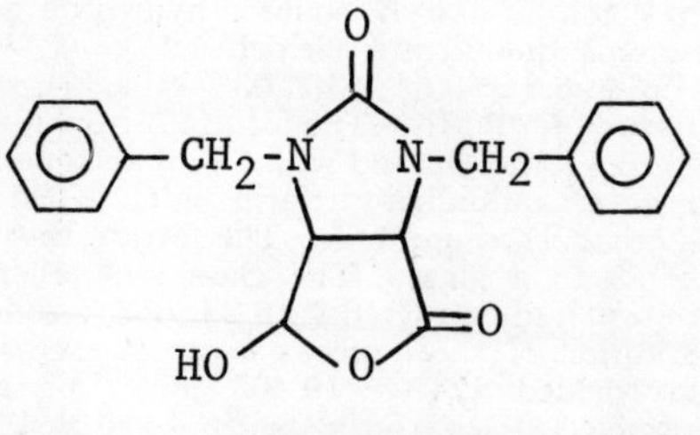

$C_{19}H_{17}N_2O_3$ Ref. 1308

EXAMPLE 1

436 g. of di-3,4-(1',3'-dibenzyl-2'-oxo-imidazolido)-2-oxo-5-hydroxy-tetrahydrofuran are dissolved in 1933 ml. of acetone. 195 g. of cinchonidine and 644 ml. of water are added to the solution. The mixture is stirred at room temperature. After cooling, the crystalline precipitate is collected by filtration. 361 g. of the salt of d-3,4-(1',3'-dibenzyl-2'-oxo-imidazolido)-2-oxo-5-hydroxy-tetrahydrofuran and cinchonidine are obtained. M.P. 138–142.5° C. $[\alpha]_D^{24}=-55.8$ (C=5, in methanol).

The product is dissolved in 800 ml. of 6.25% hydrochloric acid. The resultant solution is extracted with 900 ml. of ethyl acetate. The ethyl acetate solution is washed with water, dried and then evaporated to remove the solvent. The residue thus obtained is recrystallized from a mixture of 300 ml. of acetone, 150 ml. of ether and 350 ml. of petroleum ether. 180 g. of d-3,4-(1',3'-dibenzyl-2'-oxo-imidazolido) - 2 - oxo-5-hydroxy-tetrahydroforan are obtained. Overall yield: 84%. M.P. 129–130° C. $[\alpha]_D^{30}=+19.9$ (C=1, in methanol).

On the other hand, the mother liquid obtained by filtration of the salt of d-3,4-(1',3'-dibenzyl-2'-oxo-imidazolido)-2-oxo-5-hydroxy-tetrahydrofuran and cinchonidine is evaporated to remove acetone. The residue thus obtained is dissolved in 250 ml. of 10% hydrochloric acid and then extracted with 1500 ml. of ethyl acetate. The ethyl acetate solution is washed with water, dried and then evaporated to remove the solvent. The residue thus obtained is treated with ether. The resultant crystals are recrystallized from a mixture of acetone, ether and petroleum ether. 80 g. of 1-3,4-(1',3'-dibenzyl-2'-oxo-imidazolido)-2-oxo-5-hydroxy-tetrahydrofuran are obtained. Overall yield: 36.7%. M.P. 129–130° C. $[\alpha]_D^{20}=-19.9$ (C=1, in methanol).

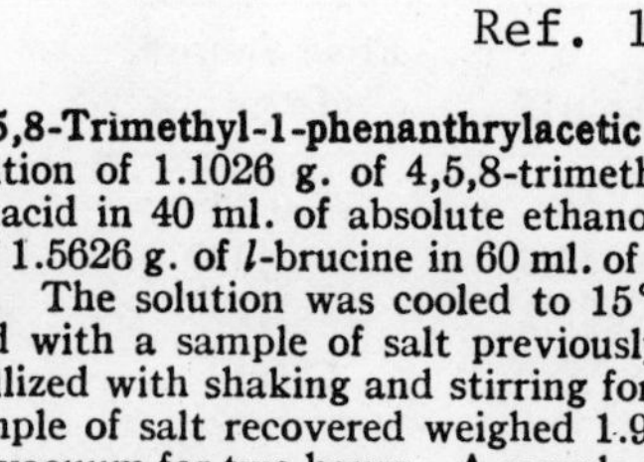

$C_{19}H_{18}O_2$ Ref. 1309

Resolution of 4,5,8-Trimethyl-1-phenanthrylacetic Acid.—To a warm solution of 1.1026 g. of 4,5,8-trimethyl-1-phenanthrylacetic acid in 40 ml. of absolute ethanol was added a solution of 1.5626 g. of *l*-brucine in 60 ml. of absolute ethyl acetate. The solution was cooled to 15° in a water-bath, seeded with a sample of salt previously obtained, and crystallized with shaking and stirring for fifty minutes. The sample of salt recovered weighed 1.968 g. after drying under vacuum for two hours. A sample of the salt (0.0831 g. in 2.00 ml. of absolute ethyl acetate), gave a rotation of −2.81° in a 2.0 dcm. tube: $(\alpha)^{24}D$ −33.8°. Two recrystallizations of the salt rapidly from 60 to 70 ml. of 2-1 absolute ethanol–ethyl acetate gave 1.034 g. of material melting at 126.8–128.3° with sintering at 123°.

Anal. Calcd. for $C_{42}H_{44}O_6N_2$: C, 75.0; H, 6.6; N, 4.2. Found[a]: C, 74.4; H, 7.0; N, 4.0.

A sample of the thrice recrystallized salt (0.6128 g. in 20.00 ml. of absolute ethyl acetate) gave a rotation of −2.01 ± 0.02° in a 2.0 dcm. tube: $(\alpha)^{24.8}D$ −32.8 ± 0.3°. After 2, 4, 6, 8, 12 and 15 hours at 24.8–24.0°, the rotations observed were −2.06, −2.09, −2.11, −2.13, −2.15, −2.15°, respectively. The specific rotation of the equilibrium mixture was −35.1 ± 0.3°.

4,5,8-Trimethyl-1-phenanthrylacetic acid, VIII, was recovered from 0.4016 g. of thrice recrystallized brucine salt by treatment with 2 ml. of concentrated hydrochloric acid in 15 ml. of water and extracting the liberated acid with ether. The ether solution was then washed with dilute hydrochloric acid, the acid extracted with sodium carbonate and the carbonate extracts acidified. Extraction of the liberated acid with ether, removal of most of the ether under reduced pressure in a stream of dry air and trituration with cold Skellysolve C gave 0.1012 g. of *d*-acid, m. p. 142.4–143.4° (no depression with *dl*-acid).

A solution of 0.0931 g. of *d*-4,5,8-trimethyl-1-phenanthrylacetic acid in 2.00 ml. of chloroform (in a 1.0 dcm. tube), gave an observed rotation of 0.11 ± 0.02; $(\alpha)^{24.8}D$ 2.3 ± 0.5°. After three, four, six and eight hours, the observed rotations were +0.09, +0.06, +0.04 and 0.00°, respectively. In other experiments, samples of *d*-4,5,8-trimethyl-1-phenanthrylacetic acid with rotations of +1.0 to +2.5° were obtained. In some of the first cases, complete racemization had occurred by the time optical measurements were tried.

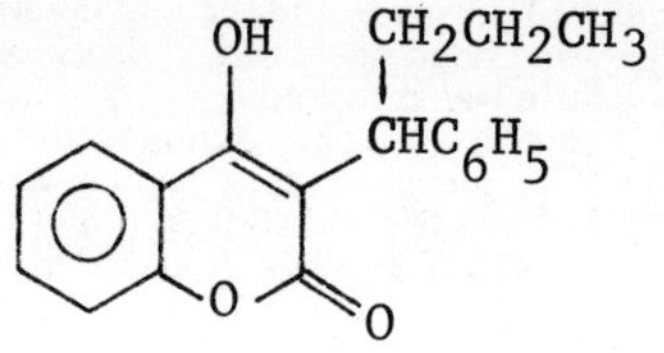

$C_{19}H_{18}O_3$ Ref. 1310

B. **By Partial Resolution.**—*rac*-3-(α-Phenylbutyl)-4-hydroxycoumarin[19] (200 g., 0.68 mole) and 225 g. (0.68 mole) of quinidine were dissolved in 6 l. of absolute ethanol. Filtration after 24 hr. at room temperature yielded 270 g. of salt, $[\alpha]^{23}D$ +97.8° (*c* 1.9, butanone-2). Recrystallization of this salt from 2 l. of absolute ethanol yielded 110 g. of salt, $[\alpha]^{25}D$ +83° (*c* 2, butanone-2). This salt was partitioned between chloroform and a slight excess of potassium hydroxide solution. The basic solution was added to excess hydrochloric acid and the precipitated solid was separated and dried. Crystallization from 450 ml. of absolute ethanol yielded a first crop of 17 g. of partially resolved (*ca.* 15%) (−)(S)-III, m.p. 180–200°, $[\alpha]^{25}D$ −26° (*c* 1.2, 1 *N* sodium hydroxide). Warm water (300 ml.) was added to the warmed filtrate. Cooling caused crystallization of 42 g. of partially resolved (*ca.* 85%) (−)(S)-III, m.p. 135–165°, $[\alpha]^{25}D$ −96 ± 1° (*c* 2, 95% ethanol) and −142 ± 1° (*c* 1.2, 1 *N* sodium hydroxide). The infrared spectrum was identical with that of the product made by method A, $\lambda_{max}^{chloroform}$ 2.95, 3.41, 5.92 (2-C=O) and 6.14 μ.

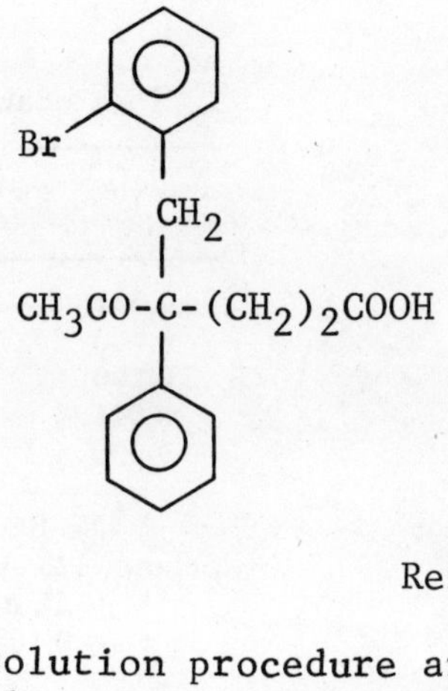

$C_{19}H_{19}BrO_3$ Ref. 1311

Note: For resolution procedure and physical constants, see Ref. 1312.

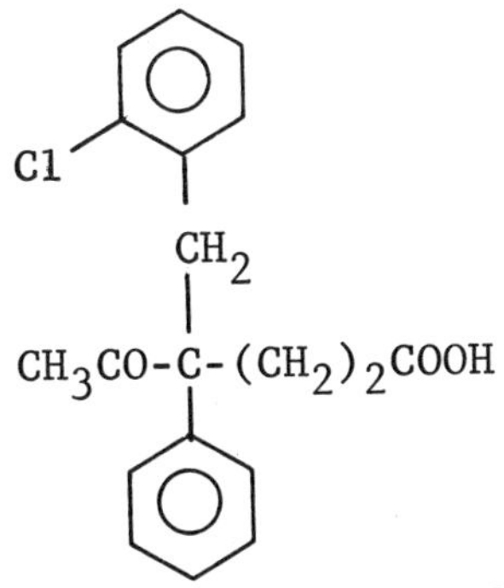

$C_{19}H_{19}ClO_3$ Ref. 1312

levo-4-(o-Chlorobenzyl)-4-phenyl-5-oxohexanoic acid. A mixture of DL-4-(*o*-chlorobenzyl)-4-phenyl-5-oxohexanoic acid (354.4 g., 1.07 moles) and brucine (422.6 g., 1.07 moles) were dissolved in boiling methanol (975 ml.). The solution was cooled and seeded with a few crystals of the product. After 24 hr. at room temperature followed by 24 hr. at 5° the white solid that separated was removed by filtration and dried. The yield was 351 g. (91% of one antipode), m.p. 97–101°. (The mother liquors were saved for recovery of the *dextro* antipode.)

One recrystallization from methanol gave 300 g., m.p. 100–102°. A second recrystallization gave 289 g. (74%), m.p. 100–102°. Analysis of the brucine salt indicated it to be solvated. Adjusting for solvation by calculation, the specific rotation of the brucine salt is −87.9° for a 2% solution in 95% ethanol at 25°.

The *levo*-acid-brucine salt was treated with dilute hydrochloric acid (1500 ml., 1*N* concn.) and then extracted twice with benzene (500 ml. portions). The combined benzene extracts were dried over sodium sulfate and the solvent removed by distillation at reduced pressure. The yield of dry solid residue was 120 g. (70%), m.p. 106–109°. Recrystallization from heptane gave 118.5 g., m.p. 109–110°. Several more recrystallizations from either acetic acid–water or heptane gave material melting at 110–111°, $[\alpha]^{25}_{D}$ −143.1° for a 2% solution in 95% ethanol.

dextro-4-(o-Chlorobenzyl)-4-phenyl-5-oxohexanoic acid. The mother liquors from the initial crystallization of the *levo*-acid-brucine salt were evaporated to dryness to give a viscous liquid residue. This crude brucine salt was treated by a procedure similar to that described for the *levo*-acid-brucine salt. The crude *dextro*-acid generated in this manner was dissolved in a small volume of acetonitrile (about 1 ml. per g.) and the solution refrigerated. The material which separated was the racemic acid (*ca.* 15%). Evaporation of the solvent gave the *dextro*-acid (63%), m.p. 97–101°. Recrystallization, first from a small volume of acetonitrile, then several times from heptane gave material melting at 109–110°, $[\alpha]^{25}_{D}$ +142° for a 2% solution in 95% ethanol.

TABLE IV

RESOLUTION OF 4-ARYLMETHYL-4-ARYL-5-OXOHEXANOIC ACIDS

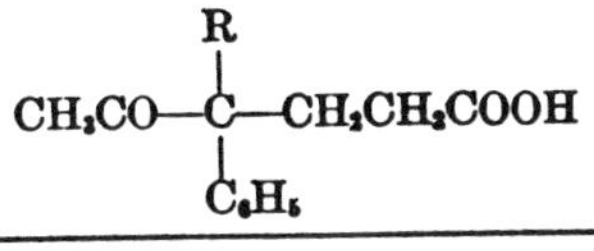

R	Yield, %[a]	M.P.	Antipode	Specific Rotation[b]	Calcd. for	Analysis Carbon Calcd.	Analysis Carbon Found	Analysis Hydrogen Calcd.	Analysis Hydrogen Found
o-Fluorobenzyl[c]	58	121–121.5	levo[d]	−137.6[e]	$C_{19}H_{19}FO_3$	72.59	72.26	6.09	6.05
o-Chlorobenzyl[f]	70	110–111	levo	−143.1	$C_{19}H_{19}ClO_3$	68.98	69.04	5.79	5.75
o-Chlorobenzyl[g]	63	109–110	dextro	+142.0	$C_{19}H_{19}ClO_3$	68.98	69.11	5.79	6.04
o-Bromobenzyl[h]	57	85.5–87.5	levo	−118.5	$C_{19}H_{19}BrO_3$	60.81	60.96	5.10	5.40
o-Bromobenzyl[i]	50	77–84	dextro	+106.6	$C_{19}H_{19}BrO_3$	...	...	..	..

[a] Calculated on the basis that 100% is the theoretical yield for each antipode. [b] Specific rotation of a 2% solution in 95% ethanol at 25°. [c] The brucine salt was recrystallized from an isopropyl alcohol–water mixture and the free acid from cyclohexane. [d] No attempt was made to isolate or purify the dextro antipode. [e] A 3% solution was used in this case. [f] The brucine salt was recrystallized from methanol; the free acid from heptane. [g] Recrystallized from acetonitrile then from heptane. [h] The brucine salt was recrystallized from methanol; the free acid was recrystallized from cyclohexane. [i] No attempt was made to obtain this antipode in pure form.

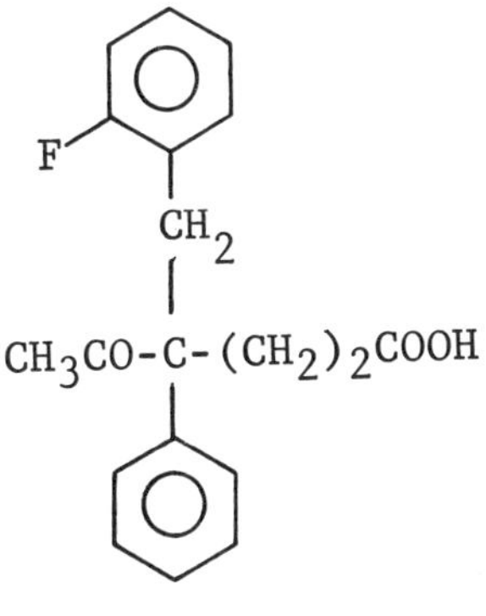

$C_{19}H_{19}FO_3$ Ref. 1313

Note:
For resolution procedure and physical constants, see Ref. 1312.

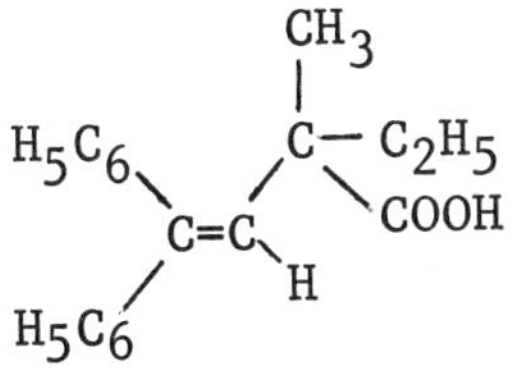

$C_{19}H_{20}O_2$ Ref. 1314

Resolution of 2-Ethyl-2-methyl-4,4-diphenyl-3-butenoic Acid. Cinchonidine (3.59 g, 12.2 mmol) was dissolved in a solution of 3.43 g (12.3 mmol) of 2-ethyl-2-methyl-4,4-diphenyl-3-butenoic acid in 20 ml of chloroform. The solution was warmed and 25 ml of hexane was added. Upon standing overnight at room temperature, the solution deposited 132 mg of crystalline salt. Reducing the volume of the solution and adding more hexane gave two additional crops of salt, increasing the total amount to 3.60 g. Four successive crystallizations of this gave 1.34 g of cinchonidine salt as colorless crystals, mp 174–174.5°, which on hydrolysis (6 *N* HCl)

afforded 0.650 g (38%) of 2-ethyl-2-methyl-4,4-diphenyl-3-butenoic acid, $[\alpha]^{27}_{365}$ 115 ± 1° (*c* 0.010, methanol),[35,37] as a colorless oil. The specific rotations were unchanged from those of a sample obtained from the previous recrystallization. The specific rotations at 27° were (λ in parentheses): 25.0 ± 0.6° (589), 26.4 ± 0.4° (578), 30.9 ± 0.4° (546), 60.6 ± 0.5° (436), 115 ± 1° (365) (*c* 0.010, methanol). The optically active acid had ir and nmr spectra identical with those of the racemic compound.

(35) All quantitative work was done on a Perkin-Elmer Model 141 polarimeter with thermostated 1-dm cells. The [α]'s of purified (+)-10-camphorsulfonic acid were measured on this instrument and found to agree to within 1.5% or less with the values published by DeTar.[36] We are grateful to Professor Harlan Goering for use of the polarimeter.

(36) D. F. DeTar, *Anal. Chem.*, **41**, 1406 (1969).

(37) All optically active compounds that were purified by recrystallization were recrystallized to constant rotation at all five wavelengths available on the Perkin-Elmer 141. And all chromatographically purified optically active compounds were checked to be sure that the earliest and latest product-containing fractions had the same [α]'s at all five wavelengths.

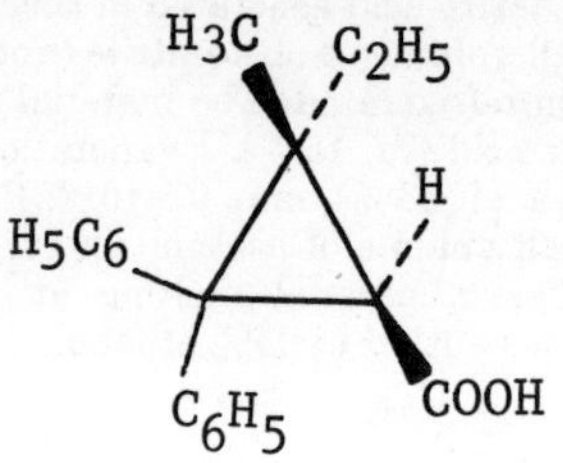

$C_{19}H_{20}O_2$ Ref. 1315

Resolution of *trans*-2-Ethyl-2-methyl-3,3-diphenylcyclopropanecarboxylic Acid. A mixture of 7.76 g (2.40 mmol) of (−)-quinine and 6.59 g (23.5 mmol) of *trans*-2-ethyl-2-methyl-3,3-diphenylcyclopropanecarboxylic acid was dissolved in 50 ml of chloroform. The solution was diluted with 50 ml of hexane and concentrated to 75 ml. Addition of 25 ml of hexane, cooling, and seeding gave 5.31 g of the salt as colorless needles, mp 127–129°. A portion of the salt on hydrolysis (3 *N* HCl) gave acid of $[\alpha]^{27}_{365}$ 701° (*c* 0.0113, $CHCl_3$). Three additional crystallizations gave 3.91 g of salt, mp 129–130°, which was hydrolyzed to 1.51 g of partly crystalline acid with $[\alpha]^{27}_{365}$ 778 ± 12° (*c* 0.006, $CHCl_3$), unchanged from the previous crystallization. Crystallization from hexane gave 1.410 g (43%) of *trans*-2-ethyl-2-methyl-3,3-diphenylcyclopropanecarboxylic acid, $[\alpha]^{27}_{365}$ 840 ± 4° (*c* 0.004, $CHCl_3$), as colorless prisms, mp 148.5–149° (sealed capillary). Further crystallization from hexane did not change the melting point or rotations. The specific rotations at 27° were (λ in parentheses): 196 ± 2° (589), 206 ± 2° (578), 238 ± 2° (546), 455 ± 4° (436), 840 ± 6° (365) (*c* 0.004, $CHCl_3$). The ir and nmr spectra of the optically pure trans acid were identical with those of the racemic compound.

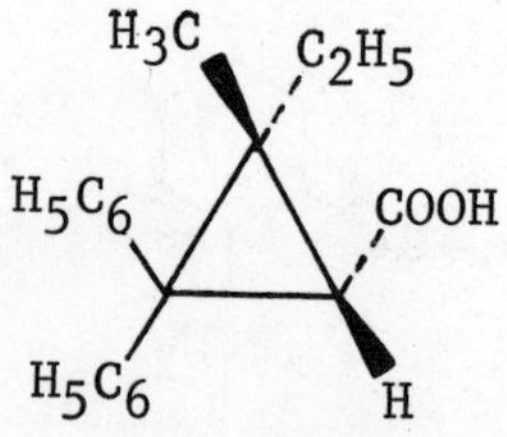

$C_{19}H_{20}O_2$ Ref. 1316

Resolution of *cis*-2-Ethyl-2-methyl-3,3-diphenylcyclopropanecarboxylic Acid. A mixture of 2.48 g (8.71 mmol) of *cis*-2-ethyl-2-methyl-3,3-diphenylcyclopropanecarboxylic acid and 2.60 g (8.71 mmol) of purified[39] (−)-cinchonidine was heated with 120 ml of ethyl acetate until solution occurred. The hot solution was concentrated to *ca.* 85 ml, then cooled, and addition of seeds (obtained by trituration with ethyl acetate at Dry Ice temperature) initiated crystallization. Three crops of the salt, 1.90 g in all, were obtained as colorless needles, mp 108–112°. Hydrolysis (3 *N* HCl) of a small portion of the salt gave acid with $[\alpha]^{27}_{365}$ −625° (*c* 0.004, $CHCl_3$). Crystallization of the salt gave 1.60 g of white needles, mp 110–112°, a little of which was hydrolyzed to acid of $[\alpha]^{27}_{365}$ −743° (*c* 0.004, $CHCl_3$). Further crystallization of the salt followed by hydrolysis gave acid of unchanged specific rotation. Consequently, the salt of the second crystallization was hydrolyzed to 650 mg of acid, which on crystallization from hexane afforded 355 mg of *cis*-2-ethyl-2-methyl-3,3-diphenylcyclopropanecarboxylic acid as colorless needles, mp 176.5–177° (sealed capillary). The specific rotations at 27° were (λ in parentheses): −171 ± 1° (589), −179 ± 1° (578), −208 ± 1° (546), −406 ± 2° (436), −765 ± 5° (365) (*c* 0.004, $CHCl_3$). The optically pure compound had nmr spectral data identical with those of the racemic acid and was not changed in any way by further crystallization.

By recrystallization of various acid and salt mother liquors, it was possible to improve the yield of optically pure cis acid to 812 mg (66%).

(39) T. A. Henry, "The Plant Alkaloids," 4th ed, Blakiston Co., Philadelphia, Pa., 1949, pp 427 and 428.

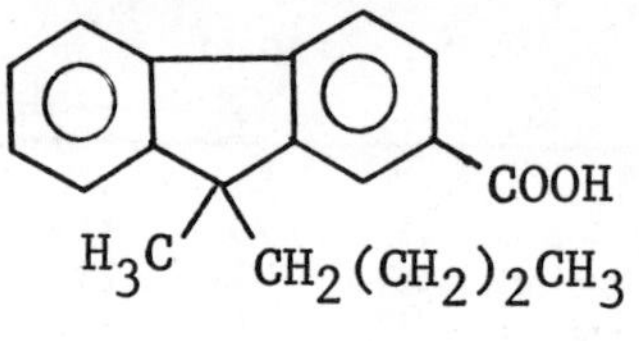

$C_{19}H_{20}O_2$ Ref. 1317

Le dédoublement de l'acide 9,9-méthylebutylefluorènecarboxylique-2 était assez difficile. L'énantiomère lévogyre a été obtenu à l'usage du sel brucinique par sa cristallisation de l'éthanol dilué. Le sel optiquement pur de l'antimère lévogyre formait des aiguilles, F. 99—101° et $(\alpha)^{20}_D$ = −33,33° (méthanol). Pour obtenir l'antimère dextrogyre on devait séparer l'acide libre des eaux-méres après la séparation de la premiere fraction du sel brucinique et le lier avec la cinchonidine. Ce sel a été cristallisé de l'acétone diluée. Le sel cinchonidinique optiquement pur présentait des aiguilles, F. 157—158° et $(\alpha)^{20}_D$ = −39,16° (méthanol).

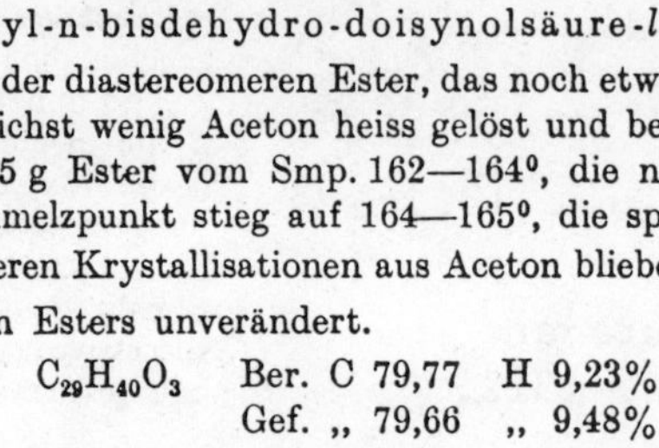

$C_{19}H_{22}O_3$ Ref. 1318

2. (+)7-Methyl-n-bisdehydro-doisynolsäure-*l*-menthylester.

Das rohe Gemisch der diastereomeren Ester, das noch etwas überschüssiges Menthol enthielt, wurde in möglichst wenig Aceton heiss gelöst und bei Zimmertemperatur krystallisiert. Man erhielt 5 g Ester vom Smp. 162—164°, die nochmals aus Aceton umgelöst wurden. Der Schmelzpunkt stieg auf 164—165°, die spezifische Drehung betrug $[\alpha]^{21}_D$ = − 5°. Nach weiteren Krystallisationen aus Aceton blieben Drehung und Schmelzpunkt des so erhaltenen Esters unverändert.

$C_{29}H_{40}O_3$	Ber.	C 79,77	H 9,23%
	Gef.	„ 79,66	„ 9,48%

Löslichkeit bei 20° pro cm³: 0,0104 g in Aceton und 0,0007 g in Methanol.

3. (+)7-Methyl-n-bisdehydro-doisynolsäure.

2 g *l*-Menthylester vom Smp. 164—165° wurden mit 5 g KOH und 20 cm³ Propylalkohol im Ölbad 30 Minuten auf 160—170° erwärmt, die erhaltene Schmelze in Wasser aufgenommen, mit Äther gewaschen, dann die (+)7-Methyl-n-bisdehydro-doisynolsäure mit HCl ausgefällt und aus verdünntem Methanol umkrystallisiert. Smp. 220—221° (219°). Drehung s. Tabelle I.

$C_{19}H_{22}O_3$	Ber. C	76,48	H 7,43%
	Gef. ,,	76,38	,, 7,66%

4. (−)7-Methyl-n-bisdehydro-doisynolsäure-*l*-menthylester.

Die Mutterlauge der 1. Krystallisation des (+)Säure-*l*-menthylesters aus Aceton wurde auf 30 cm³ eingeengt und bei 20° aufbewahrt. Es krystallisierten nochmals 0,5 g weitgehend angereicherten (+)Säure-esters. Dessen Mutterlauge wurde im Vakuum zur Trockne eingedampft. Die Drehung des Rückstandes (3,2 g) betrug $[\alpha]_D^{20} = -60°$. Nach Krystallisation aus 230 cm³ Methanol war sie auf −64° gestiegen; der Schmelzpunkt lag sehr scharf bei 113°.

$C_{29}H_{40}O_3$	Ber. C	79,77	H 9,23%
	Gef. ,,	79,56	,, 9,43%

Löslichkeit bei 20° pro cm³: 0,206 g in Aceton und 0,0053 g in Methanol.

5. (−)7-Methyl-n-bisdehydro-doisynolsäure.

2 g *l*-Menthylester vom Smp. 113° wurden, wie unter 3. angegeben, bei 150—160° verseift. Man erhielt (−)7-Methyl-n-bisdehydro-doisynolsäure vom Smp. 219—221 (218°). Drehung s. Tab. I.

$C_{19}H_{22}O_3$	Ber. C	76,48	H 7,43%
	Gef. ,,	76,68	,, 7,57%

6. (+)n-Bisdehydro-doisynolsäure.

100 mg (+)7-Methylsäure wurden mit 2 cm³ 48-proz. HBr und 2 cm³ Eisessig 2 Stunden zum Sieden erhitzt, die erkaltete Lösung mit Wasser versetzt, der entstandene Niederschlag abfiltriert und mit Tierkohle aus verdünntem Methanol umkrystallisiert. Man erhielt 30 mg (+)n-Bisdehydro-doisynolsäure vom Smp. 159—161°. Drehung s. Tab. I.

7. (−)n-Bisdehydro-doisynolsäure.

Diese Säure wurde ganz analog wie die rechtsdrehende Verbindung aus der (−)7-Methylsäure erhalten. Smp. 159—160°. Drehung s. Tab. I.

Die Analysen und die Bestimmung der Drehungen wurden in unserem Laboratorium unter der Leitung von Hrn. Dr. *Gysel* durchgeführt.

$C_{19}H_{22}O_4$

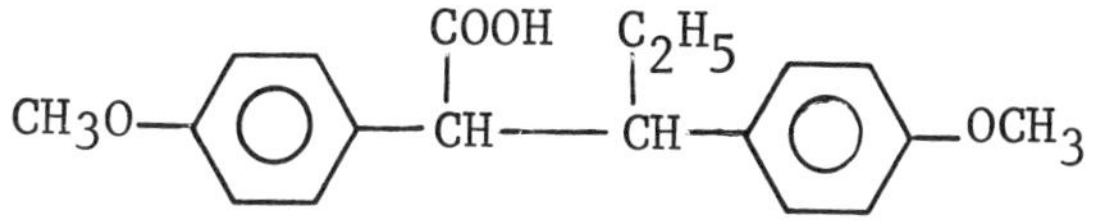

Ref. 1319

(*p*) *Resolution of* erythro-*2,3-Bis*(p-*methoxyphenyl*)*valeric Acid* (*10f*)

(i) *Dextro*.—A mixture of the acid (9·4 g) and (−)-quinine (11·4 g) was dissolved in hot absolute ethanol (600 ml) and the mixture allowed to cool slowly. After 5 hr the crude salt (10·2 g), m.p. 202–204°, was collected. Several recrystallizations from ethanol and careful fractional crystallization of mother liquors (26 crystallizations in all) gave (+)-2,3-bis(*p*-methoxyphenyl)-valeric acid (−)-quinine salt (total 7·2 g), m.p. 211–212·5°, $[\alpha]_D$ −72·4° (*c*, 1·11 in chloroform) (lit.[16] m.p. 210–210·5°, $[\alpha]_D$ −70·5° in chloroform).

Treatment of the salt with 4N hydrochloric acid, extraction with ether, and successive crystallizations from aqueous ethanol and benzene gave pure (+)-*erythro*-2,3-bis(*p*-methoxyphenyl)valeric acid, m.p. 173–174°, $[\alpha]_D$ +22·7° (*c*, 1·24 in dioxan) (lit.[16] m.p. 170–174°, $[\alpha]_D$ +18·5° in dioxan) (Found: C, 72·9; H, 7·1. $C_{19}H_{22}O_4$ requires C, 72·6; H, 7·1%).

Esterification with diazomethane gave the (+)-erythro-*methyl ester*, m.p. 129–131·5°, $[\alpha]_D$ +19·2° (*c*, 0·99 in dioxan) (Found: C, 73·0; H, 7·4. $C_{20}H_{24}O_4$ requires C, 73·1; H, 7·4%).

(ii) *Laevo*.—The (−)-enriched acid (6·5 g) recovered from early mother liquors of the (−)-quinine salt, and (−)-ephedrine (3·4 g) were dissolved in hot ethanol (90 ml) and crystallization induced. The crude salt (7·5 g), m.p. 160–164°, was recrystallized seven times from ethanol to give pure (−)-erythro-*2,3-bis*(p-*methoxyphenyl*)*valeric acid* (−)-*ephedrine salt* (5·7 g), m.p. 165–167°, $[\alpha]_D$ −34·0° (*c*, 0·97 in dioxan) (Found: C, 72·5; H, 7·7; N, 2·5. $C_{19}H_{22}O_4,C_{10}H_{15}NO$ requires C, 72·6; H, 7·8; N, 2·9%).

The acid was recovered from the salt with hydrochloric acid in the usual way, and two crystallizations from methanol gave (−)-erythro-*2,3-bis*(p-*methoxyphenyl*)*valeric acid* (2·0 g), m.p. 173–174·5°, $[\alpha]_D$ −22·4° (*c*, 1·31 in dioxan) (Found: C, 72·4; H, 7·1. $C_{19}H_{22}O_4$ requires C, 72·6; H, 7·1%). The i.r. spectrum was identical with that of the (+)-isomer.

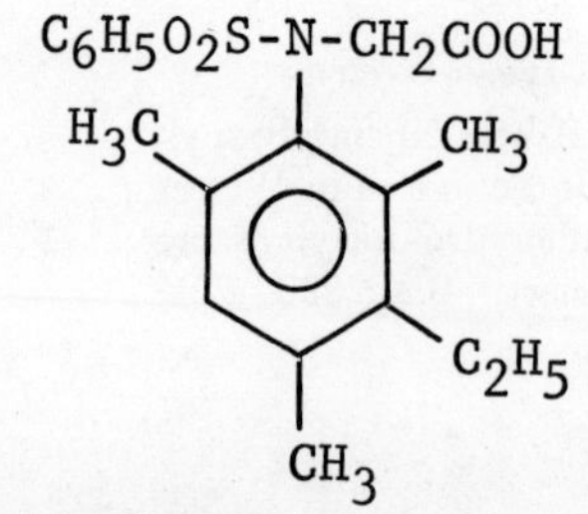

$C_{19}H_{23}NO_4S$ Ref. 1320

Resolution of N-Benzenesulfonyl-N-carboxymethylethylmesidine.—A hot solution of 4.870 g. of N-benzenesulfonyl-N-carboxymethylethylmesidine and 3.966 g. of cinchonidine in 300 ml. of ethyl acetate was filtered, then placed in a refrigerator. The solution was allowed to evaporate slowly to dryness over a period of 6 days. Four crops were collected: 1.04 g., $[\alpha]^{23}D$ − 66.7°; 1.13 g., $[\alpha]^{23}D$ − 66.4°; 3.93 g., $[\alpha]^{23}D$ − 58.9°; 2.13 g., $[\alpha]^{23}D$ − 45.6°. The rotations were determined in absolute ethanol.

The first three crops (69%) were put together and recrystallized from 350 ml. of ethyl acetate. Upon evaporation of the solvent the following crops were collected: 1.53 g., $[\alpha]^{27}D$ − 68.0°; 1.24 g., $[\alpha]^{27}D$ − 67.1°; 1.18 g., $[\alpha]^{27}D$ − 64.6°; 0.76 g., $[\alpha]^{27}D$ − 52.7°; 1.20 g. (rotation not determined). The rotations were determined in absolute ethanol.

The first three crops of this series were combined and recrystallized. The specific rotation remained unchanged, and the pure less-soluble salt crystallized, m.p. 188–189°; rotation, 0.0742 g. made up to 5 ml. with absolute ethanol at 26° gave αD − 1.01° (*l* 1), $[\alpha]^{26}D$ − 68.0°.

(−)-N-Benzenesulfonyl-N-carboxymethylethylmesidine.—The optically active acid was regenerated from the less-soluble salt in a manner previously described.[14] The product after crystallization from benzene melted at 155–157°; rotation, 0.0164 g. made up to 2 ml. with absolute ethanol at 27° gave αD − 0.10° (*l* 1), $[\alpha]^{27}D$ −12.4°. The yield was 96%.

Anal. Calcd. for $C_{19}H_{23}NO_4S$: C, 63.13; H, 6.41; N, 3.88. Found: C, 62.85; H, 6.32; N, 3.91.

(14) R. Adams and K. V. Y. Sundstrom, *J. Am. Chem. Soc.*, **76**, 5477 (1954).

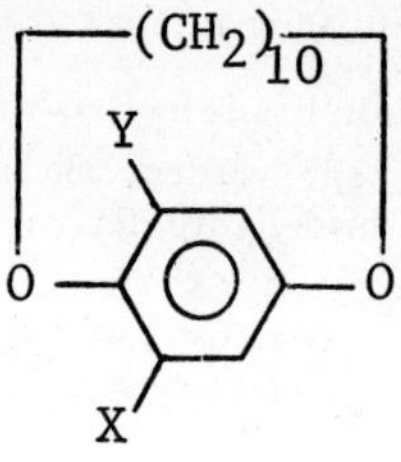

X=COOCH3
Y=COOH

Ref. 1321

$C_{19}H_{26}O_6$

Diastereomere (S)-α-*Phenyläthylamide der 17-Methoxycarbonyl-1,12-dioxa-[12]paracyclophan-15-carbonsäure* (VIIIa, VIIIb). Zu einer eisgekühlten Lösung von 533 mg (1,52 mMol) des Dicarbonsäure-monomethylesters VII in 1,8 ml Chloroform gab man 169 mg (1,67 mMol) Triäthylamin und 181 mg (1,67 mMol) Chlorameisensäureäthylester in je 1,5 ml Chloroform gelöst. Nach 2 Std. Stehen bei Raumtemperatur wurden 250 mg (2,06 mMol) (−)-(*S*)-α-Phenyläthylamin hinzugefügt und weiterhin 10 Std. stehengelassen. Durch Dünnschichtchromatographie konnte festgestellt werden, dass der Umsatz vollständig war. Nach Verteilung zwischen 100 ml Äthylacetat und 2mal je 30 ml Wasser, 2mal je 20 ml 1 N Salzsäure, 3mal je 20 ml Wasser, 2mal je 20 ml 1 N Natriumhydroxid-Lösung und Eindampfen der gewaschenen und getrockneten organischen Phase blieben 654 mg (95%) eines farblosen Öls zurück, welches im Dünnschichtchromatogramm zwei Flecken aufwies: Benzol/Äthylacetat 9:1, Rf. (−)VIIIa 0,59, (+)-VIIIb 0,50. Im präparativen Maßstab gelang die Trennung der Diastereomeren durch Chromatographie an 70 g Silikagel mit demselben Elutionsmittel, wobei im Bereich, in welchem Produkte vorkamen, Fraktionen von je 5 ml aufgefangen und dünnschichtchromatographisch analysiert wurden. Im Intervall 420–510 ml waren 225 mg Amid-ester (−)-VIIIa, im Intervall 510–570 ml 324 mg eines Gemisches und im Bereich 570–650 ml 96 mg Amid-ester (+)-VIIIb enthalten. Die beiden diastereomeren Verbindungen konnten nicht zur Kristallisation gebracht werden.

Amid-ester (−)-VIIIa mit Rf. 0,59. $[\alpha]^{21}_{578} = -3{,}2°$, $[\alpha]^{21}_{365} = -84°$ (c = 2,81, Benzol). IR. ($CHCl_3$): Banden u.a. bei 3375 (w), 1720 (s), 1650 (s), 1520 (s), 1520 (s), 1215 (breit, s), 700 (m) cm^{-1}. NMR. ($CDCl_3$): δ 0,7–2,0 (*Sh*, 16H), 1,62 (*d*, *J* = 7, 3H), 3,91 (*s*, 3H), 3,9–4,6 (*Sh*, 4H), 5,32 (*qi*, *J* = 7, 1H), 7,2–7,5 (*Sh*, 5H), 7,49 (*d*, *J* = 3,5, 1H), 7,92 (*d*, *J* = 3,5, 1H), 8,32 (*d*, breit, *J* = 8, 1H). MS.: M^+ 453.

Amid-ester (+)-VIIIb mit Rf. 0,50. $[\alpha]^{21}_{578} = +9{,}9°$, $[\alpha]^{21}_{365} = +126°$ (c = 4,28, Benzol). IR. ($CHCl_3$): Deckungsgleich dem von (−)-VIIIa. NMR. ($CDCl_3$): δ 0,6–2,0 (*Sh*, 16H), 1,58 (*d*, *J* = 7, 3H), 3,90 (*s*, 3H), 3,8–4,2 (*Sh*, 2H), 4,28 (*t*, *J* = 6, 2H), 5,35 (*qi*, *J* = 7, 1H), 7,2–7,4 (*Sh*, 5H), 7,49 (*d*, *J* = 3,5, 1H), 7,96 (*d*, *J* = 3,5, 1H), 8,32 (*d*, breit, *J* = 8, 1H). MS.: M^+ 453.

Diastereomere Mono-(S)-α-*phenyläthylamide der 1,12-Dioxa-[12]paracyclophan-15,17-dicarbonsäure* (*IXa*, *IXb*). Eine Lösung von 266 mg (0,586 mMol) Amid-methylester(−)-VIIIa in 10 ml Methanol, der man zu Beginn und nach 5 Std. 0,7 ml bzw. 0,3 ml 1 N Natriumhydroxid-Lösung hinzufügte, wurde 9 Std. zum Sieden erhitzt. Man engte auf ca. 2 ml ein, verdünnte mit 50 ml Wasser und säuerte mit 1 N Salzsäure an (pH 1–2). Den farblosen Niederschlag extrahierte man 3mal mit je 75 ml Chloroform. Der Rückstand nach dem Eindampfen der gewaschenen und getrockneten Extrakte wurde aus 60 ml Äthylacetat umkristallisiert: 231 mg farblose Nadeln der Amid-carbonsäure IXa, Smp. 255–257° (Zers.). Aus der Mutterlauge konnten durch 3malige Umkristallisation aus Äthanol/Wasser weitere 16 mg der reinen Verbindung gewonnen werden (insgesamt 96%). Die Verbindung ist relativ schwer löslich in den üblichen Lösungsmitteln. Dünnschichtchromatographisches Verhalten (Benzol/Äthylacetat/Eisessig 50:50:3): Rf. 0,64. $[\alpha]^{24}_{D} = -28°$, $[\alpha]^{24}_{546} = -37°$, $[\alpha]^{24}_{436} = -77°$, $[\alpha]^{24}_{405} = -106°$ (c = 0,274, Äthanol). IR. (KBr): Banden u.a. bei 3340 (m), 1720 (s), 1630 (s), 1595 (m), 1580 (m), 1535 (s), 1200 (breit, s), 705 (s)

cm^{-1}. MS.: M^+ 439. pK^*_{MCS} 5,88 (Äqu.-Gew.: Ber. 439,5, gef. 461).

$C_{26}H_{33}NO_5$ Ber. C 71,04 H 7,57 N 3,19% Gef. C 70,88 H 7,61 N 3,16%

Analog erhielt man aus 150 mg (+)-VIIIb 135 mg (93%) der Amid-carbonsäure (+)-IXb, Smp. 221–223° (Sintern ab 214°), nach Wiedererstarren Smp. 242–244° (Zers.), farblose Nadeln (aus Äthylacetat) oder Blättchen (aus Äthanol/Wasser), relativ schwer löslich in den üblichen Lösungsmitteln. Dünnschichtchromatographisches Verhalten (Benzol/Äthylacetat/Eisessig 50:50:3): Rf. 0,62. $[\alpha]_D^{24} = +34°$, $[\alpha]_{546}^{24} = +48°$, $[\alpha]_{436}^{24} = +137°$, $[\alpha]_{405}^{24} = +220°$ ($c = 0,315$, Äthanol). IR. (KBr): Banden u.a. bei 3360 (m), 1720 (s), 1630 (s), 1595 (m) mit Schulter 1580 (w), 1540 (s), 1200 (breit, aufgespalten, s), 705 (s) cm^{-1}, besonders im Fingerprint-Gebiet signifikant verschieden von dem des diastereomeren (−)-IXa. MS.: M^+ 439. pK^*_{MCS} 5,72 (Äqu.-Gew.: Ber. 439,5, gef. 449).

$C_{26}H_{33}NO_5$ Ber. C 71,04 H 7,57 N 3,19% Gef. C 70,97 H 7,60 N 3,25%

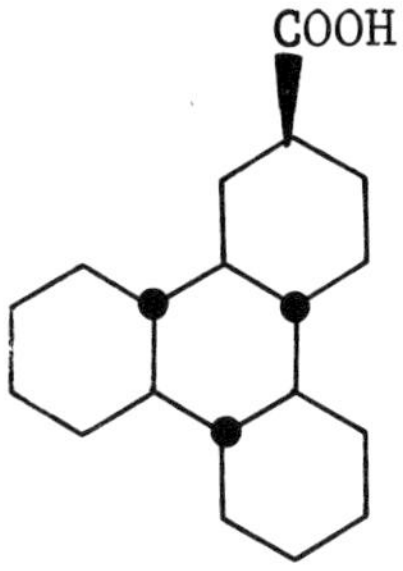

$C_{19}H_{30}O_2$ Ref. 1322

Resolution of perhydrotriphenylen-2-carboxylic acid (II)

(a) *Salt with amine D.* An etheral soln (0·23 N) of amine D (160 ml) obtained[5, 6] from commercial amine D (Hercules Powder Co) was added to a soln of acid II (10 g) in ether (1 l); 10 g of salt precipitated, its rotatory power after 6 crystallizations from EtOH reached the constant value of −23·2 ($CHCl_3$, 25°, Na-light). The highest rotatory power of the positive salt was +54.

(b) *Hydrolysis of the salt.* 20 g of salt ($[\alpha]_D^{25}$ = 23·2) wetted with a few drops of EtOH and 400 ml 5% KOH were heated in water bath for 20 hr. After ether extraction of the amine, it was acidified with 35 ml conc HCl. The ppt was recrystallized from 1:1 acetone–toluene: 8·9 g, yield 89·5% $[\alpha]_D^{25}$ = −74·5 (benzene), m.p. 232°. From a positive salt with $[\alpha]_D^{25}$ = +49·5, an acid with $[\alpha]_D^{25}$ = +40 was obtained.

[5] B. Sjöberg and S. Sjöberg, *Ark. Kemi* **22**, 447 (1964).
[6] W. J. Gottstein and L. C. Cheney, *J. Org. Chem.* **30**, 2072 (1965).

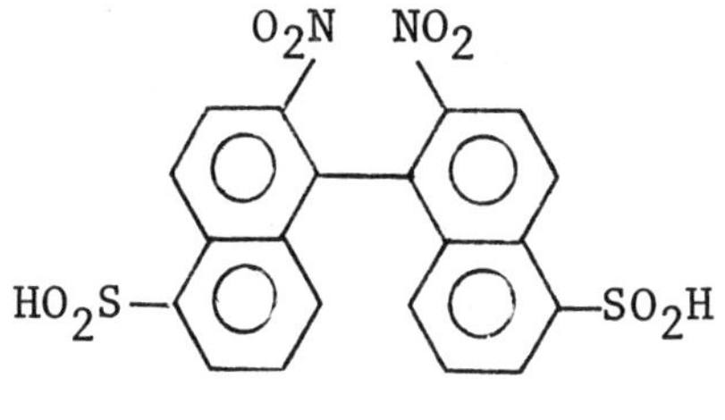

$C_{20}H_{12}N_2O_{10}S_2$ Ref. 1323

Note:

The barium salt of the racemic acid was resolved via α-phenylethylamine from H_2O. The [α] were found to be $[\alpha]_D^{33}$ 36.9° and -35.5° (c 0.32%, H_2O).

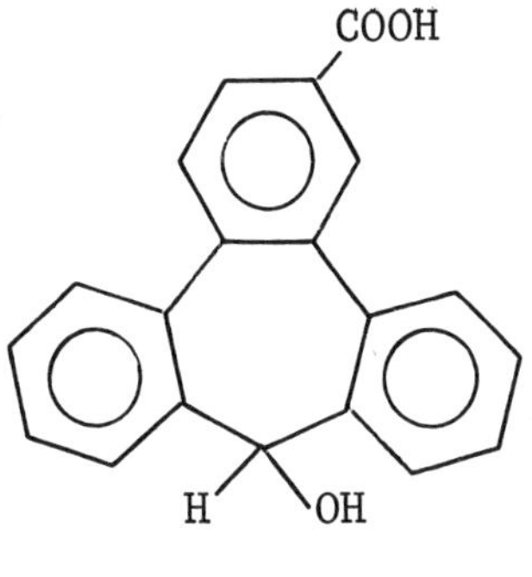

$C_{20}H_{13}O_3$ Ref. 1324

Note:

2 liess sich in die optischen Antipoden spalten, da aus Aceton bevorzugt das Brucin-Salz der rechtsdrehenden Säure kristallisierte. ((+)-2: $[\alpha]_{426}^{24}$ = +362°; (-)-2: $[\alpha]_{436}^{24}$ = -380°; c = 0.025 in DMSO).

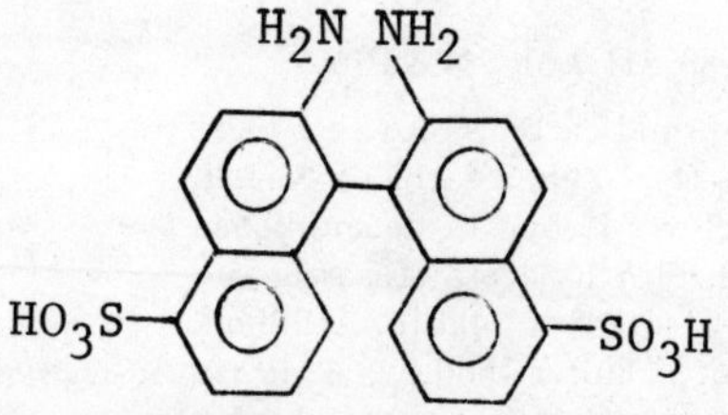

$C_{20}H_{16}N_2O_6S_2$ Ref. 1325

Note:

The barium salt of the racemic acid was resolved via α-phenylethylamine from H_2O. The [α] were found to be $[\alpha]_D^{13}$ 120.8° and -122.0° (c 1% H_2O).

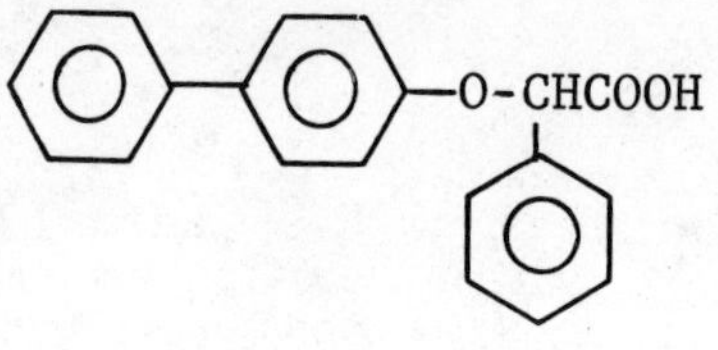

$C_{20}H_{16}O_3$ Ref. 1326

Le dédoublement de l'acide α-(4-biphényliloxy)-phénylacétique était lié avec des difficultés considérables causées par le fait que les sels alcaloïdiques le mieux cristallisants, à savoir: brucinique, strychninique, quininique et hydrocinchoninique, ne donnaient pas l'effet de séparation aux antipodes optiques. Dés résultats positifs ont été obtenus pendant la cristallisation fractionnée du sel neutre cinchonidinique mal cristallisant, qui séparait l'enantiomère lévogyre en milieu méthanolique en fractions moins solubles. Après la deuxième cristallisation nous avons obtenu un sel optiquement pur sous forme d'aiguilles bien distinctes, f. à 114° et a rot. spéc. $[\alpha]_D^{20}$ = -90,90° (c 0,33; d 1; α -0,30°) dans l'éthanol 96% (calc. pour $C_{39}H_{38}N_2O_4$: N. 4,67; tr. N. 4,79).

Isolé de façon ordinaire du sel cinchonidinique, l'enantiomère lévogyre de l'acide α-(4-biphényliloxy)-phénylacétique, après une purification soigneuse du benzène, se présentait sous forme d'aiguilles fines, f. à 195-196° et a rot. spéc. $[\alpha]_D^{20}$ = -106,06° (c 0,33; d 1; α -0,35°) dans l'éthanol 96% (calc. pour $C_{20}H_{16}O_3$; C. 78,93; H. 5,30; tr. C. 78,76; H. 5,31).

Malgré de nombreux essais, nous n'avons pas réussi à isoler l'enantiomère dextrogyre du racémat par voie de cristallisation des sels alcaloidiques. L'unique voie qui nous conduisît aux resultats positifs était celle de la séparation de cet acide des eaux-mères après la cristallisation du sel cinchonidinique de l'acide lévogyre. L'acide dextrogyre brut ($[\alpha]_D^{20}$ = +90,90° dans l'éthanol 96%) a été purifié par une double cristallisation du benzène. L'enantiomère dextrogyre ainsi obtenu formait des aiguilles fines f. à 194-195° et à rot. spec. $[\alpha]_D^{20}$ = +106,06° (c 0,33; d 1; α +0,35°) dans l'éthanol 96% (calc. pour $C_{20}H_{16}O_3$: C. 78,93; H. 5,30; tr. C. 78,79; H. 5,51).

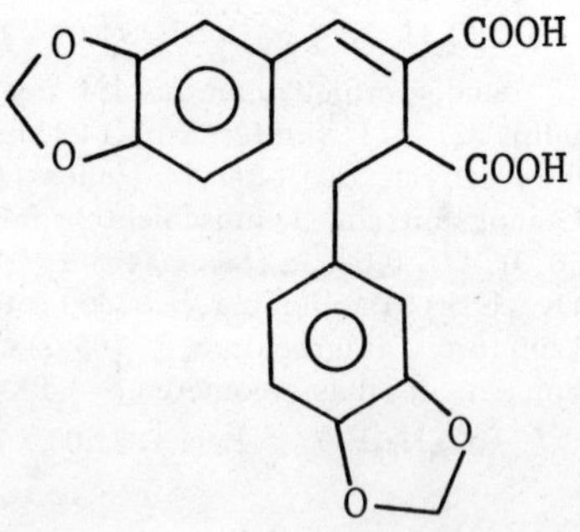

$C_{20}H_{16}O_8$ Ref. 1327

Resolution of (±)-α-(3,4-*Methylenedioxybenzyl*-β-(3,4-*methylenedioxybenzylidene*)*succinic Acid*.—The (±)-acid hydrate (26 g., 1 mol.) and (−)-quinine (48·9 g., 2 mol.) in ethanol (1·25 l.) were boiled for 2 min. On cooling, fine needles separated, and were collected. Two recrystallizations from ethanol afforded the *monoquinine salt of the* (−)-*acid* (23 g., 93%), m.p. 182—183° (Found: C, 67·7; H, 5·35; N, 4·15. $C_{20}H_{16}O_8,C_{20}H_{24}NO_2$ requires C, 67·8; H, 5·65; N, 3·95%), $\nu_{max.}$ (mull) 3185, 1724, 1686, 1613, 1580, and 926 cm.$^{-1}$, $\lambda_{max.}$ 232 (4·68), 284 (4·25), and 311 (4·12) nm. Concentration of the mother liquors gave a solid which on three more crystallizations from aqueous ethanol yielded the diquinine salt of the (+)-acid (12·6 g., 42%), m.p. 161—163° (softened 145°), $\nu_{max.}$ (mull) 3145, 1642, 1626, 1582, and 926 cm.$^{-1}$, $\lambda_{max.}$ 231 (4·92), 281 (4·39), and 316 (4·25) nm. Both quinine salts were decomposed by washing an ethereal suspension with dil. hydrochloric acid. The aqueous solutions were extracted with ether, and the combined extracts were dried and evaporated. The salt m.p. 182—183° (23 g.) yielded the (−)-*acid* (12 g., 92%), m.p. 97° (decarbox.) (Found: C, 62·7; H, 4·35. $C_{20}H_{16}O_8$ requires C, 62·5; H, 4·2%), $[\alpha]_D^{21}$ −96·5° (*c* 3·09% in acetone), $\nu_{max.}$ (mull) 1707, 1692, 1623, 1492, and 926 cm.$^{-1}$, $\lambda_{max.}$ 229 (4·20), 285 (4·14), and 306 (4·99) nm. The salt m.p. 161—163° (12·6 g.), on similar treatment, gave the (+)-*acid* (3·5 g., 78%), m.p. 97° (decarbox.) (Found: C, 62·9; H, 4·45%), $[\alpha]_D^{19.5}$ +89·9° (*c* 3·5% in acetone). It had spectra closely similar to those of its epimer. Admixture of equal amounts of the (+)- and (−)-forms gave the racemic acid, m.p. 170° (decarbox.).

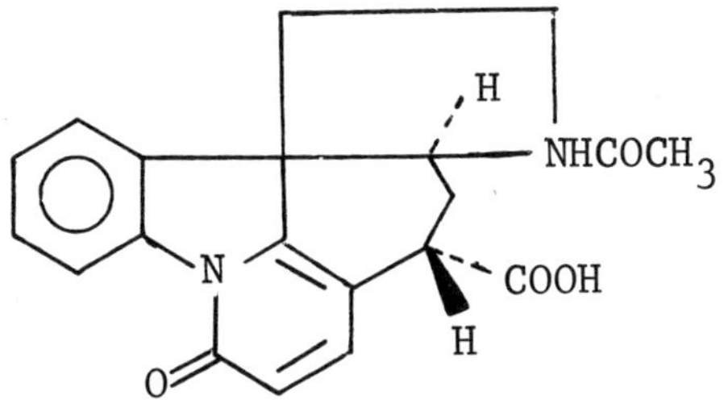

$C_{20}H_{18}N_2O_4$ Ref. 1328

Resolution of the synthetic trans N-*acetyl acid* (XXXIX) *with quinidine*

Laevorotatory trans N-*acetyl acid* (XXXIX). Synthetic *trans* acid (249 mg) was heated gently with quinidine (231 mg, recrystallized from chloroform–methanol, colorless prisms, m.p. 163–164°) in a mixture of chloroform (2 ml) and methanol (2 ml) until a clear solution was obtained. After the solvents had been evaporated the semi-solid residue was crystallized from chloroform–acetone to give the dihydrate of the quinidine salt (114 mg; 24%), m.p. 160–172°, unchanged on admixture with *trans* N-acetyl acid quinidine salt (m.p. 160–172°) prepared by degradation from natural strychnine [see *Ancillary degradative studies* (below)].

The free laevorotatory trans N-*acetyl acid* (XXXIX) was obtained in the following manner: The synthetic quinidine salt dihydrate (114 mg) was dissolved in water (5 ml) and 10% aqueous potassium carbonate (5 ml). The solution was extracted with chloroform to remove quinidine, acidified, and again extracted with chloroform to give the *trans* acid: 51 mg (87%) of colorless crystals, m.p. 295–300° after two recrystallizations from chloroform–methanol. The melting point behavior of the resolved synthetic acid was identical with that of the acid of the same structure (XXXIX), m.p. 295–300°, derived from strychnine by degradation [see *Ancillary degradative studies* (below)].

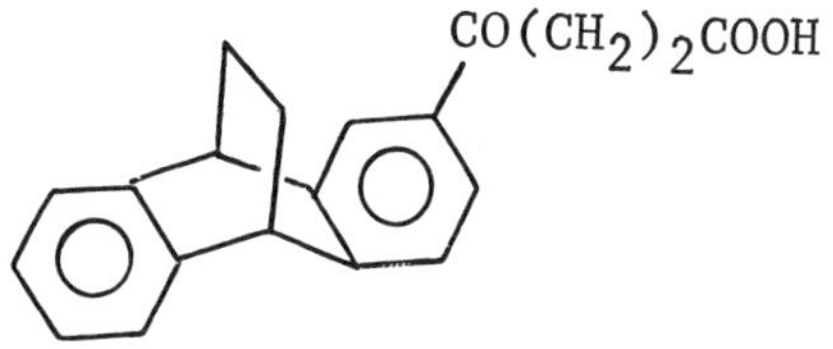

$C_{20}H_{18}O_3$ Ref. 1329

Racematspaltung der Ketosäuren **(8)**

8 a: 450 mg (1,47 mMol) racem. **8 a**[8] und 432 mg (1,47 mMol) Cinchonidin lösten wir in etwas CH_2Cl_2 und dampften im Vak. ab. Der Rückstand wurde in 10 ml Aceton und 5 ml Wasser aufgenommen, filtriert und das Salz (390 mg) nach längerem Stehen (bis 2 Wochen) im Kühlschrank abgesaugt. Daraus ließen sich 190 mg aktive Ketosäure **8 a** ($[\alpha]_D$ + 82,2°; Äthanol, *c* = 0,75) gewinnen. Aus der Mutterlauge erhielt man 240 mg **8 a**; $[\alpha]_D$ — 88,5° (Äthanol, *c* = 0,63).

[8] *J. Paul* und *K. Schlögl*, Mh. Chem. **104**, 263 (1973).

$C_{20}H_{18}O_3$ Ref. 1330

(+)(2R)-5'-Acetyl-2,2'-spirobiindan-5-carbonsäure (**2e**): Eine Lösung von 5.20 g (17 mmol) racem. **2e** (Tab. 8) in 270 ml Aceton wurde mit 2.25 g (18.6 mmol) (−)-α-Phenethylamin ($[\alpha]_D^{20}$ = −39°) versetzt und das Salz nach 24 h (Kühlschrank) abgesaugt. 4.20 g (58%).

$C_{28}H_{29}NO_3$ (427.5) Ber. N 3.28 Gef. N 3.17

Zur Racematspaltung wurde 7 mal (bis zur konstanten Drehung der freigesetzten Säure) aus Aceton umkristallisiert (4.20 g aus 95 ml bis 1.15 g aus 25 ml), wobei man 0.99 g Salz erhielt. Daraus wurde die Säure durch Behandeln mit 1 proz. wäßr. Natronlauge, Ausethern, Ansäuern mit 10 proz. Phosphorsäure und Absaugen erhalten. 0.65 g (91%; bzw. 12.5% von eingesetztem **2e**). Schmp. 215–220°C (Zers.). $[\alpha]_D^{20}$ = +27.0° (*c* = 1.2 in Aceton).

$C_{20}H_{18}O_3$ (306.4) Ber. C 78.41 H 5.92 Gef. C 78.32 H 5.98

Aus der Mutterlauge der 1. Kristallisation (3.24 g Salz) gewann man linksdrehende Säure: $[\alpha]_D^{20}$ = −9.5° (Aceton). Nach 4 Kristallisationen (1.86 g Salz) zeigte **2e** eine Drehung von +22.5°.

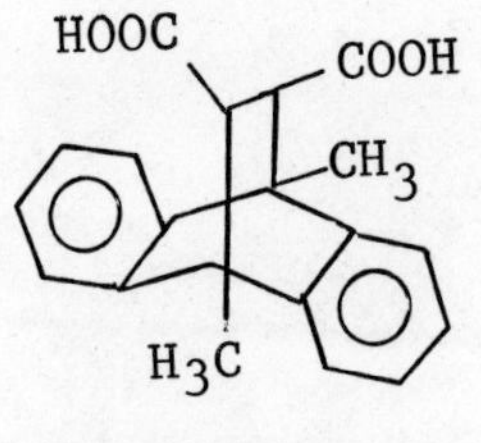

$C_{20}H_{18}O_4$ Ref. 1331

Dédoublement de l'acide **21***a*.

On dissout 40 g d'acide **21***a* (brut) et 115 g de brucine (hydratée) dans 420 cm³ d'éthanol et 220 cm³ d'eau. On obtient 61,7 g de sel qui ne se redissout que partiellement (même après ébullition prolongée) dans la même quantité de solvant. On laisse refroidir, essore le sel qu'on fait bouillir à nouveau dans 500 cm³ d'alcool et 200 cm³ d'eau pendant 1/2 h. On essore 37 g de sel qui fournit, après décomposition, 8,6 g d'acide, $[\alpha]_{578}^{25} = +20{,}6°$ (éthanol, $c = 1$).

Les premières eaux-mères de cristallisation du sel, évaporées partiellement et décomposées, fournissent 19,2 g d'acide $[\alpha]_{578} = -19{,}0°$, qui est partiellement dissous dans 50 cm³ d'éther et 50 cm³ de benzène. On filtre l'insoluble (5,4 g) qui est essentiellement de l'acide racémique ($[\alpha]_{578}^{25} = -2{,}6°$). On évapore la plus grande partie de l'éther des eaux-mères, ajoute un peu de pentane et laisse cristalliser. On essore 10 g d'acide $[\alpha]_{578}^{25} = -22{,}6°$.

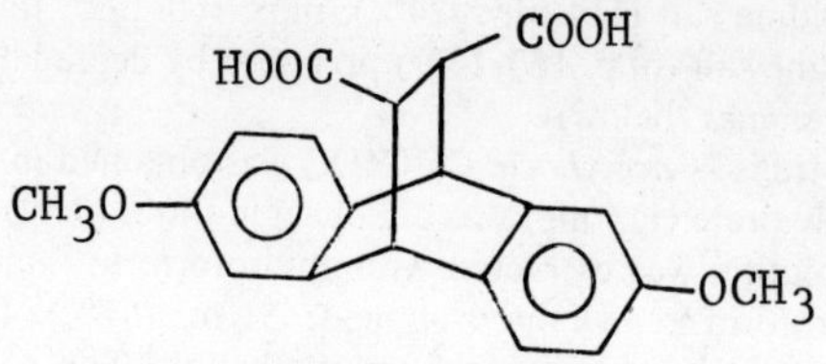

$C_{20}H_{18}O_6$ Ref. 1332

Resolution of endo-*dicarboxylic acid* (**31**). A mixture of *endo*-dicarboxylic acid (**30**, 942 mg), brucine tetrahydrate (2·29 g) and EtOAc (20 ml) was heated under reflux for two hr. After cooling, crystals were collected and recrystallized twice from MeOH (1·338 g). $[\alpha]_D$ −10·7° (MeOH, *c* 0·402). The salt was decomposed by shaking with dil. HCl for 30 min and free acid was filtered, washed with water and dried (621 mg). $[\alpha]_D$ +3·4° (dioxane, *c* 0·388).

A mixture of partially resolved *endo*-dicarboxylic acid, cinchonidine (1·031 g) and MeOH (10 ml) was warmed to 70° for 30 min. After cooling, crystals were collected and recrystallized twice from MeOH (372 mg). $[\alpha]_D$ −54·1° (MeOH, *c* 0·292). This salt was decomposed as described above and the free acid recrystallized from benzene (170 mg). $[\alpha]_D$ +35·3° (MeOH, *c* 0·317).

A mixture of this *endo*-dicarboxylic acid, quinine (220 mg) and 99% EtOH was warmed to 70° for 10 min and EtOH distilled to dryness. The residue was crystallized from acetone–EtOAc and then twice from acetone to give optically pure diastereomer (131 mg). $[\alpha]_D$ −113·5° (MeOH, *c* 0·349).

This pure salt was decomposed by adding dil. HCl to suspension in EtOAc. After the usual treatment, crude free acid was recrystallized from benzene to give optically pure acid (37 mg). $[\alpha]_D$ +39·0° (dioxane, *c* 0·331). (Found: C, 68·43; H, 5·24. $C_{20}H_{18}O_6$ requires: C, 67·78; H, 5·12%).

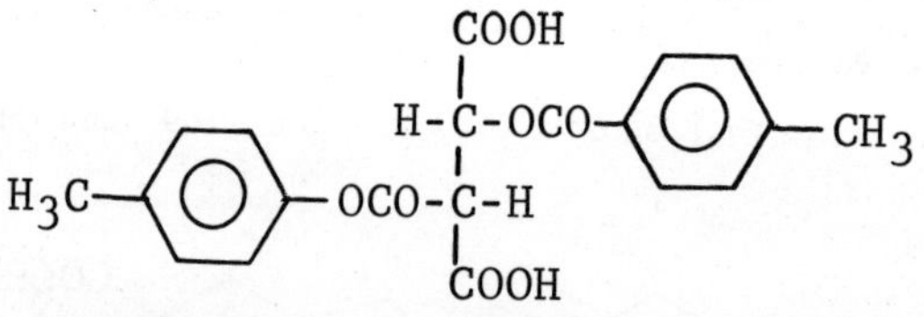

$C_{20}H_{18}O_8$ Ref. 1333

Experimental.—(±)-OO-*Di*-p-*toluoyltartaric anhydride* was prepared from racemic acid (35·6 g.) [3] and *p*-toluoyl chloride (117 g.) by Stoll and Hofmann's method.[1] Recrystallised from xylene, it had m. p. 162—163° (Found: C, 64·8; H, 4·45. $C_{20}H_{16}O_7$ requires C, 65·2; H, 4·4%).

(±)-OO-*Di*-p-*toluoyltartaric acid.* The anhydride (32 g.) was refluxed for 2 hr. with acetone (75 ml.) and water (7·5 ml.), and the mixture evaporated. The solid residue was boiled with xylene to remove unchanged anhydride and filtered hot. The air-dried insoluble *product* (25 g.) had m. p. 183—184° and was sufficiently pure for the next stage. A sample recrystallised from nitrobenzene had m. p. 188° (Found: C, 62·2; H, 4·6. $C_{20}H_{18}O_8$ requires C, 62·3; H, 4·7%).

Resolution. The racemic acid (25 g.) was added to a suspension of cinchonine (19 g.) in boiling alcohol (500 ml.). The components dissolved completely and the solution on cooling deposited crystals which after 1 hr. were filtered off. The crude salt was refluxed with alcohol (60 ml.) for 15 min., filtered off, and dried at 100°. The *cinchonine* (−)-OO-*di*-p-*toluoyltartrate* so obtained (20 g.) melted at 201° and could be used without further purification. It recrystallised when treated in dimethylformamide with an equal volume of alcohol; it then melted at 208°, $[\alpha]_D^{26}$ +79·4° (*c* 0·4 in dimethylformamide) (Found: C, 68·3; H, 5·9; N, 4·2. $C_{39}H_{40}O_9N_2$ requires C, 68·8; H, 5·9; N, 4·1%).

(−)-OO-*Di*-p-*toluoyltartaric acid.* The cinchonine salt (156 g.) was suspended in water (1 l.), ether (200 ml.) added, and the whole stirred while concentrated hydrochloric acid (75 ml.) was added. The ether was separated, the mixture was extracted with a further portion of

ether (200 ml.), and the combined extracts were dried ($MgSO_4$). Evaporation gave a gum which was refluxed for 1 hr. with benzene (600 ml.), during which a few crystals of the racemic compound were added to induce crystallisation of any traces remaining. The solution was filtered hot and allowed to cool slowly. Next morning the acid was filtered off, washed with benzene, and dried at 60° (81 g.). It had m. p. 148°, resolidified, and remelted 168°; $[\alpha]_D^{20}$ +138° (*c* 1 in alcohol). After recrystallisation from benzene the m. p. was unchanged, and $[\alpha]_D^{25}$ was +140° (Found: C, 62·3; H, 4·7%). Stoll and Hofmann [1] report m. p. 172° (corr.), $[\alpha]_D$ +140°.

The pure acid is slowly soluble in about 70 parts of boiling benzene. Its solubility is, however, greatly increased by the addition of small amounts of acetone or ether and in the

[1] Stoll and Hofmann, *Helv. Chim. Acta*, 1943, **26**, 922.
[2] Marckwald, *Ber.*, 1896, **29**, 42.
[3] Church and Blumberg, *Ind. Eng. Chem.*, 1951, **43**, 1780.

Note: Some samples prepared by both methods have shown evidence of polymorphism, melting at 148°, resolidifying, and finally melting at 168° (uncorr.) [Stoll and Hofmann [1] give 172° (corr.)]. This is especially apparent in these samples on rapid heating. After recovery of cinchonine, the residue from the mother-liquors may be worked up to give a smaller yield of the (+)-isomer or can conveniently be hydrolysed to recover *p*-toluic acid.

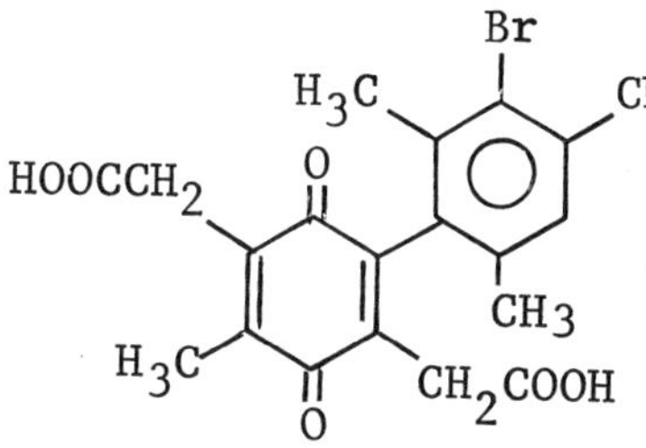

$C_{20}H_{19}BrO_6$ Ref. 1334

Resolution of 2-(3-Bromo-2,4,6-trimethylphenyl)-5-methylbenzoquinone-3,6-di-(acetic Acid) (XV).—To a solution of 1.5 g. of the diacid (XV) in 10 cc. of hot absolute alcohol was added a solution of 2.4 g. of morphine in 25 cc. of hot dry ethyl acetate. An immediate separation of a brown salt occurred which was redissolved by the addition of 15 cc. of absolute alcohol and the solution was set aside to crystallize. By this means 0.35 g. of a brown crystalline material of m. p. 199–204° (decomp. corr.) separated.

Rotation. 0.0670 g. made up to 15 cc. with methyl alcohol at 20° gave α_D −0.10°; l = 1; $[\alpha]_D^{20}$ −31.4°.

The mother liquor from this crop was heated to boiling, 65 cc. of dry ethyl acetate added and the solution again allowed to crystallize. A further 0.35 g. of brown crystalline material of m. p. 199–204° (decomp. corr.) separated.

Rotation. 0.0800 g. made up to 15 cc. with methyl alcohol at 20° gave α_D −0.16°; l = 1; $[\alpha]_D^{20}$ −32.0°.

The mother liquor was then evaporated to 50 cc. and again set aside to crystallize. Thus was obtained 0.55 g. of brown crystalline material of m. p. 198–200° (decomp. corr.).

Rotation. 0.0950 g. made up to 15 cc. with methyl alcohol at 20° gave α_D −0.27°; l = 1; $[\alpha]_D^{20}$ −45.7°.

These three crops, the latter of which obviously contained some free morphine, were combined and crystallized from a mixture of 15 cc. of methyl alcohol and 15 cc. of dry ethyl acetate. Thus 0.75 g. of brown crystalline material of m. p. 201–205° (decomp. corr.) was obtained.

Rotation. 0.0675 g. made up to 15 cc. with methyl alcohol at 20° gave α_D −0.14°; l = 1; $[\alpha]_D^{20}$ −32.6°.

Anal. (micro). Calcd. for $C_{20}H_{19}O_6Br{\cdot}2C_{14}H_{19}O_3N$: Br, 7.95. Found: Br, 8.00.

The final mother liquor from the salt fractions above was slowly evaporated in the air to 7 cc. but no separation of the more soluble salt occurred. A certain amount of morphine began to separate, however, and in view of the small quantity and the presence of morphine no attempt was made to purify the remaining salt but it was decomposed directly to obtain the active acid.

***d*-2-(3-Bromo-2,4,6-trimethylphenyl)-5-methylbenzoquinone-3,6-di-(acetic Acid).**—To 0.7 g. of the less soluble salt was added 40 cc. of cold 5% hydrochloric acid and the product extracted with ether. The ether was well washed with further quantities of acid and then with water and was dried over anhydrous magnesium sulfate. The majority of the ether was then removed on the steam-bath and petroleum ether (65–110°) was added until a faint cloudiness appeared. The solution was set to crystallize overnight and yielded 0.2 g. of an orange-colored microcrystalline material of m. p. 198–200° (corr.).

Rotation. 0.0450 g. made up to 15 cc. with methyl alcohol at 20° gave α_D −0.10°; $l = 1$; $[\alpha]^{20}_D$ −34.7°.

Anal. (micro). Calcd. for $C_{20}H_{19}O_6Br$: Br, 18.4. Found: Br, 18.3.

***l*-2-(3-Bromo-2,4,6-trimethylphenyl)-5-methylbenzoquinone-3,6-di-(acetic Acid).**— The remaining more soluble salt was decomposed as described for the less soluble salt above. Thus 0.4 g. of an orange-colored powder was obtained, with m. p. 205–207° (corr.).

Rotation. 0.0624 g. made up to 25 cc. with methyl alcohol at 20° gave α_D −0.04°; $l = 1$; $[\alpha]^{20}_D$ −16.8°.

Anal. (micro). Calcd. for $C_{20}H_{19}O_6Br$: Br, 18.4. Found: Br, 18.35.

This material was recrystallized from ether or petroleum ether as before and 0.1 g. of product with m. p. 205–207 (corr.) was obtained.

Rotation. 0.0480 g. made up to 20 cc. with methyl alcohol at 20° gave α_D −0.045°; $l = 1$; $[\alpha]^{20}_D$ −18.8°.

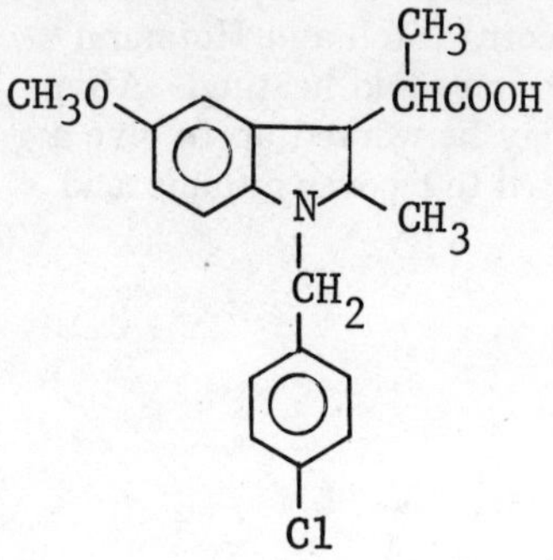

$C_{20}H_{20}ClNO_3$ Ref. 1335

EXAMPLE 1

A mixture of 10 g. of racemic α - (1 - *p*-chlorobenzyl - 2 - methyl - 5 - methoxy - 3 - indolyl) - propionic acid and 4 g. of (+) α-phenethylamine is dissolved in 100 ml. of hot isopropanol. The solution is allowed to cool slowly whereupon 2.5 g. of (+) α - (1 - *p*-chlorobenzyl - 2 - methyl - 5 - methoxy - 3-indolyl) - propionic acid (+) α - phenethylamine salt crystallizes. This salt is removed by filtration, washed with isopropanol and with ether, and dried. On further cooling of the filtrate, an additional 3.0 g. of salt crystallizes. On recrystallization from isopropanol the salt has m.p. 148—149° C. $[\alpha]_D^{22}$ + 43° (c = 1, methanol).

To a suspension of this salt in a mixture of water and ethyl ether is added an excess of dilute hydrochloric acid. The acidified mixture (pH 2) is shaken and the solvent layers are allowed to separate. The ethereal phase is removed, washed with water and dried over sodium sulphate and magnesium sulphate. The ether is then removed by evaporation *in vacuo* and the residue crystallized from aqueous ethanol to give (+) α - (1 - *p* - chlorobenzyl - 2-methyl - 5 - methoxy - 3 - indolyl) - propionic acid. On recrystallization from a 1:1 mixture of benzene and petroleum ether, the product has m.p. 156—157° $[\alpha]_D^{22}$ + 60° (c = 1, ethanol).

The isopropanol filtrate which is rich in (−) α - (1 - *p* - chlorobenzyl - 2 - methyl - 5-methoxy - 3 - indolyl) - propionic acid (+) α - phenethylamine salt is concentrated to dryness *in vacuo* and the residue treated with dilute hydrochloric acid in a water-ether mixture in the manner described above. The ether solution thus obtained is concentrated to dryness *in vacuo* and dissolved in hot acetonitrile. This solution, upon cooling, deposits crystals of *DL* α - (1 - *p* - chlorobenzyl) - 2 - methyl-5 - methoxy - 3 - indolyl) - propionic acid. The acetonitrile filtrate is concentrated to dryness and the residue thus obtained crystallized from aqueous ethanol to give (−) α - (1 - *p*-chlorobenzyl - 2 - methyl - 5 - methoxy - 3 - indolyl) - propionic acid which on recrystallization from benzene - petroleum ether has a melting point of 153—154° C., $[\alpha]_D^{23}$ − 58° (c = 1, ethanol).

When the above experiment is carried out using (−) phenethylamine as the resolving agent instead of (+) phenethylamine, the (−) α - (1 - *p* - chlorobenzyl - 2 - methyl - 5 - methoxy - 3 - indolyl) - propionic acid (−) α - phenethylamine salt is the more soluble of the two diastereoisomers and crystallizes from the isopropanol reaction medium. The (+) α - (1 - *p* - chlorobenzyl - 2 - methyl - 5 - methoxy - 3 - indolyl) - propionic acid (−) α - phenethylamine salt is found in the isopropanol filtrate. The optically active forms of the indole compound are obtained from the diastereoisomers by the procedure described above.

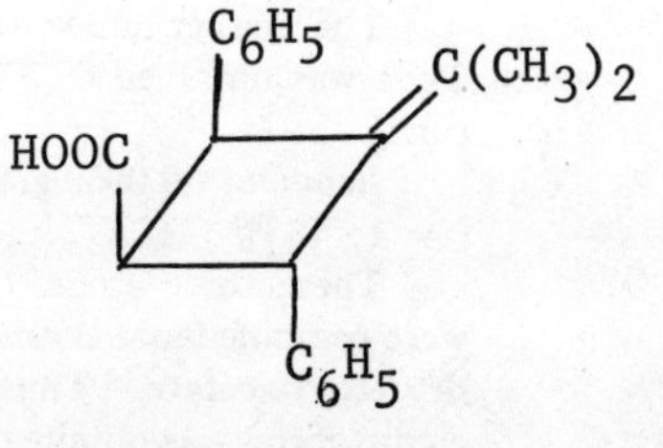

$C_{20}H_{20}O_2$ Ref. 1336

Spaltung der ungesättigten Säure I mit Morphin.

2.7 g Morphin und 2.62 g der Säure vom Schmp. 145—146° wurden in 40 ccm Methanol, dem 12 ccm Wasser zugesetzt waren, gelöst, wonach sich am nächsten Tage 2.5 g eines Salzes ausgeschieden hatten, das, aus 75-proz. Methanol umkrystallisiert, bei 117—118° schmolz. Das Salz scheint Krystallwasser zu enthalten, da es nach längerem Trocknen bei 70° einen viel höheren, aber unscharfen Schmp. zeigte. Nach der Zerlegung des Salzes mit verd. Salzsäure wurde eine Säure erhalten, die, aus verd. Methanol umgelöst, bei 144—145° schmolz und, mit der Racemsäure gemischt, eine Depression (132° bis 136°) zeigte.

0.4 g der Säure zu 10 ccm in Alkohol gelöst, zeigten im 1 dm-Rohr α = +2.70°. $[\alpha]_D$: +67.5°.

Die aus der Mutterlauge des Salzes gewonnene Antipodensäure hatte unter gleichen Bedingungen $[\alpha]_D$: —47.5°, wurde also so nicht rein erhalten.

Nicht immer gelangen die Spaltungen mittels Morphins in so vollkommener Weise, öfters wurden Säuren mit erheblich geringerem Drehungsvermögen erhalten, die dann auch einen tieferen Schmelzp. zeigten.

Spaltung der *racem.* Säure I mit Brucin.

Die Spaltung der ungesättigten Racemsäure mittels Brucins gelingt zuweilen nicht, und es fällt das Salz der ungespaltenen Säure aus. Erst als bei genügender Verdünnung und mit reinem Methanol gearbeitet wurde, fiel das Brucinsalz der linksdrehenden Säure aus, die aber nie dieselbe hohe Drehung wie die Antipodensäure zeigte.

6 g der Säure und 9.6 g Brucin wurden in 110 ccm reinem Methanol gelöst und über Nacht stehen gelassen. Es fielen aus 6.5 g eines Brucinsalzes, das, auch nach dem Umkrystallisieren aus verd. Methanol, unscharf unter Aufschäumen bei etwa 130—135° schmolz und nach dem Zerlegen mit verd. Salzsäure eine Säure lieferte, die, mehrfach aus verd. Methanol umkrystallisiert, bei 143—144° schmolz und, mit Racemsäure gemischt, etwa dieselbe Depression gab wie die Rechts-Säure.

0.4 g der Säure zu 10 ccm in Alkohol gelöst, zeigten im 1 dm-Rohr α = −2.51°. $[\alpha]_D$: −62.75°.

Das Brucinsalz krystallisiert ausgezeichnet und verwittert nach dem Trocknen, enthält also wohl Krystallalkohol. Zuweilen zeigten die daraus abgeschiedenen Säuren erheblich geringere Drehungen als angegeben. Die Spaltung mit Brucin eignet sich auch gut zur Gewinnung fast reiner *l*-Säure aus der rohen Antipodensäure, die bei der Morphinspaltung anfiel. Zum Vergleich mit der unten beschriebenen Ketonsäure, die nur in Eisessig polarisiert werden konnte, wurde auch die Drehung der *l*-Säure in Eisessig festgestellt.

0.276 g der Säure zu 10 ccm in Eisessig gelöst, zeigten α = −0.72°. $[\alpha]_D$: −26.1°.

Der Methylester der *l*-Säure, mit Diazomethan hergestellt und aus Methanol umgelöst, hatte den Schmp. 86—87°, während der ebenso gewonnene, bisher nicht dargestellte Ester der Racemsäure bei 108—109° schmolz.

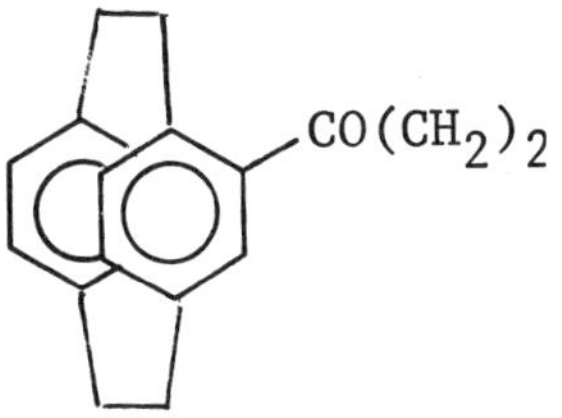

$C_{20}H_{20}O_3$ Ref. 1337

Racematspaltung. 877 mg racem. **16** (2·84 mMol) wurden in 15 ml $CHCl_3$ gelöst und mit 841 mg Cinchonidin (2·87 mMol) in 15 ml $CHCl_3$ versetzt. Durch Abdampfen, Lösen des öligen Rückstandes in Methanol (2·5 ml) und Versetzen mit Äther (90 ml) erhielt man nach 6-täg. Stehen 743 mg (43% d.Th.) des Salzes. (Die daraus freigesetzte Säure **16** $[\alpha]_D$ = +23·4°, war zu 45% optisch rein, wie sich durch Korrelation mit **13** ergab). Weitere Kristallisation des Salzes aus Methanol-Äther gab eine Säure von p = 72% ($[\alpha]_D$ +37·4°).

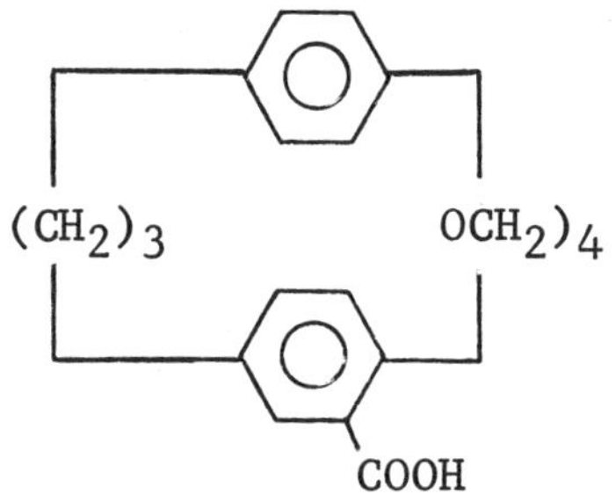

$C_{20}H_{22}O_2$ Ref. 1338

Resolution of 6-Carboxy[3.4]paracyclophane (V).—A mixture of 1.58 g. (5.36 mmoles) of acid V, 1.09 g. of brucine (2.8 mmoles) and 25 ml. of acetone was heated until solution was complete. The salt that separated at 0° was recrystallized six times from acetone until its melting point no longer changed (m.p. 159–161°). This material (0.26 g.) was shaken with ether and dilute hydrochloric acid, the ether layer was washed with water, dried, and the solvent was evaporated. The residual oil crystallized from ethanol and water to give 0.093 mg. (6%) of long thin needles, m.p. 154–154.9°, $[\alpha]^{27}D$ −154° (*c* 1.3, chloroform).

Anal. Calcd. for $C_{20}H_{22}O_2$: C, 81.61; H, 7.54. Found: C, 81.70; H, 7.46.

The mother liquor from the initial crystallization of the brucine salt was shaken with a mixture of ether and dilute hydrochloric acid, and acid V was recovered and crystallized from an ethanol–acetic acid–water mixture. This material (0.78 g. or 2.61 mmoles) was mixed with 0.502 g. (150 mmoles) of strychnine and heated with a minimum amount of acetone containing 7 ml. of ethanol to effect solution. The salt that separated at 0° was recrystallized four times from ethanol–acetone to constant rotation, $[\alpha]^{27}D$ −2.20° (*c* 0.77, chloroform). The acid was recovered in the usual way, and was crystallized from ethanol–water as long thin needles, m.p. 153.5–154.4°, wt. 0.050 g. (3%), $[\alpha]^{27}D$ +148° (*c* 1.6, chloroform).

Anal. Calcd. for $C_{20}H_{22}O_2$: C, 81.61; H, 7.54. Found: C, 81.73; H, 7.56.

A sharp-melting sample of racemic V was prepared by dissolving 6 mg. of each of the above enantiomers in a small amount of ethanol and water. The material that separated possessed a melting point of 183–185°.

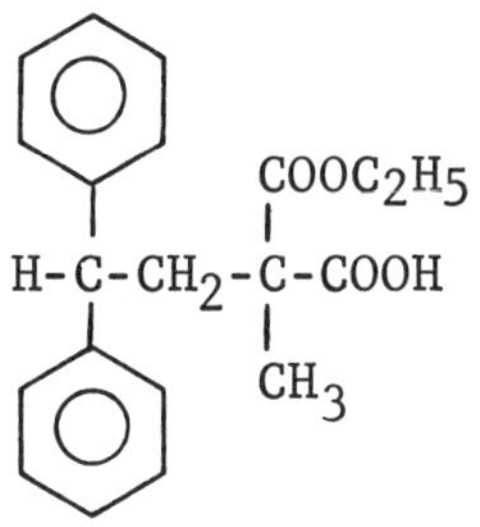

$C_{20}H_{22}O_4$ Ref. 1339

(−)-(*S*)-Carbethoxy-2-methyl-4,4-diphenylbutanoic Acid.[26] To a solution of 19.7 g (0.056 mol) of (±)-2-carbethoxy-2-methyl-4,4-diphenylbutanoic acid in 50 ml of ethyl acetate was added a solution of 2.58 g (0.028 mol) of (−)-ephedrine in 50 ml of ethyl acetate and the solution was kept at 0 to −5° for 48 hr. The salt was recrystallized five more times from ethyl acetate to give $[\alpha]_{Hg}^{25}$ −14.1° (2.5%, EtOH). Another recrystallization from chloroform gave the value $[\alpha]_{Hg}^{25}$ −14.7° (2%, EtOH); mp 131–132°; ir and NMR spectra identical with those of racemic compound.

(26) The *S* series is described in the Experimental Section but for clarity of presentation the *R* series was used in Chart II.

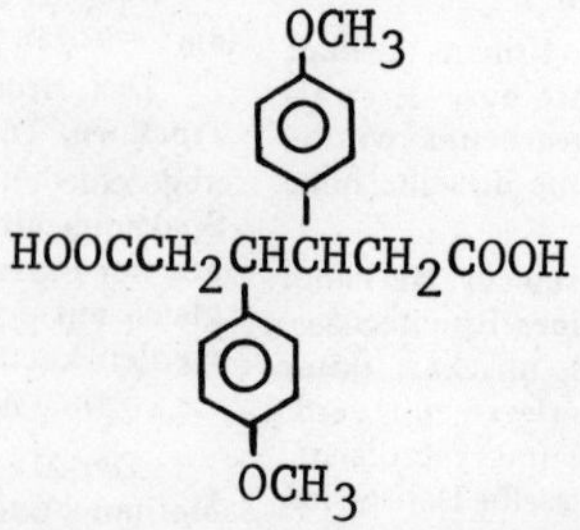

$C_{20}H_{22}O_6$ Ref. 1340

Resolution of DL-*β,γ-di-p-anisyladipic acid*. Following the procedure of Oommen and Vogel for DL-β,γ-diphenyladipic acid (7), 1.0 g. of DL-β,γ-dianisyladipic acid (m.p. 185–186°) and 2.19 g. of *l*-brucine were dissolved in 400 ml. of hot water, then the clear solution was allowed to cool slowly to room temperature, seeding with the brucine salt of the *d*-acid from a previous run. (Some difficulty was first encountered in obtaining a crystalline salt, which did result, however, using aqueous acetone as the solvent.) By further recrystallization of the first crop (1.32 g.; $[\alpha]_D^{25}$ −22°) the brucine salt of the *d*-acid was obtained with the constant $[\alpha]_D^{25}$ −19° (50 mg. in 5 ml. of 95% alcohol). By warming 310 mg. of the salt with 10 ml. of 5% hydrochloric acid until a clear solution resulted, then extracting with ether and crystallizing the acid from benzene containing a few drops of ether, 54 mg. of *d*-acid was obtained, m.p. 104–110°, $[\alpha]_D^{25}$ +47° (50 mg. in 5 ml. of 95% alcohol). Further recrystallization yielded acid of m.p. 108–110°; the product contained benzene of crystallization. After vacuum-drying it melted at 124–126.5° with previous softening.

By concentrating the original filtrate from the brucine salt of the *d*-acid to one-half its volume and seeding with the salt of the *l*-acid from a previous run, 1.41 g. of crystals slowly separated, $[\alpha]_D^{25}$ −35° (50 mg. in 5 ml. of 95% alcohol). Further recrystallization from water gave the brucine salt of the *l*-acid with the constant $[\alpha]_D^{25}$ −41°. Decomposition of the salt with 5% hydrochloric acid as above gave the crude *l*-acid, $[\alpha]_D^{25}$ −42° (50 mg. in 5 ml. of 95% alcohol); after several recrystallizations from benzene the melting point of the acid containing benzene of crystallization was 106–110°. The solvent-free acid was obtained after drying 35 hours at 100° and 0.05 mm., m.p. 127–129°.

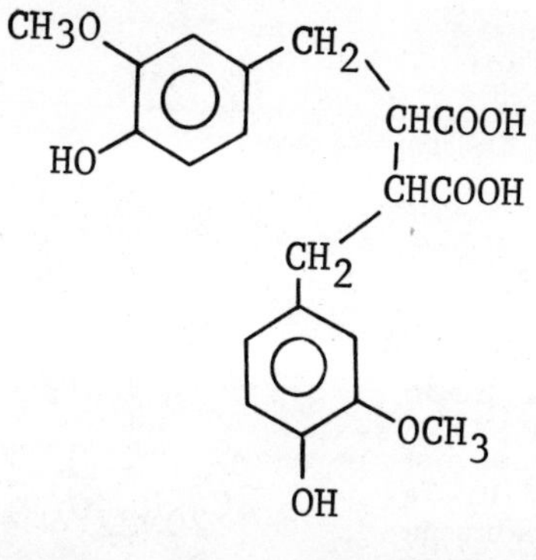

$C_{20}H_{22}O_8$ Ref. 1341

Resolution of the dl-*Acid* (I; R = H).—The acid (3·0 g.) and strychnine (5·1 g.) were mixed in chloroform solution. The solvent was removed and replaced by hot alcohol containing 10% of water. The stout prisms (3·83 g.) which separated on cooling were twice crystallised from aqueous alcohol; prisms (3·0 g.), shrinking at 145° and melting at 247°, were obtained (Found: C, 61·0; H, 7·1; loss in weight over P_2O_5, 13·6. $2C_{21}H_{22}O_2N_2,C_{20}H_{22}O_8,9H_2O$ requires C, 61·0; H, 6·9; loss in weight, 13·3%). In chloroform solution (*c*, 2·00) it gave $[\alpha]_D^{17°}$ − 18°. This *strychnine* salt was dissolved in chloroform and shaken with sodium bicarbonate solution; the l-*acid* (I; R = H), liberated by acidification of the bicarbonate extract and isolated with ether, crystallised from ether–benzene in rosettes of needles, m. p. 109° (Found: C, 60·9; H, 5·8. $C_{20}H_{22}O_8$ requires C, 61·5; H, 5·6%). In alcoholic solution (*c*, 2·00) it gave $[\alpha]_D^{17°}$ − 47°. The mother-liquors from the crystallisation of the strychnine salt described above were evaporated, the residue taken up in chloroform and decomposed with sodium bicarbonate, and the acid (1·7 g.) recovered. This was treated with brucine (3·4 g.) in chloroform, and the resultant salts crystallised from aqueous alcohol. After three crystallisations the "head" fractions yielded a brucine salt in colourless prisms (0·5 g.), which in chloroform solution (*c*, 2·00) gave $[\alpha]_D^{15°}$ − 54°. The d-*acid*, recovered with sodium bicarbonate in the usual way, separated from ether–benzene in rosettes of needles, m. p. 106—108° (Found: C, 61·2; H, 5·7%). In alcoholic solution (*c*, 2·00) it gave $[\alpha]_D^{16°}$ + 40°.

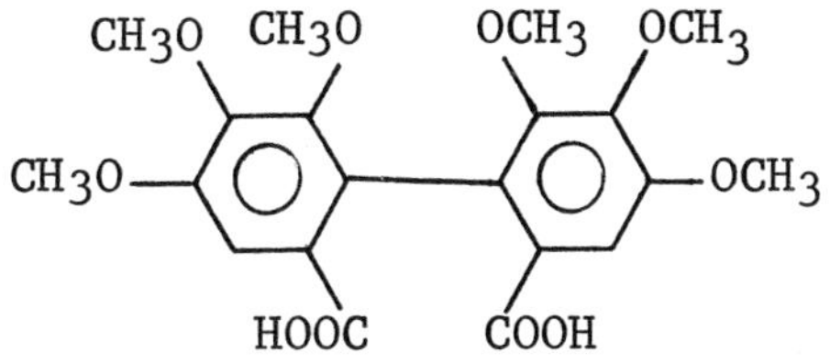

$C_{20}H_{22}O_{10}$ Ref. 1342

II. Trennung mittels Chinidin

a) *Di-chinidin-salz der l-Hexamethoxy-diphensäure*

5,11 g Hexamethoxy-diphensäure und 7,85 g Chinidin[7]) (2 Äquivalente) werden in 250 ccm 50-proc. wäßrigem Äthanol auf dem Wasserbad erwärmt. Beide Substanzen gehen dabei in Lösung. Beim Stehenlassen in der Kälte kristallisieren 5,14 g (40% der Gesamtmenge) Salz der l-Säure aus. Das Salz ändert nach zweimaligem Umkristallisieren aus Äthanol oder Aceton/Wasser seinen Schmp. und die Drehung nicht mehr. Es kristallisiert aus Äthanol in farblosen, flachen, prismatischen Kristallen, die wie feine Blättchen aussehen, und schmilzt bei 198—199° [8]). In Chloroform löst es sich schon in der Kälte, in Methanol, Äthanol, Benzol, Aceton und Dioxan in der Wärme leicht. In Tetrachlorkohlenstoff und Essigester ist es schwer löslich, in Äther nahezu unlöslich und in Wasser unlöslich. Es kristallisiert mit 4 Molen Wasser, die auch beim Erhitzen i. V. auf 120° nicht vollständig abgegeben werden; bei höherer Temperatur wird die Substanz braun. Zur Analyse und Bestimmung der Drehung wurde die lufttrockene Substanz verwandt.

$C_{20}H_{22}O_{10} \cdot 2\, C_{20}H_{24}O_2N_2 \cdot 4\, H_2O$ (1142,6)
Ber. C 63,07 H 6,83 8 OCH_3 21,71 N 4,90 H_2O 6,31
Gef. » 63,08[9]), 62,94[10]) » 7,17, 7,21 » 21,70 » 5,06 » 7,00[11])
$[\alpha]_D^{20} = +112{,}5 \pm 2°$ (abs. Methanol, c = 1).

Die Mutterlauge der 1. Kristallisation ergab beim Einengen i. V. noch eine geringe weitere kristallisierte Abscheidung, führte aber in der Hauptmenge zu einem amorphen, in verd. Alkohol oder Aceton leicht löslichen Produkt, das bei 90° zu sintern begann und bei 120° unter Blasenbildung geschmolzen war.

b) *l-Hexamethoxy-diphensäure*

1,3 g des Salzes vom Schmp. 198—199° werden mit 20 ccm einer eiskalten, 5-proc. Natronlauge in einer Reibschale verrieben und zur Entfernung des Alkaloids 5-mal mit je 10 ccm Chloroform ausgeschüttelt. Darauf wird die wäßrige Lösung unter Eiskühlung tropfenweise mit gekühlter 20-proc. Salzsäure angesäuert. Die Diphensäure scheidet sich zunächst als weiße, klebrige Masse aus, die beim Reiben mit dem Glasstab leicht kristallisiert. Ausbeute 0,40 g (83% d. Th.). Die Säure ist sofort praktisch rein und ändert durch zweimaliges Umkristallisieren weder Schmp. noch Drehung. Zum Umkristallisieren wird eine kalt gesättigte Lösung in abs. Äther tropfenweise (sehr langsam) mit tiefsiedendem Petroläther versetzt.

l-Hexamethoxy-diphensäure bildet farblose, derbe Prismen, die bei 161° klar schmelzen, bei langsamem weiterem Erhitzen zwischen 210 und 220° wieder fest werden und bei 240° zum zweiten Male scharf schmelzen. Die Löslichkeit der l-Säure in verschiedenen Lösungsmitteln ist in der nachstehenden Tabelle der Löslichkeit der d,l-Verbindung gegenübergestellt.

Lösungsmittel	d,l-Hexamethoxy-diphensäure	l-Hexamethoxy-diphensäure
Äther	schwer löslich	z. l. l. (15 mg/ccm bei 20°)
Wasser	schwer löslich	z. schw. lösl., geeignet z. Umkristallisieren
Benzol	schwer löslich	l. lösl. in d. Kälte
Eisessig	l. lösl. i. d. Hitze, krist. auf Zusatz von Wasser	l. lösl. in d. Kälte
Aceton	l. lösl. i. d. Hitze	l. lösl. in d. Kälte
Dioxan	l. lösl. i. d. Hitze	l. lösl. i. d. Kälte
Äthanol	l. lösl. i. d. Hitze (mehr als 1-proc. Lösg. i. d. Hitze)	l. lösl. i. d. Kälte (mehr als 1-proc. Lösg. i. d. Kälte)

Durch Umkristallisieren aus Äther/Petroläther haben wir mitunter Präparate erhalten, die sich weder im Schmp., noch in der Drehung in n/10-NaOH, noch im mikroskopischen Aussehen, noch in den Analysenwerten von der gewöhnlichen Form unterscheiden, aber in Äthanol nun schwerer löslich sind. Bei 20° bilden sie nur eine ½-proc. Lösung in Äthanol, in der Hitze nur schwer 1-proc. Lösungen,

aus denen beim Abkühlen — im Gegensatz zur leichter löslichen Form und selbst zur racemischen Säure — wieder ein Teil der Substanz auskristallisiert. Auf Animpfen mit der schwerer löslichen Form, oder bei längerem Stehen manchmal auch ohne Animpfen, kristallisiert aus alkoholischen Lösungen der leichter löslichen Form ein Teil der Substanz als schwerer lösliche Verbindung aus. Wird die in Äthanol schwerer lösliche Form aus Äther/Petroläther umkristallisiert, so kann wieder die in Alkohol leichter lösliche Form erhalten werden. Ein Löslichkeitsunterschied der beiden Formen in Äther war nicht festzustellen. Wenn es sich um 2 verschiedene Modifikationen handelt, von denen verschiedene Schmelzpunkte zu erwarten wären, muß man annehmen, daß die höher schmelzende vor Erreichen von 161° in die tiefer schmelzende umgewandelt wird. Dies scheint in der Tat der Fall zu sein.

Je 20 mg beider Formen wurden 15 Sek. lang in ein auf 160° erhitztes Glycerinbad getaucht, dann rasch auf 20° abgekühlt. Nun lösten sich beide Proben leicht in 2 ccm Äthanol. Die Drehung der Präparate hatte sich in dieser Zeit nicht außerhalb der Fehlergrenze verändert. Eine Racemisierung war übrigens auch deshalb nicht zu erwarten gewesen, weil d- oder l-Hexamethoxy-diphensäure bei Wiederholung der Schmelzpunktsnahme, wenn man sie nur auf 161° erhitzt hat, noch scharf bei dieser Temperatur schmelzen. Indessen konnten wir bei der mikroskopischen Beobachtung des Erhitzens beider Formen bis zum Schmelzen keine Veränderung an den Kristallen wahrnehmen.

Zur Analyse und Drehung wurde 3 Stunden bei 55° und 16 mm über P_2O_5 getrocknet.

$C_{20}H_{22}O_{10}$ (422,2)	Ber.	C 56,89	H 5,21	6 OCH_3 44,06
	Gef.	» 57,15	» 5,38	» 43,86

$[\alpha]_D^{20} = -25{,}7 \pm 1°$ (abs. Äthanol, c = 1,0).

$[\alpha]_D^{20} = -125{,}1 \pm 2°$ (n/10-NaOH, c = 1,0).

c) *d-Hexamethoxy-diphensäure*

Die Darstellung der d-Hexamethoxy-diphensäure aus dem rohen, nicht gereinigten Chinidinsalz der d-Säure gelingt deshalb, weil die racemische Säure in Äther sehr viel schwerer löslich ist als die aktive, aber sie führt nicht zur völlig reinen d-Form.

220 mg des amorphen Chinidin-salzes, das beim Eindunsten der letzten Fraktion aus dem Filtrat des Chinidin-salzes der l-Säure anfiel, wurden, wie unter b) angegeben, zerlegt. Die rohe Hexamethoxy-diphensäure (110 mg) wurde mit 7 ccm abs. Äther digeriert; dabei blieben 40 mg d,l-Säure vom Schmp. 240° ungelöst. Das Filtrat wurde mit etwa 20 ccm tiefsiedendem Petroläther gefällt. Die erhaltene d-Hexamethoxy-diphensäure schmolz klar bei 161°, wurde zwischen 210 und 220° wieder fest und schmolz erneut scharf bei 240°.

$C_{20}H_{22}O_{10}$ (422,2)	Ber.	C 56,89	H 5,21	6 OCH_3 44,06
	Gef.	» 57,12	» 5,56	» 44,11

$[\alpha]_D^{20} = +23{,}8 \pm 1°$ (abs. Äthanol, c = 0,9).

[7]) Der Firma Knoll AG und besonders Herrn Direktor Dr. K. Kraft sind wir für die freundliche Überlassung einer größeren Menge Chinidins sehr zu Dank verpflichtet.

[8]) Alle Schmelzpunkte sind unkorrigiert.

[9]) Unter Zusatz von V_2O_5 verbrannt, da die Subst. schwer verbrennt.

[10]) Unter Zusatz von $PbCrO_4$ verbrannt.

[11]) Nach K. Fischer, Angew. Chem. 48, 394 (1935).

$C_{20}H_{24}O_5$

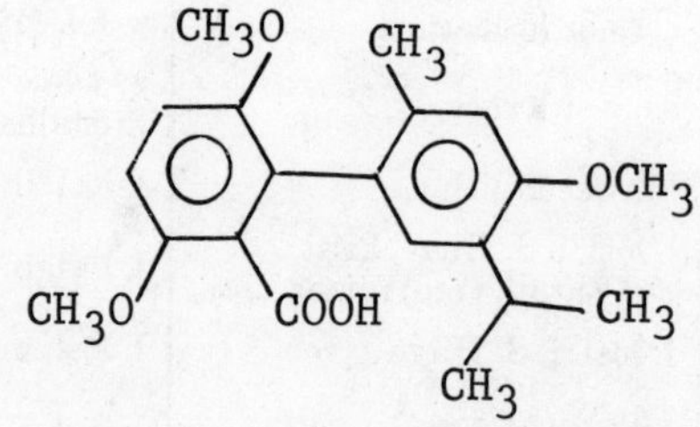

Ref. 1343

Racematspaltung von Ve. 6,26 g Carbonsäure Ve und 5,44 g Dehydroabietylamin [11], gelöst durch Erwärmen in 200 ml Äther, wurden mit Petroläther bis zur beginnenden Trübung versetzt und dann die Lösung bei − 20° aufbewahrt. Die ersten Kristalle wurden abfiltriert, die Mutterlauge eingedampft und der Rückstand aus Diisopropyläther durch Animpfen zur Kristallisation gebracht. Nach 4–5 Umkristallisationen wurden 3,0 g (+)-Salz in langen, farblosen Nadeln erhalten, mit $[\alpha]_D^{23} = +27{,}0° \pm 1°$ (Methanol). Die letzte Mutterlauge hatte dann $[\alpha]_D^{23} = +26{,}0° \pm 1°$. Smp. 110–115°. Die Zerlegung des Salzes erfolgte an Amberlite IRC 50 ($H^{\oplus}$) aus äthanolischer Lösung.

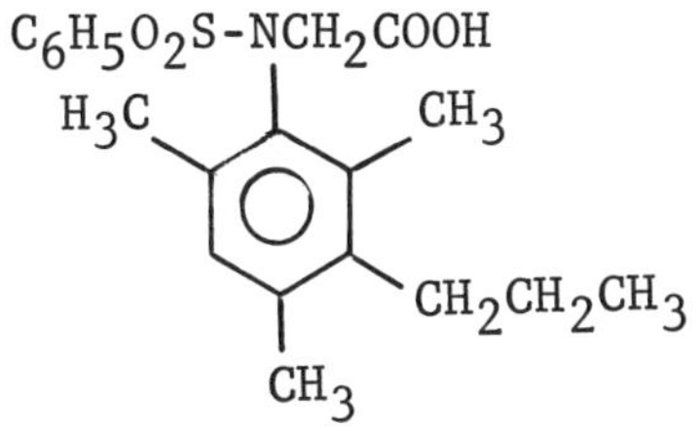

$C_{20}H_{25}NO_4S$ Ref. 1344

Resolution of N-Benzenesulfonyl-N-carboxymethyl-*n*-propylmesidine.—A solution of 4.0 g. of N-benzenesulfonyl-N-carboxymethyl-*n*-propylmesidine and 3.136 g. of cinchonidine in 65 ml. of absolute ethanol was kept at 15° for 2 days. The first crop of salt weighed 3.486 g., m.p. 206–208°; rotation, 0.0729 g. made up to 5 ml. with absolute ethanol at 23° gave α_D −1.00° (l 1), $[\alpha]^{23}_D$ −68.6°. The mother liquors yielded 3.427 g. of crystalline salt, m.p. 105–110°; rotation, 0.0710 g. made up to 5 ml. with absolute ethanol at 23° gave α_D −0.73° (l 1), $[\alpha]^{23}_D$ −51.4°. The first crop was dissolved in 40 ml. of absolute ethanol, and after standing for 24 hours at 15° yielded 2.924 g. of crystals; rotation, 0.0797 g. made up to 5 ml. with absolute ethanol at 22° gave α_D −1.13° (l 1), $[\alpha]^{22}_D$ −70.9°. Upon recrystallization the specific rotation of this crop did not change; it was considered to be pure less-soluble salt; m.p. 212–213°.

(−)-N-Benzenesulfonyl-N-carboxymethyl-*n*-propylmesidine.—The optically active acid was regenerated from the less-soluble salt by the procedure used for the ethyl analog. The product from benzene had a m.p. 148–149°; rotation, 0.0418 g. made up to 2 ml. with absolute ethanol at 28° gave α_D −0.48 (l1), $[\alpha]^{28}_D$ −22.9°. The yield was 97%.

Anal. Calcd. for $C_{20}H_{25}NO_4S$: C, 63.97; H, 6.71; N, 3.73. Found: C, 63.88; H, 6.91; N, 3.69.

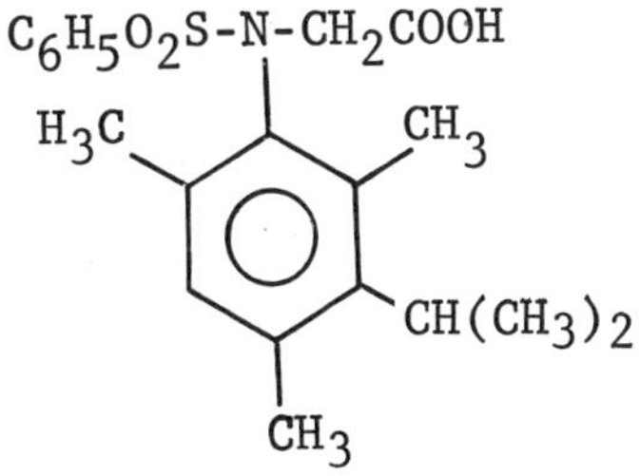

$C_{20}H_{25}NO_4S$ Ref. 1345

Resolution of N-Benzenesulfonyl-N-carboxymethylisopropylmesidine.—A solution of 3.452 g. of N-benzenesulfonyl-N-carboxymethylisopropylmesidine and 2.707 g. of cinchonidine in 65 ml. of absolute ethanol was filtered, then placed in a refrigerator. The solution was allowed to evaporate slowly to dryness over a period of 20 days. Six crops were collected: 0.298 g., $[\alpha]^{27}_D$ −47.7°; 0.077 g., $[\alpha]^{26}_D$ −47.4°; 1.415 g., $[\alpha]^{28}_D$ −52.9°; 0.162 g., $[\alpha]^{27}_D$ −52.1°; 0.710 g., $[\alpha]^{27}_D$ −62.8°; 3.015 g. (rotation not determined). The rotations were determined in absolute ethanol.

The first four crops were combined and recrystallized from 60 ml. of absolute ethanol. The specific rotation remained substantially unchanged, and the pure less-soluble salt crystallized; m.p. 194° dec.; rotation, 0.0125 g. made up to 2 ml. with absolute ethanol at 28° gave α_D −0.30 (l 1), $[\alpha]^{28}_D$ −48.0°.

(+)-N-Benzenesulfonyl-N-carboxymethylisopropylmesidine.—The optically active acid was regenerated from the less-soluble salt by the usual procedure. The product purified from benzene had an m.p. 149–150°; rotation, 0.0648 g. made up to 2 ml. with dimethylformamide at 24° gave α_D + 0.42° (l 1), $[\alpha]^{24}_D$ + 12.9°. The yield was 94%.

Anal. Calcd. for $C_{20}H_{25}NO_4S$: C, 63.97; H, 6.71; N, 3.73. Found: C, 63.64; H, 6.70; N, 3.74.

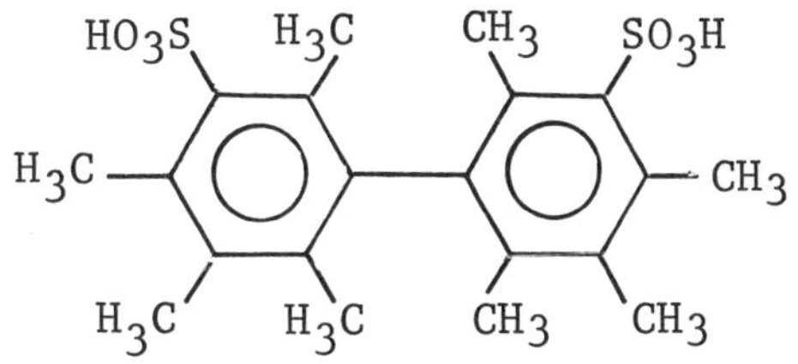

$C_{20}H_{26}O_6S_2$ Ref. 1346

Preparation and Resolution of 2,2′,4,4′,5,5′,6,6′-Octamethyldiphenyl-3,3′-disulfonic Acid (Diisoduryl Disulfonic Acid).—A mixture of 2.3 g. of V and a solution of 1 g. of sodium hydroxide in 150 cc. of water was boiled until solution was complete (about eight hours). The excess of sodium hydroxide was neutralized with dilute hydrochloric acid and the solution filtered free of solid material. The solution of sodium diisoduryl disulfonate was heated to boiling and added slowly to a solution of 4.1 g. of strychnine hydrochloride in 200 cc. of water. After standing for about twelve hours, the white crystals which had formed were filtered off and after drying first in an oven at 120° for four hours and then in an Abderhalden drier at 100° and 4 mm. pressure weighed 2.3 g. Evaporation of the mother liquor to a volume of 100 cc., followed by standing for twelve hours, yielded another crop of crystals which, when dried by the above method, weighed 2.2 g. Both fractions melted at 252–255° (with dec.). Further evaporation gave no crystals and when dry a dark brown rather gummy residue was obtained.

Rotation. 0.1786 g. of first fraction made up to 10 cc. in 80% methyl alcohol at 20° gave α_D −0.25°; l = 1; $[\alpha]^{20}_D$ −14°.

Anal. Calcd. for $C_{62}H_{70}O_{10}N_4S_2$: N, 5.12. Found: N, 5.03.

The amount of salt recovered amounted to approximately 85% of the theoretical quantity and since recrystallization of each fraction from water gave products with the same rotation, it became obvious that water was not a satisfactory solvent for resolution.

Resolution of Distrychnine Diisoduryl Disulfonate.—The two fractions were combined and 3 g. of material was dissolved in 400 cc. of boiling absolute alcohol. On standing for twelve hours, the solution deposited a considerable quantity of white crystals, 0.9 g. Evaporation of the mother liquor to 200 cc. followed by standing for twelve hours gave a further crop of crystals, 0.5 g. These fractions, both of which had a melting point of 252–255° dec., were combined.

The mother liquor was evaporated to dryness and 1.5 g. of light brown salt obtained, m. p., 248–251° dec.

Rotation. (Less soluble salt) 0.2680 g. made up to 10 cc. in 80% methyl alcohol at 20° gave α_D −0.57; l = 1; $[\alpha]_D^{20}$ −21.3°

Recrystallization from absolute alcohol did not alter the melting point.

Anal. Calcd. for $C_{62}H_{70}O_{10}N_4S_2$: S, 5.85. Found: S, 5.70.

Rotation. (Less soluble salt) 0.3140 g. made up to 10 cc. in 80% methyl alcohol at 20° gave α_D −0.68°; l = 1; $[\alpha]_D^{20}$ −21.6°.

Rotation. (More soluble salt) 0.2905 g. made up to 10 cc. with 80% methyl alcohol at 20° gave α_D −0.30; l = 1; $[\alpha]_D^{20}$ −10.3°.

This fraction was not recrystallized.

Anal. Calcd. for $C_{62}H_{70}O_{10}N_4S_2$: S, 5.85. Found: S, 5.74.

1-Ammonium Diisoduryl Disulfonate.—A suspension of 0.6580 g. of less soluble strychnine salt in 15 cc. of dilute aqueous ammonia (1:15) was extracted four times with 10-cc. portions of chloroform and the rotation of the resulting aqueous solution determined.

Rotation. The volume of the tube used was 9.2 cc. and this contained theoretically 0.1697 g. of ammonium diisoduryl disulfonate, α_D −0.21; l = 1; $[\alpha]_D^{20}$ −11.4°.

Continued extractions with chloroform did not change the rotation.

Evaporation of 9.2 cc. of solution to dryness gave 0.1701 g. of salt (theoretical quantity 0.1697 g.). After drying in an Abderhalden dryer at 140° it was analyzed.

Anal. (Parr bomb) Calcd. for $C_{20}H_{32}O_6N_2S_2$: S, 13.91. Found: S, 13.74.

***d*-Ammonium Diisoduryl Disulfonate.**—This was prepared in a similar manner to the *l*-salt from 0.6668 g. of the more soluble strychnine salt.

Rotation. The volume of the tube used was 9.2 cc. and this contained theoretically 0.1720 g. of ammonium salt: α_D +0.21°; l = 1; $[\alpha]_D^{20}$ +11.2°.

Additional extractions did not change the rotation.

Evaporation of 9.2 cc. of this solution to dryness gave 0.1725 g. of ammonium salt (theoretical quantity 0.1720 g.).

Anal. Calcd. for $C_{20}H_{32}O_6N_2S_2$: S, 13.91. Found: S, 13.69.

```
              OH
              |
CH3(CH2)7-CH-CH-(CH2)9-COOH
```

$C_{20}H_{40}O_4$ Ref. 1347

Resolution of threo-11,12-Dihydroxyeicosanoic Acid

The racemic acid (10.0 g) was treated with (−)-ephedrine hydrate (5.3 g) in a mixture of ethanol (40 ml) and water (20 ml). The salt that deposited (9.6 g) had m.p. 95–100° and $[\alpha]_D$ −26° (*c*, 2.0 in EtOH). After three crystallizations from ethyl acetate, it had $[\alpha]_D$ −27.9° (*c*, 1.3 in EtOH), unchanged by further crystallization. It was decomposed by heating with a mixture of methanol and 5 *N* hydrochloric acid (1:1), and the methanol was removed on the steam bath. The product deposited from the aqueous residue. It was crystallized from aqueous methanol and then from ethyl acetate, giving (−)-*threo*-11,12-dihydroxyeicosanoic acid, m.p. 101.0–101.5°, $[\alpha]_D$ −21.1° (*c*, 1.2 in MeOH).

Anal. Calcd. for $C_{20}H_{40}O_4$: C, 69.72; H, 11.70. Found: C, 69.68; H, 11.68.

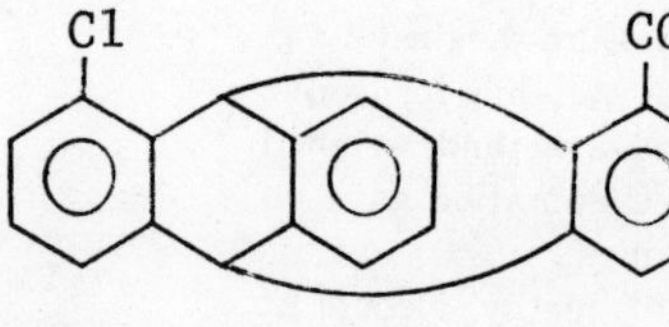

$C_{21}H_{13}ClO_2$ Ref. 1348

Optical Resolution of 5-Chloro-7-carboxytriptycene (XVIIIb). To a solution of XVIIIb (128 mg, 0.4 mmol) in ethanol (6 ml) was added brucine dihydrate (172 mg, 0.4 mmol) and the mixture was refluxed for 30 min. The mixture was allowed to stand overnight. The crystals deposited were recrystallized from methyl acetate to afford pure brucine salt, mp 225—231°C.

Found: C, 72.56; H, 5.43; N, 3.83; Cl, 4.62%. Calcd for $C_{43}H_{39}O_6N_2Cl$: C, 72.66; H, 5.41; N, 3.85; Cl, 4.88%.

A hot acetic acid solution of the brucine salt was diluted with water to result in the precipitation of (+)-XVIIIb, mp 285—277°C, CD: $\lambda_{max}^{dioxane}$ ($\Delta\varepsilon$) 285 (−0.8), 275 (+1.3) nm.

Found: C, 75.64; H, 3.75%. Calcd for $C_{21}H_{13}O_2Cl$: C, 75.79; H, 3.94%.

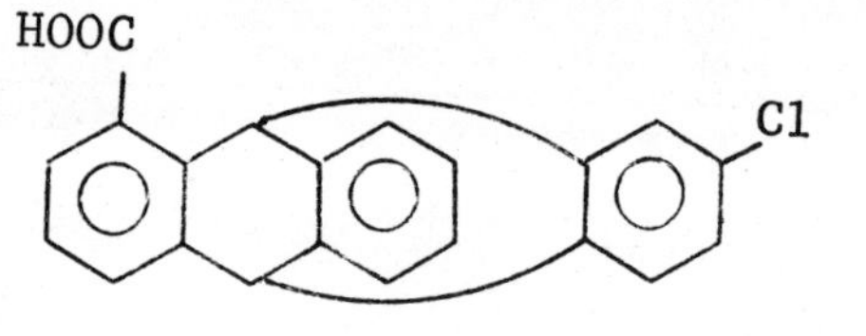

$C_{21}H_{13}ClO_2$ Ref. 1349

Optical Resolution of 4-Chlorotriptycene-7-carboxylic Acid (Xb). A solution of Xb (2.27 g, 0.00683 mol) in 99% ethanol (80 ml) was mixed with aqueous quinidine methohydroxide (0.614 M, 11.1 ml, 0.0068 mol) and left to stand overnight. The solid obtained by evaporating the solvent under reduced pressure was recrystallized from ethanol–ether. Repeated fractional recrystallization (16 times) from ethanol–ether or ethanol afforded colorless crystals of optically pure salt containing one molecule of ethanol as a solvent of crystallization, 1.134 g, mp 175—177 °C, $[\alpha]_{600}^{16}$ +133.9°, $[\alpha]_{589}^{16}$ +137.1°, $[\alpha]_{500}^{16}$ +213.4°, $[\alpha]_{400}^{16}$ +461.7° (*c* 0.440, EtOH).

Found: C, 73.76; H, 6.47; N, 3.91%. Calcd for $C_{42}H_{39}N_2O_4Cl \cdot C_2H_6O$: C, 73.67; H, 6.32; N, 3.91%.

The salt was decomposed with 5% aqueous hydrochloric acid to obtain (−)-Xb. Recrystallization of (−)-Xb from ligroin yielded colorless crystals of mp 90 °C containing some unidentified hydrocarbon as a solvent of crystallization. Upon heating *in vacuo* they gradually lost the solvent and showed a gradual rise in the melting point. After heating to 120 °C for 6 hr under reduced pressure, crystals free from the solvent were obtained, mp 204—205 °C, IR (KBr-disk): $\nu_{C=O}$ 1685 cm^{-1}, $[\alpha]_{436}^{21}$ −4.74°, $[\alpha]_{405}^{21}$ −9.95°, $[\alpha]_{365}^{21}$ −33.1° (*c* 0.980, 99% EtOH), CD: $\lambda_{max}^{99\% EtOH}$ ($\Delta\varepsilon$) 290 (−2.7), 274 (+2.0), 264* (+0.79), 250 (+2.0), 240 (−3.5), 225 (+33) nm.

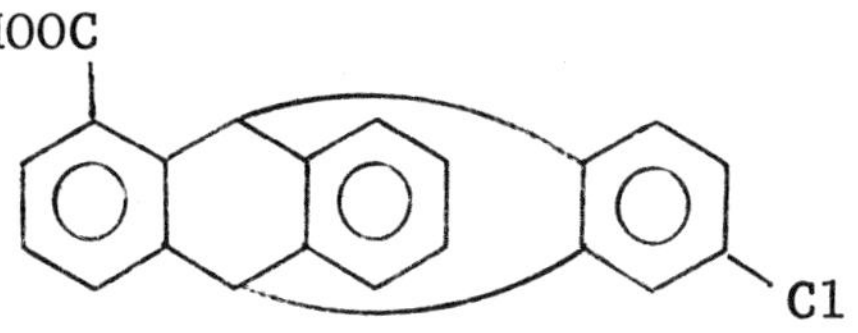

$C_{21}H_{13}ClO_2$ Ref. 1350

Optical Resolution of (±)-3-Chlorotriptycene-7-carboxylic Acid (Xa). Xa (2.157 g, 0.00648 mol) dissolved in 99% ethanol (40 ml) was mixed with aqueous quinidine methohydroxide (0.592 M, 10.9 ml, 0.0065 mol). After being left to stand overnight, the solvent was removed under reduced pressure and partly crystalline residue was recrystallized from dioxane. Repeated fractional recrystallization (7 times) afforded colorless crystals of optically pure salt, 0.389 g, mp 177—179 °C, $[\alpha]_{600}^{17.5}$ +95.10°, $[\alpha]_{589}^{17.5}$ +97.96°, $[\alpha]_{500}^{17.5}$ +154.7°, $[\alpha]_{400}^{17.5}$ +326.1° (*c* 0.490, EtOH). The crystals contained two molecules of dioxane as a solvent of crystallization and were slightly hygroscopic.

Found: C, 70.66; H, 6.47; N, 3.53%. Calcd for $C_{42}H_{39}N_2O_4 \cdot 2C_4H_8O_2$: C, 70.86; H, 6.54; N, 3.31%.

An effective resolution could not be attained by the use of ethanol or ethanol–ether.

The optically pure salt was decomposed by 5% aqueous hydrochloric acid to obtain (−)-Xa (0.13 g), which was recrystallized from ligroin, mp 236—238 °C, IR (KBr-disk): $\nu_{C=O}$ 1685 cm^{-1} (almost identical over entire region with (−)-Xb, (±)-Xa, and (±)-Xb), $[\alpha]_{600}^{16}$ −15.2°, $[\alpha]_{589}^{16}$ −16.3°, $[\alpha]_{500}^{16}$ −27.7°, $[\alpha]_{400}^{16}$ −70.8°, $[\alpha]_{350}^{16}$ −168° (*c* 0.516, 99% EtOH), CD: $\lambda_{max}^{99\%EtOH}$ ($\Delta\varepsilon$) 292 (−2.1), 278* (−0.89), 260* (+1.2), 254 (+2.1), 247 (−0.816), 240 (−1.14), 232 (−0.245), 220 (+11.4), 210 (−18.9) nm.

Found: C, 75.77; H, 4.18%. Calcd for $C_{21}H_{13}O_2Cl$: C, 75.79; H, 3.94%.

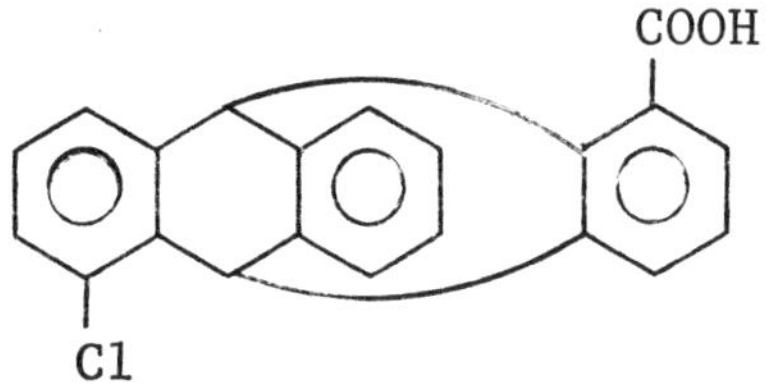

$C_{21}H_{13}ClO_2$ Ref. 1351

Optical Resolution of 2-Chloro-7-carboxytriptycene (XVIIIa). Brucine dihydrate (1034 mg, 2.40 mmol) was added to a solution of XVIIIa (796 mg, 2.40 mmol) in 99% ethanol (30 ml). After the mixture had been refluxed for 10 min, the solvent was removed under reduced pressure. The residue was recrystallized twice from acetone to yield pure brucine salt, mp 195—199°C, $[\alpha]_{350}$ −154°, $[\alpha]_{400}$ −54.0°, $[\alpha]_{500}$ −6.00°, $[\alpha]_D$ +4.00° (*c* 0.50, $CHCl_3$).

Found: C, 72.76; H, 5.32; N, 3.85; Cl, 4.62%. Calcd for $C_{44}H_{39}O_6N_2Cl$: C, 72.66; H, 5.41; N, 3.85; Cl, 4.88%.

The brucine salt was dissolved in hot acetic acid and diluted with water to precipitate (+)-XVIIIa, mp 289—291°C (decomp.), $[\alpha]_{350}^{15}$ +103°, $[\alpha]_D^{15}$ +19.4° (*c* 0.515, dioxane), CD: $\lambda_{max}^{dioxane}$ ($\Delta\varepsilon$) 287 (−1.2), 275 (+3.2), 259 (−1.3) nm.

Found: C, 75.30; H, 3.75%. Calcd for $C_{21}H_{13}O_2Cl$: C, 75.79; H, 3.94%.

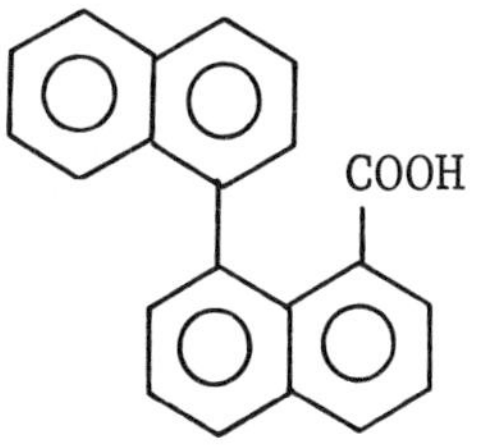

$C_{21}H_{14}O_2$ Ref. 1352

Die erkaltete und zerkleinerte Reaktionsmasse wird im Extraktionsapparat mit etwa 250 ccm Äther ausgezogen und die ätherische Lösung auf wenige ccm eingeengt. Es krystallisieren ca. 0.5 g Dinaphthyl-(1.1')-dicarbonsäure-diäthylester-(8.8'). Der Rest des Äthers wird vertrieben und das zurückbleibende, dunkle Öl der Wasserdampf-Destillation unterworfen. Dabei geht ein Gemisch von unverändertem α-Brom-naphthalin und Chlor-naphthoesäure-ester über (zusammen etwa 7 g). Der Kolbenrückstand der Wasserdampf-Destillation, ein dunkles, zähes Öl, wird vorteilhaft im Hochvakuum destilliert. Erste Hauptfraktion von 110—135°/1 mm, 1.6 g hellgelbes Öl. Es ist ein Gemisch von Chlor-naphthoesäure-ester mit wenig Di-ester und kann durch fraktionierte Krystallisation aus Methylalkohol zerlegt werden. Zweite Hauptfraktion von 230—250°/1 mm: 2.1 g zähes, dunkelgelbes Öl, erstarrt in der Vorlage glasig. Durch 4-maliges Umkrystallisieren aus Alkohol erhält man, neben ganz wenig Di-ester, 1.2 g Dinaphthyl-(1.1')-carbonsäure-äthylester-(8) vom Schmp. 146°. Er krystallisiert in kurzen, blaßgelben Prismen, ist in Alkoholen ziemlich leicht, in Schwefelkohlenstoff recht leicht löslich. In konz. Schwefelsäure löst er sich mit braunroter Farbe; aus der Lösung werden durch Wasser kanariengelbe Flocken ausgefällt[8]).

0.1206 g Sbst.: 0.3730 g CO_2, 0.0633 g H_2O.

$C_{22}H_{18}O_2$ (326.1). Ber. C 84.63, H 5.56. Gef. C 84.35, H 5.87.

Aus den von vielen derartigen Ansätzen gesammelten methylalkohol. Rest-Mutterlaugen des obigen Esters konnte durch fraktionierte Krystallisation wenig einer farblosen, in Methylalkohol spielend löslichen, halogen-haltigen Substanz isoliert werden, die in fächerförmig gruppierten Nadeln krystallisierte. Schmp. 242°; in konz. Schwefelsäure mit schwach gelber Farbe löslich. Materialmangel ließ eine weitere Untersuchung nicht zu; es mag sich um eine ähnliche Verbindung handeln, wie sie unter 4. beim Ester der andern Monocarbonsäure beschrieben ist.

Dinaphthyl-(1.1')-carbonsäure-(8): Der Ester ist, ebenso wie der der Dicarbonsäure, schwer verseifbar, weshalb wieder am besten durch Alkali-Schmelze verseift wird: Im Glycerin-Bade wird aus einem Gemisch von 1 g Dinaphthyl-(1.1')-carbonsäure-ester-(8) und 15 ccm 30-proz. methylalkohol. Kali der überschüssige Alkohol bei 120° weggekocht und schließlich die Badtemperatur auf 135° gesteigert, wobei allmählich aller Ester klar in Lösung geht. Nach etwa 1 Stde. beginnt sich ein Kaliumsalz in feinen Nadeln aus der dunkelgelben Schmelze abzuscheiden. Die Schmelze wird nach $1^1/_2$-stdg. Erhitzungs-Dauer aufgearbeitet; man löst sie in Wasser und fällt die Säure mit verd. Salzsäure aus. Schmp. der rohen Säure 240°. Die Säure ist in Alkoholen, Dioxan, Eisessig leicht, in Äther, Chloroform, Essigester schwerer, in Benzol schwer löslich. In kalter konz. Schwefelsäure löst sie sich wie der Ester mit braunroter Farbe. Die reine Säure erhält man durch Umlösen aus Methylalkohol in schwach gelben Krystallen, sie schmilzt bei 242°.

0.5504 g Säure werden in überschüssiger 0.1-n. Natronlauge gelöst und mit Salzsäure zurücktitriert; Indicator: Phenol-phthalein. Verbrauch 18.55 ccm Natronlauge, ber. 18.46 ccm.

Spaltung der Dinaphthyl-(1.1')-carbonsäure-(8): 1.305 g Säure und 2.04 g Brucin werden mit 25 ccm Essigester durch Erwärmen auf dem Wasserbade in Lösung gebracht. Nach Einengen auf die Hälfte läßt man erkalten und setzt 3 Tropfen wäßrigen Methylalkohol (1:1) zu. Beim Anreiben krystallisiert (+)-Brucinsalz in farblosen Blättchen mit typischen Streifen aus, die um 150° anfangen zu sintern, um 165° unter Blasenbildung offenbar Krystall-Lösungsmittel abgeben und sehr unscharf bei 210° unter Bräunung zusammenschmelzen. Das Salz ist in Chloroform und Alkohol spielend löslich, weniger leicht in Essigester. Im ersten Versuch erhielten wir beim Einengen der Mutterlauge und stets erneuten nachträglichen Zusatz von einigen Tropfen wäßrigem Methylalkohol lediglich (+)-Brucinsalz. In insgesamt 9 Fraktionen konnten so 3.25 g Salz isoliert werden.

0.2059 g luft-trockne Sbst. aus Fraktion 1 zu 10 ccm in Chloroform gelöst; die Chloroform-Lösung war von abgeschiedenem Krystallwasser etwas trübe. α_D = +4.18°, $[\alpha]_D^{21}$ = +101.5°. — 0.1536 g luft-trockne Substanz aus Fraktion 6, zu 10 ccm in Chloroform gelöst: α_D = +3.24°, $[\alpha]_D^{17}$ = +105.5°.

Eine Probe Brucinsalz wurde in Essigester gelöst und durch 8 Tage langes Stehen in sehr großen Krystallen gezüchtet, die Drehung war praktisch unverändert; 0.103 g Sbst. wie oben: α_D = +2.11°, $[\alpha]_D^{2?}$ = +103°. Das Brucinsalz erleidet langsame Racemisation; die angegebene erste Ablesung war 5 Min. nach Versuchs-Beginn gemacht, nach weiteren 1500 Min. war die Drehung auf α_D = +0.88° gesunken.

Beim Umlösen einer anderen Probe des Brucinsalzes aus Essigester

[8]) vergl. die analoge Reaktion des Dicarbonsäure-esters: L. Kalb, B. 47, 1728 [1914].

krystallisierten aus der vom (+)-Salz getrennten Mutterlauge spontan klare, derbe Prismen aus, die sich als linksdrehend erwiesen. Sinterung von 155° an. Löslichkeit sehr ähnlich der des (+)-Brucinsalzes.

0.2298 g luft-trocknes (—)-Brucinsalz verloren im Vakuum bei 100° binnen $3^1/_2$ Stdn. 0.0061 g an Gewicht. 0.1407 g luft-trockne Sbst.: 0.3824 g CO_2, 0.0800 g H_2O.

$C_{21}H_{14}O_2$, $C_{23}H_{26}O_4N_2$ + H_2O (710.6). Ber. C 74.34, H 5.96, H_2O 2.54.
Gef. „ 74.14, „ 6.36, „ 2.65.

0.1012 g luft-trocknes (—)-Salz, zu 10 ccm in Chloroform gelöst; im Gegensatz zum (+)-Salz tritt keine Krystallwasser-Abscheidung ein. Erste Ablesung 10 Min. nach Lösungs-Beginn α_D = —4.07°, 60 Min. nach Lösungs-Beginn α_D = —4.00°, 980 Min. nach Lösungs-Beginn α_D = —3.12°. Der theoretische Endwert des Racemisationsvorgangs wurde durch Bestimmung der Drehung des Brucinsalzes der inaktiven Säure gefunden (Gemisch von Brucin und racem. Säure in derselben Konzentration wie oben: α_D = —1.28°, $[\alpha]_D^{20}$ = —63.2°, $[M]_D^{20}$ = —449°). Daraus berechnet sich k pro Minute zu 0.00045, die Halbwertszeit zu $25^1/_2$ Stdn.; extrapolierter Anfangs-Drehwert α_D = —4.08°; damit erhält man für $[\alpha]_D^{20}$ = —201.6°, $[M]_D^{20}$ = —1432°.

Racemisierungsverlauf in Essigester: 0.0753 g luft-trockne Sbst., zu 10 ccm in Essigester gelöst. Erste Ablesung 20 Min. nach Lösungs-Beginn α_D = —2.48°, letzte Ablesung 85 Min. nach Lösungs-Beginn α_D = —2.24°.

Aus der Essigester-Lösung der Brucinsalze ließ sich eine Zeit lang nach Belieben (+)- oder (—)-Salz gewinnen, je nach Wahl des Impfkrystalles. Anwesenheit von wenig wäßrigem Methylalkohol war in beiden Fällen erforderlich. Doch gelang es plötzlich aus unersichtlichen Gründen nicht mehr, ein einheitlich krystallisierendes (+)-Salz zu isolieren.

Die optisch aktiven Säuren.

a) 0.20 g (+)-Brucinsalz ($[\alpha]_D$ = +103°) wurden mit einer wäßrigen Lösung von 0.07 g Soda in bekannter Weise zerlegt und möglichst rasch die Drehung bestimmt. Beobachtet wurde nach 35 Min. α_D = +0.64°, nach 1175 Min. α_D = +0.33° Racemisationskonstante k = 0.00082; Halbwertszeit 14 Stdn., berechnete Anfangsdrehung α_D = +0.66°. Die Konzentrations-Bestimmung des Rohr-Inhalts nach der Ablesung ergab für 5 ccm 0.0267 g *d*-Säure; daraus: $[\alpha]_D^{22}$ = +61.8°, $[M]_D^{22}$ = +184°. — b) 0.20 g (—)-Brucinsalz ($[\alpha]_D$ = —202°), genau wie oben zerlegt. Die Konzentration an Säure in 5 ccm Rohr-Inhalt wurde zu 0.0322 g *l*-Säure bestimmt. Abgelesen nach 55 Min. α_D = —0.84°, nach 1850 Min. α_D = —0.31°. Konstante k = 0.00077; Halbwertszeit 15 Stdn.; berechnete Anfangsdrehung α_D = —0.88°, also $[\alpha]_D^{20}$ = —68.3°, $[M]_D^{20}$ = —204°.

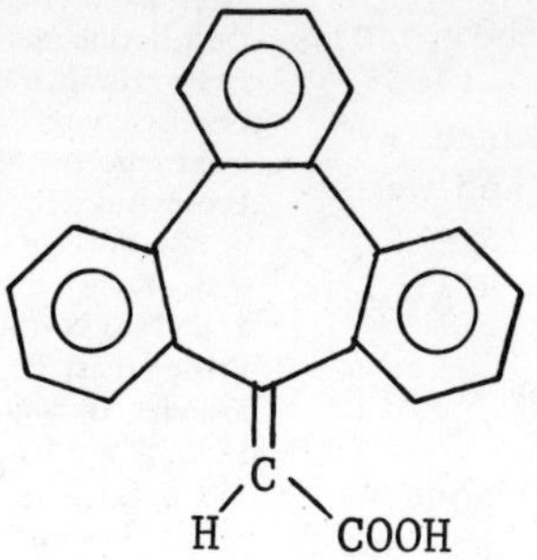

$C_{21}H_{14}O_2$ Ref. 1353

Zur Racematspaltung wurden Lösungen von 1.49 g (5 mMol) **2** in 45 ccm Aceton und von 2.00 g (5.05 mMol) *Brucin* in 40 ccm Aceton in der Siedehitze vereinigt, wobei sich entweder sofort oder beim Einengen Kristalle abschieden. Nach ca. 5 min. Erhitzen und Stehenlassen über Nacht ließ sich eines der diastereomeren *Brucin-Salze* von **2** absaugen (1.52 g; Schmp. 235.–237°).

$C_{23}H_{27}N_2O_4[C_{21}H_{13}O_2]$ (692.8) Ber. C 76.28 H 5.80 Gef. C 76.35 H 5.85

Das zweite Brucin-Salz ist in Aceton und Chloroform leicht löslich und konnte nicht rein erhalten werden.

Aus dem abgesaugten Salz erhielt man nach der Spaltung mit 2*n* H_2SO_4, Ausschütteln mit Äther und Umkristallisation aus Essigester oder Essigester/Cyclohexan eines der Enantiomeren von **2** (starkes Sintern bei 218–222°, Verfestigung, Durchschmelzen bei 249–251°). Der Misch-Schmp. mit racem. **2** ergab keine Depression. Die spezif. Drehungen sind stark vom verwendeten Lösungsmittel abhängig; es wurden folgende Werte gemessen:

Aceton, $[\alpha]_{546}^{25}$: +31.7° (*c* = 0.026 g/ccm).
Dioxan, $[\alpha]_{436}^{25}$: −49.7° (*c* = 0.025 g/ccm).
Dimethylformamid, $[\alpha]_{546}^{20}$: +52° (*c* = 0.02 g/ccm)[27], $[\alpha]_{436}^{20}$: +71° (*c* = 0.02 g/ccm).
Diäthylenglykoldimethyläther, $[\alpha]_{546}^{25}$: −7° (*c* = 0.036 g/ccm), $[\alpha]_{436}^{20}$: −47° (*c* = 0.025 g/ccm).

Aus dem in Aceton leicht löslichen Salz wurde analog eine optisch aktive Säure **2** gewonnen, welche die Ebene des polarisierten Lichtes in den obigen Lösungsmitteln in die entgegengesetzte Richtung dreht. Diese Verbindung zeigt das gleiche Schmelzpunktsverhalten wie ihr Enantiomeres.

Aceton, $[\alpha]_{546}^{25}$: −30.9° (*c* = 0.026 g/ccm).
Dimethylformamid, $[\alpha]_{546}^{20}$: −51° (*c* = 0.02 g/ccm), $[\alpha]_{436}^{20}$: −69° (*c* = 0.02 g/ccm).
Diäthylenglykoldimethyläther, $[\alpha]_{436}^{20}$: +35° (*c* = 0.025 g/ccm).

Nach 15 min. Erhitzen von 16 mg festem (−)-**2** ($[\alpha]_{546}^{20}$: −50.5°, *c* = 0.02 g/ccm in DMF) auf 230° betrug die spezif. Drehung nur noch $[\alpha]_{546}^{20}$: −2.1°.

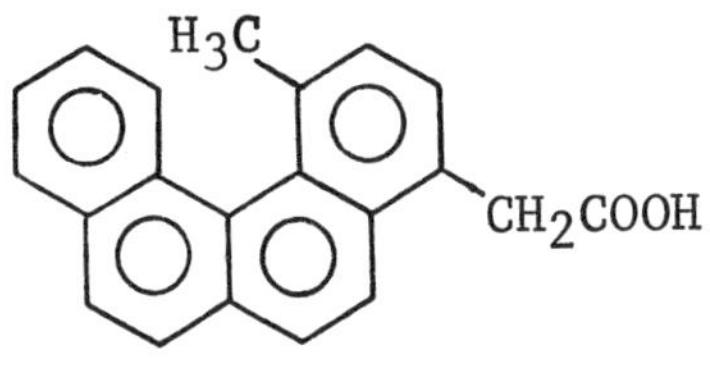

Ref. 1354

$C_{21}H_{16}O_2$

Resolution of II.—A solution of the chloride of acid II, prepared by treatment of 1.54 g. (0.0041 mole) of II with thionyl chloride and pyridine, in 50 cc. of dry benzene was added dropwise to a well-stirred ice-cold solution of 0.80 g. (0.0051 mole) of *l*-menthol ($[\alpha]_D$ −49.8°, *c*, 2 in absolute ethanol) in 25 cc. of dry benzene. After being stirred for an hour, during which time it came to room temperature, the reaction mixture was hydrolyzed. The benzene layer was separated, washed in turn with dilute hydrochloric acid, water, saturated sodium bicarbonate solution and then dried. Evaporation of the benzene under reduced pressure left an orange oil, which gave 0.39 g. of crystalline material on trituration with Skellysolve F. This material, after five recrystallizations from chloroform–Skellysolve F, melted at 185.5–187.0° and showed a specific rotation of +1.4 ± 0.2° (*c*, 1 in chloroform). Although it was at first believed that this material was the *l*-menthyl ester of II, the analysis indicated that it was impure.

Anal. (b) Calcd. for $C_{31}H_{34}O_2$ (ester): C, 84.9; H, 7.8. Calcd. for $C_{21}H_{16}O_2$ (acid): C, 84.0; H, 5.4. Found: C, 84.9, 84.9; H, 5.4, 5.4.

The five-times recrystallized material was shaken with alcoholic potassium hydroxide for ten minutes, the mixture then diluted with a large quantity of water and extracted repeatedly with ether. Acidification of the aqueous layer precipitated the acid, which was extracted with ether. Evaporation of the ether from the combined extracts left light tan crystals of acid II, m. p. 208.8–209.6°, alone and when mixed with an authentic sample of II. A solution of 0.1053 g. of this acid in 5 cc. of acetone gave an observed rotation of +0.09 ± 0.02°; $[\alpha]^{25}_D$ +2.1 ± 0.4°. No rotation could be observed the following day. Two other resolutions were carried out in the manner described above, giving samples of acid with specific rotations of +1.6 and +1.0°. The acetone solutions of both of these samples displayed no optical activity after standing for twelve hours at room temperature.

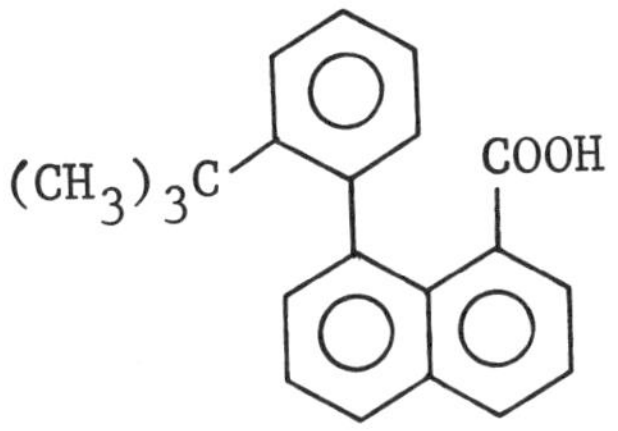

Ref. 1355

$C_{21}H_{20}O_2$

Resolution of 8-o-*t*-*Butylphenyl*-1-*naphthoic Acid*.—All rotations were measured in chloroform at room temperature (*c* ~0·5) in 2 dm. tubes unless otherwise stated. The acid (6·5 g.) and strychnine (7·2 g.) were dissolved in boiling ethanol (300 c.c.) and kept overnight at room temperature. The first fraction of salt (2·9 g.) separated as rectangular plates and had $[\alpha]_{5791}$ −22·2°, $[\alpha]_{5461}$ −31·4°. The second fraction (2·8 g.), which separated after concentration of the mother-liquor, had $[\alpha]_{5791}$ −43·7°, $[\alpha]_{5461}$ −62·2°. Evaporation of the mother-liquor to dryness gave a solid which had $[\alpha]_{5791}$ −94·7°, $[\alpha]_{5461}$ −126·3°. This fraction, the (−)-acid salt, was recrystallised from acetone until it was optically pure. The first two fractions were combined and recrystallised from ethanol. *Strychnine* (+)-8-o-*t*-*butylphenyl*-1-*naphthoate* crystallised from ethanol in hexagonal plates, m. p. 213—214° with loss of solvent at 101°, $[\alpha]_{5791}$ −14·5°, $[\alpha]_{5461}$ −19·9° (Found: C, 69·3; H, 7·6. $C_{21}H_{20}O_2,C_{21}H_{22}N_2O_2,5H_2O$ requires C, 69·2; H, 7·2%). On being heated *in vacuo* at 80° for several hours the salt lost its water of crystallisation and the loss in weight corresponded to $5H_2O$. On exposure to air the salt quickly reverted to the hydrated form.

Strychnine (−)-8-o-*t*-*butylphenyl*-1-*naphthoate* crystallised in small rectangular plates, m. p. 192—193°, $[\alpha]_{5791}$ −87·7°, $[\alpha]_{5461}$ −100·7° (Found: C, 78·6; H, 6·7. $C_{21}H_{20}O_2,C_{21}H_{22}N_2O_2$ requires C, 79·0; H, 6·6%). The optically active acids were obtained from their strychnine salts by decomposition with aqueous sodium hydroxide solution in the usual manner. (+)-8-o-*t*-*Butylphenyl*-1-*naphthoic acid*, crystallised from 1 : 5 benzene–light petroleum (b. p. 60—80°), had m. p. 145—146°, $[\alpha]_{5791}$ +44·4°, $[\alpha]_{5461}$ +49·7° (Found: C, 83·1; H, 6·7. $C_{21}H_{20}O_2$ requires C, 82·9; H, 6·6%). The (−)-*acid* had m. p. 145—146° and $[\alpha]_{5791}$ −44·6°, $[\alpha]_{5461}$ −50·0° (Found: C, 83·1; H, 6·7%). When the active acid melted, the melt solidified immediately and then remelted at 236—237°, the m. p. of the racemic acid.

Racemisation of (−)-*Acid* (V).—The racemisation of the (−)-acid was studied at temperatures between 121° and 136°. The acid (~0·15 g.) was dissolved in ethylbenzene (20 c.c.) and sealed in 8 glass tubes which were heated in a thermostat-bath at the required temperature. At intervals a tube was removed and cooled rapidly and the solution examined polarimetrically (1 dm. tube) at room temperature. As racemisation proceeded the acid became less soluble in the solvent and crystallised in the tubes. The following results were obtained:

Temp.	121°	125°	131°	136°
10^3k (min.$^{-1}$)	3·79	5·38	9·48	15·62
Half-life (min.)	183	129	73·1	44·4

The energy of activation was found to be 29 kcal. mole^{-1}.

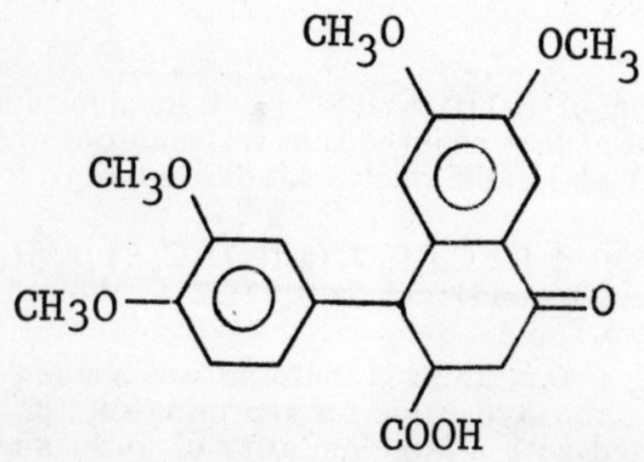

$C_{21}H_{22}O_7$ Ref. 1356

7) *Risoluzione con chinina del chetoacido* (XII) *racemico.*

G 10 del chetoacido racemico, ottenuto come descritto nel precedente paragrafo, vengono disciolti a caldo, unitamente a g 9 di chinina base anidra, in cc 70 di metanolo puro. A freddo precipita il sale (levogiro) di chinina dell'acido (+)(XII) che filtrato, lavato con poco metanolo e seccato, fonde tra 129 e 132° (con decomp.). Ricristallizzato da metanolo il prodotto fonde a 136-137° (con dec.) e puro a 148° (con dec.) con $[\alpha]_D^{20}$ = —24,01° (c = 0,63% in etanolo assoluto). La resa ammonta a g 9 circa.

	trov. %	:	C 69,08;	H 6,60;	N 3,84
per $C_{41}H_{44}O_9N_2$	calc.	:	69,28;	6,51;	3,95

Nelle acque madri metanoliche provenienti dalla filtrazione del levo-sale rimane in soluzione il sale di chinina del chetoacido stereoisomero (—)(XII).

Il sale di chinina dell'acido (+)(XII) viene disciolto in cloroformio e dibattuto ripetutamente con una soluzione di soda caustica al 50%. La fase acquosa basica, contenente il sale alcalino del chetoacido (+)(XII), viene separata dal cloroformio ed acidificata a freddo con acido solforico 50%. L'acido (+)(XII) che precipita allo stato amorfo viene separato, lavato con acqua e cristallizzato da metanolo. Il prodotto filtrato, lavato con metanolo e ricristallizzato da propanolo o da isopropanolo fonde puro a 214-215° con $[\alpha]_D^{20}$ = +81,1 (c = 0,45% in etanolo assoluto).

	trov. %	:	C 65,12;	H 5,58
per $C_{21}H_{22}O_7$	calc.	:	65,27;	5,74

Dalle acque madri metanoliche provenienti dal sale di chinina dell'acido (+)(XII) si ottiene con un trattamento analogo il cheto-acido (—)(XII) che fonde puro, dopo ricristallizzazione da propanolo od isopropanolo, a 214-215° con $[\alpha]_D^{20}$ = —81,1° (c = 0,45% in etanolo assoluto).

	trov. %	:	C 65,20;	H 5,88
per $C_{21}H_{22}O_7$	calc.	:	65,27;	5,74

Una miscela equivalente dei due chetoacidi antipodi fornisce l'isomero racemico che fonde a 211° e che risulta identico a quello descritto nel paragrafo precedente.

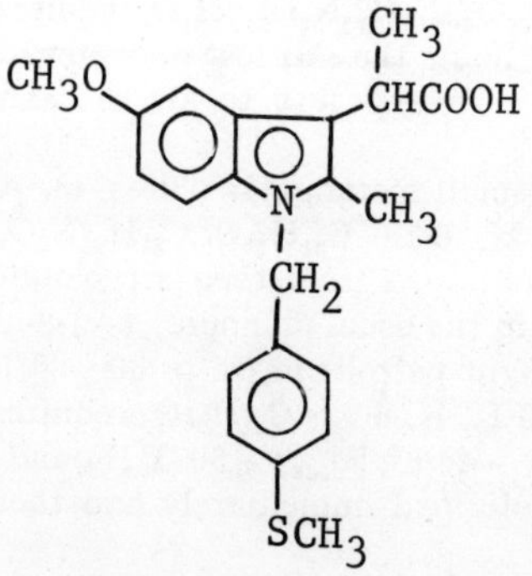

$C_{21}H_{23}NO_3S$ Ref. 1357

EXAMPLE 3

24.9 g. of racemic α - (1 - *p* - methylthiobenzyl - 2 - methyl - 5 - methoxy - 3 - indolyl) - propionic acid and 9.5 g. of (+) α - phenethylamine are dissolved in 350 ml. of boiling ethanol. The solution is then cooled to 20—25° C., and allowed to stand for 90 minutes. The crystalline material which forms is recovered by filtration, washed with cold ethanol and with ether. It is recrystallized from ethanol to give substantially pure (+) α - (1- *p* - methylthiobenzyl) - 2 - methyl - 5 - methoxy - 3 - indolyl) - propionic acid (+) α-phenethylamine salt, m.p. 170—172° C., $[\alpha]_D^{22}$ +38.5° (c = 1, methanol).

This product is added at room temperature to a mixture of 100 ml. of ether, 50 ml. of water and 2.5 ml. of concentrated hydrochloric acid. After a few minutes the ethereal layer is separated, and the aqueous acidic solution extracted with 2 x 75 ml. of ether. The combined ethereal extracts are concentrated to dryness *in vacuo*. The residue thus obtained is recrystallized from 20 ml. of ether and 12 ml. of benzene to give substantially pure (+) α-(1 - *p* - methylthiobenzyl - 2 - methyl - 5 - methoxy - 3 - indolyl) - propionic acid, m.p. 118° C., $[\alpha]_D^{22}$ + 62.4° (c = 0.94, ethanol).

(—) α - (1 - *p* - methylthiobenzyl - 2 - methyl - 5 - methoxy - 3 - indolyl) - propionic acid is obtained from a racemic mixture by the method described above using (—) α-phenethylamine as the resolving agent.

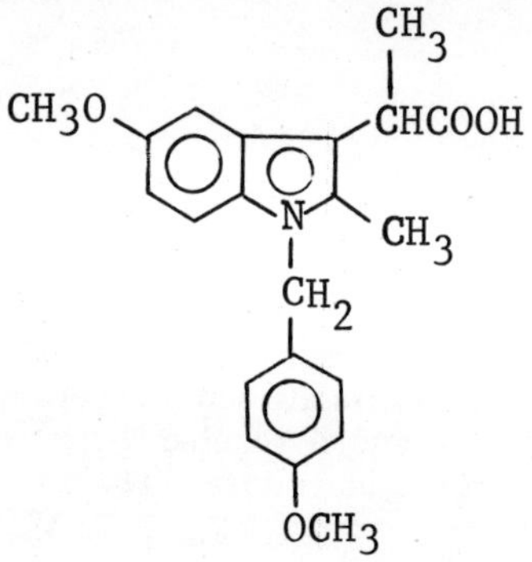

$C_{21}H_{23}NO_4$ Ref. 1358

EXAMPLE 4

40 mg. of (+) α - phenethylamine and 100 mg. of α-(1-*p*-methoxybenzyl-2-methyl - 5 - methoxy - 3 - indolyl) - propionic acid are dissolved in 1 ml. of hot isopropanol. The solution is allowed to cool to room temperature during which time (+) α - 1 - *p* - methoxy - benzyl - 2 - methyl - 5 - methoxy - 3 - indolyl) - propionic acid (+) α - phenethylamine salt crystallizes. The mixture is held at 25° C. for one hour and the crystalline material then removed by filtration, washed with isopropanol-ether (1:2) and with ether. The product has $[\alpha]_D^{22}$ + 32° (c = 1, methanol).

By treatment with aqueous hydrochloric acid and extraction with ether following the procedure of Example 3 above, there is obtained substantially pure (+) α - (1 - *p* - methoxybenzyl - 2 - methyl - 5 - methoxy - 3 - indolyl) - propionic acid.

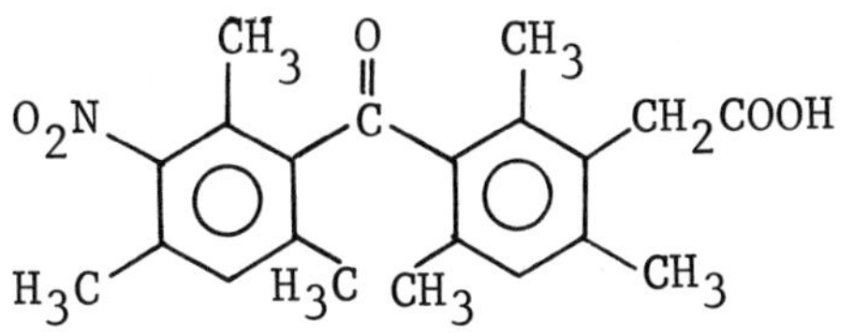

$C_{21}H_{23}NO_5$ Ref. 1359

Optical Resolution of Acid (IX).—A mixture of (−)-brucine (5·38 g.) and the acid (IX) (4·62 g.) was dissolved in ethyl acetate (112 ml.) under gentle reflux. The solution was cooled, left overnight in a refrigerator, and seeded with crystals from an earlier experiment. After 11 days in the refrigerator, the crystals (5·76 g., m. p. 124—133°) were collected and redissolved in hot ethyl acetate (40 ml.); the solution was seeded and cooled as before for 8 days, and crystals (5·17 g., m. p. 124—133°) were obtained. This product was allowed to crystallise slowly in the refrigerator during 14 days from ethyl acetate (36 ml.). The crystals (4·52 g.), m. p. 124—135°, were redissolved in hot ethyl acetate (32 ml.). The solution was filtered, seeded, and left to crystallise for 13 days in the refrigerator; when the pure *brucine salt* (2·06 g.) was obtained as the monohydrate, m. p. 128—132° (sintering from 126°) (Found: C, 67·6, 67·6; H, 6·8, 6·8; N, 5·6, 5·4. $C_{44}H_{49}N_3O_9,H_2O$ requires C, 67·6; H, 6·6; N, 5·4%), $[\alpha]_D$ −32·71° (*c* 0·90 in chloroform).

The brucine salt (1·8 g.) was powdered and added in portions to stirred concentrated hydrochloric acid (30 ml.). The mixture was stirred for a further 1 hr. at room temperature and filtered; the solid was washed with concentrated hydrochloric acid (50 ml.) and water (100 ml.), and dried *in vacuo*, to give the crude laevorotatory form of (IX) (0·83 g.), m. p. 153·5—156°, $[\alpha]_D$ −1·79° (*c* 0·84 in chloroform). A pure sample of the *acid* was obtained after five quick crystallisations from aqueous ethanol, m. p. 158·1—159·4° (Found: C, 68·4; H, 6·5; N, 4·2. $C_{21}H_{23}NO_5$ requires C, 68·3; H, 6·3; N, 3·8%), $[\alpha]_D$ −2·2° (*c* 0·86 in chloroform). It did not depress the melting point of racemic (IX).

Solvent was removed from the mother-liquor from the first fractional crystallisation of the brucine salt, the residue was suspended in water, and the acid was regenerated with concentrated hydrochloric acid. The acid was extracted with benzene, and the benzene extract was washed with more concentrated hydrochloric acid and water, and dried. Solvent was removed and a waxy material obtained. Attempts to obtain the dextrorotatory antipode from this material after salt formation with several bases were unsuccessful.

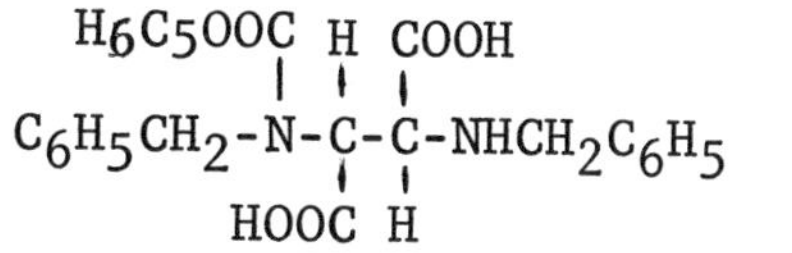

$C_{21}H_{24}N_2O_6$ Ref. 1360

Resolution of DL-threo-2-(Benzylamino)-3-[benzyl(ethoxycarbonyl)amino]-succinic Acid (II) into Its Enantiomers. A solution of 3 g of (II) in 35 ml of 1 N NaOH was heated to 50°, 7.7 g of L-(+)-threo-2-amino-1-p-nitrophenyl-1,3-propanediol sulfate was added in small portions, and the mixture was stirred at 50° for 1 h. Unchanged L-(+)-threo amine was filtered off, and when the filtrate was cooled the diastereomeric salt was precipitated and was filtered off and washed with 15 ml of cooled water. The yield of the salt was 2.8 g (90.5%), colorless prisms, mp 130-131° (decomp., from alcohol), $[\alpha]_D^{20}$ +35.2° (c 0.8, methanol). Found %: C 56.90, 57.12; H 6.23, 6.04; N 10.15, 9.95; $C_{39}H_{48}N_6O_{14}$. Calculated %: C 56.79; H 5.86; N 10.19.

A suspension of the diastereomeric salt in 10 ml of water was acidified to pH 2 with 2 N HCl, and the precipitate formed was separated. We obtained 1.2 g (88.4%) of (+)-threo-2-(benzylamino)-3-[benzyl(ethoxycarbonyl)amino]succinic acid, colorless prisms, mp 162° (decomp., from alcohol), $[\alpha]_D^{20}$+47.1° (c 0.9, methanol). Found %: C 62.95, 62.82; H 6.22, 6.13; N 6.56, 6.40. $C_{21}H_{23}N_2O_6$. Calculated %: C 62.99; H 6.04; N 6.99.

The filtrate from the separation of the diasteresomeric salt of (+)-2-(benzylamino)-3-[benzyl(ethoxycarbonyl)amino]succinic acid and the L-(+)-threo amine was extracted with chloroform. The extract was washed with water, and chloroform was removed. The residue was the diastereomeric salt of (-)-threo-2-(benzylamino)-3-[benzyl(ethoxycarbonyl)amino]succinic acid with the L-(+)-threo amine; yield 2.1 g (67.8%), colorless crystals, mp 167-168° (acetone), $[\alpha]_D^{20}$ -8.1° (c 1.48, methanol). Found %: C 56.64, 57.40; H 5.95, 5.72. $C_{39}H_{48}N_6O_{14}$. Calculated %: C 56.79; H 5.86.

Water (10 ml) was added to the diastereomeric salt, the mixture was acidified to pH 2 with 2 N HCl, and the precipitate formed was filtered off, washed with water, and crystallized from alcohol five times. We obtained 0.62 g (58.8%) of (-)-threo-2-(benzylamino)-3-[benzyl(ethoxycarbonyl)amino]succinic acid, colorless prisms, mp 161° (decomp., from alcohol), $[\alpha]_D^{20}$ -47.9° (c 0.4, methanol). Found %: C 63.32, 62.93; H 6.11, 5.80; N 6.68, 6.59. $C_{21}H_{23}N_2O_6$. Calculated %: C 62.99; H 6.04; N 6.99.

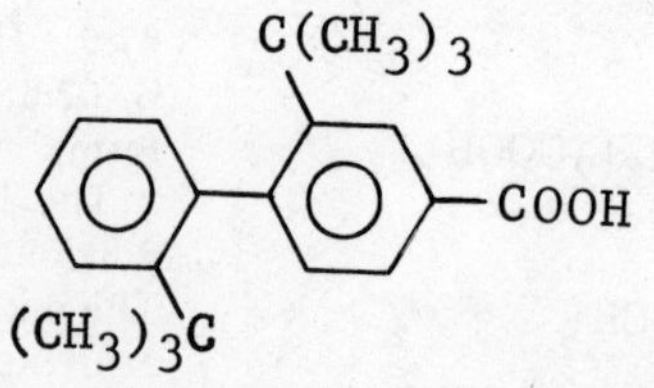

$C_{21}H_{26}O_2$

Ref. 1361

Resolution of 2',6-Di-t-butylbiphenyl-3-carboxylic Acid.—Rotations of salts and acids were measured at room temperature in " AnalaR " chloroform ($c \sim 1$) in 2 dm. tubes unless otherwise stated.

The above acid (3·1 g.) and strychnine (3·4 g.) were dissolved in ethanol (120 c.c.) and kept at room temperature overnight. The first crop of salt (1·4 g.) separated as fine needles, $[\alpha]_{5791}$ −8·9°, $[\alpha]_{5461}$ −11·0°. After concentration of the mother-liquor more salt was obtained (1·2 g.) with approximately the same rotation. On further concentration an oil was obtained that did not crystallise. This was decomposed and gave the crude (−)-acid. The crystalline (+)-acid salt was purified by recrystallisation from ethanol.

Strychnine (+)-2',6-*di-t-butylbiphenyl*-3-*carboxylate* crystallised from ethanol in slender needles, m. p. 160—161°, $[\alpha]_{5791}$ −9·5°, $[\alpha]_{5461}$ −12·6° (Found: C, 74·2; H, 7·8. $C_{21}H_{26}O_2,C_{21}H_{22}N_2O_2,2H_2O$ requires C, 74·1; H, 7·7%). When heated *in vacuo* at 80° the salt lost 2 mols. of water of crystallisation. The free acids were obtained from the strychnine salts by decomposition with formic acid. (+)-2',6-*Di-t-butylbiphenyl-3-carboxylic acid* crystallised from methanol in needles, m. p. 181—185°, $[\alpha]_{5791}$ +25·5°, $[\alpha]_{5461}$ +28·4° (Found: C, 80·8; H, 8·3. $C_{21}H_{26}O_2$ requires C, 81·2; H, 8·4%). In toluene its rotation was $[\alpha]_{5791}$ +45·4°, $[\alpha]_{5461}$ +51·8°.

The crude (−)-acid was crystallised from methanol, and a small amount of (±)-acid separated. This was filtered off and the mother-liquor was concentrated: the (−)-acid crystallised. Recrystallisation from methanol gave the pure (−)-acid, m. p. 181—185°, $[\alpha]_{5791}$ −25·8° and $[\alpha]_{5461}$ −28·3°.

The active acids melted rather indefinitely and it was suspected that they contained solvent of crystallisation since erratic analytical figures for the same sample were obtained on several occasions. The (−)-acid was therefore heated at 130°/1 mm. and sublimed under these conditions. The *acid* so obtained melted at 192—193° and had $[\alpha]_{5791}$ −65·5° and $[\alpha]_{5461}$ −72·4° in toluene (Found: C, 80·9; H, 8·6%). A portion of the pure (−)-acid was melted and allowed to solidify: its specific rotation in toluene was unchanged.

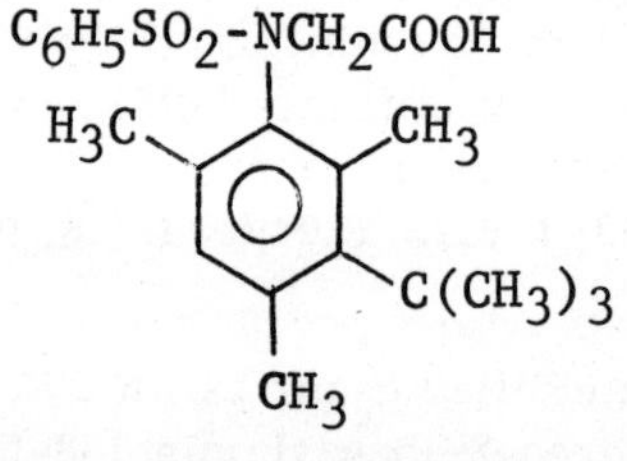

$C_{21}H_{27}NO_4S$

Ref. 1362

Resolution of N-Benzenesulfonyl-N-carboxymethyl-*t*-butylmesidine.—The cinchonidine salt of N-benzenesulfonyl-N-carboxymethyl-*t*-butylmesidine was prepared in a manner similar to that of the cinchonine salt of the isoduridine derivative, using ethyl acetate as resolving solvent. The less soluble salt was purified by recrystallization from ethyl acetate, m.p. 195–196°; rotation: 0.0611 g. made up to 10 ml. at 28° with ethanol gave α_D −0.22°, *l* 1; $[\alpha]^{28}_D$ −36.0°. It was treated in the manner previously described to yield pure (+)-N-benzenesulfonyl-N-carboxymethyl-*t*-butylmesidine, m.p. 171.5–172.5°; rotation: 0.0064 g. made up to 1.607 ml. with ethanol at 26° gave α_D +0.17°, *l* 1; $[\alpha]^{26}_D$ +42.5°.

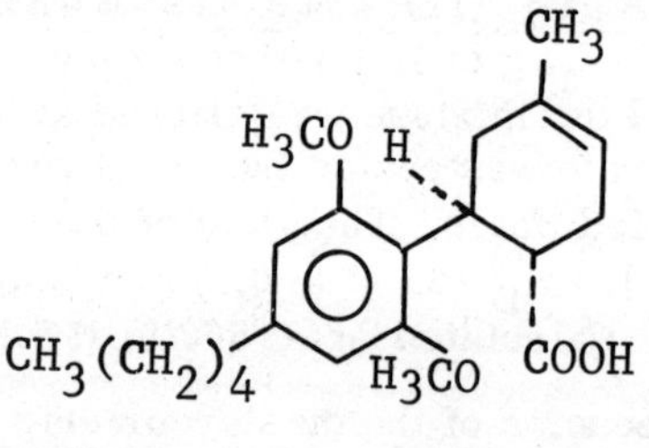

$C_{21}H_{29}O_4$

Ref. 1363

Note:

Resolved via (+)-1,-1'-naphthylethylamine in hexane. Obtained acid, m.p. 137.5-138.5° $[\alpha]^{24}_D$ -63° (c 1.00, $CHCl_3$).

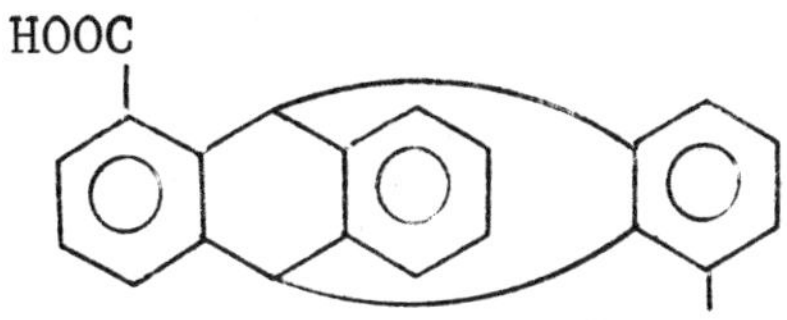

$C_{22}H_{14}O_4$

Ref. 1364

Optical Resolution of dl-2,7-*Dicarboxytriptycene* (*VII*)[.] To a hot solution of *dl*-VII (10.058 g, 0.0294 mol) in ethanol (350 ml) was added cinchonidine (8.649 g, 0.0294 mol) and the mixture was refluxed for 1 hr. Colorless solid (mp 188—195°C) obtained by concentration of the mixture was refluxed in methyl acetate (2350 ml) for 6.5 hr.[12] The mixture, on standing overnight in a refrigerator, gave crystals containing 1 mol of methyl acetate, mp 187—194°C, 8.305 g, $[\alpha]_{350}$ −261.0° (*c* 0.528, methanol). The salt was recrystallized 4 times from methyl acetate to give optically pure material, mp 186—189°C, $[\alpha]_{350}$ −146.3° (*c* 0.436, methanol).

Found: C, 74.62; H, 5.96; N, 4.19%. Calcd for $C_{41}H_{36}$-$N_2O_5 \cdot C_3H_6O_2$: C, 74.35; H, 5.96; N, 3.94%.

Decomposition of the optically pure salt with acetic acid (150 ml) yielded (+)-VII (1.053 g) as colorless crystals, mp 342.5—350.0°C (decomp.) (sublimed at 260°C), ORD: $[\alpha]_{600}$

+33.33°, $[\alpha]_D$ +33.3°, $[\alpha]_{500}$ +54.81°, $[\alpha]_{400}$ +140.7°, $[\alpha]_{350}$ +328.1° (*c* 0.540, methanol), CD: λ_{max}^{MeOH} ($\Delta\varepsilon$) 304 (+1.6), 282 (+5.3), 259 (−1.7), 244 (−4.0), 233 (+6.0), 219 (−49.7) nm.

Found: C, 76.81; H, 4.21%. Calcd for $C_{22}H_{14}O_4$: C, 77.18; H, 4.12%.

The initial mother liquor was mixed with acetic acid to afford (−)-VII with a low optical purity, mp 321—328°C (decomp.) (sublimed at 275°C), $[\alpha]_{350}$ −129.4° (*c* 0.4325, methanol).

Starting from *dl*-VII (11.338 g, 0.033 mol), ethanol (350 ml) and cinchonine (9.749 g, 0.033 mol), crude cinchonine salt was prepared by an essentially similar procedure with (+)-enantiomer. A suspension of the salt in methyl acetate (2000 ml) was refluxed for 3 hr, and then concentrated to 800 ml. Crystals deposited on standing the solution in a refrigerator overnight were recrystallized 4 times from the same solvent to yield optically pure salt, $[\alpha]_{500}^{12}$ +112.1° (*c* 0.5925, methanol). The crystals obtained on treatment of the optically pure salt with acetic acid were recrystallized from acetic acid to afford pure (−)-VII, 1.227 g, mp 342—350°C (decomp.) (sublimed at 260°C), ORD: $[\alpha]_{600}$ −33.2°, $[\alpha]_D$ −33.9°, $[\alpha]_{500}$ −56.8°, $[\alpha]_{400}$ −141.9°, $[\alpha]_{350}$ −332.9° (*c* 0.5425, methanol).

Found: C, 77.04; H, 4.15%. Calcd for $C_{22}H_{14}O_4$: C, 77.18; H, 4.12%.

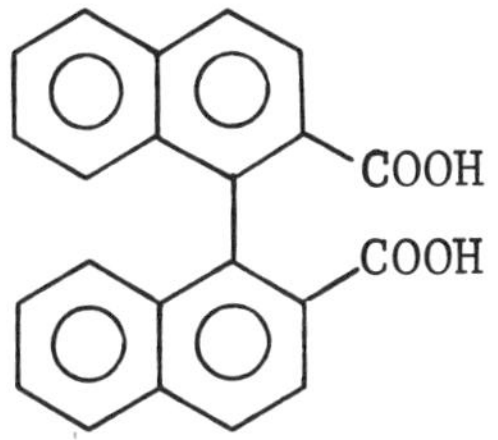

$C_{22}H_{14}O_4$

Ref. 1365

Resolution of 1 : 1′-*Dinaphthyl*-2 : 2′-*dicarboxylic Acid.*—The de-solvated acid (46·8 g., 1 mol.) and anhydrous quinine (44·3 g., 1 mol.) were dissolved together in ethanol (455 c.c.), and ether (455 c.c.) was added. The solution was kept at 4° and eventually deposited a salt (57 g.) which was subsequently recrystallised 3 times from ethanol to constant specific rotation (4 g.). The mother-liquor from the first crop was evaporated to dryness and the residue crystallised from ethanol. The more soluble salt was crystallised from highly concentrated ethanolic solutions. Intermediate crops were repeatedly recrystallised. Altogether 27·5 g. of the less soluble salt and 13·4 g. of the more soluble salt were obtained, apparently optically pure or nearly so. The less soluble *quinine salt* had m. p. 178° (decomp.), $[\alpha]_{5461}^{23}$ −103·5°, $[\alpha]_{5791}^{23}$ −89·8° (*c*, 1·101 in acetone) (Found : C, 74·15; H, 6·4. $C_{42}H_{38}O_6N_2,C_2H_5 \cdot OH$ requires C, 74·1; H, 6·2%). The more soluble *quinine salt* had m. p. 184—190° (decomp.) with previous softening, $[\alpha]_{5461}^{22}$ +11·6°, $[\alpha]_{5791}^{22}$ +8·6° (*c*, 0·989 in acetone) (Found : C, 73·2; H, 6·4. $C_{42}H_{38}O_6N_2,1·5C_2H_5 \cdot OH$ requires C, 73·45; H, 6·4%). Several crops of the more soluble salt were obtained with $[\alpha]_{5461}$ about +21°, but decomposition gave acid which was not optically pure. Some of the (+)-acid with the highest $[\alpha]$ was therefore converted into the quinine salt and this had $[\alpha]_{5461}^{22}$ +11·6°. The higher dextrorotations obtained for the optically impure salt remain anomalous.

(−)-1 : 1′-*Dinaphthyl*-2 : 2′-*dicarboxylic Acid.*—A solution of the less soluble quinine salt (3·5 g.) in chloroform (35 c.c.) was extracted 3 times with N-potassium hydroxide. The combined extracts were washed with chloroform and poured into dilute hydrochloric acid. The precipitated (−)-1 : 1′-*dinaphthyl*-2 : 2′-*dicarboxylic acid* was crystallised from aqueous acetone (yield, 1·6 g.) and had $[\alpha]_{5461}^{22}$ −125·2°, $[\alpha]_{5791}^{22}$ −108·6° (*c*, 1·023 in approx. 0·1N-NaOH). It was hydrated, the analysis corresponding to about 0·5H$_2$O, and had m. p. *ca.* 120° (decomp.) (Found : C, 74·9; H, 4·5. $C_{22}H_{14}O_4,0·5H_2O$ requires C, 75·2; H, 4·3%). It lost water when heated for some hours at 100° *in vacuo* but the anhydrous acid was very hygroscopic; to ensure reproducible results samples (*e.g.*, those obtained by precipitation) were always crystallised from aqueous acetone and air-dried at room temperature before their specific rotations were measured. The active *acid* also crystallised in needles, solvated with carbon tetrachloride, but apart from this could not be crystallised from anhydrous solvents (Found : C, 60·5; H, 3·6. $C_{22}H_{14}O_4,0·7CCl_4$ requires C, 60·6; H, 3·1%).

(+)-1 : 1′-*Dinaphthyl*-2 : 2′-*dicarboxylic Acid.*—Similar decomposition of the more soluble quinine salt gave (+)-*acid*, m. p. *ca.* 120° (decomp.), $[\alpha]_{5461}^{20}$ +124·2°, $[\alpha]_{5791}^{20}$ +107·2° (*c*, 1·115 in approx. 0·1N-NaOH) (Found : C, 74·9; H, 4·6. $C_{22}H_{14}O_4,0·5H_2O$ requires C, 75·2; H, 4·3%). Decomposition of the salt with $[\alpha]_{5461}$ *ca.* +21° gave acid with $[\alpha]_{5461}$ +84°, from which it proved possible to extract more highly active acid ($[\alpha]_{5461}$ +117°) with ether, the racemic acid being very sparingly soluble.

$C_{22}H_{14}O_4$ Ref. 1365a

Zerlegung der 1,1'-Dinaphtyl-2,2'-dicarbonsäure in optisch aktive Komponenten.

In eine Lösung von 0,831 g Säure in 30 ccm heißem 96-proc. Äthylalkohol wurden 0,977 g Chininhydrat (1 Mol) eingetragen. Die beim Erkalten klar gebliebene Lösung, welche wir mit dem gleichen Volum Äther vermischten, ließ nach Stehen über Nacht bei 0° farblose, schief auslöschende Stäbchen (0,1 g) ausfallen, welche von 180° an zusammensintern und unscharf gegen 202° unter Zersetzung zu einer roten Flüssigkeit schmelzen.

$$[\alpha]_D^{22} = (+1,15° \cdot 100) : (0,7 \cdot 0,718) = +230,4° \text{ in Chloroform.}$$

Aus dem mit 30 ccm Äther versetzten Filtrat der I. Fraktion krystallisierten nach 48 stündigem Stehen im Eisschrank farblose Stäbchen von etwas wechselnder Breite (0,55 g). Der Schmelzpunkt lag bei 197,5—198° (unkorr.). In Chloroformlösung fanden wir

$$[\alpha]_D^{24} = (+2,78° \cdot 100) : (0,7 \cdot 1,293) = +301,6°.$$

Ein weiterer Zusatz von 30 ccm Äther zu dem Filtrat der II. Fraktion bewirkte nach 3 tägigem Aufbewahren bei 0° nur noch eine ganz geringe Krystallisation. Die Mutterlauge der schwerlöslichen Chininsalze, völlig zur Trockne verdampft, hinterließ ein gelbliches Öl, das in Eis zu einer gelbbraunen Masse erstarrte (1,05 g), die wohl doppelbrechend ist, aber keine Einzelkrystalle erkennen läßt. Sie sintert von 167° an und schmilzt unscharf gegen 230° zu einer dunkelroten Schmelze unter schwacher Zersetzung.

$$[\alpha]_D^{22,5} = (+0,12° \cdot 100) : (0,7 \cdot 1,118) = +15,4° \text{ in Chloroform.}$$

l-1,1'-Dinaphtyl-2,2'-dicarbonsäure. 0,5 g Chininsalz von $[\alpha]_D^{24} = +301,6°$ wurden in 8 ccm Chloroform gelöst und auf der Maschine 4 mal mit je 10 ccm 2 n-HCl geschüttelt. Die der Chloroformlösung mit Soda als Natriumsalz entzogene aktive Säure haben wir durch Eintropfen in verdünnte Salzsäure in farbloser mikrokrystalliner Form erhalten (0,15 g). Sie sintert von 135° an, bildet bei etwa 145° einen durchscheinenden, an der Wand klebenden Kegel, der bei 177° (unkorr.) zu einer gelben, durch wenige Gasblasen getrübten Schmelze zusammenfällt. In $^n/_{10}$-NaOH dreht die Säure, deren optische Reinheit allerdings nicht feststeht,

$$[\alpha]_D^{22} = (-0,46° \cdot 100) : (0,7 \cdot 0,647) = -101,6°.$$

3,691 mg Subst.: 10,44 mg CO_2, 1,33 mg H_2O.

$C_{22}H_{14}O_4$	Ber.	C 77,17	H 4,12
	Gef.	„ 77,14	„ 4,03.

d-1,1'-Dinaphtyl-2,2'-dicarbonsäure. 0,85 g fein pulverisiertes, leicht lösliches Chininsalz haben wir mit je 15 ccm 2 n-HCl mehrmals bei 70—80° einige Zeit digeriert, bis das Filtrat mit Phosphorwolframsäure nur noch eine ganz geringe Trübung gab. Der Rückstand wurde in wenig Soda gelöst, kalt mit etwas Tierkohle geschüttelt und vorsichtig in verdünnte HCl eingetropft. Ausbeute 0,3 g. Die Säure sintert von etwa 185° an zu einem braunen Kegel, der bei 239—248° (unkorr.) zu einer braunroten Schmelze zusammenfällt.

$$[\alpha]_D^{22} = (+0,22° \cdot 100) : (0,7 \cdot 0,683) = +46° \text{ in } ^n/_{10}\text{-NaOH.}$$

Synthese des Racemats aus den Antipoden. d- und l-Säure wurden im umgekehrten Verhältnis der $[\alpha]_D$-Werte gemischt. Dabei stieg der Schmelzpunkt auf 255—257° (unkorr.; unter Dunkelfärbung nach vorangegangenem Sintern). Die ursprünglich inaktive Säure schmolz bei 257—258° (unkorr.) unter ähnlichen Erscheinungen.

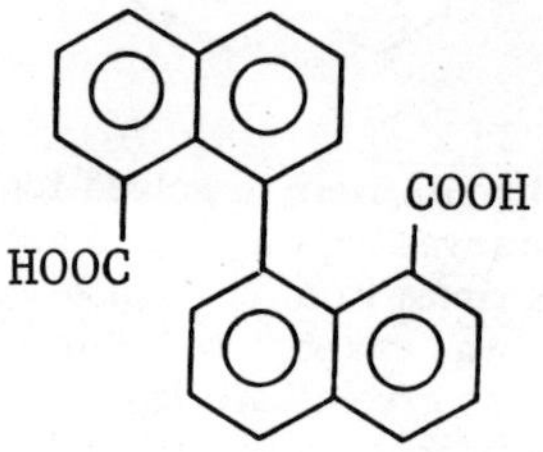

$C_{22}H_{14}O_4$ Ref. 1366

Resolution of 8,8'-Dicarboxy-1,1'-dinaphthyl.—To a cloudy solution of 0.4367 g. of 8,8'-dicarboxy-1,1'-dinaphthyl in 150 cc. of absolute ethyl alcohol was added 0.4138 g. (1 equivalent) of quinine. The solution, which became perfectly clear upon the addition of the quinine, was evaporated to dryness. The mono-quinine salt is very soluble in methyl alcohol, ethyl alcohol, acetone and chloroform, slightly soluble in benzene and insoluble in ether and water. The mono-quinine salt was taken up in 20 cc. of benzene and a few drops of ethyl alcohol was added to make the solution clear. The solution was then boiled for five minutes and allowed to stand. After standing for two days at room temperature, the clear solution was decanted from a thin glassy film (0.24 g.) which had formed on the sides and bottom of the flask.

Rotation. 0.0566 g. made up to 3 cc. with chloroform at 20° gave α_D −0.45°; $l = 1$; $[\alpha]_D^{20}$ −23.9°.

After standing two more days a mass of fine crystals (0.25 g.) and two large clusters of fine needles (0.1 g.) had separated from the decanted solution. These were removed and dried. The melting point of the 0.1-g. portion was 195° with sintering at 175°.

Rotation of the 0.1 g. portion: 0.0548 g. made up to 3 cc. with chloroform at 20° gave α_D −3.1°; $l = 1$; $[\alpha]_D^{20}$ −169.7°.

The 0.1-g. portion was recrystallized from benzene. The melting point was unchanged.

Rotation. 0.0292 g. made up to 2 cc. with chloroform at 20° gave α_D −2.42°; $l = 1$; $[\alpha]_D^{20}$ −165.8°.

Rotation of the 0.25-g. portion: 0.0604 g. made up to 3 cc. with chloroform at 20° gave α_D −2.75°; $l = 1$; $[\alpha]_D^{20}$ −136.6°.

Anal. Calcd. for $C_{42}H_{38}O_6N_2$: C, 75.64; H, 5.75. Found: C, 75.47; H. 5.71.

The remaining salt solution was evaporated to dryness and gave 0.25 g. of salt which sintered at 173° and melted at 190°.

Rotation. 0.0570 g. made up to 3 cc. with chloroform at 20° gave α_D = +3.65°; l = 1; $[\alpha]^{20}_D$ +192.1°.

The first portion (0.24 g.) of salt which was obtained in the fractionation consisted mainly of the *d,l*-salt. Upon refractionation from benzene the partially pure *d*- and *l*-salts were obtained.

***d*-8,8′-Dicarboxy-1,1′-dinaphthyl.**—To 0.24 g. of salt having a rotation of +192.1° in chloroform was added 10 cc. of 0.5 *N* hydrochloric acid. After stirring for ten minutes the mixture was filtered. This treatment was repeated twice and the precipitated acid was dissolved in 15 cc. of 0.1 *N* sodium hydroxide and extracted twice with 5 cc. of chloroform. The active acid was then precipitated from the alkaline solution with dilute hydrochloric acid. After drying, the product melted to a red liquid at 305–306°.

Rotation. (a) 0.0210 g. made up to 2 cc. with pyridine at 20° gave α_D +2.08°; l = 1; $[\alpha]^{20}_D$ +198.1°. (b) 0.0336 g. made up to 15 cc. with 0.1 *N* sodium hydroxide gave α_D −0.28°; l = 0.5; $[\alpha]^{20}_D$ −250.0°. (c) 0.0190 g. made up to 5 cc. with 2 *N* aqueous ammonia gave α_D −0.35°; l = 0.5; $[\alpha]^{20}_D$ −184.2°.

A portion of the *d*-salt having a rotation of +44.5° in chloroform was hydrolyzed in a similar manner to give partially pure *d*-acid.

Rotation. (a) 0.0250 g. made up to 9 cc. with 0.5 *N* aqueous ammonia gave α_D −0.12°; l = 1; $[\alpha]^{20}_D$ −43.2°. (b) 0.0240 g. made up to 2 cc. with pyridine at 20° gave α_D +0.88°; l = 1; $[\alpha]^{20}_D$ +73.1°.

It was necessary to use dilute alkaline solutions of the *d*-acid since concentrated alkaline solutions of the *d*-acid were always cloudy. Repeated solution in alkali, extraction with chloroform and precipitation with hydrochloric acid did not change this property.

***l*-8,8′-Dicarboxy-1,1′-dinaphthyl.**—A portion of *l*-salt having a rotation of −169.7° in chloroform was hydrolyzed by treatment with three 5-cc. portions of 0.5 *N* hydrochloric acid and extraction of the alkaline solution with chloroform. The *l*-acid so obtained melted to a red liquid at 304.5–305.5°.

Rotation. 0.0240 g. made up to 2 cc. with pyridine at 20° gave α_D −2.25°; l = 1; $[\alpha]^{20}_D$ −185.8°.

Anal. Subs., 4.447 mg.: CO_2, 12.57 mg.: H_2O, 1.68 mg. Calcd. for $C_{22}H_{14}O_4$: C, 77.17; H, 4.12. Found: C, 77.02; H, 4.23.

A portion of *l*-salt having a rotation of −136.6° in chloroform was hydrolyzed by treatment with three 10-cc. portions of 0.5 *N* hydrochloric acid, solution in 0.5 *N* aqueous ammonia and immediate precipitation with dilute hydrochloric acid.

Rotation. 0.0225 g. made up to 2 cc. with pyridine at 20° gave α_D −2.02°; l = 1; $[\alpha]^{20}_D$ −179.6°.

The *l*-acid was precipitated from the pyridine solution by the addition of concentrated hydrochloric acid at 0°. The rotation was again taken.

Rotation. 0.0187 g. made up to 2 cc. with 2 *N* ammonium hydroxide at 20° gave α_D +0.31°; l = 1; $[\alpha]^{20}_D$ +33.1°.

$C_{22}H_{14}O_4$ Ref. 1366a

Spaltung der Dinaphthyl-(1.1′)-dicarbonsäure-(8.8′): 1.914 g Dicarbonsäure werden mit 900 ccm Methylalkohol zum Sieden erhitzt, wobei die Säure zum größeren Teil in Lösung geht, und dazu 2.601 g Brucin, gelöst in 50 ccm Methylalkohol, hinzugegeben. Nachdem Lösung eingetreten ist, wird auf ca. 350 ccm eingeengt. Beim Stehen über Nacht krystallisieren 1.7 g farblose Prismen des linksdrehenden Brucinsalzes der Dinaphthyl-dicarbonsäure aus. Sinterung und Bräunung von 255° an, Schmp. 262° (unt. Zers.).

0.2247 g luft-trocknes Salz, zu 10 ccm in Chloroform gelöst: α_D = −17.76°; $[\alpha]^{18}_D$ = −395.2°. Zweimaliges Umkrystallisieren aus Methylalkohol erhöht den Schmelzpunkt nicht, die Drehung nur unwesentlich: 0.2219 g wie oben: α_D = −17.74°; $[\alpha]^{18}_D$ = −399.7°; $[M]^{18}_D$ = −3071°. Die Drehung war nach 3 Wochen unverändert.

0.3203 g (luft-trocken) verloren, im Vakuum bei 100° zur Konstanz getrocknet, binnen 11 Stdn. 0.0116 g an Gewicht; die getrocknete Substanz sinterte bei 253° und schmolz bei 263—265° (unt. Zers.). — 0.1408 g (luft-trocken): 0.3692 g CO_2, 0.0754 g H_2O.

$C_{22}H_{14}O_4$, $C_{23}H_{26}O_4N_2$ + $CH_3.OH$ (768.4)[7]). Ber. C 71.84, H 5.77, $CH_3.OH$ 4.17.
Gef. „ 71.51, „ 5.99, „ 3.62.

Die methylalkohol. Mutterlauge des linksdrehenden Brucinsalzes liefert beim Einengen nur noch sehr wenig des gleichen Salzes. Man verdampft den Methylalkohol im Vakuum und nimmt den zähen, harzigen Rückstand mit 500 ccm heißem Essigester auf. Über Nacht krystallisieren nunmehr 1.5 g farblose Nadeln des rechtsdrehenden Salzes aus, die bei 228° zu sintern anfangen und bei 234° unt. Zers. schmelzen. Durch Einengen der Mutterlauge erhält man weitere 0.5 g von gleicher Drehung. — Vertreibt man den Essigester schließlich auf dem Wasserbade vollständig, löst den Rückstand in Methylalkohol und impft mit (−)-Salz an, so kann man weitere 0.3 g Prismen des (−)-Salzes erhalten.

0.2329 g luft-trocknes (+)-Salz (Rohprodukt) wurden zu 10 ccm in Chloroform gelöst: α_D = +17.61°; $[\alpha]^{27}_D$ = +377.8°. Nach 2-maligem Umkrystallisieren aus Essigester (eine Änderung des Schmp. trat dabei nicht ein) 0.2312 g wie oben: α_D = +18.04°; $[\alpha]^{24}_D$ = +390.1°; $[M]^{24}_D$ = +3083°

0.4784 g luft-trocknes Salz verloren im Vakuum bei 100° in 7 Stdn. 0.0316 g an Gewicht. — 0.1295 g luft-trockne Sbst.: 0.3229 g CO_2, 0.0728 g H_2O.

$C_{22}H_{14}O_4$, $C_{23}H_{26}O_4N_2$ + 3 H_2O (790.4). Ber. C 68.33, H 5.86, H_2O 6.84.
Gef. „ 68.00, „ 6.29, „ 6.61.

Wie man sieht, sind die Unterschiede im Drehungsvermögen der beiden Brucinsalze, wenn man vom Vorzeichen absieht, gering; aus den gefundenen Werten ist zu schließen, daß das Drehungsvermögen des Brucinsalzes der inaktiven Säure schwach positiv sein muß. Das ist in der Tat der Fall: Ein Gemenge von 0.0649 g inaktiver Dicarbonsäure und 0.0885 g Brucin (mit 4 Mol. H_2O), entsprechend 0.1500 g Brucinsalz (mit 3 Mol. H_2O), in Chloroform zu 10 ccm gelöst, gab folgende Werte: α_D = +0.36°, $[\alpha]^{20}_D$ = +12°, $[M]^{20}_D$ = +95°.

Optisch aktive Dinaphthyl-(1.1′)-dicarbonsäuren-(8.8′): a) Zerlegung des (−)-Salzes: 0.250 g Brucinsalz, $[\alpha]_D$ = −399.7°, werden in 2 ccm Chloroform gelöst und 3 Min. heftig mit einer Lösung von 0.05 g Soda in 8 ccm Wasser durchgeschüttelt. Man trennt vom Chloroform, wäscht mit etwas Chloroform und dann mit Äther nach und filtriert wegen der großen Racemisations-Geschwindigkeit die alkalische Lösung durch ein gehärtetes Filter direkt in das Polarimeterrohr.

Erste Ablesung 15 Min. nach Beginn des Versuches α_D = +8.96°; letzte Ablesung 390 Min. nach Beginn α_D = +1.84°. Als Mittelwert für die Reaktionskonstante berechnet sich aus zahlreichen Ablesungen k = 0.0043 pro Min. für eine Temperatur von etwa 20°. Für die Anfangsdrehung läßt sich daraus ein Wert von α_D = +9.56° extrapolieren, Halbwertszeit. 160 Min.

Die Konzentration der Säure im Polarimeterrohr wurde gewichtsanalytisch bestimmt: Es wurden 5 ccm Rohrinhalt mit verd. Salzsäure ausgefällt und die ausgefallene Dicarbonsäure durch einen gewogenen Glasfilter-Tiegel filtriert. Ausbeute an Säure nach dem Trocknen 0.0560 g. — Das salzsaure Filtrat wurde 3-mal mit je 50 ccm Äther ausgeschüttelt, der Äther verdampft und der trockne Rückstand gewogen: 0.0082 g; Gesamtmenge der Dicarbonsäure also 0.0642 g. Unter Verwendung des Wertes α_D

= +9.56° berechnet sich für die Drehung des dinaphthyl-dicarbonsauren Natriums: $[\alpha]_D^{20} = +372.3°$, $[M]_D^{20} = +1274°$. Natürlich sind die Werte nur annähernd richtig, schätzungsweise auf 5—10% genau.

b) Zerlegung des (+)-Brucinsalzes: 0.160 g wurden mit einer wäßrigen Lösung von 0.03 g Soda nach oben stehender Vorschrift zerlegt.

Die gewichtsanalytische Bestimmung der Dicarbonsäure im Polarimeterrohr ergab für 5 ccm Flüssigkeit 0.0393 g. 22 Min. nach Versuchs-Beginn erste Ablesung: α_D = —4.54°, 240 Min. nach Beginn letzte Ablesung: α_D = —0.54°. Für die Racemisationskonstante wurde ein Mittelwert von k = 0.0102 pro Minute (t = 26°) berechnet, für die Halbwertszeit 68 Min., für die Anfangsdrehung ein Wert von α_D = —5.68° extrapoliert. Somit ist $[\alpha]_D^{26} = -361.3°$, $[M]_D^{26} = -1236°$.

Auf eine Bestimmung des Drehungsvermögens der freien Säuren wurde wegen ihrer Schwerlöslichkeit verzichtet.

[7]) Aus Äthylalkohol scheint das Brucinsalz, nach Corbellinis Angaben, lösungsmittelfrei zu krystallisieren.

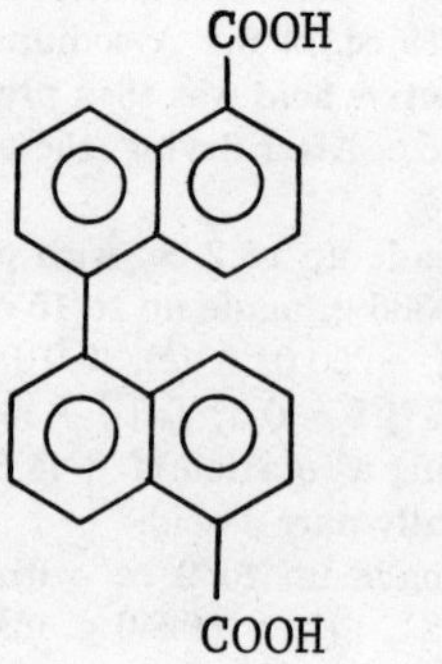

$C_{22}H_{14}O_4$ Ref. 1367

Resolution of 1 : 1′-*Dinaphthyl*-5 : 5′-*dicarboxylic Acid*.—(a) *Acid from* 1-*naphthoic acid*. Brucine (1·77 g., 2 mols.) was added to a suspension of the acid (0·65 g.) in boiling ethanol (65 c.c.). The mixture was refluxed gently for ½ hr., the clear solution first obtained beginning to deposit crystals. After cooling, the insoluble portion (1·7 g.) was filtered off and the filtrate poured into dilute hydrochloric acid. The recovered 1 : 1′-dinaphthyl-5 : 5′-dicarboxylic acid, m. p. 355°, had $[\alpha]_D$ −20·4° (*c*, 1·08 in 0·1N-NaOH). The crop of the brucine salt was purified by extraction with boiling ethanol (65 c.c.) and then formed a pale yellow powder, m. p. 210° (decomp.), $[\alpha]_D$ −10·4° (*c*, 2·5 in $CHCl_3$). This was decomposed by trituration with dilute hydrochloric acid to give (+)-1 : 1′-dinaphthyl-5 : 5′-dicarboxylic acid, m. p. 355°, $[\alpha]_D$ +66° (*c*, 1 in 0·1N-NaOH).

Note: The quinine, quinidine, cinchonine, cinchonidine, and morphine salts of this acid were non-crystallising and in solution had a strong green fluorescence.

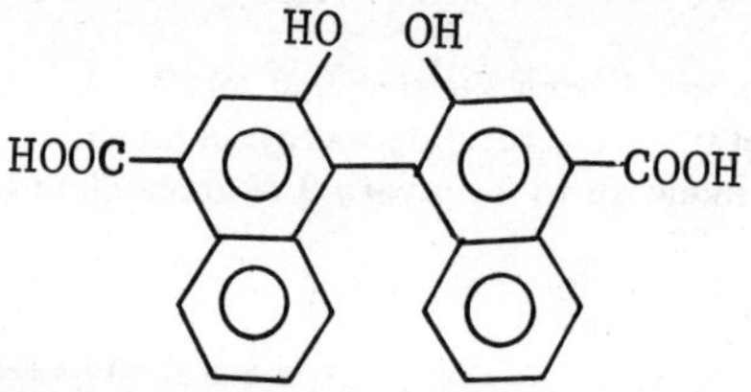

$C_{22}H_{14}O_6$ Ref. 1368

b) Spaltung des Racemates mit Hilfe von Brucin. 8 g *d,l*-Dinaphtyl-dioxy-dicarbonsäure werden in 350 cm³ siedendem absolutem Äthylakohol gelöst. Zu dieser Lösung werden 20 g Brucin zugegeben. Man erhält als Niederschlag 21 g Salz vom Smp. 236,5—237° unkorr. 20 g dieses Salzes werden in 200 cm³ heissem Pyridin gelöst. Nach mehrwöchigem Stehen bei 0° C krystallisieren etwa 14 g Salz aus; sie werden ein zweites Mal aus 150 cm³ Pyridin umkrystallisiert, wobei etwa 8 g Salz erhalten werden, welche ihrerseits ein drittes Mal aus 70 cm³ Pyridin umkrystallisiert werden. Man erhält so etwa 7 g Salz vom Drehungsvermögen $[\alpha]_D^{10} = -85{,}4°$ in 0,43-proz. Lösung in Pyridin; in Übereinstimmung mit den Angaben von *Stanley* und *Adams* l. c.

Zur Freisetzung der Dinaphtyl-dioxy-dicarbonsäure wird das Brucinsalz mit der berechneten Menge NaOH versetzt und das sich ausscheidende Brucin mit Chloroform extrahiert, worauf die linksdrehende Dinaphtyl-dioxy-dicarbonsäure durch Zufügung von konz. HCl ausgeschieden werden kann. Das Drehungsvermögen der so gewonnenen Säure in absolutem Äthylalkohol war $[\alpha]_D^{20} = -134{,}5°$, während die weiter unten zu beschreibende Trennung mit Hilfe von *d*(−)-Leucin eine Säure mit dem Drehungsvermögen $[\alpha]_D^{20} = -166°$ liefert.

Eine Literaturangabe (l. c.), wonach der Reinheitsgrad der aktiven Säure durch Umkrystallisieren aus Eisessig verbessert werden kann, konnte von uns nicht bestätigt werden; im Gegenteil: es wurde beim Umkrystallisieren aus Eisessig je nach der Dauer der Operation eine fast vollständige Racemisierung beobachtet.

c) Spaltung des Racemates mit Hilfe von *l*(+)Leucin-methylester und *d,l*-Leucin-methylester. Sie erfolgt über das neutrale Salz (1 Mol Dinaphtyl-dioxy-dicarbonsäure mit 2 Mol Leucin-methylester); eine Trennung mit Hilfe der sauren Salze gelingt nicht.

Zunächst wird der positiv drehende Antipode der Dinaphtyl-dioxy-dicarbonsäure mit Hilfe von $l(+)$-Leucin-methylester aus dem Racemat herausgenommen. Zu diesem Zwecke werden 37,4 g der racemischen Säure in ca. 450 cm³ reinem Methylalkohol suspendiert und durch Kochen am Rückfluss teilweise gelöst. Zur siedenden Lösung werden 29 g $l(+)$-Leucin-methylester, [$l(+)$L] zugegeben, wobei eine klare, dunkelgelb gefärbte Lösung entsteht. Beim Abkühlen auf Zimmertemperatur und anschliessendem Stehen bei 20° C krystallisiert 85% der Theorie an reinem [$l(+)$L; $(+)$D] vom Smp. 217,5° aus. Durch Abdunsten des Methylalkohols und Stehenlassen bei 0° C können weitere Mengen dieses Salzes, insgesamt etwa 98—99% der Theorie gewonnen werden. Durch Auswaschen mit kaltem Methylalkohol oder durch nochmaliges Umkrystallisieren kann das Salz von der anhaftenden Mutterlauge befreit werden. Es kann zur Gewinnung von reiner $(+)$Dinaphtyl-dioxy-dicarbonsäure verwendet werden. Zu letzterem Zweck wird das Salz [$l(+)$L; $(+)$D] mit der berechneten Menge verd. NaOH versetzt und der freigesetzte $l(+)$-Leucinester mit Äther aufgenommen; aus der wässerigen Lösung wird dann die optisch reine $(+)$-Dinaphtyl-dioxy-dicarbonsäure durch Zusatz von konz. HCl ausgefällt.

Drehungsvermögen in Äthylalkohol: $[\alpha]_D^{23°} = +166,5°$ in 0,574-proz. Lösung;

Drehungsvermögen in Pyridin: $[\alpha]_D^{15°} = +178,8°$ in 0,97-proz. Lösung.

Der von *Stanley* und *Adams* für die Pyridinlösung angegebene Wert ist $[\alpha]_D^{20} = 171°$ in 0,781-proz. Lösung.

Die für den Nachweis des d-Leucins benötigte $(-)$Dinaphtyl-dioxy-dicarbonsäure befindet sich als leichtlösliches Salz [$l(+)$L; $(-)$D] in den Mutterlaugen, aus denen sich die Krystalle [$l(-)$L; $(+)$D] ausgeschieden hatten. Wegen der Schwerlöslichkeit der letzteren Verbindung muss sich nach Erreichung des Löslichkeitsgleichgewichts optisch fast reine, negativ drehende Säure in der Lösung befinden. — Wenn man bei der Krystallisation des schwerlöslichen Diastereomeren den Methylalkohol soweit entfernt, dass die verbleibende Lösung zu 50% aus Estersalz besteht, so erhält man tatsächlich durch etwa 4-wöchiges Stehen bei 0° C eine Mutterlauge, aus welcher [$(-)$D] unmittelbar mit einem optischen Reinheitsgrade von 98—99% gewonnen werden kann.

Um absolut reine [$(-)$D] zu erhalten, wird die das Salz [$l(+)$L; $(-)$D] enthaltende Mutterlauge durch Eindampfen vom grössten Teil des Methylalkohols befreit, die kalte Lösung sodann mit einem gleich grossen Volumen Wasser verdünnt, worauf die optisch nicht ganz reine [$(-)$D] mit konz. HCl ausgefällt, mit Wasser gewaschen und bei 120° getrocknet wird. 37,4 g (1/10 Mol) der nahezu reinen [$(-)$D] werden darauf in etwa 400 cm³ reinem CH_3OH suspendiert und erwärmt. Zur siedenden Lösung werden 58 g (0,4 Mol) von racemischem Leucin-methylester gegeben. (Besser wäre der Zusatz von 0,2 Mol $d(-)$-Leucinester, was aber auf Grund des hohen Preises dieser Substanz nicht durchführbar war.) Beim Abkühlen der Lösung krystallisiert das Salz [$d(-)$L; $(-)$D] vom Smp. 217,5°, welches in ausgezeichneter Ausbeute erhalten wird. Die Gewinnung der freien Säure aus dem Salz ist bereits bei der Darstellung der positiv drehenden Säure beschrieben worden. Das Drehungsvermögen wurde in Alkohol gemessen; es war $[\alpha]_D^{20} = -166,0°$ in 0,57-proz. Lösung.

Sowohl die optisch aktiven Antipoden als auch das Racemat der Dinaphtyl-dioxy-dicarbonsäure sind amorph. Beim Erhitzen tritt zwischen 328—31° korr. allmähliches Zersetzen ein.

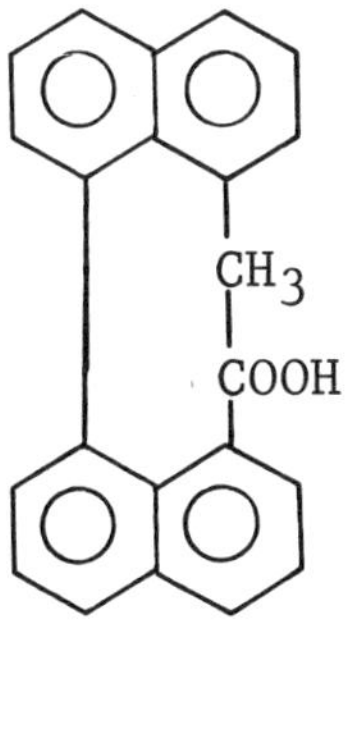

$C_{22}H_{16}O_2$ Ref. 1369

Resolution of (±)-*8′-Methyl-1,1′-binaphthyl-8-carboxylic Acid.*—The resolution was effected by crystallising the brucine salt from ethanol; various conditions were tried and the optimum procedure was as follows. The (±)-acid (2·0 g.) was dissolved in ethanol (300 c.c.) and to it was added a solution of brucine (3·0 g., 1·2 mol.) in ethanol (300 c.c.). The solution was evaporated down to 150 c.c. and allowed to cool slowly to room temperature; 1·8 g. of brucine (−)-acid salt (A) crystallised, m. p. 161—163°, $[\alpha]^{21.5}$ −239·9° (in $CHCl_3$). Concentration of the mother-liquor from (A) to half-volume gave a further 0·5 g. of brucine salt (B), m. p. 161—162·5°, $[\alpha]^{21.5}$ −211·8°; (A) and (B) together represent a 50% yield of brucine salt, based on the quantity of (±)-acid used. The salt (A) was dissolved in chloroform and twice extracted with N-sodium hydroxide; the alkaline extract was washed twice with chloroform and once with ether, and acidified with hydrochloric acid, to give 0·55 g. of the (−)-*acid*, m. p. 247·5—248°, $[\alpha]^{21.5}$ −253·4° (in $CHCl_3$). Cool evaporation of the mother-liquor from (B) gave a non-crystalline residue (C) which failed to crystallise from any of a large variety of solvents. It was therefore dissolved in chloroform and the (+)-*acid* extracted from it as described for salt (A). It had m. p. 247·5—248°, $[\alpha]^{21.5}$ +250·2° ($CHCl_3$).

The (−)-acid racemised when heated under reflux in sodium hydroxide solution; the (±)-acid recovered was identical with the (±)-acid used for the resolution (m. p., mixed m. p., infrared spectrum). Racemisation was not followed polarimetrically in sodium hydroxide solution, as the rotation of the sodium salt in water is inconveniently small in comparison with that of the acid in *NN*-dimethylformamide.

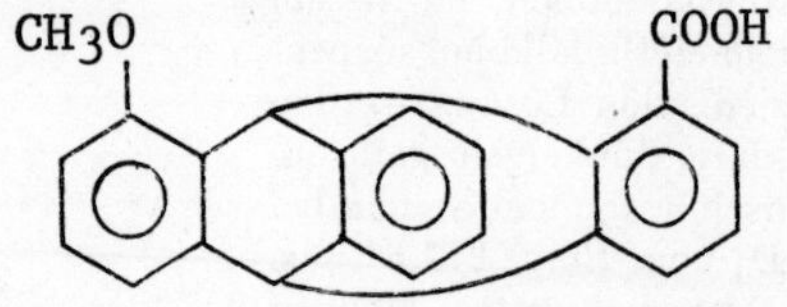

$C_{22}H_{16}O_3$ Ref. 1370

Optical Resolution of 5-Methoxy-7-carboxytriptycene (VIIb).
To a hot solution of VIIb (170 mg, 0.518 mmol) in acetone (5 ml) was added brucine dihydrate (111 mg, 0.258 mmol). After refluxing for 15 min, crystals deposited (84 mg) were recrystallized from acetone (6 ml) to give brucine salt, 31 mg, $[\alpha]^{15}_{350}$ $-206°$ (*c* 0.34, chloroform). (+)-VIIb obtained from an acetic acid solution of the brucine salt on dilution with water was sublimed *in vacuo* to give pure (+)-VIIb, mp 310—313°C, $[\alpha]_{600}$ +21.1°, $[\alpha]_D$ +23.7°, $[\alpha]_{400}$ +55.3°.

Found: C, 80.00; H, 4.85%. Calcd for $C_{22}H_{16}O_3$: C, 80.47; H, 4.91%.

The residue obtained on concentrating the mother liquor of recrystallization of brucine salt was decomposed to yield (−)-VIIb with unknown optical purity (negative rotation in the visible wavelength region).

The experiments were repeated under the same and different conditions, but no optical resolution could be achieved except for the above described run. The cause of the poor reproducibility is not clear.

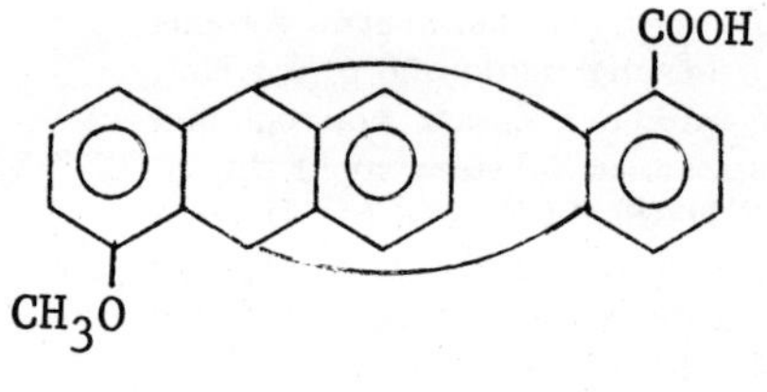

$C_{22}H_{16}O_3$ Ref. 1371

Optical Resolution of 2-Methoxy-7-carboxytriptycene (VIIa).
To a hot solution of VIIa (4.70 g, 14.3 mmol) in 99% ethanol (270 ml) was added brucine dihydrate (3.08 g, 7.80 mmol) in one portion. After refluxing for 15 min, the mixture was allowed to stand overnight to deposit brucine salt (5.1 g). The salt was recrystallized twice from 99% ethanol to yield pure material, mp 196.0—198.0°C, IR: 3510 (ν_{N-H}), 1655 ($\nu_{C=O}$, -COO⁻) cm^{-1}, $[\alpha]^{20}_{350}$ $-268°$ (*c* 0.117, dioxane).

The pure salt (1.125 g) was dissolved in acetic acid (10 ml) on warming up to 90—95°C for 5 min. White precipitate (478 mg) obtained on addition of water (30 ml) to the acetic acid solution was recrystallized from acetic acid to give pure (+)-VIIa mp 267°C (decomp.), IR: 2830 (ν_{C-H}, $-OCH_3$), 1673 ($\nu_{C=O}$, -COOH) cm^{-1}, $[\alpha]^{20}_D$ +15.4°, $[\alpha]^{20}_{405}$ $-74.4°$ (*c* 0.187, dioxane).

Found: C, 80.26; H, 4.76%. Calcd for $C_{22}H_{16}O_3$: C, 80.47; H, 4.91%.

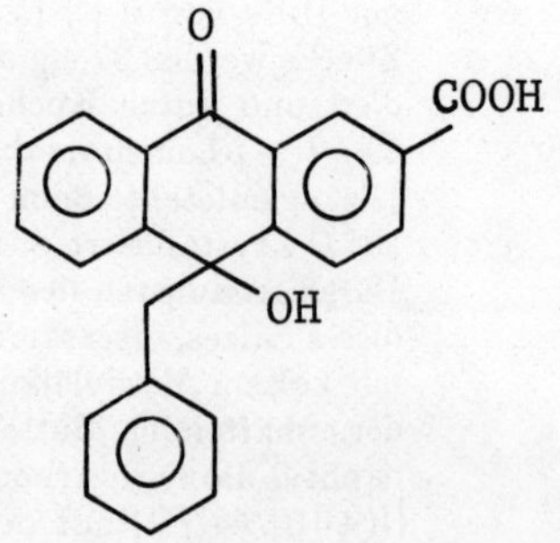

$C_{22}H_{16}O_4$ Ref. 1372

Dédoublement optique des acides benzyl-oxanthrone-β-carboniques.

Le dédoublement s'effectue par cristallisation fractionnée des sels de brucine, en solution alcoolique. On mélange les solutions alcooliques bouillantes de quantités équimoléculaires de brucine (anhydre) et d'un des acides à dédoubler. Il faut avoir soin de prendre un léger excès de brucine (1 à 2%), afin d'éviter tout risque d'avoir un excès d'acide. En effet, un léger excès de brucine n'a aucun inconvénient, tandis qu'un excès d'acide, même infime, gêne beaucoup la cristallisation. Si l'on a employé la quantité voulue d'alcool (12 à 15 cm³ d'alcool par gr. d'acide pour l'isomère A, et 7 à 8 seulement pour l'isomère B) le sel de brucine cristallise par refroidissement. On le recristallise dans l'alcool bouillant, jusqu'à ce que son pouvoir rotatoire spécifique reste constant.

Pour nos deux acides isomères, c'est le sel de brucine de l'antipode lévogyre qui est le moins soluble dans l'alcool, et que l'on isole ainsi par cristallisation fractionnée. Ces sels cristallisent en courtes aiguilles blanches, souvent groupées en rosettes.

Le sel de brucine de l'isomère A lévogyre fond à 176° (très peu net).
Pouvoir rotatoire en solution chloroformique:

$$C = 4{,}652; \quad l = 2; \quad t = 21°; \quad \alpha = -3°{,}98; \quad [\alpha]^{21}_D = -42°{,}8$$

Le sel de brucine de l'isomère B lévogyre fond à 219°.
Pouvoir rotatoire en solution chloroformique:

$$C = 5{,}023; \quad l = 2; \quad t = 17°; \quad \alpha = -7°{,}51; \quad [\alpha]^{17}_D = -74°{,}8$$

Acide actif à partir du sel de brucine. Le sel de brucine est mis en suspension dans 10 fois son poids d'alcool; on ajoute de l'acide chlorhydrique concentré jusqu'à forte réaction acide. En chauffant la liqueur alcoolique, tout doit se dissoudre; sinon, il faut ajouter un peu d'alcool. A la solution refroidie, on ajoute de l'eau jusqu'à trouble laiteux persistant, chauffe pour redissoudre, et laisse cristalliser par refroidissement lent. Les cristaux sont filtrés et lavés soigneusement à l'eau acidulée. Pour éliminer plus sûrement les dernières traces de brucine, on redissout les cristaux dans l'alcool et les reprécipite par l'eau. Les acides benzyl-oxanthrone-β-carboniques actifs cristallisent en cristaux plus gros et mieux formés que les acides inactifs.

Pouvoir rotatoire de l'isomère A lévogyre, en solution dans l'alcool absolu:

$$C = 4{,}013; \quad l = 2; \quad t = 20°; \quad \alpha = -5°{,}74; \quad [\alpha]^{20}_D = -71°{,}5$$

Pouvoir rotatoire de l'isomère B lévogyre, en solution dans l'alcool absolu:

$$C = 3{,}524; \quad l = 2; \quad t = 20°; \quad \alpha = -5°{,}71; \quad [\alpha]^{20}_D = -81°{,}0$$

Les sels de brucine des antipodes dextrogyres se trouvent dans les liqueurs-mères de la cristallisation des sels lévogyres. On arrive à les cristalliser par concentration des liqueurs-mères, mais les cristaux sont mal formés et très impurs. Leur purification optique ne semblant pas réalisable, vu leur trop grande solubilité, nous en avons retiré les acides libres dont nous avons ainsi obtenu les antipodes dextrogyres optiquement impurs. Leur purification aurait probablement pu être réalisée par l'intermédiaire de leurs sels de cinchonine; mais nous ne disposions pas d'une quantité suffisante de substance.

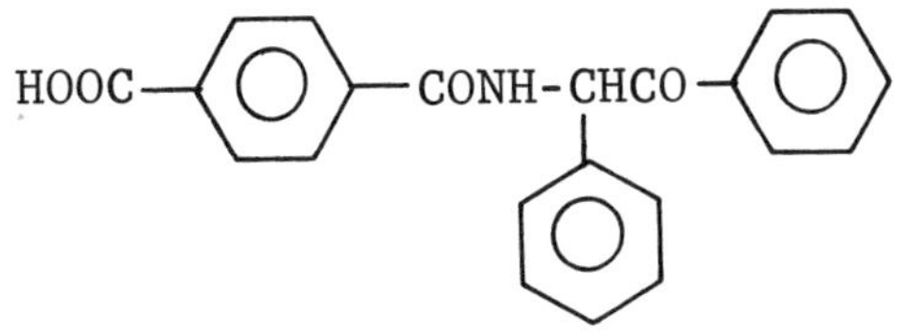

$C_{22}H_{17}NO_4$ Ref. 1373

Resolution of r-*Desylphthalamic Acid.*—270 C.c. of water were added to a solution of a mixture of 27 g. of the *r*-acid (Neumann, *Ber.*, 1890, **23**, 995) and 22·7 g. of morphine in 270 c.c. of ethyl alcohol. After 3 hours at the ordinary temperature, crystallisation started on stirring. The glassy prisms (23·5 g.), which separated over-night, were crystallised twice from 50% aqueous alcohol. Yield: 12·2 g. After decomposition of the salt by dilute sulphuric acid, the acid was extracted with ether. Yield: 6·1 g. It was almost pure, giving in acetone ($l = 2$, $c = 2·4965$), $\alpha_D^{18°}$ −7·85°, $[\alpha]_D^{18°}$ −157·2°. It was finally crystallised from ether.

l-*Desylphthalamic Acid*, $CO_2H·C_6H_4·CO·NH·CHPh·COPh$, is sparingly soluble in water, benzene, and light petroleum. It separates from ether in feathery needles, m. p. 155—157° (decomp.). In acetone: $l = 2$, $c = 2·545$, $\alpha_D^{18°}$ −8·10°, $[\alpha]_D^{18°}$ −159·1°.

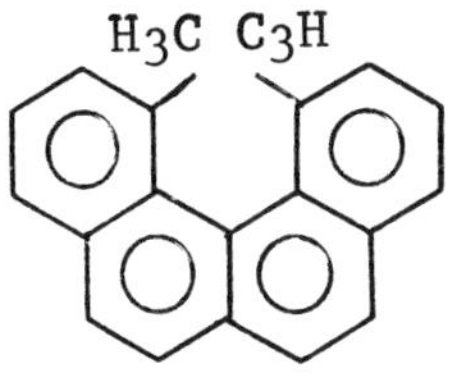

$C_{22}H_{18}O_2$ Ref. 1374

Resolution of 1,12-Dimethylbenzo(c)phenanthrene-5-acetic Acid (XIX).[34]—To 2.00 g. of XIX dissolved in hot acetone was added 1.872 g., one equivalent, of *l*-cinchonidine dissolved in hot acetone. Removal of the solvent and trituration of the residue with Skellysolve F (petroleum ether, b.p. 35–40°) afforded a cream-colored solid, m.p. 105–130°, $[\alpha]^{24}D$ −32.5° (*c* 2 in chloroform). Approximately 600 ml. of warm ether failed to dissolve all the solid. The remaining cinchonidine salt (1 g.) melted at 140–142°, and had $[\alpha]^{24}D$ −153° (*c* 2 in chloroform). Recrystallization of this material from a large volume of ether at room temperature[35] gave 0.6 g., m.p. 139.8–141.0°, $[\alpha]^{23}D$ −170° (*c* 2 in chloroform). The analytical sample, recrystallized three times from ether, formed very fine needles in rosettes, m.p. 143.7–145.1° with softening at 140°. The analysis indicated a monohydrate.

Anal. Calcd. for $C_{41}H_{40}O_3N_2·H_2O$: C, 78.6; H, 6.8; N, 4.5. Found: C, 78.5, 78.6; H, 6.9, 7.1; N, 4.2, 4.4.

The original filtrate was concentrated at room temperature and 1.5 g. of white solid which precipitated was separated. The filtrate was concentrated to a viscous oil which formed a cream-colored solid, m.p. 120–124°, $[\alpha]^{23}D$ +43.0° (*c* 2.45 in chloroform), on trituration with Skellysolve F.

Each of the cinchonidine salts, $[\alpha]D$ −170° and +43.0°, was decomposed by the addition of aqueous alcoholic hydrochloric acid. The acid from the (−)-cinchonidine salt gave a rotation of −7.97°, $[\alpha]^{23}D$ −332° (*c* 1.20 in acetone). Repeated recrystallizations from ether yielded fine crystals, m.p. 207.3–208.4° with slight darkening, $[\alpha]^{25}D$ −362.7 ± 2.5° (*c* 0.35 in acetone). The acid from the (+)-cinchonidine salt gave a rotation of +6.05°, $[\alpha]^{23}D$ +187° (*c* 1.62 in acetone). From benzene–acetone some racemic acid crystallized, m.p. 238.5–240.0°. Repeated recrystallizations from ether of the acid obtained from the filtrate yielded fine crystals, m.p. 207.7–208.7° with slight darkening, $[\alpha]^{25}D$ +347.6 ± 3.6° (*c* 0.29 in acetone). The racemic acid has an m.p. of 243.0–244.4° dec.

(33) I. Heilbron, E. R. H. Jones, M. Julia and B. Weedon, *J. Chem. Soc.*, 1823 (1949).

(34) All readings were taken using a Schmidt and Haensch polarimeter in a 2-dcm. tube.

(35) The solutions in these first experiments were not heated as the optical stability of the compound was not known. In later experiments recrystallization from acetone–ether was effective.

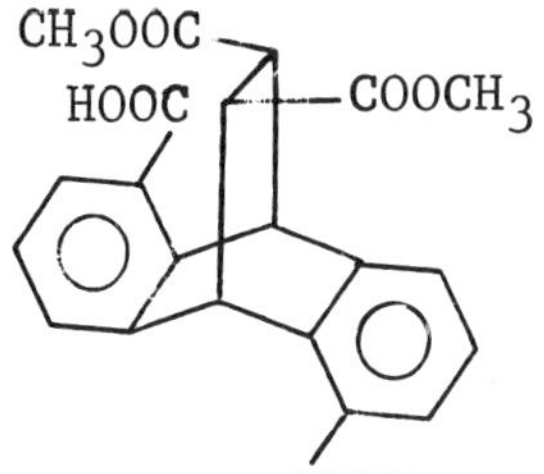

Compound 1

$C_{22}H_{18}O_8$ Ref. 1375

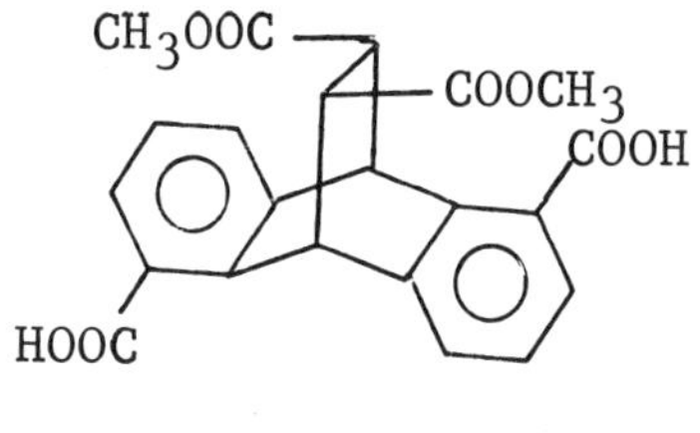

Compound 2

$C_{22}H_{18}O_8$ Ref. 1376

Resolution and isolation of **1** *and* **2**. The mixture of the acids (**1** and **2**, 17·6 g), brucine dihydrate (32·5 g) and MeOH (500 ml) were heated under reflux for 30 min and allowed to stand at room temp. overnight. Crystals were filtered and recrystallized from MeOH three times to give one diastereomer in prisms (10·6 g), $[\alpha]_D$ −33·3° (MeOH, *c* 0·195).

The mother liquor from the first recrystallization was concentrated to 200 ml and the crystals were collected by filtration and recrystallized three times from MeOH to give the other diastereomer as needles (2·5 g), $[\alpha]_D$ +50·2° (MeOH, *c* 0·233).

The (−)-salt (10·6 g) was suspended in EtOAc and dil. HCl was added. The mixture was shaken for 30 min. The organic layer was separated and the aqueous layer extracted with EtOAc. The combined EtOAc layer was washed with water and dried (Na_2SO_4). Solvent was distilled under reduced pressure and the residue recrystallized from MeOH to give prisms (**1**, 3·08 g), m.p. >300°, $[\alpha]_D$ −70·3° (MeOH, *c* 0·266); IR ν_{max}^{Nujol} cm^{-1}: 1730, 1695. (Found: C, 64·21; H, 4·62. $C_{22}H_{18}O_4$ requires: C, 64·39; H, 4·42%).

The (+)-salt (2·5 g) was treated in a similar manner and the product recrystallized from EtOAc to give a powder (**2**, 679 mg), m.p. >300°, $[\alpha]_D$ +256·1° (MeOH, *c* 0·123); IR ν_{max}^{Nujol} cm^{-1}: 1740, 1692. (Found: C, 64·58; H, 4·47. $C_{22}H_{18}O_4$ requires: C, 64·39; H, 4·42%).

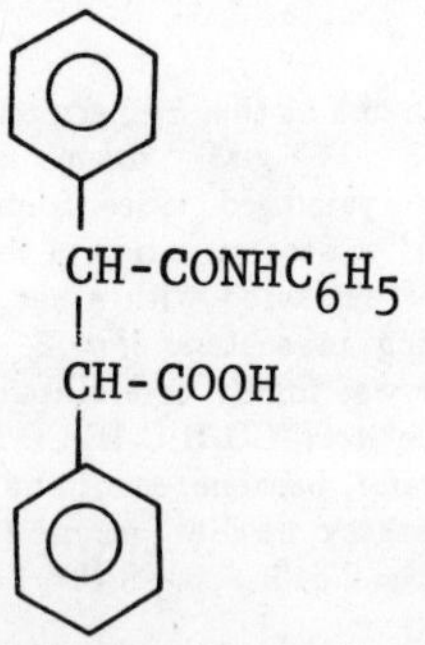

$C_{22}H_{19}NO_3$ Ref. 1377

Resolution of r-*Diphenylsuccinalic Acid into its Optical Antipodes.*—A solution of *r*-diphenylsuccinalic acid (40 gms.) and quinine (40 gms.) in boiling rectified spirit (1000 c.c.) was allowed to cool to the atmospheric temperature, and the needles (46·7 gms.) that slowly separated were crystallised four times from the same solvent. The non-homogeneous quinine *l*-diphenylsuccinalate (15·9 gms.) obtained was decomposed with dilute sulphuric acid and ether, and the l-*diphenylsuccinalic acid* (8·1 gms.; $[\alpha]_D - 326{\cdot}6°$ in acetone) crystallised from rectified spirit until the specific rotation remained constant. It melted and evolved gas at 193—194° after shrinkage at 187°, then re-solidified, and again melted at 224—226°; the observed values depend somewhat on the mode of heating (Found: C = 76·7; H = 5·6; N = 4·3. $C_{22}H_{19}O_3N$ requires C = 76·5; H = 5·6; N = 4·1 per cent.). In acetone: $l = 2$, $c = 1{\cdot}226$, $\alpha_D^{19°} - 8{\cdot}29°$, whence $[\alpha]_D^{19°} - 338{\cdot}2°$; in ethyl alcohol: $l = 2$, $c = 1{\cdot}2384$, $\alpha_D^{17°} - 8{\cdot}68°$, whence $[\alpha]_D^{17°} - 350{\cdot}3°$.

d-Diphenylsuccinalic acid ($[\alpha]_D + 143{\cdot}6°$ in acetone, 17·2 gms.; from the crude, dextrorotatory mixture of acids obtained from the first filtrates of the quinine salt) and cinchonine (14·9 gms.) were dissolved in boiling ethyl alcohol (250 c.c.), the cool solution was filtered from a small amount of diphenylsuccinanil, the formation of which is somewhat liable to complicate the course of the resolution, and the filtrate allowed to evaporate spontaneously to about 180 c.c. The non-homogeneous cinchonine *d*-diphenylsuccinalate (19·2 gms.) that separated was decomposed in the usual manner, and the d-*diphenylsuccinalic acid* ($[\alpha]_D + 257{\cdot}7°$ in acetone) repeatedly crystallised from rectified spirit. The pure acid resembled exactly its optical antipode in appearance, solubility, and melting point. It had $[\alpha]_D^{17°} + 337{\cdot}8°$ in acetone solution ($l = 2$, $c = 1{\cdot}236$, $\alpha_D^{17°} + 8{\cdot}35°$) (Found: C = 76·8; H = 5·7; N = 4·3 per cent.).

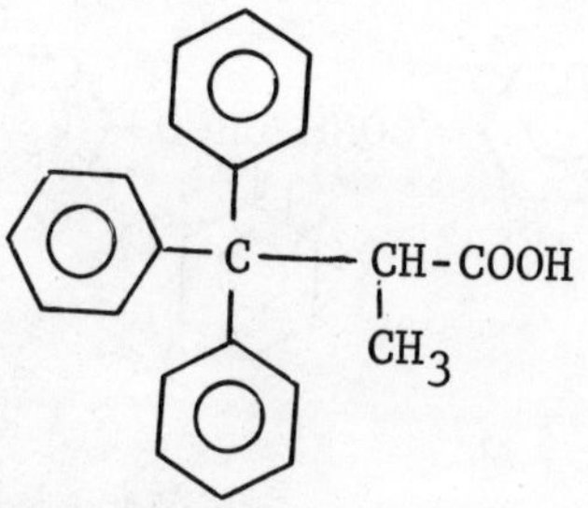

$C_{22}H_{20}O_2$ Ref. 1378

Resolution of 2-Methyl-3,3,3-triphenylpropionic Acid (IX). A mixture of 100 g of racemic IX and 100 g of quinine was dissolved in 306 ml of absolute ethanol. The ethanol was evaporated under reduced pressure and the oily residue was dissolved in 4280 ml of dry ether. After 48 hr at −18°, 46 g of quinine salt was obtained. After five crystallizations of this salt from absolute ethanol, a total of 19 g of optically pure salt was obtained. The salt was converted to the acid, and the acid was recrystallized from benzene to give white solid, 8 g: mp 172–173°; $[\alpha]^{25}{}_{546}$ +8.1° (*c* 3.69, $CHCl_3$), $[\alpha]^{25}{}_{436}$ +18.0° (*c* 3.69, $CHCl_3$), mp 173–174°. *Anal.* Calcd for $C_{22}H_{20}O_2$: C, 83.51; H, 6.37. Found: C, 83.68; H, 6.38.

The filtrate of the quinine salt was concentrated to 1200 ml and was allowed to stand at −25° for 48 hr. A further 50 g of salt was obtained whose acid showed no optical activity. The mother liquor of the second crop was concentrated, and 40 g of (−)-IX was isolated from the oily quinine salt, $[\alpha]^{25}{}_{546}$ −2.43° (*c* 3.88, $CHCl_3$), $[\alpha]^{25}{}_{436}$ −5.86° (*c* 3.9, $CHCl_3$). This (−)-acid was dissolved in 160 ml of benzene. After addition of 60 ml of pentane to the benzene solution, 30.3 g of racemic acid crystallized. By adding 160 ml of pentane to the filtrate, another 1.3 g of racemic acid was obtained. The mother liquor was evaporated, and 13 g of (−)-IX, $[\alpha]^{25}{}_{546}$ −7.1° (*c* 3.7, $CHCl_3$), was recovered. This 90% optically pure acid was recrystallized from benzene–pentane mixture. A total of 10.5 g of pure (−)-IX, $[\alpha]^{25}{}_{546}$ −8.2° (*c* 3.7, $CHCl_3$) was obtained, mp 172–173°. *Anal.* Calcd for $C_{22}H_{20}O_2$: C, 83.51; H, 6.37. Found: C, 83.34; H, 6.30.

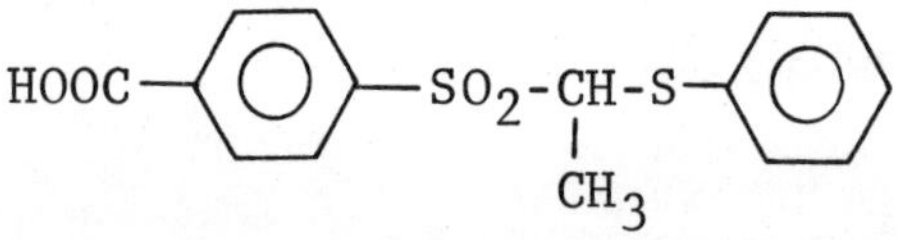

$C_{22}H_{20}O_6S_3$ Ref. 1379

Resolution of α-p-*Carboxyphenylsulphonyl*-α-p-*tolylsulphonyl*-α-*phenylthioethane.*—The acid (27 g.) and brucine (25 g.) were mixed in alcoholic solution and the sparingly soluble salt which separated (39 g.) was filtered off. It had m. p. 165—170°, $[\alpha]_{5461} - 2{\cdot}75°$ in chloroform ($c = 6{\cdot}67$). This salt was repeatedly extracted with hot alcohol insufficient to dissolve it and after six such extractions the residue (6 g.) finally crystallised in prisms, m. p. 171—172° (Found: C, 60·7; H, 5·7; loss at 80° in a vacuum, 2·0. $C_{22}H_{20}O_6S_3,C_{23}H_{26}O_4N_2,H_2O$ requires C, 60·7; H, 5·4; H_2O, 2·0%). $[\alpha]_{5461} + 14{\cdot}1°$. Further extraction did not alter these values. The acid was obtained from this final fraction by solution in acetic acid, followed by the addition of water. It had a variable m. p. (decomp.) 192—205° according to the rate of heating [Found: C, 55·9, 55·7; H, 4·7, 4·8 (dried at 60° in a vacuum). $C_{22}H_{20}O_6S_3$ requires C, 55·5; H, 4·2%]. $[\alpha]_{5461} - 16{\cdot}1°$ in acetone ($c = 3{\cdot}5$). The acid obtained from the salt from the original mother-liquor gave $[\alpha]_{5461} + 15{\cdot}0°$ in acetone ($c = 4{\cdot}8$). The *d*-acid can also be obtained with the aid of the *l*-menthylamine salt, which crystallises finally from alcohol in small needles, m. p. 220°. The acid from this gave $[\alpha]_{5461} + 15{\cdot}5°$ in acetone ($c = 0{\cdot}67$). The *l*-acid, dissolved in *N*-sodium hydroxide (1·9 equivs.), gave $[\alpha]_{5461} + 12{\cdot}2°$ (calc. on acid, $c = 1{\cdot}7$). No racemisation took place during 18 hours and the recovered acid showed $[\alpha]_{5461} - 15{\cdot}4°$ in acetone.

The *l*- and the *d*-ethyl ester, prepared in the usual way, crystallised from alcohol in needles, m. p. 148°, $[\alpha]_{5461} - 3{\cdot}2°$ ($c = 1{\cdot}55$) and $+ 4{\cdot}24°$ ($c = 4{\cdot}8$) respectively in chloroform. When equal weights in hot alcohol were mixed, the *dl*-ester, m. p. 173—174°, crystallised at once. The *d*-ester, dissolved in chloroform with the addition of sodium ethoxide, was recovered unchanged after an hour. The ester was hydrolysed by aqueous-alcoholic sodium hydroxide (1 equiv.), and the pure active acid recovered unchanged. By using larger quantities of alkali, *p*-carboxyphenylsulphonyl-α-*p*-tolylsulphonylethane, m. p. 233° (ester, m. p. 121°), was obtained.

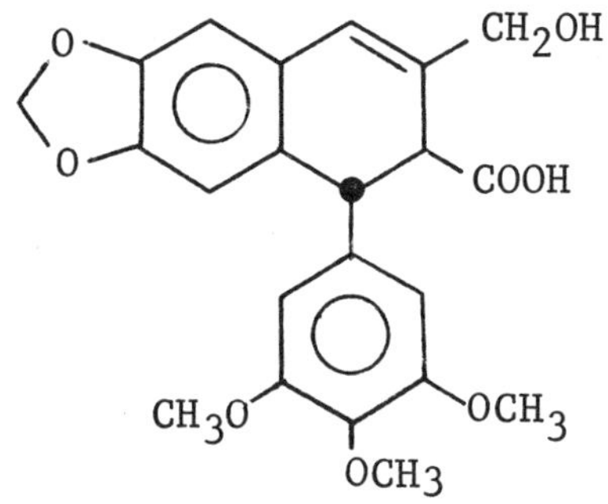

$C_{22}H_{22}O_8$ Ref. 1380

Quinine Salt of α-Apopodophyllic Acid. (a) From Synthetic DL-α-Apopodophyllic Acid (XX).—The clear solution obtained by combining 4.80 mg. of quinine (0.0148 mmole) in 1 ml. of acetone with 12.4 mg. of DL-α-apopodophyllic acid (0.03 mmole) in 1.5 ml. of acetone was allowed to stand in the cold overnight. The crystals were collected, washed with a small amount of acetone, and dried. This quinine salt (7.6 mg., 70%) of synthetic α-apopodophyllic acid showed m.p. 213–214° and $[\alpha]^{27}D$ −232° (*c* 0.42 in pyridine).

Anal. Calcd. for $C_{42}H_{46}N_2O_{10}$: C, 68.28; H, 6.28; N, 3.79. Found: C, 68.1; H, 6.2; N, 3.9.

The mixture melting point with the quinine salt (m.p. 214–215°) of α-apopodophyllic acid from natural products (see below) was 213–214°. The infrared absorption curves of the two salts, as mulls with mineral oil, were identical.

(b) From α-Apopodophyllic Acid Derived from Natural Products.—A hot solution of 0.20 g. of α-apopodophyllic acid (0.48 mmole) and 0.18 g. of quinine (0.58 mmole) in 20 ml. of acetone was cooled and allowed to stand at room temperature. The precipitated quinine salt (high yield) melted at 214–215° and showed $[\alpha]^{27}D$ −235° (*c* 0.51 in pyridine).

Anal. Calcd. for $C_{42}H_{46}N_2O_{10}$: C, 68.28; H, 6.28; N, 3.79. Found: C, 68.0; H, 6.3; N, 3.8.

Optically Active Synthetic α-Apopodophyllic Acid XXI from Its Quinine Salt.—The quinine salt (80 mg.) was shaken with 10 ml. of 2% sodium hydroxide solution and 5 ml. of ether. The alkaline aqueous layer, after further extraction with two portions of ether, was kept cold and acidified with a cold solution of 0.5 ml. of glacial acetic acid in 5 ml. of water. The mixture was stored in the cold for two days. The precipitate was collected, washed on the funnel with water, and air-dried. This crude synthetic α-apopodophyllic acid (38 mg., m.p. 161–165°) was dissolved in 5 ml. of boiling 95% alcohol, the solution was diluted slowly with 15 ml. of water, and was allowed to stand in the cold overnight. The precipitated crystals after collection and drying (29 mg., 65%) melted at 168–169° both before and after admixture with authentic α-apopodophyllic acid (m.p. 168–169°), and showed $[\alpha]^{26}D$ −158° (*c* 0.59 in chloroform). A specific rotation of $[\alpha]^{27}D$ −159.5° was observed for the authentic acid. The ultraviolet absorption curve of the synthetic α-apopodophyllic acid (XXI), which curve was the same as that of authentic α-apopodophyllic acid, had λ_{max} 295 mμ (log ε 3.89; flat) and 310 mμ (log ε 3.90) (3.78 × 10^{-5} *M* in 95% alcohol).

For infrared work a sample of synthetic acid XXI was recrystallized from benzene–chloroform. The melting point was unchanged. Degradation α-apopodophyllic acid (m.p. 169–170°) was likewise brought out of benzene–chloroform, and the infrared absorption curves of the two samples as mineral oil mulls were taken and compared.[60] All of the 20 or more features of the two curves were substantially the same, with the exception of two. The degradation material showed minor absorption maxima at 7.72 μ (T = 45%, with base line 51%) and at 13.2 μ (T = 60%, with base line 75%) that were not evident in the synthetic material. These two maxima were ascribed to trace impurities in the degradation acid.

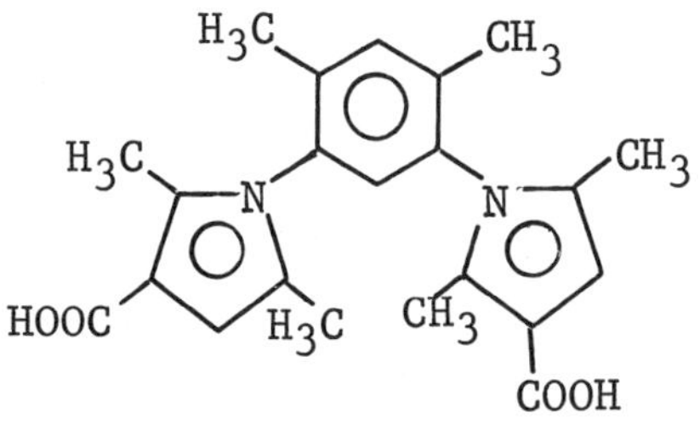

$C_{22}H_{24}N_2O_4$ Ref. 1381

Resolution of *trans*-4,6-Di-(2,5-dimethyl-3-carboxypyrryl)-1,3-dimethylbenzene.—A solution of 4.2 g. of brucine in 400 cc. of absolute methyl alcohol was heated to its boiling point and 4 g. of the powdered less soluble acid, m. p. 305°, was added slowly with stirring. After standing for several hours at 0°, the salt which separated was filtered. The first fraction thus obtained which amounted to 2.6 g. was recrystallized from absolute methyl alcohol to constant rotation, m. p. 186–190°.

Rotation. Less-soluble salt (*l*-brucine, *d*-acid): 0.1675 g. made up to 25 cc. with chloroform at 27° gave α_D +1.08; *l* = 2, $[\alpha]^{27}_D$ +80.63°.

Anal. Calcd. for $C_{46}H_{60}O_8N_4$: N, 7.23. Found: N, 7.23.

The filtrate from the less soluble salt was evaporated to about 150 cc. and again allowed to cool. The crystals separating were discarded. It was necessary to concentrate to dryness before the more soluble salt was obtained. It then separated from the methyl alcohol as a gum which, on long standing in a desiccator, solidified. It was found impossible to recrystallize this material, so the rotation was taken on the crude material, m. p. 152–159°.

Rotation. Crude more-soluble salt (*l*-brucine, *l*-acid). 0.1030 g. made up to 25 cc. with chloroform at 27° gave α_D −0.77; *l* = 2, $[\alpha]^{27}_D$ −93.44°.

***d* and *l* Acids.**—A suspension of 2 g. of either salt in 100 cc. of water was treated with 6 cc. of dilute hydrochloric acid and thoroughly stirred. The acid which precipitated was recrystallized from absolute ethyl alcohol to a constant m. p. of 275–276°.

Rotation. d-Acid. 0.09 g. made up to 25 cc. with pyridine at 27° gave α_D +1.24; *l* = 2, $[\alpha]^{27}_D$ +172.2.

Anal. Calcd. for $C_{22}H_{24}O_4N_2$: C, 69.47; H, 6.31. Found: C, 69.84; H, 6.68.

Rotation. l-Acid. 0.0792 g. made up to 25 cc. with pyridine at 27° gave α_D −1.05; *l* = 2, $[\alpha]^{27}_D$ −165.8.

Anal. Calcd. for $C_{22}H_{24}O_4N_2$: C, 69.47; H, 6.31. Found: C, 69.65; H, 6.50.

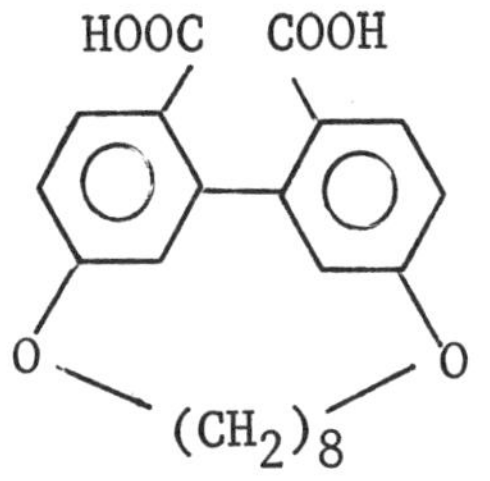

$C_{22}H_{24}O_6$ Ref. 1382

Resolution of 2,2′-Dicarboxy-5,5′-(octamethylenedioxy)-biphenyl.—While a beautifully crystalline monobrucine salt was obtained from absolute ethanol, careful fractionation gave only one compound which did not mutarotate in chloroform solution; white needles, softening at 175°, m. p. 187° (cor.) with evolution of gas.

Anal. Calcd. for $C_{22}H_{24}O_6{\cdot}C_{23}H_{26}O_4N_2$: C, 69.41; H, 6.42; N, 3.59. Found: C, 68.95; H, 6.86; N, 3.32.

Rotation. 0.0433 g. made up to 5 cc. with chloroform at 20° gave α_D +0.01°; *l*, 1; $[\alpha]^{20}_D$ +1.16°.

The acid obtained by decomposing this salt was inactive. Resolution was achieved via the dicinchonine salt.

A mixture of 0.733 g. of 2,2′-dicarboxy-5,5′-(octamethylenedioxy)-biphenyl and 1.120 g. of cinchonine was dissolved in 44 cc. of boiling absolute ethanol. The solution was allowed to stand at room temperature for twenty-four hours. Prisms separated which were freed from mother liquor by decantation; yield, 1.20 g. Occasionally seeding was necessary to induce crystallization. A second fraction, after concentration of the mother liquor to 20 cc., weighed 0.37 g. Further concentration to 5 cc. gave a third crop, 0.12 g. All three fractions had identical specific rotations. Recrystallization of the first crop did not change its rotation; m. p. 155–170° (cor.) depending on the rate of heating.

Anal. Calcd. for $C_{22}H_{24}O_6{\cdot}2C_{19}H_{22}ON_2$: N, 5.76. Found: N, 5.72.

Rotation. 0.0852 g. made up to 5 cc. with chloroform at 27° gave α_D −2.92°; *l*, 1; $[\alpha]^{27}_D$ −171°. In about sixty hours the salt had mutarotated to a constant value of −155°.

***l*-2,2′-Dicarboxy-5,5′-(octamethylenedioxy)-biphenyl.**—Decomposition of 1 g. of the cinchonine salt with 100 cc. of ice cold 20% hydrochloric acid by the procedure prescribed for *d*-2,2′-dicarboxy-5,5′-(decamethylenedioxy)-biphenyl gave the active acid; m. p. 344° (bloc Maquenne); yield, 0.396 g. (92%) (see Table I for rotation and racemization constants).

Anal. Calcd. for $C_{22}H_{24}O_6$: C, 68.75; H, 6.25. Found: C, 68.55; H, 6.29.

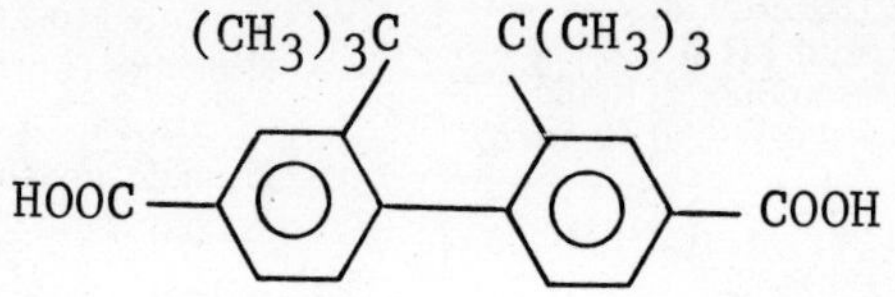

$C_{22}H_{26}O_4$ Ref. 1383

Resolution of 6,6′-*Di-t-butylbiphenyl*-3,3′-*dicarboxylic Acid.*—All rotations were measured in " AnalaR " acetone at room temperature ($c \sim 0{\cdot}5$) in 2 dm. tubes. The acid (6·5 g.) and brucine (14·4 g.) were dissolved in ethanol (450 c.c.), and the solution kept overnight at +4°. The first fraction of salt (6·1 g.) separated as rosettes of thin rectangular plates and had $[\alpha]_{5791}$ −41·8°, $[\alpha]_{5461}$ −46·8°. The second fraction (1·4 g.) which separated after concentration of the mother-liquor had $[\alpha]_{5791}$ −42·4°, $[\alpha]_{5461}$ −50·2°. Further concentration of the mother-liquor yielded a gel which contained a small amount of crystalline salt and since the gel was very soluble in ethanol it was possible to separate them. The crystalline salt was recrystallised four times from ethanol and was then optically pure.

Brucine (+)-6,6′-*di-t-butylbiphenyl*-3,3′-*dicarboxylate* crystallised from ethanol as a hydrate in rosettes of long, thin rectangular plates, m. p. 210° with previous softening, $[\alpha]_{5791}$ −37·8°, $[\alpha]_{5461}$ −43·9° (Found: C, 65·3; H, 7·4. $C_{22}H_{26}O_4,2C_{23}H_{26}N_2O_4,6H_2O$ requires C, 65·3; H, 7·3%). On being heated *in vacuo* at 70° for several hours the salt lost its water of crystallisation and the loss in weight corresponded to $6H_2O$. On exposure to air the anhydrous salt very quickly reverted to the hydrated form. Decomposition of the above salt yielded (+)-acid, and from the gel the (−)-acid was obtained.

(+)-6,6′-*Di-t-butylbiphenyl*-3,3′-*dicarboxylic acid* crystallised from ethanol in glistening plates, from glacial acetic acid in sheaves of rectangular rods, and from aqueous acetic acid in plates. From these solvents it always had solvent of crystallisation which was completely removed only by heating the products *in vacuo* at 130° for several hours. From aqueous acetic acid the (+)-acid crystallised with 1 mol. of water of crystallisation, and had m. p. 345° with loss of solvent at 200° (Kofler block), $[\alpha]_{5791}$ +18·1°, $[\alpha]_{5461}$ +23·6° (Found: C, 70·9; H, 7·2. $C_{22}H_{26}O_4,H_2O$ requires C, 70·9; H, 7·6%).

The *anhydrous acid*, m. p. 345°, had $[\alpha]_{5791}$ +18·6°, $[\alpha]_{5461}$ +24·1° (Found: C, 74·7; H, 7·6. $C_{22}H_{26}O_4$ requires C, 74·5; H, 7·4%).

The (−)-*acid* crystallised from glacial acetic acid with 1 mol. of acetic acid of crystallisation; it had m. p. 345° with loss of solvent at 240° (Kofler block), $[\alpha]_{5791}$ −17·7°, $[\alpha]_{5461}$ −22·8° (Found: C, 69·7; H, 7·2. $C_{22}H_{26}O_4,C_2H_4O_2$ requires C, 69·6; H, 7·3%). Heating *in vacuo* at 130° for several hours gave the unsolvated acid, $[\alpha]_{5791}$ −18·9°, $[\alpha]_{5461}$ −24·2°.

After being boiled in sodium hydroxide or in pyridine solution for 3 hr. the active acid was recovered unchanged.

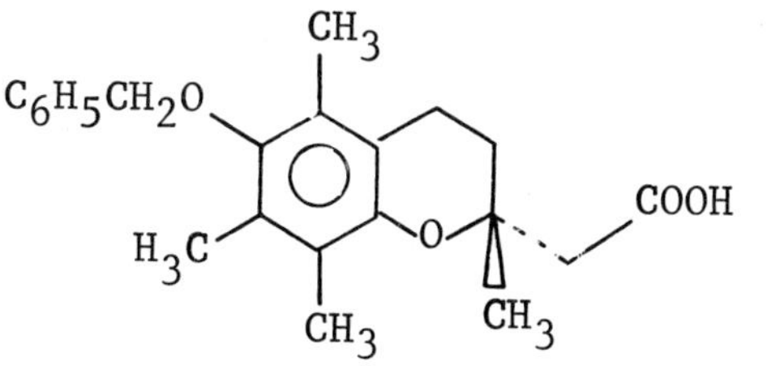

$C_{22}H_{26}O_4$ Ref. 1384

(*S*)-(−)-*2-(6-Benzyloxy-2,5,7,8-tetramethylchroman)acetic acid* (**6**). To a hot solution of 35.4 g (0.10 mol) of racemic acid **11** in 350 ml of ethyl acetate was added 32.4 g (0.10 mol) of (−)-quinine. The pale yellow solution was cooled to 25°, diluted with 250 ml of ether, seeded and stored for 16 h at 3°. The solid was collected by filtration and dried to give 22.58 g of white powder, m.p. 161-162°, $[\alpha]_D^{25} = -100.0°$ ($c = 1.07$, CH_3OH). Recrystallization of this material from ethyl acetate/ether gave two crops (combined for further use) of pure salt: a) 17.54 g, m.p. 162-163°, $[\alpha]_D^{25} = -96.5°$ ($c = 1.14$, CH_3OH); b) 3.21 g (total 20.75 g = 61.2% yield), m.p. 160-160.5°, $[\alpha]_D^{25} = -98.8°$ ($c = 1.27$, CH_3OH). To a suspension of the salt in 500 ml of ether and 120 ml of water was added 61 ml of 1.0N HCl over 15 min. The mixture was stirred another 15 min until all the salt had reacted and then worked up in the usual manner to give 10.54 g of white solid. Crystallization of this material from ether/hexane gave 9.14 g (54% yield from **11**) of pure (*S*)-acid **6**, m.p. 95-97°, $[\alpha]_D^{25} = -11.0°$ ($c = 1.08$, CH_3OH). The UV., IR., NMR., and mass spectra were identical with those of racemic acid **11**. A similarly prepared sample gave the following analysis:

$C_{22}H_{26}O_4$ (354.43) Calc. C 74.55 H 7.39% Found C 74.60 H 7.56%

(*R*)-(+)-*2-(6-Benzyloxy-2,5,7,8-tetramethylchroman)acetic acid* (**17**). To a solution of 3.54 g (10 mmol) of racemic acid **11** in 35 ml of hot benzene was added 1.71 g (10 mmol) of (*R*)-1-(1-napthyl)ethylamine. The solution was cooled to 25°, diluted with 25 ml of ether, and stored for 16 h at 3°. The solid was collected by filtration, dried and crystallized from 250 ml of ethyl acetate to give 1.71 g (66% yield) of white powder, m.p. 161.5-162°, $[\alpha]_D^{25} = +9.32°$ ($c = 1.08$, CH_3OH). A 525 mg sample of this salt was acidified as described in the preceding experiment. Crystallization of the crude product from ether/petroleum ether (30-60°) gave 302 mg (56% yield from **11**) of (*R*)-acid **17** as a white solid, m.p. 95-96°, $[\alpha]_D^{25} = +11.0°$ ($c = 1.14$, C_2H_5OH). The UV., IR., NMR., and mass spectra were identical with those of racemic acid **11**.

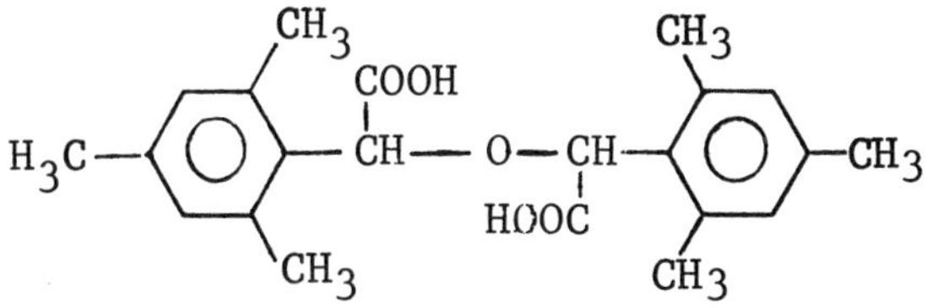

$C_{22}H_{26}O_5$ Ref. 1385

*Optical Resolution of Bis(α-carboxy-2,4,6-trimethylbenzyl) Ether, **5B**.* (1) The high-melting carboxylic acid **5B** (170 mg) was dissolved with cinchonidine (307 mg) in MeOH, after which the solution was allowed to stand overnight at room temperature. The residue, after removal of the MeOH, was crystallized from MeOH–AcOEt six times to give one optically active salt, **I** (110 mg) as prisms; $[\alpha]_D^{20}$ +1° (MeOH); mp 189—190 °C. Found: C, 73.41; H, 7.63; N, 5.62%. Calcd for $C_{60}H_{70}N_4O_7$+AcOEt: C, 73.39; H, 7.51; N, 5.35%. Into a solution of **I** in MeOH we stirred concd HCl to give (+)-**5B**; $[\alpha]_D^{20}$ +223.5° (MeOH); mp 219°C (dec). (2) **5B** (470 mg) was treated with cinchonine (250 mg) in MeOH, and the product was recrystallized from acetone–AcOEt five times to give another optically active salt, **II** (136 mg); $[\alpha]_D^{20}$ −29° (MeOH); mp 151—152 °C. Found: C, 70.07; H, 7.49; N, 3.71%. Calcd for $C_{41}H_{48}N_2O_6$ +2AcOEt: C, 69.97; H, 7.67; N, 3.33%. (−)-**5B** was afforded from **II**; $[\alpha]_D^{18}$ −235° (MeOH).

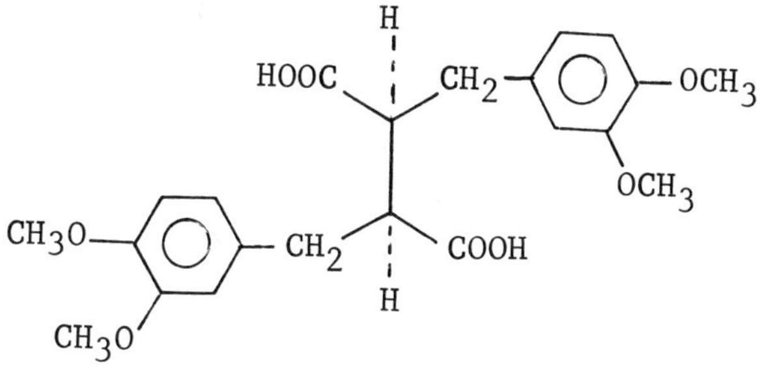

$C_{22}H_{26}O_8$ Ref. 1386

Resolution of** (+)**diveratrylsuccinic acid

A soln of (±)acid (1g)[7] and (+)cinchonine (1·2 g) in a mixture of MeOH (15 ml) and chf (10 ml) was boiled for 10 min. The solvent was removed completely and the residue crystallized from aqueous MeOH. The cinchonine salt of the (−)acid crystallized from 50% MeOH as colourless

small cubes (800 mg) m.p. foaming at 169° with dec at 285°, $[\alpha]_D^{30}$ +134° (*c*, 2·2). (Found: C, 67·3; H, 7·3; $C_{22}H_{26}O_8{\cdot}2C_{19}H_{22}N_2O$, $5H_2O$ requires: C, 67·5; H, 7·5%.) From the mother liquor on concentration, the cinchonine salt of (+)acid separated and was crystallized from aqueous MeOH as colourless flowers (700 mg) m.p. 179–186°, $[\alpha]_D^{30}$ +55° (*c*, 2·0). (Found: C, 67·4; H, 7·2; $C_{22}H_{26}O_8$·-$2C_{19}H_{22}N_2O$, $5H_2O$ requires: C, 67·5; H, 7·5%.) The cinchonine salts were decomposed with excess ammonia and extracted with chf to remove the base and then acidified with dil HCl.

(+)*Diveratrylsuccinic acid* crystallized from MeOH as colourless micro needles (200 mg) m.p. 99–105°, $[\alpha]_D^{30}$ +28° (*c*, 0·8). (Found: C, 55·9; H, 7·2; $C_{22}H_{26}O_8$, $3H_2O$ requires: C, 55·9; H, 6·7%.) The dimethyl ester (diazomethane) crystallized from EtOH as colourless needles m.p. 95–96°, $[\alpha]_D^{30}$ +22° (*c*, 2·0). (Found: C, 64·5; H, 6·6; OMe, 41·6; $C_{24}H_{30}O_8$ requires: C, 64·6; H, 6·7; 4-OMe, 41·7%.)

(−)*Diveratrylsuccinic acid* crystallized from EtOH as colourless thin laminae (250 mg) m.p. 98–105°, $[\alpha]_D^{30}$ −25° (*c*, 1·0). (Found: C, 55·9; H, 7·0; $C_{22}H_{26}O_8 3H_2O$ requires: C, 55·9; H, 6·7%.) The dimethyl ester (diazomethane) crystallized from MeOH as colourless needles m.p. 95–97°, $[\alpha]_D^{30}$ −20° (*c*, 1·5). (Found: C, 64·5; H, 6·6; OMe, 41·5; $C_{24}H_{30}O_8$ requires: C, 64·6; H, 6·8; 4-OMe, 41·7%.)

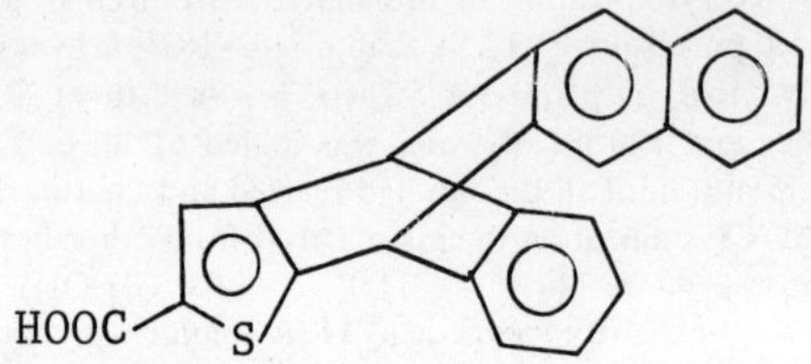

$C_{23}H_{14}O_2S$ Ref. 1387

Resolution of **4** *with dehydroabietylamine*

(a) A soln of 286 mg (1 mmole) of dehydroabietylamine, $[\alpha]_{578}^{20}$ = + 61·7, *c* = 3·07, pyridine, (lit.[26] $[\alpha]_{578}^{20}$ = + 56·1, *c* = 2·4, pyridine) in 5 ml ether was added to a boiling soln of 354 mg (1 mmole) of **4** in 30 ml ether. The mixture was refluxed for 30 min and cooled overnight at − 25°. The white ppt was collected and dried (500 mg) and crystallized 3 times from EtOH to give 82 mg of an almost white solid. This solid was boiled for 2 hr with 20 ml 2N KOH.[20b] After cooling and washing with ether the basic layer was acidified with 6N HCl; no ppt was formed. The ether layer was concentrated and the residue (80 mg) boiled for 30 min with a 50% AcOH soln. After cooling, water and ether was added. The ether layer was extracted with three 25 ml portions of 2N NaOH and the combined basic layer was acidified with 6N HCl. The ppt was collected and dried to give 26 mg of a cream coloured solid $[\alpha]_{546}^{20}$ = + 11·4, $[\alpha]_{578}^{20}$ = + 9·0 (*c* = 1·2, DMSO).

(b) A reaction between 890 mg (2·52 mmole) of **4** and 720 mg (2·52 mmole) of **12** in 200 ml ether afforded 1·1 g of an almost white solid. After 5 crystallizations from EtOH the product (210 mg) was hydrolysed with AcOH and water to give 90 mg of a slightly yellow product, $[\alpha]_{405}^{20}$ = − 13·3, $[\alpha]_{436}^{20}$ = − 10·0, $[\alpha]_{546}^{20}$ = − 1·7, $[\alpha]_{578}^{20}$ = − 1·7 (*c* = 0·3, DMSO).

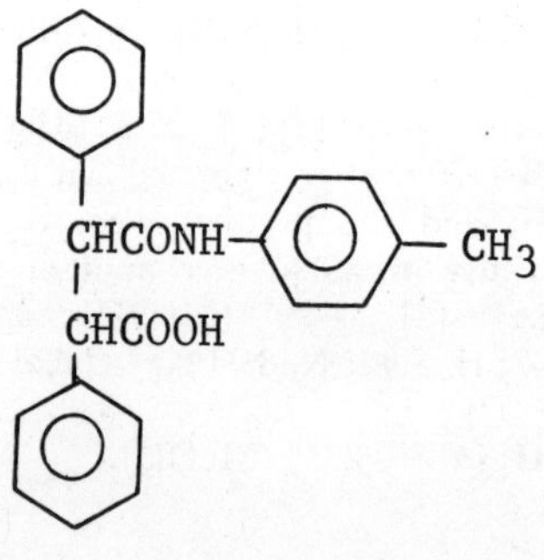

$C_{23}H_{21}NO_3$ Ref. 1388

Resolution of** r-**Diphenylsuccino**-p-**toluidic Acid into its Optical Antipodes.—Hot solutions of *r*-diphenylsuccino-*p*-toluidic acid (38·0 gms.) and of quinine (19·8 gms.) in ethyl alcohol (950 c.c.) were mixed, and crystals (29 gms.) separated readily. The solid was repeatedly extracted with boiling ethyl alcohol in portions of 500 c.c., the solutions being cooled to the atmospheric temperature previous to filtration. The specific rotations in acetone of the acids isolated from the successive filtrates were + 144·8°, + 279·4°, + 134·5°, + 49·2°, − 2·92°, − 91·62°, − 160·7°, and − 235·7°. The residual quinine salt (18·75 gms.) was decomposed with sulphuric acid and much ether, and the l-*diphenylsuccino*-p-*toluidic acid* (9·65 gms.; $[\alpha]_D^{18°}$ − 327·6° in acetone) crystallised from alcohol until the specific rotation was constant: small needles, m. p. 209—209·5° (the observed m. p. depends very greatly on the experimental conditions) (Found: C = 76·7; H = 6·1; N = 4·0. $C_{23}H_{21}O_3N$ requires C = 76·8; H = 5·9; N = 3·9 per cent.). In acetone: *l* = 2, *c* = 1·460, $\alpha_D^{18°}$ − 9·62°, whence $[\alpha]_D^{18°}$ − 329·5°.

The isolation of *d*-diphenylsuccino-*p*-toluidic acid was effected by the crystallisation of a mixture of the *d*- and *r*-acids, having $[\alpha]_D$ + 144·8° in acetone, from aqueous ethyl alcohol. After a single crystallisation, the acid had $[\alpha]_D$ + 202·7° in acetone, and the filtrate was decidedly lævorotatory. Repeated crystallisation of the acid from alcohol yielded d-*diphenylsuccino*-p-*toluidic acid*, minute needles, which resembles exactly its optical antipode (Found: C = 76·9; H = 5·9; N = 4·0 per cent.). In acetone: *l* = 2, *c* = 1·2028, $\alpha_D^{18°}$ + 7·94°, whence $[\alpha]_D^{18°}$ + 330·0°.

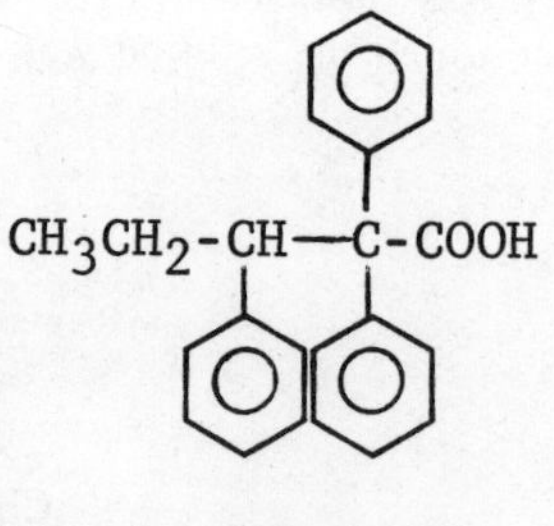

$C_{23}H_{22}O_2$ Ref. 1389

Acide R(+) triphényl-2,2,3 valérique **33**.

7,75 g d'acide (F = 202°) et 6,34 g de déhydroabiétylamine en solution dans 150 cm³ d'éthanol fournissent 7,3 g de sel qu'on recristallise 4 fois dans l'éthanol (voir tableau ci-contre).

	A	B	C	D	E
Poids de sel en g.	7,3	5,8	4,75	4,33	3,7
Volume de solvant (cm^3) de cristallisation	150	120	100	100	
$[\alpha]_J$ de l'acide régénéré du sel		+28,2°	+ 31,1°	+ 33,2°	+ 33,9°
$[\alpha]_J$ de l'acide régénéré des eaux-mères ...	— 21°	— 4°		+ 26,9°	+ 31,7°

La fraction E est traitée par la soude diluée (0,2 N). Après extraction à l'éther de la déhydroabiétylamine et neutralisation de la solution alcaline par l'acide chlorhydrique, on obtient 1,63 g d'acide $[\alpha]_J$ = + 33,9° (c = 1,4, éthanol), F = 167°.

Analyse $C_{23}H_{22}O_2$ (330,41) : Calc. % : C 83,6 H 6,7
Tr. : 83,3 6,7.

Par le même traitement, les eaux mères de A fournissent 4 g d'acide **33** *ent* $[\alpha]_J$ = — 21° (c = 1,5, éthanol). Cet acide (—) peut être obtenu par ailleurs optiquement pur en recristallisant 3 fois son sel de cinchonidine dans l'acétate d'éthyle, 4,7 g d'acide racémique fournissant 0,45 g d'acide **33** *ent* $[\alpha]_J$ = — 33,9° (c = 2, éthanol).

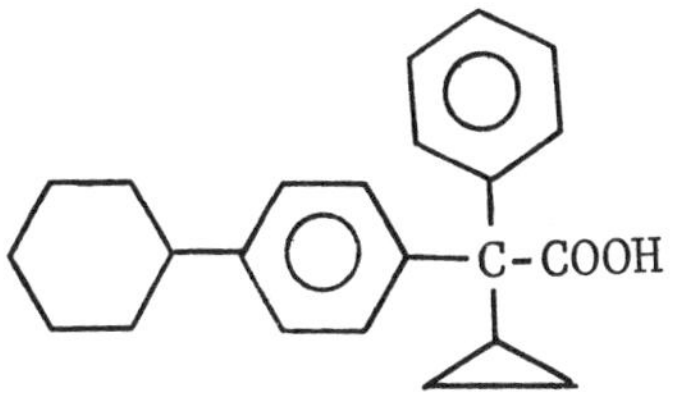

$C_{23}H_{26}O_2$ Ref. 1390

EXAMPLE 11

The mixture of 4.69 g. d,l-α-cyclopropyl-α-(4-cyclohexylphenyl)-acetic acid (M.P. 154–156°), 2.20 g. l(—)-α-phenylethylamine and 225 ml. 66% aqueous ethanol is heated to the boil and allowed to stand in the cold. The precipitate formed is filtered off and recrystallized from aqueous ethanol, to yield the l(—)-α-phenylethylammonium α-cyclopropyl - α - (4 - cyclohexylphenyl)-acetate, $[\alpha]_D^{25}$= —27.6° (methanol).

1.1 g. thereof is shaken with diethyl ether, water and 5 ml. N hydrochloric acid, the organic layer separated, dried and evaporated, to yield the l(—)-α-cyclopropyl-α-(4-cyclohexylphenyl)-acetic acid melting at 131–141°.

The combined mother liquors obtained from the above salt are evaporated, the residue taken up in aqueous sodium hydroxide and the mixture washed with diethyl ether. The aqueous phase is acidified with N hydrochloric acid and extracted with diethyl ether. The extract is washed with water, dried and evaporated. 2.35 g. of the residue is taken up in 112 ml. 66% aqueous ethanol and 1.1 g. d(+)-α-phenyl-ethylamine is added while stirring and heating. The precipitate formed after cooling is filtered off and recrystallized from aqueous ethanol, to yield the d(+)-α-phenylethyl ammonium α-cyclopropyl-α-(4-cyclohexylphenyl)-acetate, $[\alpha]_D^{25}$=+32.1° (ethanol). The corresponding d-acid prepared therefrom as shown above exhibited $[\alpha]_D^{25}$=+60.5° (ethanol).

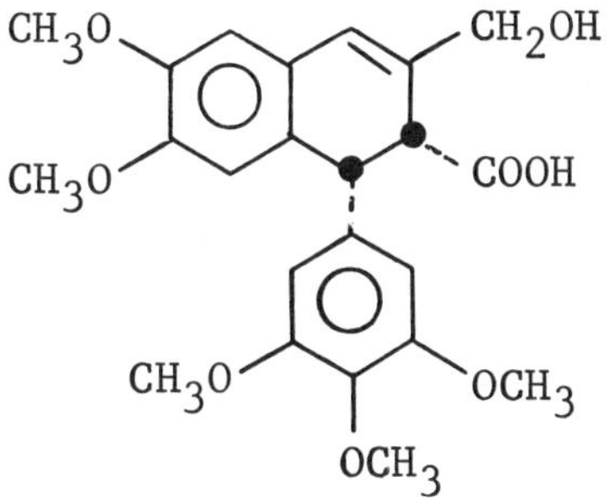

$C_{23}H_{26}O_8$ Ref. 1391

15. (+)-Pikrosikkimotoxin und (−)-*epi*-Pikrosikkimotoxin

15.1. (+)-α-*Apopikrosikkimotoxinsäure. – Ephedrinsalz der (+)-α-Apopikrosikkimotoxinsäure:* 50,8 g Eindampfrückstand (70 mMol) der Mutterlauge des Cinchoninsalzes der (−)-Apopikrosikkimotoxinsäure (vgl. Abschnitt 13.1.) werden in 500 ml Methylenchlorid gelöst, die Lösung dreimal mit 250 ml 2N Salzsäure und Eis ausgeschüttelt und dreimal mit 150 ml Eis-Wasser gewaschen. Die wässerigen Extrakte werden zweimal mit 150 ml Methylenchlorid nachgeschüttelt, die organischen Auszüge mit Natriumsulfat getrocknet, im Vakuum schonend eingedampft und die rohe α-Aposäure 2 Std. bei 60° im Vakuum getrocknet: 30 g; $[\alpha]_D$ = +115° (Chloroform).

Aus Methylenchlorid-Äther kristallisiert nach längerem Stehen *optisch inaktive α-Apopikrosikkimotoxinsäure:* 8,0 g, Smp. 151–152° (Zers.), $[\alpha]_D$ 0° (Chloroform); nach Misch-Smp., UV.- und IR.-Spektrum identisch mit XXXIV.

$C_{23}H_{26}O_8$	Ber. C 64,2	H 6,1	O 29,7	OCH_3 36,0%
(430,44)	Gef. ,, 63,8	,, 6,0	,, 29,1	,, 36,2%

Die Mutterlauge liefert nach dem Eindampfen im Vakuum 22 g (+)-α-*Aposäure*; $[\alpha]_D$ = +150° (Chloroform). Die rohe (+)-Säure (51 mMol) wird in 100 ml Methylenchlorid gelöst, eine Lösung von 9,5 g (−)-Ephedrin (51 mMol) in 50 ml Methylenchlorid zugefügt und im Vakuum eingedampft. Das *Ephedrinsalz* kristallisiert aus Aceton-Cyclohexan: Smp. 147–149°, $[\alpha]_D$ = +214° (Chloroform); nach dem Umkristallisieren aus Methylenchlorid-Benzol, Smp. 147–149°, $[\alpha]_D$ = +219 (Chloroform); 24,4 g.

$C_{33}H_{41}O_9N$	Ber. C 66,5	H 6,9	O 24,2	N 2,4	OCH_3 26,0%
(595,69)	Gef. ,, 65,3	,, 6,8	,, 23,6	,, 2,3	,, 25,2%

(+)-α-*Aposäure:* 17,9 g Ephedrinsalz (30 mMol) werden durch Ausschütteln mit verd. Salzsäure und Methylenchlorid in Ephedrin und (+)-α-Apopikrosikkimotoxinsäure zerlegt. Die aus dem Methylenchlorid-Auszug isolierte Säure liess sich nicht kristallisieren: 12,9 g, $[\alpha]_D$ = +170 (Chloroform).

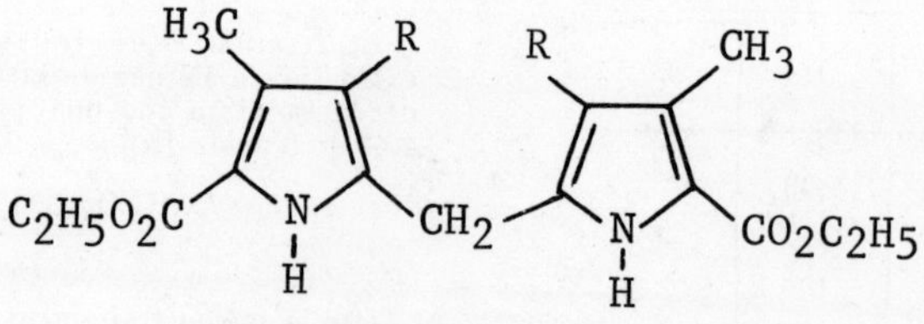

$C_{23}H_{30}N_2O_4$ R = CH_2-CH_2-COOH Ref. 1392

Optical Resolutions of Dipyrrolic Compounds.—Resolution of diethyl 4,4′-*dimethyl*-3,3′-*di*-(2-*carboxyethyl*)*dipyrrylmethane*-5,5′-*dicarboxylate* (I). Quinidine sulphate (20 g.) was suspended in water (1500 ml.), the mixture being warmed to effect complete solution. The solution was made alkaline with 4N-sodium hydroxide, and the resulting precipitate of free base was crystallised from ethanol (yield 96%); it had m. p. 168—169°, $[\alpha]_D$ +187° (in ethanol).

The dipyrrylmethane (3·89 g.) was added in portions to a solution of quinidine (12·46 g.) dissolved in stirred boiling ethanol. Crystallisation in five stages of evaporation afforded a colourless compound (6·9 g.) composed almost entirely of free quinidine, m. p. and mixed m. p. 167°. Trituration with ether of the viscous oily mother-liquor afforded crystals (4·07 g.) of the required quinidine salt. Fractional crystallisation from n-butyl acetate gave a less soluble crop (2·99 g.), and on complete evaporation of the mother-liquor, a more soluble crop (0·67 g.).

The less soluble crop, recrystallised from n-butyl acetate, attained a constant rotation, $[\alpha]_D$ +121° (in n-butyl acetate), and had m. p. 131—134° [Found: C, 65·8; H, 7·15; N, 7·0. Calc. for 1 quinidine : 1 methane($C_{43}H_{54}N_4O_{10}$): C, 65·6; H, 6·9; N, 7·1%].

The more soluble salt, recrystallised from n-butyl acetate to a constant rotation, $[\alpha]_D$ +128° (in n-butyl acetate), had m. p. 128—130° [Found: C, 66·5; H, 7·0; N, 7·15. Calc. for 1 quinidine : 1 methane($C_{43}H_{54}N_4O_{10}$): C, 65·6; H, 6·9; N, 7·1%].

The quinidine salts suspended in water (50 ml.) were decomposed by addition of concentrated hydrochloric acid (4 ml.). The precipitated enantiomorphic dipyrrylmethanes were filtered off and washed many times with water to remove free quinidine hydrochloride. The dipyrrylmethanes were crystallised from ethanol to constant rotation (both in ethanol) of $[\alpha]_D$ −2·3°, m. p. 198—199°, and +2·5°, m. p. 196—198°, respectively. For polarimetry a 10-cm. tube was used. During crystallisation of the optically active methanes, the mother-liquors underwent spontaneous oxidation to the corresponding red methenes, the solutions then showing enhanced lævo- and dextro-rotations of −0·35 and +0·55°, respectively. Rotations observed for the colourless methanes were only about ±0·05°.

Polarimetry.—This was carried out with a Hilger M.375 polarimeter. The zero rotation (an average of ten readings) for sodium light was checked before each experiment. The observed rotation for each solution examined was also obtained as an average of ten readings. Unless otherwise stated a 20-cm. polarimetry tube was used, and polarimetry was carried out between 20 and 25°.

[9] H. Fischer and K. Morgenrath, *Annalen*, 1928, **466**, 165.

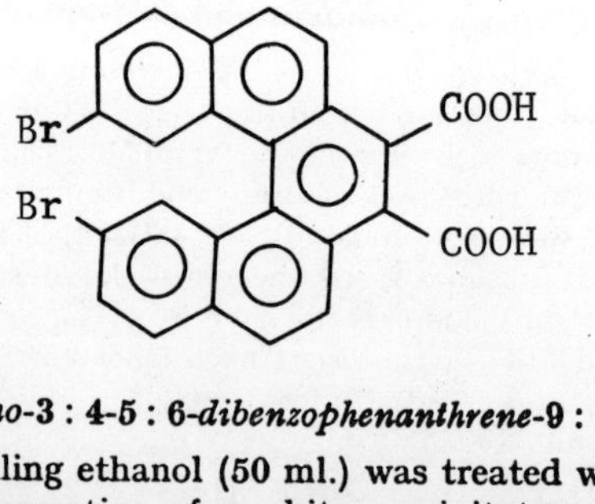

$C_{24}H_{12}Br_2O_4$ Ref. 1393

Partial Resolution of* 3′ : 2″-*Dibromo*-3 : 4-5 : 6-*dibenzophenanthrene*-9 : 10-*dicarboxylic Acid

—The acid (1·5 g.) suspended in boiling ethanol (50 ml.) was treated with morphine (0·91 g.). The orange-red colour faded with formation of a white precipitate, which was dissolved by adding ethanol (250 ml.) and refluxing. Cooling after filtration produced a crop of colourless crystals (0·8 g.). Concentration of the mother liquor under reduced pressure yielded three further crops. Only the first and the fourth (0·5 g.) were used.

(*a*) Several recrystallisations of the first crop from ethanol gave a morphine salt (0·22 g.), $[\alpha]_D^{22}$ (ethanol) = −220°, which on decomposition with hydrochloric acid afforded the orange-yellow *active acid* (0·12 g.), $[\alpha]_D^{22}$ (chloroform) = −712°, m. p. 330° after shrinkage at 120° representing conversion into the anhydride (Found: C, 56·9; H, 2·1. $C_{24}H_{10}O_3Br_2$ requires C, 56·9; H, 2·0%).

(*b*) Recrystallisation of the fourth crop from ethanol gave a morphine salt (0·35 g.), $[\alpha]_D^{22}$ = +497° (ethanol), which on decomposition afforded the acid (0·2 g.), $[\alpha]_D^{22}$ (chloroform) = +745°.

Racemisation.—The foregoing active acids in chloroform solution at 22° racemised with a half-life of 32 hr.:

t (hr.)	0	$2\frac{1}{4}$	24	26	36	87	97
α_D	$+3{\cdot}28°$	$+2{\cdot}98°$	$+2{\cdot}08°$	$+1{\cdot}92°$	$+1{\cdot}52°$	$+0{\cdot}60°$	$+0{\cdot}49°$
t (hr.)	0	13	23	49	71	95	111
α_D	$-1{\cdot}64°$	$-1{\cdot}24°$	$-0{\cdot}97°$	$-0{\cdot}59°$	$-0{\cdot}40°$	$-0{\cdot}30°$	$-0{\cdot}20°$

Alternative Partial Resolution.—To the acid (1·789 g.) dissolved in chloroform morphine (1·088 g.) suspended in chloroform was added, with stirring. On concentrating the resulting solution at room temperature under reduced pressure four fractions of morphine salt were obtained. On recrystallisation and decomposition the first fraction (0·825 g.) gave the acid $[\alpha]_D^{25} = +589°$ and the last fraction (0·936 g.) gave the acid of $[\alpha]_D^{25} = -394°$.

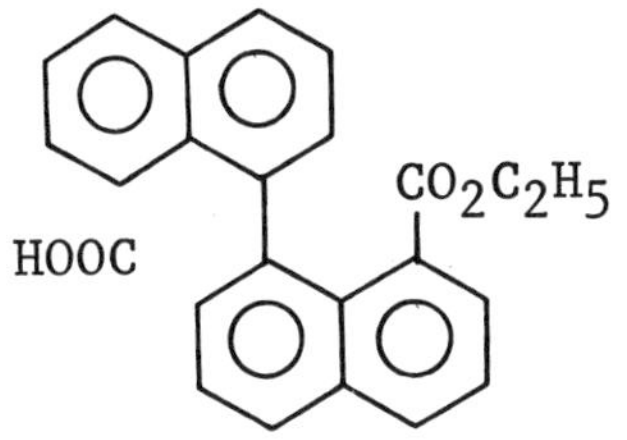

$C_{24}H_{18}O_4$ Ref. 1394

Brucinsalz der Ester-säure: Ein Gemisch von 0.652 g Ester-säure und 0.932 g Brucin (je 0.002 Mol.) wird unter Erwärmen auf dem Wasserbade in 5 ccm Essigester gelöst. Nach Zusatz von 4—5 Tropfen wäßrigem Methylalkohol (1:1) wird mit in einem Vorversuch erhaltenem Brucinsalz angeimpft. Über Nacht krystallisieren als erste Fraktion 0.75 g radial gruppierte Prismen. Sinterung um 130°, bei 140° Blasenbildung, endgültige Schmelze unter Bräunung um 210° (unt. Zers.). — Nach 8 Stdn. krystallisieren aus der Mutterlauge erneut 0.04 g und nach 3-tägigem Stehen schließlich noch 0.54 g Salz vom gleichen Schmelzpunkt und Krystallhabitus und derselben Drehung. Das Brucinsalz ist in Alkoholen und Chloroform sehr leicht, in Essigester schwerer löslich. Durch 2-maliges Umkrystallisieren aus Essigester läßt sich weder der Schmelzpunkt, noch die Drehung erhöhen.

0.1267 g luft-trockne Sbst.: 0.3037 g CO_2, 0.0656 g H_2O.
$C_{24}H_{18}O_4$, $C_{23}H_{26}O_4N_2 + 3\,H_2O$ (818.7). Ber. C 68.92, H 6.16.
Gef. ,, 68.64, ,, 6.17.

0.1511 g luft-trockne Sbst., zu 10 ccm in Chloroform gelöst; die Lösung ist zunächst vom abgeschiedenen Krystallwasser getrübt. Erste Ablesung 10 Min. nach Lösungsbeginn, $\alpha_D = -10.63°$, letzte Ablesung 1300 Min. nach Lösungsbeginn, $\alpha_D = -8.30°$. Endwert der Drehung (Gemisch von Brucin und racem. Säure in derselben Konzentration wie vorher): $\alpha_D = -2.54°$, $[\alpha]_D^{20} = -84.1°$, $[M]_D^{20} = -689°$. Daraus berechnet sich k pro Minute = 0.000261; Halbwertszeit = $44^1/_4$ Stdn. Extrapolierter Anfangsdrehwert $\alpha_D = -10.65°$, $[\alpha]_D^{20} = -352.4°$, $[M]_D^{20} = -2885°$.

Optisch aktive Ester-säure: 0.23 g Brucinsalz ($[\alpha]_D = -352.4°$) werden mit einer Lösung von 0.05 g Soda in 8 ccm Wasser zerlegt und die alkalische Lösung durch ein gehärtetes Filter in das Polarimeterrohr filtriert. — Die nachträgliche Konzentrations-Bestimmung ergab für 5 ccm Rohr-Inhalt 0.0438 g Ester-säure. Erste Ablesung 23 Min. nach Beginn des Versuchs $\alpha_D = +7.10°$, letzte Ablesung nach 457 Min. $\alpha_D = +6.12°$. Mittelwert der Racemisationskonstante für das Natriumsalz 0.00041 je Minute. Halbwertszeit 28.2 Stdn. — Extrapolierter Anfangsdrehwert: $\alpha_D = +7.10°$, $[\alpha]_D^{18} = +405.3°$, $[\alpha]_D^{18} = +1500°$.

Die freie Säure krystallisiert aus Methanol in wasserklaren Kryställchen vom Schmp. 199°. 0.0241 g, in Dioxan zu 10 ccm gelöst, zeigten 5 Min. nach Lösungsbeginn ein $\alpha_D = -2.53°$, nach 41 Stdn. $\alpha_D = 1.08°$. K = 0.00033, Halbwertszeit 35 Stdn., $[\alpha]_D^{20} = -525°$, $[M]_D^{20} = -1943°$.

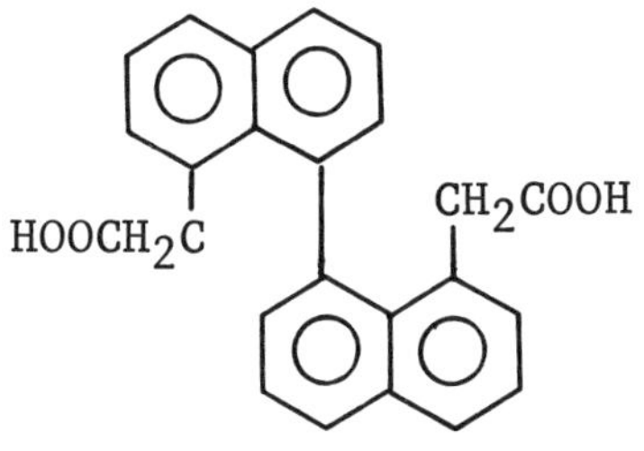

$C_{24}H_{18}O_4$ Ref. 1395

Optically Active 1,1′-Binaphthyl-8,8′-diacetic Acid.—The (±)-acid was resolved by crystallising its monoquinine salt from acetone; the less soluble diastereoisomeric salt was decomposed to give the (+)-*acid*, m.p. 308—310°, $[\alpha]_{546}^{20}$ +249° (*c* 0·18; *l* 0·5 dm; *NN*-dimethylformamide) (Found: C, 78·1; H, 5·1%). The more soluble salt gave the (−)-*acid*, $[\alpha]_{546}^{20}$ −245° (*c* 0·212; *NN*-dimethylformamide) (Found: C, 77·7; H, 5·0; O, 17·3%).

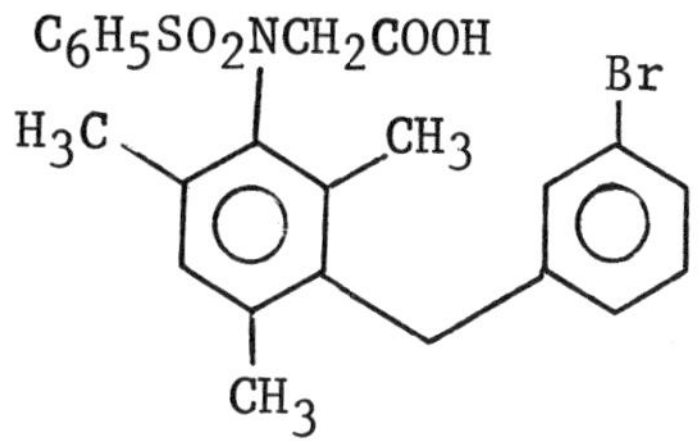

$C_{24}H_{24}BrNO_4S$ Ref. 1396

Note:

For resolution procedure and physical constants, see Ref. 1397.

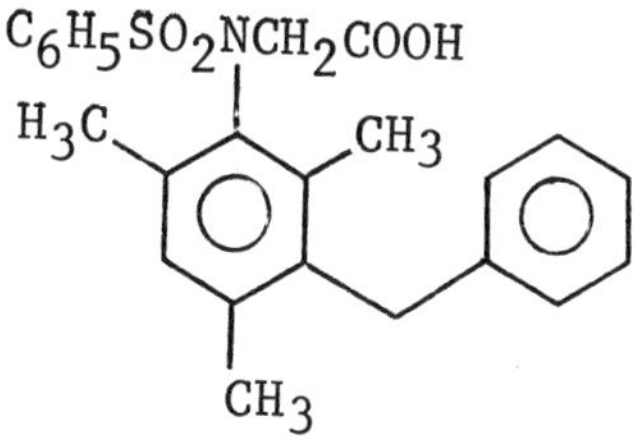

$C_{24}H_{25}NO_4S$ Ref. 1397

Resolution of Various Acids.—The cinchonidine salts of the N-benzenesulfonyl-N-carboxymethyl-3-(*m*-substituted benzyl)-mesidines were prepared by dissolving acid and alkaloid in 5 parts of methanol. Crystallization of the first salt prepared (*m*-methylbenzyl derivative) required several days, although seeds of this salt induced crystallization of other salts in a much shorter time. In every case crystalli-

TABLE V

ROTATIONS OF CINCHONIDINE SALTS OF THE MESIDINES

m-Substituent in benzyl group	M.p., °C.	$[\alpha]^t_D$ in DMF	Temp., °C.
H	120	-60.5 ± 1.0	20
CH_3	168–170	-72.5 ± 1.0	20
Br	179–180	-72.0 ± 1.0	20
CN	94	-71.8 ± 1.0	30
OCH_3	122	-62.5 ± 1.0	28

TABLE VI

ROTATIONS OF OPTICALLY ACTIVE MESIDINES

m-Substituent in benzyl group	M.p., °C.	$[\alpha]^t_D$ in DMF	Temp., °C.
H	179–180	-53.5 ± 1.0	26
CH_3	142–143	-48.5 ± 1.0	20
Br	131–133	-64.5 ± 1.0	20
CN	132–134	-59.5 ± 1.0	30
OCH_3	166–167	-59.5 ± 1.0	28

zation stopped after approximately 70% of the less soluble isomer had been removed. The first fractions were nearly optically pure, and recrystallization from ethanol did not change the specific rotation by an amount greater than the experimental error. The characteristics of the salts are described in Table V.

Isolation and Racemization of Optically Active Acids.—The technique employed was essentially the same as that previously described.[2] The characteristics of the acids and a sample rate determination are described in Table VI. The errors in the rate constants and rotations are commensurate with the error in setting and reading the polarimeter (±0.01°).

(1) R. Adams and R. H. Mattson, This Journal, **76**, 4925 (1954).
(2) R. Adams and K. V. Y. Sundstrom, *ibid.*, **76**, 5474 (1954).

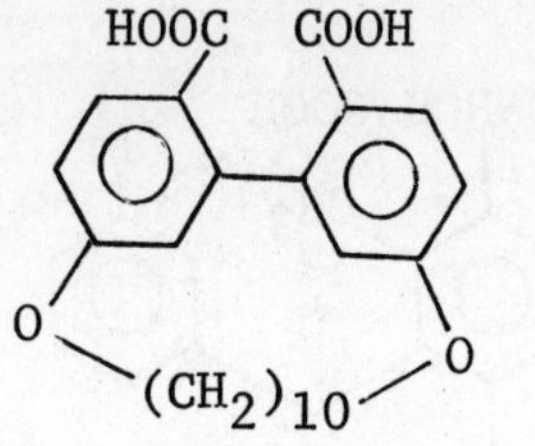

$C_{24}H_{28}O_6$ Ref. 1398

Resolution of 2,2′-Dicarboxy-5,5′-(decamethylenedioxy)-biphenyl.—To 0.629 g. of 2,2′-dicarboxy-5,5′-(decamethylenedioxy)-biphenyl in 250 cc. of hot methanol was added a solution of 1.21 g. of anhydrous brucine in 15 cc. of methanol. After removing 160 cc. of methanol, the solution was allowed to stand at room temperature for twenty-four hours. Large mushroom-like clusters of crystals separated which were freed from mother liquor by decantation; yield, 1.415 g. (77.2%). Further crops were obtained by concentration of the mother liquor. These were identical with the first crop. Furthermore, when the salt was allowed to crystallize in the course of a week it had the same rotation as the crystals obtained by more rapid precipitation; m. p. 155–163° (cor.).

Anal. Calcd. for $C_{24}H_{28}O_6 \cdot 2C_{23}H_{26}O_4N_2 \cdot 4CH_3OH$: C, 66.86; H, 7.22; N, 4.22. Found: C, 66.99; H, 6.97; N, 4.49.

Rotation. 0.052 g. made up to 5 cc. with chloroform at 20° gave α_D −0.58°; *l*, 1; $[\alpha]^{20}_D$ −55.8°. In about thirty hours the salt had mutarotated to a constant value of −33°.

d - 2,2′ - Dicarboxy - 5,5′ - (decamethylenedioxy) - biphenyl.—A mixture of 1.27 g. of finely ground dibrucine salt and 100 cc. of 20% ice cold hydrochloric acid was allowed to stand for several hours in an ice-bath. The solids were collected on a sintered glass crucible and dried overnight in a vacuum desiccator. The cold hydrochloric acid filtrate was then added to the finely powdered mixture of acid and unreacted salt. After standing in an ice-bath for three hours the mixture was filtered, the active acid washed with several hundred cubic centimeters of ice cold 20% hydrochloric acid, then with increasingly dilute acid and finally with water. After drying *in vacuo* over potassium hydroxide the product weighed 0.355 g. (90%). The active acid when plunged into a bath preheated to 250° has a m. p. 280–290° (cor.) with decomposition (see Table I for rotation and racemization constants).

Anal. Calcd. for $C_{24}H_{28}O_6$: C, 69.90; H, 6.80. Found: C, 69.91; H, 6.88.

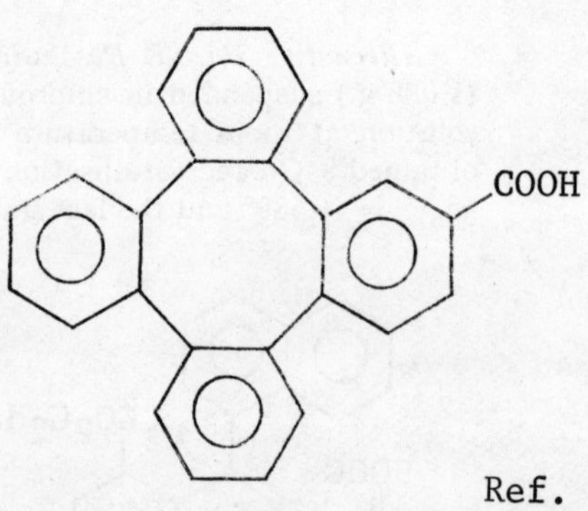

Ref. 1399

$C_{25}H_{16}O_2$

Partial resolution of (**2**) by fractional crystallization of the brucine salt from ethanol gave (+)-(**2**), m.p. 285—287°, $[\alpha]_{320}$ +23·3° (*c* 0·45 in EtOH), and (−)-(**2**), m.p. 287—288°, $[\alpha]_{320}$ −8·4° (*c* 0·57 in EtOH).

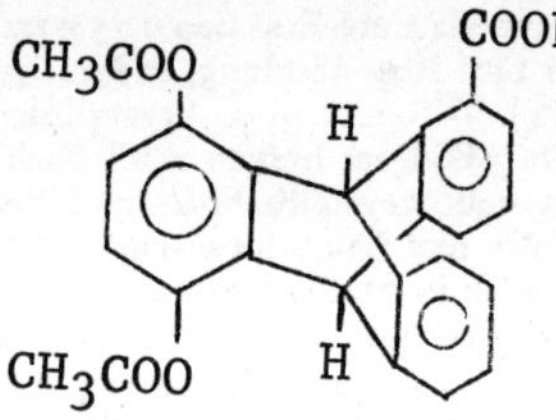

$C_{25}H_{16}O_2$ Ref. 1400

Optical Resolution of *dl*-7-Carboxy-2, 5-diacetoxytriptycene (XII).—*d-XII.*—The racemic XII (5.950 g., 0.0144 mol.) was dissolved in absolute ethanol (160 ml.). Brucine tetrahydrate (3.344 g., 0.00722 mol.) was added at once to the hot solution and the mixture was refluxed for 30 min. The mixture was allowed to stand overnight at room temperature to precipitate well-defined colorless needles. The mother liquor was separated by decantation and the crystals thus obtained was washed several times with a small amount of ethanol. The crystals obtained were dried under reduced pressure yielding the brucine salt, 5.7 g., $[\alpha]^{10}_D$ = −7.28° (*c* 0.906, acetone). The brucine salt was recrystallized 3 times from absolute ethanol yielding a salt with $[\alpha]^{10}_D$ = +6.2° (*c* 1.46, acetone). This salt was recrystallized from ethanol 2 times affording an optically pure salt with a constant specific rotation $[\alpha]^{10}_D$ = +7.5°, (*c* 0.69, acetone).

Found: C, 71.83; H, 5.40; N, 3.39. Calcd. for $C_{48}H_{44}O_{10}N_2$: C, 71.28; H, 5.48; N, 3.46%.

Water (24 ml.) was added to the hot solution of the optically pure salt (2.354 g.) in acetic acid (24 ml.) and the white precipitate formed was filtered, washed with water and dried to yield *d*-XII, 1.088 g., m. p. 263~266°C. This was recrystallized from acetic acid to give pure *d*-XII, m. p. 269~271°C, $[\alpha]^{13}_{5461}$ = +96.3°, $[\alpha]^{13}_{4358}$ = +174.8° (*c* 0.7042, dioxane).

Found: C, 72.99; H, 4.40. Calcd. for $C_{25}H_{18}O_6$ C, 72.46: H, 4.38%.

l-XII.—The above-mentioned mother liquor which was obtained by decantation of the brucine salt was concentrated under reduced pressure. Treatment of the residue with 25% acetic acid gave the optically impure *l*-XII, m. p. 261~263°C, $[\alpha]^{10}_{5461}$ =

−49.25° (*c* 0.873, acetone). Quinine (6.5 g., 0.023 mol.) was added to the hot solution of the crude *l*-XII (9.6 g., 0.023 mol.) in 95% ethanol (120 ml.) and the mixture was refluxed for 30 min. The solution was allowed to stand overnight in a refrigerator. The colorless crystals deposited were filtered, washed with 95% ethanol to yield the crude quinine salt (9.8 g.). This was recrystallized 4 times from 95% ethanol to give optically pure *l*-salt (3.2 g.). This salt showed no definite melting point. Development of yellow color was observed near 140°C and it decomposed gradually at 155∼160°C with frothing. The specific rotation of the pure salt was found to be $[\alpha]^{19.5}_{5791} = -109°$, $[\alpha]^{19.5}_{5461} = -139°$ (*c* 1.028, acetone).

Found: C, 71.59; H, 6.33; N, 3.66. Calcd. for $C_{45}H_{42}N_2O_8 \cdot H_2O$: C, 71.40; H, 5.86; N, 3.70%.

The pure quinine salt obtained (3.1 g.) was heated on a water bath with 25% acetic acid (50 ml.) for 30 min. The mixture was kept at room temperature overnight, and the precipitate formed was filtered, washed with 25% acetic acid and water successively, to result in *l*-acid, (1.5 g.), m. p. 252∼263°C. The *l*-acid was recrystallized twice from acetic acid yielding the pure *l*-XII, m. p. 269∼271°C, $[\alpha]^{24}_{5461} = -93.1°$, $[\alpha]^{24}_{4358} = -168.2°$ (*c* 1.0272, dioxane).

Found: C, 71.76; H, 4.46. Calcd. for $C_{25}H_{18}O_6$: C, 72.46; H, 4.38%.

The infrared spectra of the *d*- and *l*-acid were found to be completely identical over the entire region of wavelength.

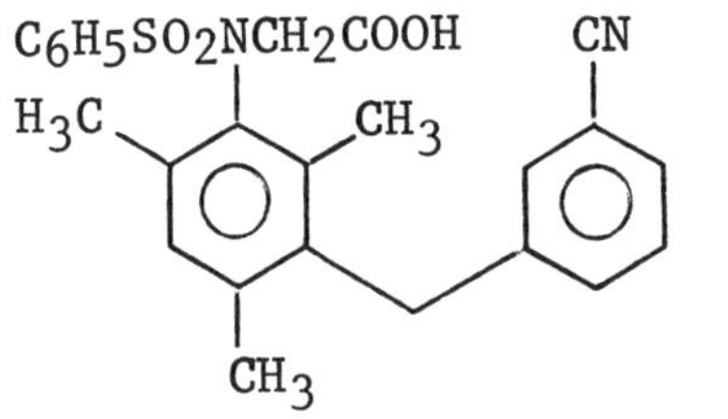

$C_{25}H_{24}N_2O_4S$ Ref. 1401

Note:

For resolution procedure and physical constants, see Ref. 1397.

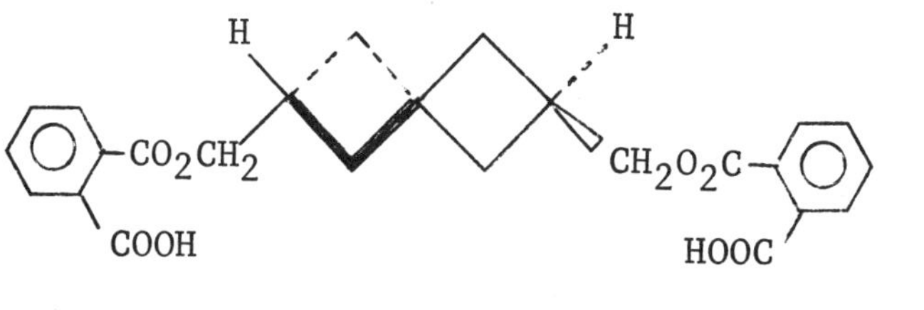

$C_{25}H_{24}O_8$ Ref. 1402

e. *Dédoublement optique de l'éther diphtalique acide.* On prépare le sel de brucine en dissolvant 0.90 g (2 m.mol) d'éther diphtalique et 1.58 g (4 m.mol) de brucine dans 10 cm³ d'alcool bouillant et en évaporant ensuite la solution dans le vide. Le résidu, recristallisé dans l'alcool dilué, donne 1.6 g de produit cristallisé. D'après l'analyse, ce produit est un mélange des sels acide et neutre de brucine.

En décomposant 0.5 g de ce sel par une lessive de soude caustique et en éliminant ensuite la brucine par extraction au chloroforme, on obtient une solution du sel sodique, qui, diluée au volume de 25 cm³, présente, dans un tube de 4 dm, la rotation: $\alpha_D = -0.03°$.

En acidifiant cette solution, on a obtenu le diphtalate acide, dont on a contrôlé le poids équivalent (224.7, calculé 226.2). Ce diphtalate acide a été dissous dans l'alcool et s'est également révélé lévogyre.

L'eau-mère dans laquelle le sel de brucine s'est déposé a été décomposée par une lessive de soude caustique, extraite au chloroforme et acidifiée. On a ainsi obtenu le diphtalate acide à l'état pur; poids équivalent 226.6, alors que le calcul donne 226.2. Rotation du sel sodique: $\alpha_D = +0.045°$ (dans un tube de 4 dm; volume 25 cm³). Par acidification, on obtient le diphtalate acide, qui, dissous dans l'alcool, se révèle également dextrogyre.

Le sel de *strychnine* cristallise mieux que celui de brucine. On le prépare en solution alcoolique, aux dépens de 0.90 g (2 m.mol) de diphtalate et de 1.34 g (4 m.mol) de strychnine.

Le sel est trituré avec de l'acétone bouillante et recristallisé dans l'alcool. On en obtient ainsi 1.5 g et, après une seconde recristallisation, 0.8 g. Le *sel neutre de strychnine* cristallise en petits cristaux brillants, unis en rosettes.

Subst. 0.4878, 0.3352 g; 11.31, 7.70 cm³ de NaOH 0.0773 n.
Trouvé: p. équiv. 558.0, 563.2.
$C_{25}H_{24}O_8 . 2\ C_{21}H_{22}O_2N_2$ (1121.25). Calculé: „ „ 560.6.

0.4878 g de sel neutre de strychnine, transformés en sel sodique, ont donné, dans un volume de 25 cm³ et dans un tube de 4 dm, la rotation: $\alpha_D = +0.035°$. Calculée à partir de cette donnée, la rotation moléculaire $[M]_D$ du sel sodique serait de +5°. Cependant, il est très probable que le pouvoir rotatoire est plus notable, car, faute de matériel, nous n'avons pu achever complètement le dédoublement.

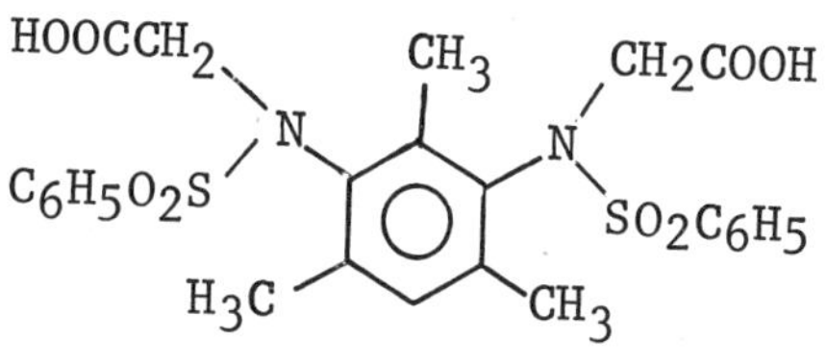

$C_{25}H_{26}N_2O_8S_2$ Ref. 1403

Resolution of N,N′-Dicarboxymethyl-N,N′-dibenzenesulfonyldiaminomesitylene (m. p. 269–271°).—A solution of 6.49 g. of quinine in 100 ml. of acetone was added to a suspension of 5.47 g. of N,N′-dicarboxymethyl-N,N′-dibenzenesulfonyldiaminomesitylene in 200 ml. of boiling acetone. The mixture was boiled and filtered. Crystallization started upon cooling in an ice-box. After thirty-six hours the crystals were collected on a filter. The yield of less-soluble salt, m. p. 194.5–195° (cor.), fraction I, was 5 g.

The filtrate was evaporated to half its volume and when cooled an oily semi-crystalline product precipitated. This, fraction II, weighed 2.5 g.

Fraction I was recrystallized from absolute ethanol, m. p. 195.5–196.5° (cor.). Fraction II was recrystallized from the mother liquor of the recrystallization of fraction I. The product also had an m. p. of 195.5–196° (cor.). The total yield was 5.5 g. The melting point rose to 203–204° (cor.) when dried for four hours *in vacuo* at 110° and the indication is that water was retained in the product as obtained directly from the solvent.

Anal. (undried salt). Calcd. for $C_{25}H_{26}O_8N_2S_2 \cdot 2C_{20}H_{24}O_2N \cdot H_2O$: C, 64.33; H, 6.32. Found: C, 64.68; H, 6.51.

Anal. (dried salt). Calcd. for $C_{25}H_{26}O_8N_2S_2 \cdot 2C_{20}H_{24}O_2N_2$: C, 65.30; H, 6.24. Found: C, 64.95; H, 6.44.

Rotation (dried less-soluble salt). 100 mg. made up to 10 ml. with methanol at 24° gave αD −8.25; *l*, 1; $[\alpha]^{24}D$ −82.5°.

The mother liquors from fractions I and II were evaporated to about half the volume, cooled and the precipitate collected on a filter. This procedure was repeated once more. These two crops were discarded. The resulting solution of about 50 ml. volume was then evaporated to dryness giving a white powder weighing 4.0 g., m. p. 147–168° (cor.). This salt was not further purified.

Decomposition of the Less-soluble Salt (m. p. 195.5–196.5°); **Preparation of *d*-N,N′-Dicarboxymethyl-N,N′-dibenzenesulfonyldiaminomesitylene.**—A suspension of 1 g. of the salt in 60 ml. of water and 10 ml. of methanol was stirred and treated with a solution of 1 g. of potassium hydroxide in 15 ml. of water. The mixture was heated for a few minutes to 75°. The solution was cooled and the quinine removed by filtration. The filtrate was acidified with

hydrochloric acid and a precipitate was formed. The solution was heated and acetone added until the precipitate dissolved. The acid crystallized upon cooling. It was recrystallized from a methanol–water mixture, m. p. 209–211° (cor.); the compound melted, crystallized and melted again at 252–253° (cor.). The yield was 275 mg.

Anal. Calcd. for $C_{25}H_{26}O_8N_2S_2$: C, 54.92; H, 4.80. Found: C, 54.51; H, 5.05.

Rotation. 100 mg. made up to 10 ml. with methanol at 24° gave α_D +0.55°; *l*, 1; $[\alpha]^{24}_D$ +55°.

Decomposition of the More-soluble Salt (m. p. 147–168°); Preparation of *l*-N,N'-Dicarboxymethyl-N,N'-dibenzenesulfonyldiaminomesitylene.—The impure more-soluble salt was decomposed in a manner similar to the decomposition of the less-soluble salt. The crude acid after crystallization from an acetone–water mixture had a m. p. of 147–163° (cor.).

Rotation. 50 mg. made up to 10 ml. with methanol at 24° gave α_D −0.24; *l*, 1; $[\alpha]^{24}_D$ −48°.

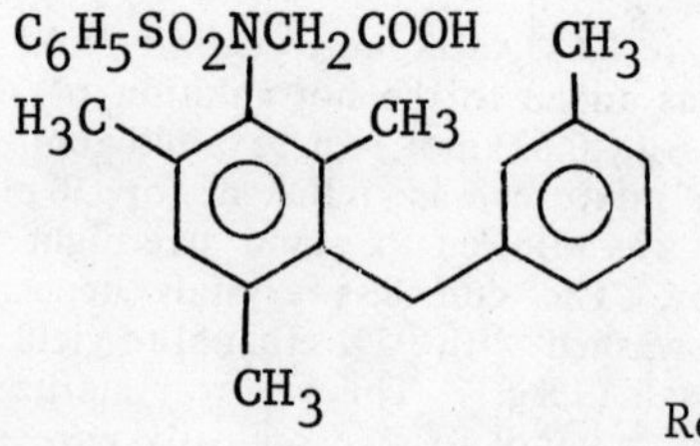

$C_{25}H_{27}NO_4S$ Ref. 1404

Note:

For resolution procedure and physical constants, see Ref. 1397.

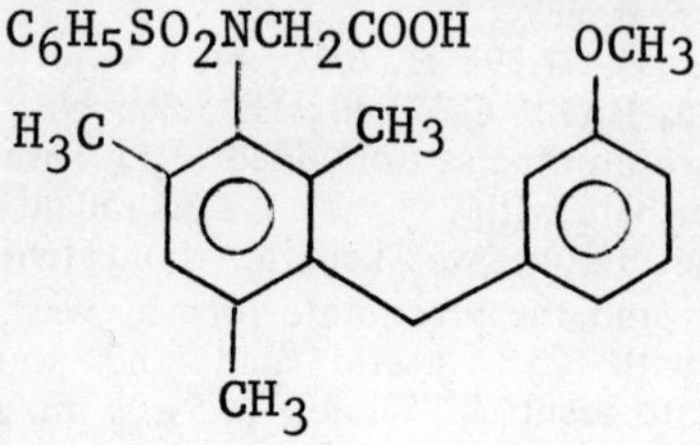

$C_{25}H_{27}NO_5S$ Ref. 1405

Note:

For resolution procedure and physical constants, see Ref. 1397.

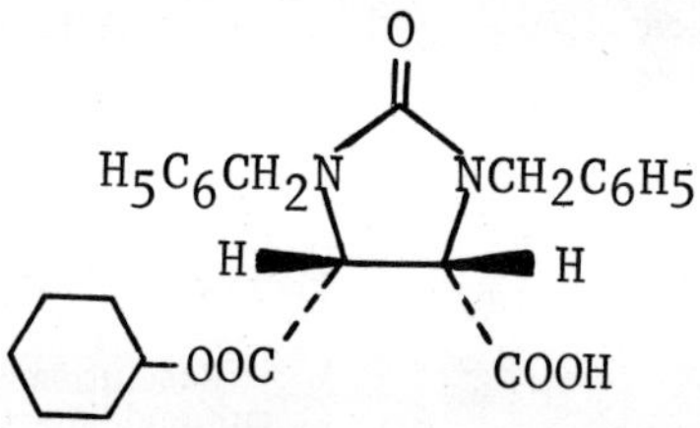

$C_{25}H_{28}N_2O_5$ Ref. 1406

(+)-*Ephedrinsalz der* (4S,5R)-*1,3-Dibenzyl-5-(cyclohexyloxycarbonyl)-2-oxo-imidazolidin-4-carbonsäure.* Zu 1 l kochendem Benzol werden portionenweise 336 g *cis*-1,3-Dibenzyl-tetrahydro-2*H*-furo[3,4-*d*]imidazol-2,4,6-trion und gleichzeitig 110 g Cyclohexanol innert 1½ Std. gefügt. Man kocht noch 16 Std. unter Rückfluss und dampft sodann im Vakuum ein. Der Rückstand enthält, neben kleinen Mengen Benzol und überschüssigem Cyclohexanol, praktisch reine *cis*-1,3-Dibenzyl-5-(cyclohexyloxycarbonyl)-2-oxo-imidazolidin-4-carbonsäure. (Diese kann durch Lösen in 800 ml Äther und Zugabe von 400 ml Hexan kristallisiert werden: Smp. 130–131°.) Der ölige Rückstand wird in 1500 ml Isopropanol bei 75–80° gelöst und mit einer auf 75° erwärmten Lösung von 110 g (+)-Ephedrin in 1500 ml Isopropanol vermischt. Man lässt innert ca. 1½ Std. auf 35° abkühlen und filtriert die Kristalle ab. Man erhält 232 g Ephedrinsalz der (4*S*,5*R*)-1,3-Dibenzyl-5-(cyclohexyloxycarbonyl)-2-oxo-imidazolidin-4-carbonsäure mit einem Zersetzungspunkt von 172–175°. $[\alpha]^{25}_D = +11°$; $[\alpha]^{25}_{365} = +33{,}3°$ (*c* = 1 in Dimethylformamid).

$C_{35}H_{43}N_3O_6$ (601,71) Ber. C 69,86 H 7,20 N 6,98% Gef. C 70,14 N 7,36 N 7,02%

Die Mutterlaugen werden im Vakuum eingedampft. Der Rückstand wird zwischen Benzol und verdünnter Schwefelsäure verteilt. Aus der wässerigen Phase kann nach Alkalinisieren mit einem Überschuss Natriumhydroxid-Lösung das (+)-Ephedrin mit Äther extrahiert werden. Die benzolische Phase enthält ein Gemisch von viel **18** und wenig **19** (R' = Cyclohexyl), welche wie die entsprechenden Cholesterinester zur Dicarbonsäure **2** verseift werden.

(3aS,6aR)-*1,3-Dibenzyl-tetrahydro-4*H-*furo*[*3,4*-d]*imidazol-2,4*(*1*H)-*dion* (**15**) *aus dem* (+)-*Ephedrinsalz von* **19** (*R' = Cyclohexyl*). 12,05 g Ephedrinsalz der (4*S*,5*R*)-1,3-Dibenzyl-5-(cyclohexyloxycarbonyl)-2-oxo-imidazolidin-4-carbonsäure werden mit 40 ml Benzol und 10 ml 3N Schwefelsäure geschüttelt. Die Benzolschicht wird 2mal mit 10 ml Wasser gewaschen und hierauf im Vakuum eingedampft. Man erhält 8,72 g rohe (4*S*,5*R*)-1,3-Dibenzyl-5-(cyclohexyloxycarbonyl)-2-oxo-imidazolidin-4-carbonsäure. [Diese kann aus Äther-Hexan kristallisiert werden; Smp. 82–84°; $[\alpha]^{25}_D = +7{,}6°$; $[\alpha]^{25}_{365} = +29{,}1°$ (*c* = 1 in Benzol).] Die rohe Säure wird in 20 ml Tetrahydrofuran gelöst und mit 2,01 g Triäthylamin versetzt. Diese Lösung wird unter Stickstoff zu einer kochenden Lösung von 1,2 g Lithiumborhydrid in 40 ml Tetrahydrofuran getropft. Man kocht noch 2 Std. unter Rückfluss und gibt dann vorsichtig 30 ml 6N Salzsäure hinzu. Man engt das Gemisch im Vakuum ein und verteilt es zwischen Wasser und Benzol. Die neutral gewaschenen organischen Phasen werden im Vakuum eingedampft und der Rückstand rasch in 25 ml Äther gelöst. Das (3a*S*,6a*R*)-1,3-Dibenzyl-tetrahydro-4*H*-furo[3,4-*d*]imidazol-2,4(1*H*)-dion (**15**) kristallisiert rasch. Man erhält 5,85 g mit einem Smp. von 120–121°. $[\alpha]^{25}_D = +58{,}2°$; $[\alpha]^{25}_{365} = +212{,}8°$ (*c* = 1 in Benzol). IR.: 1777 cm^{-1} (C=O Lacton); 1703 cm^{-1} (C=O Amid).

$C_{19}H_{18}N_2O_3$ (322,35) Ber. C 70,79 H 5,63 N 8,69% Gef. C 70,81 H 5,60 N 8,96%

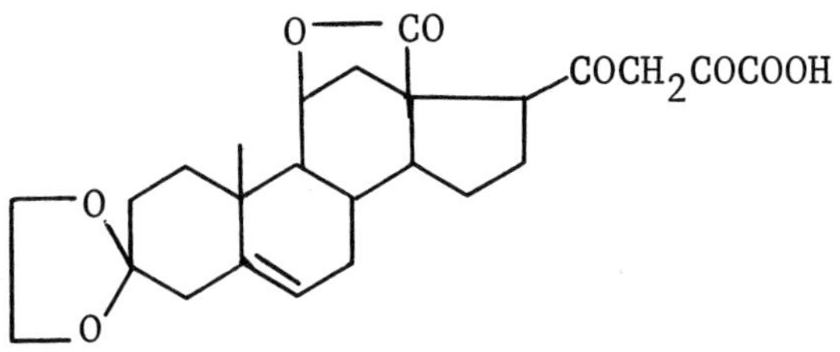

$C_{25}H_{30}O_8$ Ref. 1407

(18→11)-Lacton der *l*- bzw. *d*-Δ^5-3-Äthylendioxy-11β-hydroxy-20-oxo-pregnen-18-säure-21-oxalosäure (*l*-VI und *d*-VI): Zu einer Lösung von 1,828 g der reinen *d, l*-Oxalosäure VI und 1,333 g Strychnin in 50 ml Methylenchlorid gab man portionenweise unter gleichzeitigem Abdestillieren von Methylenchlorid insgesamt 50 ml Aceton zu und engte die entstehende Kristallsuspension auf ein Volumen von etwa 20 ml ein. Man liess zuerst 1 ½ Std. bei 20°, dann noch 1 Std. bei 0° stehen, saugte hierauf ab und wusch das Kristallisat mit kaltem Aceton und Aceton-Äther-Gemischen aus. Man erhielt 1,160 g des *schwerlöslichen* Strychninsalzes der Oxalosäure *l*-VI vom Smp. 197—199° (Zers.). $[\alpha]_D^{23} = -43°$; $-41° \pm 3°$ (c = 1,336 in $CHCl_3$).

Das Filtrat wurde weiter konzentriert und über Nacht bei 0° stehengelassen. Dabei schieden sich noch weitere 45 mg des *schwerlöslichen* Strychninsalzes vom Smp. 198—200° ab.

Die verbleibende Mutterlauge wurde im Vakuum eingedampft, der Rückstand mit Äther verrieben und getrocknet. Man erhielt 2,104 g des rohen, *leichtlöslichen* Strychninsalzes der Oxalosäure *d*-VI als amorphes Pulver. $[\alpha]_D^{23} = +3°$; $+4° \pm 4°$ (c = 0,906 in $CHCl_3$).

1,065 g des *schwerlöslichen* Strychninsalzes wurden in einer Mischung von 160 ml Methylenchlorid und 80 ml Methanol gelöst. Die Lösung kühlte man auf 0° ab und schüttelte sie zunächst mit 100 ml, dann zweimal mit je 80 ml eiskalter 10-proz. Phosphorsäure aus. Die wässerigen Auszüge extrahierte man der Reihe nach mit einer Mischung von 100 ml Methylenchlorid und 50 ml Methanol. Die organischen Lösungen ihrerseits wurden mit 3-m. Natriumchlorid gewaschen und mit Natriumsulfat getrocknet. Durch Abdestillieren des Lösungsmittels erhielt man 672 mg der Oxalosäure *l*-VI als amorphen Rückstand, der auf Zusatz von wenig Aceton grösstenteils kristallisierte. $[\alpha]_D^{23} = -44° \pm 4°$ (c = 1,133 in $CHCl_3$). IR.-Absorption in CH_2Cl_2: 2,95—3,25 μ (assoz. O—H); 5,65 μ (γ-Lacton-C=O); Schulter bei 5,75 μ (isol. Keton-C=O und Carboxyl-C=O); 6,10 μ (wahrscheinlich konj. Keton-C=O); 6,26 μ (O-induz. konj. C=C). Eine zweimal aus Aceton umkristallisierte Probe der Oxalosäure *l*-VI schmolz bei 197—200° (Zers.). $[\alpha]_D^{22} = -52° \pm 4°$ (c = 1,010 in $CHCl_3$).

$C_{25}H_{30}O_8$ (458,49) Ber. C 65,49 H 6,60% Gef. C 65,61 H 6,67%

In völlig analoger Weise wie vorstehend für das schwerlösliche Strychninsalz der Oxalosäure *l*-VI beschrieben, lieferten 2,086 g des rohen *leichtlöslichen* Strychninsalzes 1,316 g rohe Oxalosäure *d*-VI, die aber nicht kristallisiert werden konnte. $[\alpha]_D^{23} = +25°$; $+26° \pm 4°$ (c = 0,566 in $CHCl_3$).

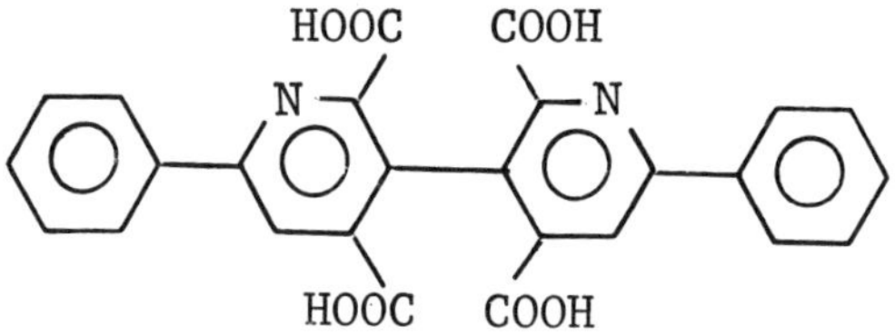

Ref. 1408

$C_{26}H_{16}N_2O_8$

Resolution of 2,2′,4,4′-Tetracarboxy-6,6′-diphenyl-3,3′-dipyridyl.—Two methods of resolution were used. The first was more extensively studied but the second proved much the simpler of the two.

First Method.—A solution of 4.84 g. (0.01 mole) of the tetracarboxydipyridyl in 200 cc. of ethyl acetate and a solution of 7.88 g. (0.02 mole) of brucine in 200 cc. of ethyl acetate were mixed together in a 2-liter beaker. Sufficient ethyl acetate was then added to dissolve almost completely the brucine salt. The hot solution was filtered, cooled and the precipitated salt filtered out by means of a Gooch crucible. About 0.5 g. was usually obtained.

Rotation. 0.2205 g. made up to 50 cc. with chloroform at 20° gave α_D −0.02 ± 0.01°; $l = 1$; $[\alpha]_D^{25}$ −4.9°.

This precipitate was extracted several times with 100-cc. portions of hot ethyl acetate, but neither the residue nor the salt which separated on cooling showed any change in rotation.

The filtrate from the 0.5 g. of salt from the original solution was then concentrated and various fractions as they precipitated were filtered. This was continued until a volume of 50 cc. was reached when no more salt could be obtained in a solid condition

upon cooling the solution. These intermediate fractions were worked up for less soluble and more soluble salt by the process just discussed.

Upon evaporating the 50 cc. to dryness and removing the last traces of solvent by suction, the more soluble salt was obtained in a dry powdery form. Generally less than a gram was obtained.

Rotation. 0.1136 g. made up to 20 cc. with chloroform at 20° gave α_D −0.20 ± 0.01°; l = 1; $[\alpha]^{25}_D$ −35.8°.

Second Method.—To a solution of 9.682 g. (0.02 mole) of the acid in 200 cc. of ethyl acetate was added 7.88 g. (0.02 mole) of brucine in 100 cc. of ethyl acetate. A precipitate (8.7 g.) was obtained which decomposed without melting at 202–207°. It was purified by boiling with ethyl acetate to dissolve any more soluble salt which had adhered.

Rotation. 0.1400 g. made up to 50 cc. with chloroform at 20° gave α_D −0.01 ± 0.01°; l = 1; $[\alpha]^{25}_D$ −3.5°.

Upon the addition of another 7.88 g. (0.02 mole) of brucine in 100 cc. of ethyl acetate, 1.9 g. more of precipitate was obtained which apparently was a less soluble form.

Rotation. 0.1623 g. made up to 50 cc. with chloroform at 20° gave α_D −0.046 ± 0.01°; l = 1; $[\alpha]^{25}_D$ −5.6°.

The solution was then evaporated to 50 cc., whereupon 14 g. of salt had precipitated.

Rotation. 0.1916 g. made up to 20 cc. with chloroform at 20° gave α_D −0.19 ± 0.01°; l = 1; $[\alpha]^{25}_D$ −19.8°.

The last 50 cc. was evaporated to dryness and 3 g. of more soluble salt was obtained. It turns brown at 155–160° and melts with decomposition at 180–184°.

Rotation. 0.1500 g. made up to 20 cc. with chloroform at 20° gave α_D −0.26 ± 0.01°; l = 1; $[\alpha]^{25}_D$ −34.7°.

By extracting the 14 g. of intermediate fraction with 50-cc. portions of the ethyl acetate, 1.5 g. of the more soluble salt was readily obtained having $[\alpha]^{25}_D$ −35°.

Anal. Calcd. for $C_{72}H_{68}N_6O_{16}$: N, 6.69. Found: for less soluble salt, N, 6.61; for more soluble salt, N, 6.66.

***d* and *l*-2,2′-4,4′-tetracarboxy-6,6′-diphenyl-3,3′-dipyridyl.**—Three grams of the salt $[\alpha]^{25}_D$ −5.0° was triturated in a small porcelain mortar with ice-cold, 5% hydrochloric acid, filtered and washed with distilled water. After partially drying, the procedure was repeated. The acid was then taken up in ice-cold, very dilute sodium hydroxide and shaken three times with 100-cc. portions of chloroform. The solution was filtered into cold dilute hydrochloric acid. (The procedure occupied about twenty minutes up to this point.) The free acid separated and was filtered and washed with distilled water and dried over phosphorus pentoxide *in vacuo* at room temperature. About 0.8 g. of the acid (entirely free from brucine) was recovered from the 3 g. of salt.

Rotation. 0.0896 g. made up to 20 cc. with acetone at 20° gave α_D +0.035 ± 0.01°; l = 1; $[\alpha]^{25}_D$ +7.8°. 0.1628 g. made up to 20 cc. with 95% alcohol at 20° gave α_D +0.05 ± 0.01°; l = 1; $[\alpha]^{25}_D$ +6.1°.

The same procedure was followed with the more soluble salt. The yield of free acid was less from this fraction.

Rotation. 0.0677 g. made up to 20 cc. with 95% alcohol at 20° gave α_D −0.04 ± 0.01°; l = 2; $[\alpha]^{25}_D$ −5.9°.

Anal. Calcd. for $C_{26}H_{16}N_2O_8$: N, 5.78. Found: for +6.1° acid, N. 5.16; for −5.9° acid, N, 5.08.

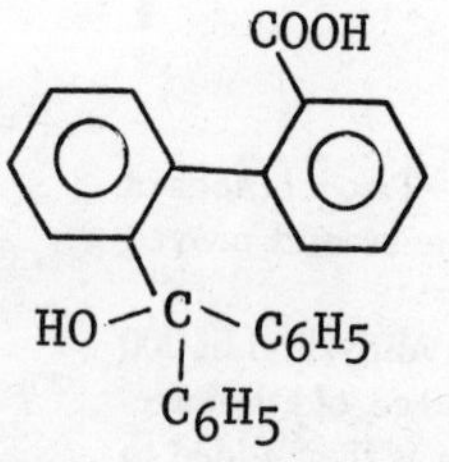

$C_{26}H_{20}O_3$ Ref. 1409

Scissione dell'acido. – Fra i diversi sali presi in esame (di cinconina, stricnina, brucina) abbiamo scelto quello di brucina che cristallizza bene da alcool.

Ad una soluzione di 2.07 gr. (1 mol.) di brucina anidra in 40 cmc. di alcool etilico 95° si aggiungono 2 gr. (1 mol.) di acido 2-[bis-fenil-ossimetil] 2′-difenilcarbossilico. Si bolle per breve tempo, si filtra la soluzione e la si concentra ponendola in essicatore a vuoto su acido solforico.

Quando il volume è ridotto a circa metà si filtra il sale separatosi (1ª frazione gr. 2.8, p. f. 200°); evaporando il filtrato a secco sempre in essicatore si ottiene una seconda frazione (gr. 1.2, p. f. 182°).

L'analisi delle due frazioni ha fornito:

	1ª frazione	trov. %	C 75.82	H 6.10	N 3.70
	2ª frazione	»			3.35
per $C_{49}H_{46}O_7N_2$		calc.	75.94	5.99	3.62;

il loro potere rotatorio in soluzione cloroformica misurato appena fatta la soluzione risulta rispettivamente:

1ª frazione . . . . $[\alpha]^{18}_D = (+0°.67 \cdot 100):(1.6280 \cdot 1) = +41°.15$

2ª frazione . . . . $[\alpha]^{18}_D = (-0°.08 \cdot 100):(1.0693 \cdot 1) = -7°.48$.

Il potere rotatorio della soluzione cloroformica della prima frazione lasciata a sè a circa 18° va diminuendo annullandosi dopo circa due tre giorni ed assumendo poi valori negativi.

Il potere rotatorio misurato dopo 150 ore dalla prima misura risulta:

$$[\alpha]^{18}_D = (-0,°18 \cdot 100):(1.6280 \cdot 1) = -11°.06.$$

Esso tende evidentemente al valore del potere rotatorio del sale di brucina della miscela racemica, che dalla misura di una soluzione di 0.1900 gr. di acido e 0. 1970 gr. di brucina anidra in 25 cmc. di cloroformio risulta essere:

$$[\alpha]_D^{18} = (-0^\circ.23 \cdot 100) : (1.5480 \cdot 1) = -14^\circ.86.$$

La scissione del sale di chinina si effettua scogliendolo a temperatura ordinaria nella minor quantità possibile di piridina, precipitando la soluzione per diluizione con acqua ghiacciata ed acidificando la sospensione con acido cloridrico ghiacciato. La parte insolubile costituita dall'acido attivo viene lavata parecchie volte prima con acido cloridrico diluito poi con acqua e si asciuga in essicatore.

Gli acidi attivi così ottenuti dalla prima e dalla seconda frazione fondono ambedue a 110° come il racemico ed in soluzione cloroformica sono ambedue destrogiri, il primo in quantità maggiore del secondo. Le soluzioni lasciate a sè a temperatura ordinaria perdono rapidamente l'attività ottica.

(1) « Ber. », 59, 659 (1926).
(2) P. G. SSERGEJEW, « Chem. Zentr. », II, 392 (1930).
(3) P. G. SSERGEJEW, loc. cit.

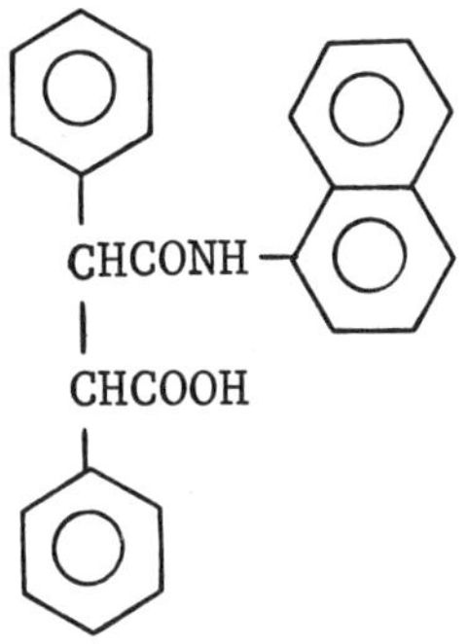

$C_{26}H_{21}NO_3$ Ref. 1410

A solution of *r*-diphenylsuccin-α-naphthylamic acid (25·1 g.) and quinine (24·1 g.) in boiling absolute ethyl alcohol (175 c.c.) was filtered and preserved in an ice-chest during 3 days. The ill-defined crystals which separated (26·5 g.) were crystallised repeatedly from the same solvent, 5 c.c. of the latter being used for each gram of material. The course of the resolution was followed by observing the specific rotations in acetone of the acids isolated from the successive filtrates, the following values being obtained: − 155·5°, − 61·4°, + 93·4°, and + 154·9°. The residual quinine salt (9·6 g.) was decomposed with dilute sulphuric acid and ether, and the crude d-*diphenylsuccin-α-naphthylamic acid* crystallised from 80% alcohol until its specific rotation remained constant. It formed small needles, m. p. 206—207° (Found: C, 78·8; H, 5·4%). In acetone ($l = 2$, $c = 0{\cdot}8432$) $\alpha_D^{16°}$ + 3·47°, whence $[\alpha]_D^{16°}$ +205·8°.

l-Diphenylsuccin-α-naphthylamic acid ($[\alpha]_D$ − 123·2° in acetone; 16·7 g.), from the crude lævorotatory mixture of acids obtained from the first filtrates of the quinine salt (see above), and cinchonidine (13 g.) were dissolved in boiling ethyl alcohol (120 c.c.). The salt, which separated very slowly from the cold solution, was recrystallised from alcohol and decomposed in the usual manner, yielding l-*diphenylsuccin-α-naphthylamic acid* having $[\alpha]_D$ − 194·3° in acetone. Crystallisation of the crude acid from 80% alcohol afforded the homogeneous acid, which exactly resembled its optical antipode in appearance, solubility and melting point. It had $[\alpha]_D^{17°}$ − 206·6° in acetone solution ($l = 2$, $c = 0{\cdot}9484$, $\alpha_D^{17°}$ − 3·92°) (Found: C, 79·2; H, 5·4%).

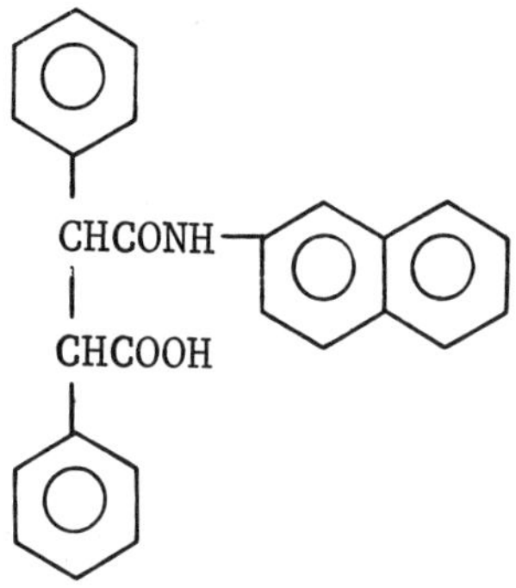

$C_{26}H_{21}NO_3$ Ref. 1411

Resolution of r-*Diphenylsuccin-β-naphthylamic Acid into its Optical Antipodes.*—*r*-Diphenylsuccin-β-naphthylamic acid (m. p. 201—202°; prepared in almost quantitative yield in the same manner as the α-acid and purified by crystallisation from rectified spirit) (49·8 g.) and quinine (23·6 g.) were dissolved in boiling absolute alcohol and the solution was preserved in an ice-chest during 3 days. The needles (27·8 g.) which slowly separated were repeatedly crystallised from the same solvent, 20 c.c. of which were used for each gram of salt. The acid recovered from the successive filtrates had $[\alpha]_D$ − 96·3°, − 56·4°, + 44·0°, + 126·2° and + 210°, respectively, in acetone. The crude dextrorotatory acid isolated from the residual salt was crystallised from 80% alcohol until successive crops had a constant specific rotation. d-*Diphenylsuccin-β-naphthylamic acid* crystallises in small needles, m. p. 188° (Found: C, 78·8; H, 5·4. $C_{26}H_{21}O_3N$ requires C, 79·0; H, 5·4%). In acetone ($l = 2$, $c = 0{\cdot}7288$) $\alpha_D^{15.5°}$ + 5·64°, whence $[\alpha]_D^{15.5°}$ + 386·9°.

Preparation of the homogeneous *l*-acid from the crude lævorotatory mixture of acids isolated from the initial filtrates obtained in the foregoing resolution could not be effected by crystallisation or by means of cinchonine, cinchonidine, or brucine.

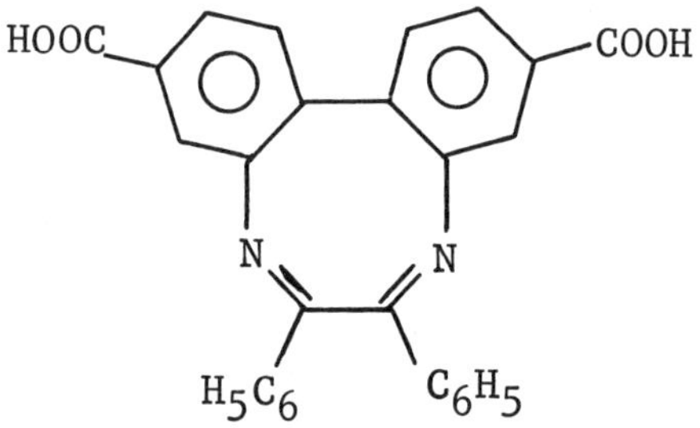

Ref. 1412

$C_{28}H_{18}N_2O_4$

On addition of (IV) (1·4 g.) to brucine (2·8 g.) in hot ethanol (50 c.c.) there was obtained a clear solution which almost immediately began to deposit rosettes of needles. The crop ($[\alpha]_D$ −540°; $c = 1$, in chloroform) was extracted with alcohol until constant rotatory power was obtained ($[\alpha]_D$ −566°). On decomposition with hydrochloric acid this gave the free acid, $[\alpha]_D$ −740° ($c = 1$, in N/2-sodium hydroxide) raised by crystallisation from aqueous alcohol to $[\alpha]_D$ −955°. The mother liquor from the brucine salt was concentrated, a small crystalline crop removed, and the residual liquor poured into dilute hydrochloric acid. The product had $[\alpha]_D$ +925° ($c = 0{\cdot}91$, in N/2-sodium hydroxide).

$C_{28}H_{18}N_2O_4$ Ref. 1412a

2,3-*Diphenyl*-5,6:7,8-*dibenzo*-1,4-*diazocine*-2′,3″-*dicarboxylic Acid* (I; R = Ph).—2,2′-Diaminobiphenyl-4,4′-dicarboxylic acid (1 g.) and benzil (0·78 g.) were heated in boiling glacial acetic acid (70 c.c.) for 25 hr. The hot solution was filtered and the filtrate concentrated to ~1/3 of its volume. Hot water was added until yellow solid began to crystallise. This was taken through the sodium salt to remove any benzil and the acid then crystallised from aqueous acetic acid. The diazocine-acid (0·4 g., 24%) had m. p. >360° (Bell [3] gives m. p. 348°).

Optical Resolution of 2,3-*Diphenyl*-5,6:7,8-*dibenzo*-1,4-*diazocine*-2′,3″-*dicarboxylic Acid.*—This was achieved through the brucine salt [3] which was repeatedly extracted with boiling ethanol until a constant rotation of $[\alpha]^{22}_{5461}$ −750° (l = 2; *c*, 0·458 in $CHCl_3$) was obtained. A chloroform solution of the salt was extracted with 10% sodium hydroxide solution, and the (−)-acid was precipitated from it and crystallised from aqueous acetic acid from which it separated in a solvated form. After being heated at 100° it had a rather variable first m. p. of *ca.* 225° but resolidified on further heating and then melted sharply at 276—277°; $[\alpha]^{24}_{5461}$ −2100° $[\alpha]^{24}_{5791}$ −1670° (*c*, 0·170 in Me_2NCHO) (Found, after being dried at 100° *in vacuo*: C, 75·1; H, 4·3; N, 6·4; O, 14·4. Calc. for $C_{28}H_{18}N_2O_4$: C, 75·3; H, 4·1; N, 6·3; O, 14·3%). Similar treatment of the original-mother-liquor of the brucine salt gave the (+)-acid with similar melting behaviour; $[\alpha]^{24}_{5461}$ +2050°, $[\alpha]^{24}_{5791}$ +1620° (*c*, 0·226 in Me_2NCHO) (Found, after being dried at 100° *in vacuo*: C, 75·35; H, 4·2; N, 6·25; O, 14·55%).

[3] Bell, *J.*, 1952, 1527.

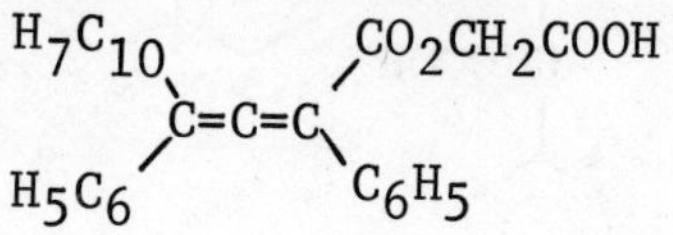

$C_{28}H_{20}O_4$ Ref. 1413

Resolution: The Dextro Acid, I.—A solution of 4.7 g. of the acid and 5.2 g. of brucine in 60 cc. of dry methyl alcohol was boiled for an hour during which time it deposited a quantity of a solid salt. The suspension was filtered while hot and the salt was washed with methyl alcohol. It weighed 4.0 g. and it melted at 145°. The melting point was not changed by three recrystallizations from a mixture of acetone and methyl alcohol from which the salt separated in small transparent prisms.

The acid was liberated by shaking a suspension of the salt in ether three times with 10% hydrochloric acid. The ethereal layer was washed and shaken with bicarbonate. From the bicarbonate solution precipitated an oil that was converted into a solid by treatment with ether–petroleum ether. The solid melted at 145–146° and its rotation in ethyl acetate was $[\alpha]_D$ +29.5°. Neither the melting point nor the rotation was changed by two recrystallizations from ether–petroleum ether.

Anal. Calcd. for $C_{28}H_{20}O_4$: C, 79.9; H, 4.8. Found: C, 79.9; H, 4.8.

The Levo Acid.—The mother liquor from which the salt of the dextro acid had been removed was allowed to cool. It deposited first an oil and then a small quantity of the dextro salt. It was set aside for twenty-four hours, then filtered. The filtrate was evaporated and the residue was treated like the salt of the dextro acid. The ether–petroleum ether solution that was obtained in this manner first deposited some of the *d,l* acid melting at 195° and then an acid melting at 144–146°. Owing to a mishap, the quantity of this acid was too small for further purification. The melting point and the rotation in ethyl acetate—$[\alpha]_D$ −28.4°—show that it was practically pure levo acid.

Anal. Calcd. for $C_{28}H_{20}O_4$: C, 79.9; H, 4.8. Found: C, 80.0; H, 4.9.

A mixture of equal weights of the *d* and *l* acids melted at 195°.

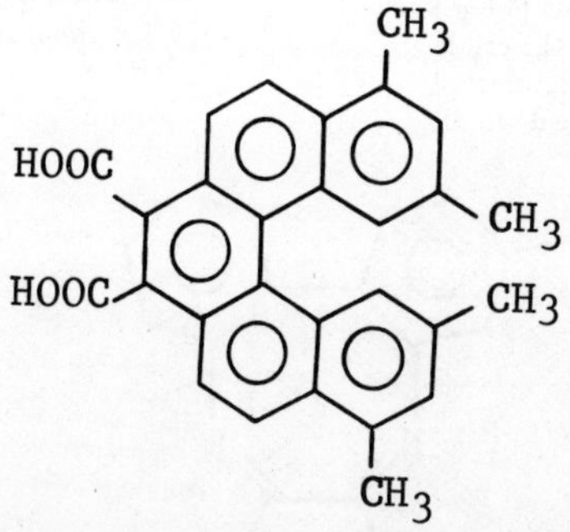

$C_{28}H_{22}O_4$ Ref. 1414

Resolution. Finely powdered morphine (0·71 g.) in alcohol (25 c.c.) was treated at the boil with 0·493 g. of the acid. The resulting solution was left overnight after being well cooled and scratched vigorously. The fine white powdery salt which separated was dried in a vacuum, desiccator; yield 0·92 g., $[\alpha]^{20}_{5461}$ −123°. Crystallisation from alcohol (18 c.c.) gave 0·54 g. of salt, $[\alpha]^{20}_{5461}$ −173°, this value being increased to $[\alpha]^{20}_{5461}$ −182° (chloroform, *c* = 0·95) by a further crystallisation from alcohol (12 c.c.). The salt was decomposed by shaking it with cold dilute hydrochloric acid, and the yellow flocculent precipitate was dissolved in cold sodium hydroxide, reprecipitated, filtered off, washed, and sucked as dry as possible on the pump. The slightly damp acid was shaken with cold acetone until dissolved; the filtered solution (20 c.c.) showed a rotation of −0·52° decreasing to −0·32° after one hour, −0·20° after 3 hours, and after 5 hours was too small to be observed with accuracy. The acetone solution and the washings of the polarimeter tube were evaporated to dryness, whereupon the weight of the acid in solution was found to be 0·11 g., giving an initial specific rotation of $[\alpha]^{20}_{5461}$ −47·2°. The original mother-liquor of the salt was diluted with water, decomposed as above, and the slightly damp acid gave an observed rotation of +0·18°, corresponding to a specific rotation of approximately +18°.

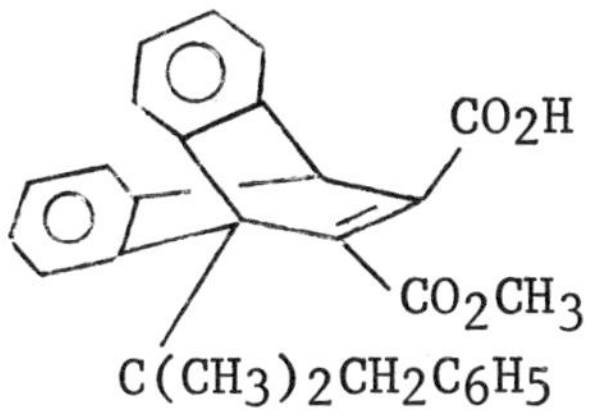

$C_{29}H_{26}O_4$ Ref. 1415

Note:

Resolution of racemic acid was carried out through crystallization of its (-)-menthyl ester. The physical constants obtained were: m.p. 188-190°, $[\alpha]_D^{32}$ +24.8° and -24.6° both in $CHCl_3$.

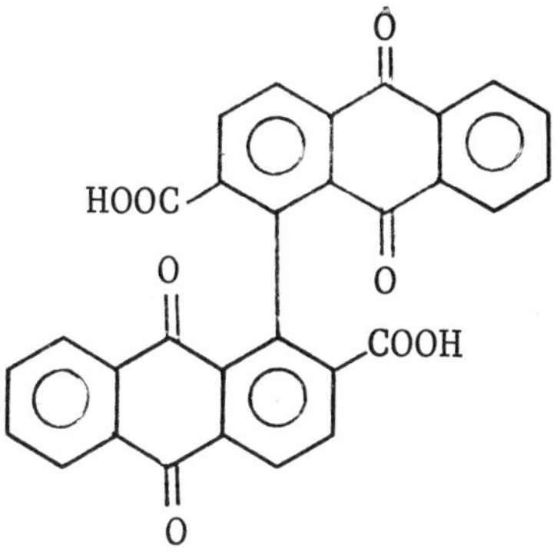

$C_{30}H_{14}O_8$ Ref. 1416

III. Zerlegung in optisch aktive Komponenten.

Zur Spaltung eignen sich die primären Brucin- oder Morphinsalze nicht, obwohl das Brucinsalz aus Aceton krystallisiert erhalten werden kann. Hingegen gelingt die Zerlegung über das saure Chininsalz, das leicht aus Aceton oder Alkohol fraktioniert krystallisiert, oder aus Chloroform mit Äther fraktioniert gefällt werden kann. Hier sei der letztere Weg beschrieben.

7,58 g Chininhydrat (1 Mol) wurden in 200 ccm Chloroform gelöst und langsam 10,06 g 1,1'-Dianthrachinonyl-2,2'-dicarbonsäure in die siedende Lösung eingetragen. Nach dem Einengen auf 160 ccm wurden die Chininsalze durch vorsichtigen Ätherzusatz unter stetem Reiben mit einem Glasstab ausgefällt.

Die I. Fraktion wurde mit 65 ccm Äther erst etwas ölig, dann in gelbroten, doppelbrechenden Flocken, welche trocken 9 g wogen (54,4 Proc. d. Th. berechnet auf primäres, wasserfreies Salz), ausgefällt. Falls das Chloroform durch Äther nicht vollständig verdrängt wird, kann sich das Chininsalz im Exsiccator verflüssigen. Schmelzpunkt unscharf bei etwa 196—210° unter Zersetzung.

$[\alpha]_D^{17}$ = (+ 2,90°.100):(0,7.2,58) = + 160,6° in Pyridin.

Als II. Fraktion wurden 5,5 g (33 Proc. d. Th.) gelbe Flocken aus dem Filtrat von I nach Zusatz von weiteren 40 ccm Äther erhalten. Schmelzpunkt unscharf bei etwa 196—210° unter Zersetzung $[\alpha]_D^{18}$ = etwa + 185° (ungenau wegen anhaftendem Chloroform).

Eine III. Fraktion von 1,3 g (7,9 Proc. d. Th.) erhielten wir aus der Mutterlauge von II nach Zugabe von 160 ccm Äther. Schmelzpunkt unscharf bei etwa 200° unter Zersetzung.

$[\alpha]_D^{17}$ = (+3,58°.100):(0,7.1,69) = + 302,6° in Pyridin.

Die Mutterlauge von III, völlig zur Trockne verdampft, lieferte als *IV. Fraktion* noch 0,7 g (4,2 Proc. d. Th.) leichter lösliches Chininsalz.

$[\alpha]_D^{17}$ = (+2,78°.100):(0,7.1,64) = + 242,2° in Pyridin.

l-1,1'-Dianthrachinonyl-2,2'-dicarbonsaures Chinin ist in Alkohol leicht löslich und läßt sich durch Extraktion der einzelnen Chininsalzfraktionen gewinnen. Nach 3 maligem Auskochen der I. Fraktion, erst mit 180 ccm, dann zweimal mit 100 ccm 96 proc. Alkohol, hinterblieben 4,6 g schwer lösliches Chininsalz, für welches wir fanden

$[\alpha]_D^{17}$ = (+2,14°.100):(0,7.1,027) = + 297,7° in Pyridin.

Der auf die Hälfte eingeengte erste alkoholische Auszug ließ nach einigem Stehen 0,65 g leicht lösliches Chininsalz ausfallen, welches drehte

$[\alpha]_D^{18}$ = (−0,36°.100):(0,7.0,703) = − 73,2° in Pyridin.

Nach völligem Verdampfen des Lösungsmittels hinterblieb 1 g Chininsalz von

$[\alpha]_D^{18}$ = (−0,53°.100):(0,7.1,023) = − 74° in Pyridin.

Beim Einengen des vereinigten 2. und 3. alkoholischen Auszuges auf etwa 50 ccm krystallisierten 0,9 g Chininsalz vom Zersetzungsp. 193° (korr.) aus.

$[\alpha]_D^{18}$ = (−0,62°.100):(0,7.0,787) = − 110,7° in Pyridin.

Das leichter lösliche Chininsalz läßt sich durch Umfällen aus Chloroform–Äther weiter reinigen. Etwa 0,6 g Chininsalz von $[\alpha]_D^{18}$ = − 73,2° wurden in 8 ccm Chloroform gelöst und durch Zusatz von Äther eine Kopffraktion von

$[\alpha]_D^{17}$ = (−0,17°.100):(0,7.0,402) = − 81,3° in Pyridin

ausgefällt. Die Endfraktion wurde nochmals in Chloroform gelöst und mit Äther eine schwer lösliche Fraktion von

$[\alpha]_D^{17}$ = (−0,19°.100):(0,5.0,468) = − 81,2° in Pyridin

erhalten, der Rest drehte

$[\alpha]_D^{17}$ = (−0,13°.100):(0,5.0,38) = − 68,4° in Pyridin.

d-1,1'-Dianthrachinonyl-2,2'-dicarbonsaures Chinin ist in Alkohol schwer löslich und wurde gewonnen durch häufiges Auskochen der II. Fraktion mit diesem Lösungsmittel. Nach 4 maligem Auskochen, erst mit 100 ccm, dann dreimal mit 50 ccm 96 proc. Alkohol stieg das Drehungsvermögen auf

$[\alpha]_D^{17}$ = (+1,25°.100):(0,7.0,573) = + 311,6° in Pyridin.

Nach weiterem 5 maligem Auskochen mit je 50 ccm Alkohol war

$[\alpha]_D^{17}$ = (+1,76.100):(0,7.0,697) = + 360,7° in Pyridin.

Wiederholung des Auskochens ergab nach Anwendung von 70, 50, 100 ccm Alkohol

$[\alpha]_D^{19}$ = (+2,02°.100):(0,7.0,787) = + 366,7° in Pyridin.

Nach weiterem Auskochen mit 100, dann mit 50 ccm Alkohol fanden wir

$[\alpha]_D^{19}$ = (+1,93°.100):(0,7.0,75) = + 367,6° in Pyridin.

Nochmals ausgekocht mit 50 ccm Alkohol hinterblieb ein Rückstand von 0,85 g vom Schmelzp. 249—250° (korr.) unter Zersetzung, welcher drehte

$[\alpha]_D^{18}$ = (+1,25°.100):(0,7.0,484) = + 369° in Pyridin.

l-1,1'-Dianthrachinonyl-2,2'-dicarbonsäure. Zur Zerlegung wurden 0,8 g fein pulverisiertes Chininsalz von $[\alpha]_D^{18}$ = −110,7° dreimal mit 20 ccm etwa 2 n-Salzsäure $^3/_4$ Stunden auf 60—70° erwärmt. Durch Umfällen aus $^n/_{10}$-NaOH/HCl (wie beim Ausgangsmaterial angegeben) wurde die aktive Säure in mikrokrystalliner Form erhalten. Sie sintert von 184° an, bildet bei 194° (unkorr.) einen durchsichtigen, an der Wand klebenden Kegel, der sich allmählich zu einem Tropfen zusammenzieht und bei 273° (unkorr.) einen Meniskus bildet.

$[\alpha]_D^{18}$ = (− 1,12°.100):(0,7.0,675) = − 237° in $^n/_{10}$-NaOH.

d-1,1'-Dianthrachinonyl-2,2'-dicarbonsäure. 0,8 g 15 mal mit Alkohol ausgekochtes Chininsalz wurde in gleicher Weise zerlegt. Die aus $^n/_{10}$-NaOH/HCl in mikrokrystalliner Form erhaltene Säure (chininfrei, mit Phosphorwolframsäure geprüft) sintert von 184° an, bildet bei 195° einen durchscheinenden Kegel, der in nicht genau reproduzierbarer Weise gegen 260° zu einer roten Schmelze zusammenfließt.

$[\alpha]_D^{19}$ = (+ 3,40°.100):(0,7.1,404) = + 346° in $^n/_{10}$-NaOH.

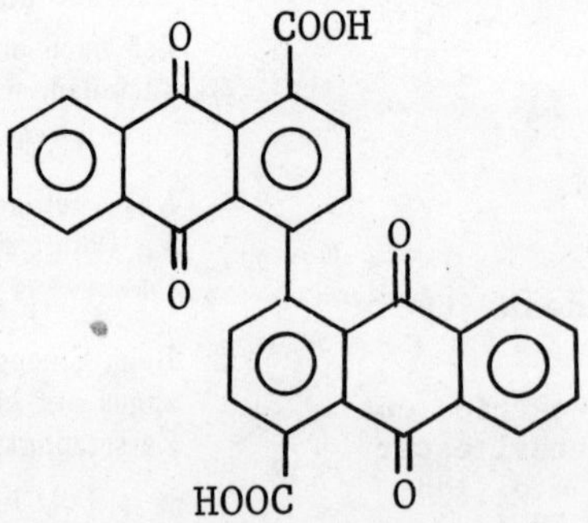

$C_{30}H_{14}O_8$

Ref. 1417

1 : 1′-Dianthraquinonyl-4 : 4′-dicarboxylic acid was prepared from 1-chloro-4-benzamidoanthraquinone by the method of Stanley and Adams (*loc. cit.*), and formed a pale yellow powder, m. p. 418°. The resolution with brucine was unsatisfactory but, nevertheless, that part of the salt which was least soluble in absolute alcohol gave an acid of small lævorotation, and the more soluble salt gave an acid of small dextrorotation. Resolution was however readily accomplished by use of cinchonine, which gave a less soluble salt of the (−)-acid, or cinchonidine, which gave a less soluble salt of the (+)-acid. The following is a typical experiment. Cinchonine (6 g., 2 mols.) was added to a suspension of the acid (5 g., 1 mol.) in boiling absolute alcohol (500 c.c.). About half of the acid rapidly dissolved but to get the remainder into solution required the addition of a further 3 g. of cinchonine. No crystallisation occurred on cooling of the solution and for this it was necessary to reduce the volume to about 100 c.c. The first crop consisted of almost pure cinchonine (3 g.), the second crop of bright yellow crystals (6 g.), and the filtrate from this was decomposed by pouring it into boiling dilute hydrochloric acid. The recovered acid ($[\alpha]_D$ about +350° in 0·1N-sodium hydroxide) was purified by combination with cinchonidine (below).

The crop of cinchonine salt was recrystallised from alcohol until of constant rotatory power, $[\alpha]_D^{21}$ +20° (*c*, 1·01 in chloroform), and then had m. p. 207° (decomp.). Decomposition gave (−)-1 : 1′-dianthraquinonyl-4 : 4′-dicarboxylic acid, m. p. 395°, $[\alpha]_D$ −443° (*c*, 1·02 in 0·1N-sodium hydroxide).

The (+)-acid (3·15 g., 1 mol.; see above) was added to a boiling solution of cinchonidine (5·7 g., 3 mols.) in absolute alcohol (250 c.c.). The liquid immediately filled with a heavy crystalline deposit of the cinchonidine salt. This was purified by repeated extraction with hot alcohol. The purified salt, m. p. 234° (decomp.), furnished (+)-1 : 1′-dianthraquinonyl-4 : 4′-dicarboxylic acid, m. p. 390°, $[\alpha]_D$ +428° (*c*, 1·04 in 0·1N-sodium hydroxide).

The sodium salts of the active acids were very much more soluble than was the sodium salt of the inactive acid, a 1% solution of which tended to crystallise in the polarimeter tube. At room temperature the solutions of the sodium salts slowly lost activity (the observed rotation had fallen to about one-third after 70 hours); at the b. p. the same loss was attained in somewhat under 1 hour. The active acid required some 6 hours' heating with thionyl chloride for complete dissolution. The chloride left after removal of the excess of thionyl chloride was insoluble in benzene, chloroform, carbon tetrachloride, acetone, *o*-dichlorobenzene, or methyl ethyl ketone, and was inactive in pyridine (*c*, 0·99).

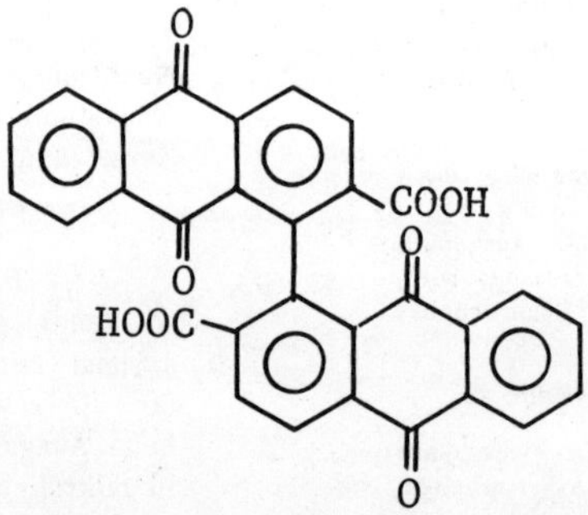

$C_{30}H_{14}O_8$

Ref. 1418

Resolution of 1 : 1′-*Dianthraquinonyl*-2 : 2′-*dicarboxylic Acid.*—Quinidine (36·5 g.) was added to the acid (24·5 g.) in boiling alcohol (1600 c.c.). The mixture, after boiling for 1 hour, was allowed to cool overnight and the crystalline crop filtered off and well washed with alcohol. The residue (23·7 g.) was repeatedly extracted with hot alcohol to remove more soluble materials, and the final residue (21·2 g.) decomposed by trituration with dilute hydrochloric acid. The material so obtained crystallised from acetic acid in compact orange-red prisms, $[\alpha]_{5791}$ −318° (*c*, 2·6 in 0·1N-sodium hydroxide). The alcoholic filtrate from this salt was evaporated to about one-eighth bulk and the crop (4·8 g.) obtained on cooling filtered off. The alcoholic filtrate was poured slowly into boiling dilute hydrochloric acid whereupon there was obtained the (+)-acid, $[\alpha]_{5791}$ +304° (*c*, 2·5 in 0·1N-sodium hydroxide).

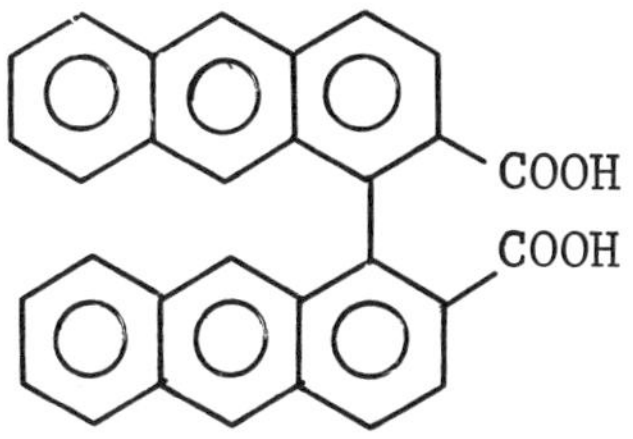

$C_{30}H_{18}O_4$ Ref. 1419

Resolution.—Results with brucine, morphine, quinine, cinchonine, or cinchonidine were negative or unsatisfactory.

A suspension of the acid (25 g.) in alcohol (1 l.) was heated under reflux on a water-bath. Finely powdered quinidine ($C_{20}H_{24}O_2N_2,2H_2O$; 41 g.) was added slowly. After addition of about 15 g. of the alkaloid the acid was in solution. Addition of the remainder of the alkaloid caused immediate precipitation of a highly crystalline alkaloidal salt. The mixture was kept warm on the water-bath for a further 10 minutes, cooled, and filtered, and the salt well washed with alcohol. Yield, 30·5 g.; $[\alpha]_{5461}^{20°}$ −509° (*c*, 0·51 in chloroform). The combined mother-liquor and washings were distilled on the water-bath until 800 c.c. of alcohol had been removed, and the residual solution set aside overnight. The small quantity (1·73 g.) of amorphous material which separated was filtered off and discarded. The alcohol was then completely removed from the filtrate, and the residual brown honey-like mass decomposed by warming on the water-bath for ½ hour with 1% sodium hydroxide solution (500 c.c.). After filtration from the precipitated alkaloid, the warm yellow solution was poured into 3·5% hydrochloric acid (200 c.c.). The gelatinous precipitate of *dextro*-1 : 1′-dianthryl-2 : 2′-dicarboxylic acid (12·5 g.) was filtered off, washed, and dried in the steam oven at 90—95°. The crude acid was pulverised in a mortar, added to boiling glacial acetic acid (250 c.c.), and freed from a little undissolved material. The solution on cooling deposited the acid as a bright canary-yellow crystalline powder, m. p. 251—253°, $[\alpha]_{5461}^{21°}$ +362° (*c*, 0·7265 in acetone). Two further crystallisations from glacial acetic acid gave the optically pure acid (8·25 g.), m. p. 251—253°, $[\alpha]_{5461}^{20°}$ +439°, $[\alpha]_{5790}^{20°}$ +392°, $[\alpha]_D^{21°}$ +382° (*c*, 0·795 in acetone). The crystalline salt of the *lævo*-acid was extracted with boiling alcohol (500 c.c.); the residual salt (27 g.) had $[\alpha]_{5461}^{20°}$ −522° (*c*, 1·03 in chloroform). Decomposition of this by the above method yielded 12·0 g. of acid which, on crystallisation from boiling glacial acetic acid (120 c.c.), yielded 11·1 g. of bright yellow crystalline powder, m. p. 253—255°, $[\alpha]_{5461}^{20°}$ −429° (*c*, 0·80). A further crystallisation from glacial acetic acid yielded 10·4 g. of optically pure acid, m. p. 253—255°, $[\alpha]_{5461}^{20°}$ −440°, $[\alpha]_{5790}^{20°}$ −395°, $[\alpha]_D^{21°}$ −386° (*c*, 0·80 in acetone).

$C_{30}H_{18}O_4$ Ref. 1419a

II. Spaltung in optisch aktive Komponenten

Am geeignetsten für die Spaltung erwies sich das saure Chininsalz, als Lösungsmittel Benzol, oder noch besser Aceton, aus dem auf Zusatz von Petroläther fraktioniert gefällt werden kann.

5,1 g Dianthryl-dicarbonsäure wurden in 60 ccm Aceton in der Wärme gelöst und bei 40—50°, 3,75 g Chininhydrat zugegeben. Die Lösung färbt sich etwas dunkel.

1. Fraktion: Sie wurde erhalten durch langsames Ausfällen mit 70 ccm Petroläther (Sdp. 48—55°) erhalten. Die Lösung trübt sich auf Zusatz des Petroläthers, dann scheidet sich plötzlich ein harzig-öliges Produkt am Boden aus, während die Lösung vollkommen klar wird. Sie wird abgegossen und das Öl bei 35—40° getrocknet. Sobald alles Lösungsmittel verdunstet ist, erstarrt das Öl zu einer braunen, glasigen Masse, die beim Verreiben in ein schwach gelb gefärbtes Pulver übergeht. Auch alle übrigen Fraktionen verhalten sich so. Der Schmelzpunkt ist nicht bestimmbar, man kann nur einen Zersetzungspunkt angeben, bei dem deutliche Gasentwicklung auftritt. Bereits lange vorher beginnt das Salz zu erweichen. Wir geben im folgenden diese beiden Temperaturen als Verflüssigungspunkt an. Verflüssigungsp. ist 120–160° u. Zers. 3,9 g.

$(\alpha)_D^{20} = (+ 0{,}13°.100) : 1.0{,}5) = + 26{,}0$ in Chloroform.

2. Fraktion: Erhalten auf weiteren Zusatz von 40 ccm Petroläther. 2,6 g, Verflüssigungspunkt 130—160° u. Zers.

$(\alpha)_D^{20} = (- 0{,}44°.100) : (0{,}5.1{,}04) = - 76{,}0°$ in Chloroform.

3. Fraktion: Durch Eindampfen der Mutterlauge von Fraktion 2. 2,1 g, Verflüssigungspunkt ist 130—175° u. Zers.

$(\alpha)_D^{20} = (- 0{,}68°.100) : (0{,}5.1{,}04) = - 130{,}8°$ in Chloroform.

d-1,1′-Dianthryl-2,2′-dicarbonsaures Chinin ist in Benzol schwer löslich und wird aus der Fraktion 1 durch mehrmaliges Umkrystallisieren als gelbliches Pulver erhalten, das bei 165—185° u. Zers. schmilzt. 1,95 g.

$(\alpha)_D^{20} = (+ 1{,}18°.100) : (0{,}5.1{,}012) = + 233{,}2°$ in Chloroform.

l-1,1′-Dianthryl-2,2′-dicarbonsaures Chinin ist sehr schwer in reiner Form zu isolieren. Am besten gelingt dies, wenn man aus Methylalkohol umkrystallisiert und die in der Mutterlauge verbleibende, leicht lösliche Fraktion in der gleichen Weise weiterverarbeitet. Man erhält so schließlich etwa 1 g des Salzes als gelbes Pulver vom Schmp. 160—185° u. Zers.

$(\alpha)_D^{20} = (- 0{,}52°.100) : (0{,}5.0{,}4325) = - 245{,}0°$ in Chloroform.

d-1,1′-Dianthryl-2,2′-dicarbonsäure. 0,85 g d-Chininsalz wurden mit 50 ccm 2/n-HCl bei 70° 2-mal nacheinander je 2 Stunden unter Rühren erwärmt, bis im Filtrat kein Chinin mehr nachweisbar. Durch Umkrystallisieren aus Eisessig erhält man die d-Säure in mikrokrystallinen Nadeln vom Schmelzpunkt 187—198°, wobei unter deutlicher Gasentwicklung Zersetzung auftritt. Die Säure ist in den üblichen, organischen Lösungsmitteln ziemlich gut löslich.

$(\alpha)_D^{19} = (+ 2{,}13°.100) : (0{,}5.1{,}21) = + 352{,}0°$ in Aceton,
$(\alpha)_D^{20} = (+ 0{,}57°.100) : (0{,}5.0{,}406) = + 279{,}4°$ in Chloroform,
$(\alpha)_D^{20} = (+ 0{,}63°.100) : (0{,}5.0{,}41\ ) = + 307{,}3°$ in Eisessig,
$(\alpha)_D^{19} = (+ 1{,}62°.100) : (0{,}5.1{,}006) = + 322{,}0°$ in n/10 alkohol. KOH.

l-1,1′-Dianthryl-2,2′-dicarbonsäure. 0,65 g l-Chininsalz wurden, wie bei der d-Säure angegeben zersetzt. Aus Eisessig oder Alkohol erhält man gelbe, mikrokrystalline Nadeln vom Schmp. 190—200°, wobei wieder unter Gasentwicklung Zersetzung erfolgt.

$(\alpha)_D^{20} = (- 1{,}88°.100) : (0{,}5.1{,}05) = - 358{,}2°$ in Aceton,
$(\alpha)_D^{20} = (- 0{,}80°.100) : (0{,}5.0{,}558) = - 286{,}7°$ in Chloroform,
$(\alpha)_D^{19} = (- 0{,}59°.100) : (0{,}5.0{,}336) = - 351{,}2°$ in Eisessig,
$(\alpha)_D^{20} = (- 0{,}98°.100) : (0{,}5.0{,}631) = - 310{,}6°$ in n/10 alkohol. KOH.

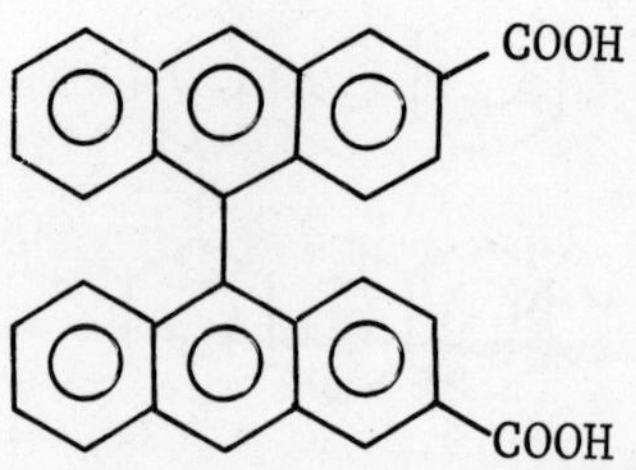

$C_{30}H_{18}O_4$ Ref. 1420

Resolution. The finely powdered acid (9·2 g.) was added slowly to a solution of quinidine (15 g.) in alcohol (250 c.c.). The clear solution was allowed to cool overnight, and the fine crystalline powder which separated weighed 9·5 g.; $[\alpha]^{21}_{5461}$ was $-127°$ (chloroform, $c = 0·09$). Three subsequent crystallisations from alcohol brought the salt to the constant rotatory power of $[\alpha]^{21}_{5461}$ $-153°$. The salt (5·2 g.) on decomposition yielded 1·9 g. of acid which when crystallised from acetic acid gave fine needles, m. p. 146—150°, $[\alpha]^{21}_{5461}$ $-132°$ (acetone, $c = 0·10$). The rotation and m. p. were unchanged by a further crystallisation.

The original mother-liquor when concentrated to 100 c.c. and kept overnight deposited 4·3 g. of a white amorphous powder. The filtrate was evaporated to dryness, and the salt when decomposed gave 3·4 g. of acid, m. p. 141—146°, $[\alpha]^{21}_{5461}$ $+123°$ (acetone, $c = 0·09$). Two crystallisations from acetic acid gave material of $[\alpha]^{21}_{5461}$ $+129°$, m. p. 145—146°. The rotation of the (+)-acid in xylene was unchanged after it had been heated under reflux (b. p. 139°) for 2 hours on an oil-bath.

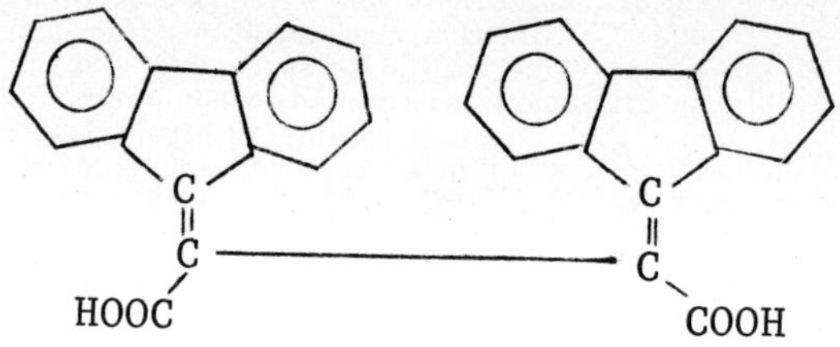

$C_{30}H_{18}O_4$ Ref. 1421

Spaltung des Bisdiphenylenfulgensäure-Racemates

Bisdiphenylenfulgensäure. Zur Lösung von 5 g NaOH in 600 ccm 50-proz. Alkohol gibt man 25 g schwarzes Fulgid und erhitzt, bis eine hellgelbe Lösung entstanden ist. Man gießt in überschüssige verd. Salzsäure, saugt den gebildeten Niederschlag ab, wäscht ihn mit dest. Wasser bis zur neutralen Reaktion des Filtrats und trocknet ihn i. Vak. Man erhält 24—25 g Rohprodukt, das zur Reinigung am besten aus Acetonitril umkristallisiert wird. Ausbeute 23 g (88% d. Th.) vom Schmp. 238° (Zers.).

Spaltung[20]: Zur Lösung von 4.4 g (0.01 Mol) der Fulgensäure in 500 ccm kochendem Äthanol gibt man 8.5 g (0.02 Mol) *Brucin*, filtriert das Gemisch schnell und läßt es in einem Dewar-Gefäß erkalten. Dabei scheiden sich bald Kristallkrusten ab, die nach einem Tag abgesaugt, mit 100 ccm Äthanol gewaschen und i. Vak. getrocknet werden. Ausbeute 2.2 g vom Schmp. 208.5—209°; $[\alpha]^{20}_D = -29.5°$ (Chloroform, c=0.420). Nach Umkristallisieren aus Chloroform verbleiben 2.0 g gelber Prismen des Mono-Brucinsalzes vom Schmp. 209—209.5° (Zers.).

$C_{53}H_{44}O_6N_2$ (Mono-Brucinsalz) Ber. N 3.35 Gef. N 3.15

Optisch aktive Fulgensäure. 1.7 g des Mono-Brucinsalzes werden mit 30 ccm 1-proz. eiskalter Natronlauge digeriert und abgesaugt. Das Filtrat läßt man unter kräftigem Rühren in die auf 0° gekühlte Mischung von 40 ccm Alkohol, 10 ccm konz. Salzsäure und 40 ccm Wasser einlaufen. Nach 10 Min. wird der gelbe Niederschlag abgesaugt, mit 5-proz. Salzsäure, zum Schluß mit Eiswasser gewaschen und getrocknet. Ausbeute 0.83 g vom Schmp. 237—238° (Zers.). — Das gelbe Produkt gibt mit konz. Salpetersäure keine Reaktion auf Brucin; der Stickstoffnachweis ist negativ.

Zur Bestimmung der *optischen Aktivität* wurden 0.246 g bei 20° in 25 ccm Chloroform gelöst; dann wurde so schnell wie möglich im 2-dm-Rohr die Drehung mehrmals gemessen:
Gef. $\alpha^{20}_D = +0.18°$ (2.5 Min. nach Lösen); $[\alpha]^{20}_D = +9.1°$; $[M]^{20}_D = +40.2°$.

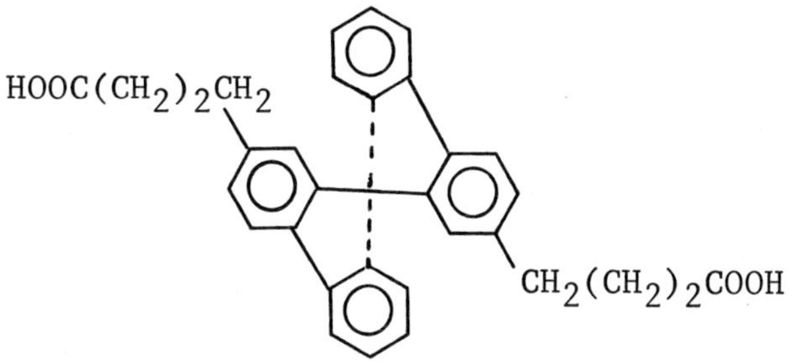

$C_{33}H_{28}O_4$ Ref. 1422

Trennung des Racemates der Dicarbonsäure VIII in Enantiomeren über die Bis-dehydroabietylamide. Eine Lösung von 5,00 g Dicarbonsäure VIII in 20 ml abs. Benzol wurde bei 0° unter Rühren mit 20 ml Oxalylchlorid versetzt, zuerst 1 Std. bei 0° und anschliessend über Nacht bei Zimmertemperatur gerührt. Die blassgelbe Lösung dampfte man unter vermindertem Druck bei Raumtemperatur zur Trockne ein. Zur vollständigen Entfernung des überschüssigen Oxalylchlorids wurde viermal mit je 10 ml abs. Benzol eingedampft. Das rohe Säurechlorid löste man in 30 ml abs. Dioxan und versetzte die Lösung unter Rühren bei 0° mit 12,8 g Dehydroabietylamin und der gleichen Menge Triäthylamin in 20 ml abs. Dioxan. Nach weiterem Rühren während 3 Std. bei Zimmertemperatur arbeitete man unter Verwendung von Äther als organischen Phase wie üblich auf. Das erhaltene Diastereomerengemisch wurde an 1,3 kg Kieselgel mit Hexan-Essigester (9:10) als Elutionsmittel (125 ml pro Fraktion) chromatographiert. Fraktionen 31–41 enthielten 3,60 g des (+)-, Fraktionen 42–50 2,65 g eines Gemisches und Fraktionen 51–60 3,33 g des (−)-Bis-dehydroabietylamides. Beide Diastereomere bildeten farblose Öle, welche nicht kristallin gewonnen werden konnten. Ihre IR. und NMR. waren nicht unterscheidbar. IR. (in $CHCl_3$): ν_{max} 3450 (*m*), 3340 (*w*), 1665 (*s*), 1515 (*s*) cm^{-1}. NMR. (in $CDCl_3$): δ 0,97 (*s*, 6 H), 1,1–2,2 (*Sh*, 42 H), 2,45 (*t*, *J* = 7, 4 H), 2,79 (*t*, *J* = 7, 4 H), 2,95–3,15 (*d*, *J* = 7, 4 H), 5,44 (*t*, *J* = 7, 2 H), 6,47 (*s*, 2 H), 6,63 (*d*, *J* = 7,5, 2 H), 6,85 (*s*, 2 H), 7,01 (*t*, *J* = 7,5, *d*, *J* = 1,2, 2 H), 7,05 (*d*, *J* = 12, 2 H), 7,11 (*d*, *J* = 7,5, *d*, *J* = 1,2, 2 H), 7,16 (*d*, *J* = 12, 2 H), 7,30 (*t*, *J* = 7,5, *d*, *J* = 1,2, 2 H), 7,67 (*d*, *J* = 7,5, 2 H), 7,77 (*d*, *J* = 7,5, 2 H).

(+)-*Bis-dehydroabietylamid.* $[\alpha]_{589}^{20} = +25,1°$, $[\alpha]_{546}^{20} = +30,4°$, $[\alpha]_{436}^{20} = +57,8°$, $[\alpha]_{405}^{20} = +73,6°$, $[\alpha]_{365}^{20} = +117°$ (c = 1,82 in $CHCl_3$).

(−)-*Bis-dehydroabietylamid.* $[\alpha]_{546}^{21} = -6,4°$, $[\alpha]_{436}^{21} = -11,6°$, $[\alpha]_{405}^{21} = -10,9°$ (c = 1,66 in $CHCl_3$).

(+)-*Dicarbonsäure VIII.* Zu 8,5 g wasserfreiem Natriumacetat wurden bei −60° 20 ml einer 1,4 M Lösung von Distickstofftetroxid in Tetrachlorkohlenstoff zugegeben. Die auf 0° erwärmte Lösung versetzte man unter Rühren mit 1,00 g des (+)-Bis-dehydroabietylamids in 10 ml kaltem Tetrachlorkohlenstoff und liess über Nacht bei 0° stehen. Zur Aufarbeitung wurde unter Eiskühlung zweimal zwischen 200 ml Äther und 100 ml 5-proz. Natriumhydrogencarbonatlösung verteilt. Die unter Kühlung gewaschene und getrocknete ätherische Lösung dampfte man bei Zimmertemperatur unter vermindertem Druck ab. Der Rückstand wurde an 40 g Kieselgel mit Benzol-Essigester-Eisessig (90:10:3) als Elutionsmittel (10 ml pro Fraktion) chromatographiert. Fraktionen 11–18 enthielten 376 mg (79%) der (+)-Dicarbonsäure VIII als farbloses Öl, das trotz vieler Versuche nicht kristallin erhalten werden konnte. $[\alpha]_{589}^{20} = +12,6°$, $[\alpha]_{546}^{20} = +14,7°$, $[\alpha]_{436}^{20} = +34,1°$, $[\alpha]_{405}^{20} = +50,0°$ (c = 10,8 in $CHCl_3$).

Auf analoge Weise erhielt man aus dem (−)-Bis-dehydroabietylamid die (−)-*Di-carbonsäure VIII.* $[\alpha]_{589}^{20} = -10,1°$, $[\alpha]_{546}^{20} = -12,9°$, $[\alpha]_{436}^{20} = -32,7°$, $[\alpha]_{405}^{20} = -47,8°$ (c = 6,62 in $CHCl_3$).

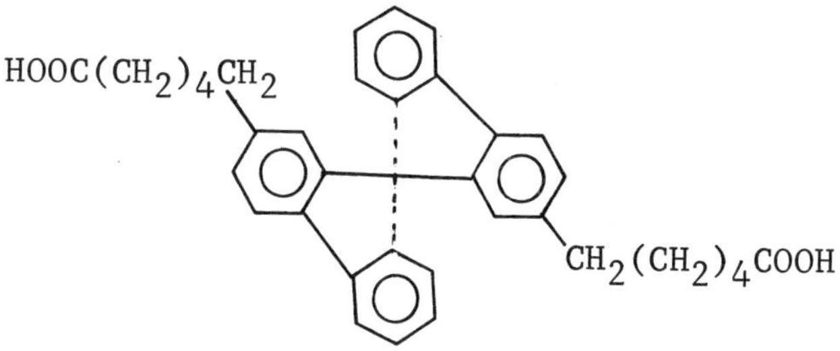

$C_{37}H_{36}O_4$ Ref. 1423

Trennung des Racemates der Dicarbonsäure XIII in die Enantiomeren. Das aus 4,55 g Dicarbonsäure XIII erhaltene Gemisch der diastereomeren Bis-dehydroabietylamide wurde an 1,1 kg Kieselgel mit Benzol:Äther (2:3) und 5 Tropfen Eisessig pro 100 ml Lösungsmittel als Elutionsmittel (Fraktionen von 200 ml) chromatographiert. Dabei enthielten die Fraktionen 19–24 das Bis-dehydroabietylamid der (+)-Dicarbonsäure, die Fraktionen 25–30 ein Gemisch und die Fraktionen 31–37 das Bis-dehydroabietylamid der (−)-Dicarbonsäure. Durch systematisches mehrmaliges Chromatographieren wurden schliesslich 1,73 g Bis-dehydroabietylamid der (+)-Dicarbonsäure und 1,28 g Bis-dehydroabietylamid der (−)-Dicarbonsäure gewonnen. Im Unterschied zum letzteren, das ein farbloses Öl bildete, lieferte das Bis-dehydroabietylamid der (+)-Dicarbonsäure nach längerem Stehenlassen bei 0° in wenig Tetrachlorkohlenstoff ein farbloses Pulver, das zwischen 116

und 121° sinterte. Die IR. und NMR. der beiden Diastereomeren sind nicht unterscheidbar. IR. (in $CHCl_3$): ν_{max} 3450 (*m*), 3340 (*w*), 1665 (*s*), 1515 (*s*) cm^{-1}. NMR. ($CDCl_3$): δ 0,92 (*s*, 6 H), 1,20 (*d*, *J* = 7, 12 H), 1,21 (*s*, 6 H), 0,8–3,0 (*Sh*, 4 H), 3,11 (*t*, *J* = 7, 4 H), 5,46 (*t*, *J* = 6, 2 H), 6,48 (*s*, 2 H), 6,67 (*d*, *J* = 7,5, 2 H), 6,88 (*s*, 2 H), 7,03 (*d*, *J* = 11,5, 2 H), 7,06 (*t*, *J* = 7,5, *d*, *J* = 1,2, 2 H), 7,13 (*d*, *J* = 7,5, 2 H), 7,30 (*d*, *J* = 11,5,2 H), 7,33 (*t*, *J* = 7,5, *d*, *J* = 1,2, 2 H), 7,74 (*d*, *J* = 7,5, 2 H), 7,81 (*d*, *J* = 7,5, 2 H). *Bis-dehydroabietylamid der (+)-Dicarbonsäure.* $[\alpha]_{578}^{22} = +26,7°$, $[\alpha]_{546}^{22} = +30,1°$ (*c* = 1, 345 in $CHCl_3$). *Bis-dehydroabietylamid der (–)-Dicarbonsäure.* $[\alpha]_{578}^{22} = +3,3°$, $[\alpha]_{546}^{22} = +4,4°$ (*c* = 0,906 in $CHCl_3$).

Die (+)-*Dicarbonsäure XIII* erhielt man aus ihrem Bis-dehydroabietylamid nach dem bei niedrigeren Homologen beschriebenen Verfahren. Die chromatographisch reine (+)-Dicarbonsäure kristallisierte aus Essigester-Hexan in farblosen kompakten Kristallen, nach 5-maligem Umkristallisieren Smp. 177–178°. Das IR. (in KBr) unterscheidet sich besonders im fingerprint-Gebiet stark von dem der racemischen Verbindung. $[\alpha]_{578}^{22} = +10,1°$, $[\alpha]_{546}^{22} = +13,0°$, $[\alpha]_{436}^{22} = +26,5°$, $[\alpha]_{405}^{22} = +37,4°$, $[\alpha]_{365}^{22} = +70,4°$ (*c* = 1,345 in $CHCl_3$).

$C_{37}H_{36}O_4$ Ber. C 81,59 H 6,66% Gef. C 81,73 H 6,96%

Die (–)-*Dicarbonsäure XIII*, auf analoge Weise aus ihrem Bis-dehydroabietylamid hergestellt, schmolz nach 6-maligem Umkristallisieren aus Essigester-Hexan bei 176,5–178°. $[\alpha]_{578}^{22} = -10,0°$, $[\alpha]_{546}^{22} = -11,3°$, $[\alpha]_{436}^{22} = -27,4°$, $[\alpha]_{405}^{22} = -39,0°$, $[\alpha]_{365}^{22} = -77,2°$ (*c* = 1,465 in $CHCl_3$).

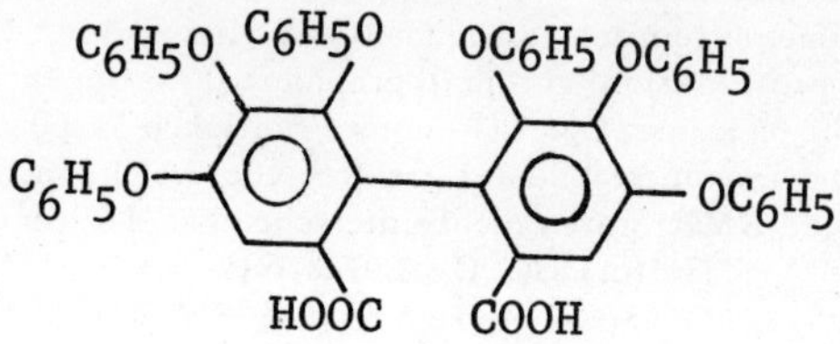

$C_{50}H_{34}O_{10}$ Ref. 1424

b) Racematspaltung mit Chinidin

1. Dichinidin-salz der D(—)-Hexabenzoxy-diphensäure

1,0121 g D,L-Hexabenzoxy-diphensäure und 0,7475 g Chinidin wurden in 25 ccm abs. Äthanol in der Wärme gelöst. Beim Stehenlassen bildeten sich farblose, prismatische Kristalle, die nach dem Umkristallisieren aus Äthanol konstant bei 196° schmolzen. Ausbeute 0,330 g, 37,4% d. Th. Zur Analyse wurde bei 120°/5 über P_2O_5 getrocknet.

$C_{56}H_{46}O_{10}$, 2 $C_{20}H_{24}O_2N_2$ (1527,68)

Ber.	C 75,47	H 6,22	N 3,67	OCH_3 4,06
Gef.	» 75,21	» 6,38	» 3,75	» 4,06

2. D(—)-Hexabenzoxy-diphensäure

250 mg des vorigen Salzes wurden mit 5 ccm 2n-HCl in der Reibschale verrieben. Nach dem Abfiltrieren wurde mit viel mit Salzsäure angesäuertem Wasser, dann mit reinem Wasser gewaschen, bis das Filtrat auf Zugabe von Ammoniak keine Trübung mehr zeigte. Ausbeute 110 mg, 65% d. Th. Nach 2maligem Umkristallisieren aus Eisessig/Wasser schmolz die Säure bei 146°. Zur Drehung wurde bei 55°/2 über P_2O_5 getrocknet.

$[\alpha]_D^{20}$ = —64,7 ± 1° (Chloroform, c = 1,4); $[M]_D$ = —569°.

ADDENDUM

$CH_3CHCOOH$ (with NH_2 on the CH)

$C_3H_7NO_2$ Ref. 1425

8.3. Versuche zur Enantiomerentrennung über diastereomere Salze

8.3.1. Racematspaltung von D,L-Alanin (Modellversuch)[11]

1,00 g (11,2 mmol) D,L-Alanin, 1,24 g (12,4 mmol) frisch destilliertes Acetylaceton und 3,85 g (11,8 mmol) Chinin wurden in 18 ml abs. Methanol 1 h unter N_2 und Rühren gekocht. Anschließend wurde die klare Lösung etwas eingeengt. Nach Stehen im Kühlschrank wurde das auskristallisierte N-(1-Methyl-2-acetylvinyl)-L-alanin-chininsalz 14a abgesaugt, mit kaltem Methanol gewaschen und über Silicagel i. Vak. getrocknet. Nach vorsichtigem Einengen der Mutterlauge fiel noch eine 2. Kristallfraktion an.

Fr.1: 1,2 g, Schmp. 143-144°C, $|\alpha|_D^{25}$ = - 82,4° (c=2; 95% EtOH)
Fr.2: 0,7 g, " 147-149°C, " = - 83,5° (c=2; 95% EtOH)
Lit.[11] " 142-143°C, " = - 73,8° (n.angegeben)
Ausbeute Fr. 1 + 2: 1,9 g (67 %)

IR (KBr): 3600-2800 breit (Maxima bei 3200, 3065, 2930), 1615, 1530, 1505, 1450, 1430, 1390, 1350, 1290, 1250, 1230, 1185, 1165, 1135, 1088, 1068, 1030, 998, 975, 917, 870, 845, 815, 790, 731, 705 cm^{-1}

Die verbliebene Mutterlauge und das darin enthaltene D-Enantiomere wurden nicht weiter aufgearbeitet.

Man vereinigte die beiden Kristallfraktionen des diastereomeren Salzes 14a. Davon wurden 1,5 g (3 mmol) in 10 ml Wasser aufgenommen und unter Rühren bei 10°C mit 5 ml 1 n NaOH-Lösung versetzt. Man extrahierte das ausgefallene Chinin mit Chloroform, säuerte die wässrige Phase in der Kälte mit 3 ml 2 n Salzsäure an und extrahierte das abgespaltene Acetylaceton wiederum mit Chloroform. Die saure, wässrige Lösung wurde auf eine Ionenaustauschersäule 2 x 30 cm mit Dowex 50 W x 8, H^+-Form, aufgetragen und mit Wasser nachgewaschen, bis das Eluat neutral und frei von Chloridionen war. Anschließend wurde die Aminosäure mit 0,5 n Ammoniaklösung eluiert, die ninhydrinpositiven Fraktionen vereinigt, mit Aktivkohle behandelt und nach Filtration zur Trockne eingeengt. Durch Umkristallisieren aus Wasser/Ethanol erhielt man nach Trocknen i. Vak. 136 mg (57 %) L-Alanin 14.

Schmp. 270-280°C; $|\alpha|_D^{25}$ = + 12,0° (c=2,5, 5 n HCL)
Lit. - " = + 12,8° (c=5, 5 n HCL)[11]
Lit. 297°C[59]

Die Probe wurde im DC und PC in verschiedenen Laufmitteln im Vergleich mit käuflichem L-Alanin identifiziert.

Note: Following is reaction sequence involved in this resolution:

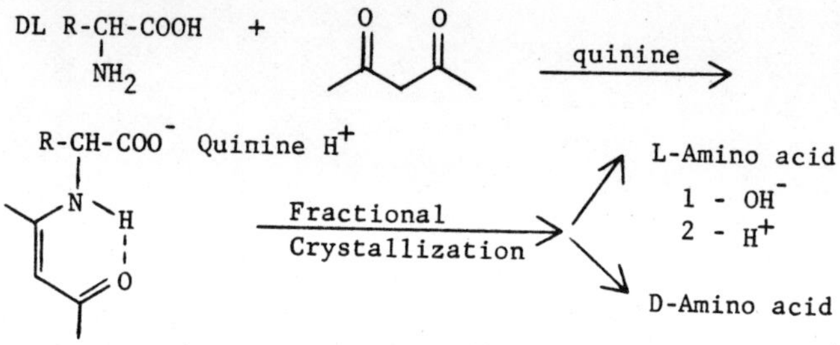

$CH_3-CH(OH)-CH(OH)-COOH$

$C_4H_8O_4$ Ref. 1426

Resolution of the Acid with Brucine.—Contrary to the experience of Morrell and Hanson, we found brucine to be an excellent resolving agent when water is used as the solvent.

The brucine salt was made in the usual way.[7] A mixture of twenty-five grams of recrystallized *dl-threo*-acid (m. p. 73–74°) in 800 cc. of water and 85 g. of anhydrous brucine was kept on the boiling water-bath until the solution was permanently alkaline (several hours). The solution was cooled, extracted twice with 100-cc. portions of benzene, and distilled to dryness at reduced pressure (water-bath at 70°); wt. of residue, 127 g. This was dissolved in 150 cc. of hot water, the solution cooled and allowed to stand first at room temperature for two hours and then for one hour in an ice-bath. The solid was then collected on a suction filter, pressed dry and kept in an oven at 70–75° until constant in weight; wt. 43.5 g. The mother liquor from Crop I was evaporated to dryness at reduced pressure as before. The residue, which weighed 60 g., was crystallized from 1 part of water. This process was repeated until four crops of crystals had been obtained. The residue from the mother liquor from Crop IV weighed 12 g. The solvent was changed at this point; the material was crystallized from 12 cc. of 50% ethyl alcohol. This yielded 2.8 g. of dry salt, Crop V. The residue from the filtrate from Crop V weighed 6.0 g. It was crystallized from 6 cc. of 50% ethyl alcohol and yielded 1.3 g. of dry material.

Five such experiments were made in each of which 25 g. of the *dl*-acid was used. Six crops of crystals were obtained in each case. The specific rotations of these (sodium light) are recorded below.

Experiment	Crop I	Crop II	Crop III	Crop IV	Crop V	Crop VI
A	−32.5	−24.5	−21.0	Lost	−21.8	−22.5
B	−33.5	−21.2	−21.3	−22.2	−20.5	−22.0
C	−32.9	−21.2	−20.6	−21.9	−21.0	−18.6
D	Lost	−21.7	−24.5	−23.7	−21.5	−23.0
E	−32.8	−21.4	−21.0	−23.0	−21.2	−19.6

It is apparent from these data that a partial resolution had been accomplished. Each Crop I was now recrystallized six times from water and from the results of these recrystallizations it is concluded that the pure anhydrous brucine salt of the levo acid has a specific rotation in water solution between −34.4° and −35.6°.

Preparation of the Levo Acid from the Brucine Salt.—To a solution of 40.5 g. of recrystallized brucine salt (−34.4 to −34.6°) in 200 cc. of water was added a hot solution of 12.5 g. of hydrated barium hydroxide in 200 cc. of water. The mixture was cooled, the brucine removed and the filtrate extracted five times with 75-cc. portions of benzene. The barium was exactly precipitated with sulfuric acid, the barium sulfate removed and the filtrate evaporated to dryness at reduced pressure. The residual sirup weighed 9 g. Solution in a large volume (200–300 cc.) of ethyl acetate, filtration to remove gummy precipitate, and distillation of filtrate to dryness, gave 6 g. of gum which crystallized when seeded with racemic acid. The crystals were brought on a filter, washed with a little cold ethyl acetate and dried; m. p. 73.5–75°, $[\alpha]_D$ −15.0°.

A second portion of 75.2 g. of brucine salt (−35.1 to −35.7°) was treated in the manner outlined above. The rotation of the acid after three recrystallizations from ethyl acetate was −15.1°.

Preparation of the Dextro Acid from the Brucine Salt.—For the preparation of the dextro acid, various crops of brucine salt, −20.7 to −22.7°, were combined; weight 134.2 g. This salt was hydrolyzed in the manner outlined above for the levo acid and yielded 27 g. of crude crystalline acid; +11.3°. Fourteen grams of this material was subjected to five successive crystallizations from two parts of ethyl acetate and the specific rotation of the final product was found to be +15.1°.

Resolution of the Acid with Quinidine.—The work of Morrell and Hanson with quinidine was repeated. To a solution of 20 g. of the acid, m. p. 73.5–74.5°, in 400 cc. of hot water, quinidine was added until the solution was neutral (59 g. of alkaloid needed). The hot solution was filtered and deposited a crop of crystals which weighed 37.3 g. after three days in a vacuum desiccator over sulfuric acid; m. p. 117–117.5°; $[\alpha]_D$ +142.7°. Morrell and Hanson give 113–114° and +143.46° for the corresponding crop of crystals. They report the specific rotation as +142.2° after the material had been recrystallized six times. Our quinidine salt was recrystallized five times and then had a specific rotation of +147.5°. Further work with this salt showed it to be so much less soluble in water than the salt of the dextro acid that an almost complete separation of the two acids was found to be possible by the use of quinidine. The results recorded below support this statement.

A mixture of 60 g. of *dl* acid, m. p. 73.5–75°, in 2.5 liters of water, and 180 g. of quinidine was kept on the boiling water-bath for a half hour, cooled, filtered (2 g. of quinidine recovered) and the filtrate extracted three times with 500-cc. portions of ether. The solution was then concentrated at reduced pressure and brought to a weight of 1455 g. (1 part salt in 5 parts water), heated until all the solid was again in solution, then cooled rapidly and allowed to stand overnight. The crystals were then removed and dried in a vacuum desiccator over sulfuric acid for three days; wt. 90.3 g., $[\alpha]_D$ +147.5°; m. p. 116–122°.

It was found that it is the hydrated form of this salt which melts at 116–122° and that the m. p. must be taken rapidly to get this low value. If it is taken slowly, a very indefinite melting is observed with the last of the material liquefying at 159–162°. If the air-dry salt is extracted with boiling anhydrous ether (as is often done to avoid possible contamination with free alkaloid) it always melts at the higher value.

The filtrate from the first crop of crystals was concentrated and adjusted as before until it weighed 1395 g., cooled, seeded with crop 1 and allowed to stand for three days. The second crop was then removed; wt. 14 g., $[\alpha]_D$ +147.5°; m. p. (after ether treatment) 159–162°. A third crop of crystals was obtained by concentration of the filtrate to 1175 g. Crystals came very slowly this time even when the solution was stored for several days in the ice box; wt. crop 3, 6.8 g., $[\alpha]_D$ +149.5°; m. p. (after ether treatment) 159–162°.

The three crops of crystals were combined, wt. 106 g. (some material lost in tests of various sorts) and the filtrates and washings concentrated to dryness at reduced pressure, wt. residue 126 g. The acids were now set free from these two lots of material.

Active Acids from Quinidine Salts.—The two lots of salts were separately treated in 4–5 liters of hot water with an excess of barium hydroxide in hot solution, the mixtures cooled, the quinidine separated by filtration, the filtrates extracted with ether, the barium exactly removed as sulfate and the filtrates distilled to dryness at reduced pressure with water-bath finally at 100°; wts. of residues 24.5 g. from the crystalline salts, and 31 g. from the non-crystalline salts. Small samples of each were removed and the specific rotation determined. Then the residues were recrystallized from one and one-half parts of ethyl acetate and the specific rotation of the crystals obtained, again determined. This process was repeated five times with both levo and dextro acids. The results are recorded in the following table:

$C_4H_8O_5$

	Levo acid			Dextro acid	
	Weight, g.	$[\alpha]_D$		Weight, g.	$[\alpha]_D$
Residue	24.5	−13.55°		31	+12.17°
Crop 1	9	−15.9°		15	+13.4°
Crop 2	7	−15.6°		11	+15.4°
Crop 3	5.5	−15.2°	Av. −15.5	10	+15.5°
Crop 4	4	−15.1°		8	+15.1°
Crop 5	2	−15.7°		6.5	+15.8°

Av. +15.45

(7) Glattfeld and Hanke, THIS JOURNAL, **40**, 976 (1918).

$$\text{HOCH}_2-\overset{\overset{\displaystyle H}{|}}{\underset{\underset{\displaystyle OH}{|}}{C}}-\overset{\overset{\displaystyle H}{|}}{\underset{\underset{\displaystyle OH}{|}}{C}}-\text{COOH}$$

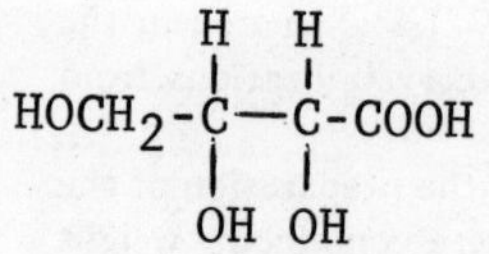

$C_4H_8O_5$

Ref. 1427

The Resolution.—Preliminary experiments showed that either brucine or quinine could be used as the resolving agent. Recrystallization of the brucine salts from water gave the pure brucine salt of the levorotatory component and recrystallization of the quinine salts from 95% alcohol gave the pure dextrorotatory component. The yields of pure lactone obtained when a single alkaloid was used, however, were not good and the two pure lactones were obtained in larger quantities by the alternate use of brucine and quinine. This procedure is made possible by the fact that of the two brucine salts it is the d-(−)-form that is the less soluble and of the two quinine salts the l-(+)-form that is the less soluble.

The procedure used was to convert the lactone into its brucine or quinine salt by the usual methods. In the case of the brucine salt, the water solution was then concentrated *in vacuo* at 60° until the ratio of water to salt was 2 to 1, cooled, and stored in the ice box for twenty-four to forty-eight hours. The crop of crystals (Crop 1) was removed by suction filtration but not washed. The mother liquor from Crop 1 was concentrated until the ratio of water to salt was again 2 to 1 and a second crop of crystals (Crop 2) obtained. Crops 1 and 2 were now united and recrystallized from 2 parts of water; Crop B1A was thus obtained. The mother liquor from Crop B1A was added to that from Crop 2. The lactone was set free from Crop B1A and found to be fairly pure d-(−)-lactone (see table below).

The combined mother liquors were now hydrolyzed and the lactone obtained was converted into the quinine salt. Again two crops of salts were obtained as in the case of the brucine salt except that 5 parts of 95% alcohol were used. The two crops were united and recrystallized from 5 parts of 95% alcohol and thus yielded Crop Q2A. The mother liquor from Crop Q2A was added to the mother liquor from quinine salt Crop 2. The lactone was set free from Crop Q2A and found to be fairly pure l-(+)-lactone (see table below).

The lactone was set free from the quinine salts in the combined mother liquors and converted back into the brucine salt and the process outlined above repeated; two crops of brucine salt obtained and recrystallized from two parts of water gave Crop B3A. The mother liquors gave a lactone that was converted into the quinine salt; this yielded two crops which were combined and recrystallized and gave Crop Q4A. This cycle was again repeated and Crops B5A and Q6A obtained. Crops B3A and B5A were now united as were also Crops Q4A and Q6A and the lactones set free.

The resolution was then repeated, starting with quinine and results similar to those in the first experiment obtained. These are recorded in the table. Rotations in this paper are for sodium light and approximately 4% aqueous solutions unless otherwise indicated.

It is seen that the total recovery of active lactone in the first case is 52% of the theoretical and in the second case 53% of the theoretical. It will be noted that the yield of lactone from the combined second and third crops of both quinine and brucine salts in Experiment 2 is low. This is due to the fact that the crude lactones obtained by the hydrolysis of these salts were of low optical activity and had to be recrystallized repeatedly from ethyl acetate in order to purify them. Thus the 38 g. of quinine salts in Experiment 2 gave 8 g. of lactone [+38°]; this was four

EXPERIMENT 1

100 g. of Lactone and 392 g. of Brucine to Start

Crop B1A, 72 g.	⟶ lactone, 16 g. (−66.4°)	} total d-(−)-lactone, 30 g.
Crop B3A, 68 g. } Crop B5A, 28 g.	⟶ lactone, 14 g. (−60.0°)	
Crop Q2A, 92 g.	⟶ lactone, 22 g. (+70.6°), total l-(+)-lactone, 22 g.	
Crop Q4A, 45 g. } Crop Q6A, 16 g.	⟶ lactone, 15 g. (+17.5°), discarded	

EXPERIMENT 2

50 g. of Lactone and 147 g. of Quinine to Start

Crop Q1A, 47 g.	⟶ lactone, 11 g. (+69.4°)	} total l-(+)-lactone, 12.87 g.
Crop Q3A, 27 g. } Crop Q5A, 11 g.	⟶ lactone, 1.87 g. (+73.0°)	
Crop B2A, 60 g.	⟶ lactone, 10.5 g. (−66.59°)	} total d-(−)-lactone, 14.0 g.
Crop B4A, 25 g. } Crop B6A, 7 g.	⟶ lactone, 2.5 g. (−71.6°)	

times recrystallized and then yielded only 1.87 g. [+73°]; similarly in the other cases where the yield of lactone seems abnormally low. Only crude lactones of specific rotation about 40° or above will yield pure lactones of proper rotation by this process of recrystallization. In Experiment 1 the 15 g. of crude lactone from 61 g. of quinine salts was of such low activity (+17.5) that it was useless to try to obtain pure lactone from it by recrystallization. Unless conservation of material is very important, it is not worth while to attempt to obtain more than two crops of brucine and quinine salts (B1A and B3A; Q2A and Q4A). Subsequent crops do not yield lactones of a very high degree of purity.

The Pure Active Lactones.—From the experiments described above and other similar ones, 51 g. of *l*-(+)-lactone and 60 g. of *d*-(−)-lactone with rotations above 60° were obtained. These two lots of material were four times recrystallized from ethyl acetate. The first crops (31.77 g. and 37.18 g.) had specific rotations of +72.53 and −72.41 and the fourth crops (6 g. and 10 g.) +73.05 and −72.98, respectively. The specific rotations of these pure lactones with mercury light (546) were found to be +87.32 and −87.62, respectively. The lactones melt at 105° (corr.). When allowed to crystallize slowly from ethyl acetate they form long glistening needles.

See also:

Anderson, *Am. Chem. J.*, **42**, 402 (1909); Lespieau, *Bull. soc. chim.*, [iv] **1**, 1117 (1907);

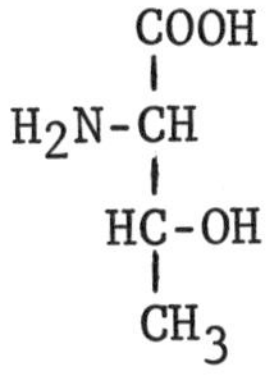

$C_4H_9NO_3$ Ref. 1428

DL-trans-5-methyl-2-oxooxazolidine-4-carboxylic acid (I), 7.5 g. prepared from DL-threonine and $COCl_2$ under basic conditions and 24.0 g. brucine (II) were dissolved in 215 ml. methanol and filtered after 8 hours to give 12.0 g. difficultly soluble salt which was crystallized from methanol and gave the first fraction of (II) salt, m.p. 145.5-146°(dec.) $[\alpha]^{25}_D$ -31.6° (C 3.29, H_2O). The first fraction was treated with alkali to give D(-)-I, m.p. 139-140° $[\alpha]^{24.5}_D$ -40.5° (C 3.07, H_2O). From the soluble part of (II) salt impure L(+)-I, m.p. 123-131°, $[\alpha]^{25.5}_D$ 20.5° (C, 3.07, H_2O) was obtained. L(-)-threonine (III), $[\alpha]^{25.5}_D$ -27.4° (C 3.24, H_2O) (6.6 g.) was dissolved in 110 ml. H_2O, mixed with 33 ml. 1.7N KOH and treated with 7.0 g. $COCl_2$ in 20 ml. toluene and 98 ml. 1.7N KOH to give 5.7 g. L(+)-I(532 mg.) in 20 ml. 1:1 HCl was heated 8 hours to give 384 mg. L(-)-III 258-9°(dec.) $[\alpha]^{15}_D$ -27.6° (C, 3.04, H_2O). Similarly, D(-)-I gave D(+)-III m.p. 258.5-259° (dec.), $[\alpha]^{25.5}_D$ 28.0 (C 3.18, H_2O).

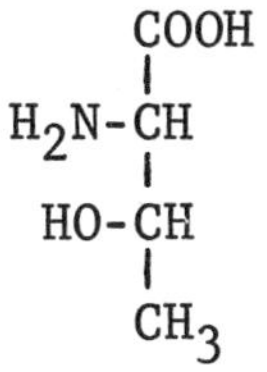

$C_4H_9NO_3$ Ref. 1429

DL-cis-5-Methyl-2-oxooxazolidine-4-carboxylic acid (IV) was resolved with brucine (II) to give difficulty soluble (II) salt, m.p. 152-3° (dec.), $[\alpha]^{25}_D$ -32.1° (C, 3.15, H_2O) which was decomposed with alkali to afford L(-)-IV, m.p. 169-170°, $[\alpha]^{16}_D$ -19.2° (C, 3.29, H_2O). The easily soluble part gave impure D(+)-IV. Using quinine, D(+)-IV salt is difficultly soluble, m.p. 136-138.5°, $[\alpha]^{17}_D$ -107.0° (C, 1.00, H_2O), and pure D(+)-IV, m.p. 170-170.5°, $[\alpha]^{19.5}_D$ 19.0° (C, 3.21, H_2O), is obtained. L(-)-IV, 505 mgs. was hydrolyzed by heating with 1:1 HCl to give L(+)-allothreonine (V), m.p. 270-270.5° (dec.), $[\alpha]^{15}_D$ 8.8° (C, 3.40, H_2O). Similarly, D(-)-V, m.p. 272-272.5° (dec.), $[\alpha]^{25}_D$ -8.5° (C, 3.17, H_2O), was obtained from D(+)-IV.

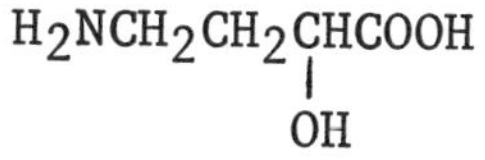

$C_4H_9NO_3$ Ref. 1430

(R)-2-Hydroxy-4-phthalimidobutyric acid. (−)-1-Phenylethylamine (46 g, 0.38 mmol) and (±)-2-hydroxy-4-phthalimidobutyric acid (95 g, 0.38 mmol) were mixed with cooling and 200 ml of ethanol was added. The mixture was warmed to effect solution and then left overnight at room temperature. The salt obtained (76 g) was recrystallized six times from about 30% solutions in ethanol before constant melting point (152−153 °C) and optical rotation $[\alpha]^{22}_D$ +4.0° (*c* 2.0, 95% ethanol) were obtained. The yield was 19.3 g (27%). Anal. $C_{20}H_{22}N_2O_5$: C, H, N.

The resolved salt (17.0 g, 0.046 mol) was treated with 1 N HCl and the liberated acid was recrystallized twice from water: m.p. 152−153 °C, $[\alpha]^{22}_D$ −5.9° (*c* 1.5, 95% ethanol), yield 8.6 g (75% based on resolved salt). Anal. $C_{12}H_{11}NO_5.H_2O$: C, H, N.

(R)-4-Amino-2-hydroxybutyric acid. To 7.5 g (0.03 mol) of (*R*)-2-hydroxy-4-phthalimidobutyric acid in hot ethanol (300 ml) was added hydrazine hydrate (2.0 g, 0.04 mol) and the solution was refluxed for 2 h. The ethanol was evaporated *in vacuo*, the residue treated with water (125 ml) and the resulting mixture adjusted to pH 5 by the addition of acetic acid. The precipitated phthaloyl hydrazide was filtered off and washed with water. The filtrate was then concentrated *in vacuo* and the residue recrystallized twice from 90% ethanol: m.p. 200−201 °C, $[\alpha]^{22}_D$ +28.0° (*c* 1.1, water), yield 2.6 g (73%). Lit.[18] m.p. 199−201 °C, $[\alpha]_D$ +27.5° (*c* 1.0, water).

18. Opfermann, A. C. J. *Brit. Patent* (1953) 688 253; *Chem. Abstr. 48* (1954) 3996.

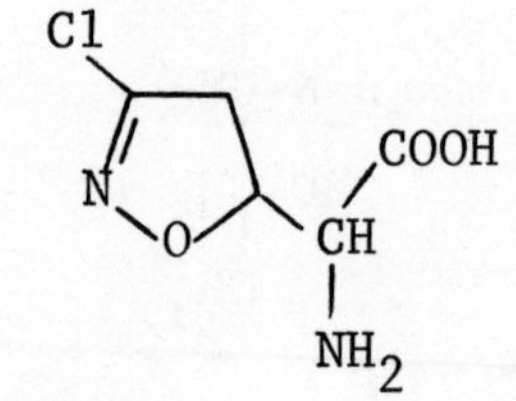

$C_5H_7ClN_2O_3$ Ref. 1431

NOTE: Optical resolution of the racemate was readily achieved via the chloroacetyl derivative by means of hog kidney acylase affording the optically pure enantiomer: $(\alpha)^{20}_{378} = 135°$ (c 0.159, H_2O).

$$CH_3CH_2-\overset{\overset{\displaystyle Cl}{|}}{\underset{\underset{\displaystyle CH_3}{|}}{C}}-COOH$$

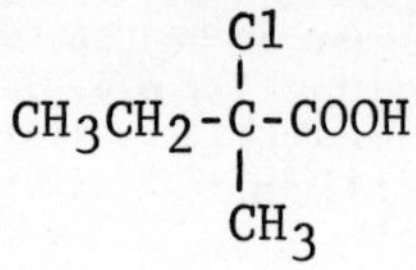

$C_5H_9ClO_2$ Ref. 1432

This chloro acid was converted by treatment with thionyl chloride into the acid chloride which without purification was allowed to interact with (−)-α-(1-naphthyl)ethylamine in dioxane containing triethylamine,[6] giving a mixture of diastereomeric amides VIIIa and VIIIb, mp 60–63°, which was separated by preparative tlc on silica gel (hexane–EtOAc, 9:1). Thus a total of 1.3 g of VIIIa, mp 72–73° (Anal. Found: C, 70.6; H, 7.0; Cl, 12.1; N, 4.8) and 1.26 g of VIIIb, mp 73–74° (Anal. Found: C, 70.6; H, 6.9; Cl, 12.1; N, 4.8) were obtained. The nmr spectrum at 100 MHz ($CDCl_3$, TMS internal standard) included, in particular, a singlet at δ 1.70 (3 H) for the methyl group on the carbon holding the chlorine atom, while in the spectrum of VIIIb this band appeared at δ 1.79 ppm. The amides were hydrolyzed by heating with a 1:1 mixture of dioxane and ~25 N sulfuric acid at 95° for 4 hr to give in 95–100% yield the enantiomeric forms of the aforementioned chloro acid, $[\alpha]^{20}$D (for isomer a, derived from VIIIa) +7.9° (c 1.6, 95% ethanol); $[\alpha]^{20}$D (for isomer b, derived from VIIIb) −7.8° (c 1.7, 95% ethanol).

$$CH_3SCH_2CH_2\underset{\underset{\displaystyle NH_2}{|}}{CH}COOH$$

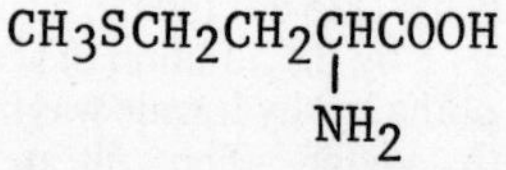

$C_5H_{11}NO_2S$ Ref. 1433

EXAMPLE 45

Resolution with Racemisation of 10% Methyl DL-Methioninate in Methanol using Anisaldehyde.

A solution of methyl DL-methioninate (2.506 g., 15.37 mmole) and (+)-tartaric acid (2.372 g., 15.82 mmole, 1.03 equiv.) and dried methanol (25 ml., i.e. 10% ester concentration) was seeded with methyl L-methioninate (+)-hemitartrate ($[\alpha]_D$ + 29.6°). Crystallisation occurred slowly and after 1½ hours at 25°, anisaldehyde (1.86 ml., 2.09 g., 15.35 mmole, 1 equiv.,

6.9% v/v) was added, the mixture was stirred at 20° to 25° for 18 days and then filtered. The product was washed with methanol (2 × 3 ml.) and dried at 20°/2 mm. for 4 hours to give methyl L-methioninate (+)-hemitartrate (2.959 g., 61.5%), m.p. 142° to 145°, $[\alpha]_D^{21}$ + 29.9° (c 3.016, H_2O).

EXAMPLE 46

Resolution with Racemisation of 10% Methyl DL-Methioninate in Methanol using Benzaldehyde, and Re-use of Filtrate

As for Example 45 but adding benzaldehyde (1.56 ml., 1.63 g., 15.36 mmole, 1 equiv.) and stirring for 6 days, to give methyl L-methioninate (+)-hemitartrate (2.209 g., 46%), $[\alpha]_D^{25}$ + 29.8° (c 3.016, H_2O).

The filtrate and first wash were combined, and used as described below:

A warm solution of (+)-tartaric acid (912 g., 12.76 mmole, 1.03 equiv.) in the above filtrate was added to methyl DL-methioninate (2.024 g., 12.40 mmole, 1 equiv.) in the filtrate (total volume, 20 ml.). The resulting solution was shaken and seeded with methyl L-methioninate (+)-hemitartrate ($[\alpha]_D$ + 29.6°). Crystallisation occurred slowly and after ca. 2 hours at 25° stirring was begun. After 28 days the product was filtered, washed, and dried as for Example 45 to give methyl L-methioninate (+)-hemitartrate (4.129 g., 106%), $[\alpha]_D^{22}$ + 29.8° (c 3.020, H_2O). The overall yield was 76%.

L-Methionine

Methyl L-methioninate (+)-hemitartrate ($[\alpha]_D$ + 29.8°, 5.914 g., 18.9 mmole) was stirred with 5N-sodium hydroxide solution [2.514 g., 62.8 mmole, 3.32 equiv. sodium hydroxide in water (12.5 ml.)]. Most of the hemitartrate dissolved immediately but after 8 minutes a solid had precipitated (disodium (+)-tartrate). After 1 hour 35 minutes the pH of the mixture was adjusted from 12.3 to 5.8 (the isoelectric point of methionine) with concentrated hydrochloric acid — solid was present all the time. The mixture was cooled in ice, filtered, and the solid washed with water (2 × 3 ml.), and dried over phosphorus pentoxide giving L-methionine (1.928 g., 68%), m.p. decomp. 210 to 215°, darkening began at 225° but the sample did not melt below 320°. An authentic sample of L-methionine decomposed at 225° to 230°, darkening and shrinking occurred at 230° but the sample did not melt below 330°, $[\alpha]_D^{22}$ + 21.7° (c 1.007, 1N-HCl) — 4 dm. tube, and $[\alpha]_D^{22}$ + 21.4° (c 1.021, 1N-HCl) — 1 dm. tube.

Note: The following is a detailed description of the theoretical basis for this resolution procedure.

It is commonly convenient in relatively largescale production to synthesise amino acids and their esters by non-stereospecific methods and to resolve the racemic product so produced.

Esters of DL-phenylglycine may be obtained readily in good yields from 2-phenylacetic esters, some of which are available in large quantities as waste by-products from the production of semi-synthetic penicillin and cephalosporin antibiotics. It is thus highly desirable commercially to be able to resolve these relatively

cheap esters of DL-phenylglycine, and other related esters described hereinafter, successfully and cheaply. Similarly, many naturally occurring amino acids can be synthesised cheaply in the racemic form but then require resolution.

We have previously attempted to resolve such esters by relatively conventional techniques, using optically active acids, and although high resolution efficiencies can be achieved, for economical production of any one optical isomer it is very desirable to find some way of racemising the remaining isomer so that this racemate may itself be subjected to resolution. However, the racemisation conditions usually tend to hydrolyse the ester grouping or, using alcohol solvents which were otherwise very convenient, lead to transesterification. Furthermore some previously suggested processes have involved changes of solvent and these are undesirable.

We have found that these problems can be avoided by providing a system in which the unwanted isomer is racemised in situ while the desired isomer is continuously removed from solution by the resolving agent.

In this way, one enantiomer can be converted into the opposite enantiomer and a racemic mixture may thus be converted into a single optically active form. In practice, this racemisation/resolution process may be rather slow and in some cases it may be preferable simply to enrich the product with respect to one optical isomer. We have found, however, that α-amino acids carrying an aryl substituent, particularly in the α-position, are converted especially rapidly and in this case virtually all of the DL-starting material can be converted into the required isomer in an economical time. The starting material may be the L-isomer, when the D-isomer is the required product or vice versa or a mixture of the two isomers may be used.

Our new method is based on the finding that Schiff bases of the above esters are more readily racemised than the parent esters and usually exist in equilibrium therewith. We have further found that the Schiff bases tend not to form insoluble salts with the resolving acids such as tartaric acid and in consequence, if a DL-ester is partially converted in solution into a Schiff base in the presence of a resolving acid, such as tartaric acid, an equilibrium is eventually reached out of which the required optically active amino acid ester is separated in the form of its salt. In the equilibration process the Schiff base of the other isomer however will continuously be racemised.

Schiff bases of amino acids are generally regarded as optically stable. It is thus surprising that the present process produces the high resolution efficiencies which are desired.

The Schiff base is formed by reaction of the parent ester or a salt thereof with an aldehyde or ketone. The optically active acid may be present during this reaction and may indeed be introduced together with the ester as a salt thereof, or may be added subsequently.

According to one feature of the present invention there is provided a process for the production of an ester of one enantiomer of an α-amino acid in the form of a salt with an optically active acid, which comprises reacting an ester of the opposite enantiomer of said α-amino acid (which may be in admixture with an ester of the desired enantiomer) with said optically active acid and an aldehyde or ketone, whereby an ester of the desired enantiomer separates out in the form of the said salt.

The α-amino acids which are conveniently used in the process of the present invention include compounds of the formula:

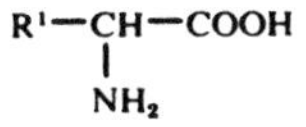

$$R^1-\underset{\underset{NH_2}{|}}{CH}-COOH \qquad\qquad I$$

wherein R^1 represents an optionally substituted alkyl, aralkyl, aryl or cycloalkyl group. Preferred alkyl groups include straight or branched chain C_{1-6} alkyl groups, which may if desired contain a sulphur or oxygen atom or an NH group or a $>C=C<$
group in the chain, and/or which may if desired contain conventional substituents found in amino acids such as esterified carboxyl (especially alkoxycarbonyl), carbamoyl, thio, etherified thio, hydroxyl or etherified hydroxyl groups or further amino or carboxyl groups. The alkyl portion of an aralkyl group may be similarly modified. Cycloalkyl groups may, if desired, contain one or two double bonds; thus R^1 may, for example, represent the cyclohexa-1,4-dien-1-yl group. The term "aryl", both in relation to aryl groups per se and also as part of an aralkyl group, includes not only carbocyclic groups but also heterocyclic aryl groups containing at least one hetero atom selected from nitrogen, sulphur and oxygen such as imidazolyl e.g. 2-or 4-imidazolyl; thien-2-yl; thien-3-yl; furyl e.g. fur-2-yl; pyridyl e.g. pyrid-3-yl; pyrrolyl or N-substituted pyrrolyl e.g. N-methyl pyrrolyl; isothiazolyl; thiadiazolyl; oxadiazolyl; 3- or 4-isoxazolyl; substituted 3- or 4-isoxazolyl e.g. 3-aryl-5-methyl isoxazol-4-yl, the aryl group being, for example, phenyl or halophenyl; and fused heterocyclic groups containing at least one hetero atom selected from nitrogen, sulphur and oxygen e.g. benzothienyl such as benzothien-3-yl, benzofuryl or indolyl such as 2- or 3- indolyl.

It will thus be seen that the process of the present invention is generally applicable to the esters of α-amino acids including for example the esters of naturally occurring α-amino acids such as alanine, valine, leucine, phenylalanine, tyrosine, serine, cysteine, methionine, tryptophan, aspartic acid, glutamic acid, lysine and histidine.

In view of the excellent results which may be obtained with aromatic amino acids, however, R^1 preferably represents phenyl and phenyl substituted by, for example, hydroxy; alkoxy e.g. methoxy; acyloxy e.g. acetoxy or benzyloxycarbonyloxy; halogen e.g. chlorine; or lower alkyl e.g. methyl. Thus R^1 may be, for example, m-or p-hydroxyphenyl, m- or p-methoxyphenyl, m- or p-chlorophenyl, m-tolyl, etc., or a di- or poly-cyclic group such as α- or β-naphthyl. Particularly preferred R^1 groups are unsubstituted phenyl and p-hydroxyphenyl.

The α-amino acid esters may conveniently be represented by the formula

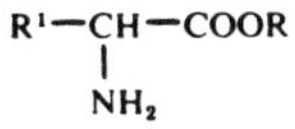

$$R^1-\underset{\underset{NH_2}{|}}{CH}-COOR \qquad\qquad II$$

where R^1 has the above meaning and R represents an unsubstituted or substituted alkyl group with 1–6 carbon atoms, an unsubstituted or substituted cycloalkyl group with 5 or 6 carbon atoms, an aralkyl group or an

aryl group. Thus R may be for example methyl, ethyl, isopropyl, butyl, isobutyl, hydroxyalkyl, cyclohexyl, benzyl, benzhydryl or phenyl. Where R^1 represents an aryl group, especially an unsubstituted phenyl or p-hydroxyphenyl group, R preferably represents a C_{1-4} alkyl group especially a methyl or ethyl group.

Before the racemisation/resolution process of the present invention is effected it may be necessary to protect any reactive substituents in the R^1 group, and subsequently remove such protecting groups. Thus, for example, protection of reactive substituents is particularly necessary with regard to certain of the naturally occurring α-amino acids. Any thiol groups and any additional carboxyl or amino groups will usually require protection. Thiol groups may, for example, be benzylated, carboxyl groups may, for example, be esterified with the same esterifying group as on the carboxyl group bonded to the asymmetric carbon atom or with a different esterifying group and amino groups may, for example, be protected by acylation e.g. N-acetylation or N-benzoylation. Hydroxyl groups present in the compound of formula II e.g. where R^1 is p-hydroxyphenyl may also be protected, which protection may be effected, for example, by the use of benzyloxycarbonyloxy group or by etherification.

The aldehyde or ketone may in general be represented by the formula

$$R^2 - CO - R^3 \qquad \text{III}$$

where R^2 and R^3, which may be the same or different, each represents hydrogen or an aliphatic, araliphatic, aromatic or heterocyclic group, e.g. an alkyl group or a monocyclic aralkyl or aryl group, which may carry substituents such as nitro or alkoxy groups. Examples include acetaldehyde, benzaldehyde, anisaldehyde, p-nitrobenzaldehyde, formaldehyde, 2-formylthiophene, furfural, pyridoxal, acetophenone, methyl ethyl ketone, methyl isobutyl ketone and acetone. R^2 and R^3 may also be joined together as in a cycloalkanone such as cyclohexanone or cyclopentanone. Simple derivatives of aldehydes and ketones such as acetals, hemiacetals, ketals and hemiketals may be used in place of the aldehyde or ketone.

The optically active resolving acid is preferably tartaric acid, more especially (+)-tartaric acid but di-esters such as dibenzoyltartaric acid may also be used. Other suitable resolving acids include (+)-mandelic acid and (+)-5-acetoxy-4-methylpentanoic acid.

By selecting the right conditions a D-isomer may be prepared from the corresponding L-isomer, the racemic mixture, or any other mixture of D- and L-isomers. Furthermore by selecting the right conditions an L-isomer may be prepared from either the corresponding D-isomer or a mixture of D- and L-isomers. The starting material may be the "wrong" isomer or a mixture of isomers in the form of a salt with the resolving acid. All such processes are included within the scope of the present invention.

Furthermore the ester may be used in the form of a Schiff base with the selected aldehyde or ketone. Thus, for example, it may be convenient to start with the preformed α-amino acid ester hemitartrate; these salts may be prepared from the crude esters.

Alternatively, the Schiff base from the α-amino acid ester and an aldehyde or ketone can be formed in solution in a solvent such as benzene, with removal of the water azeotropically or using a drying agent such as magnesium sulphate. This racemic Schiff base may then be reacted with a resolving acid such as tartaric acid in a suitable solvent to give the desired enantiomer.

Where an ester of an α-amino acid of formula I is used in which R^1 represents an aryl group (as hereinbefore defined), it is preferred to produce the D-isomer; the L-isomer may be produced in a similar way and may also find utility in the synthesis of antibiotics. Similarly, naturally occuring α-amino acids will usually be required in the L- form but nevertheless it may be useful to obtain the D- form for organic synthesis, e.g. in the preparation of analogues of the above-described cephalosporin and penicillin antibiotics.

In particularly preferred embodiments of the invention, certain combinations of DL-esters, resolving acid, carbonyl reagents and solvents have given especially good results in terms of yield and optical purity of the product.

Using DL-phenylglycinate esters with (+)-tartaric acid to obtain D-phenylglycine ester (+)-hemitartrates, we have found that the methyl ester gives best results using benzaldehyde or acetone in ethanol as solvent. The ethyl ester gives best results using benzaldehyde in methanol or, still better, ethanol as solvent or using acetone in ethanol or methanol as solvent.

Using DL-p-hydroxyphenylglycinate esters with (+)-tartaric acid to obtain D-p-hydroxyphenylglycinate ester (+)-hemitartrates, we found that the methyl ester gives best results using benzaldehyde in acetontrile or, still better, methanol/benzene as solvent. The ratio of methanol:benzene has some effect on the result and a ratio of about 4:1 is preferred. The ethyl ester gives best results with acetone in methanol as solvent or with benzaldehyde in methanol/methylene chloride as solvent. The ratio of methanol:dichloromethane is preferably about 1:1.

When an aldehyde is used in the process of our invention it may be desirable to exclude air (or oxygen) from the reaction mixture, in order to avoid oxidation of the aldehyde to the corresponding acid.

As already indicated the process of our invention is conveniently effected in the presence of a solvent other than the aldehyde or ketone although an excess of the aldehyde or ketone may serve as solvent in some cases. Any total solvent system from which the desired isomer preferentially comes out of solution may be suitable. It is advantageous to determine the preferred solvent system by appropriate preliminary "trial and error" experimentation. As indicated above, methanol, ethanol and acetonitrile as single solvents and methanol/-benzene and methanol/methylene chloride as mixed solvents find particular application in the process of the invention. Other solvents which may be used include ethylene glycol, digol, isopropanol, diglyme, tetrahydrofuran containing for example about 10% water, ethanol containing up to 10% water, methanol/1,2-dichloroethane, butane-1,3-diol/methylene chloride, dimethylacetamide/methylene chloride and hexamethyl phosphoramide/methylene chloride.

As stated above esters of p-hydroxyphenylglycine are preferred compounds for use in the process of the present invention and particularly preferred solvent systems for these esters, when the desired product is the D-isomer, include acetonitrile (as single solvent) and methanol, which is preferably in combination with a solvent which reduces the solubility of the hemitar-

trate, e.g. a chlorinated hydrocarbon such as 1,2-dichloroethane or methylene chloride or an aromatic hydrocarbon, preferably benzene. When the desired product is the L-isomer, preferred solvents with methanol include acetonitrile, carbon tetrachloride and ethyl acetate.

It is believed that the preferential crystallisation of the "right" isomer may be solvate dependent and the preferred solvates for certain given systems are exemplified in the present specification. It will be appreciated that the preferred solvate may differ from one ester to another and thus the yield of the "right" (i.e. the desired optically active isomer) isomer may be increased by choosing the most appropriate solvent. As stated above it is consequently advantageous to determine the most appropriate solvent for any particular case by preliminary "trial and error" experimentation.

The concentration of the ester may be relatively high and, for example, in methanol/acetone 1:1, the ethyl ester of DL-p-hydroxyphenylglycine was resolved in substantially higher yield at a concentration of 13.7% than at 10%. In methanol:benzene (55:45), the concentration is preferably about 5% whereas in methanol:-benzene (2:1) it is preferably about 8%.

In general, the concentration of ester in the reaction mixture may be up to 50% and as low as 0.7% but is preferably between 2.0 and 30% depending on solubilities of the various components.

It has been found advantageous to re-use the filtrate from one treatment as the solvent for the next. Thus by repeatedly re-using the filtrate from one treatment as the solvent for the next treatment improved overall yield of the desired enantiomer and good economy in respect of the particular aldehyde or ketone used may, in general, be achieved. This recycling process may, for example, be effected up to at least twelve times.

The process of our invention may conveniently be initiated at temperatures up to about 80°C. In general the whole process may conveniently be effected at ambient temperature or the process initiated at ambient temperature and the mixture cooled to a temperature as low as −30°C. It is preferred to stir the mixtures. It is useful to seed the reaction mixture with the desired product.

The yield of product, in general, increases with time. Thus, for example at room temperature, for the methyl or ethyl esters of phenylglycine and p-hydroxyphenylglycine best results usually attend reaction times of about ½–3 days, e.g. 20–24 hours, but can be as low as 6–8 hours. In general the choice of reaction conditions will follow from experiments involving isolation of the precipitate and measurement of its optical purity by rotation and its chemical purity by thin layer chromatography or spectroscopic means.

In general, where esters of formula II are used in which R^1 is other than aryl, longer reaction times are necessary, since in this case reacmisation is usually slower, and reaction times of more than two days may well be required.

Where the reaction is carried out for a relatively long time using an alcohol solvent different from that used to esterify the α-amino acid, some ester exchange may take place; we have found however that the mixed esters are optically pure, that is, they are esters of the same optical isomer of the α-amino acid.

While we do not wish to be bound by theoretical considerations, it is believed, from deuteration experiments on the methyl and ethyl esters of phenylglycine

with benzaldehyde and dimethyl sulphoxide or methanol, that the racemisation proceeds via the charged species:

$$R^1{-}\overset{\ominus}{\underset{N=CR^2R^3}{C}}{-}COOR$$

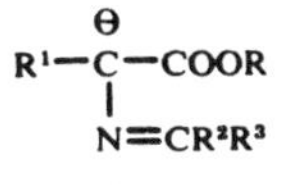

This charged species may, however, only be present in low concentration.

The conversion of the salts of the optically active α-amino acid esters into optically active α-amino acids may be carried out by first removing the optically active acid e.g. (+)-tartaric acid, e.g. on a basic ion exchange column or by formation of an insoluble salt, e.g. the tartrate, e.g. by addition of ammonia in an organic solvent such as ethanol and hydrolysing the free optically active α-amino acid ester. Alternatively the free optically active α-amino acid ester may be obtained by neutralising the optically active salt with a base, e.g. aqueous ammonium hydroxide, sodium hydroxide or sodium bicarbonate to ca. pH7 and extracting with an organic solvent or by precipitating the ester. Care must be exercised in releasing the free optically active α-amino acid ester especially a 2-amino-2-arylacetic ester since it may racemise, especially on warming or in the presence of weak acid or weak base.

Because of the risk of racemisation we have found it advantageous simply to hydrolyse directly the salt of the optically active ester (i.e. one avoids releasing the free optically active amino ester). Alternatively the salt may be converted into another salt before hydrolysis e.g. by addition of a calcium salt e.g. calcium chloride. When the process is operated in any of these ways no or very little racemisation occurs, and the α-amino acid of good optical purity can be obtained.

Free amino acids, may be obtained by hydrolysing the obtained ester, preferably using a salt as indicated above, in an aqueous solution of a strong acid e.g. having a pH of 2.5 or less, preferably 1.5 or less such as a mineral acid or an alkane- or arylsulphonic acid or a halogenated carboxylic acid, e.g. hydrochloric, hydrobromic, hydriodic, sulphuric, phosphoric, perchloric, trifluoroacetic, methanesulphonic or p-toluene sulphonic acid.

In order to achieve optimum hydrolysis it is advantageous to use at least 2.5 equivalents, preferably at least 3–4 equivalents of acid.

The hydrolysis reaction may be carried out at 20° to 150°C and is conveniently effected at the boiling point of the aqueous acid solution. It has been found that even at the boiling point little or no racemisation occurs. It is most important that strong acid hydrolysis be used.

The product of the acid hydrolysis is a solution containing a salt of the optically active amino acid. The optically active amino acid may be liberated by adjusting the pH of the hydrolysis mixture with a base to the isoelectric point of the amino acid and filtering or extracting as required. Alternatively ion exchange processes may be used.

The optically active α-amino acid esters or their salts may also be converted into their corresponding optically active α-amino acids in good yield by the use of a base i.e. a strong base having, for example, a pH greater than 10 preferably greater than 10.5, advantageously greater than 12. This is particularly surprising since the use of a base in the hydrolysis of an optically active

2-amino-2-arylacetic acid ester has been reported to lead to racemisation.

The basic conditions may be achieved by addition of a strong inorganic base capable of generating a sufficiently high pH e.g. an alkali metal hydroxide such as sodium or potassium hydroxide or an alkaline earth metal hydroxide such as barium hydroxide, ammonium hydroxide and water soluble strong organic bases may also be used. It is generally necessary to use at least 1.0 equivalent, but preferably 1–2 equivalents of sodium hydroxide or other equivalent bases together where hydrolysis is effected directly on the salt with sufficient additional base to liberate the amino acid ester from its salt.

In a single stage process under basic conditions using a hemitartrate salt, at least 3 equivalents, but preferably 3 to 4 equivalents, of base are required.

The base hydrolysis is preferably effected at temperatures of e.g.. from the freezing point of the mixture to 60°C, more preferably 20° to 40°C, conveniently for a short period of time e.g. about 15 minutes. Reaction times of 1 minute to 24 hours have, however, been used. The optimal time and temperature can be determined by a preliminary study.

The conversion of the salts of optically active esters of phenylglycine and p-hydroxyphenylglycine into their corresponding optically active acids is preferably effected by base hydrolysis.

The optically active resolving agent e.g. (+)-tartaric acid, may be recovered from the mother liquors by conventional techniques and recycled.

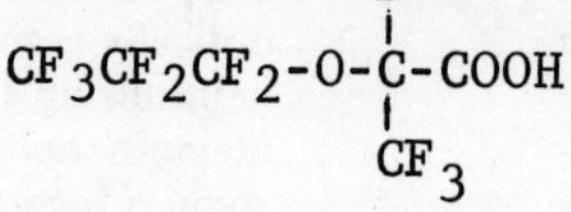

$$CF_3CF_2CF_2-O-\overset{\overset{\displaystyle F}{|}}{\underset{\underset{\displaystyle CF_3}{|}}{C}}-COOH$$

Ref. 1434

Perfluoro-2-propoxypropionyl fluoride (2), which was prepared by the anionic dimerization of perfluoro-1,2-epoxypropane (1) using tetramethylurea in diglyme,[8] was allowed to react with (-)-1-phenylethylamine, $[\alpha]^{20}$ -40.0° (neat), and an oily mixture of the diastereomeric amides (4a + 4b) was obtained quantitatively.

$$2 \quad + \quad \underset{\underset{\displaystyle Me}{|}}{(-)PhCHNH_2} \quad \xrightarrow[\substack{MeCN \\ 0.5h}]{Et_3N} \quad \underset{\underset{\displaystyle CF_3 \quad Me}{|}}{C_3F_7O\overset{\overset{\displaystyle O}{\|}}{C}FCNHCHPh} \quad \longrightarrow \quad 3 \begin{cases} a(+) \\ b(-) \end{cases}$$

$$4 \begin{cases} a(+)(-) \\ b(-)(-) \end{cases}$$

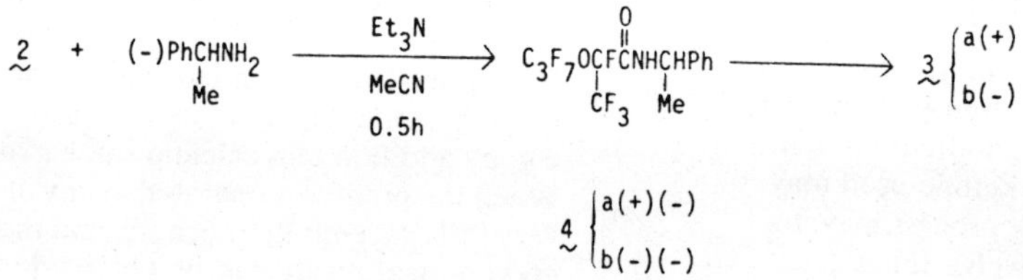

The diastereomers, 4a and 4b, were readily separated from each other by means of chromatography on silica gel using a hexane-benzene mixture (3 : 1) as a solvent and eluent. The first fraction contained (-)(-)-isomer (4b), m.p. 55.5 - 56.5 °C; $[\alpha]_D^{20}$ -82.0° (C 1.00, C_6H_6) while the second fraction gave (+)(-)-isomer (4a), m.p. 83 - 83.5 °C (from pentane); $[\alpha]_D^{20}$ -88.0° (C 1.00, C_6H_6).

The ir spectra of each isomer showed similar characteristic bands due to the NH and C=O groups at 3300 and 1700 cm^{-1}, respectively. In the ^{1}H nmr spectra (in CCl_4), each isomer gave again a similar pattern, each consists of four signals at δ 1.53 (Me), 5.12 (CH), 6.72 (NH) and 7.27 (Ph). In the ^{19}F nmr, however, a difference (9 Hz) in chemical shifts due to the terminal CF_3 of perfluoropropoxyl group was observed for the isomers. They were also characterized from the different g.l.c. retention times of 4a (11 min) and 4b (12 min).[9] Thus, the purity of each isomer could be clearly determined by both ^{19}F nmr spectra and gas chromatography.

The hydrolysis of these amides was carried out by prolonged refluxing of their aqueous ethanol solution containing 10% sodium hydroxide. The enantiomers of perfluoro-2-propoxypropionic acid thus obtained, the first example of optically active organic perfluoro compounds, were characterized as shown in Table 1.

8) Japan Kokai 52-156801 (1977).

9) G.l.c. analysis was carried out on a Shimazu GC-3BT apparatus equipped with a TCD. The 4φ x 3 steel column was packed with 15% Thermol-3 on Shimalite. Helium gas was flowed at the rate of 23 ml/min, while the column was kept at 150 °C.

Table 1 Properties of 3a and 3b

	3a	3b
Prepd. from	4a	4b
Yield (%)	69	72
B.p. (°C/mmHg)	93 - 94 / 90	
$[\alpha]^{20}_D$ ($CHCl_3$)	+16.5 (C 0.82)	-16.5 (C 0.85)
IR (film) (cm^{-1})	3200 (OH), 1780 (C=O)	
^1H NMR ($CDCl_3$)	δ 10.3	
^{19}F NMR* (neat)	2.7(1F), 5.43(3F), 6.3(3F), 10.0(1F), 53.0(2F), 54.8(1F)	

* δ ppm upfield from ext. CF_3CO_2H.

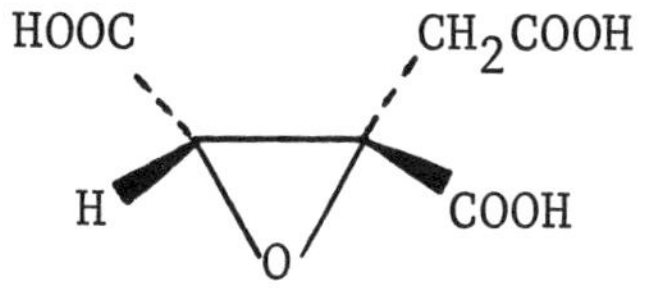

$C_6H_6O_7$ Ref. 1435

65.7 g (0.122 mole) of the bis R-(+)-α-methyl-p-nitrobenzylamine salt of (+)-threo-epoxyaconitic acid (98–99% optical purity) and 73 ml of 0.5 N HCl (0.365 mole) were heated at reflux for 16 hrs. The solution was cooled and extracted with EtOAc (2 × 100 ml). The organic layers were backwashed in turn with water (50 ml) and the combined aqueous layers were evaporated to dryness under reduced pressure. The residue was triturated with EtOAc (3 × 100 ml) and the solids were recovered by filtration to give 44.8 g (91.4%) of recovered R(+)-α-methyl-p-nitrobenzylamine hydrochloride (m.p. 246°–7°). The filtrate was dried over $MgSO_4$, evaporated in vacuo and the residue was heated at 75°–80° in vacuo for ½ hr. to ensure lactonization. Crystallization of the residue (21 g) from EtOAc-CCl_4 furnished the γ-lactone of (−)-threo-hydroxycitric acid in two crops: 6.0 g [m.p. 174°–6°; $[\alpha]_D^{25}$ +105.6°] and 3.2 g [168°–173°;$[\alpha]_D^{25}$ +100.5°].

EXAMPLE 2

38.85 g (200 mmoles) of racemic threo-epoxyaconitic acid dissolved in 250 ml of methanol-water (98:2 v/v) was treated with 59.80 g (360 mmoles) of R(+)-α-methyl-p-nitrobenzylamine in 150 ml of the same solvent. The warm solution immediately began to deposit solid and was left at room temperature overnight. The mixture set to a solid mass, which was mashed and filtered. The collected solid was rinsed with fresh solvent and dried in a vacuum oven at 45° overnight to give 50.5 g solid with $[\alpha]_{436}^{25}$ +13.07° (c=2.035% in water), approx. 87.3% optically pure. The solid was stirred and refluxed gently as a slurry with 400 ml of the same solvent for 2 hr, then allowed to cool to room temperature with stirring overnight to give 44.78 g of solid with $[\alpha]_{436}^{25}$ +14.83° (c=2% in water). This salt contained 2 moles of amine per mole of acid and was 99.1% optically pure by comparison with an authentic sample prepared by reacting optically pure (+)-threo-epoxyaconitic acid with R(+)α-methyl-p-nitrobenzylamine.

The crops were combined and recrystallized from EtOAc-CCl_4 (after decolorization using acid-washed Norit Sv charcoal) to give the γ-lactone in two crops; m.p. 178°–180°, $[\alpha]_D^{25}$ +106.2°, and m.p. 178°–180°λ ,$[\alpha]_D^{25}$ +105.9°.

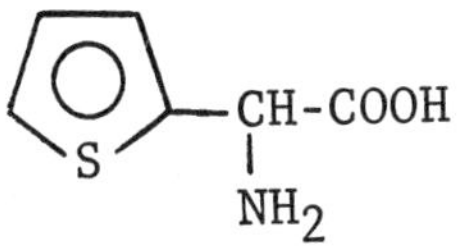

$C_6H_7NO_2S$ Ref. 1436

EXAMPLE 40

Resolution with Racemisation of Methyl DL-2-Thienylglycinate

A solution of methyl DL-2-thienylglycinate (1.232 g., 7.20 mmole) and (+)-tartaric acid (1.091 g., 7.27 mmole, 1.01 equiv.) in ethanol/acetone (1:1, 12 ml.) was stirred at 20° for 7 days. Some solid precipitated immediately but then dissolved in ca. 15 minutes. The orange solution was allowed to stand for an hour, during which little crystallisation occurred, and then stirring was restarted. The product was washed with ethanol/acetone (1:1, 2 ×) and dried at 20°/2 mm. for 5 hours to give methyl D-2-thienylglycinate (+)-hemitartrate (0.947 g., 41%), m.p. 144° to 145°, $[\alpha]_D^{23}$ − 43.6° (c 1.000, H_2O). ca. 94% optically pure.

EXAMPLE 68

D-2-Thienylglycine

Methyl D-2-thienylglycinate (+)-hemitartrate ($[\alpha]_D$ − 43.6°, 0.742 g., 2.31 mmole) was stirred with 2.22N-sodium hydroxide solution (3.45 ml., 7.65 mmole, 3.32 equiv.). The hemitartrate had dissolved after 1 minute and tlc showed that hydrolysis was complete. After 15 minutes the pH was adjusted to 6.6 with 2N-hydrochloric acid. The mixture was cooled in ice, filtered, and the solid washed with water (2 × 0.4 ml.), and dried over phosphorus pentoxide giving D-2-thienylglycine (85 mg., 23.5%), m.p. 188° to 194° (decomp.), $[\alpha]_D^{20}$ − 69.3° (c 0.8085, H_2O).

For the theoretical basis for this resolution procedure, see Ref. 1433

$C_6H_8O_2$

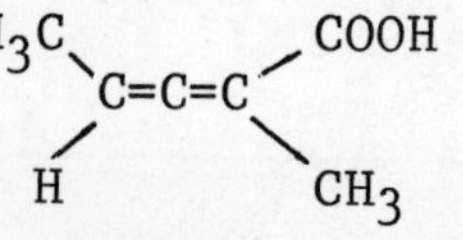

Ref. 1437

Eine feinverteilte, feste Mischung von 11,21 g (100 mmol) (*RS*)-**13** und 15,33 g (52 mmol) Cinchonidin wurde langsam auf 60° erhitzt und dann mit soviel Aceton versetzt (*ca.* 800 ml), dass eine klare Lösung vorlag. Nach dem Abkühlen wurde über Nacht bei 0° auskristallisieren gelassen. Sowohl die abfiltrierte und im RV. eingedampfte Mutterlauge, wie auch ein Aliquot des gebildeten Salzes[26]) (*ca.* 4 g) wurden zur Freisetzung der Säure aufgehoben. Der Rest des Salzes wurde in obiger Art 9mal aus siedendem Aceton umkristallisiert, wobei weitere Aliquote entnommen wurden (vgl. *Tab. 4*). Zur Rückgewinnung der freien Säuren (*R*)-**13** bzw. (*S*)-**13** wurden die einzelnen Fraktionen mit verd. Schwefelsäure [20b] aufgearbeitet und mindestens 1mal aus siedendem Pentan umkristallisiert. Nach dem Messen der Drehwinkel α (vgl. *Tab. 4*) wurden die Säuren nach Methode 1.2.4 in die entsprechenden Methylester (*R*)-**3** bzw. (*S*)-**3** übergeführt. Von den destillierten Methylestern (Sdp. 65-75°/14 Torr; GC. ≥ 99%) wurden wiederum die Drehwinkel α (vgl. *Tab. 5*) bestimmt und 90-MHz-^{1}H-NMR.-Spektren[27]) ohne und mit Zusatz der optisch aktiven Verschiebungsreagenzien aufgenommen (vgl. *Tab. 6*).

Tabelle 4. *Physikalische Eigenschaften der optisch aktiven 2-Methyl-2,3-pentadiensäuren*

Mess-reihe Nr.	Säure	Umkr.ᵃ) (Aceton)	Umkr.ᵇ) (Pentan)	Smp. [°]	cᶜ) mg/ml	$[\alpha]_\lambda$ᵈ) 365	436	546	578	589	eᵉ)	pᶠ)
1	(−)-(*R*)-**13**	1	1	54-55	9,1 und 20,5	−47,95	−27,46	−14,98	−13,02	−12,44	0,15 ± 0,02	0,17
2	(*RS*)-**13**	-	3	55	-	-	-	-	-	-	0,00	0,00
3	(+)-(*S*)-**13**	1	1	55	13,9	153,57	86,33	46,55	40,65	38,85	0,54 ± 0,02	0,53
4	(+)-(*S*)-**13**	2	1	56	13,5	184,52	104,22	56,30	48,59	46,67	0,62 ± 0,02	0,64
5	(+)-(*S*)-**13**	7	1	58	17,6	226,02	127,61	68,92	59,72	57,39	0,84 ± 0,02	0,80
6	(+)-(*S*)-**13**	10	2	64	7,7 und 15,2	279,87	157,40	85,06	74,01	70,39	0,92 ± 0,02	0,95

ᵃ) Anzahl Umkristallisationen des Cinchonidin-Adduktes (1. Kristallisation = 1).
ᵇ) Anzahl Umkristallisationen der freien Säure.
ᶜ) In mg Säure/1 ml Äthanol («Uvasol»).
ᵈ) Messtemp. 20°, λ in nm; Drehwerte in Grad, kein Vorzeichen bedeutet +.
ᵉ) Enantiomerenreinheiten e von den entsprechenden Estern **3** übernommen (vgl. *Tab. 5*).
ᶠ) Optische Reinheit p (vgl. Fussnote 2) berechnet aus den über alle Wellenlängen gemittelten Werten (rel. Fehler ≤ 2,5%).

Tabelle 5. *Physikalische Eigenschaften der optisch aktiven 2-Methyl-2,3-pentadiensäure-methylester*

Mess-reihe Nr.ᵃ)	Ester	cᵇ)	$[\alpha]_\lambda$ᶜ) 365	436	546	578	589	eᵈ)	pᵉ)
1 (1)	(−)-(*R*)-**3**	12,6	−47,46	−27,37	−14,86	−12,90	−12,32	0,15 ± 0,02	0,17
2 (2)	(*RS*)-**3**	-	-	-	-	-	-	0,00	0,00
3	(+)-(*S*)-**3**	8,2	36,59	20,85	11,59	10,00	9,60	0,13 ± 0,01	0,13
4	(+)-(*S*)-**3**	6,5	114,62	65,69	36,15	30,77	29,85	0,39 ± 0,02	0,40
5 (3)	(+)-(*S*)-**3**	4,5	141,33	80,22	44,44	39,33	37,04	0,54 ± 0,02	0,50
6 (4)	(+)-(*S*)-**3**	15,2	195,59	112,04	61,38	53,62	51,00	0,62 ± 0,02	0,67
7 (5)	(+)-(*S*)-**3**	10,0	230,40	132,00	72,30	63,50	60,10	0,84 ± 0,02	0,80
8 (6)	(+)-(*S*)-**3**	7,8	262,44	150,77	82,44	72,05	69,00	0,92 ± 0,02	0,92

ᵃ) Die Ziffern in Klammern verweisen auf die entsprechenden Säure-Fraktionen der *Tabelle 4*.
ᵇ) In mg Ester/1 ml Äthanol («Uvasol»).
ᶜ) Messtemp. 20°, λ in nm; Drehwerte in Grad, keine Vorzeichen bedeutet +.
ᵈ) Enantiomerenreinheit e (vgl. Fussnote 2) berechnet aus Q (*Tab. 6*).
ᵉ) Optische Reinheit p (vgl. Fussnote 2) berechnet aus den über alle Wellenlängen gemittelten Werten (rel. Fehler ≤ 2,5%).

Tabelle 6. *Daten der Eu(hfc)$_3$-induzierten ^{1}H-NMR.-Verschiebungen bei den optisch aktiven 2-Methyl-2,3-pentadiensäure-methylestern*ᵃ)

Messreihe Nr.ᵇ)	Ester	Lösungs-mittel	$\Delta\delta$(CH$_3$O)ᶜ) [ppm]	$\Delta\Delta\delta$(CH$_3$O) [ppm]	Qᵈ)
1 (1)	(−)-(*R*)-**3**	CCl_4	1,30	0,030	1,35 ± 0,05
2 (2)	(*RS*)-**3**	CCl_4	1,35	0,035	1,00
3	(+)-(*S*)-**3**	CCl_4	1,25	0,035	1,31 ± 0,03
4	(+)-(*S*)-**3**	CCl_4	1,25	0,035	2,28 ± 0,05
5 (3)	(+)-(*S*)-**3**	CCl_4	1,35	0,030	3,34 ± 0,07
6 (4)	(+)-(*S*)-**3**	CCl_4	1,30	0,035	4,43 ± 0,06
7 (5)	(+)-(*S*)-**3**	CCl_4	1,25	0,030	11,87 ± 0,20
8 (6)	(+)-(*S*)-**3**	TCFE	1,25	0,040	24,96 ± 0,50

ᵃ) *Ca.* 1 M Lösungen bzgl. des Esters unter Zugabe von *ca.* 0,125 Mol-Äquiv. Eu(hfc)$_3$.
ᵇ) Die Ziffern in Klammern verweisen auf die entsprechenden Säure-Fraktionen der *Tabelle 4*.
ᶜ) Im Vergleichsspektrum ohne Verschiebungsreagenz erscheint das Signal als *s* bei 3,65 (CCl_4) bzw. 3,70 ppm (TCFE); $\Delta\delta$ = Mittlerer Verschiebungswert der beiden *s* minus 3,65 (bzw. 3,70) ppm.
ᵈ) Q = Verhältnis der Enantiomeren, berechnet aus den entsprechenden Flächen (Pikhöhe × Halbhöhenbreite) von 10 in beiden Feldrichtungen aufgenommen ^{1}H-NMR.-Spektren (vgl. *Fig. 1c, d*).

[27]) ^{13}C-NMR.-Spektrum von (*RS*)-**3** (1 M in TCFE unter Zusatz von 0,125 Mol-Äquiv. Eu(hfc)$_3$): 211,4 (*s*, C(3)); 167,6 (*s*, C(1)); 96,1 (*s*, C(2)); 88,4 (*d*, C(4)); 52,5 (*qa*, CH_3O); 15,9 (*qa*, CH_3–C(2)); 12,9 (*qa*, C(5)).

[2]) e = ($E_+ - E_-$)/($E_+ + E_-$), E_+ und E_-: Molenbrüche der Enantiomeren; p = [α]/[A], [α] = spezifische Drehung einer Substanz, [A] = spezifische Drehung des reinen Enantiomeren; vgl. [1] [2].

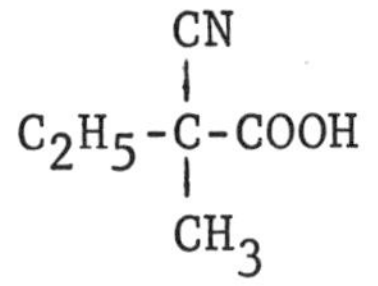

$C_6H_9NO_2$ Ref. 1438

Note: Resolved using (-)-threo-1-phenyl-2-aminopropanediol-1,3 as resolving agent in methanol/ether (1:3) as solvent. The (+)(-) diastereomer had a m.p. of 146°. The obtained (+) enantiomer had a m.p. of 44° and a $[\alpha]_D^{20}$ 4.56°. (Rotation taken in ethanol).

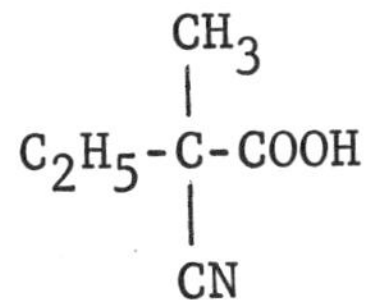

$C_6H_9NO_2$ Ref. 1439

Note: Using 1S,2S (+)-1-phenyl-2-amino-propanediol-1,3 obtained acids with the following constants:

b.p. 93°/0.2 Torr $[\alpha]_D^{20}$ -4.76° (ethanol)
b.p. 92°/0.2 Torr $[\alpha]_D^{20}$ +4.56° (ethanol)

See also Ref. 189.

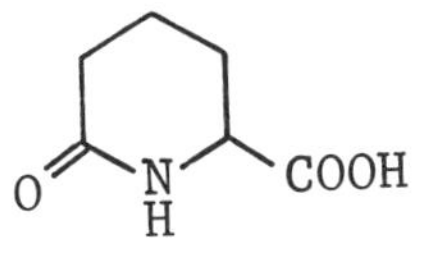

$C_6H_9NO_3$ Ref. 1440

EXAMPLE 1

Resolution of d,l-6-oxo-2-piperidinecarboxylic acid (HPCA)

A. Preparation of d-HPCA Quinine Salt

Dissolve 2.27 g of anhydrous quinine in 208 ml of acetonitrile with warming and add a suspension of 1 g of dl-HPCA in 180 ml of warm acetonitrile. Seed with the quinine salt of d-HPCA and allow to crystallize at room temperature. When crystallization is complete, filter and wash with two 5-ml portions of acetonitrile and air dry the precipitate. The yield is 1.71 g. mp 213.5°-215.5° dec.

B. Preparation of l-HPCA Quinine Salt

Concentrate the combined mother liquors and wash from the previous step to 25 ml, add 0.25 ml of water and seed with the quinine salt of l-HPCA. Allow to crystallize at room temperature. Filter and wash with two 3-ml portions of acetonitrile and air dry the precipitate. The yield is 1.19 g of solvated product, mp 180°-183°.

To purify, disperse 1 g in 67 ml of acetonitrile containing 1% water warmed to 39° and filter the solution from a trace of insoluble material. Concentrate the filtrate to 11.5 ml, seed with l-HPCA quinine salt and allow to crystallize at room temperature. Filter and wash with three 2-ml portions of acetonitrile and air dry the precipitate. The yield is 0.8759. Mp 159°-160°, resolidifying and remelting at 182°-184°. The material may be desolvated by heating in vacuo at 100°. The rotation (dry basis) $[\alpha]_D^{21}$ = -140.2°, C = 2 in 6N HCl.

C. Preparation of l-HPCA

Dissolve a 0.6495 g sample of l-HPCA quinine salt in 19.5 ml of water and make alkaline with 1 ml of 2.5N NaOH. Filter the precipitated quinine after it becomes granular. Acidify the filtrate with 0.85 ml of 2.5N HCl and evaporate to a residue. Extract the residue with anhydrous ethanol and concentrate the extract to a residue. Dissolve the residue in a small amount of water and allow the l-HPCA to crystallize. Filter and wash with water, and vacuum dry at room temperature. The yield is 0.1306 g of partially solvated material, $[\alpha]_D^{21}$ = +35.3°, C = 2 in 6N HCl; or +39.0° corrected for solvation.

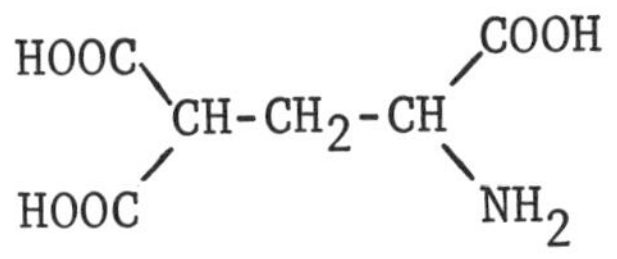

$C_6H_9NO_6$ Ref. 1441

For resolution procedure, see Ref. 1510 and 1510a.

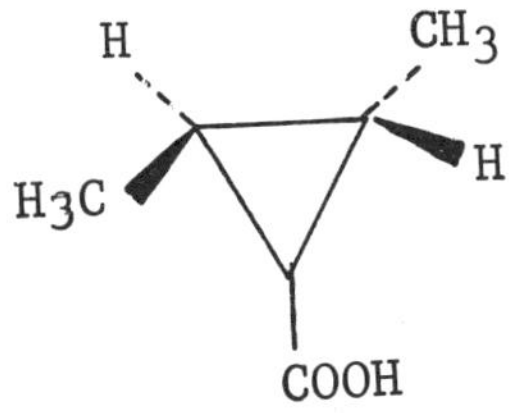

$C_6H_{10}O_2$ Ref. 1442

Resolution of (±)-*trans*-2,3-Dimethylcyclopropanecarboxylic Acid. To a solution of 12.0 g (37 mmol) of quinine in 100 ml of hot 95% ethanol, 8.0 g (70 mmol) of the acid was added. The mixture was heated to reflux for 15 min, then 400 ml of water was added. Cooling in the refrigerator for 2 days yielded 9.75 g (92%) of the white crystalline diastereomer, mp 133–135°. Recrystallization yielded 5.79 g (54%) of the diastereomer as clusters of white needles, mp 139–141°. This diastereomer and 5.61 g of potassium hydroxide were dissolved in 200 ml of 50% methanol–water and the solution heated on a steam bath for 5 hr. The methanol was removed by use of a rotary evaporator and the resulting aqueous solution continuously extracted with ether for 48 hr. The ether solution thus obtained was dried over magnesium sulfate and the ether removed by use of a rotary evaporator to yield 1.48 g (35%) of the acid, $[\alpha]^{25}D$ −10.0° (*c* 0.190, absolute ethanol). The filtrates from the first two crystallizations were combined and saponified in like manner to yield 4.36 g (54%) of the acid, $[\alpha]^{24}D$ +4.56° (*c* 0.0473, 95% ethanol).

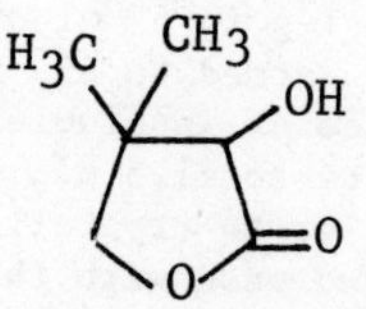

$C_6H_{10}O_3$ Ref. 1443

Optically active *l*-α-**hydroxy**-β,β-**dimethyl**-γ-**butyrolactone.** Štefan Bauer and Štefan Országh. **Czech. 88,066,** Dec. 15, 1958. *dl*-α-Hydroxy-β,β-dimethyl-γ-butyrolactone (52 g.) and 66 g. *l*-ephedrine (I) dissolved in 60 ml. H_2O, the soln. heated 1 hr. to 90°, evapd. *in vacuo* at 65°, the sirupy residue dissolved in 132 ml. PrCOMe, the soln. seeded and allowed to crystallize 3 days at −5°, the cryst. salt filtered off, washed with 12 ml. ice-cold PrCOMe and dried over P_2O_5 gives 43.2 g. *l*-ephedrine *l*-α,γ-dihydroxy-β,β-dimethylbutyric acid (II), m. 109°. The filtrate is evapd. *in vacuo*, and the sirupy residue heated with 10 ml. H_2O and 20 ml. HCl 1 hr. to 90°. To the hot mixt. was added 10.7 g. NaCl, the salted out I.HCl (47.3 g.) sepd., the acid aq. filtrate neutralized with solid Na_2CO_3 to pH 6.5, extd. continually with $CHCl_3$ 6 hrs., the $CHCl_3$ ext. evapd., the residue dissolved in 100 ml. abs. Et_2O, the undissolved I.HCl (4.7 g.) filtered off, the Et_2O filtrate evapd. and the residue distd. *in vacuo* to give 16.9 g. crude title compd., recrystd. from 9 ml. PrCOMe and dried to give 9.93 g. product, m. 83–4°, $[\alpha]^{20}_D$ −50°(H_2O). II (43.2 g.) is refluxed in 50 ml. H_2O with 18.5 ml. HCl 1 hr. to 90°; to the hot soln. is added 21.2 g. NaCl, the salted out I.HCl (24.82 g.) filtered off and the filtrate worked up as above to give 14.7 g. *d*-α-hydroxy-β,β-dimethyl-γ-butyrolactone, b_{12} 120–2°, $[\alpha]^{20}_D$ 37.1° (H_2O).

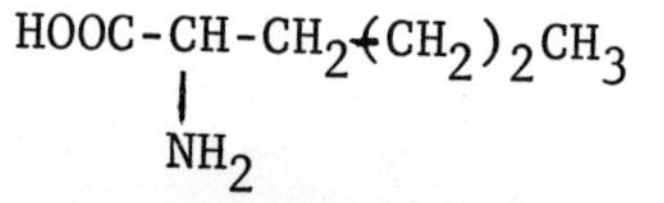

$C_6H_{13}NO_2$ Ref. 1444

N-Chloroacetyl-DL-α-aminoadipic Acid.—One hundred and sixty-eight grams of aminoadipic acid[6] was treated with chloroacetyl chloride and chilled NaOH in the usual manner. The reaction mixture was acidified to a *p*H of about 0.5 with concd. HCl and extracted several times with ethyl acetate. The combined extracts were dried over Na_2SO_4 and evaporated to dryness *in vacuo*. The residual sirup was dissolved in dry ether from which crystals separated on chilling. The yield of N-chloroacetyl-DL-α-aminoadipic acid was 74 g., m.p. 127° (cor.). After recrystallization from ethyl acetate the m.p. was 129° (cor.). The yield was 31%, but from the aqueous layer 46 g. of unaltered DL-α-aminoadipic acid (N, calcd. 8.7, found 8.6) could be recovered.

Anal.[7] Calcd. for $C_8H_{12}O_5NCl$: N, 5.9; Cl, 14.9. Found: N, 5.8; Cl, 14.6.

Enzymatic Resolution of Chloroacetyl-DL-α-aminoadipic Acid.—Eighty-six and a half grams of chloroacetyl-DL-α-aminoadipic acid was suspended in 2 liters of water and brought into solution at *p*H 7.0 by addition of 2 *N* LiOH. Water was added to bring the final volume to 3,640 cc. (0.1 *M*) and 2.8 g. of acylase I powder was dissolved in the solution. The latter was brought back to *p*H 7.0 by addition of a few drops of LiOH, and placed in a water-bath at 38°.[8] After 10 hours of incubation, manometric ninhydrin analyses on an aliquot of the digest revealed 50% hydrolysis of the racemate. Further incubation of the digest up to 24 hours did not result in a change of this figure. Accordingly, acetic acid was added to *p*H 5, and the protein filtered off with the aid of Norit. The filtrate was evaporated to about 400 cc. *in vacuo*, and the small amount of protein which flocculated was again removed by filtration. The filtrate was treated dropwise with concd. HCl to *p*H 3.2. A copious crystallization of L-α-aminoadipic acid quickly ensued. Twice the volume of absolute ethanol was added, and the mixture chilled at 5° for several hours. The L-isomer was filtered and washed with ethanol, and the mother liquor and washings combined and set aside for the preparation of the D-isomer. The yield of L-α-aminoadipic acid was 27 g. or 93%; $[\alpha]^{25}D$ +24.6° (2% in 5 *N* HCl). It was recrystallized by adding sufficient boiling water to dissolve the solid, filtering rapidly through a heated filter, and chilling quickly in a −20° alcohol-water-bath to 5°. The final yield of pure L-α-aminoadipic acid was 22 g. or 76%; $[\alpha]^{25}D$ +25.0° (2% in 5 *N* HCl).

Anal. Calcd. for $C_6H_{11}NO_4$: C, 44.7; H, 6.9; N, 8.7. Found: C, 44.8; H, 6.9; N, 8.7.

The combined alcoholic mother liquor and washings contained chloroacetic acid, chloroacetyl-D-α-aminoadipic acid, and traces of unprecipitated L-α-aminoadipic acid. It was evaporated *in vacuo* nearly to dryness, concd. HCl was added with careful cooling to a *p*H of about 0.5, and the acid solution extracted several times with ethyl acetate. The combined extracts were dried over Na_2SO_4 and evaporated *in vacuo* to a residual oil. The oil was taken up in a liter of dry acetone, filtered, the acetone removed by a stream of air, and the residue dissolved in 500 cc. of 2 *N* HCl. The solution was refluxed for 2 hours, decolorized with a little Norit, and evaporated *in vacuo* to a thick sirup. The sirup was dissolved in 400 cc. of H_2O, and the solution treated dropwise with pyridine to *p*H 3.2. The D-α-aminoadipic acid which appeared was recrystallized from water as described for the L-isomer. Yield of pure product was 12 g. or 42%; $[\alpha]^{25}D$ was −25.0° for a 2% solution, and −24.9° for a 6% solution, in 6 *N* HCl.

Anal. Found: C, 44.5; H, 7.0; N, 8.7.

Optical Purity of D-α-Aminoadipic Acid.—One thousand micromoles of D-α-aminoadipic acid at *p*H 7.2, and in the presence of catalase, was practically inert to 30 mg. of *Crotalus adamanteus* venom. When, under the same conditions, 1 micromole of the L-isomer was mixed at the beginning of the run with the 1,000 micromoles of the D-isomer, there was an oxygen consumption equivalent to that of the 1 micromole of L-isomer added. The reaction reached completion in about 1 hour. There was evidently less than 1 part of the L-isomer present in 1,000 parts of the D. Ten micromoles of the L-isomer alone in the presence of large amounts of the venom and catalase, also consumed close to the theoretical amount of oxygen. The D-isomer itself was completely inert to hog kidney D-amino acid oxidase, and therefore the optical purity of the L-isomer could not be determined in this fashion.[4]

(4) A. Meister, L. Levintow, R. B. Kingsley and J. P. Greenstein, *J. Biol. Chem.*, **192**, 535 (1952).

(5) S. M. Birnbaum and J. P. Greenstein, *Archiv. Biochem. Biophys.*, **39**, 108 (1952).

(6) Donated by Dr. Alton Meister.

(7) Analyses by R. J. Koegel and staff of this Laboratory.

(8) At *p*H 7.0 and 38°, the rate of hydrolysis of this substrate by crude hog kidney aqueous homogenate is 1.5 micromoles per hour per mg. N; with acylase I this rate is 45. Since the reaction is zero order, the amount of acylase added to the solution should be sufficient to hydrolyze the L-component of the racemate in about 8 hours.

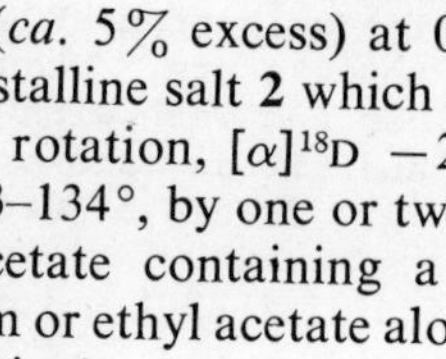

$C_7H_{10}O_3$ Ref. 1445

Addition of (+)-α-methylbenzylamine (*ca.* 5% excess) at 0° led to rapid formation of the crystalline salt **2** which could be easily purified to constant rotation, $[\alpha]^{18}D$ −25.4° (*c* 0.7 in CH_3OH) and mp 133–134°, by one or two recrystallizations from ethyl acetate containing a few per cent methanol (chloroform or ethyl acetate alone may also be used for recrystallization).

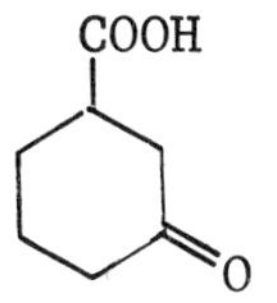

$C_7H_{10}O_3$ Ref. 1446

Note: Racemic acid was resolved using brucine. Active acid had m.p. 70.5-71.5°, $[\alpha]^{24}_D$ -8.2° (C 3.01, methanol).

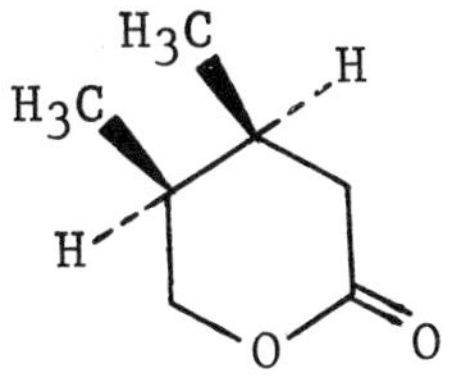

$C_7H_{12}O_2$ Ref. 1447

Note: The racemic lactone was hydrolyzed with NaOH and the resulting acid was resolved with (+)-α-phenethylamine. After recrystallizing 5 times from acetone a salt, m.p. 135.5-136.5°, $[\alpha]^{22}_D$ 5.02° (c 2.25, CH_3OH), was obtained in 12.2% yield. The salt was acidified (HCl), to give 92% optically pure (3S,4S) lactone, $[\alpha]^{22}_D$ -47.2° (c 1.23, CH_3OH). The lactone enriched in the (+)-enantiomer was recovered from the mother liquor of the recrystallization and it was resolved with (-)-α-phenethylamine to give another salt, m.p. 133-134°, $[\alpha]^{22}_D$ = -4.96° (C, 2.34, CH_3OH) in 9.1% yield. The salt was decomposed to give 90% optically pure (3R,4R)-lactone, $[\alpha]^{22}_D$ 46.3° (C 1.85, CH_3OH). The optical purity of the resolved lactones was determined by analyzing the diastereomeric ratio of the amide derivatives

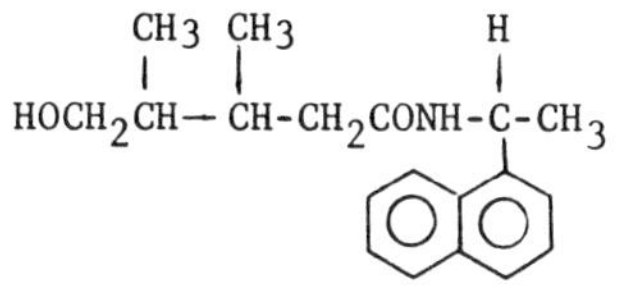

by HPLC (Zorbax SIL 25 cm. X 6.2 mm, EtOAc-MeOH 20:1, 1 ml/min.) and shown to be 90% in the case of (+)-lactone and 92% in the case of (-)-lactone.

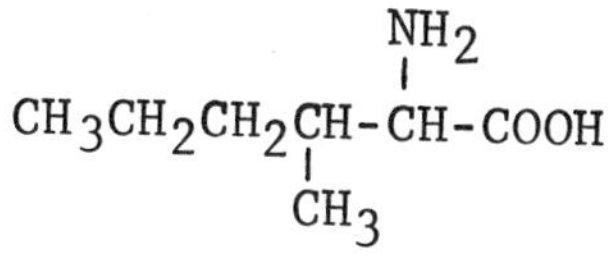

$C_7H_{15}NO_2$ Ref. 1448

Enzymatic resolution of (±)-**4**.

(*i*) *Preparation of* (2S, 3R)-**5**. The N-acetate (±)-**4** (43g) was dissolved in water (2.05 l) by adding NaOH aq (*ca* 8.6g in 100 ml water) to pH 6.7–6.8. Acylase (Acylase "Amano", 15,000 unit/g, 3g) and 7×10^{-4} M $CoCl_2$ were added to the soln and the mixture was kept at 37°. The acylase (2g) was added after 1 day. Another g of the acylase was added after 2 days. After 4 days at 37° the dark soln was concentrated *in vacuo* to *ca* 100 ml. The separated crystals of (2*S*, 3*R*)-**5** (8.1g) were collected on a filter and washed with cold water. The combined filtrate and washings were concentrated *in vacuo* and acidified with 6N HCl (32.5 ml). The partially resolved (2*R*, 3*S*)-**4** (28.3g) immediately separated from the soln and was collected on a filter. The filtrate was extracted with EtOAc. The EtOAc extract was concentrated *in vacuo* to give impure (2*R*, 3*S*)-**4** (5.0g). The aq. layer was concentrated *in vacuo* to dryness. The residue was triturated with 99% EtOH and filtered to remove insoluble materials (17.4g). The filtrate was concentrated *in vacuo*. Pyridine (1 ml) and water (5 ml) were added to the residue and the precipitated (2*S*, 3*R*)-**5** (1g) was collected on a filter. The total yield of (2*S*, 3*R*)-**5** was 9.1g (55%). An analytical sample was obtained as prisms by recrystallization from water, m. p. 230–238° (dec.), $[\alpha]^{21}_D$ +44.9 (c = 0.275, 5N HCl); ν_{max} ~3100 (m), ~2590 (m), 2100 (w), 1600 (s, sh), 1575 (s), 1505 (s), 1410 (m), 1350 (m), 1320 (m), 1295 (w), 1265 (w), 1240 (w), 1185 (w), 1120 (w), 1070 (w), 1020 (w), 945 (w), 900 (w), 860 (w), 815 (w), 790 (w), 760 (w), 740 (w), 715 (m) cm^{-1}. (Found: C, 57.68; H, 10.29; N, 9.67. Calc. for $C_7H_{15}O_2N$: C, 57.90; H, 10.41; N, 9.65%). The crude amino acid (7.3g) was recrystallized from a large volume of water to give 4.5g of pure (2*S*, 3*R*)-**5**.

(*ii*) *Preparation of* (2R, 3S)-**4**. The partially resolved N-acetate (61.4g) was fractionally recrystallized from acetone. Fractions with $[\alpha]_D$ − 13° to − 30° (EtOH) were combined (39g). This was suspended in water (2l) and dissolved by adding NaOH aq to pH 6.5. The acylase (3g) and $CoCl_2$-$6H_2O$ (44.0 mg) were added and the mixture was set aside at 37° for 5 days with the addition of further amount of the acylase (1g × 3) at intervals. Subsequent work-up as described above gave 25.5g of crude (2*R*, 3*S*)-**4**. This was fractionally recrystallized from acetone to give the first [17.5g, $[\alpha]^{22}_D$ − 28.7° (c = 1.286, EtOH)], second [5.5g, $[\alpha]^{22}_D$ − 15.6° (c = 0.973, EtOH)] and third [2.5g, $[\alpha]^{22}_D$ − 17.0° (c = 1.260, EtOH)] crops. The first crop was further purified by recrystallization from acetone to give 12.2g of pure (2*R*, 3*S*)-**4** as prisms, m.p. 146–147°, $[\alpha]^{22}_D$ − 34.3° (c = 0.936, EtOH); ν_{max} 3320 (s), ~2480 (m), ~2320 (m), ~1880 (w), 1695 (s), 1620 (s), 1540 (s), 1425 (m), 1315 (m), 1305 (m), 1275 (s), 1230 (m), 1150 (m), 1115 (w), 1085 (w), 1025 (w), 955 (m), 865 (w), 835 (w), 745 (w), 700 (m) cm^{-1}. (Found: C, 57.81; H, 9.12; N, 7.46. Calc for $C_9H_{17}O_3N$: C, 57.73; H, 9.15; N, 7.48%).

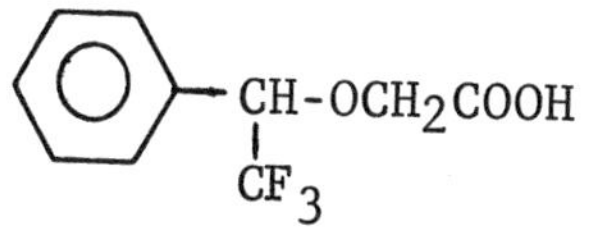

$C_8H_7N_3O_2$ Ref. 1449

Diastereoisómeros D(—) · L(+) y L(+) · D(—)

A la solución de 35,4 (0,2 mol.) de ácido α-azidofenilacético racemo en 70 ml. de acetona, se adicionaron 42,9 g. (0,2 mol.) de L(+) treo-1,p-nitrofenil-2-amino-1,3 propanodiol o idéntica cantidad del D(—) treo-isómero, calentando moderadamente (40°) hasta completa disolución; a continuación agitando se vertieron 350 ml. de cloruro de metileno caliente, lográndose así una más rápida y suave ebullición de la mezcla que mediante suave calefacción exterior se mantuvo a reflujo durante 30 m. Casi inmediatamente se inició la precipitación de la sal, que progresivamente fue aumentando. Después se dejó enfriar a 25° durante unos 60 m. aislándose por filtración y lavado con cloruro de metileno, una vez secos, 41,0 g. (≃ 0,2 mol.) de diastereoisómero D(—) · L(+), blanco, con F ≃ 145-150° (d). Procediendo exactamente con la D(—) treo base del cloranfenicol, se logró idéntico resultado en L(+) · D(—) sal. En los líquidos madres de filtración permanecieron en solución los diastereoisómeros con componentes de igual signo.

Purificación

Con la cantidad de sal anterior, distribuida en cuatro lotes (10,25 g.) fueron sucesivamente realizadas con cada uno de ellos, tres cristalizaciones utilizando

siempre las mismas aguas madres; la primera con 60 ml. de agua destilada, la segunda con 50 ml. y ambas por enfriamiento lento (reposo, 20°), causando la formación de grandes agujas. La tercera, en otros 45 ml. y mediante enfriamiento rápido en continua agitación hasta alcanzar 20°, provocándose la cristalización en diminutas agujas. La disolución de la sal, en todos los casos se produjo a 80-82°, resultando soluciones de una tonalidad amarilla pálida y cada vez el sólido aislado fue lavado con la cantidad precisa de etanol de 96° y secado.
Después del tercer tratamiento se logró una pureza óptica del 100 %, resultando 36,9 g. de distereoisómero, prismas aciculares con F = 157-60° (d) y rendimiento del 95 % del teórico.

En los líquidos acuosos, después del uso prolongado de las aguas de cristalización, con el tiempo y más rápidamente por enfriamiento se produjo la separación de sales acumuladas, de donde se logró aislar más disatereoisómero de menor pureza.

Diastereoisómero L(+) · D(—). Espectro IR, fig 2

Análisis. Calculado para $C_{17}H_{19}N_5O_6$ (389,36): C, 52,44; H, 4,91 y N, 17,98. Hallado: C,52,17; H, 4,92 y N, 17,96.
Actividad óptica: $[\alpha]^{22}_{589}$ = —1,58° (C = 2,330 %, 1 dm., DMSO y α = —0,037).

Diastereoisómero D(—) · L(+). Idéntico espectro IR al de la fig 2, e igual valor de la actividad óptica, con signo positivo. Prismas aciculares con F = 157-60° (d), iniciándose la descomposición en la superficie de los cristales, análogamente a la otra sal, con la aparición de vacuolas originadas por el desprendimiento de gases y presentando finalmente el aspecto de una superficie viscosa en ebullición.

Diastereoisómeros D(—) · D(—) y L(+) · L(+).

Los líquidos orgánicos, resultantes de la separación de las sales con componentes de signo opuesto, se evaporaron a presión reducida, calentando en baño de agua a 30° y al aceite originado se adicionó una porción de éter etílico, produciendo una solución menos viscosa; a continuación se repitió el proceso de evaporación (rota-vapor), sin calentamiento exterior, lográndose un hinchamiento o esponjamiento de la masa que al favorecer la eliminación de restos de disolventes, provocó la solidificación (espuma sólida). En algunas ocasiones este tratamiento se tuvo que efectuar tres veces consecutivas, especialmente con líquidos procedentes de resoluciones realizadas con sustancias de insuficiente grado de pureza, o con varios días de preparación. El sólido resultante (36,8-39,0 g.), cuando no fue utilizado inmediatamente se dejó en el secador de vacío, sobre potasa caústica, debido especialmente a la marcada tendencia al apelmazamiento. La solución de esta sal en acetato de etilo (40 ml.), se diluyó con cloruro de metileno hasta ligera turbidez y una vez se inició la cristalización a temperatura ambiente, luego se enfrió en baño de hielo (2 h.). Separados los cristales, se diluyeron nuevamente los líquidos de filtración, con más cloruro de metileno y se abandonaron en el refrigerador. En total se aislaron 30 g. de diastereoisómero, con F = 109-111° una vez lavados y secados. Por evaporación del disolvente y repitiendo el tratamiento con el residuo, se logró otra fracción (3 g.) de menor pureza, alcanzándose un rendimiento del 88 % del teórico.

Purificación

Se disolvieron 33 g. de sal en 240 ml. de isopropanol y a 40° se adicionaron 240 ml. de cloruro de metileno, enfriando a continuación en baño de hielo durante dos horas; seguidamente se filtró, lavó con cloruro de metileno y secado el sólido a 50-60°, resultaron 29,8 g. con rendimiento del 90 % y F = = 110-111° (d).

Diastereoisómero D(—) · (D—). Espectro IR, figura 3.

Análisis. Calculado para $C_{17}H_{19}N_5O_6$ (389,36): C, 52,44; H, 4,91 y N, 17,98. Hallado: C,52,40; H, 4,85 y N, 17,90.
Actividad óptica: $[\alpha]^{22}_{589}$ = —55,86° (C = 2,302 %, 1 dm., DMSO y α = —1,286).

Diastereoisómero L(+) · L(+). Idéntico espectro IR al de la fig. 3, e igual valor de la actividad óptica, con signo positivo. Análogamente a la otra sal, presenta F = 110-111° (d). Muy soluble en agua, acetato de etilo y acetona.

DESDOBLAMIENTO DE LAS SALES. AISLAMIENTO DE LOS ACIDOS ENANTIOMEROS

En una mezcla de 135 ml. de agua y 135 ml. de cloruro de metilo, se suspendieron 38,93 g. (0,1 mol.) de diastereoisómeros y con agitación de la masa, se vertieron 20 ml. de ácido clorhídrico concentrado, diluidos en agua (20 ml.). Inmediatamente se produjo la disolución de la fase sólida, ocasionada por el desdoblamiento; resultando por reposo, dos fases transparentes, que una vez decantadas, de la superior (acuosa) y después de lavada con cloruro de metileno, se recuperó la base utilizada en la resolución, ajustando la solución a pH 10. La fase orgánica inferior reunida con los extractos, lavada con agua (25 ml.) y secada con sulfato sódico anhidro, se evaporó completamente el disolvente a presión reducida, calentando en baño de agua a 30°. El aceite incoloro resultante se enfrió en baño de hielo, cristalizando en bellas rosetas blancas (comportamiento exotérmico) que luego se pulverizaron o desmenuzaron para eliminar vestigios del disolvente, mediante evaporación al vacío, rindiendo 17,27 g. del ácido enantiómero, con rendimiento del 97,5 % del teórico y F = 52-6° para cada uno, e indistintamente de la sal de partida usada.

Acido D(—) α-azidofenilacético. Espectro IF, fig. 4.

Análisis. Calculado para $C_8H_7N_3O_2$ (177,15): C, 54,23; H, 3, 98 y N, 23,71.

Hallado: C, 54,39; H, 4,00; y N. 23,72.

Actividad óptica: $[\alpha]^{22}_{589}$ = —146,5° (c = 1,071 %, 1 dm., DMSO y α = —1,570). $[\alpha]^{22}_{589}$ = —145,8° (c = 1,000 %, 1 dm., Etanol abs. y α = —1,458). Lit. —144° y F = 55-7 (35).

Acido L(+) α-azidofenilacético. Espectro IR idéntico a la fig 4.

Análisis. Calculado para $C_8H_7N_3O_2$ (177,15): C, 5423; H, 3,98 y N, 23,71.

Hallado: C, 54,41; H, 3,96 y N, 23,83.

Actividad óptica: $[\alpha]^{22}_{589}$ = +146,5° (c = 1,005 %, 1 dm., DMSO y α = +1,473). $[\alpha]^{22}_{589}$ = +145,6° (c = 1,013 %, 1 dm., Etanol abs. y α = +1,475). Lit. +146° y F = 56-7° (35).

(35) B. Sjöberg y B. Ekstrom: Pat. Brit. 960665: «Chem. Zent.», 137, 29-1.721 (1966).

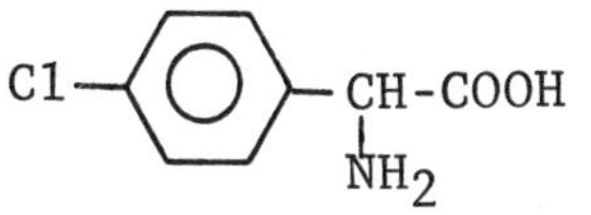

$C_8H_8ClNO_2$ Ref. 1450

Resolution with Racemisation of Methyl p-Chlorophenylglycinate

A solution of methyl DL-p-chlorophenylglycinate (0.801 g., 4.01 mmole) and (+)-tartaric acid (0.634 g., 4.2 mmole, 1.05 equiv.) in methanol (4 ml.) was stirred for 2 hours at 18°, by which time a solid had crystallised. Acetone (4 ml.) was added over 20 minutes, and the mixtures was stirred at 18° at 25° for 7 days, when it was filtered. The product was washed with methanol-:actone (1:1, 2 × 1 ml.) and dried at 20°/1 mm. Hg for 2 hours to give methyl D-p-chlorophenylglycinate (+)-hemitartrate (0.897 g., 57% yield) as a methanol(0.65M MeOH 0.2M Me_2CO 0.15M EtOH) solvate, m.p. 150° - 156° $[\alpha]_D^{22}$ − 61° (c 2.50, H_2O).

D-p-Chlorophenylglycine

A solution of methyl D-p-chlorophenylglycinate (+)-hemitartrate (0.867 g., 2.370 mmole.) in water (20 ml.) was neutralised to pH 7.0 with 10N-ammonium hydroxide solution, and extracted into methylene chloride, which was washed, dried, and evaporated to give the D-ester as a colourless oil (0.474 g., 100%). A solution of the D-ester (0.474 g., 2.370 mmole) in 6N-hydrochloric acid (1.6 ml., 9.60 mmole, 4 equiv.) was refluxed for 75 minutes. Water (1.6 ml.) was added and the pH of the warm solution adjusted to 7.0 with 10N-ammonium hydroxide solution. The mixture was cooled in ice, filtered, washed, and dried over phosphorus pentoxide to give the D-amino acid (0.337 g., 77%), m.p. 233° to 237° (decomp.), $[\alpha]_D^{20}$ − 129.0° (c 0.993, 1N-HCl), $[M]_D^{20}$ − 239°.

For the theoretical basis for this resolution procedure, see Ref. 1433

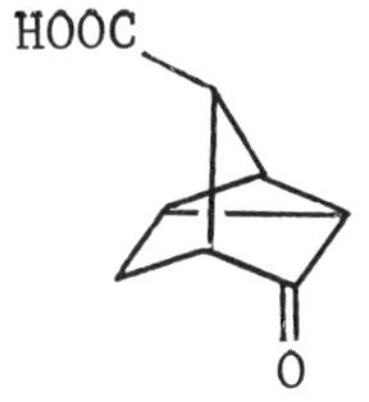

$C_8H_8O_3$ Ref. 1451

(+)-*anti*-5-Carboxytricyclo[2.2.1.0^{2,6}]heptan-3-one (2). A solution containing 27.4 g (0.18 mol) of racemic 5-carboxytricyclo[2.2.1.0^{2,6}]heptan-3-one[18] in 1.1 L of acetone was heated to 50 °C and 21.9 g (0.18 mol) of *l*-(−)-α-methylbenzylamine was added. The hot solution was swirled while 1.1 L of warm hexanes was added at such a rate so as to prevent premature crystallization. The homogeneous solution was allowed to cool to room temperature slowly. After 20 h, the ammonium salt was collected by filtration, giving 39.0 g: mp 103–107 °C (130–135 °C, evacuated sealed tube); $[\alpha]_D$ +3.5° (*c* 1.0, CH_3OH).

The above salt was dissolved in 1.5 L of acetone and heated to 50 °C. The solution was filtered hot, if necessary, prior to the slow addition of 1.5 L of warm hexanes so as to avoid crystallization. After cooling to room temperature, the homogeneous solution was allowed to stand for 20 h. Filtration provided 20.3 g of ammonium salt: mp 105–110 °C (137–141 °C, sealed tube); $[\alpha]_D$ +23.6° (*c* 1.0, CH_3OH). Recrystallization of this material from 800 mL of acetone and 800 mL of hexanes using the above techniques afforded 11.5 g of salt: mp 107–110 °C (140–143 °C, sealed tube); $[\alpha]_D$ +42.5° (*c* 1.0, CH_3OH). Further recrystallization from 470 mL of acetone and 470 mL of hexanes gave 8.2 g of salt: mp 110–112 °C (143–146 °C, sealed tube); $[\alpha]_D$ +53.2° (*c* 1.0, methanol). Optical purity was achieved by a fourth recrystallization from 350 mL of acetone and 350 mL of hexanes. There was obtained 6.1 g of pure salt: mp 114–116 °C (149.0–151.5 °C, sealed tube); $[\alpha]_D$ +58.9° (*c* 1.0, CH_3OH).

The above salt (6.1 g) was dissolved in 30 mL of 20% hydrochloric acid. After dissolution, solid sodium chloride was added to the aqueous acidic solution. The product was extracted with ethyl acetate (4 × 40 mL). The combined organic layers were washed with saturated brine solution and dried over anhydrous magnesium sulfate. Concentration under reduced pressure gave 3.2 g of pure 2: mp 142.5–143.5 °C; $[\alpha]_D$ +76° (*c* 1.0, CH_3OH) [lit.[5] mp 137–138 °C; $[\alpha]^{25}_D$ +74.0° (*c* 1.0, CH_3OH)]. Our $[\alpha]_D$ for optically pure 2 in methanol rapidly drops to +60°. Use of dioxane as solvent gave $[\alpha]_D$ +81.8° (*c* 1.0) consistently.

(18) P. A. Grieco, C. S. Pognowski, S. D. Burke, M. Nishizawa, M. Miyashita, Y. Masaki, C.-L. J. Wang, and G. Majetich, *J. Am. Chem. Soc.*, **99**, 4111 (1977).

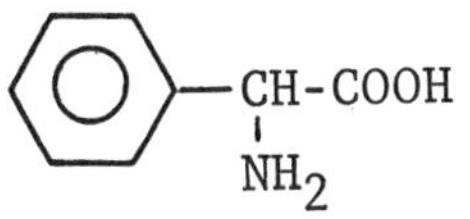

$C_8H_9NO_2$ Ref. 1452

A solution of 5.0 mg moles (930 mg) of DL-phenyl glycine amide. HCl, 50 mg of $MgCl_2$ and about 0.2 mg $MnCl_2$ in 100 ml of water is adjusted to a pH of 8.0 by means of 1-N sodium hydroxide. After addition to this solution of 250 mg of leucine aminopeptidase (Merck 25010) covalently bonded to 3-amino-propyl-triethoxysilyl Bio-Glass with a load of 0.3 % by weight, obtained as described in Biotechnology and Bioengineering Vol. XVI, pp. 275–77, 1974, the solution was stirred at room temperature for 18 hours.

After filtration of the leucine aminopeptidase bonded to glass powder, the filtrate is subjected to a thin-layer chromatographic examination. This showed that the DL-phenyl glycine amide was converted into equimolar amounts of L-phenyl glycine and D-phenyl glycine amide by leucine aminopeptidase convalently bonded to glass.

The filtrate is adjusted to a pH of 10.0 with 1-N NaOH and then passed over 100 grams of Amberite 1.R.C.—50 ion exchanger in the H^+ form. Next 100 ml of water is passed over, the ion exchanger, the eluate is evaporated to a volume of 15 ml in vacuo, and the L-phenyl glycine is isolated by filtration. The yield of L-phenyl glycine which is pure according to thin-layer chromatography is 0.34 gram(efficiency 90 %).

Specific rotation of this L-phenyl glycine: $[\alpha]_D^{25}$ = +157° (2.6 % by weight of HCl; C = 1.6). Reference: Beilstein 14 III, p. 1188: $[\alpha]_D^{25}$ = +157.5 (2.6 % by weight of HCl; C = 1.6). Selectivity: % of L-phenyl glycine= 99.8 %.

The D-phenyl glycine amide bonded to the Amberlite I.R.C.—50 is extracted with 150 ml of 0.5-N sulfuric acid. The eluate is concentrated to 10 ml by evaporation in vacuo and then boiled for 1 hour. After cooling and neutralization with concentrated aqueous ammonia, the crystallized D-phenyl glycine is filtered over a glass filter and washed on the filter with 5 ml of water. The yield of D-phenyl glycine is 0.33 gram (efficiency 90 %). Specific rotation found:

$[\alpha]_D^{25} = -152°$(C = 0.6; 2-N HCl) Reference: Beilstein 14 III, p. 1187: $[\alpha]_D^{25} = -153°$ (C = 0.6; 2-N HCl). Selectivity: % of D-phenyl glycine = 99.2 %.

$C_8H_9NO_2$ Ref. 1452a

Resolution with Racemisation of Methyl DL-phenylglycinate using Acetone

Methyl DL-phenylglycinate (4.98 g., 30.2 mmole), (+)-tartaric acid (4.54 g., 30.2 mmole, 1 equiv.) and acetone (4.5 ml., 61.2 mmole, 2 equiv.) were stirred in dry ethanol (46 ml.) at 20° to 25° for 44 hours. The mixture was filtered and the solid washed with ethanol (2 × 15 ml.) and dried at 27°/3 mm. for 2½ hours to give methyl D-phenylglycinate (+)-hemitartrate as a mono-ethanol solvate, (9.93 g., 91%), $[\alpha]_D^{23}$ −63.5° (c 2.5, H_2O).

Following the general procedure of Example 3 but using various ketones to form the Schiff base, D-phenylglycinate (+)-hemitartrate esters were prepared as set out in Table B.

TABLE A

Resolution with Racemisation of Esters of DL-Phenylglycine in Ethanol with Various Aldehydes.

Aldehyde	Equivs. Aldehyde	Ester	Conc. Ester % w/v	Time Hrs.	Temp.°	$[\alpha]_D$°	Product Hemitartrate % Optical Purity	Yield %
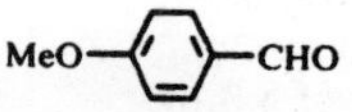	1	Et	10	19	20	−46	95	76
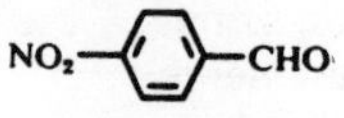	1	Et	10	19	20	−46	95	51
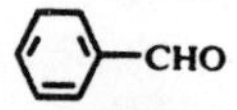	1	Et	10	18	20	−46	95	73
CH_3CHO	1	Et	10	19	20	−44.5	93	68.5
CH_2O	1	Et	10	42	20–26	−46	95	38.5
PhCHO	1	Et + Me = 57:43	20	70	20–25	−53.5	96	82.5
PhCHO	1	Et + Me = 55:45	10	24	20	−52	94	59

TABLE B

Resolution with Racemisation of Esters of DL-Phenylglycine in Ethanol in the Presence of Ketones

Ketone	Equivs. of Ketone	Ester	Conc. of Ester % w/v	Time of Stirring	Temp.°	$[\alpha]_D$°	Product - hemitartrate % Optical Purity	Yield %
Me_2CO	2	Et	10	165 hours	20–25	−46.5	96	89.5
Me_2CO	2	Me	10	44 hours	20–25	−63.5	98	91
Me_2CO	2	Me	8	142 hours	20–25	−63	98	90.5
Me \ CO / Et	2	Me	10	122 hours	20–25	−64.5	99	92
Me \ C=O / CH_2CHMe_2	2	Me	10	140 hours	20–25	−63	97	96
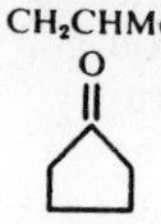	2	Me	10	141 hours	20–25	−63	97	92.5
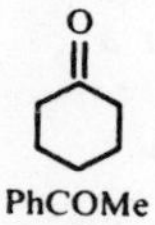	2	Me	10	141 hours	20–25	−65	100	94.5
PhCOMe	2	Me	10	288 hours	20–25	−61.5	95	94.5

Resolution with Racemisation of Pure Methyl DL-Phenylglycinate in Aqueous IMS using Benzaldehyde

A solution of pure methyl DL-phenylglycinate (4.674 g., 28.3 mmole) and (+)-tartaric acid (4.285 g., 28.6 mmole, 1.01 equiv.) in 10% aqueous IMS (47 ml.) was seeded with methyl D-phenylglycinate (+)-hemitartrate ($[\alpha]_D$ −64.6°). Crystallisation began immediately. After 2 hours, benzaldehyde (2.9 ml., 3.03 g., 28.5 mmole, 1 equiv.) was added and the mixture was stirred for 48 hours, and then filtered. The product was washed with 10% aqueous IMS (2 × 8 ml.) and dried at 20°/4 mm. for 2½ hours giving methyl D-phenylglycinate (+)-hemitartrate solvated with 1.0 mole ethanol (7.38 g., 72%), $[\alpha]_D^{20}$ −63.2° (c 2.508, H_2O).

Resolution with Racemisation of Pure Methyl DL-Phenylglycinate in Aqueous IMS using Acetone.

Similarly to Example 13 but using methyl DL-phenylglycinate (4.818 g., 29.2 mmole) and (+)-tartaric acid (4.449 g., 29.9 mole, 1.02 equiv.) in 10% aqueous IMS (48 ml.) and adding acetone (4.3 ml., 3.40 g., 58.5 mmole, 2 equiv.) instead of benzaldehyde to give methyl D-phenylglycinate (+)-hemitartrate solvated with 1.0 mole ethanol (5.195 g., 49%), $[\alpha]_D^{20}$ −63.1° (c 2.495, H_2O).

Hydrolysis of Methyl D-Phenylglycinate (+)-Hemitartrate

A solution of methyl D-phenylglycinate (+)-hemitartrate (20.49 g., — containing 0.7 mole ethanol i.e. 59.0 mmole) in 6N-hydrochoric acid (38 ml., 228 mmole, 3.9 equiv.) was refluxed for 1 hour 10 minutes, and then concentrated to remove most of the alcohols. The solution was diluted with water (19 ml.) and the pH adjusted to 7.0 with 0.880 ammonia solution. The mixture was cooled in ice for ca. 30 minutes, filtered, the solid washed with water (2 × 12 ml.) and ethanol (12 ml.), and dried over phosphorus pentoxide in vacuo giving D-phenylglycine (8.06 g., 90%) as cream coloured plates, sublimed 245° – 249°, $[\alpha]_D^{25}$ – 154° (c 1.02, 1N-HCl).

Hydrolysis of Methyl L-Phenylglycinate (−)-Hemitartrate

A solution of methyl L-phenylglycinate (−)-hemitartrate mono-ethanol solvate ($[\alpha]_D$ + 62.4°, 36.888 g., 0.102 mole) in 6N-hydrochloric acid (68 ml., 0.408 mole, 4 equiv.) was refluxed for 1 hour 10 minutes and then distilled for 15 minutes. Water (68 ml.) was added and the pH of the warm solution adjusted to 7.0 with ammonium hydroxide solution (0.880, 35 ml.). The mixture was cooled in ice, filtered, and the solid was washed with water (2 × 25 ml.) and ethanol (25 ml.) and dried over phosphorus pentoxide to give L-phenylglycine as white plates (13.406 g., 87%), $[\alpha]_D^{21}$ + 152.1° (c 1.007, 1N-HCl).

The product (5.968 g.) was dissolved in 2N-hydrochloric acid (130 ml.) and neutralised to pH7.0 with ammonium hydroxide solution (0.880, 26 ml.). The solid was filtered, washed, and dried as before to give L-phenylglycine (4.706 g., 79%), $[\alpha]_D^{24}$ + 154.7° (c 1.006 1N-HCl),

The product (4.210 g.) was reprecipitated to give L-phenylglycine (3.340 g., 79%), $[\alpha]_D^{23}$ + 155.5° (c 1.005, 1N-HCl).

This product (3.002 g.) was reprecipitated to give

L-phenylglycine (2.385 g., 79%, $[\alpha]_D^{22}$ + 152.1° (c 1.016, 1N-HCl), $[\alpha]_D^{23}$ + 153.0° (c 1.010, 1N-HCl).

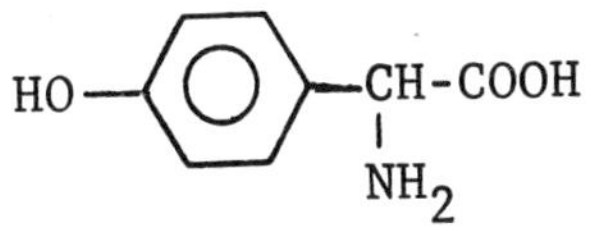

$C_8H_9NO_3$ Ref. 1453

L-(+)-2-(4-Hydroxyphenyl)glycine (25). DL-2-(4-Methoxyphenyl)glycine (93 g, 0.514 mol) was suspended in H_2O (1.3 L) and to the stirred suspension was added NaOH (21.3 g, 0.514 mol). Chloroacetic anhydride (177 g, 1.027 mol) was then slowly added over a period of 0.5 h, with cooling, followed by further addition of NaOH (42.6 g) in H_2O (200 mL). The pH was maintained at 9 by addition, if necessary, of more NaOH solution, and stirring at room temperature was continued for a 1.5 h period. The solution was then acidified to pH 2 by addition of concentrated HCl, and the resultant pale yellow precipitate of DL-*N*-(chloroacetyl)-2-(4-methoxyphenyl)glycine was filtered off, washed, and dried: yield 51 g; mp 174–178 °C (lit.[40] mp 182–183 °C).

The DL-*N*-(chloroacetyl)-2-(4-methoxyphenyl)glycine (51 g) was suspended in distilled H_2O (770 mL) and to this was added sufficient NH_4OH to maintain the pH at 7.8 and effect solution. Hog kidney acylase enzyme (2.8 g) (acylase-1, Sigma Chemical Co.) was added, and the solution was stirred at 37 °C for 22 h. A light brown precipitate of **27** was obtained and filtered off [the filtrate contains D-(–)-*N*-(chloroacetyl)-2-(4-methoxyphenyl)-glycine]. The crude **27** was added to hot 3 N HCl (100 mL) containing charcoal, and the mixture was warmed gently and filtered. The cooled filtrate was treated with 0.880 ammonia until pH 5–6 was obtained. A white crystalline solid of L-(+)-2-(4-methoxyphenyl)glycine (**27**) precipitated and was filtered off and recrystallized from water: yield 7.7 g (43%); mp 218 °C dec; $[\alpha]^{25}_D$ +137° (lit.[40] $[\alpha]^{25}_D$ +150.4°).

Compound **27** (10 g) was added to 48% HBr (100 mL), and the mixture was heated under reflux with stirring for 5 h. The resultant red solution was evaporated to dryness; the residue was then treated with H_2O (50 mL) and the mixture filtered. The filtrate was brought to pH 5 by addition of 0.880 ammonia, whereupon a solid precipitated after cooling. The solid was filtered off, washed, and recrystallized from H_2O to give **25**: yield 5.5 g (60%); mp 230 °C dec; $[\alpha]^{25}_D$ +124.5° (lit.[39] mp 225 °C dec).

(39) A. W. Long, J. H. C. Nayler, H. Smith, T. Taylor, and N. Ward, *J. Chem. Soc. C*, 1920 (1971).
(40) L. B. Crast, U.S. Patent 3 517 023 (1967).

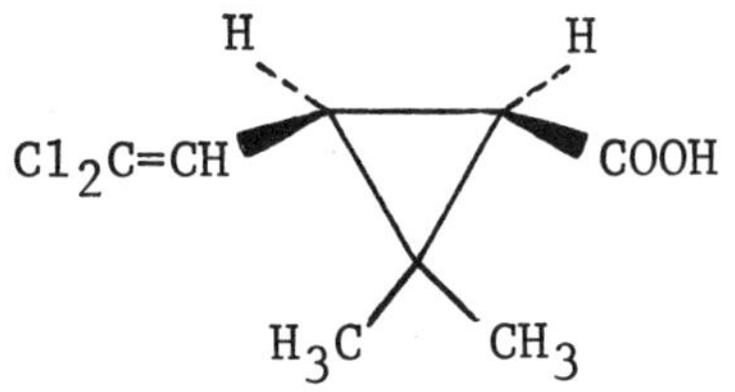

$C_8H_{10}Cl_2O_2$ Ref. 1454

2.4. Resolution of (±)-*cis*-2,2-dimethyl-3-(2,2-dichlorovinyl)-cyclopropanecarboxylic acid

The (±)-*cis* acid (14.6 g) in benzene (250 ml), and (+)-α-methylbenzylamine (8.47 g) in benzene (30 ml) were mixed at 50°, and allowed to cool to 20° overnight. The precipitate (13.2 g, 58% required isomer) was recrystallised 3 times from benzene to give the *(+)-α-methyl benzylamine salt of the* (–)-cis *acid* (4.0 g) m.p. 146° $[\alpha]_D$ + 26.9° (c, 1.5 in EtOH). From the mother liquors, the (+)-*α-methylbenzylamine salt of the* (+)-cis *acid* (1.7 g) m.p. 135°, $[\alpha]_D$ – 17.1° (c, 1.6 in EtOH) was isolated. Throughout the resolution, the degree of separation was estimated from the relative heights of the two singlets at τ8 (benzene solution) due to the different CH_3^a groups in the 2 salts (cf.[10, 11]) in the nmr spectrum. Repetition using (–)-α-methylbenzylamine gave, after 3 crystallisations, the (–)-*α-methylbenzylamine salt of the* (+)-cis *acid* (6.1 g) m.p. 147° $[\alpha]_D$ – 26.1° (c, 1.9 in EtOH) and from the mother liquors the (–)-*α-methylbenzylamine salt of the* (–)-cis *acid* (3.8 g) m.p. 139° $[\alpha]_D$ + 14.8° (c, 2.0 in EtOH).

Each of the four salts was shaken with benzene (50 ml) and 3N-HCl (50 ml) and the benzene layer processed to give the resolved acids. Thus were obtained (–)-cis-*2,2-dimethyl-3-(2,2-dichlorovinyl)-cyclopropanecarboxylic acid* (4.6 g) m.p. 90° $[\alpha]_D$ – 26.9° (c, 1.7 in $CHCl_3$) and (+)-cis-*2,2-dimethyl-3-(2,2-dichlorovinyl)-cyclopropanecarboxylic acid* (3.9 g) m.p. 90° $[\alpha]_D$ + 27.2° (c, 2.1 in $CHCl_3$).

10. Barlow, F.; Elliott, M.; Farnham, A. W.; Hadaway, A. B.; Janes, N. F.; Needham, P. H.; Wickham, J. C. *Pestic. Sci.* 1961, **2**, 115.
11. Bramwell, A. F.; Crombie, L.; Hemesley, P.; Pattenden, G.; Elliott, M.; Janes, N. F. *Tetrahedron*, 1969, **25**, 1727.

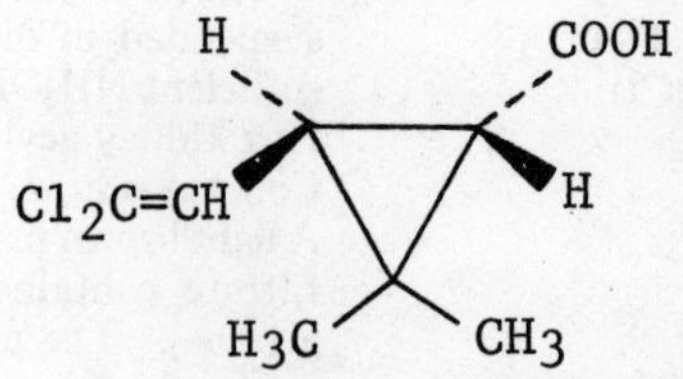

$C_8H_{10}Cl_2O_2$

Ref. 1455

2.5. Resolution of (±)-*trans*-2,2-dimethyl-3-(2,2-dichlorovinyl)-cyclopropanecarboxylic acid

The (±)-*trans* acid (15.6 g) in benzene (180 ml) and L-(+)-threo-1-*p*-nitrophenyl-2-(*N*,*N*-dimethylamino)propane-1,3-diol[12] (18.0 g) in benzene (180 ml) were mixed at 50° and cooled to 20° during 2 days. The precipitate (14.2 g) was recrystallised 3 times from trichloroethylene to give the *L-(+)-threo-1-*p*-nitrophenyl-2-N,N-dimethylamino-propane-1,3-diol salt of* (−)-trans-*2,2-dimethyl-3-(2,2-dichlorovinyl)-cyclopropane-carboxylic acid* (8.9 g) m.p. 129–131° $[\alpha]_D$ + 7.4° (c, 2.1 in EtOH). Correspondingly D-(−)-threo-1-*p*-nitrophenyl-2-(*N*,*N*-dimethylamino)propane-1,3-diol gave *the salt with the* (+)-trans *acid* (9.4 g) m.p. 129–131°, $[\alpha]_D$ − 7.3° (c, 2.0 in EtOH). Decomposition of the salts with 3N-HCl as described for the *cis* acids gave (−)-trans-*2,2-dimethyl-3-(2,2-dichlorovinyl)-cyclopropanecarboxylic acid* (3.8 g) m.p. 68–73°, $[\alpha]_D$ − 34.6° (c, 1.9 in EtOH) and (+)-trans-*2,2-dimethyl-3-(2,2-dichlorovinyl)-cyclopropanecarboxylic acid* (4.1 g) m.p. 69–73°, $[\alpha]_D$ + 33.0° (c, 2.0 in EtOH).

12. Goffinet, B.; Locatelli, A. *French Patent* 1968, 1,536,458 (*Chem. Abs.* 1969, 71, 90923w).

$C_8H_{10}Cl_2O_2$ Ref. 1455a

Beispiel 1

Zu 1 Mol (±)trans-2-(2,2-Dichlorvinyl)-3,3-dimethyl-cyclopropancarbonsäure und 1 Mol Natriumcarbonat in 10 ltr. Wasser wird bei 20°C unter Ruhren eine Lösung von 0,5 Mol (-)-Phenylglycinethylester-hydrochlorid 92% optisch rein ($[\alpha]^{20}_D$ = -91° (1 %ige Lösung in Wasser)) in 1000 ml Wasser zugetropft. Der entstehende Niederschlag wird scharf abgesaugt, mit kaltem Wasser gewaschen und durch Zugabe von 1000 ml 0,25 molarer Schwefelsäure und 1000 ml Ether bei 20° zersetzt. Die organische Phäse wird abgetrennt, getrocknet und eingeengt. Man erhält in 95 %iger Ausbeute (+)-trans-2-(2,2-Dichlorvinyl)-3,3-dimethylcyclopropancarbonsäure mit einer optischen Reinheit von 87 %. Durch Umkristallisation aus Petrolether und nach Abtrennung des restlichen schwerer löslichen Racematanteils erhält man die optisch reine (+)-trans-Saure mit einem Drehwert von $[\alpha]^{20}_D$ = +36,0° (1 %ige Losung in Chloroform).

Aus der wässrigen Phase erhält man bei entsprechender Aufarbeitung die (-)-trans-2-(2,2-Dichlorvinyl)-3,3-dimethylcyclopropancarbonsäure mit einem Drehwert von $[\alpha]^{20}_D$ = -36,0° (1 %ige Lösung in Chloroform).

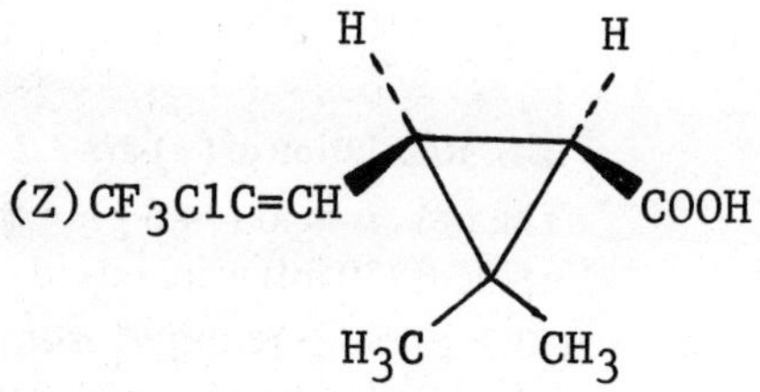

$C_9H_{10}ClF_3O_2$ Ref. 1456

EXAMPLE 13

To a stirred solution of (±)-cis-3-[(Z)-2-chloro-3,3,3-trifluoroprop-1-en-1-yl]-2,2-dimethylcyclopropane carboxylic acid (1.2 g) in 0.2 N sodium hydroxide (25 cc) is added dropwise during 15 minutes a solution of l-α-methylbenzylamine (0.3 g) in 0.2 N hydrochloric acid (12.5 cc). The mixture is filtered and the residue is washed with water. The solid is dried(0.70 g), it consists of the l-α-methylbenzylamine salt of (±)-cis-3-[(Z)-2-chloro-3,3,3-trifluoroprop-1-en-1-yl]-2,2-dimethylcyclopropane carboxylic acid, m.p. 173°. The salt is stirred with a mixture of 2N hydrochloric acid (5 cc) and dichloromethane (5 cc). The dichloromethane solution is separated and it is washed with water. The dichloromethane is distilled and the residue is (+)-cis-3-[(Z)-2-chloro-3,3,3-trifluoroprop-1-en-1-yl]-2,2-dimethylcyclopropane carboxylic acid, $[\alpha]^{25}_D$ (C, 5, chloroform) +45°. The pure isomer has $[\alpha]^{25}_D$ (C, 5, chloroform) +48°.

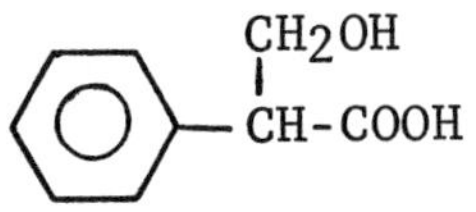

$C_9H_{10}O_3$ Ref. 1457

From this salt *l*-tropic acid was isolated and without further purification melted at 126—128° and had $[\alpha]_D - 75{\cdot}6°$ in water.

With Ethylhydrocupreidine.—From *dl*-tropic acid (4·9 grams) and ethylhydrocupreidine (10 grams), ethylhydrocupreidine *d*-tropate (4·5 grams) was isolated pure, and further quantities of slightly less pure salt were obtained from the alcoholic mother-liquors.

Ethylhydrocupreidine d-*tropate* crystallises anhydrous from alcohol in soft, white, voluminous masses of fine needles. It is sparingly soluble in cold alcohol and melts at 182—183° (Found: C = 70·8; H = 7·6. $C_{21}H_{28}O_2N_2,C_9H_{10}O_3$ requires C = 71·1; H = 7·6 per cent.). The specific rotation was determined in absolute alcohol:

$c = 1{\cdot}011$; $l = 2$ dcm.; $\alpha_D + 3{\cdot}05°$; $[\alpha]_D + 150{\cdot}8°$.
$c = 1{\cdot}012$; $l = 2$ dcm.; $\alpha_D + 3{\cdot}05°$; $[\alpha]_D + 150{\cdot}7°$.

The tropic acid isolated from this salt melted at 128—130° and gave $[\alpha]_D + 78{\cdot}1°$ in water ($c = 0{\cdot}61$).

From the alcoholic mother-liquors of this salt, the corresponding ethylhydrocupreidine *l*-tropate was isolated in small quantity.

Ethylhydrocupreidine l-*tropate monohydrate* crystallises from alcohol, in which it is readily soluble, in clusters of well-formed prisms. Air-dried, it melts at 121—123° with effervescence at 127°, and when dried at 100° it melts at 131—133° (Found: in air-dried salt, H_2O = 3·4. $C_{21}H_{28}O_2N_2,C_9H_{10}O_3,H_2O$ requires H_2O = 3·6 per cent.).

Its specific rotation was determined in absolute alcohol:

$c = 1{\cdot}029$; $l = 2$ dcm.; $\alpha_D + 2{\cdot}45°$; $[\alpha]_D + 118{\cdot}8°$;
$c = 0{\cdot}856$; $l = 2$ dcm.; $\alpha_D + 2{\cdot}04°$; $[\alpha]_D + 119{\cdot}2°$,

whence, for the anhydrous salt, $[\alpha]_D + 123{\cdot}2°$. From this salt, ethylhydrocupreidine was recovered, melting at 196° and having $[\alpha]_D + 225°$ in absolute alcohol ($c = 0{\cdot}46$) and *l*-tropic acid isolated, melting at 127—129° and having $[\alpha]_D - 78°$ ($c = 0{\cdot}29$).

$C_9H_{10}O_3$ Ref. 1457a

With Cinchotoxine.—Seventeen grams of cinchotoxine base were neutralised with 9·7 grams of *dl*-tropic acid and the salt from the syrupy solution was recrystallised several times, initially from a mixture of absolute alcohol and dry ether, and finally from 95 per cent. alcohol. The yield of cinchotoxine *l*-tropate was 60 per cent.

Cinchotoxine l-*tropate* crystallises from 95 per cent. alcohol in clusters of fine, matted needles. It melts at 145—146°. It has a cream colour when pure and forms an almost colourless solution in absolute alcohol, but readily becomes yellowish-brown in colour on boiling. As observed with quinotoxine salts, there is a tendency to resinify (Found: C = 72·8; H = 7·0. $C_{19}H_{22}ON_2,C_9H_{10}O_3$ requires C = 73·0; H = 7·0 per cent.). The specific rotation was determined in absolute alcohol: $c = 0{\cdot}996$; $l = 2$ dcm.; $\alpha_D + 0{\cdot}205°$; $[\alpha]_D + 10{\cdot}3°$.

The tropic acid isolated from 1 gram of this salt was *l*-tropic acid, $[\alpha]_D - 76°$, m. p. 127°.

$C_9H_{10}O_3$ Ref. 1457b

With Quinotoxine.—*dl*-Tropic acid (11·5 grams) and quinotoxine base (21·7 grams) in alcoholic solution gave a crystalline salt which after four crystallisations showed little signs of resolution. After a few crystallisations from water quinotoxine *l*-tropate was readily isolated pure in 58 per cent. yield.

Quinotoxine l-*tropate monohydrate* crystallises best from water, in small, cream-coloured needles. Air-dried, it melts at 112—113° with effervescence at about 130°, and when dried at 100° it melts at 116—118° without effervescence (Found: in air-dried salt, H_2O = 4·2; C = 68·6; H = 7·0. $C_{20}H_{24}O_2N_2,C_9H_{10}O_3,H_2O$ requires H_2O = 3·5; C = 68·5; H = 7·1 per cent.). The specific rotation was determined in absolute alcohol: $c = 0{\cdot}997$; $l = 2$ dcm.; $[\alpha]_D + 0{\cdot}17°$; $[\alpha]_D + 8{\cdot}4°$, whence for anhydrous salt $[\alpha]_D + 8{\cdot}71°$.

The crude tropic acid isolated from 1 gram of pure quinotoxine *l*-tropate melted at 126—128° and gave $[\alpha]_D - 72°$ in water ($c = 0{\cdot}46$).

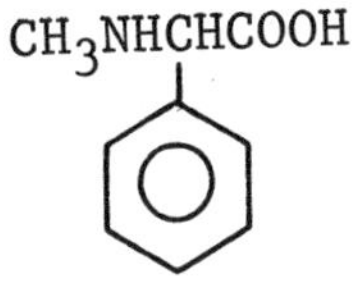

$C_9H_{11}NO_2$ Ref. 1458

The racemic acid (II) (21.1 g) in 460 ml. ethyl acetate and 26.2 g brucine (III) in 430 ml. ethyl acetate was allowed to stand overnight to give 31 g (+)-II·III salt, $[\alpha]^{11}_D$ 31.4° (C 2.32, H_2O). This salt (27.5 g) was added to approximately 4 g Na_2CO_3 in approximately 80 ml. H_2O, shaken with $CHCl_3$ to remove brucine and treated with concentrated HCl to adjust pH to 2, gave 9.0 g L-(II), m.p. 129°, $[\alpha]^8_D$ 204° (C 2.31, ethanol). From mother liquor of (+)-II·III salt, 8.3 g D-II, m.p. 129°, $[\alpha]^{11}_D$ -198° (C 2.41, ethanol) was obtained.

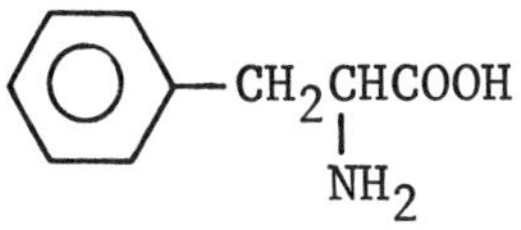

$C_9H_{11}NO_2$ Ref. 1459

Beispiel 7

Spaltung des Salzes aus Beispiel 1 und Isolierung von D(-)-p-Hydroxyphenylglycin

Eine Lösung von 20,2 g (0,045 Mol) des Salzes von 1-N-Methylephedrin und N-Salicyliden-D-p-hydroxy-phenylglycin (Beispiel 1) in 100 ml Salzsäure (7,5 %ig) werden zur Abtrennung des Salicylaldehyds dreimal mit je 50 ml Methylenchlorid extrahiert. Die verbleibende wässrige Phase wird im Vakuum auf etwa 40 ml eingeengt und mit 20 ml Wasser verdünnt. Nach Erwärmen auf 60-80°C wird mit etwa 16 ml Ammoniak (25%ig) auf pH 6,8 eingestellt und das ausgefallen p-Hydroxyphenylglycin abfiltriert. Man isoliert 5,39 g (71,9% d. Theorie) D(-)-p-Hydroxy-phenylglycin mit einer spez. Drehung $[\alpha]^{20}_D$ = -154,6° (96,6% opt. Reinheit) (c = 1,6 NHCl).

Die wässrige Mutterlauge wird mit 85 ml Natronlauge (10%) auf pH 12 eingestellt. Der dabei entstehende, helle Niederschlag wird abgesaugt und mit wenig Ammoniakwasser (10 %ig) gewaschen. Man isoliert 7.0 g (87,6% der Theorie) 1-N-Methylephedrin mit praktisch unveränderter spez. Drehung.

Zur Nachfällung der Aminosäure wird das wässrige Filtrat auf 50 ml eingeengt, mit 5 ml konz. Salz-säure auf pH 6,8 gestellt und über Nacht zur Kristal-lisation stehen gelassen. Es werden nochmals 1,36 g D(-)-p-Hydroxyphenylglycin mit einer spez. Drehung $[\alpha]^{20}_D$ = -135,5° (84,7% opt. Reinheit) isoliert. Damit ergibt sich eine Gesamtausbeute von 90,0% Hydroxyphenylglycin mit einer opt. Reinheit von 94%.

Beispiel 9

Spaltung des Salzes aus Beispiel 4 und Isolierung von D(+)-Phenylalanin

Eine Lösung von 5,85 g (0,013 Mol) des Salzes von 1-N-Methylephedrin und N-Salicyliden-D-Phenylalanin (Beispiel 4) in 25 ml Salzsäure (10 %ig) werden zur Abtrennung des Salicylaldehyds dreimal mit je 25 ml

Methylenchlorid extrahiert. Die verbleibende wässrige Phase wird mit Natronaluge (35%ig) auf pH 12,5 gestellt und das dabei auskristallisierende N-Methylephedrin durch Filtration entfernt. Anschliessend wird die Lösung mit konz. Salzsäure auf pH 6,8 gestellt und das ausfallende Phenylalanin abfiltriert. Nach dem Trocknen werden 1,3 g (60,5 % der Theorie) D(+)-Phenylalanin als farblose Kristalle $[\alpha]20_D$ = +16,7° (c = 2, H_2O) erhalten.

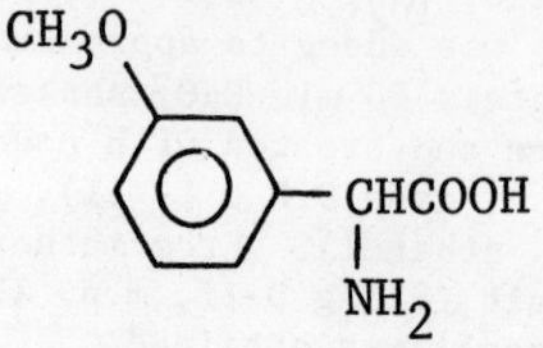

$C_9H_{11}NO_3$ Ref. 1460

EXAMPLE 33

Resolution with Racemisation of Methyl m-Methoxyphenylglycinate

A solution of (+)-tartaric acid (0.804 g., 5.35 mmole, 1.05 equiv.) was added to a solution of methyl DL-m-methoxyphenylglycinate (0.994 g., 5.09 mmole) in dry methanol (total volume 5 ml.) at 20°. Crystallisation began immediately and acetone (5 ml.) was added, with stirring, during 40 minutes. The mixture was stirred at 20° to 25° for 9 days, and was filtered. The product was washed with methanol:acetone (1:1, 2 × 2 ml.) and dried at 20°/2 mm. for 3 hours to give methyl D-m-methoxyphenylglycinate (+)-hemitartrate solvated with 0.8 mole methanol (1.631 g., 86%) m.p. 157°–158°, $[\alpha]_D^{18} - 62°$ (c 2.49, H_2O).

EXAMPLE 53

D-m-Methoxyphenylglycine

A solution of methyl D-m-methoxyphenylglycinate (+)-hemitartrate (0.909 g., 2.45 mmole) in 6N-hydrochloric acid (1.64 ml., 9.85 mmole, 4 equiv.) was refluxed for 30 minutes. Water (2 ml.) was added and the pH of the warm solution adjusted to 7.0 with 10N-ammonium hydroxide solution. The mixture was cooled in ice, filtered, washed, and dried over phosphorus pentoxide to give the D-amino acid (0.175 g., 39.5% as needles) m.p. 185° to 189°, $[\alpha]_D^{21} - 137°$ (c 0.998, 1N-HCl). The filtrate was concentrated to give a second crop (0.200 g., 32% corr.) m.p. 178° to 181°, $[\alpha]_D^{20} - 131°$ (corrected for 0.25 mole mono-ammonium tartrate and 0.45 mole ammonium chloride), τ (F_3CCO_2H) indicated the presence of 0.25 mole mono-ammonium tartrate and 0.45 mole ammonium chloride. There was no evidence for the ester at τ 6.14 in the nmr.

For the theoretical basis for this resolution procedure, see Ref. 1433

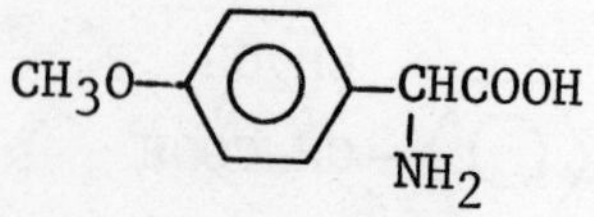

$C_9H_{11}NO_3$ Ref. 1461

For the resolution procedure for this compound, see Ref. 1452.

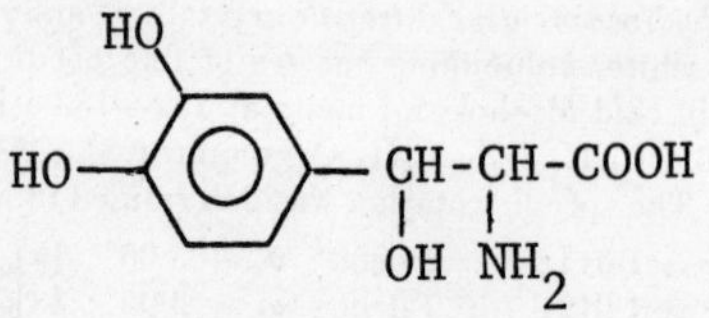

$C_9H_{11}NO_5$ Ref. 1462

EXAMPLE 6

37 g of rac-erythro-3-(3,4-dibenzyloxyphenyl)-N-carbobenzoxyserine are dissolved in 20 ml of abs. ethanol and treated with a solution of 7.5 g of (−)-threo-1-(p-nitrophenyl)-2-amino-1,3-propanediol in 180 ml of boiling hot ethanol. The mixture is left at room temperature for 2-3 hours to crystallize, filtered off and washed with ethanol and ether. The product obtained is crystallized from 200 ml of methanol. There is obtained the (−)-threo-1-(p-nitrophenyl)-2-amino-1,3-propanediol salt of (−)-erythro-3-(3,4-dibenzyloxyphenyl)-N-carbobenzoxyserine of melting point 159°–160°C; $[\alpha]_D = -24.3°$ ($c = 1$; acetone); +9.8° ($c = 1$; acetonitrile).

Anal. Calcd. for $C_{40}H_{41}O_{11}N_3$: C, 64.94; H, 5.59; N, 5.68 Found: C, 64.76; H, 5.44; N, 5.56

EXAMPLE 7

The mother liquor remaining according to Example 6 is concentrated to about 20 ml under reduced pressure and treated with a boiling hot solution of 7.5 g of (+)-threo-1-(p-nitrophenyl)-2-amino-1,3-propanediol in 180 ml of ethanol. The mixture is left at room temperature for 2-3 hours to crystallize, filtered off and washed with ethanol and ether. After recrystallization from 300 ml of methanol, there is obtained the (+)-threo-1-(p-nitrophenyl)-2-amino-1,3-propanediol salt of (+)-erythro-3-(3,4-dibenzyloxyphenyl)-N-carbobenzoxyserine of melting point 163°–165°C; $[\alpha]_D$ = +24.3° (c = 1; acetone); −9.4° (c = 1; acetonitrile).

Anal. Calcd. for $C_{40}H_{41}O_{11}N_3$: C, 64.94; H, 5.59; N, 5.68 Found: C, 64.62; H, 5.53; N, 5.57

EXAMPLE 10

The (−)-threo-1-(p-nitrophenyl)-2-amino-1,3-propanediol salt of (−)-erythro-3-(3,4-dibenzyloxyphenyl)-N-carbobenzoxyserine is converted into the free acid (−)-erythro-3-(3,4-dibenzyloxyphenyl)-N-carbobenzoxyserine in analogy to Example 8, with the difference that the crude product is crystallized from methanol. The (−)-erythro-3-(3,4-dibenzyloxyphenyl)-N-carbobenzoxyserine obtained melts at 154°–157°C; $[\alpha]_D = -42.0°$ (c = 1; chloroform).

Anal. Calcd. for $C_{31}H_{29}O_7N$: C, 70.58; H, 5.54; N, 2.65 Found: C, 70.22; H, 5.31; N, 2.57

13 g of (−)-erythro-3-(3,4-dibenzyloxyphenyl)-N-carbobenzoxyserine are suspended in a mixture of 370

$C_9H_{11}NO_5$

ml of ethanol and 120 ml of water and hydrogenated with palladium-carbon (5). After the hydrogen uptake has taken place, the catalyst is filtered off and the filtrate evaporated under reduced pressure until removal of the water (bath temperature not above 40°C). The whole is left to stand overnight at −15°C and subsequently filtered. The crystals are washed with ethanol and ether and for further purification dissolved in 15 ml of pre-boiled water, filtered and left to crystallize overnight at about 0°C. The crystals are filtered off, washed with ethanol and ether and dried in air. There is obtained (−)-erythro-3-(3,4-dihydroxyphenyl)-serine of melting point 191°–194°C (decomposition); $[\alpha]_D$ = −51.9° (c = 1; 1 N aqueous hydrochloric acid). The preparation tastes very sweet.

Anal. Calcd. for $C_9H_{11}O_5N.3H_2O$: C, 40.45; H, 6.41; N, 5.24; H_2O, 20.23 Found: C, 40.36; H, 6.17; N, 5.17; H_2O, 19.62

EXAMPLE 11

In analogy to Example 8, from the (+)-threo-1-(p-nitrophenyl)-2-amino-1,3-propanediol salt of (+)-erythro-3-(3,4-dibenzyloxyphenyl)-N-carbobenzoxyserine there is obtained the free acid (+)-erythro-3-(3,4-dibenzyloxyphenyl)-N-carbobenzoxyserine of melting point 154°–157°C; $[\alpha]_D$ = +42.5° (c = 1; chloroform).

Anal. Calcd. For $C_{31}H_{29}O_7N$: C, 70.58; H, 5.54; N, 2.65 Found: C, 70.80; H, 5.40; N, 2.57

The (+)-erythro-3-(3,4-dibenzyloxyphenyl)-N-carbobenzoxyserine obtained as subjected to hydrogenolysis in analogy to Example 10.

There is obtained (+)-erythro-3-(3,4-dihydroxyphenyl)-serine of melting point 191°–194°C (decomposition); $[\alpha]_D$=+51.9° (c = 1; 1 N aqueous hydrochloric acid). The compound is tasteless.

Anal. Calcd. for $C_9H_{11}O_5N.3H_2O$: C, 40.45; H, 6.41; N, 5.24; H_2O, 20.23 Found: C, 40.47; H, 6.17; N, 5.20; H_2O, 19.76

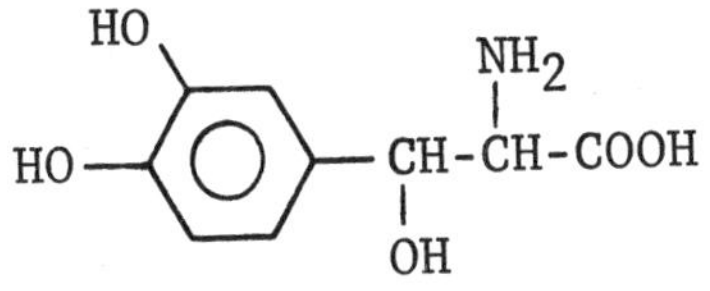

$C_9H_{11}NO_5$ Ref. 1463

EXAMPLE 3

101 g of rac-threo-3-(3,4-dibenzyloxyphenyl)-N-carbobenzoxyserine are dissolved in 2000 ml of abs. ethanol and treated with 15.6 g of (+)-epnedrine. After allowing to stand overnight at room temperature, the crystals obtained are filtered off and washed with ethanol and ether. There is obtained the (+)-ephidrine salt of (−)-threo-3-(3,4-dibenzyloxyphenyl)-N-carbobenzoxyserine which melts at 189°–190°C after recrystallization from 1,000 ml of methanol. $[\alpha]_D$=+38.5° (c = 1; dimethylformamide).

Anal. Calcd. for $C_{41}H_{44}O_8N_2$: C, 71.08; H, 6.40; N, 4.04 Found: C, 70.98; H, 6.32; N, 3.95

EXAMPLE 4

The mother liquor and ethanol washings remaining in Example 3 are evaporated under reduced pressure, the residue dissolved in ethyl acetate and shaken with 3 N aqueous hydrochloric acid. After drying over sodium sulphate, the organic phase is evaporated under reduced pressure. The residue consists of the not yet completely optically pure (+)-threo-3-(3,4-dibenzyloxyphenyl)-N-carbobenzoxyserine which is purified further as follows:

The compound is dissolved in 2,000 ml of abs. ethanol and treated with as much (−)-ephedrine to make the mixture react weakly alkaline. The mixture is left to stand 3–4 hours, filtered off and washed with ethanol and ether. The crude product obtained is recrystallized from 1,000 ml of methanol and yields optically pure (−)-ephedrine salt of (+)-threo-3-(3,4-dibenzyloxyphenyl)-N-carbobenzoxyserine which melts at 189°–190°C. $[\alpha]_D$=−38° (c = 1; dimethylformamide).

Anal. Calcd. for $C_{41}H_{44}O_8N_2$: C, 71.08; H, 6.40; N, 4.04 Found: C, 71.02; H, 6.40; N, 3.94

EXAMPLE 5

The mother liquor and the ethanol washings remaining in Example 3 are evaporated under reduced pressure, the residue dissolved in ethyl acetate and shaken with 3 N aqueous hydrochloric acid. After drying over sodium sulphate, the organic phase is evaporated under reduced pressure. The residue is dissolved in 200 ml of abs. ethanol and treated with a boiling hot solution of 23 g of (−)-threo-1-(p-nitrophenyl)-2-amino-1,3-propanediol in 1,800 ml of ethanol. The mixture is left to crystallize at room temperature for about 3 hours. After filtering off the obtained crystals and washing with ethanol and ether, there is obtained the (−)-threo-1-(p-nitrophenyl)-2-amino-1,3-propanediol salt of (+)-threo-3-(3,4-dibenzyloxyphenyl)-N-carbobenzoxyserine which melts at 183°–185°C. $[\alpha]_D$=−29.4°C (c = 1; dimethylformamide).

Anal. Calcd. for $C_{40}H_{41}O_{11}N_3$: C, 64,94; H, 5.59; N, 5.68 Found: C, 65.03; H, 5.61; N, 5.56

EXAMPLE 8

50 g of (+)-ephedrine salt of (−)-threo-3-(3,4-dibenzyloxyphenyl)-N-carbobenzoxyserine are shaken with a mixture of 500 ml of ethyl acetate and 300 ml of 3 N aqueous hydrochloric acid in a separating funnel until formation of two clear layers. The ethyl acetate phase is separated, washed once with water and the aqueous phase again extracted with ethyl acetate. The combined ethyl acetate phases are dried over sodium sulphate, evaporated under reduced pressure and crystallized from a mixture of ethyl acetate, isopropyl ether and petroleum ether. There is obtained (−)-threo-3-(3,4-dibenzyloxyphenyl)-N-carbobenzoxyserine of melting point 134°–135°C; $[\alpha]_D$=−17.2° (c = 1; chloroform).

Anal. Calcd. for $C_{31}H_{29}O_7N$: C, 70.58; H, 5.54; N, 2.65 Found: C, 70.44; H, 5.50; N, 2.55

10.4 g of (−)-threo-3-(3,4-dibenzyloxyphenyl)-N-carbobenzoxyserine are dissolved in 400 ml of ethanol and 21 ml of 1 N aqueous hydrochloric acid and hydrogenated with palladium-carbon (5%). After termination of the hydrogen uptake, the catalyst is filtered off and the filtrate completely evaporated down, the last traces of moisture being removed by repeated evporation with ethanol. The residue is dissolved in 100 ml of abs. ethanol and, with cooling, adjusted to a pH value of 5.5–6 with a dilute ethanolic diethylamine solution. A precipitate forms. The whole is left to stand overnight at −15°C, filtered and washed with ethanol and ether. For further purification, the crystals are introduced into 200 ml of boiling water and subsequently filtered. The crystallization is completed by standing overnight at about 0°C. The crystals are filtered off, washed with ethanol and ether and dried under re-

duced pressure at about 80°–90°C. There is obtained (−)-threo-3-(3,4-dihydroxyphenyl)-serine which melts at 232°–235°C under decomposition; $[\alpha]_D = -39°$ (c = 1; 1 N aqueous hydrochloric acid).

Anal. Calcd for $C_9H_{11}O_5N$: C, 50.71; H, 5.20; N, 6.57 Found: C, 50.61; H, 5.26; N, 6.45

EXAMPLE 9

In the same manner as given in Example 8, from the (−)-ephedrine salt or (−)-threo-1-(p-nitrophenyl)-2-amino-1,3-propanediol salt of (+)-threo-3-(3,4-dibenzyloxyphenyl)-N-carbobenzoxyserine there is obtained the free acid (+)-threo-3-(3,4-dibenzyloxyphenyl)-N-carbobenzoxyserine which melts at 134°–135°C; $[\alpha]_D$ = +16.9° (c = 1; chloroform).

Anal. Calcd. for $C_{31}H_{29}O_7N$: C, 70.58; H, 5.54; N, 2.65 Found: C, 70.67; H, 5.53; N, 2.61

The (+)-threo-3-(3,4-dibenzyloxyphenyl)-N-carbobenzoxyserine obtained is subjected to hydrogenolysis in analogy to Example 8. There is obtained (+)-threo-3-(3,4-dihydroxyphenyl)-serine of melting point 232°–235°C (decomposition); $[\alpha]_D$ = +39° (c = 1; 1 N aqueous hydrochloric acid).

Anal. Calcd. for $C_9H_{11}O_5N$: C, 50.71; H, 5.20; N, 6.57 Found: C, 51.07; H, 5.19; N, 6.34

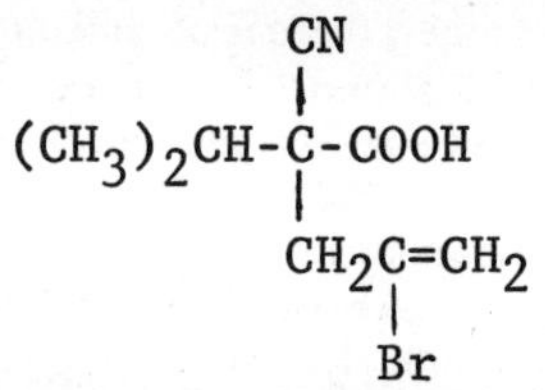

$C_9H_{12}BrNO_2$ Ref. 1464

Note: Resolved using threo-1-phenyl-2-aminopropanediol-1,3 as resolving agent and using water or acetone/ether as solvent. The (+)(+) diastereomer had a m.p. of 149-156°. The obtained (+) enantiomer had a m.p. of 46-50° and $[\alpha]^{20}_D$ 10.66°. The (−) enantiomer had a m.p. of 46-49° and $[\alpha]^{20}_D$ -10.7°. (Rotations taken in ethanol)

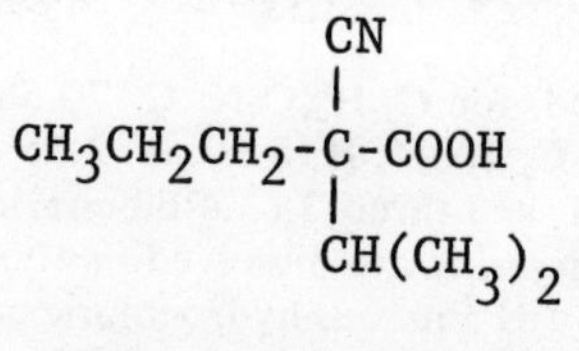

$C_9H_{15}NO_2$ Ref. 1465

Note: Resolved using (-)threo-1-phenyl-2-aminopropanediol-1,3 as resolving agent and using water as solvent. The (+)(-)diastereomer had a m.p. of 165°. The obtained (+) enantiomer had a m.p. of 93-95° and a $[\alpha]^{22}_D$ +3.0° and the (-) enantiomer had a m.p. of 92-94.5° and a $[\alpha]^{21}_D$ -3.2°. (Rotations taken in ethanol).

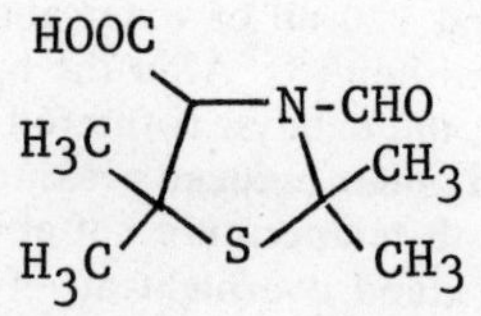

$C_9H_{15}NO_3S$ Ref. 1466

Note: Resolved using brucine in water solution. Acids obtained had $[\alpha]^{20}_{5461}$ 66° and $[\alpha]^{20}_{5461}$ -60° (C 0.8, H_2O) m.p. 179°-180°. The (+)-enantiomer is hydrolyzed by heating with 2N HCl to give penicillamine-HCl $[\alpha]^{20}_{5461}$ 1.0° (C 1.0, H_2O).

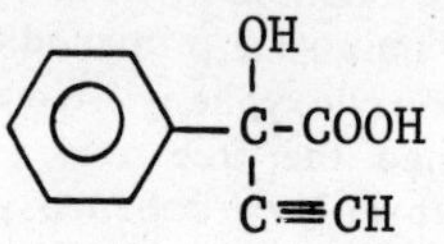

$C_{10}H_8O_3$ Ref. 1467

Note: Resolved using (+)-1-(p-nitrophenyl)-2-amino-1,3-propanediol. Obtained active acid with m.p. 130° and $[\alpha]^{26}_D$ -44.9° (C 1.0, ethanol).

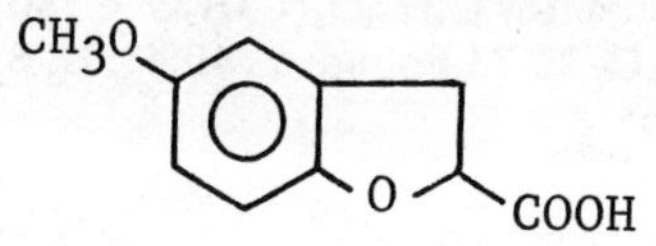

$C_{10}H_{10}O_4$ Ref. 1468

The starting material is prepared as follows: To the solution of 0.97 g of d,*l*-5-methoxy-2,3-dihydro-2-benzofurancarboxylic acid in 50 ml of diethyl ether, 0.7 g of *l*-amphetamine are added while stirring. The precipitate formed is filtered off and washed with diethyl ether, to yield the corresponding salt melting at 134°–142°. It is taken up in 125 ml of hot acetone and the solution allowed to cool to room temperature during 2 ½ hours. The precipitate formed is filtered off, washed with acetone and again dissolved in 60 ml of hot acetone. The precipitate formed after three hours cooling is again filtered off, to yield the corresponding d-salt melting at 153°–162°.

All the mother liquors obtained are concentrated to a volume of 60 ml and the solution allowed to cool to room temperature for three hours. The precipitate formed is filtered off and recrystallized once from acetone, to yield the corresponding *l*-salt melting at 150°–165°.

Both salts obtained are taken up in the minimum amount of 6N hydrochloric acid and the solution obtained extracted with diethyl ether. The extract is washed with water and saturated aqueous sodium chloride, dried and evaporated, to yield the:

a. d-5-methoxy-2,3-dihydro-2-benzofurancarboxylic acid, $[\alpha]_D = +37°$ (chloroform)

b. the *l*-antipode thereof, $[\alpha]_D = -38°$ (chloroform).

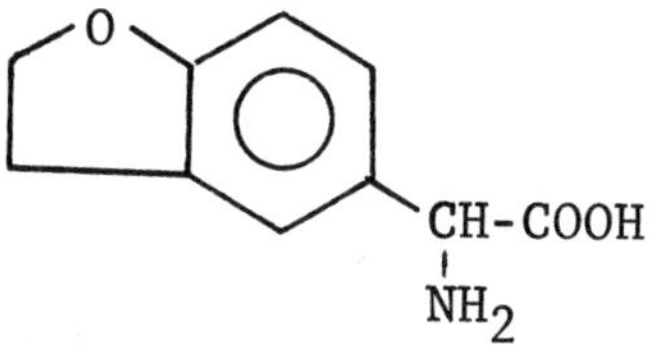

$C_{10}H_{11}NO_3$ Ref. 1469

Resolution of (±)-2-(2,3-Dihydro-5-benzofuranyl)glycine (5). A mixture of 2.7 g (13.99 mmol) of (*R*,*S*)-2-(2,3-dihydro-5-benzofuranyl)glycine and 3.5 g (10 mmol) of (+)-binaphthylphosphoric acid (BPA) was refluxed in 25 mL of methanol for 0.5 h. After the mixture was cooled to 0 °C, 2.76 g (5.08 mmol) of white solid was removed by filtration. The latter was slurried in 50 mL of methanol and treated with 0.691 g (5.08 mmol) of sodium acetate trihydrate and refluxed for 1 h. The hot solution was filtered and the solid was washed with hot methanol. After drying, 880 mg of white crystals was recovered, $[\alpha]^{20}_D$ −131° (*c* 10, 0.1 N HCl).

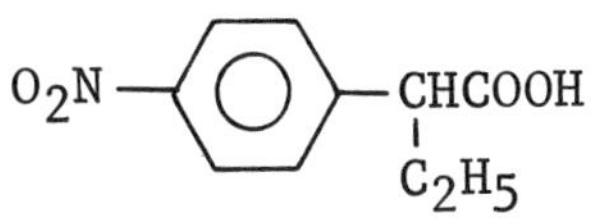

$C_{10}H_{11}NO_4$ Ref. 1470

Resolution of *α-p*-Nitrophenylbutyric Acid (VII).—To a solution of 52.2 g. of *α-p*-nitrophenylbutyric acid in 3.5 liters of dry methyl alcohol was added a solution of 40.5 g. of anhydrous quinine in 500 cc. of dry methyl alcohol. After this solution had stood for twenty-four hours at 0°, it was filtered. The crystals thus obtained weighed 29–32 g. (fraction I). The salt was recrystallized four times from methyl alcohol and then had a constant rotation and melted at 183–185°. The yield was 10–11 g. *Rotation.* 0.3800 g. subs., in 20 cc. of pyridine; *α*, −1.605°; *t*, 25°; *l*, 2 dcm.; $[\alpha]^{20}_D$ −42.2°.

Anal.[11] Calcd. for $C_{30}H_{35}N_3O_6$: N, 7.88. Found: N, 7.74.

All of the mother liquors from the original filtration and the recrystallization of this first salt were combined and a solution of 40.5 g. of anhydrous quinine in 500 cc. of dry methyl alcohol was added. The solution was allowed to stand for three hours and filtered. This fraction of crystals weighed 34–42 g. After recrystallization four times from dry methyl alcohol, 9–12 g. of salt melting at 183–185° with a rotation of −42.7° was obtained.

The original mother liquor and the solution from the purification of this salt were combined and concentrated to about 1500 cc. The solution was cooled to room temperature and allowed to stand for three hours. The crystals thus obtained weighed 30–45 g. and after six recrystallizations gave 9–10 g. of the salt melting at 183–185°, $[\alpha]^{25}_D$ −42.2°.

The mother liquors were combined and again evaporated to 1500 cc. About 40–50 g. of salt was obtained. It was a mixture and could not be purified to give either pure *d*- or pure *l*-salt. This material was discarded. The mother liquors were concentrated to 1000 cc. and 20–30 g. of mixed salt was obtained. The solution was next concentrated to 500 cc. and 16–25 g. of mixed salt was obtained. This was recrystallized from methyl alcohol and the mother liquors were added to the original filtrate. The solution was concentrated to 250 cc. and on cooling 5–10 g. of the salt was obtained. This was crystallized and the solution combined with the filtrate. The solution was evaporated to 150 cc. and cooled at 0° for twelve hours. The salt thus obtained weighed 4–6 g. On recrystallization from methyl alcohol this gave 3–4 g. of a salt which melted at 180–182°. *Rotation.* 0.1830 g. subs., in 20 cc. of pyridine; *α*, −0.984°; *t*, 25°; *l*, 2 dcm.; $[\alpha]^{25}_D$ −53.8°.

Anal.[11] Calcd. for $C_{30}H_{35}N_3O_6$: N, 7.88. Found: N, 8.05.

The filtrate was evaporated to dryness and the residue was washed with acetone to remove some colored impurities and then recrystallized from a little methyl alcohol. Another 4–6 g. of the same salt was obtained; $[\alpha]^{25}_D$ −54°.

The less soluble fraction proved to be the quinine salt of the *d*-acid and the more soluble fraction was the *l*-salt. Many different salts and different conditions were tried in an effort to obtain a more satisfactory resolution but the above procedure was the best separation that could be obtained.

The pure *d*-acid was obtained by treating 60 g. of the less soluble salt ($[\alpha]^{25}_D$ −42.2°) with 30 cc. of concentrated hydrochloric acid at 0°. This mixture was then treated with 300 cc. of water at 0° and another 10 cc. of hydrochloric acid was added. The acid separated and was collected on a Buchner funnel. The yield was 22 g. After recrystallization from 2500 cc. of hot water, 20 g. of pure *d*-acid of m. p. 120–122° was obtained. *Rotation.* 0.2845 g. subs., in 20 cc. of ethyl acetate; *α*, +0.503°; *t*, 25°; *l*, 2 dcm.; $[\alpha]^{25}_D$ +17.7°.

Anal.[11] Calcd. for $C_{10}H_{11}NO_4$: N, 6.7; neutral equivalent, 209. Found: N, 6.7; neutral equivalent, 211.

In a similar fashion 24 g. of the more soluble salt gave 8 g. of pure *l*-acid m. p. 120–122°. *Rotation.* 0.2945 g. subs., in 20 cc. of ethyl acetate; α, −0.528°; *t*, 25°; *l*, 2 dcm.; $[\alpha]^{25}_{D}$ −17.8°.

Anal.[11] Calcd. for $C_{10}H_{11}NO_4$: N, 6.7; neutral equivalent, 209. Found: N, 6.99; neutral equivalent, 208.

The active nitro acids racemized readily in hot 50% acetic acid and in boiling water some racemization occurred in two to three hours.

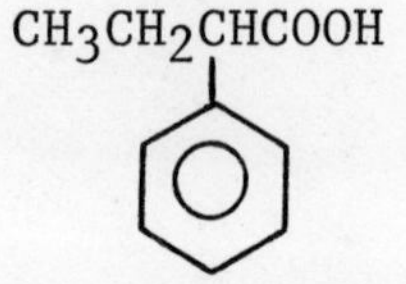

$C_{10}H_{12}O_2$ Ref. 1471

2-Phenylbutanoic acid (200 g) was resolved by repeated crystallization of its cinchonidine salt from 95% ethanol following the procedure of Levene and Marker.[10] After four recrystallizations, 250 g of white needles, mp 117–131° dec, were obtained. The salt was decomposed by suspension in 1400 ml of 4 *N* HCl, and the resolved acid was extracted with three 300-ml portions of diethyl ether. The combined ether extracts were dried over $MgSO_4$ and the solvent was removed under reduced pressure. Vacuum distillation gave 87.7 g of (+)-2-phenylbutanoic acid, bp 108–110° (0.8 mm), $n^{25}D$ 1.5142, $d^{25}{}_4$ 1.059, $[\alpha]^{25}D$ +80.0° (neat). Bonner and Greenlee[9] reported bp 115–130° (1–2 mm), $[\alpha]^{25}D$ +84.4° (neat); Levene and Marker[10] reported $[\alpha]^{25}D$ +87.3° (neat) for the resolved acid.

(9) W. A. Bonner and T. W. Greenlee, *J. Amer. Chem. Soc.*, **81**, 3336 (1959).
(10) P. A. Levene and R. E. Marker, *J. Biol. Chem.*, **100**, 685 (1933).

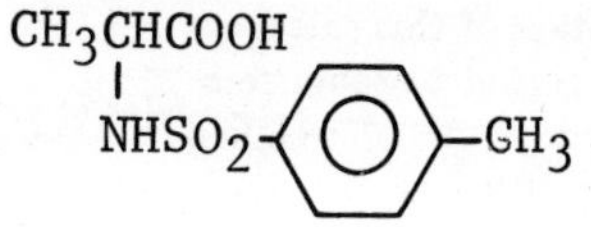

$C_{10}H_{13}NO_4S$ Ref. 1472

Note: Racemic acid was resolved with brucine to give optically active acid with m.p. 131-131.5°, $[\alpha]^{10}D$ -46.41° (solvent not specified).

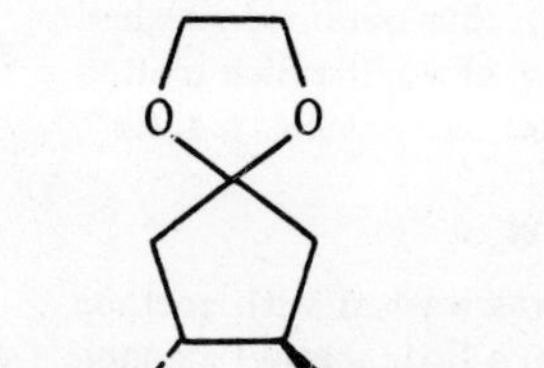

$C_{10}H_{14}O_6$ Ref. 1473

To 186 g. of the monoester, m.p. 63-65° dissolved in 740 ml. isopropanol was added 133 g. d-ephedrine and refluxed for 20 minutes. The mixture was allowed to stand overnight affording 109 g. of the ephedrine salt, $[\alpha]^{25}D$ 0.5° ($CHCl_3$) which was recrystallized from 300 ml. of isopropanol to yield 77 g. of the ephedrine salt, $[\alpha]_D$ -4.6°. Further recrystallization from 180 ml. isopropanol afforded 71.8 g. of the optically pure salt, $[\alpha]^{25}D$ -5.5° ($CHCl_3$).

To 82 g. of the salt dissolved in 500 ml. of H_2O was added 280 ml. of 10% aqueous K_2CO_3 with cooling via ice water. The solution was extracted 2 to 3 times with ether to remove d-ephedrine. The aqueous layer was carefully neutralized with HCl and acidified by the addition of 30 ml. of acetic acid using ice-water cooling. The solution was extracted 3 times with ethyl acetate, washed with H_2O saturated with NaCl and dried over Na_2SO_4. The removal of solvent in vacuo afforded the crystalline solid which was submitted to silica gel chromatography. The fraction eluted with 5% ethyl acetate-benzene was collected. The optically pure monoester was obtained as a crystalline solid, m.p. 33-34°, $[\alpha]^{25}D$ -27.1 ($CHCl_3$).

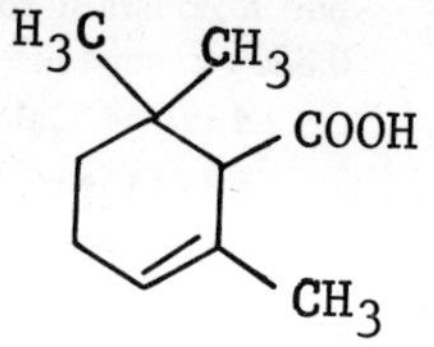

$C_{10}H_{16}O_2$ Ref. 1474

The racemic acid (12.7 g.) was mixed with 0.894N-sodium hydroxide (43.2 c.c.) and cinchonine (11.16 g.), and the hot filtered solution kept for 24 hours. A cinchonine salt (10 g.) crystallised in needles, m.p. 201-204°, sintering at 180°, $[\alpha]_{5461}$ -9.8° in chloroform (C, 4.244). Two crystallisations from methyl alcohol gave the pure salt of constant rotatory power in rosettes of soft needles, m.p. 204-206°, sintering 183°, $[\alpha]_{5461}$ -15.4° in chloroform (C, 4.015). The l-acid, regenerated from the salt, crystallised from ligroin (b.p. 60-80°) in massive prisms, m.p. 104°, $[\alpha]_{5461}$ -395.7° in ethyl alcohol (C, 4.865).

The acid (7.9 g.) regenerated from the soluble cinchonine salt had $[\alpha]_{5461}$ +200° in ethyl alcohol (C, 4.15). This acid (7.4 g.), in hot methyl alcohol (20 c.c.), was mixed with 0.894N-sodium hydroxide (11.6 c.c.) and cinchonidine (9.8 g.); on keeping, the cinchonidine salt (13.5 g.) crystallised in needles, m.p. 150°. After three recrystallisations from acetone-methyl alcohol the pure salt, which was very sparingly soluble in acetone, separated in hair-like

needles, m.p. 157-158° $[\alpha]_{5461}$ +81.1° in chloroform (C, 3.28). The d-acid, regenerated from the salt, crystallised from ligroin (b.p. 60-80°) in prisms, m.p. 104°, $[\alpha]_{5461}$ +395.7° in ethyl alcohol (C, 4.84).

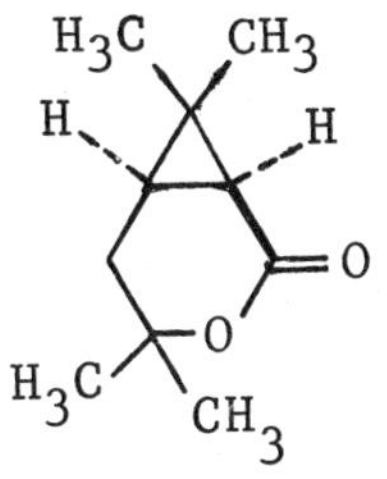

$C_{10}H_{16}O_2$ Ref. 1475

EXAMPLE 2

216 Grams of (±)-dihydrochrysanthemolactone was charged into a 3 liter flask and dissolved at an elevated temperature in 1,800 g. of n-hexane, and the resulting solution was allowed to cool to room temperature with gentle stirring. On the other hand, purified seed crystals of (+)-dihydrochrysanthemolactone and (−)-dihydrocrysanthemolactone were respectively seeded to each of 2 separate deposition poles which were capable of being cooled by recycling cooling water therethrough, and then the poles were dipped in the racemic lactone solution. Subsequently, the poles were cooled by recycling water at 23°C. through the deposition poles, while maintaining the solution temperature at 26°C., and the solution was gently stirred as it was for 24 hours. Thereafter, the deposition poles were taken out of the solution and air-dried, and then the grown crystals were collected by scraping to obtain two kinds of optically active substances. The amounts of the thus obtained substances were individually 7 g., and the melting points thereof were individually 80° – 82°C. From the optical rotations of the thus obtained substances, it was identified that the substances were optically pure (+)-dihydrochrysanthemolactone and (−)-dihydrochrysanthemolactone.

EXAMPLE 3

Example 2 was repeated, except that the room temperature was maintained at 26° to 27°C. and the solution was gently stirred for a total of 41 hours while recycling through the deposition poles water at 23°C. for 19 hours and then water at 20°C. for 8 hours, to obtain each 23 g. of (+)- and (−)-dihydrochrysanthemolactones. The (+)-dihydrochrysanthemolactone showed a specific optical rotation at 25°C. of +70.34° (in chloroform; C=4.2), which corresponds to an optical purity of 92.6 %, while the (−)-dihydrochrysanthemolactone showed a specific optical rotation at 25°C. of −73.37° (in chloroform; C=5.2), which corresponds to an optical purity of 96.5 %.

The optical rotations of pure (+)- and (−)-dihydrochrysanthemolactones are + and −76.6° (in chloroform; C=5.0), respectively.

EXAMPLE 4

Example 2 was repeated except that 432 g. of (±)-dihydrochrysanthemolactone was dissolved in 1800 g. of a solvent consisting of n-hexane 9 : benzene 1, whereby each 12 g. of optically pure lactone was obtained.

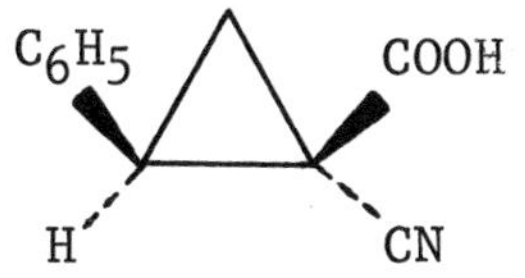

$C_{11}H_9NO_2$ Ref. 1476

Note: Resolved using quinine in methanol to give an acid $[\alpha]^{25}_{546}$ 199° (C 0.16, ethyl acetate).

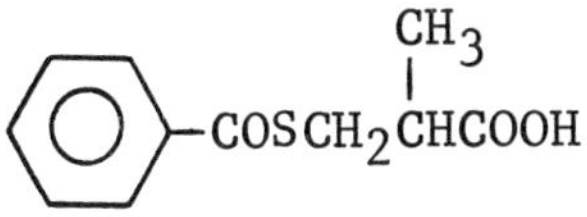

$C_{11}H_{12}O_3S$ Ref. 1477

Example 1

a Salification

A solution of 1 mol of DL-S-benzoyl-β-mercaptoisobutyric acid was prepared in 500 ml of isopropanol. To this solution 0.95 mol of NBPA was added. The resulting mixture was heated to about 45°C. After stirring the solution for half an hour at this temperature it was cooled, with stirring, to 20°C. After additional stirring for about 3 hours at that temperature, the crystallized salt was centrifuged, washed with approximately 50 ml of isopropanol and dried.

The yield was 217 g, which corresponds to approximately 50%; melting point: 104-106°C.

b Recrystallisation of the salt

The 217 g of salt obtained above were added to 500 ml of isopropanol, after which the mixture was heated with stirring, to approximately 70°C. At that temperature the salt dissolved completely. Stirring all the time, the solution was cooled slowly. Some seed crystals were added at 65°C, after which the solution was further cooled to 20°C in about an hour's time and the stirring was prolonged at this temperature for approximately 2 hours.

The crystallized salt was centrifuged, washed with 50 ml of isopropanol and dried. The yield was 180 g (= approximately 41.5%); melting point: 107-108°C and $[\alpha]^{22}{}_D$ = -3° to -4.4° (1% in 96% ethanol).

c Liberation of the D(-)-isomer form the NBPA-salt

The 180 g of purified salt obtained by the process b were added to a stirred mixture of 200 ml of 1,2-dichloroethane, 53 g of soda and 500 ml of water. After vigorous stirring for one hour the dichloroethane layer was separated from the aqueous layer. The first layer contained the NBPA, the second the desired acid in the form of the sodium salt. With stirring, concentrated hydrochloric acid was added to the aqueous layer till a pH-value of 1 was reached. The precipitated D-(-)-S-benzoyl-β-mercaptoisobutyric acid was filtered over a Buchner funnel, washed with water and dried. The overall yield was 40%; melting point: 67-69°C and $[\alpha]^{22}{}_D$ = -43° to -44° (1% in 96% ethanol).

The greater part of the NBPA started from could be recovered from the various mother liquors. Moreover the various isopropanol layers obtained during the working up process, which layers still contained remainders of the NBPA-salt of D-(-)-S-benzoyl-β-mercaptoisobutyric acid, could be reused.

Compared with the overall yield recorded in our previous European Patent Application 79200477.2 (22.4% in Example 1 and 30.7% in Example 2), the resolution according to the present invention gives considerably higher yields.

Additional advantages are that, generally, the reaction time is shorter and the number of purification steps smaller. Further, a strongly marked advantage lies in that it is possible to work in considerably more concentrated solutions. Thus, according to the Examples of our former patent application the solvent required per one mol of DL-compound or resolving agent amounts to 5,100 and 3,000 ml, respectively, whereas according to the present invention an amount of 500 ml suffices.

Another advantage is that the resolution of the DL-S-benzoyl-β-mercaptoisobutyric acid can be carried out directly after its preparation from thiobenzoic acid and methacrylic acid, id est, without the necessity of isolating first the DL-compound, which was not practicable, or scarcely so, when the resolving agents referred to above were used.

The following example may serve to illustrate this.

Example 2

With stirring, 1.05 mol of thiobenzoic acid were added to 250 ml of isopropanol. The solution was heated to about 80°C and 1.00 mol of methacrylic acid was added in about 1/2 hour's time. The resolution was heated to reflux temperature. After refluxing the solution for 2 hours it was cooled again to 40°C, and 250 ml of isopropanol, 0.95 mol of NBPA and some seed crystals of the desired salt were added.

The mixture was stirred for 1/2 hour at 40°C, was then cooled to 20°C, whereupon, the stirring was continued for 4 hours at this temperature. The salt, which had meanwhile crystallized out, was centrifuged, washed with approximately 50 ml of isopropanol and dried. The yield was approximately 50%.

The salt obtained was further treated as described in Example 1 under b and c. The overall yield of D-(-)-S-benzoyl-β-mercaptoisobutyric acid was 39%; melting point: 67-69°C.

Finally, the use of NBPA has the additional advantage that it can be recovered in a considerably simpler way than the resolving agents used before.

The recovery of the NBPA occurred as follows:

The mother liquor of the resolving step was concentrated by evaporation, in which process the isopropanol was recovered. The residue was treated with 1,2-dichloroethane and diluted sodium hydroxide. After vigorous stirring for half an hour the dichloroethane layer was separated, washed with diluted sodium hydroxide and twice with water. The dichloroethane layer was dried, the dichloroethane was evaporated and the NBPA was recovered in a practically quantitative yield. The mother liquor of the recrystallisation step could be reused for a next resolution or recrystallisation. From the dichloroethane layer liberated during the hydrolysis step the NBPA could be recovered quantitatively by washing the layer with diluted lye and water and evaporating the dichloroethane.

NBPA = D-(+)-N-benzyl-α-phenethylamine

$C_{11}H_{12}O_3S$ Ref. 1477a

1. Separation of DL-S-benzoyl-β-mercaptoisobutyric acid by means of cinchonidine.

(1) Salification with cinchonidine

294.5 g (= 1 mol) of cinchonidine were added to 5,100 ml of acetone and the mixture was heated to 45-50°C. To this mixture 224 g (= 1 mol) of DL-S-benzoyl-β-mercaptoisobutyric acid were added. The solution obtained was additionally heated to approximately 60°C (reflux temperature) and maintained at that temperature for about half an hour. The solution was then cooled, with stirring, to about 20°C. The stirring at room temperature was continued overnight and, the morning after, the precipitated cinchonidine salt of D(-)-S-benzoyl-β-mercaptoisobutyric acid was filtered off and washed three times with acetone. The yield was 233 g = 45%.

(2) Recrystallisation of the cinchonidine salt

The 233 g of cinchonidine salt obtained above were added to 2,300 ml of acetone, after which the temperature of the mixture was raised to approximately 60°C (reflux temperature). As the solution was not clear, it was filtered. The filtrate was cooled to about 20°C and allowed to stand one night. The morning after, the salt was filtered off and washed three times with 50 ml-portions of acetone. The yield was 151.5 g = 65%. This purification step had to be repeated twice before the salt crystallized out was sufficiently pure, id est, before it possessed an $[\alpha]_D \geqslant -96°$ (1% in 96% ethanol).

(3) Liberation of the D(-)-isomer from the cinchonidine salt

With stirring, 260 ml of hydrochloric acid, 800 ml of 1,2-dichloroethane and 520 g of the cinchonidine D(-)-salt prepared according to (1) and (2) were added to 2,300 ml of water. The mixture was stirred for half an hour. The organic layer was separated, the water layer was extracted twice with 200 ml-portions of dichloroethane and the organic layers were combined to form one organic phase. This organic phase was dried by means of magnesium sulphate. After evaporation of the solvent 200 g (= approximately 90%) of crude D(-)-S-benzoyl-β-mercaptoisobutyric acid with an $[\alpha]_D = -40°$ (1% in 96% ethanol) remained.

(4) Recrystallisation of the liberated D(-)-isomer

198 g of the crude product obtained by the process (3) were added to 1,300 ml of cyclohexane, after which the mixture was heated until all the salt had dissolved (about 70°C). The solution was filtrated by passing it through a pre-heated filter and the filter was washed three times with warm cyclohexane (25 ml-portions).
The filtrate was cooled slowly to approximately 10°C, after which the mixture was stirred at this temperature for about 1 hour. The precipitated D(-)-S-benzoyl-β-mercaptoisobutyric acid was filtered off and washed three times with 50 ml-portions of cyclohexane. The yield was 167 g = 85%; melting point: 67.6 - 68.7°C; $[\alpha]_D = -45.1°$ (1% in 96% ethanol).

In connection with the yields mentioned about it should be noted that from the various mother liquors and filtrates there resulted a recovery amounting to 35% of the racemic acid started from. As this acid can be reused, this means that the reaction steps referred to under (1) and (2) lead in fact to higher yields. Moreover, the cinchonidine could be recovered quantitatively.

2. Separation of DL-S-benzoyl-β-mercaptoisobutyric acid by means of D(-)-2-aminobutanol-1.

(1) Salification with D(-)-2-aminobutanol-1

With stirring, a solution of 224 g of DL-S-benzoyl-β-mercaptoisobutyric acid was prepared at room temperature in 3,000 ml of toluene. Stirring all the time, 89.2 g of D(-)-2-aminobutanol-1 were added to the solution, the temperature rising to about 30°C. Some seed crystals were added, after which the mixture was stirred slowly for another 4 hours in order to allow the desired salt to crystallize out completely. Meanwhile, the temperature had dropped to approximately 20°C. The salt was filtered off and washed three times with 50 ml-portions of toluene. After drying, the yield was 114 g - about 36%; $[\alpha]_D$ = -31° (1% in 96% ethanol).

(2) Recrystallization of the 2-aminobutanol-1-salt

110 g of the 114 g of salt obtained about were added to 1,100 ml of toluene, and the temperature of the mixture was increased to between 70 and 75°C in order to dissolve the salt completely. The solution was then cooled slowly. Some seed crystals were added at a temperature of about 60°C. The crystallization process started at a temperature between 55 and 58°C. The mixture was then further cooled to approximately 20°C, after which the salt was filtered off and washed three times with 45 ml-portions of toluene. After drying, the yield was 97.5 g = about 88%; $[\alpha]_D$ = -34.5° (1% in 96% ethanol).

(3) Liberation of the D(-)-isomer from the 2-aminobutanol-1-salt

With stirring, 50 ml of hydrochloric acid, 200 ml of ether and the 97.5 g of 2-aminobutanol-1-salt mentioned above were added to 150 ml of water. The mixture was stirred for 15 minutes. The organic layer was separated, the water layer was extracted twice with ether and the organic layers were combined to form one organic phase. This organic phase was dried with magnesium sulphate and evaporated. The yield was 68.2 g = about 97.5%; $[\alpha]_D$ = -43° (1% in 96% ethanol). In this case the purity of the D(-)-S-benzoyl-β-mercaptoisobutyric acid sufficed to render recrystallization (the 4th reaction step) superfluous.

Besides D(-)-s-aminobutanol-1 itself, a derivative thereof, such as optically active 2-benzylaminobutan-ol-1, can be used as a resolving agent.

Author's comments:

1) The patent application describes two resolution procedures, one with cinchonidine, the other one with 2-aminobutanol as the resolving agent. It turned out that the latter procedure is based on experiments carried out under non-equilibrium conditions. It is therefore difficult to reproduce the resolution using 2-aminobutanol. The resolution via the cinchonidine salt followed by further optical purification by crystallisation from hexane has been reproduced several times without problems.

2) The optical purity of the different derivatives of β-mercapto isobutyric acid could be checked by quantitative transformation of the derivatives into the S-benzoyl derivative as stated on page 9. Alternatively a HPLC control was used. Deacylation (sodium methoxide in methanol) followed by oxidation (iodine, ethanol, pH ~ 6) yields ββ'-dithiodiisobutyric acid. The meso compound and the dl compound are well separated using reversed phase HPLC.

(Waters associates analytical instrument; Bondapak C18 column, 3.9 mm x 30 cm; particle size 10 μl; eluent 40:60 (vol) mixture of methanol and 0.01N H_2SO_4, flow 2 ml/min.; detection at 254 mμ.

The ratio of the meso peak/dl peak is independent of the injected amount of sample; the surface of the dl peak is proportional to the amount of injected sample of pure dl isomer. Therefore the enantiomeric excess q of the monomeric mercapto isobutyric acid derivative can be calculated from the formula:

$$q = \sqrt{\frac{p_{rac} - p}{p_{rac} + p}} \times 100\%$$

in which p_{rac} represents p when racemic β-mercapto isobutyric is dimerized. In this way we also determined the optical purity of our S-benzoyl isobutyric acid, furnishing a reference point for the optical purities of other derivatives.

$C_{11}H_{15}NO_2$

$CH_3CH_2CH(NH_2)COOCH_2C_6H_5$

Ref. 1478

Spaltung des *d,l*-α-Amino-buttersäure-benzylesters mit Dibenzoyl-*d*-weinsäure: 9.2 g Dibenzoyl-*d*-weinsäure werden in 130 ccm absol. *n*-Propanol gelöst, die Lösung mit einer Mischung von 9.9 g des Esters in 30 ccm *n*-Propanol vereinigt und bei 18° sich selbst überlassen. Nach 2 Tagen werden die ausgeschiedenen büscheligen Nadeln von *d*-Aminobuttersäure-benzylester-dibenzoyl-*d*-tartrat abgesaugt und getrocknet. Ist die Ausbeute geringer als 7 g, so dampft man die Mutterlauge i. Vak. bei Badtemperatur 30° auf 2/3 des Gesamtvolumens ein, impft mit der gewonnenen Kristallfraktion an und läßt stehen, bis sich insgesamt 7–9 g des Estersalzes abgeschieden haben. $[\alpha]_D^{20}$: –40.5° (*c* = 0.52, in Äthanol).

[1]) W. Langenbeck u. O. Herbst, Chem. Ber. 86, 1524 [1953].

[2]) J. Amer. chem. Soc. 55, 2605 [1933].

$C_{40}H_{44}O_{12}N_2$ (744.4) Ber. C 64.50 H 5.92 N 3.76 Gef. C 64.35 H 5.70 N 3.89

Zur Abspaltung der Dibenzoylweinsäure wird das Salz mit überschüss. 10-proz. Salzsäure geschüttelt und die ausgeschiedene Säure abfiltriert; in Lösung verbliebene Reste werden mit Äther extrahiert. In Lösung verbleibt ein Gemisch von Aminosäure-hydrochlorid und Ester-hydrochlorid, das zur vollständigen Verseifung noch eine Zeitlang mit konz. Salzsäure auf dem Wasserbad erwärmt wird. Nach dem Eindampfen der Lösung und Trocknen wird rohes *d*(−)-α-Amino-buttersäure-hydrochlorid erhalten. Ausb. 95 %, bez. auf *d*-α-Amino-buttersäure-benzylester-dibenzoyl-*d*-tartrat; $[\alpha]_D^{21}$: −9.5° (*c* = 2.25 in Wasser), entspr. einer optischen Reinheit von 65%.

Das Rohprodukt kristallisiert man aus Äthanol durch vorsichtigen Ätherzusatz um, wobei sich die optisch reinen Anteile zuerst ausscheiden. Ausb. 52%, bez. auf das Rohhydrochlorid; $[\alpha]_D^{20}$: −14.0° (*c* = 2.01, in Wasser).

Nach E. Fischer und A. Mouneyrat[3]) beträgt die spezif. Drehung von optisch reinem α-Amino-buttersäure-hydrochlorid + 14.5° (−14.3°).

$C_4H_9O_2N \cdot HCl$ (139.5) Ber. C 34.40 H 7.17 N 10.03 Gef. C 34.61 H 7.24 N 10.35

Zur Gewinnung des *l*-Antipoden wird die Mutterlauge des Estersalzes i. Vak. (Badtemperatur 30°) auf 50 ccm eingeengt und durch Zusatz von viel Äther das *l*-Ester-dibenzoyl-*d*-tartrat ausgefällt. Ausb. 6–8 g; $[\alpha]_D^{20}$: −69.5° (*c* = 0.49, in Äthanol).

Die weitere Verarbeitung verläuft wie bei der *d*-Verbindung. Ausbeute an rohem *l*(+)-Aminosäure-hydrochlorid 92%, bez. auf *l*-Estersalz. $[\alpha]_D^{20}$: +8.5° (*c* = 2.10, in Wasser), entspr. einer optischen Reinheit von 59%.

Ausbeute an optisch reinem Hydrochlorid: 48%, bez. auf das Rohprodukt. $[\alpha]_D^{20}$: + 14.1° (*c* = 2.21, in Wasser).

$C_4H_9O_2N \cdot HCl$ (139.5) Ber. C 34.40 H 7.17 N 10.03 Gef. C 34.33 H 6.96 N 10.31

Gewinnung der optischen Antipoden des α-Amino-buttersäure-benzylester-hydrochlorides: *d*-α-Amino-buttersäure-benzylester-dibenzoyl-*d*-tartrat wird mit einem Überschuß von 10-proz. Salzsäure behandelt; von ausgeschiedener Dibenzoylweinsäure wird abfiltriert, Reste der Säure aus der Lösung mit Äther werden extrahiert und vorsichtig i. Vak. eingedampft. Die Temperatur der Lösung darf bei keiner dieser Operationen 30° übersteigen. Man erhält so ein rechtsdrehendes Gemisch von *d*(+)-Aminobuttersäurebenzylester-hydrochlorid und *d*(−)-Aminosäure-hydrochlorid. Das Gemisch wird in absol. Äthanol gelöst und allmählich mit Äther versetzt, wobei sich zunächst die verseiften Esteranteile körnig, später das (+)-Esterhydrochlorid in feinen Nadeln ausscheiden; $[\alpha]_D^{21}$: +15.3° (*c* = 1.52, in Wasser).

$C_{11}H_{15}O_2N \cdot HCl$ (229.7) Ber. C 57.56 H 6.97 N 6.10 Gef. C 57.83 H 6.39 N 6.15

Der optische Reinheitsgrad des *d*-(+)-Ester-hydrochlorides wurde durch Verseifung zum *d*-(−)-Aminosäure-hydrochlorid ermittelt und betrug 63%. Unter Berücksichtigung des gefundenen Drehwertes errechnet sich hieraus für das optisch reine *d*-Ester-hydrochlorid eine spezif. Drehung von $[\alpha]_D^{21}$: +25.0° (*c* = 1.52, in Wasser).

Das völlig entsprechend aus *l*-α-Amino-buttersäure-benzylester-dibenzoyl-*d*-tartrat gewonnene *l*-(−)-Ester-hydrochlorid lieferte bei einem optischen Reinheitsgrad von 65% eine spezif. Drehung von $[\alpha]_D^{21}$: −15.1° (*c* = 1.25, in Wasser), woraus sich für die optisch reine Verbindung ein Drehwert von $[\alpha]_D^{21}$: −23.3° ergibt.

$C_{11}H_{15}O_2N \cdot HCl$ (229.7) Ber. C 57.56 H 6.97 N 6.10 Gef. C 57.39 H 6.82 N 6.48

Spaltung des *d,l*-α-Amino-buttersäure-benzylesters mit *d*-Weinsäure: 4.4 g *d*-Weinsäure werden in 350 ccm absol. Äthanol gelöst und eine Lösung von 5.7 g α-Amino-buttersäure-benzylester in 20 ccm Äthanol bei 20° zugesetzt. Die Kristallisationsgeschwindigkeit des *l*-Ester-*d*-hydrogentartrates kann sehr unterschiedlich sein und seine Ausscheidung einige Stunden bis zwei Tage dauern. Am besten isoliert man solange mehrere Kristallfraktionen, bis sich insgesamt 4 g Ester-hydrogentartrat abgeschieden haben. Endet die Kristallisation, bevor die gewünschte Salzmenge gewonnen ist, so erreicht man weitere Ausscheidung durch allmählichen Ätherzusatz. *l*-α-Amino-buttersäure-benzylester-*d*-hydrogentartrat: $[\alpha]_D^{18}$: +5.1° (*c* = 0.21, in Äthanol).

$C_{15}H_{21}O_8N$ (343.3) Ber. C 52.52 H 6.11 N 4.08 Gef. C 52.61 H 6.05 N 4.10

Die Zersetzung des Ester-hydrogentartrates erfolgt, wie beim Alanin beschrieben[1]). Ausb. an rohem *l*-(+)-α-Amino-buttersäure-hydrochlorid 88%, bez. auf das Ester-hydrogentartrat. $[\alpha]_D^{18}$: +10.8° (*c* = 2.01, in Wasser), entspr. einer optischen Reinheit von 72%.

Nach dem Umkristallisieren aus Alkohol-Äther Ausb. 58%, bez. auf das rohe Hydrochlorid; $[\alpha]_D^{18}$: +13.8° (*c* = 1.98, in Wasser).

$C_4H_9O_2N \cdot HCl$ (139.5) Ber. C 34.40 H 7.17 N 10.03 Gef. C 34.56 H 7.11 N 10.38

Aus der Mutterlauge des Ansatzes wird das *d*-α-Aminobuttersäure-benzylester-*d*-hydrogentartrat durch Einengen bei Badtemperatur 30° und Ausfällen mit viel Äther gewonnen. Ausb. 4.5 g, $[\alpha]_D^{20}$: +14.2° (*c* = 0.22, in Alkohol); nach der Zersetzung Ausbeute an rohem *d*(−)-α-Amino-buttersäure-hydrochlorid 95%, bez. auf das Ester-hydrogentartrat, $[\alpha]_D^{20}$: −7.1° (*c* = 2.14, in Wasser), entspr. einer optischen Reinheit von 50%.

Nach dem Umkristallisieren Ausb. 28%, bez. auf das rohe Hydrochlorid; $[\alpha]_D^{21}$: −14.1° (*c* = 2.14, in Wasser).

$C_4H_9O_2N \cdot HCl$ (139.5) Ber. C 34.40 H 7.17 N 10.03 Gef. C 34.16 H 7.14 N 10.22

[3]) Ber. dtsch. chem. Ges. 33, 2390 [1900].

$C_{11}H_{16}O_5$

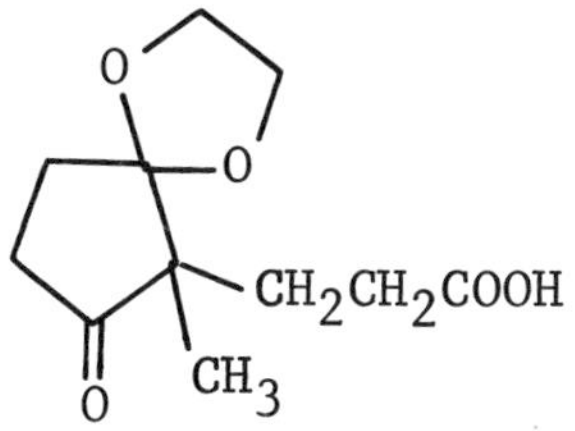

$C_{11}H_{16}O_5$ Ref. 1479

Stade D : Dédoublement.

a. *Formation du sel de cinchonine de l'acide 3-(1'-méthyl 2',2'-éthylènedioxy 5'-oxo cyclopentyl)propionique, V.*

Dans 180 cm³ d'éthanol, on introduit 11,6 g de cinchonine base, agite quinze minutes à température ambiante, puis porte au reflux sous agitation et introduit 10 g d'acide dl 3-(1'-méthyl 2',2'-éthylènedioxy 5'-oxo cyclopentyl)propionique. On agite dix minutes en maintenant au reflux, puis élimine 80 cm³ d'éthanol par distillation. On amène le mélange réactionnel à 20 °C, agite pendant une heure à cette température, puis abaisse la température du milieu réactionnel à une température comprise entre 0 et +5 °C et agite pendant deux heures à cette température. On laisse ensuite quinze heures au repos en maintenant cette température. On sépare le précipité formé par filtration, le lave à l'éthanol froid et obtient 15,4 g de sel de d-cinchonine brut $[\alpha]_D^{20}$ = +119° (*c* = 1 %, éthanol) qui est purifié par recristallisation dans l'éthanol. On obtient ainsi le sel dextrogyre de cinchonine de l'acide 3-(1'-méthyl 2',2'-éthylènedioxy 5'-oxo cyclopentyl)propionique, F = 186°, $[\alpha]^{20}$ = +127,5 °C (*c* = 1 %, méthanol).

Dichroïsme circulaire (éthanol) :
à 295 mμ, Δ ε = +1,25.

A la connaissance de la Société demanderesse, ce produit n'est pas décrit dans la littérature.

b. *Isolement de l'acide d-3-(1'-méthyl 2',2'-éthylènedioxy 5'-oxo cyclopentyl)propionique, VA.*

Dans 25 cm³ d'eau, on met en suspension 5 g de sel dextrogyre de cinchonine de l'acide 3-(1'-méthyl 2',2'-éthylènedioxy 5'-oxo cyclopentyl)-propionique, puis ajoute goutte à goutte sous agitation, 1,13 cm³ de solution aqueuse 10,7N d'ammoniaque. On agite trente minutes à température ambiante, élimine l'insoluble par filtration, sature le filtrat obtenu par du chlorure de sodium et acidifie à pH 4,0 par une solution aqueuse de sulfate acide de potassium. La phase aqueuse est extraite à l'éther, les solutions éthérées sont réunies, on lave la solution organique obtenue par une solution aqueuse saturée de chlorure de sodium, puis la sèche et la concentre à sec. Le résidu est purifié par cristallisation dans un mélange d'éther isopropylique et d'hexane et l'on obtient acide d 3-(1'-méthyl 2',2'-éthylènedioxy 5'-oxo cyclopentyl)propionique, F = 70-71 °C, $[\alpha]_D^{20}$ = +9,3 (*c* = 1,1 %, dioxane).

Dichroïsme circulaire (éthanol) :
à 302 mμ, Δ ε = +0,58.

$C_{12}H_{11}NO_4$

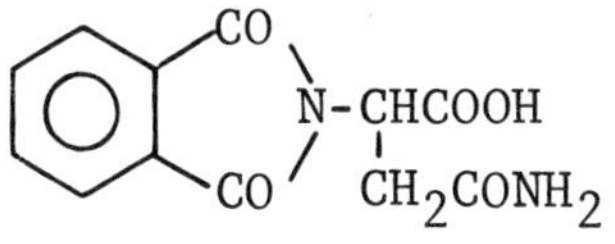

$C_{12}H_{10}N_2O_5$ Ref. 1480

Note: The racemic acid was resolved with brucine to give the active acids, m.p. 207-209° (decomp.), $[\alpha]_D$ -89° (C 0.5, methanol) and m.p. 208-209° (decomp.) $[\alpha]_D$ +89° (C 0.5, methanol).

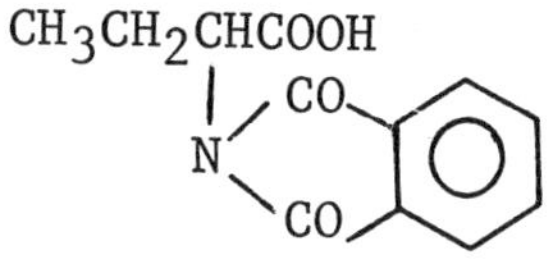

$C_{12}H_{11}NO_4$ Ref. 1481

Acido l-α-ftalimidobutirrico

G 121 di acido dl-α-ftalimidobutirrico monoidrato vengono sciolti a circa 70° in cc 310 di alcool etilico assoluto. Si aggiunge una soluzione calda di g 92 di l-efedrina base monoidrata (14) in cc 310 di alcool etilico assoluto e si lascia a riposo per 15 ore a 0-5°. Il cristallizzato ottenuto, costituito dal sale di efedrina grezzo dell'antipodo levogiro, viene quindi filtrato, mentre le acque madri (soluzione A) vengono messe da parte per il recupero dell'antipodo destrogiro. Il grezzo così separato pesa g 103 ed ha $[\alpha]_D^{20}$ = —36,2° (C = 2% in dimetilformammide). Dopo tre cristallizzazioni da alcool etilico assoluto, raffreddando ogni volta a 0-5° per una notte, si ottengono alla fine g 60 di l-α-ftalimidobutirrato di efedrina con p.f. 197-199° e $[\alpha]_D^{20}$ = —49,3°. Un campione di sale puro, ottenuto dopo ripetute cristallizzazioni, ha p.f. 199-200°, $[\alpha]_D^{20}$ = —51,7° (C = 2% in dimetilformammide) e dà all'analisi:

	trov. % :	C 66,03;	H 6,70;	N 7,13
per $C_{22}H_{26}N_2O_5$	calc. :	66,31;	6,58;	7,03

I g 60 di sale di efedrina con $[\alpha]_D^{20}$ = —49,3° vengono sciolti in cc 1050 di acqua calda. Si acidifica la soluzione con HCl conc., si raffredda, si filtra il precipitato ottenuto, lo si lava con acqua e lo si asciuga all'aria (in essiccatore sotto vuoto diviene vetroso e ritorna solido riprendendolo con acqua). Si ottengono così g 33 (54,5% d.t.) di acido l-α-ftalimdobutirrico monoidrato con p.f. 79-80° e $[\alpha]_D^{20}$ = —31,2° (C = 2% in alcool etilico assoluto). Il prodotto puro (ottenuto dal sale di efedrina con $[\alpha]_D^{20}$ = —51,7°) ha $[\alpha]_D^{20}$ = —32,2° e dà all'analisi:

	trov. % :	C 57,14;	H 5,32;	N 5,70;	H_2O 8
per $C_{12}H_{11}NO_4 \cdot H_2O$	calc. :	57,37;	5,22;	5,58;	7,2

Dopo deftaloilazione con idrato di idrazina in soluzione alcoolica (5), il prodotto fornisce un acido L-(+)-α-amminobutirrico con $[\alpha]_D^{20}$ = +20° (C = 2% in HCl 6 N) [in letteratura sono riportati i valori +20,6° (15), +19,6° (16)].

Acido d-α-ftalimidobutirrico

Le acque madri di cristallizzazione del sale di efedrina dell'acido l-α-ftalimidobutirrico (soluzione A, vedi sopra) vengono portate a secco sotto vuoto. Il residuo leggermente appiccicoso, viene spappolato con etere anidro e filtrato. Si ottengono così g 77 di sale di efedrina grezzo dell'acido d-α-ftalimidobutirrico con $[\alpha]_D^{20}$ = +3,6° (C = 2% in dimetilformammide). Questi vengono cristallizzati una prima volta da cc 126 di alcool etilico assoluto, raffreddando a 0-5° per una notte. Si ottengono g 58 di cristallizzato che vengono purificati una seconda volta sciogliendoli a caldo in cc 116 di alcool etilico assoluto ed aggiungendo cc 232 di etere anidro. Dopo una notte a 0-5° si ottengono g 45,2 di d-α-ftalimidobutirrato di efedrina con p.f. 149-150° e $[\alpha]_D^{20}$ = +7°. Questo sale ha una purezza ottica sufficiente per l'ottenimento dell'acido destrogiro corrispondente. Un campione di sale di efedrina puro, ottenuto dopo ripetute cristallizzazioni da alcool etilico, ha p.f. 151-152°, $[\alpha]_D^{20}$ = +9,5° (C = 2% in dimetilformammide) e dà all'analisi.

	trov. % :	C 66,75;	H 6,60;	N 7,13
per $C_{22}H_{26}N_2O_5$	calc. :	66,31;	6,58;	7,03

I g 45,2 di sale di efedrina, con $[\alpha]_D^{20}$ = +7°, vengono sciolti in cc 790 di acqua calda. Si acidifica la soluzione con HCl conc., si raffredda, si filtra il precipitato ottenuto, lo si lava con acqua e lo si asciuga all'aria. Si ottengono in tal modo g 25,8 (42,8% d.t.) di acido d-α-ftalimidobutirrico monoidrato con

p.f. 78-80° e $[\alpha]_D^{20}$ = +31° (C = 2% in alcool etilico assoluto). Il prodotto puro (ottenuto dal sale di efedrina con $[\alpha]_D^{20}$ = +9,5°) ha p.f. 79-80°, $[\alpha]_D^{20}$ = +32,5° e dà all'analisi:

	trov. % :	C 57,27;	H 5,35;	N 5,48;	H_2O 8,16
per $C_{12}H_{11}NO_4.H_2O$	calc. :	57,37;	5,22;	5,58;	7,2

Dopo deftaloilazione con idrato di idrazina in soluzione alcoolica, il prodotto fornisce un acido D-(—)-α-amminobutirrico con $[\alpha]_D^{20}$ = —19° (C = 2% in HCl 6 N).

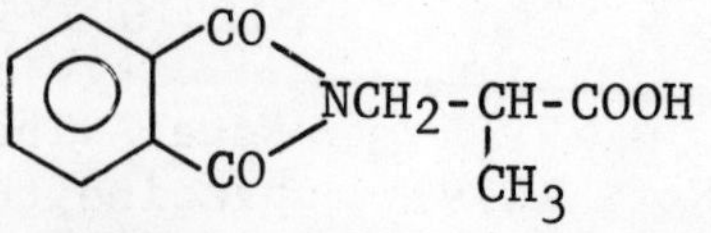

$C_{12}H_{11}NO_4$ Ref. 1482

The acid (154 g.) and brucine (260 g.) were dissolved in ethanol (1300 c.c.) and left at 0° for 10 days. The crystals formed had $[\alpha]_D^{24\cdot5}$ $-31\cdot5°$ (*c* 1·506 in $CHCl_3$). A second crop of crystals, obtained from the mother-liquor, had $[\alpha]_D^{25}$ $-37°$ (*c* 1·504 in $CHCl_3$). Fractional crystallisation of the combined crops from absolute ethanol gave the substantially pure brucine salt of low solubility which had $[\alpha]_D^{22}$ $-39\cdot7°$ (*c* 1·503 in $CHCl_3$). Bregant and Balenovic [3] report $[\alpha]_D$ $-44°$. The free acid (V) was obtained by the addition of 4N-hydrochloric acid (1700 c.c.) to a suspension of the brucine salt (100 g.) in water (3000 c.c.). Fractional crystallisation of the first two crops of crystals gave the (−)-acid (V) (9·8 g.), m. p. 145—146°, $[\alpha]_D^{21}$ $-20\cdot1°$ (*c* 1·5 in $CHCl_3$). Bregant and Balenovic [3] report m. p. 145—146°, $[\alpha]_D^{17}$ $-24\cdot4°$ (*c* 0·98 in $CHCl_3$).

[3] Bregant and Balenovic, *Tetrahedron*, 1959, **5**, 44.

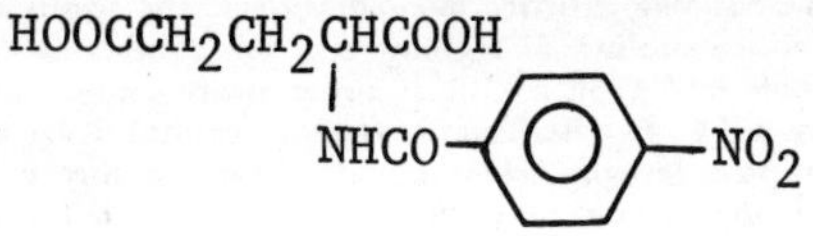

$C_{12}H_{12}N_2O_7$ Ref. 1483

p-Nitrobenzoyl-*d*(−)-glutamic acid has been prepared in this Laboratory by resolution of *p*-nitrobenzoyl-*dl*-glutamic acid through repeated recrystallization of the strychnine salt from water. The slightly soluble salt of the *d*(−)-enantiomorph was obtained in good yield. After removal of strychnine, the free acid derivative crystallized from aqueous solution in fine white needles which softened at 77° and melted at 115–116° (*Anal.* Calcd. for $C_{12}H_{12}N_2O_7$: N, 9.46. Found: N, 9.39). This is in good agreement with the melting point of the l(+)-derivative reported by Van der Scheer and Landsteiner.[1] The specific rotation of the aqueous solution containing 2 moles of alkali was −16.02°.

(1) Van der Scheer and Landsteiner, *J. Immunol.*, **29**, 371 (1935).

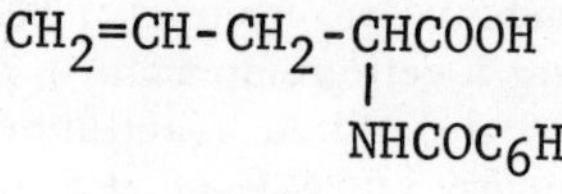

$C_{12}H_{13}NO_3$ Ref. 1484

d(—)-*Allyl-hippursaures Brucin.*

75,3 g Allyl-hippursäure (Smp. 107° unkorr.) lösten wir in 75,3 cm³ 5-n. Natronlauge. Eine gleichzeitig bereitete Lösung von 160,3 g Brucin (mit 4 Mol Krystallwasser) in 75,3 cm³ 5-n. Salzsäure und 250 cm³ Wasser, die unter schwachem Erwärmen am Wasserbad hergestellt war, filtrierte an der Saugpumpe in die Lösung des Natriumsalzes der Allyl-hippursäure ein. Die viskose Flüssigkeit wurde durch Umrühren gut gemischt und durch Einstellen in Eis auf 0° abgekühlt. Sodann impften wir die stark violett fluoreszierende Lösung mit etwas d(—)-allyl-hippursaurem Brucin, kratzten an den Gefässwänden und liessen über Nacht bei 0° stehen.

Der andern Tags reichlich abgeschiedene Krystallbrei wurde abgesogen und mit 30 cm³ eiskaltem Wasser nachgewaschen.

Die Ausbeute an schneeweissen, feine Nadeln bildenden Krystallen betrug lufttrocken 103 g. Die Drehung der im Vakuum über Phosphorpentoxyd bei 50° getrockneten Substanz war $[\alpha]_D^{20} = -27{,}3°$.

Zur Erreichung der maximalen Drehung krystallisierten wir das Brucinsalz neunmal aus je 50 cm³ Wasser um. Dabei zeigte die spezifische Drehung von der sechsten Krystallisation ab einen zwischen $[\alpha]_D^{20} = -41{,}5°$ und $[\alpha]_D^{20} = -40{,}5°$ schwankenden Wert. Die Ausbeute betrug zuletzt 32 g lufttrockenes Salz.

Als definitiven Drehwert bestimmten wir:

0,0668 g Subst., Gesamtgewicht der wässerigen Lösung 10,9294 g, Rohrlänge 1 dm

$$\alpha_D = -0{,}25° \qquad [\alpha]_D^{20} = -40{,}9°$$

Das Brucinsalz der d(—)-Allyl-hippursäure konnte auch aus einem Gemisch von gleichen Teilen Benzol und Petroläther krystallisiert erhalten werden. Jedoch wurde dieser Weg nie zur Spaltung grösserer Mengen Säure benutzt.

l(+)-*Allyl-hippursaures Brucin.*

Die nach Abtrennung der Hauptmenge des *d*(—)-allyl-hippursauren Brucins verbleibende Mutterlauge gab nach dem Eindampfen auf die Hälfte des Volumens noch eine kleine Menge von sehr unreinen d(—)-allyl-hippursaurem Salz ab.

Die nach Abtrennung dieses Restes verbleibende Mutterlauge, die auch bei stärkstem Eindampfen nicht zum Krystallisieren zu bringen war, wurde direkt zur Herstellung der (+)-Allyl-hippursäure verwendet.

d(—)-Allyl-hippursäure.

32 g (—)-allyl-hippursaures Brucin lösten wir in 50 cm³ Wasser und versetzten mit einem Überschuss konz. Salzsäure. Sodann schüttelten wir sofort dreimal mit je 50 cm³ Äther aus. Die Ätherextrakte wurden jedesmal mit je 5 cm³ Wasser gewaschen und dann zusammen über Natriumsulfat getrocknet. Nach dem Verjagen des Äthers im Vakuum blieb ein gelbes Öl, das bald krystallinisch erstarrte. Die Masse löste sich leicht in 20 cm³ kochendem Benzol. Aus der heiss filtrierten Lösung schieden sich beim Abkühlen schneeweisse Blättchen ab. Nach dem Absaugen und Trocknen an der Luft blieben 8 g reinste d(—)-Allyl-hippursäure. Aus der Benzol-Mutterlauge konnten noch weitere 1,6 g reine Säure isoliert werden.

Die d(—)-Allyl-hippursäure schmolz bei 89° (unkorr.). Sie ist in Benzol und Wasser viel leichter löslich als die racemische Verbindung. Beim Aufnehmen des Brucinsalzes in zu viel Wasser tritt deshalb beim Ansäuern mit Salzsäure keine Trübung durch sich abscheidende Allyl-hippursäure ein. Die Säure kann in diesem Fall aus der Lösung durch Extraktion mit Äther gewonnen werden.

0,01012 g Subst. gaben 0,62 cm³ N_2 (18°, 706 mm)

$C_{12}H_{13}O_3N$ Ber. N 6,39 Gef. N 6,59%

Zur Bestimmung der optischen Aktivität löste man die Substanz in Wasser und fügte pro Mol Allyl-hippursäure 1 Mol Kaliumhydroxyd hinzu.

0,1152 g Subst., 2,2018 g Gesamtgewicht der Lösung, Rohrlänge 2,5 cm

$\alpha_D = -0{,}42°$ $[\alpha]_D^{20} = -32{,}11°$

Weitere, weniger stark drehende (—)-Allyl-hippursäurepräparate konnten aus den Mutterlaugen der verschiedenen Umkrystallisationen des (—)-allyl-hippursauren Brucins gewonnen werden.

l(+)-Allyl-hippursäure.

Die nach zweimaliger Abtrennung von (—)-allyl-hippursaurem Brucin zurückbleibende, bis zur syrupösen Konsistenz eingedampfte Mutterlauge ergab nach der Aufarbeitung, die der bei der d(—)-Allyl-hippursäure beschriebenen entsprach, eine l(+)-Allyl-hippursäure vom Smp. 90° (unkorr.). Die Löslichkeitsverhältnisse waren dieselben wie die der d(—)-Allyl-hippursäure.

Drehungsbestimmung:

0,0986 g Subst., 11,207 g Gesamtgewicht der Lösung (Wasser +1 Mol KOH pro 1 Mol Säure), Rohrlänge 1 dm

$\alpha_D = +0{,}29°$ $[\alpha]_D^{18} = +32{,}9°$

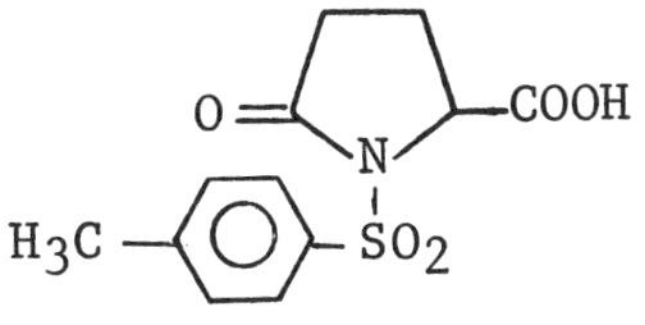

$C_{12}H_{13}NO_5S$

Ref. 1485

Resolution of Toluenesulphonyl DL-pyrrolidonecarboxylic Acid

***Brucine Salt of Toluenesulphonyl-D-pyrrolidonecarboxylic Acid*:** Toluenesulphonyl-DL-pyrrolidonecarboxylic acid monohydrate (15·07 g; 0·05 mol) was dissolved in hot 96% ethanol (300 ml) and mixed with a solution of brucine (19·5 g of the anhydrous base) in the same amount of hot ethanol. On chilling and seeding, the solution deposited the brucine salt of the D-acid in fine needles. (The first sample crystallised from the solution after about a week's standing.) After 6 hours at room temperature the product was collected at the pump, washed on the filter with 100 ml 96% ethanol, dried in air and recrystallised from the minimum amount of 96% ethanol (about 750—850 ml). The recrystallised salt was dried in a vacuum desiccator over sodium hydroxide. Yield 13·70 g (79%), m. p. 222—223°.

For $C_{12}H_{13}O_5NS.C_{23}H_{26}O_4N_2.H_2O$ (695·8)
calculated: 60·42% C, 5·94% H, 6·04% N, 4·61% S;
found: 60·20% C, 5·85% H, 5·97% N, 4·60% S.

A few mg of the salt were treated with two drops of 5% hydrochloric acid and set aside at 0° overnight. The characteristic needle-shaped crystals of the monohydrate of optically active toluenesulphonylpyrrolidonecarboxylic acid were dried on a porous tile; m. p. 68—69°. If this melting-point was not achieved, the salt was once more recrystallised in the same way.

For $C_{12}H_{13}O_5NS$ (283·3) calculated: 4·95% N;
found: 4·79% N.

The mother-liquors after removal of the first crop were evaporated to crystallisation; a second crop melting at 117—122° was obtained. This product on solution in ethanol and careful precipitation with water yielded 0·55 g (10·5%) of the *monohydrate* of toluenesulphonyl-D-pyrrolidonecarboxylic acid, m. p. 68—69°. The mixed m. p. with a sample of the L-acid was 90—110°.

The overall yield of the resolution is 73%.

p-Toluenesulphonyl-D-glutamic Acid

Anhydrous toluenesulphonyl-D-pyrrolidonecarboxylic acid (5 g; 0·0175 mol) was dissolved in 4N-NaOH (27 ml; 0·054 mol) at room temperature. After 10 minutes the solution was acidified with conc. hydrochloric acid. The toluenesulphonyl-D-glutamic acid crystallised in long needles, m. p. 143—145°, yield 4·6 g. Extraction of the mother-liquors with ether (5 × 10 ml) and evaporation of the extracts yielded a second crop (0·30 g), m. p. 142—145°. Total yield 92%.

For $C_{12}H_{15}O_6NS$ (301.3) calculated: 47·83% C, 5·02% H, 4·65% N;
found: 48·04% C, 5·12% H, 4·43% N.

D-Glutamic Acid

Toluenesulphonyl-D-glutamic acid (3·01 g; 0·01 mol) dissolved in liquid ammonia (100 ml) was reduced with sodium by the procedure previously described[14]; 1·3 g (0·055 g-at.) of the metal were required. The colour of the solution was discharged by the addition of a small amount of ammonium acetate and the ammonia allowed to evaporate. The dry residue was taken up in 10 ml of ice-water and treated with 5 g of Amberlite IRC-50(NH_4^+). After 30 minutes the resin was filtered off, washed with water, the filtrate and washings evaporated and a small excess of 1M-barium acetate added. The precipitate of barium salts was filtered off, the filtrate extracted with ether and run through a column of the ion-exchange resin (3 × 8 cm). The eluate (150 ml) was evaporated to 10 ml, acetic acid (0·5 ml) added and then excess absolute ethanol. Yield of D-glutamic acid 1·05 g (72%), after recrystallisation from aqueous ethanol 0·90 g. $[\alpha]_D^{20}$ — 32·4 ± ± 0·5° (c = 3 in 5N-HCl).

For $C_5H_9O_4N$ (147·1) calculated: 40·81% C, 6·17% H, 9·52% N;
found: 40·91% C, 6·13% H, 9·39% N.

On incubation with L-glutamic acid oxidase, 20 mg and 60 mg samples of this product caused no significant evolution of CO_2. From these results, the optical purity of the D-glutamic acid is better than 99·9%.

The literature records a number of procedures for obtaining D-glutamic acid from the racemate, based both on chemical[1–3] and on enzymic[4–6] or biological[7–10] methods.

The most advantageous of the chemical methods hitherto described appears to be that of Sugasawa[2] as modified by Hellmann and Elies[3]. It is based on the conversion of glutamic to DL-pyrrolidonecarboxylic acid, separation of the D-component of the latter as the quinine salt and acid hydrolysis to D-glutamic acid. The yield of D-glutamic acid hydrochloride, based on the DL-pyrrolidonecarboxylic acid used, is reported[3] to be 64%.

Of the enzymic methods of resolution, two appear to have found practical application. The procedure of Fruton, Irving and Bergmann[7] makes use of the selective synthesis of the α-anilide from the L-component of carbobenzoxy-DL-glutamic acid under the influence of papain;*** the method of Levintow, Greenstein and Kingsley[10] is based on the selective hydrolysis of carbobenzoxy-L-glutamic acid by hog-kidney acylase. For the second method, a yield of 85% is recorded.

References

1. Fischer E.: Ber. *32*, 2451 (1899).
2. Sugasawa S.: J. Pharm. Soc. Japan 1926, 90; Chem. Zentr. 1927, I, 1464.
3. Hellmann G., Elies A.: Z. physiol. Chem. *283*, 31 (1948).
4. Schulze E., Bosshard E.: Z. physiol. Chem. *10*, 138 (1886).
5. Pringsheim H.: Z. physiol. Chem. *65*, 96 (1910).
6. Ehrlich F.: Biochem. Z. *63*, 379 (1914).
7. Fruton J. S., Irving G. W., Bergmann M.: J. Biol. Chem. *133*, 703 (1940).
8. Fodor P. J., Price V. E., Greenstein J. P.: J. Biol. Chem. *178*, 503 (1949).
9. Price V. E., Gilbert J. B., Greenstein J. P.: J. Biol. Chem. *179*, 1169 (1949).
10. Levintow L., Greenstein J. P., Kingsley R. B.: Arch. Biochem. Biophys. *31*, 77 (1951).
11. Hanby W. E., Waley S. G., Watson J.: J. Chem. Soc. 1950, 3239.
12. Rudinger J.: Chem. listy *48*, 235 (1954). This Journal *19*, 370 (1954).
13. Harington C. R., Moggridge R. C. G.: J. Chem. Soc. 1940, 706.
14. Rudinger J.: Chem. listy *48*, 244 (1954). This Journal *19*, 380 (1954).

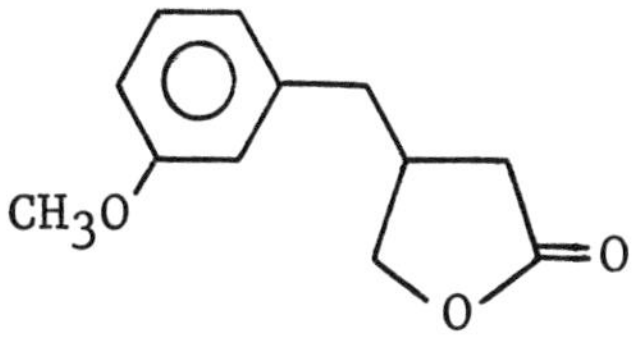

$C_{12}H_{14}O_3$ Ref. 1486

Resolution of 4-[(3-methoxyphenyl)methyl]dihydro-2-(3H)-furanone

To a solution of 4.12 g (0.02 mol) of 1 in 20 ml of methanol was added 40 ml of 4% aqueous KOH. The mixture was heated at 50°C for 30 min., resulting in a clear solution, which was cooled to 0-5°C. The reaction mixture was acidified with 2N HCl at $<$ 5°C and extracted with ice-cold ether (2 x 50 ml). The extracts were washed with water, dried briefly over anhyd. Na_2SO_4 and filtered. To the resulting solution of 11 was added 2.7 g (0.02 mol) of d-amphetamine (ex Aldrich) and the precipitated salt was collected by filtration; yield 6.5 g, mp 95-105°C. This product was recrystallized four times from ethyl acetate (300-450 ml) to give 1.7 g (25% based on 1) of pure material, mp 123-125°C, (needles). This treated with 40 ml 1N aqueous HCl at 50°C for 1 h regenerated the lactone 1, which was isolated by extraction of the cooled reaction mixture with ether (2 x 50 ml). The extracts were dried over anhyd. Na_2SO_4 and evaporated to give 0.94 g of (+)-1, $[\alpha]_D^{20}$ = +6.35° (c 1, $CHCl_3$).

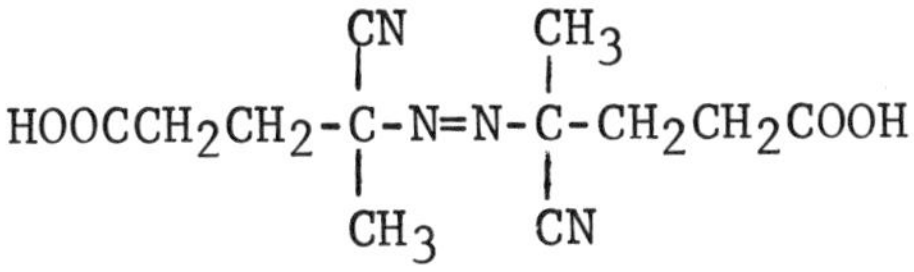

$C_{12}H_{16}N_4O_4$ Ref. 1487

Resolution of (±)-4,4'-Azobis(4-cyanopentanoic acid) with Quinine.—A mixture of 83 g (0.296 mol) of (±)-4,4'-azobis(4-cyanopentanoic acid) and 192.2 g (0.592 mol) of quinine was added portionwise and with stirring to *ca.* 6000 ml of acetone maintained at room temperature. Stirring was continued for 2 hr after the addition of the mixture to ensure complete precipitation of the quinine salt of the (+) isomer. Subsequent filtration followed by several washings of the salt with 2000-ml portions of acetone gave 180.9 g (61% yield, theoretical yield 50%) of impure quinine salt of (+) isomer, mp 120–123° dec. This salt was added portionwise and with stirring to an excess of 4 *N* hydrochloric acid (275–300 ml) kept at 0–5°. The resulting suspension was cooled at −3° for 7 hr and then filtered to give 47.5 g (0.169 mol) of impure (+) isomer, mp 119–122° dec. A further resolution of this isomer, conducted in the same manner as the first, utilizing 110 g (0.339 mol) of quinine and *ca.* 5000 ml of acetone, gave 110 g (40% yield based on the first resolution) of analytically pure quinine salt of the (+) isomer, $[\alpha]^{25}D$ −131° (*c* 3.056, methanol), mp 129–130° dec. Recrystallization of this salt from large volumes of acetone did not change its melting point or specific rotation.

Anal. Calcd for $C_{52}H_{64}N_8O_8$: C, 67.22; H, 6.94; N, 12.06. Found: C, 67.35; H, 7.03; N, 12.19.

Generation of the (+) isomer by treatment of this salt with 4 *N* hydrochloric acid in the same fashion as previously described and subsequent recrystallization of this isomer from water maintained at 60–65° gave 23 g (55.4% overall yield) of colorless platelets, $[\alpha]^{25}D$ +45.3° (*c* 3.037, methanol), mp 130–131° dec. Further recrystallization of the (+) isomer from water did not alter its melting point or specific rotation: ν_{max}^{Nujol} 2255 (C≡N) and 1715 cm^{-1} (C=O); λ_{max}^{MeOH} 348 mμ (ε 20); nmr (CF_3COOH) τ 8.24 (singlet, 6 H, CCH_3) and 7.32 (singlet, 8 H, CH_2CH_2COOH).

Anal. Calcd for $C_{12}H_{16}N_4O_4$: C, 51.43; H, 5.75; N, 19.99. Found: C, 51.60; H, 5.81; N, 19.85.

The combined acetone filtrate was evaporated under reduced pressure at room temperature, and to the remaining quinine salt of (−) isomer kept at 0–5° was added, with stirring, excess 4 *N* hydrochloric acid (275–300 ml). The resulting suspension was cooled at −3° for 10 hr, after which time filtration and subsequent recrystallization of the (−) isomer from water at 60–65° gave 20 g (48.2% overall yield) of colorless platelets, $[\alpha]^{25}D$ −44.8° (*c* 2.463, methanol), mp 130–131° dec. No change in the melting point or specific rotation could be effected by further recrystallization. The ORD and CD data for the (−) isomer are summarized in Table III; ν_{max}^{Nujol} 2255 (C≡N) and 1715 cm^{-1} (C=O); λ_{max}^{MeOH} 348 mμ (ε 20); nmr (CF_3COOH) τ 8.24 (singlet, 6 H, CCH_3) and 7.32 (singlet, 8 H, CH_2CH_2COOH).

Anal. Calcd for $C_{12}H_{16}N_4O_4$: C, 51.43; H, 5.75; N, 19.99. Found: C, 51.61; H, 5.89; N, 19.84.

Resolution of (±)-4,4'-Azobis(4-cyanopentanoic acid) by Fractional Crystallization.—(±)-4,4'-Azobis(4-cyanopentanoic acid) (33 g) was dissolved in *ca.* 1000 ml of water at 60–65°, and slow cooling of the resulting solution to room temperature afforded 25 g of a mixture of racemic isomer (colorless solid) and impure (+) isomer (colorless platelets), $[\alpha]^{25}D$ +1.36° (*c* 2.980, methanol), mp 120–122° dec. The platelets (5.5 g) were separated from the racemic isomer with tweezers and subjected to slow recrystallization from *ca.* 400 ml of water as previously described; after 4 hr, 1.5 g of colorless platelets formed, $[\alpha]^{25}D$ +8.53° (*c* 2.355, methanol), mp 125–127° dec. A third recrystallization of this material from *ca.* 250 ml of water gave 0.65 g of colorless platelets, $[\alpha]^{25}D$ +40.8° (*c* 2.875, methanol), 90% optically pure based on $[\alpha]^{25}D$ +45.3°, mp 129–130° dec.

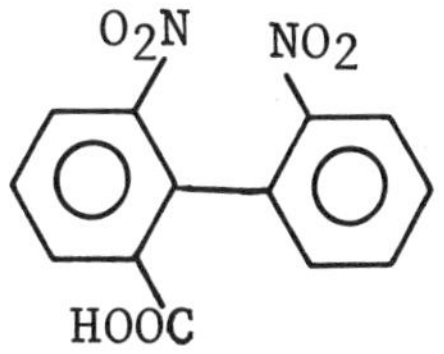

$C_{13}H_8O_6N_2$ Ref. 1488

Resolution of 2,2'-Dinitro-6-carboxybiphenyl.—To a warm solution of 4 g. of 2,2'-dinitro-6-carboxybiphenyl in 800 cc. of 75% ethanol was added with stirring 4.5 g. of quinine. After standing overnight approximately half of the salt separated. It was purified by crystallization twice from 400 cc. of 50% ethanol. The salt then had a constant rotation, m. p. 156–191°. After drying the melting point was 195–197°.

Rotation. (dry *d*-salt) 0.05 g. made up to 15 cc. in chloroform. α_D +0.35; l = 2; $[\alpha]^{25}D$ +52.5°.

Evaporation of the mother liquor from the less soluble salt resulted in the separation of an oil which after standing for a few days gradually solidified. The solid was thoroughly pulverized and allowed to stand in 200 cc. of ethanol with occasional stirring. The solution was filtered and upon evaporation of the solvent the salt obtained solidified rapidly: m. p. 121–125°; yield, 2.5 g.

Rotation. (more soluble salt) 0.1 g. made up to 15 cc. in chloroform at 25°. α_D −3.16; l = 2; $[\alpha]^{25}D$ −238°.

Anal. Calcd. for $C_{33}H_{32}O_8N_4$: N, 9.15. Found: N, 8.96.

***d*- and *l*-2,2'-Dinitro-6-carboxybiphenyl.**—The active acids were liberated from the salts in the manner previously described. The active acids were obtained as oils which solidified upon standing in a vacuum desiccator overnight. They were recrystallized from dilute acetic acid; m. p. of *d*-acid from the less soluble salt was 135–137°; the *l*-acid 127–130°.

Rotation. (*d*-acid) 0.10 g. made up to 15 cc. in ethanol at 25°. α_D +2.69; l = 2; $[\alpha]^{25}D$ +201.5°. (*l*-acid) 0.05 g. made up to 15 cc. in ethanol at 25°. α_D −1.33; l = 2; $[\alpha]^{25}D$ −199.5°.

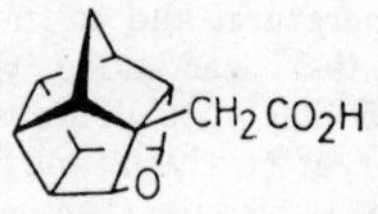

$C_{13}H_{14}O_3$ Ref. 1489

Optical Resolution of 17. A mixture of 17 (19.4 g, 89.0 mmol), cinchonidine (24.0 g, 81.6 mmol), and 95% ethanol (100 mL) was refluxed for 4 h. Allowing the mixture to stand overnight at room temperature resulted in a solid precipitate which was collected to yield 41.3 g of the salt, $[\alpha]^{22}_D$ -61.3° (*c* 0.552, EtOH). Fractional recrystallization of the salt from ethanol–water (1/4 v/v, six times) gave 24.2 g of the salt, $[\alpha]^{22}_D$ -77.9° (*c* 0.907, EtOH). A mixture of the salt (24.0 g) and 10% aqueous HCl (750 mL) was stirred for 10 h at room temperature and extracted with ether. The extract was washed with aqueous HCl and water and dried ($MgSO_4$). Evaporation of the solvent gave 8.96 g of (–)-17 ($[\alpha]^{22}_D$ -32.6° (*c* 0.690, EtOH)) which was recrystallized from ether to afford 6.15 g of (–)-17: $[\alpha]^{22}_D$ -39.3° (*c* 0.613, EtOH); mp 109–110 °C.

Anal. Calcd for $C_{13}H_{14}O_3$: C, 71.54; H, 6.47. Found: C, 71.31; H, 6.38.

Concentration of the combined mother liquors precipitated 10.0 g of the salt, $[\alpha]^{22}_D$ -49.0° (*c* 0.469, EtOH). The same treatment of this salt as described above for the diastereomeric salt afforded (+)-17 (3.10 g; $[\alpha]^{22}_D$ +20.6° (*c* 0.564, EtOH)) which was recrystallized from ether to give 1.21 g of (+)-17: $[\alpha]^{22}_D$ +29.2° (*c* 0.499, EtOH); mp 107–110 °C.

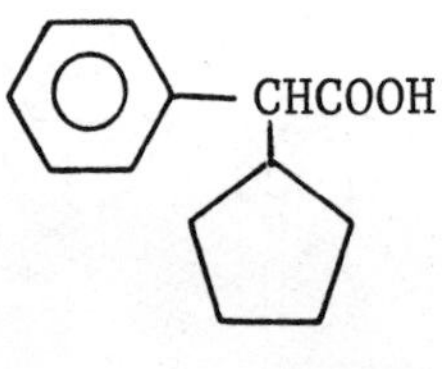

$C_{13}H_{16}O_2$ Ref. 1490

Preparation of the (–) and (+) Enantiomers of [(α-Cyclopentylphenylacetoxy)methyl]-1-methylpyrrolidinium Chloride (13ca and 13cb). 1. Resolution of the Acid. (±)-α-Cyclopentylphenylacetic acid (4.57 g, 2.24×10^{-2} mol) was dissolved in chloroform and added to a solution of strychnine (7.48 g, 2.24×10^{-2} mol) in chloroform. The solvent was removed in vacuo and the residue recrystallized repeatedly from chloroform–methanol. All of the mother liquors were stored.

The solid (3.46 g) was dissolved in water (200 mL), acidified, and extracted with ether (2×100 cm^{-3}). The ether extract was washed with 1 N hydrochloric acid (50 mL), followed by water (50 mL), dried over sodium sulfate, and evaporated in vacuo to yield a viscous oil which crystallized on standing. The product was recrystallized from *n*-hexane (1.03 g): mp 65–66 °C; $[\alpha]^{20}_D$ +60.3° (*c* 1, $CHCl_3$). The NMR of the product was identical with (±)-α-cyclopentylphenylacetic acid.

The chloroform–methanol mother liquors, containing the salts of the (–) isomer, were combined and evaporated in vacuo. The residue was extracted with excess ether. The ether was filtered, concentrated, and washed extensively with 1 N hydrochloric acid, followed by water (50 mL). The organic phase was dried over sodium sulfate and evaporated. The residue was recrystallized from *n*-hexane to yield a white solid (0.88 g): mp 73–74 °C; $[\alpha]^{20}_D$ -52.1°. The NMR of this product was identical with (±)-α-cyclopentylphenylacetic acid.

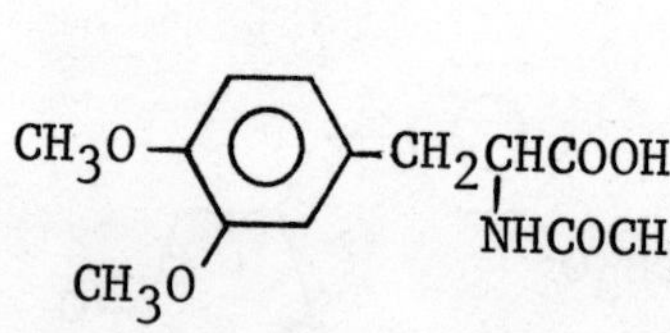

$C_{13}H_{17}NO_5$ Ref. 1491

***N*-Acetyl-3-(3,4-dimethoxyphenyl)-L-alanine-*d*-ephedrine Salt (*d*-Ephedrine-L-I Salt).**—*N*-Acetyl-3-(3,4-dimethoxyphenyl)-DL-alanine (DL-I) (53.4 g, 0.2 mole) and 33.0 g of *d*-ephedrine (0.2 mole) were dissd together in 130 ml of MeOH or in 200 ml of EtOH with warming at 55–60° for 1.0 hr, and the soln was kept in a refrigerator overnight. The colorless crystals that sepd were filtered off, washed with MeOH (*ca.* 30 ml), and dried, giving 37.9 g (87.8%) of the *d*-ephedrine-L-I salt: mp 147.5–149.5°, $[\alpha]^{20}D$ +49.8° (*c* 5, H_2O). After recrystn from 3 vol of MeOH, the mp and $[\alpha]D$ became constant: mp 152–153°; $[\alpha]^{20}D$ +54.5° (*c* 5, H_2O); yield, 28.4 g (68.1%). *Anal.* ($C_{23}H_{32}N_2O_6$) C, H, N.

***N*-Acetyl-3-(3,4-dimethoxyphenyl)-L-alanine (L-I) from the *d*-Ephedrine-L-I Salt.**—*d*-Ephedrine-L-I (20 g was dissd in 50 ml of H_2O, then this soln was added dropwise with 30% HCl with cooling and stirring, giving colorless crystals. After standing in a refrigerator overnight they were filtered off, washed with H_2O (20 ml), and dried, affording 11.4 g (91.0%) of L-I: mp 149–150°; $[\alpha]^{20}D$ +46.2° (*c* 5, MeOH). *Anal.* ($C_{13}H_{17}NO_5$) C, H, N.

***N*-Acetyl-3-(3,4-dimethoxyphenyl)-L-alanine (L-I) from the *d*-Ephedrine-L-I Salt.**—*d*-Ephedrine-L-I (20 g) was dissd in 50 ml of H_2O, then this soln was added dropwise with 20% HCl with cooling and stirring, giving colorless crystals. After standing in a refrigerator overnight they were filtered off, washed with H_2O (20 ml), and dried, affording 11.4 g (91.0%) of L-I: mp 149–150°; $[\alpha]^{20}D$ +46.2° (*c* 5, MeOH). *Anal.* ($C_{13}H_{17}NO_5$) H, C, N. From the filtrate and washings of the acid (L-I), *d*-ephedrine·HCl was nearly quant recovered as colorless crystals; mp 217–218°; $[\alpha]^{20}D$ +34.1° (*c* 1, H_2O).

L-Dopa (L-III) from L-I.—A mixt of 26.8 g (0.1 mole) of L-I, 69.8 ml (0.6 mole) of 47% HBr, and 28 ml (0.32 mole) of PhOH was heated under stirring and reflux for 6 hr, and the resulting slight brown soln was evapd to a reddish syrup. This was dissd in 30 ml of *n*-BuOAc and extd twice with 30 ml and 10 ml of H_2O. The 2 aq exts were combined and adjusted to pH 5.0 with 25% NH_4OH soln contg a little $NaHSO_3$, whereupon colorless crystals sepd. After standing in a refrigerator overnight the crystals were filtered off, washed with H_2O, and dried, giving 19.6 g (99.5%) of crude L-dopa: mp 266–269°; $[\alpha]^{15}D$ -11.6° (*c* 5, 1 *N* HCl). Recrystn from 800 ml of H_2O contg a little $NaHSO_3$ gave 15.6 g (79.5%) of L-dopa as colorless minute leaflets: mp 277–278° dec; $[\alpha]^{15}D$ -13.3° (*c* 5, N-HCl). *Anal.* ($C_9H_{11}NO_4$) C, H, N.

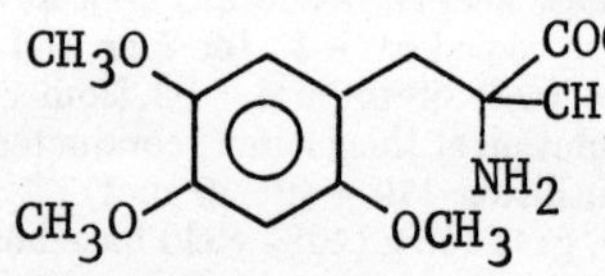

$C_{13}H_{19}NO_5$ Ref. 1492

Resolution of 6-OH-α-Me-Dopa. Racemic 17 (6.2 g, 21 mmol) in 75 mL of warm absolute ethanol was added to a warm solution of (+)-tartaric acid (3.3 g, 22 mmol) in 75 mL of absolute ethanol, and the resulting solution was immediately filtered. Crystallization, initially at room temperature (16 h), was completed at 5 °C for 12 h. The salt (4.6 g, 97%; mp 157–160 °C) was recrystallized from absolute ethanol to give an analytical sample, mp 157–159 °C. Anal. ($C_{19}H_{29}NO_{11}$) C, H, N.

The residue obtained from the above combined filtrates in 100 mL of 0.5 N NaOH was extracted with petroleum ether. After drying ($MgSO_4$) and removing solvent, 1.4 g (4.8 mmol) of the amino ester 17 was recovered. When treated with (–)-tartaric acid

$C_{14}H_7N_3O_{10}$

(0.75 g, 4.83 mmol) in a total of 40 mL of warm absolute ethanol, 0.3 g (19%) of the salt was obtained. Recrystallization from absolute ethanol gave material melting at 155–158 °C.

The above tartrate salts were converted to the corresponding free amino esters by extraction into petroleum ether from 0.5 N NaOH solutions. The melting points (41–42 °C) and NMR spectra [$(CDCl_3)$ δ 6.71 and 6.53 (2 s, Ar H, 2), 4.16 (q, CH_3CH_2, 2), 3.87, 3.82, 3.79 (3 s, OCH_3, 9), 2.96 (d, CH_2, 2), 2.27 or 1.66 (br s, NH_2, 2), 1.38 (s, CH_3, 3), 1.26 (t, CH_3CH_2), 3)] were essentially identical.

The enantiomeric purities of (+)- and (−)-**17** were estimated by GC analysis of the corresponding amide derivatives obtained by treating the free bases (1 mg each) in 0.1 mL of benzene with 2 mg of (*S*)-*N*-[(pentafluorobenzoyl)prolyl] (PFBP) 1-imidazolide. Each solution was concentrated under a stream of nitrogen gas on the steam bath to about 0.05 mL before analysis on an OV 25 column at 260 °C. The retention time of the PFBP amide from (−)-**17** was 61 min and from (+)-**17** was 68 min. In both instances, enantiomeric purity was estimated at greater than 90%.

(*R*)-(+)-6-OH-α-Me-Dopa·HCl [(*R*)-7]. Levorotatory **17** (0.5 g, 1.8 mmol) in 10 mL of freshly distilled 48% hydrobromic acid containing 1 mL of glacial acetic acid was heated under a nitrogen atmosphere for 3 h. After the solvent was removed in vacuo the brownish residue was chromatographed on a 50W-X8 ion-exchange resin, H^+ form. The resin was washed with doubly distilled water and when the eluent was halogen free the column was eluted with 2 N HCl. The solvent was removed under vacuum to to give a white glassy material (0.35 g, 48%). The product was further heated in 10 mL of distilled water under an atmosphere of nitrogen for 15 min on a steam bath. The TLC (2-propanol–HOAc–H_2O, 4:1:1; R_f 0.67), NMR, and CIMS (PFP ethyl ester derivative) were identical with (*RS*)-**7**: $[\alpha]^{25}_D$ +19.7° (*c* 1, 0.1 M aqueous HCl).

(*S*)-(−)-6-OH-α-Me-Dopa·HCl [(*S*)-(−)-7·HCl]. Dextrorotatory **17** (1.47 g, 4.95 mmol) was O-demethylated and hydrolyzed in the same manner as (−)-**17** and gave 0.750 g (57.6%) of the enantiomeric hydrochloride salt. The TLC, NMR, and CIMS (Me_3Si ethyl ester) properties were identical with (*RS*)-**7** and (*R*)-**7**: $[\alpha]^{25}_D$ −18.8° (*c* 1, 0.1 M aqueous HCl).

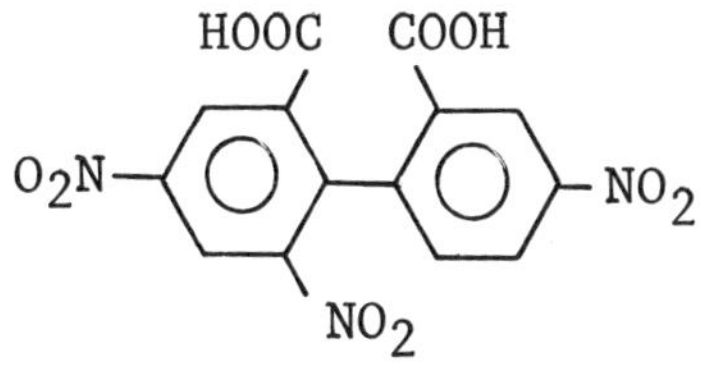

$C_{14}H_7N_3O_{10}$ Ref. 1493

Resolution of r-4 : 6 : 4′-*Trinitrodiphenic Acid.*—By fractional crystallisation of the brucine salt of the racemic acid from water, the less soluble salt was obtained in a state of purity without much difficulty, but the more soluble salt was less easy to purify, and this was not pursued further when it was found that the quinidine salts (prepared from quinidine, of which $[\alpha]^{15°}_D = +253{\cdot}0°$ for a 2 per cent. absolute alcoholic solution) were more suitable for the purpose.

Brucine d-4 : 6 : 4′-*trinitrodiphenate* consists of colourless, flat plates with rounded edges, m. p. 239—240° (decomp.), of which one part is soluble in about 1700 parts of cold water. For a 1 per cent. solution in 10*N*-acetic acid, $[\alpha]_D = -20{\cdot}79°$ (Found : H_2O = 2·32. $C_{60}H_{59}O_{18}N_7,1\frac{1}{2}H_2O$ requires H_2O = 2·28 per cent. Found : for the anhydrous material dried at 130°, N = 8·56. $C_{60}H_{59}O_{18}N_7$ requires N = 8·41 per cent.).

Quinidine d-4 : 6 : 4′-*trinitrodiphenate*,

$C_{14}H_7O_{10}N_3,C_{20}H_{24}N_2O_2,\frac{1}{2}EtOH$,

separates from absolute alcohol in clusters of hexagonal prisms, frequently truncated, m. p. 229° (decomp.). For a 0·71 per cent. solution in chloroform, $[\alpha]^{16°}_D = -191{\cdot}1°$ (Found : EtOH = 2·43. $C_{34}H_{31}O_{12}N_5,\frac{1}{2}EtOH$ requires EtOH = 2·20 per cent. Found : for the material dried at 130°, N = 9·81. $C_{34}H_{31}O_{12}N_5$ requires N = 9·57 per cent.).

Quinidine l-4 : 6 : 4′-*trinitrodiphenate*,

$C_{14}H_7O_{10}N_3,C_{20}H_{24}O_2N_2,2EtOH$,

crystallises from absolute alcohol in stout, rhombic prisms, m. p. 176° (decomp.). For a 0·71 per cent. solution in chloroform, $[\alpha]^{16°}_D = +56{\cdot}04°$ (Found : EtOH = 8·55. $C_{34}H_{31}O_{12}N_5,2EtOH$ requires EtOH = 8·24 per cent. Found : for the material dried at 130°, N = 9·51. $C_{34}H_{31}O_{12}N_5$ requires N = 9·57 per cent.).

d-4 : 6 : 4′-*Trinitrodiphenic acid*, $C_{12}H_5O_6N_3(CO_2H)_2$, prepared from the brucine salt as described in the cases of the active tetranitro-acids, was a yellow oil, which solidified after several weeks to minute prisms, m. p. 281—282° (decomp.). For a 1·50 per cent. aqueous solution of the sodium salt, $[\alpha]^{16°}_D = +156{\cdot}8°$. A somewhat less pure sample of the acid was titrated [Found : equivalent = 189·5. $C_{12}H_5O_6N_3(CO_2H)_2$ requires equivalent = 188·5]. For a preparation from the quinidine salt, a 1·27 per cent. aqueous solution of the sodium salt showed $[\alpha]^{16°}_D + 143{\cdot}1°$.

l-4 : 6 : 4′-*Trinitrodiphenic acid*, $C_{12}H_5O_6N_3(CO_2H)_2$, from the quinidine salt, remained in the oily condition for several weeks, and had not solidified at the time of writing this paper. For a 0·49 per cent. aqueous solution of the sodium salt, $[\alpha]^{16°}_D = -130{\cdot}5°$.

$C_{14}H_7N_3O_{10}$ Ref. 1493a

I. *Spaltung.*

Aus der durch Zusammengießen der siedenden Lösungen von 1,319 g Säure und 1,63 g kryst. Brucin (1 Mol) in je 40 ccm Aceton erhaltenen, gelbgefärbten Lösung waren beim Aufbewahren über Nacht gelbe Krystalle ausgefallen, die mit einem Glasstab von der Wandung des Gefäßes weggekratzt wurden. Ihre Menge betrug 1,43 g, d. h. 70,4 % der zugesetzten Brucinmenge sind als sekundäres Salz ausgefallen, falls dasselbe wasserfrei ist. Der Schmelzpunkt lag bei 235—236° (korr.) unter Zersetzung.

$[\alpha]^{20}_D = (-0{,}12° \cdot 100):(0{,}6892 \cdot 1{,}84) = -9{,}5°$. (In 10,4 n-Essigsäure.)

Aus dem Filtrat, das an der Pumpe etwas eingedunstet worden war, fielen nach kurzer Zeit 0,85 g (41,8 Proc.) flockige Krystallaggregate vom Schmelzp. 221—222° (korr., unter Zersetzung) aus.

$[\alpha]^{20}_D = (-0{,}255° \cdot 100):(0{,}6892 \cdot 2{,}26) = -16{,}4°$. (In 10,4 n-Essigsäure.)

G. H. Christie und J. Kenner[3]) geben für das schwer lösliche Brucinsalz, das sie aus Wasser erhielten, den Schmelzp. 239—240° unter Zersetzung an.

Die Mutterlauge der II. Fraktion hinterließ nach dem Verdunsten des Lösungsmittels ein rotes Öl, das nach 14 Tagen nicht erstarrt war. Mit Salpetersäure lieferte es eine schwache Rosafärbung. Dieses Öl wurde in Ammoniak aufgenommen, wobei ein gelbbrauner Rückstand von geringer Menge hinterblieb. Das Filtrat davon drehte im 0,5 dm-Rohr + 0,63°. Beim Eintropfen in verdünnte Salzsäure wurde ein zähes Öl erhalten, das allmählich erstarrte. Nach nochmaligem Auflösen in Soda wurde beim Eintropfen in etwa 1 n-Salzsäure 0,15 g einer schwach gelbbraunen Substanz erhalten, die z. T. aus farblosen sternförmigen Krystallaggregaten, z. T. aus gelblichen, tröpfchenförmigen Aggregaten besteht, die das Gesichtsfeld unter gekreuzten Nicols aufhellen.

Zerlegung des schwerlöslichen Brucinsalzes. 1,4 g Alkaloidsalz wurden in üblicher Weise mit 2 g $KHSO_4$ zerlegt und nach Zusatz von entwässertem Natriumsulfat scharf getrocknet. Achtstündige Extraktion mit absolutem Äther im Soxhletapparat lieferte etwa 0,18 g eines gelben Öles, das erst beim Stehen über Nacht im Exsiccator erstarrte. Eine weitere Menge von 0,15 g und dem Schmelzp. 281 bis 282° (korr., unter Zersetzung) wurde erhalten nach nochmaliger Extraktion während etwa 8 Stunden.

$[\alpha]^{22}_D = (-0{,}37° \cdot 100):(0{,}5 \cdot 1{,}96) = -37{,}8°$. (In 2 n-Soda.)

Eine dritte Extraktion mit Äther lieferte noch 0,05 g Säure. Gesamtausbeute 0,38 g, entsprechend 84 Proc. d. Th., berechnet auf wasserfreies, sekundäres Brucinsalz. G. H. Christie und J. Kenner[1]) fanden für die aus dem Chinidinsalz in öliger Form freigemachte Säure $[\alpha]_D = -130{,}5°$.

Die l-Trinitrodiphensäure hellt das Gesichtsfeld unter gekreuzten Nicols auf, es sind aber keine wohlausgebildeten Krystalle wahrnehmbar.

Zerlegung des leichter löslichen Brucinsalzes. 0,78 g Brucinsalz vom Schmelzp. 239—240° (korr., unter Zersetzung) wurde in üblicher Weise mit 1,2 g $KHSO_4$ zerlegt und lieferte nach 8 stündiger Extraktion mit Äther 0,22 g d-Trinitrodiphen-

säure vom Schmelzp. 279—280° (korr., unter Zersetzung), was einer Ausbeute von 87 Proc. entspricht, berechnet auf wasserfreies, sekundäres Salz. Sie ist brucinfrei, enthält aber noch eine Spur Sulfat und besteht aus beidseitig zugespitzten Stäbchen, die sternartig aggregiert sind.

$[\alpha]_D^{20} = (+0{,}28° \cdot 100) : (0{,}5 \cdot 1{,}68) = +33{,}3°$. (In 2 n-Soda.)

Die englischen Autoren[1]) geben für die aus dem Brucinsalz dargestellte d-Säure den Schmelzp. 281—282° unter Zersetzung an und für $[\alpha]_D + 156{,}8°$.

[1]) a. a. O., und zwar S. 785.

$C_{14}H_7N_3O_{10}$ Ref. 1493b

4:6:4'-Trinitrodiphenic acid was prepared and resolved by quinine as described by Christie and Kenner (loc. cit.). These workers obtained the d-acid as an oil which solidified only after standing for several months. We find that rapid crystallisation can be brought about by solution in chloroform and evaporation to dryness, the operation being repeated 3 or 4 times. Rapid solidification of the l-acid, which is much harder to obtain than the d-isomer (Christie and Kenner, J., 1923, 123, 785), was brought about in the same manner. Optically active benzene complexes, $2C_{14}H_7O_{10}N_3,C_6H_6$, were prepared by dissolving specimens of quinine-resolved acid of varying rotatory power in mixtures of benzene and ether (2:1 by volume), from which the ether was slowly distilled on the water-bath until the first signs of crystallisation were seen. The distilling flask was then rapidly cooled, and the crystals of benzene complex filtered off (Found for the d-acid complex having $[\alpha]_{5461}$ 23.14° in ether, m.p. 176° and after resolidifation, m.p. 279-281°: C, 49.7; H, 2.5. $2C_{14}H_7O_{10}N_3,C_6H_6$ requires C, 49.1; H, 2.4%).

The molecular rotations of the crystals obtained after successive recrystallisations A,B,C,D, by the above technique and of the solids left after evaporation of mother-liquors were determined in dry ether in a 2 dcm. tube for the line = 5461A. The results are collected in the table, in which the values for $[\alpha]_{5461}$ refer to free acid, having been corrected for the benzene content of the complexes by multiplying the observed rotations by the factor 1:11.

		I.	II.	III.	IV.	V.	VI.	VII.
A.	Original complex	24.6°	26.9°	26.9°	13.3°	13.1°	15.3°	-14.7°
B.	Recrystallisation of A	42.2	41.5	47.1	36.0	37.0	29.6	-33.0
B'.	Mother-liquor	12.2					8.0	
C.	Recrystallisation of B		48.2	48.1	45.2			-37.0
C'.	Mother-liquor		5.0					
D.	Recrystallisation of C				48.0			

In order to avoid complicating the presentation of the data in the table, actual rotations and the concentrations at which they were determined have been omitted. The measured values for the rotations ranged from 0.35° to 0.9° at concentrations C = ca. 0.4 g.-mol./l., giving the molecular rotations recorded in the table.

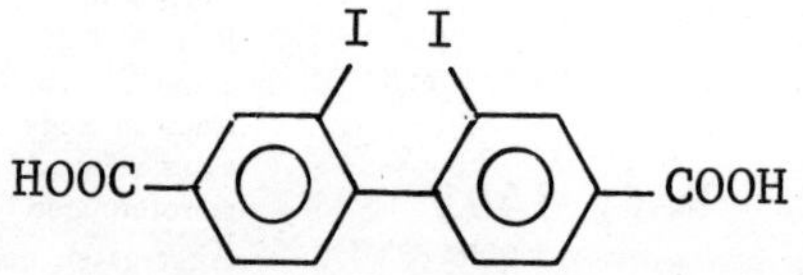

$C_{14}H_8I_2O_4$ Ref. 1494

Resolution of 2,2'-Diiodo-4,4'-dicarboxydiphenyl. (First Method)

Brucine Salt.—A solution of 3 g. of 2,2'-diiodo-4,4'-dicarboxydiphenyl in 140 cc. of absolute methanol was added to a solution of 4.8 g. of anhydrous brucine in 60 cc. of absolute methanol. After standing for one-half hour the salt came down as an oil. This was redissolved by adding 500 cc. more of absolute methanol and boiling. The solution was then evaporated to 450 cc. on the steam-cone. On standing overnight at room temperature 1.35 g. of salt precipitated as a fine powder, m. p. 212–224°. This fraction was dextrorotatory and was the salt of the *d*-acid (for rotations see Table I).

Anal. Less soluble salt—salt of *d*-acid. Calcd. for $C_{14}H_8O_4I_2{\cdot}2C_{23}H_{26}O_4N_2$: N, 4.37. Found (micro Dumas): N, 4.07.

The mother liquor from the first fraction was allowed to evaporate slowly at room temperature. After standing four days, a second fraction of 1.95 g. of salt crystals deposited. By allowing the mother liquor to evaporate spontaneously for a week at room temperature a third fraction of 2.90 g. of crystals was obtained. The second and third fractions were found to be identical in melting point and rotation and were different from the first fraction. They were levorotatory and proved to be the salt of *l*-acid, m. p. 201–212° (for rotations see Table I).

Anal. Calcd. for $C_{14}H_8O_4I_2{\cdot}2C_{23}H_{26}O_4N_2$: N, 4.37. Found (micro Dumas): N, 4.45.

(Second Method.)—Two moles of anhydrous brucine in ethyl acetate and one mole of racemic acid in ethyl acetate were mixed and allowed to stand overnight. The salt precipitated gradually and quantitatively. The mixture of the two diastereoisomeric salts was treated as follows.

A. A solution of 2.75 g. of the mixed salts in 250 cc. of ordinary methanol was allowed to evaporate slowly to 100 cc. at room temperature. At first small hard hemispherical clusters of crystals formed but later clusters of larger, transparent prismatic crystals deposited. The mother liquor was poured off and the crystals washed with methanol. After drying, the two kinds of crystals were easily separated by hand. The hemispherical clusters that first appeared were in the smaller amount and were the salt of the *d*-acid. The prismatic crystals that formed later were in the larger amount and were the salt of the *l*-acid.

B. A solution of 4.3 g. of the salt obtained from the ethyl acetate process in 500 cc. of hot 95% ethyl alcohol deposited 1.72 g. of crystals on cooling. After standing overnight 0.99 g. more of salt crystallized out. Upon evaporating at room temperature a third fraction of 0.84 g. was obtained. All three fractions were identical in melting point and rotation and were the salt of the *l*-acid.

***d*-2,2′-Diiodo-4,4′-dicarboxydiphenyl.**—The *d*-salt was ground with ice-cold 6 *N* hydrochloric acid in a small porcelain mortar cooled by an ice-bath. The fine suspension thus produced was filtered on a sintered quartz filter and continuously washed with cold 6 *N* hydrochloric acid for four hours until the acid gave a negative test for brucine. After washing thoroughly with cold water it was dried *in vacuo* over sulfuric acid. From 0.65 g. of salt, 0.30 g. of active acid was obtained, m. p. 339–341° (for rotations and racemization see Table I).

***l*-2,2′-Diiodo-4,4′-dicarboxydiphenyl.**—The *l*-acid was obtained by the method used for the *d*-acid. From 3.0 g. of the *l*-salt, 1.1 g. of the active acid was obtained, m. p. 339–341° (for rotations and racemization see Table I).

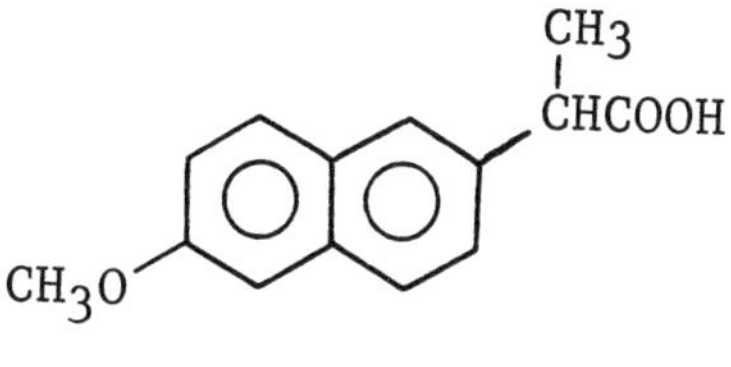

$C_{14}H_{14}O_3$ Ref. 1495

EXAMPLE 1

(+)-6-methoxy-α-methyl-2-naphthaleneacetic N-methyl-D-glucamine salt

460.7 g. of racemic 6-methoxy-α-methyl-2-naphthaleneacetic acid (2 mol) and 390.5 g of N-methyl-D-glucamine [= 1-deoxy-1-(methylamino)-D-glucitol] (2 mol) were dissolved in 4 liters of boiling methanol.

The solution was filtered to clearness and carefully cooled to 45°C with slow stirring. 1 G. of (+)-6-methoxy-α-methyl-2-naphthaleneacetic acid N-methyl-D-glucamine salt crystals (obtained in a preliminary test by cooling and rubbing with a glass rod, filtering under suction and washing with some methanol) was now added. Massive crystallization of (+)-6-methoxy-α-methyl-2-naphthaleneacetic acid N-methyl-D-glucamine salt occurred immediately after seeding. The temperature was held at 45°C and then lowered slowly to 15°C.

The precipitated crystals were filtered off and washed with a little methanol.

Yield: 360 g. of (+)-6-methoxy-α-methyl-2-naphthaleneacetic acid N-methyl-D-glucamine salt, i.e. 84% of theoretical.

Melting point: 156–158°C.

Specific rotation at 20°C; conc. = 1% in water

Wavelength λ		589	546	436	365
$[\alpha]_\lambda^{20}$	°	–18.59	–22.85	–42.53	–80.63

The product obtained (360 g.) was redissolved in 4.4 liters of boiling methanol, filtered, cooled slowly, seeded with authentic material, allowed to crystallize out, cooled, filtered and washed.

Yield: 278 g. of pure (+)-6-methoxy-α-methyl-2-naphthaleneacetic acid N-methyl-D-glucamine salt, i.e. 65% of theoretical.

Melting point: 160–161°C.
Specific rotation at 20°C; conc. = 1% in water

Wavelength λ	589	546	436	365
$[\alpha]_\lambda^{20}$ °	-20	-23.95	-44.83	-87.19

Microanalysis: $C_{21}H_{31}NO_8$:
calc. C 59.28%; N 3.29%
found C 59.58%; N 3.42%

The mother liquors were completely evaporated to recover the methanol.

The residue from evaporation was dissolved in water and dilute hydrochloric acid was added to acidify the salt solution. The (–)-6-methoxy-α-methyl-2-naphthaleneacetic acid was precipitated.

Amount: 228 g. of (–)-6-methoxy-α-methyl-2-naphthaleneacetic acid, i.e. 99.1% of theoretical.

Melting point: 145—146°C.

$[\alpha]_D^{20}$ = –45.8° (conc. = 1% in chloroform).
(589) Optical purity: 67%.15

The product can be converted by racemization back to the racemate, i.e. the starting material, and then reused in further batches during the resolution process.

EXAMPLE 2

Reuse of the mother liquors

The methanolic mother liquor can be used directly prior to regeneration, in further resolving operations.

A resolving operation as described in Example 1 was carried out with the same quantities of starting materials. Instead of fresh methanol, however, the methanolic mother liquor from a previous equal batch was used.

The first product obtained was:

431 g. of (+)-6-methoxy-α-methyl-2-naphthaleneacetic acid N-methyl-D-glucamine salt, i.e. 100% of theoretical.

Melting point: 155–158°C.
Specific rotation at 20°C; conc. = 1% in water

Wavelength λ	589	546	436	365
$[\alpha]_\lambda^{20}$ °	-18.52	-21.41	-40.5	-76.6

After recrystallization from 4.4 liters of fresh methanol, the product was:

326 g. of (+)-6-methoxy-α-methyl-2-naphthaleneacetic acid N-methyl-D-glucamine salt, i.e. 76% of theoretical.

Melting point: 159–160°C.
Specific rotation at 20°C; conc. = 1% in water

Wavelength λ	589	546	436	365
$[\alpha]_\lambda^{20}$ °	-20.02	-24.12	-45.88	-88.41

The resolution of racemic 6-methoxy-α-methyl-2-naphthaleneacetic acid was continued another 3 times, always using the mother liquor from the preceding operation.

The following material balance was obtained:

Used: 2,303.5 g. of racemic 6-methoxy-α-methyl-2-naphthaleneacetic acid.

Obtained: 1,613.5 g. of (+)-6-methoxy-α-methyl-2-naphthaleneacetic acid N-methyl-D-glucamine salt, i.e. 75.8% of theoretical,

1,120 g. of (–)-6-methoxy-α-methyl-2-naphthaleneacetic acid, $[\alpha]_D^{20} = -47 \pm 2°$, optical purity 69%.

EXAMPLE 3

(+)-6-methoxy-α-methyl-2-naphthaleneacetic acid

460.7 G. of racemic 6-methoxy-α-methyl-2-naphthaleneacetic acid (2 mol) and 390 g. of N-methyl-D-glucamine are dissolved in 4 liters of boiling methanol. The obtained diastereoisomer pairs are separated by the method described in Example 1.

Obtained: 370 g. of (+)-6-methoxy-α-methyl-2-naphthaleneacetic acid N-methyl-D-glucamine salt, i.e., 86.9% of theoretical.

Melting point: 158—159°C.

$[\alpha]_D^{20} = -19.1°$, $[\alpha]_{365}^{20} = -83.7°$ (c = 1% in water).

The methanolic mother liquors are used to recover the (—)-6-methoxy-α-methyl-2-naphthaleneacetic acid and the N-methyl-D-glucamine.

The obtained salt (370 g) is dissolved in 1750 ml. of water, and the solution is warmed to 80°C and filtered clear. The solution is acidified by slow addition of 250 ml. of 4N sulfuric acid at 80°C with stirring. The suspension obtained is cooled down to 20°C, the product is filtered off and washed with water. The mother liquor is collected. The filtered product is washed with acidified water (0.001 N hydrochloric acid) until the sulfate ions vanish.

Obtained: 196.3 g. Of (+)-6-methoxy-α-methyl-2-naphthaleneacetic acid, i.e., 98% of theoretical relative to utilized salt and 85.16% of theoretical relative to utilized racemate.

Melting point: 156—157°C; $[\alpha]_D^{20} = +65.2°$.

Content: 99.4%

By-products = negligible

(DC)

Dry loss: 0.1%.

The quality of the product obtained directly in this manner (naproxen) already meets the optical rotation requirements of the health authorities, e.g., as published in the British Pharmacopeia (Addendum 75), wherein $[\alpha]_D^{20}$ of +63 to +68.5° is required.

EXAMPLE 4

Recovery of (—)-6-methoxy-α-methyl-2-naphthaleneacetic acid (A) and recovery of N-methyl-D-glucamine (B)

Recovery of (A)

The methanolic mother liquors from the isomeric separation according to Example 3 are evaporated to dryness. The residue is dissolved in 2300 ml. of water at 80°C. By acidifying with 290 ml. of 4N sulfuric acid, cooling, filtering and drying, analogously to the method described in detail in Example 3, there is obtained: 255 g. of (—)-6-methoxy-α-methyl-2-naphthaleneacetic acid, which can then be racemized, according to known techniques, for recycling.

$$\text{Mat. Bal.} = \frac{\text{yield of (+)- and (—)-6-methoxy-}\alpha\text{-methyl-2-naphthaleneacetic acid acetic acid}}{\text{starting material (racemate)}} = 98\%$$

Recovery of (B)

The aqueous mother liquors from the isolation of the (+)- and (—)-6-methoxy-α-methyl-2-naphthaleneacetic acid from Example 3, containing N-methyl-D-glucamine sulfate; are combined, and there is slowly added to it a suspension of calcium hydroxide [obtained by slaking 63.7 g of calcium oxide (i.e., 105% of theoretical, relative to the utilized sulfuric acid) with 250 ml. of water]. Calcium sulfate is formed, most of which precipitates and is filtered off and washed with water. The filtrate is concentrated to a small volume, the newly precipitated calcium sulfate is filtered off and washed with a little water. The filtrate is now concentrated by evaporation at 85—95°C in vacuum to dryness.

The evaporation residue is dissolved in 2400 ml. of 95% ethanol with reflux boiling, filtered clear in the hot state, and cooled to 15°C. N-methyl-D-glucamine crystallizes out.

Amount: 351 g. of N-methyl-D-glucamine

Yield: 90% of theoretical

Content: 99%

Melting point: 127—128°C.

$[\alpha]_D^{20} = -16.95°$

EXAMPLE 5

Recovery of N-methyl-D-glucamine with the aid of anion exchange resin

For the decomposition of the (+)- and (—)-6-methoxy-α-methyl-2-naphthaleneacetic acid N-methyl-D-glucamine salts and precipitation of the (+)- and (—)-6-methoxy-α-methyl-2-naphthaleneacetic acid, respectively, it is also possible to use hydrochloric acid instead of the sulfuric acid used in Examples 3 and 4(A). Then, N-methyl-D-glucamine hydrochloride remains dissolved in the aqueous phase, from which the chloride ions can be removed more easily by means of ion exchangers than would be possible with sulfate ions.

From a 2 mol starting preparation, the mother liquors thereby obtained from the precipitation of (+)- and (—)-6-methoxy-α-methyl-2-naphthaleneacetic acid, which contain N-methyl-D-glucamine hydrochloride, are neutralized with ammonia to pH 7 and then percolated through an ion exchanger column coated with 1.6 liters of Amberlite® IR—120. The exchange resin is then washed with 3.2 liters of deionized water. The chloride ion-containing effluent is discarded.

The N-methyl-D-glucamine is dissolved out of the exchange resin by percolation with 2400 ml. of aqueous ammonia (2.5 N) and 3.2 liters of deionized water. The effluents are combined and concentrated by evaporation to dryness. As described in Example 4, the evaporation residue is recrystallized from 2400 ml. of 95% ethanol.

Amount: 351 g. of N-methyl-D-glucamine
Yield: 90%
Content: 99.1%
Melting point: 127—128°C
$[\alpha]_D^{20} = -17°$°.

TABLE 1

Solubility of the glucosamine salts

Solvent	Salt of (+)A with D-glucosamine $[\alpha]_D^{20}$ = 39.85° mp = 60–63°C decomp. 20°C	boiling temp.	Salt of (–)A with D-glucosamine $[\alpha]_D^{20}$ = 37.41° mp = 90–100°C decomp. 20°C	boiling temp.
H_2O	insol.	decomp.	1	decomp.
CH_3OH	50	decomp.	3.3	decomp.
C_2H_5OH, 95%	2.5	decomp.	1	decomp.
C_2H_5OH absolute	1	decomp.	1	decomp.

TABLE 2

Solubilities of the N-methyl-D-glucamine salts

Solvent	Salt of (+)A with N-methyl-D-glucamine		Salt of (–)A with N-methyl-D-glucamine	
	20°C	boiling temp.	20°C	boiling temp.
H_2O	25	100	70	100
CH_3OH	1.3	6.5	18	100
$(CH_3)_2CHOH$	0.02	0.16[1]	0.16	1.7[1]

[1]at reflux

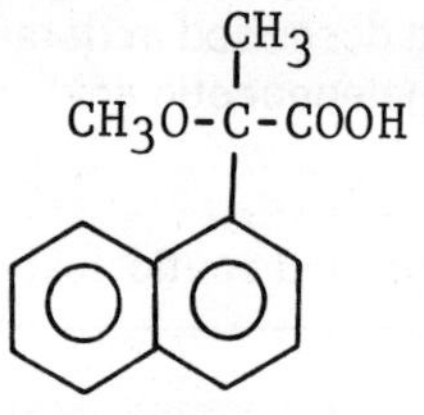

$C_{14}H_{14}O_3$ Ref. 1496

Note: The optical isomer was readily resolved by fractionally crystallizing the (+)-α-methylbenzylamine salt from ethanol. This procedure was repeated twice to provide the desired (-)-α-methoxy-α-methyl-1-naphthalene acetic acid, m.p. 111-112°, $[\alpha]^{13}_D$ -106.3° (C, 0.16, $CHCl_3$), $[\alpha]^{13}_D$ -128.8° (C, 0.10, CH_3OH). Theoretical purity was determined to be over 99.5%).

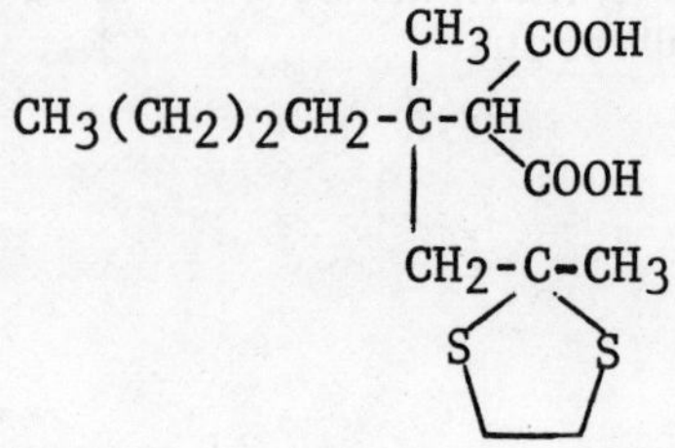

$C_{14}H_{24}O_4S_2$ Ref. 1497

(–)-Cinchonidine Salt of 34. To one portion of crude diacid **34** (ca. 82 g) in warm ethyl acetate (300 mL) was added 78 g of (–)-cinchonidine suspended in warm ethyl acetate (ca. 200 mL) (a solution of (–)-cinchonidine in 200 mL of methanol can be used as well). Immediate salt formation occurred. After the mixture was heated under slight reflux for 5 min, it was cooled to room temperature. The salt was filtered off and washed with methanol (to give ca. 70 g of salt). The filtrate was evaporated, heated under reflux with methanol (200 mL), and evaporated again, and then ethyl acetate was added to give a solid. This solid was filtered off and washed with methanol to give another 7 g of salt. The filtrate was evaporated and dissociated (see below) to afford a residue (ca. 30 g) which consisted mostly of the decarboxylated acid, **38**. This was distilled to give 20.0 g of acid **38**, bp 180–184 °C (0.1 mm). From the other portion of crude **34** (ca. 69 g) there was obtained in the same way ca. 93.5 g of (–)-cinchonidine salt and 8.0 g of acid **38**: total yield ca. 170 g of the (–)-cinchonidine salt (0.277 mol, 63% based on the diester **32**); 28.0 g of acid **38** (0.101 mol, 23% based on the diester **32**).

Resolution of the (–)-Cinchonidine Salt of 34. A 77-g sample of (–)-cinchonidine salt (salt of the first portion described above) was dissolved by heating with 5 L of methanol. The solution was cooled overnight at about 0 °C, and the crystals were filtered and washed with methanol. This gave 41.9 g of salt, mp 172.5–173 °C. The filtrate was concentrated to about 1.5 L, heated until a clear solution was obtained, and cooled again at 0 °C for 3 days. This gave another 2.94 g of salt, mp 171.5–172 °C. The two portions of salt were combined and stirred with ca. 20% sulfuric acid and benzene until two clear layers were obtained. The two layers were separated, and the benzene layer was washed with ca. 20% sulfuric acid and with water, dried, and evaporated to give 26.6 g of (+)-**34** as a viscous oil: $[\alpha]_{578}$ +4.81°, $[\alpha]_{546}$ +5.43° (*c* 9.30, chloroform).

Both diacid enantiomers, obtained in this way, presumably contained some solvent and/or other impurities which could not be removed; hence the specific rotations will be somewhat too low. Anal. Calcd for $C_{33}H_{46}N_2O_5S_2$ [(–)-cinchonidine salt with (+)-**34**]: C, 64.46; H, 7.54; N, 4.56; S, 10.43. Found: C, 64.10, 64.14; H, 7.70, 7.62; N, 4.62, 4.55; S, 10.24, 10.25.

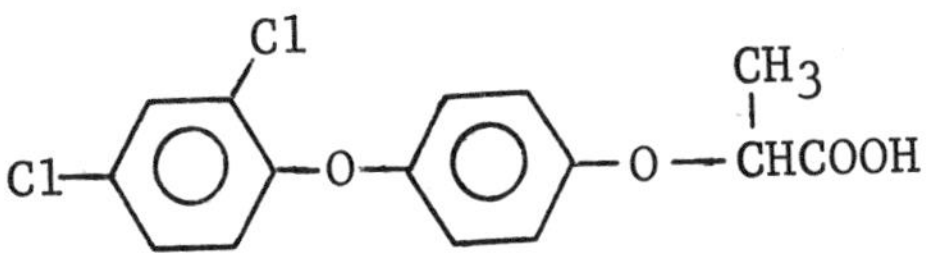

$C_{15}H_{12}Cl_2O_4$ Ref. 1498

L-(—)-2-[4-(2.4-Dichlorphenoxy)-phenoxy]-propionsäure **[(—)-2]**

98,1 g (0,3 mol) 2 werden zusammen mit 88,2 g (0,3 mol) (+)-Cinchonin in einer Mischung von 3000 ml Wasser und 2975 ml Acetonitril unter Erwärmen in Lösung gebracht. Das nach Erkalten isolierte Salz (88,5 g) wird 6× aus einem Wasser-Acetonitril-Gemisch (Volumenverhältnis 8:5) umkristallisiert. Aus den resultierenden 9,8 g Salz (ohne die für die Drehwertkontrollen abgenommenen Proben) werden durch Ansäuern mit 2 N Schwefelsäure, Aufnehmen in Chloroform und Abdampfen des Lösungsmittels 3,0 g **(—)-2** vom Schmp. 85–87 °C erhalten; $[\alpha]_D^{23}$ = —14,3° (0,61 M in $CHCl_3$).

D-(+)-2-[4-(2.4-Dichlorphenoxy)-phenoxy]-propionsäure **[(+)-2]**

Das bei der Herstellung von **(—)-2** (s.o.) nach Abtrennen des 1. Salzkristallisates (88,5 g) verbleibende Filtrat wird auf *ca.* die Hälfte seines Volumens eingeengt, mit Schwefelsäure angesäuert und 2× mit Chloroform extrahiert. Die vereinigten Chloroformauszüge liefern beim Eindampfen 58,3 g einer rechtsdrehenden Säure **(+)-2** mit $[\alpha]_D^{23}$ = + 10,4° (0,86 M in Chloroform) als langsam kristallisierendes Harz mit unscharfem Schmp. zwischen 80 und 100 °C.

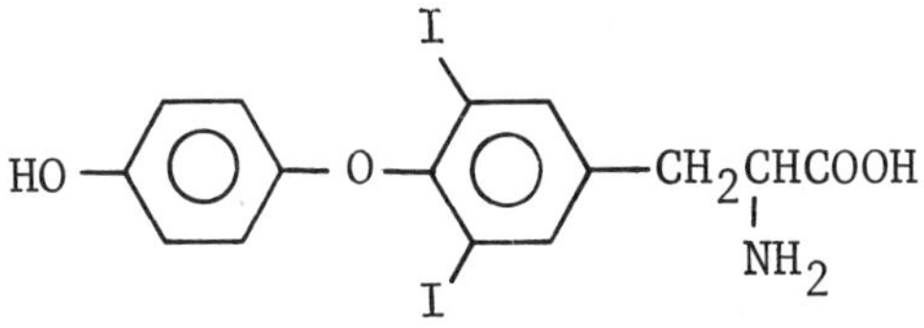

$C_{15}H_{13}I_2NO_4$ Ref. 1499

L(+)-N-Formyl-3.5-dijod-thyronin: **Das aus 350 g DL-3.5-Dijod-thyronin hergestellte rohe *DL-N-Formyl-3.5-dijod-thyronin* wird in 1500 ccm wasserfreiem Isopropylalkohol auf dem** Dampfbad erhitzt. Zu dieser Suspension gibt man eine siedend heiße Lösung von 300 g wasserfreiem *Brucin* in 1500 ccm wasserfreiem Isopropylalkohol. Bei längerem Sieden scheidet sich aus der vorübergehend klar gewordenen Lösung das *D(—)-N-Formyl-3.5-dijod-thyronin-Brucin-Salz* aus. Die Ausscheidung ist nach etwa 3 Stdn. beendet. Es wird noch heiß abgesaugt und mit Isopropylalkohol nachgewaschen. Ausb. 290 g.

Anschließend wird die Mutterlauge unter vermindertem Druck zur Trockne eingedampft. Der Rückstand wird in 1000 ccm 1 *n* Ammoniaklösung aufgenommen und durch dreimaliges Ausschütteln mit je 300 ccm Chloroform das Brucin entfernt. Nach Ansäuern der Ammoniaklösung mit Salzsäure auf pH 1—2 (unter Kühlung) scheidet sich das *L(+)-N-Formyl-3.5-dijod-thyronin* zunächst harzig aus, wird aber bald kristallin. Nach Absaugen, Waschen mit Wasser und Trocknen bleiben 146 g, Schmp. 186° (unkorr.). Aus Isopropylalkohol/Wasser umkristallisiert, zeigt es die spezif. Drehung $[\alpha]_D^{30}$: +43.8° (c = 5, in 95-proz. Äthanol).

L(+)-3.5-Dijod-thyronin: 74.3 g *N-Formyl-Derivat* werden mit 750 ccm einer Mischung von 48-proz. *Bromwasserstoffsäure* und Wasser im Verhältnis 1 : 2 2 Stdn. unter Rückfluß zum Sieden erhitzt. Es entsteht eine klare Lösung, aus der sich beim Abkühlen das bromwasserstoffsaure Salz des L(+)-3.5-Dijod-thyronins abscheidet. Es wird nach dem Absaugen in heißem Wasser suspendiert und mit gesätt. Natriumacetatlösung bis pH 6 versetzt. Das ausgeschiedene *L(+)-3.5-Dijod-thyronin* wird noch heiß abgesaugt und mit Wasser, Methanol und Aceton gewaschen. Ausb. 61.3 g, Schmp. 254° (unkorr.) (Zers.). $[\alpha]_D^{25}$: +25.2° (c = 5, in 1 *n* HCl/95-proz. Äthanol 1 : 2).

D(—)-N-Formyl-3.5-dijod-thyronin: Das bei der Gewinnung von L(+)-*N*-Formyl-3.5-dijod-thyronin (s. oben) anfallende *D(—)-N-Formyl-3.5-dijod-thyronin-Brucin-Salz* (290 g) wird aus einer Mischung von 1 *l* Dimethylformamid und 2.5 *l* Isopropylalkohol umkristallisiert, Schmp. 271°. Man trägt dieses Salz unter Rühren in 750 ccm schwach erwärmtes 2 *n* Ammoniak ein. Zur Entfernung des freigewordenen Brucins wird viermal mit je 200 ccm Methylenchlorid ausgeschüttelt. Die wäßr.-alkalische Lösung säuert man mit konz. Salzsäure bis pH 2 an. Das ausgeschiedene *D(—)-N-Formyl-3.5-dijod-thyronin* kristallisiert unter Kühlung bald durch. Ausb. 140 g (96.5% d. Th.), Schmp. 186°.

D(—)-3.5-Dijod-thyronin wird wie die L-Verbindung aus 100 g *D(—)-N-Formyl-3.5-dijod-thyronin* und 1 *l* einer Mischung von 48-proz. *Bromwasserstoffsäure* und Wasser im Verhältnis 1:2 dargestellt. Ausb. 80.5 g vom Schmp. 252° (Zers.). $[\alpha]_D^{21}$: —25.0° (c = 5, in 1 *n* HCl/95-proz. Äthanol 1:2).

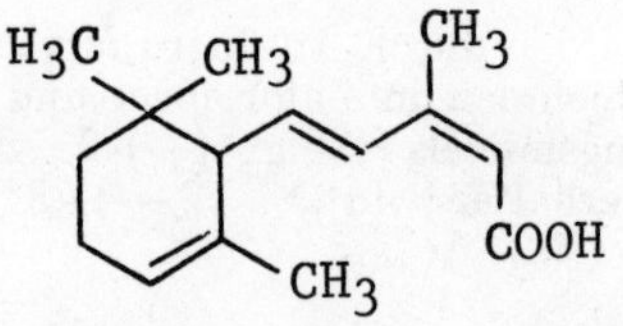

$C_{15}H_{22}O_2$ Ref. 1500

(±)-(2*E*,4*E*)-α-Ionylideneacetic acid (**IIIa**+**IIIb**) (4.3 g) was dissolved in 120 ml of methanol and 5.9 g of quinine was added to the hot solution. After cooling, a quinine salt was collected by filtration and recrystallized five times from methanol to give the optically pure salt of constant optical rotation, weighed 3.4 g, mp 191~193°C, $[\alpha]_D^{21}$ +78.6° (*c*=0.6, EtOH). The (+)-(*R*)-(2*E*)-acid (**IIIa**) regenerated from the salt was crystallized from acetonitrile to give silky needles, 1.4 g, mp 87~87.5°C, $[\alpha]_D^{21}$ +446.7° (*c*=0.8 EtOH). The IR ($CHCl_3$ solution) and PMR spectra were identical with those of racemic one. PMR $\delta_{Me_4Si}^{CDCl_3}$: 0.83 (3H, s), 0.91 (3H, s), 1.57 (3H, d, *J*=1.5 Hz), 2.28 (3H, d, *J*=1 Hz, 3*E*-CH_3).

The acid (1.5 g) regenerated from the soluble quinine salt showed $[\alpha]_D^{21}$ −150° in EtOH (*c*=1.0). But attempts to obtain pure (−)-acid salt with common chiral amines were all failed. Therefore the combined (−)-enriched acid (4.1 g) was dissolved in 150 ml of methanol and 5.7 g of quinine was added. The precipitated salt was filtered off after cooling, and the mother liquor was concentrated to about 35 ml in volume and after cooling a massy crystal was again filtered off. Regeneration from the filtrate gave the (−)-enriched acid, $[\alpha]_D^{21}$ −380° (*c*=1.0, EtOH). Recrystallization several times from acetonitrile afforded optically pure (−)-(*S*)-(2*E*)-acid (**IIIb**), 450 mg, mp 87~87.5°C. $[\alpha]_D^{21}$ −447.0° (*c*=1.0, EtOH) [(lit.[9]) mp 75~6°C, $[\alpha]_D^{18}$ −415° (*c*=1.0, EtOH)]. The IR and PMR spectra were identical with those of (+)-acid (**IIIa**).

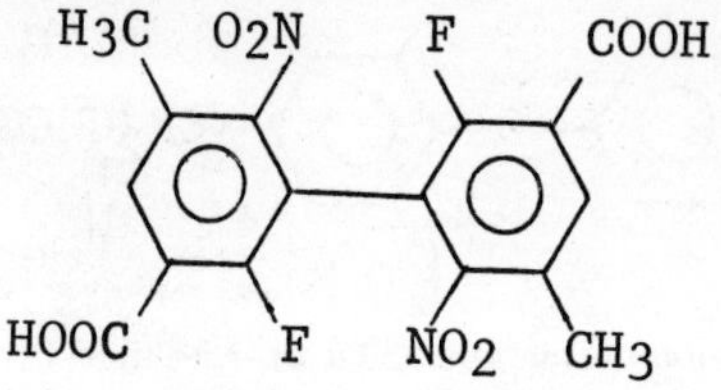

$C_{16}H_{10}F_2N_2O_8$ Ref. 1501

Resolution of 2,2′-Difluoro-3,3′-dicarboxy-5,5′-dimethyl-6,6′-dinitrodiphenyl (V.) Strychnine Salt.—To a solution of 2.1 g. of strychnine dissolved in 300 cc. of absolute methyl alcohol was added 1.23 g. of the acid (V). The solution was evaporated to 210 cc. and allowed to stand overnight in a desiccator. At the end of this time 1.5 g. of salt had crystallized.

The salt for purification was dissolved in 150 cc. of absolute methyl alcohol and allowed to stand overnight. At the end of this time the salt had crystallized out in small cubes. The melting point was 224–228° (corr.), with decomposition.

Rotation. 0.1000 g. made up to 10 cc. with pyridine at 20° gave α_D −0.75°, l = 1; $[\alpha]_D^{20}$ −75°. Further recrystallization brought no change in rotation.

Anal. Calcd. for $C_{16}H_{10}O_8F_2N_2{\cdot}2C_{21}H_{22}O_2N_2$: N, 7.89. Found: (micro Dumas) N. 7.83.

The mother liquor from the first crop of crystals was evaporated to 150 cc., when 0.35 g. of needle-like crystals came down. These were filtered off and the filtrate was evaporated to 80 cc. and allowed to stand overnight. At the end of this time 1 g. of needle-like crystals had separated. This last fraction was recrystallized from absolute methyl alcohol, m. p. 190–193° (corr.) with decomposition.

Rotation. 0.1000 g. made up to 10 cc. with pyridine at 20° gave α_D −0.50, l = 1; $[\alpha]_D^{20}$ −50.0°. Further recrystallization gave no change in rotation.

Anal. Calcd. for $C_{16}H_{10}O_8F_2N_2{\cdot}2C_{21}H_{22}O_2N_2$: N, 7.89. Found: (micro Dumas) N, 7.56.

As the nitrogen analysis will not distinguish the mono- and distrychnine salts, a portion of salt was decomposed quantitatively and acid and base isolated. The salt proved to be dibasic.

0.2230 g. of salt yielded 0.0830 g. of acid and 0.1350 g. of strychnine. For 0.0830 g. of acid, there is required 0.1400 g. of strychnine for a dibasic salt.

***l*-2,2′-Difluoro-3,3′-dicarboxy-5,5′-dimethyl-6,6′-dinitrodiphenyl.**—The less soluble salt was treated in the cold with 5% aqueous sodium hydroxide for about thirty minutes. At the end of this time the precipitated strychnine was filtered off. The acid was precipitated with dilute hydrochloric acid and purified from 50% alcohol, from which it crystallized in white needles. The melting point (tube) was 298–300° (corr.) with decomposition.

Rotations. 0.1000 g. made up to 10 cc. at 20° with methyl alcohol gave α_D −0.17°, l = 1; $[\alpha]_D^{20}$ −17.0°.

Further recrystallization did not change the rotation.

0.0750 g. made up to 10 cc. at 20° with pyridine gave α_D −0 18°, l = 1; $[\alpha]_D^{20}$ −24 0°.

0.1000 g. made up to 10 cc. at 25° with cyclohexanol gave α_D −0.12°, l = 1; $[\alpha]_D^{20}$ −12.0°.

0.1000 g. made up to 10 cc. at 20° with glacial acetic acid gave α_D −0.15°, l = 1;

$[\alpha]^{20}_{D}$ −15.0°.

0.1068 g. made up to 10 cc. at 20° with cyclohexanone gave α_D −0.154°, l = 1; $[\alpha]^{20}_{D}$ −14.4°.

0.1000 g. made up to 10 cc. at 20° with 0.1 N sodium hydroxide gave α_D −0.135°, l = 1; $[\alpha]^{20}_{D}$ −13.5°.

Anal. Calcd. for $C_{16}H_{10}O_8F_2N_2$: N, 7.07. Found: (micro Dumas) N, 7.17.

***d*-2,2′-Difluoro-3,3′-dicarboxy-5,5′-dimethyl-6,6′-dinitrodiphenyl.**—The *d*-acid was prepared in the same way as the *l*-isomer. After crystallization from 50% alcohol it melted at 297–301° (corr.) with decomposition.

Rotation. 0.1000 g. made up to 10 cc. at 20° with methyl alcohol gave α_D +0.15°, l = 1; $[\alpha]^{20}_{D}$ +15.0°.

Anal. Calcd. for $C_{16}H_{10}O_8F_2N_2$: N, 7.07. Found: (micro Dumas) N, 7.11.

Racemization Experiments.—Refluxing in 95% ethyl alcohol for five hours; in glacial acetic acid for seven hours; in cyclohexanone for three hours; in 0.1 N sodium hydroxide for three hours resulted in no appreciable change in rotation.

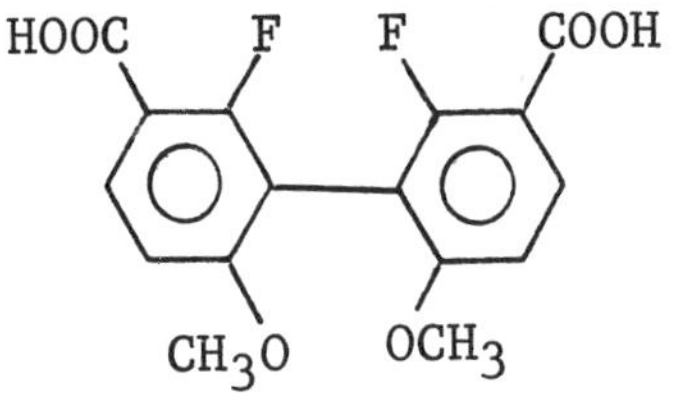

Ref. 1502

$C_{16}H_{12}F_2O_6$

Optical Resolution of 1. The racemic 1 (675 mg, 2 mmol) was dissolved in a hot mixture of ethanol (20 mL) and acetone (5 mL) and mixed with brucine dihydrate (861 mg, 2 mmol) to give a clear solution, which was left standing for 2 h. The salt obtained (1.4 g) was washed with ethanol and recrystallized four times from a mixture of pyridine and acetone (1:1 v/v). The salt obtained (190 mg) melted at 272–273 °C. Decomposition of the salt with HCl followed by recrystallization from methanol gave an optical active acid (50 mg), mp 276–277 °C. The active acid was methylated with diazomethane and the ester obtained was recrystallized from methanol to give colorless sand crystals: mp 157–158 °C; $[\alpha]^{17}_{D}$ +37.5°, $[\alpha]^{17}_{400}$ +104.2°, and $[\alpha]^{17}_{326}$ +172.9° (1.44% dioxane). The other data are given in Tables IV–VI.

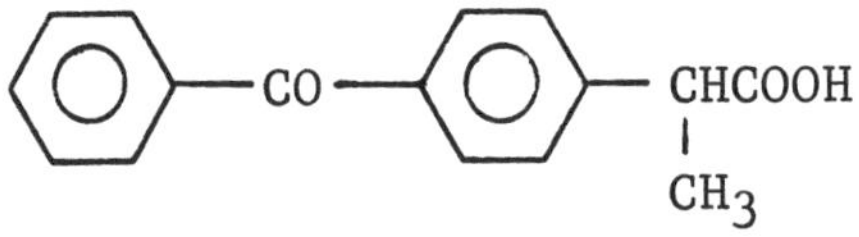

Ref. 1503

$C_{16}H_{14}O_3$

»Faster« diastereomer, (+)-α-phenylethylamide of α-(3-benzoylphenyl)-propionic acid (V). — Fractions 177—236 contained 533 mg of V, which crystallizes from ether—petroleum ether, mp. 93—95°. (We have previously reported (5) our failure to bring this diastereomer to crystallization). $[\alpha]^{22}_{D}$ +17.4° (c = 2.47 in $CHCl_3$). NMR ($CDCl_3$: 1.25, 1.40 and 1.54 (the three signals correspond to superimposed doublets from two CH_3-groups), 3.62 (q, 1H), 5.18 (p, 1H), 6.11 (m, NH), 7.28 (s, 5H), 7.3—8.0 (m, 9H).

»Slower« diastereomer, (+)-α-phenylethylamide of α-(3-benzoylphenyl)-propionic acid (VI). — Fractions 262—299 contained 566 mg of VI which, on crystallization from ether-cyclohexane, had mp. 116—118°. $[\alpha]^{23}_{D}$ —8.6° (c = 2.47 in $CHCl_3$). NMR ($CDCl_3$): 1.24, 1.35, 1.42 and 1.55 (two doublets of two CH_3-groups), 3.66 (q, H1), 5.18 (p, 1H), 6.11 (d, NH), 7.17 (s, 5H), 7.3—8.0 (m, 9H).

Anal. for $C_{24}H_{23}NO_2$ (357.46

Calc'd: C 80.63 H 6.49, N 3.92%

Found: C 80.71, H 6.65, N 4.07%.

(+)-α-(3-Benzoylphenyl)-propionic acid (+)-I. — To a solution of N_2O_4 in carbon tetrachloride (15 ml), dry sodium acetate (3 g) was added, the suspension was stirred and cooled to —15°, then a solution of VI (440 mg) in carbon tetrachloride (10 ml) was added dropwise. After 2 hrs. stirring at —10 to 0 °C the reaction mixture was poured on 50 g of crushed ice, after which 50 ml of 5% solution of sodium bicarbonate was added. This mixture was extracted with ether (3 × 50 ml), extracts were dried (Na_2SO_4), evaporated, and the residual oil dissolved in carbon tetrachloride (30 ml). The solution was heated under reflux for 20 hrs, at which point only one spot of pure I can be observed on a TL chromatogram (silicagel chloroform — methanol — conc. ammonia 7 : 3 : 0.3, Rf 0.75). After the evaporation of solvent the residual oil was purified on a column (10 g silicagel, chloroform — methanol 7 : 3 as the eluant). Fractions 27—16 (5 ml per fraction) contained 222 mg of pure (+)-I. After crystallization from ether — cyclohexane it had $[\alpha]^{23}_{D}$ +57.1° (c = 0.76, in CH_2Cl_2).

(—)-α-(3-Benzoylphenyl)-propionic Acid (—)-I. — This enantiomer was obtained from VII (450 mg) using the same procedure as described for (+)-I. Yield 230 mg, $[\alpha]^{23}_D$ —57.4° (c = 0.88 in CH_2Cl_2).

IR spectra (in KBr) of both enantiomers were superimposable with those of the racemic mixture.

(+)-α-Phenylethylamides of (±)-α-(3-Benzoylphenyl)-propionic acid. — (+)-α-Phenylethylamine (621 mg, 5.0 mmol) and (±)-α-(3-benzoylmethyl)-propionic acid (1.27 g, 5.0 mmol) were dissolved in methylene chloride (10 ml), and to this solution dicyclohexylcarbodiimide (DCC, 1.08 g, 5.25 mmol) dissolved in 5 ml of methylene chloride, were added dropwise. After standing overnight in a refrigerator, the precipitate was removed by filtration (dicyclohexylurea, 615 mg, 54.5%), the solvent was evaporated and the residual oil was purified by column chromatography (90 g silicagel, methylene chloride — ther — light petroleum 2 : 2 : 6 as the eluent).

N,N'-Dicyclohexyl-N-α-(3'-benzoylphenyl)-propionyl-urea (IV). — Fractions 121—146 (10 ml per fraction) contained 720 mg of IV, which after crystallization from ether, had a mp. 142—144°. NMR ($CDCl_3$): 0.9—2.2 (m, 23H), 3.4—4.2 (broad signal, 2H), 4.06 (q, 1H), 6.4 (broad s, NH), 7.3—8.0 (m, 9H).

Anal. for $C_{29}H_{36}N_2O_3$ (460.623)

Calc'd: C 75.62, H 7.88, N 6.08%

Found: C 75.84, H 7.94, N 5.78%.

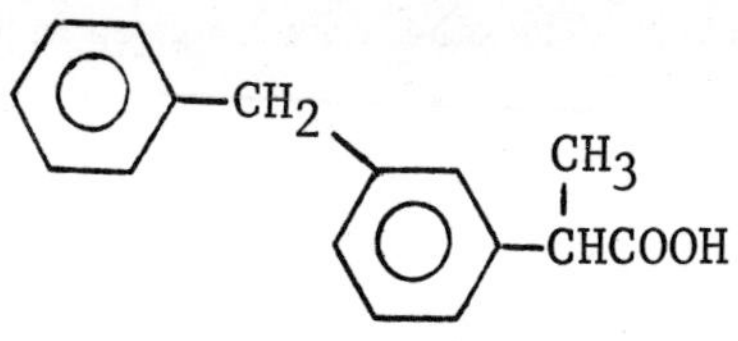

$C_{16}H_{16}O_2$

Ref. 1504

RESOLUTION OF (+)-**6** WITH (−)-α-PHENYLETHYLAMINE

Compound **6** (14.4 g, 60 mmol) was dissolved in dry benzene (360 ml) and 7.66 g (60 mmol) of (−)-PEA was added. The solution was set aside for 4 h at room temperature for crystallization. 10 g of the salt were obtained: $[\alpha]_D=-7.15°$ (*c*=2.59 in 96% EtOH). On evaporation of the mother liquors, 11.6 g of the diastereomeric salt were obtained: $[\alpha]_D=-1.20°$ (*c*=2.49 in 96% EtOH). The first was recrystallized three times from benzene to afford 7.8 g of material with $[\alpha]_D=-8.89°$ from which the free acid (−)-**6** was obtained: m.p. 58-9 °C, $[\alpha]_D=-51.83°$ (*c*=1.69, CH_2Cl_2) (lit. [25]: $[\alpha]_D=50\pm1°$). The second diastereomeric salt was crystallized twice to $[\alpha]_D=-0.53°$. From it the free acid (+)-**6** was obtained in impure form, $[\alpha]_D=+20.8°$. After three recrystallizations, $[\alpha]_D$ rose to +40.3° (*c*=1.64 in CH_2Cl_2).

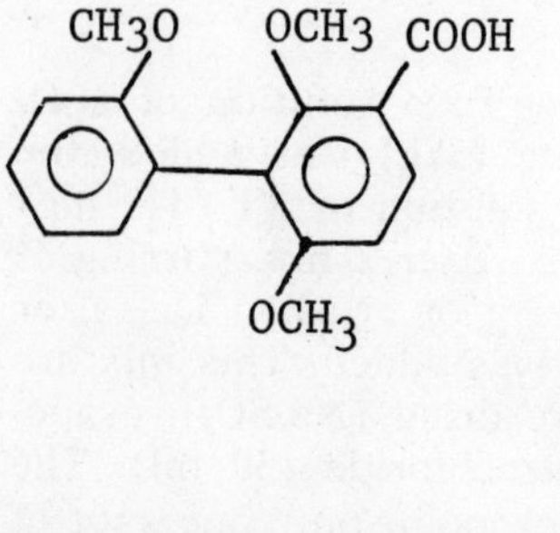

$C_{16}H_{16}O_5$

Ref. 1505

(-)-2,2',6-Trimethoxy-3-carboxybiphenyl. Racemic acid (424 mg) and brucine dihydrate (630 mg) were dissolved in acetone (8 mL) and left to stand overnight. The brucine salt (550 mg) produced was recrystallized two times from acetone to give 400 mg of salt, mp 117–120 °C, which was dissolved in water (15 mL) and acidified with HCl. White precipitates (155 mg) were recrystallized from a mixture of benzene and hexane (1:1 v/v) to give colorless minute crystals (120 mg): mp 151–153 °C; $[\alpha]^{15}_D$ −12.3° and $[\alpha]^{15}_{400}$ −58.5° (1.3%, $CHCl_3$).

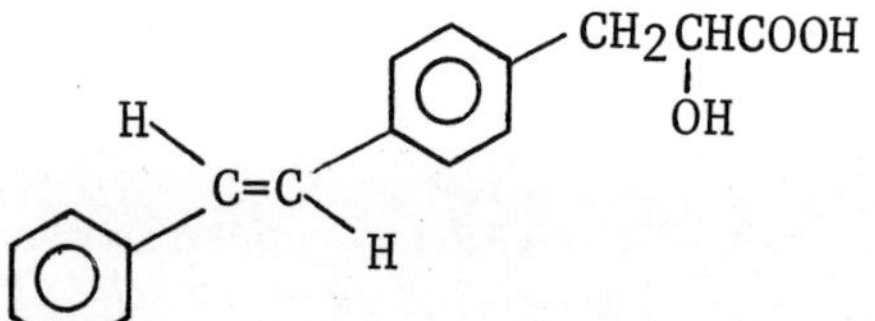

$C_{17}H_{16}O_3$

Ref. 1506

Brucine salt of I was obtained by keeping a soln. of 0.025 mole I and 0.025 mole brucine in 300 ml. 1:1 dioxane–H_2O at room temp. The first fraction obtained m. 116–17°, $[\alpha]^{20}_D$ −23° ($CHCl_3$), and the 2nd fraction m. 120–2°, $[\alpha]^{20}_D$ −36° ($CHCl_3$). An aq. suspension of the brucine salt was mixed with 10% aq. KOH, vigorously stirred brucine removed, the filtrate extd. with $CHCl_3$, and acidified with HCl to give (−)-I, m. 172–3°, $[\alpha]^{20}_D$ −21° (dioxane); Me ester and hydrazide m. 83–5° and 189–99°, and $[\alpha]^{20}_D$ −14° and −18° (dioxane), resp. Brucine salt of (+)-I was obtained from the liquor which remained after crystn. of brucine salt of (−)-I. After partial evapn. and cooling a product m. 128–30°, $[\alpha]^{20}_D$ −18°, was obtained. Fractional crystn. from 1:1 Me_2CO–H_2O gave a product, m. 132–4°, $[\alpha]^{20}_D$ 28° (EtOH). The brucine salt of (+)-I was decompd. in aq. KOH to give (+)-I, m. 172–3°, $[\alpha]^{20}_D$ 20.5° (dioxane).

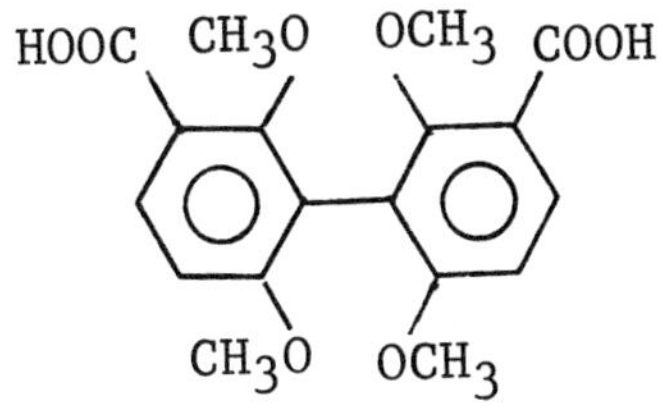

$C_{18}H_{18}O_8$ Ref. 1507

(-)-2,2′,6,6′-Tetramethoxy-3,3′-dicarboxybiphenyl. Racemic acid **3** (724 mg, 2 mmol) and brucine dihydrate (1.77 g, 4.1 mmol) were dissolved in hot ethanol (7 mL) and left to stand overnight. Brucine salt obtained (650 mg) was recrystallized three times from ethanol to afford colorless sand crystals (300 mg), mp 203–204 °C dec, which were decomposed with 10% hydrochloric acid and recrystallized from ethyl acetate to give optically active acid (100 mg): mp 183–184 °C; $[\alpha]^{22}_D$ -18.5° and $[\alpha]^{22}_{400}$ -31.5° (5%, $CHCl_3$).

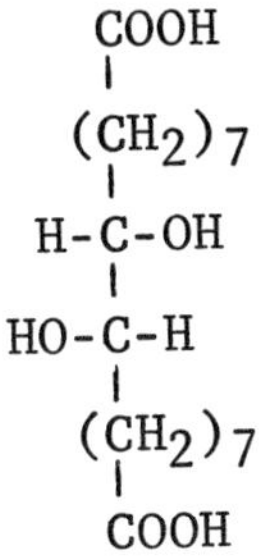

$C_{18}H_{34}O_6$ Ref. 1508

Brucine Salt (1:1) of Optically Active 9,10-Dihydroxyoctadecanedioic Acid (I).—A solution of 1.1 g. of brucine (0.0030 mole) and 0.5 g. (0.0015 mole) of 9,10-dihydroxyoctadecanedioic acid, m.p. 121–122°, in 50 ml. of absolute ethanol was boiled for one hour. Alcohol was removed by distillation until the volume was 15 ml., and the concentrated solution was held at 0° for three days. The small white cubic crystals were collected, washed on the funnel with a small volume of cold ethanol and air-dried. The salt weighed 1.15 g. and melted at 115–117°. Repeated crystallizations from ethanol–water as well as from ethanol did not change the melting point and did not give any sign of separation into two compounds. The following procedure did effect separation.

A mixture of 3.6 g. of the brucine salt, m.p. 115–117°, and 10 ml. of absolute ethanol was allowed to stand at room temperature for two days. The mixture was filtered, and the undissolved solids were treated in the same way with a fresh 10-ml. portion of absolute ethanol. After a total of eight successive exposures of the brucine salt to ethanol, 1.3 g. remained undissolved. Crystallization of this solid (m.p. 118–119°) from 8 ml. of ethanol afforded 0.92 g. of a white product, which was dried in vacuum at 78°.

Anal. Calcd. for $C_{41}H_{60}O_{10}N_2$: C, 66.5; H, 8.2. Found: C, 66.6; H, 8.4.

The rotation of the salt before the alcohol leaching was $[\alpha]^{26}D$ −68° (0.108 g. in 10 ml. of alcohol solution), and after the leaching was $[\alpha]^{26}D$ −65° (0.103 g. in 10 ml. of alcohol solution).

Optically Active 9,10-Dihydroxyoctadecanedioic Acid.—A mixture of 0.41 g. of brucine salt ($[\alpha]^{26}D$ −65°) with 50 ml. of water and 1 ml. of concentrated hydrochloric acid was allowed to stand at room temperature. After addition of another 1 ml. of hydrochloric acid, the mixture was extracted with ether. The ether extract was washed with water until the washings were at *p*H 5, and the ether was dried over calcium chloride. Removal of drying agent and of solvent left 0.17 g. (88%) of 9,10-dihydroxyoctadecanedioic acid, m.p. 122–123°. Crystallization from ethyl acetate gave 0.15 g. of the acid with the same melting point, and with $[\alpha]^{26}D$ 4.6 ± 0.4° (standard deviation) (0.112 g. in 5 ml. of ethanol).

Anal. Calcd. for $C_{18}H_{34}O_6$: C, 62.4; H, 9.9; N, 0.0. Found: C, 62.7; H, 10.0; N, 0.0.

Note: The following other constants have been reported for this compound:

Melting point 134-135°, J. F. McGhie, W.A. Ross, J.W. Spence and F.J. James, Chem. Inc., 536 (1972).

Melting point 135-136°, $[\alpha]_D^{22.5}$ = +12.20° and -18.71° for the sodium salt in water, R. Alvarez-Vázques and I. Marqués-Ribas, Anales de la Real Soc. Esp. de Fisica y Quimica 64B, 783 (1968).

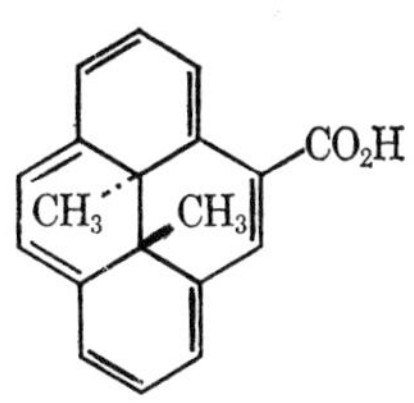

18

$C_{19}H_{16}O_2$ Ref. 1509

Optical Resolution of 4-Carboxy-*trans*-15,16-dimethyldihydropyrene (18). To a solution of 200 mg of **18** in 20 ml of hot acetone there was added 216 mg of cinchonidine in a minimum of acetone for solution. The hot solution was filtered and allowed to stand in the cold. After 24 hr, 73 mg of green crystals, mp 194–196°, had separated and were collected. These were recrystallized several times from an acetone–hexane mixture to give 40 mg of green crystals, mp 198–200°, corresponding to the cinchonidine salt of one enantiomorph of **18**.

Anal. Calcd for $C_{38}H_{38}N_2O_3$: C, 79.97; H, 6.71. Found: C, 79.79; H, 6.89.

A solution of 40 mg of the cinchonidine salt of **18**, as described above, was dissolved in 50 ml of ether and shaken with aqueous dilute hydrochloric acid. The ether layer was separated, dried, and concentrated to give nice green crystals. These, after recrystallization from a benzene–hexane mixture, gave 16 mg of green-black crystals, mp 197–198°, corresponding to the levorotatory enantiomorph of **18**. The spectral properties of these crystals were identical with those described for racemic **18**. The optical rotatory dispersion curve was taken with a solution containing 1.150 mg of the above sample in 5 ml of ethanol. The specific rotations of the peaks and troughs at the various wavelengths were 660 mμ (+438°), 651 (0°), 637.5 (−244°), 550 (−128°), 505 (348°), 480 (0°), 393 (+230°), 388 (0°), 365 (−4132°), 346 (0°), 277 (−113°), 275 (0°), 261 (+2969°), 240 (0°), 225 (−8874°), 210 (−7586°), and 200 (0°).

To isolate the dextrorotatory enantiomorph the mother liquor from the cinchonidine salt recrystallization was concentrated causing the separation of an additional 20 mg of crystals which were collected. The mother liquor was then concentrated to dryness, and the crystalline residue was recrystallized from a hexane–acetone mixture to separate 60 mg of crystals, mp 184–188°. The mother liquor from this crystallization was concentrated; the residue was dissolved in ether and treated with dilute aqueous hydrochloric acid, as before, to recover the free acid. This gave 110 mg of green crystals, mp 180–184°. Fractional crystallization of these from a petroleum ether–benzene mixture gave 60 mg of dark green crystals, mp 195–197°. Solution spectra of these crystals were the same as those described for racemic **18**. That these crystals were the dextrorotatory enantiomorph of **18** containing a small impurity of the levorotatory isomer was demonstrated by its optical rotatory dispersion curve taken on a solution of 1.13 mg of these crystals in 5 ml of ethanol. The specific rotations of the peaks and troughs at the various wavelengths were 660 mμ (−305°), 651 (0°), 637 (+243°), 550 (+120°), 503 (+340°), 480 (0°), 393 (−182°), 387 (0°), 365 (+3000°), 348 (0°), 278 (+222°), 275 (0°), 261 (−2120°), 240 (0°), 227 (+7150°), 213 (+6450°), and 200 (0°).

$C_{20}H_{22}N_2O_4$

$C_{20}H_{22}N_2O_5$

$C_{20}H_{22}N_2O_4$

$$\text{HOOCCH}\overset{\displaystyle H_5C_2}{\underset{}{|}}\!-\!\bigcirc\!-\!N=N\!-\!\bigcirc\!-\!\overset{}{\underset{\displaystyle C_2H_5}{|}}\text{CHCOOH}$$

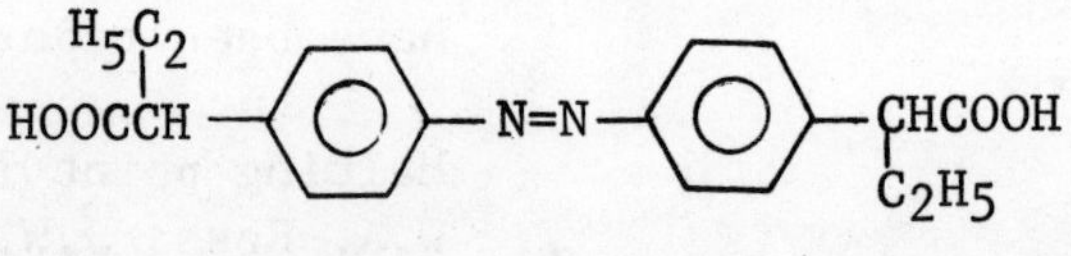

Ref. 1510

Resolution of *dl-α-p*-Azophenylbutyric Acid (XIII).—Salts of the low melting azo acid were made with brucine, strychnine, quinine, cinchonine, cinchonidine, nicotine, morphine and *d-α*-phenylethylamine and these salts were crystallized from various solvents. The most satisfactory resolution was obtained when the strychnine salt was fractionally crystallized from a mixture of methyl alcohol and ethyl acetate.

To 3 g. of the low-melting azo acid dissolved in 200 cc. of dry ethyl acetate was added a solution of 5.68 g. of strychnine in a mixture of 300 cc. of absolute methyl alcohol and 300 cc. of dry ethyl acetate. The mixture was boiled to get a clear solution. No material separated on cooling. The solution was concentrated to about 70–80 cc. On cooling and filtering 1.8 g. of crystals was obtained. This material was found to contain some strychnine.

The mother liquors from the first crop of crystals were concentrated to about 15–20 cc. On cooling a viscous, reddish liquid was obtained. This viscous material was heated with 50 cc. of dry ethyl acetate. The material gradually crystallized, giving 5 g. of fine orange crystals. The product was dried at 80–90°. It softened at 190° and melted at 195–197°. *Rotation.* 0.2 g. subs., in 25 cc. of pyridine; α, $-1.506°$; t, 25°; l, 2 dcm.; $[\alpha]_D^{25}$ $-94.12°$.

This salt was recrystallized from dry ethyl acetate three or four times. The least soluble portions were separated at one end of the series and the more soluble at the other end of the series.

The least soluble fraction melted at 197–199°. *Rotation.* 0.215 g. subs., in 25 cc. of pyridine; α, $-1.37°$; t, 25°; l, 2 dcm.; $[\alpha]_D^{25}$ $-79.6°$.

Anal.[12] Calcd. for $C_{62}H_{66}N_6O_8$: N, 8.21. Found: N, 8.21.

The more soluble material was isolated by evaporating the mother liquors and washing the sticky red material with petroleum ether (b. p. 30–60°). After drying at 70–80°, this material softened at 115° and melted at 130–136°. It was dissolved in dry ethyl acetate and on slow evaporation of the solution a small amount of crystalline material which softened at 130° and melted at 140–146° was obtained. *Rotation.* 0.215 g. subs., in 25 cc. of pyridine; α, $-1.63°$; t, 25°; l, 2 dcm.; $[\alpha]_D^{25}$ $-94.7°$.

Anal.[12] Calcd. for $C_{62}H_{66}N_6O_8$: N, 8.21. Found: N, 8.16.

The active azo acid was prepared from each salt by dissolving it in a mixture of equal parts of pyridine and water and then acidifying the solution with hydrochloric acid at 0°. The free acids were recrystallized from dilute alcohol.

The acid from the least soluble salt melted at 195–196° with some decomposition. *Rotation.* 0.1760 g. subs., in 25 cc. of absolute alcohol; α, $+0.741°$; t, 25°; l, 2 dcm.; $[\alpha]_D^{25}$ $+52.6°$. From a slightly less pure salt a dextro acid with a rotation of $+50.5°$ was obtained.

Anal.[11] Calcd. for $C_{20}H_{22}N_2O_4$: N, 7.93. Found: N, 7.92.

The acid from the more soluble salt melted at 194–196° with some decomposition. *Rotation.* 0.2320 g. subs., in 25 cc. of absolute alcohol; α, $-0.784°$; t, 25°; l, 2 dcm.; $[\alpha]_D^{25}$ $-42.2°$.

Anal.[11] Calcd. for $C_{20}H_{22}N_2O_4$: N, 7.93. Found: N, 7.89.

(11) This analysis was made by Mr. K. Eder.
(12) This analysis was made by Mr. J. M. Fulton.

$$\text{HOOCCH}\overset{\displaystyle H_5C_2}{\underset{}{|}}\!-\!\bigcirc\!-\!\underset{\displaystyle \downarrow O}{N\!=\!N}\!-\!\bigcirc\!-\!\overset{\displaystyle C_2H_5}{\underset{}{|}}\text{CHCOOH}$$

$$\text{HOOCCH}\overset{\displaystyle H_5C_2}{\underset{}{|}}\!-\!\bigcirc\!-\!\underset{\displaystyle \downarrow O}{N\!=\!N}\!-\!\bigcirc\!-\!\text{CHCOOH}\underset{\displaystyle C_2H_5}{\underset{}{|}}$$

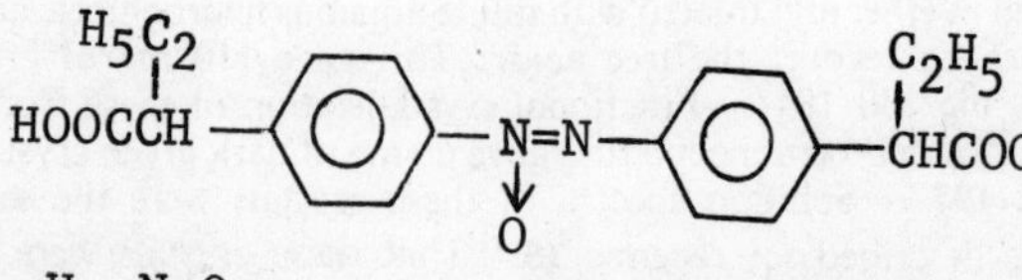

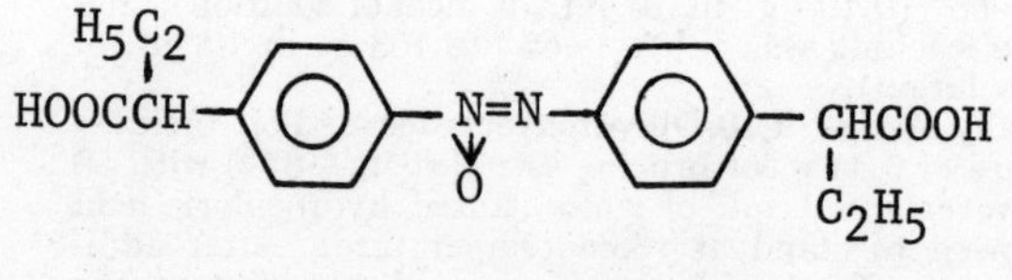

$C_{20}H_{22}N_2O_5$

Ref. 1511

Resolution of *α-p*-Azoxyphenylbutyric Acid (XV) Prepared from the Meso Azo Acid.—The resolution of the azoxy acid was not satisfactorily accomplished by use of strychnine, brucine, quinine or cinchonine using as solvents, ethyl alcohol, methyl alcohol, acetone, ethyl acetate and chloroform. *d-α*-Phenylethylamine gave a neutral salt which separated into two fractions when ethyl acetate was used as a solvent.

To a solution of 4 g. of the high melting azoxy acid (m. p. 199–201°) in 2 liters of dry ethyl acetate was added a solution of 2.6 g. of *d-α*-phenylethylamine in 700 cc. of the same solvent. Crystals separated at once. The solution was heated to boiling until these redissolved. This solution was allowed to stand overnight and the first fraction

of crystals was collected on a suction filter. The yield was 4.8 g. of a product which sintered at 196° and melted at 205–208°. This material was recrystallized from 2400 cc. of ethyl acetate and then twice more from a mixture of 400–500 cc. of chloroform and 20–40 cc. of methyl alcohol. This gave 1.5 g. of a product which sintered at 205° and melted at 207–210°. Further crystallization did not change the melting point or the optical rotation. *Rotation.* 0.313 g. subs., in 25 cc. of absolute methyl alcohol; α, +0.21°; t, 25°; l, 2 dcm.; $[\alpha]^{25}_{D}$, +8.3°.

Anal.[12] Calcd. for $C_{36}H_{44}N_4O_5$: N, 9.15. Found: N, 9.27.

The filtrate from the first fraction was concentrated to 500 cc. and allowed to stand overnight. A second fraction of salt weighing 1.2 g. was obtained. This fraction was recrystallized from ethyl acetate until it had a constant melting point and rotation; m. p. 192–196°. *Rotation.* 0.1800 g. subs., in 25 cc. of methyl alcohol; α, +0.15°; t, 25°; l, 2 dcm.; $[\alpha]^{25}_{D}$, +9.7°.

Anal.[12] Calcd. for $C_{36}H_{44}N_4O_5$: N, 9.15. Found: N, 9.16.

The filtrate from the second fraction was evaporated to dryness and another 0.5 g. of less pure salt with a rotation of +9.1° was obtained.

The free *l*-azoxy acid was obtained by treating a solution of 1.6 g. of the less soluble salt in 180 cc. of methyl alcohol at 0° with ice-cold concentrated hydrochloric acid and diluting with 250 cc. of water. The acid was collected on a suction filter and recrystallized from 30% methyl alcohol. The product thus obtained weighed 0.92 g.; m. p. 206–208°. *Rotation.* 0.4420 g. subs., in 25 cc. of absolute methyl alcohol; α, −0.47°; t, 25°; l, 2 dcm.; $[\alpha]^{25}_{D}$ −13.3°.

Anal.[12] Calcd. for $C_{20}H_{22}N_2O_5$: N, 7.57. Found: N, 7.75.

In the same manner 0.8 g. of the more soluble salt gave 0.45 g. of *d*-azoxy acid; m. p. 206–208°; rotation, 0.4040 g. subs., in 25 cc. of methyl alcohol; α, +0.478°; t, 25°; l, 2 dcm.; $[\alpha]^{25}_{D}$ +14.7°.

Anal.[12] Calcd. for $C_{20}H_{22}N_2O_5$: N, 7.57. Found: N, 7.58.

The last fraction of the salt obtained above gave a sample of azoxy acid which melted at 195–199° and had a rotation of +11°.

Resolution of the Low Melting *dl*-α-*p*-Azoxyphenylbutyric Acid (XIV).—The resolution of the low melting (178–182°) azoxy acid was accomplished in essentially the same manner. The salt was prepared from 1.5 g. of the azoxy acid and 0.98 g. of *d*-α-phenylethylamine in 2 liters of ethyl acetate. The first fraction which separated weighed 1.1 g. and after recrystallization to constant melting point and rotation gave 0.42 g. of a product; m. p. 204–206°. *Rotation.* 0.3510 g. subs., in 25 cc. of methyl alcohol; α, +0.22°; t, 25°; l, 2 dcm.; $[\alpha]^{25}_{D}$ +7.8°.

Anal.[12] Calcd. for $C_{36}H_{44}O_5$: N, 9.15. Found: N, 9.16.

Evaporation of the original mother liquor to 450 cc., cooling and filtering gave 0.75 g. of product; m. p. 200–203°. After crystallization to constant melting point, the yield was 0.41 g.; m. p. 201–203°. *Rotation.* 0.3180 g. subs., in 25 cc. of methyl alcohol; α, +0.14°; t, 25°; l, 2 dcm.; $[\alpha]^{25}_{D}$ +5.5°.

Anal.[12] Calcd. for $C_{36}H_{44}N_4O_5$: N, 9.15. Found: N, 9.15.

Another less pure fraction with a rotation of +5.1° was obtained from the further concentration of the mother liquors.

The *l*-azoxy acid was obtained by the procedure described before; 0.38 g. of the less soluble salt yielded 0.21 g. of acid; m. p. 182–183°. *Rotation.* 0.2000 g. subs., in 25 cc. of methyl alcohol; α, −0.061°; t, 25°; l, 2 dcm.: $[\alpha]^{25}_{D}$ −3.8°.

Anal.[12] Calcd. for $C_{20}H_{22}N_2O_5$: N, 7.57. Found: N, 7.72.

In the same manner 0.38 g. of the more soluble salt yielded 0.2 g. of product; m. p. 182–184°. *Rotation.* 0.2000 g. subs., in 25 cc. of methyl alcohol; α, +0.06°; t, 25°; l, 2 dcm.; $[\alpha]^{25}_{D}$ +3.7°.

Anal.[12] Calcd. for $C_{20}H_{22}N_2O_5$: N, 7.57. Found: N, 7.72.

---

(17) Angeli, *Atti Accad. Lincei*, [5] **19**, i, 793 (1910); **20**, i, 896 (1911).

```
                  NHCO2CH2C6H5
                  |
(CH3)3CO2C-CH-CH2CHCOOH
           |
           CO2C(CH3)3
```

$C_{22}H_{31}NO_8$

Ref. 1512

*Quinine salt of γ,γ'-di-*t*-butyl* D(−)-N*-benzyloxycarbonyl-γ-carboxyglutamate.* 2.66 g (6.08 mmol) of DL-Z · Gla(O*t*Bu)$_2$ · OH (**1**) and 1.97 g (6.08 mmol) of quinine (m.p. 175°; $[\alpha]^{20}_{546} = -154 \pm 3°$, $c = 1.5$, $CHCl_3$) were dissolved in 50 ml of hot ethyl acetate and kept at RT. for 12 h. Crystallization was completed by cooling to 4° for 15 h. The colourless needles were gathered by filtration and washed with ice-cold ethyl acetate: 1.82 g (2.4 mmol, 40% of the theoretical yield), m.p. 132–133°; $[\alpha]^{20}_{D} = -76.8°$ and $[\alpha]^{20}_{546} = -94.1°$ (both $c = 1$, $CHCl_3$).

The filtrate and washings were evaporated to dryness, the residue dissolved in CCl_4 and treated with pentane. Another 204 mg of the salt (4.4% yield) were obtained.

*γ,γ'-Di-*t*-butyl* D(−)-N*-benzyloxycarbonyl-γ-carboxyglutamate* (**1a**). The quinine was removed according to the general procedure. The viscous residue was crystallized from CCl_4/pentane in the form of dense aggregates of needles. 1.63 g (2.1 mmol) of the quinine salt yielded 781 mg (1.79 mmol, 83%) **1a;** m.p. 86–88°; Rf 0.68 CM, 0.37 CME. - NMR.: 10.05 (*broad signal,* 1H); 7.4 (*s,* 5H); 5.6–5.3 (*broad signal,* 1H); 5.15 (*s,* 2H); 4.7–4.3 (*m,* 1H); 3.35 (*t,* 1H); 2.6–2.2 (*many signals,* 2H); 1.45 (2*s,* 18H).

$C_{22}H_{31}NO_8$ (437.5) Calc. C 60.40 H 7.14 N 3.20% Found C 60.32 H 7.19 N 3.28%

*γ,γ'-Di-*t*-butyl* L(+)-N*-benzyloxycarbonyl-γ-carboxyglutamate* (**1b**). The filtrate and washings of the crystalline quinine salt were evaporated to dryness. The quinine was removed from the residue according to the general procedure. Attempts to further resolve the mixture of L- and DL-acids *via* the quinidine salts were only partly successful, because the L-Z · Gla(O*t*Bu)$_2$ · OH salt was only obtained as a gel (m.p. 83–93°, $[\alpha]^{20}_{D} = +100 \pm 0.5°$ and $[\alpha]^{20}_{546} = 123 \pm 0.5°$, both $c = 1$, $CHCl_3$).

Therefore the acid mixture was simply recrystallized. The L-isomer appeared from CCl_4/pentane mixtures at 4° as dense aggregates of needles and from diisopropyl ether/pentane at 4° usually as colourless needles, m.p. 87–89°, in seldom cases as hard, thick crystals. The TLC. and NMR. results were identical with those of the D-isomer, **1a.** The (−)-ephedrine salt of **1b** (below) yielded an identical product in 62% over-all yield from **1.**

$C_{22}H_{31}NO_8$ (437.5) Calc. C 60.40 H 7.14 N 3.20% Found C 60.23 H 7.11 N 3.13%

The cyclohexylamine salt was obtained as colourless needles from ethyl acetate, m.p. 122–126°, $[\alpha]^{20}_{D} = +11.7°$, $[\alpha]^{20}_{546} = +14.7°$ (both $c = 1.1$, $CHCl_3$).

*(−)-Ephedrine salt of γ,γ'-di-*t*-butyl* L(+)-N*-benzyloxycarbonyl-γ-carboxyglutamate.* 437 mg (6.08 mmol) **1** were dissolved in 0.3 ml ethyl acetate and combined with a solution of 83 mg (0.5 mmol) (−)-ephedrine in 0.2 ml ethyl acetate. The clear mixture was diluted with much pentane and kept at 4° for 2 days. The solid precipitate was recrystallized from ethyl acetate/pentane: 173 mg (58%) large, colourless needles, m.p. 122–124°. $[\alpha]^{20}_{546} = -7.7°$, $[\alpha]^{20}_{D} = -6.7°$ (both $c = 1.2$, $CHCl_3$); $[\alpha]^{20}_{546} = -17.7°$, $[\alpha]^{20}_{D} = -14.5°$ (both $C = 1.0$, MeOH).

$C_{32}H_{46}N_2O_9$ (602.7) Calc. C 63.77 H 7.69 N 4.65 C 62.03 H 7.73 N 4.52%
with 2.73% EtOAc Found C 62.03 H 7.71 N 4.60%

The product was decomposed to **1b** with Amberlyst 15, yield 85%. Treatment of the mother liquors with (−)-ephedrine resulted in another 13% of pure salt, or 11% of **1b.** Total yield of **1b** from **1** = 62%.

*γ,γ'-Di-*t*-butyl* D(−)*-γ-carboxyglutamate,* **2a.** 219 mg (0.5 mmol) **1a** were catalytically hydrogenated according to [8] in order to remove the benzyloxycarbonyl group. The crude solid product was washed with diethyl ether, yield 144 mg (0.48 mmol or 95%). It was pure without recrystallization from water, m.p. 165.5–167.5 (dec.); Rf 0.46 BEWl.

$C_{14}H_{25}NO_6$ (303.36) Calc. C 55.43 H 8.31 N 4.62% Found C 55.42 H 8.43 N 4.76%

*γ,γ'-Di-*t*-butyl* L(+)*-γ-carboxyglutamate,* **2b.** This isomer was prepared in exactly the same manner as its antipode, **2a.** Yield 96% (precipitated from methanol with diethyl ether), pure solid, m.p. 166–167° (dec.). Crystallization from water with a small amount of methanol resulted in colourless needles, yield 70%; m.p. 170–171° (dec.).

$C_{14}H_{25}NO_6$ (303.36) Calc. C 55.43 H 8.31 N 4.62% Found C 55.23 H 8.30 N 4.55%

D(−) *γ-Carboxyglutamic acid monoammonium salt* (**3a**). 94 mg (0.31 mmol) of D-H · Gla(O*t*Bu)$_2$ · OH (**2a**) were dissolved in 1 ml of cold, concentrated hydrochloric acid and kept at 0° for 15 min. The solution was evaporated at 0.001 Torr over P_2O_5 and KOH. The hygroscopic residue was quickly dissolved in 1 ml of glacial acetic acid, treated with a slight excess of ammonium acetate (35 mg = 0.42 mmol), and lyophilized. The residue was repeatedly triturated with ethanol: yield 53 mg (0.25 mmol, 82%) colourless solid; m.p. 157–159° (decomposition with evolution of CO_2). At pH 6.4 and 40 V/cm, the compound migrates about 50 mm towards the anode in 50 min. This corresponds to about 1.4 times the distance travelled by aspartic acid under the same conditions. The electrophoretic and TLC. aspects are those of a pure compound, Rf 0.23 I. - ^{1}H-NMR. confirmed the expected structure and the analytical purity (see *Fig. 1).*

$C_6H_{12}N_2O_6$ (208.1) Calc. C 34.62 H 5.81 N 13.46% Found C 34.63 H 6.00 N 13.66%

L(+)-γ-*Carboxyglutamic acid* **(3b)**. This isomer was obtained by dissolving **2b** in trifluoroacetic acid/water, 9:1 *(v/v)*, evaporating the solution after 90 min at 20°, azeotropic removal of the reagent with toluene, triturating with ether, and recrystallizing from water/ethanol, 1:1 *(v/v)*. Colourless, very small crystals, yield 75%, m.p. 167–167.5° (dec.).

$C_6H_9NO_6$ (191.14) Calc. C 37.70 H 4.75 N 7.32% Found C 37.59 H 4.85 N 7.29%

Table 1. *Determination of the absolute configuration and optical purity of γ-carboxyglutamic acid derivatives*

Educt	Hydrolysis, 3h, 110°C	Product (electro-phoresis)	$[\alpha]^{21}_{546}$°	$[\alpha]^{21}_{D}$°	c, H_2O	% Optical purity	Absolute configu-ration
L-Glu	6N HCl	Glu	+25.2±0.2	+21.4	1.5	= 100	L
L-Z · Glu(O*t*Bu)	6N HCl	Glu	+24.6±0.2	+20.6	1.5	= 100	L
L-Z · Glu(O*t*Bu)	conc. HCl	Glu	+23.2±0.4	+19.3	2	= 100	L
(+)-Z · Gla(O*t*Bu)$_2$[a])	6N HCl	Glu	+24.2±0.4	+20.4	1	99	L
(+)-Z · Gla(O*t*Bu)$_2$[a])	conc. HCl	Glu	+21.7±0.6	+15.9	0.4	94–96	L
(−)-Z · Gla(O*t*Bu)$_2$[b])	6N HCl	Glu	−24.0±0.4	−20.5	1	98–99	D
(−)-Z · Gla(O*t*Bu)$_2$[b])	conc. HCl	Glu	−23.6±0.5	−21.3	0.4	100	D
(+)-Ac · Gla(O*t*Bu)$_2$[c])	6N HCl, 16 h, 108°	Glu	+10.5±0.2	+ 8.8	2	50–55	L>D

[a]) *Dextro* in chloroform, *laevo* in methanol.
[b]) *Laevo* in chloroform, *dextro* in methanol.
[c]) *Dextro* in chloroform.

Table 2. *Physical data of glutamic acid* (Glu), *γ-carboxyglutamic acid* (Gla), *and derivatives*

Compound	$[\alpha]^{20}_{546}$	(c, solvent)	$[\alpha]^{20}_{D}$	(c, solvent)
D-Gla, NH_3	−44.6±0.5°	(1, 6N HCl)	−37.5±0.5°	(1, 6N HCl)
L-Gla	+41.7±0.5°	(1, 6N HCl)	+35.3±0.5°	(1, 6N HCl)
L-Glu	+36°	(5, 5N HCl)	+31.4°	(1, 6N HCl)
D-Gla(O*t*Bu)$_2$	− 6.8±0.3°	(1, methanol)	− 5.7±0.3°	(1, methanol)
L-Gla(O*t*Bu)$_2$	+ 6.6±0.3°	(1, methanol)	+ 5.6±0.3°	(1, methanol)
L-Glu(O*t*Bu)	–	–	+10.1°	(1, water)
D-Z · Gla(O*t*Bu)$_2$	−13.7±0.3°	(1.1, chloroform)	−11.3±0.3°	(1.1, chloroform)
L-Z · Gla(O*t*Bu)$_2$	+14.7±0.3°	(1.1, chloroform)	+12.3±0.3°	(1.1, chloroform)
	−13.8±0.3°	(1.1, methanol)	−10.9±0.3°	(1.1, methanol)
L-Z · Glu(O*t*Bu)	+13.3±0.3°	(1.1, chloroform)	+11.5±0.3°	(1.1, chloroform)
	−16.0±1°	(2, methanol)	− 9.4°	(1, ethanol)

Ref. 1512a

$C_{22}H_{31}NO_8$

Resolution of 4c Using a Combination of the Quinine and Tyrosine Hydrazide Salts. Isolation of the D Enantiomer. The lithium salt of 167 g of di-*tert*-butyl malonate in 242 mL of tetrahydrofuran was prepared as described above using 108 mL of diisopropylamine, 604 mL of tetrahydrofuran, and 322 mL of 2.4 M *n*-butyllithium in hexane. After being warmed to room temperature and stirred for an additional hour, the reaction mixture was added over 5 h to a solution of 157 g of *d,l*- **1a** (prepared in the same manner as **1a**, mp 103–105 °C) in 242 mL of tetrahydrofuran cooled to 0 °C. The reaction was allowed to stir for an additional 24 h, during which time it warmed to room temperature. After the dropwise addition of 44 mL of glacial acetic acid and removal of the solvent in vacuo, the mixture was worked up in the usual fashion to yield 240 g of oil. The oil was dissolved in 3 L of 0.48 N potassium hydroxide in ethanol and stirred for 25 min at room temperature. After adjustment to pH 7 with ice-cold 1.0 N hydrochloric acid, the ethanol was removed in vacuo. After workup as before, 225 g of crude oil was isolated.

The oil was dissolved in 150 mL of hot anhydrous methanol, 48.2 g of L-tyrosine hydrazide was added, and the mixture was warmed until all solid dissolved. After the mixture was cooled to room temperature, 1000 mL of anhydrous ether was added followed 15 min later by a second 1000 mL. The mixture was filtered after standing at −15 °C for 1 h, and the solid was air-dried, leaving 158 g of **5d:** mp 125–130 °C; $[\alpha]^{22}{}_D$ +22.6° (*c* 2.0, methanol). The free acid **5a** was recovered by partitioning the crude salt between ether and a solution of 48 g of citric acid in 150 mL of water. The ether extracts were washed with saturated brine, dried, and condensed in vacuo to 111 g of oil. Mixing of a solution of the oil in 50 mL of hot ethyl acetate with a dispersion of 80.8 g of L-quinine in 700 mL of hot ethyl acetate resulted in solution of all solids. Filtration after slow cooling and standing for 2 days gave 42.4 g of quinine salt, mp 130–135 °C. A second crop of 30.7 g was obtained from the filtrate for a total yield of 73.1 g (37% of the *d,l* free acid). The remaining material in the final filtrate (110.4 g) was a brown viscous oil (representing 56.4% of the *d,l* free acid). The conversion to the first set of separated quinine salts proceeded with 93% overall yield.

Following the procedure of Schwyzer et al.,[7] the quinine salt was recrystallized several times from ethyl acetate. Careful cooling procedures yielded a total of 46 g of salt (15% from **2** or 23% of the *d,l* acid **5a**). The salt was contained in four fractions of various levels of purity, including 28.2 g of highly purified salt: mp 139.5–140 °C; $[\alpha]^{22}{}_D$ −68.6° (*c* 1.0, methanol).

Anal. Calcd: C, 66.21; H, 7.28; N, 5.52. Found: C, 65.98; H, 7.28; N, 5.46.

The salt **5d** could be converted into **5a** by partitioning the purified salt between 20% citric acid and ether: mp 87–88 °C; $[\alpha]^{22}{}_D$ +11.4° (*c* 1.1, methanol). Hydrolysis of 150 mg of **5a** as previously described above yielded 61.4 mg of glutamic acid hydrochloride, $[\alpha]^{20}{}_D$ −20.3° (*c* 1.0, H_2O). The isolated free acid **5a** is therefore *N*-(benzyloxycarbonyl)-D-γ,γ-di-*tert*-butyl-γ-carboxyglutamic acid with an enantiomeric excess of 98.1 ± 1.5%.

Isolation of the L Enantiomer of 4c via 4a. The oily L-enriched quinine salt obtained on the first separation was partitioned between 20% citric acid and ether. The combined organic extracts were washed with saturated brine and dried over magnesium sulfate, and the solvent was removed in vacuo to leave 58.6 g of oil (representing 55.4% of the *d,l* free acid). The oil was dissolved in 140 mL of hot anhydrous

methanol, 25.3 g of L-tyrosine hydrazide was added, and the solution was heated until all of the solid dissolved. Careful cooling overnight gave on first separation 56.7 g of solid: mp 134–137 °C; $[\alpha]^{24}_D$ +22.3° (*c* 2.0, methanol). Further crystallization and collection of fractions gave a total of 64 g of salt (27.2% from **1a**, representing 41.9% of *d,l*-**5a**) distributed among several fractions of differing purity, including 21 g of highly purified salt (9% from **1a**, 13.7% from *d,l*-**4c**): mp 149–150 °C; $[\alpha]^{22}_D$ −21.6° (*c* 1.0, methanol).

Anal. Calcd for $C_{31}H_{44}N_4O_{10}$: C, 58.84; H, 7.01; N, 8.86. Found: C, 58.72; H, 7.04; N, 8.84.

The free acid **5a** was obtained from the most highly purified fraction as previously described: mp 87–89 °C; $[\alpha]^{21}_D$ −12.4° (*c* 1.1, methanol).

Anal. Calcd for $C_{22}H_{31}NO_8$: C, 60.40; H, 7.14; N, 3.20. Found: C, 60.29; H, 7.17; N, 3.19.

Hydrolysis of 150 mg of this material as described above yielded 67.2 mg of glutamic acid hydrochloride, $[\alpha]^{20}_D$ +20.4° (*c* 1.0, water), indicating on comparison with the appropriate standards an enantiomeric excess of 98.6%. The absolute configuration of the material obtained from the tyrosine hydrazide salt is established as L.

Isolation of the L Enantiomer of 5a by Crystallization. The low-melting solid obtained from the filtrates of the recrystallization of the quinine salt obtained from 144.0 g of **5a** was partitioned between 20% citric acid and ether, and the combined organic fractions were washed with water and saturated brine. After the mixture was dried over magnesium sulfate, the solvent was removed in vacuo to leave 91.5 g of viscous oil (representing 66% of the *d,l*-**5a**). Several recrystallizations of this material from a carbon tetrachloride and petroleum ether solvent pair yielded essentially two fractions: 38 g (15% from *d,l*-**1a**) of highly purified *N*-(benzyloxycarbonyl)-L-γ,γ-di-*tert*-butyl-γ-carboxyglutamic acid [mp 85–86 °C, $[\alpha]^{20}_D$ −12.1° (*c* 1.1 methanol)], and 40 g of oil (16% from *d,l*-**1a**) from which no more L-**5a** could be crystallized.

Comparison of the Effectiveness of L-Tyrosine Hydrazide, Quinine, and (−)-Ephedrine in the Purification of the L Enantiomer of 5a. The rotation of 40 g of oil obtained from the mother liquor when purification of the L enantiomer of **5a** was accomplished by recrystallization of an L enriched sample of **5a**, $[\alpha]^{21}_D$ −2.7° (*c* 1.1, methanol), indicates an excess of 22% of the L enantiomer. In order to compare the separation effectiveness of L-tyrosine hydrazide and quinine with that of (−)-ephedrine, the oil was divided into three 15-g portions and transformed into salt with the appropriate bases as indicated below.

(i) Quinine. As might have been expected, quinine was essentially ineffective at separating a mixture with this level of enantiomeric excess.

(ii) Tyrosine Hydrazide. The tyrosine hydrazide salt of a second aliquot (21.8 g) was recrystallized from methanol until no further solid could be obtained from the filtrate. Three fractions of crystals (a total of 10.5 g) and 7.83 g of oil were obtained from the filtrate. The filtrate was converted as before to 5.4 g of free acid, $[\alpha]^{22}_D$ +1.0° (*c* 1.0, methanol). The collected 10.5 g of salt was recrystallized as before from methanol, giving three fractions of crystals (a total of 6.4 g) and 2.69 g of filtrate. The filtrate was converted to 1.77 g of free acid, $[\alpha]^{23}_D$ +0.15° (*c* 1.0, methanol). The pooled salt fractions were converted to 4.59 g of oil, $[\alpha]^{23}_D$ −8.0° (*c* 1.0, methanol). The oil was dissolved in 11.1 mL of warm carbon tetrachloride, and 35.6 mL of pentane was added. Slow cooling followed by filtration gave 2.86 g of solid **5a**, $[\alpha]^{23}_D$ −10.9° (*c* 1.0, methanol). The filtrate yielded 1.20 g of oil as well, $[\alpha]^{23}_D$ −1.8° (*c* 1.0, methanol).

(iii) Ephedrine. The ephedrine salt of a third aliquot (20.7 g) was recrystallized from ethyl acetate/petroleum ether until no further salt could be obtained from the filtrate, giving four fractions of crystals (a total of 11.9 g) and 6.5 g of oil from the filtrate. The oil was converted as above to 4.69 g of **5a** as an oil, $[\alpha]^{22}_D$ +1.6° (*c* 1.0, methanol). The collected 11.9 g of solid was recrystallized as before from ethyl acetate/petroleum ether, giving three fractions of salt (a total of 8.8 g) and 2.25 g of oil from the filtrate. The filtrate was converted to 1.54 g of free acid as an oil, $[\alpha]^{23}_D$ −2.0° (*c* 1.0, methanol). The pooled salt fractions were converted to 5.24 g of oil, $[\alpha]^{23}_D$ −5.2° (*c* 1.0, methanol). The oil was dissolved in 12.5 mL of warm carbon tetrachloride, and 41 mL of pentane was added. Slow cooling followed by filtration gave 1.57 g of solid **5a**, $[\alpha]^{23}_D$ −10.1° (*c* 1.0, methanol). The filtrate yielded 3.00 g of oil as well, $[\alpha]^{23}_D$ −1.9° (*c* 1.0, methanol).

***N*-(Benzyloxycarbonyl)-γ,γ-di-*tert*-butyl-D-γ-carboxyglutamic Acid Hydrazide (D-4).** The optically pure free acid **5a** was obtained from 2.24 g of the quinine salt in the usual manner and dissolved in 3 mL of anhydrous ether. An ether solution of diazomethane[21] was added until the yellow color persisted. After 10 min additional, the reaction mixture was quenched with acetic acid in ether and extracted with saturated brine. The dried ether layer was evaporated to yield 1.24 g (100%) of D-**3a** as a clear oil, $[\alpha]^{21}_D$ 1.25° (*c* 1.2, $CHCl_3$). The NMR spectrum and TLC mobility were identical with those of a sample of *d,l*-**3a**.

To a solution of 1.62 g of **3a** in 7.9 mL of methanol was added 0.52 mL of hydrazine hydrate, and the reaction mixture was stirred at room temperature for 4.5 h. Removal of the solvent and drying over P_2O_5 and 96% sulfuric acid provided 1.62 g of glassy solid. Crystallization from ether provided 1.05 g (65%) of optically pure **4**: mp 63.5–65 °C; $[\alpha]^{24}_D$ −6.2° (*c* 1.0, $CHCl_3$).

Anal. Calcd for $C_{22}H_{33}N_3O_7$: C, 58.52; H, 7.37; N, 9.31. Found: C, 58.46; H, 7.38; N, 9.29.

γ,γ-Di-*tert*-butyl-D-γ-carboxyglutamic Acid (D-6a). The free acid **5a** from 2.24 g of quinine salt was obtained by partitioning the salt between 20% citric acid and ether. The ether layer was washed with water and saturated brine and dried over anhydrous magnesium sulfate. The 1.25 g of oil obtained on removal of the solvent in vacuo was dissolved in 20 mL of anhydrous methanol and hydrogenated at 1 atm in the presence of 200 mg of 10% palladium on charcoal. After 1 h, the flow of hydrogen was discontinued, the catalyst was removed by filtration through a Celite bed, and the methanol was evaporated in vacuo to leave 808 mg of white solid (98% based on starting quinine salt): mp 163–164 °C; $[\alpha]^{26}_D$ −5.7° (*c* 1.0, CH_3OH) [literature values:[7b] mp 165–167.5 °C, $[\alpha]^{20}_D$ −5.7 ° (*c* 1, CH_3OH)].

Authors' comments:

Another route to the L enantiomer of **5a** was reported by Schwyzer et al.[7a] and was used successfully in our laboratory. Recrystallization of the crude L enantiomer fraction of **5a** (liberated from the oily D-quinine L-acid fraction with 20% citric acid) from carbon tetrachloride or carbon tetrachloride/pentane provided a 15% overall yield of the optically pure L enantiomer of **5a** and 16% of recovered mother liquor enriched in the L enantiomer (Scheme V). This route to the L-enantiomer of **5a** is the method of choice for the rapid preparation of synthetically useful quantities of this substance.

Attempts to further enrich the mother liquors by formation and separation of the quinine salt were unsuccessful; however, both the tyrosine hydrazide and ephedrine[7b] salts could be obtained and purified. Recrystallization of the salts was pursued until no more solid could be obtained from either filtrate. Each filtrate was then reconverted to the acid **5a**, and the rotation of the oil was determined; virtually no difference between the amount of rotation of the acid remaining in the filtrate from either salt was observed. The crystalline salt fractions from ephedrine and tyrosine hydrazide were collected and likewise converted into **5a**. Rotations indicated that although the percent yield of solid salt was higher with ephedrine, the enantiomeric excess of the acid obtained from the tyrosine hydrazide salt was considerably greater.

Determination of Optical Purity. The criteria that were developed for the determination of the optical purity of **5a** are given in Table I. Conversion of **5a** or *N*-(benzyloxycarbonyl)-γ-*tert*-butyl-L-glutamic acid to the optically pure glutamic acid hydrochloride by hydrolysis with hydrochloric acid was accompanied by a 1–2% loss of enantiomeric excess. The value of 20.3 ± 0.5° (*c* 1, H_2O) for the specific rotation of glutamic acid hydrochloride was used as the standard value.

The specific rotations for the enantiomers of **5a** were found to be most reliable when methanol was used as the solvent. Consistent with the previous reports,[2b,7b] we have found an inversion of the Cotton effect of both glutamic and γ-carboxyglutamic acid derivatives on changing solvent from methanol to chloroform. The problems of reproducibility encountered with chloroform as a solvent could have been due

to the presence of either water or alcohol in the chloroform, although alumina-filtered chloroform was not more reliable.

Scheme V

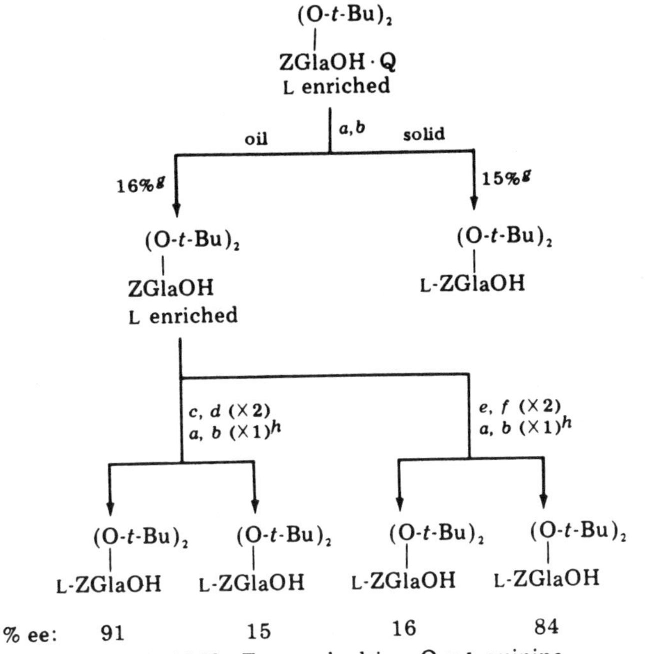

T = L-HTryN$_2$H$_3$, E = L-ephedrine, Q = L-quinine

[a] 20% citric acid. [b] CCl_4/pentane recrystallization. [c] 1 equiv of T. [d] CH_3OH recrystallization. [e] 1 equiv of E. [f] Ethyl acetate/pentane recrystallization. [g] % based on starting serine tosylate. [h] Ratios are the same in each case; volumes are proportional to the amount of solid obtained from each salt.

Table I. Optical Purity Criteria for Z-Gla(O-*t*-Bu)$_2$-OH

	mp, °C	$[\alpha]^{22}_D$, deg
1. quinine salt	139.5–140	−71.9 (c 1, $CHCl_3$)
tyrosine hydrazide salt	149–150	−21.6 (c 1, CH_3OH)
2. free acid (D)	87–88	+11.4 (c 1.1, CH_3OH)
(L)	87–89	−11.2 (c 1.1, CH_3OH)
3. glutamic acid hydrochloride (98%)		±20.0 (c 1, H_2O)

(2) Some of these results were outlined in preliminary communications: (a) N. T. Boggs III, R. E. Gawley, K. A. Koehler, and R. G. Hiskey, *J. Org. Chem.*, **40,** 2850 (1975); (b) N. T. Boggs III and R. G. Hiskey in "Peptides, Proceedings of the Fifth American Peptide Symposium", M. Goodman and J. Meienhofer, Eds., Wiley, New York, 1977, p 465.

(7) (a) W. Marki and R. Schwyzer, *Helv. Chim. Acta*, **59,** 1591 (1976); (b) W. Marki, M. Oppliger, P. Thanei, and R. Schwyzer, *ibid.*, **60,** 798 (1977).

T. J. DeBoer and H. J. Backer, *Recl. Trav. Chim. Pays Bas*, **73,** 229 (1954).

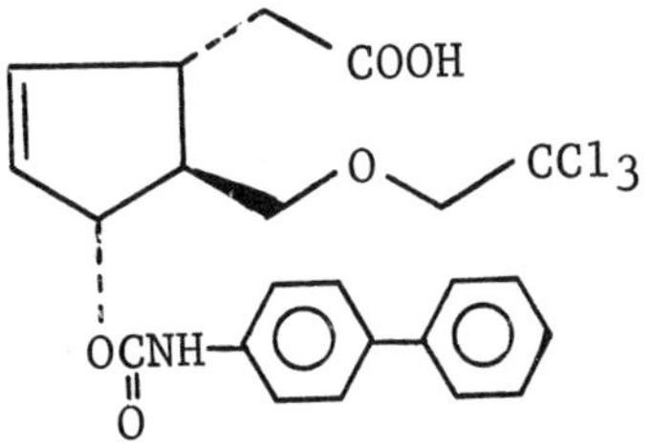

$C_{23}H_{22}Cl_3NO_5$ Ref. 1513

The acid **3a** upon treatment with (+)-amphetamine yielded a crystalline salt which could be fully resolved by one or two recrystallizations from isoamyl acetate–ethyl acetate (2:1); the fully resolved salt, mp 149–150°, had $[\alpha]^{20}D$ −58° (*c* 1.16 in CH_3OH). The resolved form of **3a**, mp 129–130°, $[\alpha]^{20}D$ −55.5° (*c* 1.02 in $CHCl_3$), obtained from the salt by treatment with aqueous acid and extraction, was converted quantitatively to the methyl ester **3b**, mp 100°, $[\alpha]^{20}D$ −54° (*c* 1.0 in $CHCl_3$), using diazomethane.

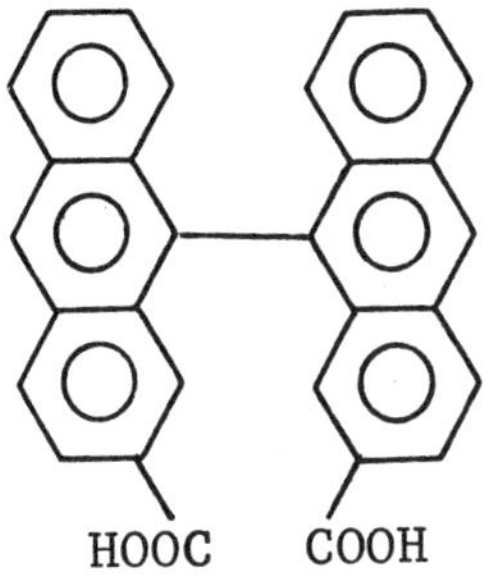

$C_{30}H_{18}O_4$ Ref. 1514

Note: Resolved with quinidine. Obtained (+)-diacid $[\alpha]^{23.5}_D$ 101° (C, 0.65, acetone) and (-)-diacid $[\alpha]^{22}_D$ -114° (C, 0.65, acetone).

SECTION 3

OPTICAL RESOLUTION OF ACIDS BY CHROMATOGRAPHIC METHODS

There are three basic approaches to the resolution of a racemic pair by gas or liquid chromatography. In the first, one converts the enantiomers into diastereomers by reaction with an optically active compound and the diastereomers are separated by chromatography on an achiral or chiral stationary phase. In the second, one passes the enantiomers or derivatives of the enantiomers through an optically active stationary phase which results in varying diastereomeric interactions between the components of the stationary and mobile phases, affording partial or complete separation. Finally, one may use an achiral stationary phase but include in the mobile phase which contains the enantiomer or their derivatives, a chiral eluant. This section will review the uses of these methods in the resolution of acids, as gleaned from papers published from 1974 through 1980. (For work published prior to 1974, see, 1) C.H. Lochmuller and R.W. Souter, J. Chromatog., *113,* 283 (1975), and 2) E. Gil-Av and D. Nurok, Advances in Chromatography, Vol. 10, J.C. Giddings and R.A. Keller, Eds., Marcel Dekker, N.Y., pgs. 99-172 (1974).)

For excellent recent reviews discussing the chromatographic resolution of racemates which contain material not found in this compilation, see, 1) I. Krull in "Advances in Chromatography," Volume 18, Marcel Dekker, New York (1979), 2) R. Audebert, J. Liquid Chromatog., *2,* 1063 (1979), and 3) G. Blaschke, Angew. Chem. Int. Ed. Engl., *19,* 13 (1980).

OPTICAL RESOLUTION OF ACIDS BY CHROMATOGRAPHIC METHODS

Page

Gas Liquid Chromatography on Chiral Phases

- Enantiomers 875

- Diastereomers 915

Gas Liquid Chromatography on Achiral Phases

- Diastereomers 916

Liquid Chromatography on Chiral Phases

- Chiral Ligands Bonded to Silica or Sephadex 934

- Ligand Exchange Chromatography 944

- Chiral Crown Ethers Bonded to Silica or Polystyrene 987

- Microcrystalline Cellulose Triacetate 1000

- Chiral Polyamides 1005

- Potato Starch 1007

- Affinity Chromatography 1010

- Crosslinked Cyclodextrin Gels 1011

Liquid Chromatography on Achiral Phases

- Enantiomers using Chiral Eluants 1014

- Diastereomers 1022

Reference

R. Charles, U. Beitler, B. Feibush and E. Gil-Av, J. Chromatog., 112, 121 (1975).

Summary

The authors have prepared the higher homologues of the highly efficient chiral diamide stationary phase N-lauroyl-L-valine tert-butyl amide (I) which was introduced by Feibush in 1971 for the gas-liquid chromatographic resolution of α-amino acids. The chiral phases are N-docosanoyl-L-valine tert-butyl amide (II) and N-lauroyl-L-valine 2-methyl-2-heptadecyl amide (III). Unlike (I) which suffers from relatively high column bleeding which limits the working temperature to 130-140°, these two materials show no loss of weight by thermogravimetric analysis until 190° and 180° respectively. Their melting points are also convenient being 85-86° and 47-48° respectively. A dozen racemic α-amino acids could be resolved using these phases on packed short columns (2-4 meters) with resolution factors ≫1 in many instances. The separation of the enantiomers of proline, however, require the use of capillaries. Experimental details and results follow.

EXPERIMENTAL

Materials

The N-TFA-amino acid esters were synthesized as described previously[5]. Phase I was supplied by Miles-Yeda, Rehovot, Israel; the other phases were prepared according to the procedures given below.

N-Docosanoyl-L-valine tert.-butylamide (II). Docosanoic (behenic) acid (10.2 g) in 100 ml of dry dioxane was cooled in an ice-water bath; N-hydroxysuccinimide (3.45 g) and N,N'-dicyclohexylcarbodiimide (6.18 g) were added successively and the mixture was stirred for 48 h (ref. 6). The reaction mass was then filtered, the dioxane distilled off and the residue dissolved in diethyl ether and re-filtered. Evaporation of the ether left a white solid, which was stirred overnight with light petroleum (b.p. 40–60°). The docosanoate of N-hydroxysuccinimide (3.5 g) was obtained in 27% yield; m.p. 91–94°; the nuclear magnetic resonance (NMR) spectrum agreed with the expected structure.

The above active ester (2.5 g) was condensed with L-valine *tert.*-butyalmide[7] (1 g) in the presence of triethylamine (0.63 g) in 100 ml of dry chloroform[6]. The mixture was first stirred in an ice-water bath and then at room temperature for 48 h, treated with active charcoal, filtered and the solvent distilled off. The remaining solid was dissolved in diethyl ether and filtered. The ether solution was washed successively with 2% hydrochloric acid, water, 5% sodium hydrogencarbonate solution, again with water, dried over sodium sulphate and filtered. Evaporation of the ether left a solid (4.5 g), which was chromatographed on silica gel (containing 6% of water) with ethyl acetate–*n*-hexane (15:85) as the eluent. The resulting N-docosanoyl-L-valine *tert.*-butylamide (II) (0.9 g) had an NMR spectrum that agreed with the expected structure; m.p. 85–86°. Elemental analysis: found: C, 74.94; H, 12.48; N, 6.07%; calculated for $C_{31}H_{62}N_2O_2$: C, 75.24; H, 12.63; N, 5.66%. TGA showed that II does not lose any material at temperatures up to 190°.

The optical purity of II was found to be 89% by hydrolysis, derivatization of the valine formed and gas chromatography on a chiral phase.

N-Lauroyl-L-valine 2-methyl-2-heptadecylamide (III). 2-Methyl-2-heptadecanol was obtained by the action of methylmagnesium iodide on methyl palmitate; yield 90%; m.p. 36–38° [ref. 8, 36°]. The alcohol (45 g) was refluxed for 3 h with an excess of acetyl chloride (20 ml). The 2-chloro-2-methylheptadecane obtained was washed with 90 ml of 5% sodium hydrogen carbonate solution; yield 93%; b.p. 118–122°/0.2 mm. To a solution of the chloroalkane (44 g) in 400 ml of absolute ethanol, 60 ml of liquid ammonia was added in an autoclave. The mixture was stirred at 120° for 1 week. The product was filtered, the ethanol distilled off in a rotatory evaporator, the residue dissolved in diethyl ether, filtered, the solid re-dissolved in chloroform and refiltered. Evaporation of the chloroform gave 2-methyl-2-heptadecylamine hydrochloride (3.5 g); m.p. 106–110°; yield 7%; 34 g of the chloroalkane were recovered unchanged.

In the final step of the synthesis[6], the hydrochloride (3.5 g) in 300 ml of dry chloroform was cooled in an ice-water bath and a solution of the N-lauroyl-L-valine derivative of N-hydroxysuccinimide[7] in 150 ml of chloroform and triethylamine (2.44 g) was added, the reaction mixture being stirred for 48 h. The product was treated with active charcoal, filtered and the chloroform distilled off. The remaining solid was worked up as for II, followed by chromatography on silica gel (containing 6% of water) with ethyl acetate–*n*-hexane (1:9) as the eluent. The final product, N-lauroyl-L-valine 2-methyl-2-heptadecylamide (III), had m.p. 47–48° and its infrared (IR) and NMR spectra were in agreement with the expected structure. Elementary analysis: found: C, 76.11; H, 12.30; N, 4.96%; calculated for $C_{35}H_{70}N_2O_2$: C, 76.3; H, 12.81; N, 5.09%. TGA showed that III could be used up to 180° as a gas chromatographic stationary phase. By hydrolysis of III and enantiomeric analysis of the valine formed, the optically purity of the synthetic product was found to be 83%.

Chromatographic conditions

A Hewlett-Packard 7626A research chromatograph equipped with a dual flame ionization detector was used. Aluminium tubing of length 1.9–4 m and I.D. 2 mm was used for the columns, which were filled with Chromosorb W AW or P AW DMCS, coated with 10% of phase. Helium pressure was 60 p.s.i. More details of the chromatographic conditions are given in the tables and the legends of the figures.

5 S. Nakaparksin, P. Birrell, E. Gil-Av and J. Oró, *J. Chromatogr. Sci.*, 8 (1970) 177.

6 G. W. Anderson, J. E. Zimmermann and F. M. Callahan, *J. Amer. Chem. Soc.*, 86 (1964) 1839.

7 U. Beitler and B. Feibush, in preparation (see also U. Beitler, *M.Sc. Thesis*, Feinberg Graduate School, Weizmann Institute of Science, Rehovot, 1974).

8 A. D. Petrov and J. E. Lapteva, *J. Gen. Chem. U.S.S.R.*, 11 (1941) 1107.

R. Charles, U. Beitler, B. Feibush and E. Gil-Av., J. Chromatogr., 112, 121 (1975). continued.

TABLE II

SEPARATION OF THE ENANTIOMERS OF N-TFA ISOPROPYL ESTERS OF PROTEIN AMINO ACIDS

Retention times and resolution factors for N-trifluoroacetyl isopropyl esters on packed columns containing chiral diamide phases. Columns as in Table I.

N-TFA isopropyl ester of	Enantiomer	Column I			Column II			Column III		
		Temperature (°C)	Corr. retention time (min)	$r_{L/D}$	Temperature (°C)	Corr. retention time (min)	$r_{L/D}$	Temperature (°C)	Corr. retention time (min)	$r_{L/D}$
Ala	D	120	11.52	1.187	130	6.69	1.196	130	12.05	1.138
	L		13.68			8.00			13.71	
Thr	D		18.35	1.133		8.86	1.128		16.00	1.102
	L		20.80			10.00			17.63	
Val	D		17.41	1.162		10.80	1.167		18.27	1.096
	L		20.24			12.60			20.03	
Gly	—		24.32	—		12.16	—		23.52	—
*allo*Ile	D		25.75	1.174		16.26	1.176		26.75	1.098
	L		30.24			19.12			29.36	
Ile	D		28.56	1.156		17.92	1.153		29.36	1.101
	L		33.04			20.67			32.32	
Ser	D		30.96	1.106		17.92	1.118			
	L		34.24			20.03				
Leu	D		39.76	1.257		22.08	1.273		36.01	1.212
	L		50.00			28.11			43.65	
Pro	D		39.44	1.022		28.16	1.000		54.88	1.000
	L		40.32	(shoulder)						
Asp	D	140	46.96	1.037	190	11.36	1.000	180	23.20	1.000
	L		48.72							
Met	D		75.68	1.160		17.15	1.077		35.16	1.084
	L		87.84			18.48			38.14	
Glu	D		104.56	1.132		21.92	1.065		46.08	1.066
	L		125.60			23.36			49.12	
Phe	D		110.98	1.147		24.91	1.066		50.72	1.056
	L		127.36			26.56			53.57	
Orn	D					77.52	1.098		170.72	1.103
	L					85.12			184.40	
Lys	D					108.88	1.080		244.80	1.083
	L					117.60			265.28	

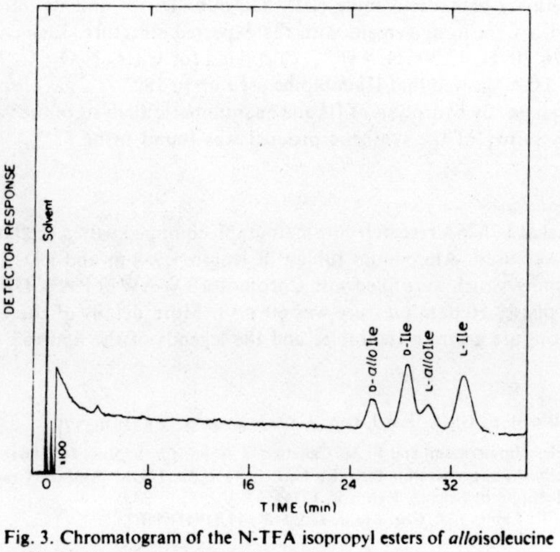

Fig. 3. Chromatogram of the N-TFA isopropyl esters of *allo*isoleucine and isoleucine. Chromatographic conditions as in Fig. 2.

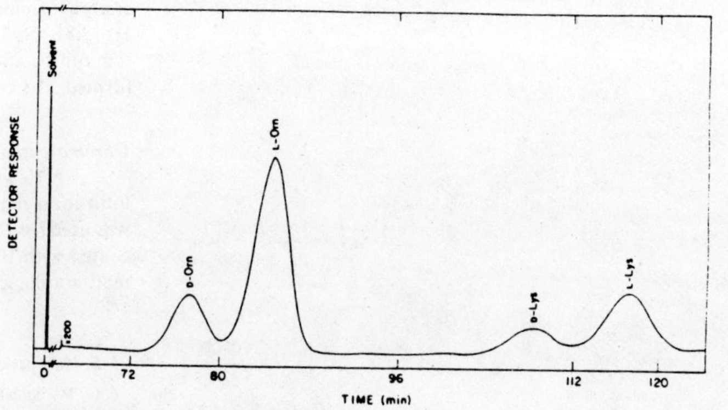

Fig. 4. Chromatogram of the di-TFA isopropyl esters of ornithine and lysine. Chromatographic conditions: column, 3 m × 2 mm I.D., containing 80–100 mesh Chromosorb P AW DMCS coated with phase II; temperature, 190°.

R. Charles, U. Beitler, B. Feibush and E. Gil-Av., J. Chromatogr., 112, 121 (1975) continued.

TABLE I

SEPARATION OF THE ENANTIOMERS OF N-TFA METHYL ESTERS OF PROTEIN AMINO ACIDS

Retention times and resolution factors for N-trifluoroacetyl methyl esters on packed columns containing chiral diamide phases.

N-TFA methyl ester of	*Enantiomer*	*Column I**			*Column II***			*Column III****		
		Temperature (°C)	*Corr. retention time (min)*	$r_{L/D}$	*Temperature (°C)*	*Corr. retention time (min)*	$r_{L/D}$	*Temperature (°C)*	*Corr. retention time (min)*	$r_{L/D}$
Ala	D	110	9.05	1.173	120	4.80	1.183	130	8.32	1.096
	L		11.15			5.68			9.12	
Thr	D		17.28	1.102		7.95	1.126		11.55	1.077
	L		19.04			8.96			12.45	
Val	D		14.32	1.145		7.76	1.148		11.84	1.071
	L		16.40			8.91			12.69	
Gly			18.80	—		9.04	—		17.36	—
*allo*Ile	D		22.91	1.165		12.56	1.167		18.08	1.076
	L		(26.68)§			14.67			19.45	
Ile	D		(25.12)§	1.143		13.55	1.145		19.45	1.081
	L		28.72			15.52			21.04	
Ser	D		40.88	1.095		16.96	1.108		—	
	L		44.76			18.80				
Leu	D		39.68	1.256		18.75	1.269		26.24	1.167
	L		49.84			23.80			30.64	
Pro	D		32.88	1.039		20.73	1.000		40.80	1.000
	L		34.17	(shoulder)						
Asp	D	140§§	27.04	1.038	180	7.52	1.000	170	17.46	1.000
	L		28.08	(shoulder)						
Met	D		71.44	1.135		17.52	1.079		38.67	1.070
	L		81.15			18.91			41.39	
Glu	D		70.00	1.107		16.06	1.064		38.67	1.044
	L		77.52			17.10			40.37	
Phe	D		100.16	1.124		24.75	1.064		52.96	1.052
	L		112.40			26.35			55.76	

* Column I: 4 m × 2 mm I.D., containing 60–80 mesh Chromosorb W AW, coated with 10% N-lauroyl-L-valine *tert.*-butylamide (I).
** Column II: 3 m × 2 mm I.D., containing 80–100 mesh Chromosorb P AW DMCS, coated with 10% N-docosanoyl-L-valine *tert.*-butylamide (II).
*** Column III: 3 m × 2 mm I.D., containing 80–100 mesh Chromosorb P AW DMCS, coated with 10% N-lauroyl-L-valine 2-methyl-2-heptadecylamide (III).
§ These two peaks overlapped partially.
§§ Maximum permissible temperature.

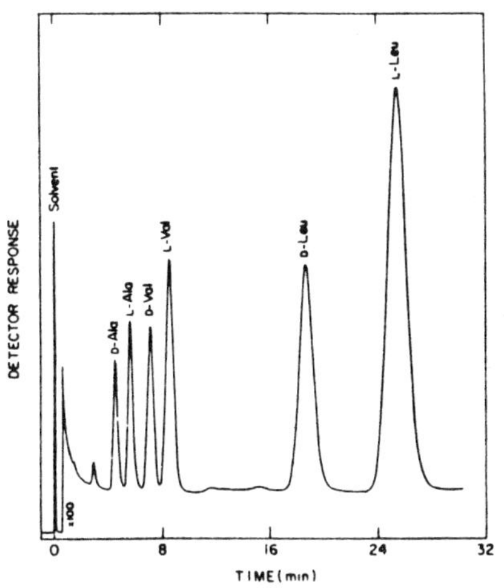

Fig. 1. Chromatogram of the N-TFA methyl esters of alanine, valine and leucine (enriched in the L-isomer). Chromatographic conditions: column, 1.9 m × 4 mm I.D., containing 60–80 mesh Chromosorb W AW coated with 10% of phase I; temperature, 110°.

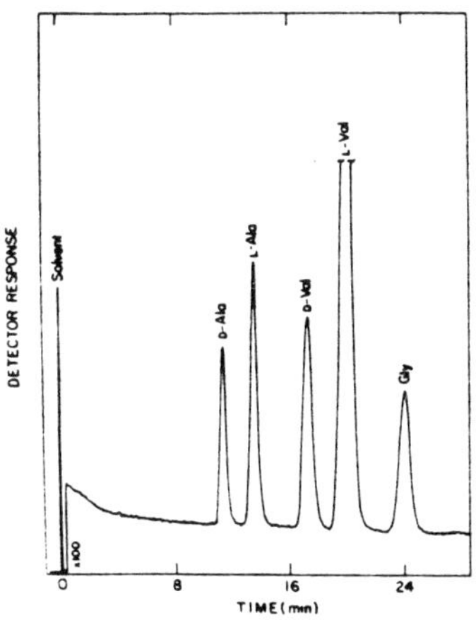

Fig. 2. Chromatogram of the N-TFA isopropyl esters of alanine, valine (enriched in the L-isomer) and of glycine. Chromatographic conditions: column, 4 m × 2 mm I.D., containing 60–80 mesh Chromosorb W AW coated with 10% of phase I; temperature, 120°.

R. Charles, U. Beitler, B. Feibush and E. Gil-Av., J. Chromatogr., 112, 121 (1975) continued.

TABLE III

SEPARATION OF THE N-TRIFLUOROACETYL ISOPROPYL ESTERS OF PROTEIN AMINO ACIDS ON DUAL PACKED COLUMNS CONTAINING A CHIRAL AND AN ACHIRAL PHASE

The columns consisted of column III (see Table I, footnote), followed by a 3 m × 2 mm I.D. column containing 80–100 mesh Chromosorb P AW DMCS, coated with 10% SE-30.

N-TFA isopropyl ester of	*Enantiomer*	*Temperature (°C)*	*Corr. retention time (min)*	*N-TFA isopropyl ester of*	*Enantiomer*	*Temperature (°C)*	*Corr. retention time (min)*
Ala	D	130	23.40	Leu	D		70.24
	L		25.12		L		78.24
Thr	D		34.00	Pro	D } L		97.92
	L		35.60				
Val	D		38.32	Asp	D } L	180	39.20
	L		41.04				
Gly	—		39.36	Met	D		59.97
*allo*Ile	D		52.00		L		63.49
	L		60.00	Glu	D		76.27
Ile	D		55.20		L		80.19
	L		62.64	Phe	D		85.97
					L		90.43

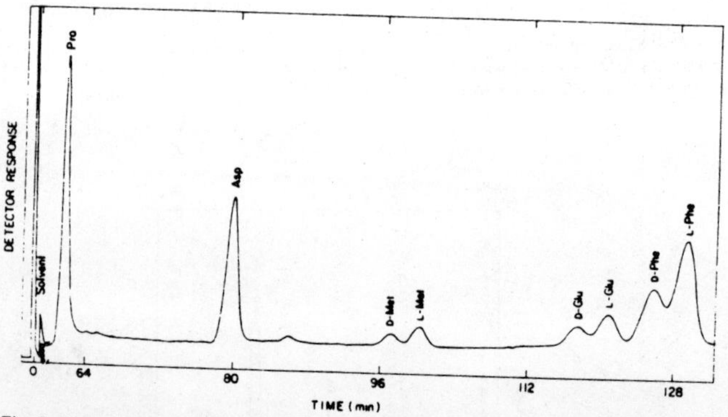

Fig. 6. Chromatogram of the N-TFA isopropyl esters of proline, aspartic acid, methionine, glutamic acid and phenylalanine (enriched in the L-isomer). Chromatographic conditions: columns as in Fig. 5; temperature, isothermal at 130° for 30 min, programmed at 1°/min up to 150° and then at 2°/min up to 180° (final temperature). Neither proline nor aspartic acid show any resolution under these conditions.

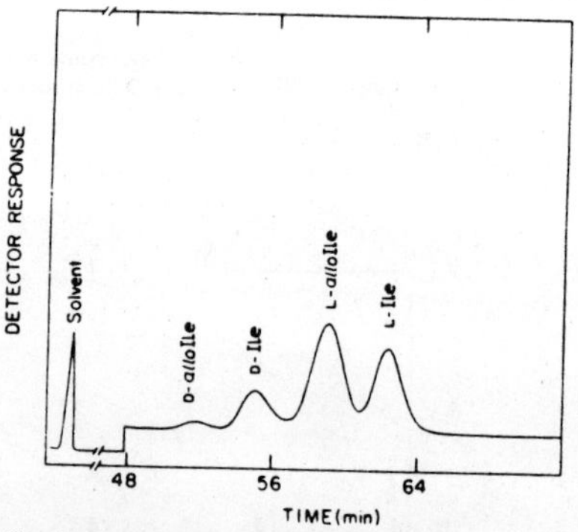

Fig. 5. Chromatogram of the N-TFA isopropyl esters of *allo*isoleucine and isoleucine. Chromatographic conditions: dual column consisting of (1) 3 m × 2 mm I.D. tube containing 80–100 mesh and (2) 3 m × 2 mm I.D. tube containing Chromosorb P AW DMCS coated with 10% phase III, 80–100 mesh Chromosorb P AW DMCS coated with 10% SE-30; temperature, 130°.

Reference

F. Andrawes, R. Brazell, W. Parr and A. Zlatkis, J. Chromatogr., 112, 197 (1975).

Summary

The authors report the synthesis of N-trifluoroacetyl-L-methionyl-L-methionine cyclohexyl ester as a stationary phase for the resolution of racemic α-amino acids and use it to resolve a number of α-amino acids. Proline could not be resolved. The stationary phase could be used at temperatures ranging from 70 to 150°. Experimental details and results follow:

Synthesis of N-TFA-L-methionyl-L-methionine cyclohexyl ester

L-Methionine cyclohexyl ester was prepared as previously described[7]. Yield, 95%. M.p., 93–94°.

N-TFA-L-methionine was synthesized according to the procedure of Weygand and Geiger[12]. Yield, 94%. M.p., 80–82°.

N-TFA-L-methionyl-L-methionine cyclohexyl ester was synthesized as follows. 10 mmoles of L-methionine cyclohexyl ester hydrogen chloride were dissolved in 10 ml of tetrahydrofuran (THF). The solution was neutralized with 10 mmoles of triethylamine. 10 mmoles of N-TFA-L-methionine were dissolved in 15 ml THF, and 11 mmoles of N,N'-carbonyldiimidazole were dissolved in 10 ml of THF. The three solutions were combined and stirred at room temperature for 12 h, after which the mixture was filtered and the solvent evaporated. The remaining clear oil was dissolved in ethyl acetate and then extracted once with a 10% solution of sodium bicarbonate and once with a 2 *N* solution of citric acid. It was then extracted with distilled water until neutral. The organic layer was dried over anhydrous sodium sulfate and excess solvent was removed *in vacuo*. The remaining oil was further purified by column chromatography over neutral alumina using an LKB ultrorac (R) Model 7000 fraction collector and collecting fractions absorbing at 254 nm. The final product was a clear oil. Yield, 86%. The structure was confirmed by infrared (IR) spectroscopy, mass spectroscopy and elemental analysis.

Gas chromatography

Analyses were carried out on a Varian 1200 gas chromatograph equipped with a flame ionization detector. Stainless-steel capillary columns (100 and 135 m × 0.5 mm I.D.) were used for the analysis. The columns were coated with 10% solutions of the phases in methylene chloride and conditioned for 24 h at 160° while helium carrier gas was passed through at 6 p.s.i.

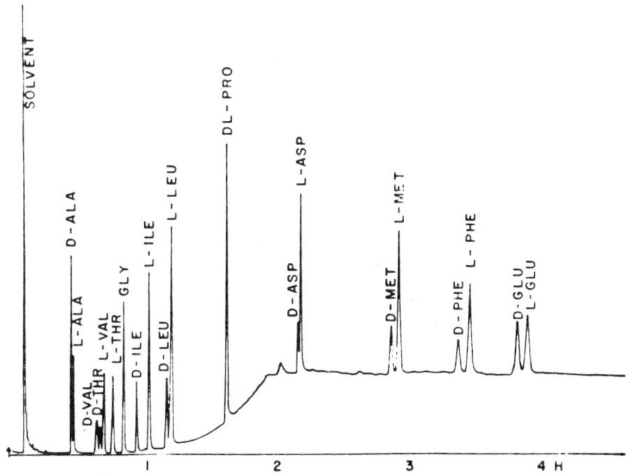

Fig. 1. Chromatogram of N-TFA-D,L-amino acid isopropyl esters with N-TFA-L-methionyl-L-methionine cyclohexyl ester as stationary phase. Conditions: 100 m × 0.5 mm I.D. stainless-steel capillary column, operation at 70° isothermal for 30 min, then temperature-programmed 0.5°/min to 110°; injector temperature, 180°; detector temperature, 275°; carrier gas, helium at 20 p.s.i.

F. Andrawes, R. Brazell, W. Parr and A. Zlatkis, J. Chromatogr., 112, 197 (1975) continued.

TABLE I

RELATIVE RETENTION TIMES AND SEPARATION FACTORS FOR N-TFA-D,L-AMINO ACID ISOPROPYL ESTERS ON N-TFA-L-METHIONYL-L-METHIONINE CYCLOHEXYL ESTER AS STATIONARY PHASE

Amino acid	*Relative retention time**	*Separation factor*
D-Alanine	0.320	1.037
L-Alanine	0.334	
D-Valine	0.495	1.078
L-Valine	0.544	
D-Threonine	0.518	1.131
L-Threonine	0.602	
Glycine	0.667	
D-Isoleucine	0.761	1.103
L-Isoleucine	0.845	
D-Leucine	0.962	1.037
L-Leucine	1.000	
D-Proline	1.374	1.00
L-Proline	1.374	
D-Aspartic acid	1.840	1.010
L-Aspartic acid	1.868	
D-Methionine	2.476	1.024
L-Methionine	2.528	
D-Phenylalanine	2.919	1.027
L-Phenylalanine	2.997	
D-Glutamic acid	3.317	1.022
L-Glutamic acid	3.389	

* Relative retention time with respect to L-leucine.

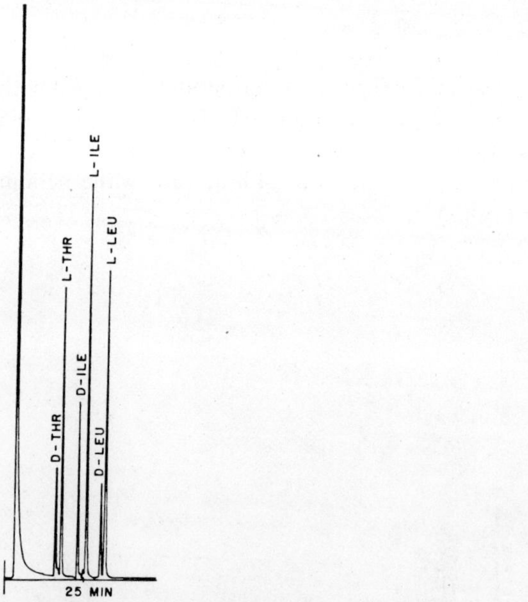

Fig. 2. Chromatogram of N-TFA-D,L-threonine, isoleucine, and leucine isopropyl esters on N-TFA-L-methionyl-L-methionine cyclohexyl ester as stationary phase. Conditions: 100 m × 0.5 mm I.D. stainless-steel capillary column, 90° isothermal operation; injection temperature, 185°; detector temperature, 275°; carrier gas, helium at 20 p.s.i.

7 W. Parr and P. Howard, *Anal. Chem.*, 45 (1973) 716.

12 F. Weygand and R. Geiger, *Chem. Ber.*, 89 (1956) 647.

Reference
H. Iwase, Chem. Pharm. Bull., 23, 217 (1975).

Summary
The authors reported their studies of the resolution of tryptophane, tyrosine, 3,4-dihydroxyphenylalanine and α-methyl-3,4-dihydroxyphenylalanine as their trimethylsilylated N-trifluoroacetyl-L-prolyl n-butyl esters by gas-liquid chromatography on achiral phases. Tyrosine and 3,4-dihydroxyphenylalanine were resolved. Tryptophane was not resolved completely and α-methyl-3,4-dihydroxyphenylalanine could not be resolved. Experimental details and results follow:

Apparatus and Conditions——A Hewlett-Packard Model 402 gas chromatograph equipped with dual flame ionization detector was used for the analysis of tryptophan. A glass column of 5.5 ft × 1/4 in. O.D. packed with 5% OV-1 on 100—120 mesh Supelcoport was used. Column temperature and injection temperature were 230° and 250°, respectively. Helium was used as carrier gas at a flow rate of 60 ml/min, 40 p.s.i.

A Perkin-Elmer Model 900 gas chromatograph equipped with attachments for scot[3] column and dual flame ionization detector was used for the analysis of tyrosine and related compounds. A stainless steel scot column of 100 ft × 0.02 in. I.D. coated with Dexsil 300 GC was used. Column temperature and injection temperature were 225° and 250°, respectively. Helium was used as the carrier gas at a flow rate of 1 ml/min, 50 p.s.i.

Reagents and Materials——All solvents used in this study were of reagent grade. Amino acids were obtained from Ajinomoto Co. and Nakarai Chemical Co., dopamine hydrochloride from Wako Pure Chemical Co., epinephrine hydrochloride and norepinephrine hydrochloride from Tokyo Kasei Co., metanephrine hydrochloride from Sigma Chemical Co., normetanephrine hydrochloride from Tokyo Kasei Co. Trifluoroacetic anhydride and BSTFA with 1% TMCS were obtained from Pierce Chemical Co. Pyridine was used after drying over NaOH pellets. N-TFA-L-PC was prepared in the same manner as described previously.[4] Hypovial was obtained from Pierce Chemical Co. Scot column was purchased from Perkin-Elmer Co.

Preparation of Derivatives——Each amino acid *n*-butyl ester was prepared by the method of Roach, *et al.*[5] and Imai, *et al.*[6] N-TFA-L-prolyl amino acid *n*-butyl ester derivatives prepared in the same manner as described in the preceding paper[1] were mixed with 0.5 ml of pyridine and 0.5 ml of BSTFA with 1% TMCS, and allowed to stand for 15 min at room temperature. N-TFA-L-prolyl catecholamines prepared in the similar manner as described in the previous paper[4] were mixed with 0.5 ml of pyridine and 0.5 ml of BSTFA with 1% TMCS and allowed to stand for 15 min at room temperature. A 0.3 μl portion of each solution was injected into gas chromatograph.

Separation Factors——Separation factors, α, were calculated from the following definition:

$$\alpha = \frac{\text{retention time of L enantiomer from solvent}}{\text{retention time of D enantiomer from solvent}}$$

1) Part IV: H. Iwase, *Chem. Pharm. Bull.* (Tokyo), **22**, 2075 (1974).
2) Location: *1-1, Suzuki-cho, Kawasaki-ku, 210, Japan.*
3) Abbreviations: scot, support coated open tubular; N-TFA-L-PC, N-trifluoroacetyl-L-prolyl chloride; BSTFA, N.O-bis-(trimethylsilyl)trifluoroacetamide; TMCS, trimethylchlorosilane; RRT, relative retention time; DOPA, 3,4-dihydroxyphenylalanine, p.s.i: pound square inch.
4) H. Iwase and A. Murai, *Chem. Pharm. Bull.* (Tokyo), **22**, 8 (1974).
5) D. Roach and C.W. Gehrke, *J. Chromatogr.*, **44**, 269 (1969).
6) K. Imai, N. Arizumi, M. Wang, S. Yoshine, and Z. Tamura, *Chem. Pharm. Bull.* (Tokyo), **20**, 2436 (1972).

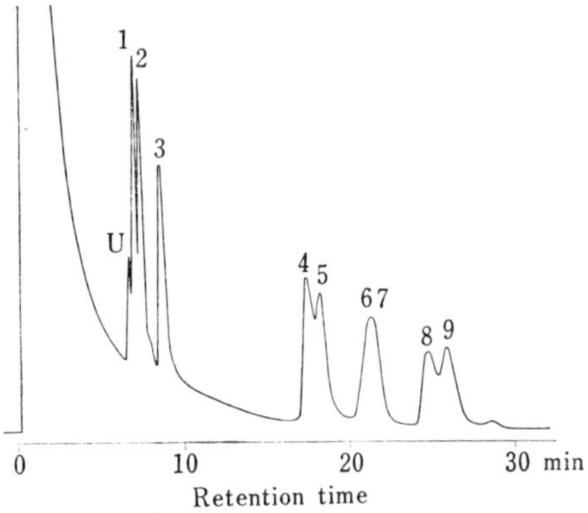

Fig. 1. Gas Chromatogram of N-TFA-L-Prolyl Amino Acid *n*-Butyl Esters on Scot Column coated with Dexsil 300GC

1: D-phenylalanine, 2: L-phenylalanine, 3: dopamine, 4: D-tyrosine, 5: L-tyrosine, 6: D-α-methyl DOPA, 7: L-α-methyl DOPA, 8: D-DOPA, 9: L-DOPA, U: unknown

TABLE I. Gas Chromatographic Data for Racemic Amino Acids as Their N-TFA-L-Prolyl *n*-Butyl Esters at 225°

Compound	RRT[a]	rL/D
D-Phenylalanine	0.382	1.065
L-Phenylalanine	0.407	
Dopamine	0.473	—
D-Tyrosine	0.959	1.042
L-Tyrosine	1.000	
D-α-Methyl DOPA	1.173	1.000
L-α-Methyl DOPA	1.173	
D-DOPA	1.363	1.046
L-DOPA	1.426	

a) RRT, reference compound is N-TFA-L-prolyl-L-tyrosine *n*-butyl ester, t_R=18.2 min.

Summary

Two new dipeptide stationary phases, N-TFA-L-phenylalanyl-L-phenylalanine cyclohexyl ester (phe-phe) and N-TFA-L-phenylalanyl-L-aspartic acid bis(cyclohexyl) ester (phe-asp) were synthesized and their properties in relation to enantiomer separation, temperature range of operation and thermal stability investigated using glass capillaries. Phe-asp was found to have high temperature stability (low volatility). Its upper temperature limit is 165°C and it also has a low melting point (96°C). Experimental details and results follow:

Reference

W.A. Koenig and G.J. Nicholson, Anal. Chem., 47, 951 (1975).

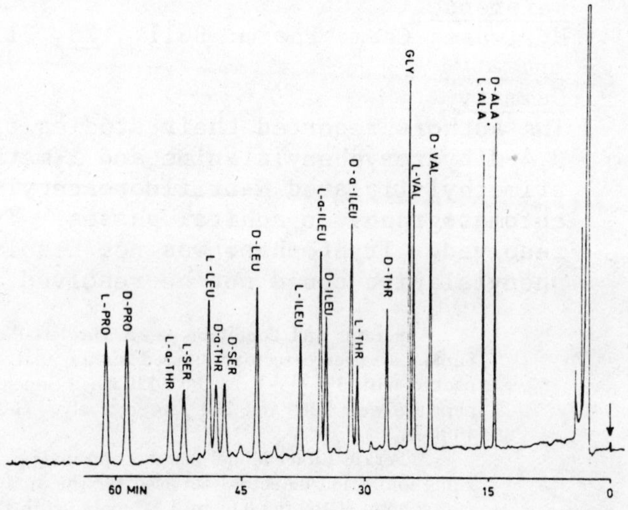

Figure 1. Separation of TFA-amino acid isopropyl esters on 39-m glass capillary coated with *N*-TFA-L-val-L-val cyclohexyl ester. Column temperature, 110 °C

EXPERIMENTAL

Gas Chromatography. A Carlo Erba gas chromatograph model Fractovap 2101 Milan, Italy) equipped with an all glass injection port, inlet splitter, and flame ionization detector was used. Hydrogen was employed as carrier gas.

Preparation of Glass Capillary Columns. Glass capillaries were drawn to the dimensions 0.9-mm o.d. and 0.30-mm i.d. with the glass drawing apparatus from Hupe and Busch (Karlsruhe-Groetzingen, Germany). The length of the capillaries used varied between 14 and 40 meters.

The following two methods were found to improve the stability of the coating (up to two months constant usage).

Method 1. A solution of 1% 3-aminopropyl triethoxy silane (Merck, Darmstadt, Germany) in CH_2Cl_2 was forced through the column, the ends were sealed, and the remaining film of reagent was allowed to react at 120–130 °C. Excess reagent was removed by washing with CH_2Cl_2, and the column subsequently coated by the static method as described by Bouche and Verzele (*16*) using 0.2% stationary phase dissolved in CH_2Cl_2. The column was then conditioned by slowly raising the temperature to above the melting point of the stationary phase.

In this way, we intended to form a stable chemical bond between the glass surface (Si-OH) and the aminopropyl-triethoxy silane and to link the stationary phase to the reagent by means of an aminolysis of the cyclohexyl ester.

Method 2. Soda-lime glass capillaries were etched with dry HCl gas according to the method of Novotny and Tesarik (*17*).

Synthesis of Dipeptide Derivatives. *N*-TFA-L-valyl-L-valine cyclohexyl ester was purchased from Miles Laboratories, Elkhart, IN. The phe-leu, phe-asp, and phe-phe phases were analogously synthesized by the method described by Koenig et al. (*10*) and recrystallized from diethyl ether. (Melting points: phe-leu 113 °C, phe-phe 136 °C, phe-asp 96 °C.)

Retention Indices. In order to measure the relative volatility of the dipeptide phases, the retention indices were determined on a 2-m glass column packed with 3% OV 17 on Gas Chrom Q at 280 °C. ($I_{\text{phe-asp}} = 3545$, $I_{\text{phe-phe}} = 3342$, $I_{\text{phe-leu}} = 2825$, $I_{N\text{-Lauroyl-L-val-}tert\text{-butylamide}} = 2400$, $I_{\text{val-val}} = 2260$).

Preparation of Amino Acid Derivatives was carried out according to (*10*).

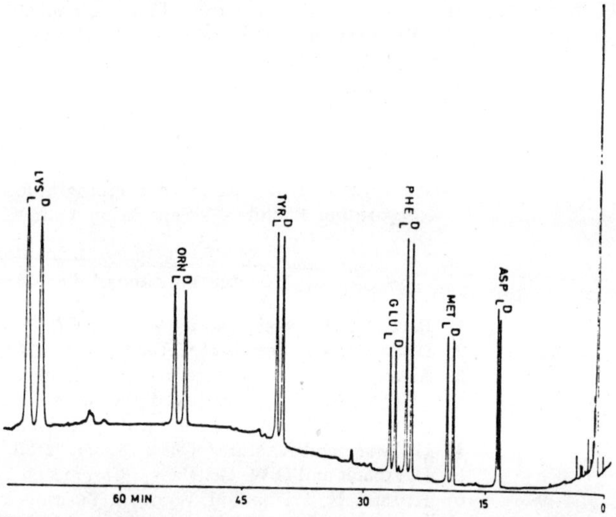

Figure 2. Separation of pentafluoropropionyl amino acid isopropyl esters on 20-m glass capillary coated with *N*-TFA-L-phe-L-asp bis-(cyclohexyl) ester. Column temperature, 130 °C, temperature program, 1 °C/min to 165 °C

(10) W. A. Koenig, W. Parr, H. A. Lichtenstein, E. Bayer, and J. Oró, *J. Chromatogr. Sci.*, **8**, 183 (1970).

(16) J. Bouche and M. Verzele, *J. Gas Chromatogr.*, **6**, 501 (1968).

(17) M. Novotny and K. Tesarik, *Chromatographia*, **1**, 332 (1968).

Reference
H. Iwase, Chem. Pharm. Bull., 23, 1608 (1975).

Summary
The authors report the gas-liquid chromatographic resolution of a number of racemic α-amino acids and two β-amino acids as their N-trifluoroacetyl esters on an optically acid stationary phase, N-lauroyl-L-valine-L-valine lauryl esters. The relation between the separation factor and structure of amino acid and relative retention times were studied. It was concluded that the separation factor depended on the relative size of the substituent on the chiral carbon and the position of the amino group. Experimental details and results follow:

Apparatus and Condition——A Perkin-Elmer Model 900 gas chromatograph equipped with attachments for capillary column and dual flame ionization detector was used. A stainless steel capillary column of 200 ft ×0.02 in. I.D. was cleaned as described by Koenig, *et al.*[4] and coated using 10% w/v solution of N-lauroyl-L-valyl-L-valine lauryl ester in methylene chloride, at 14 p.s.i. (dry nitrogen).

Reagents and Material——All solvents used in this study were of reagent grade. Amino acids were obtained from Ajinomoto Co., Tokyo Kasei Co., and K & K Laboratories. N-Lauroyl-L-valine and L-valine lauryl ester hydrochloride were obtained from Ajinomoto Co. Hypovial and trifluoroacetic anhydride were purchased from Pierce Chemical Co.

Preparation of Amino Acid Derivatives——N-TFA amino acid esters were prepared according to the method of Roach, *et al.*[5] N-lauroyl-L-valyl-L-valine lauryl ester was synthesized from N-lauroyl-L-valine and L-valine lauryl ester hydrochloride by the mixed anhydride method.[6]

Separation Factor——Separation factor, α, was calculated from the following definition:

$$\alpha = \frac{\text{retention time of L enantiomer}}{\text{retention time of D enantiomer}}$$

4) W.A. Koenig, W. Parr, H.A. Lichtenstein, E. Bayer, and J. Oró, *J. Chromatogr. Sci.*, **8**, 183 (1970).
5) D. Roach and C.W. Gehrke, *J. Chromatogr.*, **44**, 269 (1969).
6) D. Theodoropoulos and L.C. Craig, *J. Org. Chem.*, **20**, 1169 (1955).

Result and Discussion

The experimental data of the relative retention times and separation factors of N-TFA amino acid esters are given in Table I.

TABLE I. Comparison of Gas Chromatographic Data of Different N-TFA-Amino Acid Esters at 135°, 30. p.s.i

Ester	iso-Propyl		*n*-Propyl		iso-Butyl		*n*-Butyl	
Amino acid	RRT	α	RRT[a]	α	RRT	α	RRT	α
D-Isovaline	0.277	1.000	0.412	1.000	0.559	1.000	0.684	1.000
L-Isovaline	0.277		0.412		0.559		0.684	
D-Alanine	0.328	1.052	0.525	1.043	0.718	1.047	0.842	1.054
L-Alanine	0.345		0.548		0.751		0.887	
D-*tert*-Leucine	0.435	1.000	0.638	1.000	0.836	1.000	1.056	1.000
L-*tert*-Luecine	0.435		0.638		0.836		1.056	
D-Valine	0.446	1.038	0.684	1.033	0.898	1.037	1.136	1.040
L-Valine	0.463		0.706		0.932		1.181	
D-α-Amino-*n*-butyric acid	0.435	1.052	0.689	1.041	0.932	1.043	1.090	1.052
L-α-Amino-*n*-butyric acid	0.458		0.716		0.972		1.147	
Glycine	0.621	—	1.000	—	1.395	—	1.746	—
D-Isoleucine	0.706	1.032	1.068	1.037	1.395	1.032	1.751	1.039
L-Isoleucine	0.729		1.107		1.441		1.819	
L-Norvaline	0.701	1.040	1.113	1.041	1.463	1.042	1.723	1.046
D-Norvaline	0.729		1.158		1.525		1.802	
D-β-Amino-*n*-butyric acid	0.819	1.000	1.271	1.000	1.689	1.000	2.079	1.000
L-β-Amino-*n*-butyric acid	0.819		1.271		1.689		2.079	
D-β-Aminoisobutyric acid	0.864	1.000	1.299	1.000	1.723	1.000	2.141	1.000
L-β-Aminoisobutyric acid	0.864		1.299		1.723		2.141	
D-Leucine	0.927	1.054	1.486	1.053	1.949	1.052	2.288	1.057
L-Leucine	0.977		1.565		2.051		2.412	
D-Norleucine	1.102	1.051	1.746	1.049	2.299	1.044	2.695	1.054
L-Norleucine	1.158		1.831		2.401		2.841	
D-Proline	1.181	1.000	1.814	1.000	2.389	1.000	3.000	1.000
L-Proline	1.181		1.814		2.389		3.000	

a) RRT, relative retention time, reference compound is N-TFA-glycine *n*-propyl ester, t_R=8.85 min

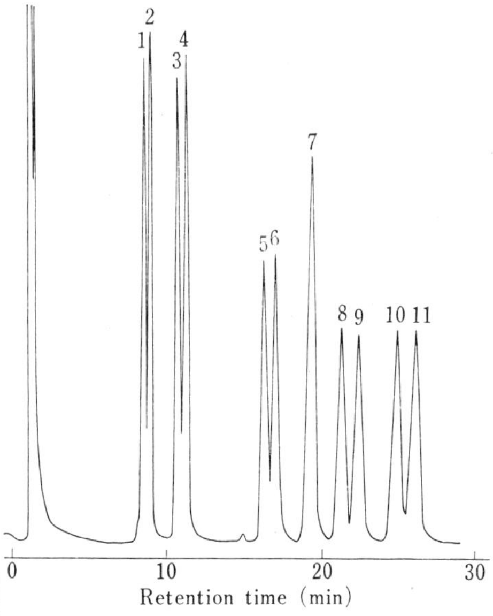

Fig. 1. Gas Chromatogram of N-TFA-Amino Acid *n*-Butyl Esters at 135°, 30 p.s.i.

1: D-alanine, 2: L-alanine, 3: D-α-amino-*n*-butyric acid, 4: L-α-amino-*n*-butyric acid, 5: D-norvaline, 6: L-norvaline, 7: D- and L-β-amino-*n*-butyric acids, 8: D-leucine, 9: L-leucine, 10: D-norleucine, 11: L-norleucine

Reference

W.A. Koenig and G.J. Nicholson, Anal. Chem., 47, 951 (1975).

Summary

The authors reported the synthesis of two new dipeptide stationary phases for use in gas-liquid chromatography namely N-TFA-L-phenylalanyl-L-phenylalanine cyclohexyl ester (phe-phe) and N-TFA-L-phenylalanyl-L-aspartic acid bis(cyclohexyl)ester(phe-asp) and their properties in relation to enantiomer separation, temperature range of operation and thermal stability investigated. Glass capillaries were used rather than steel capillaries because of their higher efficiency and lower catalytic activity in causing decomposition of certain amino acids at elevated temperatures. The phase phe-asp has an upper temperature of around 165° which is considerably higher than that found in all previously reported phases of this type (it also has a m.p. of 96°C). Experimental details and results follow.

Gas Chromatography. A Carlo Erba gas chromatograph model Fractovap 2101 Milan, Italy) equipped with an all glass injection port, inlet splitter, and flame ionization detector was used. Hydrogen was employed as carrier gas.

Preparation of Glass Capillary Columns. Glass capillaries were drawn to the dimensions 0.9-mm o.d. and 0.30-mm i.d. with the glass drawing apparatus from Hupe and Busch (Karlsruhe-Groetzingen, Germany). The length of the capillaries used varied between 14 and 40 meters.

The following two methods were found to improve the stability of the coating (up to two months constant usage).

Method 1. A solution of 1% 3-aminopropyl triethoxy silane (Merck, Darmstadt, Germany) in CH_2Cl_2 was forced through the column, the ends were sealed, and the remaining film of reagent was allowed to react at 120–130 °C. Excess reagent was removed by washing with CH_2Cl_2, and the column subsequently coated by the static method as described by Bouche and Verzele (*16*) using 0.2% stationary phase dissolved in CH_2Cl_2. The column was then conditioned by slowly raising the temperature to above the melting point of the stationary phase.

In this way, we intended to form a stable chemical bond between the glass surface (Si-OH) and the aminopropyl-triethoxy silane and to link the stationary phase to the reagent by means of an aminolysis of the cyclohexyl ester.

Method 2. Soda-lime glass capillaries were etched with dry HCl gas according to the method of Novotny and Tesarik (*17*).

Synthesis of Dipeptide Derivatives. *N*-TFA-L-valyl-L-valine cyclohexyl ester was purchased from Miles Laboratories, Elkhart, IN. The phe-leu, phe-asp, and phe-phe phases were analogously synthesized by the method described by Koenig et al. (*10*) and recrystallized from diethyl ether. (Melting points: phe-leu 113 °C, phe-phe 136 °C, phe-asp 96 °C.)

Retention Indices. In order to measure the relative volatility of the dipeptide phases, the retention indices were determined on a 2-m glass column packed with 3% OV 17 on Gas Chrom Q at 280 °C. ($I_{\text{phe-asp}} = 3545$, $I_{\text{phe-phe}} = 3342$, $I_{\text{phe-leu}} = 2825$, $I_{N\text{-Lauroyl-L-val-}tert\text{-butylamide}} = 2400$, $I_{\text{val-val}} = 2260$).

Preparation of Amino Acid Derivatives was carried out according to (*10*).

(10) W. A. Koenig, W. Parr, H. A. Lichtenstein, E. Bayer, and J. Orò, *J. Chromatogr. Sci.*, **8**, 183 (1970).

(16) J. Bouche and M. Verzele, *J. Gas Chromatogr.*, **6**, 501 (1968).
(17) M. Novotny and K. Tesarik, *Chromatographia*, **1**, 332 (1968).

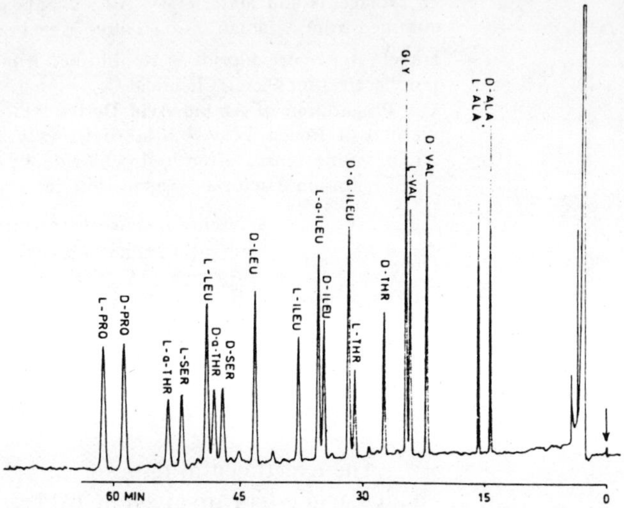

Figure 1. Separation of TFA-amino acid isopropyl esters on 39-m glass capillary coated with *N*-TFA-L-val-L-val cyclohexyl ester. Column temperature, 110 °C

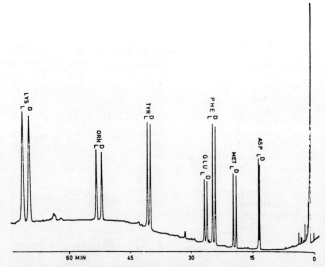

Figure 2. Separation of pentafluoropropionyl amino acid isopropyl esters on 20-m glass capillary coated with *N*-TFA-L-phe-L-asp bis-(cyclohexyl) ester. Column temperature, 130 °C, temperature program, 1 °C/min to 165 °C

Reference
S. Weinstein, B. Feibush and E. Gil-Av, J. Chromatogr., 126, 97 (1976).

Summary
The authors demonstrate via the results reported in the paper that it sufficies for a chiral stationary phase used in gas-liquid chromatography to contain an amide group and an asymmetric carbon atom attached to the nitrogen atom [$RCONHCH(CH_3)R'$], in order to show selectivity in its interaction with the enantiomers of amides such as N-trifluoroacetyl amines, N-trifluoroacetylamino acid esters and α-methyl- and α-phenylcarboxylic acid amides. The best efficiency is obtained when R' is aromatic, particularly α-naphthyl, as in N-lauroyl-S-α-(1-naphthyl)ethylamine.

The highest resolution factors were found for aromatic solutes, such as N-trifluoroacetyl-α-phenylethylamine and α-phenylbutyric acid amides which could be resolved readily on packed columns.

The enantiomers of α-branched carboxylic acids were separated for the first time by gas chromatography. Experimental details and results follow:

Synthesis of amides

Equimolar ice-cold solutions of freshly distilled lauroyl chloride and the corresponding chiral amine in dry chloroform were slowly mixed. A 10% excess of triethylamine was added and the solution left overnight in the cold (5–10°). The solution was washed successively with water, saturated sodium hydrogen carbonate solution, 2% hydrochloric acid and water. After drying over magnesium sulphate and evaporation, the amides were crystallized several times from chloroform–*n*-hexane**.

Synthesis of hydroaromatic amides

These amides were prepared by catalytic hydrogenation of the corresponding aromatic amides with 5% rhodium–alumina in methanolic solution at a hydrogen pressure of 60 p.s.i. for 24 h. The catalyst was filtered off, the solution evaporated and the amides were purified by column chromatography with silica gel and light petroleum–dichloromethane as the eluent.

Synthesis of N-methylamides

N-Methylamides were prepared from the amides by treatment with methyl iodide in dimethylformamide in the presence of silver oxide for several days at room temperature[7].

Carbonylbis-(N-L-valine isopropyl ester) (V). This phase was purchased from Miles-Yeda, Rehovot, Israel.

The properties of the *S*-monoamide phases were as follows:

Phase	*M.p. (°C)*	$[\alpha]_D$	*(c in $CHCl_3$)*
I	62	−66.0	(1.5)
II	86	−10.0	(1.5)
III	96–97	−59.6	(1.5)
IV	76–80	+ 6.4	(2.0)

The structures of all of the phases were confirmed by NMR and IR spectroscopy and microanalysis.

* TFA = trifluoroacetyl.
** Phase III can be obtained from Yeda, Rehovot, Israel.

Synthesis of solutes

N-TFA amines[5] and N-TFA amino acid esters[8] were synthesized as described previously.

Aliphatic α-methylcarboxylic acids were prepared from α-methyl diethylmalonate[9] by the malonic ester synthesis[10] with the corresponding alkyl bromide.

α-Phenylbutyric acid and α-phenylpropionic acid were purchased from Norse

S. Weinstein, B. Feibush and E. Gil-Av, J. Chromatogr., <u>126</u>, 97 (1976) continued.

TABLE II

RESOLUTION OF N-TFA-AMINO ACID ESTERS ON N-LAUROYL-*S*-α-(1-NAPHTHYL)ETHYLAMINE (III)*

α-Amino acid	*t* (°C)	*Alcohol residue* Me			Et			*n*-Pr			*i*-Pr			*n*-Butyl			3-*n*-Pentyl		
		*r(min)***	$r_{L/D}$***	R_s†	*r(min)***	$r_{L/D}$***	R_s†	*r(min)***	$r_{L/D}$***	R_s†	*r(min)***	$r_{L,D}$***	R_s†	*r(min)***	$r_{L/D}$***	R_s†	*r(min)***	$r_{L,D}$***	R_s†
Ala	100	59.7 56.7	1.053	0.95	82.3 78.3	1.052	0.95	157.0 149.0	1.054	1.0	85.6 82.2	1.042	0.9	303.5 288.5	1.052	1.5	86.8 83.0	1.046	1.0
	120	28.8 27.6	1.043	0.9	37.5 36.0	1.042	0.9	78.4 75.0	1.045	0.9	39.2 37.8	1.037	0.9	126.4 120.9	1.045	1.5	37.5 36.0	1.042	1.0
Val	100	71.1 67.4	1.054	1.0							104.3 98.8	1.055	0.9						
	120	33.8 32.5	1.040	0.9							36.0 34.5	1.042	0.9						
Leu	100	200.0 ~200.0	sh††	—	270.0 270.0	sh††	—	549.0 538.0	1.020	0.9	320.0 320.0	1.000	—	1015.0 990.0	1.025	1.0			
	120	75.0 75.0	1.000	—	120.0 120.0	1.000	—				95.0 95.0	1.000	—				80.0 80.0	1.000	—
tert.-Leu	100	59.1 56.5	1.044	0.9							58.2 56.1	1.034	0.3						
	130										20.3 19.7	1.030	0.6						
Pro	100	203.1 195.5	1.039	0.9							170.0 166.0	1.024	0.5						
	130	61.0 59.2	1.028	0.3															
Phenyl-Gly	130										62.7 61.0	1.027	—						
Phe	130	270.0 270.0	1.000	—															
α-Methyl α-amino acid																			
α-Me-*tert.*-Leu	100	82.2 80.7	1.018	0.3															
α-Me-Val	100	72.9 72.3	1.008	—															
α-Me-Leu	100	60.0 60.0	1.000	—															
α-Me-Norleu	100	105.5 102.5	1.029	0.5															
α-Me-Norval	100	62.8 61.7	1.018	0.3															

* See Table I.
** See Table I.
*** Ratio of the corrected retention times of the L-enantiomer over that of the D-isomer. Assignment was made with optically enriched mixtures, except for *tert.*-leucine for which the order of emergence was deduced by extrapolation.
† See Table I.
†† sh = shoulder.

S. Weinstein, B. Feibush and E. Gil-Av, J. Chromatogr., 126, 97 (1976) continued.

Labs., Santa Barbara, Calif., U.S.A.

The acids were converted to the amides via the acyl chlorides by treatment with the corresponding amine in the presence of a 10% excess of triethylamine.

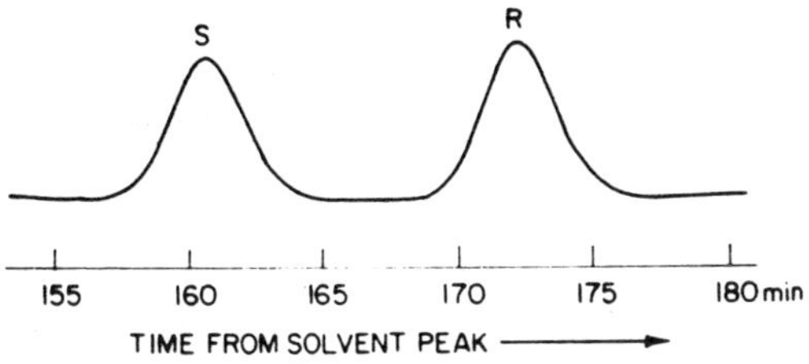

Fig. 3. Resolution of α-phenylbutyric acid *tert.*-butylamide. Chromatographic conditions as in Fig. 2; temperature, 150°.

TABLE III

RESOLUTION OF α-METHYL- AND α-PHENYLCARBOXYLIC ACID AMIDES

Compound	*Optically active stationary phase*							
	N-Lauroyl-S-α-phenylethylamine (I) *			*N-Lauroyl-S-α-(1-naphthyl)ethylamine (III)* *			*Carbonylbis-(N-L-valine isopropyl ester) (V)* *	
	r (min) **	$r_{II/I}$ ***	R_s §	*r (min)* **	$r_{II/I}$ ***	R_s §	*r (min)* **	$r_{II/I}$ ***
Aliphatic acids, RCHCONHR' (with CH_3 on CH)								
$R=CH_3CH_2$ $R'=(CH_3)_3C$	45.0 45.0	1.000 (120°)	—	175.0 175.0	1.000 (100°)	—		
$R=(CH_3)_2CHCH_2CH_2$ $R'=(CH_3)_3C$	76.0 74.1	1.026 (140°)	0.7	119.6 115.3	1.037 (130°)	0.6	47.1 45.1	1.043 (120°)
				756.3 714.0	1.059 (100°)	2.0		
$R'=(CH_3)_2CH$ $R'=CH_3$	149.3 146.2	1.021 (140°)	0.4	230.5 222.7	1.035 (130°)	0.8	98.6 96.3	1.024 (120°)
							147.0 142.9	1.028 (120°)
Aromatic acids $RCHCONHC(CH_3)_3$ (with C_6H_5 on CH)								
$R=CH_3$	*R* 212.5 *S* 205.0	1.036 (130°)	1.5	*R* 352.5 *S* 335.5	1.051 (130°)	1.0		
$R=CH_3CH_2$				*R* 482.0 *S* 441.0	1.093 (130°)	3.0		

* Chromatographed on stainless-steel columns of the following dimensions: (I) 400 ft. × 0.02 in. I.D.; (III) 400 ft. × 0.02 in. I.D.; (V) 150 ft. × 0.02 in. I.D.

** See Table I.

*** Ratio of the corrected retention time of the second peak over that of the first peak.

§ See Table I.

5 B. Feibush and E. Gil-Av, *J. Gas Chromatogr.*, 5 (1967) 257.
6 J. A. Corbin and L. B. Rogers, *Anal. Chem.*, 42 (1970) 974.
7 B. C. Das, S. D. Gero and E. Lederer, *Biochem. Biophys. Res. Commun.*, 29 (1967) 211.
8 S. Nakaparksin, P. Birrell, E. Gil-Av and J. Oró, *J. Chromatogr. Sci.*, 8 (1970) 177.
9 *Org. Syn.*, Collect Vol. II (1943) 272 and 279.
10 A. I. Vogel, *Practical Organic Chemistry*, Longmans, London, 3rd ed., 1955, p. 483.

Reference

K. Stölting and W.A. König, Chromatographia, 9, 331 (1976).

Summary

The authors report the separation of the enantiomers of a number of α-amino acids on a chiral stationary phase N-TFA-L-prolyl-L-proline cyclohexyl ester which does not allow the formation of hydrogen bonds between solvent and solutes. Based on molecular model studies, the authors rationalize that van der Waal attractive forces and dipole-dipole interactions are responsible for the selectivities of separation and that closer association is possible between the L-phase and the L-enantiomer than between the L-phase and the D-enantiomer. Experimental details and results follow:

Die Synthese von N-Trifluoracetyl-L-Prolyl-L-Prolin-Cyclohexylester erfolgte analog zu der in [2] beschriebenen Vorschrift durch Kupplung von N-t-BOC-L-Prolin mit L-Prolincyclohexylester. Dicyclohexylcarbodiimid wurde als Kondensationsmittel eingesetzt. Das Endprodukt fiel als dünnschicht- und gas-chromatographisch einheitliches Öl an (MS: M^+ = m/e 320; $[\alpha]_D^{23} = -126{,}2°$, CH_3OH).

Tabelle I. Trennfaktor α für verschiedene enantiomere Aminosäure-Derivate, getrennt an N-Trifluoracetyl-L-Prolyl-L-Prolin-Cyclohexylester [a].

N-Trifluoracetyl-Aminosäure-Isopropylester[c]	Trennfaktor
DL-Ala	1,047
DL-Val	1,048
DL-Thr[b]	1,034
DL-Nval	1,022
DL-*a*-Thr[b]	1,050
DL-Leu	1,006
DL-*a*-Ile	1,040
DL-Ile	1,018
DL-Pro	1,03

[a] 30 m Glaskapillare, 118 °C Säulentemperatur, Trägergas: He, 0,5 atü; Splitverhältnis 1 : 50; Gerät: Carlo Erba Modell 2101

[b] N, O-Bis-Trifluoracetyl-Derivat

[c] Herstellung der Derivate nach [2]

[2] *König, W.A., Parr, W., Lichtenstein, H.A., Bayer, E.* und *Oró, J.*, J. Chromatogr. Sci. 8, 177 (1970).

Reference
M.A. van Dort and W.A. Bonner, J. Chromatogr., 133, 210 (1977).

Summary
The authors report the resolution by gas liquid chromatography of DL-leucine as the diastereomeric (+) and (-)-2-butyl esters on chiral N-lauroyl-S-valyl-tert-butylamide stationary phase, followed by a Ucon H 90,000 achiral phase placed in tandem. Experimental conditions and results follow:

Gas chromatographic analyses

All GC analyses were performed using a Hewlett-Packard Model 5700A gas chromatograph coupled to a Hewlett-Packard Model 3380A digital electronic integrator–recorder. Column A consisted of a 150 ft. × 0.02 in. stainless-steel capillary column coated with N-lauroyl-*S*-valyl-*tert*.-butylamide phase[7]. Column B consisted of a similar 150 ft. × 0.02 in. column coated with Ucon H 90,000 phase. Operating conditions for the GC traces in Fig. 1 were: 1A, 120° isothermal, nitrogen flow-rate *ca.* 1.6 ml/min; 1B, 125° isothermal, nitrogen flow-rate *ca.* 1 ml/min; 1C, 119° isothermal, nitrogen flow-rate *ca.* 1 ml/min. The eflux times (min) at each peak maximum are shown adjacent to each corresponding peak in Fig. 1.

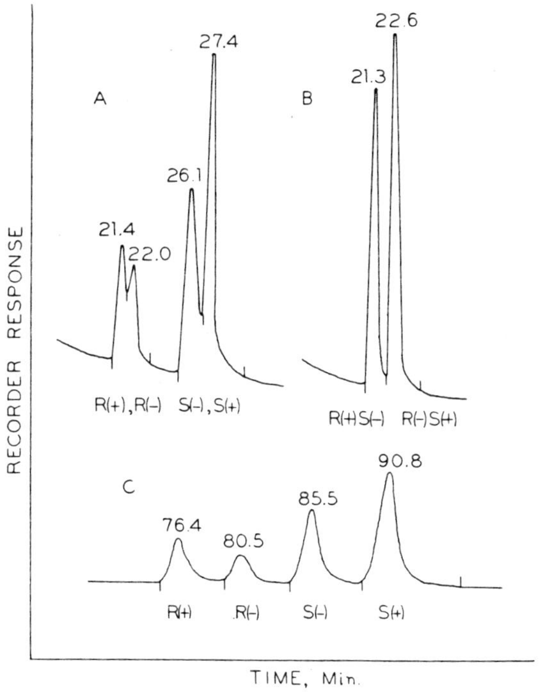

Fig. 1. Gas chromatograms of *RS*-leucine (±)-2-butyl ester diastereomer mixture with various columns. A, N-Lauroyl-*S*-valyl-*tert*.-butylamide phase; B, Ucon H 90,000 phase; C, columns A and B *in tandem*. Operational conditions: see Experimental.

TABLE I

GAS CHROMATOGRAPHIC ANALYSES OF *RS*-LEUCINE (±)-2-BUTYL ESTER DIASTEREOMERS

Column	*Percent of diastereomer in mixture*						*Figure*
	R(+)	*R(−)*	*S(−)*	*S(+)*	*R(+)S(−)*	*R(−)S(+)*	
Known composition	15.7	10.2	29.0	45.1	44.7	55.3	
A	12.8	11.9	26.6	48.7	39.4	60.6	1A
B	—	—	—	—	44.9	55.1	1B
A + B ± st. dev.	15.6* ± 0.3	9.3* ± 0.3	29.5* ± 0.4	45.5* ± 0.4	45.1 ± 0.5	54.8 ± 0.5	1C
B (error)**	—	—	—	—	−0.2	0.2	
A + B (error)**	0.1	0.9	−0.5	−0.4	−0.4	0.5	

* Average of closest 5 out of 6 replicate analyses.
** Percent known − percent observed.

7 B. Feibush, *Chem. Commun.*, (1971) 544.

Reference

J.P. Kamerling, G.J. Gerwig, J.F.G. Vliegenthart, M. Duran, D. Ketting and S.K. Wadman, J. Chromatogr., 143, 117 (1977).

Summary

The separation of the enantiomers of lactic and glyceric acids was achieved by capillary gas chromatography on SP-1000 using the O-acetylated menthyl esters. Experimental details and results follow:

Synthesis of O-acetylated menthyl esters of lactic and glyceric acids

(−)-Menthol (300 mg) was added to 1—5 mg of dry hydroxy acid and esterified at 110° for 2 h by bubbling dry HCl gas through the solution [10]. Subsequently, the excess of HCl and menthol was removed by a gentle stream of nitrogen at 110°. To avoid possible losses of the volatile menthyl ester of lactic acid, it is advisable not to remove menthol completely. The residue was acetylated in 1 ml of pyridine—acetic anhydride (1:1) at 100° for 30 min. Finally, the solvent was evaporated in the presence of absolute ethanol and the residue dissolved in chloroform.

Capillary gas—liquid chromatography

A Varian Aerograph 2740-30-01 gas chromatograph equipped with a flame-ionization detector and a glass capillary column (25 m × 0.3 mm I.D.) coated with SP-1000 (LKB, Stockholm, Sweden) as stationary phase was used. For direct on-column injection (0.1—0.2 μl) without a stream splitter, a Pasteur pipette (length 140 mm, I.D. 1 mm) was used as the inlet, connected to the column with shrinkable PTFE. As the outlet to the detector, a second pipette (length 110 mm, I.D. 0.5 mm) was used. The carrier gas (nitrogen) flow-rate was 1 ml/min and the make-up gas (nitrogen) flow-rate was 30 ml/min. The injection port temperature was 200° and the detector temperature 220°; the oven temperature was 150° for lactic acid and 200° for glyceric acid.

Proton magnetic resonance spectroscopy

The proton magnetic resonance (PMR) spectra of the menthyl esters of *R,S*-lactic acid and *R,S*-glyceric acid as well as those of (−)-menthol, *R,S*-lactic acid and *R,S*-glyceric acid were recorded at 60 MHz with a Varian EM-360 spectrometer in CD_3OD as solvent and tetramethylsilane as internal standard at room temperature.

Gas chromatography—mass spectrometry

The 75-eV mass spectra of the O-acetylated menthyl esters of *R,S*-lactic acid and *R,S*-glyceric acid were recorded on a Jeol JGC-20 KP/JMS-D100/W-JMA combination at an ion-source temperature of 150°, an accelerating voltage of 3 kV and an ionizing current of 300 μA. As the column material, 5% GESE-52 on Chromosorb W AW DMCS, 100—120 mesh (HP), was used. The oven temperature was dependent on the sample.

10 M. Hasegawa and I. Matsubara, Anal. Biochem., 63 (1975) 308.

J.P. Kamerling, J.G. Gerwig, J.F.G. Vliegenthart, M. Duran, D. Ketting and S.K. Wadman, J. Chromatogr., 143, 117 (1977) continued.

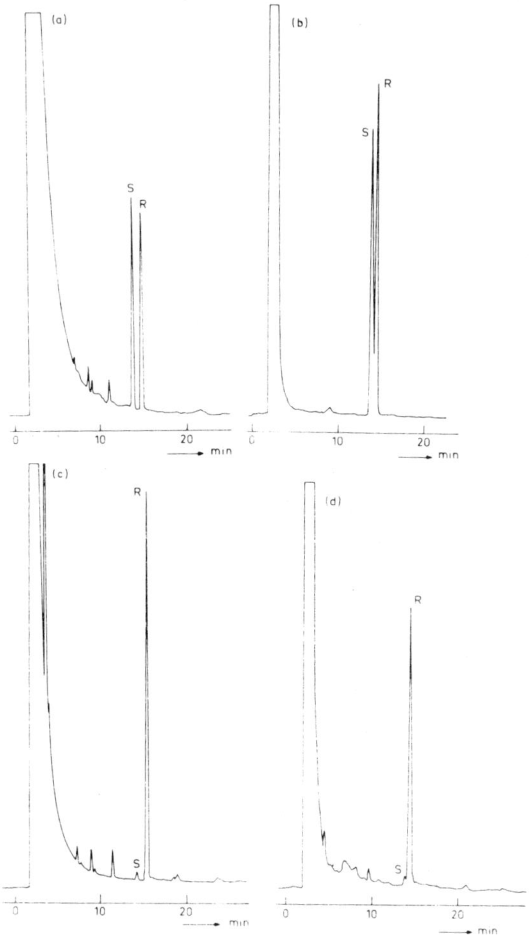

Fig. 3. Gas chromatograms of the O-acetylated menthyl esters of (a) synthetic *R,S*-lactic acid (150°), (b) synthetic *R,S*-glyceric acid (200°), (c) *R*-lactic acid isolated from urine (150°) and (d) *R*-glyceric acid isolated from urine (200°) on a glass capillary column (25 m × 0.3 mm I.D.) coated with SP-1000 as stationary phase (WCOT). The nitrogen flow-rate was 1 ml/min.

Reference
W.A. Koenig, K. Stoelting and K. Kruse, Chromatographia, 10, 444 (1977).

Summary
The authors report on the separation of α-amino acid enantiomers by gas-liquid chromatography in glass capillaries of their diastereomeric derivatives on chiral stationary phases in which hydrogen bond interactions are not the basis for the separation. To introduce a second chiral center into the enantiomers being separated, they were acylated with L-α-chloroisovaleryl chloride. Experimental details and results follow:

Experimental

Preparation of glass capillaries: capillaries (0.25 mm i d) were drawn from pyrex glass tubes with a Hupe and Busch glass drawing machine. Before coating the glass capillary was treated with 0.2 % suspension of Silanox (Cabot, Boston, Mass., USA) in CH_2Cl_2. The coating was performed according to the static procedure [18] with 0.1–0.2 % solutions of the stationary phase in CH_2Cl_2.

Formation of derivatives: L-α-chloroisovaleryl chloride was prepared according to *Greenstein* et al. [19]. Samples of about 10^{-4} g of amino acid methyl esters, amines or amino alcohols were treated with a mixture of 80 mm^3 CH_2Cl_2 and 20 mm^3 of L-α-chloroisovaleryl chloride at room temperature in a screw cap vial with Teflon lining in the cap. After removal of excess reagent in a N_2-stream the samples were injected into a Carlo Erba gas chromatograph, model 2101. The derivatives of amino alcohols and of hydroxy amino acids were dissolved in 50 mm^3 CH_2Cl_2 and 50 mm^3 N-methyl-N-trimethylsilyl-trifluoroacetamide (MSTFA, Macherey u. Nagel, Germany) and kept at room temperature for 30 min. The derivatives of chiral alcohols were obtained by adding about 1 mg of K_2CO_3 to the acylation mixture.

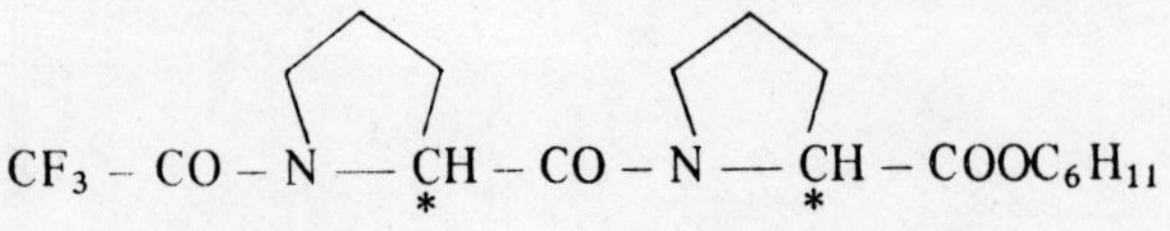
(1)

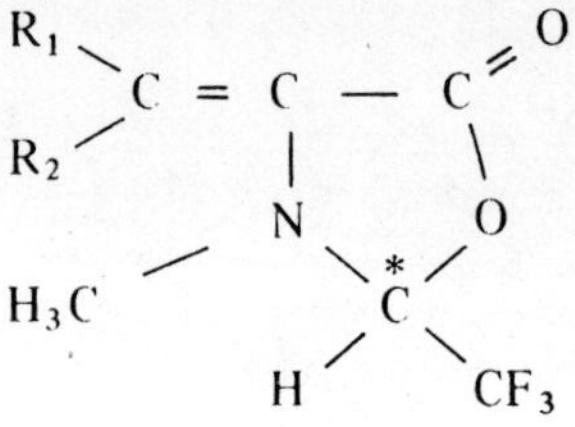
(2)

R_1	R_2
CH_3	CH_3
CH_3	CH_2CH_3
C_6H_5	H
C_3H_7	H

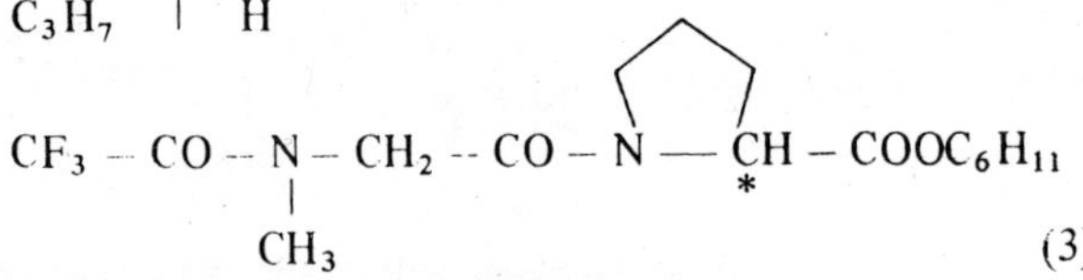
(3)

Stationary phases: chiral stationary phases were synthesized by the method described in [2].

[2] *W. A. Koenig, W. Parr, H. A. Lichtenstein, E. Bayer* and *J. Oró*, J. Chromatogr. Sci. 8, 183–186.

[8] *J. A. Corbin, J. E. Rhoad* and *L. B. Rogers*, Anal. Chem 43, 327–331 (1971).

[9] *W. Parr* and *P. Y. Howard*, J. Chromatogr. 71, 193–201 (1972).

W.A. Koenig, K. Stoelting and K. Kruse, Chromatographia, 10, 444 (1977) continued.

Table I. Separation factors α for L-α-chloroisovaleryl derivatives of DL-amino acid methyl esters in glass capillaries with different types of stationary phases

	Column I	Temp. [°C]	Column II	Temp. [°C]	Column III	Temp. [°C]
DL-ala	1.07	150	1.06	150	1.15	130
DL-abu	1.10	150	1.10	150	1.20	130
DL-val	1.13	150	1.11	150	1.22	130
DL-ile	1.10	150	1.09	150	1.20	130
DL-a-ile	1.10	150	1.09	150	1.21	130
DL-leu	1.07	150	1.06	150	1.19	130
DL-ser(OTMS)	1.07	150	–	–	–	–
DL-ser*	–	–	1.02	200	–	–
DL-thr(OTMS)	1.10	150	–	–	1.18	130
DL-thr*	–	–	1.07	200	–	–
DL-pro	1.07	150	1.04	200	1.24	130
DL-asp	1.02	150	1.03	200	1.04	150
DL-phe	–	–	1.06	200	1.12	150
DL-glu	–	–	1.03	200	1.14	150
DL-met	–	–	1.03	200	–	–
DL-orn	–	–	1.03	250	–	–
DL-lys	–	–	1.04	250	–	–
DL-trp	–	–	1.02	250	–	–
DL-N-Me-val	–	–	–	–	1.03	130
DL-N-Me-ile	1.08	150	–	–	1.06	130

* N,O-bis-L-α-chloroisovaleryl derivative

Column I = 33 m SE 30

Column II = 25 m AmAc (LKB)

Column III = 14 m N-TFA-L-phe-L-asp-bis-cyclohexyl ester

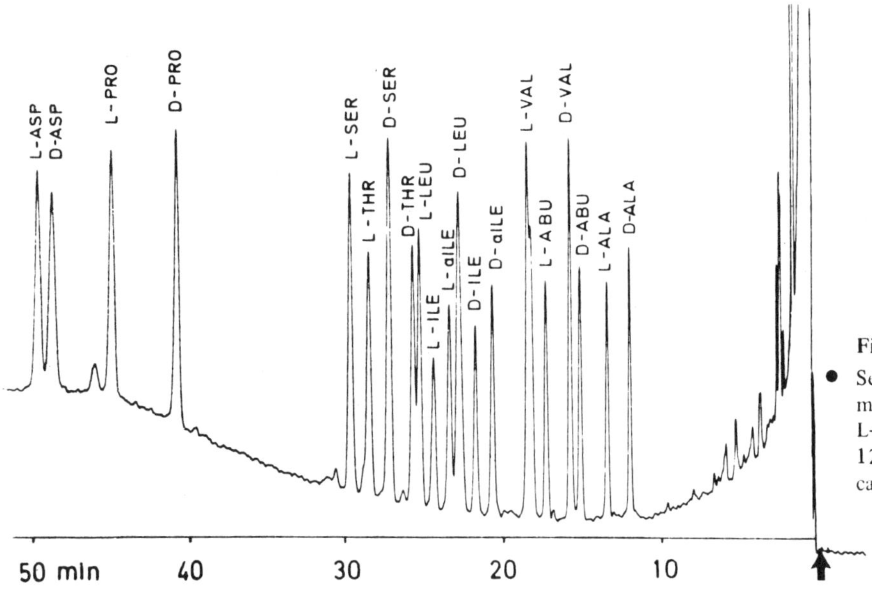

Fig. 1

Separation of N-(L-α-chloroisovaleryl)-DL-amino acid methyl esters. 14 m glass capillary coated with N-TFA-L-phe-L-asp-bis-cyclohexyl ester; column temperature 125 °C; temperature program: 1.5 °C min^{-1} to 160 °C; carrier gas H_2, 0.4 × $10^5 Nm^{-2}$

Reference

H. Frank, G.J. Nicholson and E. Bayer, J. Chromatogr. Sci., 15, 174 (1977).

Summary

Using a copolymer of dimethylsiloxane and carboxyalkylmethylsiloxane units onto which was grafted N-propionyl-L-valine-t-butylamide enabled the authors to separate most of the amino acid enantiomers as their N-pentafluoropropionylisopropylesters in less than 30 minutes. The most striking advantage of the adsorbent is its thermal stability at temperatures of up to 175° for extended periods of time. Experimental details and results follow:

Gas chromatography is carried out on a Carlo Erba, model 2101, with hydrogen as carrier gas on open tubular columns made of AR-Glass (Schott & Gen.), about 20 m × 0.3 mm, pretreated with colloidal silicic acid (10) or aerosil (11) to stabilize the film of stationary phase. The columns are coated with 0.15% stationary phase in chloroform by the static method and conditioned at 175°C with a slow hydrogen stream. Amino acid derivatives are prepared by heating 300 - 500 μg of D,L-amino acids for one hour at 100°C with 2 N hydrogen chloride in isopropanol, evaporating the reagent and dissolving it in 250 μl methylene chloride and 50 μl pentafluoropropionic anhydride. After one hour at room temperature the solvent is evaporated and the residue dissolved in 200 μl chloroform.

Table I. Retention times (t_{m+s}) and resolution factors ($\alpha_{L/D}$) of N(O,S)-pentafluoropropionyl-D,L-amino acid isopropylesters at given temperatures.
A: N-Propionyl-L-valine t-butylamide polysiloxane, conditioned for 3 days at 170°C.
B: N-n-docosanoyl-L-valine t-butylamide.

	A: T(°C)	$\alpha_{L/D}$	t_{m+s}(min)	B: T(°C)	$\alpha_{L/D}$	t_{m+s}(min)
Ala	100	1.129	3	100	1.240	2.1
Val	100	1.117	3.5	100	1.200	2.8
Thr	100	1.069	4.5	100	1.125	2.5
a-Ile	100	1.148	5	100	1.200	4.0
Ile	100	1.158	6	100	1.192	4.4
Pro	100	1.005	7	100	1.025	6.3
Leu	100	1.222	8	100	1.375	6.3
Ser	120	1.052	4.5	100	1.081	4.6
Cys	120	1.060	5.0	120	1.118	4.1
Asp	120	1.031	9	120	1.027	6.3
Met	140	1.079	7	140	1.140	5.8
Glu	140	1.108	8	*		
Phe	140	1.086	8	140	1.132	8.5
Tyr	170	1.078	6	*		
Orn	170	1.081		*		
Lys	170	1.065		*		
Trp	170	1.044	16	*		

*The column bled severely and expired after a few hours.

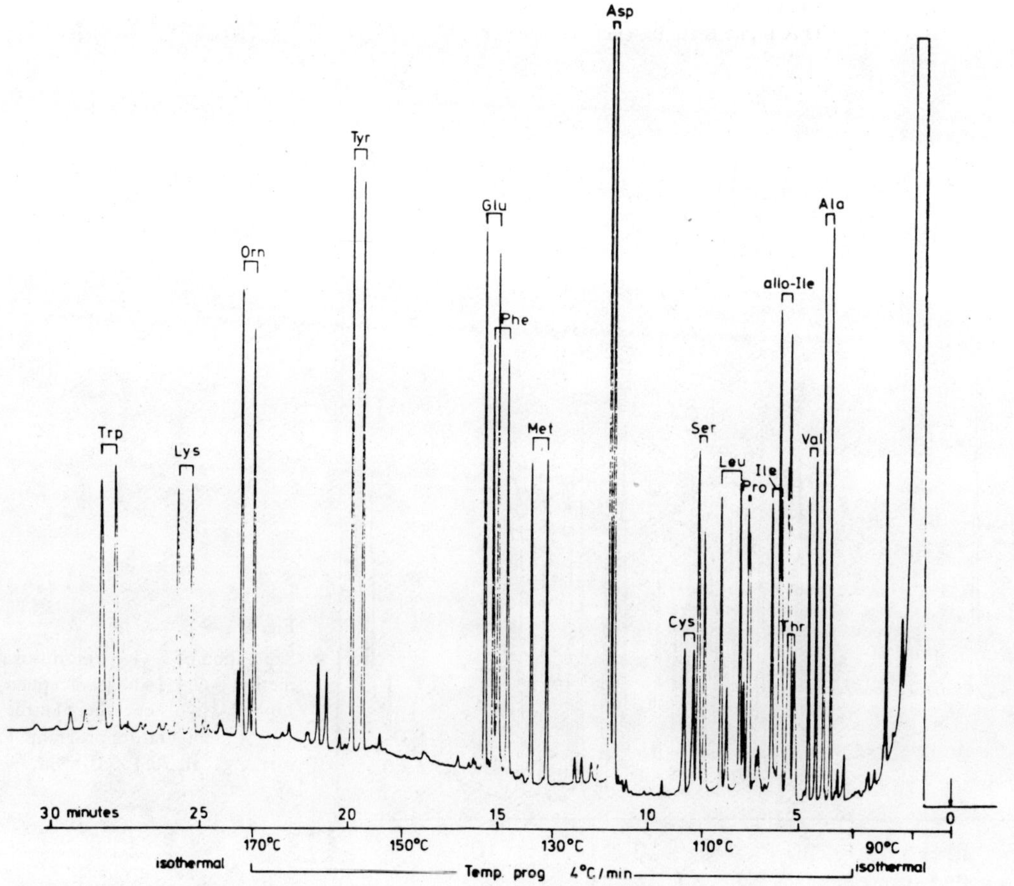

Figure 1. Gas chromatogram of a synthetic mixture of 17 N-pentafluoropropionyl-D,L-amino acid iso-propylesters on a 18 m X 0.3 mm open tubular column coated with N-propionyl-L-valine t-butylamide polysiloxane.

The first peak of each amino acid represents the D-enantiomer.

Reference

I. Abe, T. Kohno and S. Musha, Chromatographia, 11, 393 (1978).

Summary

N-trifluoroacetylmethyl and isopropyl ester derivatives of 16 racemic α-amino acids were resolved by chromatography on N-caproyl-L-valyl-L-valine as a chiral stationary phase. This phase is temperature stable and can even be operated at temperatures up to 150°C when coated on a glass capillary column. The experimental details and results follow:

Apparatus and Measurements

The analyses were carried out in a Hitachi Model 063 gas chromatograph equipped with a flame ionization detector and a Hitachi Model 056 chart recorder. The following conditions were used: injector temperature, 200 °C; detector temperature, 250 °C; split ratio, 1:80. Helium was used as the carrier gas.

The relative retention (r L/D) data were calculated using the adjusted retention time (t'_R) values:

$$r\,(L/D) = t'_R\ (\text{L enantiomer}) \,/\, t'_R\ (\text{D enantiomer}).$$

For the calculation of the adjusted retention time, the retention time of methane was taken as the gas holdup time. In order to simplify the measurements, methane gas was bubbled into the sample solutions prior to determination.

Synthesis of N-caproyl-L-valyl-L-valine cyclohexyl ester

N-caproyl-L-valine [13] and L-valine cyclohexyl ester hydrogen chloride [6] were synthesized according to the references. N-caproyl-L-valyl-L-valine cyclohexyl ester (CVV) was prepared by a coupling procedure similar to that described by *Parr* and *Howard* [13]. This product was recrystallized from n-hexane and dried under high vacuum over P_2O_5 for 24 hours. The end product had the following characteristic data:

m.p. = 113 °C; $[\alpha]_D^{25} = -28.6°$ (c = 0.7 in $CHCl_3$)

elementary composition:
theoretical $C = 66.63\,\%$, $H = 10.17\,\%$, $N = 7.06\,\%$
found: $C = 66.25\,\%$, $H = 10.54\,\%$, $N = 7.19\,\%$

Preparation of N-TFA-amino acid methyl and isopropyl ester derivatives

The amino acid derivatives were prepared as described [6]. A 2-mg aliquot of the DL-amino acid or 1:3 mixture of enantiomeric amino acids was dissolved in about 3 cm³ of methanol or isopropanol containing about 3N HCl. Pyrex 16 X 75 mm glass screw-top culture tubes with teflon-lined caps (Corning 9826) were used. The solution was heated to 100 °C for three hours and then the excess solvent and HCl removed on a rotary evaporator. About 3 cm³ of methylene chloride was added to the residue and the reaction vessel with $CaCl_2$ drying tube was cooled in acetone-dry ice bath. About 1 cm³ of trifluoroacetic anhydride was added to this solution and then left at room temperature for one hour. The excess reagents and solvent were eliminated by evaporation to dryness on a rotary evaporator. The remaining derivative was then dissolved in 1 cm³ of chloroform. From this solution, 2–6 mm³ aliquots were injected into gas chromatograph.

Column preparation

The column used in this study was prepared of a Pyrex glass capillary tube, 50 m long with 0.25 mm ID. The capillary tube was drawn by a machine which was a slightly modified version of the type described by *Desty* et al. [15]. The glass tubing was first filled with 2 % HF solution for 24 hours in order to etch the inner surface. After this etching, the capillary was washed with water, acetone and methylene chloride. Finally dry nitrogen gas was passed through the capillary overnight. A 0.5 cm³ plug of a 10 % solution (0.1 g in 1 cm³ CH_2Cl_2) of the CVV was passed through the capillary according to the dynamic coating method, at a plug velocity of about 2 cm/sec. One end of the column was connected to a second glass capillary tubing, 10-m long with 0.25 mm ID, in order to prevent the coating film from rupturing due to changes in the flow rate as the plug emerged from the column proper. After the coating solution has completely passed through the capillary, the remaining solvent traces were removed by continuing the passage of nitrogen gas for overnight. The column was conditioned in the chromatograph by slowly rising the temperature at a rate of 1 °C/min from room temperature to 160 °C and then maintaining at this temperature for 24 hours.

Fig. 2

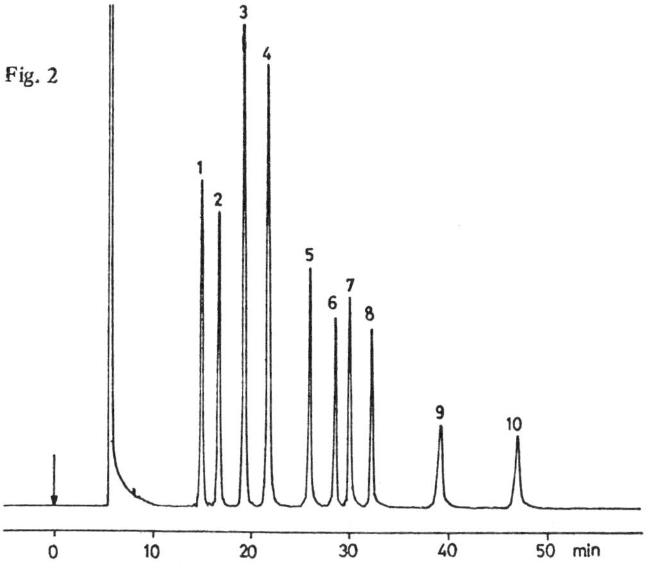

Chromatogram of TFA-DL-amino acid isopropyl esters, at 110 °C. Peaks: *1* D-alanine, *2* L-alanine, *3* D-valine, *4* L-valine, *5* D-allo-isoleucine, *6* D-isoleucine, *7* L-allo-isoleucine, *8* L-isoleucine, *9* D-leucine, *10* L-leucine.

I. Abe, T. Kohno and S. Musha, Chromatographia, 11, 393 (1978) continued.

Table I. Retention data of volatile N,0-trifluoroacetyl amino acid esters at 110 °C*

Amino Acid		Methyl Ester retention time (min)	r (L/D)	Isopropyl Ester retention time (min)	r (L/D)
Alanine	D	13.4	1.134	14.5	1.179
	L	14.5		16.2	
α-amino-n-butyric acid	D	16.3	1.147	18.1	1.194
	L	18.0		20.6	
Valine	D	16.5	1.123	18.6	1.166
	L	17.9		20.9	
Threonine	D	21.2	1.098	21.9	1.150
	L	22.8		24.4	
allo-Isoleucine	D	22.9	1.166	25.2	1.193
	L	25.9		29.1	
Isoleucine	D	24.9	1.118	27.6	1.161
	L	27.3		31.3	
Norvaline	D	25.9	1.145	27.7	1.192
	L	28.9		32.1	
Glycine		24.4		27.8	
Leucine	D	36.8	1.174	37.9	1.231
	L	42.4		45.5	
Proline	D	36.4	1.026	40.1	1.025
	L	37.3		41.0	
Norleucine	D	40.7	1.155	43.3	1.208
	L	46.2		51.2	
Serine	D	45.8	1.070	43.7	1.108
	L	48.7		47.9	

* gas holdup time (methane): 5.01 min.

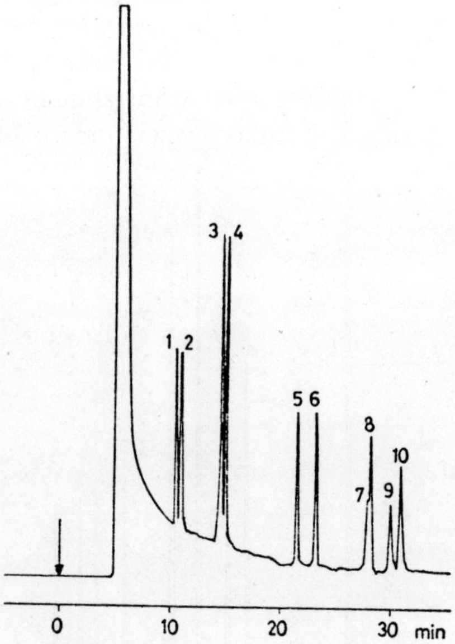

Fig. 3

Chromatogram of less volatile TFA-DL-amino acid isopropyl esters at 150 °C. Peaks: *1* D-cysteine, *2* L-cysteine, *3* D-aspartic acid, *4* L-aspartic acid, *5* D-methionine, *6* L-methionine, *7* D-glutamic acid, *8* D-phenylalanine, *9* L-glutamic acid, *10* L-phenylalanine.

Table II. Retention data of volatile N,O-trifluoroacetyl amino acid esters at 130 °C*

Amino Acid		Methyl Ester retention time (min)	r (L/D)	Isopropyl Ester retention time (min)	r (L/D)
Alanine	D	12.4	1.105	14.5	1.135
	L	13.2		15.7	
α-amino-n-butyric acid	D	14.7	1.103	17.6	1.138
	L	15.7		19.3	
Valine	D	14.6	1.085	18.1	1.121
	L	15.4		19.7	
Threonine	D	17.7	1.075	20.7	1.112
	L	18.6		22.4	
allo-Isoleucine	D	19.2	1.113	23.4	1.140
	L	20.8		25.9	
Isoleucine	D	20.3	1.091	25.2	1.117
	L	21.7		27.5	
Norvaline	D	21.5	1.110	25.3	1.146
	L	23.2		28.3	
Glycine		22.9		25.7	
Leucine	D	28.2	1.125	32.8	1.168
	L	31.1		37.5	
Proline	D	30.2	1.025	37.0	1.020
	L	30.9		37.7	
Norleucine	D	31.6	1.112	37.6	1.152
	L	34.6		42.6	
Serine	D	35.0	1.061	38.4	1.085
	L	36.8		41.2	

* gas holdup time (methane): 5.24 min.

Table III. Retention data of less volatile N,S-trifluoroacetyl amino acid esters at 150 °C*

Amino Acid		Methyl Ester retention time (min)	r (L/D)	Isopropyl Ester retention time (min)	r (L/D)
Cysteine	D	14.9	1.060	16.6	1.072
	L	15.5		17.4	
Aspartic acid	D	16.8	1.031	24.2	1.042
	L	17.2		25.0	
Methionine	D	34.6	1.091	39.2	1.117
	L	37.3		43.1	
Glutamic acid	D	36.1	1.069	52.4	1.097
	L	38.2		57.0	
Phenylalanine	D	44.4	1.095	52.8	1.121
	L	48.2		58.6	

* gas holdup time (methane): 5.22 min.

[6] *S. Nakaparksin, P. Birrel, E. Gil-Av* and *J. Oró*, J. Chromatogr. Sci. 8, 177 (1970).

[13] *K. Grohman* and *W. Parr*, Chromatographia 5, 18 (1972).

[15] *D. H. Desty, J. N. Haresnape* and *B. H. F. Whyman*, Anal. Chem. 32, 303 (1960).

Reference
T. Saeed, P. Sandra and M. Verzele, J. Chromatogr., 186, 611 (1979).

Summary
A chiral stationary phase has been synthesized by grafting L-valine-tert-butyl-amide onto a modified form of the well known gas chromatographic stationary phase polycyanopropylmethyl phenylmethylsilicone (OV-225). This chiral phase can be used for the separation of α-amino acid enantiomers at temperatures ranging from 60° to 230°. Experimental details and results follow:

Synthesis of the chiral phase

The synthetic pathway is shown in Fig. 1.

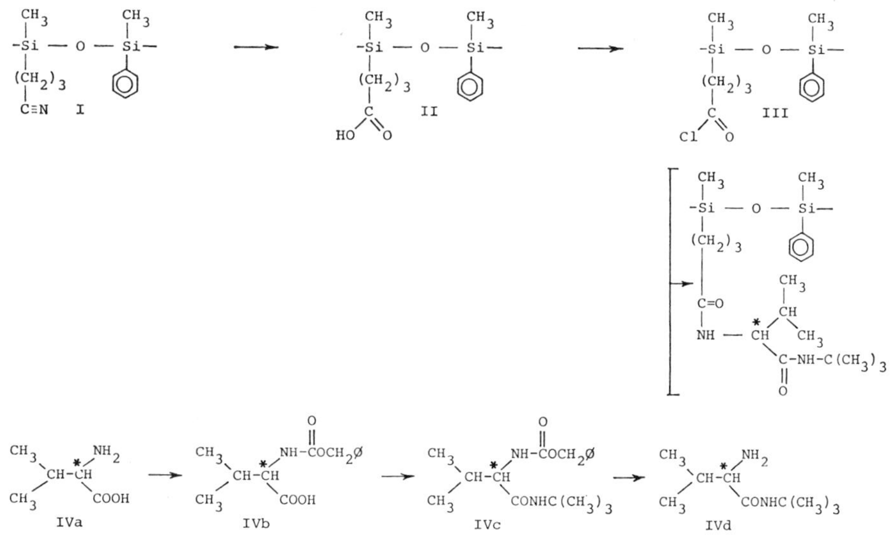

Fig. 1. Synthetic pathway for the chiral stationary phase.

The cyano group (I) of OV-225 is hydrolysed to the carboxylic function (II). By conversion to the acid chloride (III), a site is created for reaction with L-valine–*tert.*-butylamide. The latter compound (IVd) is synthesized by coupling carbobenzoxy-L-valine (IVb) and *tert.*-butylamine (IVc). The protecting group is removed and the amide is linked to the polymer. Details of the synthesis are given below.

Synthesis of chloropropionylmethyl phenylmethyl silicone. OV-225 (1–10 g) is dissolved in diethyl ether and the cyano group is converted into the carboxylic function by acid hydrolysis. The reaction is followed by infrared (IR) spectroscopy. The total conversion of the cyano group (IR band 2270 cm^{-1}) to the carboxylic group (IR band 1730 cm^{-1}) marks the completion of the reaction. A 1-g amount of the acid thus obtained is dissolved in 50 ml of dry benzene. The mixture is cooled in an ice–salt bath and 3 ml of freshly distilled oxalyl chloride are added dropwise with constant stirring. After the evolution of hydrogen chloride gas, the mixture is refluxed for 1 h. The acid group is quantitatively converted to the acid chloride function as can be followed by IR spectroscopy (the 1730 cm^{-1} IR band shifts to 1815 cm^{-1}). Benzene and residual oxalyl chloride are removed on a rotary evaporator and the acid chloride is immediately dissolved in dry diethyl ether.

Synthesis of L*-valine–tert.-butylamide.* To a solution of 0.01 mole (1.17 g) of L-valine in 20 ml of water, 0.1 *N* sodium hydroxide solution is added until the pH of the solution is 10. The mixture is cooled in an ice–salt bath and 0.01 mole (1.7 g) of carbobenzoxy chloride, dissolved in 10 ml of diethyl ether, is added dropwise. During the reaction, the pH of the mixture is maintained at 10 by adding 0.1 *N* sodium hydroxide solution. Stirring is continued until the pH remains constant. Unreacted carbobenzoxy chloride is extracted with diethyl ether. The aqueous layer is acidified to pH 2 and extracted with diethyl ether. The ether extract is washed with water,

T. Saeed, P. Sandra and M. Verzele, J. Chromatogr., 186, 611 (1979) continued.

dried over magnesium sulphate and the solvent removed. The dried derivatized or Z-amino acid is dissolved in dry tetrahydrofuran (THF) (20 ml). One equivalent (2.47 g) of N-ethoxycarbonyl-2-ethoxy-1,2-dihydroquinoline (EEDQ) is added and the mixture is stirred for 1 h at room temperature. Thereafter one equivalent (0.73 g) of *tert.*-butylamine is added; the mixture is stirred for 30 min at room temperature and then refluxed for 2–3 h until the precipitate dissolves completely. The reaction mixture is cooled and washed three times with 0.1 *N* hydrochloric acid and with water to remove unreacted amine and quinoline. The solvent is evaporated and the compound crystallized from *n*-pentane–chloroform (9:1). The blocked L-valine–*tert.*-butylamide is dissolved in absolute methanol (30 ml). A few drops of glacial acetic acid are added and the mixture is stirred with 1 g of 10% Pd/C for 3 h at room temperature while hydrogen gas is blown just above the surface of the solution. After the reaction is completed, the mixture is filtered and methanol evaporated. The liberated amine is extracted with 0.1 *N* hydrochloric acid, regenerated with sodium hydroxide, extracted with chloroform and dried. L-Valine–*tert.*-butylamide is crystallized from isooctane, with the following properties. Yield, 60%, M.p., 48°. Spectroscopic values: 360 MHz. Proton nuclear magnetic resonance (NMR): γH 0.81δ; γ'H 0.97δ; βH 2.28δ; αH 3.10δ; *tert.*-Bu 1.36δ; NH_2 1.21δ; NH 7.13δ; $^3J_{\alpha,\beta}$ 3.1 Hz; $^3J_{\beta,\gamma}$ 7.0 Hz. Mass spectrum: $M^{+\cdot}$ 172, m/z 72 (100%). IR spectrum: 3370, 1675, 1540 cm^{-1}.

Coupling of chloropropionylmethyl phenylmethyl silicone and L-*valine–tert.-bytylamide.* The acid chloride solution is cooled in an ice–salt bath and an excess of L-valine–*tert.*-butylamide dissolved in diethyl ether is added dropwise. The mixture is stirred for 30 min. Excess valine reagent is extracted with 0.1 *N* hydrochloric acid. The ether layer is washed with water, dried over magnesium sulphate and the solvent removed. The absorption bands of L-valine–*tert.*-butylamide are present in the infrared spectrum of the chiral phase. The NMR data indicate the presence of *tert.*-butyl (δ = 1.36) and isopropyl protons (δ 0.92, overlap of γ,γ' Hs).

Capillary columns

Borosilicate glass capillaries, drawn on a Hupe Bush apparatus, were washed with methanol and dichloromethane and then heated overnight with dry nitrogen at 300°. The surface was modified by whisker formation[21,22] and deactivated with N,OH-containing compounds[23]. The columns were coated statically[24] with 0.2% solutions in dichloromethane or dynamically[25] with 4% solutions. In both instances a relatively thin film of *ca.* 0.2 μm is obtained.

Equipment

The GC separations were carried out on a Varian 3700 or a Carlo Erba 2900 gas chromatograph, both equipped with a flame-ionization detector.

Preparation of derivatives

N-TFA-D,L-amino acid isopropyl and *n*-butyl esters, N-pentafluoropropionyl (PFP)-D,L-amino acid isopropyl and *n*-butyl esters and N-heptafluorobutyryl (HFB)-D,L-amino acid isopropyl and *n*-butyl esters were prepared according to the methods described in the literature[1,20,26].

T. Saeed, P. Sandra and M. Verzele, J. Chromatogr., 186, 611 (1979) continued.

TABLE I

ADJUSTED RETENTION TIMES OF DERIVATIVES OF SOME PROTEIN D,L-AMINO ACIDS ON A 22 m × 0.25 mm I.D. WHISKERED CAPILLARY COLUMN TEMPERATURE PROGRAMMED FROM 90° TO 190° AT 2°/min

Amino acid	*Derivative*					
	TFA-i-Pr	*TFA-n-Bu*	*PFP-i-Pr*	*PFP-n-Bu*	*HFB-i-Pr*	**HFB-n-Bu*
D-Val	4.00	8.96	3.00	7.02	2.90	6.40
L-Val	4.40	9.42	3.28	7.40	3.10	6.72
Gly	6.24	13.00	5.40	11.36	5.26	10.80
D-Leu	7.80	14.70	6.24	12.16	5.90	11.30
L-Leu	8.70	15.52	6.90	12.90	6.60	12.04
D-Pro	10.90	18.70	9.14	16.10	8.30	14.60
L-Pro	11.00	18.80	9.22	16.22	8.40	14.68
D-Asp	17.48	33.10	15.22	29.96	14.16	28.20
L-Asp	17.80	33.22	15.44	30.12	14.40	28.40
D-Phe	25.70	33.60	22.90	30.50	21.80	28.74
L-Phe	26.40	34.08	23.56	31.00	22.44	29.22
D-Glu	26.26	41.64	23.30	38.26	22.00	36.00
L-Glu	26.80	42.10	23.90	38.62	22.60	36.40

* The carrier gas flow-rate was slightly higher; normally retention times of PFP and HFB derivatives are identical.

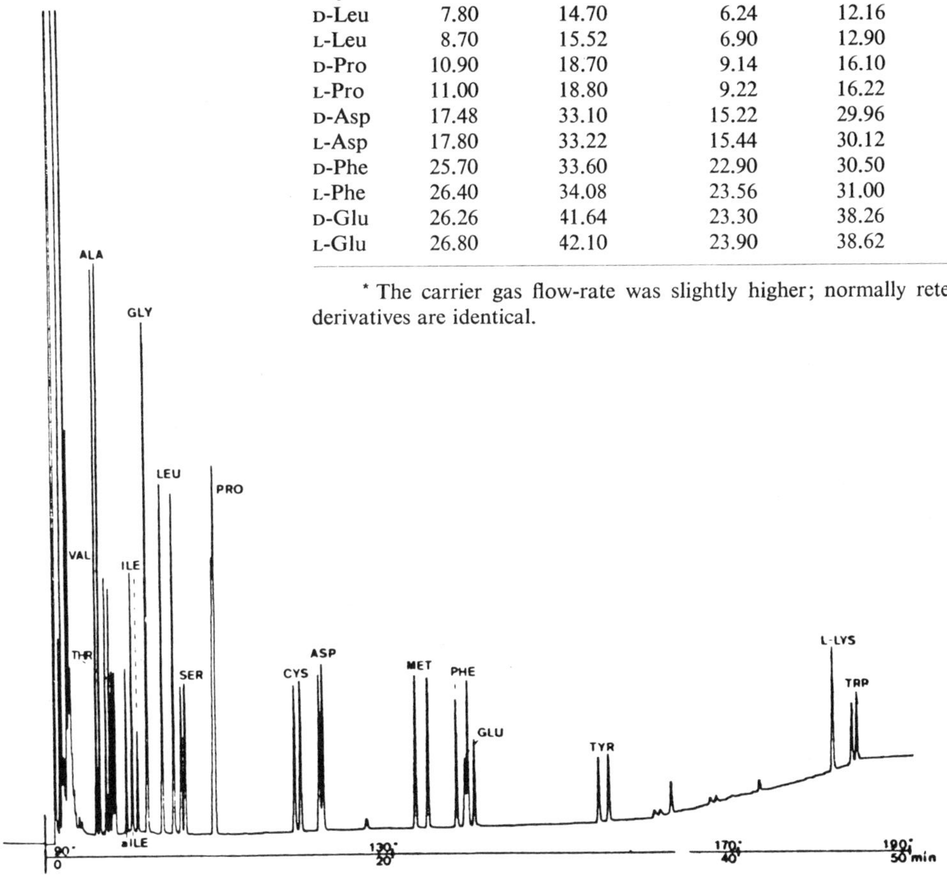

Fig. 2. Chromatogram of the N-PFP-amino acid isopropyl esters of sixteen pairs of amino acid enantiomers together with L-lysine. Conditions: 22 m × 0.25 mm I.D. whiskered capillary column; temperature-programmed at 2°/min from 90° to 190°; injector and detector temperature, 250°; carrier gas, hydrogen at a linear velocity 50 cm/sec.

20 H. Frank, G. J. Nicholson and E. Bayer, *J. Chromatogr. Sci.*, 15 (1977) 174.
21 J. D. Schieke, N. R. Comins and V. Pretorius, *J. Chromatogr.*, 112 (1975) 97.
22 P. Sandra and M. Verzele, *Chromatographia*, 10 (1977) 419.
23 P. Sandra, M. Verstappe and M. Verzele, *J. High Resol. Chromatogr. Chromatogr. Commun.*, 1 (1978) 28.
24 J. Bouche and M. Verzele, *J. Gas Chromatogr.*, 5 (1968) 501.
25 G. Dykstra and J. De Goey, in D. H. Desty (Editor), *Gas Chromatography 1958*, Butterworths, London, 1958, p. 56.
26 C. F. Poole and M. Verzele, *J. Chromatogr.*, 150 (1978) 439.

T. Saeed, P. Sandra and M. Verzele, J. Chromatogr., 186, 611 (1979) continued.

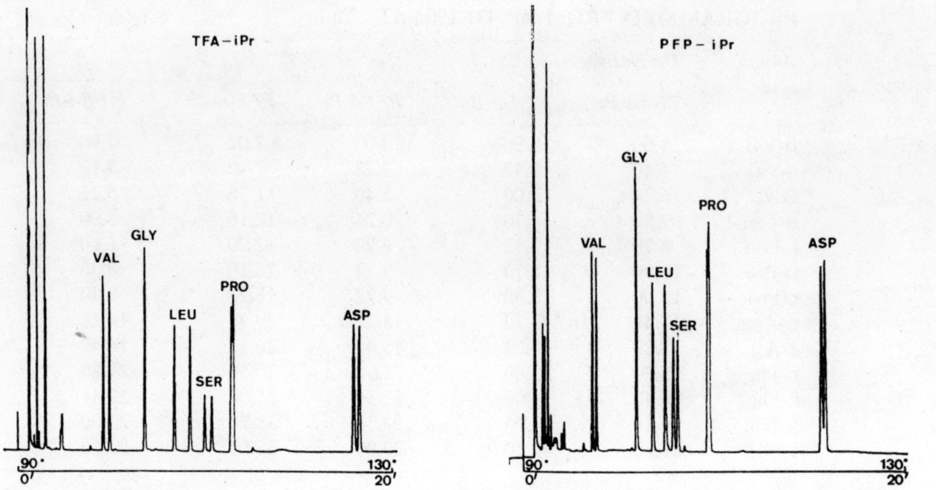

Fig. 3. Chromatogram of the N-TFA-D,L-amino acid isopropyl esters (TFA-*i*-Pr) and N-PFP-D,L-amino acid isopropyl esters (PFP-*i*-Pr) of valine, glycine, leucine, serine, proline and aspartic acid. Conditions as in Fig. 2.

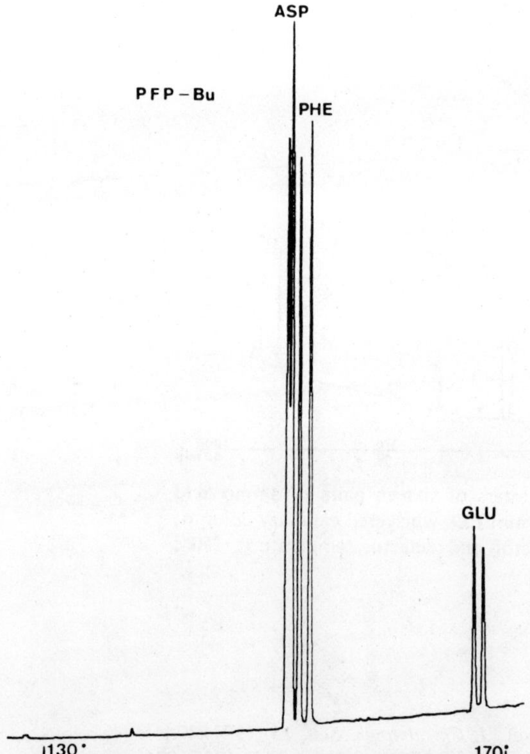

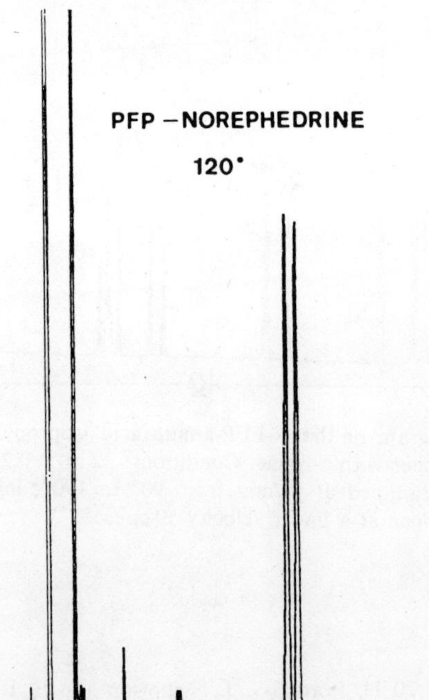

Fig. 4. Chromatogram illustrating the peak shift of the N-PFP-D,L-amino acid *n*-butyl esters (PFP-Bu) of aspartic acid, phenylalanine and glutamic acid. Conditions as in Fig. 2.

Fig. 5. Enantiomer separation of the pentafluoropropionyl derivative of D,L-norephedrine. Conditions: 18 m × 0.25 mm I.D. whiskered capillary column; temperature, 120°; carrier gas, hydrogen at a linear velocity of 40 cm/sec.

Reference

N. Oi, K. Moriguchi, M. Matsuda, H. Shimada and O. Hiroaki, Bunseki Kagaku, 27, 637 (1978).

Summary

The authors report the preparation of some new s-triazine derivatives of amino acid esters to be used as stationary phases for the resolution of α-amino acid (and amine) enantiomers by gas liquid chromatography. One of the new phases, N,N',N"-[2,4,6-(1,3,5-triazine)trilyl]-tris(L-valine isopropyl ester) is especially notable in that its maximum permissible operating temperature of about 150°C is considerably higher than those of all published phases containing amino acid ester groups. Some gas chromatograms illustrating the resolutions obtained using these phases are shown below:

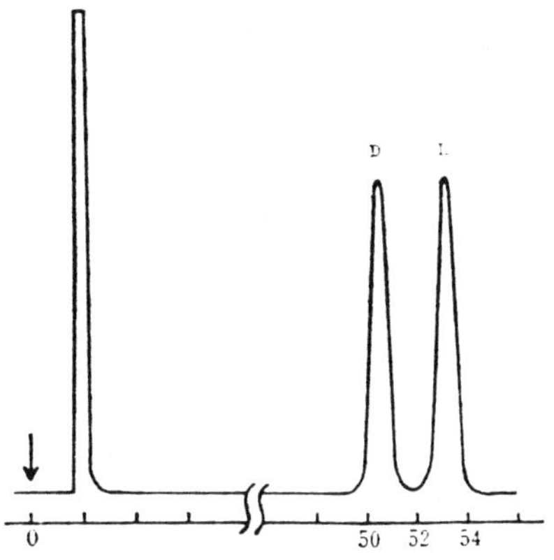

Fig. 1 Gas chromatogram of *N*-TFA-DL-alanine *t*-butyl ester on a glass capillary (30 m × 0.25 mm i.d.) coated with *N*, *N'*-[2,4-(6-ethoxy-1,3,5-triazine)diyl]-bis-(L-valine isopropyl ester

Column temperature : 95°C

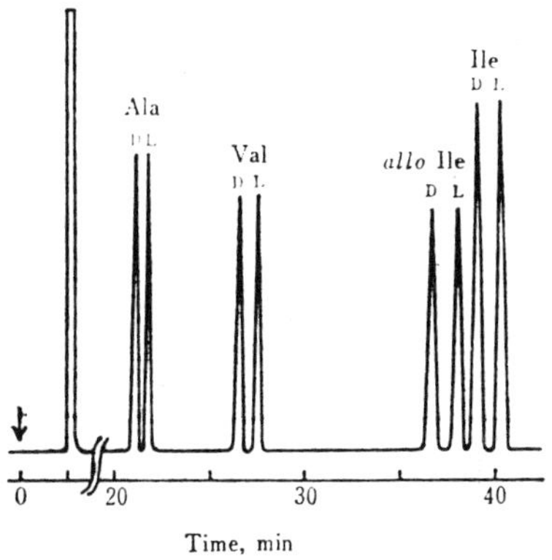

Fig. 3 Gas chromatogram of *N*-TFA isopropyl esters of DL-alanine, DL-valine, DL-allo-isoleucine and DL-isoleucine on a glass capillary (60 m × 0.25 mm i.d.) coated with *N*, *N'*, *N''*-[2,4,6-(1,3,5-triazine)-triyl]-tris-(L-valine isopropyl ester)

Column temperature : 100°C

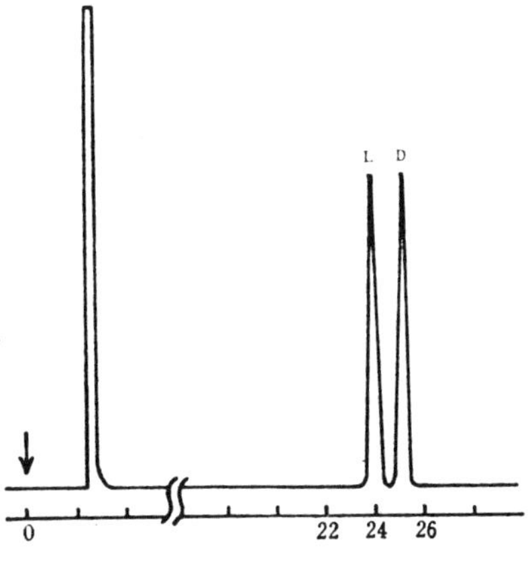

Fig. 5 Gas chromatogram of *N*-TFA-DL-alanine *t*-butyl ester on a glass capillary (30 m × 0.25 mm i.d.) coated with *N*, *N'*, *N''*-[2,4,6-(1,3,5-triazine)triyl]-tris-(D-valine isopropyl ester)

Column temperature : 100°C

Reference
G.G. Smith and D.M. Wonnacott. Presented in part at the Northwest Regional Meeting of the American Chemical Society in Portland, Oregon, June 1977 and in partial fulfillment for a Ph.D. degree by David M. Wonnacott at Utah State University, 1979.

Summary
A 150 ft. stainless steel capillary column loaded with a mixed phase of N-docosanoyl-L-val-t-butylamide and N-octadecanoyl-L-val-L-val-cyclohexylester has satisfactorily separated N-TFA isopropyl ester derivatives of neutral and acidic amino acid enantiomers in less than 200 minutes. Aspartic acid was separated better by this glc column than by any other reported so far. Experimental details and results follow:

MATERIALS AND METHODS

Chiral Phases

The syntheses of the chiral phases and intermediates leading up to them were similar to other published procedures (2g,6a,6b,7) and are only briefly discussed here.

N-Docosanoyl-L-val-t-Butylamide. L-Val-t-butylamide hydrochloride (0.5 g, 2.5 mmoles) and docosanoyl-N-hydroxysuccinimide (1.1 g, 2.5 mmoles) were dissolved in 80 ml of tetrahydrofuran in which 0.34 ml of triethylamine was added. The solution was stirred overnight. The solvent was removed on the rotary evaporator and the residue taken up in ethyl acetate (100 ml) and washed with 1% hydrochloric acid, water, 5% sodium bicarbonate solution and water. The ethyl acetate was dried over anhydrous magnesium sulfate. The solvent was removed on the rotary evaporator. The product was recrystallized from ethyl acetate yielding 0.8 g (64%) of the purified amide m.p. 80-82; lit. m.p. 85-86, (2g).

N-Octadecanoyl-L-val-L-val-cyclohexylester. Octadecanoic acid N-hydroxy succinimide active ester (0.95 g, 2.5 mmoles) and the trifluoroacetic acid (TFA) salt of L-NH_2-val-L-valine cyclohexyl ester (0.103 g, 2.5 mmoles) were dissolved in 80 ml of tetrahydrofuran. To this solution was added triethylamine (0.35 ml, 2.5 mmoles) and the solution was stirred overnight. The solvent was removed on the rotary evaporator and the residue was taken up in 100 ml of hot ethyl acetate. The hot solution was washed with 3-5 ml portions of the following: 1% hydrochloric acid, water, 5% sodium becarbonate solution, and water. It was necessary to keep the solution hot while washing to prevent the product from crystallizing. The ethyl acetate solution was dried with anhydrous magnesium sulfate and filtered hot. The product crystallized on standing at room temperature to produce 0.85 g (60%) m.p. 105-106.5°C.

L-Val-L-val-cyclohexylester. N-t-Butoxycarbonyl-L-valine (BOC valine) (4.92 g, 22.7 mmoles) and L-valine cyclohexyl ester hydrogen chloride (5.34 g, 22.7 mmoles) were dissolved in methylene chloride and cooled in an ice bath. Triethylamine (2.27 g, 22.7 mmoles), N-hydroxybenzotriazole hydrate (N-HOBT) (46 g, 34 mmoles) and dicyclohexylcarbodiimide (5.1 g, 24 mmoles) were added to the methylene chloride solution in the order given. The solution was stirred for two hours in an ice bath, then stirred for three hours at room temperature. The dicyclohexylurea (DCU) was filtered and 1 ml of acetic acid was added; after one half hour it was filtered again. The solvent was removed on the rotary evaporator. The product was dissolved in ethyl acetate and washed twice with 10% sodium bicarbonate solution, water, 0.1 N hydrochloric acid and water. The ethyl acetate was dried over anhydrous magnesium sulfate and subsequently removed on the rotary evaporator. The BOC group was removed by treatment with trifluoracetic acid (TFA) yielding 9.71 g (85%) as the TFA salt, m.p. 198-200°C; lit. m.p. for HCl salt, 96-9°C (7a).

Derivatization

Derivatization Procedure (5c,8). The amino acid solutions, generally obtained from racemization experiments contained in a small pyrex tube, were taken to dryness by blowing a stream of nitrogen over the surface of the solution while placing the tubes in an oil bath (110°). When dry, the amino acids were esterified with a solution (2 ml) of isopropanol in which dry hydrogen chloride (2.5-4N) had been added. The tubes were sealed in an oxygen torch and ultrasonicated for 15 min. at 40°, then heated in an oil bath for 2-3 hours. After the alcohol was evaporated in the same manner as described above for the aqueous solutions, methylene chloride (0.5 ml) was added and subsequently evaporated, azeotroping the remaining hydrochloric acid. If hydroxy acids, (ser, thr) were being derivatized, the tubes were further dried in a vacuum oven at 40-50° for an hour. The resulting amino acid ester hydrochlorides salts were acylated with 1-1.5 ml of 30% trifluoroacetic anhydride in methylene chloride. After thorough mixing, the solution was allowed to stand at room temperature for 30 minutes then transferred to gc sampling vials where it was allowed to evaporate to dryness. Methylene chloride (0.5 ml) was added to the N-TFA ester derivative and the vials were capped with septum seals, ready for gc analysis.

Cleaning and Loading the Stainless Steel Capillary Column

Stainless steel capillary tubing (0.0625" OD ± 0.002" by 0.020 ID ± 0.001") was obtained from Handy and Harmon Tube Company, Norristown, PA in one thousand foot lengths and cut and wound into 150' lengths or longer. Before the stainless steel capillary was coated with the chiral phase it was necessary that it be rigorously cleaned. The stainless steel capillary was attached to a solvent reservoir with a 1/16" Sweglok nut and a flexible ferrule. The ferrules were readily made by punching out a septa with a #1 cork borer. The capillary was cleaned by passing 20 ml each of methylene chloride, chloroform, methanol, water, conc. nitric acid and water through in this sequence with 700 psi of hydrogen pressure (hood). While heating the capillary in hot water it was further washed with 20 ml of water, 20% sodium hydroxy solution, water, methanol, chloroform and ether. After the washing sequence, any powdered residues that may have dislodged in the column were removed by forcing hydrogen gas through at 1000 psi for several minutes. The capillary was further dried by passing nitrogen gas through at 10 psi for an hour.

A 5% solution of stationary phase (150 mg of phase dissolved in 2.0 ml of $CHCl_3$) was put in a 5 ml solvent reservoir and pushed through at 10-15 psi. When a 50-50 mixed phase was used to coat the column, 75 mg of N-docosanoyl-L-val-t-butylamide and 75 mg of N-octadecanoyl-L-val-L-val cyclohexyl ester were dissolved in 2 ml of $CHCl_3$ and this solution was dynamically coated as previously described.

The solution was collected as it came out of the column and saved for future use. The amount of phase left on the column was determined by removing solvent from the collected solution and subtracting the weight of this from 150 mg. Generally 30-60 mg were coated on a 150' x 0.020" tube. The column was made ready

G.G. Smith and D.M. Wonnacott (continued).

for use by drying with nitrogen at 10 psi for 3-4 hours. The column was conditioned by passing nitrogen through at 4 ml/min while it was heated slowly from 70°C to 125°. The temperature was maintained at the upper limit for at least 5 hours. When the capillary and column were prepared in this way and used below 150°, they gave base-line resolution for the amino acid discussed and lasted for a year with almost day and night operation resolving thousands of enantiomeric mixtures. If resolution time is important the column can be suitably operated at 170° with a life time of two months. The phase is readily removed from the stainless steel by using the same washing procedure.

Gas Chromatograph

The results were obtained on a Hewlett-Packard (HP)-5830A gc modified to use a capillary column and an inlet splitter. The inlet was adapted with a carefully constructed glass liner, properly silanized and the dead space taken up with silanized glass beads. Flow through the column was readily adjusted with a needle valve attached to the splitter which was regulated such that the solvent (methylene chloride) elutes at approximately 7 minutes. By adjusting the flow and temperature the relative retention of enantiomers were suitably attained. For continued use of the gc and more uniform injections a HP auto sampler was employed. The sampler was modified to use Hamilton 801 syringes.

The basic amino acid derivatives are so non-volatile that they do not elute as gc peaks. Occasionally it is necessary to heat the column for an extended period of time to remove them from the column packing.

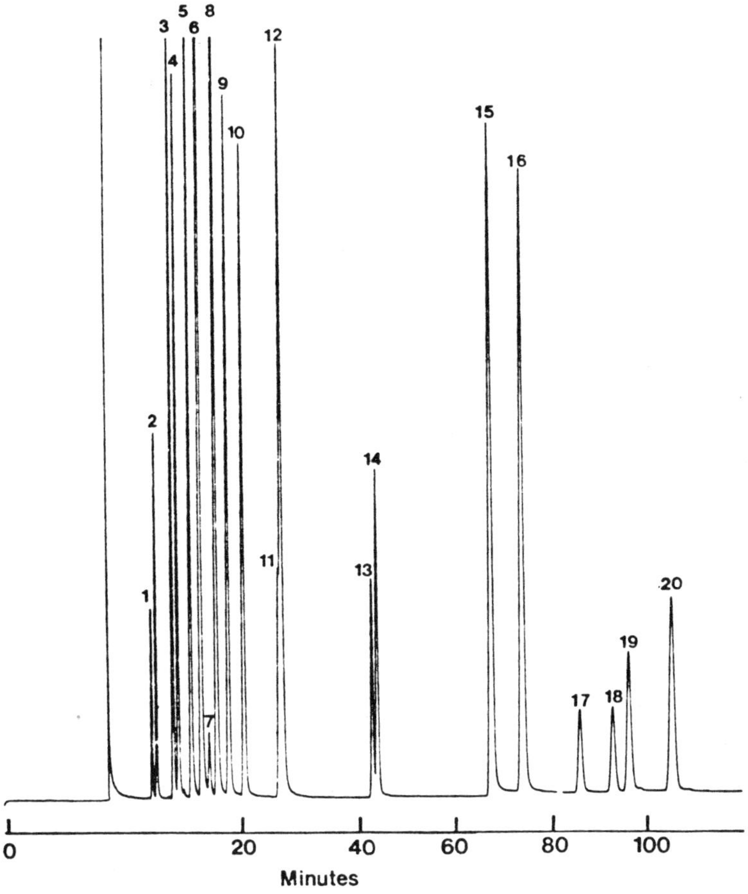

In normal operation the column is kept heated (100-120°) and purged when not in use which keeps the column clean. If a raised background is observed this indicates the column needs purging.

TABLE 2

Retention Data of Volatile N-trifluoroacetyl amino acid isopropyl ester at 170°[a]

Amino Acid		Retention time (min)	r(L/D)[b]
Alanine	D	11.97	1.10
	L	12.47	
Valine	D	14.21	1.08
	L	14.77	
Isoleucine	D-alloisoleu	17.20	1.16
	L	18.85	
Leucine	D	20.09	1.12
	L	21.72	
Aspartic acid	D	43.21	1.07
	L	44.31	
Methionine	D	67.91	1.11
	L	74.41	
Glutamic acid	D	86.28	1.09
	L	93.27	
Phenylalanine	D	96.67	1.10
	L	105.54	

[a]A 150' stainless steel capillary column (0.20" i.d.) coated with 65% N-octadecanoyl-L-valyl-L-valine cyclohexyl ester and 35% N-decosanoyl-L-valyl-t-butylamide mixture.

[b]Solvent hold up time (CH_2Cl_2) 6.98 min

(2g) R. Charles, U. Beitler, B. Feibush and E. Gil-Av, J. of Chromatogr., 112, 121-133 (1975).
(6a) W.A. Konig, W. Parr, H.A. Lichtenstein, E. Bayer and J. Oro, J. Chromatogr. Sci., 8, 183-186 (1971).
(6b) W. Parr, J. Pleterski, C. Yang and E. Bayer, J. Chromatogr. Sci., 9, 141-147 (1971).
(7a) B. Feibush and E. Gil-Av, Tetrahedron Lett., 26, 1361-1368 (1970).
(7b) B. Feibush, Chem. Commun., 544-545 (1971).

Fig. 1. Gas chromatogram of N-TFA-amino acid isopropyl ester. Instrument: Hewlett-Packard 5830A. Column: A 150' stainless steel capillary column (0.020" i.d.) coated with 65% N-octadecanoyl-L-valyl-L-valine cyclohexyl ester and 35% N-decosanoyl-L-valyl-t-butylamide mixture. Flame ionization detector (FID), temperature 250°C, column temperature 170°C, injector 200°C, injection splitter carrier gas N_2 pressure 50 psi.

(1) D-Ala, (2) L-Ala, (3) D-Val, (4) L-Val, (5) Gly, (6) D-AIle, (7) D-Ile or L-AIle, (8) L-Ile, (9) D-Leu, (10) L-Leu, (11) D-Pro, (12) L-Pro, (13) D-Asp, (14) L-Asp, (15) D-Met, (16) L-Met, (17) D-Glu, (18) L-Glu, (19) D-Phe, (20) L-Phe

Reference

W.A. König and S. Sievers, J. Chromatogr., 200, 189 (1980).

Summary

A number of new optically active stationary phases were synthesized and were used to investigate the structural requirements for enantioselectivity in the gas-liquid separation of racemic α-hydroxy acids, racemic α-amino acids and other compounds. Experimental details and results follow:

EXPERIMENTAL

Synthesis of compounds I–XIII

The compounds used as liquid phases on glass capillary columns are represented in Table I.

The *Z*-derivative of *S*(*R*)-mandelic acid was prepared according to Thamm[17] and coupled with α-phenylethylamine after formation of the mixed anhydride with chloro-carbonic acid ethyl ester. Analogously, *Z*-mandelic acid was coupled to *tert.*-butylamine, L-valine cyclohexyl ester, L-valine *tert.*-butylamide and *R*-phenylglycinol. Compound XI was prepared by esterification of *S*-mandelic acid with cyclohexanol and *p*-toluenesulfonic acid as a catalyst[18]. The *Z*-derivative XII was obtained as indicated above. VII was obtained from *S*-mandelic acid by reaction with dodecanoyl chloride and coupling with *tert.*-butylamine. X was prepared according to Staab[19] from *Z*-*S*-mandelic acid and XI with N,N′-carbonyldiimidazole. Racemic 2-phenylbutyric acid could be separated by fractional crystallization from diisopropyl ether of the diastereoisomeric *S*-2-phenylethylamides, obtained according to the mixed anhydride method described above.

Preparation of glass capillary columns

Glass capillaries were drawn from Pyrex glass tubes with a Hupe and Busch capillary drawing machine and coated as described in a previous publication[16]. Gas chromatography was performed with hydrogen as carrier gas in Carlo Erba model 2101 gas chromatographs.

Formation of derivatives

Isopropyl esters of amino acids and α-hydroxy acids were prepared by reaction of 100–200 μg of sample with isopropanol–HCl gas (1.5 *N*) at 100°C for 30 min. After removing the excess of reagent in a stream of dry nitrogen the samples were trifluoroacetylated at room temperature (30 min) in a mixture of 200 μl of methylene chloride and 50 μl of trifluoroacetic anhydride. The excess of reagent was evaporated in a smooth stream of dry nitrogen and the samples were dissolved in 100 μl of methylene chloride and used for gas chromatography. The esters of higher alcohols and pentafluoropropionyl and heptafluorobutyryl derivatives were prepared analogously.

16 W. A. König, K. Stölting and K. Kruse, *Chromatographia*, 10 (1977) 444.
17 P. Thamm, in *Houben-Weyl*, *Methoden der Organischen Chemie*, Vol. 15/1, G. Thieme Verlag, Stuttgart, 1974, p. 869.
18 I. Ojima, T. Kogure and M. Kumagai, *J. Org. Chem.*, 42 (1977) 1671.
19 H. A. Staab, *Angew. Chem.*, 71 (1959) 194.

TABLE I

STRUCTURE, CONFIGURATION AND MELTING POINT OF COMPOUNDS USED AS STATIONARY PHASES FOR ENANTIOMER SEPARATION

Structure/configuration	*Melting point (°C)*
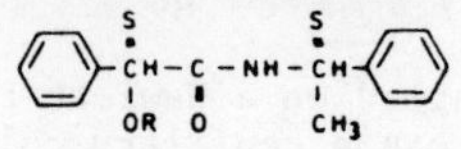 I : R=H , II : R=Z	I:oil II: 93
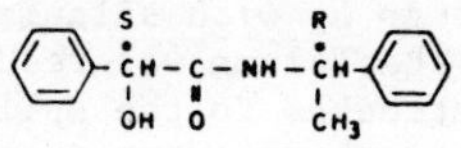	III:oil
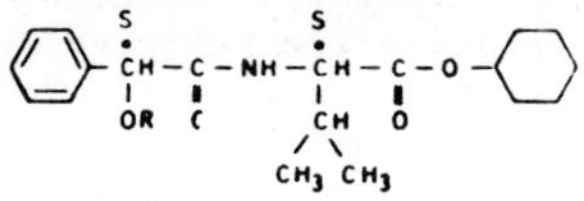 IV : R=H , V : R=Z	IV:oil V: 70
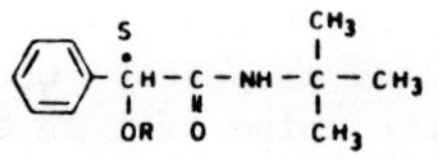 VI R=Z , VII R= n-$C_{11}H_{23}$-CO-	VI: 78 VII: 47
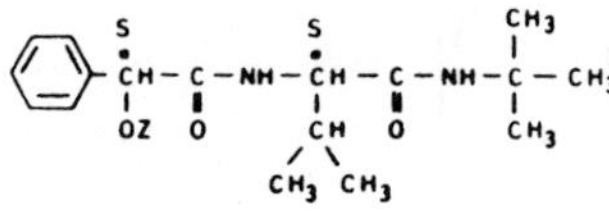	VIII:145
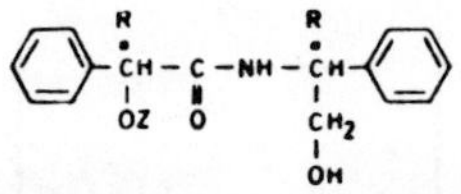	IX:139
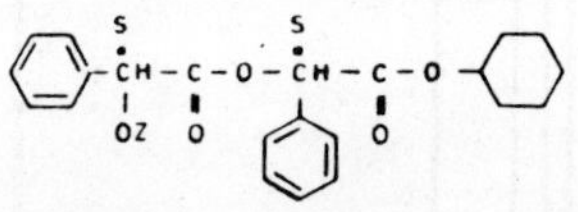	X:oil
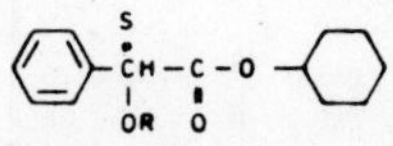 XI R=H, XII R=Z	XI: 27 XII: 57
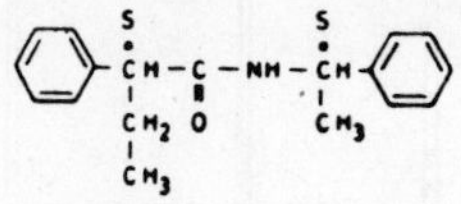	XIII:116

W.A. Konig and S. Sievers, J. Chromatogr., 200, 189 (1980) continued.

TABLE II

SEPARATION FACTORS (α) AND OPERATING TEMPERATURES FOR ENANTIOMER SEPARATION ON GLASS CAPILLARY COLUMNS COATED WITH STATIONARY PHASES VI, VII AND XIII

Racemate	*Phase VI on 44.5-m glass capillary*	*Phase VII on 26.5-m glass capillary*	*Phase XIII on 39-m glass capillary*
R,S-Alanine	1.02/90	1.037/80	1.038/120
R,S-Valine	1.02/90	1.031/80	1.044/120
R,S-Alaninol	shoulder/110	1.016/100	1.018/120
R,S-Valinol	1.005/110	–	1.018/120
R,S-2-Aminopentane	1.01/100	1.012/100	–
R,S-2-Aminohexane	1.012/100	1.013/100	not tested
R,S-2-Amino-5-methylhexane	1.015/100	1.013/100	not tested
R,S-2-Aminoheptane	1.015/100	1.013/100	1.023/120
R,S-2-Amino-6-methylheptane	1.015/100	1.014/100	not tested
R,S-2-Amino-octane	1.014/100	1.015/100	not tested
R,S-α-Phenylethylamine	1.033/110	1.039/100	1.107/120
R,S-2-Hydroxybutyric acid	1.007/80	–	not tested
R,S-2-Hydroxyisopentanoic acid	1.009/80	–	not tested
R,S-2-Hydroxyisohexanoic acid	1.014/80	shoulder/60	not tested
R,S-2-Hydroxyoctanoic acid	1.015/80	–	–
R,S-2-Hydroxydodecanoic acid	not tested	not tested	1.010/120
R,S-Mandelic acid	1.018/110	1.012/100	1.029/120
R,S-3-Phenyllactic acid	1.008/110	–	–

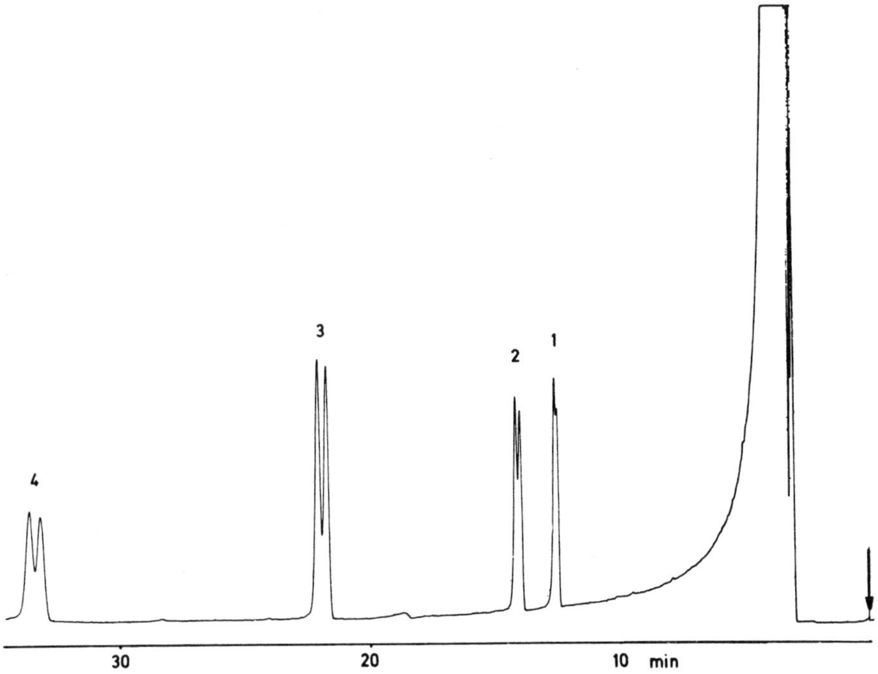

Fig. 1. Separation of *R,S*-O-TFA-α-hydroxybutyric acid isopropyl ester (1), *R,S*-O-TFA-α-hydroxyisopentanoic acid isopropyl ester (2), *R,S*-O-TFA-α-hydroxyisohexanoic acid isopropyl ester (3), and *R,S*-O-TFA-α-hydroxyhexanoic acid (4) on a 44.5-m glass capillary column, coated with compound VI. Column temperature, 76°C; carrier gas, 0.2 bar hydrogen.

Reference

I. Abe and S. Musha, J. Chromatogr., 200, 195 (1980).

Summary

The authors report the preparation of new, easily synthesized optically active stationary phases of the dipeptide ester type for use in gas-liquid chromatography of racemic α-amino acids by coupling N-lauroyl-L-valine with L-valine cyclohexyl ester or L-leucine cyclohexyl ester. The melting points of N-lauroyl-L-valyl-L-leucine cyclohexyl ester are 85-87° and 74-76°C respectively. These two phases were coated on glass capillary columns 17 m long and were found to be stable up to 170°C in use. Sixteen racemic α-amino acids including tryptophane were resolved on both phases. Proline, however, could not be completely resolved. Experimental details and results follow:

Apparatus

A Hitachi O63 gas chromatograph equipped with a flame ionization detector and an all-glass inlet splitter was used throughout this work.

Reagents and materials

All of the amino acids used were obtained from Wako (Osaka, Japan). Anhydrous HCl (>99.9%) was purchased from Seitetsu Kagaku (Osaka, Japan).

Isopropanol was first refluxed over BaO and then redistilled. Trifluoroacetic anhydride (TFAA) and pentafluoropropionic anhydride (PFPA) were obtained from Tokyo Kasei (Tokyo, Japan). Methylene chloride and chloroform were distilled before use. Anhydrous HCl was dissolved in isopropanol and its normality verified by titration.

N-Lauroyl-L-valyl-L-valine cyclohexyl ester (Lau-Val-Val) was synthesized as follows. First, N-lauroyl-L-valine was prepared by the Schotten–Baumann reaction[10] and L-valine cyclohexyl ester hydrogen chloride by Fischer's method[11]. Next, N-lauroyl-L-valine (10 mmole), 1-hydroxybenzotriazole (10 mmole) and dicyclohexylcarbodiimide (11 mmole) were dissolved in 40 ml of chloroform. After cooling the mixture to about 2°C, L-valine cyclohexyl ester hydrogen chloride (10 mmole) and N-ethylmorpholine (10 mmole) were added and the mixture stirred for 2 h, and then for another 6 h at room temperature.

The precipitate was filtered off, the filtrate evaporated *in vacuo* and the residue dissolved in 30 ml of ethyl acetate. The solution was filtered, and extracted successively with 5% sodium bicarbonate and (twice) with water. The ethyl acetate layer was dried over sodium sulphate overnight and the solvent removed *in vacuo*. The final compound was recrystallized twice from petroleum ether. Its yield was 42% and its melting point 85–87°C.

N-Lauroyl-L-valyl-L-leucine cyclohexyl ester (Lau-Val-Leu) was prepared in the same manner. Its yield was 69% and its melting point 74–76°C.

The optical purity of Lau-Val-Leu was determined by gas chromatography (GC) after hydrolysis in 6 *N* HCl at 120°C for 10 h and conversion of the hydrolysis products into their TFA-isopropyl esters. According to this method, the optical purities of L-valine and L-leucine were determined to be 82% and 97% respectively. The optical purity of the valine residue at the amide side of Lau-Val-Val could not be determined accurately because hydrolysis yielded a mixture of the valine residues in the lauroyl end and the cyclohexyl ester end.

Preparation of glass capillary columns

Coiled glass capillaries were drawn from Pyrex tubing on a home-made drawing machine[12]. Glass capillaries (17m × 0.25 mm I.D.) were pretreated with 0.5% HF solution for 1 h and silanized with 3-aminopropyltriethoxysilane. Coating was performed by the dynamic method. A methylene chloride solution containing about 12% of these phases was passed through the pretreated capillary. Finally, the capillary columns were conditioned at 170°C overnight with a flow of helium as carrier gas.

Sample preparation

All amino acid derivatives were prepared according to the usual method. About 0.5 mg of the individual DL-amino acids or their mixtures were heated in 2 *N* HCl–isopropanol at 110°C for 1 h. After evaporating the HCl and isopropanol, 2 ml of methylene chloride were added to the residue which was then cooled to about −10°C.

Finally, 0.2 ml of TFAA or PFPA were added to the solution and left to stand for 1 h at room temperature. Solvent and excess of reagents were evaporated and the final product was dissolved in 0.2–0.5 ml of chloroform.

I. Abe and S. Musha, J. Chromatogr., 200, 195 (1980) continued.

TABLE I

RETENTION TIMES AND RESOLUTION FACTORS OF N(O)-TFA-AMINO ACID ISOPROPYL ESTERS

Temp. = column temperature; t_R = retention time; r(L/D) = resolution factor calculated from corrected retention times; nd = not determined.

Amino acid		Lau-Val-Val			Lau-Val-Leu		
		Temp. (°C)	t_R (min)	r(L/D)	Temp. (°C)	t_R (min)	r(L/D)
Ala	D	110	4.6	1.174	110	3.2	1.163
	L		5.3			3.6	
Val	D	110	6.6	1.158	110	4.7	1.135
	L		7.6			5.2	
Thr	D	110	7.3	1.132	110	4.9	1.123
	L		8.1			5.5	
Gly		110	9.4	—	110	6.2	—
allo-Ile	D	110	9.8	1.175	110	6.8	1.161
	L		11.3			7.8	
Ile	D	110	10.8	1.150	110	7.4	1.139
	L		12.3			8.4	
Leu	D	110	14.5	1.228	130	4.3	1.161
	L		17.6			4.9	
Ser	D	110	15.2	1.097	130	4.3	1.074
	L		16.6			4.6	
Pro	D	110	16.0	1.022	130	5.1	1.000
	L		16.3			5.1	
Asp	D	150	8.5	1.035	150	5.7	1.030
	L		8.8			5.9	
Met	D	150	14.8	1.108	150	9.8	1.103
	L		16.3			10.7	
Glu	D	170	8.9	1.064	170	6.1	1.061
	L		9.4			6.5	
Phe	D	170	9.7	1.072	170	6.7	1.070
	L		10.4			7.1	
Tyr	D		nd		170	14.5	1.086
	L					15.7	
Orn	D		nd		170	32.9	1.078
	L					35.4	
Lys	D		nd		170	47.7	1.080
	L					51.5	

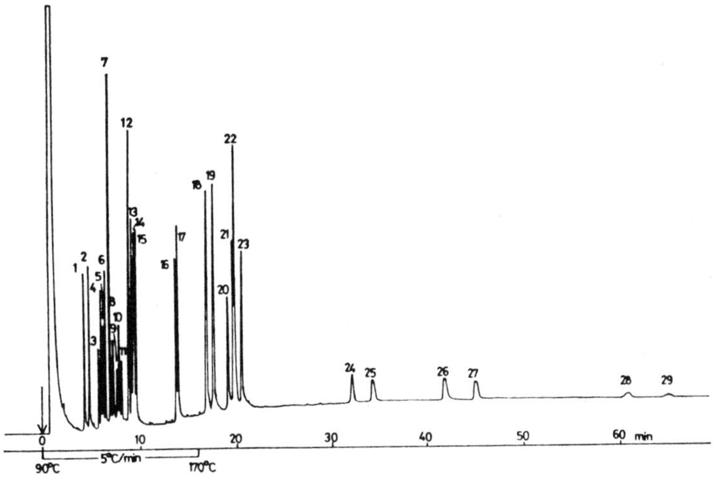

Fig. 1. Chromatogram of N(O)-TFA isopropyl esters of racemic amino acid mixtures with temperature programming. Column: Lau-Val-Leu (17 m × 0.25 mm). Carrier gas: helium. Peaks: 1 = D-Ala; 2 = L-Ala; 3 = D-Val; 4 = D-Thr; 5 = L-Val; 6 = L-Thr; 7 = Gly; 8 = D-*allo*-Ile; 9 = D-Ile; 10 = L-*allo*-Ile; 11 = L-Ile; 12 = D-Leu + D-Ser; 13 = L-Ser; 14 = DL-Pro; 15 = L-Leu; 16 = D-Asp; 17 = L-Asp; 18 = D-Met; 19 = L-Met; 20 = D-Glu; 21 = L-Glu; 22 = D-Phe; 23 = L-Phe; 24 = D-Tyr; 25 = L-Tyr; 26 = D-Orn; 27 = L-Orn; 28 = D-Lys; 29 = L-Lys.

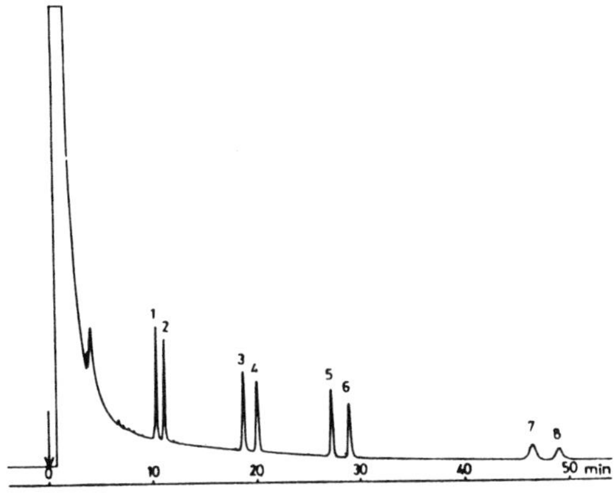

Fig. 2. Chromatogram of N(O)-PFP isopropyl esters of racemic amino acid mixtures. Column: Lau-Val-Leu (17 m × 0.25 mm). Column temperature: 170°C. Carrier gas: helium. Peaks: 1 = D-Tyr; 2 = L-Tyr; 3 = D-Orn; 4 = L-Orn; 5 = D-Lys; 6 = L-Lys; 7 = D-Trp; 8 = L-Trp.

9 N. Ohi, K. Moriguchi, M. Matsuda, H. Shimada and O. Hiroaki, *Bunseki Kagaku (Jap. Anal.)*, 27 (1978) 637.
10 A. W. Ingersoll and S. H. Babcock, *Org. Synth.*, 2 (1943) 328.
11 E. Fischer and F. Fourneau, *Chem. Ber.*, 34 (1901) 2868.
12 D. H. Desty, J. N. Haresnape and B. H. F. Whyman, *Anal. Chem.*, 32 (1960) 303.

Reference

S-C. Chang, R. Charles and E. Gil-Av, J. Chromatog., 202, 247 (1980).

Summary

The resolution of N-trifluoroacetyl (N-TFA) *tert.*-butylamides of Ala, Val, Leu and Pro by gas chromatography on the N-lauroyl *tert.*-butylamide derivatives of L-alanine (I), L-leucine (II), D-phenylglycine (III) and L-phenylalanine (IV) as stationary phases was investigated, and the results compared with those obtained for the corresponding N-TFA isopropyl esters.

Efficiency of resolution of the two classes of compounds and the differences between them depend greatly on the nature of the phase. N-Lauroyl-L-Phe-*tert.*-butylamide (IV), which is highly efficient for the resolution of the N-TFA esters of α-amino acids, shows even more selectivity for the N-TFA *tert.*-butylamides.

Proline, which is resolved only with great difficulty as its N-TFA ester, behaves distinctly differently from the amino acids having a primary amine group, and on all phases shows high resolution factors, ranging from 1.173 to 1.384.

Experimental details and results follow.

Materials

Chromatographic resolution was carried out on the following stationary phases: N-lauroyl-L-alanine *tert.*-butylamide (I)[4]; N-lauroyl-L-leucine *tert.*-butylamide (II)[5]; N-lauroyl-D-phenylglycine *tert.*-butylamide (III)[5] and N-lauroyl-L-phenylalanine *tert.*-butylamide (IV)[5]. These compounds were synthesized according to the general procedure described previously[3]; full details will be reported elsewhere[5].

The N-TFA *tert.*-butylamides of Ala, Val, Leu and Pro were prepared from the N-TFA-amino acids, synthesized according to Weygand and Geiger[9], by one of the following procedures.

(1) To a solution of N-TFA-α-amino acid in chloroform or ethyl acetate, kept at -5 to -10°C, N-hydroxysuccinimide (1.1 equiv.) and dicyclohexylcarbodiimide (1.0 equiv.) were added. After 24 h the dicyclohexylurea formed was filtered off, and into the stirred solution, cooled as above, was added dropwise a mixture of *tert.*-butylamine and N-methylmorpholine (1.0 equiv. each); stirring was then continued in the cold (48 h). The reaction mixture was washed successively with 2% HCl, water, 5% $NaHCO_3$, water and then dried over $MgSO_4$. The residue left on evaporation of the solvent was the desired compound, as checked by NMR spectroscopy. During this reaction no racemization was observed to occur in analogous cases[5].

(2) First, the acid chloride of the N-TFA-α-amino acid in dry dichloromethane was formed by reaction with a slight excess of thionyl chloride at room temperature for 1 h. The solvent was removed by evaporation with a nitrogen stream. The residue was redissolved in dry dichloromethane, cooled in a water–ice bath and *tert.*-butylamine (2 equiv.) was added dropwise. The solution was then stirred for another hour. The reaction mixture was washed as above, and the desired compound obtained on evaporation of the solvent.

The second procedure is more rapid and convenient than the first. However, some racemization of the α-amino acids with a primary amine group (but not of proline) occurs under the above conditions. For the purpose of the present study, where non-racemic mixtures were prepared only for peak identification, both methods can be used.

Chromatographic conditions

Stainless-steel capillary columns (100 ft. × 0.02 in.) were coated by the plug method with I and II (mounted in a Varian Series 2700 chromatograph) and (150 ft. × 0.02 in.) with III and IV (mounted in a Varian Series 1200 chromatograph). Both instruments were provided with a splitter and a flame ionization detector. The temperatures of the injector and detector were 240°C; column temperatures used are given in Table I. The helium flow-rate was 3 ml/min for all columns. The order of elution of the peaks was established for Ala and Pro by operating with mixtures enriched in the D and the L enantiomer, respectively. The result was extrapolated to Val and Leu.

S-C. Chang, R. Charles and E. Gil-Av, J. Chromatog., 202, 247 (1980) continued.

TABLE I

RESOLUTION OF N-TFA ISOPROPYL ESTERS AND OF N-TFA *tert.*-BUTYLAMIDES OF α-AMINO ACIDS ON DIAMIDES, R'''CONHCH(R'')CONHR', AS STATIONARY PHASES

Optical purity: 98% (I), 99% (II), 81% (III) and 99% (IV). For chromatographic conditions, see Experimental.
r = Corrected retention time (min). $r_{L/D}$ = resolution factor = ratio of the corrected retention time of the enantiomer eluting last over that of the enantiomer eluting first, calculated with r values expressed to the second decimal.

Phase	*N-TFA-alanine*						*N-TFA-valine*		
	Isopropyl ester			*tert.-Butylamide*			*Isopropyl ester*		
	r	$r_{L/D}$	*T(°C)*	r	$r_{L/D}$	*T(°C)*	r	$r_{L/D}$	*T(°C)*
I. N-Lauroyl-L-alanine *tert*-butylamide	D 5.00 L 5.40	1.080	130	46.6 50.5	1.083	140	6.60 7.00	1.061	130
II. N-Lauroyl-L-leucine *tert.*-butylamide	D 8.46 L 9.84	1.163	150	48.2 55.1	1.143	160	12.50 14.22	1.138	150
III. N-Lauroyl-D-phenylglycine *tert.*-butylamide*	L 8.60 D 9.80	(1.140)	130	65.20 68.80	(1.055)	150	12.00 13.40	(1.117)	130
IV. N-Lauroyl-L-phenylalanine *tert.*-butylamide	D 4.82 L 5.84	1.212	130	30.24 37.00	1.223	150	7.42 8.96	1.207	130

* III being a D phase, the order of elution is reversed. Resolution factors listed are $r_{D/L}$.

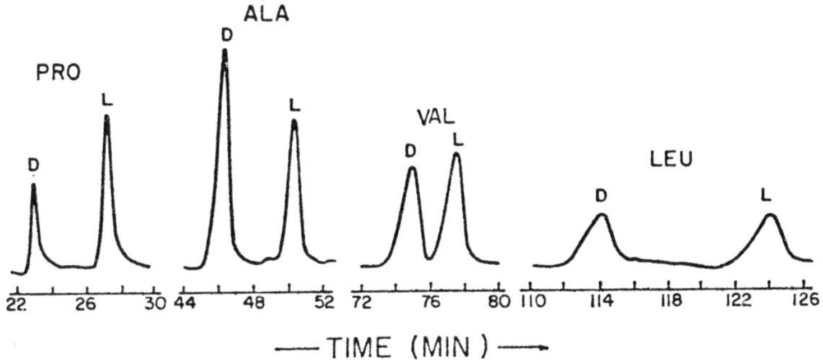

Fig. 1. Chromatogram of N-TFA *tert.*-butylamides of L-enriched Pro, D-enriched Ala, D,L-Val and D,L-Leu on a stainless-steel capillary column (100 ft. × 0.02 in.) coated with N-lauroyl-L-alanine *tert.*-butylamide. For chromatographic conditions, see Experimental. Temperature, 140°C.

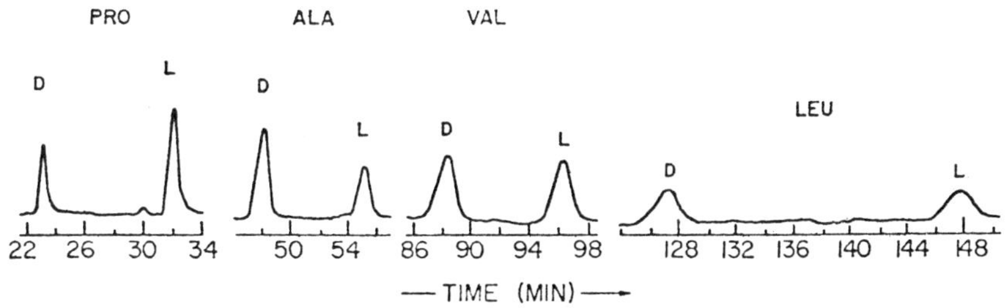

Fig. 2. Chromatogram of N-TFA *tert.*-butylamides of L-enriched Pro, D-enriched Ala, D,L,Val and D,L-Leu on a stainless-steel capillary column (100 ft. × 0.02 in.) coated with N-lauroyl-L-leucine *tert.*-butylamide. For chromatographic conditions, see Experimental. Temperature, 160°C.

S-C. Chang, R. Charles and E. Gil-Av, J. Chromatog., 202, 247 (1980) continued.

			N-TFA-leucine						N-TFA-proline					
tert.-Butylamide			*Isopropyl ester*			*tert.-Butylamide*			*Isopropyl ester*			*tert.-butylamide*		
r	$r_{L/D}$	*T(°C)*	*r*	$r_{L/D}$	*T(°C)*	*r*	$r_{L/D}$	*T(°C)*	*r*	$r_{L/D}$	*T(°C)*	*r*	$r_{L/D}$	*T(C°)*
75.20	1.034	140	15.70	1.095	130	114.30	1.087	140	17.00	1.000	130	23.10	1.186	140
77.80			17.20			124.20			17.00			27.40		
88.40	1.089	160	24.30	1.216	150	127.20	1.162	160	29.02	1.036	150	23.20	1.384	160
96.30			29.54			147.80			30.06			32.10		
90.80	(1.066)	150	11.00	(1.145)	150	140.80	(1.020)	150	40.40	(1.000)	130	43.80	(1.173)	150
96.80			12.60			143.80			40.40			51.40		
53.00	1.216	150	6.50	1.215	150	78.32	1.343	150	22.42	1.000	130	17.18	1.314	150
64.48			7.90			105.20			22.42			23.40		

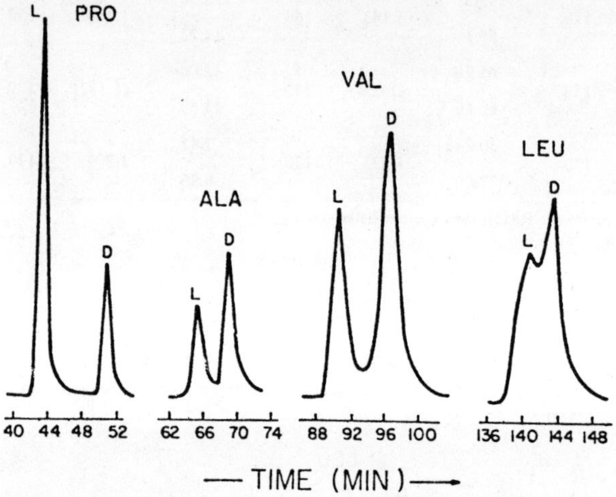

Fig. 3. Chromatogram of N-TFA *tert.*-butylamides of L-enriched Pro, D-enriched Ala, D,L-Val and D,L-Leu on a stainless-steel capillary column (150 ft. × 0.02 in.) coated with N-lauroyl-D-phenylglycine *tert.*-butylamide. For chromatographic conditions, see Experimental. Temperature, 150°C.

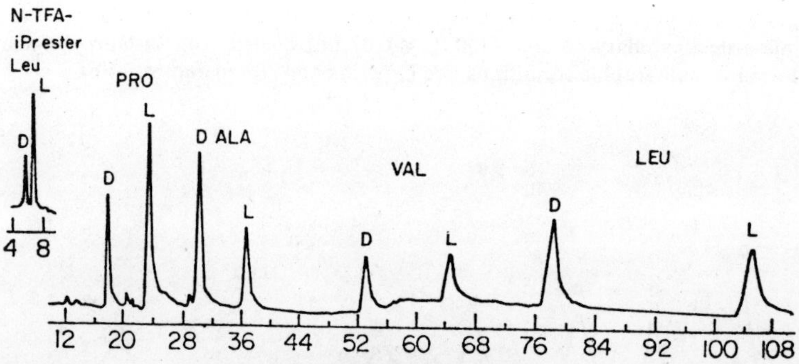

Fig. 4. Chromatogram of N-TFA *tert.*-butylamides of L-enriched Pro, D-enriched Ala, D,L-Val and D,L-Leu and of the N-TFA isopropyl esters of L-enriched Leu on a stainless-steel capillary column (150 ft. × 0.02 in.) coated with N-lauroyl-L-phenylalanine *tert.*-butylamide. For chromatographic conditions, see Experimental. Temperature, 150°C.

3 R. Charles and E. Gil-Av, *J. Chromatogr.*, 195 (1980) 317.
4 Shu-Cheng Chang, R. Charles and E. Gil-Av, Poster presented at the *Franco-Israeli Symposium on Chiral Structures, Milly La Forêt, May 1979.*
5 S.-C. Chang, R. Charles and E. Gil-Av, to be published.

Reference

W.A. König, S. Sievers and U. Schulze, Angew. Chem. Int. Ed. Engl., 19, 910 (1980).

Summary

The authors report the development of some new chiral stationary phases for the separation of the trifluoroacetylated esters of racemic 2-hydroxycarboxylic acids by gas-liquid chromatography. The selectivity of the phases was rationalized in the paper. Experimental details and results follow:

Table 1. Gas chromatographic separation of enantiomers on the stationary phases *(1)*—*(4)*.
Phase *(1)*: (*S*)-mandelic acid-(*S*)-α-phenylethylamide
Phase *(2)*: *O*-benzyloxycarbonyl-(*S*)-mandelic acid (*S*)-α-phenylethylamide
Phase *(3)*: *O*-benzyloxycarbonyl-(*S*)-mandelic acid *tert*-butylamide
Phase *(4)*: *N*-[(*S*)-mandeloyl]-(*S*)-valine cyclohexyl ester

Racemate	Separation factor α/Column temperature [°C]			
	Phase *(1)*	Phase *(2)*	Phase *(3)*	Phase *(4)*
DL-Mandelic acid [a]	1.032/90	1.019/118	1.018/110	1.018/90
DL-3-Phenyllactic acid [a]	—	1.010/113	1.008/110	—
DL-2-Hydroxy-4-methylpentanoic acid [a]	—	1.008/89	1.014/80	—
DL-2-Hydroxyhexanoic acid [a]	—	1.010/89	1.011/80	—
DL-2-Hydroxyoctanoic acid [a]	—	1.014/89	1.015/80	—
DL-2-Hydroxydodecanoic acid [a]	—	1.014/120	[e]	—
DL-Alanine [b]	1.053/70	1.016/100	1.020/90	1.020/90
DL-Valine [b]	1.075/70	1.017/100	1.020/90	1.025/90
DL-Alaninol [c]	1.029/90	1.010/123	—	1.017/90
DL-Valinol [c]	1.025/90	—	1.005/110	1.012/90
DL-2-Aminopentane [d]	—	—	1.010/100	1.014/90
DL-2-Aminoheptane [d]	[e]	—	1.015/100	1.022/90
DL-2-Amino-6-methylheptane [d]	[e]	—	1.015/100	1.024/90
DL-2-Aminooctane [d]	1.048/80	—	1.014/100	1.024/90
DL-α-Phenylethylamine [d]	1.090/90	—	1.033/110	1.055/110

[a] Separated as 2-(trifluoroacetoxy)carboxylic acid isopropyl ester. [b] Separated as 2-(trifluoroacetylamino)carboxylic acid isopropyl ester. [c] Separated as 2-(trifluoroacetylamino)alkyl trifluoroacetate. [d] Separated as *N*-(2-methylalkyl)trifluoroacetamide. [e] Not tested.

Reference

N. Oi, H. Kitahara, M. Horiba and T. Doi, J. Chromatog., __206__, 143 (1981).

Summary

The authors report the direct separation by gas-liquid chromatography of the enantiomers of α-hydroxycarboxylic acid esters using amino acid derivatives as chiral stationary phases. Experimental details and results follow.

A Shimadzu GC-7A gas chromatograph equipped with a flame ionization detector was employed. Glass capillary columns (40 m × 0.25 mm I.D.) were coated with the optically active stationary phases N,N′-[2,4-(6-ethoxy-1,3,5-triazine)diyl]bis (L-valyl-L-valine isopropyl ester) (OA-200)[5], N,N′-[2,4-(6-ethoxy-1,3,5-triazine)diyl] bis(L-valyl-L-valyl-L-valine isopropyl ester) (OA-300)[6] and N,N′,N″-[2,4,6-(1,3,5-triazine)triyl]tris(N$^\alpha$-lauroyl-L-lysine tert.-butylamide) (OA-400)[7] which were prepared as described previously.

L- and DL-lactic acid and DL-α-hydroxybutyric acid were purchased from Wako (Osaka, Japan). The various esters or amines for GC were prepared from these acids by treatment with corresponding alcohols or amides. Some esters and amides were O-acylated with acetic anhydride or trifluoroacetic anhydride.

TABLE I

GC SEPARATION OF α-HYDROXYCARBOXYLIC ACID ESTER ENANTIOMERS

Chromatographed on 40 m × 0.25 mm I.D. glass capillary columns. Carrier gas: helium at 0.7 ml/min.

$$\begin{array}{c} H \\ | \\ R\text{--}C^*\text{--}COOR' \\ | \\ OH \end{array}$$

X	R	R′	OA-400 Column temp. (°C)	Retention time* (min) 1st peak	2nd peak	Separation factor, α (2nd/1st)	OA-300 + OA-200 (1:1) Column temp. (°C)	Retention time* (min) 1st peak	2nd peak	Separation factor, α (2nd/1st)
H	CH₃	C₂H₅	90	3.48	3.60	1.034	130	1.4	1.4	1.000
H	CH₃	CH(CH₃)₂	90	3.84	3.95	1.029				
H	CH₃	CH₂CH(CH₃)₂	90	9.85	10.20	1.036	130	3.36	3.43	1.021
COCH₃	CH₃	CH₂CH(CH₃)₂	90	10.8	10.8	1.000	130	4.5	4.5	1.000
H	CH₃	cyclo-C₆H₁₁	100	32.0 (L)	33.1 (D)	1.034	130	16.9 (L)	17.4 (D)	1.030
H	CH₃	n-C₆H₁₃	100	24.5 (L)	25.4 (D)	1.037	130	12.5 (L)	12.8 (D)	1.024
COCH₃	CH₃	n-C₆H₁₃	100	24.4	24.4	1.000	130	16.1	16.1	1.000
H	C₂H₅	n-C₆H₁₃					130	18.1	18.6	1.028

* Measured from solvent peak.

TABLE II

GC SEPARATION OF LACTIC ACID AMIDE ENANTIOMERS

Chromatographed on 40 m × 0.25 mm I.D. glass capillary columns coated with OA-300 + OA-200 (1:1). Carrier gas: helium at 0.6 ml/min. Column temperature: 150°C.

$$\begin{array}{c} H \\ | \\ CH_3\text{--}C^*\text{--}CONHR \\ | \\ OX \end{array}$$

X	R	Retention time* (min) 1st peak	2nd peak	Separation factor, α (2nd/1st)
H	n-C₆H₁₃	161.1 (D)	163.8 (L)	1.017
COCF₃	n-C₆H₁₃	20.5 (D)	20.7 (L)	1.010
H	cyclo-C₆H₁₁	181.3 (D)	182.7 (L)	1.008
COCF₃	cyclo-C₆H₁₁	14.7 (D)	15.0 (L)	1.020
H	$\begin{array}{c}CH_3\\|\\C\text{--}CH_3\\|\\CH_3\end{array}$	14.4	14.6	1.014
H	$\begin{array}{c}CH_3\quad CH_3\\|\qquad|\\C\text{--}CH_2\text{--}C\text{--}CH_3\\|\qquad|\\CH_3\quad CH_3\end{array}$	60.8	62.3	1.025

* Measured from solvent peak.

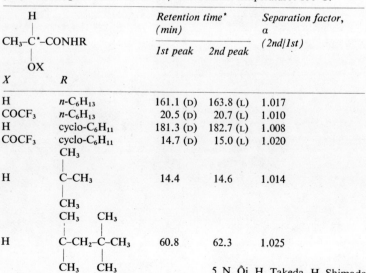

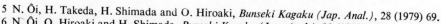

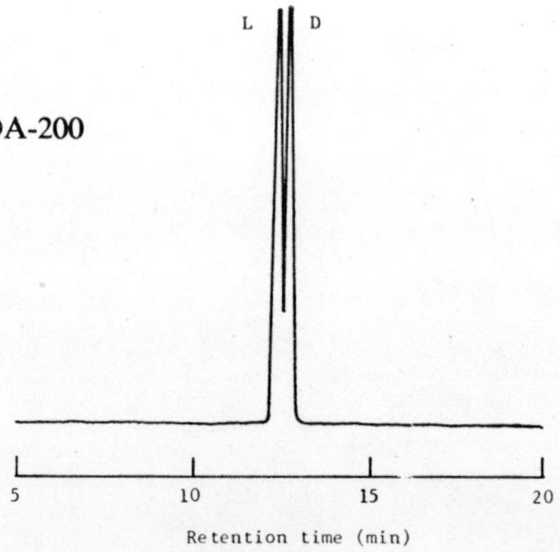

Fig. 1. Gas chromatogram of DL-n-hexyl lactate. Column: glass capillary (40 m × 0.25 mm I.D.) coated with OA-300 + OA-200 (1:1). Temperature: 130°C.

5 N. Ôi, H. Takeda, H. Shimada and O. Hiroaki, Bunseki Kagaku (Jap. Anal.), 28 (1979) 69.
6 N. Ôi, O. Hiroaki and H. Shimada, Bunseki Kagaku (Jap. Anal.), 28 (1979) 125.
7 N. Ôi, O. Hiroaki, H. Shimada, M. Horiba and H. Kitahara, Bunseki Kagaku (Jap. Anal.), 29 (1980) 270.

Reference

N. Oi, H. Kitahara and T. Doi, J. Chromatog., 207, 252 (1981).

Summary

The authors report the resolution by means of gas chromatography of several acids using di-l-menthyl (+)-tartrate and di-dl-menthyl (-) malate as stationary phases. Experimental details and results follow:

Gas chromatography was carried out with a Shimadzu GC-7A gas chromatograph equipped with a flame-ionization detector. Glass capillary columns (40 m × 0.25 mm I.D.) coated with *α*-hydroxycarboxylic acid esters were used.

Di-*l*-menthyl (+)-tartrate was prepared from (+)-tartaric acid by treatment with *l*-menthol in the presence of concentrated sulphuric acid for several hours at 100°C. The ester was extracted with chloroform and the solution was washed successively with water, 1 *N* hydrochloric acid and water. After drying over sodium sulphate and evaporation, the ester was purified by column chromatography with silica gel and *n*-hexane–ethyl acetate as the eluent. Di-*dl*-menthyl (—)-malate was similarly prepared from (—)-malic acid by treatment with *dl*-menthol. The structures of these esters were confirmed by infrared and nuclear magnetic resonance spectroscopy and microanalysis. Their specific rotations were $[\alpha]_D^{25} = -69°$ ($c = 1.0\%$, chloroform) in di-*l*-menthyl (+)-tartrate and $[\alpha]_D^{25} = -8°$ ($c = 1.2\%$, chloroform) in di-*dl*-menthyl (—)-malate.

(+)-Tartaric acid, (—)-malic acid and *l*- and *dl*-menthol were commercially available. Various racemic amino acids, amines and carboxylic acids shown in Table I were also commercially available. *α*-Bromo-*β*,*β*-dimethylbutyric acid was prepared in our laboratory.

TABLE I

GAS CHROMATOGRAPHIC SEPARATION OF AMINO ACID, AMINE AND CARBOXYLIC ACID ENANTIOMERS ON OPTICALLY ACTIVE *α*-HYDROXYCARBOXYLIC ACID ESTERS

Glass capillary columns, 40 m × 0.25 mm I.D. Column temperature, 100°C. Carrier gas, helium at a flow-rate of 0.7 ml/min. Stationary phases: A, di-*l*-menthyl (+)-tartrate; B, di-*dl*-menthyl (—)-malate.

Compound	*Stationary phase*	*Retention time* (min)*		*Separation factor, α (second/first)*
		First peak	*Second peak*	
Amino acids**:				
Alanine	A	22.26 (L)	22.71 (D)	1.020
	B	111.60 (L)	112.80 (D)	1.011
Valine	A	33.54 (L)	33.97 (D)	1.013
	B	191.00 (L)	192.50 (D)	1.008
Leucine	A	67.07 (L)	68.93 (D)	1.028
Amines:				
α-Phenylethylamine***	A	82.34 (—)	84.39 (+)	1.025
α-(2,5-Xylyl)ethylamine§	A	272.00 (—)	281.20 (+)	1.034
α-Phenylpropylamine§	A	164.01 (—)	169.63 (+)	1.034
Carboxylic acids:				
α-Phenylpropionic acid§§	A	176.00 (—)	178.80 (+)	1.016
α-Bromo-*β*,*β*-dimethylbutyric acid§§§	A	62.10 (+)	63.60 (—)	1.024

* Measured from solvent peak.

** Resolved as N-trifluoroacetyl isopropyl ester.

*** Resolved as N-pentafluoropropyl derivatives.

§ Resolved as N-trifluoroacetyl derivatives.

§§ Chromatographed on 20 m × 0.25 mm I.D. glass capillary column using helium at a flow-rate of 1.3 ml/min. Resolved as isopropylamide.

§§§ Resolved as *tert*.-butylamide.

N. Oi, H. Kitahara and T. Doi, J. Chromatog., 207, 252 (1981) (continued).

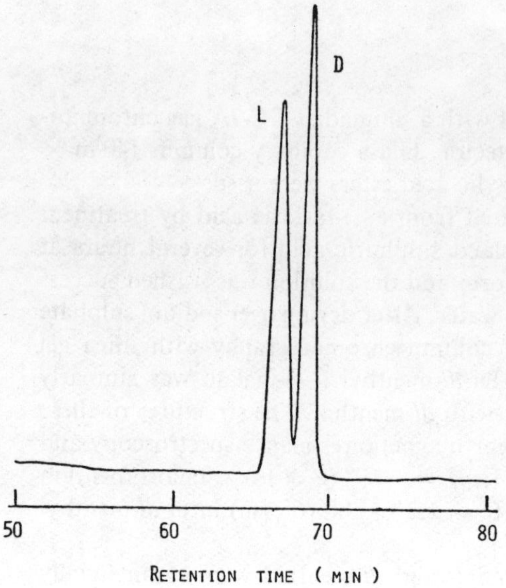

Fig. 1. Gas chromatogram of N-trifluoroacetyl-DL-leucine isopropyl ester. Glass capillary column (40 m × 0.25 mm I.D.) coated with di-*l*-menthyl (+)-tartrate. Temperature: 100°C. Carrier gas (helium) flow-rate: 0.7 ml/min.

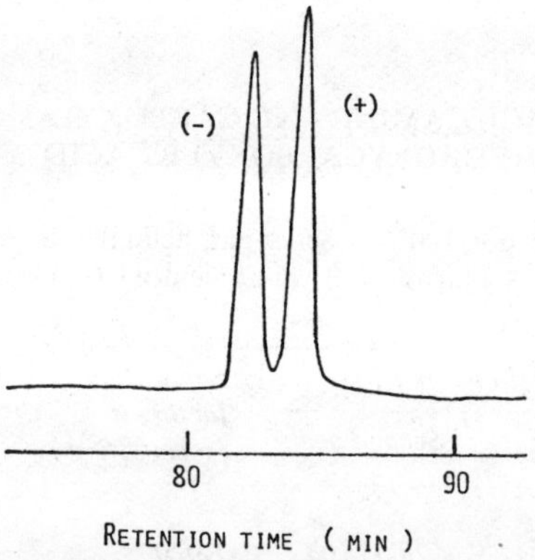

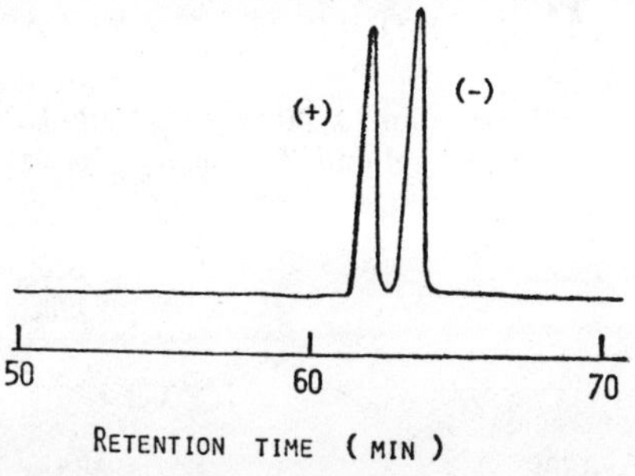

Fig. 2. Gas chromatogram of racemic N-pentafluoropropyl-α-phenylethylamine. Chromatographic conditions as in Fig. 1.

Fig. 3. Gas chromatogram of racemic α-bromo-β,β-dimethylbutyric acid *tert.*-butylamide. Chromatographic conditions as in Fig. 1.

Reference

W.A. König, Chromatographia, 9, 72 (1976).

Summary

A quantitative analysis of racemic amino acids by gas chromatographic separation of diastereoisomeric esters on non-chiral stationary phases is inaccurate when optically impure reagents are used for the formation of derivatives. This problem can be solved by using a chiral stationary phase, on which all optical isomers are separated. Experimental details and results follow:

- Gas chromatogram of N-pentafluoropropionyl-D, L-leu-O-D, L-(3-methyl)-2-butyl ester on (a) 50 m glass capillary, 0.3 mm i.d., SE 30; column temperature 130 °C; carrier gas H_2, $0.75 \cdot 10^5$ Nm^{-2}.

  Peak 1: N-PFP-D-leu-O-D-(3-methyl)-2-butyl ester
  und N-PFP-L-leu-O-L-(3-methyl)-2-butyl ester

  Peak 2: N-PFP-D-leu-O-L-(3-methyl)-2-butyl ester
  and N-PFP-L-leu-O-D-(3-methyl)-2-butyl ester.

  (b) 26 m glass capillary, 0.3 mm i.d., coated with N-trifluoroacetyl-L-phenylalanyl-L-aspartic acid-bis-cyclohexyl ester; column temperature 130 °C; carrier gas H_2, $0.5 \cdot 10^5$ Nm^{-2}.

  Peak 1: N-PFP-D-leu-O-D-(3-methyl)-2-butyl ester
  Peak 2: N-PFP-L-leu-O-L-(3-methyl)-2-butyl ester
  Peak 3: N-PFP-D-leu-O-L-(3-methyl)-2-butyl ester
  Peak 4: N-PFP-L-leu-O-D-(3-methyl)-2-butyl ester.

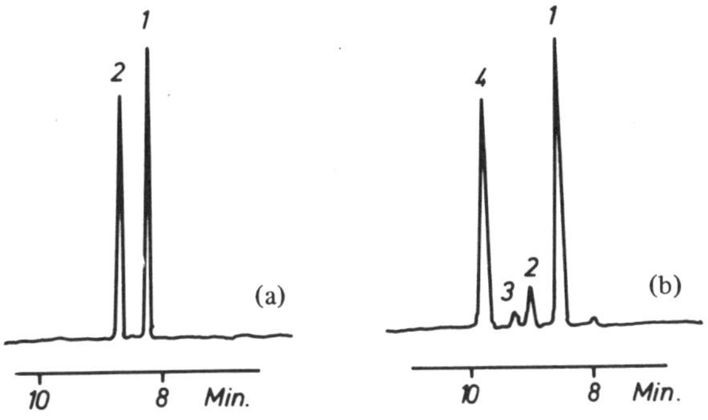

Fig. 1

Reference
S. Hammarström and M. Hamberg, Anal. Biochem., 52, 169 (1973).

Summary
The authors reported the resolution of some hydroxyoctadecanoic acids by gas-liquid chromatography of their diastereomers on achiral phases. Experimental details and results follow:

2D-Phenylpropionic Acid

To a solution of 2.42 g (20 mmole) of (+)-1-phenylethylamine (Fluka AG, Switzerland) in 20 ml of acetone was added a solution of 3 g (20 mmole) of 2DL-phenylpropionic acid in 60 ml of acetone. The mixture was kept at 70° for 5 min. A crystalline salt (2.8 g) was obtained on cooling to −20°. The salt was recrystallized 3 times from acetone at +4° yielding 0.3 g of the (+)-1-phenylethylammonium salt of 2D-phenylpropionic acid. A solution of the salt in water was treated with 2N-hydrochloric acid and extracted 3 times with diethyl ether. After evaporation of the ether, 2D-phenylpropionic acid was obtained as a pale yellowish syrup [yield, 11% of the theoretical; $[\alpha]_D^{25}$ = +88.0° (C1, benzene); earlier reported for 2D-phenylpropionic acid, $[\alpha]_D^{20}$ = +92.5° (benzene) (19)].

2D-Phenylpropionyl Chloride (PPC)

Two hundred milligrams of 2D-phenylpropionic acid and 0.24 ml of thionyl chloride (distilled from beeswax) were mixed at 0° and then kept at 70° for 30 min. Dry benzene was added and the mixture was evaporated to dryness. Another portion of dry benzene was then added and the mixture was re-evaporated to remove the last traces of $SOCl_2$. The residue was dissolved in 2.40 ml dry benzene and stored in the refrigerator in a glass-stoppered flask. The solution contained about 0.5 μmole of PPC per ml.

D-Phenylpropionate Derivatives (PP-Derivatives) of Hydroxy Esters and Alkanols

To 100 μg of hydroxy compound was added 80 μl of PPC solution and 20 μl of dry pyridine. The mixture was left for 2 hr at room temperature in a desiccator, then evaporated to dryness and dissolved in about 100 μl of $CHCl_3$. This solution was quantitatively applied to a thin-layer plate coated with a 250-μm-thick layer of Silica Gel G and activated at 120° for 60 min just before use. The plate was developed with $CHCl_3$ (E. Merck AG., *pro analysi*, containing 0.6–1.0% ethanol as stabilizer) and the compounds were detected in uv light after spraying the plate with 2′,7′-dichlorofluorescein. The PP-derivatives were eluted from the plate with ethyl acetate.

Gas-Liquid Chromatography (glc)

An F&M Biomedical gas chromatograph model 400 with a glass column containing 5% QF-1 on Gas Chrom Q and a hydrogen flame ionization detector was used. For combined glc–mass spectrometry the LKB model 9000 instrument was used instead. The electron energy was 22.5 eV, the trap current 60 μA and the accelerating voltage 3.5 kV. An on-line digital computer was used for automatic background subtraction and plotting of mass spectra (20).

20. Sweeley, C. C., Ray, B. D., Wood, W. I. and Holland, J. F. (1970) *Anal. Chem.* 42, 1505.

S. Hammarström and M. Hamberg, Anal. Biochem., 52, 169 (1973) continued.

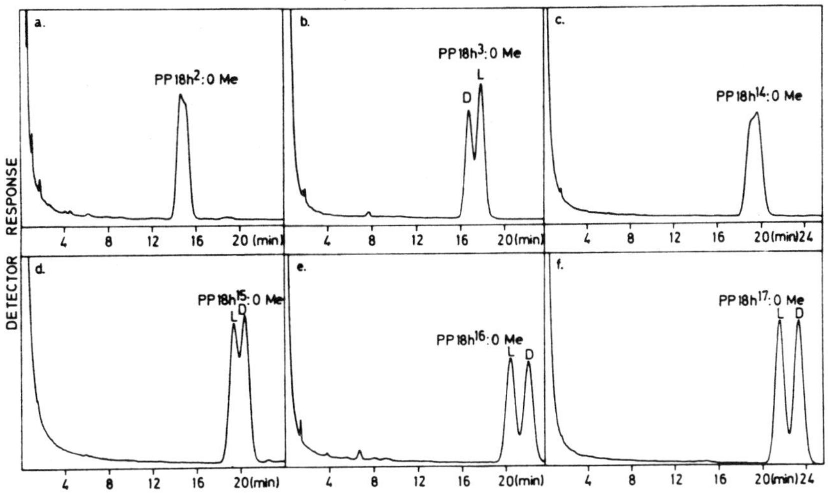

FIG. 1. Gas-liquid chromatograms of six racemic hydroxyoctadecanoic acids as 2D-phenylpropionate-methyl ester derivatives. The hydroxyoctadecanoates have substituents at (a) C-2, (b) C-3, (c) C-14, (d) C-15, (e) C-16 and (f) C-17. *Conditions for* glc: stationary phase, 5% QF-1 on Gas Chrom Q; carrier gas, helium; column temperature, 230°.

TABLE 1

C-Values of 2D-Phenylpropionate Derivatives of Hydroxy Acid Methyl Esters with 5% QF-1 on Gas Chrom Q as Stationary Phase and Helium as Carrier Gas

Hydroxy acid	C-values[a]	Separation factor (ratio of retention times of diastereoisomers)	Column temp. °C
17D-hydroxy 18:0	31.00	1.08	230
17L-hydroxy 18:0	30.60		230
16DL-hydroxy 18:0	29.80/30.10	1.08	230
15DL-hydroxy 18:0	29.65/29.80	1.05	230
14DL-hydroxy 18:0	29.60/29.65	1.03	230
13DL-hydroxy 18:0	29.50	—	230
7DL-hydroxy 18:0	29.10	—	230
4DL-hydroxy 18:0	28.80	—	230
3DL-hydroxy 18:0	28.80/29.05	1.07	230
2DL-hydroxy 18:0	28.35/28.50	1.03	230
3DL-hydroxy 10:0	20.70/20.90	1.06	200
3DL-hydroxy 13:0	23.65/23.90	1.08	200
3DL-hydroxy 14:0	24.60/24.85	1.08	200
3DL-hydroxy 16:0	26.55/26.85	1.08	200
3DL-hydroxy 18:0	28.50/28.80	1.08	200

[a] See Footnote 1.

[2] Hammarström, S., unpublished results.
[3] Hamberg, M., unpublished results.

Reference
H. Iwase and A. Murai, Chem. Pharm. Bull., 22, 8 (1974).

Summary
A number of racemic α-amino acids were resolved by gas-liquid chromatography by first reacting them with N-trifluoroacetylprolyl chloride to form their diastereomeric amides and then chromatographing them on achiral phases. The relation between separation factors and structure of amino acid was discussed. Experimental details and results follow:

Apparatus and Condition——Apparatus: A Hewlett-Packard Model 402 gas chromatograph equipped with dual flame ionization detector was used. Two glass column of 5.5 ft × 1/4 liter in. O.D. and 4 ft × 1/4 liter in. O.D. were used. The column packings were 5% OV-1 on 100—120 mesh Supercoport for monoaminocarboxylic acids and diaminocarboxylic acids and 2% PEGA, stabilized grade, for monoaminodicarboxylic acids. Helium was used as the carrier gas at 60 ml/min.

Reagents and Materials——All solvents used in this study were reagent grade. Amino acids were obtained from Ajinomoto Co., Sigma Chemical Co., and Tokyo Kasei Co. L-Proline was twice recrystallized from absolute ethanol-diethylether. Thionyl chloride was distilled according to the method described elsewhere.[11] BSTFA, TMCS and acetonitrile were obtained from Pierce Chemical Co. The stationary phase, OV-1 and PEGA, were obtained from Analabs Inc. The support materials, 100—120 mesh Supelcoport, was obtained from Supelco. Inc. L-TPC was prepared according to the method of Dabrowiak.[12] Hypovial was purchased from Pierce Chemical Co.

Preparation of Amino Acid Derivatives——TPAM were prepared according to the method of Halpern[9] and Dabrowiak[12] with some modification as follows: the neutral amino acid mixture (alanine, valine, leucine and proline) containing each 5 mg was esterified with 5 ml of thionyl chloride-methanol (1+9) for 2 hr, and excess of the reagent and the solvent were removed *in vacuo*. To the residue, a 2 ml portion of L-TPC containing 0.017 mole in 100 ml chloroform was added and the mixture was neutralized with 0.1 ml of triethylamine and allowed to stand for 15 min at room temperature. The mixture was washed with 2—3 ml of distilled water for 30 sec in a 10 ml separating funnel and dried over anhydrous sodium sulfate. A 3 μl portion of this solution was injected into gas chromatograph.

After triethylamine and L-TPC were added to the hydroxy amino acid methyl ester (threonine), the solvent was removed *in vacuo* and followed by addition 1 ml of acetonitrile, 0.5 ml of BSTFA and 5—6 drops of TMCS. After standing it for 15 min at room temperature, a 3 μl portion of this solution was injected into gas chromatograph.

Acidic and basic amino acids were treated in the same manner as those with the neutral amino acids.

9) B. Halpern and J.W. Westley, *Tetrahedron Letters*, **1966**, 2283; B. Halpern and J.W. Westley, *Biochem. Biophys. Res. Commun.*, **19**, 361 (1965).

11) L.F. Fieser "Experiments in Organic Chemistry," 3rd ed., Heath, Boston, 1957, p. 345.

12) J.C. Dabrowiak and D.W. Cooke, *Anal. Chem.*, **43**, 791 (1971).

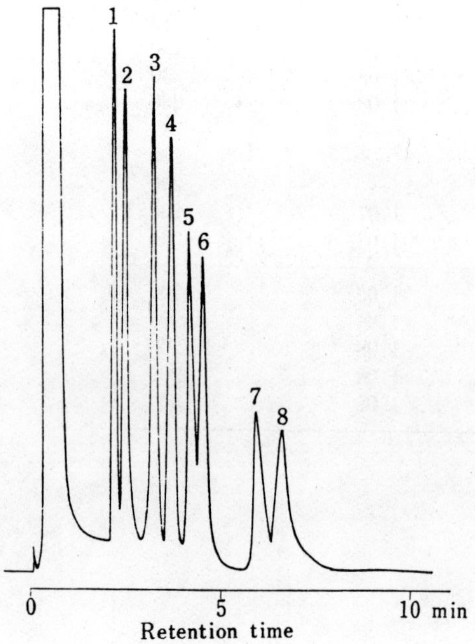

Fig. 1. Gas Chromatogram of Diastereomeric Esters of Amino Acids on OV-1

1: D-alanine, 2: L-alanine, 3: D-valine, 4: L-valine, 5: D-leucine, 6: L-leucine, 7: D-proline, 8: L-proline

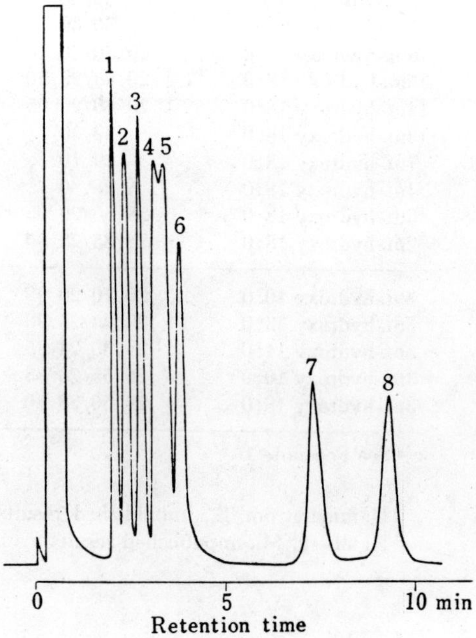

Fig. 2. Gas Chromatogram of Diastereomeric Esters of Amino Acids on OV-25

1: D-alanine, 2: L-alanine, 3: D-valine, 4: L-valine, 5: D-leucine, 6: L-leucine, 7: D-proline, 8: L-proline

H. Iwase and A. Murai, Chem. Pharm. Bull., 22, 8 (1974) continued.

TABLE VI. Gas Chromatographic Data for Racemic Amino Acids as Their N-Trifluoroacetyl L-Prolyl Peptide Methyl Esters with 5% OV-1 on Supelcoport at 180°

Amino acid	Enantiomer	RRT[a]	r L/D
Alanine	D	0.428	1.156
	L	0.494	
Glycine	—	0.517	—
Valine	D	0.678	1.172
	L	0.794	
Norvaline	D	0.806	1.103
	L	0.889	
Leucine	D	0.917	1.109
	L	1.000	
Isoleucine	D	0.967	1.132
	L	1.094	
Norleucine	D	1.139	1.098
	L	1.250	
Serine	D	1.128	1.104
	L	1.417	
Threonine	D	1.339	1.158
	L	1.550	
Proline	D	1.406	1.115
	L	1.567	
Methionine	D	2.672	1.075
	L	2.878	
Phenylalanine	D	3.956	1.077
	L	4.439	

a) Relative retention time, reference compound is N-TFA-L-leucine prolyl peptide methylester. t_R=4.73 min

TABLE VII. Gas Chromatographic Data for Racemic Amino Acids as Their N'-Trifluoroacetyl L-Prolyl Peptide Methyl Esters with 2% PEGA on Supelcoport at 205°

Amino acid	Enantiomer	RRT[a]	r L/D
Threonine	D	0.192	1.262
	L	0.243	
Isoleucine	D	0.231	1.246
	L	0.287	
Serine	D	0.239	1.223
	L	0.293	
Proline	D	0.558	1.248
	L	0.697	
Aspartic acid	D	1.000	1.069
	L	1.069	
Methionine	D	1.483	1.143
	L	1.694	
Glutamic acid	D	1.694	1.126
	L	1.909	
Phenylalanine	D	2.111	1.057
	L	2.231	

a) RRT, reference compound is N-TFA-D-aspartic acid prolyl peptide methylester. t_R=7.92 min

TABLE VIII. Gas Chromatographic Data for Racemic Amino Acids as Their N-Trifluoroacetyl L-Prolyl Peptide Methyl Esters with 5% OV-1 on Supelcoport at 270°

Amino acid	Enantiomer	RRT[a]	r L/D
Ornithine	D	0.860	0.916
	L	0.788	
Lysine	D	1.106	0.904
	L	1.000	

a) RRT, reference compound is N-TFA-L-lysineprolyl peptide methyl ester. t_R=6.05 min

Reference

H. Iwase and A. Murai, Chem. Pharm. Bull., 22, 1455 (1974).

Summary

Several racemic α-amino acids were resolved by gas-liquid chromatography of the diastereomeric N-perfluoroacyl prolyl amino acids esters on achiral phases. The relation between the separation factors of the amino acids and a) the number of CF_2 groups in the N-perfluoroacylpropyl groups, and b) the number of CH_2 groups in the primary alcohols were studied. The order of elution of the amino acids was not influenced by the perfluoroacyl groups or the ester groups.

Experimental details and results follow:

Experimental

Apparatus and Condition——A Hewlett-Packard Model 402 gas chromatograph equipped with dual flame ionization detector was used. A glass column of 5.5 ft × 1/4 in. O.D. packed with 5% OV-1 on 100—120 mesh Supelcoport was used. Column temperature was 250° for *l*-menthyl ester derivatives and 185° for the other ester derivatives.

Reagents——All the solvents used in this study were of reagent grade. Amino acids were purchased from Ajinomoto Co., trifluoroacetic, pentafluoropropionic, heptafluorobutyric, and pentadecafluorooctanoic anhydrides from Pierce Chemical Co., and *l*-menthol from Aldrich Chemical Co.

N-PFP-L-PC, N-HFB-L-PC, and N-PDFO-L-PC were prepared in the same manner as N-TFA-L-PC.[1)]

Preparation of Amino Acid Derivatives——Each amino acid was esterified with thionyl chloride–methanol (1+9), 5% HCl–ethanol, isopropanol, *n*-propanol, *n*-butanol, and cyclopentanol. Amino acid *l*-menthyl esters were prepared according to the method of Harada, *et al.*,[6)] amino acid *tert*-butyl esters were prepared with isobutene,[7)] and N-perfluoroacyl-L-prolyl amino acid esters in the same manner as described in the preceding paper.[1)]

Separation Factors——Separation factors, α,(rL/D) were calculated from the following definition:

$$\alpha = (t_{R_2} - t_a)/(t_{R_1} - t_a)$$

where t_{R_1} and t_{R_2} are the retention times (from injection) of the first and the second components, respectively, and t_a is the retention time of non-adsorbed species (methane).

1) Part I: H. Iwase and A. Murai, *Chem. Pharm. Bull.* (Tokyo), **22**, 8 (1974).

6) K. Harada and T. Hayakawa, *Bull. Chem. Soc. Japan*, **37**, 191 (1964).
7) R.W. Rorske, *Chem. & Ind.* (London), **1950**, 1121.

H. Iwase and A. Murai, Chem. Pharm. Bull., 22, 1455 (1974) continued.

Table I. Comparison of Gas Chromatographic Data of Different N-Perfluoroacyl Prolyl Amino Acid Esters at 185°

Perfluoroacyl	Ester	Enantiomer	Alanine RRT[a]	Alanine rL/D	Valine RRT	Valine rL/D	Leucine RRT	Leucine rL/D	Proline RRT	Proline rL/D
TFA	methyl	D L	0.259 0.296	1.139	0.408 0.466	1.142	0.537 0.584	1.081	0.805 0.888	1.103
	ethyl	D L	0.329 0.379	1.141	0.513 0.588	1.148	0.667 0.726	1.082	0.986 1.094	1.109
	n-propyl	D L	0.469 0.542	1.154	0.704 0.815	1.159	0.913 1.000	1.095	1.368 1.531	1.119
	isopropyl	D L	0.383 0.429	1.123	0.581 0.657	1.130	0.740 0.797	1.078	1.094 1.209	1.106
	n-butyl	D L	0.671 0.779	1.161	1.007 1.173	1.165	1.296 1.422	1.097	1.921 2.173	1.132
	tert-butyl	D L	0.429 0.487	1.134	0.664 0.755	1.136	0.819 0.877	1.071	1.231 1.332	1.082
	cyclopentyl	D L	1.209 1.389	1.149	1.765 2.029	1.151	2.238 2.444	1.092	3.332 3.765	1.130
PFP	methyl	D L	0.256 0.292	1.141	0.399 0.462	1.164	0.523 0.577	1.103	0.747 0.815	1.092
	ethyl	D L	0.299 0.345	1.151	0.480 0.559	1.165	0.661 0.693	1.109	0.906 0.992	1.096
	n-propyl	D L	0.466 0.542	1.163	0.703 0.812	1.169	0.895 0.998	1.115	1.267 1.397	1.103
	isopropyl	D L	0.365 0.415	1.137	0.566 0.646	1.140	0.707 0.776	1.097	1.004 1.083	1.079
	n-butyl	D L	0.661 0.776	1.175	0.996 1.173	1.177	1.253 1.404	1.121	1.787 1.985	1.111
	tert-butyl	D L	0.415 0.473	1.139	0.632 0.729	1.154	0.769 0.841	1.094	1.151 1.191	1.034
	cyclopentyl	D L	1.137 1.315	1.156	1.693 1.960	1.158	2.083 2.329	1.118	3.007 3.343	1.112
HFB	methyl	D L	0.283 0.325	1.146	0.443 0.502	1.168	0.559 0.621	1.109	0.797 0.861	1.081
	ethyl	D L	0.359 0.412	1.152	0.538 0.632	1.174	0.693 0.776	1.118	0.982 1.072	1.092
	n-propyl	D L	0.516 0.602	1.168	0.769 0.906	1.178	0.963 1.094	1.135	1.361 1.494	1.098
	isopropyl	D L	0.386 0.444	1.149	0.595 0.689	1.158	0.747 0.830	1.111	1.064 1.148	1.078
	n-butyl	D L	0.726 0.859	1.184	1.075 1.288	1.198	1.339 1.534	1.146	1.909 2.111	1.106
	tert-butyl	D L	0.466 0.545	1.171	0.711 0.834	1.173	0.863 0.949	1.100	1.223 1.259	1.029
	cyclopentyl	D L	1.265 1.509	1.174	1.881 2.256	1.197	2.355 2.635	1.134	3.299 3.661	1.109

a) Relative retention time, reference compound is N–TFA–L-prolyl–L-leucine *n*-propyl ester, t_R=7.15 min.

Table II. Comparsion of Gas Chromatographic Data of Different N-Perfluoroacyl Prolyl Amino Acid *l*-Menthyl Esters at 250°

Perfluoroacyl	Enantiomer	Alanine RRT[a]	Alanine rL/D	Valine RRT	Valine rL/D	Leucine RRT	Leucine rL/D	Proline RRT	Proline rL/D
TFA	D L	0.692 0.747	1.078	0.901 0.973	1.081	1.018 1.045	1.027	1.462 1.525	1.043
PFP	D L	0.665 0.719	1.082	0.837 0.919	1.097	0.946 1.000	1.057	1.281 1.344	1.049
HFB	D L	0.683 0.746	1.093	0.873 0.964	1.104	0.957 1.036	1.085	1.308 1.385	1.059

a) RRT, reference compound is N-PFP-L-prolyl-L-leucine *l*-menthyl ester, t_R=5.53 min.

Reference
H. Iwase, Chem. Pharm. Bull., 22, 2075 (1974).

Summary
This paper deals with the relative retention times and the relation between the separation factors and structure of 25 racemic amino acids which were converted to their N-TFA-L-prolyl-n-butyl esters and separated by gas-liquid chromatography on achiral phases. Experimental details and results follow:

Apparatus and Conditions——A Hewlett-Packard Model 402 gas chromatograph equipped with a dual flame ionization detector was used. Two glass columns of 5.5 ft × 1/4 in O.D. packed with 5% OV-1 on 100—120 mesh Supelcoport, and 4 ft × 1/4 in O.D. packed with 2% PEGA, stabilized grade, were used. Helium was used as the carrier gas at a flow rate of 60 ml/min.

Reagents and Material——All solvents used in this study were of reagent grade. Amino acids were obtained from Ajinomoto Co., Sigma Chemical Co., K & K Laboratories, and Tokyo Kasei Co. Trifluoroacetic anhydride, N,O-bis-(trimethylsilyl)trifluoroacetamide, trimethylchlorosilane, and acetonitrile were purchased from Pierce Chemical Co. N-TFA-L-PC was prepared in the same manner as described in the previous paper.[3a)] Hypovial was obtained from Pierce Chemical Co.

Preparation of Amino Acid Derivatives——Amino acid *n*-butyl esters were prepared according to the method of Roach, *et al.*[6)] N-TFA-L-prolyl amino acid *n*-butyl esters were prepared according to the method reported previously.[3a)]

3) *a*) H. Iwase and A. Murai, *Chem. Pharm. Bull.* (Tokyo), **22**, 8 (1974);

6) D. Roach and C.W. Gehrke, *J. Chromatogr.*, **44**, 269 (1969).

Table I. Gas Chromatographic Data for Racemic Amino Acids as Their N-TFA-L-Prolyl Amino Acid *n*-Butyl Esters with 5% OV-1 on Supelcoport at 210°

Amino acid	Structure	Emantiomer	RRT[a)]	(r L/D)
Alanine	CH_3-CH-COOH NH_2	D- L-	0.519 0.583	1.124
Glycine	H-CH-COOH NH_2	—	0.615	—
α-Amino-*n*-buturic acid	CH_3CH_2-CH-COOH NH_2	D- L-	0.658 0.733	1.114
Isovaline	CH_3 CH_3CH_2-C-COOH NH_2	D- L-	0.689 0.689	1.000
β-Amino-*n*-butyric acid	CH_3CH-CH_2-COOH NH_2	D- L-	0.743 0.806	1.086
Valine	CH_3>CH-CH-COOH CH_3 NH_2	D- L-	0.743 0.845	1.137
Norvaline	$CH_3CH_2CH_2$-CH-COOH NH_2	D- L-	0.818 0.904	1.105
β-Amino-iso-butyric acid	CH_2-CH-COOH NH_2 CH_3	D- L-	0.845 0.845	1.000
tert-Leucine	CH_3 CH_3-C-CH-COOH CH_3 NH_2	D- L-	0.818 0.936	1.144
Leucine	CH_3>CH-CH_2-CH-COOH CH_3 NH_2	D- L-	0.914 1.000	1.094
Isoleucine	CH_3>CH-CH-COOH CH_3CH_2 NH_2	D- L-	0.979 1.075	1.098
Norleucine	$CH_3CH_2CH_2CH_2$-CH-COOH NH_2	D- L-	1.096 1.198	1.088
Serine	CH_2-CH-COOH OH NH_2	D- L-	1.214 1.332	1.097
Threonine	CH_3CH-CH-COOH OH NH_2	D- L-	1.278 1.406	1.100
Proline	(pyrrolidine ring, N-H)-COOH	D- L-	1.332 1.471	1.104
Penicillamine	CH_3>C-CH-COOH CH_3 SH NH_2	D- L-	1.427 1.535	1.075
Pipecolic acid	(piperidine ring, N-H)-COOH	D- L-	1.834 1.995	1.087
α-Amino-*n*-caprylic acid	$CH_3CH_2CH_2CH_2CH_2CH_2$-CH-COOH NH_2	D- L-	2.016 2.166	1.074
Methionine	$CH_3SCH_2CH_2$-CH-COOH NH_2	D- L-	2.326 2.471	1.062
Phenylglycine	C_6H_5-CH-COOH NH_2	D- L-	2.588 2.588	1.000
Ethionine	$CH_3CH_2SCH_2CH_2$-CH-COOH NH_2	D- L-	2.919 3.107	1.064
Phenylalanine	$C_6H_5CH_2$-CH-COOH NH_2	D- L-	3.417 3.631	1.063

a) Relative retention time, reference compound is N-TFA-L-prolyl-L-leucine *n*-butyl ester. t_R = 4.92 min

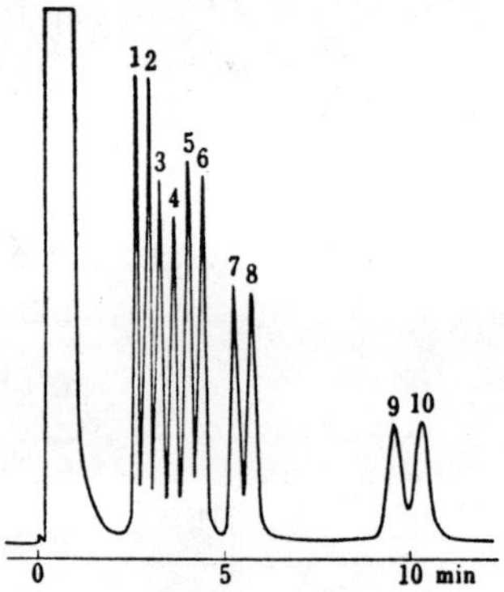

Fig. 1. Gas Chromatogram of N-TFA-L-Prolyl Amino Acid *n*-Butyl Esters on OV-1

1: D-alanine, 2: L-alanine, 3: D-α-amino-*n*-butyric acid, 4: L-α-amino-*n*-butyric acid, 5: D-norvaline, 6: L-norvaline, 7: D-Norleucine, 8: L-norleucine, 9: D-α-amino-*n*-caprylic acid, 10: L-α-amino-*n*-caprylic acid

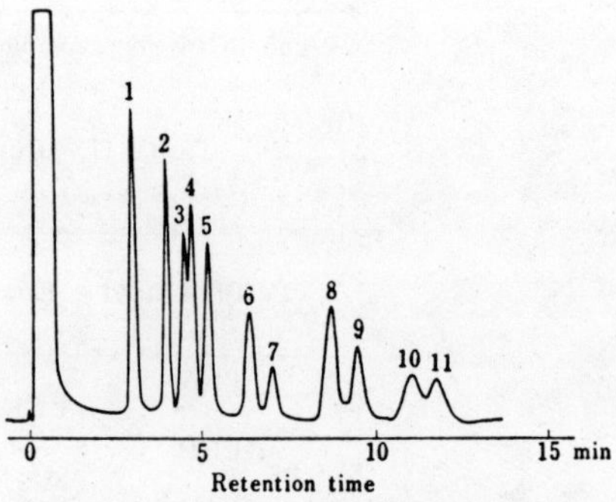

Fig. 2. Gas Chromatogram of N-TFA-L-Prolyl Amino Acid *n*-Butyl Esters on OV-1

1: glycine, 2: D-*tert*-leucine, 3: L-*tert*-leucine, 4: D-isoleucine, 5: L-isoleucine, 6: D-proline, 7: L-proline, 8: D-pipecolic acid, 9: L-pipecolic acid, 10: D-methionine, 11: L-methionine

H. Iwase, Chem. Pharm. Bull., 22, 2075 (1974) continued.

Separation Factors——Separation factors, α, were calculated from the following equation:

$$\alpha = (tR_2 - t_a)/(tR_1 - t_a)$$

were t_{R_1} and t_{R_2} are the retention times from injection of the first and the second components, respectively, and t_a is the retention time of non-adsorbed species (methane).

Result and Discussion

The experimental data of the relative retention times and separation factors of N-TFA-L-prolyl amino acid *n*-butyl esters are given in Tables I, II, and III.

TABLE II. Gas Chromatographic Data for Racemic Amino Acids as Their N-TFA L-Prolyl Amino Acid *n*-Butyl Esters with 2% PEGA on Supelcoport at 220°

Amino acid	Enantiomer	RRT[a)]	(r L/D)
tert-Leucine	D- L-	0.325 0.391	1.204
Threonine	D- L-	0.351 0.404	1.151
Serine	D- L-	0.431 0.497	1.153
Isoleucine	D- L-	0.444 0.536	1.209
β-Amino-*n*-butyric acid	D- L-	0.536 0.616	1.148
β-Amino-iso-butyric acid	D- L-	0.576 0.616	1.069
Glycine	—	0.788	—
α-Amino-*n*-caprylic acid	D- L-	0.947 1.106	1.168
Penicillamine	D- L-	1.039 1.146	1.102
Proline	D- L-	1.000 1.583	1.252
Pipecolic acid	D- L-	1.252 1.384	1.106
Phenylglycine	D- L-	2.325 2.569	1.105
Methionine	D- L-	2.404 2.709	1.127
Ethionine	D- L-	2.815 3.185	1.132
Aspartic acid	D- L-	2.848 2.974	1.044
Glutamic acid	D- L-	4.563 5.113	1.120

a) RRT, reference compound is N-TFA-L-prolyl-D-proline *n*-butyl ester. t_R=4.05 min

TABLE III. Gas Chromatographic Data for Racemic Amino Acids as Their N-TFA L-Prolyl Amino Acid *n*-Butyl Esters with 5% OV-1 on Supelcoport at 290°

Amino acid	Structure	Enantiomer	RRT[a)]	(r L/D)
Ornithine	$NH_2(CH_2)_3\text{-}CH(NH_2)\text{-}COOH$	L- D-	0.812 0.852	0.953
Lysine	$NH_2(CH_2)_4\text{-}CH(NH_2)\text{-}COOH$	L- D-	1.000 1.068	0.936

a) RRT, reference compound is N-TFA-L-prolyl-L-lysine *n*-butyl ester. t_R=6.35 min

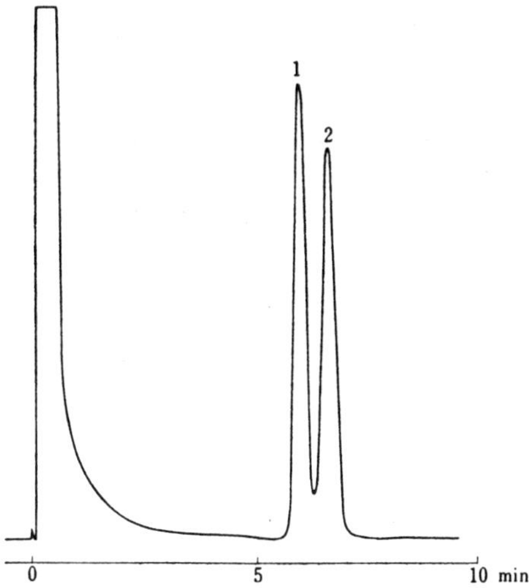

Fig. 3. Gas Chromatogram of N-TFA-L-Prolyl Amino Acid *n*-Butyl Esters on OV-1

1: D-threonine, 2: L-threonine

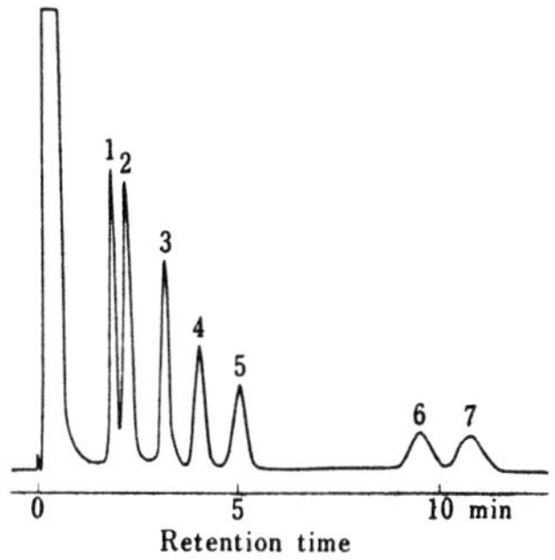

Fig. 4. Gas Chromatogram of N-TFA-L-Prolyl Amino Acid *n*-Butvl Esters on PEGA

1: D-isoleucine, 2: L-isoleucine, 3: glycine, 4: D-proline, 5: L-proline, 6: D-methionine, 7: L-methionine

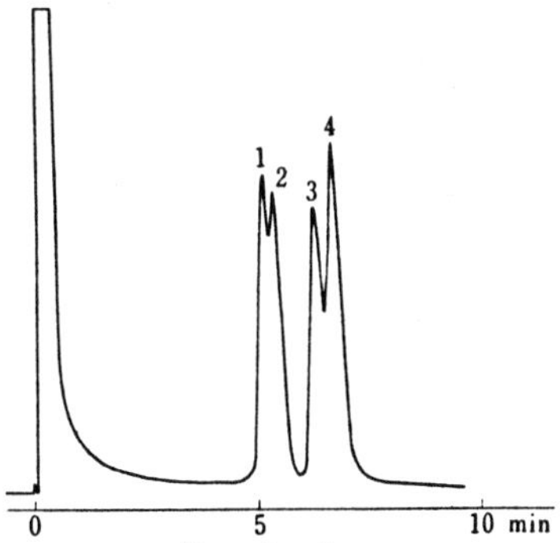

Fig. 5. Gas Chromatogram of N-TFA-L-Prolyl Amino Acid *n*-Butyl Esters on OV-1

1: L-ornithine, 2: D-ornithine, 3: L-lysine, 4: D-lysine

Reference

M. Hasegawa and I. Matsubara, Anal. Biochem., 63, 308 (1975).

Summary
The authors report the resolution via gas liquid chromatography of 19 racemic α-amino acids and 1 β-amino acid as their N-trifluoroacetyl menthyl esters on packed or capillary columns. For the resolution of neutral and basic amino acids conventional packed columns were used. For the complete resolution of acid amino acids a capillary column was used. The resolutions were rationalized as being due to the differences in the abilities of the derivatives to form intermolecular hydrogen bonds with the stationary phases. Experimental details and results follow:

Preparation of Derivatives

All the compounds studied were obtained from commercial sources with exception of amidases used for the resolution of racemic phenylglycine.

Aliphatic and aromatic amino acids. 250 mg of 1-menthol was added to 1.0 mg of amino acid and esterified at 105°C for 1–3 hr in an oil bath by Fisher's method. Then the excess HCl and menthol were completely removed bubbling with dry N_2 gas, followed by addition of 0.5 ml of trifluoroacetic anhydride (TFAA). The reaction mixture was vibrated for 5 min at room temperature and the excess TFAA was removed by the gentle stream of dry N_2 gas. 0.5 ml of dry ethylacetate was added and a 1 μl aliquot was applied to glc.

In order to examine the difference in the reaction velocity between the enantiomeric pairs, menthylation and *N*-trifluoroacetylation were stopped at each interval.

Hydroxy amino acids. To the trifluoroacetylated menthyl esters obtained as described above, 0.5 ml of TMS-HT (hexamethyldisilazane and trimethylchlorosilane in anhydrous pyridine, Tokyo Kasei Co.) was added and stirred for 5 min at room temperature. After removal of the excess TMS reagent by the gentle stream of N_2 gas, the residual products were dissolved in 0.5 ml of ethylacetate.

Acidic and basic amino acids. 5.0 mg of amino acids were added into 3 ml of dry HCl-methanol and esterified at 80°C for 1 hr. After removal of the excess reagent under *vacuo*, 2.0 g of 1-menthol was added and interesterified at 105°C for 3 hr bubbling with dry HCl gas. The menthyl esters obtained thus were then *N*-trifluoroacetylated.

Preparation of L- *and* D-*alanine derivatives.* Following the method for the aliphatic amino acids, L- and D-alanine were added to 3.0 g of 1-menthol and esterified agitating by a magnetic stirrer for 5 hr. After cooling, 50 ml of acetone was added and the resulted precipitates were gathered by filtration, washed with diethylether and then with a small volume of acetone for several times, and crystallized from acetone to form white fine platy crystal for the L-isomer and needle-like crystal for the D-isomer. These esters were then *N*-trifluoroacetylated. The derivatives thus obtained were identified by infrared and NMR spectrometry.

M. Hasegawa and I. Matsubara, Anal. Biochem., <u>63</u>, 308 (1975) continued.

Gas Chromatography

A Yanagimoto model 550F dual flame ionization detector gas chromatograph was used for all amino acids. The stainless steel columns (0.75–4 m × 3 mm i.d.) were packed with various commercial 5% coated stationary phases on 80/100 mesh Chromosorb W.AW. A Perkin Elmer model 900 gas chromatograph equipped with a stainless steel capillary column (300 ft × 0.01 in. i.d.) coated with Apiezon L was used for acidic and basic amino acids. Chromatographic conditions are described in each figure.

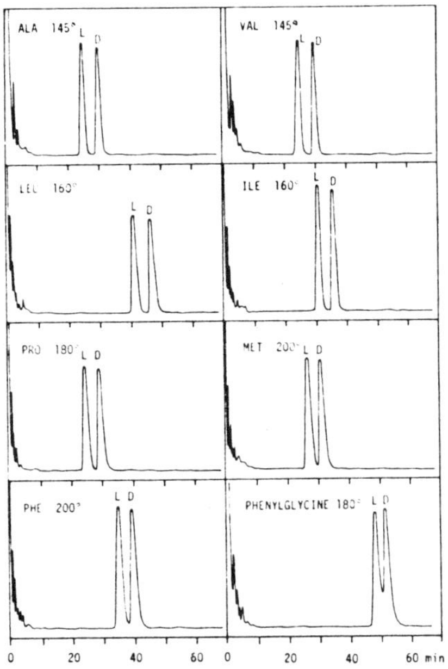

Fig. 1. Resolution of aliphatic and aromatic amino acids on PEG-adipate column. *Conditions:* 5% PEG-adipate column (4 m × 3 mm i.d.), carrier flow = He 10 ml/min, sample size = 1 μl, injection = 250°C.

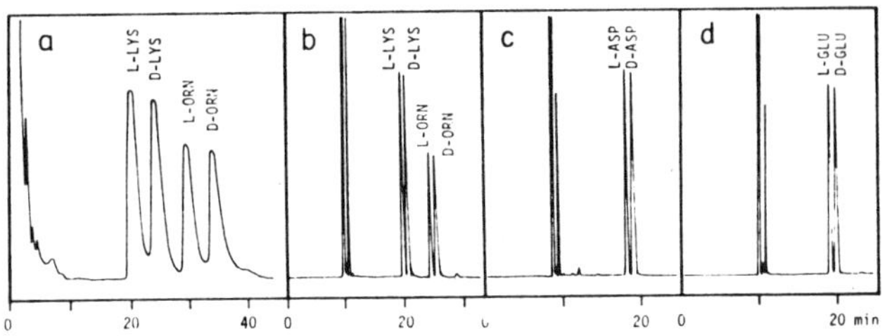

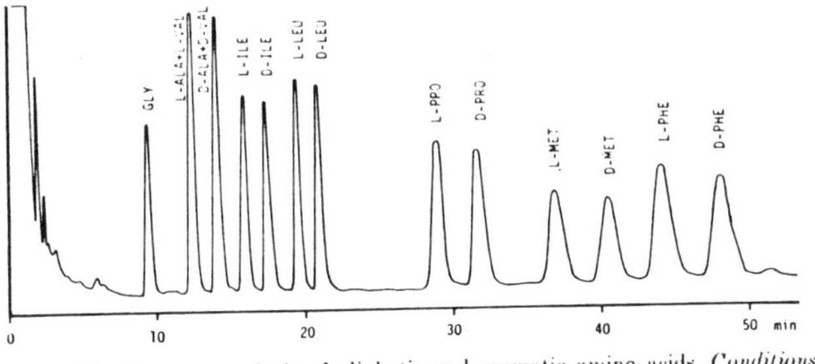

Fig. 2. Simultaneous analysis of aliphatic and aromatic amino acids. *Conditions:* 5% PEG-adipate column (4 m × 3 mm i.d.), 140–200°C at 2°C min, carrier flow = He 10 ml/min, sample size = 1 μl.

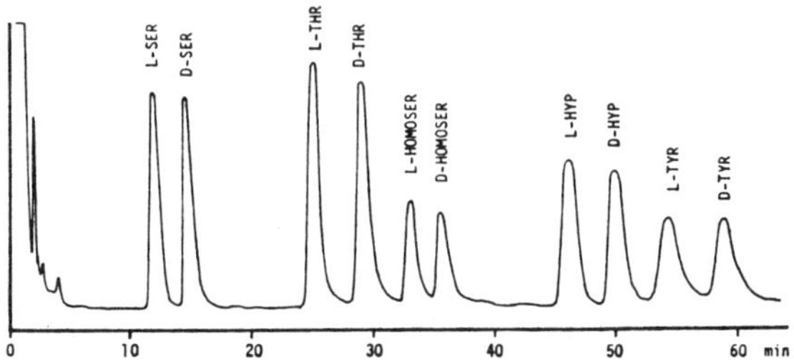

Fig. 3. Resolution of hydroxy amino acids on PEG-adipate column. *Conditions:* 5% PEG-adipate column (4 m × 3 mm i.d.), isothermal at 190°C, carrier flow = HE 10 ml/min, sample size = 1 μl.

Fig. 4. Resolution of basic and acidic amino acids. *Conditions:* (a) 5% Apiezon L column (0.75 m × 3 mm i.d.), isothermal at 180°C, carrier flow = He 15 ml/min. (b) Capillary column (Apiezon L, 300 ft × 0.01 in. i.d.), isothermal at 245°C. (C) Capillary column (Apiezon L, 300 ft × 0.01 in. i.d.), isothermal at 240°C. (d) Capillary column (Apiezon L, 300 ft × 0.01 in. i.d.), isothermal at 265°C.

TABLE 1
Separation Factors Measured on Various Stationary Phases

Amino acid	Structure of side chain R	Separation factor α^a			
		PEG-20M	PEG-A	Apie-zon-L	DC-550
Alanine	—CH$_3$	1.147	1.114	1.111	1.073
Leucine	—CH$_2$CH(CH$_3$)CH$_3$	1.156	1.141	1.117	1.083
Valine	—CH(CH$_3$)CH$_3$	1.160	1.144	1.139	1.077
Isoleucine	—CH(CH$_3$)CH$_2$CH$_3$	1.177	1.161	1.171	1.081
Phenylglycine	—C$_6$H$_5$	—^{b}	1.045	1.070	—
Phenylalanine	—CH$_2$—C$_6$H$_5$	—	1.167	1.113	1.081
α-ABA^d	—CH$_2$CH$_3$	1.149	1.128	1.119	1.077
α-AVA^e	—CH$_2$CH$_2$CH$_3$	1.154	1.135	1.119	1.080
β-ABA^f	(see Fig. 7b)	1.0^c	1.0	1.0	1.0
β-AIBA^g	(see Fig. 7c)	1.050	1.052	1.0	1.0

^{a} Mean values obtained from three times chromatography; 4 m columns packed with 5% coated stationary phases were used at the column temperature 180°C, and the carrier flow (He) was 10 ml/min.
^{b} Not determined.
^{c} No resolution. The pair have just the same retention times.
^{d} α-Amino-n-butyric acid.
^{e} α-Amino-n-valeric acid.
^{f} β-Amino-n-butyric acid.
^{g} β-Aminoisobutyric acid.

Reference
H. Iwase, Chem. Pharm. Bull., 23, 1604 (1975).

Summary
The gas-liquid chromatographic resolution of a number of racemic α-amino acids and a β-amino acid as their N-perfluoroacyl-1-menthyl ester derivatives and as their 1-bornyl ester derivatives on a number of achiral stationary phases was studied for their selectivities. The relation between separation factor and structure of amino acid was discussed. Experimental details and results follow:

Apparatus——A Perkin-Elmer Model 900 gas chromatograph equipped with attachments for scot column and dual flame ionization detector was used. The stainless steel scot column of 100 ft × 0.02 in. i.d. coated with Apiezon L was used.

Reagents and Materials——All solvents used in this study were of reagent grade. Amino acids were obtained from Ajinomoto Co., Tokyo Kasei Co., and K & K Laboratories, trifluoroacetic, pentafluoropropionic, heptafluorobutyric, and pentadecafluorooctanoic anhydrides from Pierce Chemical Co., and chlorodifluoroacetic anhydride from K & K Laboratories, and *l*-menthol, *i*-isopulegol and *l*-borneol from Aldrich Chemical Co. Scot columns were purchased from Perkin-Elmer Co. Hypovial was purchased from Pierce Chemical Co.

Preparation of Amino Acid Derivatives——Amino acid *l*-menthyl esters were prepared according to the procedure of Harada, *et al.*[8] N-Perfluoroacyl-amino acid *l*-menthyl esters were obtained by the known method.[9] N-Perfluoroacyl-amino acid *l*-bornyl esters were prepared in the same manner as *l*-menthyl ester derivatives.

Separation Factor——Separation factor, α, was calculated from the following definition:

$$\alpha = \frac{\text{retention time of D enantiomer}}{\text{retention time of L enantiomer}}$$

Stationary Phases

Seven stationary phases (Carbowax 20M, PEGA, BDS, Apiezon L, SE-30, SE-52, and Dexsil 300 GC) of scot columns were tested for the resolution of racemic amino acids.

The resolution of proline was poor on non-polar stationary phases (SE-30, SE-52 and Dexsil 300 GC) with tailing of the peaks, but it was much improved without tailing on polar stationary phases (BDS, Carbowax 20M and PEGA) and a non-polar stationary phase (Apiezon L). Apiezon L was used for the resolution of racemic amino acids, considering the separation of racemic amino acids and the asymmetric peaks. It is of interest that retention times increase in the order of valine, alanine, leucine and proline on Carbowax 20M, while in the order of alanine, valine, leucine and proline on Apiezon L.

Table I. Gas Chromatographic Data for Racemic Amino Acid as Their N-TFA *l*-Menthyl Esters at Different Temperatures

Amino acid	150°		170°	
	RRT[a]	α	RRT[a]	α
L-Alanine	0.550	1.117	0.580	1.116
D-Alanine	0.614		0.647	
L-α-Amino-*n*-butyric acid	0.735	1.109	0.765	1.099
D-α-Amino-*n*-butyric acid	0.815		0.840	
Glycine	0.751	—	0.765	—
L-Valine	0.823	1.117	0.849	1.099
D-Valine	0.920		0.933	
L-*tert*-Leucine	0.843	1.162	0.866	1.146
D-*tert*-Leucine	0.980		0.992	
L-Norvaline	1.000	1.120	1.000	1.118
D-Norvaline	1.120		1.118	
L-Leucine	1.129	1.121	1.118	1.105
D-Leucine	1.265		1.235	
L-β-Amino-*n*-butyric acid	1.129	1.000	1.126	1.000
D-β-Amino-*n*-butyric acid	1.129		1.126	
L-Isoleucine	1.181	1.153	1.168	1.129
D-Isoleucine	1.361		1.319	
L-Norleucine	1.482	1.130	1.420	1.124
D-Norleucine	1.675		1.597	
L-Proline	2.570	1.072	2.445	1.062
D-Proline	2.755		2.597	

a) RRT, relative retention time, reference compound is N-TFA-L-norvaline *l*-Menthyl ester, $t_{R150°}=12.45$ min, $t_{R170°}=5.95$ min

H. Iwase, Chem. Pharm. Bull., 23, 1604 (1975) continued.

TABLE II. Gas Chromatographic Data for Racemic Amino Acid as Their N-TFA *l*-Menthyl Esters at 190°

Amino acid	RRT[a)]	α
L-Methionine	0.927	1.079
D-Methionine	1.000	
L-Phenylalanine	1.466	1.081
D-Phenylalanine	1.584	

a) RRT, reference compound is N-TFA-D-methionine *l*-menthyl ester, t_R=10.95 min

TABLE III. Gas Chromatographic Data for Racemic Amino Acids as Their N-TFA *l*-Menthyl Esters at 215°

Amino acid	RRT[a)]	α
L-Aspartic acid	0.622	1.000
D-Aspartic acid	0.622	
L-Glutamic acid	1.000	1.065
D-Glutamic acid	1.065	

a) RRT, reference compound is N-TFA-L-glutamic acid *l*-menthyl ester, t_R=38.75 min

TABLE IV. Comparison of Gas Chromatographic Data of Different N-Perfluoroacyl-Amino Acid Esters at 165°

Perfluoroacyl	Ester	Enantiomer	α-Amino-*n*-butyric acid RRT[a)]	α-Amino-*n*-butyric acid α	Leucine RRT	Leucine α
TFA	menthyl	L	0.698	1.108	1.038	1.109
		D	0.774		1.151	
	bornyl	L	0.799	1.059	1.214	1.052
		D	0.846		1.277	
PFP	menthyl	L	0.597	1.105	0.862	1.102
		D	0.660		0.950	
	bornyl	L	0.679	1.056	1.000	1.050
		D	0.717		1.050	
HFB	menthyl	L	0.635	1.099	0.912	1.097
		D	0.698		1.000	
	bornyl	L	0.723	1.052	1.057	1.042
		D	0.761		1.101	
PDFO	menthyl	L	1.157	1.092	1.597	1.091
		D	1.264		1.742	
	bornyl	L	partially resolved		partially resolved	
		D				
CDF	menthyl	L	1.717	1.110	2.484	1.111
		D	1.906		2.761	
	bornyl	L	1.962	1.061	2.950	1.053
		D	2.082		3.107	

a) RRT, reference compound is N-HFB-D-leucine *l*-methyl ester, t_R=7.95 min

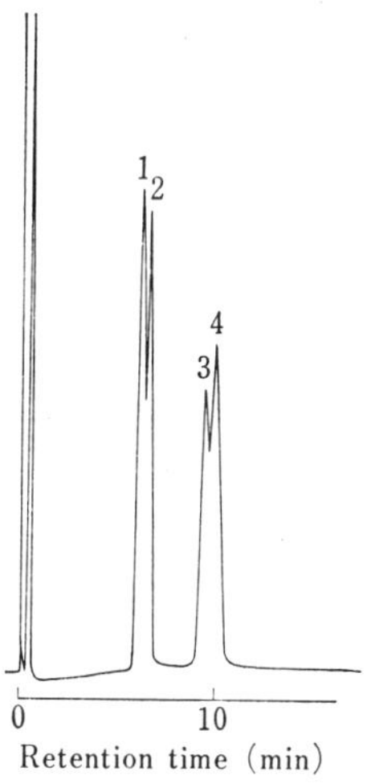

Fig. 1. Gas Chromatogram of N-TFA-Amino Acid *l*-Bornyl Esters at 165°

1: L-α-amino-*n*-butyric acid,
2: D-α-amino-*n*-butyric acid,
3: L-leucine,
4: D-leucine

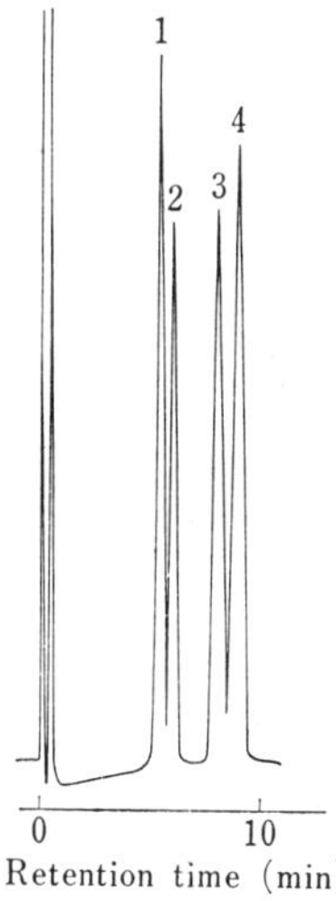

Fig. 2. Gas Chromatogram of N-TFA-Amino Acid *l*-Menthyl Esters at 165°

1: L-α- amino-*n*-butyric acid,
2: D-α-amino-*n*-butyric acid,
3: L-leucine,
4: D-leucine

Reference

D.G. Kaiser, G.J. Vangiessen, R.J. Reischer and W.J. Wechter, J. Pharm. Sci., 65, 269 (1976).

Summary

The enantiomers of 2-(4-isobutylphenyl)propionic acid (A) and 2-(α-hydroxy-4-isobutylphenyl)propionic acid (B) were converted to their diastereomeric (S)-(-)-α-methylbenzyl amide derivatives and separated via gas-liquid chromatography. Experimental details and results follow:

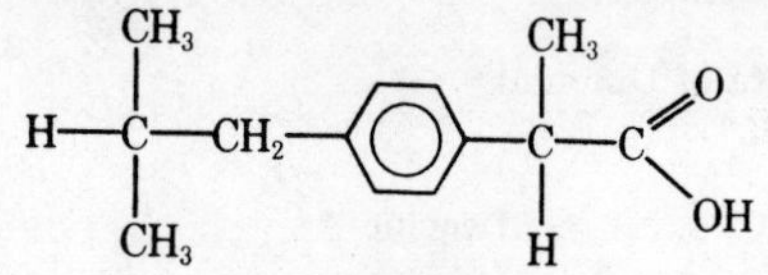

(A)

ibuprofen
I: racemate
II: (S)-(+)
III: (R)-(−)

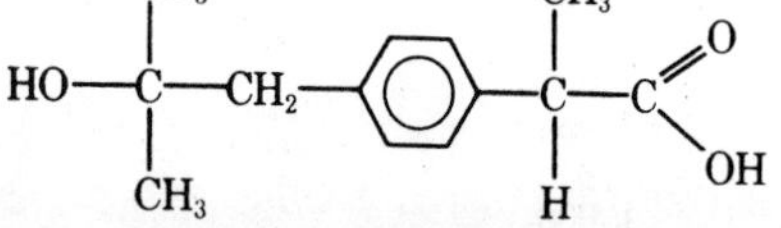

(B)

hydroxy metabolite
IV: isomeric mixture
V: (S)-(+)
VI: (R)-(−)

Resolution of Ibuprofen—(S)-(−)-α-Methylbenzylamine (0.291 mole) was added dropwise, with stirring, to an ice-cooled solution of I (0.291 mole) in 600 ml of ether. The resulting solid, *i.e.*, the more insoluble (S)-(−)-α-methylbenzylamine salt of II (mp 155–170°), was filtered and recrystallized from 300 ml of isopropanol. Two additional recrystallizations, from 200 and 150 ml of absolute ethanol, afforded 12.9 g of white crystals (mp 179–185°). The material was acidified with 3 *N* aqueous sulfuric acid and extracted into ether.

After washing with water and saline, the ether extract was evaporated to dryness. The resulting white solid (mp 49–51°) was recrystallized twice from absolute ethanol to afford 4.5 g of II (mp 50–52°, $[\alpha]_D$ + 57°). GLC analysis, as the (S)-(−)-α-methylbenzylamide derivative (*vide infra*), showed an optical purity of 95%.

Anal.—Calc. for $C_{13}H_{18}O_2$: C, 75.69; H, 8.79. Found: C, 75.88; H, 8.92.

The procedure was repeated using (R)-(+)-α-methylbenzylamine as the resolving agent. The (R)-(+)-α-methylbenzylamine salt of III (mp 153–172°) was filtered and recrystallized from isopropanol. Two additional recrystallizations from absolute ethanol afforded 15.5 g of white crystals (mp 181–185°). The material was acidified with 3 *N* aqueous sulfuric acid and extracted into ether.

After washing with water and saline, the ether extract was evaporated to dryness. The resulting white solid (mp 49–52°) was recrystallized twice from absolute ethanol to afford 6.3 g of III (mp 50–52°, $[\alpha]_D$ −57°). GLC analysis, as the (S)-(−)-α-methylbenzylamide derivative (*vide infra*), showed an optical purity of 96%.

Anal.—Calc. for $C_{13}H_{18}O_2$: C, 75.69; H, 8.79. Found: C, 75.86; H, 9.09.

Instrumentation—All GLC measurements were made with a gas chromatograph[12] equipped with dual hydrogen flame-ionization detectors and a −0.2–1.0-mv dual-pen recorder[13]. All gas cylinders used for chromatography (*i.e.*, helium, hydrogen, and oxygen) were fitted with filters containing molecular sieve 4A. All mass spectrometric measurements were made with a combined GLC–mass spectrometer interfaced to a computer (16). Optical rotation measurements, $[\alpha]_D$ in 95% ethanol, were made with a polarimeter[14] at 25° in a 1-dm tube.

[12] HP model 402, Hewlett-Packard Co., Avondale, Pa.
[13] HP model 7128A, Hewlett-Packard Co., Avondale, Pa.
[14] PE model 141, Perkin-Elmer Corp., Norwalk, Conn.

(16) L. Baczynskyj, D. J. DuChamp, J. F. Zieserl, Jr., and U. F. Axen, *Anal. Chem.*, **45**, 479(1973).

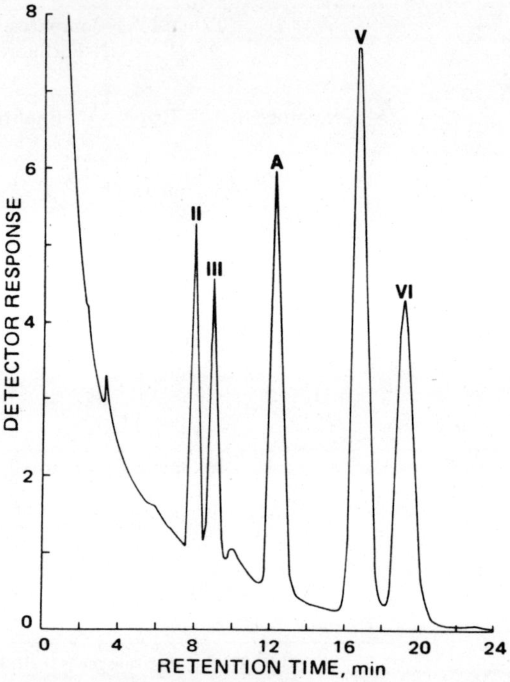

Figure 2—*Gas–liquid chromatogram of* (S)-(−)-α-*methylbenzylamide derivatives of ibuprofen enantiomers and enantiomers of hydroxy metabolite. Key: II,* (S)-(+)-*enantiomer of ibuprofen; III,* (R)-(−)-*enantiomer of ibuprofen; A,* n-*tridecanoic acid standard; V,* (S)-(+)-*enantiomer of hydroxy metabolite; and VI,* (R)-(−)-*enantiomer of hydroxy metabolite.*

The individual enantiomers of I, IV, and VII excreted in human urine were measured as the (S)-(−)-α-methylbenzylamide derivatives *via* GLC on a column of 3% (w/w) OV-17 (10, 12). With the column temperature maintained isothermally at 220°, the retention times for the derivatives of II, III, V, and VI were 8.0, 9.0, 16.9, and 19.1 min, respectively (Fig. 2).

Reference

G. Saucy, R. Borer, D.P. Trullinger, J.B. Jones and K.P. Lok, J. Org. Chem., 42, 3206 (1977).

Summary

A convenient new general method for determining the enantiomeric purities of chiral δ-lactones was developed. The method involves conversion of the lactones to their ortho esters with (-)-(2R,3R)-2,3-butanediol, followed by gas-liquid chromatographic analysis of the obtained diastereomers (see Scheme I). Experimental details and results follow.

[For another method for the determination of enantiomeric purities of 2- and 3-substituted butyrolactones, see G. Helmchen, G. Nill, D. Flockerzi and M.S.K. Youssef, Angew. Chem. Int. Ed. Engl., 18, 63 (1979)]

Scheme I

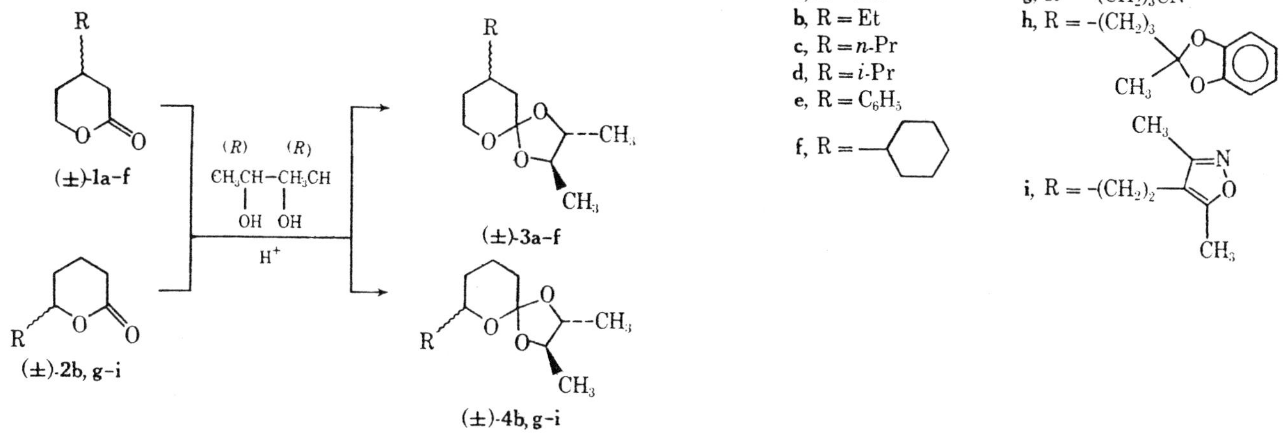

Table I. Diastereomeric Ortho Ester Mixtures

Compd[a]	Method[b]	Yield, %[c]	Formula[d]	GC retention times, min[e]		Column temp, °C
3a	A	52	$C_{10}H_{18}O_3$	6.30	6.89	100
3b	A	73	$C_{11}H_{20}O_3$	8.90	9.55	110
3c	A	57	$C_{12}H_{22}O_3$	9.91	10.69	120
3d	A	50	$C_{12}H_{22}O_3$	8.97	9.82	125
3e	A	54	$C_{15}H_{20}O_3$	17.20	18.50	165
3f	A	43	$C_{15}H_{26}O_3$	16.20	17.30	155
4b	A	60[h]	$C_{11}H_{20}O_3$	2.18[i]	2.47[i]	220
4g	B	62	$C_{13}H_{21}NO_3$	5.25	5.76	220
4h	A	60[h]	$C_{20}H_{28}O_5$	13.08	14.24	220
4i	A	53[h]	$C_{16}H_{25}NO_4$	13.25	14.51	220
4i	B	86[f,h]		84.60[g]	85.60[g]	

[a] All ortho ester mixtures prepared from racemic lactone. [b] See Experimental Section. [c] Data refer to ortho ester mixtures purified by column chromatography. [d] Microanalyses within ±0.3% of theory (C, H) (also N in the case of **4g** and **4i**) were obtained for these compounds. [e] The observed ratios of diastereomers were within 3% of the expected 50:50 relative proportions. [f] Reaction mixture heated for a total of 19 h. [g] Analysis performed on a 3 m, 10% OV-101 column packed on GCQ 100/120 mesh with a temperature program of 2 °C/min over 80–260 °C; N_2 carrier gas flow rate 30 mL/min. [h] Purified by chromatography on alumina (method B) rather than silica gel. [i] Retention times of 37 and 40 min, respectively, observed when analysis was carried out using a 3 m × 0.4 mm (i.d.) column of 10% OV-17, at 130 °C, N_2 carrier gas flow rate of 30 mL/min; these conditions were employed for analyzing the sample derived from (−)-(*S*)-**2b**.

Reference
W.A. König, W. Rahn and J. Eyem, J. Chromatogr., 133, 141 (1977).

Summary
The authors report the resolution via gas liquid chromatography of the diastereomeric (+)-3-methyl-2-butyl esters of N-pentafluoropropionyl-D,L-amino acids on glass capillaries. Separation factors of between 1.03 and 1.09 were obtained and the separation of a mixture of commmon amino acids took less than 1 hour. Experimental conditions and results follow:

Gas chromatography and mass spectrometry

A Carlo Erba Model 2101 gas chromatograph equipped with an all-glass injection port, inlet splitter and flame-ionization detector was used with a 25-m glass capillary coated with SE-30 (LKB, Type 2101-210, AmAc). Hydrogen was used as the carrier gas. The number of theoretical plates was 114,000 at 120° for *n*-tetradecane and nitrogen as carrier gas.

Formation of derivatives

About 100 μg of the D,L-amino acid sample were heated in 150 μl of a 7 *N* solution of hydrogen chloride in (+)-3-methyl-2-butanol of about 99% optical purity (Norse Labs., Santa Barbara, Calif., U.S.A.) for 90 min at 100° (ref. 14). Basic amino acids were esterified before with a solution of hydrogen chloride in methanol (1.25 *N*) for 60 min and 100°. After removal of the excess of reagent under reduced pressure, the sample was acylated in a mixture of 200 μl of dichloromethane and 50 μl of pentafluoropropionic anhydride for 30 min at room temperature. After removing excess of reagent, the sample was dissolved in 100 μl of ethyl acetate and the solution obtained was used for gas chromatography.

TABLE I

SEPARATION FACTORS, α, FOR THE SEPARATION OF N-PENTAFLUOROPROPIONYL-L-AMINO ACID (+)-3-METHYL-2-BUTYL ESTERS (LONGER RETENTION TIME) *versus* N-PENTAFLUOROPROPIONYL-D-AMINO ACID (+)-3-METHYL-2-BUTYL ESTERS (SHORTER RETENTION TIME)

Amino acid (in order of emergence)	*α*	*Column temperature (°C)*
Ala	1.09	100
Gly	—	100
α-Aminobutyric acid	1.09	100
Thr	1.03	100
Val	1.08	100
Ser	1.05	100
Leu	1.09	100
a-Ile	1.08	100
Ile	1.09	100
Cys	1.07	100
Pro	1.06	100
Diaminopropionic acid	1.04	140
Met	1.05	140
Orn	1.06	140
Phe	1.04	140
Asp	1.04	140
His	1.03	140
Lys	1.05	140
Tyr	1.04	140
Glu	1.05	140
Arg	1.05	140
Trp	1.04	200

W.A. König, W. Rahn and J. Eyem, J. Chromatogr., 133, 141 (1977) continued.

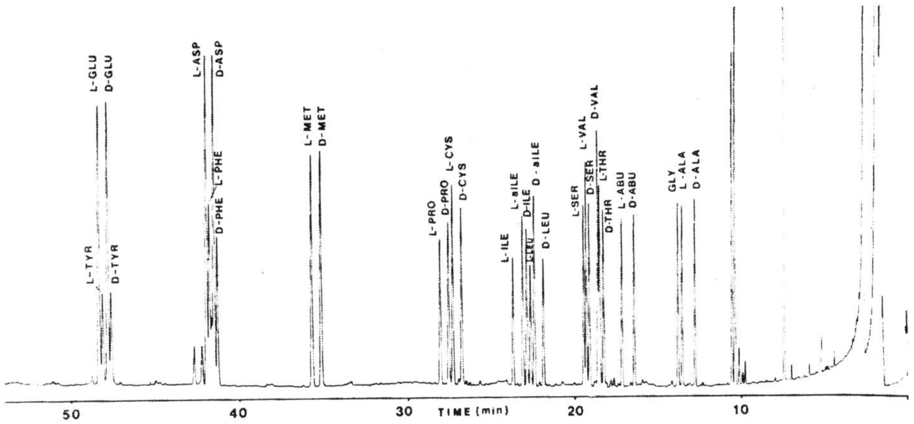

Fig. 1. Gas chromatogram of diastereoisomeric pentafluoropropionyl-amino acid (+)-3-methyl-2-butyl esters on a 25-m glass capillary column (SE-30 AmAc, LKB 2101-210). Column temperature: 85°, temperature program: 2°/min to 220°. Carrier gas: hydrogen, split ratio 1:30.

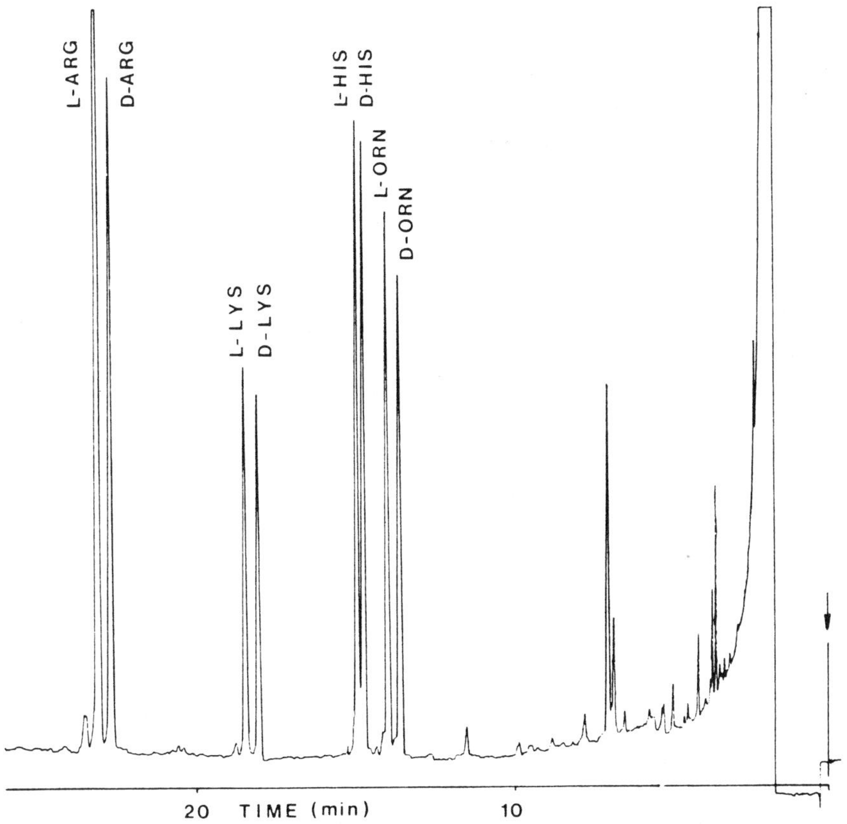

Fig. 2. Gas chromatogram of diastereoisomeric derivatives of basic amino acids. Column and carrier gas as in Fig. 1. Column temperature: 150°, temperature program: 2°/min to 220°.

Reference

E.A. Hoopes, E.T. Peltzer and J.L. Bada, J. Chromatogr. Sci., 16, 556 (1978).

Summary

The authors report the resolution by gas liquid chromatography of several racemic α-amino acids as their diastereomeric N-trifluoroacetyl-L-prolyl methyl esters on an achiral stationary phase. Experimental details and results follow:

TPC Synthesis: Due to the presence of 3-12% D-isomer in commercially available TPC (Regis Chemical Co., Morton Grove, Illinois), which unnecessarily complicates the analysis, we proceeded to synthesize our own. The method of Dabrowiak and Cooke (13) was used, with the following modifications.

Because acid chlorides are extremely reactive reagents, due caution was exercised to keep TPC out of contact with water and alcohols. The reaction flask was kept under a stream of dry nitrogen except for stripping of solvents and excess reagents, which were removed using a rotary vacuum evaporator connected to a vacuum pump through a dry ice-acetone trap. A water aspirator was not used, as the water vapor would react with the product.

Ten mmole (1.151 g) of proline was suspended with magnetic stirring in 15 ml of anhydrous ether in a weighed reaction flask. This mixture was cooled in a dry ice-acetone bath, and 10 ml of trifluoroacetic anhydride was added dropwise. When the addition was complete, the bath was removed immediately and the mixture was allowed to warm slowly to room temperature. Magnetic stirring was continued under the nitrogen atmosphere, and after one hour the ether and unreacted anhydride were removed by rotary vacuum evaporation at room temperature.

The flask containing the light-yellow oily product was then returned to the nitrogen atmosphere. A mixture of 9 ml of dry benzene and 6 ml of doubly distilled thionyl chloride was added dropwise with magnetic stirring in a room-temperature bath. When the addition was complete, the stirring was continued for an additional 2½ hours. The excess reagent and solvent were again removed by rotary evaporation at room temperature. The final product was weighed and sufficient dichloromethane (spectral grade) was added to make a 0.1*M* solution. We found that chloroform (which Dabrowiak and Cooke used as a final solvent) is often preserved with ~1% ethanol, which subsequently reacts with the TPC. Thus, its use is to be carefully avoided. The TPC solution was then stored under nitrogen at 0°C in twenty 5 ml bottles with Teflon-lined septum stoppers. Dabrowiak and Cooke reported that TPC stored under nitrogen at -20°C is stable (no racemization or loss of activity) for six months.

Gas Chromatography

Column Preparation: Two glass columns were used, one 3.6 m x 2 mm and one 6 m x 2 mm (i.d.). The 3.6 m column was obtained empty from Hewlett-Packard, while the 6 m column was custom made by Curtis Associates (San Diego, California). It is interesting to note that the 3.6 m column gave slightly better separations, which was attributed to better flow characteristics of the shorter column.

The following procedures are summarized here for convenience. To facilitate the addition of reagents, the column was attached to an aspirator so that by varying the water flow through the aspirator it was possible to control the rate at which reagents were pulled through the column. Approximately 10 column volumes of each reagent were used.

First, a 1:1:1 mixture of acetone, ethyl acetate and methanol was added to the column, followed by doubly distilled water. A freshly prepared solution of 20% NaOH was added and the flow rate adjusted so that it required 15 to 20 minutes for 10 column volumes to flow through. Excess NaOH was flushed from the column with 2x water, followed by anhydrous methanol. The column was next washed with toluene and then a 20% (v/v) solution of dimethyldichlorosilane (DMCS) in toluene was added, with the flow rate adjusted so that 15-20 minutes were required for the 10-column addition. Without admitting any air, the DMCS was washed from the column with anhydrous methanol and the column then was dried in a stream of dry nitrogen.

Preparation of Support: The following procedure was taken from a paper by Liebrand and Dunham (17).

The support is very fragile and should be handled as gently as possible in all phases of preparation. Approximately 50 g of Chromosorb W (Supelco, Inc., Bellefonte, Pennsylvania), 100/120 mesh range, was covered with doubly distilled 6*M* HCl in a 1000 ml suction flask. (A house vacuum was applied for two hours to degas the slurried support.) The acid was decanted, along with any fines present, and the procedure was repeated until acid washes were clear. This required two weeks, with the acid changed twice daily. The support was washed with doubly distilled water until the pH of the wash was 7. It was then transferred to a fritted glass funnel, washed with more doubly distilled water, and then washed with methanol. The dried support was transferred to an Erylenmeyer flask with a septum-stopper (Kontes, Vineland, New Jersey) and allowed to dry overnight in a vacuum oven at 110°C. As the vacuum was released, N_2 was bled into the oven and the septum-stopper put in place. After cooling, 100 μl of DMCS (2 μl per gram of support) was injected through the septum stopper into the N_2-filled flask and allowed to stand overnight at 60°C. Anhydrous methanol (5 μl per gram of support) was then injected and allowed to stand overnight at 45°C. (Caution should be observed when adding methanol because of the increase in pressure due to the methanol evaporation.) Support was transferred to a fritted glass funnel and washed with 300 ml anhydrous methanol. When dry, the support was transferred to a storage container and dried in a vacuum oven overnight at 70°C.

E.A. Hoopes, E.T. Peltzer and J.L. Bada, J. Chromatogr. Sci., 16, 556 (1978) continued.

Coating the Support: A 7% (w/v) solution of SP-2250 in chloroform was prepared, allowing for about 10 ml of solution per gram of support. This solution was cooled and added to the solid support in a vacuum flask. After swirling to ensure complete wetting, house vacuum was applied to degas the support. Degassing was repeated several times until no more air appeared to be escaping; then the vacuum was left on for 10 minutes. When the vacuum was released, the support was transferred to a fluidized drier and the solution drawn off. When the dripping ceased, the coated support was fluidized and dried in a stream of dry nitrogen until no odor of chloroform could be detected. It was then transferred to a storage container and further dried overnight in a vacuum desiccator. The support, prepared as above, yields approximately 10% liquid loading.

Instrumentation

A Hewlett-Packard HP5711A Dual Flame-Ionization Detector Gas Chromatograph (Hewlett-Packard, Avondale, Pennsylvania) was used. Helium (L&V Industrial Supply, Encinitas, California) was used as the carrier gas after purification by drierite and molecular sieves to remove any traces of water and organic compounds, followed by an OXY-TRAP (Alltech Associates, Arlington Heights, Illinois) to remove any oxygen present. Hydrogen (L&V Industrial Supply) and Synthetic Air (20% O_2 in N_2; L&V Industrial Supply) were used for the flame ionization detectors. Gas chromatography of the standards and samples was done in the single detector mode. Electrometer output was recorded with a Linear Instruments Model 252A Integrating Chart Recorder (Linear Instruments Corp., Costa Mesa, California). Samples were injected, using Hamilton 801N syringes (Hamilton Co., Reno, Nevada). Due to the high inlet pressures, 80 psig, Vespel ferrules (Alltech Associates) were used to connect the glass columns to the GC oven fittings. Combined gas chromatography-mass spectrometry (GC/MS) was accomplished with a Hewlett-Packard HP5710 Gas Chromatograph coupled to a Hewlett-Packard HP5930A Mass Spectrometer with a Hewlett-Packard HP5933A Data System and Tektronix 4012 CRT Display. A 2 m column was interfaced with the mass spectrometer via a silicone membrane separator.

Procedure for Synthesizing N-trifluoroacetyl-L-prolyl-dipeptide methyl esters

10^{-4} to 10^{-7} Mole of amino acids were placed in a 16 x 75 mm screw-capped (Teflon-lined) culture tube. One ml of acidic methanol was added and the mixture heated in a heating block at 90°C without being capped. The reaction was complete when the excess methanol had evaporated off. One ml of dichloromethane (DCM) was added after the methyl ester residue had returned to room temperature. Sufficient TPC reagent was then added to the residue to provide a X5 excess. Triethylamine was then added dropwise (generally 1 to 3 drops) with thorough mixing until DUAL TINT pH paper (J.T. Baker, Phillipsburg, New Jersey) indicated in the 10-12 pH range. (In this nonaqueous system, the color change of the paper can be speeded up greatly by gently blowing on the paper and reading the most intense color development.) The culture tube was capped and allowed to stand for one hour at room temperature. During the reaction time, the pH was occasionally monitored to make sure the basic condition (pH 10-12) was maintained.

An equal volume of doubly distilled 6*M* HCl was added and the tube tightly sealed with a Teflon-lined cap and vigorously shaken. The phases were then separated with the aid of a low-speed centrifuge and the aqueous upper layer removed. The organic lower layer, containing the dipeptide, was dried with anhydrous magnesium sulfate and then filtered through pyrex glass wool into a separate 16 x 75 mm culture tube. The magnesium sulfate was then washed with 1-2 ml of DCM, filtered, and combined with the initial solution. The DCM was evaporated with a stream of dry nitrogen at room temperature, and the residue was redissolved in ~1 ml of anhydrous ether for standards and 10-500 μl for samples. One to five μl of this solution was then injected into the gas chromatograph.

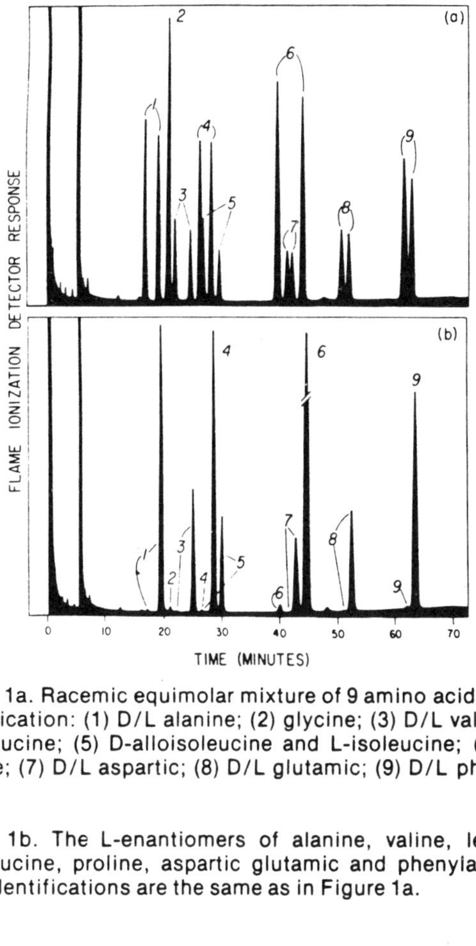

Figure 1a. Racemic equimolar mixture of 9 amino acids. Peak identification: (1) D/L alanine; (2) glycine; (3) D/L valine; (4) D/L leucine; (5) D-alloisoleucine and L-isoleucine; (6) D/L proline; (7) D/L aspartic; (8) D/L glutamic; (9) D/L phenylalanine.

Figure 1b. The L-enantiomers of alanine, valine, leucine, L-isoleucine, proline, aspartic glutamic and phenylalanine. Peak identifications are the same as in Figure 1a.

Reference

S. Hara and A. Dobashi, J. Chromatog., 186, 543 (1979).

Summary

New chiral phases for the resolution of α-amino acids by HPLC were synthesized.

New chiral phases [N-n-valeryl-L-valyl-aminopropylsilanized silica (VVA-silica), N-N-butyryl-L-valylaminopropylsilanized silica (VA-silica), N-propionyl-L-valyl-aminopropylsilanized silica (PVA-silica), N-acetyl-L-valylaminopropylsilanized silica (AVA-silica) and N-pivaloyl-L-valylaminopropylsilanized silica (PivVA-silica)] were synthesized for the resolution of α-amino acids and benzyloxycarbonyldipeptide by HPLC. These phases were designed to have less specific and milder diastereomeric association with the solute molecules than previously known phases. Experimental details and results follow:

EXPERIMENTAL

Preparation of 3-aminopropylsilanized silica (APS-silica)[10,11]

APS-silica was prepared from microparticulate spherical shaped silica gel (Kusano Scientific Co., Tokyo, Japan; average particle size 10 μm, average pore diameter 95 Å, specific surface area 380 m^2/g). Toluene for silanization was dried by distillation over calcium hydride under argon and 3-aminopropyltriethoxysilane (APS) was distilled twice *in vacuo* (boiling point 108°/15 torr). Before reaction, the physically adsorbed water was removed from the silica and glassware by heating at 200° *in vacuo* for 12 h.

The bonding reaction was carried out in a dry argon atmosphere. About 20 g of dried silica gel were suspended in 400 ml of absolute toluene and 20 ml of APS were added to the suspension. The mixture was heated at 100° for 12 h with gentle stirring and the ethanol formed was removed by azeotropic distillation. After the reaction, the suspension was cooled to room temperature, filtered off and washed successively with toluene, acetone, absolute methanol and diethyl ether. Finally, APS-silica was dried over phosphorus pentoxide *in vacuo* for 12 h at room temperature. The results of the elemental analysis (C, N) yielded 1.59% of nitrogen of APS-silica and a surface concentration of 3.0 μmole/m^2 of APS monomers.

Preparation of N-n-valeryl-L-valyl-aminopropylsilanized silica (VVA-silica) and other N-acyl homologues

Condensation of acyl chloride (*n*-valeryl, *n*-butyryl, propionyl and pivaloyl chloride) with L-valine to give the desired N-acyl-L-valine was carried out by the usual Schotten-Baumann procedure. A typical procedure is as follows.

L-Valine (1.5 g, 12.8 mmole) was dissolved in 7.1 ml of ice-cold 2 *N* sodium hydroxide solution and five additions of 9.6 ml of 2 *N* sodium hydroxide solution and 1.86 ml of *n*-valeryl chloride (15.4 mmole) were made at intervals of 10 min with vigorous stirring and cooling in an ice-bath. After the addition of reagents, the mixture was stirred for a further 2 h at room temperature. It was then washed once with diethyl ether, acidified (pH 2) by the careful addition of 5 *N* hydrochloric acid and extracted three times with ethyl acetate. The ethyl acetate fraction was dried over anhydrous sodium sulphate and evaporated *in vacuo*. The residue was recrystallized from ethyl acetate (melting point 139.5–140.5°). Other N-acyl-L-valine derivatives prepared by the procedure described above, and identified by NMR and IR spectrometry and melting point determinations, were N-*n*-butyryl-L-valine (m.p. 149–150.5°), N-propionyl-L-valine (m.p. 131–132°) and N-pivaloyl-L-valine (m.p 144.5–145°).

To a suspension of APS-silica (2.2 g) in 8 ml of dimethylformamide (DMF) degassed *in vacuo* for 5 min were added a solution of 1-hydroxybenzotriazole (1.02 g, 7.53 mmole) in 3 ml of DMF and a solution of N-acyl-L-valine (5.02 mmole; N-*n*-valeryl-L-valine 1.01 g, N-*n*-butyryl-L-valine 940 mg, N-propionyl-L-valine 869 mg) in 3 ml of DMF. The resulting mixture was treated with 3 ml of DMF containing 1.14 g of dicyclohexylcarbodiimide at 0° for 1 h with stirring, and then stirred at room temperature for 48 h. The grafted silica was separated from dicyclohexylurea by centrifugation and washed successively with chloroform, acetone, absolute methanol and diethyl ether, and then dried over phosphorus pentoxide *in vacuo* for 6 h. BVA-, PVA- and PivVA-silica were obtained by the same procedure.

As formyl-L-valine, when used in conjunction with the carbodiimide procedure, does not racemize, there is no necessity to add 1-hydroxybenzotriazole. However, this reagent was, in fact, added in order to keep grafting conditions constant.

IR spectra were obtained using a Hitachi Model-215 spectrometer. As the IR spectra taken in potassium bromide were too weak, tablets were obtained from direct pressurization of the grafted silica at 600 bar for 35 min. IR spectra of the grafted silica showed absorption peak at 1660 cm^{-1} due to C=O in the amide group.

Microelemental analysis was performed by the Microanalytical Centre of this college. The results are given in Table I.

Column packing procedure

Columns were packing using a high-pressure slurry packing apparatus equip- ped with a constant-pressure pump (Model DSTV-122G, Haskel Eng. and Supply Co. Burbank, Calif., U.S.A.) shown schematically Fig. 1. This pump can deliver a maximum pressure of 20,000 p.s.i. The slurry reservoir was constructed of stainless-steel tubing and was 50 cm in length with I.D. 10 mm (Chemco Co., Osaka, Japan). To 2.1 g of grafted silica dried over phosphorus pentoxide was added a solution that contained 5 ml of tetrachloromethane, 10 ml of chloroform and 10 ml of dioxan and which had been degassed in an ultrasonic bath for 3 min. Slurry Solvent B conc (Macherey, Nagel & Co., Düren G.F.R.) was added for stabilization and the slurry was further homogenized in an ultrasonic bath for 3 min. A solution consisting of chloroform and methanol (1:1, 200 ml) was used to pressurize the slurry. This solution was introduced to the bottom of the slurry reservoir. The slurry was transferred to a reservoir. The chromatographic column (precision-bore stainless-steel tubing of length 20 cm and I.D. 4 mm) was attached to the slurry reservoir. The slurry packing apparatus was initially pressurized to 6000 p.s.i. with the valve closed. The valve was opened, and the slurry was forced from the reservoir into the column. After half of the slurry solvent had been eluted, the pressure was increased to 8000 p.s.i. Just before the solvent reservoir became empty, *n*-hexane was added and 200 ml of *n*-hexane were passed through the column at 8000 p.s.i. in order to remove the slurry solvent from the packed column. Then the pump was shut off and column pressure relieved.

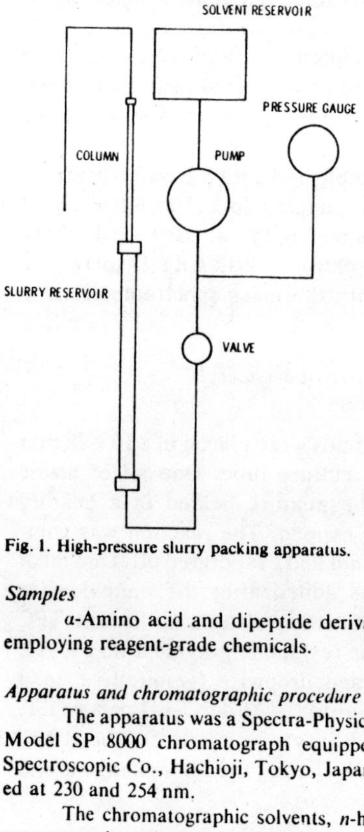

Fig. 1. High-pressure slurry packing apparatus.

Samples

α-Amino acid and dipeptide derivatives were prepared in our laboratory by employing reagent-grade chemicals.

Apparatus and chromatographic procedure

The apparatus was a Spectra-Physics (Stenderway, Santa Clara, Calif., U.S.A. Model SP 8000 chromatograph equipped with a Jasco UVIDEC-100-II (Japan Spectroscopic Co., Hachioji, Tokyo, Japan) variable-wavelength UV detector operated at 230 and 254 nm.

The chromatographic solvents, *n*-hexane and 2-propanol were of analytical reagent grade and were distilled once over calcium hydride.

The amount of N-acetylamino acid methyl esters injected was 40 μg, dissolved in 4 μl of chloroform. The amount of dipeptide derivatives was 80 μg in 8 μl of chloroform.

S. Hara and A. Dobashi, J. Chromatog., 186, 543 (1979) continued.

TABLE I

PHYSICAL PROPERTIES OF CHIRAL AMIDE-BONDED SILICA PHASES AND COLUMNS

Property	*FVA-silica*	*AVA-silica*	*PVA-silica*	*BVA-silica*	*VVA-silica*	*PivVA-silica*
Elemental analysis, N (%)	2.11	2.04	1.65	1.95	1.85	1.93
Surface coverage (%)*	37	42	53	59	61	39
Number of theoretical plates per 20 cm**	1300	1300	1100	1200	1000	900

* The ratio of N-acyl-L-valine grafted on APS-silica is shown.

** Number of theoretical plates per 20 cm was obtained by using N-Ac-L-Leu-OMe as the solute employing a linear velocity of *ca.* 0.18 cm/sec, a temperature of 40° and a mobile phase consisting of 8% (v/v) 2-propanol in *n*-hexane ($k' \approx 2.9$).

TABLE II

RESOLUTION OF DL-α-AMINO ACID AND DIPEPTIDE DERIVATIVES USING N-ACYL HOMOLOGUES OF L-VALYLAMINOPROPYL-SILANIZED SILICA

DL-α-Amino acid and dipeptide derivatives were analysed on six chiral columns under the following conditions: column dimensions, 20 × 0.4 cm I.D.; temperature, 40°; linear velocity, (1) FVA-silica 0.080 cm/sec, (2) AVA-silica 0.093 cm/sec, (3) PVA-silica 0.090 cm/sec, (4) BVA-silica 0.104 cm/sec, (5) VVA-silica 0.095 cm/sec, (6) PivVA silica 0.096 cm/sec.

Racemate	*FVA-silica*[8]	*AVA-silica*[9]	*PVA-silica*				*BVA-silica*				*VVA-silica*				*PivVA-silica*			*Mobile phase: concentration of 2-propanol in n-hexane (%)*
	R_s*	R_s	k_1'	k_2'	α	R_s	k_1'	k_2'	α	R_s	k_1'	k_2'	α	R_s	k_1'	k_2'	α	
N-Ac-Leu-OMe	0.79	0.71	5.63	6.39	1.13	0.92	6.90	7.78	1.13	0.99	6.83	7.61	1.11	0.76	7.55		**	4
N-Ac-Nle-OMe	0.70	0.63	5.89	6.60	1.12	0.86	6.69	7.51	1.12	0.91	6.61	7.38	1.12	0.83	—		—	4
N-Ac-Ile-OMe	0.62	0.54	5.37	6.00	1.12	0.85	5.98	6.67	1.12	0.90	6.01	6.63	1.10	0.68	—		—	4
N-Ac-Val-OMe	0.63	0.55	5.23	5.78	1.11	0.77	6.86	7.55	1.10	0.76	7.23	7.91	1.09	0.63	7.84		1.00	4
N-Ac-Phe-OMe	0.56	0.57	8.15	8.94	1.10	0.74	8.59	9.36	1.09	0.70	9.13	9.93	1.09	0.64	10.26		1.00	4
N-Ac-S-Bz-Cys-OMe	0.40	0.24	8.98	9.41	1.05	0.37	9.37	9.76	1.04	0.31	10.01	10.33	1.03	0.22	—		—	4
N-Ac-Met-OMe	0.39	0.31	7.36	7.73	1.05	0.37	6.90	7.24	1.05	0.38	6.50	6.89	1.06	0.41	—		—	8
N-Ac-Ala-OMe	0.31	**	6.28	6.68	1.06	0.43	5.92	6.32	1.07	0.52	7.20	7.49	1.04	0.28	—		—	8
Z-Leu-Leu-OMe	0.84	0.46	5.48	5.89	1.07	0.49	5.51	5.98	1.09	0.66	5.47	5.88	1.07	0.47	6.42		1.00	2
Z-Phe-Phe-OMe	0.70	**	6.23	6.54	1.05	0.36	6.51	6.85	1.05	0.38	6.29	6.46	1.03	0.20	—		—	3

* Resolution (R_s) was calculated according to the equation $R_s = 1/4\,(\alpha - 1)\sqrt{N}[k'/(1+k')]$, where k' is the capacity factor and α is the separation factor, calculated according to the equations $k' = (k_1' + k_2')/2$ and $\alpha = k_1'/k_2'$.

** Shoulders could be definitely detected in all instances.

A typical chromatogram is shown in Fig. 2. As a further effort in determining the features of the stationary phase, columns prepared from silica grafted with higher homologues of N-acyl-L-valine were examined. These homologues include the N-propionyl-(PVA-), N-*n*-butyryl-(BVA-), N-*n*-valeryl-(VVA) and N-pivaloyl-L-valyl-aminopropylsilanized silica (PivVA-silica) derivatives.

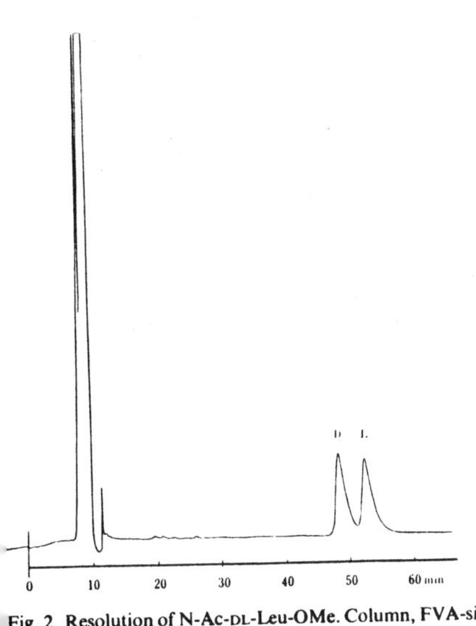

Fig. 2. Resolution of N-Ac-DL-Leu-OMe. Column, FVA-silica × 2; mobile phase 4% (v/v) 2-propanol in *n*-hexane; temperature, 40°; linear velocity, 0.086 cm/sec; detection, UV at 230 nm, 0.16 a.u.f.s.

In addition to the D,D- and L,L-enantiomers, D,L- and L-leucyl-D-leucine derivatives were prepared as another pair of antipodes. These four stereoisomers were resolved simultaneously using an FVA-silica column. The chromatogram is shown in Fig. 3. The elution sequence of the four dipeptide derivatives was as follows: L,L- > D,D- > D,L- > L,D-. The results indicated that protected dipeptides containing a D-α-amino acid as a C-terminal constituent were more retained than the antipodes on a column having an L-α-amino acid moiety.

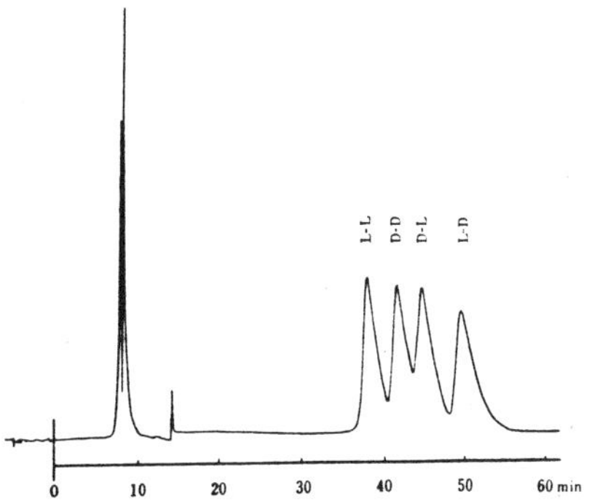

Fig. 3. Resolution of Z-Leu-Leu-OMe. (L-L, D-D, D-L, L-D). Column, FVA-silica × 2; mobile phase, 2% (v/v) 2-propanol in *n*-hexane; temperature, 40°; linear velocity, 0.086 cm/sec; detection, UV at 254 nm, 0.16 a.u.f.s.

Reference

S. Hara and A. Dobashi, J. Liquid Chromatogr., $\underline{2}$, 883 (1979).

Summary

A new chiral stationary phase N-acetyl-L-valyl-aminopropylsilanized silica (A) was prepared by grafting N-acetyl-L-valine onto 3-aminopropylsilanized silica gel.

$$(CH_3)_2CH\text{-}\overset{\displaystyle \overset{NHCOCH_3}{|}}{\underset{\displaystyle \underset{H}{|}}{C^*}}\text{-}\overset{\displaystyle}{\underset{\displaystyle \underset{O}{\|}}{C}}\text{-}NH\text{-}CH_2CH_2CH_2\text{-}Si\overset{\displaystyle \overset{OC_2H_5}{|}}{\big\langle}\genfrac{}{}{0pt}{}{O-}{O-}\Big($$

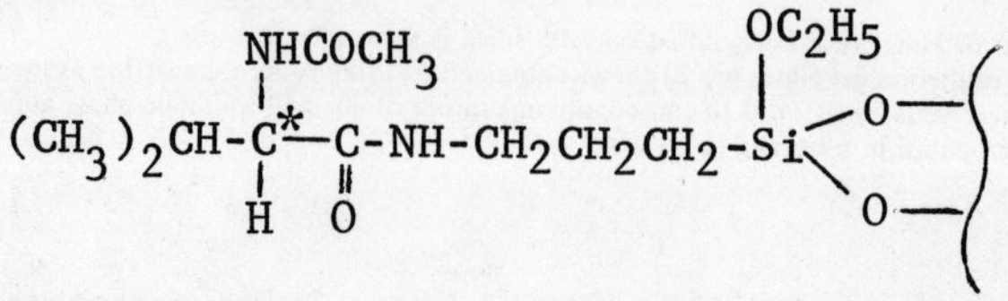

This chiral stationary phase was used for the direct resolution of racemic N-acyl-alkyl α-amino acid esters via high performance liquid chromatography. The experimental details and results follow:

The preparation of N-formyl-L-valyl-aminopropylsilanized silica (FVA-silica) and the column packing procedure are described below. 3-aminopropylsilanized silica (APS-silica) was prepared from microparticulate silica gel (Kusano Scientific Co., Ltd., Tokyo, Japan, average particule size 10 µm, average pore size 95 Å, specific surface area 380 m²/g) and freshly distilled 3-aminopropyltriethoxysilane (b. p. 108°C/15 torr) in absolute toluene, according to the procedure described by *Engelhardt* and *Mathes* [7]. The results of elemental analysis (C,N) revealed 1.59% of nitrogen per gram of APS-silica and a surface concentration of 3.0 µmol/m² of APS-monomers. To a suspension of APS-silica (2.1 g) in 8 ml of dimethylformamide (DMF), degassed under vacuum for 5 minutes, were added a solution of 1-hydroxybenztriazole 970 mg, 7.2 mmol) in 3 ml of DMF and a solution of N-formyl-L-valine (695 mg, 4.79 mmol) in 3 ml of DMF. The resulting mixture was treated with 3 ml of DMF containing 1.09 g of dicyclohexylcarbodiimide at 0°C for 1 hour under stirring, and then stirred at room temperature for 48 hours. The grafted silica was separated from dicyclohexylurea by centrifugation and washed successively with chloroform, acetone, methanol, and diethyl ether, and then dried over phosphorous pentoxide under vacuum for 6 hours. Elemental analysis (C,N) gave 2.11% of

nitrogen per gram of grafted silica. From this value, the ratio of N-formyl-L-valine grafted on the APS-silica was estimated at about 32.7%. The column packing procedure was as follows: To 2.1 g of FVA-silica was added a solution containing 5 ml of tetrachloromethane, 10 ml of chloroform, and 10 ml of dioxan, degassed in an ultrasonic bath for 3 minutes. Then 10 ml of Slurry Solvent, B concentration (Macherey-Nagel & Co., Düren, Germany) was added to stabilize the slurry. The slurry was transferred to a reservoir and pumped into a column (precision-bore stainless steel, length 20 cm, I.D. 4 mm) with a constant pressure pump (Model DSTV-122G, Haskel Eng. and Supply Co., Burbank, Calif., U.S.A.) at 6000 psi initial pressure. A solution consisting of chloroform and methanol (50:50, 200 ml) was used to pressurize the slurry. When half the volume of slurry solvent had been eluted, the pressure was increased at 8000 psi. After 200 ml of *n*-hexane had been flushed through, the pump was shut off and the pressure in the column was allowed to fall.

The apparatus was a Spectra-Physics (Stenderway, Santa Clara, U.S.A.) Model SP 8000 Chromatograph equipped with a Jasco UVIDEC-100-II (Japan Spectroscopic Co., Ltd., Hachioji, Tokyo, Japan) variable wave length UV detector.

[7]   *H. Engelhardt* and *D. Mathes*, J. Chromatogr. **142** (1977) 311.

S. Hara and A. Dobashi, J. Liquid Chromatogr., 2, 883 (1979) continued.

Table 1

Resolution of DL-α-amino acid and dipeptide derivatives by HPLC using FVA-silica

Racemates	k_1	k_2	α	R_s	Mobile phase 2-propanol in *n*-hexane v/v %
N-Ac-Leu-OMe	6.49	7.12	1.10	0.79	4
N-Ac-Norleu-OMe	6.34	6.91	1.09	0.70	4
N-Ac-Ile-OMe	5.70	6.18	1.08	0.62	4
N-Ac-Val-OMe	6.59	7.10	1.08	0.63	4
N-Ac-Phe-OMe	8.08	8.62	1.07	0.56	4
N-Ac-S-Bz-Cys-OMe	8.62	9.02	1.05	0.40	4
N-Ac-Met-OMe	6.65	6.98	1.05	0.39	8
N-Ac-Ala-OMe	6.04	6.29	1.04	0.31	8
Z-Leu-Leu-OMe	5.08	5.66	1.11	0.84	2
Z-Phe-Phe-OMe	6.27	6.85	1.09	0.70	3

(1) Resolution R_S was calculated by $R_S = 1/4\ (\alpha-1)\ \sqrt{N}[k/(1+k)]$. Retention k and relative retention were calculated by $k = (k_1+k_2)/2$, $\alpha = k_2/k_1$

(2) The column gave about 1300 theoretical plates per 20 cm when using N-Ac-L-Leu-OMe as the solute and employing a linear velocity: u = 0.18 cm/sec, temperature: 40°C and mobile phase: 8 v/v% 2-propanol in *n*-hexane (k = 3.1).

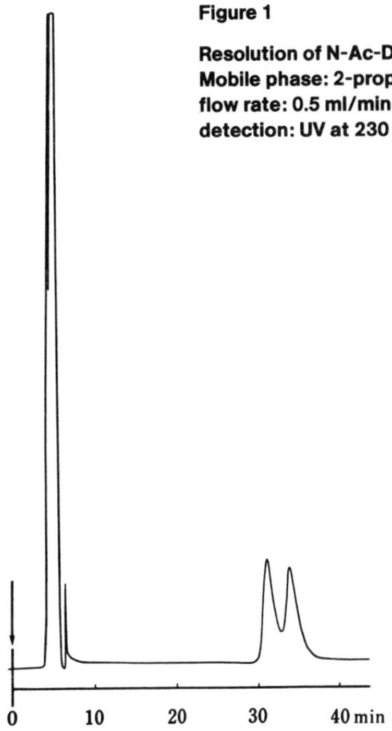

Figure 1

Resolution of N-Ac-DL-Leu-OMe.
Mobile phase: 2-propanol in *n*-hexane, 4 v/v%;
flow rate: 0.5 ml/min;
detection: UV at 230 nm, 0.16 a.u.f.s.

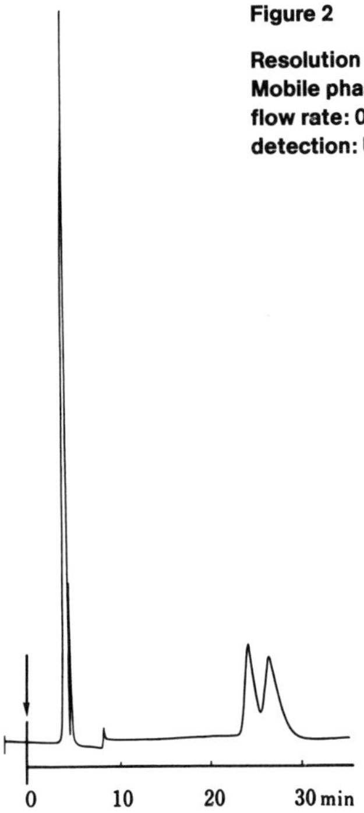

Figure 2

Resolution of Z-Leu-Leu-OMe (L-L, D-D).
Mobile phase: 2-propanol in *n*-hexane, 2 v/v%;
flow rate: 0.5 ml/min;
detection: UV at 254 nm, 0.16 a.u.f.s.

Reference
W.H. Pirkle, D.W. House and J.M. Finn, J. Chromatogr., 192, 143 (1980).

Summary
A chiral trifluoromethyl carbinol bearing stationary phase IV has been synthesized which proved capable of resolving a large number of racemates including α-amino acids and α-hydroxy acids using HPLC.

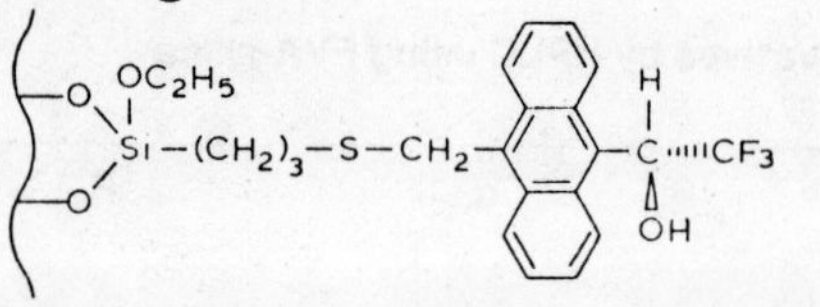

IV

The experimental details and results follow: (see W.H. Pirkle and D.W. House, J. Org. Chem., 44, 1957 (1979) for details of preparation of chiral stationary phase.

Chromatography was performed using an Altex 100A pump, a Valco 7000 p.s.i. injector with a 10-μl loop and an Altex Model 152 dual wavelength (254 and 280 nm) detector. Columns were slurry packed using conventional methods. Solutes were available from prior studies, prepared from commercially available materials, or generously provided by colleagues throughout the world.

TABLE III SEPARATION OF THE ENANTIOMERS OF 3,5-DINITROBENZOYL DERIVATIVES OF AMINO ACIDS, AMINO ALCOHOLS AND HYDROXY ACIDS

Separations were performed using 20% isopropyl alcohol in hexane unless otherwise specified. The elution order of each starred solute was determined by chromatography of a partially resolved configurationally established sample. In every instance, the configuration of the initially eluted enantiomer proved to be that shown above. The presumption is that the elution orders of the remaining solutes also follow this pattern.

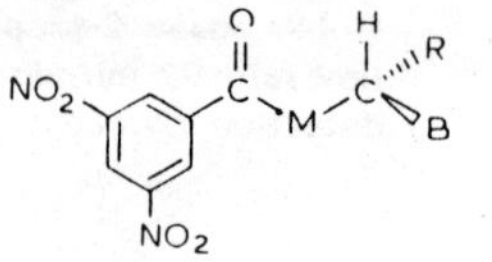

R	*B*	*M*	*α*	k'_1
CH_3	CO_2CH_3	NH	1.08*	4.16
CH_3	$CO_2C_2H_5$	NH	1.10	3.32
CH_3	CO_2-*i*-C_3H_7	NH	1.14	2.76
iso-C_3H_7	CO_2CH_3	NH	1.05*	2.75
iso-C_4H_9	CO_2CH_3	NH	1.07*	2.00
$CH_3S(CH_2)_2$	CO_2CH_3	NH	1.04*	4.81
Phenyl	CO_2CH_3	NH	1.19*	4.17
Benzyl	CO_2CH_3	NH	1.10*	4.00
CH_3	$CONHC_4H_9$	NH	1.34*	12.24§
iso-C_3H_7	$CONHC_4H_9$	NH	1.33*	0.82
Isobutyl	$CONHC_4H_9$	NH	1.65*	3.76§
$CH_3S(CH_2)_2$–	$CONHC_4H_9$	NH	1.38*	9.93§
Phenyl	$CONHC_4H_9$	NH	1.78*	0.75
Benzyl	$CONHC_4H_9$	NH	1.52*	6.78§
α-Naphthyl	$CONHC_4H_9$	NH	1.65	1.15
Phenyl	CH_2OH	NH	1.38*	2.36
Benzyl	$CH_2O(CH_2)_2OCH_3$	NH	1.18	5.00
Phenyl	$CH_2O_2CCH_3$	NH	1.18	5.30
Phenyl	$C(CH_3)_2OH$	NH	1.35	5.94§§
CH_3	CH_2OH	NH	1.06*	8.40§§
Isopropyl	CH_2OH	NH	1.19*	3.68§§
CH_3	$(CH_2)_2OH$	NH	1.15	4.30§§
CH_3	CO_2CH_3	O	1.05*	3.39
Phenyl	$CONHCH_3$	O	1.12	9.88
CH_3	$CONH_2$	O	1.10	8.90
2,5-$(CH_3)_2C_6H_3$	CO_2CH_3	O	1.05	2.51
CCl_3	$CH_2CO_2CH_3$	O	1.06	1.80
$CH_3O_2CCH_2$	CO_2CH_3	O	1.12	6.95
Phenyl	$PO(OC_2H_5)_2$	NH	1.38	4.75§§
p-Tolyl	$PO(OC_2H_5)_2$	NH	1.40	4.38§§
p-Anisyl	$PO(OC_2H_2)_5$	NH	1.37	7.50§§
p-ClC_6H_4	$PO(OC_2H_5)_2$	NH	1.26	4.38§§
p-BrC_6H_4	$PO(OC_2H_5)_2$	NH	1.25	4.50§§

§ 5% Isopropyl alcohol in hexane.
§§ 10% Isopropyl alcohol in hexane.

W.H. Pirkle, D.W. House and J.M. Finn, J. Chromatogr., 192, 143 (1980) continued.

TABLE IV DIRECT AND REVERSED-PHASE SEPARATION OF ENANTIOMERS OF 3,5-DINITROBENZOYL DERIVATIVES OF α-AMINO ACIDS UPON CHIRAL STATIONARY PHASE IV

The elution order of each starred solute was determined by chromatography of a partially resolved configurationally established sample. In every instance, the configuration of the initially eluted enantiomer proved to be that shown above. The presumption is that the elution orders of the remaining solutes also follow this pattern.

a 10% isopropyl alcohol in hexane. b = 80% water, 20% methanol, 0.25% $NaHCO_3$. In this solvent, the carboxyl group is ionized.

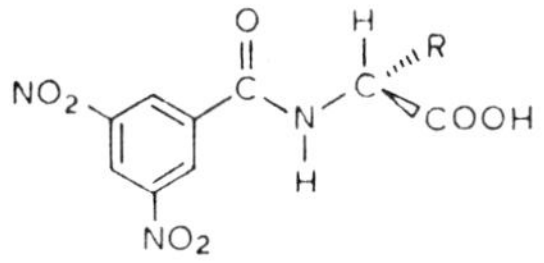

	α a/b	k_1 a/b
Alanine	1.17/1.40*	6.05/0.75
Valine	1.14/1.36*	3.76/1.4
Leucine	1.12/1.42*	2.82/2.8
Phenylalanine	1.17/1.40*	4.88/6.0
Methionine	1.12/1.31*	6.10/3.2
Phenylglycine	1.27/1.73*	7.48/3.0
α-Naphthylglycine	1.21/1.74	10.0/15.5
Tyrosine	1.16/1.41*	11.9/2.2
Glutamic acid	1.09/--	10.6/*ca.* 0.0
Isoleucine	1.16/1.50	3.26/2.1

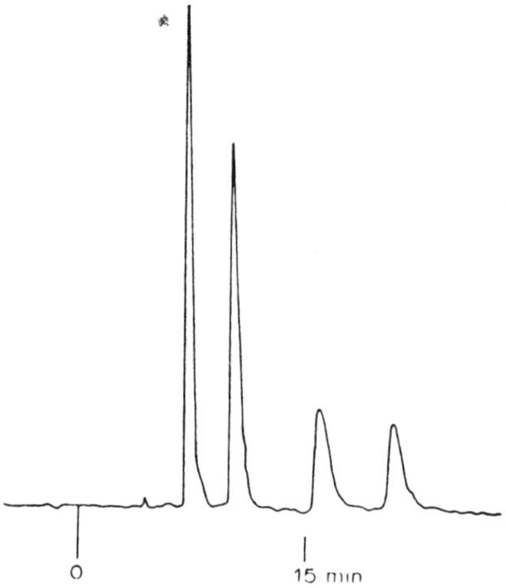

Fig. 5. Separation of the enantiomers of the racemic N-3,5-dinitrobenzoyl derivatives of leucine and alanine *n*-butyl amides upon chiral stationary phase IV using 5% isopropyl alcohol in hexane. The order of elution is D-leu, L-leu, D-ala and L-ala.

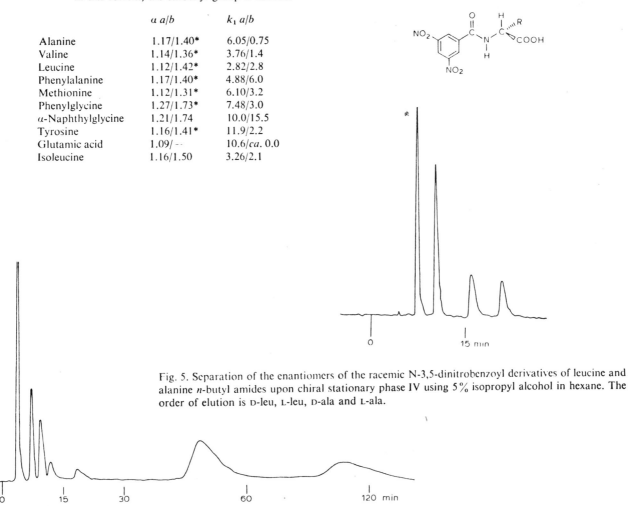

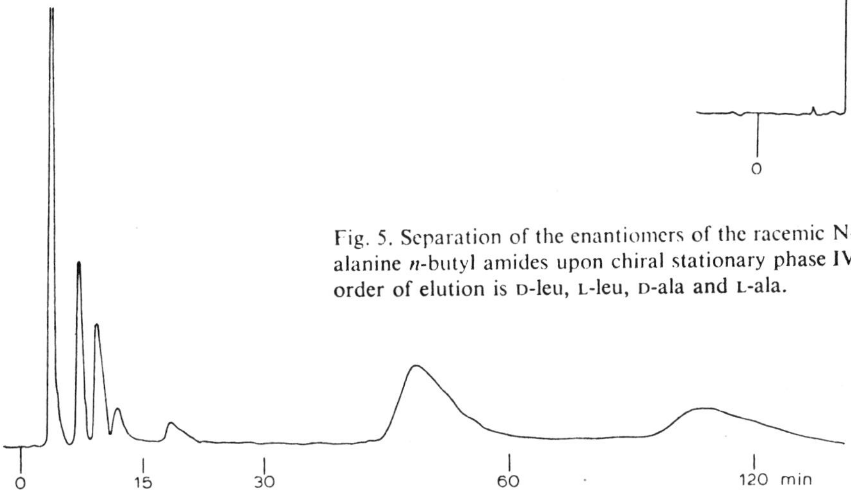

Fig. 6. Reversed-phase separation of the enantiomers of the N-3,5-dinitrobenzoyl derivatives of racemic isoleucine, phenylglycine, and α-naphthyl glycine. In order of elution: 3,5-dinitrobenzoic acid, D-isoleu, L-isoleu, D-phenyl gly, L-phenyl gly, D-α-naphthyl gly and L-α-naphthyl gly. Solvent was 80% water, 20% methanol and 0.25% sodium bicarbonate.

(*R*)-(−)-2,2,2-Trifluoro-1-[9-(10,-α-bromomethyl)anthryl]-ethanol, 1c. This alcohol was prepared by the method of Pavlin[9] from (*R*)-(−)-**1b**. The preparation and resolution of **1b** has been described[9] and proceeds along the same lines as those reported for **1a**.[10a,b]

Preparation of Chiral Stationary Phase 3. Porasil [10μ, 21 g, dried 24 h at 160 °C (0.01 torr)] was treated under a nitrogen blanket with 84 mL of freshly distilled (3-mercaptopropyl)trimethoxysilane dissolved in 75 mL of 1:1 dry benzene–dry pyridine to afford a slurry stirrable with a magnetic bar. The slurry was heated to 80 °C for 24 h with occasional stirring. After cooling, the supernatant was decanted and the wet silica was thrice washed with benzene using centrifugation–decantation. The silica was thoroughly washed (fine pore sintered glass funnel) with acetone, ether, and pentane and dried for 12 h at 0.01 torr.

Anal. Found: C, 4.64; H, 1.22; Si, 42.54; S, 2.69.

The above silica (21 g) was suspended in 75 mL of absolute ethanol (nitrogen blanket) and stirred magnetically. After addition of a twofold excess of solid sodium hydroxide (1.54 g), the slurry was heated to ~75 °C for 3 h with occasional stirring. A twofold excess of (*R*)-(−)-2,2,2-trifluoro-1-[9-(10-α-bromomethyl)anthryl]-ethanol, **1c** (14.21 g), dissolved in 15 mL of absolute ethanol was added and heating was continued for 48 h under nitrogen with occasional stirring. After cooling, the modified silica was collected, washed exhaustively with methanol, acetone, ether, and pentane, and dried as before to afford 24.05 g of light yellow solid.

Anal. Found: C, 11.90; H, 1.40; F, 2.20; Si, 37.81; S, 1.84.

The 10 × 254 mm column was slurry packed (CCl_4) using conventional techniques.

(9) M. S. Pavlin, Ph.D. Thesis, University of Illinois, 1977.
(10) (a) W. H. Pirkle, D. L. Sikkenga, *J. Org. Chem.*, **42**, 384 (1977); (b) W. H. Pirkle and J. R. Hauske, *ibid.*, **42**, 1839 (1977).

Reference

A. Dobashi, K. Oka and S. Hara, J. Am. Chem. Soc., 102, 7123 (1980).

Summary

Using (N-formyl-L-valylamino)propyl (FVA) silica gel [S. Hara and A. Dobashi, J. Chromatogr., 186, 543 (1979)] as a stationary phase, a number of derivatized α-amino acid racemates were resolved by HPLC. Experimental details and results follow:

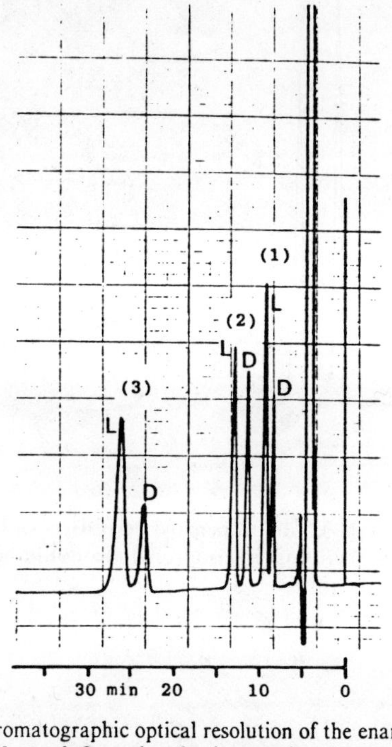

Figure 1. Chromatographic optical resolution of the enantiomeric mixtures of (1) *N*-acetyl-*O*-*tert*-butylserine *tert*-butyl ester, (2) *N*-acetylleucine *tert*-butyl ester, and (3) *N,O*-diacetyltyrosine *tert*-butyl ester. The chromatographic conditions were as described in Table I legend. Mobile phase: 4% (v/v) 2-PrOH in *n*-hexane. A mixture of three pairs of D- and L-amino acid derivatives, each consisting of an enriched concentration of the L enantiomers, was injected onto the FVA column.

Table I. Resolution of D- and L-Leucine Derivatives $(CH_3)_2CHCH_2CH(COOR^1)NHCOR^2$ with a FVA Column[a]

derivative		mobile phase, % (v/v) of 2-PrOH in	capacity factor,[b] k'		separation factor,[c]
R^1	R^2	*n*-hexane	D	L	a
Me	H	6	3.25		1.00
Me	Me	6	3.35	3.66	1.09
Me	Et	4	2.36	2.63	1.11
Me	*i*-Pr	2	3.00	3.39	1.13
Me	*t*-Bu	0.5	2.65	2.93	1.11
Me	Me	4	5.50	6.05	1.10
Et	Me	3	4.98	5.74	1.15
i-Pr	Me	2.5	4.71	5.65	1.20
t-Bu	Me	4	2.03	2.54	1.25
t-Bu	Me	2	4.84	6.70	1.38

[a] The column was 20 × 0.4 (i.d.) cm stainless-steel tubing and was packed by a high-pressure slurry technique.[3] It contained approximately 2 g of FVA silica gel and possessed a dead volume of 1.70 mL with it attached to the liquid chromatograph. The chromatographic runs were made at a constant flow rate of 1 mL/min for doubled FVA columns. The column temperature was 40 °C. In all runs, about 40 μg of racemic leucine derivatives, dissolved in 4 μL of chloroform, was injected onto the column during flow. The appearance of enantiomers in the column eluate was detected by ultraviolet absorption at 230 nm. [b] k' = (retention time of enantiomer – dead time)/dead time. [c] $a = k'$ of L enantiomer/k' of D enantiomer.

Table II. Resolution of Enantiomers of *N*-Acetyl Amino Acid *tert*-Butyl Esters[a]

separation	amino acid	strong solvent in *n*-hexane (%, v/v)	k' D	k' L	a	resolution,[b] R_s
1	Leu	Et_2O (80)	3.12	4.33	1.39	4.21
2	Val	Et_2O (80)	3.41	4.69	1.38	4.17
3	Nle	Et_2O (80)	3.13	4.28	1.37	3.99
4	Nva	Et_2O (80)	3.63	4.89	1.35	3.88
5	Abu	Et_2O (80)	4.12	5.37	1.30	3.39
6	Ala	Et_2O (80)	4.83	5.95	1.23	2.66
7	Ile	Et_2O (80)	3.16	4.32	1.37	4.00
8	*O*-*t*-BuSer	Et_2O (80)	2.13	2.82	1.32	3.12
9	*O*-AcTyr	Et_2O (80)	7.67	9.33	1.22	2.70
10	*O*-*t*-BuAsp	Et_2O (80)	2.57	3.10	1.21	2.13
11	*O*-*t*-BuGlu	Et_2O (80)	3.57	4.33	1.21	2.30
12	*S*-BzlCys	CH_2Cl_2 (30)	1.77	2.31	1.31	2.85
13	*N*-*t*-BuTrp	CH_2Cl_2 (30)	1.88	2.58	1.37	3.50
14	PheGly	$CHCl_3$ (30)	2.28	3.02	1.32	3.18
15	Phe	$CHCl_3$ (30)	1.96	2.71	1.38	3.64
16	*N*-AcLys	2-PrOH (12)	6.83	7.17	1.05	0.60
17	Gln	2-PrOH (8)	17.63[c]		>1.00	<0.30
18	Pro	2-PrOH (4)	2.77		1.00	

[a] The column temperature was 20 °C for separation 1–15, and detection for separations 12–15 was done at 254 nm with all others at 230 nm. Columns and other operating details are as described in Table I legend. [b] $R_s = \frac{1}{4}(a - 1)N^{1/2}[k/(1 + k)]$, where k = (k' of D enantiomer + k' of L enantiomer)/2 and N = 16(retention time of enantiomer/bandwidth of peak)^2. [c] Shoulder was definitely detected.

Reference
R.J. Baczuk, G.K. Landram, R.J. Dubois and H.C. Dehm, J. Chromatog., 60, 351 (1971).

Summary
The enantiomers of β-3,4-dihydroxyphenylalanine (DOPA) were resolved by liquid chromatography using a chiral adsorbent prepared by bonding L-arginine through a cyanuric chloride linkage to Sephadex G-25. In an analytic column with water as the eluent, a separation factor of 1.60 was obtained. Partial resolution of the enantiomers of tyrosine but not of phenylalanine supported the importance of "three-point contact" between sorbent and sorbate for resolving these enantiomers. Experimental details and results follow:

Reagents

Chemicals other than the following were reagent grade. Cyanuric chloride (2,4,6-trichloro-1,3,5-triazine) and L-arginine were purchased from Aldrich Chemical Co., Inc. Sephadex G-25 (gel filtration medium), 20 to 80 μm particle size, was purchased from Pharmacia Fine Chemicals, Inc. The following amino acids were purchased from Nutritional Biochemicals Corporation: L-, D-, and D,L-DOPA; L- and D-tyrosine (β-4-hydroxyphenylalanine); and D- and L-phenylalanine. N-Acetyl-L-phenylalanine was purchased from Pfaltz and Bauer.

The N,O,O-triacetyl-D,L-DOPA derivative was prepared by use of acetic anhydride. D,L-DOPA was dissolved in chilled, nitrogen-purged, 2.5 *N* sodium hydroxide. A five-fold excess of chilled acetic anhydride was incrementally added over a period of 1 h with stirring. The mixture was acidified to pH 2.5 with hydrochloric acid and stored at 0° C overnight. Upon rubbing the cold solution with a glass rod, the derivative crystallized in 60% yield. The product was readily recrystallized from water. The derivative was very soluble in alcohol and quite soluble in water. The melting point was 120° C. An IR spectrum revealed characteristic substituted amide and ester bands, the ester at 1763 cm^{-1} being especially prominent. The molecular weight was determined to be 323, equal to the theoretical value. The carbon and nitrogen contents were 55.5% and 4.3%, respectively, *versus* theoretical values of 55.7% and 4.3%, respectively.

Apparatus for chromatographic evaluation

A Milton Roy Instrument Minipump (Milton Roy Co.) with a maximum pumping capacity of about 3 ml/min was used without pulse dampening to deliver the eluent. Chromatographic columns (Chromatronix Inc.) measured 2.8 × 500 mm, 2.8 × 300 mm and 0.5 × 300 mm. The same sample injection port, Chromatronix No. 107B25, was used in conjunction with the above columns. The detection system consisted of a Beckman DK-2A spectrophotometer equipped with a microflow cell, having an internal volume of 0.125 ml and a path length of 5 mm and a reference beam attenuator. The amplifier of this spectrophotometer was wired to a Sargent Model XXI Polarograph recorder.

Packing preparations

L-Arginine on Sephadex. Dry Sephadex (50 g) was added to a 400-ml beaker, containing 250 ml of distilled water. The Sephadex was heated and maintained at the boiling point of water and was agitated by magnetic stirring. A solution composed of 20 g of cyanuric chloride in 200 ml of acetone was then prepared. About 50 ml of distilled water were added and the pH of the solution was adjusted to about 6 with sodium hydroxide. The hydrated Sephadex was then added to the cyanuric chloride solution in small increments, maintaining the pH at 6. When all the gel had been added, the pH was adjusted to 11 and maintained there for 1 min. Then 100 ml of

R.J. Baczuk, G.K. Landram, R.J. Dubois and H.C. Dehm, J. Chromatog., 60, 351 (1971) continued.

glacial acetic acid were added and the gel was filtered and washed well with distilled water.

The Sephadex/cyanuric chloride derivative was re-suspended in 300 ml of distilled water and the pH adjusted to 6 with sodium hydroxide. L-Arginine (5 g) was then added and the pH was maintained between 10 and 11 during this addition and then for a further 16 h. The product was washed well with distilled water and was filtered and dried *in vacuo*.

An attempt was made to characterize the Sephadex/cyanuric chloride intermediate and the final L-arginine-tailored packing to determine the quantity of each substituent added and to estimate the capacity of this packing. Nitrogen analyses on both the intermediate and final products were performed and also an attempt was made to determine the quantity of L-arginine on the packing by non-aqueous titrations of the amine groups present. From the nitrogen data on the intermediate product, an approximate addition of 0.63% of cyanuric chloride (0.042 m*M*/g support) was obtained. This represents an addition of only one triazine group per hundred fifty repeating anhydroglucose units of the Sephadex. Nitrogen analysis and a non-aqueous amine titration of the final product indicated that an addition of 0.19% (0.011 m*M*/g support) of L-arginine had been achieved. This represents an addition of about one L-arginine molecule per four triazine units present. We made no attempt to increase this loading by employing such techniques as swelling in an alkaline medium or converting the Sephadex to an alkali species as is commonly done with cellulose. We do feel, however, that this low capacity was due at least in part to the fact that only secondary alcohol groups were predominantly available for bonding in the Sephadex structure.

L-*Arginine on cellulose*. The cellulose-based support was prepared in a manner similar to the Sephadex preparation except that no attempt was made to swell this material initially. Whatman Cellulose Powder, CF-1, was the starting material.

L-*Arginine on chloromethylated polystyrene (S·X-2)*. Biorad S·X-2, chloromethylated polystyrene beads (20 g), was added to 100 ml of pyridine. L-Arginine (5 g) was dissolved in 60 ml of distilled water and the dissolved amino acid was added to the pyridine–S·X-2 suspension. The mixture was transferred to a jacketed beaker and hot water was run through at 50° C. The mixture was stirred for several hours and 10 ml of triethylamine were added to assure deprotonization of the bonded L-arginine. The resin was filtered and washed thoroughly with acetone and water.

Chromatographic evaluations

Prior to evaluating the microbore columns, containing the L-arginine-tailored supports, the columns were conditioned by eluting degassed distilled water through them at least over a 16-h period at flow rates of about 3–4 ml/h. This conditioning was necessary to physically pack the support, and we also found that the retention volume of the enantiomers and hence separation factors increased during this period to constant values. Though the exact explanation has not been established, we feel that it was necessary to achieve a steady state of support protonation with degassed distilled water, such that the amino groups were just basic enough to provide for an attraction of the phenolic hydroxyl groups of DOPA. Deprotonation of the support via exposure to a tertiary amine resulted in complete retention of both DOPA enantiomers, and acidifying the support caused the DOPA enantiomers to elute at

R.J. Baczuk, G.K. Landram, R.J. Dubois and H.C. Dehm, J. Chromatog., 60, 351 (1971) continued.

the solvent front. Extended periods of washing after both treatments re-established the activity of the column, however.

Collection of enantiomers for polarimetric measurements

Racemic DOPA was repetitively applied to a preparative column and separated. The column measured 0.5 × 300 mm and was packed and conditioned in a manner identical to the analytical column except that flow rates were increased to 3 ml/min. Three equal-volume cuts of the DOPA-containing eluate were taken from each run. Flash evaporation was used to concentrate these fractions to minimize the possibility of degradation of DOPA. Thus, daily, each pooled fraction was stripped of excess water and added to one of three 250-ml flasks wrapped in aluminum foil to eliminate UV radiation. The flasks were purged with nitrogen and were stored at 5°C. Flash evaporation was then used to reduce each fraction to about 50 ml. The DOPA was stabilized during evaporation by addition of several drops of concentrated hydrochloric acid. The concentrations were conducted under vacuum with the aid of the careful application of heat to permit evaporation, though the flasks never exceeded 30°C in temperature. The resulting solutions were purged with nitrogen and also stored at 5°C. Just before polarimetric measurements, a final concentration was made and consisted of flash evaporating the samples to a volume of 10 ml and permitting evaporation to dryness without applying heat. In this manner, the slight excess of hydrochloric acid was removed, leaving the hydrochloride of each resolved fraction. The dry residues were taken up in 2.00 ml of water at 25°C for determining the optical activities. Measurements were made at 25°C using a Perkin-Elmer Model 141 Polarimeter with a 3-ml capacity, 10-cm path length cell at 589 nm.

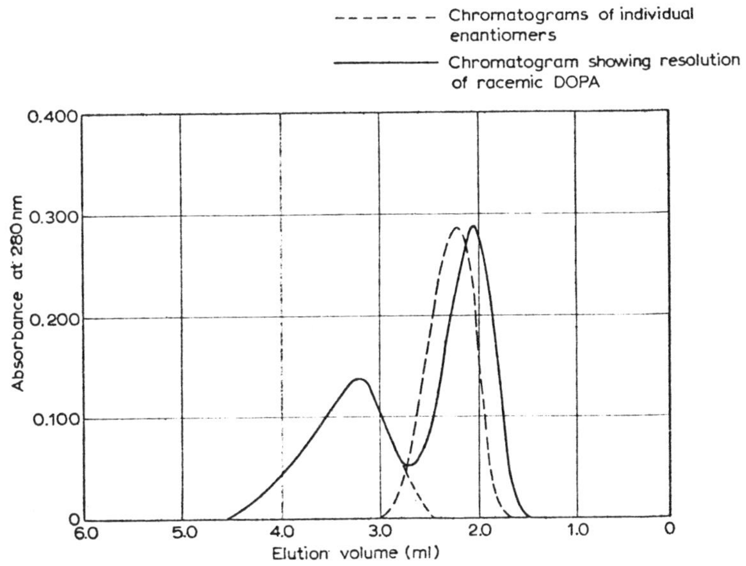

Fig. 1. Chromatogram of D-, L- and D,L-DOPA on L-arginine–Sephadex quantities, 10 μg D-10 μg L-, and 20 μg D,L-DOPA; flow, 0.7 ml/h (linear, 5 mm/min); column. 300 × 2.8 mm glass microbore; solvent, distilled water.

LIGAND EXCHANGE CHROMATOGRAPHY

Principle of method as reported by Davankov[1].

A copolymer of chloromethylated styrene and divinylbenzene is reacted with L-proline to produce an optically active resin. This resin is treated with an ammoniacal copper complex solution to form a complex in which the copper has saturated its 4 coordination sites as shown in Fig. 1 via two neighboring polymer-bound proline units.

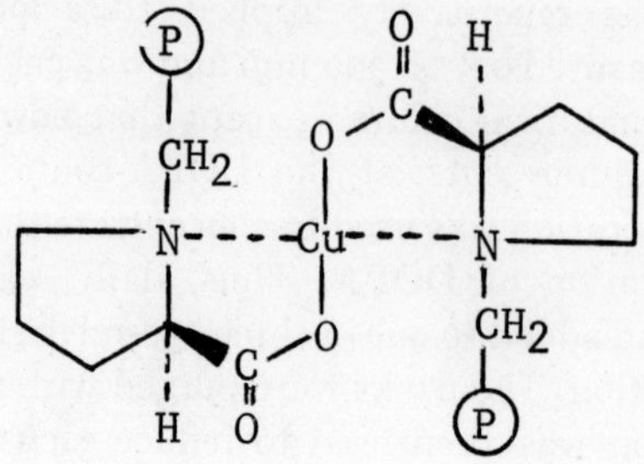

Fig. 1

The resin is washed with water and packed onto a column. This column is connected to a small column containing adsorbent that has not been treated with copper and whose function is to trap any copper ions that are introduced into the eluate from the main column. The removal of the Cu^{++} is necessary because of its interference with the rotation measurement. Each amino acid enantiomer displaces a polymer-bound proline ligand originally complexed to the Cu^{++} to form a mixed complex (Fig. 2). The individual complexes are diastereomeric and hence of differing stabilities and can thus be eluted selectively with eluants of differing nucleophylicities.

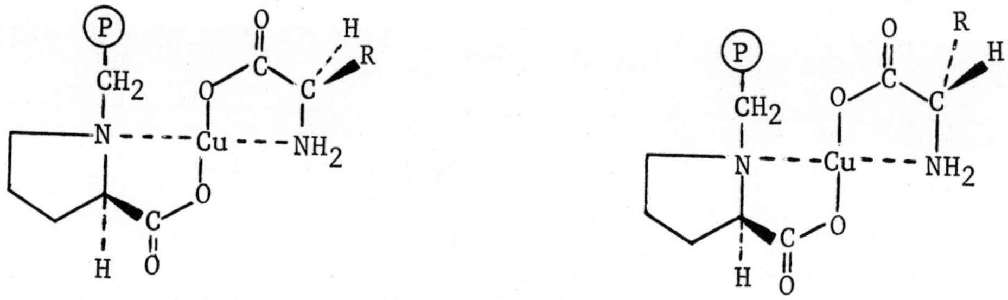

Fig. 2

Usually the complex which contains the L-amino acid is thermodynamically less stable and is eluted more readily. A typical experiment reported by Davankov[1] is the following.

The optically active adsorbent was obtained by treating a chloromethylated polymer of styrene and 0.8% p-divinylbenzene with L-proline. The analytical exchange capacity was 1.96 meq/g. A 12 gm. portion of the adsorbent (particle size 0.03 to 0.05 mm.) was treated with an excess of 0.1N $CuSO_4$ in ammonia solution, washed with water, and charged onto the column (diameter = 9 mm., length = 500 mm.). The column was connected in series with a small column containing 2 gms. of adsorbent that has not been treated with copper salt solution. A solution of 0.5 gm. of DL-proline in 5 mls. of water was introduced into the column and eluted with water at a rate of 10 mls./hr. Evaporation of the eluate, which gave a positive reaction with ninhydrin, resulted in 0.25 gm. of L-proline with $[\alpha]^{20}_D$ -80.5 (C, 1, H_2O). Evaporation of the eluate obtained by passing 100 mls. of 1N NH_3 through the column resulted in 0.25 gm. of optically pure D-proline. To regenerate the column, one washes out the excess ammonia with water.

(1) S.V. Rogozhin and V.A. Davankov, Doklady Akad. Nauk SSSR., 192, 1288 (1970).

Reference

V.A. Davankov, S.V. Rogozhin, I.I. Peslyakas, A.V. Semichkin and T.P. Sachkova, Dokl. Akad. Nauk SSSR., 986 (1971).

Summary

The authors reported the resolution of a number of racemic α-amino acids by ligand-exchange chromatography on an asymmetric resin containing optically active L-proline and L-hydroxyproline in the Cu^{++} and Ni^{++} form. Experimental conditions, results and some authors' comments follow:

The repeat units in the sorbents can be represented as

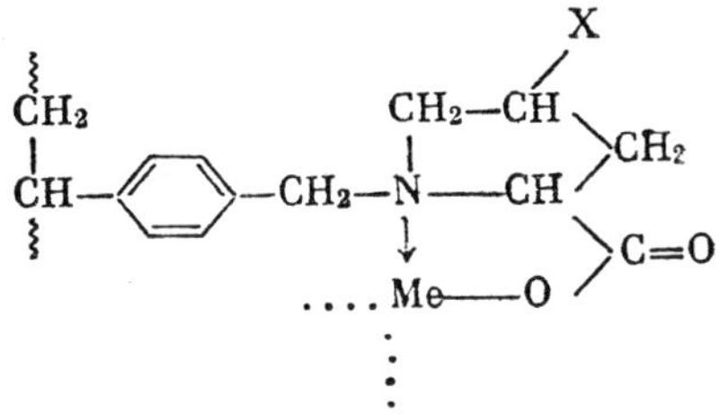

X=H (I); X=OH (II).

The sorbents were prepared by reacting the macrolattice (5 mol. % cross-linking agent) of chloromethylated styrene polymer with L-proline or the methyl ester of L-hydroxyproline in the presence of sodium iodide as a catalyst [2, 3]. The ester groups of the second sorbent were subjected to alkaline hydrolysis. The analytical exchange capacities of sorbents I and II were 1.98 and 2.96 meq/g. Both sorbents swelled considerably in aqueous media.

Optical isomers are separated by chromatography of racemates on sorbents saturated with copper ions. As a rule, the first isomer is eluted by water or dilute ammonia and the second by 1-2 N ammonia. From measurements of the optical activities of the eluate fractions it is possible to calculate the yields of isomers on the assumption of 100% optical purity (or, alternatively, optical purity can be calculated assuming 100% yield). The isomers can be obtained by evaporation of the eluate, and the column can be regenerated by simply washing with water. Some results of the chromatographic resolution of racemates on sorbents saturated with Cu^{2+} and Ni^{2+} ions are given in Table 1.

It should be emphasized that the degrees of separation reported in Table 1 are not limits, since optimum chromatographic conditions were not used. The dependence of separation on metal ion loading, on elution rate, on racemate loading, on temperature, etc. was not studied, and the optimum eluent concentration for the first isomer was not selected. The importance of the last factor can be demonstrated by an example. A change from 0.05 N NH_4OH to 0.1 M CH_3COONH_4 + NH_4OH buffer with a pH of 9.0 immediately increased the yield of threonine isomers from 70 to 100% when the racemate was chromatographed on sorbent II in the Cu^{2+} form. Nevertheless, the results permit a number of fundamentally important conclusions.

The use of Cu^{2+} ions on sorbents I and II leads to significantly better separation of the optical isomers of α-amino acids than is obtained with Ni^{2+} and Zn^{2+} ions. This is associated with insufficient stability of complexes of the latter with bidentate amino acid ligands. Indeed, interaction of the antipodes with sorbents in the Ni^{2+} form is so weak that in the majority of cases both antipodes are eluted by water. The decreased efficiency of antipode separation when Ni^{2+} and Zn^{2+} ions are used could also be due to structural ambiguity of the mixed complexes formed, whereas the Cu^{2+} ion presents only two free coordination sites for sorption of the bidentate amino acid from the mobile phase.

V.A. Davankov, S.V. Rogozhin, I.I. Peslyakas, A.V. Semichkin and T.P. Sachkova, Dokl. Akad. Nauk SSSR., 986, (1971) continued.

TABLE 1. Chromatography of Racemates on Sorbents I and II (column d = 9 mm, l = 420 mm); Elution Rate 10 ml/sec

Sorbent	Metal ion Me^{2+}	Racemate resolved		Yield of isomer, %		Elution conditions for L-isomer
		name	amt.	*L*	*D*	
I	Cu	Proline	0,10	98	100	H_2O
II	Cu	»	0,15	76	96	0,1 *N* NH_4OH
II	Ni	»	0,15	15	17	H_2O
I	Cu	Valine	0,10	47	62	H_2O
II	Cu	»	0,15	79	90	0,1 *N* $CH_3COOH + NH_4OH$, pH 9,0
II	Cu	Isovaline	0,16	74	100	0,1 *N* $CH_3COOH + NH_4OH$, pH 8,8
II	Ni	»	0,15	22	22	H_2O
I	Cu	Isoleucine	0,10	38	48	0,1 *N* NH_4OH
II	Ni	»	0,12	23	25	0,1 *N* NH_4OH
II	Cu	Threonine	0,16	100	100	0,1 N $CH_3COOH + NH_4OH$ pH 9,0
II	Ni	»	0,15	10	17	H_2O
II	Cu	Serine	0,09	76	81	0,1 *N* $CH_3COOH + NH_4OH$, pH 9,1
I	Cu	α-Aminophenyl-acetic acid	0,05	32	20	0,15 *N* NH_4OH
II	Cu	Mandelic acid	0,16	28	37	0,1 *N* $CH_3COOH + NH_4OH$, pH 8,7
II	Ni	» »	0,16	3	3,6	H_2O

Reference

V.A. Davankov, S.V. Rogozhin, A.V. Semechkin and T.P. Sachkova, J. Chromatogr., 82, 359 (1973).

Summary

The authors reported the application of an asymmetric resin containing optically active L-proline in the Cu^{++} form for the effective resolution of DL-proline by means of ligand-exchange chromatography. It was found in the static sorption of proline enantiomers that the difference in its sorption energy reaches 450 cals/mole and depends on the degree of saturation of the resin by copper ion. Experimental conditions and results follow:

The asymmetric resin I contained 5 mole% of crosslinking bridges of the structure

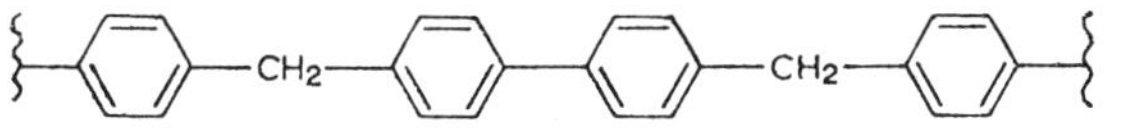

between the polystyrene chains and 1.68 mequiv./g of L-proline residues. The diameter of the particles was 0.2–0.4 mm.

A 1.785-g amount of dry resin (containing 3 mequiv. of active groups) was treated with 25 ml of aqueous solution containing 0.345 g (3 mequiv.) of DL-proline, 0.28–4.19 mequiv. of $Cu(NO_3)_2$ and the appropriate amount of NaOH such that during equilibration of the mixture its pH was 10.3.

In order to prevent crystallization of $Cu(Pro)_2$, the total volumes of the last three of the eleven samples were increased to 30, 35 and 50 ml, respectively, the pH value of the final sample having decreased to 10.0 After shaking the mixtures for 70 h at 25°, the resin was filtered and washed with 5 ml of water. The liquid and resin phases, after extraction with 2 *N* HCl, were analyzed for their total copper content[14], total proline content[14,15] and optical activity (Roussel–Jouan Quick-polarimetre; $\lambda=436$ nm; $l=7$ cm; 1 *N* HCl; for the optically pure proline, $[\alpha]^{25}_{436}=123°$).

For the chromatographic experiments, 10-g portions of resin I were treated with solutions of different amounts of $Cu(NO_3)_2$ in 1 *N* ammonia solution, washed with 0.5 *N* $CH_3COONa+NaOH$ solutions of pH 10.3 and loaded on to columns of I.D. 9 mm (thickness of resin layer *ca.* 200 mm). The chromatography of 0.100 g of DL-proline dissolved in 1 ml of 0.5 *N* $CH_3COONa+NaOH$ solution of pH 10.3 was carried out at a flow-rate of 6 ml/h of ammonia solutions prepared by using the above CH_3COONa buffer. Fractions of 5 ml were collected and their optical activities measured at 436 nm in a 2-cm cell.

The asymmetric resin II, containing 5 mole% of crosslinking bridges and 2.96 mequiv./g of L-hydroxyproline residues, had a particle diameter of 0.16–0.20 mm and was used in the Cu(II) form in a column 60 mm long and 9 mm I.D. for the chromatographic resolution of 1.5 mg of DL-proline in a 1.0 *M* pyridine solution at the rate of 15 ml/h and a temperature of 56°.

14 A. Woiwood, *Biochem. J.*, 45 (1949) 412.
15 C. Pope and M. Stevens, *Biochem. J.*, 33 (1939) 1070.

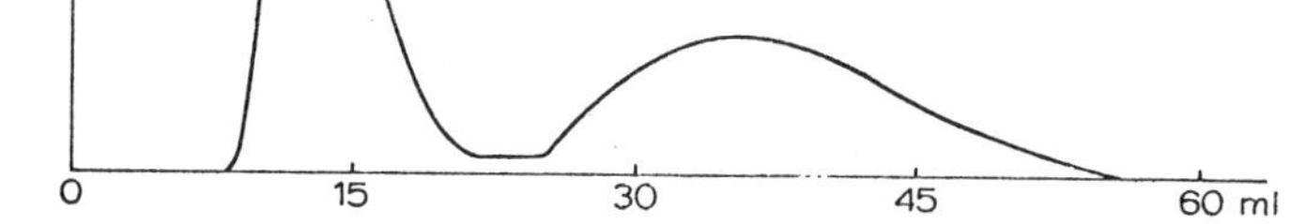

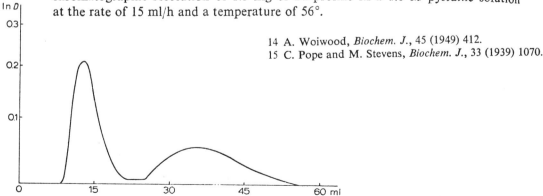

Fig. 3. Resolution of 1.5 mg of DL-proline on the asymmetric resin II containing L-hydroxy-proline–Cu(II) fixed complexes.

Reference

I.I. Peslyakas, S.V. Rogozhin and V.A. Davankov, Izv. Akad. Nauk SSSR., Ser. Khim. 174 (1974).

Summary

The authors describe the resolution of a number of racemic α-amino acids and mandelic acid by ligand-exchange chromatography on an asymmetric resin containing the bidentate α-amino acids D-alanine, L-valine and L-isoleucine in their Cu^{++}, Ni^{++} or Zn^{++} form as the fixed ligands. The results they obtained indicate that a) resolution is accomplished most effectively by adsorbents charged with Cu^{++} and b) although in most cases that enenatiomer of the bidentate α-amino acid ligand whose absolute configuration is opposite to the absolute configuration of the fixed ligand is retained more firmly by the adsorbent, on adsorbents with L-valine and L-isoleucine the complexes with two ligands of the same configuration frequently proved to be the more stable. Experimental details and results follow:

The sorbents were obtained by the reaction of macrosieve (5 mole % of crosslinking agent) chloromethylated polystyrene with the esters of amino acids and subsequent hydrolysis of the ester groups [3, 4]. The sorbents have a high analytical capacity [respectively 2.22, 2.32 and 2.51 mequiv/g for (I), (II) and (III)], and show good swelling in water and organic solvents. When sorbents are used in ligand chromatography processes it is important that they retain the metal ion-complexing agent firmly. The strength of bonding the metal ions by the fixed ligands of the sorbents was determined as described in [5], as the decomplexing pH. The found relative stability of the complexes, formed by the fixed ligands of the sorbents, is in agreement with the order of stability established [6, 7] for the complexes of composition ML_2 of the divalent metals: Co(II) < Ni(II) < Cu(II) > Zn(II), as follows from the decomplexing pH values

Metal ion	Cu^{2+}	Ni^{2+}	Zn^{2+}
Sorbent I	2.75	6.32	6.75
Sorbent II	2.50	6.00	6.81
Sorbent III	2.50	5.80	6.80

For a comparative estimate of the resolving capacity of the sorbents we fixed the principal parameters of the chromatographic process, like the racemate charge, the size of the chromatographic columns, and the degree of sorbent saturation by the metal ions. The elution rate was maintained at ~10 ml/h. The yield of the optical isomers was calculated from the optical activity values of the collected fractions of the eluate. Here the fractions with the same rotation sign were combined, evaporated under reduced pressure, the residue was dissolved in 25 ml of 1 N HCl solution, and the optical activity of the solution was measured with an accuracy of 0.001° in a cell 0.7-dm long. As a rule, the analysis results for the degree of enrichment in the D- and L-antipodes show good agreement. After chromatographing, the column was regenerated with water. The results of the chromatographic resolution of the racemates on the sorbents with a maximum saturation by the Cu^{2+}, Ni^{2+} and Zn^{2+} ions are given in Table 1.

3. V. A. Davankov, S. V. Rogozhin, and I. I. Peslyakas, Vysokomolekul.Soedin., B14, 276 (1972).
4. V. A. Davankov, S. V. Rogozhin, I. I. Peslyakas, and V. V. Vesa, Vysokomolekul. Soedin., B15, 115 (1973).
5. R. Hering, J. Prakt. Chem., 34, 69 (1966).
6. H. Irving, R. J. P. Williams, D. J. Ferrett, and A. E. J. Williams, J. Chem. Soc., 1954, 3494.
7. W. F. Stask and H. A. Skinner, Trans. Faraday Soc., 63, 1136 (1967).

I.I. Peslyakas, S.V. Rogozhin and V.A. Davenkov, Izv. Akad. Nauk SSSR., Ser. Khim. 174 (1974) continued.

TABLE 1. Ligand-Exchange Chromatography of Racemates on Sorbents I, II and III (Column 9 × 390 mm)

Cation M^{2+}	Racemate		Sorbent I with D-alanine			Sorbent II with L-valine			Sorbent III with L-isoleucine		
	name	amount, g	eluant, NH_4OH, N	rate, ml/h	order of exit of antipodes, degree of separation, %	eluant, NH_4OH, N	rate, ml/h	order of exit of antipodes, degree of separation, %	eluant, NH_4OH, N	rate, ml/h	order of exit of antipodes, degree of separation, %
Cu	Alanine	0,16	0,05	14	*D*—*L*, 13	0*	8	*D*—*L*, 19	0*	8	*D*—*L*, 26
Cu	Proline	0,16	0,10*	14	*D*—*L*, 64	0,05*	12	*D*—*L*, 17	†	9	*D*—*L*, 21
Ni	"	0,16	0,01*	12	*L*—*D*, 3	0,05*	12	*L*—*D*, 11	0,05*	8	*L*—*D*, 9
Zn	"	0,16	0,04	12	*D*—*L*, 3	0,06	12	*D*—*L*, 2	0,06	10	*D*—*L*, 8
Cu	Valine	0,15	0,10*	12	*D*—*L*, 32	0,04*	12	*L*—*D*, 31	0,07*	12	*L*—*D*, 23
Ni	"	0,15	0,07*	12	*D*—*L*, 6	0,06	12	*L*—*D*, 5	0,05*	8	*L*—*D*, 6
Cu	Isovaline	0,16	0,15*	14	*D*—*L*, 41	0,05*	11	*L*—*D*, 37	0,07*	12	*L*—*D*, 68
Cu	Isoleucine	0,12	0,25*	14	*D*—*L*, 20	0,10*	8	*L*—*D*, 37	0,22*	8	*L*—*D*, 23
Cu	Serine	0,09	0*	14	*D*—*L*, 37	0,05	9	*D*—*L*, 15	0,05	12	*D*—*L*, 10
Cu	Threonine	0,16	0*	14	*L*—*D*, 20	0,02*	8	*D*—*L*, 20	0,04*	12	*D*—*L*, 21
Ni	"	0,16	0,08*	12	*D*—*L*, 8	0,05	12	*L*—*D*, 24	0,05*	12	*L*—*D*, 25
Zn	"	0,16	0,06*	9	*D*—*L*, 5	0,06	12	*D*—*L*, 4	0,06*	10	*D*—*L*, 10
Cu	Mandelic acid	0,16	0,05	14	*D*—*L*, 13	0,03	8	*L*—*D*, 16	0,02	12	*L*—*D*, 8
Ni	The same	0,16	0,13	12	*D*—*L*, 1	0,06	12	*L*—*D*, 6	0,05	8	*L*—*D*, 7
Zn	" "	0,16	0,08	9	*D*—*L*, 4	0,06	10	*L*—*D*, 8	0,06	10	*L*—*D*, 5
Cu	Aspartic acid	0,09	0,05	14	*L*—*D*, 8	0,05	9	*D*—*L*, 15	0,05	12	*D*—*L*, 9
Ni	The same	0,09	0,09	14	*L*—*D*, 13	0,06	12	*D*—*L*, 10	0,05*	8	*D*—*L*, 25
Zn	" "	0,09	0,07*	12	*D*—*L*, 7	—	—	0	—	—	0
Cu	Ornithine	0,16	—	—	0	0,05	9	*D*—*L*, 6	0,05	12	*D*—*L*, 4
Ni	"	0,16	0,09*	9	*L*—*D*, 7	0,13	12	*D*—*L*, 1	0,06*	10	*D*—*L*, 4
Zn	"	0,16	0,07*	12	*L*—*D*, 3	—	—	0	—	—	0

*After the rotation sign of the eluate had changed to the opposite the NH_4OH concentration in the eluant was increased by 10-20 times, bringing it up to a maximum of 2.5 N.

†0.1 M CH_3COONH_4 + NH_4OH, pH 9, then 0.75 N NH_4OH.

Reference

I.I. Peslyakas, S.V. Rogozhin and V.A. Davankov, Izv. Akad. Nauk SSSR., Ser. Khim. 1872 (1974).

Summary

The authors describe the resolution of a number of racemic α-amino acids and mandelic acid by ligand-exchange chromatography on an asymmetric resin to which is attached resin to which is attached the hydroxyl containing α-amino acids L-serine (Sorbent I), L-threonine (Sorbent 2) and L-tyrosine (Sorbent 3) in their Cu^{++}, Ni^{++} or Zn^{++} form. The results they obtained indicate that a) the best resolutions are observed on adsorbents that are charged with Cu^{++} and b) the D-enantiomers of bidentate α-amino acid ligands are retained more tenaciously on an adsorbent that contains L-tyrosine in the Cu^{++} form. Experimental details and results follow:

The asymmetric sorbents were obtained by reacting the chloromethylated isoporous macrosieve (5 mole % of the crosslinking agent) styrene polymer with the methyl esters of the amino acids (AA) and subsequent alkaline hydrolysis of the ester groups [2]. The unit links of the sorbents have the following structure:

R = —CH$_2$OH (I); —CH(OH)—CH$_3$ (II);

—CH$_2$—⟨benzene⟩—OH (III); CH$_3$ (IV)

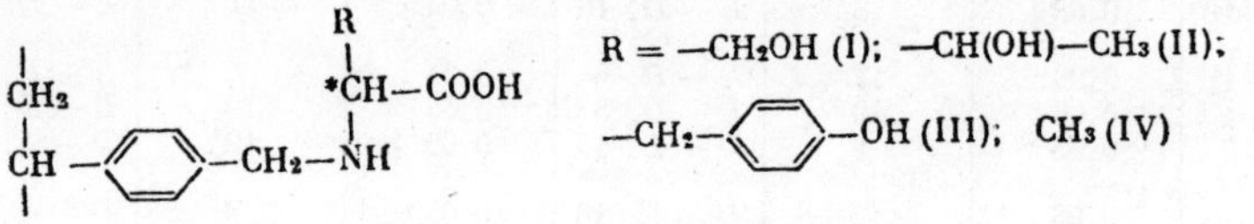

Sorbent	Cu^{2+}	Ni^{2+}	Zn^{2+}
(I)	2.30	5.00	6.40
(II)	2.25	3.90	4.35
(III)	2.80	6.03	6.93
(IV)	2.75	6.32	6.75

The analytical capacity of the sorbents is, respectively, 2.95, 2.88, and 2.11 mg-equiv/g. The sorbents exhibit good swelling in media of variable solvating capacity [2]. A study of the complexing ability toward the ions of the transition metals (Cu, Ni, Zn) disclosed that sorbents (I) and (II) retain the metal ions more tenaciously than does (III) or sorbents with neutral α-amino acid residues, for example (IV), which do not contain hydroxyl groupings [3]. The probable involvement of the β-hydroxyl group in the coordination should be manifested more strongly for the metals with a coordination number of 6 than for the Cu(II) ion. The pH values for decomplexing the metals (obtained when they are desorbed using 0.1 N HNO$_3$ solution) show that the thr complexes are quite stable.

TABLE 1. Ligand-Exchange Chromatography of Racemates on Sorbents (I)-(III) (Column 390 mm × 9 mm; racemate load 0.09-0.16 g)

Cation M^{2+}	Racemate	Sorbent (I)			Sorbent (II)			Sorbent (III)		
		eluant NH$_4$OH,N	flow rate, ml/h	exit order of antipodes and degree of resolution %	eluant NH$_4$OH,N	flow rate, ml/h	exit order of antipodes and degree of resolution, %	eluant NH$_4$OH,N	flow rate, ml/h	exit order of antipodes and degree of resolution, %
Cu	Pro	*	11	L-D-12	0,1	12	L-D-19	*	11	L-D-21
Ni	Pro	0,05	9	D-L-22	0,06	9	D-L-32	0,05	14	D-L-13
Zn	Pro	0,06	13	L-D-3	0,06	12	L-D-19	0,06	10	L-D-05
Cu	Val	0,13	12	L-D-23	0,1	9	L-D-23	0,07	9	L-D-21
Ni	Val	0,05	9	D-L-13	0,07	12	D-L-7	0,05	14	L-D-9
Cu	Iva	*	11	D-L-17	0,15	12	D-L-40	*	11	L-D-54
Cu	Ile				0,5	12	L-D-49	0,13	9	L-D-21
Cu	Ser				0,07	12	L-D-8	0,03	9	L-D-30
Cu	Thr	*	12	D-L-22	0	12	D-L-21	*	12	L-D-14
Ni	Thr	0,05	12	D-L-12	0,05	9	D-L-17	0,05	14	L-D-10
Zn	Thr	0,06	13	D-L-4	0,08	11	D-L-11	0,06	10	L-D-18
Cu	Mandelic acid	0,04	9	L-D-18	0,05	12	L-D-28	0,04	9	L-D-17
Ni	The same	0,05	9	D-L-1,3	0,09	12	L-D-3,5	0,04	14	L-D-3,5
Zn	"	0,06	13	L-D-3	0,03	9	L-D-3,5	0,06	10	L-D-6
Cu	Asp	0,05	12	D-L-13	0,05	12	D-L-14	0,07	9	D-L-13
Ni	Asp	0,05	9	D-L-0,5	0,09	12	D-L-12	0,05	14	D-L-13
Zn	Asp	0,05	9	0	0,05	9	L-D-4	0,06	12	0
Cu	Orn	0,05	10	0	0,05	9	0	0,05	9	D-L-18
Ni	Orn	0,06	9	0	0,05	9	D-L-6	0,13	10	L-D-8
Zn	Orn	0,06	9	0	0,05	9	L-D-4	0,10	11	0

*Buffer solution 0.1 M CH$_3$COONH$_4$ + NH$_4$OH, pH 9.

2. V. A. Davankov, S. V. Rogozhin, and I. I. Peslyakas, Vysokomolekul. Soed., B14, 276 (1972).
3. I. I. Peslyakas, S. V. Rogozhin, and V. A. Davankov, Izv. Akad. Nauk SSSR, Ser. Khim., 174 (1974).

Summary

Ligand exchange chromatography was used to separate the enantiomers of [^3H] valine. The adsorbent used was a copolymer of polystyrene and divinylbenzene onto which was grafted L-hydroxyproline which was complexed with Cu^{++}. The method allows one to obtain both enantiomers of [^3H] valine with an optical purity close to 100% in about 2 hours with a simultaneous radiochemical purification. The method does not require any preliminary chemical modification of the amino acid and does not impose any limitations to specific activity values. The experimental details and results follow:

Reference

N.F. Myasoedov, O.B. Kuznetsova, O.V. Petrenik, V.A. Davankov and Y. A. Zolotarev, J. Labelled Comp. and Radiopharm., 17, 439 (1974).

We synthesized sorbents 1,2,3 using the macro-net polystyrene containing 11 percent of cross-links of the structure

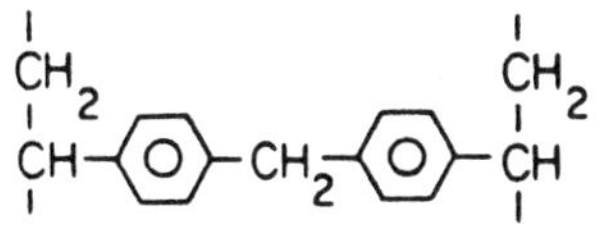

Sorbents 4 and 5 were obtained on a gel styrene copolymer containing 1% and 0.1% of divinylbenzene respectively. Sorbents 6 and 7 were obtained on a matrix including 0.7% divinylbenzene and 5.3% of additional cross-links of the diphenylmethylene type introduced as previously described [16].

Saturation of sorbents with copper(II) ions. 2-3g of air dried sorbent was equilibrated with an excess of copper(II) ammonia solution. To obtain the required extent of saturation, the excess copper was removed by washing with 2N NH_4OH containing a certain amount of KCl [17]. After phase separation the sorbent was finally washed on a filter with 0.1N NH_4OH.

Sorbents. Asymmetric sorbents with L-hydroxyproline (see Table 1) were obtained by aminating chloromethylated macro-net polystyrene matrix with methyl-L-hydroxyprolinate hydrochloride according to the procedure previously described [16]. The active sites of the final sorbent have the following structure:

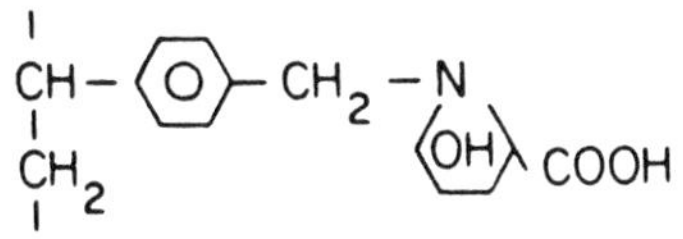

Table I

THE PROPERTIES OF SORBENTS WITH L-HYDROXYPROLINE GROUPINGS

Sorbent	Extent of cross-linking %	Capacity mmol/g	Swelling capacity weight %	Size of particles μm
1	11	3,44	200	100
2	11	2,46	120	100
3	11	1,48	70	100
4	1	3,52	200	100
5	0,1	3,50	1000	100
6	6	3,86	250	300
7	6	3,86	250	50

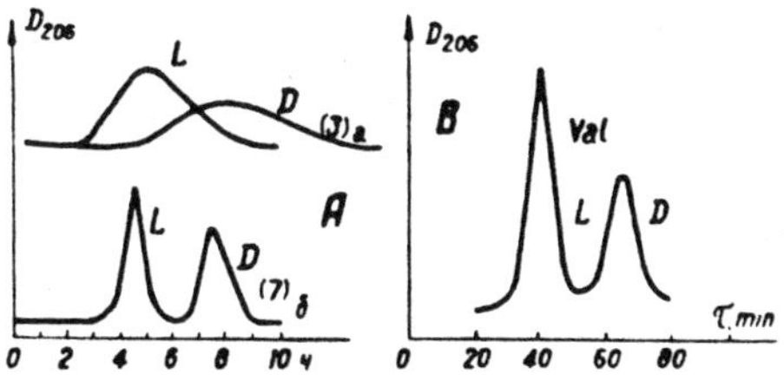

Figure 3 Chromatography of valine enantiomers on asymmetric sorbents (3) and (7), with 100% (A) and on sorbent (7) with 65% (B) saturation with Cu(II) ions.

Figure 4 shows the elution curve for 54.5mCi of D,L-[^3H]valine with a specific activity of 38Ci/mmol and a radiochemical purity of 90%. About 170μg of tritium-labelled D,L-valine in a volume of 250μl were introduced

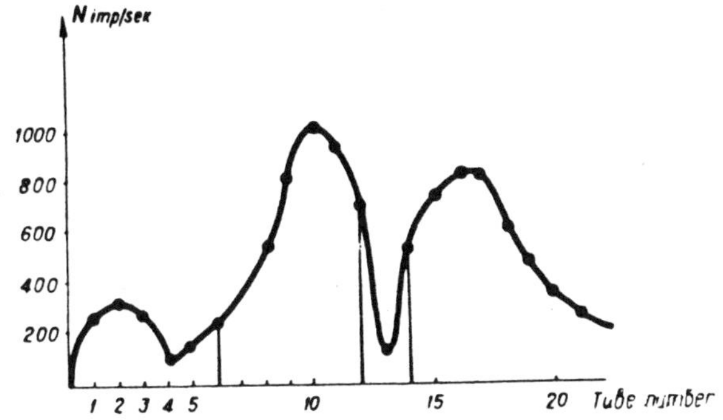

Figure 4 Elution curve for the chromatography of D,L-[^3H]valine (38Ci/mmol) on a column (7.8 x 140mm). Sorbent (7) had a Cu(II) saturation degree of 65%. Elution by 0.1N NH_4OH at a flow rate of 13ml per hour.

into the column (7.8mm I.D., height 140mm) filled with sorbent (7). Unlike the situation in Figure 3, the elution curve for the labelled D,L-valine shows three peaks with respect of radioactivity. The first peak (4.4mCi), eluting immediately after the void volume, comprises non-amino acid products. L-Valine (20.6mCi) was collected in fractions 6-12 and D-valine (24.8mCi) in fractions 14-25. During the purification of the solutions from traces of copper no more than 3% of the product were lost.

The optical purity of both isomers, determined by use of the appropriate stereoselective oxidases, was over 99%. According to the results of repeated ligand-exchange chromatography, the value was no worse than 99%. Hence we had obtained optically pure isomers of [^3H]valine.

The radioactivity eluted within the 1 peak of ligand-exchange chromatography coincides with the value of radiochemical purity of the initial preparation, obtained by thin-layer chromatography. This means that the ligand-exchange chromatography of racemic amino acids radiochemically purifies the preparations also from all non-amino acid impurities.

The specific activity of [^3H]valine preparations remains unchanged after the chromatographic separation of enantiomers.

The sorbent used showed practically no non-specific sorption: the balance of the collected radioactivity amounted to 96.3%.

7. GORDAY Ch., VERLY W.G. - J.Lab.Comp., 4 (1968), 334.

16. ZOLOTAREV Yu.A., KURGANOV A.A., DAVANKOV V.A. - Talanta, 25 (1978), 493.

17. DAVANKOV V.A., ZOLOTAREV Yu.A., TEVLIN A.B. - Bioorg.Khim. (USSR), 4, (1978), 1164.

Reference

V.A. Davankov, S.V. Rogozhin and A.V. Semechkin, J. Chromatogr., 91, 493 (1974).

Summary

The authors reported the resolution of several racemic α-amino acids by ligand-exchange chromatography on asymmetric resins produced from a macronet isoporous polystyrene matrix (see Refs. 4,8,9,10) containing optically active bi- or tridentate α-amino acids as fixed ligands coordinated with Cu^{++} or Ni^{++}. The degree of resolution of the enantiomers was found to depend on the nature of the fixed and mobile ligands and on the metal ion used. Experimental conditions and results follow:

TABLE I

EXTENT OF RESOLUTION (%) OF RACEMIC α-AMINO ACIDS

Column, *ca.* 30 ml; resin beads, 0.1–0.2 mm; rate of elution: 10–15 ml/h; 0.1–0.2 g of racemate.

Stationary ligand	Me^{2+}	*Mobile ligand*			
		Proline	*Valine*	*Threonine*	*Aspartic acid*
L-Valine	Cu	17.0	31.0	20.0	15.0
	Ni	11.0	5.0	24.0	10.0
L-Hydroxyproline	Cu	96.0	90.0	100.0	0
	Ni	15.0	21.0	10.0	6.0
L-Proline	Cu	100.0	53.0	0	0
L-Histidine	Cu	94.0	7.0	10.0	35.0
	Ni	47.0	4.0	14.0	36.0
L-Cysteic acid	Cu	33.0	15.0	9.0	0
	Ni	14.0	5.0	2.0	0
L-Aspartic acid	Cu	90.0	–	16.0	12.0
	Ni	6.0	–	2.0	12.0

4 S. V. Rogozhin and V. A. Davankov, *Dokl. Akad. Nauk SSSR*, 192 (1970) 1288; *Chem. Commun.*, (1971) 490.

8 V. A. Davankov, S. V. Rogozhin, A. V. Semechkin and T. P. Sachkova, *J. Chromatogr.*, 82 (1973) 359.

9 V. A. Davankov, S. V. Rogozhin, A. V. Semechkin and T. P. Sachkova, *Zh. Fiz. Khim.*, 47 (1973) 1254.

10 V. A. Davankov, S. V. Rogozhin, A. V. Semechkin, V. A. Baranov and G. S. Sannikova, *J. Chromatogr.*, to be published.

Reference

B. Lefebvre, R. Audebert and C. Quivoron, Isr. J. Chem., 15, 69 (1976/77).

Summary

A chiral macromolecular adsorbent was synthesized by copolymerization of acrylamide and methylenebis acrylamide onto which was grafted L-proline which was complexed with Cu^{++}. This adsorbent was found to be able to efficiently resolve a number of underivatized α-amino acids by HPLC. The experimental details and results follow:

Table 1. Capacity Factor for Some Amino Acids Eluted on a Packing Grafted with L-Proline and Complexed by Cupric Ion

Retention data: $k = (V - V_0)/V_0$

Amino acid	k_D	k_L	k_L/k_D
Alanine	0.76	0.83	1.1
Aminobutyric acid	0.72	1	1.4
Valine	0.78	1.5	1.9
Norvaline	0.87	1.2	1.4
Leucine	1.7	1.7	1
Isoleucine	1.2	1.9	1.6
Norleucine	1.3	1.7	1.3
Proline	1.1	0.72	0.65
Serine	1.6	3.1	1.9
Threonine	1.6	3.2	2
Phenylglycine	4.9	5.8	1.2
Phenylalanine	4.3	9.8	2.3
Tyrosine	9.7	24	2.5
Tryptophan	22	54	2.5
Methionine	2.6	2.6	1
Asparagine	2.3	3.4	1.5

Table 2. Relative Capacity Factor of Amino Acid Isomers Eluted on a Packing Grafted by L-Proline and Complexed by Various Ions

Relative capacity factor: k_L/k_D

	Cu(II)	Ni(II)	Co(II)	Zn(II)	Cd(II)	Hg(II)	Eu(III)	Th(IV)	U(VI)
Valine	1.9	0.61	0.72	0.74	1	>1	0.8	0.77	0.71
Proline	0.65	<1	0.7	1.2	0.84	1.6	1.1	0.77	0.79
Serine	1.9	<1	1	1	1	1	1	1	0.7
Phenylalanine	2.3	0.72	0.77	1	<1	1	1	1	0.8

Reference
D. Muller, M-A. Petit, A. Szubarga and J. Jozefonvicz, C. R. Acad. Sc. Paris, Ser. C., 285, 531 (1977).

Summary
The enantiomers of histidine were separated by ligand exchange chromatography. The adsorbent was a copolymer of polystyrene and divinylbenzene onto which was grafted L-proline which was complexed with Cu^{++}. The experimental details and results follow:

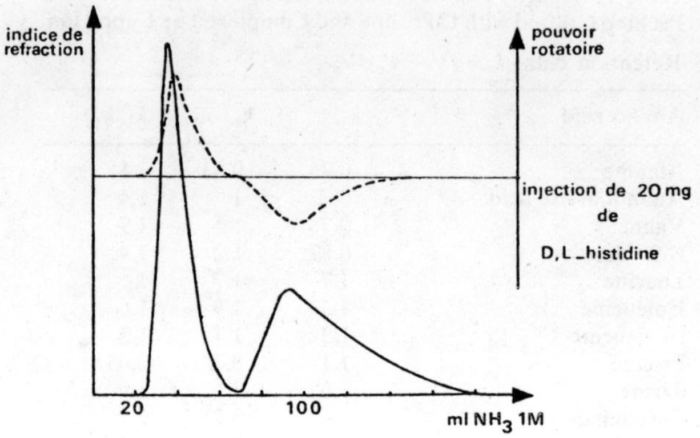

Fig. 1. — Chromatogramme de la D, L-histidine.

RÉSULTATS EXPÉRIMENTAUX. — La résolution par chromatographie d'échange de coordinats a été réalisée sur une colonne de longueur de 220 mm et de diamètre intérieur de 7,2 mm. L'ensemble chromatographique « Waters Associates » comprend une pompe 6 000 A, un injecteur U 6 K, un détecteur réfractométrique R 401. Un polarimètre « Perkin Elmer » 241 MC est placé à la suite du détecteur réfractométrique. La colonne est alimentée par de l'ammoniaque 1 M à un débit de 0,5 ml/mn. Le chromatogramme présenté sur la figure 1 montre une résolution totale de la D, L-histidine avec une sélectivité de 2,8 sur le support poly (styrène) à 1 % de divinylbenzène, 200-400 mesh. La capacité de la résine est de 1,53 méq de L-proline par gramme de résine sèche. La complexation par les ions cuivriques a été limitée à 90 % de la valeur maximale calculée sur la base du complexe stable associant deux coordinats L-proline à un ion cuivrique ([5]). Les deux isomères sont fortement retenus sur le support, notamment l'énantiomère L dont l'élution totale nécessite un grand volume d'éluant.

Reference

B. Lefebvre, R. Audebert and C. Quivoron, J. Liq. Chromatog., 1, 761 (1978).

Summary

The authors report the total resolution of several α-amino acids by HPLC using porous gels based on acrylamide grafted with L-proline and complexed with Cu^{++}. All the racemates with relative retention (α values) greater than 1.5 are completely resolved with a 30 cm. long column (or shorter) in less than one hour. The authors discuss the influence of the structue of the gel, the kinetics of the ligand exchange, the nature of the complexing ion and the structure of chiral graft on the resolution. Experimental details and results follow:

Nature of the packing

The packing is obtained in two steps (28,29,31) : 1) by pearl copolymerization of acrylamide and methylene bisacrylamide, we obtained a porous gel. The typical feature of the beads, *i.e.* granulometry between ten and twenty microns, porosity of about 0.4.cm^3/cm^3 of wet resin and good mechanical properties, are suitable for use in H P L C. 2) An L-α aminoacid is easily grafted onto these pearls through a reaction with formaldehyde. An illustration of the structure is given in Fig.1 with proline, the amont of graft linked varies from 0 to 3 meq./g of dry resin.

Finally, the beads are shaken with a aqueous salt solution of the complexing metal (*i.e.* sulfate or nitrate), filtered and washed. The ion complexed on the packing is practically not washed off by pure water but sometimes to a slight extent by the elution of solutes. Pure solutes are then freed of metal ions by just adding, at the outlet of the chromatographic column filled with uncomplexed packing.

Chromatographic conditions

The supports obtained are slurry packed in stainless steel column 30 cm x 4.8 mm i.d. The efficiency of the columns is greatly dependent on the filling conditions. In Fig.2, the efficiency of the columns (measured by the total number, N, of theoretical plates) is plotted versus the packing flow rate (eluent : pure water).

For low flow rates, peaks tail and efficiency is low. A maximum is observed because, at high flow rates, beads are compacted, a steep back asymmetry appears, and the efficiency decreases.

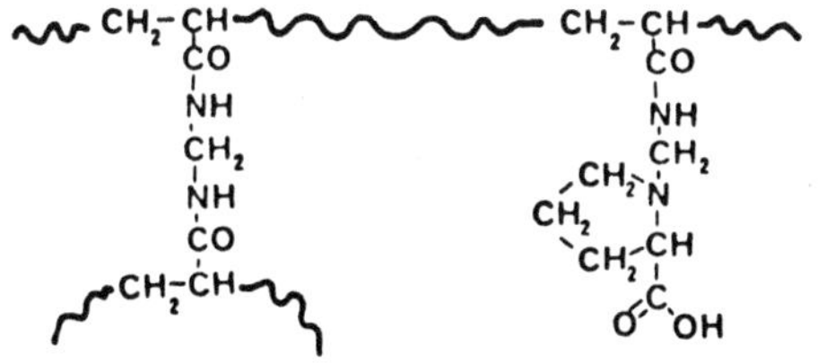

Figure 1 : Structure of the gel. After copolymerization of acrylamide and methylenebisacrylamide an L-α aminoacid is grafted through formaldehyde (proline, in this case).

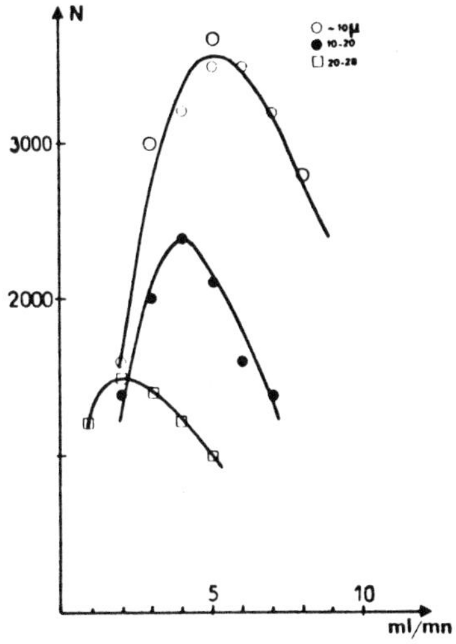

Figure 2 : Number of theoretical plates, N, versus the flow rate of filling (30 cm x 0.48 cm ID Column). N is calculated from the ethyleneglycoldimethylether granulometrie : □ 20-28μ ; ● 10-20μ ; ○ ≈ 10μ.

The same shape of curves - with a maximum - is also observed by plotting N, versus the dilution of the slurry before filling. The existence of such optimum conditions for the dilution and the packing flow rate is probably a general rule for semi-rigid beads.

Chromatographic apparatus

We used a Waters liquid chromatograph (ALC 201) and added to the classical refractometer a polarimetric detector (Perkin Elmer 241 MC) which continuously measures the rotatory power of the eluates.

28. Lefebvre B., Audebert R. and Quivoron C., French Patent ANVAR.

29. Lefebvre B., Audebert R. and Quivoron C., Information Chimie - Hauts Polymères, 165, 165, 1977.

31. Lefebvre B., Thesis University P. and M. Curie (Paris VI) 29/6/1977.

B. Lefebvre, R. Audebert and C. Quivoron, J. Liq. Chromatog., 1, 761 (1978) (continued).

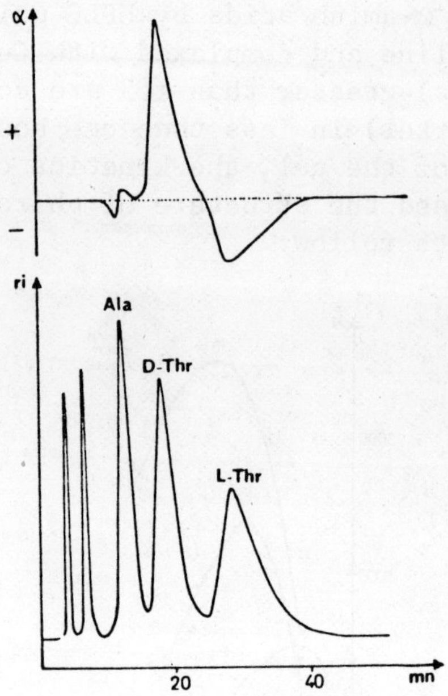

Figure 3 : Upper curve : polarimetric detector
Lower curve : refractometric detector
Elution order : 1) polyoxyethylene $\bar{M}_n$ = 6 000 ;
2) ethyleneglycoldimethylether ;
3) D and L alanine (partial resolution) ;
4) D threonine ;
5) L threonine ;
Stainless steel column 30 cm x 0.48 cm ID. Pressure drop of about 8 bars for a flow rate of 0.5 ml/m.
Gel : the graft is L proline, complexing ion Cu^{++} (0,4 cupric ion for one proline grafted). Capacity (in graft) 2.5 meq/g.
Eluent : water, room temperature.

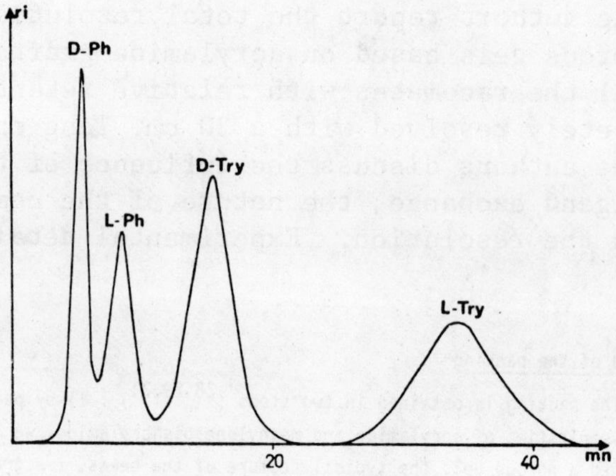

igure 4 : Elution order : 1) D phenylalanine ;
2) L phenylalanine ;
3) D tryptophan ;
4) L tryptophan.
Gel : graft is L proline and complexing ion Cu^{++}($r = 0.2$).
Capacity 0.95 meq/g.
Column : 5 cm x 0.48 cm ID
Eluent : water (0.4 ml/mn).

Reference

V.A. Davankov, Y.A. Zolotarev and A.V. Tevlin, Bioorgan. Khim., 4, 1164 (1978).

Summary

The authors reported the quantitative resolution of a number of racemic α-amino acids by ligand-exchange chromatography on an optically active resin with fixed L-hydroxyproline residues charged with Cu^{++}. The enantiomers of valine, norvaline, leucine, norleucine, isoleucine, threonine, proline, hydroxyproline, allo-hydroxyproline, phenylglycine, phenylalanine, tyrosine, phenylserine, tryptophane and histidine were completely separated on sorbent 2 (see Table 1) in 1 to 2 hours. Thus using LEC one can achieve the complete separation of the enantiomers of a majority of α-amino acids in a time comparable with the time it takes for enantiomer separation of α-amino acids by GLC, but in contrast to the latter one does not need to chemically modify the original compounds. Experimental conditions and results follow:

TABLE 1. Properties of Sorbents Containing Fixed L-Hydroxyproline Groupings

Sorbent	Degree of cross-linkage, %	Capacity, meq/g	Swellability, %	Particle size, μ	HEEP, mm	
					L-Val	L-Pro
1	11	1,48	80	100	15	20
2	6	3,86	250	50	1	1,4

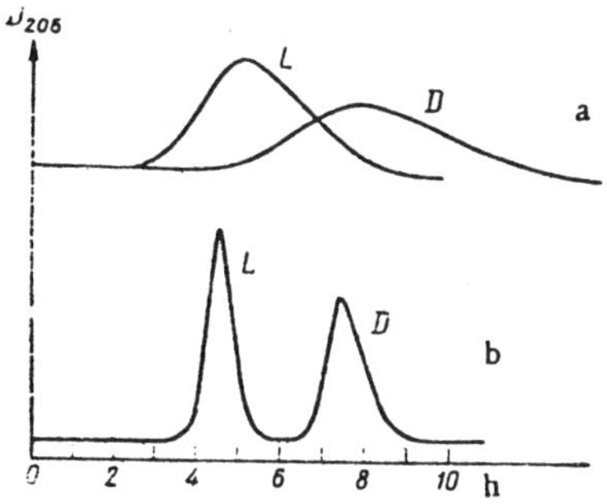

Fig. 1

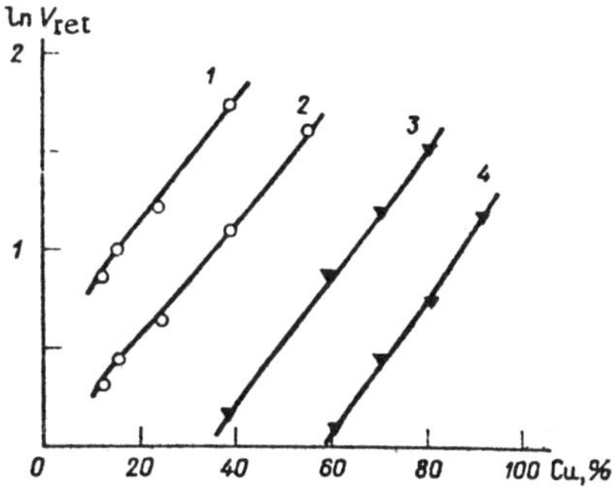

Fig. 2

Fig. 1. Chromatography of valine enantiomers on the disymmetric sorbents 1 (a) and 2 (b) containing fixed L-hydroxyproline groupings. Column (here and below) 7.8 × 140 mm, 0.1 M NH_4OH, 10 ml/h.

Fig. 2. Dependence of the retention of enantiomers of tryptophan and proline in elution on the degree of charging of the hydroxyproline sorbent 2 with Cu(II) ions: 1) D-Trp; 2) L-Trp; 3) D-Pro; 4) L-Pro.

V.A. Davankov, Y.A. Zolotarev and A.V. Tevlin, Bioorgan. Khim., 4, 1164 (1978) continued.

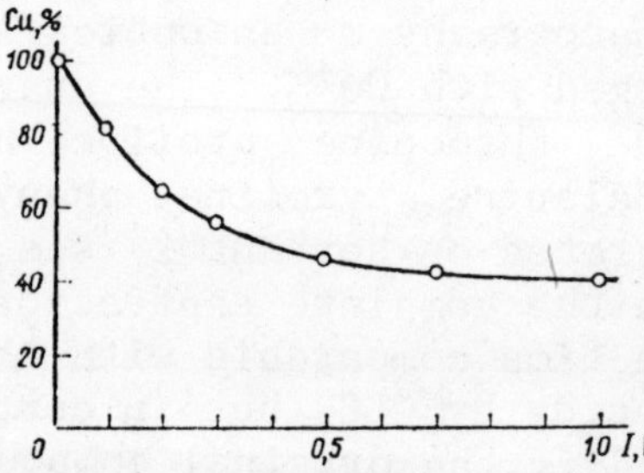

Fig. 3. Dependence of the absorption of Cu(II) ions by sorbent 2 containing L-hydroxyproline groupings on the ionic strength of equilibrium 2 N NH_4OH containing KCl (see the Experimental part).

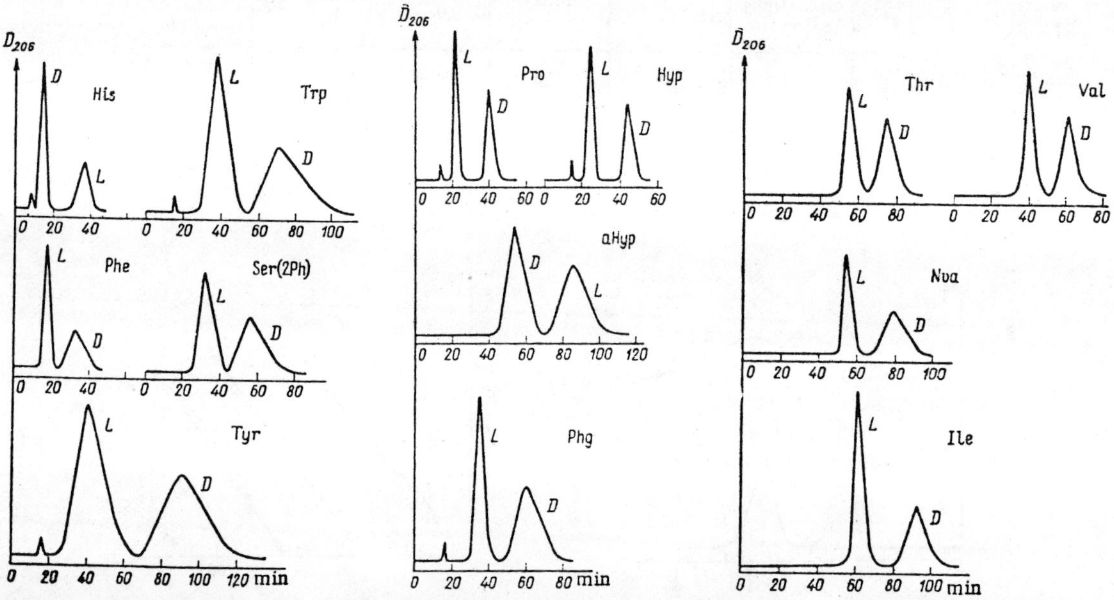

Fig. 4. Chromatography of racemates of amino acids on the L-hydroxyproline resin 2 in the Cu(II) form. For each experiment the following conditions are given in parentheses: the degree of charging, %; the concentration of eluent, NH_4OH, M; and the rate of elution, ml/h: His (30; 0.5; 25), Trp (30; 0.4; 20), Phe (45; 0.1; 20), Ser(2Ph) (45; 0.5; 14), Tyr (65; 0.1; 16), Pro (65; 1; 20), Hyp (65; 0.5; 20), aHyp (55; 0.05; 20), Phg (65; 0.1; 13), Thr (30; 0.05; 20), Val (65; 0.1; 13); Nva (65; 0.05; 16), Ile (65; 0.1; 13) [Ser(2Ph) and Phg represent phenylserine and phenylglycine, respectively].

Reference

V.A. Davankov and Y.A. Zolotarev, J Chromatog., 155, 285 (1978).

Summary

The authors reported the resolution of a large number of racemic α-amino acids by ligand-exchange chromatography on an asymmetric resin containing optically active L-hydroxyproline in the Cu^{++} form. The resin's selectivity and the column efficiency were determined and their dependence on the degree of saturation of the resin with Cu^{++}, ammonia concentration, and column parameters were discussed. Experimental conditions and results follow:

The asymmetric resin was prepared by aminating a chloromethylated polystyrene containing 11 mol% of cross-links of structure I with methyl L-hydroxyprolinate hydrochloride[6]. According to the nitrogen content and potentiometric titration of the resin obtained, the content of fixed ligand of structure II amounted to 3.44 mmol per gram of dry resin, taken in the zwitterionic form. The resin particles were of irregular shape and had an average size in the swollen state of 100 μm.

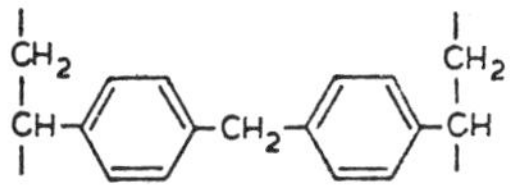

I

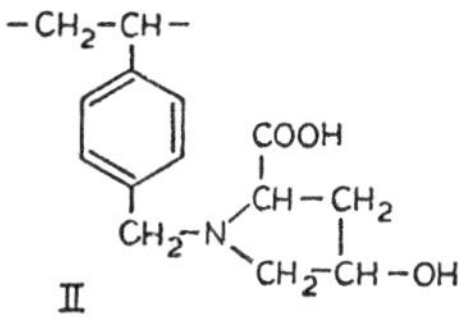

II

On treatment with excess copper–ammonia solution, the resin was saturated with copper(II) ions to an extent of 92% of the theoretical capacity calculated for the fixed complexes containing two fixed ligands per copper(II) ion. The equilibrium water content of the copper-containing resin in neutral media amounted to 200%. To maintain the copper saturation of the resin at 92%, the eluents used contained copper(II) ions in the following concentrations: $1.2 \cdot 10^{-5}$ *M* in 0.1 *M* NH_4OH for the chromatography of neutral amino acids; $2.5 \cdot 10^{-5}$ *M* in 0.025 *M* $Na(NH_4)_2PO_4$ solution of pH 8.3 for acidic amino acids and $2.0 \cdot 10^{-4}$ *M* in 1.5 *M* NH_4OH for basic amino acids.

The resin (6.3 ml) was packed into a column of 140 × 7.8 mm I.D. Portions of 1.0–1.5 mg of optically active or 2–3 mg of racemic amino acids were introduced into the column and eluted at a rate of 10 ml/h. Elution curves were recorded with a Uvicord III (LKB) detector at 206 nm. The void column volume of 4.7 ml was determined using acetone, which was assumed to be able to enter the resin phase without being strongly retained.

The retention volumes, V_L and V_D, of amino acid enantiomers L and D were determined from the distance between their peak maxima and that of acetone and expressed in void column volumes. The ratio of V_D to V_L is the enantioselectivity, α, of the sorption process and was used for calculating the difference, $\delta\Delta G^\circ$, between the free energies of the two diastereomeric sorption complexes formed in the resin phase:

$$\delta\Delta G^\circ = \Delta G^\circ_{R-Cu-D} - \Delta G^\circ_{R-Cu-L} = -RT \ln \alpha = -RT \ln \frac{V_D}{V_L}$$

If insufficient resolution of the racemate rendered a precise determination of the maxima positions or calculation of HETP values impossible, a separate chromatography of D- and L-enantiomers was performed.

6 Yu. A. Zolotarev, A. A. Kurganov and V. A. Davankov, *Talanta*, (1978) in press.

V.A. Davankov and Y.A. Zolotarev, J. Chromatog., 155, 285 (1978) continued.

TABLE I

ELUTION PARAMETERS OF AMINO ACIDS ON THE L-HYDROXY-PROLINE RESIN IN THE COPPER(II) FORM

Eluents: 0.1 *M* NH_4OH (N = 1–28); 1.5 *M* NH_4OH (N = 29–32); 0.025 *M* $Na(NH_4)_2PO_4$, pH 8.3 (N = 33–36).

N	*Amino acid*	*α-Radicals or molecular structure*	*V* L	*V* D	*α*	*δΔG°* (*cal/mol*)	*HEEP (cm)* L	*HEEP (cm)* D
1	Glycine	H–	6.44		—	—	0.31	
2	β-Alanine	$H_2NCH_2CH_2COOH$	0.28		—	—	~100	
3	Alanine	CH_3–	5.82	6.04	1.04	24	0.38	0.56
4	Aminobutyric acid	CH_3CH_2–	6.48	7.95	1.22	120	0.29	0.32
5	Norvaline	$CH_3CH_2CH_2$–	11.2	19.9	1.65	290	0.30	0.21
6	Norleucine	$CH_3CH_2CH_2CH_2$–	21.4	47.4	2.20	460	0.26	0.17
7	Valine	$CH_3CH(CH_3)$–	7.27	11.8	1.61	280	0.31	0.43
8	Isovaline	CH_3CH_2–; CH_3–	6.8	8.5	1.25	130		
9	Leucine	$CH_3CH(CH_3)CH_2$–	14.2	24.2	1.70	310	0.44	0.51
10	Isoleucine	$CH_3CH_2CH(CH_3)$–	11.1	20.9	1.89	370	0.53	0.49
11	Serine	$HOCH_2$–	3.47	4.48	1.29	150	0.94	0.90
12	Threonine	$HOCH(CH_3)$–	3.47	5.27	1.52	245	1.03	0.63
13	allo-Threonine	$HOCH(CH_3)$–	2.65	3.85	1.45	220		
14	Homoserine	$HOCH_2CH_2$–	5.32	6.65	1.25	130	0.35	
15	Methionine	$CH_3SCH_2CH_2$–	11.7	14.3	1.22	120	0.53	0.53
16	Asparagine	H_2NCOCH_2–	4.60	5.37	1.17	90	0.39	0.38
17	Glutamine	$H_2NCOCH_2CH_2$–	2.46	3.70	1.50	240	0.52	
18	Phenylglycine	C_6H_5–	6.15	13.6	2.22	465	0.70	0.74
19	Phenylalanine	$C_6H_5CH_2$–	33.8	97.6	2.89	620	0.59	0.62
20	α-Phenyl-α-alanine	C_6H_5–; CH_3–	11.9	12.5	1.07	39	1.25	1.25
21	Tyrosine	$HOC_6H_4CH_2$–	8.95	19.8	2.23	465	1.25	0.83
22	Phenylserine	$C_6H_5CH(OH)$–	22.6	41.1	1.82	350	0.98	0.94
23	β-Phenyl-β-alanine	$C_6H_5CHCH_2COOH$ NH_2	1.25	2.23	1.79	340		
24	Proline	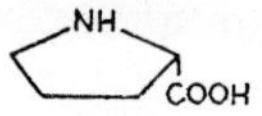	14.6	57.8	3.95	800	0.60	0.88
25	Hydroxyproline	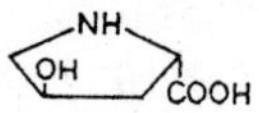	9.18	29.1	3.17	680	0.67	0.48
26	allo-Hydroxy-proline	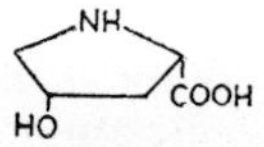	29.4	17.7	1.65	290	0.68	0.51
27	Azetidinecarboxylic acid	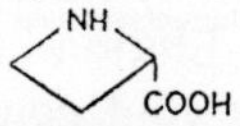	14.0	31.5	2.25	475	1.02	0.92
28	Ornithine	$H_2NCH_2CH_2CH_2$–	34.4					
29	Ornithine	$H_2NCH_2CH_2CH_2$–	2.0	2.0	1.0	0	1.2	1.2
30	Lysine	$H_2NCH_2CH_2CH_2CH_2$–	2.5	3.04	1.22	120	0.84	0.87
31	Histidine	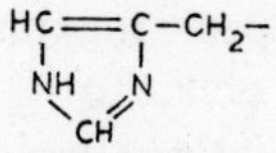	14.6	5.22	2.80	600	0.49	0.51
32	Tryptophan	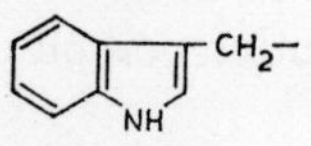	20.7	36.5	1.77	330	0.81	0.63
33	Aspartic acid	$HOOCCH_2$–	11.5	11.5	1.0	0	1.34	1.45
34	Glutamic acid	$HOOCCH_2CH_2$–	2.2	1.8	1.22	120	1.63	1.42
35	Iminodiacetic acid	$HN(CH_2COOH)_2$	32.6		—	—	1.28	
36	Serine	$HOCH_2$–	42.5					

V.A. Davankov and Y.A. Zolotarev, J. Chromatog., 155, 285 (1978) continued.

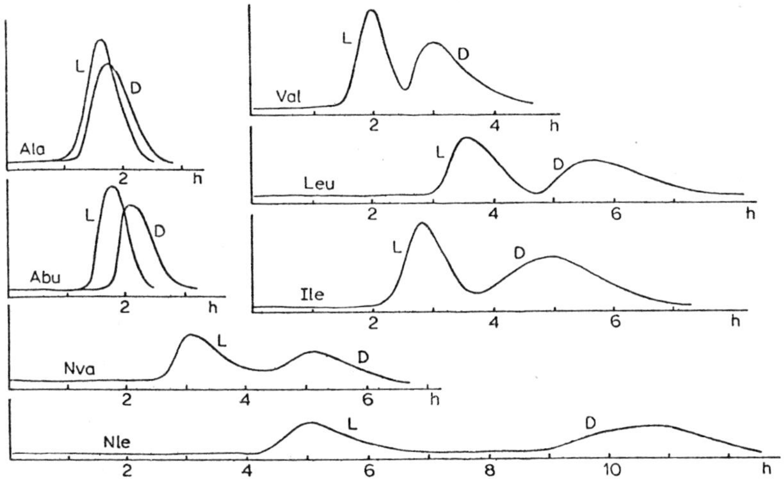

Fig. 1. Chromatography of the enantiomers of alanine ($\alpha = 1.04$), aminobutyric acid ($\alpha = 1.22$), norvaline ($\alpha = 1.65$), norleucine ($\alpha = 2.20$), valine ($\alpha = 1.61$), leucine ($\alpha = 1.70$) and isoleucine ($\alpha = 1.89$). Column 7.8 × 140 mm; 0.1 M NH_4OH; 10 ml/h. The degree of saturation of the L-hydroxyproline resin by copper(II) ions was 92%. Particle size *ca.* 100 μm.

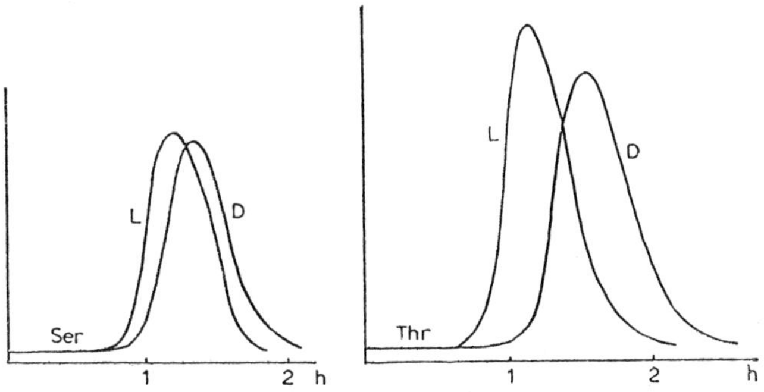

Fig. 2. Chromatography of the enantiomers of serine ($\alpha = 1.29$) and threonine ($\alpha = 1.52$). Conditions as given in Fig. 1.

Fig. 3

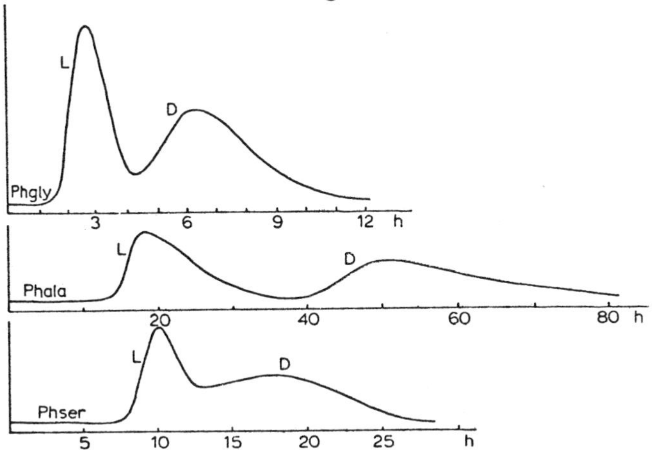

Fig. 4

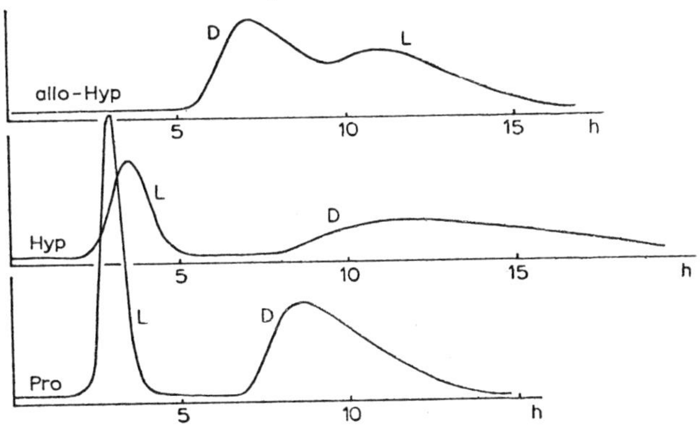

Fig. 3. Chromatography of the enantiomers of phenylglycine ($\alpha = 2.22$), phenylalanine ($\alpha = 2.89$) and phenylserine ($\alpha = 1.82$). Conditions as given in Fig. 1.

Fig. 4. Chromatography of the enantiomers of allo-hydroxyproline ($\alpha = 1.65$) and hydroxyproline ($\alpha = 3.17$) in 0.2 M NH_4OH at a flow-rate of 20 ml/h and proline ($\alpha = 3.95$) in 0.5 M NH_4OH at a flow-rate of 8 ml/h. Other conditions as given in Fig. 1.

V.A. Davankov and Y.A. Zolotarev, J. Chromatog., 155, 285 (1978) continued.

Fig. 5

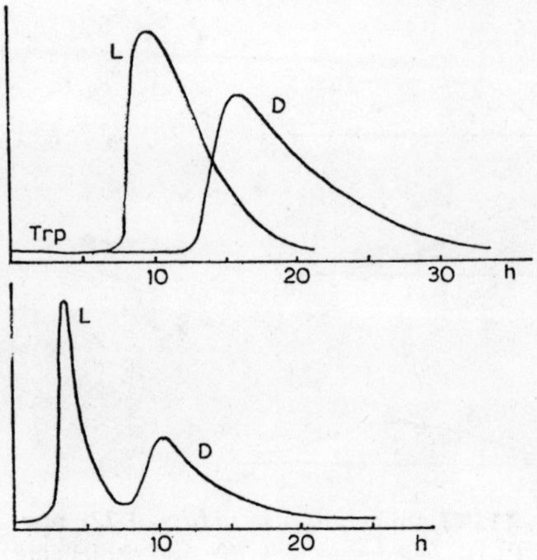

Fig. 6

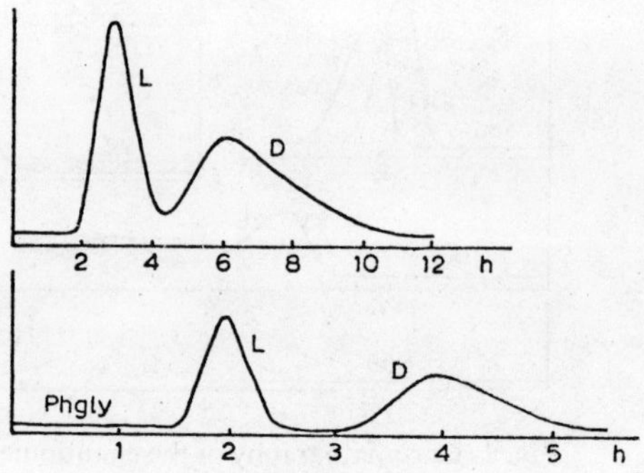

Fig. 5. Chromatography of the enantiomers of tryptophan. *Above:* in 1.5 *M* NH_4OH, other conditions as given in Fig. 1; $\alpha = 1.77$. *Below:* in 0.2 *M* NH_4OH at a flow-rate of 6 ml/h on a column of 4.5 × 280 mm with the L-hydroxyproline resin saturated by copper(II) ions to an extent of 15%, particle size 20–30 μm; $\alpha = 3.09$.

Fig. 6. Chromatography of the enantiomers of phenylglycine. *Above:* under standard conditions (see Fig. 1); HETP = 7 mm, $\alpha = 2.22$, $R_s = 0.75$. *Below:* on a column of 3.5 × 190 mm at a flow-rate of 8.2 ml/h, particle size 20–30 μm; HETP = 2.8 mm, $\alpha = 2.22$, $R_s = 1.22$.

Fig. 7

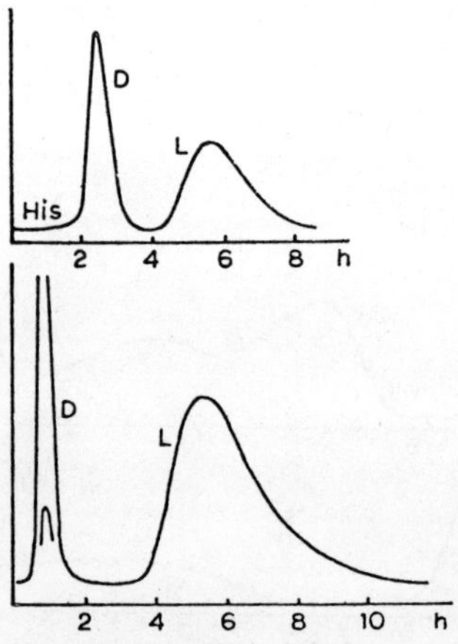

Fig. 8

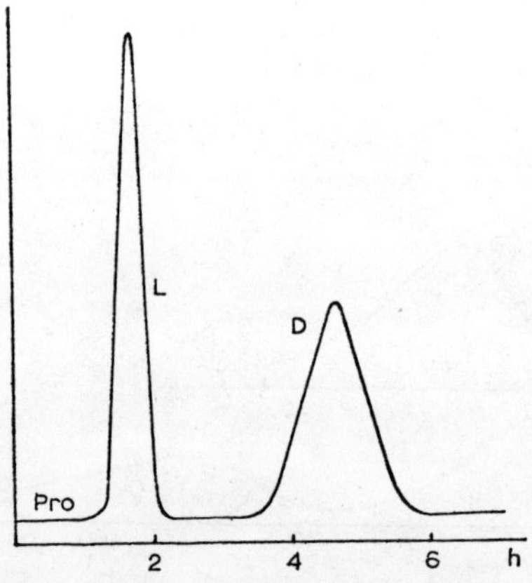

Fig. 7. Chromatography of the enantiomers of histidine. *Above:* in 1.5 *M* NH_4OH, other conditions as given in Fig. 1; $\alpha = 2.80$. *Below:* in 0.5 *M* NH_4OH at a flow-rate of 20 ml/h; the degree of resin saturation by copper(II) ions was 70%; $\alpha = 8.0$.

Fig. 8. Chromatography of the enantiomers of proline in a 0.5–1.5 *M* gradient of ammonia. Other conditions as given in Fig. 1.

Reference
V.A. Davankov and Y.A. Zolotarev, J. Chromatogr., 155, 295 (1978).

Summary
The authors describe the resolution of a large number of racemic α-amino acids by ligand-exchange chromatography on an asymmetric resin containing optically active L-proline and L-azetidine carboxylic acid in the Cu^{++} form. The enantioselectivity of the adsorbents with respect to the enantiomers of many α-amino acids is high enough (200-800 cal/mole) to allow their quantitative separation. The separating capacity of the adsorbent containing L-proline residues was generally found to be higher than that of the adsorbent containing L-azetidine carboxylic acid residues. Experimental conditions and results follow:

The asymmetric resins were prepared by aminating the chloromethylated macronet polystyrene matrix containing 11 mol% of cross-links of diphenylmethane structure by methyl esters of proline or azetidine carboxylic acid, as described in ref. 2. The sorbent capacity was 2.78 (for II) and 2.40 (for III) mmol fixed ligands per gram of dry resin in its zwitterionic form. The resin particles were of irregular shape, and their size in the swollen form was *ca.* 100 μm. The resins were charged with copper(II) ions from a copper–ammonia solution, until they contained 80% of the theoretical amount of copper corresponding to the formation of fixed complexes containing two fixed ligands per copper ion. The equilibrium water content in the copper form of the resin was 170% for sorbent II and 140% for sorbent III.

As in the previous study[1], the chromatographic column (14 cm × 7.8 mm I.D.) contained 6.3 ml resin. The detector used was Uvicord III (LKB) with the 206 nm light filter. Elution at the rate 10 ml/h was carried out at room temperature by ammonia solutions of concentration 0.1, 0.3 and 1.5 *M* containing $1.2 \cdot 10^{-5}$, $3.8 \cdot 10^{-5}$ and $2.0 \cdot 10^{-4}$ *M* $CuSO_4$ respectively, and by an 0.017 *M* ammonium phosphate solution (pH 8.8) containing $2.5 \cdot 10^{-5}$ *M* $CuSO_4$. In each experimental run either 2–3 mg of racemic amino acid or 1.0–1.5 mg of each enantiomer were chromatographed.

1 V. A. Davankov and Yu. A. Zolotarev, *J. Chromatogr.*, 155 (1978) 285.

Fig. 1

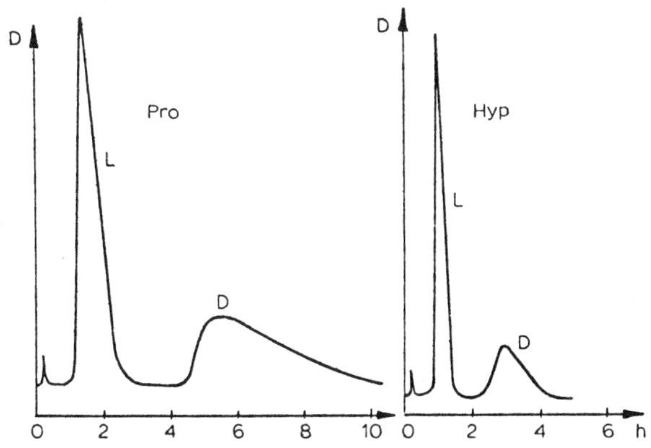

Fig. 2

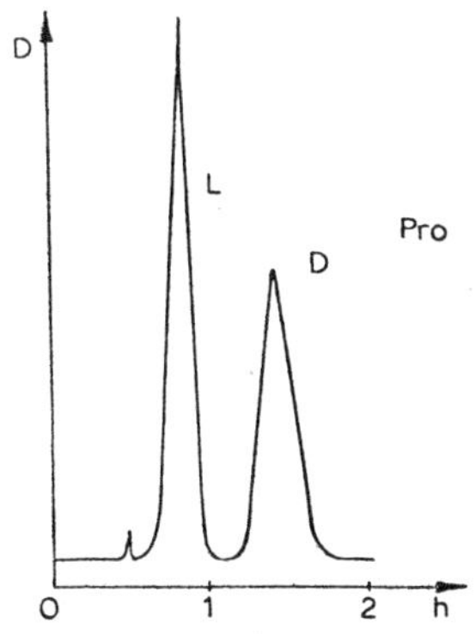

Fig. 3

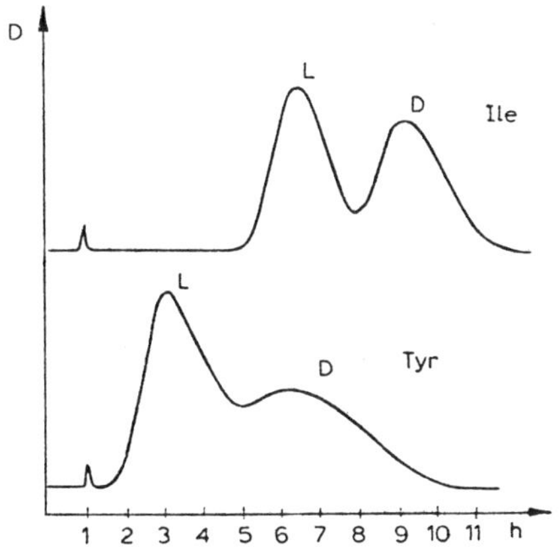

Fig. 1. Chromatography of racemic proline and hydroxyproline. Column 7.8 × 140 mm; 0.3 *M* NH_4OH; 10 ml/h. The degree of saturation of the L-proline resin by copper(II) ions was 80%. Particle size *ca.* 100 μm. Degree of cross-linking 11%.

Fig. 2. Chromatography of racemic proline. Column 7.8 × 140 mm; 1.0 *M* NH_4OH; 10 ml/h. The degree of saturation of the L-proline resin by copper(II) ions was 60%. Particle size *ca.* 70 μm. Degree of cross-linking 1%.

Fig. 3. Chromatography of racemic isoleucine and tyrosine. Column 7.8 × 140 mm; 0.1 *M* NH_4OH; 5 ml/h. The degree of saturation of the L-proline resin by copper(II) ions was 70%. Other resin parameters as given in Fig. 2.

V.A. Davankov and Y.A. Zolotarev, J. Chromatogr., 155, 295 (1978) continued.

TABLE II

ELUTION PARAMETERS OF AMINO ACIDS ON THE AZETIDINE-CARBOXYLIC ACID RESIN III IN THE COPPER(II) FORM

Eluents: 0.1 *M* NH_4OH ($N = 1$–6); 0.3 *M* NH_4OH ($N = 7$–17); 1.5 *M* NH_4OH ($N = 18$–23); 0.017 *M* $(NH_4)_3PO_4$, pH 8.8 ($N = 24$–31).

N	*Amino acid*	*α-Radicals or molecular structure*	*V*		*α*	*δΔG°* *(cal/mol)*	*HEEP (cm)*	
			L	D			L	D
1	Glycine	H–	7.2		—	—	1.72	
2	Alanine	CH_3–	11.2	11.9	1.06	35	1.68	1.70
3	Aminobutyric acid	CH_3CH_2–	15.0	19.2	1.28	145	1.91	1.84
4	Valine	$CH_3CH(CH_3)$–	24.0	41.0	1.78	315	1.87	1.93
5	Norvaline	$CH_3CH_2CH_2$–	52	64	1.23	120	1.66	1.74
6	Tyrosine	$HOC_6H_4CH_2$–	9.6	19.0	1.78	335	2.04	2.01
7	Valine	$CH_3CH(CH_3)$–	3.1	5.4	1.74	320	1.92	1.96
8	Aminobutyric acid	CH_3CH_2–	1.85	2.4	1.30	155	1.97	1.93
9	Methionine	$CH_3SCH_2CH_2$–	7.2	9.3	1.29	150	1.59	1.67
10	Proline	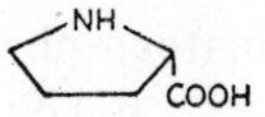	7.5	18.6	2.48	530	1.93	1.84
11	Hydroxyproline	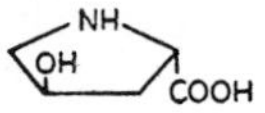	3.6	8.1	2.25	475	1.86	1.85
12	allo-Hydroxyproline	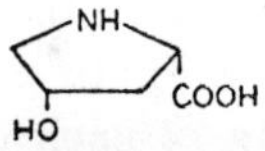	8.3	5.7	1.46	220	1.84	1.93
13	Leucine	$CH_3CH(CH_3)CH_2$–	18.2	22.5	1.24	125	1.62	1.69
14	Isoleucine	$CH_3CH_2CH(CH_3)$–	15.1	25.5	1.68	305	1.57	1.63
15	Norvaline	$CH_3CH_2CH_2$–	9.12	11.4	1.25	130	1.69	1.74
16	Norleucine	$CH_3CH_2CH_2CH_2$–	25.2	35.4	1.41	200	1.63	1.60
17	Phenylglycine	C_6H_5–	4.8	6.6	1.38	190	1.94	1.97
18	Ornithine	$H_2NCH_2CH_2CH_2$–	2.1	2.1	1.0	—	2.4	2.4
19	Lysine	$H_2NCH_2CH_2CH_2CH_2$–	1.8	1.91	1.06	35	2.3	2.25
20	Histidine	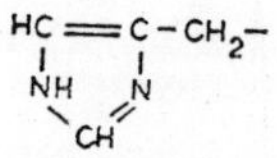	27.6	15.3	1.80	340	2.1	2.2
21	Tryptophan	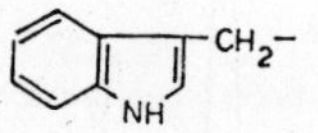	33.2	37.4	1.13	70	2.25	2.16
22	Phenylalanine	$C_6H_5CH_2$–	7.25	13.5	1.86	360	2.24	2.20
23	Norleucine	$CH_3CH_2CH_2CH_2$–	3.10	4.28	1.38	190	1.80	1.73
24	Serine	$HOCH_2$–	6.0	12.9	2.15	445	1.92	1.96
25	Threonine	$HOCH(CH_3)$–	13.7	10.7	1.28	145	1.94	1.92
26	Asparagine	H_2NCOCH_2–	13.8	9.6	1.44	210	1.78	1.83
27	Glutamine	$H_2NCOCH_2CH_2$–	17.4	21.8	1.25	130	1.84	1.96
28	Glycine	H–	36		—	—	1.78	
29	Aspartic acid	$HOOCCH_2$–	3.05	2.7	1.13	70	2.15	2.23
30	Glutamic acid	$HOOCCH_2CH_2$–	9.0	7.2	1.29	150	2.08	2.18
31	Iminodiacetic acid	$HN(CH_2COOH)_2$	2.4		—	—	2.04	

V.A. Davankov and Y.A. Zolotarev, J. Chromatogr., 155, 295 (1978) continued.

TABLE I

ELUTION PARAMETERS OF AMINO ACIDS ON THE L-PROLINE RESIN IN THE COPPER(II) FORM

Eluents: 0.1 *M* NH_4OH (N = 1–15); 0.3 *M* NH_4OH (N = 16–24); 1.5 *M* NH_4OH (N = 25–29); 0.017 *M* $(NH_4)_3PO_4$, pH 8.8 (N = 30–32).

N	*Amino acid*	*α-Radicals or molecular structure*	*V* L	*V* D	*α*	*δΔG°* *(cal/mol)*	*HEEP (cm)* L	*HEEP (cm)* D
1	Glycine	H–	5.0		—	—	0.66	
2	Alanine	CH_3–	6.75	7.25	1.08	46	0.67	0.64
3	Aminobutyric acid	CH_3CH_2–	7.20	8.50	1.17	92	0.70	0.68
4	Norvaline	$CH_3CH_2CH_2$–	14.2	18.2	1.28	145	0.68	0.70
5	Norleucine	$CH_3CH_2CH_2CH_2$–	25.5	39.4	1.54	225	0.65	0.67
6	Valine	$CH_3CH(CH_3)$–	9.0	11.6	1.29	150	1.00	0.95
7	Serine	$HOCH_2$–	4.0	4.35	1.09	52	0.85	0.90
8	Threonine	$HOCH(CH_3)$–	4.0	5.5	1.38	190	1.00	0.95
9	allo-Threonine	$HOCH(CH_3)$–	3.25	5.0	1.55	260	1.05	1.00
10	Asparagine	H_2NCOCH_2–	4.25	5.0	1.18	97	0.70	0.62
11	Glutamine	$H_2NCOCH_2CH_2$–	3.75	4.5	1.20	110	0.90	0.74
12	Proline	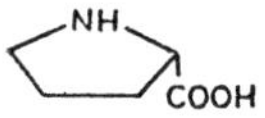	17.0	70	4.10	825	0.62	0.60
13	Hydroxyproline	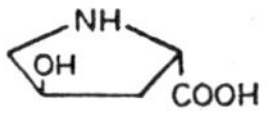	9.9	38.2	3.85	790	0.42	0.46
14	allo-Hydroxyproline	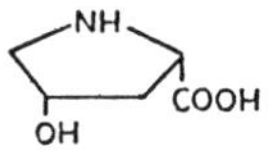	43.5	18.8	2.32	490	0.96	0.92
15	Phenylglycine	C_6H_5–	11.3	18.8	1.67	300	1.40	1.20
16	Norvaline	$CH_3CH_2CH_2$–	4.10	5.75	1.40	200	0.66	0.68
17	Norleucine	$CH_3CH_2CH_2CH_2$–	12.0	18.5	1.54	250	0.65	0.68
18	Leucine	$CH_3CH(CH_3)CH_2$–	13.0	16.5	1.27	140	0.56	0.58
19	Isoleucine	$CH_3CH_2CH(CH_3)$–	7.0	10.5	1.50	240	0.49	0.48
20	Phenylalanine	$C_6H_5CH_2$–	31.5	51.5	1.63	286	1.05	0.98
21	Tyrosine	$HOC_6H_4CH_2$–	2.65	6.5	2.46	530	1.20	1.06
22	Proline	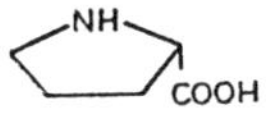	6.25	25.0	4.00	815	0.67	0.62
23	Hydroxyproline	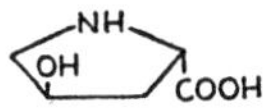	3.50	13.5	3.85	790	0.37	0.43
24	Methionine	$CH_3SCH_2CH_2$–	6.25	6.5	1.04	24	0.46	0.48
25	Lysine	$H_2NCH_2CH_2CH_2CH_2$–	2.5	2.75	1.10	57	1.80	1.64
26	Ornithine	$H_2NCH_2CH_2CH_2$–	2.5	2.5	1.0	—	2.6	2.2
27	Histidine	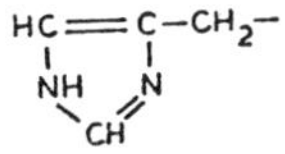	15.5	5.75	2.70	365	1.00	0.95
28	Tryptophan	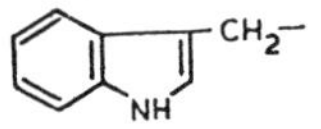	5.5	7.8	1.40	200	1.1	1.03
29	Phenylalanine	$C_6H_5CH_2$–	6.0	9.25	1.54	255	0.95	0.96
30	Aspartic acid	$HOOCCH_2$–	4.25	3.75	1.10	57	1.6	1.4
31	Glutamic acid	$HOOCCH_2CH_2$–	2.0	1.25	1.60	275	1.75	1.6
32	Iminodiacetic acid	$HN(CH_2COOH)_2$	7.5		—	—	1.2	

Reference

V.A. Davankov and Y.A. Zolotarev, J. Chromatogr., 155, 303 (1978).

Summary

The authors describe the resolution of a large number of racemic α-amino acids by ligand-exchange chromatography on an asymmetric resin containing L-allo-hydroxy-proline groups in the Cu^{++} form. The γ-hydroxy group in allo-hydroxyproline like the carboxyl and amino group is capable of coordinating Cu^{++}. The resolving power of this adsorbent with respect to racemates of acidic and basic α-amino acids as well as methionine and phenylalanine is higher than that of resins containing L-hydroxyproline, L-proline, or L-azetidine carboxylic acid residues loaded with Cu^{++}. Experimental conditions and results follow:

The asymmetric sorbent IV was prepared by aminating chloromethylated polystyrene containing 11 mol% cross-links of diphenylmethane structure[6] using methyl-L-allo-hydroxyprolinate hydrochloride, according to a procedure described in ref. 6 for methyl-L-prolinate hydrochloride. The initial L-allo-Hyp was synthesized from L-Hyp according to a scheme[7] involving inversion of configuration at the γ-carbon atom:

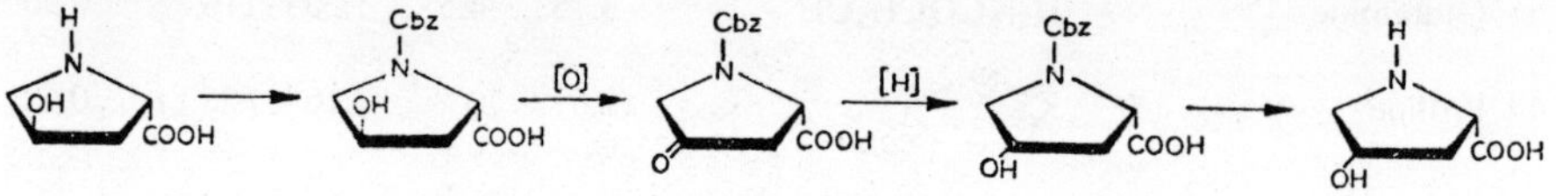

According to elemental analysis and potentiometric titration, the sorbent IV contains 2.82 mmol of fixed ligands per gram of dry resin in its zwitterionic form. The resin particles have an irregular shape, with an average size of *ca.* 100 μm when swollen. The resin was charged with copper ions from a copper–ammonia solution, resulting in quantitative formation of complexes containing two fixed ligands per copper ion. The equilibrium water content in the copper-saturated resin was 140%.

The chromatographic technique is described in detail in ref. 3. The column was 14 cm × 7.8 mm I.D. and contained 6.3 ml of resin. The eluents used were ammonia solutions of concentration 0.1, 0.3 and 1.5 *M*, containing $1.2 \cdot 10^{-5}$, $3.8 \cdot 10^{-5}$ and $2.0 \cdot 10^{-4}$ *M* $CuSO_4$, respectively, as well as a 0.017 *M* ammonium phosphate solution (pH 8.8) containing 2.0×10^{-5} *M* $CuSO_4$. Aliquots of 1.5–2.0 mg of the amino acid enantiomers introduced into the column were eluted at a flow-rate of 10 ml/h. The detector used was Uvicord-III with a 206-nm light filter.

The complex-formation properties of the resins were estimated by potentiometric titration[6], by studying the sorption of copper from copper–ammonia solutions[8] and by measuring the pH decomplexation values (DpH) of copper(II) ions, as described by Hering[9]. The sorption constant of L-proline on resins I and IV was studied and calculated according to the procedure given in ref. 8.

The enantioselectivity of the sorption of proline isomers under static conditions was estimated from the equilibrium distribution of the amino acid enantiomers between the aqueous phase and the asymmetric sorbent in batch experiments. Equilibration was carried out in 15-ml vials equipped with a porous glass filter and capable of being stoppered at both ends[6]. Into the vials were placed 0.300 g of air-dried resin containing 0.540 mmol of functional groups, 1 ml of a 0.5 *M* solution of D,L-Pro, differing amounts of copper nitrate (0.05–0.5 mmol) and 2 ml of 0.520 *M* KOH. After the volume was made up to 10 ml with water, the vials were closed and shaken for 72 h at 25°.

The resin phase was then separated by centrifugation at 1600 *g* for 15 min. To analyse the resin phase copper ions and L-proline were desorbed by washing the sorbent in the same vial with 25 ml of 5 *M* HCl.

Copper in both phases was determined spectrocolorimetrically with sodium N,N-diethyldithiocarbamate using a Specol spectrocolorimeter at λ = 440 nm.

V.A. Davankov and Y.A. Zolotarev, J. Chromatogr., 155, 303 (1978) continued.

Proline was determined by the technique of Pope and Stevens[10], modified by Woiwod[11], *i.e.* the pH of the solution was increased to 8.0 and then a four-fold volume of a colloidal suspension of copper hydroxy phosphate in 0.2 *M* Na_2HPO_4 was added. The resulting mixture was kept at 80° for 30 min. The residual copper phosphate was then filtered off and the copper content in the filtrate, which is equivalent to the proline content, was determined by the method cited above. The predominance of one proline enantiomer over the other (in both phases) was determined polarimetrically, the specific rotation of L-Pro in 5.0 *M* HCl being assumed to be $[\alpha]^{20}_{436} = -123°$.

The quantitative analysis of both phases makes it possible to calculate the difference between the standard free energies of the two diastereomeric mixed-ligand sorption complexes, R–Cu–D-Pro and R–Cu–L-Pro, according to the equation

$$\delta \Delta G^0 = -RT \ln \frac{[\text{R–Cu–D-Pro}]}{[\text{R–Cu–L-Pro}]} \cdot \frac{[\text{L-Pro}]}{[\text{D-Pro}]}$$

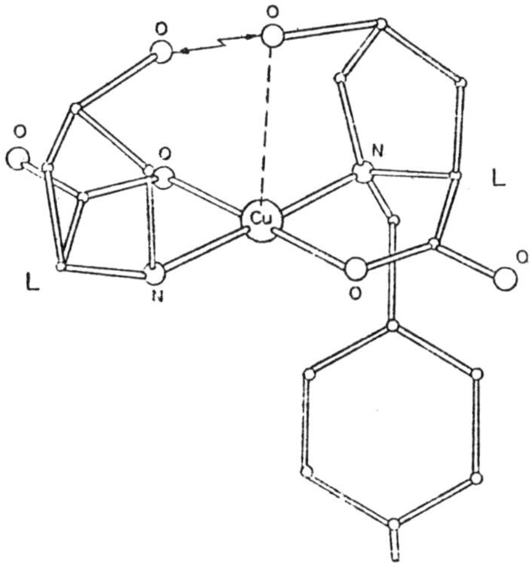

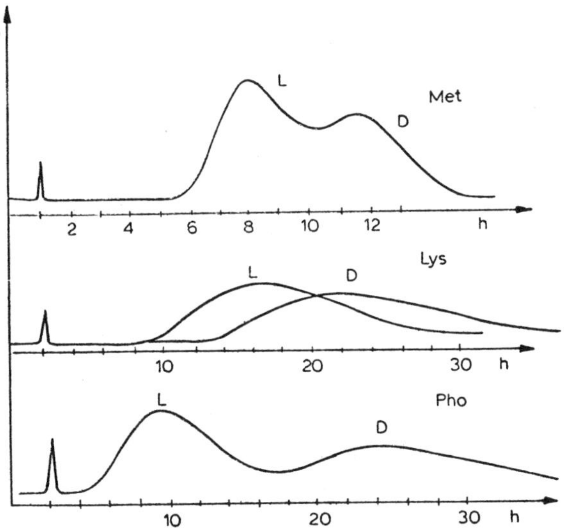

Fig. 4. Repulsion of the two hydroxy groups in the mixed-ligand sorption complex formed by L-allo-hydroxyproline on the asymmetric sorbent IV containing L-allo-hydroxyproline fixed ligands.

Fig. 5. Chromatography of enantiomers of Met, Lys and Phe. The degree of saturation of the L-allo-hydroxyproline resin IV by copper(II) ions was 50%. Column, 5 × 560 mm; 0.1 *M* NH_4OH; 6 ml/h. Particle size, *ca.* 50 μm.

6 Yu. A. Zolotarev, A. A. Kurganov and V. A. Davankov, *Talanta*, in press.
7 A. A. Patchett and B. Witkop, *J. Amer. Chem. Soc.*, 79 (1957) 185.
8 Yu. A. Zolotarev, A. A. Kurganov, A. V. Semechkin and V. A. Davankov, *Talanta*, in press.
9 R. Hering, *Chelatbildende Ionenaustauscher*, Akademieverlag, Berlin, 1967, p. 104.
10 C. Pope and M. Stevens, *Biochem. J.*, 33 (1939) 1070.
11 A. Woiwod, *Biochem. J.*, 45 (1949) 412.

V.A. Davankov and Y.A. Zolotarev, J. Chromatogr., 155, 303 (1978) continued.

TABLE II

ELUTION PARAMETERS OF AMINO ACIDS ON THE COPPER(II) FORM OF THE ALLO-HYDROXYPROLINE RESIN

Eluents: 0.1 *M* NH_4OH (N = 1–16); 0.3 *M* NH_4OH (N = 17–23); 1.5 *M* NH_4OH (N = 24–29); 0.017 *M* $(NH_4)_3PO_4$, pH 8.8 (N = 30–32).

N Amino acid	*α-Radicals or molecular structure*	*V*		*α*	*δΔG°* *(cal/mol)*	*HEEP (cm)*	
		L	D			L	D
1 Glycine	H–	5.55		—	—	1.23	
2 Alanine	CH_3–	8.9	9.2	1.04	24	1.16	1.10
3 Aminobutyric acid	CH_3CH_2–	9.6	11.0	1.14	77	1.36	1.22
4 Norvaline	$CH_3CH_2CH_2$–	13.4	19.0	1.42	205	1.32	1.3
5 Norleucine	$CH_3CH_2CH_2CH_2$–	22.9	33.4	1.46	220	1.2	1.25
6 Valine	$CH_3CH(CH_3)$–	8.6	13.6	1.58	270	1.3	1.25
7 Leucine	$CH_3CH(CH_3)CH_2$–	21.6	33.7	1.52	245	1.43	1.35
8 Isoleucine	$CH_3CH_2CH(CH_3)$–	16.2	28.2	1.74	325	1.1	1.0
9 Serine	$HOCH_2$–	4.38	5.25	1.24	125	1.43	1.41
10 Threonine	$HOCH(CH_3)$–	4.82	7.15	1.48	230	1.46	1.35
11 Asparagine	H_2NCOCH_2–	4.38	5.25	1.20	110	1.48	1.56
12 Glutamine	$H_2NCOCH_2CH_2$–	3.94	5.52	1.40	200	1.86	1.84
13 Phenylglycine	C_6H_5–	9.35	16.7	1.78	335	1.85	1.75
14 allo-Hydroxyproline	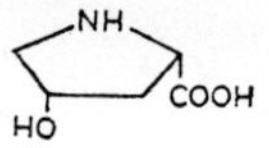	18.7	27.8	1.48	230	1.48	1.40
15 Hydroxyproline	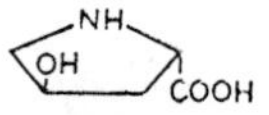	21.3	34.1	1.63	285	1.2	1.3
16 Proline	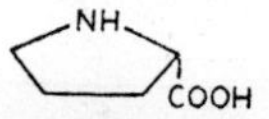	52.5	96.0	1.83	355	1.1	1.05
17 Phenylalanine	$C_6H_5CH_2$–	15.2	47.2	3.10	660	1.98	1.85
18 Tyrosine	$HOC_6H_4CH_2$–	3.21	7.58	2.36	505	2.6	2.5
19 Methionine	$CH_3SCH_2CH_2$–	8.62	13.1	1.52	245	1.75	1.70
20 Proline	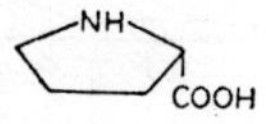	20.5	38.1	1.85	360	1.0	0.95
21 Leucine	$CH_3CH(CH_3)CH_2$–	8.8	13.8	1.56	325	1.40	1.38
22 Isoleucine	$CH_3CH_2CH(CH_3)$–	7.03	12.2	1.74	325	1.05	1.0
23 Aminobutyric acid	CH_3CH_2–	4.1	6.0	1.21	112	0.9	0.85
24 Lysine	$H_2NCH_2CH_2CH_2CH_2$–	2.25	3.0	1.33	165	1.45	1.0
25 Ornithine	$H_2NCH_2CH_2CH_2$–	1.0	1.2	1.2	110	1.75	1.65
26 Histidine	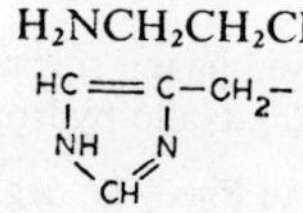	6.8	9.1	1.32	160	1.3	1.1
27 Tryptophan	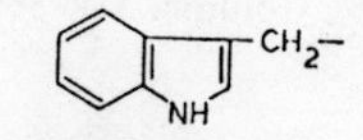	63.0	68.8	1.1	57	1.88	1.7
28 Proline	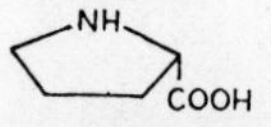	3.15	5.75	1.82	350	1.0	1.0
29 Leucine	$CH_3CH(CH_3)CH_2$–	1.3	2.0	1.54	255	1.75	1.75
30 Aspartic acid	$HOOCCH_2$–	9.8	6.8	1.23	120	2.0	1.9
31 Glutamic acid	$HOOCCH_2CH_2$–	16.0	11.0	1.45	215	2.2	2.1
32 Iminodiacetic acid	$HN(CH_2COOH)_2$	8.0		—	—	2.1	

Reference

N. Spassky, M Reix, J.-P. Guetté, M. Guetté, M.-O. Sepulchre and J.M. Blanchard, Compt. Rend. Acad. Sc. Paris, 287, 589 (1978).

Summary

Using asymmetric resins containing L-histidine ligands in the Ni^{++} form the authors report the resolution of racemic histidine by ligand-exchange chromatography. Experimental conditions and details follow:

Le deuxième support (B) a été synthétisé en prenant exemple sur une méthode récemment décrite par Takahaishi, Stille et coll. ([6]). La copolymérisation radicalaire du N-*p*-vinyl-benzyl-L-histidinate de méthyle (NVBH), avec le méthacrylate d'hydroxyéthyle (MAHE), en présence de diméthacrylate d'éthylène servant d'agent de réticulation, nous a permis d'obtenir une résine contenant les motifs NVBH/MAHE dans le rapport 0,22/0,78. Cette résine traitée par le chlorure de nickel possède une capacité en complexe L-histidine-nickel de 0,8 mmol/g de résine.

DÉDOUBLEMENT CHROMATOGRAPHIQUE DES ACIDES α-AMINÉS. — La résine (B) nous a permis de réaliser le dédoublement chromatographique partiel de l'histidine racémique. Par percolation d'une colonne remplie de cette résine à l'aide d'une solution d'histidine racémique, on isole 30 à 40 % de fractions présentant une pureté optique supérieure à 65 %. Au cours d'une expérience, les fractions de tête contenaient de la L-histidine pure. L'ordre d'élution à pH 8 des isomères correspond à celui qui a été observé par Yamskov et coll. ([7]) en utilisant une résine de Merrifield immobilisant le complexe de nickel de la L-histidine à pH 11. La quantité d'histidine racémique éluée sur 3 g de résine est 10 fois supérieure à à celle mise en œuvre par les auteurs précédents.

([6]) N. TAKAHAISHI, H. IMAI, C. A. BERTELO et J. K. STILLE, *J. Amer. Chem. Soc.*, 98, 1976, p. 5400 et 100, 1978, p. 264.

([7]) I. A. YAMSKOV, S. V. ROGOZHIN et V. A. DAVANKOV, *Bioorgan. Khim.*, 3, 1977, p. 200.

Reference

I.A. Yamskov, B.B. Berezin, V.E. Tikhonov and V.A. Davankov, Bioorgan. Khim., 4, 149 (1978).

Summary

The authors reported the synthesis of an optically active adsorbent with tetrafunctional fixed ligands, namely R-1, 2-bis(2'-carboxyethylamino)propane residues in the Cu^{++} and Ni^{++} forms and used it in the ligand-exchange chromatography of a number of racemic α-amino acids. The greatest enantioselectivity was observed in the case of the Ni^{++} complex for histidine and phenylalanine and in the case of the Cu^{++} complex for phenylalanine and proline. The HETP values, with respect to which the efficiency of the chromatographic process was evaluated, were between 10 and 50 mm. Experimental details and results follow:

TABLE 1. Results of the Ligand-Exchange Chromatography of L- and D-Enantiomers of Amino Acids

AA	Mt	V_L	V_D	α	$\delta\Delta G_{298}$ cal/mole	Eluent	HETP, mm L-AA	HETP, mm D-AA
Proline	Cu^{2+}	18,1	12,6	1,4	210	0,1N. NH_3	9,8	9,3
	Ni^{2+}	11,5	9,3	1,25	130	0,05 N NH_3	32,7	32,2
Valine	Cu^{2+}	14,9	12,2	1,22	120	0,1N NH_3	15,5	15,1
	Ni^{2+}	12,8	14,2	0,89	70	0,05 NNH_3	15,2	15,6
Alanine	Cu^{2+}	10,6	9,2	1,15	80	0,1 N NH_3	13,5	10,9
	Ni^{2+}	13,1	11,7	1,11	60	0,05 N NH_3	14,6	14,8
Leucine	Cu^{2+}	26,4	36,8	0,72	190	0,1 N NH_3	18,1	18,3
	Ni^{2+}	21,9	28.9	0,76	160	0,05N NH_3	19,0	23,8
Threonine	Cu^{2+}	5,3	5,8	0,92	70	0,1 N NH_3	17,9	18,1
	Ni^{2+}	12,5	17,3	0,73	180	H_2O	15,4	16,0
Phenylalanine	Cu^{2+}	28,8	52,5	0,55	350	0,1 N NH_3	11,3	12,2
	Ni^{2+}	40,0	25,1	1,59	270	0,05 N NH_3	15,4	14,5
Histidine	Cu^{2+}	9,2	7,4	1,25	130	0,1 N NH_3	39,6	39,3
	Ni^{2+}	4,9	12,2	0,39	560	H_2O	42,1	51,3
Methionine	Cu^{2+}	9,6	11,6	0,83	160	0,1 N NH_3	14,9	15,1
	Ni^{2+}	16,8	19,2	0,88	70	0,05N NH_3	14,1	14,8

Note. V_L and V_D are the dimensionless ratios V_L/V_o and V_D/V_o, where V_o is the free volume of the column.

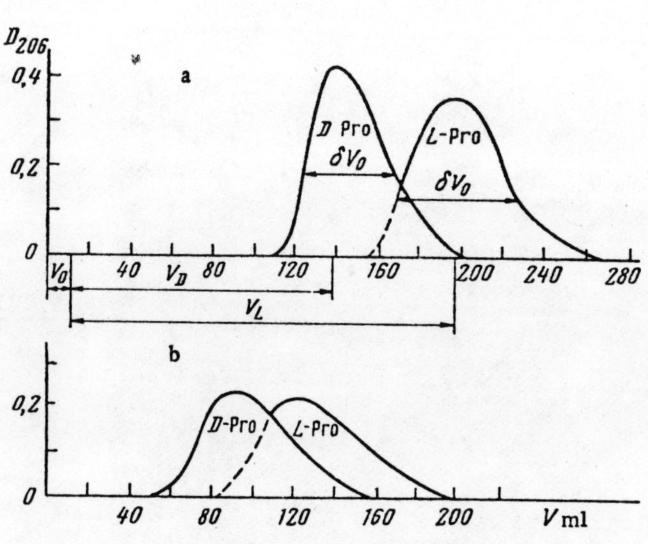

Fig. 1. Elution curves of the proline enantiomers: a) on the sorbent in the copper form; eluent 0.1 N NH_3; b) on the sorbent in the nickel form; eluent 0.05 N NH_3.

I.A. Yamskov, B.B. Berezin, V.E. Tikhonov and V.A. Davankov, Bioorgan. Khim., 4, 149 (1978) continued.

EXPERIMENTAL

R-1,2-Propylenediamine was obtained by the method of Dwyer et al. [7]. Yield 50%. Optical purity 95.0%.

R-1,8-Dicyano-4-methyl-3,6-diazaoctane was obtained by the method of DeHayes and Busch [8]. Yield 54%, bp 195-198°C/1 mm.

Synthesis of the Sorbent. A mixture of 11 g of the chloromethylated copolymer (22% of chlorine, 7 mole % of cross-linked agent — p,p'-xylylene dichloride), 20 g (0.11 mole) of R-1,8-dicyano-4-methyl-3,6-diazaoctane, 3.2 g (0.019 mole) of KI, and 13 g (0.15 mole) of $NaHCO_3$ was suspended in a mixture of dioxane (120 ml) and methanol (20 ml) and heated at 60°C for 50 h. The polymer was washed with water and with methanol. The nitrogen content of the product was 9.97%. To hydrolyze the nitrile groups, the polymer was boiled in 75 ml of 6 N HCl for 20 h. The nitrogen content after hydrolysis was 5.0% and the analytical capacity of the sorbent was 1.8 mmole of SL/g.

The swellability of the sorbent was determined by the gravimetric method [9].

Ligand-exchange chromatography was performed in columns with dimensions of 1 × 20 cm; the volume of the column filled with sorbent was 17 cm^3, corresponding to 6-7 g of dry sorbent. The volume rate of elution was 10 ml/h. The sorbent was charged with Cu^{2+} ions by keeping it in a 0.02 N solution of $CuCl_2 \cdot 2H_2O$ in 0.5 N NH_3 for 3 h. The sorbent was charged with Ni^{2+} ions by keeping it in a 0.015 M solution of $NiCl_2 \cdot 6H_2O$ in 0.5 N NH_3 for 3 h. The amount of metal bound to the ion-exchange resin was determined by complexometric titration with complexone III in the presence of murexide [10]; the ratio of the stationary ligand to metal for Cu^{2+} was 2:1 and for Ni^{2+} 1.5:1. Chromatography was carried out by adding solutions of the L and D isomers of amino acids to the column alternately (~2 mg). The eluent used was 0.1 N NH_3 containing $2 \cdot 10^{-5}$ M $CuCl_2 \cdot 2H_2O$ in order to compensate for the copper washed out, 0.05 N NH_3 containing $2 \cdot 10^{-6}$ M $NiCl_2 \cdot 6H_2O$, or H_2O. The optical densities of the fractions were measured at 206 nm on a Spectronom-204 spectrophotometer (Hungary). In the chromatography of methionine, histidine, and threonine on the sorbent in the copper form and of histidine on the sorbent in the Ni^{2+} form fractions were collected every 15 min, and in all the other cases every 50 min.

Typical elution curves are shown in Fig. 1.

The absence of a blue coloration of the fractions in the chromatography of the aliphati amino acids shows the fairly high strength of binding of the Cu(II) and Ni(II) with the SLs, appreciable entrainment of the metal being observed only in the case of histidine and threonine.

7. F. Dwyer, E. Garvan, and A. Shulman, J. Amer. Chem. Soc., 81, 290 (1959).
8. J. DeHayes and D. Busch, Inorg. Chem., 12, 2010 (1973).
9. S. V. Rogozhin, V. A. Davankov, S. G. Vyrbanov, and V. V. Korshak, Vysokomol. Soedin., 10A, 1277 (1968).
10. G. Schwartzenbach, Die Komplexometrische Titration 5th ed., Ferdinand Enke, Stuttgart (1965) [Russian translation, Goskhimizdat, Moscow (1968), p. 107] [2nd English ed., Methuen, London (1969)].

Reference

G. Gübitz, W. Jellenz, G. Löfler and W. Santi, J. High Resolut. Chromatogr. & Chromatogr. Comm., 2, 145 (1979).

Summary

A chiral stationary phase was prepared from silica gel which was reacted first with 3-glycidoxy propyltrimethoxysilane and then bonded with L-proline which was subsequently complexed with Cu^{++}.

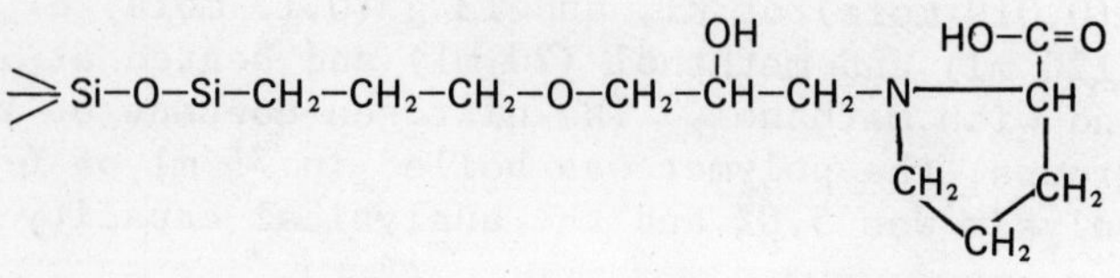

Complete separation of DL-tryptophane and DL-tyrosine was achieved in relatively short times on 10 cm. columns using this adsorbent. Experimental details and results follow:

Table 1

Separation of DL-tryptophane and DL-tyrosine

	K'_1	K'_2	α	R_s
DL-tryptophane	16.3	53	3.2	2.98
DL-tyrosine	18.5	50	2.1	1.40

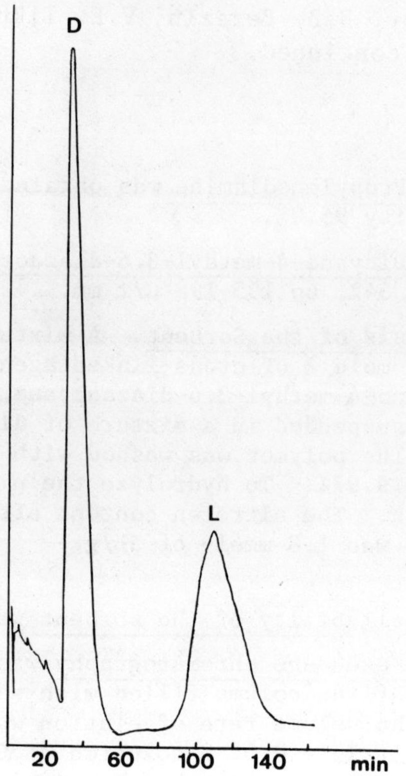

Figure 1

Separation of DL-tryptophane
Mobile phase: 0.05 M phosphate buffer
Flow rate: 0.8 ml/min.
Detection: UV 280 nm

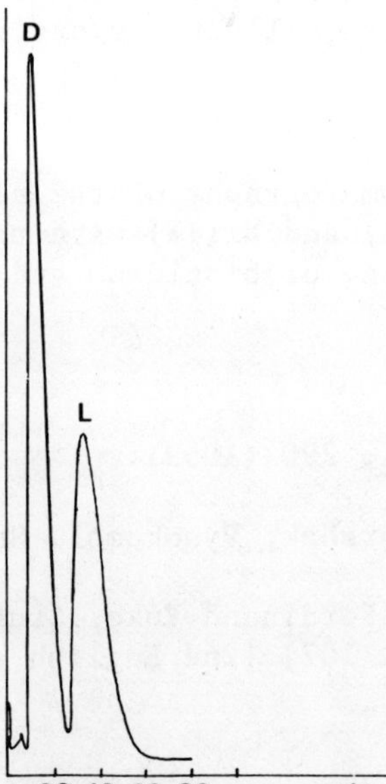

Figure 3

Separation of DL-tryptophane
Mobile phase: 0.6 M phosphate buffer
Flow rate: 1 ml/min.
Detection: UV 280 nm

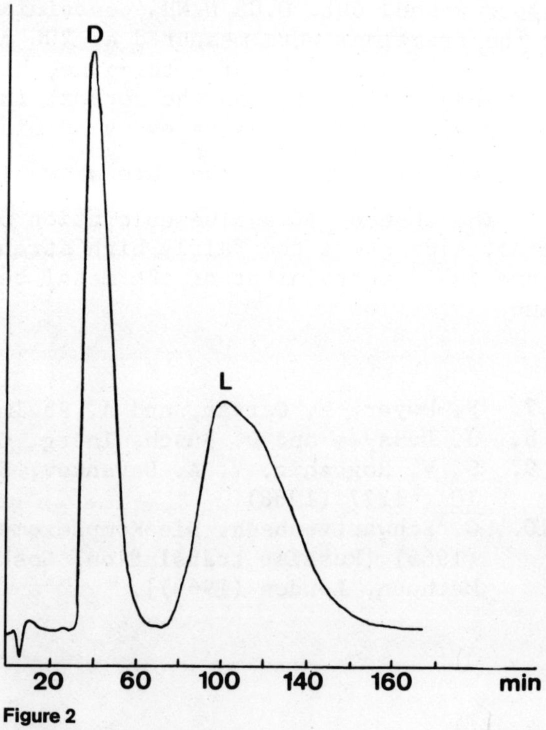

Figure 2

Separation of DL-tyrosine
Mobile phase: 0.06 M phosphate buffer
Flow rate: 0.5 ml/min.
Detection: UV 280 nm

Reference

J. Jozefonvicz, D. Muller and M.A. Petit, J. Chem. Soc., Dalton, 76 (1980).

Summary

Chromatographic elutions of DL-phenylalanine, D,L-proline and D,L-histidine were made on a styrene-divinyl benzene copolymer to which had been grafted L-proline which was complexed with Cu^{++}. The D,L-phenylalanine enantiomers were not separated while D,L-proline and D,L-histidine were completely resolved. It was found that D-proline had a higher retention time than L-proline (α value of 2.3). A reverse elution order was observed for histidine with an α value of 2.9. The experimental details and results follow:

EXPERIMENTAL

Reagents.—The α-amino-acids were obtained from Fluka (puriss grade). The styrene–divinylbenzene copolymer with 1% crosslinkage (Biobeads S-X1, 200—400 mesh) was from Bio.rad Labs. The resin was treated as previously described[9] so that it contained fixed L-proline ligands complexed by copper(II).

The amount of fixed L-proline ligands in the asymmetric resin was determined by potentiometric titration. A limited capacity value of 1.53 milliequivalents of L-proline per gram of dry resin was chosen so that very few broken beads were produced. Copper(II) ions were chelated to the resin to an extent of 90% of the theoretical capacity calculated on the basis of one copper(II) ion bound to two fixed L-proline ligands.

Chromatographic Experiments.—The liquid chromatography system consisted of a Waters Assoc. 6 000 A pump and U6K injector. Two detection cells were kept at 25 °C and used in series so that both the differential refractive index and the optical rotation of the eluate could be recorded. The resin was packed in a column of length 220 mm and internal diameter 7.4 mm.

[9] M. A. Petit and J. Jozefonvicz, *J. Appl. Polymer Sci.*, 1977, 2589.

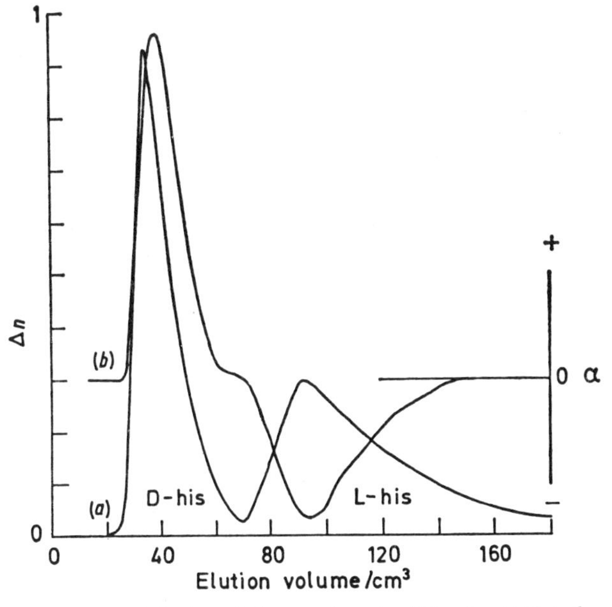

FIGURE 2 Elution of 20 mg of D,L-histidine by 0.98 mol dm^{-3} NH_3 at a flow rate of 30 cm^3 h^{-1}. Details as in Figure 1

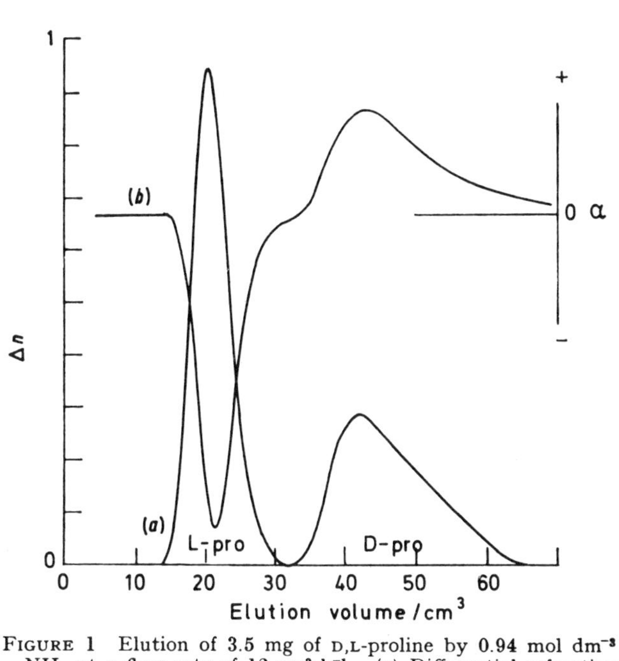

FIGURE 1 Elution of 3.5 mg of D,L-proline by 0.94 mol dm^{-3} NH_3 at a flow rate of 12 cm^3 h^{-1}. (*a*) Differential refractive index, Δ*n*; (*b*) rotation power α (both in arbitrary units)

Reference

D. Muller, J. Jozefonvicz and M.A. Petit, J. Inorg. Nucl. Chem., 42, 1083 (1980).

Summary

Resolution of D,L-valine, D,L-phenylalanine and D,L-proline were achieved by ligand exchange chromatography on a polyacrylamide resin onto which was grafted L-proline which was complexed with Cu^{++}. The experimental details and results follow:

MATERIALS AND METHODS

PAAPRO resin. The asymmetric PAAPRO resin was prepared according to a previously described method[16], the starting matrix was a "Biogel P4" (minus 400 mesh) from BIORAD LAB. An acidimetric titration revealed a capacity of 1.53 meq. of L-proline per g of dry resin. The resin was suspended in water in the presence of 80% of the theoretical amount of copper(II) which can be complexed on the basis of one copper(II) for two L-proline residues. The resin obtained had the following properties: bead size, mainly 25 μm; porosity, 0.50 cm^3/cm^3 of swollen gel.

Chromatographic system. The liquid chromatography system consisted of a 6000 A pump and U6K injector "Waters Assoc.". Two detection cells were kept at 25°C and used in series so that both the differential refractive index and the optical rotation of the eluate could be recorded. The PAAPRO resin was packed in a column of length 220 mm and internal diameter 7.4 mm. Samples of 1 to 5 mg of D,L-valine, D,L-phenylalanine or D,L-proline were injected and eluted with water at room temperature at a flow rate of 0.5 ml per min.

Table 1. Capacity factors, *k'*, of each enantiomer of valine, phenylalanine and proline

SUPPORT	VALINE		PHENYLALANINE		PROLINE	
	D	L	D	L	D	L
PAAPRO resin	0.26	0.41	1.15	2.08	0.23	0.23
25 microns	two peaks		two peaks		partial résolution	
1.53 meq/g	S* = 1.6		S = 1.8		S = 1	
	log S = 0.20		log S = 0.25		log S = 0	
PAAPRO resin	0.79	1.50	4.30	9.80	1.10	0.72
previous work (8)	two peaks		two peaks			
10-15 microns	S* = 1.9		S = 2.3		S = 0.65	
2 meq/g	log S = 0.28		log S = 0.36		Log S = - 0.19	

* S : Selectivity is the ratio of capacity factors k'_L / k'_D.

16. B. Lefebvre, *Thesis Univ.* P. and M. Curie (*Paris VI*), 29/6/1977.

Reference
V.A. Davankov and A.A. Kurganov, Chromatographia, 13, 339 (1980).

Summary
The authors describe a chiral resin (crosslinked polystyrene with covalently bonded (R)-N,N-dibenzyl-1,2-propanediamine in the form of a cupric complex) which displayed high enantioselectivity in ligand-exchange chromatography of unmodified α-amino acids. A microbore column (100 mm. X 1 mm. i.d.) packed with angular particles of d_p= 5-10μm was used to resolve a mixture of three racemic α-amino acids. Experimental conditions and results follow:

The first one includes sorbents with the resolving chiral ligand covalently fixed onto the stationary phase [1,3,5–8]. In this case, separation of enantiomers of the mobile phase ligands results from the enantioselectivity in formation of the mixed-ligand sorption complexes comprising of the chiral fixed ligand, metal ion and the mobile ligand. The separation selectivity, α (the ratio of the capacity factors, k′, of the two enantiomers), can approach its limiting value given by the ratio of the thermodynamic stability constants of the two diastereomeric mixed-ligand sorption complexes [9]. The less retained isomer forms sorption complexes of lower stability.

The second group comprises of systems where the sorbent itself is not chiral, but the mobile phase contains a complexing metal ion and a chiral ligand (besides the enantiomers to be resolved).

Experimental

The synthesis of the asymmetric resin has been described earlier [14]. The resin contained 2.7 mmole of fixed ligands (R)-N′, N′-dibenzyl-1,2-propanediamine (I) per g substance. The polymer matrix was a "macronet isoporous" styrene copolymer with 0.3% divinylbenzene, containing 5 mole-% of additional cross-links of type (II).

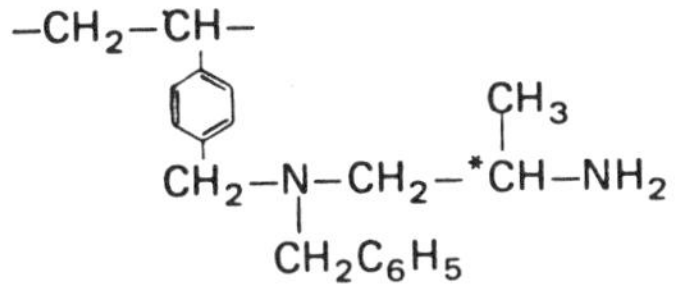

I

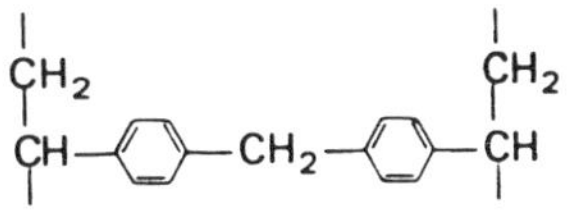

II

The resin beads were crushed in a mortar and the resulting irregular-shape particles fractionated by sedimentation. The resin suspension tends to flocculation, especially in the basic pH range, less in neutral media. Therefore the sedimentation was carried out in a 2N HCl solution and the fraction with d_p = 7.5 ± 2.5 μm was used for the chromatographic experiments.

Glass microcolumns (100 mm x 1 mm i.d.) were packed upwards at constant flow of 1 cm^3/min with a dilute suspension of the resin. The slurry liquid employed was identical with the eluent: 0.25 – 1 M sodium acetate solution containing $1.5 \cdot 10^{-3}$ M copper(II) acetate and adjusted to the desired pH value with acetic acid.

A Microcolumn Liquid Chromatograph Model 1305 (USSR) was used, fitted with a variable wavelength UV detector. The columns were operated at room temperature and at a flow rate of 1 cm^3/h. The injection volume was 8 mm^3 containing ca. 0.8 μg amino acid. Solutes were detected at 260 nm.

Pure water was used to mark the t_0 time. The enantioselectivity of the column was expressed as $\alpha = k'_L/k'_D$ where k'_L and k'_D are the capacity factors of the L-enantiomer and D-enantiomer, respectively.

References

[1] *V.A. Davankov, Yu.A. Zolotarev, A.A. Kurganov*, J. Liquid Chromatogr. **2**, 1191 (1979).

[2] *V.A. Davankov* in *J.C. Giddings, E. Grushka*, eds., "Advances in Chromatography", M. Dekker, Inc., New York, N.Y. 1980; Vol. 18, pp. 139–195.

[3] *S. V. Rogozhin, V.A. Davankov*, Ger. Pat. No. 1932190; C.A. **72**, 90875C (1970).

[4] *K. Bernauer*, Swiss Pat. No. 509239; C.A. **76**, 60602 (1972).

[5] *V.A. Davankov, Yu.A. Zolotarev*, J. Chromatogr. **155**, 285, 295, 303 (1978).

[6] *B. Lefebvre, R. Audebert, C. Quivoron*, J. Liquid Chromatogr. **1**, 761 (1978).

[7] *G. Gübitz, W. Jellenz, G. Löfler, W. Santi*, J. High Res. Chromatogr./Chromatogr. Commun. **2**, 145 (1979).

[8] *A. Foucault, M. Caude, L. Oliveros*, J. Chromatogr. **185**, 345 (1979).

[9] *V.A. Davankov, S.V. Rogozhin*, J. Chromatogr. **60**, 280 (1971).

[10] *J.N. LePage, W. Lindner, G. Davies, D.E. Seitz, B.L. Karger*, Anal. Chem. **51**, 433 (1979).

[11] *W. Lindner, J.N. LePage, G. Davies, D.E. Seitz, B.L. Karger*, J. Chromatogr. **185**, 323 (1979).

[12] *J. Gaal, J. Inczèdy*, Talanta **23**, 78 (1976).

[13] *P.E. Hare, E. Gil-Av*, Science **204**, 1226 (1979).

[14] *A. A. Kurganov, L. Ya. Zhuchkova, V. A. Davankov*, Makromol. Chem. **180**, 2101 (1979).

V.A. Davankov and A.A. Kurganov, Chromatographia, 13, 339 (1980) continued.

Table I. Retention and resolution parameters of amino acid enantiomers

Amino acid	k'_L	k'_D	α (L/D)	Eluent pH	Eluent sodium acetate mole
1. Pipecolinic Acid	1.19	0.83	1.43	6.0	0.25
2. Proline	0.87	0.41	2.11	5.7	0.25
3. Ornithine	~ 0.10	~ 0.10		5.5	0.25
4. Asparagine	1.99	1.40	1.42	–	–
5. Threonine	2.05	0.91	2.25	–	–
6. Alanine	0.56	0.39	1.43	5.2	0.25
7. α-Aminobutyric Acid	1.14	0.56	2.02	–	–
8. Valine	2.32	2.72	3.19	–	–
9. Leucine	3.23	1.59	2.03	–	–
10. Serine	1.09	0.68	1.60	–	–
11. Methionine	3.95	2.36	1.67	–	–
12. Norvaline	0.94	0.45	2.10	5.2	1.00
13. Isoleucine	2.24	1.40	1.60	5.0	1.00
14. Norleucine	2.40	1.18	2.03	–	–
15. Phenylglycine	3.41	1.68	2.03	–	–
16. β-Phenyl-α-alanine	10.68	5.58	1.90	–	–
17. α-Phenyl-α-alanine	3.95	1.50	2.63	–	–
18. β-Phenyl-β-alanine	0.74	0.74	1.00	–	–
19. Aspartic Acid	2.39	2.40	1.00	–	–

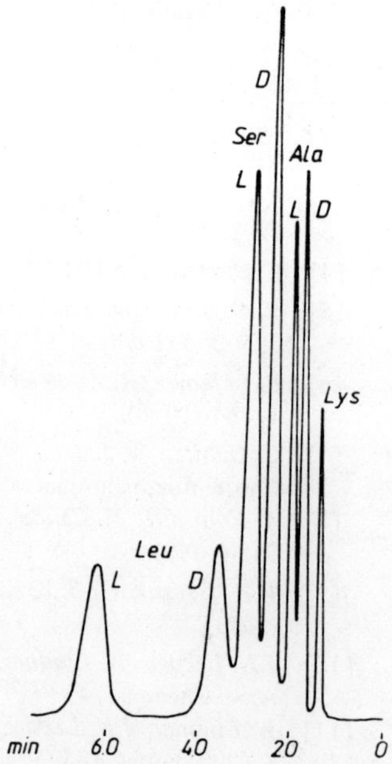

Fig. 1

Chromatogram of a mixture of racemic lysine, alanine, serine and leucine on a glass microcolumn (100 mm x 1 mm i.d.) packed with the chiral diamine resin.
Eluent: 0.25M sodium acetate + $1.5 \cdot 10^{-3}$M copper(II) acetate, pH 5.2, flow rate 1 cm^3/h, room temperature.

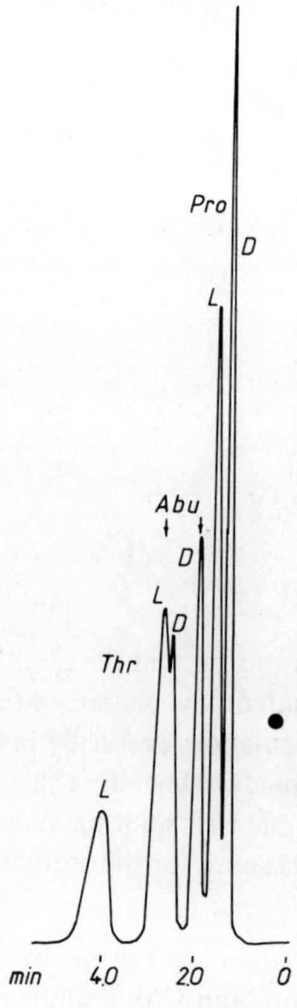

Fig. 2

- Chromatogram of a mixture of racemic proline, α-aminobutyric acid and threonine. Conditions as in Fig. 1.

Reference

V.A. Davankov, A.S. Bochkov, A.A. Kurganov, P. Roumeliotis, K.K. Unger, Chromatographia, 13, 677 (1980).

Summary

The authors describe the resolution of unmodified α-amino acid enantiomers by adsorbing N-alkyl-L-hydroxyprolines (where alkyl is n-C_7H_{15}-, n-$C_{10}H_{21}$ or n-($C_{16}H_{33}$-) onto the surface of a conventional reverse phase packing (LiChrosorb RP-18) and using a complexing metal-ion solution (copper acetate in methanol-water) as eluent. The factors controlling retention and enantioselectivity such as Cu^{++} concentration, pH of eluent, addition of ammonium acetate to eluent, effect of solvent variation and column temperature were studied. The extremely high enantioselectivity observed (α up to 16) is assumed to be caused by a three site sorbate-sorbent interaction involving bidentate coordination of two amino acids to a Cu^{++} ion and hydrophobic attractions between hydrocarbon side chains of amino acids and the n-octadecyl groups of the support. The efficiency and selectivity of the system permits resolution of up to 7 racemic α-amino acids within 35 minutes using a conventional HPLC apparatus. Experimental conditions and results follow:

2 Experimental

Columns, 100 x 4.2 mm, were packed with LiChrosorb® RP-18, dp = 5 μm (kindly supplied by E. Merck, Darmstadt, FRG) following the usual slurry technique. N-Heptyl-L-hydroxyproline (C_7-L-Hyp), N-decyl-L-hydroxyproline (C_{10}-L-Hyp) and N-hexadecyl-L-hydroxyproline (C_{16}-L-Hyp) were prepared by procedures which will be described elsewhere [11]. (The structure of L-hydroxyproline is indicated in Fig. 3.) The coating of the respective N-alkyl-L-Hyp on the reverse phase support was accomplished by forcing first 2 cm^3 of a solution of 100 mg N-alkyl-L-Hyp in methanol or methanol/water through the column followed by washing with 2–4 cm^3 concentrated solution of copper(II) acetate in methanol/water (15/85 v/v). To achieve an effective coating N-alkyl-L-Hyp was dissolved in the following solutions:

C_7-L-Hyp in methanol/water (40/60 v/v),
C_{10}-L-Hyp in methanol/water (20/80 v/v) and
C_{16}-L-Hyp in pure methanol.

The racemic α-amino acids from Serva, Heidelberg, FRG, are listed in Table I. All chemicals and solvents used were of reagent grade and supplied by E. Merck. Two liquid chromatographs were used, (1) a DuPont Model 830 fitted with a fixed wavelength UV detector of 254 nm and a Rheodyne injection system. Volume of the sample loop was 20 mm^3, (2) a Hewlett-Packard 1084 A fitted with a UV detector of 254 nm and an automatic injection device. Both UV detectors had a cell volume of 8 mm^3 Capacity factors k'_D and k'_L, respectively, were calculated based on a slightly modified eluent as t_0 marker, where k'_D and k'_L refer to the D and L enantiomer of the corresponding amino acid. Enantioselectivity was expressed by the ratio $\alpha = k'_D/k'_L$.

V.A. Davankov, A.S. Bochkov, A.A. Kurganov, P. Roumeliotis, K.K. Unger, Chromatographia, 13, 677 (1980) continued.

Table I. Representative capacity factors k'_L and k'_D and enantioselectivity α for amino acids on C_{16}-L-Hyp coated LiChrosorb® RP-18 column (100 x 4.2 mm); eluent 10^{-4} M $CuAc_2$ in methanol/water of 15/85 (v/v), column temperature 298 K

	Amino acid		k'_L	k'_D	α
Cysteic acid		$HO_3SCH_2CH(NH_2)COOH$	0	0	
Aspartic acid	Asp	$HOOCCH_2CH(NH_2)COOH$	0.08	0.10	1.17
Glutamic acid	Glu	$HOOC(CH_2)_2CH(NH_2)COOH$	0.13	0.17	1.33
Glycine	Gly	$CH_2(NH_2)COOH$	0.63		
Histidine*	His	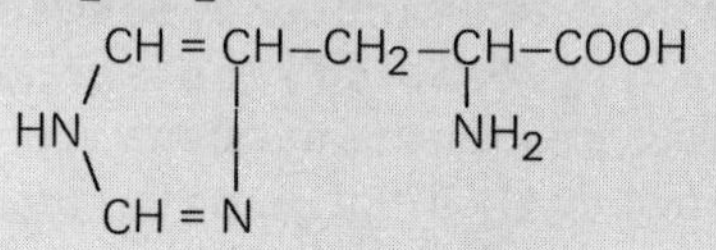	0.97	0.57	0.59
Alanine	Ala	$CH_3CH(NH_2)COOH$	0.58	0.91	1.56
Asparagine	Asn	$H_2NCOCH_2CH(NH_2)COOH$	0.66	0.66	1.00
Hydroxyproline	Hyp	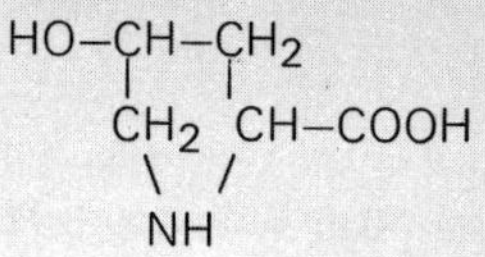	0.65		1.91
allo-Hydroxyproline	a-Hyp			1.24	
Glutamine	Gln	$H_2NCO(CH_2)_2CH(NH_2)COOH$	0.68	0.85	1.25
Serine	Ser	$HOCH_2CH(NH_2)COOH$	0.73	0.73	1.00
Methioninesulfone	Met(SO_2)	$CH_3SO_2(CH_2)_2CH(NH_2)COOH$	0.79	0.98	1.25
Proline	Pro	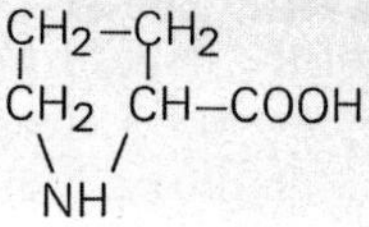	0.81	6.10	7.54
Citrulline	Cit	$H_2NCONH(CH_2)_3CH(NH_2)COOH$	0.82	1.06	1.29
Threonine	Thr	$CH_3CH(OH)CH(NH_2)COOH$	0.83	0.85	1.02
Aminobutyric acid	Abu	$CH_3CH_2CH(NH_2)COOH$	1.00	2.49	2.49
Valine	Val	$(CH_3)_2CHCH(NH_2)COOH$	1.63	7.42	4.55
3,4-Dihydroxy-phenylalanine	DOPA	$(HO)_2C_6H_3CH_2CH(NH_2)COOH$	1.94	4.51	2.32
Lysine	Lys	$H_2N(CH_2)_4CH(NH_2)COOH$	2.24	–	–
Norvaline	Nval	$CH_3(CH_2)_2CH(NH_2)COOH$	2.33	7.94	3.41
Tyrosine	Tyr	$HOC_6H_4CH_2CH(NH_2)COOH$	2.51	7.01	2.79
Methionine	Met	$CH_3S(CH_2)_2CH(NH_2)COOH$	2.54	5.06	1.99
Arginine	Arg	$H_2NC(NH)NH(CH_2)_3CH(NH_2)COOH$	2.97	3.67	1.24
Ornitine	Orn	$H_2N(CH_2)_3CH(NH_2)COOH$	3.00	3.00	1.00
Isoleucine	Ileu	$CH_3CH_2CH(CH_3)CH(NH_2)COOH$	3.18	–	
allo-Isoleucine	a-Ileu		–	18.92	5.95
Leucine	Leu	$(CH_3)_2CHCH_2CH(NH_2)COOH$	5.01	17.82	3.56
Norleucine	Nleu	$CH_3(CH_2)_3CH(NH_2)COOH$	6.25	25.05	4.01
Ethionine	Eth	$CH_3CH_2S(CH_2)_2CH(NH_2)COOH$	6.57	18.15	2.76
Phenylalanine	Phe	$C_6H_5CH_2CH(NH_2)COOH$	10.33	38.30	3.71
Tryptophane	Trp	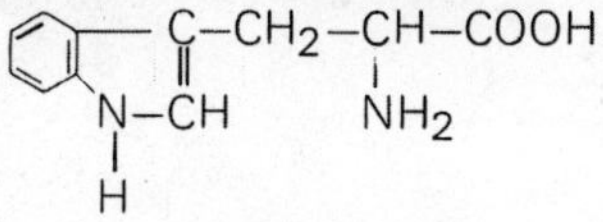	21.52	54.22	2.52

* D-Histidine eluates ahead of L-Histidine.

V.A. Davankov, A.S. Bochkov, A.A. Kurganov, P. Roumeliotis, K.K. Unger, Chromatographia, 13, 677 (1980) continued.

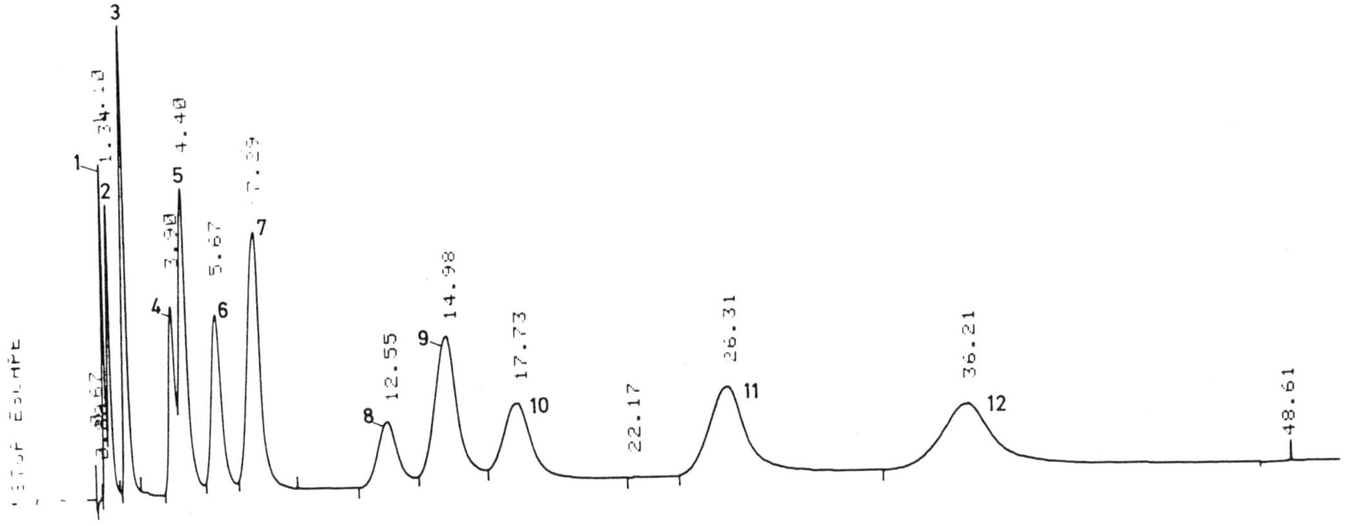

Fig. 1

- Separation of 6 racemic α-amino acids on C_{16}-L-Hyp coated LiChrosorb RP-18 5μm column (100 x 4.2 mm).

Conditions:
eluent: methanol/water of 15/85 (v/v), 10^{-4} M $CuAc_2$, pH 5.0; flow rate: 2 cm^3/min; column temperature: 293 K; chromatograph: DuPont Model 830; detection: UV 254 nm; elution sequence: 1 L-Ala, 2 D-Ala, 3 L-Nval, 4 L-Leu, 5 L-Nleu, 6 D-Nval, 7 L-Phe, 8 D-Leu, 9 L-Trp, 10 D-Nleu, 11 D-Phe, 12 D-Trp.

The additional numbers in the chromatogram indicate the retention time in minutes.

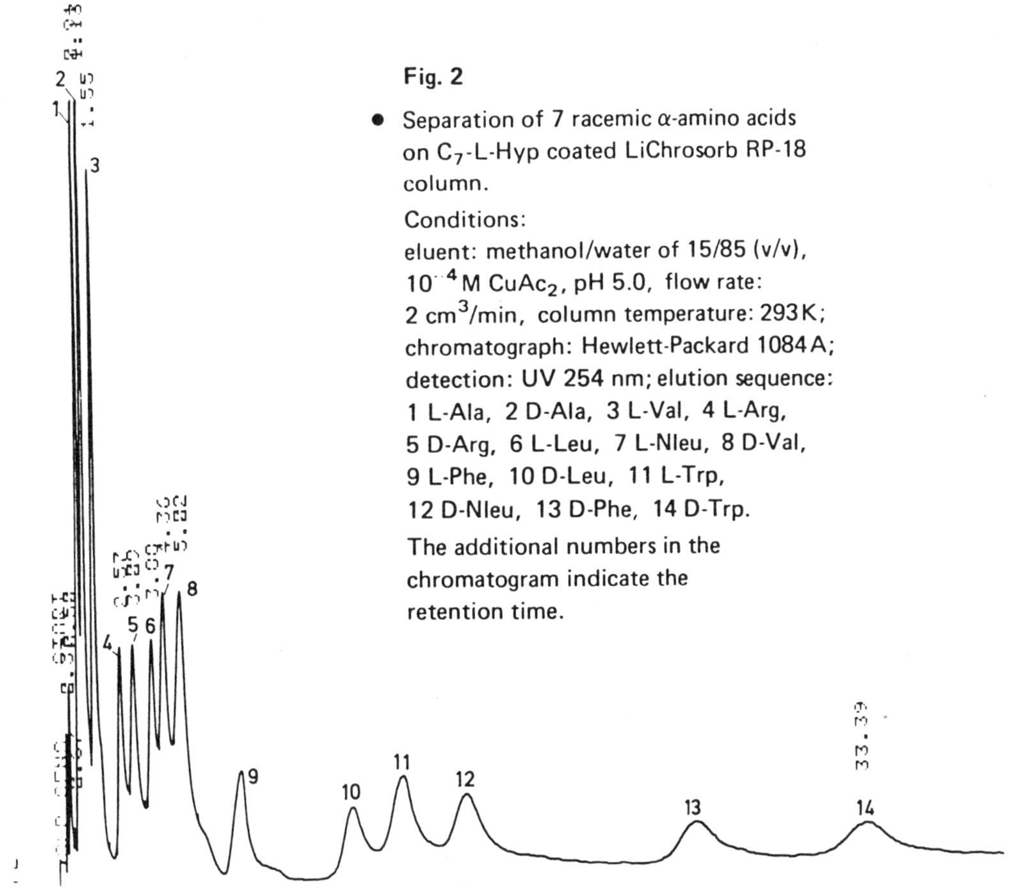

Fig. 2

- Separation of 7 racemic α-amino acids on C_7-L-Hyp coated LiChrosorb RP-18 column.

Conditions:
eluent: methanol/water of 15/85 (v/v), 10^{-4} M $CuAc_2$, pH 5.0, flow rate: 2 cm^3/min, column temperature: 293 K; chromatograph: Hewlett-Packard 1084 A; detection: UV 254 nm; elution sequence: 1 L-Ala, 2 D-Ala, 3 L-Val, 4 L-Arg, 5 D-Arg, 6 L-Leu, 7 L-Nleu, 8 D-Val, 9 L-Phe, 10 D-Leu, 11 L-Trp, 12 D-Nleu, 13 D-Phe, 14 D-Trp.

The additional numbers in the chromatogram indicate the retention time.

Reference

K. Sugden, C. Hunter and G. Lloyd-Jones, J. Chromatogr., 192, 228 (1980).

Summary

Resolution of DL-proline was achieved by HPLC on an adsorbent prepared by reaction of silica gel with 3-chloropropyltrichlorsilane followed by reaction with L-proline. The L-proline was complexed with Cu^{++}.

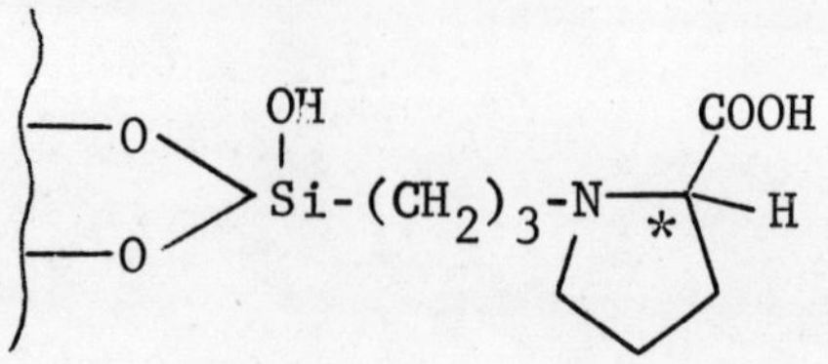

Complete resolution of DL-proline and DL-3,3-dimethylproline and partial resolution of DL-phenylalanine have been achieved. Histidine, alanine and glutamic acid were not resolved. The experimental details and results follow:

Preparation of the chiral stationary phase

LiChrosorb SI 60 (5 μm silica gel) (BDH, Poole, Great Britain) was refluxed with 2 *M* hydrochloric acid for 4 h, filtered, washed with water and acetone and dried in an oven at 110° for 16 h. The acid-washed material (10 g) was suspended in dry dioxane (200 ml) and 3-chloropropyltrichlorosilane (4 ml) was added. The mixture was refluxed for 4 h, filtered, washed with dioxane, water and acetone and dried on a water pump. The silanized silica gel was suspended in chloroform–methanol (85:15) (200 ml) containing L-proline (3 g), potassium iodide (1 g) and diisopropylethylamine (2.8 ml). The mixture was refluxed for 17 h, filtered, washed with methanol and acetone and dried on a water pump.

Column

The chiral phase was packed, as a methanol slurry, into a 25 × 0.46 cm I.D. stainless-steel tube using a Magnus P5000 Slurry Packing Unit (Magnus Scientific, Sandbach, Great Britain). The copper(II)–proline complex was formed *in situ* by eluting the column with a mobile phase of 1 m*M* copper(II) acetate.

Apparatus

A Waters Model 6000A constant flow pump (Waters Assoc., Northwich, Great Britain) was used to provide mobile phase flow and an ACS ultraviolet detector model 750/11 (Applied Chromatography System, Luton, Great Britain), fitted with a 240 nm filter, was employed to monitor column eluent.

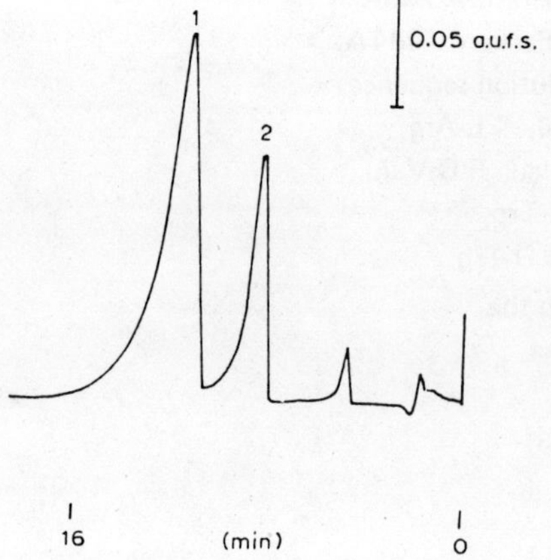

Fig. 1. Separation of D-proline (1) and L-proline (2). Column, copper (II) proline complex bound to LiChrosorb 5 μm silica gel, 25 × 0.46 cm I.D. Mobile phase, 1 m*M* copper(II) acetate (pH 4.6) delivered at 3 ml min^{-1}. Detection, UV at 240 nm.

Reference
J. Boue', R. Audebert and C. Quivoron, J. Chromatog., 204, 185 (1981).

Summary
A chiral polymer obtained by treatment of a linear polyacrylamide with L-proline in the presence of formaldehyde (see below) was adsorbed on silica beads. The adsorbent was complexed with Cu^{++} and used for the direct resolution of α-amino acids by ligand exchange chromatography.

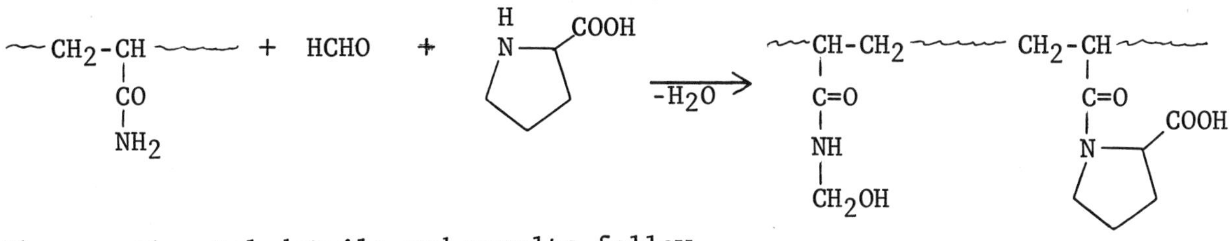

The experimental details and results follow.

Stationary phase

To 7 g of polyacrylamide ($\overline{M}_n$ = 23,000) dissolved in 50 ml of water, were added successively the following reagents: 0.68 g of potassium hydroxide (in 10 ml of water); 4.9 g of formaldehyde (in the form of polyoxymethylene) and 2.38 g of L-proline. The mixture was stirred for 1.5 h at room temperature and finally neutralized by hydrochloric acid. The capacity in proline was obtained by titration of this purified polymer. We think that the crude reaction mixture may be used directly (after neutralization) for the coating of the silica beads.

These conditions yield a capacity for proline of $x = 0.86$ mequiv./g. By increasing the concentration of the reactants and the reaction time, polymers with capacities in the range of 0–4.2 mequiv./g may be obtained (*i.e.*, *p* values between 0 and 0.90)[6].

Packing material

The polymers obtained were adsorbed on mineral beads. LiChrosorb (E. Marck, Darmstadt, G.F.R.) and Spherosil (Rhône Poulenc, Paris, France) were tested. The best results were obtained with silica Spherosil XOA 600 (particle diameter 5–7 μm).

For a 15-cm column, 400 mg of polymer (dissolved in 15 ml of water) were used. To this solution were added 2 g of silica beads (in suspension in 10 ml of water) and the mixture was stirred for 15 min. The unadsorbed polymer was removed by filtration of the beads, and by washing them with water on the filter. The packing was then complexed by stirring with a large excess of cupric ions in a buffer (generally acetate). After filtration and washing with water (pH 6–7) the stationary phase is ready to be packed.

The degree of loading of the beads can be deduced from a titration of the non-adsorbed polymer or from the capacity for cupric ions. Saturation in Cu(II) ($r = 0.5$) was obtained with a buffer of pH > 5[5], typically, after contact with Cu(II) and glutarate buffer (pH 5.4). The beads were washed with water (pH = 6–7), the Cu^{2+} was displaced in acid medium and titrated (spectrophotometric titration with diethyldithiocarbamate at 450 nm gives good results).

Packing and chromatographic apparatus

The columns were packed in water (2 g of packing per 20 cm³ of water) under pressure (400 bars) with an Haskel MCP 110 pump. A Waters ALC 201 chromatograph with an U6 K injector, R 401 refractometer, a MC 440 spectrophotometer and a Perkin-Elmer 241 MC polarimeter was used.

5 B. Lefebvre, R. Audebert and C. Quivoron, *J. Liquid Chromatogr.*, 1 (1978) 761.
6 J. Boué, *Thesis University P. and M. Curie*, Paris, 1980.

J. Boue', R. Audebert and C. Quivoron, J. Chromatog., 204, 185 (1981) (continued).

TABLE I

CAPACITY FACTORS, k', AND SELECTIVITY FACTORS, α, FOR SOME SOLUTES

Column: 25 × 0.48 cm I.D.; $r = 0.4$; $x = 0.86$ mequiv./g. Eluent: 0.1 M KNO_3 with $0.2 \cdot 10^{-4} M$ Cu(II); flow-rate, 0.4 ml/min.

Solute (D,L *form*)	*Amount injected**	k'_D	k'_L	α
Alanine	$\approx 10^{-4}$g	≈ 1.80	≈ 1.80	≈ 1 (but > 1)
Aminobutyric acid	$\approx 10^{-3}$g	1.49	1.94	1.25
Norvaline	10 μl	1.80	2.34	1.30
Norleucine	5 μl	3.94	4.81	1.20
Valine	10 μl $\approx 10^{-3}$g	1.76	3.09	1.75
Isoleucine	5 μl	2.84	4.37	1.55
Proline	$\approx 10^{-3}$g	3.20	2.06	0.70
Phenylalanine	10 μl $\approx 10^{-4}$g	6.10	12.35	2.00
Tyrosine	10 μl	16.31	36.27	2.20
Tryptophan	50 μl	15.73	38.28	2.45
Asparagine	10 μl	3.29	4.16	1.25
Serine	10 μl $\approx 5 \cdot 10^{-4}$g	2.27	4.20	1.85
Threonine	3 μl	2.80	5.31	1.90

* All volumes were of saturated solutions.

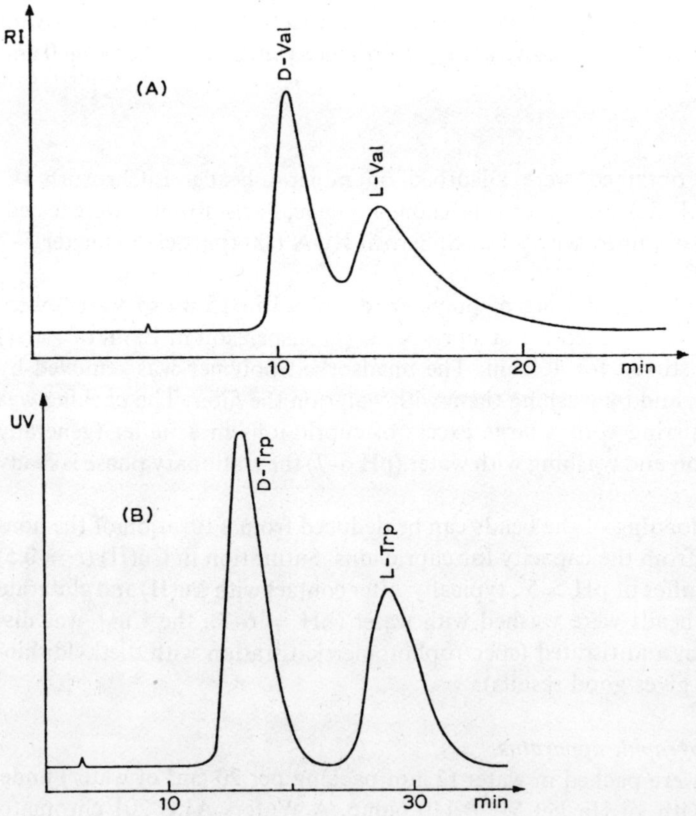

Fig. 3. Chromatograms of amino acids. (A), Column 10 × 0.48 cm I.D., eluent 0.5 ml/min water, $r = 0.3$, $x = 1.8$ mequiv./g, injection of 3 μl of a saturated water solution of D,L-valine, refractive index (RI) detection; (B), column as in (A), eluent 0.1 M KNO_3 (1 ml/min), $r = 0.4$, $x = 0.56$ mequiv./g, injection of 0.1 μl of a saturated water solution of D,L-tryptophan, UV detection.

Reference
Y.A. Zolotarev, N.F. Myasoedov, V.I. Penkina, O.R. Petrenik and V.A. Davankov, J. Chromatogr., 207, 63 (1981).

Summary
The authors presented data on the enantioselectivity and efficiency of ligand-exchange chromatographic resolution of DL-leucine using an asymmetric resin with L-hydroxyproline groups saturated with Cu^{++}. Experimental conditions and results follow:

An asymmetric sorbent with L-hydroxyproline groups was obtained by amination of the chloromethylated macronet polystyrene matrix with methyl L-hydroxyprolinate hydrochloride as described in ref. 8. The sorbent capacity was 3.86 mmol/g, its swelling capacity in water was 250% and the particle size was *ca.* 50 μm. A styrene copolymer with 0.7% divinylbenzene containing 5.3% of additional cross-links of the diphenylmethylene type[6] was used as a matrix.

Sorbent saturated to the required degree with Cu^{2+} (ref. 5) was suspended in 0.1 *N* NH_4OH and transferred into a column. Samples of L-leucine and L,D-leucine in the form of 5% solutions were introduced into the column by a microsyringe and eluted by 0.1–1.0 *N* NH_4OH at a flow-rate of 5–50 ml/h. A liquid-flow spectrophotometer was used as detector. Chromatographic studies were conducted with the aid of the LKB Vario Perpex peristaltic pump.

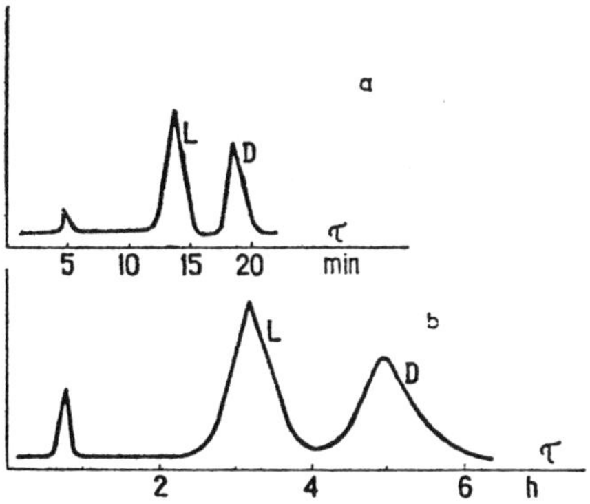

Fig. 7. Chromatography of L,D-leucine on a sorbent with L-hydroxyproline groups, satureted by Cu^{2+}. a, Particle size 10 μm, column 100 × 2 mm, sample 0.01 mg L,D-leucine, eluent 0.2 *N* NH_4OH, flow-rate 5 ml/h. b, Particle size 50 μm, column 340 × 10 mm, sample 20 mg L,D-leucine, eluent 0.1 *N* NH_4OH, flow-rate 60 ml/h.

5 V. A. Davankov, Yu. A. Zolotarev and A. B. Tevlin, *Bioorg. Khum.*, 4 (1978) 1164.

8 Yu. A. Zolotarev, A. A. Kurganov and V. A. Davankov, *Talanta*, 25 (1978) 493.

Reference

Yu. A. Zolotarev, N.F. Myasoedov, V.I. Penkina, I.N. Dostovalov, O.V. Petrenik and V.A. Davankov, J. Chromatog., 207, 231 (1981).

Summary

Racemic multiple tritiated valine, histidine and alanine with high specific activities were resolved into enantiomers using ligand-exchange chromatography on Cu^{++} saturated L-hydroxyproline modified polystyrene (I) and L-phenylalanine modified polyacrylamide (II). These two resins allow the resolution of all common amino acids on a preparative scale and their optical and radiochemical purity to be established. The method does not require any chemical modification of the racemate to be resolved, does not impose any limitations on its specific activity and provides for the simultaneous radiochemical purifications of the enantiomers. Experimental details and results follow.

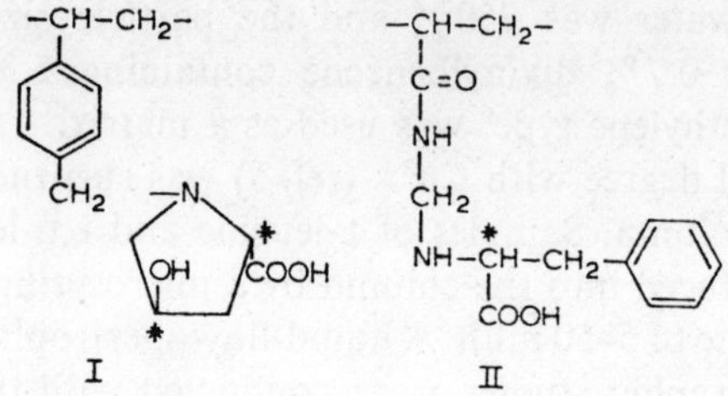

I II

EXPERIMENTAL

Sorbents

The synthesis of sorbent I by interaction of methyl L-hydroxyprolinate with chloromethylated cross-linked polystyrene was described earlier[3]. The starting copolymer contained 0.7% of divinylbenzene and was additionally cross-linked with monochlorodimethyl ether to give a total degree of cross-linking of 6 mol%. The water content of the swollen resin was 250% and the exchange capacity was 3.8 mmol of residues of L-hydroxyproline per gram of sorbent.

Sorbent II was obtained by treatment of Bio-Gel P-4 polyacrylamide beads (Serva, Heidelberg, G.F.R.)with formaldehyde and L-phenylalanine. The sorbent contained 1.4 mmol of groupings of L-phenylalanine per gram. The water uptake was 300%.

Before packing into columns, the sorbents were treated with an excess of copper(II)–ammonia solution and subsequently with a solution of potassium chloride in 1.0 *N* ammonia to achieve the desired content of Cu^{2+} ions in the sorbent.

Chromatography of racemates

The copper-loaded sorbents I and II suspended in 0.1 *N* ammonia or 1% ammonium phosphate solution (pH 9.2), respectively, were slurry-packed into glass columns and conditioned by passing the same eluents through them.

The racemic amino acids were introduced into the top of the column with the help of a micro-syringe. To detect the enantiomers resolved, the Radiochromatograph 2301 chromatographic system (U.S.S.R.) was used, equipped with a flow radioactivity detector cell of volume 170 μl and made of scintillating quartz. Another detector was a flow photometer operated at 210, 250 or 280 nm.

Isolation and characterization of enantiomers

Using the hydrolytical stable resin of type I and ammonia solutions as the eluent, the resolved amino acid enantiomers can be easily obtained by evaporation of the corresponding eluate fractions, which should be previously purified to remove trace amounts of Cu^{2+}. The purification consists in filtering the eluate through a small column (15 × 8 mm I.D.) with ANKB-50 chelating resin (polystyrene bearing iminodiacetate groups).

Yu. A. Zolotarev, N.F. Myasoedov, V.I. Penkina, I.N. Dostovalov and V.A. Davankov, J. Chromatog., 207, 231 (1981) (continued).

To obtain directly D- and L-enantiomers of [^{3}H]histidine in a copper-free state, the lower part (20 mm) of the chromatographic column was packed with copper-free resin I and the remainder of the resin (100 mm) was saturated with Cu^{2+} ions to 45% of the theoretical capacity. In contrast to many other amino acids, histidine enantiomers can be detected photometrically without being complexed with Cu^{2+}.

With resin II and phosphate-containing eluents, the fractions of resolved enantiomers have to be purified to remove mineral salts. Therefore, the enantiomers were sorbed on the Cu^{2+} form of the ANKB-50 iminodiacetate resin, washed with water and desorbed with 0.3 *N* ammonia solution.

The purity of the isolated enantiomers was tested by thin-layer chromatography (TLC) on Silufol UV-254 plates and by treatment with specific amino acid oxidases in a standard manner.

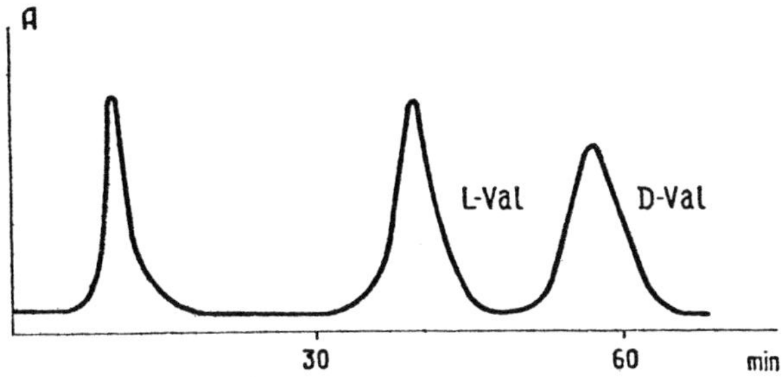

Fig. 1. Chromatography of DL-[^{3}H]valine (40 μg in 0.1 ml of water; activity $7.4 \cdot 10^8$ Bq; specific activity $2.1 \cdot 10^{12}$ Bq/mmol) on the L-hydroxyproline-containing resin I (particle diameter, d_p = 25–32 μm; saturation with Cu^{2+} 70%). Column, 300 × 4 mm I.D.; eluent, 0.15 *N* ammonia solution; flow-rate, 16 ml/h.

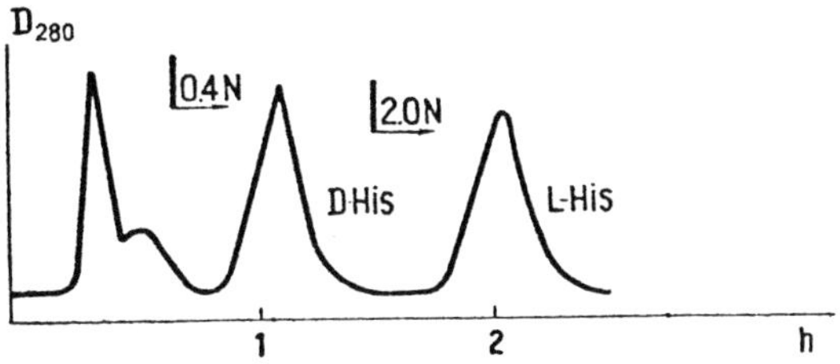

Fig. 2. Chromatography of DL-[^{3}H]histidine (500 μg in 0.1 ml of water; activity $7.4 \cdot 10^9$ Bq; specific activity $2.4 \cdot 10^{12}$ Bq/mmol) on the L-hydroproline-containing resin I (d_p = 25–32 μm; saturation with Cu^{2+} 45%). Column, 120 × 8 mm I.D. (lower 20 mm of the resin bed free of copper); eluent, 0.1, 0.4 and 2.0 *N* ammonia solution; flow-rate, 40 ml/h.

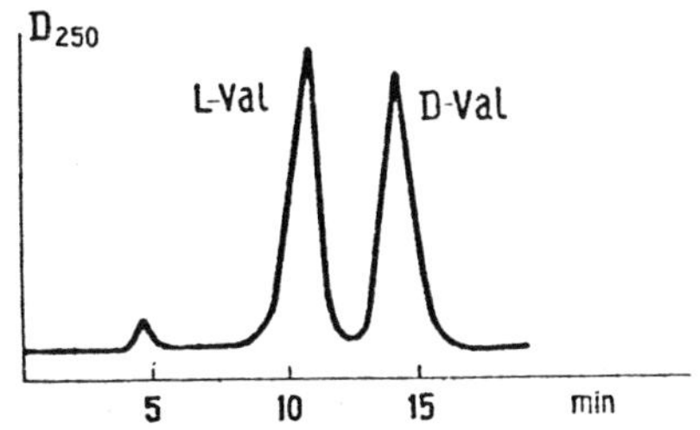

Fig. 3. Chromatography of DL-valine (15 μg) on the L-hydroproline-containing resin I ($d_p \approx$ 10 μm; saturation with Cu^{2+} 70%). Column, 100 × 2 mm I.D.; eluent, 0.25 *N* ammonia solution; flow-rate, 5 ml/h; pressure, 20 bar.

Yu. A. Zolotarev, N.F. Myasoedov, V.I. Penkina, I.N. Dostovalov and V.A. Davankov, J. Chromatog., 207, 231 (1981) (continued).

TABLE I PARAMETERS OF AMINO ACID ELUTION ON THE L-PHENYLALANINE-CONTAINING POLYACRYLAMIDE RESIN II SATURATED WITH Cu^{2+} IONS TO 60%

Eluent, 2% ammonium phosphate solution, pH 9.2. k' = Capacity factor; α = separation factor.

Amino acid	k'_L	k'_D	α
Aspartic acid	1.02	1.34	1.31
Glutamic acid	1.13	1.50	1.32
Asparagine	3.04	4.12	1.35
Glutamine	1.47	2.20	1.50
Ornithine	2.84	3.78	1.33
Lysine	6.85	9.34	1.36
Serine	2.04	2.67	1.31
Threonine	2.52	3.36	1.33
Methionine	3.15	4.98	1.58
Alanine	1.68	2.31	1.36
Valine	1.53	2.35	1.55
Leucine	2.29	3.26	1.42
Norleucine	2.33	3.68	1.58
Isoleucine	1.74	2.79	1.60
Proline	3.19	5.33	1.65
allo-Hydroxyproline	5.25	6.59	1.25
Tyrosine	5.17	7.58	1.37
Phenylglycine	1.51	2.54	1.66
Phenylalanine	3.61	4.85	1.34
Tryptophan	8.95	12.7	1.42

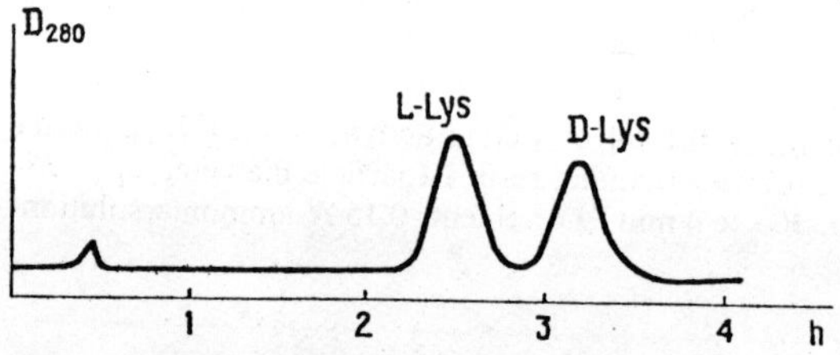

Fig. 4. Chromatography of DL-lysine (300 μg) on the L-phenylalanine-containing resin II ($d_p \leqslant 64$ μm; saturation with Cu^{2+} 60%). Column, 300 × 9 mm I.D.; eluent, 2% ammonium phosphate solution, pH 9.2; flow-rate, 30 ml/h.

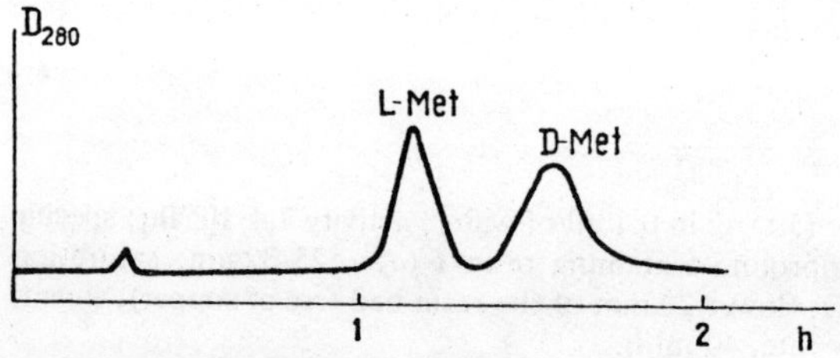

Fig. 5. Chromatography of DL-methionine (300 μg) on the L-phenylalanine-containing resin II ($d_p <$ 64 μm; saturation with Cu^{2+} 70%). Column, 190 × 8 mm I.D.; eluent, 2.5% ammonium phosphate solution, pH 9.2; flow-rate, 25 ml/h.

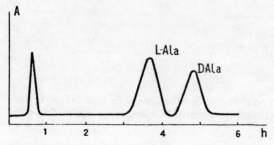

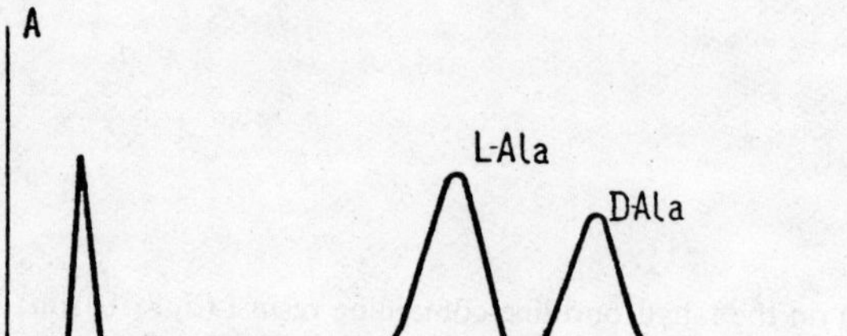

Fig. 6. Chromatography of DL-[^{3}H]alanine (315 μg in 0.1 ml of water; activity $5.5 \cdot 10^9$ Bq; specific activity $1.7 \cdot 10^{12}$ Bq/mmol) on the L-phenylalanine-containing resin II ($d_p < 64$ μm; saturation with Cu^{2+} 70%). Column, 300 × 9 mm I.D.; eluent, 0.1% ammonium phosphate solution, pH 9.2; flow-rate, 25 ml/h.

Reference

G. Dotsevi, Y. Sogah and D.J. Cram, J. Am. Chem. Soc., 97, 1259 (1975).

Summary

The optically active crown ether host (1) has previously been shown to exhibit chiral recognition in complexation in solution of the enantiomers of primary amines and amino ester salts as guests[2a,2b,2c]. The authors now report the bonding of (1) to silica gel and the use of the chiral host sites to totally resolve amino ester salts by solid-liquid chromatography. (See also, Vol. 1, this series, page 583ff.) Experimental details and results follow.

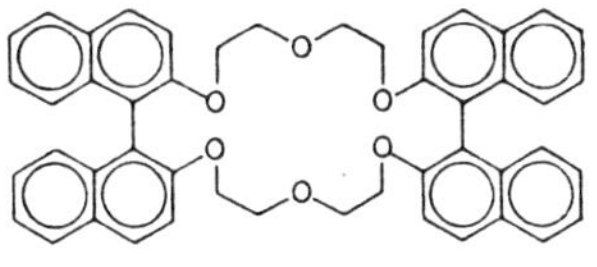

(1)

Bromination (7 mol of Br_2 in CH_2Cl_2 added at $-5°$ over 1 hr) of the isomers of **1** (1 mol) gave **2** whose four bromine

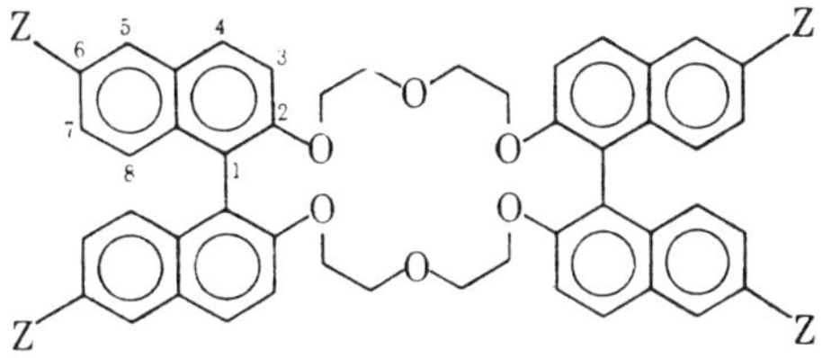

(*RR*)(*SS*)-**1**, Z = H;[2a] (*RR*)-**1**, Z = H;[2a] (*RS*)-**1**, Z = H[2a]

Compd no.	Z	Mp, °C	Yld, %
(*RR*)(*SS*)-**2**[3a,b]	Br	299–300	80
(*RR*)-**2**[3a]	Br	189–191	91
(*RS*)-**2**[3]	Br	334–335	90
(*RS*)-**3**[3a,c]	$Si(CH_3)_2OCH_3$	95–96	84

atoms were substituted in the 6-positions.[4] Addition of (*RS*)-**2** to butyllithium in dry glyme under nitrogen at $-75°$ followed by dichlorodimethylsilane at $-75°$ (mixture then refluxed) followed (after evaporation) by dry methanol gave (*RS*)-**3**. Treatment of the tetrakis(dimethylchlorosilyl) compound (similarly prepared from optically pure (*RR*)-**2**)[5] with dry carbon-free silica gel followed by methanol gave after washing and drying, host-bound silica gel, 3.94% by weight carbon by combustion. If each cycle is covalently bound at only one site, and the other three are capped with CH_3O groups, the silica gel is 0.059 mmol per gram in host residues, or each host site has an average molecular weight of 17,000. Further treatment of this silica gel with excess trimethylsilyl chloride to cap the more hindered SiOH groups gave (*RR*)-**4**[5] (H), 4.65% by weight carbon by combustion, or 0.20 mmol/g in $(CH_3)_3Si$ groups.

Table I reports the results of chromatograms run[6] on racemic α-phenylethylammonium hexafluorophosphate, the methyl or isopropyl esters of phenylglycine hexafluorophosphate or hydrochloride salts, and the methyl esters of the hydrochloride salts of valine, phenylalanine, and tryptophan. The configurational identities of the enantiomers in the bands eluted were established by their signs of rotation (e.g., in runs 1, 3, 4, and 6) or by comparisons of their retention volumes with those of pure enantiomers put through the same column under the same conditions as their racemates (runs 7, 8, and 9). Plots of the relative conductance vs. milliliters of eluate gave curves for each run from which the separation factors, α, were calculated.[7] Figure 1 records the plot for run 8. Good base-line separation was observed for the enantiomers of the ester salts of phenylalanine and tryptophan, but the minima between the two peaks did not come to base line in the other runs. Host-bound silica gel non-capped with $(CH_3)_3Si$ groups gave poorer curves, and bad tailing was observed. With capped material (*RR*)-**4** tailing was observed for the less hindered alkylammonium salts, but little for the more hindered. These facts suggest that even with capped material SiOH groups are still available for complexing less hindered RNH_3^+ guests (G) and cause band overlap. Although dichloromethane as the mobile phase gave less tailing, it also gave lower separation factors.

In liquid-liquid (chloroform-water) chromatography with (*RR*)-**1** as host and amine salts as guest, $\alpha \sim (D_A/D_B)$, where D_A is the distribution coefficient of the more and D_B that of the less complexed enantiomer in the chloroform phase.[2b,c] The results obtained with complexation at the silica gel–chloroform interface qualitatively resemble those observed in chloroform. The formula of Figure 1 illustrates the structure visualized for the complex of the ester salt of phenylalanine, and illustrates the *four-point binding model* as the more stable diastereomeric complex. This model also explains the results with valine. The *three-point binding model* **5** is illustrated by the results obtained with the salts of α-phenylethylamine, of the phenylglycine esters, and of the tryptophan ester. Similar models applied in chloroform solution, but only to the *hexafluorophosphate salts* of α-phenylethylamine and the methyl esters of valine, phenylalanine, and phenylglycine.[2] The hydrochloride salts failed to extract, or if they did, no chiral recognition was observed.[8] Possibly at the silica interface, the chloride ion is in a more polar environment, and does not destructure the host–guest complex by hydrogen bonding the alkylammonium ion as in chloroform.[8] Another difference between complexation at the interface and in solution is that chiral recognition on the three-point model side is lower and on the four-point model side is higher at the interface than in solution.

These results demonstrate that, by rational design of host

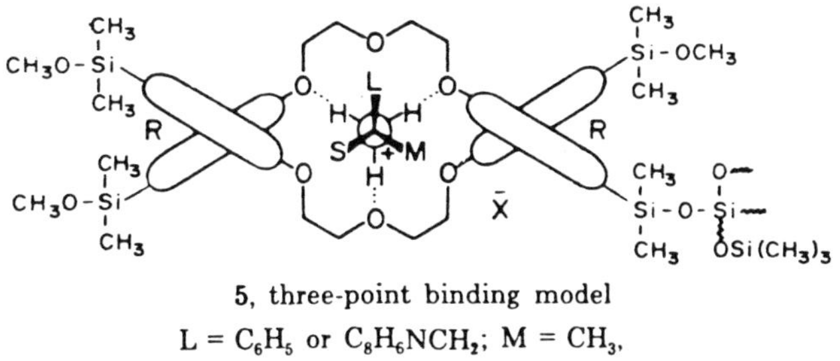

5, three-point binding model

L = C_6H_5 or $C_8H_6NCH_2$; M = CH_3, CO_2CH_3, or $CO_2CH(CH_3)_2$; S = H

G. Dotsevi, Y. Sogah and D.J. Cram, J. Am. Chem. Soc., 97, 1259 (1975) continued.

Table I. Optical Resolution by Solid–Liquid Chromatography at 25°

Run no.	$RR'CH\overset{+}{N}H_3\bar{X}$ R	R'	X^-	Molar ratio, H[a]/G	Mobile phase	Carrier[b] concn, *M*	Separat factor α	Configur better bound enantiomer
1	C_6H_5	CH_3	PF_6	21	CH_2Cl_2	4.4×10^{-5}	1.47	*S*
2	C_6H_5	CH_3	PF_6	84	$CHCl_3$	2.0×10^{-4}	1.67	*S*
3	C_6H_5	CO_2CH_3	Cl	20	CH_2Cl_2	4.4×10^{-6}	1.20	*R* or *D*
4	C_6H_5	CO_2CH_3	PF_6	50	$CHCl_3$	2×10^{-4}	1.40	*R* or *D*
5	C_6H_5	CO_2CH_3	PF_6	128	$CHCl_3$	0.8%(v/v)[c]	1.52	*R* or *D*
6	C_6H_5	$CO_2CH(CH_3)_2$	Cl	80	CH_2Cl_2	5%(v/v)[d]	2.93	*R* or *D*
7	$(CH_3)_2CH$	CO_2CH_3	Cl	23	$CHCl_3$	1×10^{-2}	1.73	*S* or *L*
8	$C_6H_5CH_2$	CO_2CH_3	Cl	23	$CHCl_3$	5×10^{-3}	4.4	*S* or *L*
9	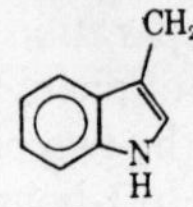	CO_2CH_3	Cl	70	$CHCl_3$	2×10^{-4}	6.4	*R* or *D*

[a] Column contained 0.82 mmol of host. [b] 18-crown-6. [c] Ethanol was carrier. [d] Isopropyl alcohol was carrier.

compounds covalently bound at a remote site to silica gel, complete optical resolution by highly structured complexation of guest compounds at the solid–liquid interface can be accomplished. We anticipate that covalent binding of **1** and its derivatives to macroreticular polystyrene resins will produce higher concentrations of host per unit weight and a chromatographic support free of unwanted binding sites.

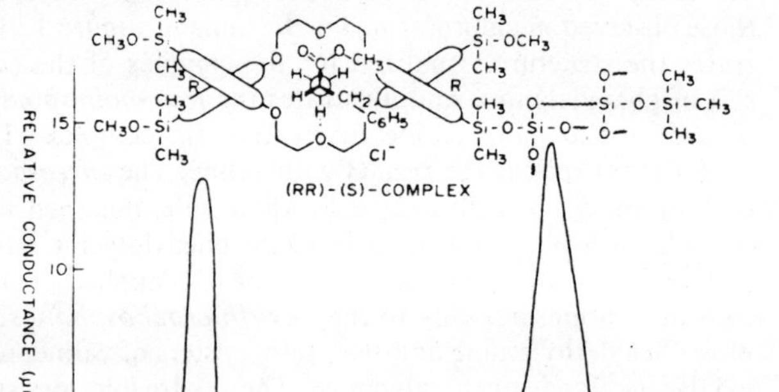

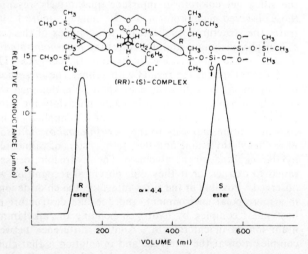

Figure 1. Chromatographic optical resolution by host-bound silica gel of methyl phenylalaninate hydrochloride salt.

(2) (a) E. P. Kyba, K. Koga, L. R. Sousa, M. G. Siegel, and D. J. Cram, *J. Am. Chem. Soc.*, **95**, 2692 (1973); (b) R. C. Helgeson, J. M. Timko, P. Moreau, S. C. Peacock, J. M. Mayer, and D. J. Cram, *ibid.*, **96**, 6762 (1974); (c) L. R. Sousa, D. H. Hoffman, L. Kaplan, and D. J. Cram, *ibid.*, **96**, 7100 (1974); (d) in the synthesis of (*S*)- and (*R*)-**4** of ref 2c, 2-(2′-chloroethoxy)ethyl 2′-tetrahydropyranyl ether was treated with (*S*)- or (*R*)-**1** of ref 2c in sodium hydride–DMF at 70°, not sodium hydroxide–butanol as erroneously reported.

(3) (a) Carbon and hydrogen analyses were within 0.30% of theory. (b) ^1H NMR spectra in $CDCl_3$ were consistent with assigned structures. (c) Mass spectra exhibited molecular ions.

(4) The structural assignments depend on the 100-MHz ^1H NMR first-order spectrum ($CDCl_3$) of (*RR*)(*SS*)-**2**, δ 3.17 (m, CH_2OCH_2, 16 H), 3.81 (m, $ArOCH_2$, 8 H), 6.85 (d, ArH-8, $J_{7,8}$ = 9 Hz, 4 H), 7.20 (d of d, ArH-7, $J_{7,8}$ = 9 Hz, $J_{5,7}$ = 2 Hz, 4H), 7.25 (d, ArH-3, $J_{3,4}$ = 9 Hz, 4 H), 7.80 (d, ArH-4, $J_{3,4}$ = 9 Hz, 4 H), 7.97 (d, ArH-5, $J_{5,7}$ = 2 Hz, 4 H). ArH-8 is shielded by the naphthalene ring bound at the 1-position and split by ArH-7; ArH-7 is split by both ArH-8 and ArH-5; ArH-5 is deshielded by its ortho bromine and peri interaction; ArH-3 and ArH-4 split one another; ArH-3 is shielded by its ortho RO group; ArH-4 is deshielded by its peri interaction. We thank M. S. Siegel for first preparing (*RR*)(*SS*)-**2** and assigning its structure.

(5) To 2.11 g of optically pure (*RR*)-**2** in 200 ml of dry glyme stirred under pure nitrogen at −75° was added a trace of triphenylmethane indicator and dropwise 10 ml of butyllithium (2.2 *M* in hexane). After 2 hr of stirring the reaction mixture was added to 12 g of dichlorodimethylsilane stirred under nitrogen at −75°. The reaction mixture was stirred at 25° for 4 hr, heated at reflux for 12 hr, cooled, and filtered, and the solids were washed with dry glyme. Volatile materials were removed (ultimately at 0.1 mm), and the residue was dissolved in dry (P_2O_5) chloroform (15 ml) and filtered into a stirred slurry of 40.0 g of dry (constant weight at 300°) Davidson No.56 Silica Gel (200–325 mesh, pore volume 1.20 ml/g, surface area 285 m^2/g, average pore diameter 168 Å) and 250 ml of dry (P_2O_5) chloroform under nitrogen. The mixture was stirred for 10 hr (while the evolved HCl was purged with pure nitrogen) and filtered, and the filtrate was washed successively with dry chloroform, methanol, benzene, and chloroform. The material was dried at 90° at 0.01 mm pressure for 18 hr to constant weight, ~41.6 g. From the washings was obtained 0.10 g of optically pure (*RR*)-**1**. Treatment of the host-bound silica gel with 10 g of $(CH_3)_3SiCl$ gave by a similar procedure ~41.7 g of trimethylsilyl-capped final useful solid phase host, (*RR*)-**4**. This material absorbs little water, a little methanol, but 2.6 g absorbs 6.6 g of chloroform before looking wet. The dry material (14.0 g) packed (tamping) into a stainless steel column (0.75 i.d. by 56 cm) provided a mobile phase volume of chloroform of 23 ml.

(6) Chromatograms were run at constant flow rates that ranged in different runs from 0.60 to 1 ml/min with pressure drops of 300–975 psi. Amine salts (1–8 mg) dissolved in 2 ml of the mobile phase were injected at the top of the column. The mobile phase of chloroform or dichloromethane contained low concentrations of 18-crown-6 (G. W. Gokel, D. J. Cram, C. L. Liotta, H. P. Harris, and F. L. Cook, *J. Org. Chem.*, **39**, 2445 (1974)) to act as a salt carrier. The column eluate was passed through a conductivity cell (ref 2c) to detect eluted salt. Between runs, the column was washed with methanol and was unchanged over a period of months.

(7) L. R. Snyder and J. J. Kirkland, "Introduction to Modern Liquid Chromatography", Wiley, New York, N.Y., 1974, pp 25–29, 35–37.

(8) J. M. Timko, F. de Jong, and D. J. Cram, unpublished results.

Reference
G. Dotsevi, Y. Sogah and D.J. Cram, J. Am. Chem. Soc., 98, 3038 (1976).

Summary
The authors report the covalent bonding of chiral crown ether (RR)-1 to macroreticular crosslinked polystyrene p-divinylbenzene resin and the use of the resin for the total optical resolution (both preparative and analytical) of amino acids and ester salts. Experimental details and results follow.

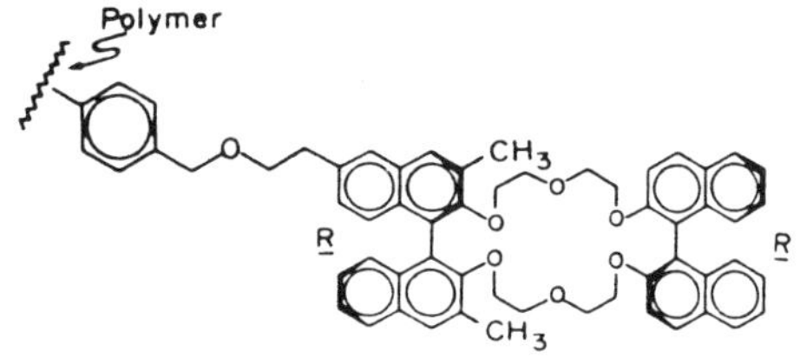

(RR)-1

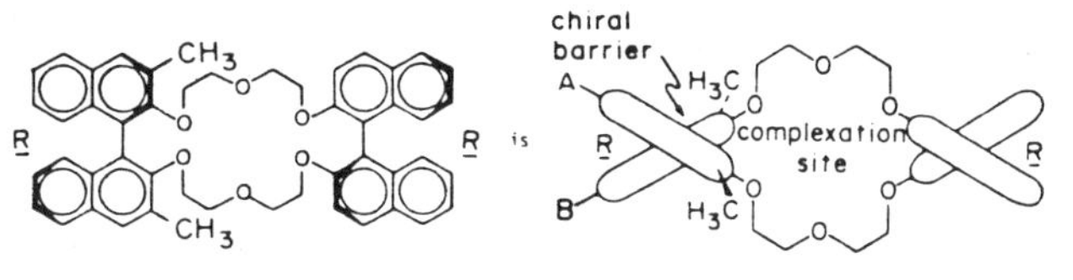

1, A = B = H; 2, A = B = Br; 3, A = B = CH_2CH_2OH;
4, A = CH_2CH_2OH; B = H; 5, A = CH_2CH_2-PS-CH_2Cl (PS = polystyrene), B = H; 6, A = CH_2CH_2-PS-CH_2OCH_3, B = H

Optically pure (*R*)-2,2′-dihydroxy-3,3′-dimethyl-1,1′-binaphthyl[3] was brominated in dichloromethane (−78° to 25°) to give (90%) (*R*)-6,6′-dibromo-3,3′-dimethyl-2,2′-dihydroxy-1,1′-binaphthyl,[4] mp 115–119° ($CHCl_3$ solvate), $[\alpha]^{25}{}_{578}$ −68°.[5] This dibromide when refluxed for 17 h in $(CH_2)_4O$-KOH with mole for mole optically pure (*R*)-2,2′-bis-(1,4-dioxa-6-tosyloxyhexyl)-1,1′-binaphthyl[3] gave cycle (*RR*)-**2**[4] (69%), mp 135–143° (solvate from benzene-cyclohexane), $[\alpha]^{25}{}_{578}$ +172°.[5] In dry glyme under nitrogen, (*RR*)-**2** was metalated at −75° with 2 equiv of BuLi, and 4 equiv of dry ethylene oxide was added (−75°) to give after chromatography on alumina: optically pure (*RR*)-**1**[3] (25%), $[\alpha]^{25}{}_{578}$ +152° (*c* 1.0, $CHCl_3$); (*RR*)-**3**[4b] (6%, glass); and (*RR*)-**4**[4] (60%, glass), $[\alpha]^{25}{}_{578}$ +164° (*c* 1.7, CH_2Cl_2). Host (*RR*)-**4** was covalently attached to chloromethylated and highly cross-linked polystyrene–divinylbenzene resin[6] to give first (*RR*)-**5** and (*RR*)-**6**[7] after CH_3ONa treatment, which was packed into a chromatographic column.[8] The resin volume did not change observably with solvent changes.

Runs were made[9] at 0° and monitored by passing the column eluate ($CHCl_3$-CH_3CN) through a conductivity detector.[2a,b] Plots of relative conductance vs. volume of column eluate were made from which the parameters of Table I were calculated.[10] The peaks were Gaussian (little tailing). The configurational identities and optical purities of the less complexed and faster moving, and more complexed and slower moving enantiomers were identified by isolation and characterization of the pure antipodes in runs 5, 7, 9, 15, and 18–20 (or runs that simulated them). In the other runs the enantiomers were identified either by comparisons of their retention volumes with those of authentic enantiomers or from signs of rotations of eluate fractions. Runs 18–20 involved esters[11] not previously resolved. Their optically pure enantiomers were obtained by preparative chromatography.[12] Comparisons of the CD curves of the more and less bound enantiomers in these runs with those of runs 5, 7, 8, and 9 (configurations known) provided the needed configurational assignments.[13] In the many runs with baseline separation of enantiomers, the areas under the two peaks were equal within experimental error.

(2) Amino esters as a family have been previously resolved by: (a) solid-liquid chromatography, G. Dotsevi Y. Sogah and D. J. Cram, *J. Am. Chem. Soc.*, **97**, 1259 (1975) (the first author's name appeared as if he were two rather than one person in the original reference); (b) liquid-liquid chromatography, L. R. Sousa, D. H. Hoffman, L. Kaplan, and D. J. Cram, *J. Am. Chem. Soc.*, **96**, 7367 (1974); (c) gas–liquid chromatography, α's as high as 1.3, R. Charles, U. Beitler, B. Feibush, and E. Gil-Av, *J. Chromatogr.*, in press. The covalent attachment of L-arginine to Sephadex G-25 provided a liquid–solid column that gave α = 1.60 in the resolution of racemic Dopa, 1.19 for racemic tyrosine, and 1.00 for phenylalanine; (d) R. J. Baczuk, G. K. Landram, R. J. Dubois, and H. C. Dehm, *J. Chromatogr.*, **60**, 351 (1971). No chromatographic resolution of amino acids as a class have been reported prior to our paper.

(3) R. C. Helgeson, J. M. Timko, P. Moreau, S. C. Peacock, J. M. Mayer, and D. J. Cram, *J. Am. Chem. Soc.*, **96**, 6762 (1974).

(4) (a) Carbon and hydrogen analyses were within 0.30% of theory; (b) ^1H NMR spectra in $CDCl_3$ were as expected; (c) 70 eV mass spectra gave parent ion.

(5) Solvent free, *c* 1.0–1.4, CH_2Cl_2.

(6) We warmly thank Rohm and Haas for this material and a description of its properties.

(7) Amberlite XAD-2 ground through a 150 mesh sieve was chloromethylated with 3 mol of chloromethyl methyl ether–aluminum chloride in 1,2-dichloroethane at 25° for 4 h, washed, and dried under vacuum at 90° for 20 h. Anal. Found: C, 86.58, H, 7.98; Cl, 3.97 (1.12 mequiv of Cl per g, or 15% of aromatic rings chloromethylated based on 130 for equivalent weight of polymer). To 2.63 g of (*RR*)-**4** and 2.5 g of NaH in refluxing $(CH_2)_4O$ under nitrogen was added 29.0 g of dry chloromethylated resin. The mixture was refluxed for 7 days and filtered, and the solids were washed with CH_3OH, H_2O, CH_2Cl_2, and CH_3OH and dried at 90° for 12 h under vacuum to give 30.3 g of (*RR*)-**5**, analysis for chlorine, 3.71%. Recovered from the filtrates was 1.8 g of crude and 1.3 g of chromatographed (*RR*)-**4**. The resin was refluxed 15 h with excess CH_3ONa in CH_3OH, washed, and dried to give 30.0 g of (*RR*)-**6**, 0.65% Cl, or 0.18 mequiv/g of Cl, 0.87 mequiv/g of CH_3O, and 0.073 mmol of host/g (based on the difference between (*RR*)-**4** used and recovered, and consistent with the difference in percent Cl of chlorinated resin and (*RR*)-**5**). Almost one in every hundred benzene rings of the polymer carries a host, and the remaining polymer provides structural support, channels, and environment.

(8) A 60 by 0.75 cm (i.d.) stainless steel jacketed (insulated) column was packed by a balanced-density slurry method in 50% (v) CH_3CN-$CHCl_3$ at 3 ml/min (800–900 psi) and was washed with methanol and then chloroform. It contained 9.5 g of 250–325 mesh (*RR*)-**6**, and possessed a dead volume of 18.4 ml.

(9) Samples dissolved in a minimum of mobile phase solvent were injected on the column through an injection loop. Corrections (less than one-third of dead volume) were made for loop, detector, and tubing volumes. Chromatograms were run at constant flow rates of 0.36–2.0 ml/min with pressure drops of 350–700 psi. After runs, the columns were washed and stored under methanol.

(10) L. R. Snyder and J. J. Kirkland, "Introduction to Modern Liquid Chromatography", Wiley, New York, N.Y., 1974, pp 25–29, 35–37.

(11) The authors warmly thank Ms. Linda A. Domeier for preparing these compounds, which were characterized for the first time (ref 4a): p-$ClC_6H_4CHNH_3Cl(CO_2CH_3)$, mp 194–197°; p-$CH_3O_2CC_6H_4CH$-$NH_3Cl(CO_2CH_3)$, mp 200–201°. The corresponding acids are known, e.g., A. H. Neims, D. C. DeLuca, and L. Hellerman, *Biochemistry*, **5**, 203 (1966).

G. Dotsevi, Y. Sogah and D.J. Cram, J. Am. Chem. Soc., 98 3038 (1976) continued.

Table I. Optical Resolution of $RC^*H(NH_3)CO_2R'^+ ClO_4^-$ Guest (G) by Solid–Liquid Chromatography on a 9.5-g Column of Resin Containing 0.694 mmol of Host (H) Sites[a]

	Guest					Separation				
	Structure									
Run no.	R	R′	Wt (mg)	H/G[b]	% (v) CH_3CN in $CHCl_3$	Factor[c] (α)	Kind[d]	Δ(ΔG)[e] (cal/mol)	Resol factor,[f] R_s	Config more bound guest
1	C_6H_5	H	0.013	14 000	10	5.5	B.l.	926	1.99	*R*
2	C_6H_5	H	0.32	550	10	11	B.l.	1303	2.90	*R*
3	C_6H_5	H	5.0	35	10	15	B.l.	1471	1.13	*R*
4	C_6H_5	H	10.1	17	10	24	B.l.	1726	0.74	*R*
5	C_6H_5	H	15.2	11	10	12	B.l.	1350	0.76	*R*
6	C_6H_5	H	84	2	10	11	Min.	1303	0.21	*R*
7	*p*-HOC_6H_4	H	6.6	28	10	6.1	B.l.	982	2.31	*R*
8	*p*-HOC_6H_4-CH_2	H	5.8	36	10	1.9	Min.	349	0.42	*R*
9	$C_6H_5CH_2$	H	4.6	40	4	2.3	B.l.	453	0.97	*S*
10	$C_8H_6NCH_2$[g]	H	2.0	104	20	6.1	B.l.	982	1.61	*R*
11	$(CH_3)_2CH$	H	1.6	97	10	2.3	Min.	452	0.45	*R*
12	$C_2H_5(CH_3)$-CH	H	2.3	69	5	1.9	Min.	349	0.24	*R*
13	$(CH_3)_3C$	H	2.0	79	5	1.9	Min.	349	0.37	*R*
14	CH_3	H	1.6	82	4	1.5	Min.	220	0.21	*R*
15	CH_3SCH_2-CH_2	H	6.6	26	4	1.4	Min.	183	0.25	*R*
16	*p*-HOC_6H_4	CH_3	9.5	50	10	26	B.l.	1770	3.0	*R*
17	C_6H_5	CH_3	9.5	48	10	18.5	B.l.	1585	4.5	*R*
18	*p*-CH_3O_2C-C_6H_4	CH_3	9.5	50	10	12.6	B.l.	1376	2.3	*R*
19	*p*-ClC_6H_4	CH_3	9.5	47	10	8.5	B.l.	1163	2.2	*R*
20	*p*-$FC_6H_4CH_2$	CH_3	9.5	50	10	8.5	B.l.	1163	2.7	*S*
21	$C_6H_5CH_2$	CH_3	9.5	50	10	6.4	B.l.	1008	1.9	*S*
22	*p*-HOC_6H_4-CH_2	CH_3	9.5	47	10	4.7	B.l.	841	1.7	*R*

[a] Average host site ~14 000 mass units, or 0.073 mmol of host per gram. [b] Ratio of total moles of host to total moles of guest. [c] Separation factor (α) = (retention volume of less mobile component minus total dead volume)/(retention volume of more mobile component minus total dead volume). [d] B.l. means baseline separation and Min., minimum between fractions. [e] $\Delta(\Delta G) = RT \ln \alpha$ (ref 10) and measures the free energy differences of the diastereomeric complexes. [f] R_s = 2(retention volume of less mobile component minus that of more mobile component)/(sum of bandwidths of two peaks). [g] Tryptophane side chain.

(12) The methyl ester perchlorate salts of the phenylglycines gave: for the para chloro derivative, mp 82.5° for the less retained enantiomer, $[\alpha]^{25}_{578}$ +73.7° (*c* 0.83, MeOH), mp 82° for the more retained, $[\alpha]^{25}_{578}$ −69.5° (*c* 0.77, MeOH); for the para carbomethoxy derivative, less retained, mp 53.5°, $[\alpha]^{25}_{578}$ +75.9° (*c* 0.80, MeOH), more retained, mp 53°, $[\alpha]^{25}_{578}$ −76.0° (*c* 0.80, MeOH). The methyl ester perchlorate salts of *p*-fluorophenylalanine gave: mp 79° for the less retained, $[\alpha]^{25}_{578}$ +35.5° (*c* 0.80, MeOH); mp 79.5° for the more retained, $[\alpha]^{25}_{578}$ −33.8° (*c* 0.80, MeOH).

(13) The CD spectrum of all four phenylglycine and three phenylalanine methyl ester salts in MeOH (*c* 0.8 ± 0.1) gave Cotton effects at 215–220 nm ($\pi \rightarrow \pi^*$) whose sign was configuration dependent, and at 250–260 nm whose sign was configuration independent and negative. The ester salts of known configuration correlated as follows: (*S*)-phenylglycine, ~220 nm, $[\theta]$ = +1260°; (*R*)-*p*-hydroxyphenylglycine, ~215 nm, $[\theta]$ = −950°; (*S*)-phenylalanine, ~220 nm, $[\theta]$ = +800°; (*S*)-tyrosine, ~220 nm, $[\theta]$ = +1100°; (+)-*p*-chlorophenylglycine, less bound, ~215 nm, $[\theta]$ = +240°, thus *S* configuration and (−)-*p*-chlorophenylglycine, more bound, ~215 nm, $[\theta]$ = −240°, thus *R* configuration; (+)-*p*-carbomethoxyphenylglycine, less bound, ~220 nm, $[\theta]$ = +300°, thus *S* configuration, and (−)-*p*-carbomethoxyphenylglycine, more bound, ~220 nm, $[\theta]$ = −310°, thus *R* configuration;(+)-*p*-fluorophenylalanine, less bound, ~220 nm, $[\theta]$ = −275°, thus *R* configuration, and (−)-*p*-fluorophenylalanine, more bound, ~220 nm, $[\theta]$ = +280°, thus *S* configuration.

G. Dotsevi, Y. Sogah and D.J. Cram, J. Am. Chem. Soc., 98, 3038 (1976) continued.

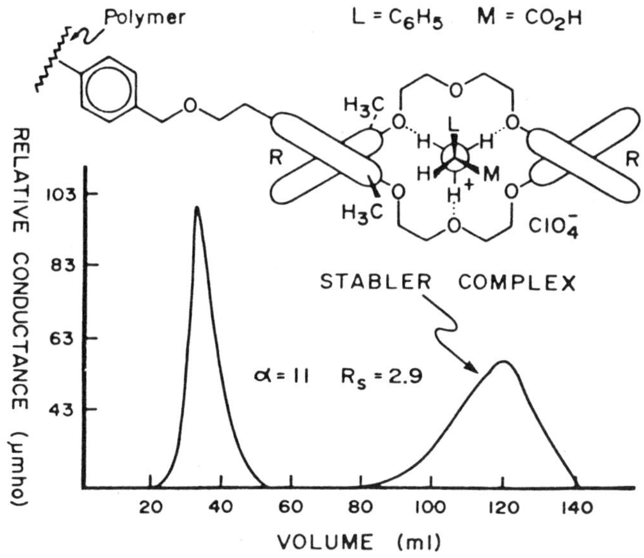

Figure 1. Plot of relative conductance vs. volume of column eluate for phenylglycine perchlorate (run 2).

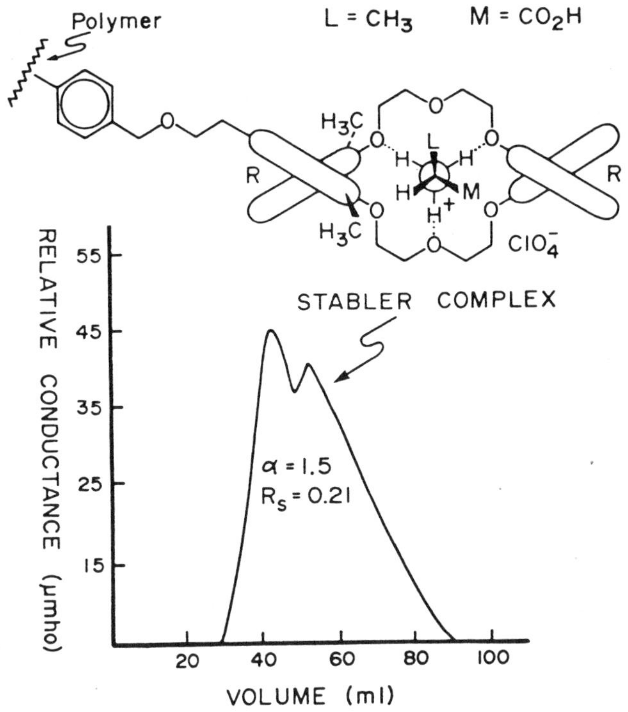

Figure 2. Plot of relative conductance vs. volume of column eluate for alanine perchlorate (run 14).

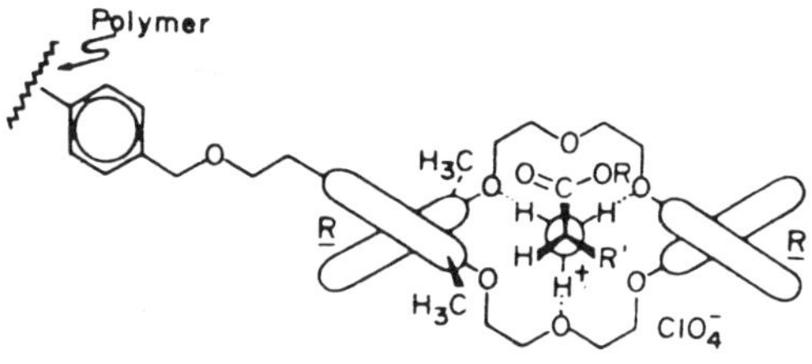

(RR)-(S)-7

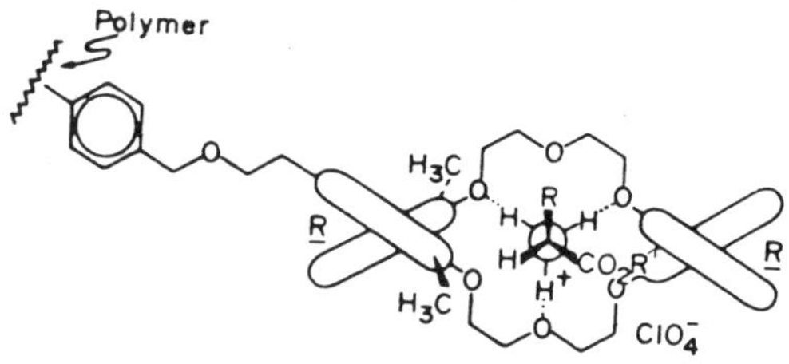

(RR)-(R)-7

Reference

L.R. Sousa, G.D.Y. Sogah, D.H. Hoffman and D.J. Cram, J. Am. Chem. Soc., 100, 4569 (1978).

Summary

The authors report two new methods for the optical resolution of amino esters (guests). The first method involved liquid-liquid chromatography with H_2O-$NaPF_6$ or H_2O-$LiPF_6$ solution supported on Celite or silica gel as the stationary phase. The mobile phase consisted of $CHCl_3$ solutions of (RR)-(bis[dinaphthyl]-22-crown-6) as host. The appearance of the host-guest complex in the column eluate was monitored conductometrically. The second method utilized liquid-solid chromatography at 25°. The same (RR)-bis[dinaphthyl]-22-crown-6 host was attached to silica gel through Ar-Si$(CH_3)_2$O-Si bonds at the 6 position of the naphthalene rings to provide a solid phase in which each host site had an average molecular weight of ~17,000. This position is remote from the complexing site of the host. The mobile phase consisted of $CHCl_3$ or CH_2Cl_2 solutions of primary amine salts as guests and 18-crown-6 ethanol, or isopropyl alcohol as carriers. The appearance of salt in the column eluate was monitored conductometrically. Models for the host-guest complexes are discussed. Experimental details and results follow.

General. All solvents were reagent grade and were distilled before use. Chloroform was freed of ethanol by washing it six times with water containing a trace of H_2SO_4 and dried over $MgSO_4$. Optical rotations were determined at 25 °C in thermostated 1-dm cells with a Perkin-Elmer polarimeter Model 141. NMR spectra were taken on a Varian T-60 Spectrophotometer with Me_4Si as internal standard. All solutions for chromatography were carefully filtered before use. The sources and properties of the various amine and amino ester salts used here have been described,[9b] except for the hydrochloride methyl ester salt of racemic and L-tryptophane, which were purchased from Sigma and stored at 0 °. Salts $LiPF_6$ and $NaPF_6$ were purchased from Ventron (98+% pure). Hexafluorophosphoric acid diethyl etherate (Aldrich) was used to prepare aqueous HPF_6 solutions or amine salt solutions. The syntheses and properties of optically pure host (*R,R*)-**1** and tetrabromide (*R,R*)-**3** have been reported.[8a,10] The jacketed chromatographic columns were insulated with two layers of Presstite insulation tape (Virginia Chemicals) and were cooled by circulating constant temperature ethylene glycol-water through their jackets.

Liquid-Liquid Chromatographic Runs. The solid supports for the liquid-liquid chromatographic columns were Celite (Johns-Manville Purified) or silica gel (Davidson No. 56, surface area 285 m^2/g, pore volume of 1.20 mL/g, and average pore diameter of 168 Å).

Run 1. The stationary phase was prepared by rolling (8 h) 90 g of Celite, dried to constant weight at 180 °C at 50 μm, with 39 mL of $CHCl_3$-saturated distilled water containing 6.52 g of $NaPF_6$ (0.94 M). This not quite moist material was dry packed in small portions onto a 57 by a 2.5 (i.d.) cm jacketed chromatographic column. The stationary phase was 29% water, 5% salt, and 66% Celite by weight. A solution of 0.75 mL of $CHCl_3$ saturated with distilled water containing 0.200 g of racemic α-phenylethylammonium bromide and 0.175 g of $NaPF_6$ was mixed with 1.6 g of Celite. This material was packed at the top of the column (0.75-cm band). The column was cooled to 0.5 °C and was developed by gravity flow with a 0.0375 M solution of (*R,R*)-**1** of $[\alpha]^{25}{}_{578}$ +221° (*c* 1.0, CH_2Cl_2) in $CHCl_3$ saturated with water at 0 °C. The free volume (V_M) was 164 mL, as shown by the amount of solution added before eluate appeared. Fractions of the column eluate were collected, the flow rate being 0.3 mL/min. The relative conductivity of each fraction was measured with a dip cell with a constant of about 0.19 cm^{-1} and an Industrial Instruments Inc. conductivity null bridge instrument. Figure 2 provides a plot of milliliters of eluate vs. relative conductivity of eluate for run 1. Fractions 8-12 (120 mL) were combined and washed with three 40-ml portions of water containing one drop of concentrated hydrochloric acid per 100 mL of water. The amine salt in this aqueous solution was converted to its tosylamide derivative to give 117 mg (42%) of material nonoptically fractionated during derivatization (control experiment), $[\alpha]^{25}{}_{546}$ −102° (*c* 1.5, CH_2Cl_2). Fractions 19-28 (120 mL) were combined and similarly converted to the tosylamide derivative to give 84 mg (30%) of material nonoptically fractionated during preparation, $[\alpha]^{25}{}_{546}$ +101° (*c* 1.5, CH_2Cl_2). A sample of (−)-(*S*)-α-phenylethylamine, $[\alpha]^{25}{}_D$ −40.8° (neat, 1 dm) of maximum rotation[13] when converted to its tosylamide derivative on the same scale by the same method gave a 90% yield of nonpurified material, $[\alpha]^{25}{}_{546}$ −102°(*c* 1.5, CH_2Cl_2). A much larger sample prepared and recrystallized four times from dichloromethane-ether gave mp 99-100 °C, $[\alpha]^{25}{}_{546}$ −108° (*c* 0.9, CH_2Cl_2), and $[\alpha]^{25}{}_D$ −79.7° (*c* 2.0, C_6H_6), essentially identical to literature values.[16] Thus, a minimum of 84% of the original (*S*) salt put on the column was eluted as optically pure (*S*) salt in the first peak of run 1, and a minimum of 60% of the original (*R*) salt was eluted optically pure in the second peak. The amine salt in fraction 16, which occurred immediately after the conductivity minimum in Figure 2, was converted to its tosylamide derivative (4.9 mg) and had a rotation of $[\alpha]^{25}{}_{546}$ +14° (*c* 0.5, CH_2Cl_2). Thus, the material eluted at this crossover point was only 14% optically pure in (*R*) salt. An estimate of the relative peak areas (planimeter) of Figure 2 gave (area A)/(area B) = 0.94. Table I records the parameters derived from the plot for run 1.

The other chromatographic runs were monitored by passing the column eluate through a conductivity cell constructed as follows. Teflon tubing, ⅛ in. o.d., was used for all connections. Two brass plates held apart by a slotted Teflon gasket were held together by two outer Teflon plates. The five-layered apparatus was secured with six nylon bolts around the perimeter. Tapped holes in one face of the cell provided inlet and outlet ports. The cell volume was about 0.1 mL, and the cell constant was 0.017 cm^{-1}. The conductance of flow through cell was continuously monitored with a Philips PR 9501 direct-reading conductivity bridge attached to a strip-chart recorder. The linearity of conductance of the cell with the concentration of complexed α-phenylethylammonium hexafluorophosphate in 0.0375 M solutions of (*R,R*)-**1** in $CHCl_3$ is indicated in Figure 1 for concentrations of salt ranging from 0.80 to 8.24 × 10^{-3} M.

Run 2. A 60 by 0.76 (i.d.) cm stainless steel jacketed and insulated chromatographic column was dry packed in small portions, with tamping, with 34% (by weight) silica gel on which was absorbed 9% $NaPF_6$ (0.94 M) in 57% distilled water. This support was prepared by shaking the dried silica gel (see above) with the aqueous $NaPF_6$ salt solution for 15 h. A 0.0375 M solution of (*R,R*)-**1** in $CHCl_3$ saturated with distilled water was pumped through the column with a Milton-Roy Mini-pump, Model 3365-290, whose stroke length was varied between 6 and 20% to attain the proper pressure drop (30 psi) and flow rate (0.15 mL/min). Although tiny air bubbles were noted in all runs, they did not interfere with detection. The free volume (V_M) was determined by measuring the volume of solution pumped into the dry-packed column before eluate appeared. The column was equilibrated with the $CHCl_3$-host solution at 25 °C. Racemic α-phen-

L.R. Sousa, G.D.Y. Sogah, D.H. Hoffman and D.J. Cram, J. Am. Chem. Soc., 100, 4569 (1978) continued.

ylethylammonium bromide (25 mg) dissolved in 0.5 mL of the $CHCl_3$-host solution was introduced onto the column through a SV 8031 Chromatronix Sample Injection Valve Block. Table I reports the results.

Run 3. The chromatographic column, 60 by 0.76 (i.d.) cm, was packed with 40% (by weight) silica gel and 19% $NaPF_6$ (2.4M) in 41% H_2O. The $CHCl_3$ solution of the host (0.0375 M) was saturated with water at the temperature of the run (−13 °C) before use. The racemic methyl phenylglycinate hydrochloride (100 mg) to be resolved was dissolved in a minimum of the aqueous $NaPF_6$ solution used as the stationary phase. This solution was mixed with sufficient silica gel to provide slightly damp-appearing material. This solid was loaded onto the top 3 cm of the column after removal of an equivalent amount of column packing material. The column was cooled to −13 °C. At a constant temperature bath of −21.5 °C in a test run, the coolant returning to the bath was −20.4 °C. Run 3 was made with a pressure drop of 80 psi (0.50 mL/min). Table I reports the column parameters, and Figure 3 records the volume–conductance plot. The column eluate was divided into three fractions: fraction A (0–90 mL), a second fraction consisting of a few drops of eluate which gave a negative ninhydrin test, and fraction B (90–200 mL). Both A and B gave very strong ninhydrin tests. Fraction A was washed with three 20-mL portions of water. The combined aqueous layers were washed with CH_2Cl_2 to remove all traces of host, and the pH of the aqueous layer was adjusted to 9 with dilute aqueous NH_4OH. The free amino ester was extracted into CH_2Cl_2, the solution was dried with $MgSO_4$, concentrated under vacuum, and transferred to a tared vial. The concentrated solution was evaporated to dryness and the traces of CH_2Cl_2 were removed under high vacuum. The vial was weighed, the contents were quantitatively transferred into a 2-mL volumetric flask with CH_2Cl_2, and the rotation of the contents was determined. Fraction B was submitted to the same procedure. As a control, 38 mg of D-methyl phenylglycinate hydrochloride of 97.2% optical purity,[15] $[\alpha]^{25}_{546}$ −155.0° (*c* 1, CH_3OH) was subjected to the same procedure to give 29.1 mg (93%) of the amino ester, $[\alpha]^{25}_{546}$ −181° (*c* 2.9, CH_2Cl_2). Optically pure amino ester prepared on a large scale gave $[\alpha]^{25}_{546}$ −185° (*c* 2.4, CH_2Cl_2). From fraction A was obtained 40% of the total racemic amino ester salt initially used, $[\alpha]^{25}_{546}$ −180° (*c* 2.4, CH_2Cl_2). From B was obtained a 38% recovery, $[\alpha]^{25}_{546}$ +180° (*c* 2.4, CH_2Cl_2).

Run 4. Due to the greater hydrophilicity of the methyl *p*-hydroxyphenylglycinate salt, a 4 M solution of $LiPF_6$ was used as the stationary phase. The $LiPF_6$ salted the guest out of the stationary aqueous phase yet did not complex with the host. The $LiPF_6$ solution was prepared by adding the salt, with stirring, to water at such a rate that the temperature never exceeded 0 °C. The addition rate was controlled to maintain the temperature near 0 °C. After addition, the pH of solution was raised to 4 by adding an appropriate amount of 5 M LiOH. Finally, the solution was cooled to −15 °C, filtered, and shaken with dried silica gel as before. A sample of the resulting material underwent no visible change on extended refrigeration at −15 °C. However, a sample of 4 M $LiPF_6$ in water at −15 °C deposited a small amount of LiF after several days, but maintained its pH. It finally became acidic by hydrolysis of the PF_6^-. A 60 by 0.76 (i.d.) cm column was packed, as in run 3, with 41% (by weight) silica gel and 26% $LiPF_6$ (4.0 M, pH 6) in 33% H_2O. The 108 mg of racemic methyl *p*-hydroxyphenylglycinate hydrochloride salt was loaded on the column as in run 3. The mobile phase was a 0.0750 M solution of (*RR*)-**1** in $CHCl_3$ equilibrated with water at −15 °C. The pressure drop during the run was 22 psi (0.52 mL/min). Table I records the results and Figure 4 records the conductance–volume plot.

The column eluate was collected in 25-mL fractions which were analyzed for amino ester by ninhydrin. These tests qualitatively paralleled the conductivity measurements. Fraction 6 collected between 125 and 150 mL gave a negative test for the amino ester, whereas fractions 5 and 7 gave strong positive tests. Fractions 1–5 were combined to give A and fractions 7–12 to give B.

The amino esters in fractions A and B were isolated as follows. Each solution was extracted with two 20-mL portions of 0.1 N aqueous HCl solution and the combined aqueous extracts were washed with CH_2Cl_2 to remove traces of (*R,R*)-**1**. Each aqueous solution was adjusted to pH 9 with Na_2CO_3 and extracted six times with ethyl acetate. Ninhydrin tests indicated extraction was nearly complete. The ethyl acetate solution from A was concentrated at 30 °C. The residue was dissolved in 0.1 N aqueous HCl solution and extracted as before with ethyl acetate, which was again evaporated, finally in a tared vial to give 24.1 mg (54%) of the free amine. Similar treatment of the solution from B gave 15.2 mg (34%) of free amine. The amine from each source was transferred quantitatively, using 1.0 N aqueous HCl, into a 2 mL volumetric flask after having been filtered from a small amount of insoluble material. The following specific rotations were calculated, assuming quantitative conversion of the amino ester to its corresponding hydrochloride salt: from band A, $[\alpha]^{25}_{589}$ −105°, $[\alpha]^{25}_{578}$ −110°, $[\alpha]^{25}_{546}$ −127° (*c* 1.44, 1 N HCl); from band B, $[\alpha]^{25}_{589}$ +105°, $[\alpha]^{25}_{578}$ +111°, $[\alpha]^{25}_{546}$ +127° (*c* 0.92, 1 N HCl). The hydrochloride salt of D-methyl *p*-hydroxyphenylglycinate was prepared from a sample of D-*p*-hydroxyphenylglycine of 98.3% optical purity of rotations: $[\alpha]^{25}_{589}$ −106.2°, $[\alpha]^{25}_{578}$ −110.7°, $[\alpha]^{25}_{546}$ −127.9°, $[\alpha]^{25}_{436}$ −231.8° (*c* 1.03, H_2O), lit.[16] $[\alpha]^{25}_{589}$ −108° (*c* 1.0, H_2O). The amino ester salt produced gave $[\alpha]^{25}_{589}$ −141.8°, $[\alpha]^{25}_{578}$ −147.8°, $[\alpha]^{25}_{546}$ −171.1°, $[\alpha]^{25}_{436}$ −317.6° (*c* 0.99, CH_3OH) (which compares with a sample provided by the Upjohn Co., $[\alpha]^{25}_{546}$ −172.8° (*c* 1.0, CH_3OH)) and $[\alpha]^{25}_{589}$ −121.1°, $[\alpha]^{25}_{578}$ −125.9°, $[\alpha]^{25}_{546}$ −145.5°, and $[\alpha]^{25}_{436}$ −267.3° (*c* 0.99, 1 N HCl). A 54-mg sample of this prepared ester salt was treated according to the procedure outlined for the isolation of material from bands A and B to give 32.3 mg (72%) of the isolated amino ester: $[\alpha]^{25}_{589}$ −103°, $[\alpha]^{25}_{578}$ −107°, $[\alpha]^{25}_{546}$ −124° (*c* 1.6, 1 N HCl).

These experiments indicate that bands A and B are 87% chemically pure and ~100% optically pure since the 98.3% optically pure material when submitted to the same isolation procedure gives an optical rotation of only 85% of the maximum.

Run 5. The procedure for run 5 was identical to that for run 4 except that CH_2Cl_2 was substituted for $CHCl_3$. Table I records the results.

Host (*R,R*)-**1** used in runs 1–5 was recovered in the following manner: The organic layers containing (*R,R*)-**1** were extracted with several portions of dilute HCl and dried with $MgSO_4$, and the solvent was removed under reduced pressure to give ~95% of (*R,R*)-**1** $[\alpha]^{25}_{578}$ +221° (*c* 1.0, CH_2Cl_2). This rotation is the same as that of host (*R,R*)-**1** used in the five runs.

Preparation of Silica Gel Bound Host. To 2.11 g of optically pure (*R,R*)-2,3,4,5,13,14,15,16-tetra-1,2-(6-bromonaphtho)-1,6,9,12,-17,20-hexaoxacyclodocosa-2,4,13,15-tetraene ((*R,R*)-**3**)[8b] in 200 mL of dry glyme (freshly distilled from CaH_2) and stirred under pure N_2 (passed through concentrated H_2SO_4 and a tower of KOH pellets) at −75 °C was added a trace of triphenylmethane indicator and 10 mL of BuLi (2.2 M in hexane) dropwise. A pink color resulted. After 2 h of stirring, the reaction mixture was added to 12 g of dichlorodimethylsilane stirred under N_2 at −75 °C. The mixture was then stirred at 25 °C for 4 h, cooled, and filtered and the solids were washed with dry glyme. Volatile components were evaporated at 0.1 mmHg, and the residue was dissolved in 15 mL of dry (P_2O_5) $CHCl_3$. The residue was filtered onto a stirred slurry of 40.0 g of Davidson Grade 56 silica gel (200–325 mesh, pore volume 1.20 mL/g, surface area 285 m^2/g, average pore diameter 168 Å), and dried at 300 °C for 24 h under argon to constant weight. The mixture was stirred for 10 h while the evolved HCl was purged with pure N_2. It was then filtered and the filtrate was washed successively with dry pure $CHCl_3$, CH_3OH, C_6H_6, and $CHCl_3$. This material was then dried at 90 °C at 0.01 mmHg pressure for 18 h to a constant weight of 41.6 g. Combustion of this solid gave 3.94% carbon and 0.58% hydrogen by weight. This material was mixed with 200 mL of dry glyme (freshly distilled from CaH_2). To this mixture, stirred under dry pure N_2 at −70 °C was added 10 g of trimethylchlorosilane. The liberated HCl was swept out of the reaction flask with dry nitrogen as the mixture, with stirring, was allowed to come to 25 °C. After stirring for 5 h at 25 °C, the silica gel was filtered and washed successively with dry (P_2O_5)$CHCl_3$, CH_3OH, C_6H_6, and $CHCl_3$. This final product was dried at 90 °C at 0.01 mmHg pressure for 24 h to give 41.7 g of solid. Combustion analysis

L.R. Sousa, G.D.Y. Sogah, D.H. Hoffman and D.J. Cram, J. Am. Chem. Soc., 100, 4569 (1978) continued.

gave 4.65% by weight of carbon and 0.77 of hydrogen, corresponding to 0.059 mmol of host per g of material. This material absorbed hydroxylic solvents such as methanol to only a small extent, but 2.6 g of it absorbed 6.6 g of $CHCl_3$ before appearing wet.

The filtrate and washings from the reaction of the lithiated host with dichlorodimethylsilane were combined and evaporated. The brown residue was dissolved in CH_2Cl_2, and the solution was water washed, dried, and evaporated to give a foam. This material was chromatographed on silica gel with CH_2Cl_2, and the product was crystallized from benzene–cyclohexane (1:3 v:v) to give 0.10 g of optically pure (*R,R*)-**1**, mp 123–126 °C, which, after drying out the solvent of crystallization, gave $[\alpha]^{25}_{578}$ +220° (*c* 1.0, CH_2Cl_2), which compares with the original (*R,R*)-**1** (starting material for preparing (*R,R*)-**2**), $[\alpha]^{25}_{578}$ +221° (*c* 1.0, CH_2Cl_2)).

The recovery of optically pure (*R,R*)-**1** from the sequence, (*R,R*)-**1** → (*R,R*)-**2** → lithiated material → (*R,R*)-**1** demonstrates that no racemization occurred during any of these reactions, that tetralithiated host existed at one point in the sequence, and that this material scavenged enough H^+ from the glass, medium, and reagents to produce (*R,R*)-**1**. By implication, host bound on the silica gel is also optically pure.

Solid–Liquid Chromatographic Runs on Silica Gel Bound Host. A 60 cm by 0.75 cm (i.d.) stainless steel column was dry packed with 14.0 g of silica gel containing 76.8 mg (0.82 mmol) of (*R,R*) host (see previous section). The column was equilibrated with the elution medium of $CHCl_3$ or CH_2Cl_2 containing the salt carrier, usually 18-crown-6[17] at concentrations ranging from 10^{-2} to 4.4×10^{-5} M, 0.8% ethanol (by volume), or 5–10% isopropyl alcohol. The jacketed column was insulated with three layers of Presstite insulation tape, glass wool, and thin aluminum foil and was maintained at 25 °C by circulating ethylene glycol–water solution from a constant temperature bath through the column's jacket. A constant flow rate of solvent through the column was maintained by use of a Milton-Roy Mini-Pump, whose percent stroke was varied between 5 and 20% to attain a pressure drop of 300 to 975 psi and a flow rate between 0.42 and 1.0 mL/min. The same column was used for all runs, and the column was flushed and stored under pure dry methanol when not in use. The column did not noticeably deteriorate over about a 9-month period. Pure, freshly distilled solvents were used. The racemic amine salt dissolved in a measured amount of the mobile phase was pumped into the top of the column through a valve device (0.50 mL volume) interposed between the pump and the column. Between runs, the column was washed with several column volumes of methanol, then chloroform , and finally the carrier solution. The column eluates were passed through the same conductivity cell described above, which was connected to a Philips PR 9501 direct reading conductivity meter, which in turn was connected to a 1.0 mV strip-chart recorder.

For each run, plots of relative conductance vs. the volume of eluate were made, and from the retention volumes of the two maxima observed for the two enantiomers, the separation factors (α) were calculated. The V_M values for the column varied from 23 to 26 mL.

In runs preliminary to runs 1–6 using the same salts, the column was deliberately overloaded with 20–45 mg of guest. The signs of rotations of the better bound enantiomer (band A, or last appearing) and of the less bound enantiomer (band B, or first appearing) were determined polarimetrically, and their absolute configurations were assigned accordingly. In runs 7–11, the retention volumes of either one (runs 10 and 11) or both enantiomeric guests (runs 7–9) were determined immediately after the runs were made and under the same conditions. The configurations of bands A and B were assigned accordingly. Excellent correspondence was observed for the retention volumes for the single enantiomer and the corresponding enantiomers when racemates were separated.

For runs 1–11 of Table II, the flow rates in milliliters per minute and the pressure drops over the column in psi were respectively: 1, 1.0, 900; 2, 0.6, 975; 3, 1.0, 900; 4, 0.6, 400; 5, 0.5, 300; 6, 0.5, 600; 7, 0.5, 650; 8, 0.5, 600; 9, 0.6, 975; 10, 0.5, 650; and 11, 0.6, 600.

The racemic methyl ester hydrochloride salts of serine and methionine in $CHCl_3$–10% (v:v) isopropyl alcohol were also run through the column, but only one peak was observed. However, fractions were cut, and their signs of rotation were determined. The D-serine and L-methionine derivatives were better complexed by the silica gel bound (*R,R*) host.

Table I. Liquid–Liquid Chromatographic Runs with Host (*R,R*)-**1** in $CHCl_3$ in the Mobile Phase and Racemic Guest in the Aqueous Stationary Phase

Run[a] no.	*T*, °C	G(R*NH$_3$PF$_6$) RNH$_3^+$	G(R*NH$_3$PF$_6$) Amt, mg	Separation factor α	EDC (K_A/K_B)	Resolution R_s	Band integrals (A/B)	Theor plates *N*	([H]/[G])$_A$	([H]/[G])$_B$	M_H/M_G	Configuration of a more complex enantiomer
1	0	$C_6H_5CH(CH_3)$-NH_3^+	200	1.8	1.8	0.6	0.94	24	4.5	8	16	*S*
2	25	$C_6H_5CH(CH_3)$-NH_3^+	25	1.5	1.5	0.6		19	65	136	155	*S*
3	−13	$C_6H_5CH(CO_2$-$CH_3)NH_3^+$	100	2.5	2.5	1.25	1.08	34	2.1	3.3	9	D
4	−15	*p*-HOC_6H_4CH-(CO_2CH_3)-NH_3^+	108	3.6	5	1.57	0.83	34	9	25	10	D
5[b]	−15	*p*-HOC_6H_4CH-(CO_2CH_3)-NH_3^+	100	2.4		1.28	0.93	74	2.7	4.1	5	D

[a] See Experimental Section for details. [b] Same as run 4 except CH_2Cl_2 was substituted for $CHCl_3$.

L.R. Sousa, G.D.Y. Sogah, D.H. Hoffman and D.J. Cram, J. Am. Chem. Soc., 100, 4569 (1978) continued.

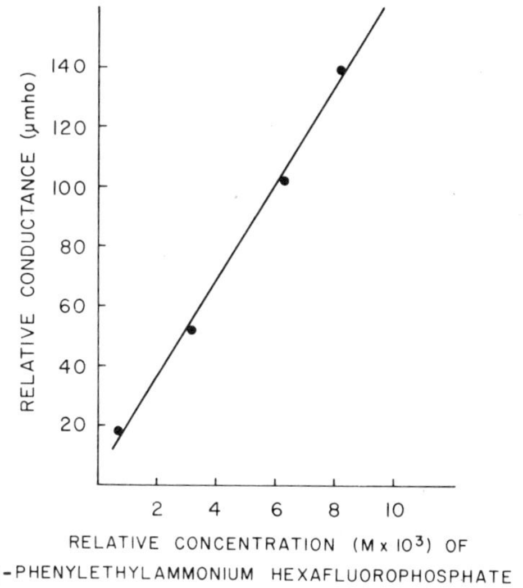

Figure 1. Plot of relative conductance vs. concentration of alkyl ammonium salt in $CHCl_3$ ~0.0375 M in (+)-(*R,R*)-**1**.

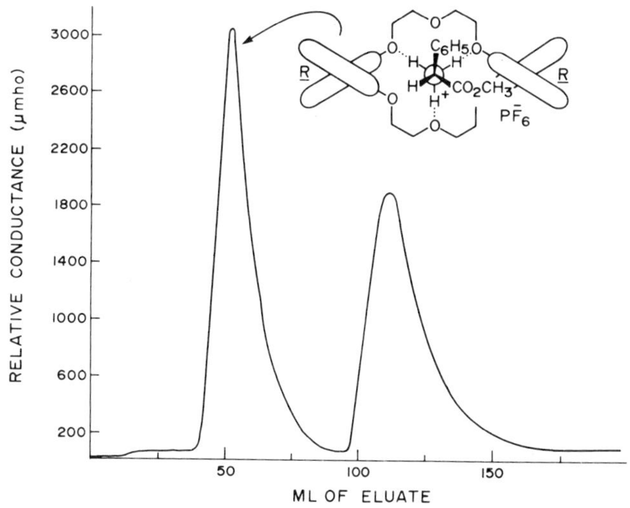

Figure 3. Chromatographic optical resolution by (*R,R*)-**1** of methyl phenylglycinate hexafluorophosphate salt.

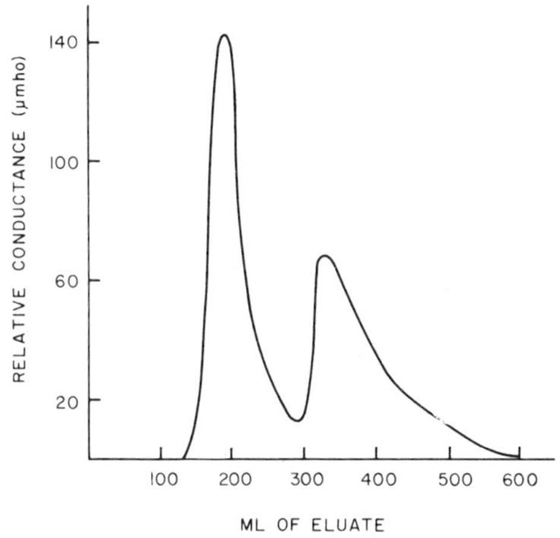

Figure 2. Chromatographic optical resolution by (*R,R*)-**1** of α-phenylethylammonium hexafluorophosphate.

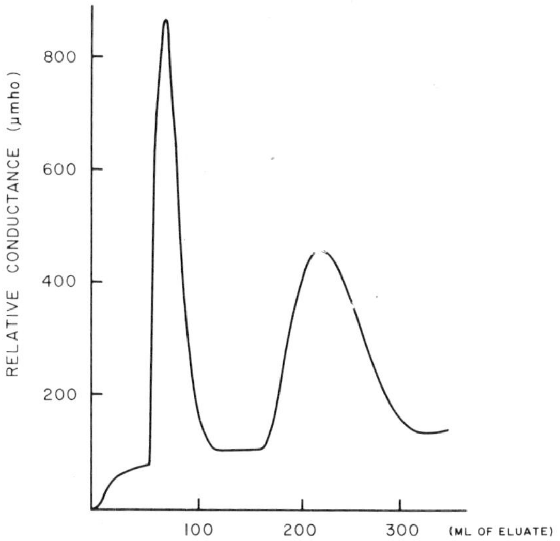

Figure 4. Chromatographic optical resolution by (*R,R*)-**1** of methyl *p*-hydroxyphenylglycinate hexafluorophosphate salt.

L.R. Sousa, G.D.Y. Sogah, D.H. Hoffman and D.J. Cram, J. Am. Chem. Soc., 100, 4569 (1978) continued.

Table II. Optical Resolution at 25 °C of Amine Salts by Solid–Liquid Chromatography on a 14 g Silica Gel Column Containing 0.82 mmol (768 mg) of (*R,R*)-Host

Run no.	G(R*NH$_3$X) RNH$_3$X	Amt, mg	Mobile phase	Carrier concn, M[a]	H/G[b]	Separation factor α	Resolution R_s	Band integrals A/B[c]	Theor plates N	Configuration of more complex enantiomer
1	$C_6H_5CH(CH_3)NH_3PF_6$	8.0	CH_2Cl_2	4.4×10^{-5}	21	1.5	~0.3	~0.9	≈60	*S*
2	$C_6H_5CH(CH_3)NH_3PF_6$	2.0	$CHCl_3$	2.0×10^{-4}	84	1.7	~0.6	~1	≈50	*S*
3	$C_6H_5CH(CO_2CH_3)NH_3Cl$	6.0	CH_2Cl_2	4.4×10^{-5}	20	1.2	~0.2	~1	≈70	D
4	$C_6H_5CH(CO_2CH_3)NH_3PF_6$	5.0	$CHCl_3$	2.0×10^{-4}	50	1.4	~0.3	~1	≈80	D
5	$C_6H_5CH(CO_2CH_3)NH_3PF_6$	2.0	$CHCl_3$	0.8% (v/v)[d]	128	1.6	0.45	1	90	D
6	$C_6H_5CH(CO_2CH(CH_3)_2)$-NH_3Cl	2.3	CH_2Cl_2	5% (v/v)[e]	80	2.9	2.3	1	50	D
7	*p*-$HOC_6H_4CH(CO_2CH_3)$-NH_3Cl	2.7	$CHCl_3$	10% (v/v)[e]	70	6.4	2.4	1	50	D
8	$(CH_3)_2CHCH(CO_2CH_3)$-NH_3Cl	6.0	$CHCl_3$	1.0×10^{-2}	23	1.7	1.4	1.1	30	L
9	$C_6H_5CH_2CH(CO_2CH_3)$-NH_3Cl	5.9	$CHCl_3$	5.0×10^{-3}	23	4.4	3.1	1.2	290	L
10	*p*-$HOC_6H_4CH_2CH(CO_2$-$CH_3)NH_3Cl$	2.4	$CHCl_3$	10% (v/v)[e]	82	2.3	0.9	1.0	50	L
11	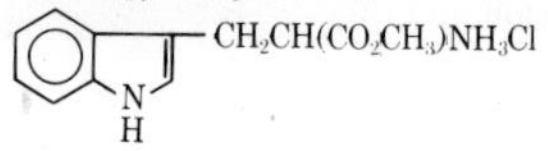	3.0	$CHCl_3$	2.0×10^{-4}	70	6.4	2.5	1.1	40	D

[a] 18-Crown-6, unless indicated otherwise. [b] Moles of host to moles of guest. [c] A is the better complexed diastereomer. [d] Ethanol. [e] Isopropyl alcohol.

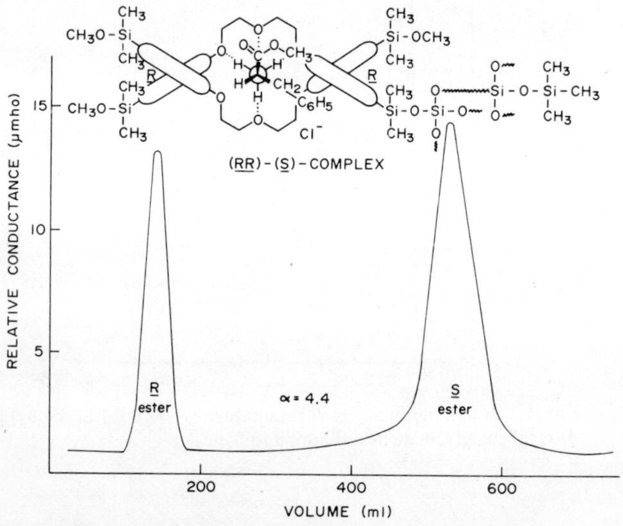

Figure 5. Chromatographic optical resolution by host-bound silica of methyl phenylalaninate hydrochloride salt.

(8) (a) E. P. Kyba, G. W. Gokel, F. de Jong, K. Koga, L. R. Sousa, M. G. Siegel, L. Kaplan, G. D. Y. Sogah, and D. J. Cram, *J. Org. Chem.*, **42**, 4173 (1977); (b) D. J. Cram, R. C. Helgeson, S. C. Peacock, L. J. Kaplan, L. H. Domeier, P. Moreau, K. Koga, J. M. Mayer, Y. Chao, M. G. Siegel, D. H. Hoffman, and G. D. Y. Sogah, *ibid.*, in press; (c) D. J. Cram, R. C. Helgeson, K. Koga, E. P. Kyba, K. Madan, L. R. Sousa, M. G. Siegel, P. Moreau, G. W. Gokel, J. M. Timko, and G. D. Y. Sogah, *ibid.*, in press.
(9) (a) J. M. Timko, R. C. Helgeson and D. J. Cram, *J. Am. Chem. Soc.*, **100**, 2828 (1978); (b) E. P. Kyba, J. M. Timko, L. J. Kaplan, F. de Jong, G. W. Gokel, and D. J. Cram, *ibid.*, preceding paper in this issue.
(10) The authors warmly thank Dr. Lester Kaplan for preparing the ~20 g of optically pure (*RR*)-**1** used in these experiments (ref 9a).
(11) B. L. Karger in "Modern Practice of Liquid Chromatography", J. J. Kirkland, Ed., Wiley, New York, N.Y., 1971, pp 8–14.
(12) J. L. Toner and D. J. Cram, unpublished results.
(13) (a) W. Theilacker and H. G. Winkler, *Chem. Ber.*, **87**, 690 (1954); (b) W. Leithe, *ibid.*, **64**, 2827 (1931).
(14) M. B. Watson and G. W. Youngson, *J. Chem. Soc.*, 2145 (1954).
(15) (a) M. Goodman and J. M. McGahren, *Tetrahedron*, **23**, 2031 (1967); (b) H. Reihlen and L. Knöpfle, *Justus Liebigs Ann. Chem.*, **523**, 199 (1936).
(16) A. W. Long, J. H. C. Nayler, H. Smith, T. Taylor, and N. Ward, *J. Chem. Soc. C*, 1920 (1971).
(17) G. W. Gokel, D. J. Cram, C. L. Liotta, H. P. Harris, and F. L. Cooke, *J. Org. Chem.*, **39**, 2445 (1974).

Reference

G.D.Y. Sogah and D.J. Cram, J. Am. Chem. Soc., 101, 3035 (1979).

Summary

In a continuation of his work on host-guest complexation as a method of resolving racemic α-amino acids (see references in paper for previous work), Dr. Cram and coworkers have synthesized a host which is covalently bound to a polystyreneresin which can be used for preparative or analytical chromatographic resolution of racemic amino acids and esters. The host is $CH_3OCH_2PSCH_2OED(CH_3)_2(OEOEO)D$ [(R,R)-12]. In (R,R)-12, PS is crosslinked polystyrene ∿12% of whose phenyl groups are substituted in the para position with a CH_3OCH_2 group and 0.8% with a spacer unit ($CH_2OCH_2CH_2$), which in turn is attached to a designed complexing site. This site is a macrocycle composed of two 1,1'-dinaphthyl or D units of the same R configuration attached to one another at their 2,2' positions by two OEOEO units (E is CH_2CH_2). The spacer is attached to the remote 6 position of that D unit which contains two methyl groups substituted in its 3,3' positions. Separation factors ranged from 26 to 1.4 and resolution factors from 4.5 to 0.21. Host of the R,R configuration bound D guest more firmly than L guest by from 1.8 to 0.18 kcal/mol. in all cases. A column packed with 9.5 g of (R,R)-12 containing the equivalent of 0.42 g of complexing site gave base-line separation of enantiomers of $C_6H_5CH(CO_2H)NH_3ClO_4$ in runs that involved as much as 15 mg to as little as 0.013 mg of racemate. Experimental details and results follow:

Chart I[a]

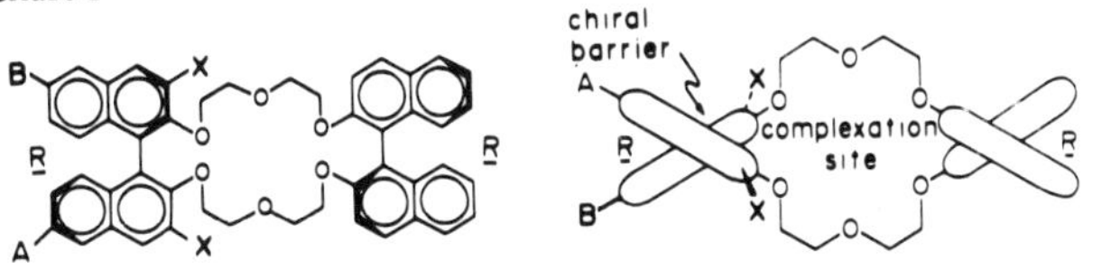

[a] (*R,R*)-**1**, A = B = X = H; (*R,R*)-**2**, A = B = H, X = CH_3; (*R,R*)-**3**, A = B = Br, X = H; (*R,R*)-**4**, A = B = Br, X = CH_3; (*R,R*)-**5**, A = B = CH_2CH_2OH, X = H; (*R,R*)-**6**, A = B = CH_2CH_2OH, X = CH_3; (*R,R*)-**7**, A = CH_2CH_2OH, B = X = H; (*R,R*)-**8**, A = CH_2CH_2OH, B = H, X = CH_3; (*R,R*)-**9**, A = $CH_2CH_2OCH_2$-PS-CH_2Cl (PS = polystyrene), B = X = H; (*R,R*)-**10**, A = $CH_2CH_2OCH_2$-PS-CH_2Cl_3, B = H, X = CH_3; (*R,R*)-**11**, A = $CH_2CH_2OCH_2$-PS-CH_2OCH_3, B = X = H; (*R,R*)-**12** = $CH_2CH_2OCH_2$-PS-CH_2OCH_3, B = H, X = CH_3.

Results

Syntheses of the Host-Bound Resins. Optically pure (*R*)-2,2′-dihydroxy-1,1′-dinaphthyl[6a] and (*R*)-2,2′-dihydroxy-3,3′-dimethyl-1,1′-dinaphthyl[6b] were brominated to give (*R*)-6,6′-dibromo-2,2′-dihydroxy-1,1′-dinaphthyl (94%) and (*R*)-6,6′-dibromo-3,3′-dimethyl-2,2′-dihydroxy-1,1′-dinaphthyl (90%), respectively. These substances, with optically pure (*R*)-2,2′-bis(1,4-dioxa-6-tosyloxyhexyl)-1,1′-dinaphthyl[6a] and KOH–THF, gave cycles (*R,R*)-**3** (74%) and (*R,R*)-**4** (69%), respectively. Metallation of (*R,R*)-**3** with BuLi and treatment of the product with ethylene oxide gave optically pure parent cycle (*R,R*)-**1** (30%), diethoxylated cycle (*R,R*)-**5** (10%), and monoethoxylated cycle (*R,R*)-**7** (55%). Similarly, (*R,R*)-**4** gave optically pure (*R,R*)-**2** (25%), (*R,R*)-**6** (6%), and (*R,R*)-**8** (60%).

Hosts (*R,R*)-**7** and (*R,R*)-**8** were attached through their 6-substituted CH_2CH_2O spacer units to a solid phase by reaction of their sodium alkoxides with ~15% chloromethylated macroreticular polystyrene-divinylbenzene copolymer to give (*R,R*)-**9** and (*R,R*)-**10**, respectively. The differences between the amounts of (*R,R*)-**7** and (*R,R*)-**8** used and recovered from the reactions were used to calculate the amounts of cycles covalently bound to the resin. These amounts were consistent within experimental error with the loss in the amounts of chlorine content of the resins during the reactions. To destroy the CH_2Cl groups on the resin unavailable to the large cyclic alkoxides, (*R,R*)-**9** and (*R,R*)-**10** were treated with $NaOCH_3$ to give (*R,R*)-**11** and (*R,R*)-**12**, respectively. Grafted polymer (*R,R*)-**11** contained ~0.048 mmol of cycle/g, 0.17 mequiv of Cl/g, and 0.90 mequiv of CH_3O groups/g. Grafted polymer (*R,R*)-**12** contained ~0.056 mmol of cycle/g, 0.18 mequiv of Cl/g, and 0.87 mequiv of CH_3O groups/g.

Chromatographic Columns. The host-bound resins were sieved, suspended in CH_3CN-$CHCl_3$, and pumped into jacketed and insulated stainless steel columns, which were conditioned by pumping through their beds, in turn, degassed CH_3OH, $CHCl_3$, and, finally, the solvent used for the runs. The columns were fitted with injection loops for sample introduction. The bottoms of the columns led to conductivity cells attached to a recorder. The relative conductivity of the cell was found to be proportional to the concentration of the alkylammonium salt in chloroform-host solutions.[4c] The dead volume of each column was determined by injecting the nonretained compounds methanol, benzene, hexane, and pentane as samples onto the columns, and determining their retention volumes (see Experimental Section).

Column A was 60 by 0.75 (i.d.) cm in dimension and was packed with 9.5 g of 250–325 mesh (*R,R*)-**12.** Column B was 60 by 0.40 (i.d.) cm and was packed with 4.0 g of 325–400 mesh (*R,R*)-**12.** Column C was the same size as B and was packed with 4.0 g of 325–400 mesh (*R,R*)-**11.**

G.D.Y. Sogah and D.J. Cram, J. Am. Chem. Soc., 101, 3035 (1979) continued.

Table I. Resolution of Enantiomers of $RCH(CO_2H)NH_3ClO_4$ Guests (G) by Solid–Liquid Chromatography with *R,R* Hosts (H)

		guest			mobile phase[c]				sepn factor		−Δ(ΔG°),	resl	guest enantiomers				
						carrier							more bound			less bound	
run no.	column used[a]	structure of R	wt, mg	H/G[b]	solvent	kind	%[d]	T, °C	α[e]	kind[f]	kcal/mol[g]	factor, R_s[h]	confign[i]	sign of α_{obsd}[j]	V_{RA}, mL	sign of α_{obsd}[j]	V_{RB}, mL
1	A	C_6H_5	0.013	11 000	$CHCl_3$	MeCN	10	0	5.5	base line	0.9	1.99	D		100		38
2	A	C_6H_5	0.13	1 100	$CHCl_3$	MeCN	10	0	8.9	base line	1.2	2.72	D		116		34
3	A	C_6H_5	0.32	420	$CHCl_3$	MeCN	10	0	11.0	base line	1.3	2.89	D		119		32
4	A	C_6H_5	0.60	220	$CHCl_3$	MeCN	10	0	11.6	base line	1.3	2.86	D		114		32
5	A	C_6H_5	1.9	70	$CHCl_3$	MeCN	10	0	12.2	base line	1.4	1.76	D		89		29
6	A	C_6H_5	5.0	27	$CHCl_3$	MeCN	10	0	14.6	base line	1.5	1.13	D	−	72	+	27
7	A	C_6H_5	10.1	13	$CHCl_3$	MeCN	10	0	24.3	base line	1.7	0.74	D	−	54	+	25
8	A	C_6H_5	15.2	8	$CHCl_3$	MeCN	10	0	12.2	base line	1.4	0.76	D	−	51	+	26
9	A	C_6H_5	20.5	6	$CHCl_3$	MeCN	10	0	10.0	minimum	1.25	0.54	D	−	30	+	25
10	A	C_6H_5	84	1.5	$CHCl_3$	MeCN	10	0	10.7	minimum	1.2	0.20	D	−	30	+	24
11	A	C_6H_5	5.08	27	$CHCl_3$	EtOAc	5	25	4.5	base line	0.9	1.35	D	mins	69	+	34
12	A	C_6H_5	5.04	27	$CHCl_3$	EtOAc	5	0	10.9	base line	1.3	1.92	D		134		34
13	A	C_6H_5	16.1	8	$CHCl_3$	EtOAc	10	0	7.4	base line	1.1	1.23	D	−	62	+	28
14	A	C_6H_5	16.0	8	$CHCl_3$	EtOAc	15	0	4.7	minimum	0.8	0.61	D	−	49	+	29
15	A	C_6H_5	5.1	26	$CHCl_3$	EtOAc	25	0	4.3	base line	0.8	0.85	D		45		28
16	A	C_6H_5	15.7	8	CH_2Cl_2	MeCN	5	0	5.3	base line	0.9	1.22	D	−	140	+	45
17	A	C_6H_5	14.5	9	CH_2Cl_2	MeCN	17	0	3.4	minimum	0.7	0.39	D	−	37	+	28
18	A	C_6H_5	14.7	9	Et_2O	MeCN	10	0	1.0	none	0.0	0.00	D		36		36
19	A	*p*-HOC_6H_4	6.6	21	$CHCl_3$	MeCN	10	0	6.1	base line	1.0	2.31	D	−	426		90
20	A	$C_6H_5CH_2$	4.6	31	$CHCl_3$	MeCN	4	0	2.3	base line	0.45	0.97	D	−	123	+	67
21	A	*p*-HOC_6H_4-CH_2	5.8	28	$CHCl_3$	MeCN	10	0	1.9	minimum	0.35	0.42	D	−	89	+	59
22	A	$C_8H_6NCH_2$[k]	2.0	80	$CHCl_3$	MeCN	20	0	6.1	base line	1.0	1.61	D	+[l]	278	−[l]	66
23	A	$(CH_3)_2CH$	1.6	74	$CHCl_3$	MeCN	10	0	2.3	minimum	0.45	0.45	D	−[l]	69	+[l]	44
24	A	$C_2H_5(CH_3)$-CH	2.3	53	$CHCl_3$	MeCN	5	0	1.9	minimum	0.3	0.24	D	−[l]	59	+[l]	42
25	A	$(CH_3)_3C$	2.0	61	$CHCl_3$	MeCN	5	0	1.9	minimum	0.3	0.37	D	−[l]	61	+[l]	44
26	A	CH_3	1.6	63	$CHCl_3$	MeCN	4	0	1.5	minimum	0.2	0.21	D	−[l]	52	+[l]	43
27	A	CH_3SCH_2-CH_2	6.6	20	$CHCl_3$	MeCN	4	0	1.4	minimum	0.8	0.25	D	−	86	+	67
28	B	C_6H_5	1.7	33	$CHCl_3$	MeCN	10	25	4.1	base line	0.8	0.89	D		19		12
29	B	*p*-HOC_6H_4	2.4	25	$CHCl_3$	MeCN	10	25	4.2	base line	0.85	1.55	D		71		24
30	B	$C_6H_5CH_2$	1.0	58	$CHCl_3$	MeCN	10	25	1.2	minimum	0.1	0.25	D		14		13
31	B	$(CH_3)_3C$	1.4	36	$CHCl_3$	MeCN	5	25	1.4	minimum	0.2	0.52	D		25		21
32	C	C_6H_5	2.0	23	$CHCl_3$	MeCN	2.5	0	2.4	minimum	0.5	0.35	D	−[l]	17	+[l]	13
33	C	*p*-HOC_6H_4	1.7	30	$CHCl_3$	MeCN	10	0	1.8	minimum	0.3	0.23	D	−[l]	32	+[l]	22
34	C	*p*-HOC_6H_4-CH_2	1.1	48	$CHCl_3$	MeCN	5	0	1.6	minimum	0.3	0.21	D	−[l]	33	+[l]	24

[a] Column A contained 9.5 g of (*R,R*)-**12** or 0.53 mmol of host (H) sites; column B, 4.0 g of (*R,R*)-**12** or 0.22 mmol of H sites; column C, 4.0 g of (*R,R*)-**11** or 0.19 mmol of H sites. [b] Ratio of moles of H to moles of G. [c] Reagent-grade solvents. $CHCl_3$ contained 0.75% EtOH. [d] By volume. [e] Equation 1. [f] Base line means base line separation. [g] Equation 3. [h] Equation 2. [i] Enantiomer A. [j] λ 578 and 546 nm; solvent is column eluant unless otherwise noted. [k] β-indolylmethyl. [l] MeOH as solvent.

Chromatographic Resolutions of Enantiomers. The runs were made at constant temperature maintained by passing water–ethylene glycol at constant temperature through the jackets of the columns. During the runs, constant flow rates were maintained between 0.27 and 2.0 mL/min with pressure drops between 350 and 900 psi. Between 0.013 and 84 mg/run of racemic $^*RNH_3ClO_4$ or $^*RNH_3PF_6$ was injected into the loop at the top of the column. Corrections, which were less than one third of the dead volume, were made for the loop, detector, and tubing volumes. The appearance of enantiomers in the column eluate was detected conductometrically. The mobile phases were $CHCl_3$ or CH_2Cl_2 containing 5–25% by volume of CH_3CN or EtO_2CCH_3 to act as salt carriers. The use of ethers or alcohols as the main solvents gave no enantiomer separation. However, small amounts of CH_3OH or $(CH_3)_2CHOH$ as salt carriers in $CHCl_3$ or CH_2Cl_2 gave moderately good results, but were not generally investigated.

Plots of relative conductance (μmho) against volume of column eluate (mL) for each chromatographic run provided the parameters that indicate the effectiveness of the separations.[8] The peaks were Gaussian and showed little tailing. The enantiomer separation factor (α) is defined by eq 1, in which V_{RA} is the retention volume of enantiomer A (more firmly complexed by the stationary phase and appearing last in the column eluate); V_{RB} is the retention volume of enantiomer B (less firmly complexed and appearing first in the eluate); and V_M is the dead volume of the column. The enantiomer resolution factor (R_s) is defined by eq 2, in which W_A is the bandwidth (mL) of enantiomer A and W_B is that of enantiomer B. Under ideal conditions, the differences in free energies of complexed enantiomers A and B are represented by eq 3.[8] In some runs, the conditions were probably not ideal. The results of these runs can be conveniently discussed in terms of the −Δ(ΔG°) values even though they are only approximations.

G.D.Y. Sogah and D.J. Cram, J. Am. Chem. Soc., 101, 3035 (1979) continued.

The configurational identities and optical purities of the faster (less complexed) and slower (more complexed) moving enantiomers were identified by isolation and characterization of the pure antipodes in runs 9, 20, and 26 of Table I, which records the results obtained with amino acid perchlorates as guests. In runs 6–21 and 27, the identifications of the faster and slower moving enantiomers were made by determinations of the signs of rotation of the eluate fractions. The signs of rotations of authentic L-amino acids salts were taken in the solvents used in these runs, and the signs and configurations correlated. In runs 22–26 and 32–34, each peak was collected, the solvent evaporated, and the residue dissolved in absolute methanol. The signs of rotation were taken. The correlations with configurations reported are based on the signs of rotations of authentic L-amino acid salts taken in absolute methanol. In those runs with base-line separation, the areas under the two bands were essentially equal to one another.

$$\alpha = (V_{RA} - V_M)/(V_{RB} - V_M) \quad (1)$$

$$R_s = 2[(V_{RA} - V_{RB})/(W_A + W_B)] \quad (2)$$

$$-\Delta(\Delta G^\circ) = RT \ln \alpha \quad (3)$$

Table II reports the results of chromatographic runs made with methyl esters of six different amino acid salts and columns A, B, and C. Both perchlorate and hexafluorophosphate salts were examined. Base-line separations were observed for all runs except 12–15. In those runs with base-line separation, the areas under the bands were essentially equal to one another. The more complexed and slower moving enantiomers were identified by isolation and characterization of the pure antipodes in runs 2, 4, and 5 (or ones like them). In the other runs, the more and the less bound enantiomers were identified by their signs of rotation. In runs 1–3 and 7–15, the signs were determined in the column eluate. Configurations were assigned based on the signs of rotation of authentic L-amino ester salts taken in the solvent of the run. In runs 4–6, the two eluant bands were evaporated, and the signs of rotation of their salts were determined in methanol. Runs 4–6 and 11 involved esters not previously resolved.[9] With column A and larger amounts of the salts than in these runs, $p\text{-}CH_3O_2CC_6H_4CH(CO_2CH_3)NH_3ClO_4$ and $p\text{-}ClC_6H_4CH(CO_2CH_3)NH_3ClO_4$ were totally resolved. The CD spectra of all four phenylglycine and two phenylalanine methyl ester perchlorate salts were determined in CH_3OH. Each of the six salts gave two Cotton effects, one at 215–220 nm ($\pi \rightarrow \pi^*$ transitions) whose sign was configuration dependent and the other at 250–260 nm whose sign was configuration independent and negative. The L enantiomers of the four salts of known absolute configuration all gave a positive Cotton effect at the lower wavelength, and this correlation was used to assign configurations to the two salts of unknown configuration (see Experimental Section).

(4) (a) G. D. Y. Sogah and D. J. Cram, *J. Am. Chem. Soc.*, **97**, 1259–1261 (1975); (b) L. R. Sousa, D. H. Hoffman, L. Kaplan, and D. J. Cram, *ibid.*, **96**, 7100–7101 (1974); (c) L. R. Sousa, G. D. Y. Sogah, D. H. Hoffman, and D. J. Cram, *ibid.*, **100**, 4569–4576 (1978).

(6) (a) E. P. Kyba, G. W. Gokel, F. de Jong, K. Koga, L. R. Sousa, M. G. Siegel, L. Kaplan, G. D. Y. Sogah, and D. J. Cram, *J. Org. Chem.*, **42**, 4173–4184 (1977); (b) D. J. Cram, R. C. Helgeson, S. C. Peacock, L. J. Kaplan, L. A. Domeier, P. Moreau, K. Koga, J. M. Mayer, Y. Chao, M. G. Siegel, D. H. Hoffman, and G. D. Y. Sogah, *ibid.*, **43**, 1930–1946 (1978).

(9) The corresponding acids were previously prepared, e.g., A. H. Neims, D. C. De Luca, and L. Hellerman, *Biochemistry*, **5**, 203–213 (1966).

Table II. Resolution of Enantiomers of $RCH(CO_2CH_3)NH_3X$ Guests (G) by Solid–Liquid Chromatography on *R,R* Hosts (H)

		guest									guest enantiomers				
		structure									more bound			less bound	
run no.	column used[a]	R	X	wt, mg	H/G[b]	% CH_3CN in $CHCl_3$ as mobile phase[c]	*T*, °C	sepn factor α[d]	$-\Delta(\Delta G^\circ)$, kcal/mol[e]	resln factor R_s[f]	confign[g]	sign of α_{obsd}[h]	V_{RA}, mL	sign of α_{obsd}[h]	V_{RB}, mL
1	A	$p\text{-}HOC_6H_4$	ClO_4^-	9.5	16	10	0	26	1.8	3.0	D	−		+	
2	A	C_6H_5	ClO_4^-	9.5	15	10	0	18.5	1.6	4.5	D	−		+	
3	A	C_6H_5	PF_6^-	2.1	77	5	0	18.2	1.6	4.5.	D	−	39	+	22
4	A	$p\text{-}CH_3O_2C\text{-}C_6H_4$	ClO_4^-	9.5	18	10	0	12.6	1.4	2.3	D	−[i]		+[i]	
5	A	$p\text{-}ClC_6H_4$	ClO_4	9.5	17	10	0	8.5	1.2	2.2	D	−[i]		+[i]	
6	A	$p\text{-}ClC_6H_4$	PF_6^-	5.0	37	10	0	8.1	1.1	1.2	D	−[i]	76	+[i]	30
7	A	$C_6H_5CH_2$	ClO_4^-	9.5	16	10	0	6.4	1.0	1.9	D	−		+	
8	A	$p\text{-}HOC_6H_4\text{-}CH_2$	ClO_4^-	9.5	17	10	0	4.7	0.8	1.7	D	−		+	
9	B	C_6H_5	ClO_4^-	2.0	29	10	25	4.3	0.9	1.02	D	−	28	+	14
10	B	C_6H_5	PF_6^-	2.5	28	5	25	4.3	0.9	0.77	D	−	23	+	13
11	B	$p\text{-}CH_3O_2\text{-}CC_6H_4$	PF_6^-	2.2	36	5	25	9.0	1.3	0.84	D	−	30	+	25
12	B	$C_6H_5CH_2$	ClO_4^-	2.6	24	5	25	3.2	0.7	0.58	D	−	15	+	11
13	B	$p\text{-}HOC_6H_4\text{-}CH_2$	ClO_4^-	2.7	24	10	25	2.2	0.6	0.24	D	−	14	+	12
14	C	C_6H_5	PF_6^-	5.4	11	5	0	4.1	0.8	0.48	D	−	20	+	12
15	C	C_6H_5	PF_6^-	0.5	116	10	0	1.7	0.3	0.25	D	−	15	+	13

[a] Column A contained 9.5 g of (*R,R*)-**12**, or 0.53 mmol of host (H) sites; column B, 4.0 g of (*R,R*)-**12**, or 0.22 mmol of H sites; column C, 4.0 g of (*R,R*)-**11**, or 0.19 mmol of H sites. [b] Ratio of moles of H to moles of G. [c] Reagent-grade solvents. $CHCl_3$ contained 0.75% EtOH, percent by volume. [d] Equation 1. [e] Equation 3. [f] Equation 2. [g] Enantiomer A. [h] λ 578 and 546 nm; solvent is column eluant, unless otherwise noted. [i] CH_3OH as solvent.

MICROCRYSTALLINE CELLULOSE TRIACETATE

Professor G. Hesse and Dr. R. Hagel, at the Universitat Erlangen-Nurnberg, West Germany, demonstrated (1) that if one prepares cellulose triacetate by heterogeneous acetylation, the conformations and the mutual arrangement of the glucose units on the parallel chains which make for a rigid molecule with crystalline regions due to hydrogen bonding is maintained. The cavities bounded by the atoms shown below are asymmetric and large enough to allow molecules or parts of molecules to be included within them. In principle, an asymmetric cavity would allow for diastereomeric interactions for enantiomers of a given chiral compound. Resolution of racemates might then be achievable. The inclusion of a chiral molecule in the "niche" between each two acetylated glucose units is dependent mainly on the shape and size of the molecule and apparently only to a small extent by the nature of the functional groups it contains. (Because of the ability of the acetyl group to rotate, the cavity which it helps to form can be larger or smaller.) Hesse and Hagel used this adsorbent successfully to chromatographically resolve a number of racemates containing various functional groups. The separations were usually more effective if one of the substituents at the chiral center was a phenyl group with at least 3 adjacent positions unsubstituted.

Dr. H. Markgraf (2) at the University of Bonn, recently reported the complete resolution of some N-methylated barbiturates by chromatography on microcrystalline cellulose triacetate as shown by the data that follow on the next five pages.

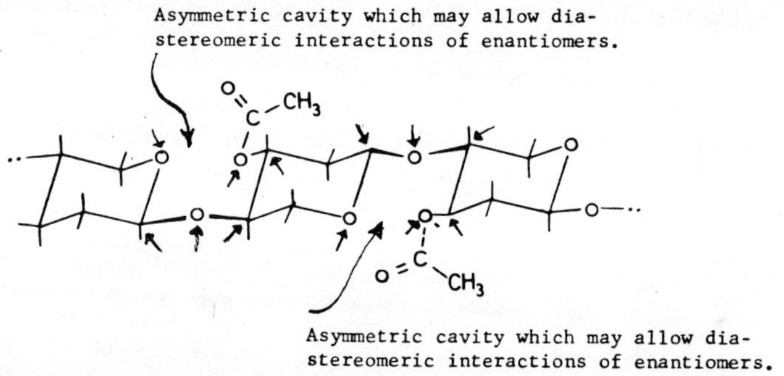

(1) G. Hesse, R. Hagel, Chromatographia, 6, 277 (1973); ibid, 9, 62 (1976); Liebigs Ann. Chem., 996 (1976).
(2) From the Ph.D. dissertation of Dr. H. Markgraf, University of Bonn, West Germany (1980). (Obtained through the kindness of Prof. G. Blaschke.)

The racemate (30) was resolved chromatographically using microcrystalline cellulose triacetate as adsorbent (205 mgs. adsorbent, 85 x 2.5 cm. chromatography tube, 301 mgs. racemate using 95% ethanol as eluent under a pressure of 2.5 bars). The active acids obtained had a m.p. of 100° and a $[\alpha]^{22}_{365}$ -26.6° (C, 0.645, ethanol) (125 mgs.) and $[\alpha]^{22}_{365}$ 26.8° (C, 0.670, ethanol) (127 mgs.).

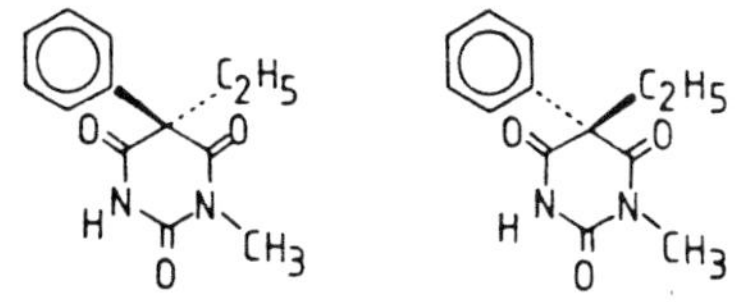

30a 30b

(R)-(-)-1-Methyl-5, 5-phenylethylbarbitursäure (30a)
(S)-(+)-1-Methyl-5, 5-phenylethylbarbitursäure (30b)

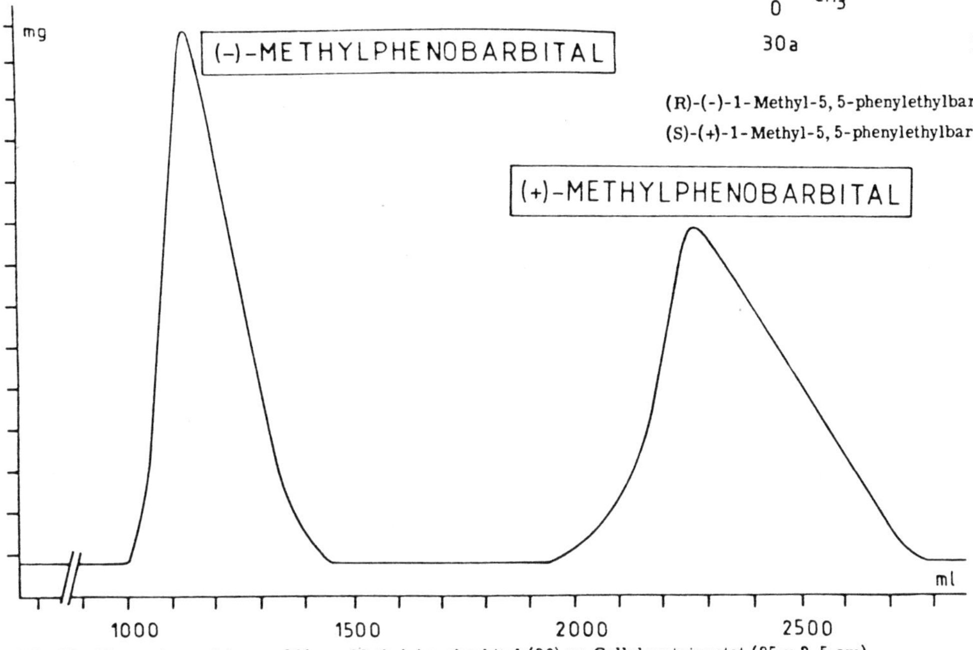

Abb. 10: Chromatographie von 301 mg Methylphenobarbital (30) an Cellulosetriacetat (85 x 2, 5 cm)
Elutionsmittel: 95 % ETOH

The racemate (31) was resolved chromatographically using microcrystalline cellulose triacetate as adsorbent (205 mgs. adsorbent, 85 x 2.5 cm. chromatography tube, 160.6 mgs. racemate, using 95% ethanol as eluent under 2.5 bars pressure). The active acids had a m.p. 152° and a $[\alpha]^{20}_{365}$ -42.3° (C, 0.635, ethanol) and $[\alpha]^{20}_{365}$ 41° (C, 0.380, ethanol).

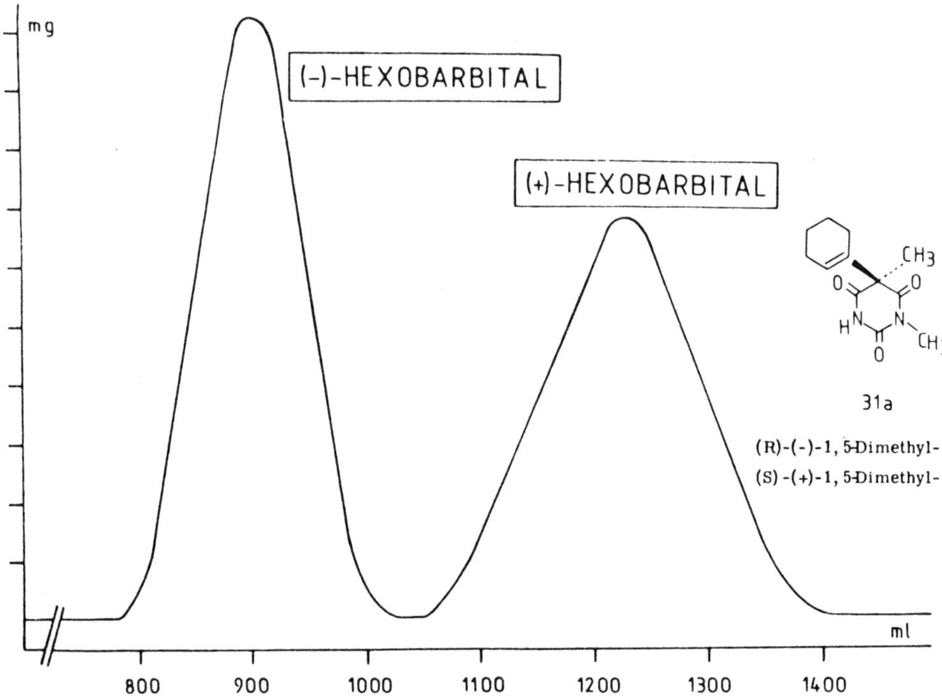

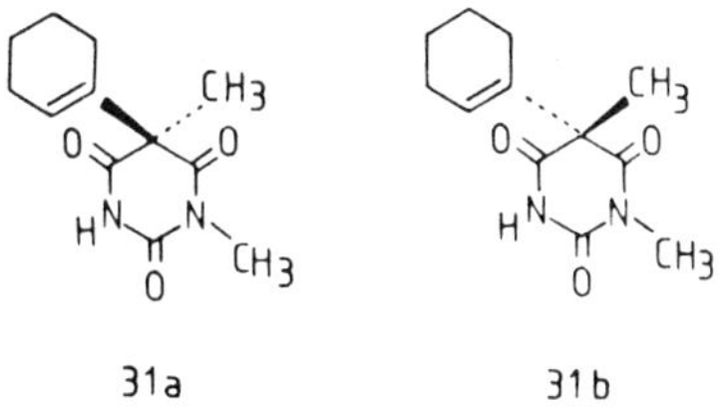

31a 31b

(R)-(-)-1, 5-Dimethyl-5-cyclohexenyl-barbitursäure (31a)
(S) -(+)-1, 5-Dimethyl-

Abb. 11: Chromatographie von 160,6 mg Hexobarbital (31) an 205 g Cellulosetriacetat (85 x 2, 5 cm)
Elutionsmittel: 95 % ETOH

The racemate (32) was resolved chromatographically using microcrystalline cellulose triacetate as adsorbent (205 mgs. adsorbent, 85 x 2.5 cm. chromatography tube, 160 mgs. racemate using 95% ethanol as eluent under a pressure of 2.5 bars.). The active acid obtained has a m.p. 141°C and $[\alpha]^{20}_{365}$ -51.2° (C, 0.580, ethanol) and $[\alpha]^{20}_{365}$ +51.8° (C, 0.550, ethanol).

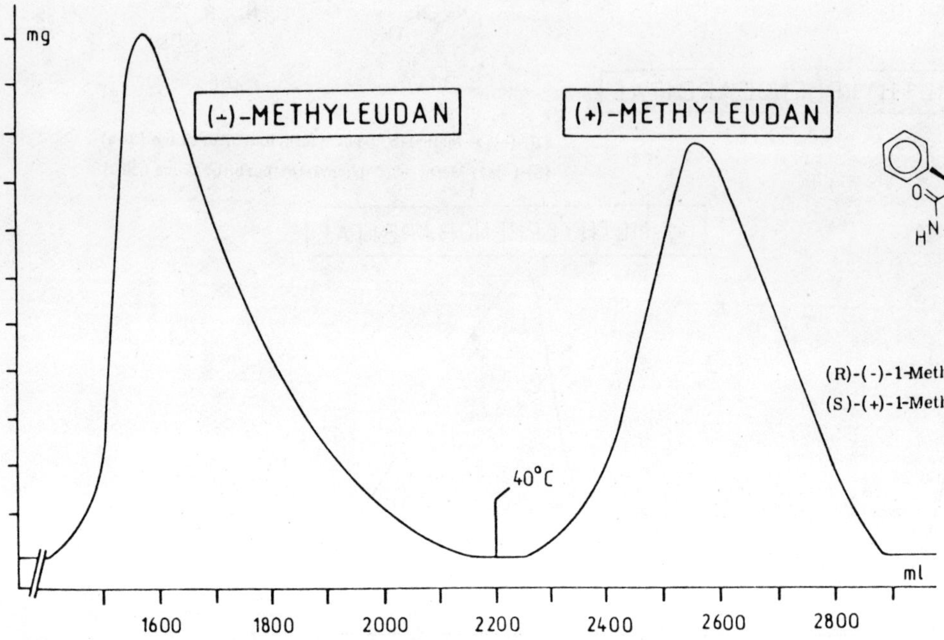

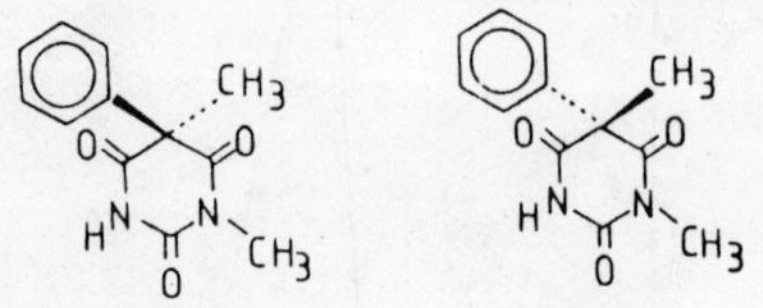

32a 32b

(R)-(-)-1-Methyl-5, 5 phenylmethylbarbitursäure (32 a)
(S)-(+)-1-Methyl-5, 5 phenylmethylbarbitursäure ((32 b)

Abb. 12: Chromatographie von 160 mg Methyleudan (32) an 205 g Cellulosetriacetat (85 x 2, 5 cm)
Elutionsmittel: 95 % ETOH

The racemate (33) was resolved chromatographically using microcrystalline cellulose triacetate as adsorbent (205 mgs. adsorbent, 85 x 2.5 cm. chromatography tube, 140 mgs. racemate using 95% ethanol as eluent under a pressure of 2.5 bars). There was obtained fractions of $[\alpha]_{365}$ -25.5 (ethanol) and $[\alpha]_{365}$ +22.2° (ethanol). Literature[1] value for S-enantiomer is $[\alpha]_{365}$ +25.5° (ethanol).

(1) J. Knabe and H. Junginger, Pharmazie, 27, 443 (1972).

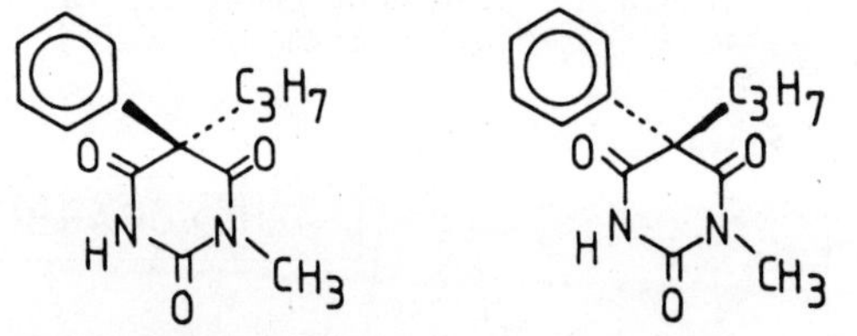

33a 33b

(R)-(-)-1-Methyl-5, 5-phenylpropylbarbitursäure (33 a)
(S)-(+)-1-Methyl-5, 5-phenylpropylbarbitursäure (33 b)

The racemate (34) was resolved chromatographically using microcrystalline cellulose triacetate as adsorbent (205 mgs. adsorbent, 85 x 2.5 cm. chromatography tube, 205 mgs. racemate using 95% ethanol as eluent under a pressure of 2.5 bars.). There was obtained active acids with m.p. 122°, $[\alpha]_{365}^{20}$ 21° (C, 0.520, ethanol) (80 Mgs.) and a m.p. 121°, $[\alpha]_{365}^{20}$ -21.1° (C, 0.540, ethanol)(83 mgs.). Literature[1] value for S-enantiomer is $[\alpha]_{365}$ 20.5° (ethanol).

(1) J. Knabe and D. Strauss, Arch. Pharm. (Weinheim), 305, 54 (1972).

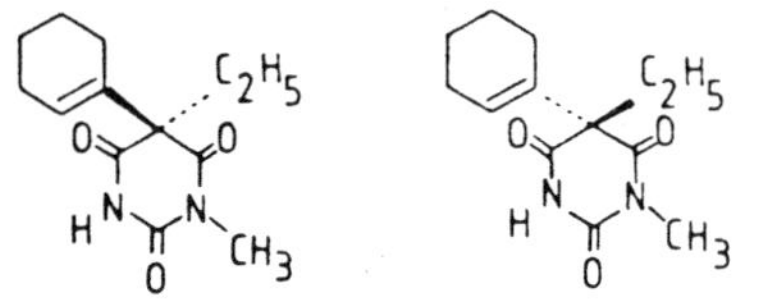

34a 34b

(R)-(-)-1-Methyl-5, 5-cyclohexenylethylbarbitursäure (34 a)

(S)-(+)-1-Methyl-5, 5-cyclohexenylethylbarbitursäure (34 b)

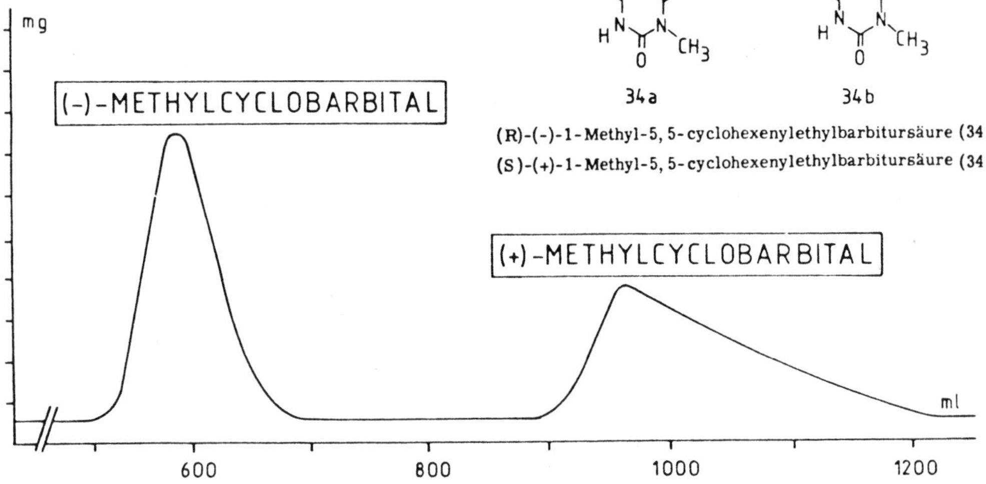

Abb. 13 : Chromatographie von 208,7 mg Methylcyclobarbital (34) an 205 g Cellulosetriacetat (85 x 2,5 cm)
Elutionsmittel : 95 % ETOH

The racemate (35) was resolved chromatographically using microcrystalline cellulose triacetate as adsorbent (205 mgs. adsorbent, 85 x 2.5 cm. chromatography tube, 200 mgs. racemate, using 95% ethanol as eluent under a pressure of 2.5 bars). There was obtained active acids with m.p. 180°, $[\alpha]_{365}^{20}$ 42.5° (C, 0.600, ethanol) (80 mgs.) and m.p. 179°, $[\alpha]_{365}^{20}$ -43.1° (C, 0.515, ethanol) (87 mgs.). Literature[1] value for S-enantiomer $[\alpha]_{365}$ 41.8° (ethanol).

(1) H.P Buch, F. Schneider-Affeld, W. Rummel and J. Knabe, Naunyn-Schmiedeberg's Arch. Pharmacol., 277, 191 (1973).

35a 35b

(R)-(-)-1, 5-Dimethyl-5-cyclohexylbarbitursäure (35 a)

(S)-(+)-1, 5-Dimethyl-5-cyclohexylbarbitursäure (35 a)

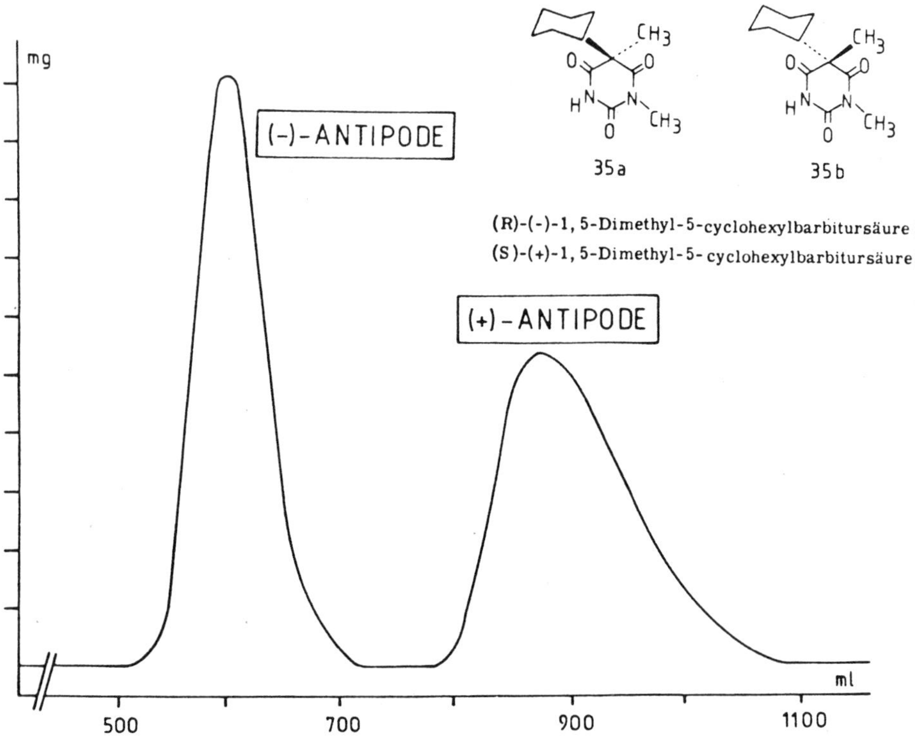

Abb. 14 : Chromatographie von Dimethylcyclohexylbarbitursäure (35) an 205 g Cellulosetriacetat (85 x 2,5 cm)
Elutionsmittel: 95 % ETOH

The racemate (36) was resolved chromatographically using microcrystalline cellulose triacetate as adsorbent (205 mgs. adsorbent, 85 x 2.5 cm. chromatography tube, 200.2 mgs. racemate, using 95% ethanol as eluent under a pressure of 2.5 bars.) There was obtained active acids with m.p. 153°, $[\alpha]^{20}_{365}$ 20° (C, 0.500, ethanol) (80 mgs.) and m.p. 152°, $[\alpha]^{20}_{365}$ -20.6° (C, 0.510, ethanol) (79 mgs.). Literature[1] value for S-enantiomer $[\alpha]_{365}$ 20.3° (ethanol).

(1) H.P. Buch, F. Schneider-Affeld, W. Rummel and J. Knabe, Naunyn-Schmiedeberg's Arch. Pharmacol., 277, 191 (1973).

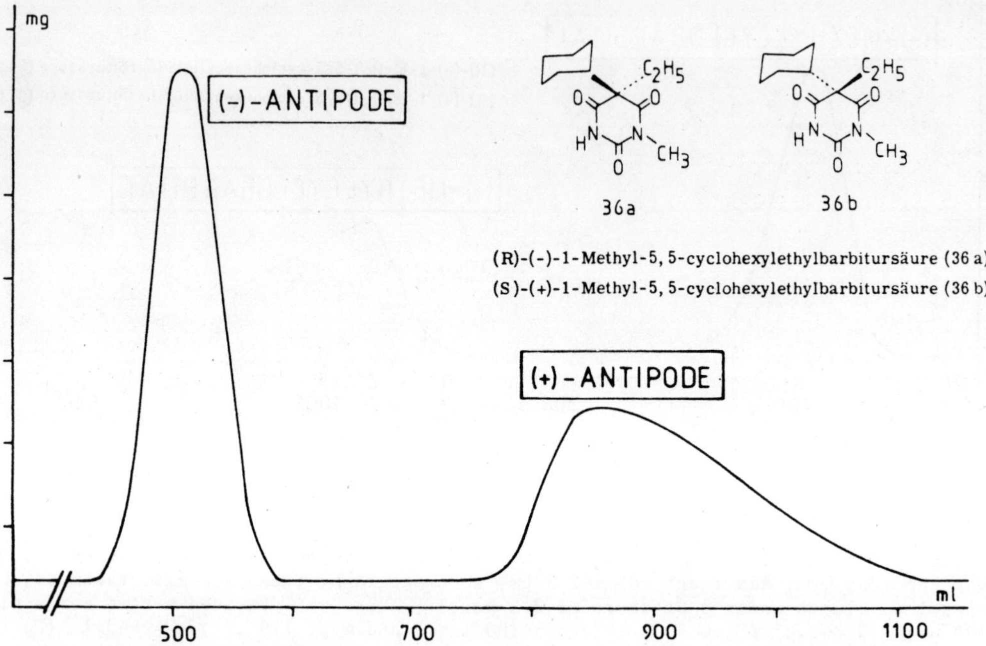

36a 36b

(R)-(-)-1-Methyl-5, 5-cyclohexylethylbarbitursäure (36 a)
(S)-(+)-1-Methyl-5, 5-cyclohexylethylbarbitursäure (36 b)

Abb. 15 : Chromatographie von Methylcyclohexylethylbarbitursäure (36) an 205 g Cellulosetriacetat (85 x 2, 5 cm)
Elutionsmittel : 95 % ETOH

The racemate (37) was resolved chromatographically using microcrystalline cellulose triacetate as adsorbent (205 mgs. adsorbent, 85 x 2.5 cm. chromatography tube, 257.3 racemate, using 95% ethanol as eluent under a pressure of 2.5 bars). There was obtained fractions with $[\alpha]_{365}$ 25.3° (ethanol) and $[\alpha]_{365}$ -25.3° (ethanol). Literature[1] value for S-enantiomer $[\alpha]_{365}$ 25.6° (ethanol)

(1) J. Knabe and H. Junginger, Pharmazie, 27, 443 (1972).

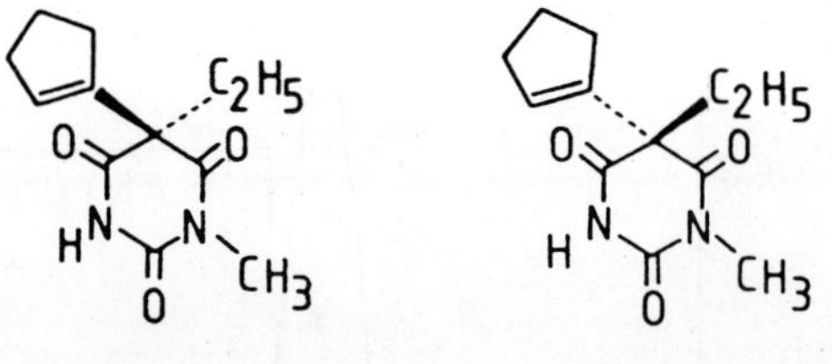

37a 37b

(R)-(-)-1-Methyl-5, 5-cyclopentenyl-ethylbarbitursäure (37 a)
(S)-(+)-1-Methyl-5, 5-cyclopentenyl-ethylbarbitursäure (37 b)

The racemate (44) was resolved chromatographically (recycling chromatography) using adsorbent 2 (263.1 mgs. racemate using toluene:dioxane 1:1 as eluent under a pressure of 2 bars). There was obtained fractions of $[\alpha]_{589}$ -128.5° (dioxane) and $[\alpha]_{589}$ 127.5° (dioxane) and also finally a recrystallized fraction of $[\alpha]_{589}$ -127° (C, 0.2576, dioxane).

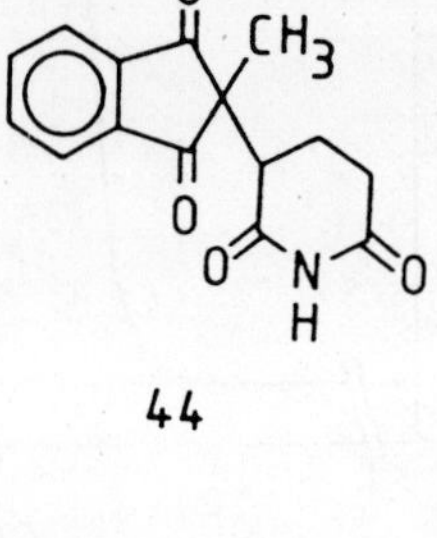

44

CHROMATOGRAPHIC RESOLUTION OF RACEMATES USING CHIRAL POLYAMIDES AS ADSORBENTS

ADSORBENT 1

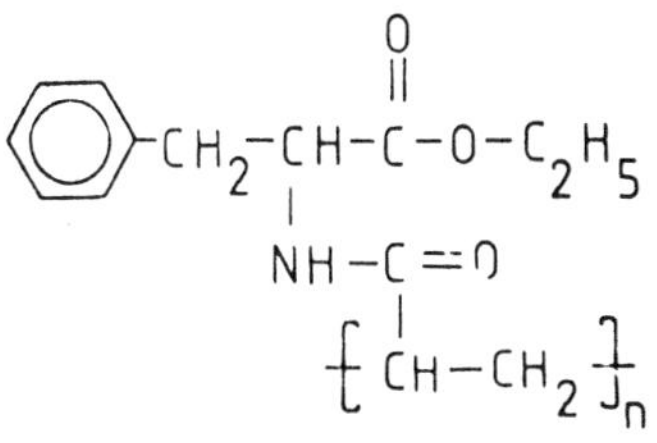

ADSORBENT 2

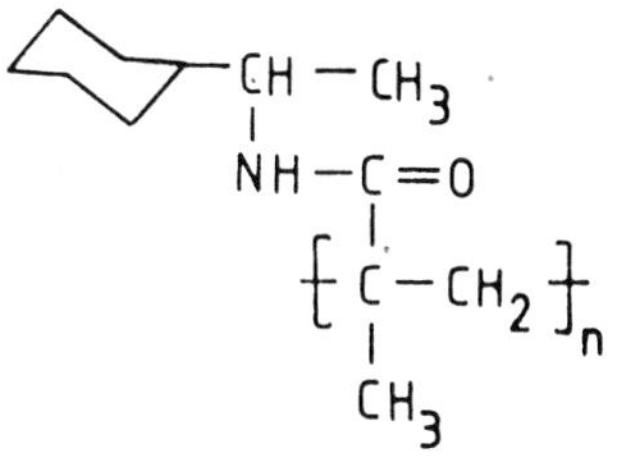

Oxazepam

Racemic oxazepam (45.6 mgs.) was chromatographically resolved using adsorbent 1. There was finally obtained 22.8 mgs. of (+)-enantiomer with m.p. 205° and $[\alpha]^{22}_{589}$ 432.9° (dioxane) and $[\alpha]^{22}_{589}$ -431.2° (dioxane).

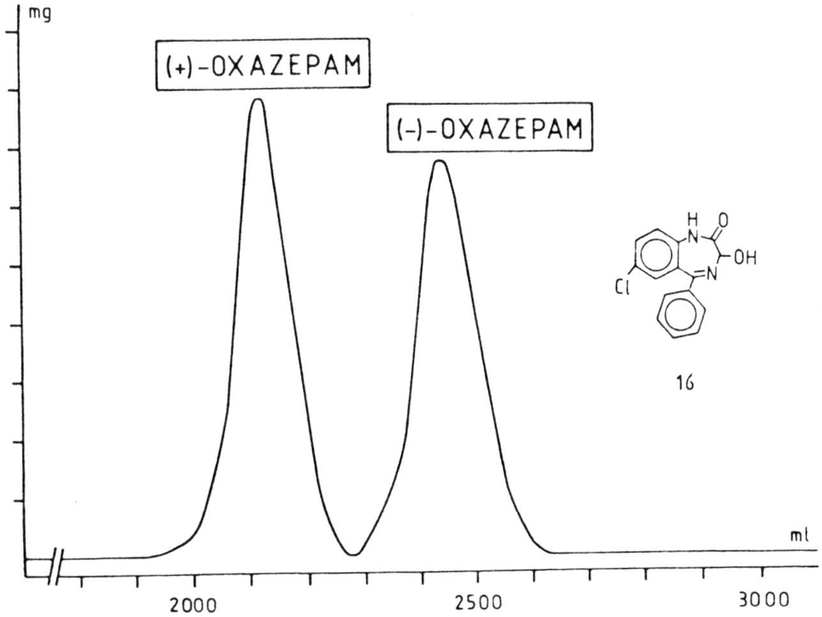

Abb. 7: Chromatographie von 45,6 mg Oxazepam (16) an 250 g Polyamid 1 (76 x 3,2 cm)
Elutionsmittel Toluol/Dioxan 1:1

Chlorthalidone

Racemic chlorthalidone (530 mgs.) was chromatographically resolved using adsorbent 1. There was finally obtained 250 mgs. of (-)-enantiomer with m.p. 264° (dec.) and $[\alpha]^{25}_{589}$ -140.1° (C, 0.2527, dioxane) and 220 mgs. of (+)-enantiomer with 264° (dec.) and $[\alpha]^{25}_{589}$ 140.0°, (C, 0.2505, dioxane).
Reference: From the Ph.D. disseration of Dr. H. Markgraf, University of Bonn (1980).

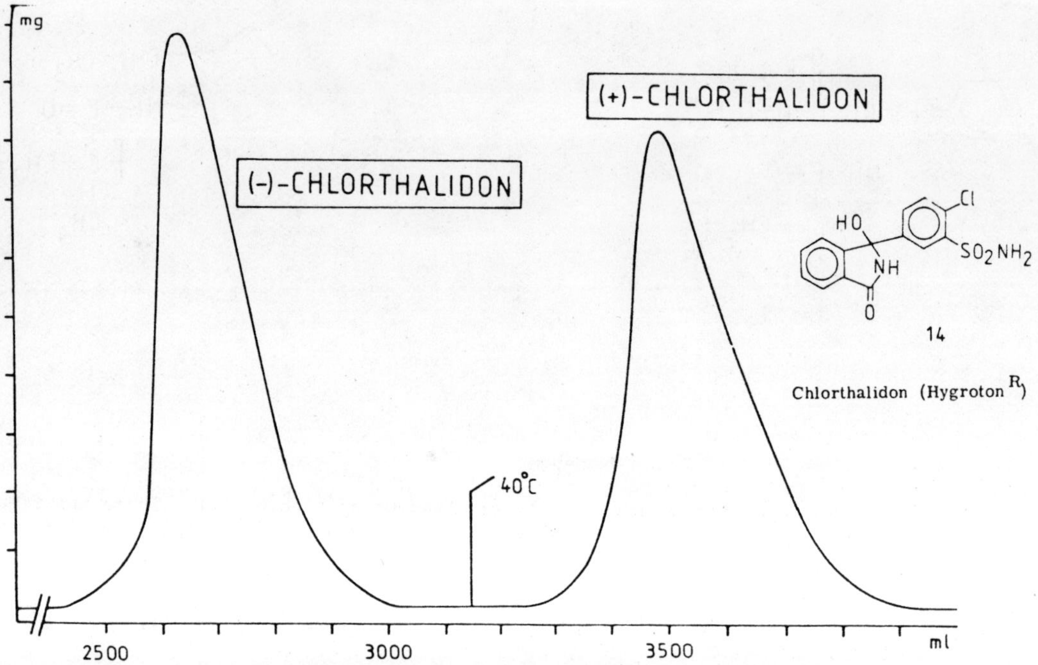

Abb. 4 : Chromatographie von 530 mg Chlorthalidon (14) an 250 g Polyamid 1 (76 x 3, 2 cm)
Elutionsmittel Toluol/Dioxan 1 : 1

2-(Bicyclo-2,2,1-heptan-2-endo-3-endodicarboimido-2,6-piperidindione (Biglumide)

Racemic Biglumide (600 mgs) was chromatographically resolved using adsorbent 2. There was finally obtained (after 2 crystallizations from ethanol) 86.3 mgs. of (+)-enantiomer with m.p. 242° (decomp.) and $[\alpha]^{25}_{589}$ 30° (C, 0.452, DMF) and 179.5 mgs. of (-)-enantiomer with m.p. 242° (decomp.) and $[\alpha]^{25}_{589}$ -29.6° (C, 0.486, DMF).
Reference: From the Ph.D. dissertation of Dr. H. Markgraf, University of Bonn (1980).

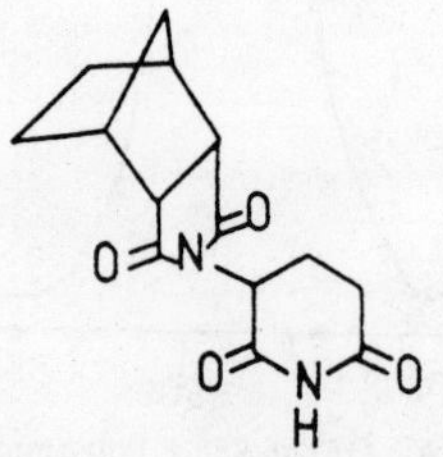

Biglumid

(R, S)-2-(Bicydo- 2, 2, 1 -heptan-2 -endo-3-
-endodicarboximido-2, 6-piperidindion

Reference
H. Hess, G. Burger and H. Musso, Angew. Chem. Int. Ed. Engl., 17, 612 (1978).

Summary
Chromatography on potato starch has been used to resolve, on a preparative scale, the enantiomers of 2,2'-dinitro-6,6'-diphenic acid. Experimental details and results follow.

9.3.6. Racemattrennung von 6,6'-Dinitrodiphensäure (DNDP) durch Stärkesäulenchromatographie (SSC)

Die Optimierungsversuche zur stärkechromatographischen Racemattrennung der DNDP wurden in 6.1. ausführlich geschildert. Im folgenden wird eine Versuchsvorschrift zur quantitativen Racemattrennung der DNDP durch SSC gegeben.

Zunächst wurde Na-Citrat durch Neutralisation von 576 g (3 Mol) Citronensäure (DAB 7) und 360 g (9Mol) NaOH (p.a.) direkt in wäßriger Lösung hergestellt. Nach dem Abkühlen und Auffüllen der neutralen wäßrigen Lösung auf 2 ℓ ist diese 1,5-molar an Na-Citrat. Die Sättigungsgrenze für Na-Citrat liegt bei Raumtemperatur etwa bei 1,6 Mol/ℓ.

Eine Lösung von 500 mg (1,5 mmol) DNDP und 120 mg (3 mmol) NaOH in 5 ml 1,5 m Na-Citrat-Lösung pH 7,9 wurde auf eine Kartoffelstärkesäule 5,2x136 cm aufgetragen. Chromatographiertemperatur: 80°C; Fluß: 70 ml/h. Durch die hohe Viskosität des Fließmittels konnte mit voll geöffnetem Säulen-Hahn eluiert werden. Fraktionen zu 16 oder 17 min; Detektor: $E_{254}, E_{343}, E_{376,5}$ = 25/5/1. Die Fraktionen von 5600 bis 6610 ml enthielten optisch reine (S)(-)-DNDP, die von 6740 bis 7850 ml optisch reine (R)(+)-DNDP. Die Mischfraktionen von 6610 bis 6740 ml enthielten 1,2 % des eingesetzten Materials. Die Grenze der Trennkapazität der beschriebenen Säule gegenüber DNDP war also gerade eben überschritten.

Die zusammengehörenden Fraktionen wurden vereinigt und mit 150 g H_3PO_4 pro ℓ Eluat auf pH 4 angesäuert. Es wurde 10 mal mit wenig Essigester ausgeschüttelt und der über Na_2SO_4 filtrierte Extrakt eingedampft. Die rohen Enantiomeren wurden mit jeweils 10 bis 12 ml siedendem H_2O aufgenommen, dem etwas CH_3OH zugesetzt war. Es wurde einige h bei Raumtemperatur offen stehengelassen, anschließend noch über Nacht bei 0°C zur Vervollständigung der Kristallisation. Es wurden je etwa 150 mg hellgelbe blättchenförmige Kristalle abgesaugt. Aus der vereinigten Mutterlauge und Waschwasser konnten nach Einengen nochmals je etwa 40 mg reines kristallisiertes Produkt erhalten werden.

Nach dem Trocknen ergaben sich:

etwa 190 mg (R)(+)-DNDP, Schmp. 230-233°C, $[\alpha]_D^{20}$ +138,0° (A, c=1)

und 190 mg (S)(-)-DNDP, Schmp. 230-233°C, $[\alpha]_D^{20}$ -137,6° (A, c=1)

Lit: 231-233°C[27a), $[\alpha]_D^{27}$ +133,7° (A, c=2)[27b)]

Die Übereinstimmung der gemessenen Drehwerte mit dem Literaturwert ist unter Berücksichtigung ihrer Temperaturabhängigkeit im Falle der (S)(-)-DNDP quantitativ; der Drehwert der (R)(+)-DNDP liegt um 0,4° höher. Scharf getrocknete DNDP zieht beim Liegen an der Luft kein Wasser an.

Fig. 1. Elution diagram for 2 mg each of (+)- and (–)-6,6'-dinitrodiphenic acid (1) on a 1.6 cm × 135 cm column.

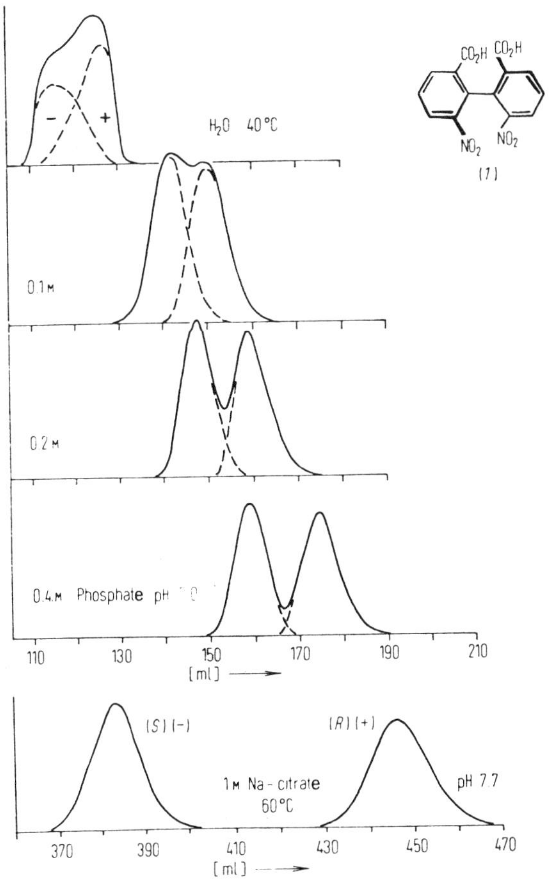

Reference

(1) H. Hess, G. Burger and H. Musso, Angew. Chem. Int. Ed. Engl., 17, 612 (1978); (2) The Ph.D. dissertation of Dr. Heinrich Hess, University of Karlsruhe, West Germany (1978). (Dissertation kindly furnished by Prof. H. Musso.)

Summary

Chromatography on potato starch has been used to resolve the enantiomers of meta linked trimers of orcinol (3a) and the diastereomeric racemic tetramers (RRR,SSS), (RRS, SSR), and (RSR,SRS)-2,4,2',4',2",4",2"',4"'-octahydroxy-6,6',6",6"'-tetramethyl-m,m-quatrephenyl, compounds 4a, 4b and 4c respectively. The experimental details and results follow.

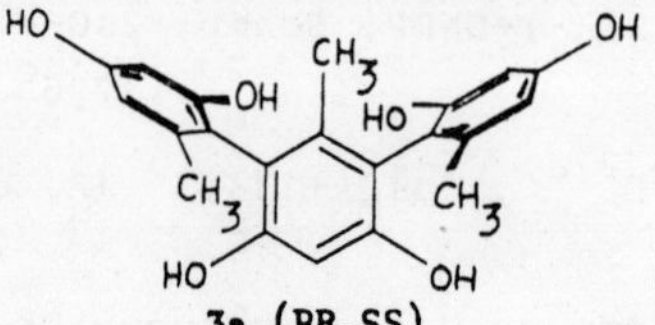

3a (RR,SS)

9.3.1. Trimeres 3a

Eine Lösung von 900 mg 3a in etwa 3 ml warmem CH_3OH wurde mit 30 ml 0,8 m Na-Phosphatpuffer pH 7 verdünnt und das CH_3OH am Rotationsverdampfer abgezogen. Die auf 60°C erwärmte Lösung wurde auf eine Kartoffelstärke-Säule 2,00x138 cm aufgetragen. Fließmittel: 0,8m Na-Phosphatpuffer pH 7; Fluß: 7 ml/h; Fraktionen zu 60 min; T: 50°C; Detektor: E_{283}, E_{295}, E_{301} bei d = 5 mm.

Die Fraktionen von 420 bis 560 ml enthielten optisch reines (SS)(-)-3a, die von 630 bis 850 ml enthielten optisch reines (RR)(+)-3a, in den Zwischenfraktionen war praktisch keine Substanz enthalten. Die Rohprodukte besaßen honigartige Konsistenz und enthielten noch eine beträchtliche Menge Lösungsmittel. Sie wurden jeweils an drei DC-Platten mit Essigester/$CHCl_3$ = 55/45 gereinigt und aus 20 ml Ether, dem etwas $CHCl_3$ zugegeben werden kann, umkristallisiert. Die reinen Enantiomeren kristallisieren beim Stehenlassen im Kühlschrank in großen farblosen (RR) bzw. fast farblosen (SS) hexagonalen Blättchen vom Schmp. 300-302°C, $[\alpha]_D^{20}$ = ±59,0° (A, c=5), Ausbeute je etwa 400 mg. Die Trennkapazität der verwendeten Säule bezüglich 3a war gut ausgenutzt.

Beim 3a wurde der in 3.2. diskutierte Einfluß der Temperatur auf die Trennwirksamkeit einer Stärkesäule erstmals beobachtet. Abb.9 stellt diesen Einfluß anschaulich dar.

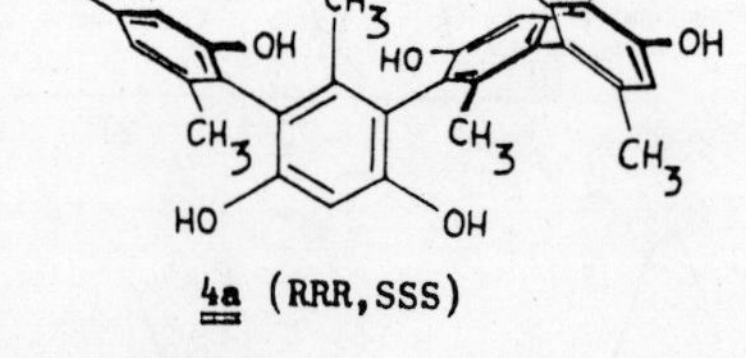

4a (RRR,SSS)

9.3.4. Tetrameres 4a

Eine Lösung von 200 mg 4a in etwa 2 ml heißem CH_3OH wurde in 40 ml heißes H_2O gegeben und das CH_3OH über dem Bunsenbrenner verkocht. Die 70°C warme Lösung wurde auf eine nicht thermostatisierte Kartoffelstärkesäule 5,5x34 cm aufgetragen. Es wurde bei Raumtemperatur zunächst mit reinem H_2O eluiert. Fluß: etwa 40 ml/h; Fraktionen zu 20 min; Detektor: E_{283}, $E_{296,7}$, $E_{302,7}$ bei d=5 mm. Die Fraktionen von 630 bis 1080 ml enthielten optisch reines (SSS)(-)-4a. Sie wurden vereinigt und zur Trockne eingedampft. Aus dem rötlichen Rückstand, der zu zwei Dritteln aus löslicher Stärke bestand, wurde das optisch aktive 4a durch 1-stündiges Behandeln mit warmem Aceton herausgelöst. Der filtrierte rohe Aceton-Extrakt wurde an drei DC-Platten 20x40 cm mit Essigester/$CHCl_3$ = 7/3 gereinigt. Der Aceton-Extrakt der 4a-Zone wurde bis zur schaumigen Konsistenz eingedampft, mit 2 ml Ether aufgenommen und bis zur beginnenden Trübung mit $CHCl_3$ versetzt. Es wurde abgedeckt bei Raumtemperatur einige h stehengelassen. Die nun nur noch $CHCl_3$ enthaltende Lösung wurde zur Vervollständigung der Kristallisation über Nacht im Eisschrank aufbewahrt. Der Kristallbrei, bestehend aus Büscheln von feinen, fast farblosen Nadeln, wurde rasch abgesaugt und mit wenig $CHCl_3$ gewaschen. Beim Versuch, die Kristallmasse an der Luft trockenzusaugen, zerläuft sie in Spuren kondensierter Luftfeuchtigkeit sofort zu einer hellbraunen klebrigen Masse. Am besten verzichtet man ganz auf das Absaugen und zieht statt dessen die über den Kristallen stehende Mutterlauge mit einer Pipette ab.

Ab 900 ml wurde mit einem CH_3OH-Gradienten eluiert: 600 ml H_2O im Vorratsgefäß wurden kontinuierlich durch reines CH_3OH ergänzt. Die Fraktionen von 1700 ml (30 % CH_3OH) bis 2200 ml (70 % CH_3OH) enthielten optisch reines (RRR)(+)-4a. Der Eindampfrückstand der vereinigten Fraktionen enthielt nur wenig lösliche Stärke. Die weitere Aufarbeitung erfolgte wie beim linksdrehenden Enantiomeren. Das kristallisierte Produkt war im Gegensatz zum (-)-4a deutlich rosa gefärbt:

etwa 80 mg (SSS)(-)-4a, $[\alpha]_D^{20}$=-6,8° (A, c=3,5), Schmp. 277-279°C
und 60 mg (RRR)(+)-4a, $[\alpha]_D^{20}$=+5,2° (A, c=2,2), Schmp. 240-266°C

Die Diskrepanz zwischen den Drehwerten beider Enantiomeren kommt einzig und allein von der unterschiedlichen Konzentration bei der Messung. Im Bereich von c=1 bis 4 wurde für beide Enantiomeren reproduzierbar folgende Konzentrationsabhängigkeit der spezifischen Drehung gefunden:

$[\alpha]_D = (\pm)[3,5(\pm)5,6 \cdot \lg c]^\circ$. Der Grenzwert der spezifischen Drehung für kleine Konzentrationen liegt anscheinend bei etwa 3°. Die Drehwerte der Enantiomeren von 4a sollten gemäß obiger Gleichung bei c = 2,2 ±5,4°, bei c = 3,5 ±6,5° betragen. Sie entsprechen sich also innerhalb einer Fehlergrenze von ±0,3°. Die optische Reinheit des zweiten Enantiomeren war sicher besser als 99,99 %, denn zwischen beiden Enantiomeren-Peaks wurde über ein großes Volumen kein 4a eluiert. Beim optisch aktiven 3a, 4b und 4c waren die Drehwerte der Enantiomeren innerhalb der Meßgenauigkeit dem Betrag nach genau gleich. Bei diesen Verbindungen bestand daher kein Anlaß, die Konzentrationsabhängigkeit der

Reference

(1) H. Hess, G. Burger and H. Musso, Angew. Chem. Int. Engl., 17, 612 (1978); (2) The Ph.D. dissertation of Dr. Heinrich Hess, University of Karlsruhe, West Germany (1978) (continued).

spezifischen Drehung zu untersuchen.

Das stärkechromatographische Verhalten der drei Tetrameren wird in Abb.11 veranschaulicht:

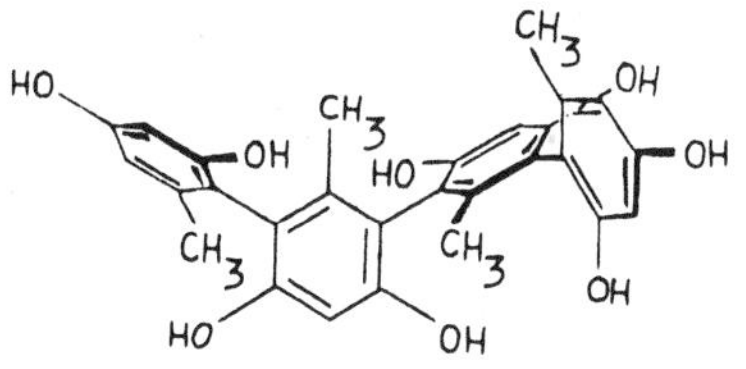

4b (RRS,SSR)

9.3.2. Tetrameres 4b

Zu einer Lösung von 200 mg 4b in 0,5 ml CH_3OH wurden 5 ml 0,4 m Na-Phosphatpuffer pH 7 zugegeben. Die Lösung wurde leicht erwärmt und auf eine Kartoffelstärkesäule 2,00x133 cm aufgetregen, T: 40°C; Fließmittel: 0,4 m Na-Phosphatpuffer pH 7 mit 10 % CH_3OH; Fluß: 6-7 ml/h; Fraktionen zu 60 min; Detektor: E_{283}, E_{295}, E_{301}. Die Fraktionen von 300 bis 460 ml enthielten optisch reines (SSR)(+)-4b. Ab 520 ml wurde mit 15 % CH_3OH eluiert. Die Fraktionen von 900 bis 1200 ml enthielten optisch reines (RRS)(-)-4b. Die vereinigten Fraktionen wurden jeweils auf etwa ein Drittel eingeengt und mit Essigester extrahiert. Die rohen öligen Enantiomeren wurden an drei Platten 20x40 cm mit Essigester/$CHCl_3$ = 7/3 gereinigt. Zu der filtrierten Aceton-Lösung der nun optisch und chemisch reinen 4b-Enantiomeren wurde Benzol gegeben, damit das nicht kristallisierbare 4b beim Einengen gleich flockig ausfällt. Es wurde noch 1 h am Rotationsverdampfer bei 90°C und über Nacht bei 80°C im Ölpumpenvakuum über P_2O_5 getrocknet. Es wurden erhalten:

etwa 80 mg (SSR)(+)-4b, $[\alpha]_D^{20}$=+47,8° (A, c=3,7), Schmp. 199-201°C

und 80 mg (RRS)(-)-4b, $[\alpha]_D^{20}$=-47,9° (A, c=3,8), Schmp. 204-206°C

Die optische Reinheit des zuletzt eluierten Enantiomeren wurde durch Rechromatographie an der gleichen Stärkesäule überprüft. Die (SSR)-Zone des "rohen" (RRS) enthielt nur etwa 1/1000 mg 4b. Seine optische Reinheit betrug also vor der Rechromatographie schon mindestens 99,998 %.

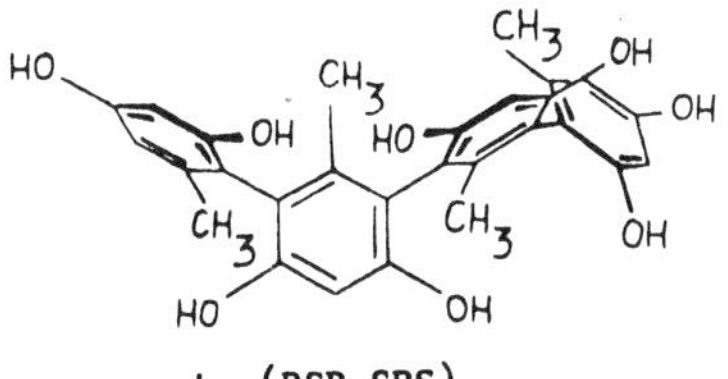

4c (RSR,SRS)

9.3.3. Tetrameres 4c

Hier war im präparativen Maßstab eine einigermaßen vollständige Racemattrennung erst nach Erhöhung der Pufferkonzentration von 0,2 m auf 0,4 m möglich.

4c wurde zunächst in zwei aufeinanderfolgenden Durchgängen an der gleichen Stärkesäule grob aufgetrennt: Eine Lösung von 140 (200) mg 4c in 30 (45) ml CH_3OH wurde mit 270 (400) ml 0,4 m Na-Phosphatpuffer pH 7 aufgefüllt und die auf 60°C erwärmte Lösung auf eine Kartoffelstärkesäule 5,2x132 cm aufgetragen. Nach dem Einziehen der Aufgabelösung wurde mit 400 ml 60°C warmem Fließmittel (0,4 m Na-Phosphatpuffer pH 7 mit 10 % CH_3OH) nachgewaschen. Chromatographier-Temperatur: 40°C; Fluß: etwa 50 ml/h; Fraktionen zu 20 min; Detektor: E_{283}, $E_{294,8}$ (5mm), α_{340}(5cm). Die Fraktionen von 3200 bis 4600 ml enthielten rechtsdrehendes 4c. Es folgten Mischfraktionen, die etwa 3 % des eingesetzten Racemats enthielten. Ab 5200 ml wurde mit 15 % CH_3OH eluiert. Die Fraktionen von 5500 bis 7700 ml enthielten linksdrehendes 4c. Die Enantiomeren-Zonen wurden jeweils auf etwa zwei Drittel ihres Volumens eingeengt und mit Essigester extrahiert. Die gut wasserlöslichen rohen Enantiomeren beider Trennansätze wurden zur Stärke-Rechromatographie gemeinsam und ohne Kieselgel-chromatographische Zwischenreinigung in je 6 ml warmem Fließmittel gelöst. Wegen des kleinen Aufgabe-Volumens waren die Zonen der Enantiomeren hier wesentlich schärfer als bei der Trennung des Racemats: Die Fraktionen von 3700 bis 4200 ml enthielten optisch reines (RSR)(+)-4c. Bei der Rechromatographie des rohen linksdrehenden 4c enthielten die Fraktionen von 5000 bis 7100 ml optisch reines (SRS)(-)-4c. Die optischen Reinheiten der rohen Enantiomeren betrugen vor der Rechromatographie, wie durch Ausmessen der Enantiomeren-Peaks bei der Rechromatographie festgestellt wurde: 99,5 % für das rechtsdrehende und 97 % für das linksdrehende 4c. Eine Reinigung der rohen Enantiomeren durch Ausscheidung von Racemat aus wäßriger Lösung ist möglich, aber mühevoll und verlustreich, da nach jeder Kristallisation die Mutterlaugen kieselgelchromatographisch gereinigt werden müssen, sonst findet keine weitere Kristallisation statt. Eine Reinigung durch Rechromatographie an der gleichen Stärkesäule ist dem vorzuziehen. Die Grenze der Trennkapazität der beschriebenen Säule bezüglich 4c war erreicht. Sie läßt sich durch Anwendung von 0,8 m Phosphatpuffer und einer höheren Temperatur (vielleicht ist Na-Citrat-Puffer noch viel besser) sicher erhöhen. Die optisch reinen Enantiomeren wurden jeweils an drei Platten 20x40 cm mit Essigester/$CHCl_3$ = 9/1 gereinigt. Die Aceton-Extrakte der nun optisch und chemisch reinen Enantiomeren wurden eingedampft, mit CH_3OH aufgenommen, mit 1 ml H_2O versetzt und bei Raumtemperatur einige h offen stehengelassen. Nach Animpfen schieden sich feine farblose Kristallnadeln ab. Zur Vervollständigung der Kristallisation wurde einige Tage bei 0°C stehengelassen und zwischendurch am Rotationsverdampfer weiter eingeengt. Nach dem Absaugen wurden die Mutterlauge und das Waschwasser nochmals eingeengt, um weiteres kristallisiertes Material zu erhalten.

Es wurden erhalten:

je etwa 90 mg (RSR)(+)-4c, $[\alpha]_D^{20}$=+117,4° (A, c=3,4), Schmp. 316-317°C und

(SRS)(-)-4c, $[\alpha]_D^{20}$=-117,7° (A, c=4), Schmp. 315,5-318°C

Affinity chromatography is based on the ability of biologically active substances to bind specifically and reversibly other substances generally called ligands. If an insoluble ligand is prepared, usually by covalently coupling to a solid support, and a solution containing the biologically active product to be isolated is passed through a column of this ligand, then all compounds having no affinity for the ligand will pass through unretarded. In contrast, a compound that shows an affinity for the insoluble ligand would be adsorbed in the column. It can be later released from the complex with the attached ligand by altering the composition of the solvent passing down the column.

Reference

K.K. Stewart and R.F. Doherty, Proc. Nat. Acad. Sci. U.S.A., 70, 2850 (1973).

Summary

The authors report the resolution of DL-tryptophane by affinity chromatography on bovine-serum albumin-agarose columns. Experimental details and results follow.

L-Amino acid oxidase (Type 1) (EC 1.4.3.2) from *Crotalus adamanteus* venom, peroxidase (Type II) (horse radish; EC 1.11.1.7), Tris (free base), Sepharose 4B-200, and homovanillic acid were obtained from Sigma Chemical Co. Cyanogen bromide, ethylenediamine, succinic anhydride, and 3-(3-dimethylaminopropyl)-1-ethylcarbodiimide were obtained from Eastman Chemical Co. Bovine-serum albumin (Cohn powder fraction V) was purchased from Schwarz-Mann and used either without further purification or after being defatted by the method of Chen (3).

The D, L, and the DL mixture of tryptophan were obtained from Merck and Co. L-Glutamic acid *N*-carboxyanhydride was a generous gift of Dr. J. M. Manning, who had obtained the reagent from Dr. D. F. Veber of Merck and Co.

Amino-acid analyses of the hydrolysates were performed by the method of Spackman, Stein, and Moore (4). D- and L-tryptophan contents were determined by the ion-exchange method of Manning and Moore (5), in which dipeptides are formed by reaction of the tryptophan with L-glutamic acid *N*-carboxyanhydride, the L-glutamyl-D-tryptophan is separated from the L-glutamyl-L-tryptophan by ion-exchange chromatography, and each diastereomer is quantitated. L-Tryptophan content was determined by the method of Guilbault and Hieserman (6) with L-amino-acid oxidase, and an Aminco fluoromicrophotometer with a CS 7-60 primary filter and a 47B, 2A combination secondary filter.

The substituted agarose supports were prepared according to Cuatrecasas (7) with cyanogen bromide. The extent of coupling was determined from amino-acid analyses of hydrolysates of the support material, and coupling efficiencies of 5–6% were normally obtained. Chromatographic columns were packed with either bovine-serum albumin linked directly to the agarose beads (bovine-serum albumin–agarose), bovine-serum albumin linked to the agarose beads by an ethylenediamine-succinic acid leash (bovine-serum albumin–succinoylaminoethyl–agarose), or defatted bovine-serum albumin linked to the agarose beads by the same leash (defatted bovine-serum albumin–succinoylaminoethyl-agarose). Control columns were packed with agarose or leashed agarose (no bovine-serum albumin) as appropriate.

4. Spackman, D. H., Stein, W. H. & Moore, S. (1958) *Anal. Chem.* **30**, 1190–1206.
5. Manning, J. M. & Moore, S. (1968) *J. Biol. Chem.* **243**, 5591–5597.
6. Guilbault, G. & Hieserman, J. (1968) *Anal. Biochem.* **26**, 1–11.
7. Cuatrecasas, P. (1970) *J. Biol. Chem.* **245**, 3059–3065.

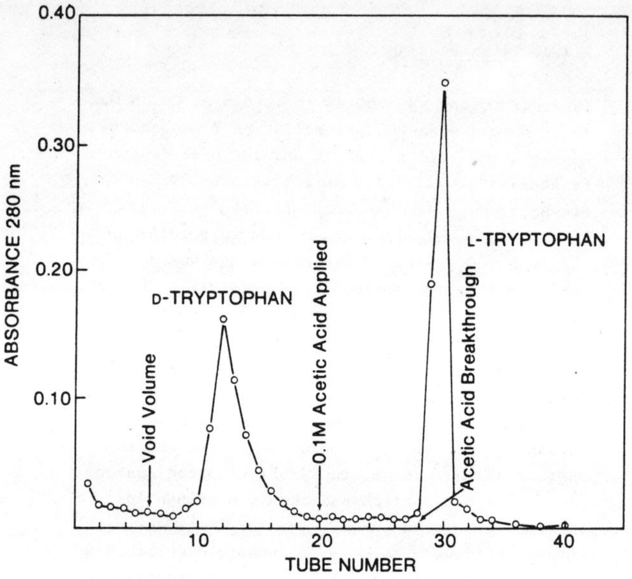

FIG. 1. Chromatography of DL-tryptophan on defatted bovine-serum albumin–succinoylaminoethyl-agarose. DL-tryptophan (500 nmol) dissolved in 0.1 ml of 0.1 M borate buffer (pH 9.2) containing 1% (v/v) $(CH_3)_2SO$, was applied to a 0.9 × 25-cm column of defatted bovine-serum albumin-succinoyl-aminoethyl-agarose. The column contained a total of 630 nmol of bovine-serum albumin. The column was eluted at 30 ml/hr with the borate buffer [no$(CH_3)_2SO$] for 20 tubes then with 0.1 N acetic acid. The void volume was determined from the elution volume of $(CH_3)_2SO$.

Author's comments:

Traditionally, affinity chromatography is considered to be an isolation technique for macromolecules such as enzymes, antibodies, and antigens. However, since the key concept in affinity chromatography is the use of specific biological interactions for separation of compounds (9), we feel that the term affinity chromatography should be extended to all chromatographic separations based on a specific biological interaction. Under this broader definition, resolution of DL-tryptophan on the bovine-serum albumin-succinoylaminoethyl-agarose columns is an example of affinity chromatography.

9. Cuatrecasas, P. & Anfinsen, C. B. (1971) in *Methods in Enzymology*, ed. Jakoby, W. B. (Academic Press, New York), Vol. 22, pp. 345–378.

Reference

A. Harada, M. Furue and S. Nozakura, J. Polymer Sci. Poly. Chem., 16, 189 (1978).

Summary

Crosslinked α- and β-cyclodextrin gels (α-CD-E and β-CD-E) were used for the chromatographic resolution of racemic mandelic acid and its derivatives. β-CD-E bound L-(+)-isomers preferentially over D-(−)-isomers and resolved DL-methyl mandelate to give a D-(−)-isomer of 100% optical purity in the first fraction. Mandelic acid, ethyl mandelate, and O-methylated mandelic acid yielded resolutions of 65–83% in initial fractions. α-CD-E, on the contrary, bound D-(−)-isomers more strongly than L-(+)-isomers, resolving DL-methyl mandelate to a smaller extent than β-CD-E. Binding of DL-mandelic acid and DL-methyl mandelate on β-CD-E was studied quantitatively by the equilibrium method. β-CD-E has a similar binding capacity to starch with 1:1 stoichiometry but bound much more strongly than starch. β-CD-E has the same mode of selectivity as starch for the asymmetric binding of the mandelic acid derivatives, but α-CD-E has a reverse selectivity to β-CD-E and starch. Experimental details and results follow.

Materials

α-Cyclodextrin and β-cyclodextrin were kindly supplied by Hayashibara Biochemical Laboratories Inc. DL-Mandelic acid was purchased from Nakarai Chemicals Ltd, DL-ethyl mandelate from Tokyo Kasei Ltd, and DL-methyl mandelate and DL-β-phenyllactic acid from Sigma Chemical Co. O-Methyl mandelic acid was prepared by the reaction of DL-mandelic acid with dimethyl sulfate.[11]

Preparation of Gels

β-Cyclodextrin gel (β-CD-E) was prepared by the reaction of β-CD with epichlorohydrin according to the procedure of Hoffman.[12] α-Cyclodextrin gel (α-CD-E) was prepared similarly, but gel formation required a longer time. The particle size of the swollen gel was reduced to a size suitable for column chromatography by treatment in a homogenizer and particles of 0.1–0.4 mm in diameter were used.

Column Chromatography

The gel was loaded into a column 10 mm in diameter and 82 cm in length. A solution of a DL-mandelic acid derivative (100–200 mg) in water/acetonitrile (4:1 v/v, 1 ml) was introduced into the column and the column was eluted with water at a flow rate of 10 ml/min. The eluate was collected in fractions of 5 g. The total amount of mandelic acid derivative in each fraction was calculated from the optical absorption at 263 nm, and the amount of the D-isomer in each fraction was determined by optical rotation measurements.

11. R. A. Moss and W. I. Sunshine, *J. Org. Chem.*, **39**, 1083 (1974).
12. J. L. Hoffman. *J. Macromol. Sci.-Chem*, **A7**, 1147 (1973).

A. Harada, M. Furue and S. Nozakura, J. Polymer Sci. Poly. Chem., 16, 189 (1978) continued.

Binding Equilibria

A 1-g portion of well-dried β-CD-E was immersed in 10 ml of aqueous DL-mandelic acid or DL-methyl mandelate solution of an appropriate concentration. In the case of DL-methyl mandelate, 20% acetonitrile–water was used as solvent due to its limited solubility in pure water. The system was degassed under reduced pressure and was kept at 25°C for 48 hr with occasional agitation. After equilibrium was attained, the supernatant liquid was withdrawn and the optical absorption and optical rotation were measured. The specific rotation $[\alpha]_D$ was calculated by the equation $[\alpha]_D = 100\alpha/dc$, where c is concentration (g/dl), α the observed angle of rotation, and d the cell length (dm).

Apparatus

The optical rotation was measured by a JASCO digital polarimeter Model DIP-4 within a ±0.001° accuracy. The optical absorption was measured by using a Hitachi spectrometer, Model 124.

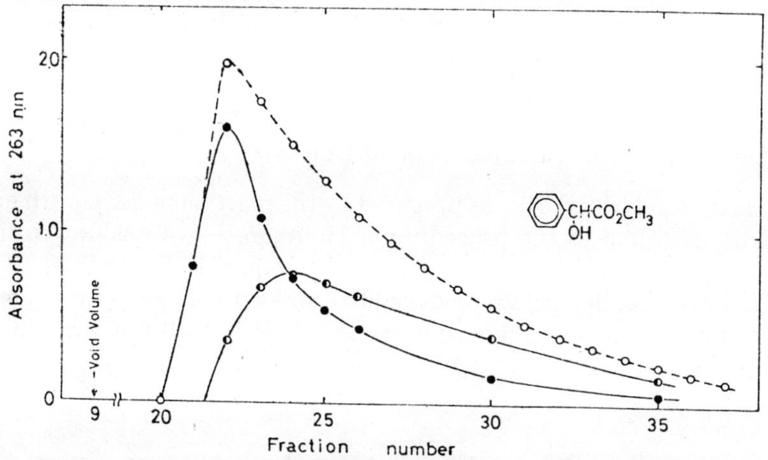

Fig. 1. Chromatography of DL-methyl mandelate on β-CD-E: (○) total; (●) D-(−); (◐) L-(+). Column 1 × 82 cm, 5 g/fraction.

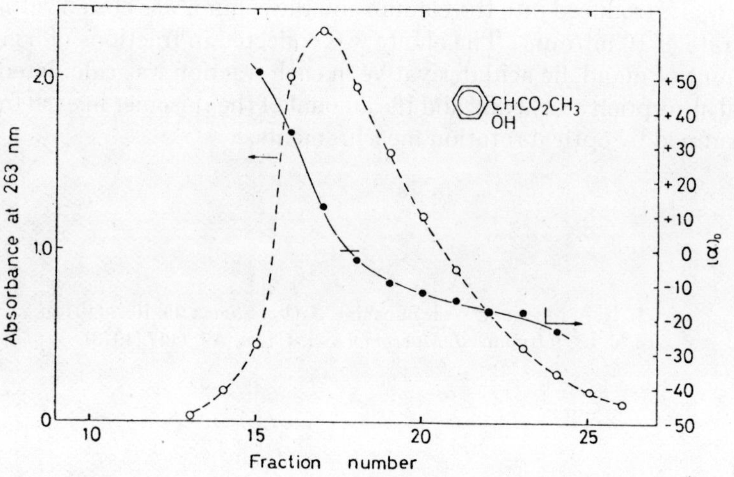

Fig. 4. Chromatography of DL-methyl mandelate on α-CD-E. Column 1 × 82 cm, 5 g/fraction.

A. Harada, M. Furue and S. Nozakura, J. Polymer Sci. Poly. Chem., 16, 189 (1978) continued.

TABLE I
Amount of D-Isomer (%) in the First Two Fractions (β-CD-E)[a]

Racemate	Amount of racemate, mg	D-isomer in fractions, % 1st	2nd	Ratio of V_R L/D
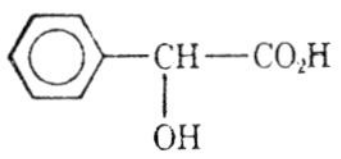	100	67	57	
	200	65	54	
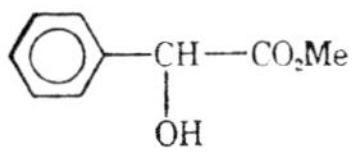	100	100	80	1.09
	100	100	76	
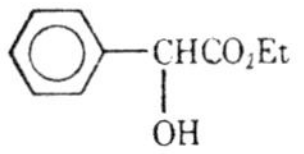	100	75	73	1.08
	200	67	—	
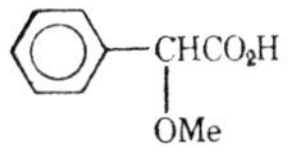	200	83	79	

[a] Column: 1 × 82 cm.; 5 g/fraction.

TABLE II
Binding Equilibrium on β-CD-E[a]

Racemate	C_i mg/ml[b]	C_e mg/ml[c]	Amount bound, mg	Optical rotation α[d]	$[\alpha]_D$
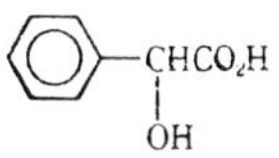	5	2.24	27.7	−0.005	−2.2
	10	5.23	47.7	−0.005	−1.0
	25	16.0	89.4	−0.009	−0.6
	50	36.8	131	+0.004	+0.1
	75	60.4	146	+0.010	+0.2
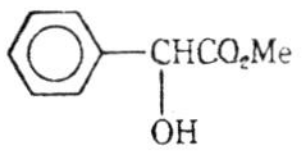	5	3.1	22.8	−0.003	−1.3
	15	10.6	52.8	−0.005	−0.5
	20	15.1	58.8	−0.009	−0.6
	25	19.3	68.4	−0.005	−0.3
	35	29.0	72.0	−0.005	−0.2

[a] β-CD-E, 1 g.
[b] C_i = initial concentration of substrate.
[c] C_e = equilibrium concentration of substrate.
[d] Observed rotation, 1 dm cell, accuracy ± 0.001°.

Reference

J.N. LePage, W. Lindner, G. Davies, D.E. Seitz and B.L. Karger, Anal. Chem., 51, 433 (1979).

Summary

The addition of L-2-R-4-octyldiethylenetriamine-M^{++} (R = ethyl, isopropyl, isobutyl; M = Zn or Cd), I to the mobile phase of a bonded reversed phase column results in the resolution of the dansyl derivatives of racemic amino acids, II. This is the first published report of the use of optically active counterions for the successful high performance reversed phase separation of enantiomers. The experimental details and results follow:

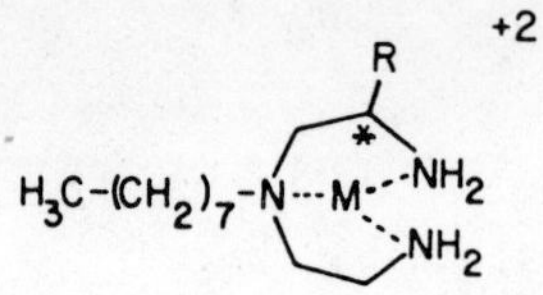

I

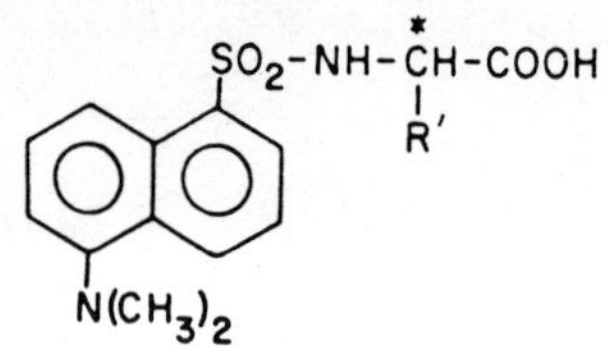

II

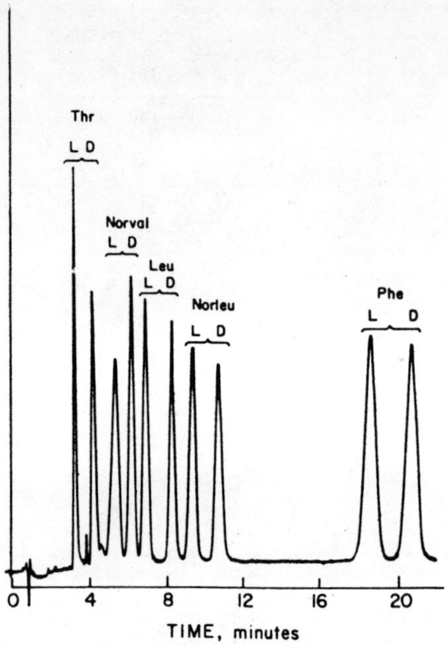

Figure 2. Separation of D,L-dansyl amino acids. Conditions as in Figure 1. Solutes: Thr = threonine; Norval = norvaline; Leu = leucine; Norleu = norleucine; Phe = phenylalanine

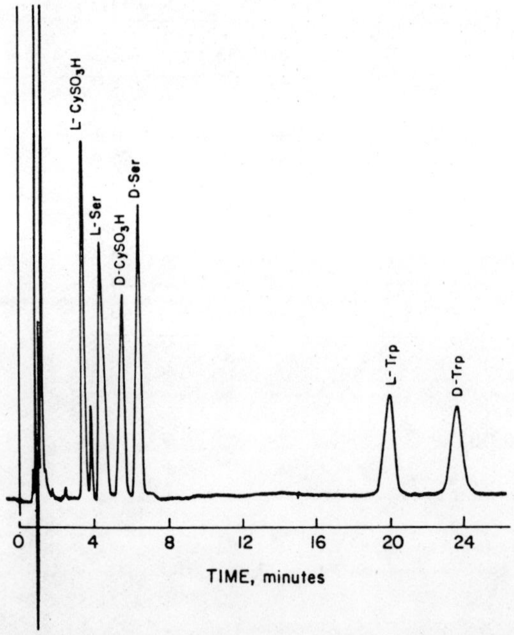

Figure 1. Separation of D,L-dansyl amino acids. Conditions: 0.65 mM L-2-isopropyl-dien-Zn(II); 0.17 M NH_4Ac to pH 9.0 with aqueous NH_3; 35/65 AN/H_2O; T = 30 °C; flow-rate 2mL/min; column: 15 cm by 4.6 mm i.d. Hypersil 5 μm C_8; solutes: $CySO_3H$ = cysteic acid; Ser = serine; Trp = tryptophan

Table I. Retention and Selectivity Parameters for Dansyl Amino Acid Derivatives[a]

	R^d = ethyl		R = isopropyl		R = isobutyl	
solute[b]	k'	α^c	k'	α^c	k'	α^c
α-Ala	3.4 3.4	1.00	3.65 4.6	0.79	6.5 7.6	0.86
α-NH_2 butyric	2.5 2.5	1.00	2.85 3.25	0.88	4.8 5.4	0.89
Norleu	8.25 8.60	0.96	10.0 11.6	0.86	18.0 19.5	0.92
Leu	6.15 6.50	0.94	7.3 8.7	0.84	14.2 13.1	1.08
Thr	2.55 2.15	1.19	2.7 3.8	0.71	5.1 6.2	0.82
Ser	4.0 3.2	1.25	4.1 6.1	0.67	7.8 10.5	0.74
Asp	1.9 1.9	1.00	2.9 2.5	1.16	5.4 5.4	1.00

[a] Common conditions: 0.65 mM L-2-R-dien-Zn, other conditions as in Figure 1. [b] Solutes are dansyl amino acids: α-Ala = α-alanine; α-NH_2 butyric = α-NH_2 butyric acid; Asp = aspartic acid. Other amino acid abbreviations may be found in Figures 1 and 2. [c] $\alpha = k_L'/k_D'$. [d] R = alkyl substituent on metal chelate in I.

Reference

P.E. Hare and E. Gil-Av, Science, 204, 1226 (1979).

Summary

A number of racemic α-amino acids were resolved without prior derivatization on an ion-exchange column (DC4a resin) [Dionex Corp., 1228 Titan Way, Sunnyside, Calif., 94086] using a L-proline-Cu^{++} complex as a chiral eluant. The experimental details and results follow:

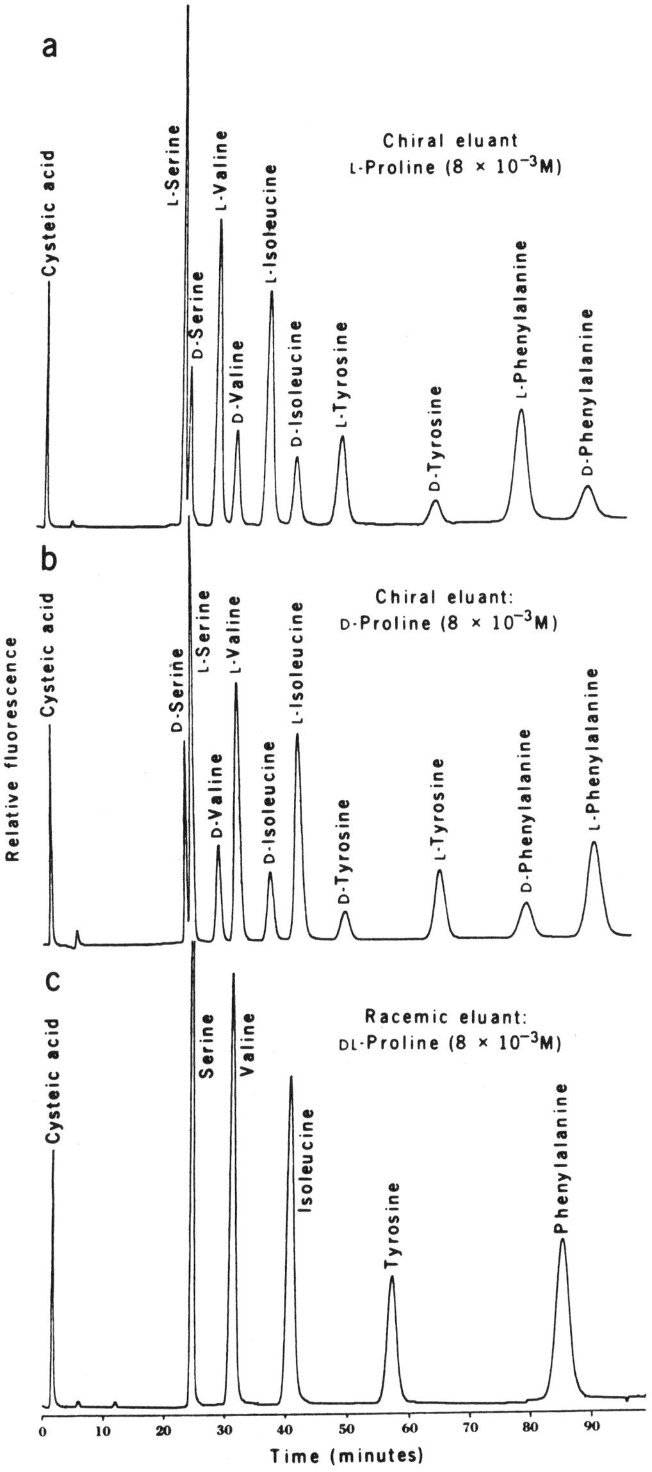

Fig. 1. Effect of the chirality of the eluant on the separation of D- and L-amino acid enantiomers by ligand-exchange chromatography. Identical portions of a mixture of five pairs of amino acid enantiomers, each consisting of 0.375 nmole of L form and 0.125 nmole D form, were injected in each run. Sodium acetate buffer (0.05*N*, *p*H 5.5) containing 4 × $10^{-3}M$ $CUSO_4$ and 8 × $10^{-3}M$ proline was used as eluant. The chirality of the proline ligand was as indicated. The column was equilibrated with each separate eluant for 15 minutes before the sample was injected. The column was 12 by 0.2 cm (inside diameter) packed with DC 4a resin. The eluant flow rate was 10 ml/hour, the reagent flow rate was 10 ml/hour, the column pressure was 200 bars, and the column temperature was 75°C. (a) L-Proline effected the separation of all five pairs of enantiomers with the L enantiomers eluting before the corresponding D enantiomers. (b) D-Proline reversed the order of elution. (c) With racemic proline no resolution occurred. The amino acids eluted halfway between the corresponding enantiomeric peaks in (a) and (b).

Table 1. Adjusted retention times (t'_R) and separation factors ($r = t'_{R(D)}/t'_{R(L)} = k'_D/k'_L$) for some amino acid enantiomers in ligand-exchange chromatography with a chiral eluant. Mobile phase: 0.1*N* sodium acetate with 8 × $10^{-3}M$ $CuSO_4 \cdot 5H_2O$ and 16 × $10^{-3}M$ L-proline. Column and operating details are as described in the Fig. 1 legend. Retention time for cysteic acid taken as column void volume.

Amino acid	Form	t'_R (min)	Separation factor (r)
(Cysteic acid)		(0)	
Aspartic acid	L	2.2	1.00
	D	2.2	
Glutamic acid	L	3.3	1.00
	D	3.3	
Allothreonine	L	10.0	1.14
	D	11.4	
Glutamine	L	12.9	1.00
	D	12.9	
Serine	L	12.9	1.04
	D	13.4	
Threonine	L	13.0	1.05
	D	13.7	
Asparagine	L	14.0	1.00
	D	14.0	
α-Amino-*n*-butyric acid	L	16.2	1.02
	D	16.6	
Valine	L	16.3	1.09
	D	17.7	
Alanine	L	17.2	1.00
	D	17.2	
Isoleucine	L	21.5	1.10
	D	23.7	
Norvaline	L	21.5	1.04
	D	22.3	
3,4-Dihydroxyphenylalanine	L	22.3	1.28
	D	28.5	
Alloisoleucine	L	23.5	1.09
	D	25.5	
Methionine	L	23.8	1.03
	D	24.6	
Leucine	L	28.3	1.01
	D	28.6	
Ethionine	L	29.0	1.04
	D	30.3	
Norleucine	L	30.8	1.05
	D	32.3	
Tyrosine	L	30.8	1.28
	D	39.4	
m-Tyrosine	L	34.1	1.21
	D	41.1	
o-Tyrosine	L	36.7	1.18
	D	43.2	
Phenylalanine	L	48.7	1.13
	D	55.0	
p-Fluorophenylalanine	L	64.0	1.18
	D	75.6	

Reference

C. Gilon, R. Leshem, Y. Tapuhi and E. Grushka, J. Am. Chem. Soc., 101, 7612 (1979).

Summary

D,L-dopa, D,L-tyrosine, D,L-phenylalanine and D,L-tryptophane have been resolved by reverse phase resolution on an ODS column using Cu^{++} or Zn^{++} complexes of L-aspartyl-L-phenylalanine methyl ester as chiral eluants. The experimental details and results follow:

Table I. The Capacity Ratios k' and Selectivity Factors α^a of Some Amino Acid Enantiomers as a Function of the Acetonitrile (ACN) in the Mobile Phase. The Mobile Phase Contains 10^{-3} M Copper–Aspartame Complex

solute	0% ACN k'	0% ACN α	7% ACN k'	7% ACN α	8% ACN k'	8% ACN α	10% ACN k'	10% ACN α
L-Dopa	3.2	1.5						
D-Dopa	4.8							
L-tyrosine	5.4	1.6	1.2	1.5	1.0	1.7		
D-tyrosine	8.9		1.8		1.7			
L-phenylalanine	*b*		4.8	1.6	4.3	1.3		
D-phenylalanine	*b*		7.8		5.4			
L-tryptophan	*b*		*b*		13.2	1.3	5.6	1.2
D-tryptophan	*b*		*b*		16.7		6.8	

[a] See note 18. [b] Retention times too long for accurate measurements.

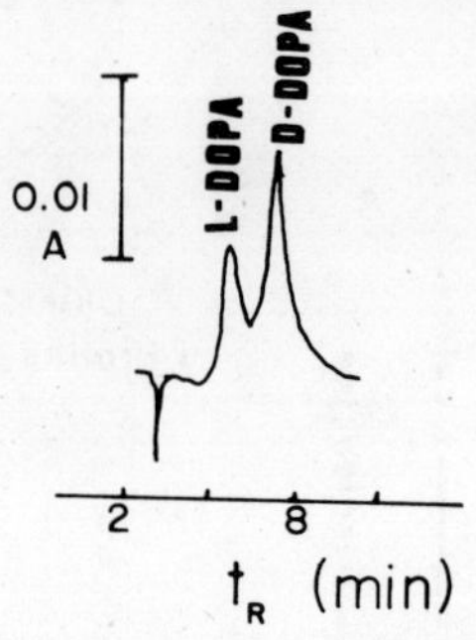

Figure 1. Separation of DL-Dopa on a reversed phase column. The mobile phase is H_2O with 10^{-3} M Aspartame and 10^{-3} M Cu(II). Chromatographic conditions are given in note 17.

Table II. The Capacity Ratios k' and Selectivity Factors α^a of Some Amino Acid Enantiomers as a Function of the Concentration of the Zinc–Aspartame Complex in the Mobile Phase

solute	10^{-3} M k'	10^{-3} M α	5×10^{-4} M k'	5×10^{-4} M α	2.5×10^{-4} M k'	2.5×10^{-4} M α
L-tyrosine	1.9	1.3	2.9	1.4	5.3	1.5
D-tyrosine	2.5		4.2		7.9	
L-phenylalanine	5.5	1.6	9.3	1.7	16	1.9
D-phenylalanine	9.0		16.0		30	
L-tryptophan	19.4	1.2	34	1.2	*b*	
D-tryptophan	23.0		42		*b*	

[a] See note 18. [b] Retention times too long for accurate measurements.

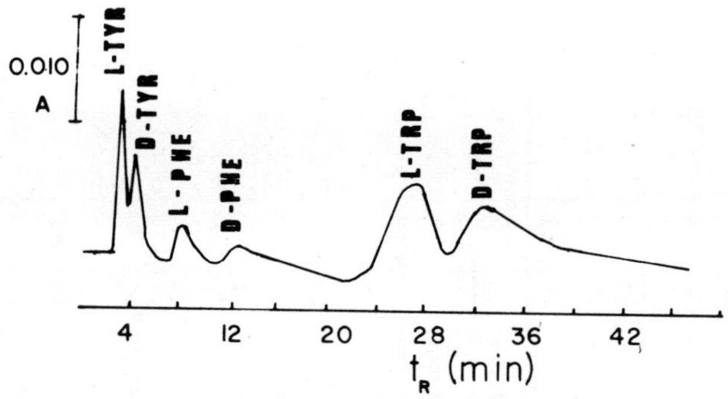

Figure 2. Separation of DL-tyrosine, DL-phenylalanine, and DL-tryptophan on a reversed phase column. The mobile phase is H_2O with 5×10^{-4} M Aspartame and 5×10^{-4} M Zn(II). Chromatographic conditions are given in note 17.

(17) The chromatographic conditions were as follows: a Spectra Physics chromatograph Model 8000 was used; the column was an ODS one, 25 cm long; the mobile phase flow rate was 2 mL/min; column temperature was 32 °C; detection was done at 275 or 254 nm.

(18) The selectivity factor α is defined as the ratio of the partition coefficients of the solutes of interest; the capacity factor k' is defined as the amount of the solute in the stationary phase proportional to that in the mobile phase. It is directly proportional to the partition coefficient. Large k' values indicate long retention times.

Reference

C. Gilon, R. Leshem and E. Grushka, Anal. Chem., 52, 1206 (1980).

Summary

The chromatographic resolution of enantiomeric amino acids is accomplished on reversed phase columns using aqueous mobile phases containing the chiral reagent L-aspartylcyclohexylamide–Cu(II) [AspcHex–Cu(II)]. This reagent has the additional advantage that the copper ions allow the detection of nonaromatic amino acids at 230 nm. The separation seems to be a result of hydrophobic interactions between the cyclohexylamide moiety of the chiral additive and the side chain of the amino acids. The results indicate that the composition of the chiral reagent in the mobile phase is $(AspcHex)_2Cu(II)$ and that the amino acids must replace one of the AspcHex for the resolution to occur.

Experimental details and results follow.

Apparatus. A Spectra-Physics model 8000 liquid chromatograph was used in this study. The UV detector was operated mostly at 230 nm. The mobile phase flow rate was 2 mL/min at a pressure of about 2500 psi. The column was 25 cm long by 4.1-mm i.d. The stationary phase was ODS bonded to Partisil 10. It was prepared by refluxing chlorodimethyloctadecyl silane with the silica gel in dry toluene.

The mobile phase was an aqueous mixture of Aspartame–Cu(II) complex or L-aspartylcyclohexylamide–Cu(II) complex.

Preparation of L-Aspartylcyclohexylamide (AspcHex). ZAsp(OBzl)OH (3.7 g, 10.2 mmol) was dissolved in dimethyl formamide (DMF; 25 mL). *N*-Methymorpholine (1.13 mL) was added and the mixture was cooled to −15 °C. Isobutyl chloroformate (1.26 mL, 9 mmol) was added and after 2 min, freshly distilled cyclohexylamine (1.15 mL, 10 mmol) was also added to the reaction. The mixture was kept 1 h at −15 °C and then at 0 °C. $KHCO_3$ (2 M, 15 mL) was added under vigorous stirring. After 0.5 h, a solution of NaCl (25% 100 mL) was added. The white precipitate was collected by filtration and washed with water until pH 7 was reached, and no traces of Cl^- were found in the wash. The product was then dried. The yield was 85% and its melting point was 139–141 °C. Elemental analysis performed on the product showed C, 68.23%; H, 7.02%; N, 6.71%. The calculated values for the product ($C_{25}H_{32}N_2O_5$) are C, 68.47%; H, 6.90%; N, 6.39%. To a solution of ZAsp(OBzl)-cHex (3 g) in acetic acid (90% 30 mL), Pd/C 10% (300 mg) was added and the mixture was hydrogenated at room temperature (5 atm). The catalyst was removed by filtration and the solvent was evaporated. The residue was recrystallized from water with a yield of 86%, and exhibited a melting point of 235 °C. Elemental analysis of the product found C, 56.12%; H, 8.32%; N, 13.23%. The calculated values for $C_{10}H_{18}N_2O_3$ are C, 56.06%; H, 8.47%; N, 13.07%. The structure of AspcHex (I) is shown below.

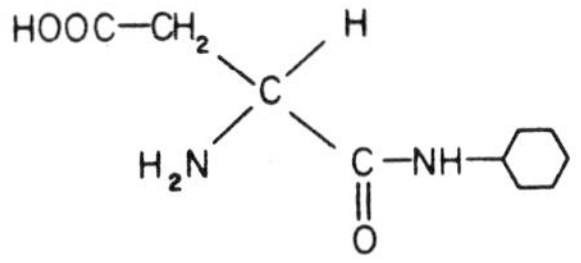

I

Chromatographic Studies. The mobile phases were prepared by dissolving the chiral reagent and Cu(II) to yield 10^{-4}–10^{-3} M solutions. When measuring separation factors, each of the enantiomers was injected individually.

Chemicals. All the amino acids as well as the Aspartame, were purchased from Sigma Chemicals. The water in the mobile phase was triple distilled in our laboratory. Spectroscopic grade acetonitrile was obtained from Aldrich.

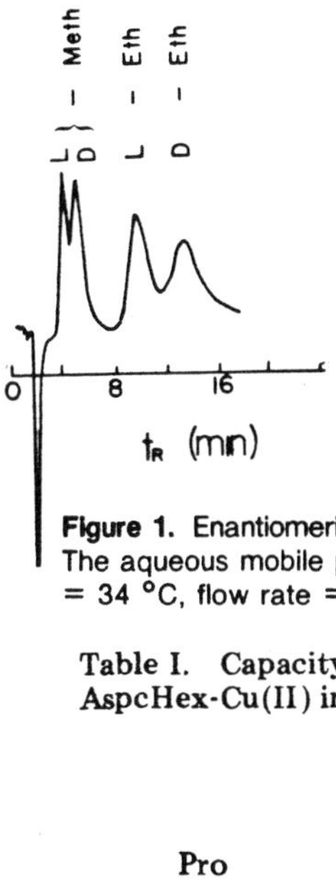

Figure 1. Enantiomeric separation of D,L-methionine and D,L-ethionine. The aqueous mobile phase contains 10^{-3} M AspcHex and Cu(II). T = 34 °C, flow rate = 2 mL/min. Detection: UV at 230 nm

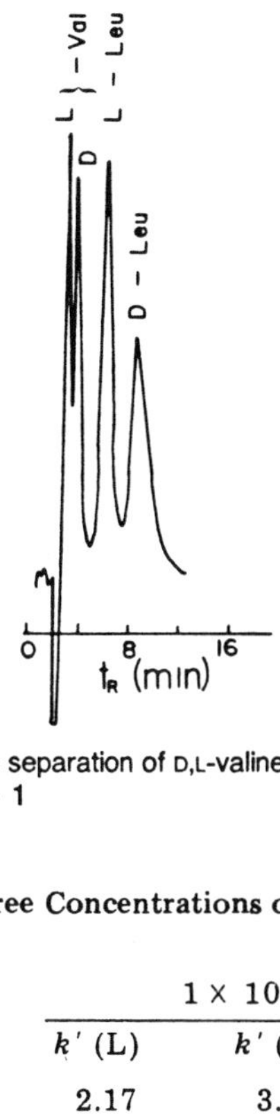

Figure 2. Enantiomeric separation of D,L-valine and D,L-leucine. Same conditions as in Figure 1

Table I. Capacity Ratios and Selectivities of Some Amino Acid Enantiomers at Three Concentrations of AspcHex-Cu(II) in the Mobile Phase

	1×10^{-3} M			2.5×10^{-4} M			1×10^{-4} M		
	k' (L)	k' (D)	α	k' (L)	k' (D)	α	k' (L)	k' (D)	α
Pro	0.24	1.12	4.46	0.55	1.42	2.58	2.17	3.0	1.38
Val	0.41	0.82	2.0	1.07	1.52	1.42	1.83	2.17	1.18
Nvl	0.56	0.89	1.59	1.14	1.43	1.25	1.74	2.0	1.15
Cys	0.76	1.15	1.51	1.81	2.43	1.34	--	--	--
Met	1.41	2.06	1.46	2.52	3.29	1.30	3.7	4.4	1.19
Dopa	1.78	2.33	1.31	3.21	3.90	1.22	5.67	6.86	1.21
Ilu	1.76	3.76	2.14	2.86	5.0	1.75	4.5	7.0	1.55
Leu	2.35	3.88	1.65	3.23	4.63	1.43	5.19	6.81	1.31
Nlu	2.47	4.23	1.71	3.67	5.40	1.47	5.13	6.76	1.32
Tyr	3.03	4.5	1.48	5.02	6.98	1.39	7.03	8.86	1.26
Eth	4.65	6.64	1.43	7.14	9.43	1.32	10.7	12.8	1.2

Reference
S. Lam, F. Chow and A. Karmen, J. Chromatogr., 199, 295 (1980).

Summary
Dansyl derivatives of 12 racemic amino acids were resolved by reverse-phase HPLC using L-proline-Cu^{++}, L-arginine-Cu^{++} and L-histidine-Cu^{++} complexes in the mobile phase. Each complex gave a different degree of separation of the enantiomers. The selectivity of separation for any chiral complex is postulated as being due to differing steric interactions between the alkyl side chains of the amino acids and structural moeities of the chiral mobile additive. Thus postulated structures for the L-proline and L-arginine ternary mixed complexes are:

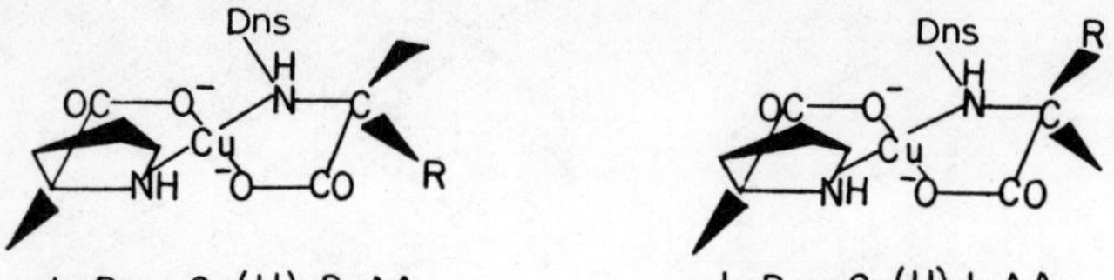

Fig. 10. Structure of L-proline mixed complexes.

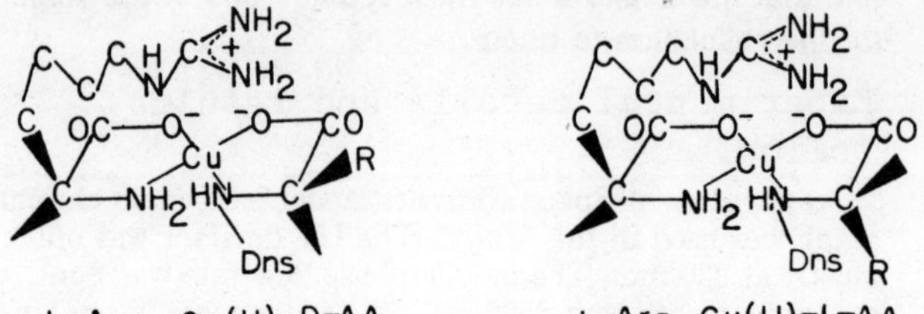

Fig. 11. Structure of L-arginine mixed complexes.

which rationalizes elution of the L- before the D-enantiomer in the proline system and of the D- before the L-enantiomer in the arginine system. The experimental details and results follow:

Instrumentation

The chromatograph was a Perkin-Elmer (Norwalk, CT, U.S.A.) Model 601 LC equipped with a Rheodyne 7105 injection valve, a Model LC 650-10 fluorescence spectrophotometer and a Model 56 chart recorder. The analytical column for the proline system was a 25 × 0.26 cm C_{18} column, ODS-HC SIL-X-1, from Perkin-Elmer. The columns for the arginine and histidine studies were packed with Nucleosil 5 purchased from Chrompack (Whittier, CA, U.S.A.). The column was packed by the downward slurry technique.

Reagents

Acetonitrile distilled in glass was bought from Burdick & Jackson Labs. (Muskegon, MI, U.S.A.). D- and L-Dns-amino acids were bought from Sigma (St. Louis, MO, U.S.A.) and Pierce (Rockford, IL, U.S.A.). Some were also prepared by the procedure of Olson *et al.*[13].

Procedures

The fluorescence at 480 nm was monitored with excitation at 340 nm.

13 D. C. Olson, G. J. Schmidt and W. Slavin, *Chromatogr. Newslett.*, 7 (1979) 22.

S. Lam, F. Chow and A. Karman, J. Chromatogr., 199, 295 (1980) (continued)

TABLE I

CAPACITY RATIO (k') AND SELECTIVITY (α) AS A FUNCTION OF ACETONITRILE CONCENTRATION

Mobile phase: acetonitrile (percentage indicated in the table) in an aqueous buffer containing $5 \cdot 10^{-3}$ *M* L-proline and ammonium acetate, and $2.5 \cdot 10^{-3}$ *M* $CuSO_4 \cdot 5H_2O$; pH 7.

Solute	*Acetonitrile (%)*					
	25		*20*		*15*	
	k'	*α*	*k'*	*α*	*k'*	*α*
D-Thr	0.34	1.00	0.97	1.37	5.17	1.24
L-Thr	0.34		0.71		4.17	
D-Ser	0.35	1.00	0.79	1.00	3.83	1.00
L-Ser	0.35		0.79		3.83	
D-Met	1.57	1.15	4.71	1.37	22.93	1.27
L-Met	1.36		3.43		18.03	
D-Val	1.86	1.16	3.83	1.37	16.67	1.22
L-Val	1.60		2.79		13.67	
D-Leu	3.00	1.27	9.86	1.50	41.40	1.29
L-Leu	2.36		6.57		31.97	
D-N-Val	1 64	1.21	5.07	1.39	21.83	1.27
L-N-Val	1.35		3.64		17.17	
D-N-Leu	3.54	1.38	12.43	1.47	55.50	1.31
L-N-Leu	2.86		8.43		42.33	
D-Phe	4.21	1.39	11.64	1.75	71.83	1.77
L-Phe	3.03		6.64		40.67	
D-Trp	4.43	1.72	19.37	1.97	73.67	1.60
L-Trp	2.57		9.80		46.07	

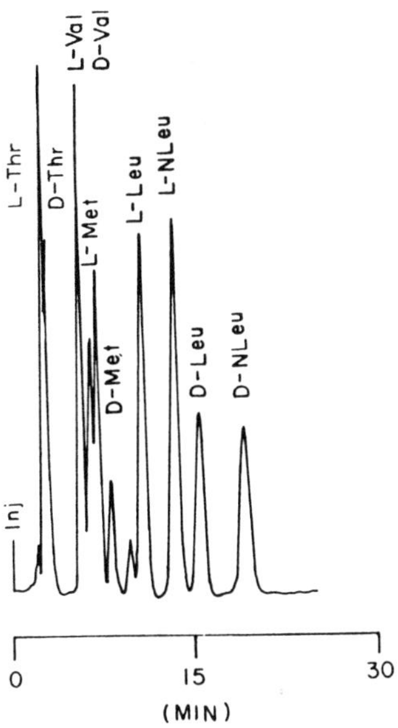

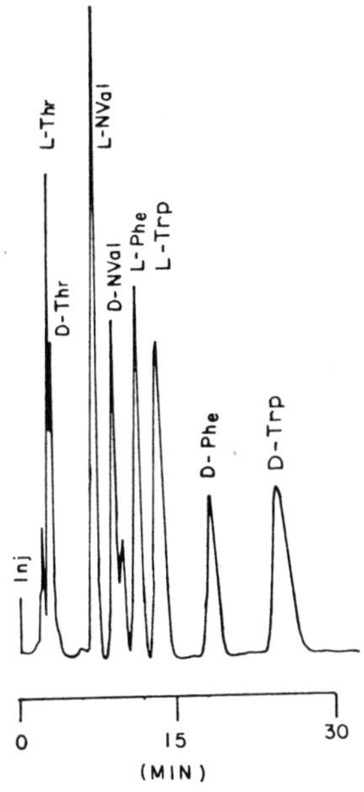

Fig. 1. Separation of D,L-Dns-amino acids with L-proline–Cu(II) eluent. Mobile phase: 20% acetonitrile in an aqueous solution containing $5 \cdot 10^{-3}$ *M* L-proline and ammonium acetate, and $2.5 \cdot 10^{-3}$ *M* $CuSO_4 \cdot 5H_2O$, pH 7.0. Flow-rate: 1.0 ml/min.

Fig. 2. Separation of D,L-Dns-amino acids with L-proline–Cu(II) eluent. Mobile phase: 20% acetonitrile in an aqueous solution containing $5 \cdot 10^{-3}$ *M* L-proline and ammonium acetate, and $2.5 \cdot 10^{-3}$ *M* $CuSO_4 \cdot 5H_2O$, pH 7.0. Flow-rate: 1.0 ml/min.

S. Lam, F. Chow and A. Karman, J. Chromatogr., 199, 295 (1980) (continued)

TABLE III

CAPACITY RATIO (k') AND SELECTIVITY (α) OF D- AND L-Dns-AMINO ACIDS

Mobile phase: 1:4 ratio of acetonitrile–aqueous solution containing $5 \cdot 10^{-3}$ M L-arginine, $2.5 \cdot 10^{-3}$ M $CuSO_4 \cdot 5H_2O$, and $2.5 \cdot 10^{-2}$ M ammonium acetate, pH 7.5.

Solutes	*k' (D)*	*k' (L)*	*α*
Ser	3.00	3.00	1.00
Thr	3.00	3.00	1.00
Ala	4.17	4.42	1.05
α-Ab	5.67	6.16	1.09
Met	10.33	11.66	1.14
Val	8.33	9.50	1.14
N-Val	11.00	13.00	1.18
Leu	18.50	20.83	1.12
Iso-Leu	17.16	20.83	1.21
N-Leu	22.33	28.16	1.26
Phe	20.33	23.00	1.13
Trp	24.83	31.17	1.26

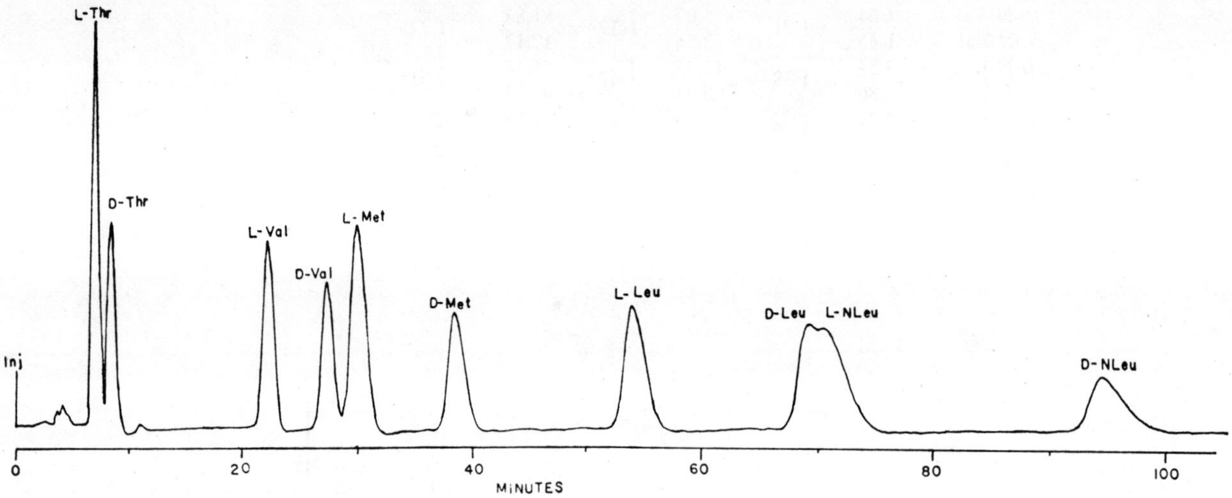

Fig. 3. Separation of D,L-Dns-amino acids with L-proline–Cu(II) eluent. Conditions as in Figs. 1 and 2, except the mobile phase acetonitrile concentration was changed to 15%.

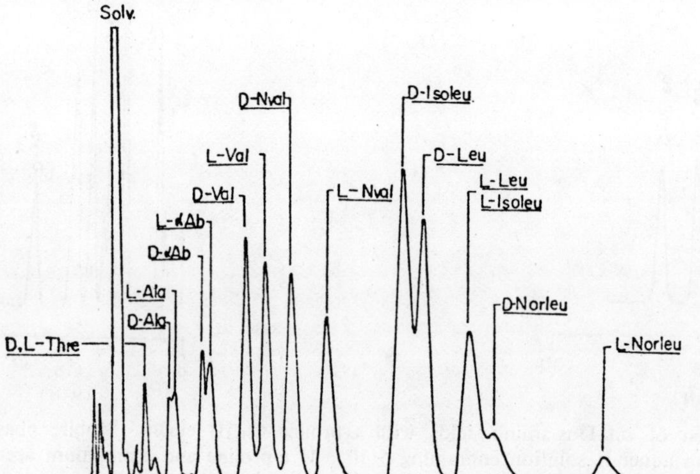

Fig. 7. Separation of D,L-Dns-amino acids with L-arginine–Cu(II) eluent. Mobile phase: 1:4 ratio of acetonitrile–aqueous solution containing $5 \cdot 10^{-3}$ M L-arginine, $2.5 \cdot 10^{-3}$ M $CuSO_4 \cdot 5H_2O$ and $2.5 \cdot 10^{-2}$ M ammonium acetate, pH 7.5. Flow-rate: 2.0 ml/min.

S. Lam, F. Chow and A. Karman, J. Chromatogr., 199, 295 (1980) (continued).

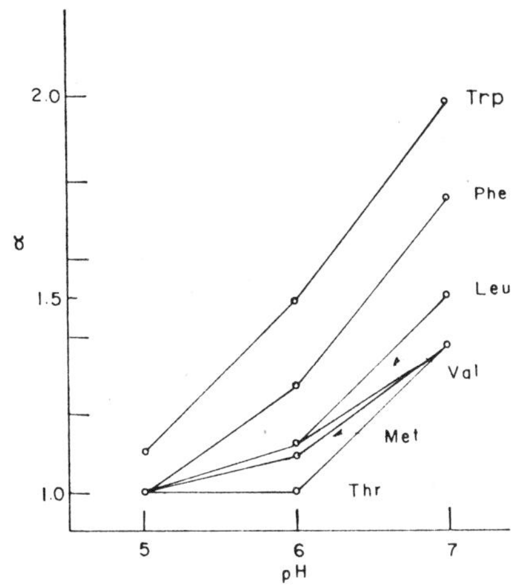

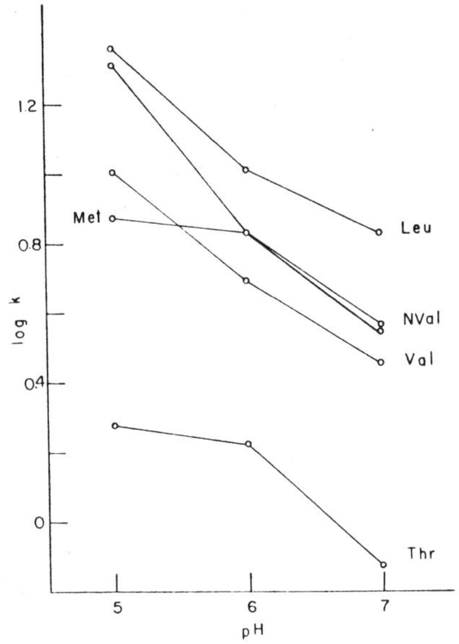

Fig. 4. Selectivity (α) as a function of pH. Mobile phase: 20% of acetonitrile in an aqueous buffer containing $5 \cdot 10^{-3}$ M L-proline and ammonium acetate, and $2.5 \cdot 10^{-3}$ M $CuSO_4 \cdot 5H_2O$, pH as given in the figure.

Fig. 5. Influence of pH on the retention of L-Dns-amino acids. Conditions as in Fig. 4.

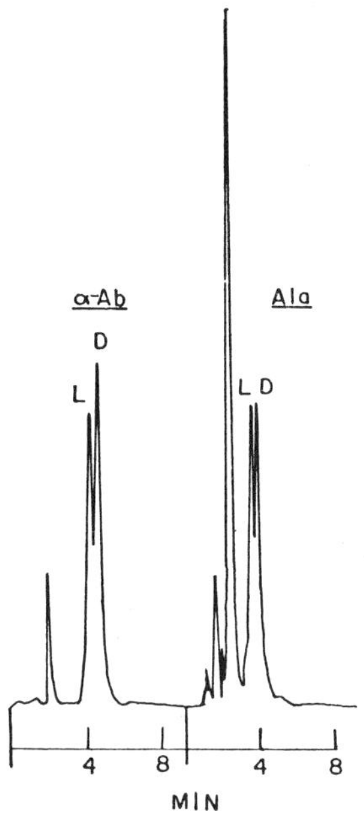

Fig. 8. Separation of D,L-Dns-α-aminobutyric acid and D,L-Dns-alanine with L-histidine–Cu(II) eluent. Mobile phase: 20% acetonitrile in an aqueous solution containing $5 \cdot 10^{-3}$ M L-histidine and ammonium acetate, and $2.5 \cdot 10^{-3}$ M $CuSO_4 \cdot 5H_2O$, pH 7.5. Flow-rate: 2.0 ml/min.

Reference
H. Furukawa, E. Sakakibara, A. Kamei and K. Ito, Chem. Pharm. Bull., 23, 1625 (1975).

Summary
Four α-amino acids were resolved as their diastereomeric N-d-10-camphorsulfonyl-p-nitrobenzyl esters by high performance liquid chromatography. Experimental details and results follow:

The derivatives (I) were prepared by the reaction of amino acids (0.5 mmole) and *d*-10-camphorsulfonyl chloride[2] (0.5 mmole) in ether (10 ml) and 1N NaOH aqueous solution (10 ml) under vigorous stirring at room temperature for one hour, and then, the reaction mixture was acidified with 1N HCl and extracted with ether. The resulting sulfonylamide was treated with *p*-nitrobenzyl bromide (0.5 mmole) in chloroform solution under reflux for 30 min, and the chloroform solution was washed with H_2O, dried with anhyd. Na_2SO_4, and evaporated.

2) P.D. Bartlett and L.H. Knox, "Organic Syntheses," Vol. 45, John Wiley & Sons, Inc., N. Y., 1965, p. 45.

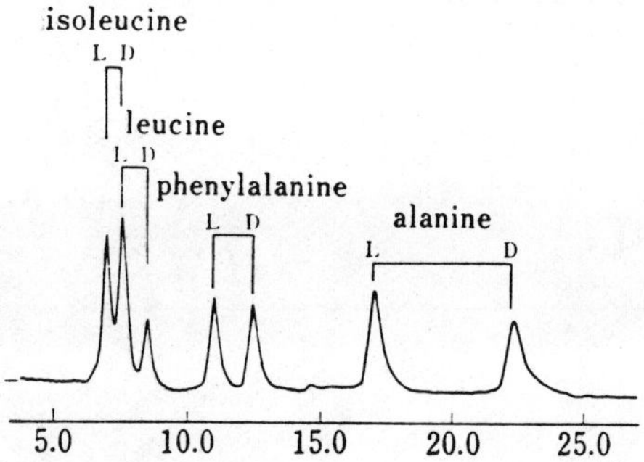

Fig. 1. Chromatogram of the Derivatives of Amino Acids

apparatus: FLC 350 equipped with a 254 nm UV-detector (JASCO); column: MicroPak Si-5 (2.0/250 mm) (Varian); solvent: 1.5% iso-PrOH in isooctane; flow-rate: 0.5 ml/min (pressure: 50—150 kg); column temperature: room temp

TABLE I. Retention Times of N-*d*-10-Camphorsulfonyl *p*-Nitrobenzyl Esters of Amino Acids

Amino acids	Retention times (min)	
	L-Enantiomer	D-Enantiomer
Isoleucine	7.0	7.6
Leucine	7.6	8.6
Phenylalanine	11.0	12.4
Alanine	17.0	22.3

Reference
C.G. Scott, M.J. Petrin and T. McCorkle, J. Chromatogr., 125, 157 (1976).

Summary
Several racemic acyclic isoprenoid acids were converted to diastereomeric amides by reaction with chiral α-methyl-p-nitrobenzylamine and the amides were separated using HPLC with ultraviolet detection at 254 nm. Separation factors ranged from 2.2 to 1.0 depending upon the distance of the secondary methyl chiral center from the amide functionality. Experimental details and results follow:

Preparation of α-methyl-p-nitrobenzylamides

The acids were converted to the acid chlorides by refluxing with oxalyl chloride and the crude acid chlorides were reacted with optically pure *S*(−)-α-methyl-*p*-nitrobenzylamine in the case of 2-methylhexanoic acid and *R*(+)-α-methyl-*p*-nitrobenzylamine for all other acids. The procedures are detailed in ref. 1. The derivatives of corresponding racemic acids were also prepared to allow co-injection with the derivative of each optically active acid into the liquid chromatograph. The samples were received by the liquid chromatography laboratory as the crude benzylamides which were diluted with ethyl acetate (5 mg in 0.5 ml) to give a 1% (w/v) solution for analysis.

Liquid chromatography

The liquid chromatographic apparatus consisted of a pump (Milton Roy Milroyal D or Minipump), a stop-flow type injection system, and either one 50 cm × 4 mm I.D. silica gel column (slurry packed with 10-μm Partisil from Whatman, Clifton, N.J., U.S.A.) or two such columns in series, depending on the difficulty of the separation. The mobile phase was 20% (v/v) tetrahydrofuran (Burdick and Jackson Labs., Muskegon, Mass., U.S.A.; distilled in glass) in *n*-heptane (Mallinckrodt, St. Louis, Mo., U.S.A.; spectral grade) at a flow-rate of 1.5 ml/min. The detection system was a Laboratory Data Control Model 1222 UV monitor operated at 254 nm. Elution volumes were obtained by direct measurement of volume, either by collection in a graduated cylinder or connecting the outlet from the detector to the base of a burette. The dead volume was determined for each system using a 50-μl injection of *n*-heptane and a refractive index detector. Plate heights for the columns were typically 0.5 mm for benzene ($k' = 0.4$), naphthalene ($k' = 0.6$) and anthracene ($k' = 0.9$) using *n*-heptane as the mobile phase; however, *h* for the benzylamides at k' of about 8 were considerably lower at between 2 and 4 mm.

1 D. Valentine, K. K. Chan, C. G. Scott, K. K. Johnson, K. Toth and G. Saucy, *J. Org. Chem.*, 41 (1976) 62.

C.G. Scott, M.J. Petrin and T. McCorkle, J. Chromatogr., 125, 157 (1976) continued.

TABLE I

RESULTS FOR THE LIQUID CHROMATOGRAPHIC SEPARATION OF DIASTEREOMERIC ACYCLIC ISOPRENOID ACIDS

No.	*Acid*	*Chiral position*	*k'*		*α*	*First eluted pair*		*Column*[*]
			1st eluted	*2nd eluted*		*Reagent*	*Acid*	
I	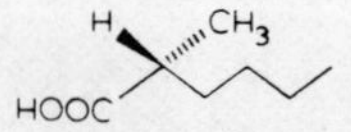	2	3.13	6.92	2.21	*S*	*R*	b
II		3	7.79	9.22	1.18	*R*	*R*	a, b, c, d
III	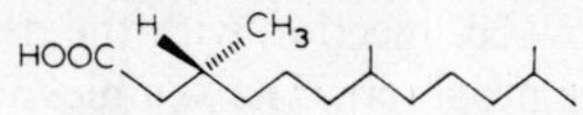	3, 7	6.52	8.04	1.23	*R*	*R*	b, d
IV	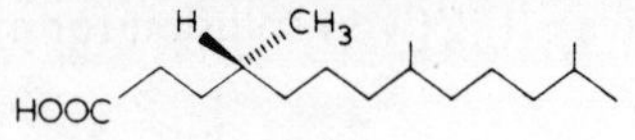	4, 8	7.83	8.25	1.05	*R*	*S*	d
V	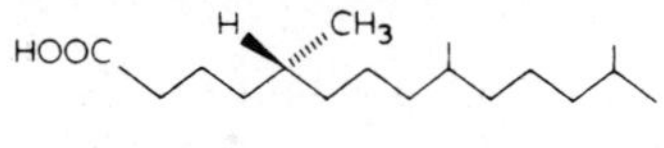	5, 9	7.67	7.67	1.00	—	—	c
VI	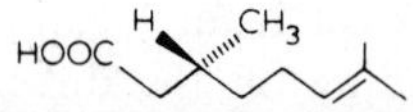	3	9.00	11.00	1.22	*R*	*R*	c
VII	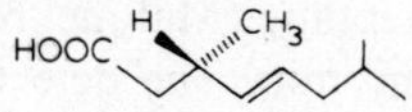	3	8.71	12.80	1.47	*R*	*S*	c
VIII		3	9.25	9.50	1.03	—	—[**]	a
IX	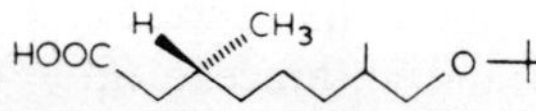	3, 7	7.58	8.71	1.15	*R*	*R*[***]	a

[*] Columns a, c and d were 2 × 50 cm columns in series; column b was 50 cm.
[**] No assignment made.
[***] Assignment on basis of chemical synthetic route only.

Reference

D. Valentine,Jr., K.K. Chan, C.G. Scott, K.K. Johnson, K. Toth and G. Saucy, J. Org. Chem., 41, 62 (1976).

Summary

A method for the direct determination of the enantiomeric ratios of 3,7-dimethyl-6-octenoic acid (6), 3,7-dimethyloctanoic acid (10) and 3,7,11-trimethyldodecanoic acid (15) was described. It is based on analytical separations by HPLC of diastereomeric amides obtained by reaction of the acids with (R)-(+)-α-methyl-p-nitrobenzylamine. Experimental details and results follow:

Preparation and Analysis of (*R*)-(+)-*p*-Nitro-*α*-methylbenzylamides by HPLC. The acid (0.50 mmol) and oxalyl chloride (1.50 mmol) were refluxed for 30 min in 5 ml of benzene. Solvent and excess oxalyl chloride were removed at 45° and 20 mm. The crude acid chloride was dissolved in 5 ml of ether and cooled in an ice bath. A solution of (*R*)-(+)-*α*-methyl-*p*-nitrobenzylamine,[7] $[\alpha]^{25}D$ +17.7° (neat) (2.0 mmol), in 3 ml of ether was added in small portions. The mixture was stirred for 1 hr at 0–5° and then diluted with 100 ml of ether, washed successively with 1 *N* HCl, saturated $NaHCO_3$, and water, and dried over $MgSO_4$. Crude amide, obtained by evaporation of the ether, was analyzed by HPLC without further purification.

Six microliters of a 1% solution of the crude amide in ethyl acetate (5 mg in 0.5 ml) was injected into a 4 mm i.d. × 100 cm chromatographic column obtained by connecting, in series with minimum volume fittings, two 50-cm stainless steel columns which had been slurry packed with 10 μm silica gel (Partisil 10 from H. Reeve Angel & Co., Inc.). The mobile phase was 20% v/v tetrahydrofuran (distilled in glass from Burdick and Jackson) in spectral grade *n*-heptane pumped at a flow rate of 1.5 ml min^{-1}. The column effluent was monitored at 254 nm (Model 1222 uv monitor from Laboratory Data Control) and quantitative results were obtained from peak area measurements. The HETP values for all components ranged from 0.17 mm to 0.23 mm. Corrected elution volumes ($V_R^1 = \bar{V} - V_m$) and capacity ratios (k^1) for the diastereoisomers were as follows.

Compd	Con-fign,	V_R^1, ml	k^1	Con-fign,	V_R^1, ml	k^1
6	*RR*	108.5	7.2	*SR*	121.0	8.1
10	*RR*	94.0	6.3	*SR*	114.0	7.6
15	*RRR* *SRR*	77.0	5.1	*RSR* *SSR*	95.0	6.3

Reference
H. Furukawa, Y. Mori, Y. Takeuchi and K. Ito, J. Chromatogr., 136, 428 (1977).

Summary
A number of α-amino acids were resolved as their diastereomeric N-d-10-camphorsulfonyl p-nitrobenzoates by HPLC [see also H. Furukawa, Y. Mori, Y. Takeuchi and K. Ito, Chem. Pharm. Bull., 23, 1625 (1975)]. Experimental details and results follow:

EXPERIMENTAL

Apparatus and conditions

An FLC 350 high-performance liquid chromatograph (JASCO) with gradient capability and a UV-254 detector monitoring at 253.7 nm were used. The column employed was a stainless-steel tube, 25 cm × 2.2 mm I.D., slurry-packed with microporous chemically bonded silica gel (Varian MicroPak-NH_2, average particle size 10 μm) and operated at ambient temperature. The flow-rate of the mobile phase was adjusted using pressures of 20–50 kg/cm².

Reagents and chemicals

All solvents were of reagent grade and were distilled prior to use. Amino acids were obtained from Katayama (Osaka, Japan), while *d*-10-camphorsulphonyl chloride was prepared from the corresponding acid[2].

Preparation of amino acid derivatives

A 30-ml volume of a solution of 2.0 mmole of *d*-10-camphorsulphonyl chloride in anhydrous diethyl ether was added dropwise to a solution of 1.0 mmole of amino acid in 10 ml of diethyl ether plus 20 ml of 1 *N* sodium hydroxide solution with vigorous stirring at 0°. Stirring was subsequently continued at room temperature for 3 h. The aqueous layer was separated from the ethereal layer, washed with twice diethyl ether, acidified with concentrated hydrochloric acid and then extracted with diethyl ether. The ethereal solution was dried over anhydrous sodium sulphate and evaporated to dryness. The residue was dissolved in 10 ml of N,N-dimethylformamide, then one drop of trimethylamine and 1.1 mmole of *p*-nitrobenzyl bromide were added. The reaction mixture was heated at 55° for 2 h, diluted with 40 ml of chloroform, washed with water, dried over anhydrous sodium sulphate and then evaporated to dryness to obtain the N-*d*-10-camphorsulphonyl *p*-nitrobenzoate of the amino acid.

Unless otherwise stated, a chloroform solution of the diastereomeric mixture of the derivatives of DL-amino acids was used for HPLC.

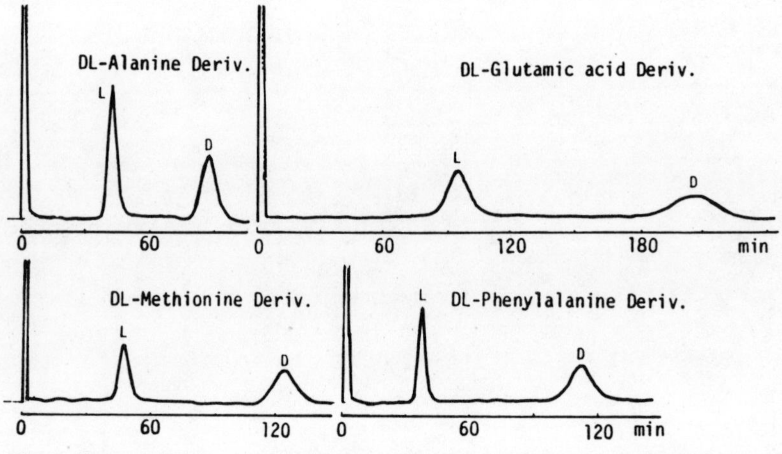

Fig. 1. Chromatograms of the diastereomers of N-*d*-10-camphorsulphonyl *p*-nitrobenzyl amino acids. Flow-rate, 0.4 ml/min; column, MicroPak-NH_2; eluent, dichloromethane.

H. Furukawa, Y. Mori, Y. Takeuchi and K. Ito, J. Chromatogr., 136, 428 (1977) continued.

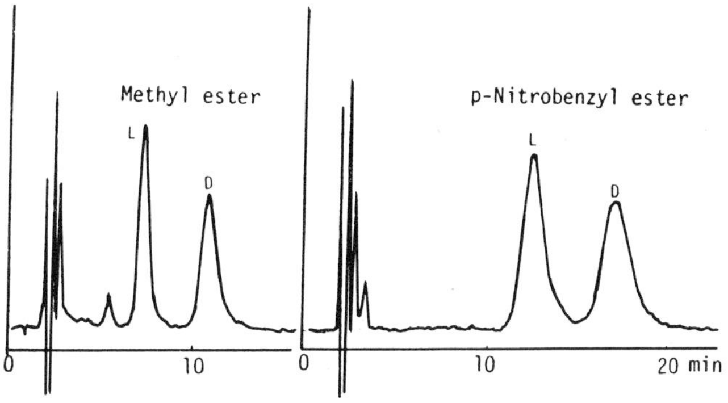

Fig. 4. Chromatograms of the methyl ester and *p*-nitrobenzyl ester of the diastereomers of N-*d*-10-camphorsulphonyl phenylalanine. Flow-rate, 0.4 ml/min; column, MicroPak-NH_2; eluent, isooctane–dichloromethane–isopropanol (87:8:5).

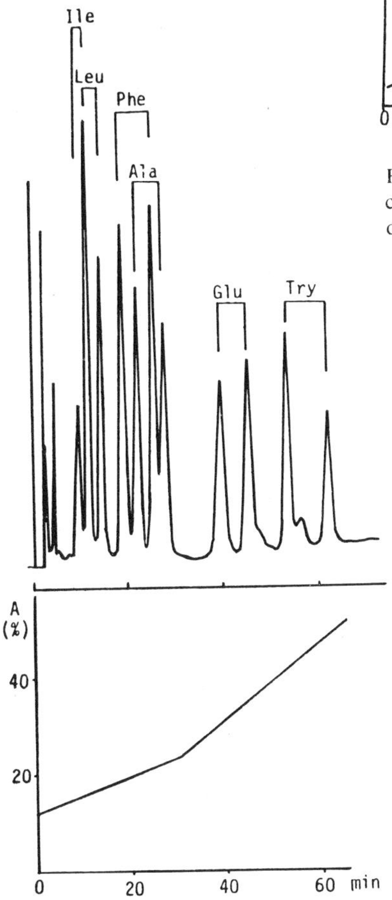

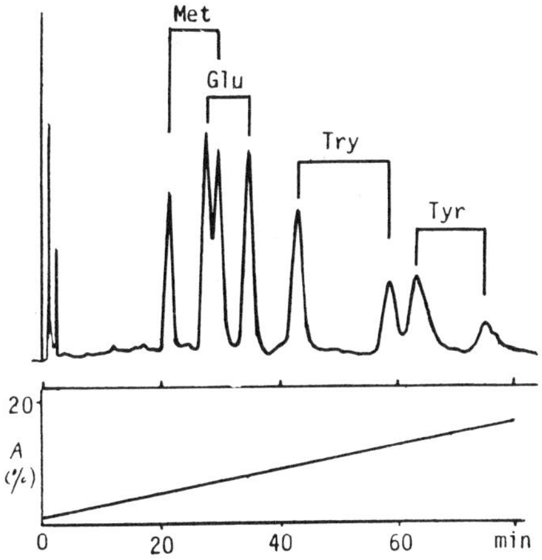

Fig. 2. Chromatogram and gradient diagram of the diastereomers of N-*d*-10-camphorsulphonyl *p*-nitrobenzyl amino acids. Flow-rate, 0.5 ml/min; column, MicroPak-NH_2. Eluent: A, isooctane–dichloromethane–isopropanol (70:15:15); B, isooctane–dichloromethane (90:10).

Fig. 3. Chromatogram and gradient diagram of N-*d*-10-camphorsulphonyl *p*-nitrobenzyl amino acids. Flow-rate, 0.7 ml/min; column, MicroPak-NH_2. Eluent: A, isooctane–dichloromethane–isopropanol (35:50:15); B, isooctane–dichloromethane (50:50).

TABLE I

RETENTION TIMES (min) OF D- AND L-AMINO ACID DERIVATIVES

Eluent: A, isooctane–dichloromethane–isopropanol (79:16:5); B, isooctane–dichloromethane–isopropanol (63:32:5). Flow-rate, 0.4 ml/min. Column, MicroPak-NH_2.

Amino acid	*Eluent A*			*Eluent B*		
	L	D	D/L	L	D	D/L
Leucine	3.9	4.4	1.1	2.7	2.8	1.0
Isoleucine	4.4	5.0	1.1	2.9	3.1	1.1
Phenylalanine	6.2	8.5	1.4	3.3	4.1	1,2
Methionine	7.4	10.0	1.4	3.6	4.6	1.3
Alanine	7.2	9.3	1.3	3.7	4.4	1.2
Glutamic acid	12.8	16.8	1.3	4.2	5.2	1.2
Tryptophan	29.2	49.6	1.7	9.0	14.9	1.7
Tyrosine	33.2	47.2	1.4	11.6	16.2	1.4

Reference

J. Goto, M. Hasegawa, S. Nakamura, K. Shimada and T. Nambara, Chem. Pharm. Bull., 25, 847 (1977).

Summary

Amino acids as their methyl esters were resolved by chromatographing the diastereomeric amides formed by reacting the methyl esters with (-)-α-methoxy-α-methyl-1-naphthaleneacetic acid on an achiral column using high performance liquid chromatography. Experimental details and results follow:

The apparatus used was a Waters Model ALC/GPC 202 R401 high-pressure liquid chromatograph (Waters Associates Inc., Milford) equipped with an UV monitor operated at 280 nm and a μ-Porasil column (1′×1/4″ i.d.). The mobile phase was cyclohexane-ethyl acetate (4:1—2:3, v/v) at a flow rate of 0.7 ml/min.

TABLE I. Separation of Diastereomeric N-(−)-α-Methoxy-α-methyl-1-naphthaleneacetyl Amino Acid Methyl Esters

Amino acid	k′		Relative retention value (α)	Mobile phase[a]
	D	L		
Alanine	1.91	3.10	1.62	A
Valine	1.76	1.06	1.66	A
Norvaline	2.17	1.22	1.78	A
Leucine	1.83	0.78	2.35	A
Isoleucine	1.53	0.88	1.74	A
Norleucine	1.92	0.96	2.00	A
Proline	1.42	2.38	1.68	A
Phenylglycine	2.56	1.32	1.94	A
Phenylalanine	2.41	1.52	1.59	A
Aspartic acid	5.61	7.00	1.25	A
Glutamic acid	6.46	6.81	1.05[b]	A
Serine	2.52	7.32	2.90	C
Tyrosine	2.02	1.74	1.16	B
DOPA	2.32	2.04	1.14[b]	C
Ornithine	2.00	3.52	1.76	D
Lysine	1.60	2.20	1.38	D
Cysteine	2.08	0.98	2.12	C

a) The ratio (v/v) of cyclohexane to ethyl acetate: A) 4:1; B) 2:1; C) 1:1; D) 2:3.
b) The two peaks were not completely resolved.

Reference

J. Goto, M. Hasegawa, S. Nakamura, K. Shimada and T. Nambara, J. Chromatogr., 152, 413 (1978).

Summary

A series of racemic amino acids were resolved via their diastereomeric amides formed from the amino acid methyl esters and (-)-α-methoxy-α-methyl-1-naphthaleneacetic acid by HPLC. The experimental details and results follow:

High-performance liquid chromatography

The apparatus used was a Waters Model ALC/GPC 202 R401 high-performance liquid chromatograph (Waters Assoc., Milford, Mass., U.S.A.) equipped with a UV detector monitoring the absorbance at 280 nm. The test samples were applied to the chromatograph by a Waters Model U6K sample loop injector with an effective volume of 2 ml. The μPorasil (1 ft. × ¼ in. I.D.) and μBondapak C_{18} (1 ft. × ¼ in. I.D.) columns (Waters Assoc.) were used under ambient conditions.

Preparation of derivatives

To a solution of amino acid methyl esters (*ca.* 100 μg) in pyridine (0.2 ml) were added IVb or VIIb (*ca.* 2 mg) and N,N'-dicyclohexylcarbodiimide (*ca.* 2 mg). The mixture was allowed to stand at room temperature for 30 min, and then diluted with ethyl acetate (*ca.* 0.5 ml), successively washed with 5% HCl, 5% $NaHCO_3$ and water, and dried over anhydrous Na_2SO_4. A 5-μl aliquot was injected with a microsyringe into the chromatograph.

TABLE II

SEPARATION OF DIASTEREOMERIC N-(−)-α-METHOXY-α-METHYL-1-NAPHTHALENEACETYLAMINO ACID METHYL ESTERS ON A REVERSED-PHASE COLUMN

Conditions: column, μBondapak C_{18} (1 ft. × ¼ in. I.D.); mobile phase, methanol–water, (A) 2:1, (B) 3:2, 1 ml/min; detection, 280 nm.

Amino acid	*k'**		*α*	*R*	*Mobile phase*
	D	L			
Alanine	1.83	1.83	1.00	0.00	A
Valine	3.06	2.66	1.15	0.92	A
Norvaline	3.33	2.95	1.13	0.75	A
Leucine	3.49	3.20	1.09	0.50	A
Norleucine	4.80	3.87	1.24	1.00	A
Isoleucine	4.36	3.81	1.14	0.95	A
Proline	3.30	3.00	1.10	0.50	A
Phenylglycine	3.73	3.57	1.05	0.27	A
Phenylalanine	4.00	3.67	1.09	0.56	A
Threonine	2.80	2.64	1.06	0.23	B
Tyrosine	4.60	4.60	1.00	0.00	B
Methionine	7.53	6.42	1.17	0.97	B
Tryptophan	11.21	11.00	1.02	0.15	B
Histidine	2.50	2.34	1.07	0.28	B

* t_0 = 2.4 min.

TABLE III

SEPARATION OF DIASTEREOMERIC N-(−)-α-METHOXY-α-METHYL-1-NAPHTHALENEACETYLAMINO ACID METHYL ESTERS ON A NORMAL-PHASE COLUMN

Conditions: column, μPorasil (1 ft. × ¼ in. I.D.); mobile phase, cyclohexane–ethyl acetate, (A) 4:1, (B) 2:1, (C) 1:1, (D) 2:3, 0.7 ml/min; detection 280 nm.

Amino acid	*k'**		*α*	*R*	*Mobile phase*
	D	L			
Alanine	1.91	3.10	1.62	5.84	A
Valine	1.76	1.06	1.66	9.17	A
Norvaline	2.17	1.22	1.78	5.90	A
Leucine	1.83	0.78	2.35	6.14	A
Norleucine	1.92	0.96	2.00	6.00	A
Isoleucine	1.53	0.88	1.74	4.26	A
Proline	1.42	2.38	1.68	2.48	A
Phenylglycine	2.56	1.32	1.94	6.22	A
Phenylalanine	2.41	1.52	1.59	4.35	A
Serine	2.52	7.32	2.90	8.63	C
Threonine	1.20	1.85	1.55	2.98	D
Tyrosine	2.02	1.74	1.16	1.02	B
DOPA	2.32	2.04	1.14	0.67	C
Cysteine	2.08	0.98	2.12	2.80	C
Methionine	1.60	1.24	1.29	1.61	B
Aspartic acid	5.61	7.00	1.25	2.52	A
Glutamic acid	6.46	6.81	1.05	0.62	A
Ornithine	2.00	3.52	1.76	3.33	D
Lysine	1.60	2.20	1.38	1.97	D
Histidine	1.36	1.96	1.45	1.47	D

* t_0 = 5.0 min.

Reference
B.J. Bergot, R.J. Anderson, D.A.
Schooley and C.A. Henrick, J.
Chromatogr., 155, 97 (1978).

Summary

The racemic monoterpenoid acids, citronellic acid (III), dihydrocitronellic acid (IV) and 7-methoxycitronellic acid (V) were converted to their diastereomeric amides by reaction with (+)-1-(1-naphthyl)-ethylamine. The amides were rapidly and completely separated using HPLC with ultraviolet detection at 254 nm. Experimental details and results follow:

(III) $(CH_3)_2C=CH(CH_2)_3CHCH_2COOH$
         $\qquad\qquad\qquad\qquad |$
         $\qquad\qquad\qquad\qquad CH_3$

(IV) $(CH_3)_2CH(CH_2)_3CHCH_2COOH$
         $\qquad\qquad\qquad\qquad |$
         $\qquad\qquad\qquad\qquad CH_3$

(V) $\qquad\quad CH_3$
       $\qquad\qquad |$
       $CH_3O-C-(CH_2)_3CHCH_2COOH$
       $\qquad\quad |\qquad\qquad\quad |$
       $\qquad\quad CH_3\qquad\quad CH_3$

Analytical procedure

The liquid chromatograph consisted of a Haskel Model 26920-4 pneumatic amplifier pump, a Valco Model CV-6-HPax loop injector and a Chromatronix Model 230 UV absorbance detector set on the 254-nm channel. All separations were performed on a single Zorbax-SIL (DuPont, Wilmington, Del., U.S.A.) silica column (22 × 0.46 cm I.D.) using 14 or 22% ethyl acetate in pentane. Solvents were either 50% or 100% saturated with water. Diastereomeric ratios were determined by peak area computation.

Table I shows important chromatographic parameters for the separation of the diastereomeric pairs studied. The commercially available column exhibited excellent N values (equivalent to ≥35,000 plates per meter). The resolution factor R_s greatly exceeds unity in all cases.

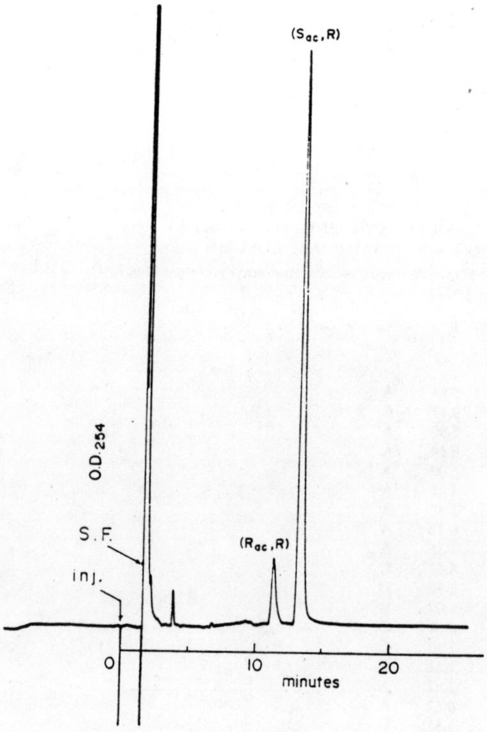

Fig. 1. HRLC analysis of diastereomeric amides III from citronellic acid and (R)-(+)-1-(1-naphthyl)-ethylamine. Conditions: Zorbax-SIL (22 × 0.46 cm I.D.) column, eluted with pentane–ethyl acetate (86:14) ("50% water-saturated"), 1.8 ml/min at 400 p.s.i.g.

B.J. Bergot, R.J. Anderson, D.A. Schooley and C.A. Henrick, J. Chromatogr., 155, 97 (1978).

TABLE I CHROMATOGRAPHIC PARAMETERS OF VARIOUS 1-(1-NAPHTHYL)ETHYLAMIDES

Parameter	*Compound I*		*Compound II*	
	(R_{ac},S)	*(R_{ac},R)*	*[17β(S)$_{ac}$,R]*	*[17β(S)$_{ac}$,S]*
N	13000	13800	7900	8600
k'	5.8	7.1	3.2	7.2
R_s	5.0		13	
α	1.22		2.25	
Eluent	pentane–ethyl acetate (95:5), "100% water-saturated"		pentane–ethyl acetate (80:20), "100% water-saturated"	

Compound III		*Compound IV*		*Compound V*	
(R_{ac},R)	*(S_{ac},R)*	*(R_{ac},R)*	*(S_{ac},R)*	*(S_{ac},R)*	*(R_{ac},R)*
7300	8100	7500	9200	7600	8900
6.6	8.0	5.5	6.8	16.5	18.0
3.8		4.2		1.9	
1.21		1.24		1.09	
pentane–ethyl acetate (86:14), "50% water-saturated"		pentane–ethyl acetate (86:14), "50% water saturated"		pentane–ethyl acetate (78:22), "100% water-saturated"	

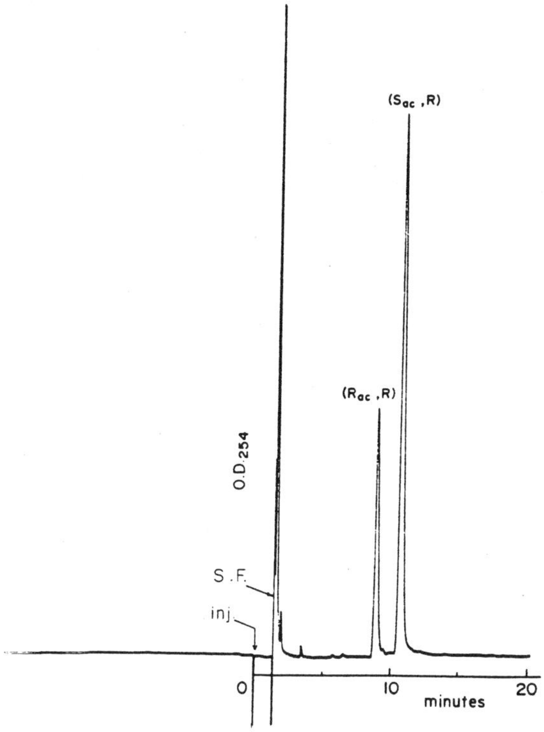

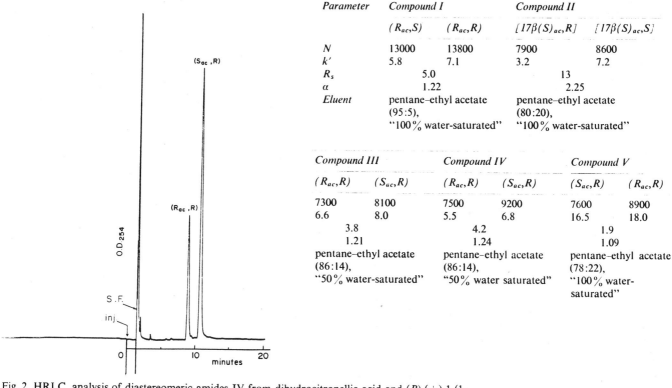

Fig. 2. HRLC analysis of diastereomeric amides IV from dihydrocitronellic acid and (*R*)-(+)-1-(1-naphthyl)ethylamine. Eluent flow-rate, 2.2 ml/min at 480 p.s.i.g. Other conditions as in Fig. 1.

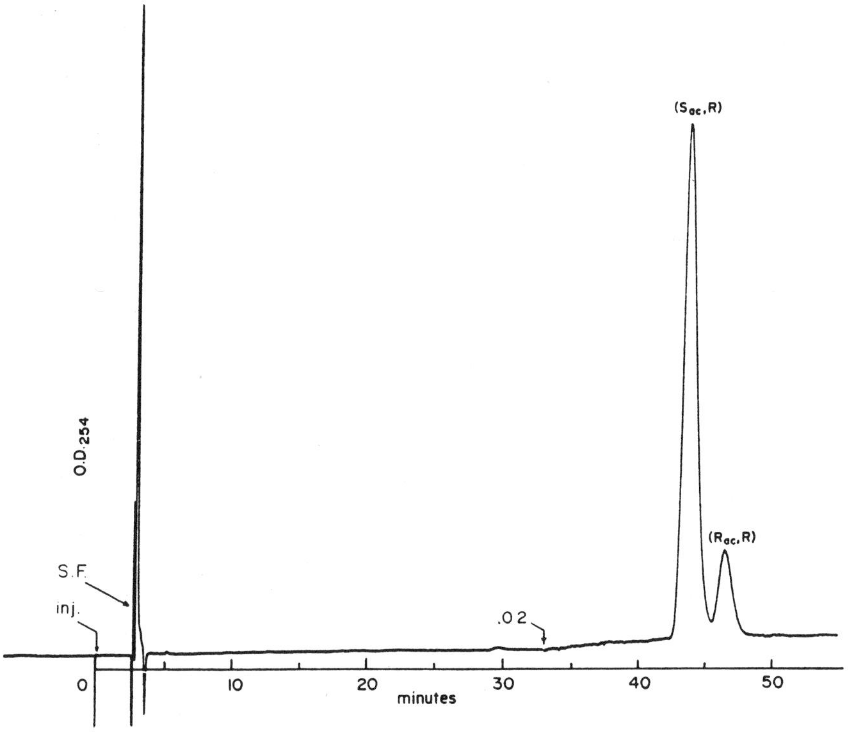

Fig. 3. HRLC analysis of diastereomeric amides V from 7-methoxycitronellic acid and (*R*)-(+)-1-(1-naphthyl)ethylamine. Conditions: Zorbax-SIL (22 × 0.46 cm I.D.) column, eluted with pentane–ethyl acetate (78:22) ("100% water saturated"), 1.3 ml/min at 300 p.s.i.g.

Reference

T. Nambara, S. Ikegawa, M. Hasegawa and J. Goto, Anal. Chim. Acta, 101, 111 (1978).

Summary

Two new chiral derivatizing reagants (-)-1,7-dimethyl-7-norbornyl isothiocyanate (I) and (+)-neomenthyl isothiocyanate (II) were synthesized from the corresponding amines. A series of racemic amino acids were readily transformed with the chiral reagents into diastereomeric thiourea derivatives which absorb at 243 nm. (ϵ = 17,000). The tert-butyldimethylsilyl esters of the diastereomeric thiourea derivatives were efficiently resolved by high performance liquid chromatography. Experimental details and results follow:

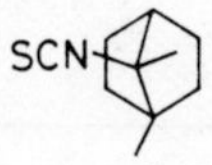

I

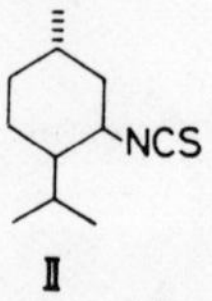

II

Synthesis of derivatization reagents

(-)-1,7-Dimethyl-7-norbornyl isothiocyanate (I). (-)-1,7-Dimethyl-7-norbornylamine (1.81 g) obtainable from (+)-isoketopinic acid [10] was added to water (3 ml)—carbon disulfide (2 ml) under ice-cooling and stirred at room temperature for 5 min. After the addition of KOH (1.25 g) in water (1.5 ml), the solution was heated in a sealed tube on the boiling water bath for 25 min. To the reaction mixture ethyl chloroformate (1.8 g) was added under ice-cooling, and the mixture was stirred at room temperature for 1 h. To the resulting solution was added KOH (1 g) in water (1.5 ml), and the solution was stirred at room temperature for 1 h and extracted with ether. The organic layer was washed with water, dried (Na_2SO_4), and evaporated. The crude product was distilled under reduced pressure to give (I) (1.4 g) as a colorless oil (b.p.$_5$ 94°C; $[\alpha]_D^{20} - 69.9°$; c = 1.3, $CHCl_3$). Calcd. for $C_{10}H_{15}NS$: 66.2%C, 8.3%H, 7.7%N; found: 65.7%C, 8.1%H, 7.8%N. N.m.r. ($CDCl_3$)δ: 1.00 (3H, s, 1-CH_3), 1.32 (3H, s, 7-CH_3). I.r. ν_{max}, $CHCl_3$: 2080 cm^{-1} (SCN—).

(+)-Neomenthyl isothiocyanate (II). (+)-Neomenthylamine (1 g) obtainable from (—)-menthol [11] was added to water (1.2 ml)—carbon disulfide (0.6 ml) under ice-cooling with stirring at room temperature for 5 min. After the addition of KOH (0.5 g) in water (0.6 ml) the solution was heated in a sealed tube on the boiling water bath for 25 min. To the reaction mixture ethyl chloroformate (0.72 g) was added under ice-cooling, and the mixture was stirred at room temperature for 1 h. To the resulting solution was added KOH (0.4 g) in water (0.6 ml), and the solution was stirred at room temperature for 1 h and extracted with ether. The organic layer was washed with water, dried (Na_2SO_4), and evaporated. The crude product was distilled under reduced pressure to give (II) (0.6 g) as a colorless oil (b.p.$_5$ 55°C; $[\alpha]_D^{17} + 34.5°$; c = 2.0, $CHCl_3$). Calcd. for $C_{11}H_{19}NS$: 67.0%C, 9.7%H, 7.1%N; found: 66.1%C, 9.5%H, 7.0%N. N.m.r. ($CDCl_3$)δ: 0.94 (6H, d, J = 6 Hz, 9- and 10-CH_3), 0.88 (3H, d, J = 6 Hz, 5-CH_3), 4.1 (1H, m, W1/2 = 6 Hz). I.r. ν_{max}, $CHCl_3$: 2160 cm^{-1} (SCN—).

High-pressure liquid chromatography

A Model ALC/GPC 202 R401 high-performance liquid chromatograph (Waters Assoc., Milford, Mass., U.S.A.) with a u.v. detector (254 nm) was used. Samples were applied by a Waters Model U6K sample loop injector (effective volume, 2 ml). The μPorasil (1 ft. × 0.25 in. i.d.) and μBondapak C_{18} (1 ft. × 0.25 in. i.d.) columns (Waters Assoc.) were used under ambient conditions.

Derivatization

Methyl ester method. To a solution of amino acid methyl ester (ca. 100 μg) in acetonitrile (0.2 ml) were added (I) or (II) (ca. 2 mg) and sodium acetate (ca. 2 mg), and the resulting solution was allowed to stand at 37°C for 1 h. The reaction mixture was diluted with ethyl acetate (0.5 ml), washed successively with 5% HCl, 5% $NaHCO_3$ and water, and dried (Na_2SO_4). An aliquot was injected into the chromatograph.

T. Nambara, S. Ikegawa, M. Hasegawa and J. Goto, Anal. Chim. Acta, 101, 111 (1978) continued.

tert-Butyldimethylsilyl ester method. To a solution of amino acid (ca. 100 μg) in aqueous 50% pyridine (0.2 ml) were added (I) or (II) (ca. 1 mg) and 2 M NaOH (10 μl), and the resulting solution was heated at 90°C for 1 h. The reaction mixture was diluted with water and extracted with ether to remove the excess of reagents. The aqueous layer was adjusted to pH 4 with 3% HCl and extracted with ethyl acetate. The organic layer was washed with water, dried (Na_2SO_4), and evaporated. To the residue was added the freshly prepared silylating agent (50 μl), and the resulting solution was allowed to stand at room temperature for 1 h. The reaction mixture was diluted with ethyl acetate. (0.5 ml), washed successively with 5% $NaHCO_3$ and water, and dried (Na_2SO_4). An aliquot (5 μl) was injected into the chromatograph.

10 M. Ishidate and A. Kawada, Chem. Pharm. Bull. (Tokyo), 4 (1956) 483.
11 A. K. Bose, J. F. Kistner and L. Farber, J. Org. Chem., 27 (1962) 2925.

TABLE 1

Separation of diastereomeric thiourea derivatives of amino acid methyl esters (t_0 = 3.0 min. Column, μPorasil. Mobile phase, cyclohexane/ethyl acetate (A) 2:1, (B) 3:1, (C) 10:1, (D) 20:1. Flow rate, 1.0 ml min^{-1}.)

Amino acid	IIIa k' D	IIIa k' L	α	R	Mobile phase	IVa k' D	IVa k' L	α	R	Mobile phase
Alanine	4.97	4.57	1.09	1.10	C	3.49	3.04	1.15	1.73	C
Valine	8.06	7.25	1.11	1.30	D	6.07	5.71	1.06	0.75	D
Norvaline	9.13	8.00	1.14	1.48	D	6.49	6.49	1.00	0.00	D
Leucine	8.62	7.95	1.08	1.00	D	3.70	3.91	1.06	0.70	D
Norleucine	6.49	5.86	1.11	1.47	D	5.18	5.46	1.05	0.66	D
Isoleucine	7.44	6.55	1.14	1.05	D	3.70	3.91	1.06	0.63	D
Proline	5.91	6.64	1.12	1.69	C	4.13	4.72	1.14	1.79	C
Phenylglycine	9.38	8.96	1.05	0.45	D	7.30	7.53	1.03	0.36	D
Phenylalanine	8.81	7.50	1.17	1.77	D	5.23	5.47	1.05	0.62	D
Serine	4.10	4.20	1.02	0.07	A	7.00	6.46	1.08	0.59	B
Threonine	3.14	3.25	1.04	0.36	A	5.75	5.54	1.04	0.39	B
Aspartic acid	7.87	8.13	1.03	0.48	C	5.72	5.66	1.01	0.15	C
Glutamic acid	16.33	15.40	1.06	0.94	C	11.25	10.10	1.11	1.43	C

TABLE 2

Separation of diastereomeric thiourea derivatives of amino acid tert-butyldimethylsilyl esters (t_0 = 3.0 min. Column, μPorasil. Mobile phase, cyclohexane/ethyl acetate (A) 30:1, (B) 40:1, (C) 50:1, (D) 80:1. Flow rate, 1.0 ml min^{-1}.)

Amino acid	IIIb k' D	IIIb k' L	α	R	Mobile phase	IVb k' D	IVb k' L	α	R	Mobile phase
Alanine	5.90	5.50	1.07	0.84	A	3.87	3.10	1.25	2.32	A
Valine	4.37	3.53	1.24	2.31	A	2.27	1.67	1.36	2.65	A
Norvaline	4.07	3.43	1.19	1.78	A	1.83	1.47	1.24	1.90	A
Leucine	4.03	3.37	1.20	2.00	A	1.93	1.67	1.16	1.19	A
Norleucine	3.60	2.93	1.23	2.06	A	1.37	1.10	1.25	1.51	A
Isoleucine	3.70	3.03	1.22	1.92	A	1.67	1.47	1.14	2.00	A
Proline	7.90	8.20	1.04	0.45	A	5.63	6.27	1.11	1.13	A
Phenylglycine	4.77	4.30	1.11	1.21	A	4.23	3.80	1.11	1.08	B
Phenylalanine	4.13	3.03	1.36	3.00	A	2.47	1.73	1.43	2.09	C
Serine	3.00	2.33	1.29	2.30	A	3.27	2.80	1.17	1.36	D
Threonine	6.57	5.53	1.19	1.90	A	1.60	1.07	1.50	3.33	A
Aspartic acid	3.00	2.60	1.15	1.43	A	2.03	1.63	1.25	1.82	B
Glutamic acid	6.57	6.23	1.05	0.90	A	4.83	3.87	1.25	2.38	A

Reference
M.G. Young, J. Chromatogr., 150, 221 (1978).

Summary
The diastereomers of a series of 7-ureidoacetamido cephalosporins were efficiently and conveniently separated and quantitated by reverse-phase HPLC. Determination of the diastereomeric purity of the compounds was necessary to evaluate their antimicrobial activity. Experimental details and results follow:

A high-performance liquid chromatograph (Waters Assoc., Milford, Mass., U.S.A.; Model ALC-GPC-202) was equipped with a Rheodyne Model 905-42 septumless injector and a UV detector operating at 254 nm. The column used was a μBondapak C_{18} (300 × 4.0 mm I.D.) custom-packed by Waters Assoc. and the chromatograms were recorded on a Varian A-25 strip chart recorder. The pressure employed was ≤ 2500 p.s.i. The eluting mixtures were prepared from reagent methanol (Mallinckrodt, St. Louis, Mo., U.S.A.) and diammonium hydrogen phosphate dissolved in water (de-ionized and distilled in glass) and filtered through a Millipore HAWPO4700 filter.

TABLE I

SEPARATION OF DIASTEREOMERIC CEPHALOSPORINS

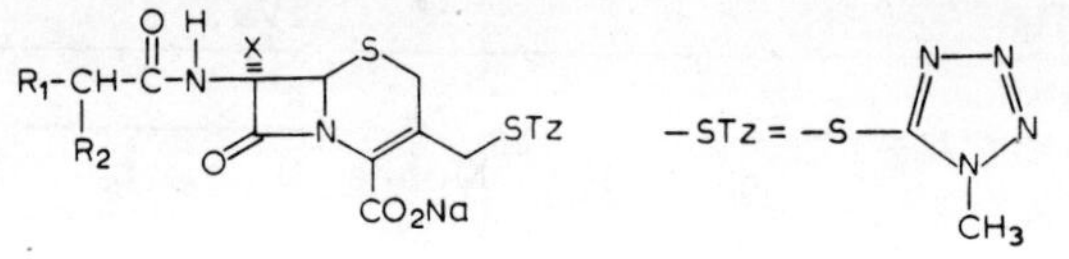

1-7

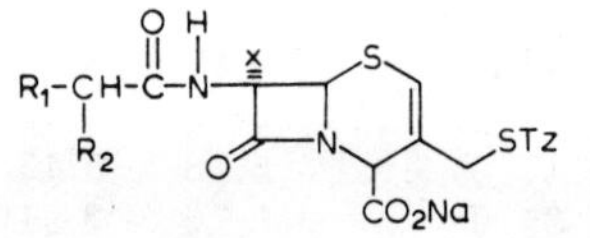

Compound	R_1	R_2	*X*	CH_3OH (%)	*Flow-rate (ml/min)*	L*, *time (min)*	D, *time (min)*
1	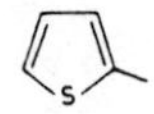	NH / C=O / $NHCH_2CN$	H	20	1.0	11	20
2	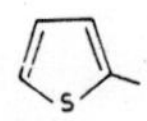	NH / C=O / $NHCH_2CN$	OCH_3	20	0.4	12	14
3	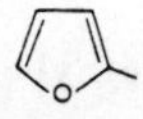	NH / C=O / NH_2	H	10	1.4	7	11
4	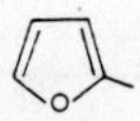	NH / C=O / NH_2	OCH_3	5	0.4	18	20
5	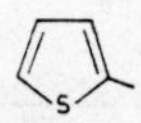	NH / C=O / NH_2	H	10	1.5	11	20
6	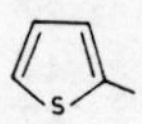	NH / C=O / NH_2	OCH_3	10	0.8	16	19
7	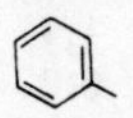	NH / C=O / NH_2	H	10	1.0	23	44
8	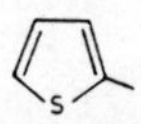	NH / C=O / NH_2	OCH_3	10	0.8	21	31

* The L and D nomenclature designates the stereochemistry of the intermediate arylglycine side chains utilized in the preparation of 1–8.

Reference

B.J. Bergot, R.J. Anderson, D.A. Schooley and C.A. Henrick, J. Chromatog., 155, 97 (1978).

Summary

A rapid high-resolution liquid chromatographic (HRLC) analysis for enantiomeric purity of chiral monoterpenoid acids is described. The acids are converted to diastereomeric amides using commercially available (+)-1-(1-naphthyl)ethylamine. The amides are chromatographed on microparticulate silica HRLC columns with ultraviolet detection at 254 nm; the enantiomeric composition is then derived from the diastereomeric ratios. Good separation of various pairs of diastereomers are reported, with very low loadings ($\leqslant 1\ \mu g$) required because of high molecular extinction coefficients. No conclusive correlations between elution order and absolute configuration could be determined. Experimental details and results follow.

Purification and analysis of chiral amine

An enantiomerically pure sample of (+)-1-(1-naphthyl)ethylamine was prepared from commercial material (*ca.* 93% optical purity; Cyclo Chemicals, Los Angeles, Calif., U.S.A.) by recrystallization of the bitartrate salt. A 0.13 *M* solution of equimolar amounts of (+)-amine and L-tartaric acid (J. T. Baker, Phillipsburgh, N.J., U.S.A.) in 94% methanol was heated to 55–60°. Overnight cooling to room temperature gave crystals which were filtered and subsequently reconverted to free amine by extraction into diethyl ether from aqueous base.

The (+)-form of the amine resolving agent is reported to have the *R*-configuration, based upon X-ray crystallography studies[12]. In order to check the enantiomeric purity of the amine, it was converted to the amide I or II, using the acid chlorides of (+)-α-methoxy-α-trifluoromethylphenylacetic acid (Aldrich, Milwaukee, Wisc., U.S.A.) and 3β-acetoxyetienic acid (Steraloids, Wilton, N.H., U.S.A.) respectively.

Following thin-layer chromatographic (TLC) purification, the amides were then analyzed by HRLC to obtain the purity values cited.

Formation of derivatives

Typically, (3*RS*)-citronellol was oxidized to the corresponding acid by an excess of Jones reagent. The recovered acid was then treated with thionyl chloride in diethyl ether containing a catalytic amount of dimethylformamide to generate the acid chloride. Treatment with excess enantiomerically pure (*R*)-(+)-1-(1-naphthyl)-ethylamine gave the crude diastereomeric amides III*, which were purified by preparative TLC before HRLC analysis. (3*RS*)-7-Methoxycitronellic acid was synthesized via methoxymercuration of (±)-citronellol, and converted to the amide V as above. (3*RS*)-Dihydrocitronellic acid was prepared via hydrogenation of (±)-citronellol, and treated as above to ultimately produce the amide IV.

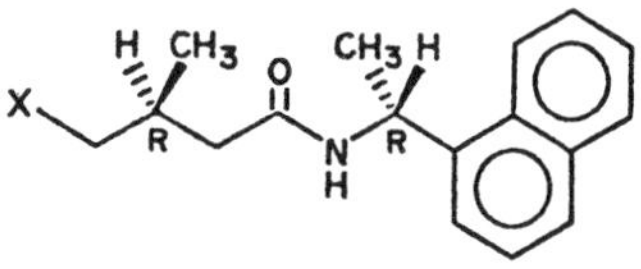

(Rac, R)

III X= 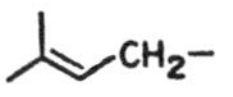

IV X= 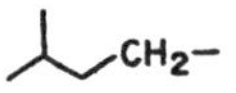

V X= 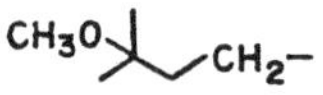

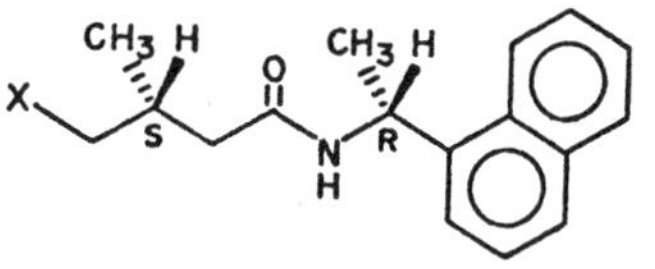

(Sac, R)

12 M. G. B. Drew, *Acta Crystallogr.*, B25 (1969) 1320.

B.J. Bergot, R.J. Anderson, D.A. Schooley and C.A. Henrick, J. Chromatog., 155, 97 (1978) continued.

Analytical procedure

The liquid chromatograph consisted of a Haskel Model 26920-4 pneumatic amplifier pump, a Valco Model CV-6-HPax loop injector and a Chromatronix Model 230 UV absorbance detector set on the 254-nm channel. All separations were performed on a single Zorbax-SIL (DuPont, Wilmington, Del., U.S.A.) silica column (22 × 0.46 cm I.D.) using 14 or 22% ethyl acetate in pentane. Solvents were either 50% or 100% saturated with water. Diastereomeric ratios were determined by peak area computation.

Table I shows important chromatographic parameters for the separation of the diastereomeric pairs studied. The commercially available column exhibited excellent N values (equivalent to ≥35,000 plates per meter). The resolution factor R_s greatly exceeds unity in all cases.

* R_{ac} (or S_{ac}) designates the absolute configuration of the acyl moiety of the diastereomeric amides, while the R refers to the amino moiety.

TABLE I

CHROMATOGRAPHIC PARAMETERS OF VARIOUS 1-(1-NAPHTHYL)ETHYLAMIDES

Parameter	*Compound I*		*Compound II*		*Compound III*		*Compound IV*		*Compound V*	
	(R_{ac},S)	(R_{ac},R)	$[17\beta(S)_{ac},R]$	$[17\beta(S)_{ac},S]$	(R_{ac},R)	(S_{ac},R)	(R_{ac},R)	(S_{ac},R)	(S_{ac},R)	(R_{ac},R)
N	13000	13800	7900	8600	7300	8100	7500	9200	7600	8900
k'	5.8	7.1	3.2	7.2	6.6	8.0	5.5	6.8	16.5	18.0
R_s	5.0		13		3.8		4.2		1.9	
α	1.22		2.25		1.21		1.24		1.09	
Eluent	pentane–ethyl acetate (95:5), "100% water-saturated"		pentane–ethyl acetate (80:20), "100% water-saturated"		pentane–ethyl acetate (86:14), "50% water-saturated"		pentane–ethyl acetate (86:14), "50% water saturated"		pentane–ethyl acetate (78:22), "100% water-saturated"	

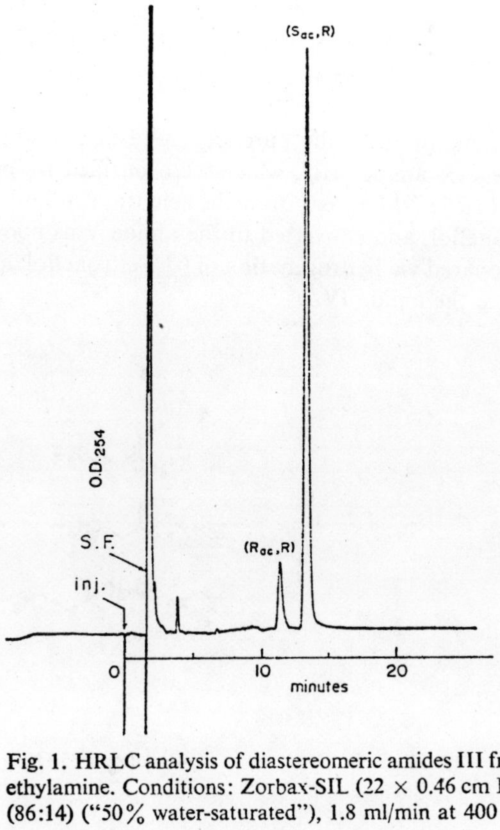

Fig. 1. HRLC analysis of diastereomeric amides III from citronellic acid and (*R*)-(+)-1-(1-naphthyl)-ethylamine. Conditions: Zorbax-SIL (22 × 0.46 cm I.D.) column, eluted with pentane–ethyl acetate (86:14) ("50% water-saturated"), 1.8 ml/min at 400 p.s.i.g.

B.J. Bergot, R.J. Anderson, D.A. Schooley and C.A. Henrick, J. Chromatog., 155, 97 (1978) continued.

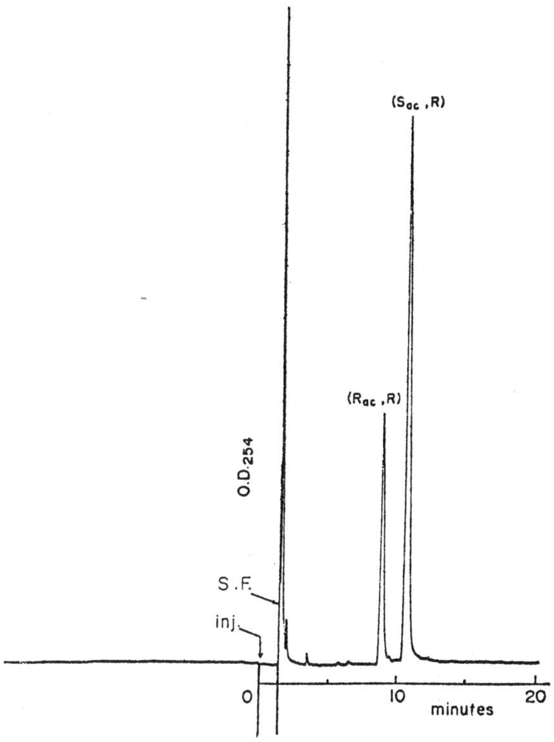

Fig. 2. HRLC analysis of diastereomeric amides IV from dihydrocitronellic acid and (*R*)-(+)-1-(1-naphthyl)ethylamine. Eluent flow-rate, 2.2 ml/min at 480 p.s.i.g. Other conditions as in Fig. 1.

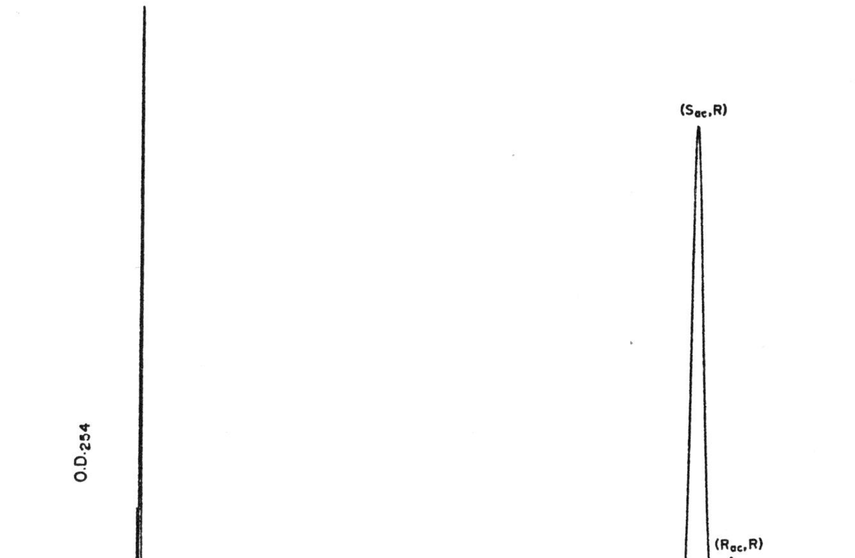

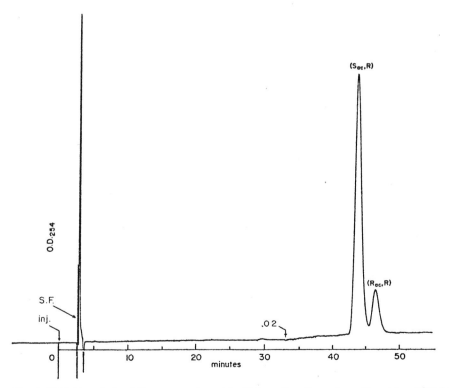

Fig. 3. HRLC analysis of diastereomeric amides V from 7-methoxycitronellic acid and (*R*)-(+)-1-(1-naphthyl)ethylamine. Conditions: Zorbax-SIL (22 × 0.46 cm I.D.) column, eluted with pentane–ethyl acetate (78:22) ("100% water saturated"), 1.3 ml/min at 300 p.s.i.g.

Reference

A.R. Mitchell, S.B.H. Kent, I.C. Chu and R.B. Merrifield, Anal. Chem., 50, 637 (1978).

Summary

Racemic amino acids were reacted with tert-butyloxycarbonyl-L-leucine-N-hydroxy-succinimide to form after acidic cleavage of the tert-butyloxycarbonyl group the diastereomeric dipeptides, L-leu-D-amino acid and L-leu-L-amino acid in high yield (> 95%) and without detectable racemization (C 0.1%). The diastereomeric dipeptides were separated on a standard amino acid analyzer using a sulfonated polystyrene column. A long column (0.9 x 58 cm.) was used for the chromatography of L-[leu]-dipeptides containing tyrosine, phenylalanine and lysine, while a short column (0.9 x 10.5 cm.) sufficed to resolve L-[leu]-dipeptides containing histidine and arginine. The experimental details and results follow:

Boc-L-Leu-OSu. Boc-L-Leu-OSu was prepared from Boc-L-Leu (Chemalog) as described by Anderson et al. (*9*). Boc-L-leucine (4.62 g, 20 mmol) and *N*-hydroxysuccinimide (2.76 g, 24 mmol) were dissolved in 60 mL THF and chilled to 0 °C. Dicyclohexylcarbodiimide (4.12 g, 20 mmol) was added with stirring and the solution kept at 0–5 °C for 18 h. Acetic acid (0.23 mL, 4 mmol) was added. After 15 min the insoluble urea was removed by filtration and the solvent removed at 35–40 °C under reduced pressure. Recrystallization of the residual oil from diisopropyl ether (650 mL) gave crystals, 2.70 g, mp. 111–112 °C.

Anal. Calcd. for $C_{15}H_{24}N_2O_6$: C, 54.86; H, 7.37; N, 8.53. Found: C, 54.94; H, 7.41; N, 8.59. Boc-L-Leu-OSu is also available from suppliers of amino acid and peptide derivatives (Bachem, Chemalog, Fluka, Peninsula, Vega-Fox).

Stock solutions of sodium bicarbonate (0.333 M) in water and Boc-L-Leu-OSu (0.333 M) in tetrahydrofuran were used in the derivatization reactions. The Boc-L-Leu-OSu solution was stable for at least 1 week at room temperature, and at least 1 month if stored at 4 °C.

Procedure. *A. Reaction of Tyr, Phe, His, and Arg with Boc-L-Leu-OSu.* Sodium bicarbonate stock solution (0.12 mL, 40 μmol) was added to a 1-mL reaction vial (Wheaton Vitro "200" Vial, SGA-5050, with a Teflon-lined cap) containing free amino acid (20 μmol) and a 4-mm Teflon coated magnetic stirring bar. The solution was stirred for 1 min on a stirring plate and Boc-L-Leu-OSu stock solution (0.12 mL, 40 μmol) in THF was added. The reaction mixture was stirred at room temperature for 1 h, washed with THF into a 50-mL round bottom flask, and evaporated to dryness using a rotary evaporator at 45–50 °C. The residue was dissolved in trifluoroacetic acid (1 mL) and allowed to stand in a stoppered flask for 1 h at room temperature to remove the Boc group. The trifluoroacetic acid was evaporated in vacuo with the aid of dichloromethane on the rotary evaporator. The residue was dissolved in pH 2.2 sodium citrate buffer (20 mL), filtered through a Millipore filter (0.22) μm, No. GSWP 01300) in a Swinny adaptor (No. XX 3001200), and an aliquot (1 mL) was injected onto the appropriate column of the amino acid analyzer. Elution conditions and peak widths for the [L-Leu[1]]dipeptides prepared by this procedure are given in Table I. The reactions went to over 94% completion in 1 h as judged by the amount of free amino acid remaining.

B. Reaction of Acidic and Neutral Amino Acids with Boc-L-Leu-OSu. The procedure described above was applied to all the neutral amino acids. For glutamic and aspartic acids, an additional two equivalents of sodium bicarbonate was added to ensure neutralization of the acid side chains. Yields of all dipeptides were greater than 95% based on the residual free amino acid.

C. Reaction of Lys, N^{α}-Z-Lys, and N^{ϵ}-Z-Lys with Boc-L-Leu-OSu. Sodium bicarbonate (40 μmol), L-Lys (20 μmol), and Boc-L-Leu-OSu (200 μmol) were reacted and worked up as described for *A*. The reaction went to 97% completion as judged by depletion of amino acid and the presence of only trace amounts of the monoacylated products N^{α}-L-Leu-L-Lys and N^{ϵ}-L-Leu-L-Lys.

The above procedure was repeated with N^{α}-Z-L-Lys and N^{ϵ}-Z-L-Lys in place of L-Lys and DL-Lys. Anhydrous HBr (32%) in acetic acid (Eastman) was used to remove both the Boc and Z groups after the coupling reactions. In this manner, N^{α}-Z-L-Lys gave rise to N^{ϵ}-L-Leu-L-Lys and N^{ϵ}-Z-L-Lys afforded N^{α}-L-Leu-L-Lys. Elution conditions and peak widths for the L-leucyl derivatives of lysine are given in Table II.

D. Protected Amino Acids. After removal of the protecting groups, the protocols described above can be used on the free amino acids. The reaction mixture must be kept at about pH 9 for the reaction with Boc-L-Leu-OSu. Where strong acid conditions were used to remove protecting groups, it is important to thoroughly remove traces of acid and to check and adjust, if necessary, the pH of the amino acid solution prior to the addition of Boc-L-Leu-OSu.

Chromatography. Ion exchange chromatography was performed with a Beckman Model 120B amino acid analyzer based on the design of Spackman, Stein, and Moore (*14*). Conditions for the analysis of the [L-Leu[1]]dipeptides of the acidic and neutral amino acids have been reported (*4, 5*). A long column (0.9 × 58 cm; Beckman AA-15 sulfonated polystyrene) was used for the chromatography of [L-Leu[1]]dipeptides containing Tyr (pH 4.25), Phe (pH 5.26), and Lys (pH 7.00), while a short column (0.9 × 10.5 cm; Beckman PA-35 sulfonated polystyrene) sufficed to resolve [L-Leu[1]]dipeptides containing His (pH 4.66) and Arg (pH 5.26). Both columns were operated at a flow rate of 61 mL/h and 57 °C. Samples (1.0 mL) were applied with an Altex rotary-valve sample injector.

The pH 2.2 sodium citrate buffer (0.2 N in sodium) was used for samples applied to the analyzer column (*14*). The pH 4.25 (0.2 N in sodium) and pH 5.26 (0.35 N in sodium) citrate buffers were prepared from Beckman concentrates. The pH 4.25 buffer used in the resolution of L-Leu-DL-Tyr diastereomers also contained 1.5% benzyl alcohol (v/v) and 2% 1-propanol (v/v). The pH 4.66 buffer was prepared by mixing three parts pH 4.25 buffer with one part of pH 5.26 buffer. The pH 7.00 buffer was prepared by titration of the pH 5.26 buffer with 50% NaOH. A Corning Digital Research pH meter was used to measure the pH of the buffer solutions.

Check for Racemization. Boc-L-Leu was deprotected with trifluoroacetic acid for 1 h at room temperature and converted to the [L-Leu[1]]dipeptide according to the above procedures. The Boc-L-Leu-OSu used had been prepared from this same lot of Boc-L-Leu. The product was chromatographed as previously described (*5*) at a 5-μmol loading.

A.R. Mitchell, S.B.H. Kent, I.C. Chu and R.B. Merrifield, Anal. Chem., 50, 637 (1978) continued.

Table I. Elution Conditions for L-Leucyl Derivatives of Tyr, Phe, His, and Arg

			Elution time, min[b]				
DL-AA	pH	Column,[a] cm	L-Leu	Unreacted DL-AA	LD Dipeptide	LL Dipeptide	NH_4^+
Tyr	4.25[c]	58	58 (<4)	71 (3)	140 (10.5)	217 (11)	300
Phe	5.26	58	39 (<4)	63 (3)	104 (7.5)	86 (6)	>130
His	4.66	10.5	20	95 (4.5)	148 (8)	198 (11.5)	101
Arg	5.26	10.5	17	105 (5)	200 (13.5)	161 (11)	71

[a] The 0.9 × 58 cm column contained Beckman AA-15 resin, while the 0.9 × 10.5 cm column contained Beckman PA-35 resin. Both columns were operated at 61 mL/h, 57 °C. [b] Figures in parentheses are peak widths given in minutes. [c] Containing 1.5% (v/v) benzyl alcohol and 2% (v/v) 1-propanol.

Table II. Elution Conditions for L-Leucyl Derivatives of Lys[a]

Derivative	Elution time, min	Peak width, min
L-Leu	38	<4
N^{α}-L-Leu-L-Lys	112	4.5
$N^{\alpha,\epsilon}$-(di-L-Leu)-L-Lys	128	7.5
DL-Lys	164	4
N^{ϵ}-L-Leu-L-Lys	208	7.5
$N^{\alpha,\epsilon}$-(di-L-Leu)-D-Lys	240	14
NH_4^+	258	6

[a] 0.9 × 58 cm Beckman AA-15 column, pH 7.00, 61 mL/h, 57 °C.

Table III. Elution Conditions for Diastereomeric Dipeptides

Dipeptide	pH	Column length, cm	Elution time, min
L-Leu-D-Tyr	4.25[a]	58	140
L-Leu-L-Tyr	4.25[a]	58	217
L-Leu-D-Phe	5.26	58	104
L-Leu-L-Phe	5.26	58	86
$N^{\alpha,\epsilon}$-(di-L-Leu)-D-Lys	7.00	58	240
$N^{\alpha,\epsilon}$-(di-L-Leu)-L-Lys	7.00	58	128
L-Leu-D-His	4.66	10.5	148
L-Leu-L-His	4.66	10.5	198
L-Leu-D-Arg	5.26	10.5	200
L-Leu-L-Arg	5.26	10.5	161

[a] Containing 1.5% (v/v) benzyl alcohol and 2% (v/v) 1-propanol.

(1) P. Sieber, B. Riniker, M. Brugger, B. Kamber, and W. Rittel, *Helv. Chim. Acta*, **53**, 2135 (1970).
(2) P. M. Helfman and J. L. Bada, *Proc. Natl. Acad. Sci. U.S.A.*, **72**, 2891 (1975).
(3) J. M. Chalovich, C. T. Burt, S. M. Cohen, T. Glonek, and M. Barany, *Arch. Biochem. Biophys.*, **182**, 683 (1977).
(4) J. M. Manning and S. Moore, *J. Biol. Chem.*, **243**, 5591 (1968).
(5) R. S. Feinberg and R. B. Merrifield, *Tetrahedron*, **28**, 5865 (1972).
(6) R. Hirschmann, R. G. Strachan, H. Schwam, E. F. Schoenewaldt, H. Joshua, B. Barkemeyer, D. F. Veber, W. J. Paleveda, Jr., T. A. Jacob, T. E. Beesley, and R. G. Denkewalter, *J. Org. Chem.*, **32**, 3415 (1967).
(7) R. G. Denkewalter, H. Schwam, R. G. Strachan, T. E. Beesley, D. F. Veber, E. F. Schoenewaldt, H. Barkemeyer, W. J. Paleveda, Jr., T. A. Jacob, and R. Hirschmann, *J. Am. Chem. Soc.*, **88**, 3163 (1966).
(8) Observations of this laboratory.
(9) G. W. Anderson, J. E. Zimmerman, and F. M. Callahan, *J. Am. Chem. Soc.*, **86**, 1839 (1964).
(10) F. M. Finn and K. Hofman, in "The Proteins", 3rd ed., Vol. 2, H. Neurath and R. L. Hill, Ed., Academic Press, New York, N.Y., 1976. pp 105–253.
(11) Y. Shimohigashi, S. Lee, and N. Izumiya, *Bull. Chem. Soc. Jpn.*, **49**, 3280 (1976).
(12) V. du Vigneaud and C. E. Meyer, *J. Biol. Chem.*, **98**, 295 (1932).
(13) B. Bezas and L. Zervas, *J. Am. Chem. Soc.*, **83**, 719 (1961).
(14) D. H. Spackman, W. H. Stein, and S. Moore, *Anal. Chem.*, **30**, 1190 (1958).
(15) J. M. Manning, *J. Am. Chem. Soc.*, **92**, 7449 (1970).
(16) J. M. Manning, A. Marglin, and S. Moore in "Progress in Peptide Research", Vol. 2, S. Lande, Ed., Gordon and Breach, London, 1972, p 173–183.

Reference

T. Tamegai, M. Ohmae, K. Kawabe and M. Tomoeda, J. Liq. Chromatogr., 2, 1229 (1979).

Summary

A series of diastereomeric amides of racemic 2-[3-(chlorophenoxyphenyl)]propionic acid (A) was separated by high performance liquid chromatography.

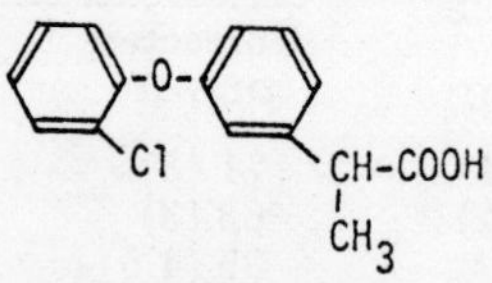

The experimental details and results follow:

TABLE 2 Resolution of enantiomeric 2-[3-(chlorophenoxyphenyl)]propionic acid

Amino compound	Resolution factor	Minimum detectable quantities (ng)
(+)-2-aminobutane	1.25	100
(+)-2-aminoheptane	2.71	100
D-(+)-1-phenylethylamine	2.27	15
(+)-1-(1-naphthyl)ethylamine	4.11	5
(-)-leucine methylester	1.09	100
(-)-phenylalanine methylester	4.25	50
(-)-glycine methylester	1.00	100

Conditions of HPLC

Column ; Nucleosil NH_2, 10μm, 4.6 mm I.D. X 250 mm

Mobile phase ; cyclohexane · ethyl acetate (5:1)

Detector ; UV_{280} , Flow rate ; 1.5 ml/min.

Reference

D.M. Johnson, A. Reuter, J.M. Collins and G.F. Thompson, J. Pharm. Sci., 68, 112 (1979).

Summary

The enantiomers of 2-(6'-methoxy-2'-naphthyl)propionic acid were converted to their diastereomeric esters by reaction with (S)-(+)-2-octanol. These esters were completely separated using high performance liquid chromatography on a silica column. The experimental details and results follow:

Liquid Chromatography Equipment and Operating Conditions—A liquid chromatograph[7] equipped with a variable wavelength UV detector[8] and a 100-μl fixed loop injector[9] were used. The wavelength chosen for detection was 332 nm (0.04 aufs); at lower wavelengths, an impurity found in all batches of octanol gave a detectable peak coincident with that for (*SS*)-III. Integration of peak areas was obtained through the use of a programmed digital integration system[10] interfaced to the detector. A 25-cm × 3-mm (i.d.) commercially available microparticle silica[11] column was operated at ambient temperature. With 0.5% (v/v) ethyl acetate in hexane as the mobile phase and a flow rate of 1.2 ml/min, the column developed a pressure of approximately 49.21 atmospheres.

Esterification Procedure—Approximately 1 mg of I was weighed into a test tube fitted with a polytef-faced screw cap. To this solid was added 100 μl of (*S*)-(+)-II and, on dissolution, 900 μl of purified toluene and 5 μl of concentrated sulfuric acid were also added. The capped tubes were placed in an oil bath for 2 hr at 100°[12]. After cooling to room temperature, 1 ml of 0.02 *M* sodium bicarbonate was added and the mixture was agitated vigorously.

The toluene layer was transferred to a new tube and dried over sodium sulfate. A 100-μl aliquot of this solution was then brought to 10 ml with the mobile phase, and the resulting solution (~10 μg/ml) was analyzed by injecting 100 μl (1 μg) into the chromatograph. The percent (*SS*)-III is then calculated from:

$$\text{percent } (SS)\text{-III} = \frac{\text{area peak 1}}{\text{area peak 1} + \text{area peak 2}} \times 100 \quad \text{(Eq. 1)}$$

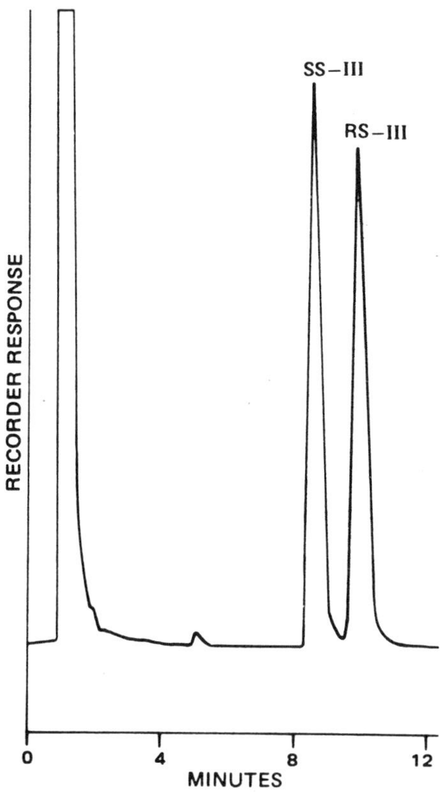

Figure 1—*Chromatogram of the mixture of diastereomeric octyl esters (III) prepared from racemic I and* (S)-(+)-*II.*

where peak 1 is the first eluting peak and corresponds to the (*SS*)-ester and the second peak corresponds to the (*RS*)-ester[13].

Scale-up of this reaction gave a crystalline product (mp 53°) upon workup whose spectral properties were consistent with those of the expected ester III.

Calibration Curve—Approximately 10 mg of (*S*)-(+)-I of high optical purity[14], $[\alpha]_D^{25}$ +67.4° (c 1.0, $CHCl_3$), was accurately weighed into a 10-ml volumetric flask. The solid was dissolved by addition of 1 ml of (*S*)-(+)-II, and the resulting solution was brought to 10 ml with purified toluene. This procedure was repeated using racemic I. Into six culture tubes were added aliquots of the solutions as shown below to give a final volume of 1 ml in each tube:

volume of (*S*)-(+)-I, ml	volume of (±)-I, ml	approximate enantiomeric purity, %
1.0	0	100
0.8	0.2	80
0.6	0.4	60
0.4	0.6	40
0.2	0.8	20
0	1.0	0

To each sample was added 5 μl of concentrated sulfuric acid, and the resulting reaction mixtures were treated as described and analyzed by liquid chromatography. The enantiomeric purity of (*S*)-(+)-I in each calibration sample can be calculated from the following equation[15].

percent enantiomeric purity

$$= 200 \left[\frac{V_+W_+F + \frac{1}{2}V_\pm W_\pm}{V_+W_+ + V_\pm W_\pm}\right] - 100 \quad \text{(Eq. 2)}$$

---

[7] Spectra-Physics model 3500B.
[8] Schoeffel model 770.
[9] Valco universal inlet.
[10] Spectra-Physics Systems I.
[11] Spectra-Physics prepacked with 5-μm Spherisorb silica.
[12] The progress of the reaction was followed by TLC. The reaction mixture (50 μl) was spotted directly onto silica gel GF plates and developed with hexane–tetrahydrofuran–acetic acid (50:50:1). In this solvent system, I (R_f 0.71) and III (R_f 0.86) are well separated.

[13] Actually each peak represents an enantiomeric pair. Peak 1 represents both (*SS*)-III and (*RR*)-III while peak 2 represents both (*RS*)-III and (*SR*)-III. Due to the high degree of optical purity of (*S*)-(+)-II, contributions that (*RR*)-III and (*SR*)-III may make to each peak were ignored.
[14] Optical rotations were measured on a Perkin-Elmer model 141 polarimeter.
[15] If $W_+ = W_\pm$, *i.e.*, if the weights used to prepare the two standard solutions are the same, then Eq. 2 simplifies to:

$$\text{percent enantiomeric purity} = 200\,[V_+F + \tfrac{1}{2}V_\pm/V_+ + V_\pm] - 100$$

D.M. Johnson, A. Reuter, J.M. Collins and G.F. Thompson, J. Pharm. Sci., 68, 112 (1979) continued.

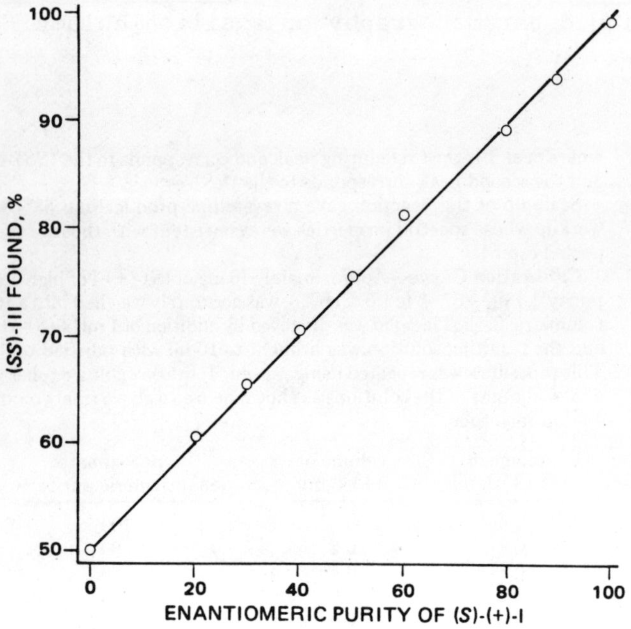

Figure 2—*Calibration plot showing the relationship between the known enantiomeric purity (by weight) of prepared samples of I and the diastereomeric composition of III found after esterification.*

where:

V_+ = volume of (*S*)-(+)-I standard solution in milliliters
$V_\pm$ = volume of racemic I standard solution in milliliters
W_+ = weight of (*S*)-(+)-I used to prepare the standard solution
$W_\pm$ = weight of racemic I used to prepare the standard solution
F = mole fraction of the (*S*)-(+) enantiomer known to be in the batch of I used to prepare the (*S*)-(+)-I standard solution

RESULTS AND DISCUSSION

The esterification reaction rate was followed by TLC. The reaction was complete in approximately 1.5 hr at 100° under the conditions specified. Complete loss of I was observed, and no side products were apparent by TLC. When (*S*)-(+)-I and (*S*)-(+)-II were allowed to react for 23 hr under these same conditions, no evidence of degradation of the ester [(*SS*)-III] was observed by TLC and liquid chromatography. Racemization of I or epimerization of (*SS*)-III under these severe conditions was also ruled out since the percent (*SS*)-diastereomer found (98%) compares well with that found after only 2 hr of reaction (99%). These results indicate that the reaction of I with (*S*)-(+)-II gives only III with no competing reactions and that this ester is completely stable, both chemically and stereochemically, under the reaction conditions.

The liquid chromatographic method used to analyze the reaction mixtures displayed baseline separation of the (*SS*)- and (*RS*)-diastereomers of III (Fig. 1). The specificity of the method for I in the presence of 2-(6′-hydroxy-2′-naphthyl)propionic acid (IV), a major metabolite in humans (7, 8), was also demonstrated by the large separation found between the octyl esters of I and IV on liquid chromatography.

A plot of the percent (*SS*)-III found experimentally *versus* the known enantiomeric purity of (*S*)-(+)-I in each sample is shown in Fig. 2. The excellent fit of the points in this calibration curve to a line of slope 0.5 clearly demonstrates that for each sample the ratio of the diastereomeric esters produced is identical to the ratio of enantiomers present in the original sample. If, however, enantiomerically impure (*S*)-(+)-II were used, the slope of the line in Fig. 2 would be less than 0.5 and could be calculated from:

$$\text{slope} = \frac{\text{enantiomeric purity of }(S)\text{-}(+)\text{-II}}{200} \qquad \text{(Eq. 3)}$$

Table I—Enantiomeric Purity of Several Samples of I [a] by Esterification followed by Liquid Chromatography

Sample	Enantiomeric Purity of (*S*)-(+)-I, %
1	79.2
2	79.9
3	79.8
4	79.2
5	79.9
Mean ± *SD*	79.6 ± 0.4

[a] Samples are 80.0% enantiomerically pure.

Table I shows the results of the liquid chromatographic analysis of five samples of (*S*)-(+)-I (80% enantiomerically pure). The data clearly demonstrate the excellent reproducibility of the method. This result is expected since the measurement is not dependent on quantitative recovery of III but rather involves comparison of relative peak areas of two closely eluting diastereomers. The applicability of this method to other

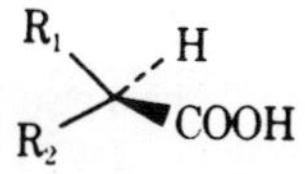

A

carboxylic acids of this type (Structure A) can only be speculative but is perhaps not unlikely if R_1 and R_2 are sufficiently dissimilar.

Reference

H. Nakazawa, Y. Kanamaru and A. Murano, Chem. Pharm. Bull., 27, 1694 (1979).

Summary
A method for the separation and determination of the enantiomers of 2,2'-(4,4'-cyclohexylidenediphenoxy)-2,2'-dimethyldibutyric acid (clinofibrate) by HPLC as the diastereomeric amide derivatives with (+)-α-methylbenzylamine was reported by the authors. Experimental details and results follow:

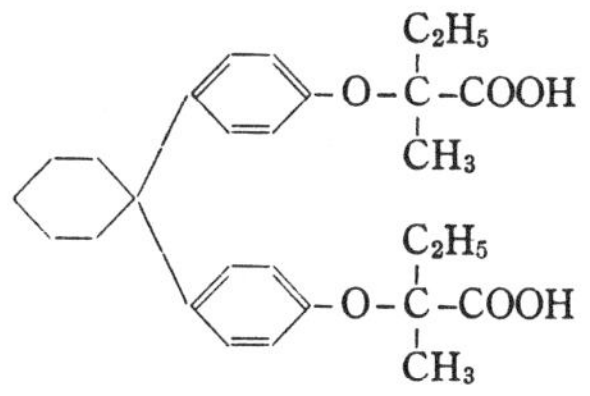

Fig. 1. Chemical Formula of 2,2'-(4,4'-Cyclohexylidenediphenoxy)-2,2'-dimethyldibutyric Acid (Clinofibrate)

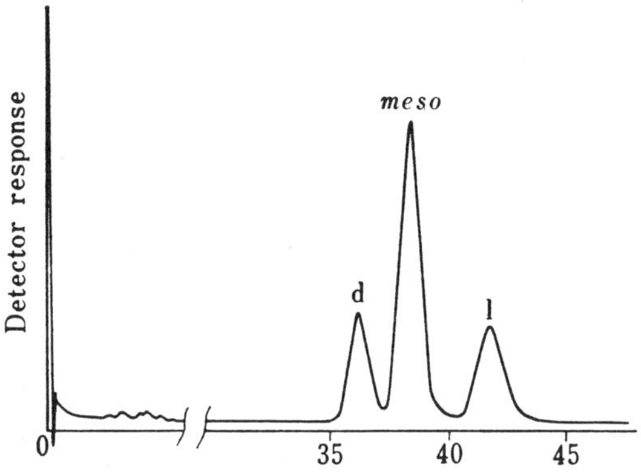

Fig. 2. Chromatogram of the Diastereomer Amide of Clinofibrate

Conditions: column LiChrosorb SI-60 (5 μm) (300 mm × 4 mm i.d.); mobile phase, *n*-hexane/isopropanol (500/3 v/v); flow rate, 1.6 ml/min; detection, UV (254 nm).

Experimental

Apparatus——A Jasco Trirotar liquid chromatograph coupled with a Jasco UVIDEC-100 ultraviolet detector for monitoring at 254 nm (Japan Spectroscopic Co., Ltd.), a Shimadzu E1A computing integrator and a Shimadzu LKB-9000 mass spectrometer equipped with the GC-MS PAC-300 data processing system (Shimadzu Seisakusho Co., Ltd.) were used.

Column——LiChrosorb SI-60 (5 μm) silica packing (E. Merck, Darmstadt) was suspended in tetrabromoethane–carbon tetrachloride–dioxane (1 : 2 : 2, v/v) and packed into a stainless-steel column 150 mm in length and 4 mm i.d. under a pressure of 400—500 kg/cm^2 by the balanced-density slurry method.[6]

Reagents——Toluene (JIS guaranteed reagent) was dried on Molecular Sieve 4A (Union Carbide). D-(+)-α-Methylbenzylamine toluene solution was prepared by dissolving 3.0 g of D-(+)-α-methylbenzylamine (Aldrich, $[\alpha]_D^{20}$: +39°, neat) in 100 ml of dried toluene. Other reagents used were of analytical reagent grade.

Procedure——About 50 mg of clinofibrate was weighed into a 10 ml round-bottomed flask and 0.4 ml of thionyl chloride was added. The flask was stoppered tightly, the mixture was warmed for 5 minutes in a water bath at 60° with occasional shaking and then the excess thionyl chloride was removed *in vacuo* below 60°. Dried toluene and D-(+)-α-methylbenzylamine toluene solution (2 ml each) were added successively, and mixed well. The mixture was allowed to stand at room temperature for 10 minutes, and then the solvent was removed *in vacuo*. Chloroform (5 ml) was added to the residue and mixed well to make a sample solution. 5.0 μl of the sample solution was chromatographed under the following HPLC conditions: column, stainless-steel two connecting columns (150 mm in length and 4 mm in i.d.) packed with LiChrosorb SI-60 (5 μm); column temperature, ambient; mobile phase, *n*-hexane/isopropanol (500/3, v/v); flow rate, 1.6 ml/min; detector, UV photometer at 254 nm. The isomer composition of the sample was determined according to the following equation;

$$\textit{meso},\ d\text{- or } l\text{-isomer ratio } (\%) = \frac{A_1, A_2 \text{ or } A_3}{A_1 + A_2 + A_3} \times 100$$

where A_1, A_2 and A_3 are the peak areas of *meso*, *d*- and *l*-isomers of clinofibrate, respectively.

Reference

T. Tamegai, T. Tanaka, T. Kaneko, S. Ozaki, M. Ohmae and K. Kawabe, J. Liq. Chromatogr., 2, 551 (1979).

Summary

The enantiomers of 2-[3-(2-chlorophenoxyphenyl)]-propionic acid were converted to their diastereomeric amide derivatives by reaction first with oxalyl chloride and then with (+)-2-aminobutane and separated by high performance liquid chromatography using a Nucleosil NH_2 column with cyclohexane-ethyl acetate (5:1) as the mobile phase. The experimental details and results follow:

High Performance Liquid Chromatography

The chromatographic system was composed of an Altex 110 A pump (Berkeley, CA, U.S.A.), a Rheodyne 7120 loop injector (Calf., U.S.A.) and a JASCO UVIDEC 100-II multi-wavelength detector (JAPAN).

The column was 25 cm x 4.6 mm I.D. stainless-steel tubing slurry packed with Nucleosil NH_2 (Macherey-Nagel, Düren, G.F.R.) having an average particle diameter of 10 µm and the mobile phase consisted of cyclohexane and ethyl acetate in the ratio of 5 : 1. The flow rate was maintained at 1.5 ml/min. and the procedure was carried out at ambient temperature. Twenty µl of the sample solution were injected onto the chromatographic column and the effluent was monitored at 280 nm.

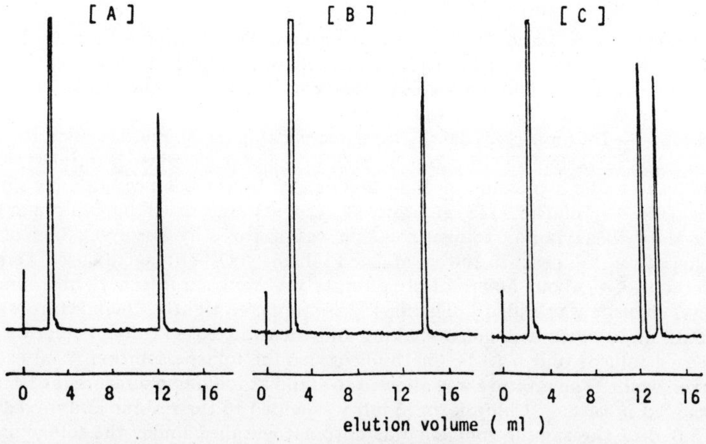

FIGURE 3

The chromatograms of authentic d-, l- and dl-CPA

Conditions , Column: Nucleosil NH_2 10 µm, 4.6 mm I.D. x 250 mm
Mobile phase: cyclohexane · ethyl acetate (5:1)
Detector: UV_{280}, Flow rate: 1.5 ml/min.
Materials , [A] d-CPA, [B] l-CPA, [C] dl-CPA

Reference

G. Helmchen, G. Nill, D. Flockerzi, W. Schuhle and M.S.K. Youssef, Angew. Chem. Int. Ed. Engl., 18, 62 (1979).

Summary

A series of diastereomeric amides were separated via HPLC on silica gel with very high separation factors. From chromatographic data, using silica gel as adsorbent, four postulates were derived which serve as guidelines in the search for structural features necessary for high separation effects. Experimental details and results follow:

In contrast to the classical method *via* fractional crystallization of diastereomeric salts the separation of the enantiomers of chiral carboxylic acids and amines can be carried out by liquid adsorption chromatography of diastereomeric amides in a directed way, *i. e.* with pre-estimation of separation effects[1a] and with simultaneous determination of the enantiomeric purity[1b] and absolute configuration[1c]. Besides the low efficiency of the—now superseded—conventional column chromatography[2], non-optimal separation factors and especially the extreme difficulty of amide hydrolysis[3] were obstacles to wider preparative application of the method.

We have now developed reagents which not only ensure very high separation factors but also ready hydrolysis (cf. [4]).

Particularly well suited for demonstrating the effects are the diastereomeric amides *(1)/(2)*, since their conformation in solution, the starting point of our model considerations, is well defined[1a] and the substituents R and A can be easily varied. From chromatographic data (adsorbent: silica gel[5]) four simple postulates were derived which serve as guidelines in the search for structural features necessary for high separation effects.

1. The conformation of the amides is the same in the dissolved state and in the adsorbed state[6]. In cases *(1)/(2)*, for both diastereomers it is determined by the planar structural element *(3)* (common plane) provided neither R^1 nor R^2 form a hydrogen bond to the amide group[7].

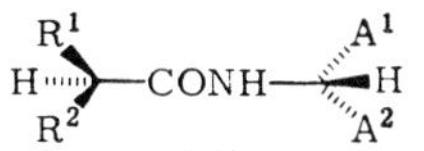

(1)

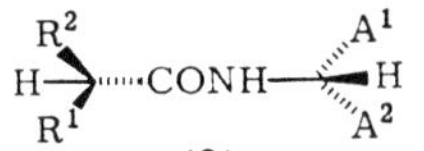

(2)

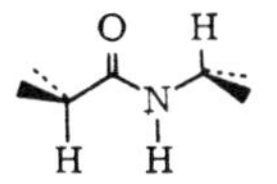

(3)

2. Binding to silica gel preferentially takes place *via* hydrogen bonding[9]. Hence the contribution of the amide group, which can be bound as described by *(4)* and *(5)*, is particularly high.

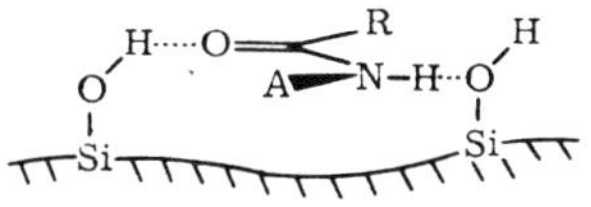

(4)

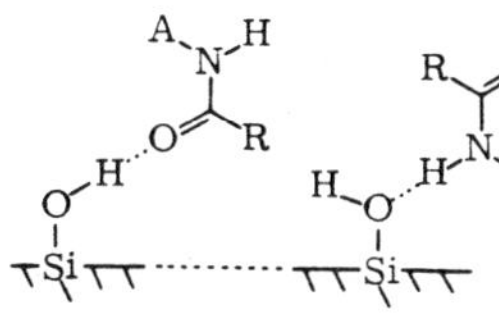

(5)

3. Significant diastereoselectivity is to be expected only for the state *(4)*. This arrangement is perturbed in favor of unbound or states *(5)* by substituents R and A with weak affinity to the silica gel. The perturbing effect of a substituent must be determined empirically. We assess it formally by the designations chromatographically large (cL) and small (cS), since for alkyl and aryl groups it approximately parallels the steric bulk in the direction perpendicular to the amide plane[9].

4. (Configuration rule) The groups R^1 and R^2 as well as A^1 and A^2 are classified according to their perturbing effect as R^{cL} and R^{cS} and A^{cL} and A^{cS}. Due to the better shielding of the amide group, the diastereomer whose R^{cL}/A^{cL} groups are situated on opposite faces of the common plane is eluted first.

Which structural features, according to these postulates, ought to lead to particularly good separating effects, as assessed by the separation factor α? Postulate 3 implies that α increases with the difference in steric bulk between A^1 and A^2 or R^1 and R^2. This is so for the amides *(a)* and *(b)* (cf. Table 1) but not in the series *(c)*—*(e)*, even though postulate 4 remains correct. Apparently the proportion of diastereoselectively acting states *(4)* decreases for *both* diastereomers with increasing size—especially broadening—of the apolar substituents. An extreme case is *(f)*.

Table 1. High-pressure liquid chromatographic separation [a] of diastereomeric amides *(1)/(2)* [b] on silica gel (23°C; hexane ethyl acetate (x:y) [c]).

	R^1 (cS)	R^2 (cL)	A^1 (cS)	A^2 (cL)	α[d]	$-\Delta(\Delta G)$ [cal] [e]	(x:y)
(a)	Et	Ph	Me	Ph	1.51	242	4:1
(b)	Et	Ph	Me	p-C_6H_4Ph	1.70	313	4:1
(c)	Me	Ph	Me	Ph	1.81	348	4:1
(d)	Me	CH_2Ph	Me	Ph	1.68	306	4:1
(e)	Me	$CHPh_2$	Me	Ph	1.45	220	4:1
(f)	Me	$CHPh_2$	Me	$CHPh_2$	1.15	82	4:1
(g)	Me	Ph	CH_2OH	Ph	2.56	553	1:1
(h)	Me	CH_2Ph	CH_2OH	Ph	2.56	553	1:1
(i)	Me	$CHPh_2$	CH_2OH	Ph	2.73	591	1:1
(i)					3.06	658	4:1
(j)	CH_2OH	Ph	Me	Ph	2.81	608	1:1
(k)	$(CH_2)_2OH$	Ph	Me	Ph	2.83	613	1:1
(l)	$(CH_2)_3OH$	Ph	Me	Ph	2.13	445	1:1
(m)	CH_2OAc	Ph	Me	Ph	2.06	424	4:1
(n)	CH_2CO_2Me	Ph	Me	Ph	1.91	380	1:1
(o)	$(CH_2)_2CO_2Me$	Ph	Me	Ph	1.71	314	1:1
(p)	$(CH_2)_2OH$	Ph	CH_2OH	Ph	5.77	1031	0:1
(q)	CH_2CO_2Me	Ph	CH_2OH	Ph	3.36	713	1:1

[a] Apparatus: see [1b]; pressure: 150 bar; inert substance: pentane; column: 30 × 0.3 cm for *(a)*—*(f)*, 20 × 0.3 cm for *(g)*—*(q)*, packed with Merckosorb SI 60, 5 μm. [b] All the new compounds were prepared diastereomerically pure and gave correct analyses and spectra; the configuration of *(l)* and *(o)* was confirmed by ^{1}H-NMR (method: *G. Helmchen*, Tetrahedron Lett. *1974*, 1527), otherwise by synthesis. [c] The composition of the eluent could not be held constant because of the difference in polarity of the compounds. As shown by case *(i)*, α decreases with increasing content of ethyl acetate. [d] $\alpha = (t_2 - t_0)/(t_1 - t_0)$; t_1, t_2: retention time of the first and second eluted amide, respectively; t_0: retention time of pentane. [e] $\Delta(\Delta G) = -RT\ln\alpha$.

<u>Reference</u>

G. Helmchen, G. Nill, D. Flockerzi and M.S.K. Youssef, Angew. Chem. Int. Ed. Engl., <u>18</u>, 63 (1979).

<u>Summary</u>

A number of racemic 2-methylcarboxylic acids and γ- and δ-lactones were resolved as their diastereomeric amides on a preparative scale via HPLC and hydrolyzed to give each of the enantiomers in high yield and enantiomerically pure. Experimental details and results follow:

The diastereomeric amides *(1)*/*(2)* with OH groups located in the γ or δ position to the carbonyl group [R^1 or $R^2=(CH_2)_nOH$ and/or A^1 or $A^2=(CH_2)_{n-1}OH$, $n=2, 3$] show high, in certain cases extreme separation factors in liquid absorption chromatography[1]. We now report that these amides also have favorable chemical properties. Their cleavage takes place under acidic conditions mild enough, so that relatively sensitive compounds can be worked with, but not under such mild conditions that reaction occurs on the weakly acidic adsorbent silica gel. In cases where R^1 or $R^2=(CH_2)_nOH$, $n=2$, 3, reaction with 0.5–1 N mineral acid at 50–90°C leads to formation of lactones *(3)*, $n=2$, 3[2] and amines *(4)*. In cases where A^1 or $A^2=(CH_2)_{n-1}OH$, $n=2, 3$, *N,O*-acyl transfer[3] occurs, followed by ester hydrolysis to give the carboxylic acids *(5)* and amines *(4)*. Depending upon the properties of R^1 and R^2, 0.5–3 N mineral acid is necessary at *ca.* 50–100°C. As a rule the yields are almost quantitative.

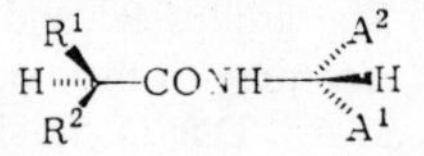

(1)

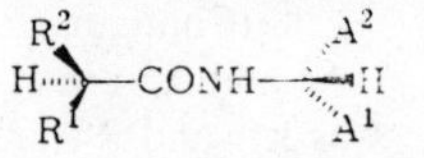

(2)

[*] Dr. G. Helmchen, Dipl.-Chem. G. Nill, Dipl.-Chem. D. Flockerzi, Dr. M. S. K. Youssef
Institut für Organische Chemie, Biochemie und Isotopenforschung der Universität
Pfaffenwaldring 55, D-7000 Stuttgart 80 (Germany)

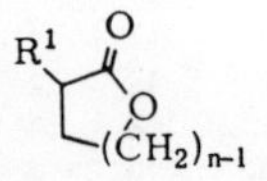

(3)

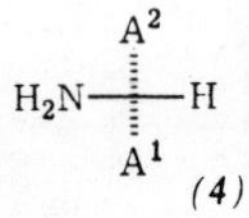

(4)

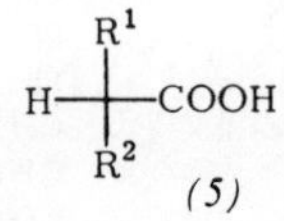

(5)

(4a) A^1 = CH_2OH, A^2 = Ph
(4b) A^1 = CH_3, A^2 = Ph

These results thus demonstrate that the sought-after method (see [1]) for directed resolution of enantiomeric carboxylic acids or amines has in principle been realized, as has also a method for the separation of enantiomeric lactones:

1. Racemic carboxylic acids *(5)* *via* the usual activated derivatives (acyl chlorides, imidazolides *etc.*) can be reacted with amino alcohols *(4)*, A^1 or $A^2=(CH_2)_nOH$, $n=1$, 2, to give the diastereomeric amides *(1)*/*(2)*, which can be separated chromatographically and subsequently hydrolyzed. (−)-(*R*)-phenylglycinol *(4a)* is a suitable reagent here, since it is UV-active (chromatographic detection), is commercially available[4], and is easily recoverable almost quantitatively (cf. Table 1 and Experimental). Other compounds that can be prepared from amino acids, *e.g.* phenyl alaninol, alaninol, valinol, leucinol, and amides or esters of serine also give good results[5]. The nitrosamide rearrangement, an alternative for the hydrolysis in the case of extremely sensitive carboxylic acids, can also be employed in the case of *N*-acyl derivatives of amino alcohols, cf. *(5d)* in Table 1.

2. Racemic lactones *(3)* can by direct reaction with amines *(4)* be converted into amides *(1)*/*(2)*, R^1 or $R^2=(CH_2)_nOH$, $n=2, 3$ (catalyst: 2-hydroxypyridine[6]). Since these amides show high separation factors even in the case of apolar substituents A^1, A^2[1], amines such as (−)-(*S*)-1-phenylethylamine *(4b)*[7] are sufficiently good separating reagents. Cleavage of the chromatographically separated amides affords (apart from in the case where R^1 = Ph) enantiomerically pure lactones *(3)* (cf. Experimental and Table 1).

Such lactones have a strong tendency to racemization. We have therefore determined the enantiomeric purity of the particularly sensitive lactone *(3c)* in the following way: (+)-*(3c)* (for data see Table 1) was treated with hydrogen bromide/glacial acetic acid and then with zinc/glacial acetic acid; the 2-benzylbutyric acid formed was > 99.9 % enantiomerically pure [HPLC of the diastereomeric amides with *(4b)*][8].

3. Enantiomerically pure lactones *(3)* are now readily available for the first time. However, they are not suitable as separating reagents for amines since they partially racemize upon direct conversion to amides (for a solution to this problem see [9]).

Experimental

(1)/*(2)* from *(5)*: 1 mol *(5)* is converted with oxalyl chloride into the crude acyl chloride, whose solution in anhydrous dioxane is added dropwise to a solution of 1.0 mol *(4a)* and 1.2 mol triethylamine in dioxane at 5–10°C. After removal of the solvent 1 N hydrochloric acid is added and the amides *(1)*/*(2)* are extracted with methylene chloride.

(1)/*(2)* from *(3)*: A solution of 1 mol *(3)*, 2 mol *(4a)* or *(4b)* and 1 mol 2-hydroxypyridine in 0.5 l anhydrous toluene is heated to boiling for 25 h under an inert gas, then partially evaporated down and the residue partitioned between CH_2Cl_2 and 0.5 N hydrochloric acid.

Separation of *(1)* and *(2)*: The crude mixture of *(1)*/*(2)* is chromatographed, either on a column as mentioned in Ref.[1] or on a Merck-Lobar column (UV detection, eluent: petroleum ether (low-boiling)/ethyl acetate in a ratio shown to be optimal by TLC). Alternatively, the mixture can be fractionally crystallized with TLC monitoring of the separation progress (in all cases widely separated spots).

[**] Directed Resolution of Enantiomers *via* Liquid Chromatography of Diastereomeric Derivatives, Part 5.—This work was supported by the Deutsche Forschungsgemeinschaft (Projekt He 880/6).—Part 4: [1].

G. Helmchen, G. Nill, D. Flockerzi and M.S.K. Youssef, Angew. Chem. Int. Ed. Engl., 18, 63 (1979) continued.

Amide cleavage: For recovery of *(3)* the vigorously stirred mixture of 1 mol of the diastereomerically pure *(1)* or *(2)* and 21 l N H_2SO_4 in dioxane/water (1:1) is heated at 80–90°C for 16 h then diluted with water and extracted with methylene chloride to afford *(3)* in the neutral part. The recovery of *(5)* is carried out analogously, but as a rule up to 3 N H_2SO_4 is used and the mixture is heated to boiling. Since the rate of reaction varies greatly with the nature of the acyl group (reaction time a few minutes to several hours) the conversion is monitored by TLC. For recovery (*ca.* 90%) of *(4a)* the acidic aqueous phases from the extraction step are brought to pH 9–10 and extracted six times with *n*-butanol/ethyl acetate/heptane (2:1:0.02): the organic phase is washed with a little water and evaporated down without previous drying.

[1] *G. Helmchen, G. Nill, D. Flockerzi, W. Schühle, M. S. K. Youssef*, Angew. Chem. *91*, 64 (1979): Angew. Chem. Int. Ed. Engl. *18*, 62 (1979), references cited therein.

[2] *L. Zürn*, Justus Liebigs Ann. Chem. *631*, 56 (1960).

[3] *A. P. Phillips, R. Baltzly*, J. Am. Chem. Soc. *69*, 200 (1947).

[4] Of the commercially available products tested by us those obtainable from Sigma showed the highest chemical and enantiomeric purity: E.P. = 99.2%, determined by HPLC according to the method of *G. Helmchen, W. Strubert*, Chromatographia *7*, 713 (1974).

[5] Refractometric detection is necessary for compounds without aryl groups.

[6] *H. C. Openshaw, N. Whittaker*, J. Chem. Soc. *C 1969*, 89.

[7] Enantiomerically pure (>99.9%) (−)-*(4b)* can be obtained from commercially available products (96–99%) by single precipitation of the salt with D-tartaric acid.

[8] This procedure constitutes a new method for the determination of the enantiomeric purity of 2- and 3-substituted butyrolactones (and presumably also valerolactones): for other methods see *G. Saucy, R. Borer, D. P. Trullinger, J. B. Jones, K. P. Lok*, J. Org. Chem. *42*, 3206 (1977), and references cited therein.

[9] *G. Helmchen, G. Nill*, Angew. Chem. *91*, 66 (1979): Angew. Chem. Int. Ed. Engl. *18*, 65 (1979).

Table 1. Separation of enantiomeric lactones *(3)* and carboxylic acids *(5)* by chromatography of diastereomeric amides *(1)*/*(2)* (A^2 = Ph, A^1 = CH_2OH or CH_3) and their cleavage under acid conditions (cf. Experimental).

	n	R^1	R^2	Separating reagent	*(1)*/*(2)* [a]	Yield [%] (+)-*(3)* or *(5)* [b]	Yield [%] (−)-*(3)* or *(5)* [b]	$[\alpha]_D$ [°] of *(3)* or *(5)* from first eluted amide [c]	$[\alpha]_D$ [°] of *(3)* or *(5)* from second eluted amide [c]	Configuration according to Lit.	Configuration according to Rule in [1]
(3a)	2	CH_3		*(4b)*	67	76	67	− 23.1	+ 23.1 (*c* = 9.7, EtOH, 23°C) [d]	(+)-(*R*) [d]	(+)-(*R*)
(3b)	2	*n*-C_4H_9		*(4b)*	76	99	99	+ 12.5	− 12.5 (*c* = 5.0, MeOH, 20°C) [e]	(−)-(*R*) [e]	(−)-(*R*)
(3c)	2	CH_2Ph		*(4b)*	77	98	99	+ 67.7	− 67.9 (*c* = 5.0, CCl_4, 20°C)		(−)-(*R*)
(3d)	2	$(CH_2)_3Ph$		*(4b)*	68	95	95	+ 7.4	− 7.3 (*c* = 10.0, CCl_4, 20°C)		(−)-(*R*)
(3e)	2	$CHPh_2$		*(4b)*	69	100	100	+ 206	− 210 (*c* = 3.0, CCl_4, 20°C)		(+)-(*R*)
(3f)	3	CH_2Ph		*(4b)*	93	84	82	+ 63.4	− 63.1 (*c* = 3.0, MeOH, 20°C)		(+)-(*R*)
(5a)		*n*-C_3H_7	CH_3	*(4a)*	97	85	91	− 18.8 (25°C) [f]	+ 18.4 (neat, 16°C) [g]	(+)-(*S*) [g]	(+)-(*S*)
(5b)		CH_2Ph	CH_3	*(4a)*	93	92	98	− 25.2	+ 25.4 (neat, 22°C) [h]	(−)-(*R*) [h]	(−)-(*R*)
(5c)		$CHPh_2$	CH_3	*(4a)*	97	95	94	+ 54.3	− 54.6 (*c* = 1.6, $CHCl_3$, 26.5°C) [i]	(−)-(*S*) [i]	(−)-(*S*)
(5d)		Ph	CH_3	*(4a)*	92	96			+ 86.2 (*c* = 1.2, C_6H_6, 20°C) [j]	(+)-(*S*) [j]	(+)-(*S*)
(5d)						75 [k]			+ 94.3 (*c* = 2.5, C_6H_6, 20°C)		

[a] Chromatographically pure compounds; max. difference between *(1)* and *(2)*: 2%. [b] Analytically pure products: yield w.r.t. the amide. [c] Highest rotation found in the literature. [d] *T. Kaneko, K. Wakabayashi, H. Katsura*, Bull. Chem. Soc. Jpn. *35*, 1149 (1962): $[\alpha]_D^{15} = -21.5°$ (*c* = 5.5, EtOH). [e] $[\alpha]_D^{23} = -12.8°$ (*c* = 9.9, EtOH); *A. I. Meyers, E. D. Mihelich*, J. Org. Chem. *40*, 1186 (1975): $[\alpha]_D^{23} = -7.3°$ (*c* = 9.7, EtOH). [f] *P. A. Levene, R. E. Marker*, J. Biol. Chem. *98*, 5 (1932): $[\alpha]_D^{25} = -18.4°$ (neat). [g] *S. Ställberg-Stenhagen, E. Stenhagen*, Ark. Kemi *23 A*, 7 (1947): $[\alpha]_D^{16} = +18.5°$ (neat). [h] *A. W. Schrecker*, J. Org. Chem. *22*, 33 (1957): $[\alpha]_D^{22} = -24.56°$ (neat). [i] *H. M. Walborsky, C. G. Pitt*, J. Am. Chem. Soc. *84*, 4832 (1962): $[\alpha]_D^{26.5} = -52.6°$ (*c* = 1.6, $CHCl_3$). [j] *K. Petersen*, Ark. Kemi *10*, 283 (1956) (repeated by us): $[\alpha]_D^{20} = +94.2°$ (*c* = 3.1, C_6H_6). [k] Nitrosamine rearrangement: see [1], footnote 3.

Reference

A.I. Meyers and J. Slade, J. Org. Chem., 45, 2912 (1980).

Summary

Resolution of α-substituted mandelic acids was accomplished by (a) asymmetric alkylation of the benzoyl oxazoline (1) with organolithium reagents or Grignard reagents to afford the α-phenyl-α-hydroxy adduct (2) enriched (30-87%) in one diastereomer (b) separation of the diastereomers via medium pressure liquid chromatography [A.I. Meyers, J. Slade, R.K. Smith, E.D. Mihelich, F.M. Hershenson and C.D. Liang, J. Org. Chem. 44, 2247 (1979)] and (c) hydrolysis of (2) to give the α-hydroxy acid. The enantiomers were obtained in at least 99% optical purity. Experimental details and results follow:

Experimental Section

Medium-pressure liquid chromatography was performed on a home-built unit described in detail elsewhere.[1] The solvent system chosen for elution in Table I was based on obtaining an R_f of 0.1–0.15 on silica gel TLC plates (0.5 mm). Empirically this was found to be useful for achieving optimum separation and recovery of material. Samples of mixtures of **2** were introduced as 25–50% (by volume) solutions in the chosen eluting solvent and then chromatographed at a median pressure of 50 psi (extremes were 10–90 psi during the pump cycle) and at a flow rate of 15–20 mL/min. Fractions (5, 10, or 15 mL) were collected, and the presence of eluted materials was monitored by thin-layer chromatography (Merck, silica gel PF254, visualized by ultraviolet light). All the fractions possessing identical material and showing only a single spot were combined and the solvents evaporated to give pure material as indicated in Table I.

High-pressure liquid chromatography was performed on a Waters Associates instrument comprised of the following units: a Model 440 absorbance detector (UV); a Model R401 differential refractometer; a Model 6000A solvent delivery system; a Model U6K universal injector; a μ-Porasil No. 27477 3.9 mm × 30 cm column or a reverse-phase μ-Bondapak C_{18}, No. 27324, 3.9 mm × 30 cm column; a Houston Instrument Omniscribe Series B-5000 recorder. Samples of 0.5–2.0 μL were introduced as 5% (by volume) solutions in the appropriate eluting solvent and were chromatographed at pressures of 500–3000 psi at flow rates of 1–3 mL/min. Retention times and other parameters are given in Table II.

α-Substituted Madelic Acids 3. The fractions of **2** collected by medium-pressure LC which indicated the absence of any diastereomeric material were, after combination and concentration, subjected to the hydrolysis conditions reported in the accompanying paper.[3] The residue remaining, on concentration, gave analytically pure acids whose specific rotations are given in Table III.

Table I. Medium-Pressure Liquid Chromatography of Diastereomers 2 at 25 °C and 90 psi

	R in 2	column load, g[a]	acetone/hexane, % by volume	grams recovd	pure diastereomer 2[c]: mp, °C[d]	pure diastereomer 2[c]: $[\alpha]^{22}_D$, deg (c, solvent)
2a	Me	3.85[b]	25/75	1.96	92-94	−22.4 (10.2, $CHCl_3$)
b	Et	1.73[b]	10/90	0.48	oil	−9.23 (1.3, $CHCl_3$)
c	*n*-propyl	1.62	10/90	0.32	oil	−20.8 (1.3, EtOH)
d	isopropyl	0.97	6/94	0.07	76-78	−0.45 (2.2, $CHCl_3$)
e	isobutyl	0.91	6/94	0.20	wax	−9.04 (2.1, $CHCl_3$)
f	*p*-tolyl	0.91	12/88	0.27	wax	+12.1 (2.8, $CHCl_3$)
g	*p*-anisyl	1.17	14/86	0.51	69-71	+18.3 (2.4, $CHCl_3$)
h	α-naphthyl	1.02	12/88	0.48	oil	−40.8 (1.3, $CHCl_3$)
i	2-thienyl	0.89	16/84	0.45	120-122	−6.3 (8.7, $CHCl_3$)

[a] A 15 × 1000 cm glass column packed with silica gel 60 was used except where noted. [b] A 25 × 1000 cm glass column packed with silica gel 60 was used. [c] Purity was confirmed by high-pressure liquid chromatography; see Table II. [d] All the pure oxazolines 2 showed characteristic infrared frequencies (mineral oil) at 1650-1670 (C=N) and 3275-3450 cm^{-1} (OH). Complete spectral data for 2 and 3 can be found in the Ph.D. thesis of J. Slade, Colorado State University, 1979.

A.I. Meyers and J. Slade, J. Org. Chem., 45, 2912 (1980) continued.

Table II. High-Pressure Liquid Chromatography Data for Determining Diastereomeric Purity of 2

R in 2	column	elution solvent(s)	flow rate, mL/min	retention time, min[b] major	minor
Me	μ-Porasil	10% acetone/hexane	3.0	6.0	7.0
Et	μ-Porasil	10% acetone/hexane	2.0	4.4	5.0
n-propyl	μ-Porasil	10% acetone/hexane	1.0	8.1	9.1
isopropyl	μ-Porasil	10% acetone/hexane	1.0	5.7	6.0
isobutyl	μ-Porasil	10% acetone/hexane	1.0	6.6	6.9
p-tolyl	μ-Bondpak[a]	acetonitrile	1.5	5.0	5.3
p-anisyl	μ-Bondpak[a]	methanol	1.5	4.3	4.5
α-naphthyl	μ-Bondpak[a]	acetonitrile	1.5	4.8	5.5
2-thienyl	μ-Porasil	20% acetone/hexane	2.0	2.5	2.8

[a] Two reverse-phase columns (3.9 mm × 30 cm) in series were employed. [b] Monitored at 254 nm.

Table III. α-Hydroxy Acids 3 from Diastereomerically Pure Oxazolines 2

R in 3	mp, °C	$[\alpha]^{25}_D$, deg (*c*, EtOH)	config	anal. calcd C	calcd H	found C	found H
Me	114-116[a]	+36.3 (2.7)	*S*[f]				
Et	124-125[b]	+33.3 (0.87)	*S*[f]				
n-propyl	97-99	+21.6 (2.5)	*S*[f]	74.34	7.37[c]	74.43	7.23
isopropyl	103-105	+32.5 (2.0)	*S*[f]	68.04	7.22	68.32	7.18
isobutyl	118-120	+20.0 (2.0)	*S*[f]	69.23	7.69	68.62	7.76[d]
p-tolyl	122-123[e]	−2.4 (5.0)[g]	*S*[f]				
p-anisyl	137-139	−4.2 (1.3)	*S*	69.77	5.43	69.69	5.60
α-naphthyl	83-86	−4.0 (4.0)	*S*[f]	79.43	5.91[c]	79.15	5.92
2-thienyl	109-111	−20.0 (2.0)	*S*	61.54	4.27	61.38	4.35

[a] R. Barnes and B. Juliano, *J. Am. Chem. Soc.*, 81, 6462 (1959), report a melting point of 116–117 °C. [b] S. Mitsui et al., *Chem. Ind. (London)*, 233 (1964), report a melting point of 126 °C. [c] Analyses performed on corresponding oxazoline 2. [d] Contained trace of solvent which could not be removed. [e] A. McKenzie and E. W. Christie, *Biochem. Z.*, 277, 426 (1935), report a melting point of 125 °C. [f] Absolute configurations are known for these enantiomers: A. I. Meyers and J. Slade, *J. Org. Chem.*, companion paper in this issue. [g] Rotation at 546 nm.

Reference
E. Ade, G. Helmchen and G. Heiligenmann, Tetrahedron Lett., 21, 1137 (1980).

Summary
Racemic 2-methyloctadecanoic acid was resolved via HPLC of the diastereomeric amides with (-)-R-phenylglycinol by methods previously described [G. Helmchen, G. Nill, D. Flockerzi, M.S.K. Youssef, Angew Chem. Int. Ed. Engl., 18, 63 (1979)]. Complete separation was achieved at a throughput of ca. 4 g. per hour on a high performance preparative LC system developed by Dr. Helmchen and co-workers. Both acids were obtained in 99 ± 0.5% purity. Experimental details and results follow:

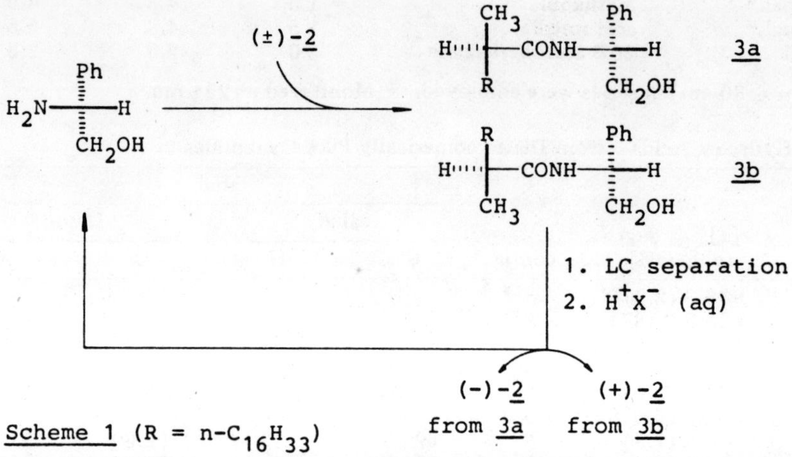

Scheme 1 (R = n-$C_{16}H_{33}$)

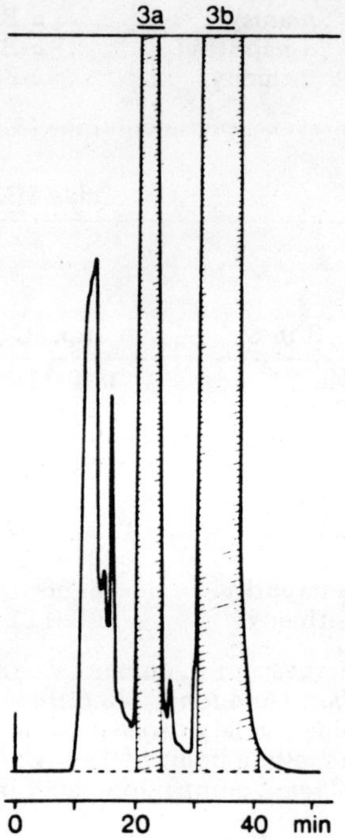

Fig. 1. Preparative LC separation of the diastereomeric amides 3a and 3b. Column: 45 × 4 cm, 270 g silica gel Merck LiChroprep 15-25 µm (9000 theoretical plates, standard test conditions: naphthalene, hexane-ethyl acetate 95/5 (50 ml/min));eluent: chloroform-ethyl acetate 6/4 (30 ml/min); detector: UV 254 nm; substance load: 3 g of raw reaction product, dissolved in 60 ml eluent.

Reference
N. Nimura, H. Ogura and T. Kinoshita, J. Chromatog., 202, 375 (1980).

Summary
A new method for the resolution of amino acid enantiomers by HPLC using 2,3,4,6-tetra-O-acetyl-β-D-glucopyranosyl isothiocyanate as resolving agent is reported. The diastereomeric thiourea derivatives were detected spectrophotometrically at 250 nm. Experimental details and results follow.

Amino acids and other reagents were obtained from Wako (Osaka, Japan) and Tokyo Chemical Industry Co. (Tokyo, Japan). All the reagents were of analytical reagent grade. Methanol and water were distilled before use. Amino acid ethyl esters were prepared by treatment with absolute ethanol and hydrogen chloride in the usual manner. Ultraviolet (UV) spectra were taken with a Model 200-20 spectrophotometer (Hitachi Ltd., Tokyo, Japan).

Preparation of GITC

α-Acetobromoglucose (4.1 g) was heated at about 100°C in dry xylene (20 ml) with thoroughly dried silver thiocyanate (5.0 g) under efficient stirring. After 1 h, silver thiocyanate (3.4 g) was added in two equal portions at intervals of 30 min, and the heating and stirring were continued for another 30 min. The reaction mixture was then filtered while still hot and the precipitate was washed twice with 10-ml portions of hot xylene. To the combined filtrates was added light petroleum (60 ml), and the crystalline isothiocyanate deposited almost instantaneously. The product was collected after 16 h and dried over P_2O_5 under reduced pressure. Yield 2.9 g (75%), m.p. 113–115°C.

Chromatography

The modular liquid chromatographic system consisted of a NSP-800-9DX pump equipped with NV1-3001 valve injector and NPG-800L pressure gauge (Sanuki Industry Co., Tokyo, Japan), and SPD-2A spectrophotometric detector (Shimadzu, Kyoto, Japan). A stainless-steel column (250 × 4 mm I.D.) was packed with LiChrosorb RP-18 (particle size 5 μm; E. Merck, Darmstadt, G.F.R.) by a slurry packing method[15].

TABLE I

SEPARATION OF DIASTEREOMERIC THIOUREA DERIVATIVES FORMED FROM AMINO ACID ETHYL ESTERS WITH GITC

t_0 = 4.0 min. Column, LiChrosorb RP-18 (25 cm × 0.4 mm I.D.). Mobile phase, 50% aqueous methanol (A), 60% aqueous methanol (B); flow-rate, 0.4 ml/min. k', α and R refer to the capacity ratio, separation factor and resolution value for a pair of diastereomers, respectively.

Amino acid	*k'*		*α*	*R*	*Mobile phase*
	L	*D*			
Serine	1.70	1.50	1.13	1.12	A
	0.95	0.83	1.13	0.71	B
Alanine	2.69	2.93	1.09	1.63	A
	1.50	1.62	1.08	1.16	B
Proline	4.28	4.67	1.21	1.21	A
	1.58	1.61	1.02	0.38	B
Aspartic acid	5.38	5.71	1.06	1.01	A
	2.67	2.83	1.06	0.62	B
Glutamic acid	5.90	6.26	1.06	0.95	A
	2.85	2.97	1.04	0.47	B
Tyrosine	2.57	2.90	1.13	1.56	B
Valine	3.50	4.13	1.18	2.48	B
Phenylglycine	4.31	4.81	1.12	1.78	B
Tryptophan	5.66	6.64	1.17	3.09	B
Isoleucine	5.67	6.71	1.18	2.90	B
Leucine	5.70	6.73	1.18	3.00	B
Phenylalanine	6.85	8.65	1.26	4.28	B

15 R. M. Cassidy, D. S. Legay and R. W. Frei, *Anal. Chem.*, 46 (1974) 340.

N. Nimura, H. Ogura and T. Kinoshita, J. Chromatog., <u>202</u>, 375 (1980) continued.

Derivatization and separation procedure

A 5-mg amount of amino acid ethyl ester was dissolved in acetonitrile containing 0.2% (w/v) triethylamine to give a volume of 5 ml. To a 50-μl aliquot of this amino acid solution were added 50 μl of 0.5% (w/v) GITC in acetonitrile. The resulting mixture was allowed to stand at room temperature for 60 min, and a 5-μl aliquot was injected directly into the chromatograph and eluted with either 50% or 60% (v/v) aqueous methanol at a constant flow-rate of 0.4 ml/min, at room temperature.

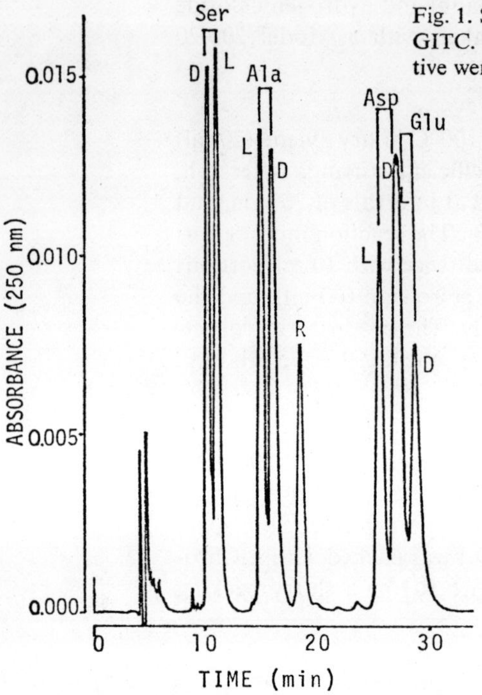

Fig. 1. Separation of diastereometic thiourea derivatives formed from amino acid ethyl esters with GITC. Mobile phase: 50% aqueous methanol; flow-rate, 0.4 ml/min. About 250 ng of each derivative were injected. R = Peak of excess of reagent (GITC).

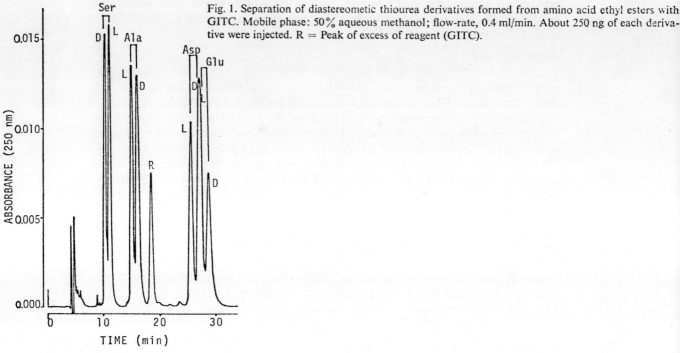

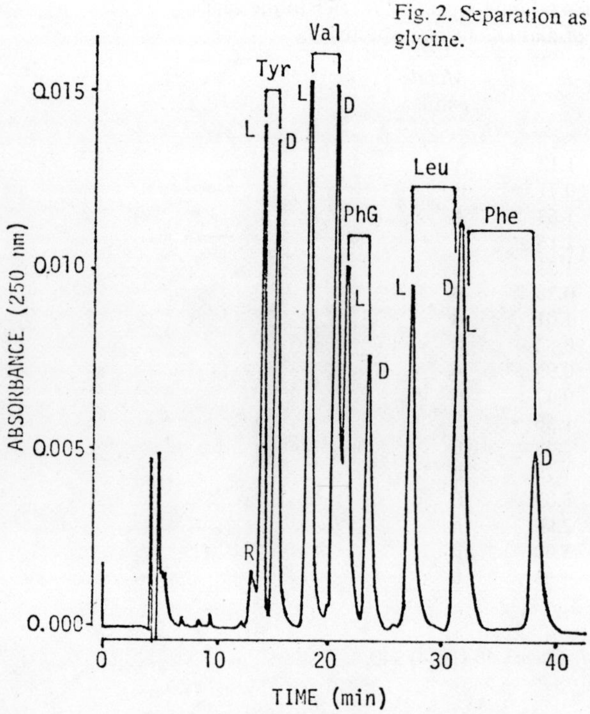

Fig. 2. Separation as in Fig. 1 except with 60% aqueous methanol as mobile phase. PhG = Phenylglycine.

Reference
J. Goto, N. Goto, A. Hikichi, T. Nishimaki and T. Nambara, Anal. Chim. Acta, 120, 187 (1980).

Summary
Two new highly sensitive chiral derivatization reagents for the resolution of racemic carboxylic acids D-and L-1-aminoethyl-4-dimethylaminonaphthalene were reported. The diastereomeric amides formed from N-acetylamino acid and α-aryl-propanoic acid enantiomers were efficiently resolved by normal phase chromatography. With a fluorescence detector (excitation 320 nm, emission 395 nm). The detection limit was 0.1 ng. Experimental details and results follow.

Optical resolution of IVa. To a solution of IVa (384 mg) in ethanol (2 ml) was added a solution of D-α-methoxy-α-methyl-1-naphthaleneacetic acid [4] (428 mg) in ethanol (5 ml). The resulting precipitate was collected by filtration and fractionally crystallized from ethanol several times. The salt was decomposed with 10% NaOH solution and the free base was extracted with ether. The organic layer was washed with water, dried (Na_2SO_4), and evaporated to provide the L-base (IVb; 100 mg) as a colorless oil. Treatment with hydrogen chloride gave the hydrochloride of IVb as colorless needles (m.p. 240–241°C, decomp.; $[\alpha]_D^{15}$ − 17.7°; c = 0.37, methanol). Calculated for $C_{14}H_{19}ClN_2$: 67.0% C, 7.6% H, 11.2% N; found: 66.8% C, 7.7% H, 11.0% N. The mother liquor was treated with L-α-methoxy-α-methyl-1-naphthalene-acetic acid [4] in the manner described above to give the hydrochloride of the D-base (IVc; 80 mg) as colorless needles (m.p. 243–244°C, decomp.; $[\alpha]_D^{15}$ + 17.3°; c = 1.4, methanol). Calculated for $C_{14}H_{19}ClN_2$: 67.0% C, 7.6% H, 11.2% N; found: 67.2% C, 7.7% H, 11.3% N.

TABLE 1

Separation of diastereoisomeric amide derivatives of N-acetyl-DL-amino acids (Column, μPorasil. Mobile phase, hexane/ethyl acetate (1:3). Flow rate, (A) 1.0 ml min^{-1}, t_0 = 2.5 min, (B) 3.0 ml min^{-1}, t_0 = 0.8 min)

Amino acid	k'		α	R	Flow rate
	L	D			
Alanine	11.20	13.40	1.20	1.17	B
α-Aminobutyric acid	6.93	11.33	1.63	3.47	A
Valine	3.20	7.07	2.21	6.44	A
Norvaline	4.00	8.60	2.15	6.27	A
Leucine	2.73	7.00	2.56	8.10	A
Norleucine	4.00	7.73	1.93	5.83	A
Proline	22.80	34.00	1.49	1.89	B
Phenylglycine	2.00	4.63	2.32	6.53	A
Phenylalanine	3.10	6.33	2.04	6.30	A

J. Goto, N. Goto, A. Hikichi, T. Nishimaki and T. Nambara, Anal. Chim. Acta, 120, 187 (1980) continued.

Derivatization procedure

To a solution of carboxylic acid (ca. 500 μg) in pyridine (0.2 ml) or dichloromethane (0.2 ml) containing tri-n-butylamine (20 μl) were added reagent IVc (ca. 500 μg) and 1-ethyl-3-(3-dimethylaminopropyl)-carbodiimide hydrochloride (ca. 1 mg); the solution was then allowed to stand at room temperature for 3 h. The reaction mixture was extracted with ethyl acetate. An aliquot (5 μl) was injected into the chromatograph.

TABLE 2

Separation of diastereoisomeric amide derivatives of DL-α- arylpropionic acids (Column, μPorasil. Mobile phase, (A) hexane/ethyl acetate (10:3), (B) hexane/tetrahydrofuran (5:1). Flow rate, 1.0 ml min^{-1}, t_0 = 2.5 min)

Drug	*k'*		α	*R*	Mobile phase
	D	L			
Ibuprofen	1.36	2.05	1.51	4.30	A
	1.32	1.98	1.50	3.80	B
Indoprofen	19.10	24.70	1.30	3.65	A
	15.40	18.30	1.18	3.00	B
Naproxen	3.04	4.37	1.44	3.60	A
	2.79	3.80	1.36	3.14	B

4 J. Goto, M. Hasegawa, S. Nakamura, K. Shimada and T. Nambara, J. Chromatogr., 152 (1978) 413.

Reference
T. Kinoshita, Y. Kasahara and N. Nimura, J. Chromatog., 210, 77 (1981).

Summary
The authors report the reversed-phase HPLC resolution of non-esterified amino acid enantiomers by the formation of diastereomers using the chiral reagents 2,3,4,6-tetra-O-acetyl-β-D-glucopyranosyl isothiocyanate and 2,3,4-tri-O-acetyl-α-D-arabinopyranosyl isothiocyanate. These compounds react readily with amino acids at room temperature and the reaction mixture can be directly chromatographed. The separation of the enantiomers was monitored spectrophotometrically at 250 nm. Complete resolution were observed for all enantiomers examined on a reversed-phase column eluted with methanol-10 mM potassium phosphate (pH 2.8). Experimental details and results follow.

Amino acids and other reagents were obtained from Wako (Osaka, Japan) and Tokyo Chemical Industry Co. (Tokyo, Japan). All the reagents were of analytical reagent grade. Methanol and water were distilled before use. GITC and AITC were prepared by treatment of α-acetobromoglucose and β-acetobromoarabinose with silver thiocyanate as described previously[9]. The 10 mM phosphate buffer was prepared from monobasic potassium phosphate and was adjusted to pH 2.8 with perchloric acid.

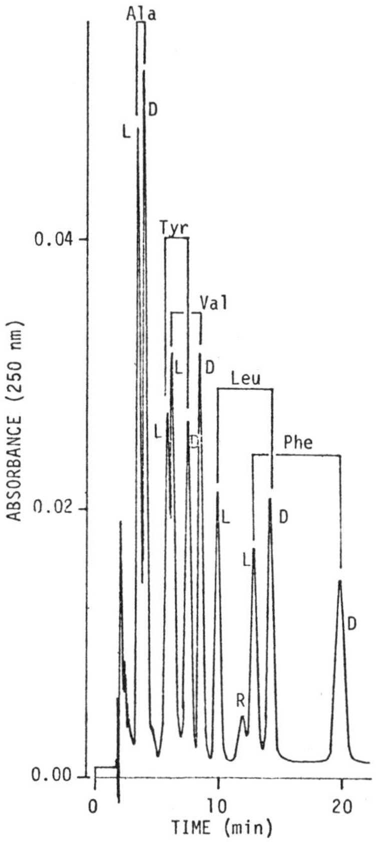

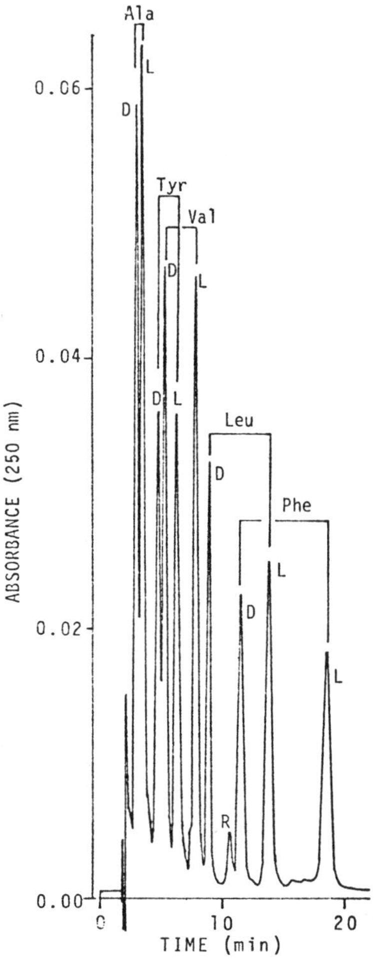

Fig. 1. Separation of diastereomeric thiourea derivatives formed from amino acids with GITC. Mobile phase: methanol–10 mM phosphate buffer (pH 2.8) (55:45); flow-rate 0.9 ml/min. About 250 ng of each derivative were injected. R = Reagent (GITC).

Fig. 2. Separation of diastereomeric thiourea derivatives formed from amino acids with AITC. Mobile phase: methanol–10 mM phosphate buffer (pH 2.8) (50:50); flow-rate 0.9 ml/min. About 250 ng of each derivative were injected. R = Reagent (AITC).

T. Kinoshita, Y. Kasahara and N. Nimura, J. Chromatog., 210, 77 (1981) continued.

Equipment

The chromatographic system consisted of a high pressure pump equipped with a universal valve injector (Sanuki Industry Co., Tokyo, Japan), a Develosil ODS-5 column (15 cm × 4.6 mm I.D., particle size 5 μm; Nomura Chemical, Seto, Japan) and an SPD-2A spectrophotometric detector (Shimadzu Seisakusho, Kyoto, Japan).

Derivatization and separation

A 5-mg amount of each amino acid was dissolved in 50% (v/v) aqueous acetonitrile containing 0.4% (w/v) triethylamine to give a final volume of 10 ml. To a 50-μl aliquot of this stock solution were added 50 μl of 0.2% (w/v) chiral reagent, either GITC or AITC, in acetonitrile. The resulting mixture was allowed to stand at room temperature for 30 min and a 2-μl aliquot was injected directly into the chromatograph. The column was eluted at room temperature and at a flow-rate of 0.9 ml/min with a mobile phase prepared by mixing methanol and 10 m*M* phosphate buffer, pH 2.8, in an appropriate ratio.

For the resolution of phenylalanine diastereomers, the reagent peak was removed as follows. To the reaction mixture described above were added 10 μl of 0.25% (w/v) monoethanolamine in acetonitrile and the resulting mixture was allowed to stand for 10 min at room temperature prior to the injection.

TABLE I

SEPARATION OF DIASTEREOMERIC THIOUREA DERIVATIVES FORMED FROM FREE AMINO ACIDS WITH GITC AND AITC

t_0 = 2.0 min. Column, Develosil ODS-5 (15 cm × 4.6 mm I.D.). Mobile phase: methanol–10 m*M* phosphate buffer (pH 2.8) (40:60) (A), (45:55) (B), (50:50) (C), (55:45) (D); flow-rate 0.9 ml/min. k', α and R_s are defined in the text.

Amino acid	*GITC*					*AITC*				
	k'		α	R_s	Mobile phase	k'		α	R_s	Mobile phase
	L	*D*				*D*	*L*			
Glutamic acid	2.70	3.15	1.17	1.80	B	1.20	1.40	1.17	1.14	A
Aspartic acid	3.80	4.35	1.14	1.69	B	1.40	1.65	1.18	1.43	A
Proline	2.80	3.70	1.32	3.00	B	1.55	2.15	1.39	3.00	A
Alanine	3.85	5.50	1.43	4.40	B	1.60	2.45	1.53	3.78	A
Tyrosine	1.75	2.55	1.46	3.20	D	1.65	2.45	1.48	3.56	C
Valine	2.00	3.10	1.55	4.00	D	1.95	3.45	1.77	4.96	C
Phenylglycine	2.10	2.80	1.33	2.80	D	2.15	3.25	1.51	4.40	C
Isoleucine	3.55	5.50	1.55	5.01	D	4.05	7.25	1.79	6.94	C
Leucine	3.75	5.65	1.51	5.43	D	4.25	7.35	1.73	7.75	C
Tryptophan	4.95	7.25	1.46	5.11	D	6.55	9.85	1.50	6.00	C
Phenylalanine	5.00	8.10	1.62	6.89	D	6.25	11.10	1.78	8.43	C

9 N. Nimura, H. Ogura and T. Kinoshita, *J. Chromatogr.*, 202 (1980) 375.

SECTION 4

METHODS OTHER THAN CLASSICAL CHEMICAL AND CHROMATOGRAPHIC FOR THE OPTICAL RESOLUTION OF RACEMIC α-AMINO ACIDS

The first section of this volume contains classical chemical procedures for the resolution of racemic α-amino acids, that is, those which involve the formation of diastereomeric derivatives of the original mixture of enantiomers in solution followed by their separation by fractional crystallization, decomposition of the derivative and isolation of the separated enantiomers. However, because of their great commercial importance in the food and pharmaceutical industries and because the classical chemical procedures are uneconomical, too laborious, and unsatisfactory for various reasons in many cases when applied on an industrial scale,[1] a tremendous amount of research has been carried out in recent years to develop suitable industrial methods for the resolution of α-amino acids. To attempt to bring all this information together in this volume would have been impractical because of space limitations. In addition, there are a number of excellent books and reviews which describe these alternative methods with voluminous literature references. This section, therefore, summarizes these methods, gives some examples of the application of the methods, and gives the reader leading references which describe these methods in great detail.

A. Preferential Crystallization Methods or Resolution by Entrainment

Two recent reviews describing this method are:

1) A. Collet, M.-J. Brienne and J. Jacques, Chem. Rev., 80, 215 (1980).

An in-depth, lucid and interesting discussion from a historial and practical point of view of the theory and practice of resolution by entrainment of α-amino acids is presented with a tabulation of some 250 amino acids which have been resolved by this method.

2) I. Chibata, in "Synthetic Production and Utilization of Amino Acids," Kodansha, Ltd., (1974), pages 18-25.*

A lucid discussion of crystallization procedures for the resolution of α-amino acids by a recognized expert and pioneer in the development of this method for industrial application with many literature and patent references to examples.

To illustrate this method and give some background information, two papers have been chosen from the recent work of Dr. Chibata and his coworkers at Tanabe Seiyaku Co., Osaka, Japan, and are reproduced in their entirety.

Optical Resolution of DL-Amino Acids by Preferential Crystallization Procedure

Shigeki Yamada,* Masao Yamamoto, and Ichiro Chibata

[J. Org. Chem., 38, 4408 (1973)]

Although a number of methods for optical resolution of DL-amino acids have been reported, most of them have employed chemical or enzymatic procedures and only a few reports on preferential crystallization procedure have appeared.[1] If successfully applied, preferential crystallization procedure is a very advantageous method for the production of optically active amino acids, since the procedure can be easily accomplished by providing seed crystals of one antipode in a supersaturated solution of the racemic modification.[2] However, in nearly a century since the first example of this type of resolution was reported, satisfactory application of this simple procedure has been restricted to several amino acids such as asparagine,[3] histidine,[4] threonine,[5] glutamic acids,[6,7] and aspartic acid.[8,9] The reason for this limited applicability is that most amino acids form racemic compounds instead of racemic mixtures and have no properties suitable for this resolution procedure. Although it was suggested[10] that resolution is possible when the solubility of each of the pure optical isomers is less than that of the racemic modification, resolution by preferential crystallization is more easily accomplished when the racemic modification forms a racemic mixture. Therefore, if it becomes possible to find out the conditions under which respective amino acid crystallizes as a racemic mixture, this convenient method is expected to be applied for all synthetic amino acids as a general method. To realize this expectation, the optical resolution of amino acids was carried out in the form of their aromatic sulfonates. Aromatic sulfonic acids were chosen because they vary greatly in properties and easily form salts with any kinds of amino acids, so that it is very likely that some of their salts will form racemic mixtures and can be resolved by preferential crystallization procedure. Previously, it was found that DL-lysine, as an example of basic amino acids, was resolved in the form of the salt with *p*-aminobenzenesulfonic acid.[11] Subsequently, under this idea, optical resolution of other amino acids was investigated, and it became possible to resolve many amino acids, for example, DL-alanine and DL-leucine as typical aliphatic amino acids, DL-serine as a hydroxy amino acid, DL-3,4-dihydroxyphenylalanine as an aromatic amino acid, DL-tryptophan as a heterocyclic amino acid, and DL-3-(3,4-methylenedioxyphenyl)-2-methylalanine as an α-alkyl amino acid. The optically active forms of these amino acids are important in nutritional and pharmaceutical fields. Especially, L-3,4-dihydroxyphenylalanine (L-DOPA) has been in large commercial demand as a specific drug for treatment of Parkinson's disease and L-3-(3,4-

*The volume entitled, "Synthetic Production and Utilization of Amino Acids," T. Kaneko, Y. Izumi, I. Chibata and T. Itoh, Eds., is an invaluable compilation of information on 1) the discovery of the individual amino acids, 2) a summary of methods of synthesis and resolution, both chemical and biological, of each of the amino acids, and 3) the utilization of amino acids as food, animal feed, medicines and cosmetics, in the chemical industry.

methylenedioxyphenyl)-2-methylalanine (L-MDPMA) is useful for an intermediate of the antihypertensive drug, L-3,4-dihydroxyphenyl-2-methylalanine (L-α-methyl DOPA).

Generally it is well recognized that the solid state infrared spectra of respective optical isomers are identical but different from that of the corresponding racemic compound.[12] However, in the case where racemic amino acids exist as a racemic mixture, the infrared spectrum of a racemic modification should be identical with that of the respective optical isomers. Thus the above amino acids were converted to the wide variety of the salts with aromatic sulfonic acids and the spectra of their optically active salts were compared with those of the respective racemic modifications. This method was very useful for screening the salts which form racemic mixtures. As a result, the spectra of DL-alanine *p*-chlorobenzenesulfonate (DL-Ala-*p*-ClBS), DL-leucine benzenesulfonate (DL-Leu-BS), DL-serine *m*-xylene-4-sulfonate (DL-Ser-*m*-XS), DL-3,4-dihydroxyphenylalanine 2-naphthol-6-sulfonate (DL-DOPA-NS·$^3/_2H_2O$), DL-tryptophan benzenesulfonate (DL-Trp-BS), and DL-3-(3,4-methylenedioxyphenyl)-2-methylalanine *p*-phenolsulfonate (DL-MDPMA-*p*-PS·H_2O), were found to be exactly identical with those of the corresponding optical isomers. The result suggests that these racemic modifications exist as racemic mixtures. This was also supported by the melting point–composition diagram. In each case, the melting point of the racemic modification was identical with that of the mechanical mixture of equal amount of the two antipodes, and admixture of one of the pure isomers to the racemic modification increased the melting point. Also, the solubility of the racemic modifications was much higher than that of the corresponding isomers. The saturated solution of the racemic modifications no longer dissolved the optically active isomers. Thus, DL-Ala-*p*-ClBS, DL-Leu-BS, DL-Ser-*m*-XS, DL-DOPA-NS·$^3/_2H_2O$, DL-Trp-BS, and DL-MDPMA-*p*-PS·H_2O could be easily screened as the simple salts forming the racemic mixtures.

The resolutions of these salts were accomplished in the usual manner. Seeding a supersaturated solution of each racemic modification with the crystals of the desired isomer (for example, L isomer) brought about preferential crystallization of the L isomer, while the nonseeded D isomer remained in the mother liquor as supersaturation. The resolutions were also carried out without seeding by spontaneous crystallization of an excess isomer (L isomer) from a supersaturated solution containing an excess of one isomer (L isomer). This procedure of using an excess of one isomer in the initial solution was equivalent, in principle, to adding seed crystals because the L isomer present in higher concentration began to crystallize initially and it played a role of seed crystals. However, the most favorable resolution procedure in a practical purpose was that described in the Experimental Section. This was started with a supersaturated solution containing an excess of one isomer (L isomer). Furthermore, the solution was nucleated with the isomer (L isomer) present in excess. In this case, preferential crystallization of L isomer occurred more rapidly and smoothly without crystallization of D isomer. The presence in the initial solution of an excess of the isomer being crystallized seemed to be important for the successful functioning of the resolution procedure. It was also desirable that the amount of an excess isomer (L isomer) dissolved initially in a supersaturated solution of racemic modification was adjusted to almost the same amount of L isomer resolved in a single cycle, and that the amount of crystallization was controlled to about twofold of the excess of L isomer employed initially. In that case, almost the same conditions as the first, except that the solution contained D isomer in excess, could be obtained by adding the same amount of the racemic modification as that of the L isomer previously separated into the mother liquor. Then D isomer was separated in the same way. Thus, the entire cycle could be repeated and both L and D isomers were obtained reciprocally. However, the amount of a desired isomer resolved in a single cycle should be limited in order to avoid crystallization of the antipode. As shown in Table IV, optimal conditions for resolution were dependent on the properties of the individual racemic modification. The isomers obtained by this procedure were almost optically pure. If the optical purity is not satisfactory and further purification is required, the crude products can be easily purified by recrystallization without loss of the optically active isomer. The optically active enantiomorph no longer dissolves in the saturated solution of the racemic modification. Therefore, this purification can be performed by dissolving the mixture in a minimum amount of water required to dissolve the racemic modification in the crude crystals, and allowing the pure crystals to crystallize out. However, the operation is not so easy because the amount of water required to dissolve the racemic impurity is very small. So it was convenient to carry out the above operation by adding an appropriate amount of the solution saturated with the racemic modification. Thus, obtained optically pure sulfonates were easily converted to optically pure amino acids by neutralization with alkali or by use of ion exchange resin.

In the present work we cannot establish a theory to predict what kind of racemic modification forms a racemic mixture suitable for the resolution by preferential crystallization. By the use of aromatic sulfonates, however, it becomes easy to find out the simple salts which form racemic mixtures and can be resolved by the preferential crystallization procedure. Consequently, it is very likely that the present simple method using aromatic sulfonates may be applied more generally for resolution of synthetic amino acids.

Experimental Section

Materials.—Analytical standard grade amino acids manufactured by our company, Tanabe Seiyaku Co., Ltd., were used, except MDPMA.[13] All aromatic sulfonic acids were obtained from Tokyo Kasei Kogyo Co., Ltd., and E. Merck AG. These were used without further purification.

Analyses.—All samples for analyses were dried overnight *in vacuo* at 45–50° unless otherwise noted. Melting points were measured with a Yamato MP-21 melting point apparatus in an unsealed capillary tube and were uncorrected. Infrared spectra of samples were determined in KBr disks using a Shimazu infrared spectrophotometer, Model IR-27G. Optical rotations were measured with a Perkin-Elmer 141 automatic polarimeter. Elemental analyses were performed by a Perkin-Elmer 240 elemental analyzer. Solubility was determined by approaching

saturation equilibrium from both sides of undersaturation and supersaturation. Concentration of solutes was measured by a Karl Zeiss immersion refractometer.

Preparation of Aromatic Sulfonates of Amino Acids.—DL-Alanine *p*-chlorobenzenesulfonate (DL-Ala-*p*-ClBS), DL-3,4-dihydroxyphenylalanine 2-naphthol-6-sulfonate (DL-DOPA-NS·$^3/_2H_2O$), DL-leucine benzenesulfonate (DL-Leu-BS), DL-lysine *p*-aminobenzenesulfonate (DL-Lys-*p*-ABS), DL-3-(3,4-methylenedioxyphenyl)-2-methylalanine *p*-phenolsulfonate (DL-MDPMA-*p*-PS·H_2O), DL-serine *m*-xylenesulfonate (DL-Ser-*m*-XS), and DL-tryptophan benzenesulfonate (DL-Trp-BS) were easily prepared from amino acids and the corresponding aromatic sulfonic acids.

A mixture of 1 mol of amino acids and 1.03 mol of aromatic sulfonic acids was dissolved in water by heating, treated with charcoal, concentrated *in vacuo*, and cooled in a refrigerator. The resulting precipitates and further crops obtained by successive concentrations of the combined filtrate were collected, washed with cold water, and dried *in vacuo* at 45°. The products were almost pure and could be used for optical resolution without further purification. The optically active isomers were prepared in the same way. The total yields based on the amino acids were from 95 to 98%. The elemental analyses are summarized in Table I.

TABLE I

AROMATIC SULFONATES OF AMINO ACIDS

Aromatic sulfonate of amino acids (elemental composition)		Elemental analysis, % Calcd	Found DL	Found L
	C	38.37	38.48	38.23
Ala-*p*-ClBS	H	4.29	4.40	4.42
($C_9H_{12}ClNO_5S$)	N	4.97	4.87	4.80
	S	11.38	11.52	11.20
	C	50.89	50.83	50.95
DOPA-NS·$^3/_2H_2O$	H	4.97	4.70	4.97
($C_{19}H_{19}NO_8S\cdot{}^3/_2H_2O$)	N	3.12	3.03	3.13
	S	7.15	7.27	7.29
	C	49.81	50.04	50.06
Leu-BS	H	6.62	6.65	6.64
($C_{12}H_{19}NO_5S$)	N	4.84	4.97	4.82
	S	11.08	10.93	11.20
	C	45.12	45.20	45.00
Lys-*p*-ABS	H	6.63	6.73	6.74
($C_{12}H_{21}N_3O_5S$)	N	13.16	13.09	13.14
	S	10.04	10.01	10.06
	C	49.15	49.27	49.27
MDPMA-*p*-PS·H_2O[a]	H	5.10	5.21	5.10
($C_{17}H_{19}NO_8S\cdot H_2O$)	N	3.37	3.32	3.32
	S	7.72	7.70	7.66
	C	45.35	45.38	45.43
Ser-*m*-XS	H	5.88	5.91	5.92
($C_{11}H_{17}NO_6S$)	N	4.81	4.70	4.76
	S	11.01	11.06	10.93
	C	40.36	40.25	40.55
Ser-*m*-XS·$2H_2O$[b]	H	6.47	6.32	6.47
($C_{11}H_{17}NO_6S\cdot 2H_2O$)	N	4.28	4.33	4.23
	S	9.80	9.78	9.75
	C	56.34	56.63	56.53
Trp-BS	H	5.01	5.04	5.07
($C_{17}H_{18}N_2O_5S$)	N	7.73	7.88	7.80
	S	8.85	8.57	8.82

[a] Recrystallized from 0.25 mol of an aqueous solution of *p*-phenolsulfonic acid. [b] Dried in air at room temperature.

The samples for elemental analysis were recrystallized from water except for MDPMA-*p*-PS·H_2O. Recrystallization of DL-MDPMA-*p*-PS·H_2O from water gave DL-MDPMA-$^1/_2$*p*-PS (hemisulfonate) as colorless prisms, mp 237–238° dec. *Anal.* Calcd for $C_{11}H_{13}O_4N\cdot{}^1/_2(C_6H_6O_4S)$: C, 54.19; H, 5.20; N, 4.51; S, 5.17. Found: C, 53.99; H, 5.28; N, 4.45; S, 4.96. On the other hand, recrystallization from 0.25 mol of an aqueous solution of *p*-phenolsulfonic acid gave a monosulfonate as needles. It was stable as a hydrate and melted at 110–120, 184–186, and 192–193° with decomposition. For the optically active MDPMA-*p*-PS·H_2O, the hemisulfonates were not obtained. The optically active and racemic Ser-*m*-XS·$2H_2O$ crystallized from water as dihydrate. Elemental analyses of the samples dried in air at room temperature corresponded to $C_{11}H_{17}NO_6S\cdot 2H_2O$. Drying the samples *in vacuo* over P_2O_5 or at elevated temperatures yielded their anhydrates.

The properties of the aromatic sulfonates of amino acids thus obtained are shown in Table II.

Optical Resolution.—A typical experiment for the resolution was carried out as follows. DL-Ser-*m*-XS (94.00 g) and L-Ser-*m*-XS (6.00 g) were dissolved in 100 ml of water at elevated temperature. The mixture was cooled to 25°, seeded with L-Ser-*m*-XS·$2H_2O$ (0.10 g), and stirred for 50 min at the same temperature. The precipitated crystals were collected by filtration, washed with small amount of cold water, and dried. The crystals thus obtained were optically pure, yield 12.66 g, $[\alpha]^{25}D$ +4.1° (*c* 4, H_2O), mp 172–173°. *Anal.* Found: C, 45.37; H, 5.87; N, 4.85; S, 11.14. After the separation of the L isomer, DL-Ser-*m*-XS (13.88 g) and a small amount of water were added to the mother liquor. The amounts of the addition were adjusted by refractometric measurement and weighing according to a standard curve previously constructed. Thus, almost the same composition as in the previous resolution was obtained, except that the predominant enantiomorph was D isomer. This supersaturated solution was seeded with D-Ser-*m*-XS·$2H_2O$ (0.10 g) at 25° and stirred for 50 min. Drying the precipitated crystals yielded D-Ser-*m*-XS (12.52 g) which had 98% optical purity. By repeating these procedures, L and D isomers were successively obtained as shown in Table III.

Other sulfonates of amino acids could also be resolved in the same manner as described above. Conditions for the resolution and the analyses for separated crystals are summarized in Table IV.

Optical Purification of Optically Impure Isomers.—The isomers obtained by the above procedure were practically pure. If the optical purification is, however, required, it can be performed as follows. Crude L-Ser-*m*-XS (10.00 g, optical purity 87.7%) was mixed with 1.5 ml of water and an appropriate amount (30 ml) of the solution saturated with DL-Ser-*m*-XS at 25° and dissolved at elevated temperature. The mixture was then stirred for 2 hr at 25°. The resulting crystals were collected by filtration, washed with a small amount of cold water, and dried. By this operation, optically pure crystals of L-Ser-*m*-XS were obtained, yield 8.62 g, $[\alpha]^{25}D$ +4.1° (*c* 4, H_2O).

Preparation of Optically Active Amino Acids.—From optically pure aromatic sulfonates of amino acids, the free amino acids were easily obtained either by neutralization with alkali or by use of an ion exchange resin. In the former, an aqueous solution of aromatic sulfonates was adjusted with alkali to the isoelectric point of the amino acids and cooled in a refrigerator overnight. The crystallized free amino acids were filtered off, washed with cold water, and dried. This method was convenient for sparingly soluble amino acids. For readily soluble amino acids, the latter method was employed. Aromatic sulfonates were taken up in a tenfold amount of water. The solution was passed through an ion exchange column of Amberlite IR-120 (in H form). The column was washed with water and the amino acid was eluted with 2 *N* NH_4OH. The eluate was concentrated, treated with charcoal, and concentrated again until the crystalline precipitate appeared. To the residue MeOH was added and the mixture was allowed to stand in a refrigerator overnight to give the colorless amino acid.

Table V indicates the yields and the specific rotations of optically active amino acids obtained by this process.

For the preparation of L-α-methyl DOPA, the L-MDPMA (50.0 g) obtained above was hydrolyzed with 20% hydrochloric acid (930 ml) and phenol (47 g) for 17 hr. After evaporation, the residue was dissolved in 120 ml of water and adjusted to pH 5.8 with 5 *N* NH_4OH containing a small amount of sodium bisulfite. The precipitate was collected, and further crops were obtained by successive concentrations of the filtrate. The total yield of L-α-methyl DOPA·$^3/_2H_2O$ was 43.6 g (81.6%). Recrystallization from sulfurous acid solution (0.5%) gave a white powder of L-α-methyl DOPA·$^3/_2H_2O$, and drying of the sesquihydrate *in vacuo* at 100° gave the anhydrous form, mp 306–307° dec, $[\alpha]^{25}D$ −5.2°, $[\alpha]^{25}_{578}$ −5.5° (*c* 2, 0.1 *N* HCl). *Anal.* Calcd for $C_{10}H_{13}NO_4$: C, 56.86; H, 6.20; N, 6.63. Found: C, 56.63; H, 6.24; N, 6.59.

Table II

Properties of Aromatic Sulfonates of Amino Acids

Aromatic sulfonate of amino acids	Isomer	Mp, °C	$[\alpha]^{25}_D$, deg (*c* 2, water)	$[\alpha]^{25}_{365}$, deg (*c* 2, water)	Solubility in water, g/100 ml (°C)		
Ala-*p*-ClBS	DL	190–192			50.2 (15)	86.3 (30)	139.2 (45)
	L	222–223	+3.6	+15.4	24.2 (15)	37.2 (30)	67.5 (45)
DOPA-NS · $^3/_2H_2O$	DL	152–154			1.6 (10)	3.3 (30)	9.0 (50)
	L	162–164	−8.6	−19.7	1.1 (10)	2.0 (30)	5.3 (50)
Leu-BS	DL	152–154			39.4 (15)	58.0 (25)	
	L	172–173	+3.2	+18.6	17.0 (15)	22.9 (25)	
Lys-*p*-ABS	DL	238–239			54.0 (15)	66.1 (25)	90.6 (45)
	L	250–251	+6.2	+23.0	33.8 (15)	42.7 (25)	63.1 (45)
MDPMA-*p*-PS · H_2O[c]	DL	192–193			10.8 (10)	18.6 (25)	76.3 (45)
	L	212–213	+0.8[a]	+14.0[a]	5.0 (10)	8.3 (25)	25.0 (45)
Ser-*m*-XS	DL	157–158			45.1 (15)	80.9 (25)	175.4 (40)
	L	172–173	+4.1[b]	+19.6[b]	23.5 (15)	39.5 (25)	86.8 (40)
Trp-BS	DL	210–211			5.7 (15)	10.7 (35)	20.9 (50)
	L	234–235	−2.9	+16.8	3.5 (15)	5.6 (35)	8.9 (50)

[a] 1% in 1 *N* HCl. [b] 4%. [c] Solubility was determined in 0.25 mol of *p*-phenolsulfonic acid aqueous solution.

Table III

Successive Resolution of DL-Ser-*m*-XS[a]

Expt	Amount of addition: DL form, g	Amount of addition: Active form, g	Composition of solution: DL form, g	Composition of solution: Active form, g	Crystals separated: Yield, g	Crystals separated: Optical purity, %
1 (L)	94.00	6.00	94.00	6.00	12.66	100
2 (D)	13.88		93.84[b]	6.16[b]	12.52	98
3 (L)	13.08		94.02[b]	5.98[b]	11.34	100
4 (D)	13.34		94.74[b]	5.26[b]	13.24	98
5 (L)	14.24		92.36[b]	7.64[b]	12.20	97
6 (D)	12.20		95.92[b]	4.08[b]	12.42	98
7 (L)	14.40		92.04[b]	7.96[b]	13.10	97
8 (D)	14.84		95.36[b]	4.64[b]	13.54	97
9 (L)	15.32		91.62[b]	8.38[b]	12.56	98
10 (D)	14.42		96.14[b]	3.86[b]	12.18	96
Mean	13.97		94.00	6.00	12.58	98

[a] Resolution was carried out on a 100-ml scale. Crystallization time was 50 min in every case. [b] Values calculated theoretically from analysis of separated crystals.

Table IV

Optical Resolution of Aromatic Sulfonates of Amino Acids[a]

Aromatic sulfonate of amino acids	Resoln no.	Registry no.	Amount of addition: DL form, g	Amount of addition: Registry no.	Amount of addition: Active form, g	Composition of solution: DL form, g	Composition of solution: Active form, g	Crystn: Temp, °C	Crystn: Time, min	Separated crystals: Yield, g	Separated crystals: Optical purity, %
Ala-*p*-ClBS	1 (L)	36760-85-7	97.00	42334-78-1	5.00	97.00	5.00	30	40	10.56	98
	2 (D)	36760-86-8	11.00			96.71[b]	5.29[b]	30	40	10.34	98
DOPA-NS · $^3/_2H_2O$	1 (L)	42334-82-7	16.00	42334-81-6	3.00	16.00	3.00	50	25	6.44	100
	2 (D)	42334-83-8	6.50			15.66[b]	3.34[b]	50	25	6.52	100
Leu-BS	1 (L)	42398-40-3	66.50	42398-39-0	1.00	66.50	1.00	25	50	2.23	93
	2 (D)	42398-41-4	2.32			66.53[b]	0.97[b]	25	50	2.12	93
Lys-*p*-ABS	1 (L)	27168-73-6	77.00	42719-79-9	5.00	77.00	5.00	25	65	11.04	98
	2 (D)	42398-44-7	11.54			76.26[b]	5.74[b]	25	65	11.72	98
MDPMA-*p*-PS · H_2O[c]	1 (L)	42334-84-9	50.00	42398-45-8	7.50	50.00	7.50	25	120	17.83	95
	2 (D)	42398-46-9	18.40			48.36[b]	9.14[b]	25	120	17.92	97
Ser-*m*-XS[d]	1 (L)	27168-77-0	94.00	27168-75-8	6.00	94.00	6.00	25	50	12.66	100
	2 (D)	27168-76-9	13.88			93.84[b]	6.16[b]	25	50	12.52	98
Try-BS	1 (L)	42719-78-8	16.00	42719-79-9	1.20	16.00	1.20	35	50	2.84	92
	2 (D)	42746-61-2	2.93			15.88[b]	1.32[b]	35	50	2.78	92

[a] Resolution was carried out on a 100-ml scale by use of 0.10 g of seed crystals. [b] Values calculated theoretically from analysis of separated crystals. [c] Resolution was carried out in 0.25 mol of *p*-phenolsulfonic acid aqueous solution. [d] Dihydrates of this compound were used as seed crystals.

Table V
Optically Active Amino Acids Prepared from Their Aromatic Sulfonates

Amino acid	Registry no. D	Registry no. L	Method	Yield, %	N analysis, % Calcd	Found L	Found D	$[\alpha]^{25}D$, deg (c 2, 5 N HCl) L	D
Alanine	338-69-2	56-41-7	Ion exchange	96	15.72	15.72	15.73	+14.6	−14.6
DOPA	5796-17-8	59-92-7	LiOH	96	7.10	7.08	7.11	−12.2[a]	+12.3[a]
Leucine	328-38-1	61-90-5	Ion exchange	95	10.68	10.63	10.64	+15.9	−16.0
Lysine HCl	42334-88-3	10098-89-2	Ion exchange	96	15.34	15.41	15.45	+20.8	−20.8
MDPMA	42334-90-7	42334-89-4	NH_4OH	96	6.28	6.27	6.27	+25.4[b]	−25.4[b]
Serine	312-84-5	56-45-1	Ion exchange	98	13.33	13.37	13.35	+15.0[c]	−15.1[c]
Tryptophan	153-94-6	73-22-3	NH_4OH	95	13.72	13.74	13.73	−32.4[d]	+32.5[d]

[a] 4%, in 1 N HCl, at 20°. [b] $[\alpha]^{25}_{365}$, 1% in 1 N HCl. [c] In 1 N HCl. [d] 1% in H_2O.

(1) J. P. Greenstein and M. Winitz, "Chemistry of the Amino Acids," Vol. 1, Wiley, New York, N. Y., 1961, pp 715–716.
(2) R. M. Secor, *Chem. Rev.*, **63**, 297 (1963).
(3) A. Piutti, *C. R. Acad. Sci.*, **103**, 134 (1886).
(4) R. Duschinsky, *Chem. Ind. (London)*, **53**, 10 (1934); "Festschrift Emil Barell," Friendrich Reinhardt A. G., Basel, 1936, p 375.
(5) L. Velluz and G. Amiard, *Bull. Soc. Chim. Fr.*, **20**, 903 (1953).
(6) F. Kögl, H. Erxleben, and G. J. van Veersen, *Z. Physiol. Chem.*, **277**, 260 (1943).
(7) T. Akashi, *Nippon Kagaku Zasshi*, **83**, 417 (1962).
(8) T. Haga, M. Sato, and K. Miura, Japanese Patent 42-3290 (1967).
(9) K. Harada, *Bull. Chem. Soc. Jap.*, **38**, 1552 (1965).
(10) A. Werner, *Ber.*, **47**, 2171 (1914).
(11) S. Yamada, M. Yamamoto, and I. Chibata, *J. Agr. Food Chem.*, **21**, 889 (1973).
(12) R. J. Koegel, R. A. McCallum, J. P. Greenstein, M. Winitz, and S. M. Birnbaum, *Ann. N. Y. Acad. Sci.*, **69**, 94 (1957).
(13) DL-MDPMA was prepared from 3,4-methylenedioxyphenylacetone according to the method of G. A. Stein, H. A. Bronner, and K. Pfister, III, *J. Amer. Chem. Soc.*, **77**, 700 (1955). Optically pure L- and D-MDPMA were prepared by the optical resolution of the *N*-acetyl menthyl ester according to the method of S. Terashima, K. Achiwa, and S. Yamada, *Chem. Pharm. Bull.*, **13**, 1399 (1965).

Optical Resolution of *N*-Acyl-DL-amino Acids by Preferential Crystallization Procedure. Preparation of L-DOPA and L-α-Methyl DOPA[1]

Shigeki Yamada,* Masao Yamamoto, and Ichiro Chibata

[J. Org. Chem., 40, 3360 (1975)]

L-3-(3,4-Dihydroxyphenyl)alanine (L-DOPA) and L-3-(3,4-dihydroxyphenyl)-2-methylalanine (L-α-methyl DOPA) are important substances in biochemical and pharmaceutical fields,[2,3] and their markets have been expanding rapidly in recent years. It is therefore desirable to establish practical methods for the production of optically active DOPA and α-methyl DOPA.

Generally, optical resolution of the synthesized DL amino acids is more facile and practical for the production of optically active amino acids than the asymmetric synthesis of amino acids, because the latter method has not yet reached the stage of practicability and is still in a state of investigation. Among the various techniques for optical resolution of DL amino acids,[4] the preferential crystallization procedure[5] is considered to be one of the most useful for industrial application since it enables the desired optically active isomer to crystallize preferentially from a supersaturated solution of DL amino acid. However, it has the disadvantage that it cannot be applied to all kinds of amino acids because most amino acids form racemic compounds and are not suitable for this resolution method. In order to resolve this problem, a method of resolution using aromatic sulfonic acid has recently been developed by us and reported in the previous papers.[6-9] In this manner optical resolution of DL-DOPA and DL-3-(3,4-methylenedioxyphenyl)-2-methylalanine (DL-MDPMA), α-methyl DOPA precursor, became possible as the salts with 2-naphthol-6-sulfonic acid and *p*-phenolsulfonic acid, respectively.[9]

On the other hand, the synthetic route via acyl derivatives has often been used for the synthesis of DL amino acids. For example, DL–DOPA is synthesized in good yield via *N*-acetyl-DL-3-(3,4-methylenedioxyphenyl)alanine (*N*-Ac-DL-MDPA) from piperonal and acetylglycine.[10] In such cases, it is more desirable that an intermediate in the process of amino acid synthesis be easily resolved into the optical antipodes, and the undesired antipode be easily racemized to the DL form and then reused for the resolution step. In this study, therefore, the optical resolution of *N*-Ac-DL-MDPA and *N*-acetyl-DL-3-(3,4-methylenedioxyphenyl)-2-methylalanine (*N*-Ac-DL-MDPMA) have been investigated as a first approach to establish the general method for the optical resolution of *N*-acyl-DL-amino acids by preferential crystallization procedure.

Until now, the ammonium salts of the acyl derivatives of certain amino acids, including DL-tryptophan,[11] DL-phenylalanine,[12] DL-valine,[12] DL-methionine,[12] DL-serine,[13] DL-phenylglycine,[14] and DL-MDPA,[15] have been resolved by the preferential crystallization procedure. Although this type of resolution using the ammonium salts is very valuable, its application is restricted to a limited number of amino acids. In fact, the ammonium salt of *N*-Ac-DL-MDPMA could not be resolved since it formed a racemic compound. With respect to the ammonium salt of *N*-Ac-DL-MDPA, it formed a racemic mixture and was resolvable. However, the operation was not so easy in practice and the resolution results was unsatisfactory since the form of the crystals was unsuitable for the filtration process after crystallization.[1] Generally speaking, even though the ammonium salts of acyl derivatives are resolvable, the practical resolution is often difficult in cases where the salts have no adequate solubility and no suitable characteristics for easy handling.

Therefore, we attempted the optical resolution of the acylamino acids in the form of their salts with commercially available (optically inactive) amines instead of the ammonium salts. This idea is similar to that in our previous method using aromatic sulfonates. Namely, amines vary greatly in their properties and readily form salts with all kinds of *N*-acylamino acids, so that it becomes very easy to screen the salts suitable for the preferential crystallization procedure. Thus, we prepared a wide variety of amine salts of *N*-Ac-DL-MDPA and of *N*-Ac-DL-MDPMA, and screened the salts forming racemic mixtures by comparing the infrared spectrum, melting point, and solubility relationships of the racemic modifications and the optically active isomers.[8] As a result, it was found that the di-*n*-butylamine salt of *N*-Ac-DL-MDPA (*N*-Ac-DL-MDPA·DBA) and the hydrazine salt of *N*-Ac-DL-MDPMA (*N*-Ac-DL-MDPMA·HZ) readily crystallize as a racemic mixture from water, and the crystals have adequate solubility and suitable characteristics for easy handling. Then both salts were resolved by the usual manner described in our previous reports[8,9] and in the Experimental Section (see Tables I and II).

The optically active *N*-Ac-MDPA·DBA and *N*-Ac-MDPMA·HZ obtained above had an optical purity of about 98% on the average. When the optical purity is not satisfactory and further purification is required, the optically impure crystals can be purified without loss of the optically active isomer using the property of a saturated solution of the racemic mixture that it no longer dissolved the optically active isomer. Thus obtained optically active *N*-Ac-MDPA·DBA and *N*-Ac-MDPMA·HZ were decomposed with HCl to yield optically active *N*-Ac-MDPA and *N*-Ac-MDPMA quantitatively. The undesired *N*-Ac-D-MDPA was completely racemized by melting and the resulting *N*-Ac-DL-MDPA was reused for the resolution. However, *N*-Ac-D-MDPMA cannot be racemized in the usual way used for *N*-acylamino acids, because of the character of substitution at the optically active α position. The optically active *N*-Ac derivatives were converted to L-DOPA and L-α-methyl DOPA by the usual hydrolysis.

Table I
Successive Resoluions of *N*-Ac-DL-MDPA·DBA[a]

Expt	Amount of addition: DL form, g	Amount of addition: Active form, g	Composition of solution: DL form, g	Composition of solution: Active form, g	Separated crystals: Yield, g	Separated crystals: Optical purity,[b] %
1 (L)	37.50	4.00	37.50	4.00	8.95	97.8
2 (D)	9.23		36.85[c]	4.65[c]	7.93	97.7
3 (L)	8.18		38.50[c]	3.00[c]	8.36	97.5
4 (D)	8.62		36.45[c]	5.05[c]	7.81	98.2
5 (L)	8.05		38.98[c]	2.52[c]	8.27	97.5
6 (D)	8.53		36.06[c]	5.44[c]	8.12	97.6
Mean	8.52		37.39[c]	4.11[c]	8.24	97.7

[a] Resolutions were carried out at 35° on a 50-ml scale. Crystallization time was 90 min in every case. [b] The optical purity was calculated with the assumption that the specific rotation of the pure sample is $[\alpha]^{25}_{D}$ ±42.4° (*c* 2, water). [c] Values calculated theoretically from analysis of separated crystals.

Table II
Successive Resolutions of DL-*N*-Ac-MDPMA·HZ[a]

Expt	Amount of addition: DL form, g	Amount of addition: Active form, g	Composition of solution: DL form, g	Composition of solution: Active form, g	Separated crystals: Yield, g	Separated crystals: Optical purity, %
1 (L)	16.50	2.00	16.50	2.00	3.96	100
2 (D)	4.00		16.59[c]	1.91[c]	4.03	97.5
3 (L)	4.08		16.53[c]	1.97[c]	4.11	96.8
4 (D)	4.24		16.54[c]	1.96[c]	4.05	98.2
Mean	4.11		16.54[c]	1.96[c]	4.04	98.1

[a] Resolutions were carried out at 25° on a 50-ml scale. Crystallization time was 60 min in every case. [b] The optical purity was calculated with the assumption that the specific rotation of the pure sample is $[\alpha]^{25}_{D}$ ±87.8° (*c* 0.5, MeOH). [c] Values calculated theoretically from analysis of separated crystals.

The optical resolution methods now presented are very advantageous providing the optical isomers are available because they require neither an optically active resolving agent nor conversion of the intermediates into complicated derivatives, the yield per unit volume is very high, and the operation is so simple that all processes are expected to be operated automatically in a sequence control system. Therefore, application of the present method for the industrial production of L-DOPA and L-α-methyl DOPA is considered to be very promising if combined with a proper synthetic method for *N*-Ac-DL-MDPA and *N*-Ac-DL-MDPMA.

Furthermore, although we cannot find a guiding rule that predicts the kind of amine salts which can be resolved by the preferential crystallization procedure, it becomes very easy to screen the suitable salts by the use of various amines. Therefore, the present simple resolution method using amine salts is expected to be applied more generally for resolution of synthetic acylamino acids.

Experimental Section

Materials. *N*-Ac-DL-MDPA was prepared in our laboratory from piperonal and *N*-acetylglycine via the azlactone as usual,[10,16] colorless needles, mp 180–182° (lit.[16] mp 178–180°). Anal. Calcd for $C_{12}H_{13}NO_5$: C, 57.37; H, 5.22; N, 5.58. Found: C, 57.22; H, 5.32; N, 5.67. A small amount of *N*-Ac-D-MDPA used for initial seed crystals was obtained by the optical resolution of *N*-Ac-DL-MDPA by asymmetric hydrolysis using a mold aminoacylase preparation.[16] The optically active *N*-Ac-L- and -D-MDPA used for seed crystals were obtained by the present preferential crystallization procedure. *N*-Ac-L-MDPA: colorless needles, $[\alpha]^{20}_{D}$ +53.9° (*c* 1.5, EtOH), mp 158–159° [lit.[16] $[\alpha]^{13}_{D}$ +53.4° (*c* 2.262, EtOH), mp 158–159°]. *N*-Ac-D-MDPA: colorless needles, $[\alpha]^{20}_{D}$ −53.9° (*c* 1.5, EtOH), mp 158–159° [lit.[16] $[\alpha]^{18}_{D}$ −53.4° (*c* 1.841, EtOH), mp 158–159°].

N-Ac-L-, -D-, and -DL-MDPMA were obtained as usual[17] by acetylating L-, D-, and DL-MDPMA, which were used in the previous report.[9] *N*-Ac-L-MDPMA: colorless needles, $[\alpha]^{20}_{D}$ −58.8° (*c* 0.5, MeOH), mp 219–220° [lit.[17] $[\alpha]^{20}_{D}$ −58.0° (*c* 0.5, MeOH), mp 214–215°]. *N*-Ac-D-MDPMA: colorless needles, $[\alpha]^{20}_{D}$ +58.8° (*c* 0.5, MeOH), mp 219–220° [lit.[17] $[\alpha]^{20}_{D}$ +58.0° (*c* 0.5, MeOH), mp 214–215°]. *N*-Ac-DL-MDPMA: colorless needles, mp 191–192° (lit.[17] mp 189–191°). Anal. Calcd for $C_{13}H_{15}NO_5$: C, 58.86; H, 5.70; N, 5.28. Found: C, 58.78; H, 5.65; N, 5.30. Di-*n*-butylamine and hydrazine hydrate were obtained from Katayama Chemical Industries Co., Ltd.

Analyses. All samples were dried overnight at 45–50° unless otherwise noted. Melting points were measured with a Yamato MP-21 melting point apparatus in an unsealed capillary tube and are uncorrected. Infrared spectra of samples were determined in KBr disks using a Shimadzu infrared spectrophotometer, Model IR-27G. Optical rotations were measured with a Perkin-Elmer 141 automatic polarimeter. Elemental analyses were performed with a Perkin-Elmer 240 elemental analyzer. Solubility was determined by approaching saturation equilibrium from both undersaturation and supersaturation. Solute concentration was measured with a Karl Zeiss immersion refractometer.

Preparation of *N*-Ac-L-, -D-, and -DL-MDPA·DBA. Di-*n*-butylamine (133.0 g, 1.03 mol) and water (350 ml) were added to *N*-Ac-DL-MDPA (251.2 g, 1 mol). The mixture was heated, treated with charcoal, and filtered. The filtrate was allowed to stand in a refrigerator overnight. The precipitate was collected, washed with cold water, and dried in vacuo to give *N*-Ac-DL-MDPA·DBA (267.4 g), mp 142–145°. A second crop was obtained by successive concentrations of the combined filtrates. The total yield was 355.2 g (93.4%). The products were almost pure and could be used for optical resolution without further purification. Recrystallization from water gave colorless prisms, mp 143–145°. Anal. Calcd for $C_{20}H_{32}N_2O_5$: C, 63.14; H, 8.48; N, 7.36. Found: C, 62.83; H, 8.50; N, 7.18. Solubility in water (g/100 ml): 22.8 (15°), 26.5 (25°), 38.3 (35°).

The optically active *N*-Ac-L- and -D-MDPA·DBA were prepared from *N*-Ac-L- and -D-MDPA, respectively, in the same way as described above. The L isomer: $[\alpha]^{25}D$ +42.4° (*c* 2, H_2O); mp 160–162°. Anal. Found: C, 62.96; H, 8.68; N, 7.14. Solubility in water (g/100 ml): 12.7 (15°), 13.3 (25°), 16.6 (35°). The D isomer: $[\alpha]^{25}D$ −42.4° (*c* 2, water); mp 160–162°. The infrared spectra of *N*-Ac-L-, -D-, and -DL-MDPA·DBA in KBr were identical: ir (KBr) 3225, 3050, 2950, 2870, 2500–2100, 1625, 1590–1550, 1500, 1445, 1380, 1300, 1240, 1193, 1035, 930, 855, 823, 812, 735 cm^{-1}.

Optical Resolution of *N*-Ac-DL-MDPA·DBA. In a typical experiment, *N*-Ac-DL-MDPA·DBA (37.50 g) and *N*-Ac-L-MDPA·DBA (4.00 g) were dissolved in water (50 ml) at elevated temperature. The solution was cooled to 35°, seeded with fine pulverized crystals of *N*-Ac-L-MDPA·DBA (0.10 g), and stirred for 90 min at the same temperature. The precipitated crystals were collected by filtration, washed with a small amount of cold water (2 ml), and dried to give *N*-Ac-L-MDPA·DBA (8.95 g). Its optical purity was 97.8%, $[\alpha]^{25}D$ +41.4° (*c* 2, H_2O).

After the separation of the L isomer, *N*-Ac-DL-MDPA·DBA (9.23 g) and a small amount of water were added to the mother liquor in order to prepare the supersaturated solution of almost the same composition as in the previous resolution except that the predominant isomer was D isomer. The amounts of the addition were adjusted by refractometric measurement and weighing according to a standard curve previously constructed. The solution thus obtained was cooled to 35°, seeded with *N*-Ac-D-MDPA·DBA (0.10 g), and stirred. After 90 min, the precipitated crystals were treated in the same manner as described above to yield *N*-Ac-D-MDPA·DBA (7.93 g), which had 97.7% optical purity. By repeating these procedures, L and D isomers were successively obtained. The examples of the several runs are shown in Table I.

Purification of Optically Impure *N*-Ac-MDPA·DBA. The optical isomers separated by the above procedure are practically pure. When further purification is necessary, it can easily be performed by ordinary recrystallization. On the other hand, optically impure *N*-Ac-L-MDPA·DBA could be purified without loss of optically active isomer as follows. Optically impure *N*-Ac-L-MDPA·DBA (8.53 g, optical purity 85.0%) was dissolved at elevated temperature in a solution comprised of water (3.3 ml) and a saturated solution of *N*-Ac-DL-MDPA·DBA (appropriate amount 10 ml). The mixture was then stirred for 1 hr at 35°. The resulting crystals were collected by filtration, washed with a small amount of water, and dried to give *N*-Ac-L-MDPA·DBA (7.29 g), $[\alpha]^{25}D$ +42.0° (*c* 2, H_2O), optical purity 99.1%. Recrystallization from water gave optically pure *N*-Ac-L-MDPA·DBA, $[\alpha]^{25}D$ +42.4° (*c* 2, H_2O), mp 160–162°.

Optically Active *N*-Ac-L- and -D-MDPA from the Corresponding Di-*n*-butylamine Salts. Optically pure *N*-Ac-L-MDPA·DBA (10.00 g) was dissolved in hot water (25 ml) and decomposed with a slight excess of 5 *N* HCl to liberate the *N*-Ac-L-MDPA. The mixture was allowed to stand in a refrigerator overnight. The precipitate was filtered off, washed with water, and dried to give *N*-Ac-L-MDPA (6.28 g, 95.1%), $[\alpha]^{20}D$ +53.9° (*c* 1.5, EtOH), mp 158–159° [lit.[16] $[\alpha]^{13}D$ +53.4° (*c* 2.262, EtOH), mp 158–159°].

N-Ac-D-MDPA was obtained similarly from *N*-Ac-D-MDPA·DBA and had $[\alpha]^{20}D$ −53.9° (*c* 1.5, EtOH), mp 158–159° [lit.[16] $[\alpha]^{18}D$ −53.4° (*c* 1.841, EtOH), mp 158–159°]. Their specific optical rotations and melting points did not change after recrystallization from water. From the filtrate, di-*n*-butylamine satisfactory for reuse was recovered in 90% yield.

Racemization of *N*-Ac-D-MDPA and Preparation of *N*-Ac-DL-MDPA·DBA. *N*-Ac-D-MDPA (1.00 g) was melted in an unsealed tube by heating at 160–165°. After 15 min, to the solidified crystals, an equivalent amounts of di-*n*-butylamine (0.53 g) and water (5 ml) were added. The mixture was dissolved at elevated temperature, treated with charcoal, and concentrated nearly to dryness. The residual crystals were suspended in acetone, filtered, and dried in vacuo to give *N*-Ac-DL-MDPA·DBA (1.38 g), mp 138–142°. The product could be reused for the resolution step. Recrystallization from water gave pure *N*-Ac-DL-MDPA·DBA as colorless prisms, $[\alpha]^{25}D$ 0.0° (*c* 2, H_2O), mp 142–145°. This sample was found to be identical by admixture and ir comparison with the authentic sample prepared from the starting material.

Preparation of L-DOPA. *N*-Ac-L-MDPA (2.00 g) obtained above was added to a mixture of 20% HCl (40 ml) and phenol (2.0 g). The mixture was refluxed for 17 hr under stirring. After filtration, the filtrate was treated with charcoal and concentrated to dryness to remove excess HCl. The residue was taken up in water (10 ml) and the solution was treated with charcoal, adjusted to pH 5 with 5 *N* NH_4OH containing a small amount of sodium bisulfite, and allowed to stand in a refrigerator overnight. The precipitate was filtered and washed with cold water to give crude L-DOPA (1.12 g, 71.4%). Recrystallization from a diluted sulfurous acid solution afforded colorless needles, $[\alpha]^{20}D$ −12.2° (*c* 4, 1 *N* HCl), mp 278–279° dec [lit.[18] $[\alpha]^{20}D$ −12.1° (*c* 4, 1 *N* HCl)]. Anal. Calcd for $C_9H_{11}NO_4$: C, 54.82; H, 5.62; N, 7.10. Found: C, 54.85; H, 5.59; N, 7.08.

Preparation of *N*-Ac-L-, -D-, and -DL-MDPMA·HZ. *N*-Ac-DL-MDPMA·HZ was obtained from *N*-Ac-DL-MDPMA (265.1 g, 1 mol) and hydrazine hydrate (52.6 g, 1.05 mol) in the same way as *N*-Ac-DL-MDPA·DBA. Total yield was 216.7 g (97.5%). The products were almost pure and could be used for optical resolution without further purification. Recrystallization from water gave colorless needles, mp 189–190° dec. Anal. Calcd for $C_{13}H_{19}N_3O_5$: C, 52.51; H, 6.44; N, 14.13. Found: C, 52.61; H, 6.51; N, 14.01. Solubility in water (g/100 ml): 17.0 (10°), 21.1 (25°), 31.7 (40°).

The optically active forms were prepared in the same way. The L isomer: $[\alpha]^{25}D$ +87.8° (*c* 0.5, MeOH), mp 206–207° dec. Anal. Found: C, 52.59; H, 6.54; N, 14.15. Solubility in water (g/100 ml): 10.6 (10°), 12.8 (25°), 17.3 (40°). The D isomer: $[\alpha]^{25}D$ −87.8° (*c* 0.5, MeOH), mp 206–207° dec. The infrared spectra of *N*-Ac-L-, -D-, and -DL-MDPMA·HZ in KBr were identical: ir (KBr) 3320, 3120, 2120, 1650, 1625, 1565–1490, 1440, 1395, 1365, 1255, 1230, 1190, 1100, 1035, 930, 825, 705, 645 cm^{-1}.

Optical Resolution of *N*-Ac-DL-MDPMA·HZ. *N*-Ac-DL-MDPMA·HZ (16.50 g) and *N*-Ac-L-MDPMA·HZ (2.00 g) were dissolved in water (50 ml) at elevated temperature. The solution was cooled to 25°, seeded with *N*-Ac-L-MDPMA·HZ (0.05 g), and stirred at the same temperature. After 60 min, the precipitated crystals were filtered and washed with cold water (2 ml). *N*-Ac-L-MDPMA·HZ (3.96 g) thus obtained was optically pure, $[\alpha]^{25}D$ +87.8° (*c* 0.5, MeOH).

After the separation of the L isomer, *N*-Ac-DL-MDPMA·HZ (4.00 g) and a small amount of water were added to the mother liquor in the same way as described in the case of *N*-Ac-MDPA·DBA. The solution was cooled to 25°, seeded with *N*-Ac-D-MDPMA·HZ (0.05 g), and stirred for 60 min. The precipitated crystals were treated as described above to yield *N*-Ac-D-MDPMA·HZ (4.03 g), which had 97.5% optical purity, $[\alpha]^{25}D$ −85.6° (*c* 0.5, MeOH). The first several runs on a 50-ml scale are given in Table II.

Purification of Optically Impure *N*-Ac-MDPMA·HZ. *N*-Ac-L-MDPMA·HZ (10.00 g, optical purity 56.5%) was dissolved in water (21 ml) by heating. The solution was then stirred for 3 hr at 25°. The precipitated crystals were collected by filtration to give optically pure *N*-Ac-L-MDPMA·HZ (5.52 g), $[\alpha]^{25}D$ +87.8° (*c* 0.5, MeOH), mp 205–206° dec.

Optically Active *N*-Ac-L- and -D-MDPMA from the Corresponding Hydrazine Salts. The optically pure *N*-Ac-L-MDPMA·HZ (5.00 g) obtained above was dissolved in hot water (50 ml) and decomposed with excess 6 *N* HCl to liberate the *N*-Ac-L-MDPMA. After the mixture was allowed to stand in a refrigerator overnight, the precipitate was filtered, washed with water, and dried in vacuo to yield *N*-Ac-L-MDPMA (4.39, 98.5%), showing $[\alpha]^{25}D$ −58.6° (*c* 0.5, MeOH), mp 218–219°. Recrystallization from MeOH afforded colorless needles, $[\alpha]^{20}D$ −58.8° (*c* 0.5, MeOH), mp 219–220° [lit.[17] $[\alpha]^{20}D$ −58.0° (*c* 0.5, MeOH), mp 214–215°].

N-Ac-D-MDPMA was obtained similarly from *N*-Ac-D-MDPMA·HZ and had $[\alpha]^{20}D$ +58.8° (*c* 0.5, MeOH), mp 219–220° [lit.[17] $[\alpha]^{20}D$ +58.0° (*c* 0.5, MeOH), mp 214–215°].

Preparation of L-α-Methyl DOPA. The *N*-Ac-L-MDPMA (4.00 g) obtained above was hydrolyzed with 20% HCl in the presence of phenol in the same way as described in the preparation of L-DOPA from *N*-Ac-L-MDPA. The total yield of L-α-methyl DOPA·$\frac{3}{2}H_2O$ was 2.57 g (71.5%). Recrystallization from a sulfurous acid solution (0.5%) gave a white powder of L-α-methyl DOPA·$\frac{3}{2}H_2O$, and drying of the sesquihydrate in vacuo at 100° gave the anhydrous form, $[\alpha]^{25}D$ −5.2°, $[\alpha]^{25}_{578}$ −5.5° (*c* 2, 0.1 *N* HCl), mp 306–307° dec [lit.[19] $[\alpha]^{25}D$ −4° (*c* 2, 0.1 *N* HCl) and $[\alpha]^{25}_{578}$ +5.5° (*c* 2, 0.1 *N* HCl) for D-α-methyl DOPA]. Anal. Calcd for $C_{10}H_{13}NO_4$: C, 56.86; H, 6.20; N, 6.63. Found: C, 56.75; H, 6.23; N, 6.58.

Registry No.—*N*-Ac-DL-MDPA, 30657-34-2; piperonal, 120-57-0; *N*-acetylglycine, 543-24-8; *N*-Ac-L-MDPA, 28104-71-4; *N*-Ac-D-MDPA, 55629-70-4; *N*-Ac-DL-MDPMA, 23541-10-8; dibutylamine, 111-92-2; *N*-Ac-DL-MDPA·DBA, 55657-00-6; *N*-Ac-L-MDPA·DBA, 55656-80-9; *N*-Ac-D-MDPA·DBA, 55657-01-7; L-DOPA, 59-92-7; *N*-Ac-DL-MDPMA·HZ, 56599-11-2; hydrazine, 302-01-2; *N*-Ac-L-MDPMA·HZ, 56599-12-3; *N*-Ac-D-MDPMA·HZ, 56599-13-4; *N*-Ac-L-MDPMA, 23402-51-9; *N*-Ac-D-MDPMA, 24951-50-6; L-α-methyl DOPA, 555-30-6.

References and Notes

(1) A part of this work was presented at the 20th Meeting of the Association of Amino Acid and Nucleic Acid, in cooperation with the Annual Meeting of the Society of Fermentation Technology, Osaka, Japan, Nov 1971; see Abstracts, p 69.
(2) G. C. Cotzias, P. S. Papavasiliou, and R. Gellene, *N. Engl. J. Med.*, **280**, 337 (1969).
(3) A. Sjoerdsma and S. Udenfriend, *Biochem. Pharmacol.*, **8**, 164 (1961); Merck & Co., Inc. (by R. T. Jones, K. H. Krieger, and J. Lago), Belgian Patent 620,113 (1973), U.S. Patent 3,158,648 (1964).
(4) J. P. Greenstein and M. Winitz, "Chemistry of the Amino Acids", Vol. 1, Wiley, New York, N.Y., 1961, pp 715–716.
(5) R. M. Secor, *Chem. Rev.*, **63**, 297 (1963).
(6) I. Chibata, S. Yamada, M. Yamamoto, and M. Wada, *Experientia*, **24**, 638 (1968).
(7) S. Yamada, M. Yamamoto, and I. Chibata, *Chem. Ind.* (*London*), 528 (1973).
(8) S. Yamada, M. Yamamoto, and I. Chibata, *J. Agric. Food Chem.*, **21**, 889 (1973).
(9) S. Yamada, M. Yamamoto, and I. Chibata, *J. Org. Chem.*, **38**, 4408 (1973).
(10) T. Okuda and Y. Fujii, *Bull. Chem. Soc. Jpn.*, **30**, 698 (1957).
(11) I. Sasaji, K. Ohno, and J. Kato, Japanese Patent 38-6183 (1963).
(12) M. Shibasaki and T. Fukuro, JAPANESE Patent 39-24440 (1964).
(13) N. Sugimoto, I. Chibata, S. Yamada, and M. Yamamoto, U.S. Patent 3,440,279 (1969).
(14) I. Chibata, S. Yamada, and M. Yamamoto, U.S. Patent 3,660,474 (1972).
(15) K. Toi, T. Uzuki, M. Yuda, N. Nakayama, and N. Sato, Swiss Patent 511,774 (1971).
(16) S. Yamada, T. Fujii, and T. Shioiri, *Chem. Pharm. Bull.*, **10**, 680 (1962).
(17) T. Kurano, M. Fukuda, and M. Horiuchi, Japan Patent 45-2733 (1970).
(18) D. D. Appleby and W. Mitchell, *Chem. Ind.* (*London*), 461 (1971).
(19) E. W. Tristram, J. ten Broeke, D. F. Reinhold, M. Sletzinger, and D. E. Williams, *J. Org. Chem.*, **29**, 2053 (1964).

B. Enzymatic Methods

1) Resolution by Asymmetric Synthesis

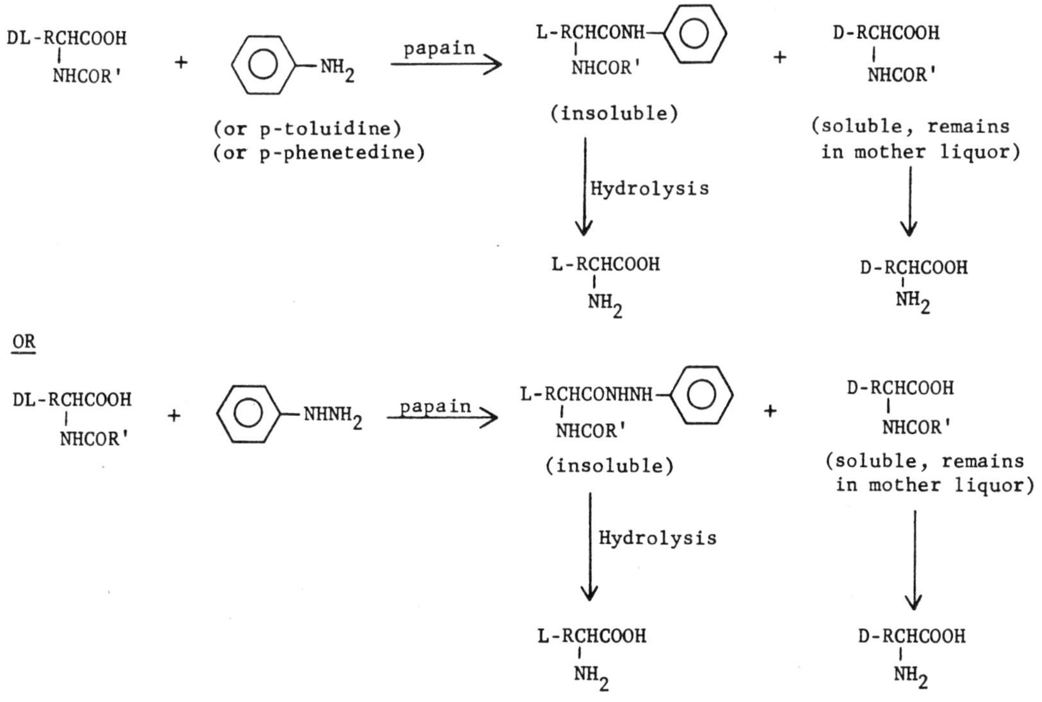

The following[6] is an example of the application of this method of resolution of α-amino acids:

Experimental

N-Benzoyl-3-fluoro-*dl*-tyrosine.—3-Fluoro-*dl*-tyrosine[2] (20 g.) was benzoylated following the procedure of Carter and Stevens[5] to give 20.1 g. (66%) of N-benzoyl-3-fluoro-*dl*-tyrosine, m. p. 178–179° after recrystallization from a mixture of ethyl acetate and ligroin.

Anal. Calcd. for $C_{16}H_{14}O_4NF$ (303); C, 63.4; H, 4.7; N, 4.6. Found: C, 63.5; H, 4.4; N, 4.5.

3-Fluoro-*l*(−)-tyrosine.—N-Benzoyl-3-fluoro-*dl*-tyrosine (8.75 g.) was dissolved in 35 ml. of *N* sodium hydroxide and 44 ml. of 2 *M* sodium acetate and the solution filtered prior to the addition of 88 ml. of 0.1 *M* citrate buffer (*p*H 5.0), 0.65 g. of cysteine hydrochloride, 5.25 ml. of aniline, 88 ml. of a filtered papain solution prepared by dissolving 0.9 g. of purified papain[3a] in 100 ml. of 0.05 *M* citrate buffer (*p*H 5.0) and 170 ml. of water. After the addition of 1 ml. of 50% acetic acid the solution (*p*H 5.8) was incubated at 40° for seven days adding 1 ml. of 50% acetic acid on the second and third days. The precipitate was collected, washed with cold water and 50% aqueous ethanol and dried to give 3.25 g. of crude N-benzoyl-3-fluoro-*l*(−)-tyrosylanilide, m. p. 194–197° dec. The filtrate obtained after the removal of the precipitated anilide was adjusted to *p*H 5.5 with 50% acetic acid and incubated at 40° for another week. A second crop of 1.70 g. of anilide, m. p. 192–196°, was obtained to give a total yield of 4.95 g. or 91% of the theoretical quantity. A suspension of 4.95 g. of the above anilide in 200 ml. of 10% hydrochloric acid was refluxed for eighteen hours, the hydrolysate cooled to 25°, filtered and the filtrate extracted with ether. The aqueous phase was concentrated *in vacuo* to 50 ml. and neutralized by the addition of sodium acetate. The addition of ether to the solution induced crystallization whereupon the ethereal phase was decanted, the product collected and recrystallized twice from water to give 1.2 g. (48%) of 3-fluoro-*l*(−)-tyrosine, m. p. 278–279° with decomposition starting at 265° when heated at the rate of 5°/min.

Anal. Calcd. for $C_9H_{10}O_3NF$ (199): C, 54.3; H, 5.1; N, 7.0. Found: C, 54.5; H, 5.2; N, 6.9: $[\alpha]^{26}_D = \frac{-0.29 \times 1.95}{1 \times 0.100} = -5.7°$ (in 4% hydrochloric acid).

3-Fluoro-*d*(+)-tyrosine.—The filtrate remaining after the removal of the second crop of N-benzoyl-3-fluoro-*l*(−)-tyrosylanilide was acidified with concd. hydrochloric acid to *p*H 1–2 and exhaustively extracted with ethyl acetate. The ethyl acetate phase was dried over sodium sulfate, the solvent removed and the residual oil refluxed with 200 ml. of 10% hydrochloric acid for eighteen hours. The hydrolysate was treated as described above and 2.2 g. of a mixture of 25% of 3-fluoro-*l*(−)-tyrosine and 75% of 3-fluoro-*d*(+)-tyrosine was obtained. This product was dissolved in the minimum quantity of hot water, the solution cooled, the precipitate discarded and the filtrate evaporated to dryness. The residue was recrystallized from water to give 0.9 g. of 3-fluoro-*d*(+)-tyrosine, m. p. 279–280° with decomposition starting at 265° when heated at the rate of 5°/min.

Anal. Calcd. for $C_9H_{10}O_3NF$ (199): C, 54.3; H, 5.1; N, 7.0. Found: C, 54.3; H, 5.1; N, 6.9: $[\alpha]^{26}_D = \frac{0.29 \times 1.95}{1 \times 0.100} = 5.7°$ (in 4% hydrochloric acid).

(2) C. Niemann, A. A. Benson and J. F. Mead, THIS JOURNAL, **63**, 2204 (1941).

(3) (a) M. Bergmann and H. Fraenkel-Conrat, *J. Biol. Chem.*, **119**, 707 (1937);

2) Resolution by Asymmetric Hydrolysis[7] (see also Ref. 33).

a) Hydrolysis of DL-α-amino acid esters

$$\text{DL-R}\underset{\substack{|\\ NH_2}}{\text{CH}}\text{COOR'} \xrightarrow[H_2O]{\text{esterase}} \text{L-R}\underset{\substack{|\\ NH_2}}{\text{CH}}\text{COOH} + \text{D-R}\underset{\substack{|\\ NH_2}}{\text{CH}}\text{COOR'} + \text{R'OH}$$

The esterases employed include chymotrypsin, pancreatin and subtilisin-BPN' and the products are separated by solubility differences.

The following[8] is an example of the application of this method of resolution of α-amino acids:

Acetyl-D-phenylalanine Methyl Ester (IV).—To a solution of 22.1 g. of acetyl-DL-phenylalanine methyl ester in 75 ml. of methanol and 500 ml. of water, contained in a beaker thermostated at 30° was added 50 mg. of α-chymotrypsin and the *p*H of the solution maintained at approximately 7.8 by the addition of 1 *N* aqueous sodium hydroxide. Although the reaction appeared to be completed in two hours, the solution was stirred for another half-hour and then evaporated, at room temperature in a current of air, to about 200 ml. The reaction mixture was stored at 0° overnight, the precipitate recovered, washed with a small quantity of cold water and dried in air to give 9.7 g. of crude IV. The crude IV was recrystallized twice from ether to give IV, dense prisms, m.p. 90–91°, $[\alpha]^{25}_D$ −19° (*c* 2% in methanol).

Anal. Calcd. for $C_{12}H_{15}O_3N$ (221): C, 65.2; H, 6.8; N, 6.3. Found: C, 65.2; H, 6.8; N, 6.4.

b) Hydrolysis of DL-α-amino acid amides

$$\text{DL-R}\underset{\substack{|\\ NH_2}}{\text{CH}}\text{CONH}_2 \xrightarrow[H_2O]{\text{amidase}} \text{L-R}\underset{\substack{|\\ NH_2}}{\text{CH}}\text{COOH} + \text{D-R}\underset{\substack{|\\ NH_2}}{\text{CH}}\text{CONH}_2 + NH_3$$

The amidase from hog kidney has been most widely studied and acts only on the L-enantiomer. Mn^{++} is a potent activator for the enzyme. D-Amidases are available from mushrooms[9]. The products can be readily separated by ion-exchange chromatography or by the differences of the solubility of the products in solvents. Amidase mediated resolutions are used when hydrolysis of acylaminoacids via aminoacylase catalysis are either very slow or unsuccessful.

The following[10] is an example of the application of this method of resolution of α-amino acids:

Enzymic Resolution.—The *p*H of a solution of 4 g. of S-benzyl-DL-penicillamine amide hydrobromide and 50 mg. of $MnCl_2 \cdot 4H_2O$, in water, was adjusted to 8.0 with 2 *N* LiOH; 30 ml. of a hog kidney amidase[44] solution containing 5 mg. of nitrogen per ml. was added thereto, and the final volume diluted to 250 ml. The mixture was subsequently digested at 38° for 18 hr., at which point the manometric ninhydrin-CO_2 procedure revealed 50% hydrolysis of the total substrate. No change in the degree of hydrolysis was revealed upon digestion for an additional 24 hr. after the addition of 7 ml. more of amidase solution. The digest was adjusted to *p*H 5.2 with glacial acetic acid, deproteinized by filtration in the presence of Norite, the precipitate washed with water and the filtrate and washings combined. Since the precipitate contained some adsorbed substrate, this was extracted twice with hot methanol, filtered, the filtrate evaporated to dryness *in vacuo* at 35° and the resulting residue taken up in the pooled aqueous filtrate. This latter was concentrated to about 250 ml. *in vacuo* and the concentrate run onto an Amberlite XE-64 column (28 × 2.5 cm.) in the acid phase. With water as the eluent, fractions were collected every 8 ml. and examined for ninhydrin-positive material. The presence of S-benzyl-L-penicillamine in tubes 10 to 170 was so indicated. After emergence of the L-amino acid, the column was washed with 2 l. of distilled water and the S-benzyl-D-penicillamine amide then eluted with 0.3 *N* HCl (fractions tested for ninhydrin positive material, as previously).

S-Benzyl-L-penicillamine.—The combined eluate of tubes 10 to 170 was concentrated to dryness *in vacuo* at 40°. The residue was dissolved in 1 *N* HCl and the *p*H brought to 5.5 with aqueous ammonia. A crystalline precipitate of S-benzyl-L-penicillamine was so obtained in 96% yield. Recrystallization was effected from water; $[\alpha]^{24}_D$ +87.5° (1% in NaOH) and $[\alpha]^{24}_D$ +91.3° (1% in *N* HCl).

Anal. Calcd. for $C_{12}H_{17}O_2NS$: C, 60.3; H, 7.1; N, 5.9; S, 13.4. Found: C, 60.2; H, 7.3; N, 5.8; S, 13.1.

S-Benzyl-D-penicillamine Amide Hydrochloride.—The 0.3 *N* HCl eluate from the column, which contained the D-amide, was brought to *p*H 4.5 with silver carbonate and filtered. Adsorbed material on the silver chloride precipitate was eluted off with hot methanol, the methanol extracts filtered, concentrated to dryness and the residue taken up in the aqueous filtrate. Hydrogen sulfide was passed through the latter to remove silver ions, the suspension filtered, and the filtrate concentrated to dryness *in vacuo*. The residue was dissolved in approximately 100 ml. of methanol, the solution filtered, the filtrate concentrated to dryness, and the residue crystallized from 80% ethanol to yield S-benzyl-D-penicillamine amide hydrochloride. This material contained approximately one molecule of water of crystallization which could be removed upon drying *in vacuo* at 80°; yield 1.4 g. (81%) of anhydrous product, m.p. 182–183°, $[\alpha]^{24}_D$ −73.0 (1% in ethanol).

Anal. Calcd. for $C_{12}H_{19}ON_2SCl$: C, 52.4; H, 6.9; N, 10.2; S, 11.7; Cl, 12.9. Found: C, 52.4; H, 7.0; N, 10.0; S, 12.0; Cl, 13.0.

S-Benzyl-D-penicillamine.—A solution of 0.7 g. of S-benzyl-D-penicillamine amide hydrochloride in 20 ml. of 5 *N* HCl was refluxed for 6 hr. and the hydrolysate then concentrated to dryness *in vacuo* at 38°. After the addition of a little water, the evaporation was repeated. The residue was dissolved in a few ml. of water and the *p*H adjusted to 5.5 with 2 *N* LiOH. The D-isomer, which crystallized out on standing, was filtered, washed with water and dried; yield 0.58 g. Recrystallization was effected from water; $[\alpha]^{24}_D$ −90.6 (1% in 1 *N* HCl).

(28) D. Hamer and J. P. Greenstein, *ibid.*, **193**, 8 (1951); S. M. Birnbaum in "Methods in Enzymology," Vol. II, Academic Press, Inc., New York, N. Y., 1955, p. 397.

(44) The amidase preparation employed was prepared as described previously,[28] but without prior adsorption on calcium phosphate gel. Its rate of hydrolysis toward L-leucine amide, under the same conditions as utilized for the S-benzylpenicillamine amide, was 2880 μmoles per hr. per mg. of N.

c) Hydrolysis of acyl-DL-α-amino acids

$$\text{DL-R}\underset{\text{NHCOR}'}{\underset{|}{\text{CH}}}\text{COOH} \xrightarrow[\text{H}_2\text{O}]{\text{aminoacylase or carboxypeptidase}} \text{L-R}\underset{\text{NH}_2}{\underset{|}{\text{CH}}}\text{COOH} + \text{D-R}\underset{\text{NHCOR}'}{\underset{|}{\text{CH}}}\text{COOH} + \text{R}'\text{COOH}$$

This enzymatic method of resolution has been most extensively studied and used. The aminoacylases employed have been obtained from hog and rat kidney[11], commercial enzyme preparations[12], molds[13], bacteria[14] and plants[15]. Hog kidney aminoacylases are commercially available. The unhydrolyzed acyl-α-amino is separated from the produced α-amino acid either by the difference in solubility of the two substances in solvents (thus the produced α-amino acids are generally water soluble and ethanol insoluble whereas the unhydrolyzed amino acid amide is generally ethanol soluble), or by the use of ion exchange chromatography.

The following[16,17] is an example of the application of this method of resolution of α-amino acids on a laboratory scale.

Ref. 16

(*b*) Resolution procedure (83; cf. 84). Twenty-four and two-tenths grams (0.1 mole) of chloroacetyl-DL-phenylalanine is suspended in 800 ml. of water, 2*N* lithium hydroxide is added to solution of the compound and a *p*H between 7.0 and 7.2, and finally water is added to 1 l. "Crude" pancreatic carboxypeptidase (Chapter 20) or renal acylase I, about 150 mg. of either one or the other, is added to solution and the digest allowed to stand at 38° until the enzymic hydrolysis is complete (as measured manometrically by the Van Slyke ninhydrin-CO_2 procedure). The mixture is brought to *p*H 5, the protein filtered off with the aid of charcoal, and the filtrate concentrated *in vacuo* to about 50–100 ml. At this point the L-isomer begins to crystallize, and the mixture is chilled for several hours. The crystals of L-phenylalanine are filtered over suction, the filtrate saved for recovery of the chloroacetyl-D-isomer, and the crystals washed first with ethanol, then with ether, and finally recrystallized from water with the aid of a little charcoal.

Chloroacetyl-D-phenylalanine is isolated by acidification to *p*H 1.7 of the resolution filtrate; m.p. 125°; $[\alpha]_D = -50.4°$ in ethanol. Chloroacetyl-L-phenylalanine, prepared in the same way as the corresponding racemate, possesses m.p. 125° and $[\alpha]_D = +50.4°$ in ethanol (85; cf. 86). The L- and D-isomers of phenylalanine are recrystallized from the minimum amount of water, the yields being 80% and 65%, respectively.

(*c*) Optical purity of the products. The L- and D-isomers of phenylalanine are pure, white crystalline compounds. When tested for optical purity with D-amino acid oxidase, or with *Crotalus adamanteus* snake venom L-amino acid oxidase (see Chapter 19), the L- and D-isomers, respectively, reveal no contamination with the opposite isomer, i.e., less than 0.1%, which is the limit of error of the method (87; cf. 88).

The enzymatic procedure for the resolution of amino acids developed in this Laboratory[2a,b] depends upon the asymmetric enzymatic hydrolysis of the N-acyl or amide derivative of the racemic amino acid. The liberated free L-amino acid is separated from the unhydrolyzed D-derivative by the addition of ethanol; the latter derivative is subsequently converted into the D-amino acid by acid hydrolysis. However, since certain amino acids, *e.g.*, isovaline, are soluble in alcohol, and hence cannot be separated in this manner, another isolation procedure was devised. This alternative procedure, employing ion-exchange chromatography for the separation of the products of the asymmetric enzymatic hydrolysis, was designed to permit the use of the small amounts of material usually involved in the synthesis of isotopically labeled amino acids. The method also has been used for the large scale preparation of the enantiomorphs of isovaline.[3]

If cation-exchange chromatography is applied to the mixture obtained after enzymatic resolution of the N-acyl derivative, the free L-amino acid is retained by the column and the unhydrolyzed D-amino acid derivative is eluted with water. After action of the enzyme upon the amide derivative, however, a weaker cation-exchange resin is used, which permits the free amino acid to pass through the column, while the unhydrolyzed derivative is retained and subsequently removed from the column with weak acid. Cation exchange therefore affords sufficiently mild conditions to avoid hydrolysis of the N-acyl or amide derivative.

Experimental

Preparation of the Ion-exchange Resin Columns.—Dowex-50[4] and Amberlite XE-64[5] in the acid phase were used. The resin as received from the manufacturer was subjected to two cycles of washing with 5 *N* HCl, water, 1 *N* NaOH, water, and followed by a final 5 *N* HCl and water wash. Washing with water in each case was continued to completion as indicated by congo red and phenolphthalein. Resin columns (see Table I for dimensions) were prepared from suspensions of the washed resin, allowed to settle in a glass column and then washed with an additional liter of distilled water. Dowex-50 was used for alanine, methionine, valine, aspartic acid, serine, ornithine and isovaline, and XE-64 was used for proline, histidine and arginine.

Substrates and Enzymes.—Many of the amino acid derivatives used were donated by Dr. J. P. Greenstein. All gave melting points in agreement with those in the literature[2] and the theoretical elemental analyses. The purified hog kidney enzymes, acylase I and II,[2] were prepared by Drs. S. M. Birnbaum and K. R. Rao, respectively. Crystalline carboxypeptidase was obtained from the Worthington Biochemical Sales Company.

Incubation with Enzyme.—N-Acyl-DL-amino acid, equivalent in amount to one gram of each enantiomorph, was dissolved in water and the *p*H adjusted to 7.6 (cresol red) with 6 *N* lithium hydroxide. Sufficient acylase was added to produce the theoretical 50% hydrolysis in one to two hours[2] and the *p*H was readjusted to 7.6. The mixture was diluted to a final substrate concentration of 0.1 *M* and incubated at 37°, the progress of the hydrolysis being followed by manometric-ninhydrin determinations. When 50% hydrolysis had been attained, the incubation mixture was deproteinized at the isoelectric point of the enzyme[2] with Norit, and the solution was reduced *in vacuo*[6] to a small volume.

Chromatography and Isolation of the D-Amino Acid.—The concentrated solution from the enzymatic run was added to the top of the appropriate resin column at a rate of about 0.5 ml. per minute and carefully washed into the resin with several 1-ml. aliquots of water. The N-acyl-D-amino acid was then eluted from the resin by water at a rate of about 10 ml./hr. and collected in fractions of 5–15 ml. The D-amino acid can be detected in the fractions most simply by the drop in *p*H which results from the acidic nature of the derivative.[7] Alternatively, aliquots of each fraction may be spotted on filter paper and examined with: (a) ninhydrin for the appearance of a ninhydrin positive color *only after* preliminary hydrolysis at 100° in 2 *N* HCl,[8] (b) various specific amino acid reagents,[9] or (c) the reagent of Rydon and Smith.[10]

The fractions containing the N-acyl-D-amino acid were combined and evaporated to dryness *in vacuo*. The residue was taken up in about 150 ml. of absolute ethanol or dry acetone and filtered to remove any residual protein. The filtrate was evaporated to dryness *in vacuo*, and the residue was hydrolyzed at 100° for 2 to 3 hours in 2 to 2.5 *N* HCl. The solution was then treated with Norit, filtered and taken to dryness *in vacuo* four times to remove excess HCl. The residue of D-amino acid hydrochloride was then converted to the free amino acid by the reagents indicated in Table I. The compounds were recrystallized from water-ethanol, with the exception of proline, in which case absolute ethanol was employed. Occasionally a second recrystallization was required.

Isolation of the L-Amino Acid.—Several hundred ml. of water was passed through the column subsequent to the complete emergence of the N-acyl-D-amino acid derivative from the column. Elution of the free amino acid was accomplished with hydrochloric acid at concentrations depending upon the resin and the particular amino acid involved. The conditions used are given in Table I. Detection of the fractions containing the L-amino acid was accomplished most conveniently by means of the ninhydrin spot test on paper,[11] although specific reagents also may be used.[9]

The fractions containing the L-amino acid were combined and evaporated to dryness *in vacuo*. The residue was taken up in about 150 ml. of concentrated HCl and filtered to remove salts which usually are eluted with some of the later fractions. The filtrate was diluted and after treatment with Norit the filtered solution was taken to dryness *in vacuo* four times to remove excess HCl. The L-amino acid hydrochloride was converted into the free amino acid in the manner used for its enantiomorph.

Determination of Optical Purity.—Optical rotations were all performed in a two-decimeter tube with a Hilger M375 polarimeter with triple field-type polarizer at 27°. Several of the isomers (*cf.* Table II) were examined for their enantiomorphs by the enzymatic procedure of Meister, Levintow, Kingsley and Greenstein[12] which is sensitive to at least one part of enantiomorph in one thousand parts of the assayed material.

TABLE I EXPERIMENTAL CONDITIONS FOR OBTAINING THE OPTICAL ISOMERS OF AMINO ACIDS (SEE TEXT)

DL-Amino acid derivative	Wt. of derivative, g.	Wt. of added enzyme, mg.	Time of incubation, hr.	Resin used	Column size height × diam., cm.	Hydrochloric acid eluting agent, *N*	Agent for converting the hydrochloride into the free amino acid
N-Chloroacetylaspartic acid	3.15	Acylase II 90.0	20.5	Dowex-50	32.5 × 2.5	1	Aniline
N-Acetylhistidine	2.77	Acylase I 194.0[b]	40.0	XE-64	55.0 × 2.5	1	LiOH
Proline amide[a]	[a]	[a]	[a]	XE-64	38.0 × 2.5	0.12	Ag_2CO_3
N-Chloroacetylserine	3.45	Acylase I 3.0	6.5	Dowex-50	57.0 × 2.5	2.5	Aniline
N-Chloroacetylphenylalanine	2.94	Carboxypeptidase 33.0	10.0	Dowex-50	35.0 × 2.0	5	Aniline
N,N′-Dichloroacetylornithine	4.32	Acylase I 115.0[c]	42.0	Dowex-50	43.0 × 2.5	5	.....
N-Acetylalanine	2.94	Acylase I 2.2	13.5	Dowex-50	31.3 × 1.1	2.5	Aniline
N-Acetylmethionine	2.56	Acylase I 0.2	13.5	Dowex-50	31.5 × 2.5	5	Aniline
N-Acetylvaline	2.72	Acylase I 5.0	7.0	Dowex-50	36.4 × 2.5	5	Aniline

[a] Non-enzymatic experiment: 0.880 g. of L-proline amide plus 0.887 g. of L-proline (see text). [b] Added in two portions: 179 mg. initially and an additional 15 mg. at 18 hr. [c] Added in two portions: 105 mg. initially and an additional 10 mg. at 18 hr.

The general procedure given above was followed for the individual amino acids and the specific details are given in Table I. In order to test the feasibility of the column separation, as indicated in Table I, a preliminary non-enzymatic experiment was performed wherein a concentrated solution of L-proline and L-proline amide was put directly on the column. Since proline is not retained by the XE-64 column used, it was eluted by the passage of water through

TABLE II

YIELDS AND PROPERTIES OF RESOLVED AMINO ACIDS

Amino acid	Isomer	Yield, %	Concn. mg. per 2 ml.	Solvent	$[\alpha]_D$ Found, degrees	Nitrogen, % Calcd.	Nitrogen, % Found
Aspartic acid	D[b]	63	38.3	6 *N* HCl	−24.7	10.5	10.4
	L	92	40.0	6 *N* HCl	+25.3		10.6
Histidine	D	55	37.5	H_2O	+38.5	27.1	27.1
	L	49	33.5	H_2O	−38.4		27.1
Proline	L[a]	54	32.0	H_2O	−84.4	12.2	12.2
	L	47	26.8	H_2O	−85.1		12.1
Serine	D	69	82.7	1 *N* HCl	−14.5	13.3	13.2
	L	48	95.6	1 *N* HCl	+14.4		13.2
Phenyl-	D[b]	36	32.4	H_2O	+35.1	8.5	8.7
alanine	L[b]	35	31.9	H_2O	−34.5		8.6
Ornithine·2	D	46	65.4	5 *N* HCl	−18.2[c]	13.7	13.9
HCl	L	60	62.3	5 *N* HCl	+17.9[c]		13.7
Alanine	D	65	55.9	5 *N* HCl	−14.2	15.7	15.9
	L[b]	61	81.7	5 *N* HCl	+14.2		15.8
Methionine	D	66	52.4	6 *N* HCl	−22.7	9.4	9.4
	L	54	40.0	6 *N* HCl	+23.6		9.4
Valine	D[b]	52	35.5	6 *N* HCl	−27.3	11.9	11.9
	L[b]	74	46.0	6 *N* HCl	+28.2		11.9

[a] Derived from the amide (see text). [b] Examined by the enzymatic test[12] and shown to contain less than 0.1% enantiomorph. [c] The only recorded value in 5 *N* HCl is ±18.2°, S-C. J. Fu, K. R. Rao, S. M. Birnbaum and J. P. Greenstein, *J. Biol. Chem.*, 199, 207 (1952).

the column. After an additional several hundred ml. of water had passed through, proline amide was eluted with weak acid. In a similar non-enzymatic experiment with L-arginine and N-acetyl-DL-arginine, the acetyl derivative was eluted from the XE-64 column with water and the free amino acid removed with weak acid.

It should be pointed out that although the di-amino acids would be retained by the weak cation exchanger, XE-64, it was necessary to use the strong cation-exchange resin, Dowex-50, for the column separation in the ornithine resolution reported here. Starting with the N,N′-dichloroacetyl-amino acid, only the α-amino group is liberated. The products of the enzymatic hydrolysis are similar in their behavior on the strong exchange resin to those obtained in the resolution of the monoamino-monocarboxylic amino acids.

(2) (a) S. M. Birnbaum, L. Levintow, R. B. Kingsley and J. P. Greenstein, *J. Biol. Chem.*, **194**, 455 (1952); (b) J. P. Greenstein, S. M. Birnbaum and M. C. Otey, *ibid.*, in press.

(3) C. G. Baker, S-C. J. Fu, S. M. Birnbaum, H. A. Sober and J. P. Greenstein, THIS JOURNAL, **74**, 4701 (1952).

(4) A strong cation-exchange resin with sulfonic acid functional groups (200–400 mesh) obtained from the Dow Chemical Company, Midland, Mich.

(5) A weak cation-exchange resin with carboxylic acid exchange groups obtained from the Resinous Products Division, Rohm and Haas, Philadelphia, Penna.

(6) All concentration procedures were performed *in vacuo* below 40°.

(7) Indicator paper is sufficiently sensitive. This test will apply only when the acyl derivative is used, since with the amide derivatives, the free amino acid emerges first from the XE-64 column.

(8) A 0.25% solution of ninhydrin in acetone is used; *cf.* G. Toennies and J. J. Kolb, *Anal. Chem.*, **23**, 823 (1951). A positive ninhydrin test in the early non-acidic as well as in the acid fractions, except where the amide derivative has been used, should be taken as evidence that the capacity of the resin column for that particular amino acid has been exceeded.

(9) The Sakaguchi test for arginine, the isatin test for proline and hydroxyproline, the Pauly test for histidine and tyrosine, the platinic iodide test for methionine, and the periodate-Nesslerization procedure for hydroxy amino acids; *cf.*, R. J. Block and D. Bolling, "The Amino Acid Composition of Foods. Analytical Methods and Results," 2nd Edition, C. C. Thomas, Springfield, Ill., 1952. The corresponding colors in the tests for proline amide and for the N-acetyl derivatives of histidine, arginine and methionine develop somewhat more slowly. The N-acetyl derivatives of the hydroxy amino acids do not give NH_3 after treatment with periodate.

(10) Except for methionine, tyrosine, cysteine and cystine, a blue starch–iodine color is given in this test with amino acids, peptides, proteins, amides and N-acyl derivatives previously exposed to chlorine; *cf.* H. N. Rydon and P. W. C. Smith, *Nature*, **169**, 923 (1952). A positive test with this reagent in the absence of a positive ninhydrin reaction, locates the N-acyl amino acids.

(11) Because of the acidity of the effluent fractions, the paper containing the aliquot spots should be exposed to an atmosphere of NH_3 for about 5 minutes and the excess NH_3 blown off before the paper is dipped into the ninhydrin solution.[8]

(12) A. Meister, L. Levintow, R. B. Kingsley and J. P. Greenstein, *J. Biol. Chem.*, **192**, 535 (1951).

(13) Analyses by R. J. Koegel and his staff.

(14) S. Moore and W. H. Stein, *Cold Spring Harbor Symposia*, **14**, 179 (1949).

Chibata and coworkers[18] at Tanabe Seiyaku Co., Ltd., Osaka, Japan, from 1953-1969 pioneered the use of mold aminoacylases for the industrial production of several L-amino acids in a batchwise process in which the substrate racemic acyl-DL-amino acid was stereospecifically hydrolyzed by incubating the substrate amino acids with a soluble enzyme (L-aminoacylase). However, this procedure had some disadvantages as an industrial process. Thus, in order to isolate the produced L-amino acid, one had to remove the enzyme and discard it even though it still showed activity since there was no economical process for separating the active from the inactive enzyme. Furthermore, since the enzyme preparations used were relatively crude mixtures, a rather involved purification process was required to remove contaminating proteins and coloring materials. This decreased the yield of L-amino acid. To overcome these disadvantages, Chibata and coworkers[19-28] developed procedures for the immobilization of aminoacylases and designed a reactor (see figure) for the continuous production of L-amino acids using aminoacylase bound to DEAE-Sephadex. This

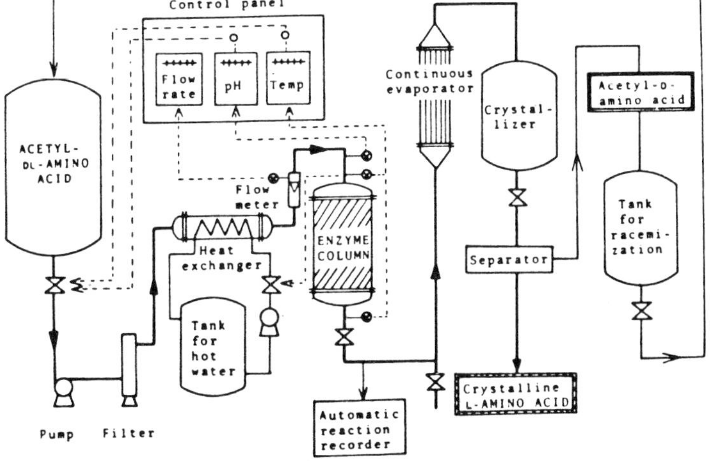

procedure has the following advantages over the batch process: 1) the immobilized aminoacylase is very stable and maintains 60-70% of its initial activity after continuous operation for 30 days at 50°C, 2) the enzyme column can be completely regenerated after prolonged operation by the addition of an amount of aminoacylase corresponding to the lost activity, 3) the carrier, DEAE-Sephadex, is very stable and has been used for 5 years without any change in adsorption capacity for the enzyme shape or pressure drop, 4) the method gives a high product yield because contamination of the effluent by impurities such as proteins and coloring matter does not occur, so the product can be obtained by a simple purification step, and 5) automatic operation reduces labor costs compared to a batch process. A detailed description of the immobilization of aminoacylases, properties of the immobilized aminoacylase and a discussion of the continuous production of L-α-amino acids by the use of a column packed with immobilized aminoacylase (DEAE-Sephadex-aminoacylase) may be found in, "Methods in Enzymology," Volume XLIV, pages 746-759, I. Chibata, T. Tosa, T. Sato and T. Mori (authors), Academic Press, New York, N. Y. (1976).

d) Other Enzymatic Methods for the Resolution of α-Amino Acids

In addition to the methods of resolution of α-amino acids by asymmetric synthesis and hydrolysis described above, α-amino acids have been "resolved" via enzymatic assisted asymmetric oxidation[29] or decarboxylation[30] of one of the two enantiomers. Thus L-amino acid oxidases obtained from snake venom and D-amino acid oxidases obtained from mammalian kidney have been used to prepare the enantiomers of α-amino acids as shown by the following reaction:

$$\text{DL-}\alpha\text{-amino acid} + \text{oxidase} \xrightarrow{O_2} \alpha\text{-keto acid} + NH_3 + \text{unreacted } \alpha\text{-amino acid enantiomer}$$

Unlike the previous described methods, wherein both enantiomers are separatedly recovered at the end of the enzymatic reaction, in this approach one of the two enantiomers is selectively destroyed. Using L-amino acid oxidase, 13 D-α-amino acids were prepared and using hog renal D-amino acid oxidase, 9 L-α-amino acids were prepared. All obtained α-amino acids were found to be optically pure. Experimental procedures and results for a series of amino acids follow:

Ref. 29

Preparation of the D-Amino Acids.—The L-amino acid oxidase preparation was dried *Crotalus adamanteus* venom obtained from the Ross Allen Reptile Institute of Silver Springs, Florida. The venom was dissolved in the appropriate volume of 0.2 *M tris* buffer at *p*H 7.2, dialyzed against running tap water for 5–6 hours at 5°, and the solution centrifuged before use. Crystalline liver catalase was obtained from the Worthington Co. and its aqueous solution thoroughly dialyzed at 5°.

D-Alanine.—In the main compartment of a 125-ml. Warburg respirometer was placed a solution of 0.89 g. (0.01 mole) of DL-alanine in 30 ml. of water[19] together with 10 ml. of 0.2 *M tris* buffer at *p*H 7.2. Immediately thereafter was added 10 ml. of a dialyzed solution of the venom and 0.4 ml. of a solution containing 100 units of catalase.[20] To the center cup was added 2 ml. of 20% KOH provided with a filter paper strip. Inasmuch as it was necessary to prepare enough material for analytical, optical rotation and purity determinations in replicate, three such flasks and their contents were so prepared. The three flasks together with a control flask wherein the substrate was omitted were attached to the manometric assembly and shaken at 37° in an atmosphere of oxygen for 18 to 24 hours. At intervals the oxygen supply was shut off, the side-arms were closed, and the oxygen consumption noted. When no further oxygen was being consumed, 0.3 ml. of a freshly-prepared solution of the venom was added to the side-arm of each flask. After a brief equilibration period, the enzyme solution was tipped into the flask and the oxygen consumption noted. In this manner the end-point of the reaction was ascertained. At the end of the reaction the three substrate suspensions were combined, brought to isoelectric *p*H by addition of a few drops of glacial acetic acid, and concentrated *in vacuo* at 45–50° to about 30 ml. The concentrate was dialyzed with agitation against 4 changes of 150 ml. each of distilled water at intervals of 2 hours.[21] The combined dialysates were warmed with Norit and filtered, the filtrate and washings concentrated to a low bulk, and ethanol added to 80%. The D-alanine which appeared on chilling was recrystallized in the same manner. In the earlier studies of this reaction, the products in each flask were worked up separately in order to check the yields under these conditions, and to note the applicability of the method to small-scale preparations. At the 10-mmole level the isolation of the D-isomers was quite successful, the combined yield being little below that obtained from the combined reaction mixtures as described above. Optical purity[3] and rotation measurements were carried out on the analyzed product. These determinations required approximately 700 mg. (about 180 mg. for optical purity, 400 mg. for rotation, and 100 mg. for elemental analyses) or close to the 900 mg. yield of twice-crystallized and pure D-alanine finally obtained (*cf.* Table II).

D-Alloisoleucine, D-methionine, D-phenylalanine, D-tryptophan and D-valine were prepared from the corresponding racemates (the isoleucine racemate was a nearly equal mixture of D-isoleucine and D-alloisoleucine) in a manner similar to that described for D-alanine, with modifications in regard to the amount of venom employed as noted in Table I. More water was also employed in the dialytic step for these compounds. Norit was not employed in the purification procedures for the aromatic amino acids.

D-Arginine.—This preparation was achieved in the same manner as with D-alanine, except that the final product was isolated as the benzylidine derivative,[22] and from this converted to the pure monohydrochloride.

D-Aspartic Acid and D-Glutamic Acid.—The corresponding racemates were brought into solution at neutrality by addition of LiOH, and the oxidation carried on as described for alanine. At the end of the usual 24-hour period the consumption of oxygen had apparently ceased. Addition of fresh venom revealed renewed oxygen uptake, so that the reaction was essentially uncompleted. Rather than continuing with the same digests and fresh enzyme, it was decided to isolate the crude products and resume the oxidation with fresh solutions. The concentrates obtained from the combined dialysates were adjusted by addition of 1 *N* HCl to *p*H 2.8, and the D-isomers isolated in the usual manner from water:ethanol in 1:4 ratio. Optical purity determinations revealed the presence of appreciable amounts of the respective L-isomers. The products were therefore each divided into 3 parts and subjected to reoxidation using the same amount of venom as before. The new products obtained thereby were optically pure.

D-**Histidine.**—The solution of racemic histidine·HCl was brought to neutrality by addition of 1 *N* LiOH prior to oxidation. If catalase is used in this reaction, the mixture assumes a strong cherry-red color which turns to a dark brown at the end, and the yields are remarkably poor. This phenomenon appears to be unique for histidine. In the absence of catalase the reaction proceeded normally and the D-histidine was isolated in good yield as the monohydrochloride monohydrate.

D-**Lysine.**—The substrate for this reaction was DL-ε-carbobenzoxylysine. Despite its insolubility the oxidation reaction proceeded normally to completion. At the end of the oxidation period the reaction mixtures were combined, brought to *p*H 5 with acetic acid, filtered with suction, and washed with ice-water. The precipitate, D-ε-carbobenzoxylysine, was recrystallized twice from water with the aid of Norit and Cello-cel to remove the coagulated venom protein. The product was catalytically hydrogenated and the D-lysine isolated first as the dihydrochloride and subsequently as the monohydrochloride.

D-**Tyrosine.**—Because of the very considerable insolubility of this amino acid and its lack of wetting, the shaking procedure in the Warburg vessel was initially ineffective. The racemic tyrosine (1.81 g. = 10 mmoles) was therefore suspended in a 500-ml. volumetric cylinder in a mixture of 120 ml. of water, 40 ml. of 0.2 *M tris* buffer at *p*H 7.2, 0.4 ml. of dialyzed solution containing 100 units of catalase and 40 ml. of a dialyzed solution of venom. Three cylinders with the above contents and one serving as blank without substrate were placed in a bath at 37°. A steady stream of oxygen was bubbled through each reaction mixture by means of gas dispersion tubes, and foaming was controlled by occasional addition of caprylic alcohol. Care was taken to prevent climbing of tyrosine crystals up to the walls of the cylinders. After 24 hours of oxidation, 2-ml. representative samples were withdrawn from each mixture and transferred to Warburg respirometers. The end-point of the reaction was checked with fresh venom solution, and it was found that there was still some unoxidized L-tyrosine present. Fresh venom solution to the same amount was added and the reaction continued for another 24-hour period when it was complete. The mixtures were combined, brought to *p*H 5, the D-tyrosine filtered and washed. The filtrate was concentrated to about 100 ml. *in vacuo* and chilled for several hours. The first and second crops of D-tyrosine were combined and recrystallized from water with the aid of Norit to remove venom protein.

D-**Leucine.**—The oxidation reaction with DL-leucine was carried out in a manner similar to that described for DL-tyrosine, except that the leucine was suspended in each cylinder in a mixture of 60 ml. of water, 20 ml. of *tris* buffer, 20 ml. of venom solution and 0.4 ml. of catalase solution (100 units). The reaction was completed readily in less than 24 hours, and the mixtures were combined, adjusted to *p*H 5, and condensed *in vacuo* to about 35 ml. The concentrate was dialyzed against 4 changes of 300 ml. of distilled water each time at 2-hour intervals. The combined dialysates were concentrated *in vacuo* to about 200 ml. and the concentrate poured onto a Dowex-50 resin column, 4 × 30 cm. (200–400 mesh) in the hydrogen form. After thorough washing of the column with water to neutrality, the D-leucine was displaced by a 1 *N* ammonium hydroxide solution and collected. The eluate was evaporated to dryness *in vacuo*, the residue taken up in water, and the evaporation repeated. This procedure was repeated again in order to remove the last trace of ammonia. The residue was dissolved in about 100 ml. of water and the solution poured onto a Dowex-1 resin column, 2.5 × 22 cm. (50–100 mesh) in the hydroxyl form. After washing with water to neutrality, the D-leucine was eluted with 1 *N* acetic acid. The collected ninhydrin-positive fractions were combined, filtered, and evaporated *in vacuo* several times to dryness, each time after dissolution of the residue in water. The residue was taken up in about 50 ml. of hot ethanol and the solution allowed to chill for several hours. The colorless crystals of D-leucine were collected by filtration, washed with chilled ethanol, and recrystallized from aqueous ethanol.

Preparation of the L-Amino Acids.—The D-amino acid oxidase preparation was derived from hog kidney. Some 600 g. of previously frozen kidneys was minced and extracted with about 4 l. of cold C.P. acetone in a Waring Blendor. The suspension was filtered and the filter-cake extracted as above. The final preparation was dried *in vacuo* over P_2O_5. Several batches were prepared in this manner, and yielded an average of 130 g. of acetone powder from 600 g. of raw kidney. An amount of 65 g. of this powder was extracted with 350 ml. of cold distilled water in a Waring Blendor, the extract was centrifuged in a Spinco centrifuge at 18,000 r.p.m. for 30 minutes, and supernatant set aside in the cold. The solid residue was re-extracted as above, and the combined supernatant solutions lyophilized and stored at −5°. The average yield of lyophilized material was 18 g.

Because quite large amounts of this crude enzymic preparation were employed in the oxidation of the various amino acids, with the consequent danger of contamination of the isomers by amino acids liberated by autolysis of the enzyme, each of the L-isomers in the final, purified state (Table II) was subjected to two-dimensional paper chromatography using 40-μg. samples. One solvent was phenol–NH_3 or phenol saturated with 10% trisodium citrate, the other was formic acid:H_2O:*sec*-butyl alcohol (15:15:70). In every case of the L-amino acids described in Table II, only a single ninhydrin-reactive spot could be developed except in the case of L-methionine which showed faint evidence for the usual presence of the corresponding sulfoxide.

L-**Alanine.**—In a 500-ml. volumetric cylinder were placed 0.89 g. (10 mmoles) of DL-alanine, 40 ml. of water and 10 ml. of a solution containing D-amino acid oxidase (*cf.* Table I) in 0.1 *M* sodium pyrophosphate buffer at *p*H 8.2. Three such cylinders with similar contents plus one cylinder in which the substrate was omitted were placed in a constant temperature water-bath at 37°, and a steady stream of oxygen bubbled through the reaction mixtures, caprylic alcohol being added to reduce foaming. The *p*H was maintained at 8.0 by appropriate addition of LiOH solution. The end-point of the reaction was determined as in the case of D-tyrosine described above. When this was established (less than 24 hours incubation) the combined mixtures were brought to *p*H 5, evaporated *in vacuo* to about 30 ml., and dialyzed against 4 changes of 500 ml. of water each at 2-hour intervals. The combined dialysates were evaporated *in vacuo* to a small bulk and the solution passed through first a Dowex-50 resin column and then a Dowex-1 resin column in acetate form as described in the case of D-leucine above. Two crystallizations from water–ethanol (1:4) yielded a pure product of L-alanine.[23]

L-**Isoleucine,** L-**leucine,** L-**methionine,** L-**proline,** L-**serine and** L-**valine** were obtained from the respective racemates by treatment similar to that described for L-alanine, except that in the cases of isoleucine, leucine, methionine and valine, twice the volume of water and of buffer solution was employed. Each of the isomers except proline and serine was readily crystallized from water–ethanol in white, pure condition. L-Proline and L-serine come off the Dowex-1 resin (in hydroxyl or acetate form) in a highly colored state. Further treatment with the Dowex-1 resin removed some but not all of the colored impurity. Proline was dissolved in hot absolute ethanol, whilst serine was dissolved in hot water and treated with hot ethanol to 85%; on cooling to room temperature each solution deposited a small amount of a highly colored oil, leaving the supernatant solution clear and colorless. The supernatant solutions were each decanted from the oil and chilled at 0° for 1–2 days, whereby pure, colorless crystals of L-proline and of L-serine separated. Repetition of the preparation of these two isomers in the presence of 0.01 *M* KCN led to the isolation of L-serine and of L-proline in yield and state of purity reported in Table II.

L-**Phenylalanine.**—The racemic phenylalanine was subjected to oxidation in the same manner as that described for L-isoleucine but with the addition of KCN to 0.01 *M* final concentration to each reaction mixture. The product obtained after a 24-hour period of incubation when the oxygen consumption was apparently at an end was examined for optical purity[3] and revealed the presence of approximately 5% of the D-isomer. (If cyanide is omitted from the reaction mixture, the product at this stage contains about 20% of the D-form.) It was subjected to reoxidation in twice the volume of water and buffer as before, with twice the amount of enzyme, and once more in the presence of 0.01 *M* cyanide. After a further 24-hour period of oxidation at 37°, the isolated product after crystallization from water–ethanol was analytically and optically pure (Table II). In the case of DL-tyrosine oxidized by D-amino acid oxidase in the presence or absence of cyanide, the product in either

case contained about 30% of the D-isomer; reoxidation in the presence of 0.01 *M* cyanide yielded a product still grossly contaminated with the D-form. A quite similar situation appeared to hold in the case of DL-tryptophan. It appeared probable that in these cases the lower fatty acid was about as inhibitory as the α-keto acid, and attempts to prepare the L-isomers of tyrosine and of tryptophan by the present procedures were therefore abandoned.

L-Hydroxyproline.—DL-Hydroxyproline is not readily available, and to test the present procedure for the preparation of the L-isomer, a suitable substrate was obtained by the epimerization of L-hydroxyproline in hot baryta solution. Leuchs and Geiger[14] prepared the epimeric mixture of L-hydroxyproline and D-allohydroxyproline (app. 1:1) in this manner, isolating the mixture after quantitative removal of barium ion with sulfate. Their procedure was modified to the extent of heating a solution of 20 g. of L-hydroxyproline in 250 ml. of water containing 150 g. of crystalline baryta at 120° for 24 hours, diluting with water and removing excess barium ion with CO_2 gas, and pouring the filtrate on a Dowex-50 resin (H^+) column, followed by a water wash. This was followed by 1 *N* NH_4OH until the ninhydrin reaction was negative, the eluate was evaporated to dryness to remove ammonia, and the crystalline, ammonia-free residue dried; yield 95%, $[\alpha]^{26}_D$ −6.4° (*c* 2, H_2O).[24]

The epimeric mixture was subjected to oxidation for 24 hours as described above for L-alanine, with the amount of enzyme given in Table I, and in the presence of 0.005 *M* potassium cyanide. The L-isomer was isolated in the usual way and, after crystallization from water in the presence of excess ethanol, was found to be analytically and optically pure (Table II).

TABLE I

INITIAL QUANTITIES OF *Crotalus adamanteus* VENOM AND OF LYOPHILIZED HOG KIDNEY D-AMINO ACID OXIDASE EMPLOYED IN EACH REACTION VESSEL CONTAINING 10 MILLIMOLES OF RACEMIC AMINO ACID

Racemate	*Crotalus adamanteus*, g.	Lyophilized D-amino acid oxidase, g.
Alanine	0.5	0.833
Arginine·HCl	.8	. .
Aspartic acid	.5	. .
Glutamic acid	.5	.
Histidine·HCl	.23	. .
L-Hydroxyproline plus D-allohydroxyproline (app. 1:1)	. . .	9.0
L-Isoleucine plus D-alloisoleucine (app. 1:1)	0.11	2.8
Leucine	0.1	2.0
ε-Carbobenzoxylysine	1.0	. .
Methionine	0.03	1.0
Phenylalanine	0.04	1.7
Proline	. .	0.86
Serine	. .	6.0
Tryptophan	0.04	(6.0)
Tyrosine	.17	(9.0)
Valine	.83	0.85

TABLE II

CHARACTERISTICS OF THE AMINO ACID ISOMERS PREPARED

Amino acids	Yield, %[a]	Analyses, % Calculated C	H	N	Found C	H	N	$[\alpha]_D$[b]
D-Alanine	68	40.44	7.92	15.72	40.64	8.11	15.56	−14.6
D-Arginine·HCl	37	34.20	7.17	26.59	34.37	7.25	26.31	−21.8
D-Aspartic acid	58	36.09	5.30	10.52	35.97	5.52	10.64	−24.6
D-Glutamic acid	79	40.81	6.16	9.52	40.91	6.25	9.34	−30.3
D-Histidine·HCl monohydrate[c]	80	34.37	5.76	20.04	34.21	5.96	19.81	−10.29
D-Alloisoleucine	83	54.94	9.99	10.67	54.85	10.02	10.69	−37.8
D-Leucine	71	54.94	9.99	10.67	54.68	9.77	10.65	−15.1
ε-Carbobenzoxy-D-lysine	70	59.98	7.19	9.99	59.83	7.33	10.12	− 5.65[d]
D-Lysine·HCl	. .	39.45	8.27	15.33	39.27	8.27	15.32	−20.6[f]
D-Methionine	79	40.25	7.43	9.39	40.08	7.33	9.27	−23.9
D-Phenylalanine[e]	64	65.51	6.81	8.48	65.43	6.71	8.56	+33.9[g]
D-Tryptophan	39	64.69	5.92	13.72	64.30	5.85	13.57	+31.7[h]
D-Tyrosine	77	59.66	6.12	7.73	59.55	6.15	7.72	+ 7.56
D-Valine	68	51.26	9.46	11.96	51.13	9.41	12.07	−26.4
L-Hydroxproline	56	45.79	6.91	10.68	45.74	6.92	10.74	−75.4[g]
L-Alanine	92	40.44	7.92	15.72	40.36	8.06	15.59	+14.1
L-Isoleucine	70	54.94	9.99	10.67	54.71	9.91	10.57	+37.5
L-Leucine	92	54.94	9.99	10.67	54.70	9.80	10.81	+15.6
L-Methionine	70	40.25	7.43	9.39	40.24	7.56	9.35	+23.1
L-Phenylalanine	74	65.43	6.71	8.48	65.41	6.90	8.58	−33.2
L-Proline	40	52.16	7.88	12.17	51.90	7.95	12.15	−83.8[g]
L-Serine	50	34.28	6.71	13.33	34.00	6.81	13.35	+14.6[i]
L-Valine	86	51.26	9.46	11.96	51.10	9.49	12.06	+26.7

[a] The yields reported are for analytically pure products. [b] Optical rotations were determined with 2% solutions in 5 *N* HCl, at temperatures between 24 and 28°, unless stated otherwise. The optical purity determined for each isomer[c] was in all cases >99.9%. [c] When dried at 140° and 1 mm. for 12 hours, histidine hydrochloride monohydrate loses water and turns brown. *Anal.* Calcd. for $C_6H_{10}N_3O_2Cl$: C, 37.60; H, 5.26; N, 21.92. Found: C, 37.90; H, 5.30; N, 21.64. [d] 2% solution in 1 *N* NaOH. [e] D- (or L)-phenylalanine when recrystallized from water–ethanol mixture and dried at 25° and 1 mm. analyzes for phenylalanine hemihydrate. *Anal.* Calcd. for $C_9H_{11}NO_2\cdot{}^1/_2H_2O$: C, 62.05; H, 6.94; N, 8.04. Found: C, 62.35; H, 6.95; N, 8.12. When dried at 90° under the same conditions it loses the water of crystallization. [f] 4% solution in 5 *N* HCl. [g] 2% aqueous solution. [h] 0.5% aqueous solution. [i] 2% solution in 1 *N* HCl.

Preparation of L- and D-Methionine from 1 Mmole of DL-Methionine.—The oxidation of 149 mg. of DL-methionine was conducted in a 125-ml. Warburg vessel in the presence of one-tenth the volume of solvents, buffers, and amount of respective enzymes described above for the larger preparations. At the end of the oxidative reaction, the dialysis step was undertaken as above and the combined dialysates from either the L- or D-amino acid oxidase reaction treated successively on Dowex-50 and Dowex-1 resin columns as described above for D-leucine. The yield of D-methionine was 69.6 mg. (93%) and of L-methionine 63.0 mg. (85%).

(3) A. Meister, L. Levintow, R. B. Kingsley and J. P. Greenstein, *J. Biol. Chem.*, **192**, 535 (1951).

(14) H. Leuchs and W. Geiger, *Ber.*, **41**, 1731 (1908).

(19) All of the racemic amino acids employed herein were recrystallized before use.

(20) Catalase was omitted in the preparation of the D-isomers of aspartic acid, glutamic acid, histidine, alloisoleucine, lysine and methionine.

(21) For more insoluble amino acids the quantity of water employed for dialysis was considerably increased.

(22) M. Bergmann and L. Zervas, *Z. physiol. Chem.*, **152**, 282 (1926); **172**, 277 (1927); S. M. Birnbaum, M. Winitz and J. P. Greenstein, *Arch. Biochem. Biophys.*, **60**, 496 (1956).

(23) The eluate from the acid Dowex-50 column contains yellowish impurities which seemingly cannot be removed readily from the amino acid, and which are essentially degradation products of the D-amino acid oxidase preparation. These contaminants are removed on the Dowex-1 resin column.

(24) L-Allohydroxyproline treated in the same way yielded an epimeric mixture (app. 1:1) of L-allohydroxyproline and D-hydroxyproline with $[\alpha]^{25}_D$ +7.4° (*c* 2, H_2O).

Ref. 30

Preparation of compounds

Preparation of d-*lysine by the bacterial decarboxylase.* Gale & Epps (1943) have shown that the purified cell-free preparation of lysine decarboxylase obtained from *Bact. cadaveris* is stereochemically specific for *l*-lysine; they have also demonstrated that the reaction goes almost to completion and is not inhibited by the *d*-isomer. This method has been adapted to preparative work. *d*-Lysine was separated from cadaverine by benzoylation (Udransky & Baumann, 1889) and the dibenzoyl-*d*-lysine was then hydrolyzed to the free amino-acid. It was found that the preparations of *d*-lysine thus obtained contained small amounts—usually about 3–4%—of the *l*-isomer; this is probably due not so much to the incompleteness of the enzymic reaction as to a slight racemization during the benzoylation.

An extract of the acetone-dried tissues of the organism was adsorbed on alumina as described by Gale & Epps (1943); for preparative purposes the centrifuged alumina, suspended in phosphate buffer, was used as such. The activity of the enzyme was estimated manometrically and the amount of enzyme suspension used was twice as much as would be required to finish the reaction, with the amount of substrate taken, in 30 min.

To the enzyme alumina suspension (100 ml.) was added 0·25M-phosphate of pH 6·0 (700 ml.) containing *dl*-lysine hydrochloride (2 g.). The mixture was shaken at 37° for 90 min.; an estimation with fresh enzyme on a sample of the mixture indicated that no *l*-lysine was then left in the solution. The alumina was then filtered off and the filtrate made alkaline to phenolphthalein with $Ba(OH)_2$; the precipitate of $Ba_3(PO_4)_2$ was filtered off and well washed with boiling water. The combined filtrate and washings were made neutral with H_2SO_4, and the $BaSO_4$ was filtered off and washed. The solution was then evaporated to dryness *in vacuo*, the residue was taken up in water, and benzoylation with benzoyl chloride (9·2 g.) and N-NaOH (160 ml.) was then carried out in the usual way. Dibenzoyl-cadaverine, which precipitated during the reaction, was filtered off; the filtrate was then extracted with chloroform and acidified. The precipitate, which consisted of benzoic acid and dibenzoyl-lysine, was filtered off and dried. The dry material was extracted with boiling ligroin and the residue dissolved in warm acetone. On careful addition of water, and cooling, dibenzoyl-*d*-lysine of m.p. 145° was obtained. This was hydrolyzed by boiling with 20% HCl for 8 hr. Benzoic acid was then removed by filtration and extraction with ether, and the aqueous solution concentrated to dryness *in vacuo*. The residue was taken up in ethanol, and addition of pyridine precipitated the monohydrochloride, which was recrystallized from aqueous ethanol. The yield was 45% of the amount of *d*-lysine used. It gave N, 15·3 (calc. 15·3) and $[\alpha]_D$ (5% HCl, $c = 2·1$) = −14·7°. The latter compares with a value of −15·6° obtained by Berg (1936*b*); if the optical purity of Berg's preparation is accepted, it follows that *d*-lysine obtained by this method contains about 3% of the *l*-isomer.

e) Fermentation [31, 32.]

Finally, L-alanine, L-arginine, L-aspartic acid, L-citrulline, L-glutamic acid, L-glutamine, L-glutathione, L-histidine, L-homoserine, L-isoleucine, L-leucine, L-lysine, L-methionine, L-ornithine, L-phenylalanine, L-proline, L-serine, L-threonine, L-tryptophane, L-tyrosine and L-valine are all produced by fermentation procedures industrially. (Ajinomoto Company, Tokyo, Japan, and Kyowa Kakko, Kogyo Company, Tokyo, Japan).

REFERENCES

1. I. Chibata, in "Synthetic Production and Utilization of Amino Acids," pages 17-51, Kodansha Ltd., Tokyo, Japan (1974).
2. J.R. Mohrig and S.M. Shapiro, J. Chem. Ed., 53, 586 (1976).
3. J.P. Greenstein and M. Winitz, "Chemistry of The Amino Acids," Vol. 1., pages 733ff, Wiley, New York, N.Y. (1961).
4. J.B. Jones and J.F. Beck, in "Techniques of Chemistry," Vol. X, Part 1, pages 193ff, Wiley, New York, N.Y. (1976).
5. H.B. Milne and C.-H. Peng, J. Am. Chem. Soc., 79, 645 (1957).
6. C.Niemann and M.M. Rapport, J. Am. Chem. Soc., 68, 1671 (1946).
7. J.P. Greenstein and M. Winitz, "Chemistry of The Amino Acids," Vol. 1, pages 735ff, Wiley, New York, N.Y. (1961); J. B. Jones and J.F. Beck, in "Techniques of Chemistry," Volume X, Part 1, pages 116ff., Wiley, New York, N.Y. (1976).
8. H.J. Huang, R.J. Foster and C. Niemann, J. Am. Chem. Soc., 74, 105 (1952).
9. J.P. Greenstein, Methods Enzymol., 3, 554 (1957).
10. R. Marshall, M. Winitz, S.M. Birnbaum and J.P. Greenstein, J. Am. Chem. Soc., 79, 4538 (1957).
11. J.P. Greenstein and M. Winitz, "Chemistry of The Amino Acids," Vols. 2,3, Wiley, New York, N.Y. (1961).
12. C. Neuberg and I. Mandl, Enzymologia, 14, 128 (1950).
13. K. Michi and H. Nonaka, J. Agr. Chem. Soc. Japan, 18, 343 (1954); K. Michi and H. Nonaka, ibid., 19, 153 (1955); K. Michi and H. Tsuda, J. Agr. Chem. Soc. Japan, 21, 18 (1957); S. Jamada, I. Chibata and S. Yamada, J. Pharm. Soc. Japan, 75, 113 (1955); I. Chibata and S. Yamada, ibid., 21, 58 (1957); I. Chibata, T. Ishikawa and S. Yamada, Bull. Agr. Chem. Soc. Japan, 21, 304 (1957).
14. Y. Kameda, E. Toyoura, Y. Kimura and H. Yamazoe, Nature, 169, 1016 (1952); Y. Kameda, T. Toyoura and K. Matsui, J. Pharm. Soc. Japan, 78, 202 (1958); Y. Kameda, E. Toyoura and Y. Kimura, Nature, 181, 1225 (1958); M. Sugie and H. Suzuki, Agr. Biol. Chem., 44, 1089 (1980).
15. I. Chibata and T. Osa, Bull. Agr. Chem. Soc. Japan, 23, 370 (1959).
16. Reference 3 above, Vol. 3, page 2173.
17. C.G. Baker and H.A. Sober, J. Am. Chem. Soc., 75, 4058 (1953).
18. I. Chibata, T. Ishikawa and S. Yamada, Bull. Agr. Chem. Soc. Japan, 21, 291, 300, 304 (1957).
19. T. Tosa, T. Mori, N. Fuse, and I. Chibata, Enzymologia, 31, 214 (1966).
20. T. Tosa, T. Mori, N. Fuse, and I. Chibata, Enzymologia, 31, 225 (1966).
21. T. Tosa, T. Mori, N. Fuse, and I. Chibata, Enzymologia, 32, 153 (1967).
22. T. Tosa, T. Mori, N. Fuse, and I. Chibata, Biotechnol. Bioend., 9, 603 (1967).
23. T. Tosa, T. Mori, N. Fuse, and I. Chibata, Agr. Biol. Chem., 33, 1047 (1969).
24. T. Tosa, T. Mori, and I. Chibata, Agr. Biol. Chem., 33, 1053 (1969).
25. T. Tosa, T. Mori, and I. Chibata, Enzymologia, 40, 49 (1971).
26. T. Tosa, T. Mori, and I. Chibata, J. Ferment. Technol., 49, 522 (1971).
27. T. Sato, T. Mori, T. Tosa, and I. Chibata, Arch. Biochem. Biophys., 147, 788 (1971).
28. T. Mori, T. Sato, T. Tosa and I. Chibata, Enzymologia, 43, 213 (1972).
29. J.R. Parikh, J.P. Greenstein, M. Winitz and S.M. Birnbaum, J. Am. Chem. Soc., 80, 953 (1958).
30. M.N. Camien, L.E. McClure and M.S. Dunn, Arch. Biochem., 28, 220 (1950); A. Neuberger and F. Sanger, Biochem, J., 37, 515 (1943); ibid., 38, 125 (1944).
31. D. Perlman, Chemtech, 210 (1974).
32. D. Perlman, Chemtech, 434 (1977).
33. C-S. Chen, Y. Fujimoto and C.J. Sih, J. Am. Chem. Soc., 103, 3580 (1981).

SECTION 5

OPTICAL PURITY OF ACIDS AND LACTONES

During the course of a resolution by classical chemical methods, i.e., via the formation of diastereomers of differing solubilities, if one observed that the specific rotation or melting point of the more insoluble salt reached a constant value following repeated crystallizations, or that the specific rotation of the finally obtained enantiomers reached constant and equal values, it was assumed that the resolution was complete, that is, that the enantiomers were optically pure. Though the above criteria have, in many cases, resulted in the experimentalist obtaining material of high optical purity, there are many cases where the use of the above criteria yielded material of less than complete optical purity.[1]

In recent years, a number of methods have been developed which allow one with accuracy to determine the optical purity of the enantiomers obtained as a result of resolution or asymmetric synthesis. Raban and Mislow,[2] in their classic review, have discussed these methods in detail and divided them into four categories. These categories are:

Method 1. Determination of optical purity after separation of enantiomers.

Method 2. Determination of optical purity without separation of enantiomers.

Method 3. Determination of optical purity by conversion to diastereomers with separation.

Method 4. Determination of optical purity by conversion to diastereomers without separation.

Recently, an additional method has been reported. We shall denote it as:

Method 5. Determination of optical purity by converting the original enantiomeric mixture into other chiral compounds with the same enantiomeric ratio.

These categories shall be used here to summarize the reported methods for determining the optical purities of chiral acids and lactones.[3]

1. S.H. Wilen, "Topics in Stereochemistry," Volume 6, p. 107ff, J. Wiley, N.Y. (1971).
2. M. Raban and K. Mislow, "Topics in Stereochemistry," Volume 2, p. 199ff, J. Wiley, N.Y. (1967).
3. For additional examples illustrating Methods 1 and 3, see E. Gil-Av and D. Nurok in "Advances in Chromatography," Volume 10, M. Dekker, New York (1974).

METHOD 1. Determination of Optical Purity After Separation of Enantiomers

Compound Class	Reference
Carboxylic acid	J.A. Berson and D.A. Ben-Efraim, J. Am. Chem. Soc., 81, 4083 (1959).
α-Amino acid	R.B. Loftfield and E.A. Eigner, Biochim. Biophys. Acta, 130, 449 (1966).
α-Amino acid	I.B. Rubin and G. Goldstein, Anal. Biochem., 33, 244 (1970).
α-Amino acid	W. Parr and P.Y. Howard, Angew. Chem. Int. Ed., 11, 529 (1972).
α-Amino acid	M.J. Hardy, Anal. Biochem., 57, 529 (1974).
α-Amino acid*	C.P. Berg and F.A. Rodden, Anal. Biochem., 71, 214 (1976).
Barbiturates	J. Knabe and V. Gradmann, Arch. Pharm., (Weinheim), 306, 306 (1973).

*For a discussion of enzymatic methods for determing optical purity of amino acids, see J.P. Greenstein and M. Winitz, "Chemistry of the Amino Acids," J. Wiley and Sons, New York, N.Y., 1961, Vol. 2, pp. 1734-1749.

METHOD 2. Determination of Optical Purity Without Separation of Enantiomers

Compound Class	Reference
α-Amino acid	W.H. Pirkle and S.D. Beare, J. Am. Chem. Soc., 91, 5150 (1969).
α-Amino acid	Y. Fujii, Bull. Chem. Soc. Japan, 47, 2856 (1974).
α-Amino acid	Y. Fujii and H. Yoneda, Chem. Lett., 43 (1974).
α-Amino acid	Y. Fujii, S. Hirasawa and S. Takahashi, Chem. Lett. 817 (1976).
α-Amino acid	F. Yasuhara, K. Kabuto and S. Yamaguchi, Tetrahedron Lett., 4289 (1978).
Ester	C-S. Chen, Y. Fujimoto and C.J. Sih, J. Am. Chem. Soc., 103, 3580 (1981).

METHOD 2. Determination of Optical Purity Without Separation of Enantiomers (continued)

Compound Class	Reference
Carboxylic acid	J-P. Guette, L. Lacombe and A. Horeau, Compt. Rend., 267C, 166 (1968).
Carboxylic acid	A. Horeau and J-P. Guette, Compt. Rend., 267C, 257 (1968).
Carboxylic acid	O. Korver and M. van Gorkom, Tetrahedron, 30, 4041 (1974).
Carboxylic acid	K. Kabuto, F. Yasuhara and S. Yamaguchi, Tetrahedron Lett., 307 (1980).
2-Hydroxy acid	W.H. Pirkle and S.D. Beare, Tetrahedron Lett., 2579 (1968).
3-Hydroxy acid	E.B. Dongala, A. Solladie-Cavallo and G. Solladie, Tetrahedron Lett., 4233 (1972).
3-Hydroxy acid	C. Mioskowski and G. Solladie, Tetrahedron, 29, 3669 (1973).
3-Hydroxy acid	A. Tai, M. Nakahata, T. Harada and Y. Izumi, Chem. Lett., 1125 (1980).
5-Methoxy acid	A.I. Meyers and C.E. Whitten, Tetrahedron Lett., 1947 (1976).
Lactone	W.H. Pirkle and D. Sikkenga, J. Org. Chem., 42, 1370 (1977).
Lactone	W.H. Pirkle and P.E. Adams, J. Org. Chem., 45, 4111 (1980).
Glyceride	J. Bus, C.M. Lok and A. Groenewegen, Chem. Phys. Lipids, 16, 123 (1976).

METHOD 3. Determination of Optical Purity By Conversion To Diastereomers With Separation

Compound Class	Reference
Carboxylic acid	R. Eberhardt, C. Glotzmann, H. Lehner and K. Schlogl, Etrahedron Lett., 4365 (1974).
Monoterpenoid acid	B.J. Bergot, R.J. Anderson, D.A. Schooley and C.A. Henrick, J. Chromatog., 155, 97 (1978).

METHOD 3. Determination of Optical Purity By Conversion To Diastereomers With Separation (continued)

Compound Class	Reference
α-Amino acid	R.B. Loftfield and E.A. Eigner, Biochim. Biophys. Acta, 130, 449 (1966).
α-Amino acid	J.M. Manning and S. Moore, J. Biol. Chem., 243, 5591 (1968).
α-Amino acid	J.W. Westley and B. Halpern, J. Org. Chem., 33, 3978 (1968).
α-Amino acid	G.E. Pollock and A.H. Kawauchi, Anal. Chem., 40, 1356 (1968).
α-Amino acid	A.V. Barooshian, M.J. Lautenschleger and W.G. Harris, Anal. Biochem., 44, 543 (1971).
α-Amino acid	A.V. Barooshian, M.J. Lautenschleger, J.M. Greenwood and W.G. Harris, Anal. Biochem., 49, 602 (1972).
α-Amino acid	M. Hasegawa and I. Matsubara, Anal. Biochem., 63, 308 (1975).
α-Amino acid	N.L. Benoiton, K. Kuroda, S.T. Cheung and F.M.F. Chen, Can. J. Biochem., 57, 776 (1979).
α-Amino acid	A.M. Kolodziejczyk and A. Arendt, Pol. J. Chem., 53, 1017 (1979).
2-Hydroxy acid	J.W. Westley and B. Halpern, J. Org. Chem., 33, 3978 (1968).
2-Hydroxy acid	K. Tatsumi, Y. Kishimoto and C. Hignite, Arch. Biochem. Biophys., 165, 656 (1974).
2-Hydroxy acid	K. Mori and H. Iwasawa, Tetrahedron, 36, 2209 (1980).
Mandelic acid	I.W. Wainer, J. Chromatog., 202, 478 (1980).
3-Hydroxy acid	K. Tatsumi, Y. Kishimoto and C. Hignite, Arch. Biochem. Biophys., 165, 656 (1974).
N-Methyl-2-Amino acid	J.R. Coggins and N.L. Benoiton, J. Chromatog., 52, 251 (1970).
N-Methyl-2-Amino acid	S.T. Cheung and N.L. Benoiton, Can. J. Chem., 55, 916 (1977).
Carboxylic acid	M. Miyakado, N. Ohno, Y. Okuno, M. Hirano, K. Fujimoto and H. Yoshioka, Agr. Biol. Chem., 39, 267 (1975).

METHOD 4. Determination of Optical Purity By Conversion To Diastereomers Without Separation

Compound Class	Reference
Carboxylic acid	M. Miyakado, N. Ohno, Y. Okuno, M. Hirano, K. Fujimoto and H. Yoshioka, Agr. Biol. Chem., 39, 267 (1975).
Carboxylic acid	W.T. Hoeve and H. Wynberg, J. Org. Chem., 45, 2754 (1980).
2-Hydroxy acid	K. Mori and H. Iwasawa, Tetrahedron, 36, 2209 (1980).

METHOD 5. Determination of Optical Purity By Converting The Original Enantiomeric Mixture Into Other Chiral Compounds With The Same Enantiomeric Ratio

Compound Class	Reference
Carboxylic acid	R.W. Lang and H.J. Hansen, Helv. Chim. Acta, 62, 1025 (1979).
Carboxylic acid	W.S. Johnson, B.E. McCarry, R.L. Markezich and S.G. Boots, J. Am. Chem. Soc., 102, 352 (1980).
Lactones	I.J. Jakovac and J.B. Jones, J. Org. Chem., 44, 2165 (1979).
Lactones	C-S. Chen, Y. Fujimoto and C.J. Sih, J. Am. Chem. Soc., 103, 3580 (1981).
δ-Lactone	G. Saucy, R. Borer, D.P. Trullinger, J.B. Jones and K.P. Lok, J. Org. Chem., 42, 3206 (1977).

SECTION 6

THE ASYMMETRIC SYNTHESIS OF CARBOXYLIC ACIDS

A General Overview

Spiro Alexandratos

University of Tennessee
Department of Chemistry
Knoxville, Tennessee 37916

Introduction 1081

Asymmetric Hydrogenation Reactions 1082
- A. Hydrogenation Catalysts: Phosphine Ligand Structure 1082
- B. Hydrogenation Catalysts: Metal Chelate Structure 1083
- C. Mechanism of the Hydrogenation Reaction 1084
- D. Work with other than Rh Metal and Phosphine Ligands 1085
- E. Induction of Chirality through Optical Activity Centered at the Metal 1085
- F. Heterogeneous Catalysts 1085

Asymmetric Synthesis Using Chiral Reagents 1086

References 1088

The Compilation of Data: Explanatory Note 1089

Data 1090
- Monodentate phosphine ligands 1090
- Biodentate phosphines:
  - The DIOP ligand and analogues 1091
  - Pyrrolidine-based ligands 1094
  - Symmetrical dimethano ligands 1099
  - Other phosphine-hydrocarbon ligands 1102
  - Phosphinoamino, phosphinoxy ligands 1107
  - Comparative studies 1111
- Use of Raney Ni 1113
- Use of Pd metal 1114
- Use of chiral reagents (with no metal catalyst) 1115

THE ASYMMETRIC SYNTHESIS OF CARBOXYLIC ACIDS

A General Overview

INTRODUCTION

Currently, optical resolution procedures may be considered to comprise the method of choice for the synthesis of chiral compounds: the researcher will synthesize a racemic mixture of the desired optically active compound and then carry out the resolution procedure which will give the highest optical yield. A more efficient method would be, of course, to synthesize the optically active compound directly. In this regard, the study of asymmetric synthesis has made significant contributions. From an initially achiral compound, a chiral product can be synthesized wherein one enantiomer is present in great excess thus obviating any need for an optical resolution. The methods for accomplishing this usually fall into the general categories of either a utilization of an optically active catalyst or the utilization of an optically active reagent which is temporarily bound to the achiral reactant. While it is true that optical resolution procedures will continue to be used for some time to come, it is also true that asymmetric syntheses will gain widespread use as the methodologies improve and become more economical. It is these methodologies which this review examines. Only methods which provide at least a 60% excess of one enantiomer over the racemic pair are presented here with values less than 60% reported only when necessary to, say, examine a trend. Results are reported as found in the original literature in terms of % optical purity (or optical yield) or in terms of % enantiomeric excess (% ee). The terms, though sometimes used as if they were interchangeable, are actually distinct. The % ee does not depend on optical rotation measurements but, rather, is determined by reacting the product mix with an enantiomerically pure reagent and then having the resulting diastereomeric compounds analyzed by, say NMR, or separated analytically. The optical yield, on the other hand, is defined in terms of the ratio of the specific rotation of the purified product mix and the pure enantiomer:

$$\text{optical purity (optical yield)} = \frac{\text{specific rotation of the enantiomeric mixture}}{\text{specific rotation of pure enantiomer}} \times 100$$

Determination of the optical purity presupposes that the specific rotation of the pure enantiomer is known; very often as a result, the optical purity is reported based on the highest specific rotation reported to date for the enantiomer and is thus subject to revision as more work on the purification of the enantiomer is done.

A number of reviews exist which examine selected aspects of asymmetric synthesis.[1-12]

ASYMMETRIC HYDROGENATION REACTIONS

A good deal of work in the area of asymmetric synthesis has been in the study of hydrogenation reactions. This is due in large measure to Wilkinson's discovery of phosphinated Rh catalysts for homogeneous hydrogenation reactions,[13] followed by the discovery that chiral phosphine ligands can hydrogenate prochiral olefins into chiral products with best results obtainable using substituted α-acylaminoacrylic acids.[14-16] The use of Rh as the central metal ion coordinated to various phosphine ligands with acrylic acid substrates has led to some very promising results as will be shown later in this review.

In a general sense, the reaction of interest for hydrogenation is

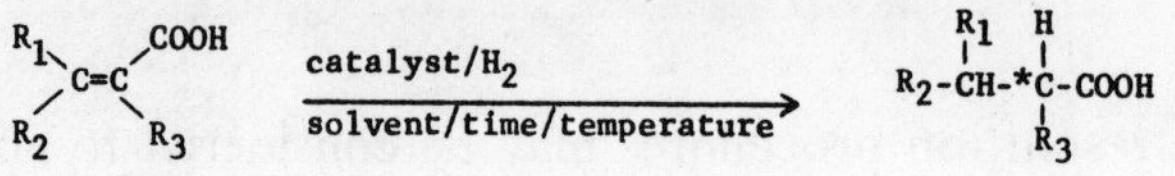

R_1 = alkyl; aryl
R_2 = H
R_3 = NHCO (alkyl,aryl); alkyl; aryl

A. *Hydrogenation Catalysts: Phosphine Ligand Structure*

Most studies have emphasized Rh(I) catalysts with Ru(II) also receiving some attention.[4] The most important variable determining enantiomeric excess has been found to be the phosphine ligands attached to the metal as they strongly affect the substrate-metal coordination through steric and possibly electronic interactions. Before examining the nature of the catalyst structure, note that the phosphine ligands can be placed into the following categories:

(a) Phosphines with chirality centered at phosphorus, e.g.,

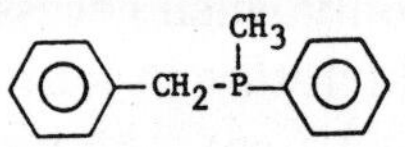

Benzylmethylphenylphosphine

(BMPP)

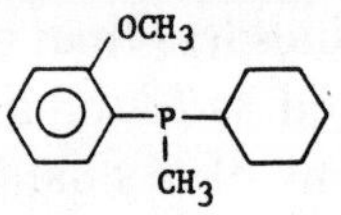

Anisylcyclohexylmethylphosphine

(ACMP)

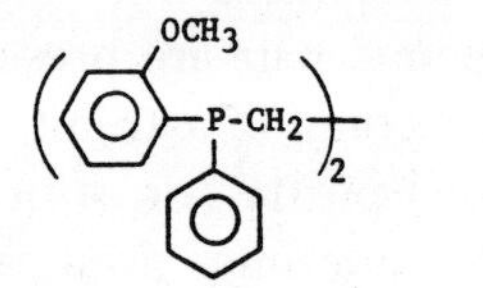

1,2-Bis(anisylphenylphosphino)ethane

(DIPAMP)

The straightforward synthesis of ACMP has been described by Knowles, et al.[6]

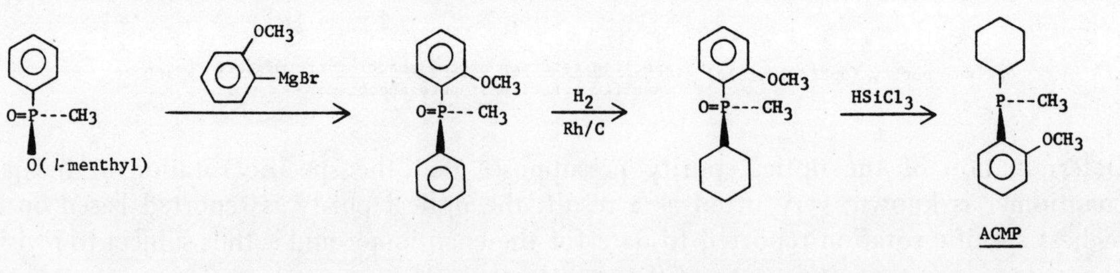

With α-acylaminoacrylic acid substrates, (R)p-ACMP gave L-amino acids upon hydrogenation and (S)p-ACMP gave D-amino acids. DIPAMP was readily synthesized by coupling the Grignard product (o-anisylmethylphenylphosphine oxide) and reducing to the phosphine.[17]

(b) Phosphines with chirality centered at carbon, e.g.,

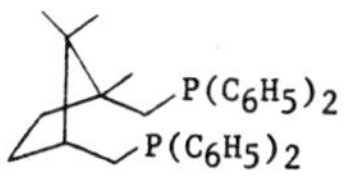

(+)-1,2,2-trimethyl-1,3-bis(diphenylphosphino-methyl)cyclopentane

(CAMPHOS)

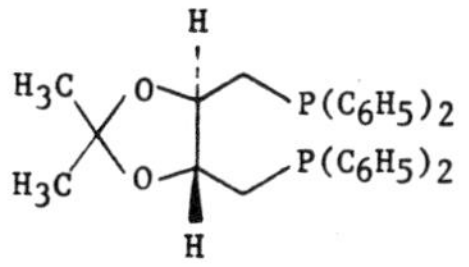

2,3-O-isopropylidene-2,3-dihydroxy-1,4-bis(diphenyl-phosphino)butane

[(-)-DIOP]

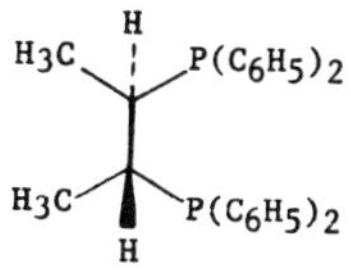

2,3-bis(diphenyl-phosphino)butane

(S,S)-CHIRAPHOS

The primary advantage of these ligands is that they are synthesized from readily available starting materials which are optically active: CAMPHOS from (+)-camphoric acid,[18] DIOP from (+) or (-)-tartaric acid,[19] and CHIRAPHOS from 2R,3R-butanediol.[20]

(c) Phosphines which are chiral at both phosphorous and carbon, e.g.,

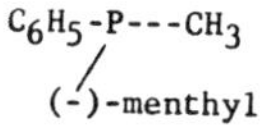

(R)$_P$ or (S)$_P$-((-)-menthyl) methylphenylphosphine

The configuration of the final product seems to depend more on the configuration at the P than at the chiral C.[21]

(d) Phosphines which are chiral due to atropisomerism, e.g.,

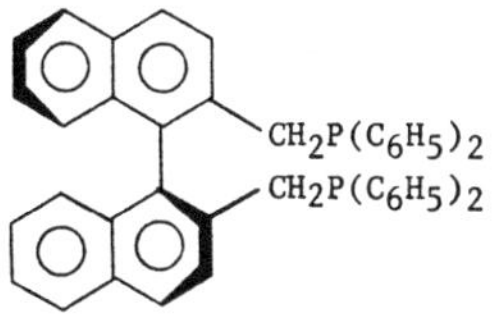

1,1'-Bi-2-naphthylbis(diphenylmethylphosphine)

(NAPHOS)

Such phosphines require the binaphthyl system to be resolved prior to complexation with the metal.[22]

B. *Hydrogenation Catalysts: Metal Chelate Structure*

In Rh(I) catalyzed hydrogenation reactions, two phosphine groups are complexed to the metal; the phosphine groups can belong to two separate molecules (e.g. ACMP) or to one molecule (e.g. DIOP). The phosphine groups displace two olefinic bonds that the Rh(I) is complexed to originally:

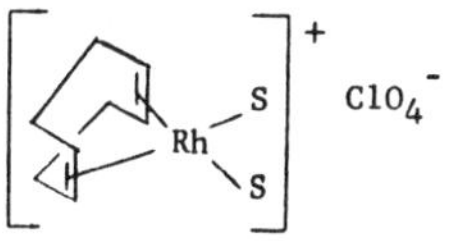

Rh(ClO$_4$)(1,5-COD) precursor

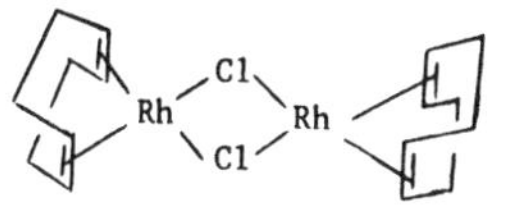

[RhCl(1,5-COD)]$_2$ precursor

(COD = cyclooctadiene)
(S = solvent)

↓ CHIRAPHOS

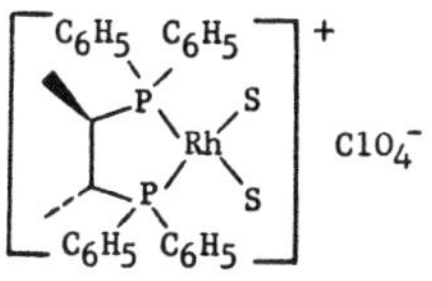

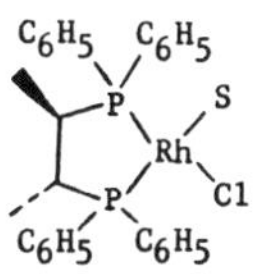

Both the solvent used and the size of the ring formed by the ligand-Rh moiety are important variables. In studying the solvent effect, Kagan noted that for a given α-acylaminoacrylic acid, changing the solvent from alcohol:benzene to benzene alone resulted in a complete reversal of the enantiomer formed as product.[23] Kagan also found that the effect of ring size on catalyst activity as measured by chemical yield (not optical yield) was pronounced in the hydrogenation of α-acetamidocinnamic acid (ethanol:benzene solvent); for monodentate and bidentate $(C_6H_5)_2P\text{-}R\text{-}P(C_6H_5)_2$ the variation found was

$$-(CH_2)_4-,\ -(CH_2)_5- > DIOP > -CH_2OCH_2- > P(C_6H_5)_3 > P(Et)(C_6H_5)_2,\ -(CH_2)_3-,\ -(CH_2)_6- > -(CH_2)_2- > -CH{=}CH-$$

with $(C_6H_5)_2P\text{-}CH_2\text{-}P(C_6H_5)_2$ being inactive.[24]

C. *Mechanism of the Hydrogenation Reaction*

Halpern and co-workers have done a great deal to elucidate the mechanism of the hydrogenation reaction.[25,26] Initial addition of the olefin to the RhL_4 (L=ligand) phosphine intermediates shown above (thus displacing solvent), followed by addition of H_2 to yield an octahedral complex, yields the chiral product upon cis-addition of the H_2 to the double bond on the side facing the metal. With α-acylaminoacrylic acids, coordination to the metal is not only through the olefinic bond but also via the amide oxygen which probably contributes to the large stereospecificity observed in the reaction. The reaction sequence may be schematically depicted as:

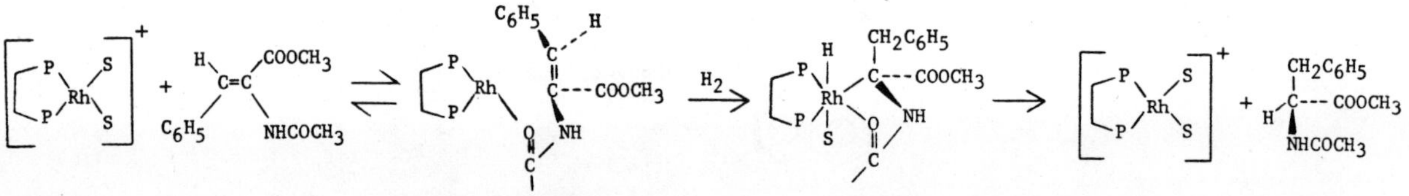

(I) (II)

When using the achiral 1,2-(diphenylphosphino)ethane (diphos) as ligand, II was observed at -78°C via ^1H, ^{31}P and ^{13}C NMR and the transformation of I to II determined to be the rate determining step.[25] I has been observed via NMR when using CHIRAPHOS as the ligand.[26]

A number of factors are important in obtaining a high enantiomeric excess. Knowles reasoned that an anisyl group was important on an optically active phosphine ligand in conjunction with an α-acylaminoacrylic acid substrate due to a weak interaction between the methoxy group and the amide hydrogen which would increase the rigidity of the intermediate.[5] Secondary electronic interactions are thought to make the α-acylamino-acrylic acids more facile substrates for hydrogenation than simple olefins, though their exact nature is still open to question.[27] Increased conformational rigidity of the intermediate is also thought to be central to the success of CHIRAPHOS in giving chiral amino acid products with 83-100% optical yield; the resulting five-membered ring is locked into one conformation by two methyl groups in the equatorial position.[20] In DIOP-type systems, the dihedral angles θ_1 and θ_2 were found to be important determiners of product optical purity though neither the oxygen atoms nor the gem-dimethyl group were found to be crucial for high purity.[28]

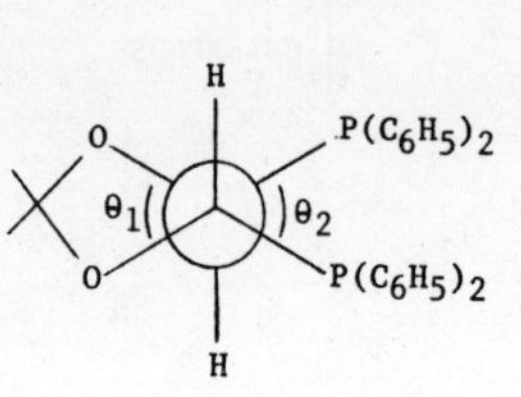

At least for the DIOP system, free acid substrates usually gave higher optical yields than the corresponding esters, pointing again to the importance of secondary interactions increasing the conformational rigidity of the intermediate.[29]

D. *Work with other than Rh Metal and Phosphine Ligands*

Studies have emphasized the phosphine ligands as the means of achieving 100% optical purity with only moderate effort aimed at examining metals other than Rh. In this respect, work employing ruthenium has been reported.[4] Along with DIOP, sulfoxide ligands have been complexed with the Ru:

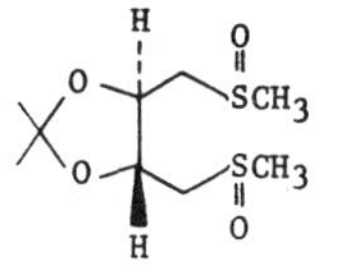

2,3-O-isopropylidene-2,3-dihydroxy-1,4-bis(methylsulfinyl)butane

(-)-DIOS

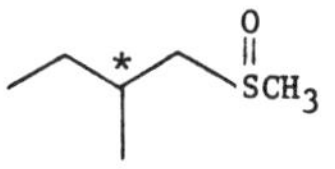

(S,R;S,S)-(+)-2-methylbutylmethyl sulfoxide

MBMSO

[chiral at carbon]

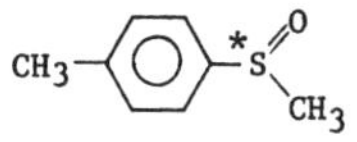

R-(+)-methyl-para-tolyl sulfoxide

MPTSO

[chiral at sulfur]

The DIOP complex provides the most active Ru catalyst giving optical yields up to 60% with carboxylic acid substrates.[30]

E. *Induction of Chirality through Optical Activity Centered at the Metal*

Work in synthesizing optically active organometallic catalysts chiral at the transition metal ion rather than the ligand has been initiated.[11,31,32] If a catalyst of the form III could be synthesized, it could, in principle,

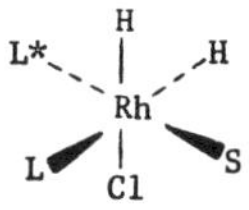

S = solvent

III

be resolved when L=L*=$P(C_6H_5)_3$ given that it has no plane of symmetry. Such compounds may not be configurationally stable, though, and it may be necessary to have at least one L group be an optically active phosphine in order to better control the configuration about the metal through optical induction. The concept remains to be applied to asymmetric hydrogenation.

F. *Heterogeneous Catalysts*

All of the work described so far has had in common the fact that the catalysis was carried out under homogeneous conditions. In fact, work has progressed in heterogenizing the catalysts thus gaining the principal benefit that the catalyst can easily be recovered from the product mix and re-used.[3] Heterogeneous catalysis has involved using a chiral support (e.g., silk fibroin)[33] and hydrogenating with, say, a Pd catalyst, or using a chiral phosphine ligand and supporting it on an achiral backbone. The most common supports are styrene

crosslinked with divinylbenzene (DVB) and various aluminosilicates (see compilation for details).

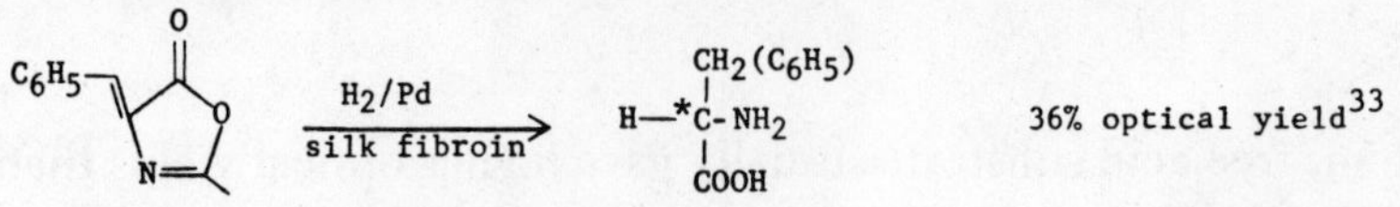

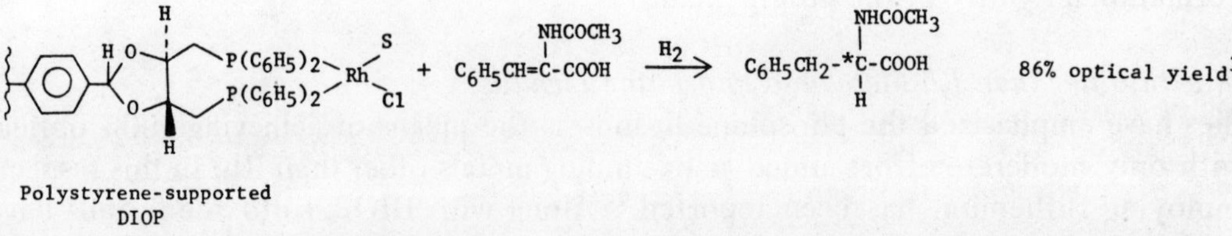

The main difficulty with polymer-supported catalysts is inaccessibility of the groups in the inner part of the polymer should the polymer not swell in the solvent chosen for reaction; this problem can usually be remedied by making the support compatible with the solvent usually by changing the polar nature of the polymer via copolymerization with other monomers.[34] Non-enantioselective catalysts, such as Raney Ni have also been modified into optically active catalysts by having them adsorb chiral amino acids or hydroxy acids such as tartaric acid.[9,35]

ASYMMETRIC SYNTHESES USING CHIRAL REAGENTS

Methods which have been taken to the point of routinely giving product with more than 60% enantiomeric excess involve the process of bonding a chiral reagent to a given moiety, having it induce asymmetry on the moiety in a subsequent reaction, and then removing the reagent to yield a chiral product. The following is intended as a short summary of the methods that will be considered in the compilation; detailed results are to be found there.

A method has been developed by Meyers and co-workers involving an optically active oxazoline which induces asymmetry on a methylene moiety in a subsequent electrophilic reaction; hydrolysis of the oxazoline yields a chiral carboxylic acid.[12,36,37]

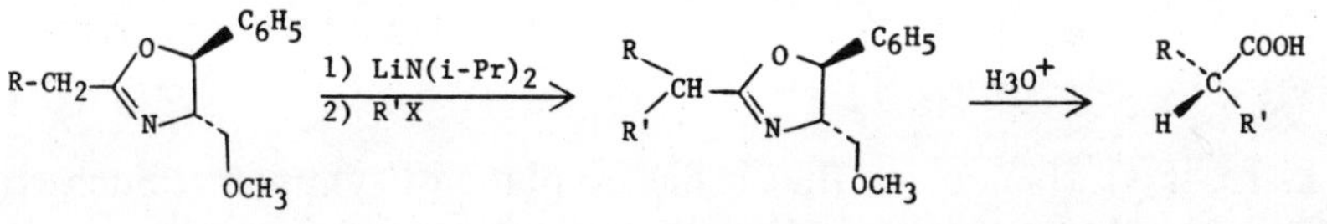

Product with up to 98% ee is obtained.

Along the same lines, Schollkopf and co-workers have synthesized optically active imidazolinones[38] and pyrazines[39] from chiral amines which can then be alkylated and hydrolyzed to give chiral di-substituted α-amino acids in 90-100% enantiomeric excess.

Chiral amines have also been employed in asymmetric halolactonization[40] and asymmetric hydrocyanation[41] reactions by addition to achiral acids and aldehydes respectively. The former yields halolactones and the latter yields Schiff bases which upon eventual hydrolysis yield chiral acids.

The use of chiral amines in transamination reactions to yield optically active α-amino acids from keto-acids is known. Hydrogenation of the addition product between the amine and keto group make this a very straightforward reaction.[8,42]

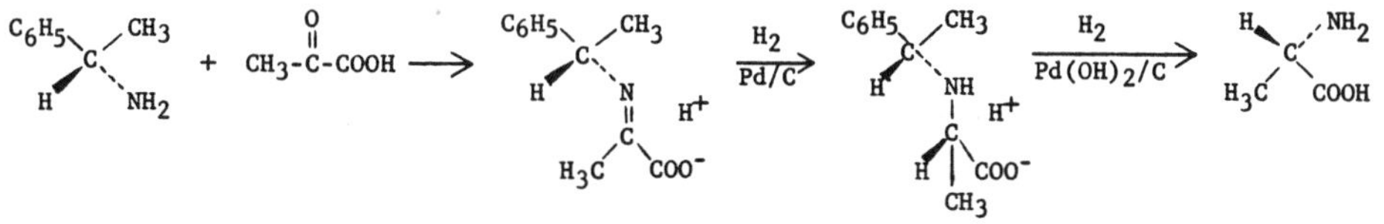

The α-amino acid shown above is formed in 63% ee.

Simple amino acids can be used to synthesize more complex amino acids with the chirality being maintained throughout the transformation. This is accomplished by forming the cyclic dimer of glycine and alanine, adding an aldehyde to the methylene moiety to form an olefinic center, and hydrogenating, with the alanine part of the dipeptide inducing the asymmetry; hydrolysis yields the more complex amino acid.[43] The asymmetric induction can be up to 99%.

REFERENCES

1. R. Pearce, Chem. Soc. Spec. Period. Rep., 11, 176 (1979).
2. a) J.M. Brown, P.A. Chaloner, B.A. Murrer, D. Parker, Am. Chem. Soc. Symp. Ser., 119, 169 (1980).
   b) R.E. Merrill, Chemtech, 118 (1981).
3. B.R. James, Adv. in Organomet. Chem., 17, 319 (1979).
4. B.R. James, R.S. McMillan, R.H. Morris, D.K.W. Wang, Am. Chem. Soc., Adv. in Chem. Ser., 167, 122 (1978).
5. W.S. Knowles, M.J. Sabacky, B.D. Vineyard, Chemtech, 590 (1972).
6. W.S. Knowles, M.J. Sabacky, B.D. Vineyard, Adv. Chem. Ser., 132, 274 (1974).
7. J.D. Morrison, H.S. Mosher, Asymmetric Organic Reactions, Prentice-Hall, Englewood Cliffs, N.J. (1971).
8. D.W. Valentine, J.W. Scott, Synthesis, 329 (1978).
9. M.J. Fish, D.F. Ollis, Catal. Rev.-Sci. Eng., 18, 259 (1978).
10. L. Marko, B. Heil, Catal. Rev., 8, 269 (1973).
11. H. Brunner, Acc. Chem. Res., 12, 250 (1979).
12. A.I. Meyers, Acc. Chem. Res., 11, 375 (1978).
13. J.A. Osborn, F.H. Jardine, J.F. Young, G. Wilkinson, J. Chem. Soc., (A), 1711 (1966).
14. a) L. Horner, H. Buthe, H. Siegel, Tetrahedron Lett., 4023 (1968).
    b) L. Horner, H. Siegel, H. Buthe, Angew. Chem. Int. Ed. Engl., 7, 942 (1968).
15. T.P. Dang, H.B. Kagan, J. Chem. Soc., Chem. Commun., 481 (1971).
16. H.B. Kagan, T.P. Dang, J. Am. Chem. Soc., 94, 6429 (1972).
17. W.S. Knowles, M.J. Sabacky, B.D. Vineyard, B.J. Weinkauff, J. Am. Chem. Soc., 97, 2567 (1975).
18. J.D. Morrison, W.F. Masler, M.K. Neuberg, Adv. Catalysis, 25, 81 (1976).
19. T.P. Dang, H.B. Kagan, J. Chem. Soc., Chem. Commun., 481 (1971).
20. M.D. Fryzuk, B. Bosnich, J. Am. Chem. Soc., 99, 6262 (1977).
21. C. Fisher, H.S. Mosher, Tetrahedron Lett., 2487 (1977).
22. a) K. Tamao, H. Yamamoto, H. Matsumoto, N. Miyake, T. Hayashi, M. Kumada, Tetrahedron Lett., 1389 (1977).
    b) R.H. Grubbs, R.A. DeVries, ibid, 1879 (1977).
23. H.B. Kagan, N. Langlois, T.P. Dang, J. Organomet. Chem., 90, 353 (1975).
24. J.-C. Poulin, T.P. Dang, H.B. Kagan, J. Organomet. Chem., 84, 87 (1975).
25. A.S.C. Chan, J. Halpern, J. Am. Chem. Soc., 102, 838 (1980).
26. A.S.C. Chan, J.J. Pluth, J. Halpern, ibid., 102, 5952 (1980).
27. B.D. Vineyard, W.S. Knowles, M.J. Sabacky, G.L. Bachman, D.J. Weinkauff, J. Am. Chem. Soc., 99, 5946 (1977).
28. R. Glaser, M. Twaik, S. Geresh, J. Blumenfeld, Tetrahedron Lett., 4635 (1977).
29. G. Gelbard, H.B. Kagan, R. Stern, Tetrahedron, 32, 233 (1976).
30. B.R. James, D.K.W. Wang, R.F. Voist, J. Chem. Soc., Chem. Commun., 574 (1975).
31. H. Brunner, Angew. Chem. Int. Ed. Engl., 10, 249 (1971).
32. H. Brunner, Ann. N. Y. Acad. Sci., 239, 213 (1974).
33. S. Akabori, S. Sakurai, Y. Izumi, Y. Fujii, Nature, 178, 323 (1956).
34. N. Takaishi, H. Imai, C.A. Bertelo, J.K. Stille, J. Am. Chem. Soc., 98, 5400 (1976).
35. a) Y. Izumi, Bull. Chem. Soc. Japan, 36, 21 (1963).
    b) Y. Izumi, ibid., 36, 155 (1963).
36. A.I. Meyers, G. Knaus, K. Kamata, M.E. Ford, J. Am. Chem. Soc., 98, 567 (1976).
37. A.I. Meyers, C.E. Whitten, J. Am. Chem. Soc., 97, 1266 (1975).
38. U. Schollkopf, H.H. Hausberg, I. Hoppe, M. Segal, U. Reiter, Angew. Chem. Int. Ed. Engl., 17, 117 (1978).
39. U. Schollkopf, W. Hartwig, U. Groth, Angew. Chem. Int. Ed. Engl., 18, 863 (1979).
40. S. Terashima, S.-S. Jew, K. Koga, Tetrahedron Lett., 4507 (1977).
41. S. Yamada, S. Hashimoto, Chem. Lett., 921 (1976).
42. K. Harada, K. Matsumoto, J. Org. Chem., 32, 1794 (1967).
43. T. Kanmera, S. Lee, H. Aoyagi, N. Izumiya, Tetrahedron Lett., 4483 (1979).

THE COMPILATION OF DATA: EXPLANATORY NOTE

As noted earlier, the concepts summarized involving both chiral catalysts and chiral reagents are explored more fully in the following compilation. While perhaps not fully comprehensive, it does provide a fairly detailed look at the experimental work which has been carried out to date. The compilation is broadly divided according to the type of reaction being carried out with hydrogenation reactions being dealt with first followed by the section on chiral reagents. In each case, the catalyst, the chiral ligand, the substrates, and the experimental conditions are abstracted from the original papers. Where the authors assigned a particular number to a ligand or substrate, it was kept in the compilation; where no number was given, a Roman numeral or upper case letter was employed. The optical yields or enantiomeric excesses and the configuration of the product from each substrate are also listed.

REACTION TYPE: Hydrogenation of α-acylaminoacrylic acids.

CATALYST: Rh(I) complex of anisylcyclohexylmethylphosphine; $[RhCl(1,5\text{-}COD)]_2$ precursor (COD = cyclooctadiene)

LIGAND:

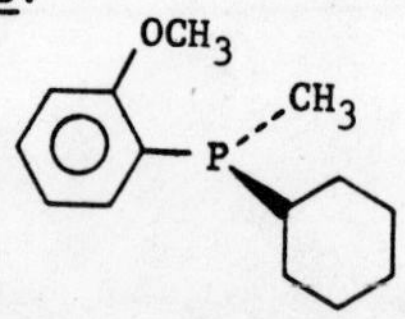

ACMP

SUBSTRATES:

$R^a\text{-}CH\text{=}C(NHCOR^b)\text{-}COOH$

I	R^a = 3-(CH_3O)-4-(OH)C_6H_3,	R^b = C_6H_5
II	R^a = 3-(CH_3O)-4-(OAc)C_6H_3,	R^b = CH_3
III	R^a = C_6H_5	R^b = CH_3
IV	R^a = C_6H_5	R^b = C_6H_5
V	R^a = H	R^b = CH_3

CONDITIONS: Solvent as noted; 25°C (unless otherwise noted) for 3 hrs.; 10 psia H_2 (unless otherwise noted); 0.05% metal

Substrate	Optical Purity,%		Substrate	Optical Purity,%	
I	87	(95% EtOH)	II	88	(i-PrOH)
I	90	(i-PrOH)	III	85	(95% EtOH)
II	77	(MeOH)*	IV	85	(95% EtOH)
II	85	(95% EtOH)	V	60	(95% EtOH)

*50°C; 55 psia; NEt_3 added; substrate/catalyst molar ratio of 3000:1

REFERENCE: W.S. Knowles, M.J. Sabacky, B.D. Vineyard, J. Chem. Soc., Chem. Commun., 10 (1972).

REACTION TYPE: Hydrogenation of substituted acrylic acids.

CATALYST: Rh(I) complex of 1-menthylmethylphenylphosphine; $[RhCl(1,5\text{-}COD)]_2$ precursor

LIGANDS:

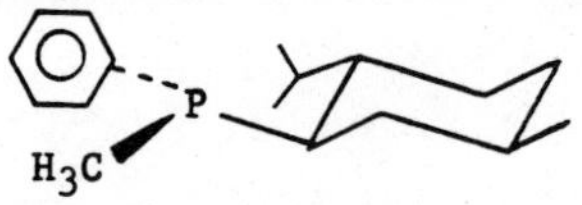

(S)-MMPP

(S)p-1

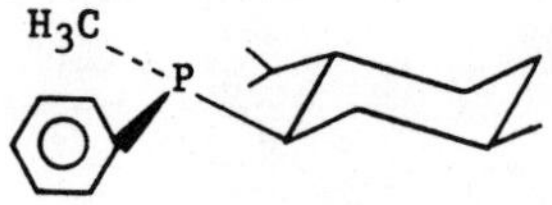

(R)-MMPP

(R)p-2

SUBSTRATES:

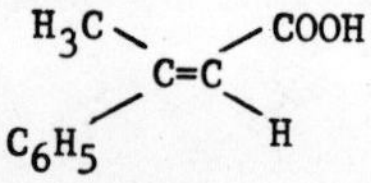

I

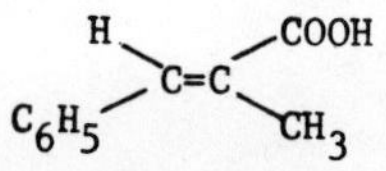

II

$C_6H_5\text{-}CH\text{=}C(NHCOCH_3)\text{-}COOH$

III

$CH_2\text{=}C(CH_2COOH)\text{-}COOH$

IV

CONDITIONS: EtOH/C_6H_6(1:1, v/v); 30°C for 24-48 hrs.; catalyst prereduced with 40 psig H_2 for 1 hr.; substrate/catalyst molar ratio of 75:1; NEt_3 added.

Substrate	Ligand	% asymmetric induction****	Configuration
I	1*	67.1	R
	2**	70.6	S
II	2***	61.4	R
III	2***	43.7	R
IV	2***	52.1	S

* By ^{31}P NMR analysis, MMPP 1 is 98% 1 and 2% 2
** By ^{31}P NMR analysis, MMPP 2 is 87% 2 and 13% 1
*** By ^{31}P NMR analysis, this sample of MMPP 2 is 75% 2 and 25% 1
**** Data uncorrected for impure ligand used.

REFERENCE: C. Fisher, H.S. Mosher, Tetrahedron Lett., (29), 2487 (1977).

REACTION TYPE: Hydrogenation of substituted acrylic acids.

CATALYST: Rh(I) complex of 2,3-O-isopropylidene-2,3-dihydroxy-1,4-bis(diphenylphosphino)butane; $[RhCl(cyclooctene)_2]_2$ precursor

LIGAND:

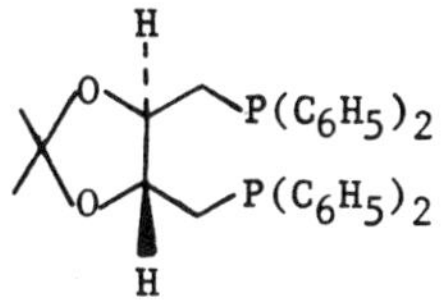

(-)-DIOP

SUBSTRATES:

$R^1-CH=C(R^2)-COOH$

4 R^1 = H, R^2 = C_6H_5
6 R^1 = C_6H_5, R^2 = NHAc
8 R^1 = H, R^2 = $NHCOCH_2C_6H_5$

CONDITIONS: C_6H_6/EtOH (1:2); room temperature; atmospheric pressure; in the presence of NEt_3.

Substrate	% Optical Purity	Configuration
4	63	S
6	72	R
8	68 (after hydrolysis to R-alanine).	

REFERENCE: T.B. Dang, H.B. Kagan, J. Chem. Soc. Chem. Commun., 481 (1971).

REACTION TYPE: Hydrogenation of α-acylaminoacrylic acids and derivatives.

CATALYST: Rh(I) complex of (-)-DIOP; $[RhCl(cyclooctene)_2]_2$ precursor

LIGAND:

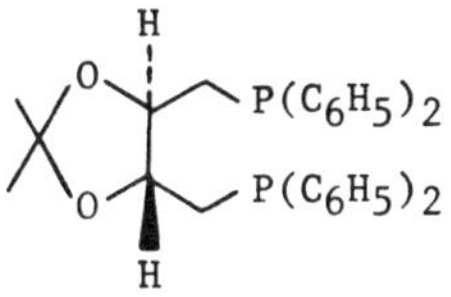

SUBSTRATES:

$C_6H_5-CH=C(NHCOR)-COR'$

I R=CH_3, R'=OH
II R=C_6H_5, R'=OH
III R=CH_3, R'=OCH_3
IV R=CH_3, R'=NH_2

$R^2-CH=C(NHCOR^3)-COOH$

V R^2=H, R^3=CH_3
VI R^2=HOC_6H_4, R^3=CH_3
VII R^2= $CH_2(O)_2C_6H_3$, R^3=CH_3
VIII R^2=HOC_6H_4, R^3=C_6H_5

CONDITIONS: C_6H_6/EtOH (1:2); room temperature; atmospheric pressure; substrate/catalyst molar ratio of (30-200):1

Substrate	% Optical Purity	Configuration	Substrate	% Optical Purity	Configuration
I	72	R	V	73	R
II	64	R	VI	80	R
III	55	R	VII	79	R
IV	71	R	VIII	62	R

(+)-DIOP prepared from D(-)-tartaric acid gives the natural S or L-amino acids.

REFERENCE: H.B. Kagan, T.P. Dang, J. Am. Chem. Soc., 94, 6429 (1972).

REACTION TYPE: Hydrogenation of substituted acrylic acids.

CATALYST: Polymer supported Rh(I) complex of a DIOP analogue; $[RhCl(C_2H_4)_2]_2$ precursor

LIGAND:

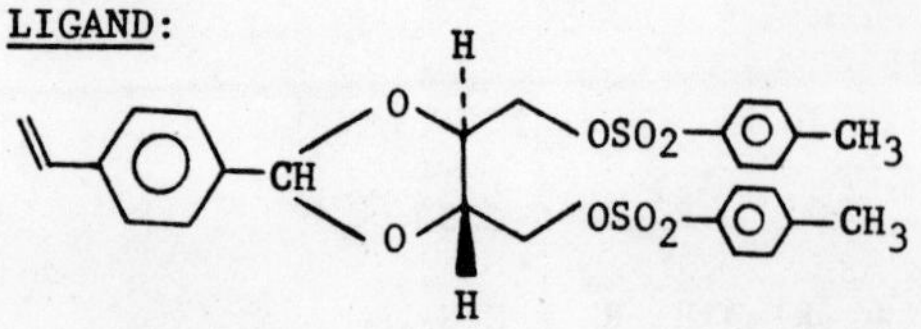

copolymerized with

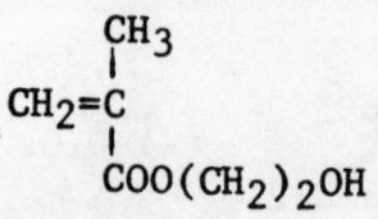

and reacted with $NaP(C_6H_5)_2$ to give

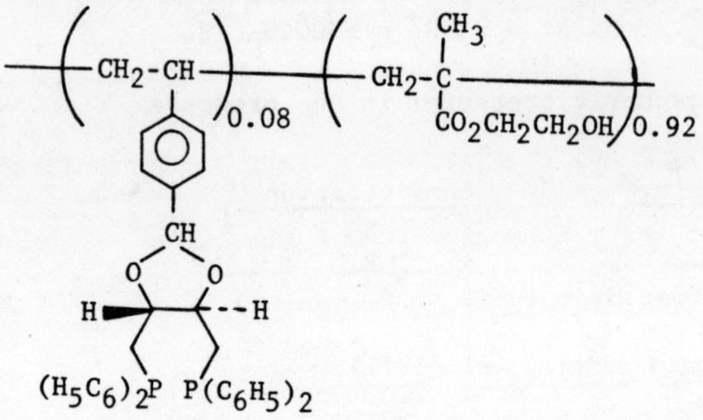

SUBSTRATES:

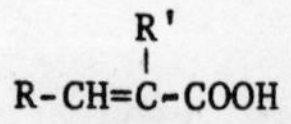

a R=H, R'=$NHCOCH_3$
b R=C_6H_5, R'=$NHCOCH_3$
c R=H, R'=C_6H_5

CONDITIONS: C_6H_6/EtOH (1:5, v/v); 25°C for 5-12 hrs.; 1-2.5 atm H_2; substrate/catalyst molar ratio of 50:1

Substrate	% Optical Yield	Configuration
a	52-60, (73)*	R
b	86, (81)*	R
c	58-62, (63)*	S

*results from using homogeneous Rh(I)-DIOP catalyst.

REFERENCE: N. Takaishi, H. Imai, C.A. Bertelo, J.K. Stille, J. Am. Chem. Soc., 98, 5400 (1976).

REACTION TYPE: Hydrogenation of α-acetamidoacrylic acids.

CATALYST: Rh(I) complex of (2R,3R)-DIOP(I), (1R,2R)-trans-1,2-bis(diphenylphosphinomethyl)cyclobutane (II), (1R,2R)-trans-1,2-bis(diphenylphosphinomethyl)-cyclopentane (III), and (1S,2S)-trans-1,2-bis(diphenylphosphinomethyl)-cyclohexane (IV); $[RhCl(1,5\text{-}COD)]_2$ precursor

LIGANDS:

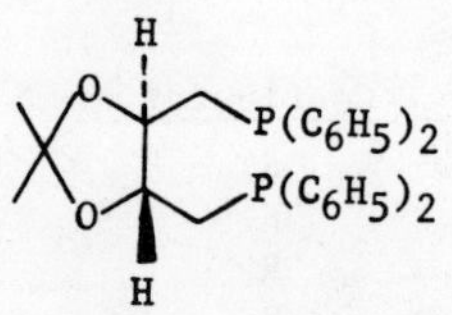

I

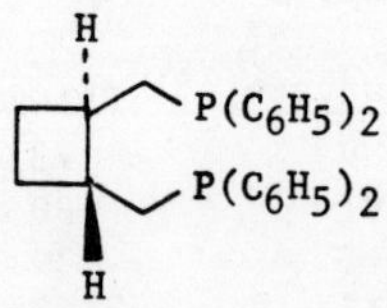

II

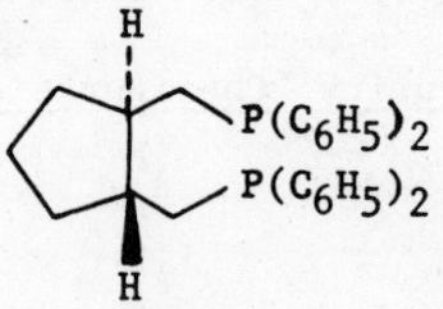

III

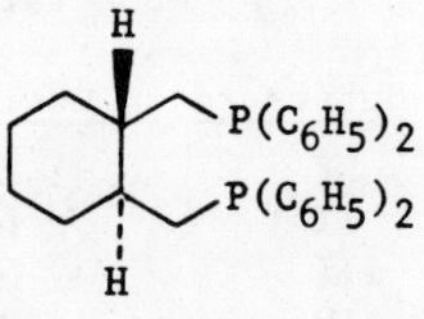

IV

SUBSTRATES:

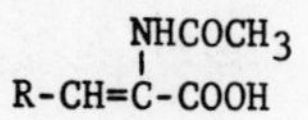

A R=H
B R=C_6H_5

CONDITIONS: EtOH/C_6H_6(2.3:1); 25°C; 1 atm H_2; substrate/catalyst molar ratio of 50:1

Substrate A

Ligand	% Optical Purity	Configuration
II	72	R
III	72	R
IV	40	S
I	73	R

Substrate B

Ligand	% Optical Purity	Configuration
II	86	R
III	63	R
IV	35	S
I	82	R

REFERENCE: R. Glaser, M. Twaik, S. Geresh, J. Blumenfeld, Tetrahedron Lett., (52), 4635 (1977).

REACTION TYPE: Hydrogenation of α-acetamidoacrylic acids and ester derivatives.

CATALYST: Rh(I) complex of DIOP and (1R,2R)-II; $[RhCl(1,5\text{-}COD)]_2$ precursor

LIGANDS:

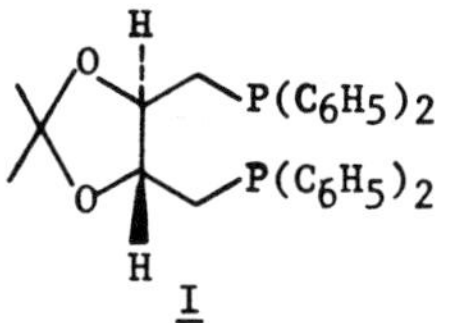

I

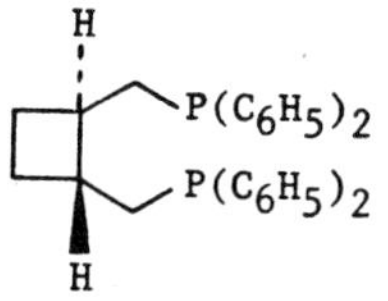

II

SUBSTRATES:

$NHCOCH_3$
$C_6H_5-CH=C-COOR$

A R=H
B R=Me
C R=Et
D R=i-Pr
E R=t-Bu

$NHCOCH_3$
$R-CH=C-COOH$

A $R=C_6H_5$
F $R=3,4\text{-}(OCH_2O)C_6H_3$
G $R=4\text{-}(AcO)C_6H_4$
H $R=4\text{-}(AcO)\text{-}3\text{-}(OCH_3)C_6H_3$

CONDITIONS: $EtOH/C_6H_6$(2.3:1); 25°C; 1 atm H_2; substrate/catalyst molar ratio of 50:1 (acids) and 25:1 (esters)

Substrate	Ligand	% Optical Purity	Configuration
A	I	82	R
B	I	69	R
C	I	72	R
D	I	76	R
E	I	77	R
A	II	86	R
B	II	44	R
C	II	42	R
D	II	41	R
E	II	40	R

Substrate	Ligand	% Optical Purity	Configuration
A	I	82	R
F	I	79	R
G	I	-	
H	I	84	R
A*	I	79	R
F*	I	76	R
A	II	86	R
F	II	80	R
G	II	85	R
H	II	87	R
A*	II	91	R
F*	II	85	R

*NEt_3 added

REFERENCE: R. Glaser, J. Blumenfeld, M. Twaik, Tetrahedron Lett., (52), 4639 (1977).

REACTION TYPE: Hydrogenation of α-acylaminoacrylic acids and ester derivatives.

CATALYST: Rh(I) complex of DIOP; $[RhCl(1,5\text{-}COD)]_2$ precursor

LIGAND:

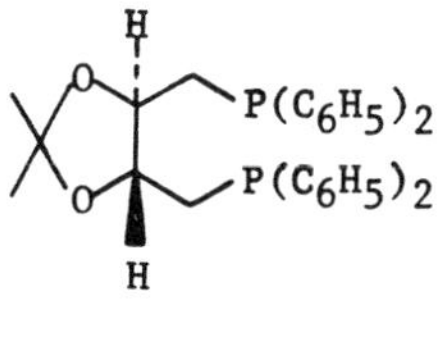

SUBSTRATES:

$NHCOR$
$C_6H_5-CH=C-COOH$

I R=H
II R=Me
III R=i-Pr
IV R=t-Bu
V R=1-adamantyl
VI $R=C_6H_5$

$NHCOR^2$
$C_6H_5-CH=C-COOR^1$

VII $R^1=Me$ $R^2=H$
VIII $R^1=Me$ $R^2=Me$
IX $R^1=Et$ $R^2=Me$
X $R^1=i\text{-}Pr$ $R^2=Me$
XI $R^1=t\text{-}Bu$ $R^2=Me$

CONDITIONS: $EtOH/C_6H_6$(2.3:1); 25°C; 1 atm H_2; substrate/catalyst ratio of 25:1

Substrate	% Optical Purity	Configuration
I	60	R
II	83	R
III	57	R
IV	52	R
V	46	R
VI	68	R

Substrate	% Optical Purity	Configuration
VII	58	R
VIII	69	R
IX	72	R
X	76	R
XI	77	R

REFERENCE: R. Glaser, S. Geresh, Tetrahedron, 35, 2381 (1979).

REACTION TYPE: Hydrogenation of an α-acylaminoacrylic acid.

CATALYST: Rh(I) complex of substituted DIOP ligands; [RhCl(1,5-COD)]$_2$ precursor

LIGANDS:

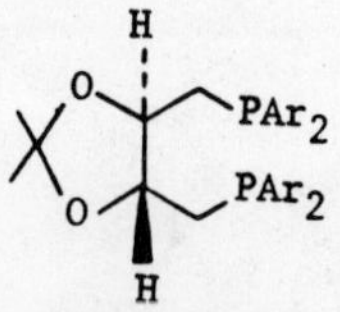

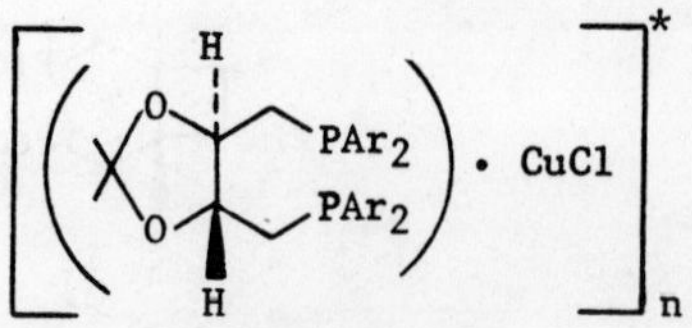

SUBSTRATE:

5a Ar=C$_6$H$_5$
5b Ar=3-MeC$_6$H$_4$
5c Ar=3,5-Me$_2$C$_6$H$_3$

6a Ar=C$_6$H$_5$
6b Ar=3-MeC$_6$H$_4$
6c Ar=3,5-MeC$_6$H$_3$

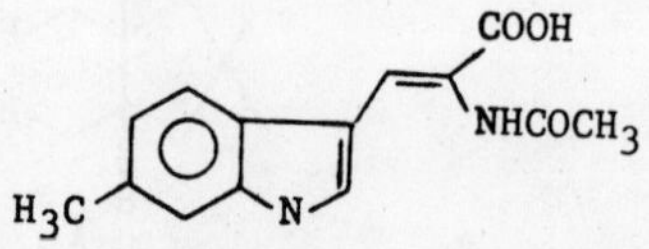

*5a-c obtained as the crude products of typical synthetic procedures, were reacted with cuprous chloride to form complexes which were easily purified and which were found to transfer their diphosphine ligand quantitatively to Rh under mild conditions.

CONDITIONS: Deoxygenated MeOH; room temperature; 40 psi initial H$_2$ pressure; substrate/catalyst molar ratio of (1350-9500):1

Ligand	% ee	Configuration	Ligand	% ee	Configuration
5a	73**	R	6b	84	R
6a	75	R	5c	86	R
5b	82	R	6c	87	R

**The % ee values correspond well with those given in J. Org. Chem., 44, 3741 (1979) for 5b and 5c; the value for 5a was listed there as 93.2% and therefore may be a misprint here.

REFERENCE: J.M. Townsend, J.F. Blount, R.C. Sun, S. Zawoiski, D. Valentine, Jr., J. Org. Chem., 45, 2995 (1980).

REACTION TYPE: Hydrogenation of α-acylaminoacrylic acids.

CATALYST: Rh(I) complex of (2S,4S)-N-butoxycarbonyl-4-diphenylphosphino-2-diphenyl-phosphinomethylpyrrolidine; [RhCl(1,5-hexadiene)]$_2$ precursor

LIGAND:

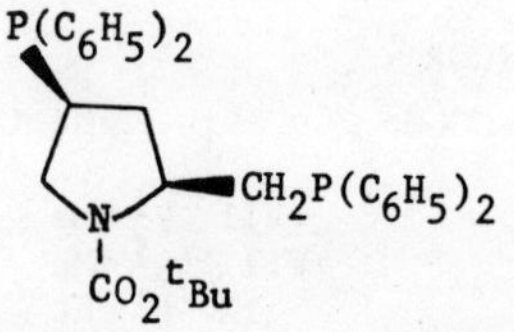

SUBSTRATES:

$$R-CH=\overset{\overset{\displaystyle NHCOCH_3}{|}}{C}-COOH$$

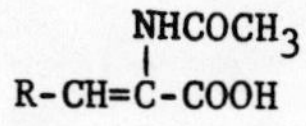

8a R=C$_6$H$_5$
8c R=3,4-methylenedioxyphenyl
8d R=4-(AcO)-3-(OCH$_3$)C$_6$H$_3$
8e R=4-(AcO)C$_6$H$_4$

CONDITIONS: Solvent as noted; 20°C for 20 hrs.; 50 atm H$_2$; substrate/catalyst molar ratio of 100:1; NEt$_3$ added.

Substrate	% Optical Yield (solvent)	Configuration
8a	83 (MeOH)	R
8a	91 (EtOH)	R
8c	83 (EtOH)	R
8d	86 (EtOH)	R
8e	87 (EtOH)	R

REFERENCE: K. Achiwa, J. Am. Chem. Soc., 98, 8265 (1976).

REACTION TYPE: Hydrogenation of α-keto acid derivatives (esters).

CATALYST: Rh(I) complex of BPPM and (2S,4S)-N-cholesteryloxycarbonyl-4-diphenylphosphino-2-diphenylphosphinomethylpyrrolidine (CPPM); $[RhCl(1,5\text{-hexadiene})]_2$ precursor

LIGANDS:

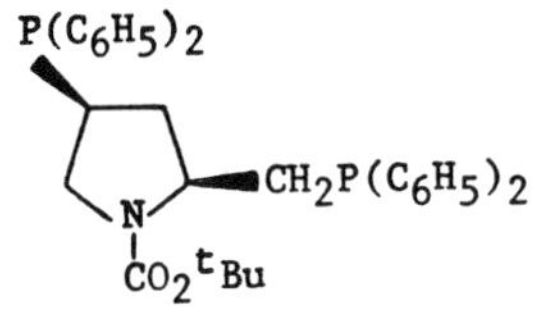

BPPM

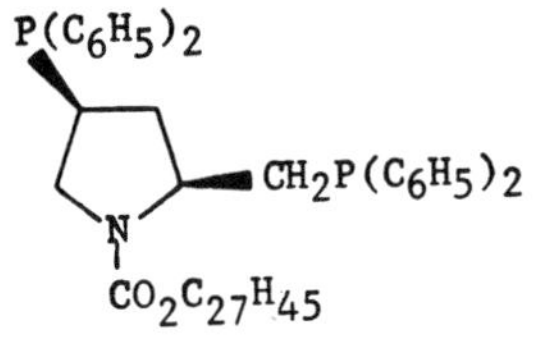

CPPM

SUBSTRATES:

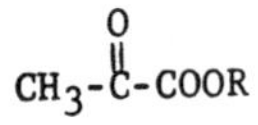

5a R=Et
5b R=n-Bu

CONDITIONS: Solvent as noted; 20°C for 24-90 hrs.; 20 atm H_2; substrate/catalyst molar ratio of 200:1

Substrate	Ligand	% Optical Yield (solvent)	Configuration
5a	BPPM	65.3 (benzene)	R
5a	CPPM	63.8 (benzene)	R
5a	CPPM	67.3 (cyclohexane)	R
5b	CPPM	61.7 (benzene)	R
5b	CPPM	62.8 (cyclohexane)	R

REFERENCE: K. Achiwa, Tetrahedron Lett., (42), 3735 (1977).

REACTION TYPE: Hydrogenation of an α-keto acid derivative (lactone).

CATALYST: Rh(I) complex of BPPM and 4 of its derivatives; $[RhCl(1,5\text{-hexadiene})]_2$ and $[RhCl(1,5\text{-COD})]_2$ precursors

LIGANDS:

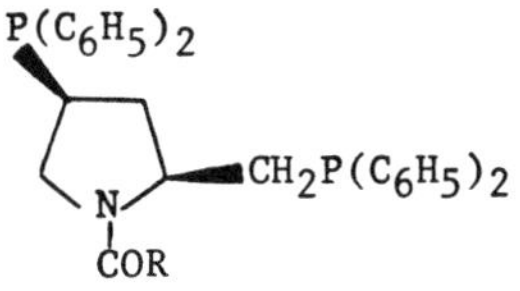

3a RCO = Me_3COCO (BPPM)
3b RCO = HCO (FPPM)
3c RCO = CH_3CO (APPM)
3d RCO = C_6H_5CO (BZPPM)
3e RCO = Me_3CCO (PPPM)

SUBSTRATE:

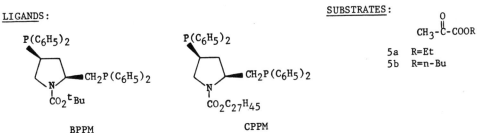

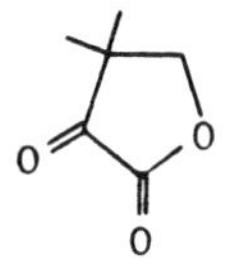

α-keto-β,β-dimethyl-γ-butyrolactone

CONDITIONS: C_6H_6; 50°C for 45 hrs.; 50 atm H_2; substrate/catalyst molar ratio of 100:1

Ligand	Catalyst Precursor	% Optical Yield	Configuration
3a	$[RhCl(1,5\text{-hexadiene})]_2$	54.6	R
3b	"	75.1	R
3c	"	70.8	R
3d	"	75.9	R
3e	"	59.2	R

Ligand	Catalyst Precursor	% Optical Yield	Configuration
3a	$[RhCl(1,5\text{-COD})]_2$	80.5	R
3b	"	78.9	R
3c	"	73.4	R
3d	"	78.5	R
3e	"	67.5	R

REFERENCE: K. Achiwa, T. Kogure, I. Ojima, Chem. Lett., 297 (1978).

REACTION TYPE: Hydrogenation of an α-keto acid derivative (lactone).

CATALYST: Rh(I) complex of BPPM; [RhCl(1,5-COD)]$_2$ precursor

LIGAND:

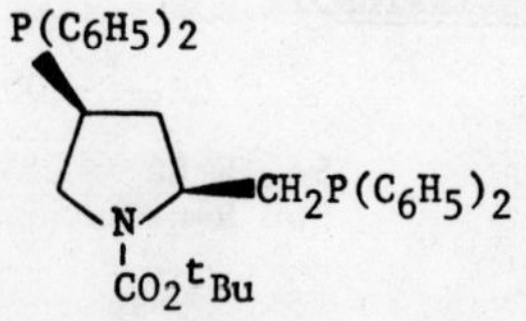

BPPM

SUBSTRATE:

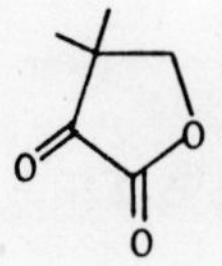

CONDITIONS: Solvent as noted; temperature as noted for 48 hrs.; 50 atm H_2; substrate/catalyst molar ratio of 1000:1

Solvent/temperature	% ee
C_6H_6/20°	85.5
C_6H_6/30°	86.7
C_6H_6/50°	84.8
THF/15°	82.6
THF/30°	80.7
C_6H_5Cl/50°	63.5
$C_6H_5CH_3$/50°	77.7

REFERENCE: I. Ojima, T. Kogure, T. Terasaki, K. Achiwa, J. Org. Chem., 43, 3444 (1978).

REACTION TYPE: Hydrogenation of an acrylic diacid.

CATALYST: Rh(I) complex of two derivatives of BPPM; [RhCl(1,5-COD)]$_2$ precursor

LIGANDS:

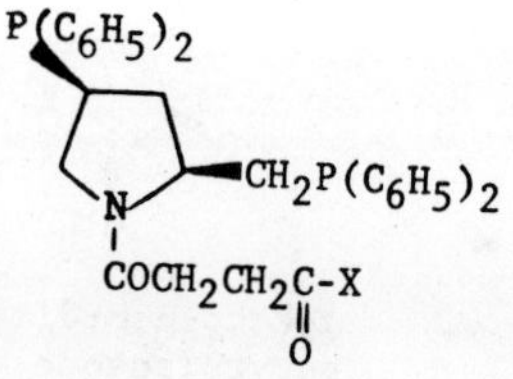

X = OCH_3 (MSPPM)
X = OH (HSPPM)

SUBSTRATE:

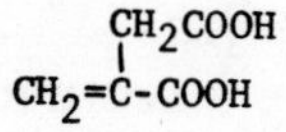

CONDITIONS: MeOH; 20°C for 20 hrs.; 50 atm H_2; substrate/catalyst molar ratio of 50:1

Ligand	% Optical Yield	Configuration
MSPPM	77.6	S
MSPPM	80.0*	S
HSPPM	86.0	S
HSPPM	93.9*	S

*NEt_3 added

REFERENCE: K. Achiwa, Y. Ohga, Y. Iitaka, Tetrahedron Lett., (47), 4683 (1978).

REACTION TYPE: Hydrogenation of an acrylic diacid.

CATALYST: Rh(I) complex of BPPM and 4 of its derivatives: $[RhCl(1,5\text{-}COD)]_2$ precursor

LIGANDS:

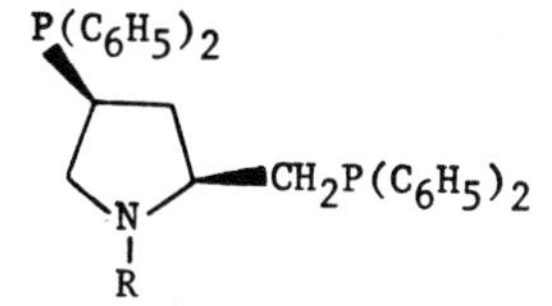

SUBSTRATE:

$CH_2=C(CH_2COOH)\text{-}COOH$

3a R=$(CH_3)_3COCO$ (BPPM)
3b R=C_6H_5CO (BZPPM)
3c R=(2-pyridyl)CO (PCPPM)
3d R=(3-pyridyl)CO (NPPM)
3e R=(4-pyridyl)CO (INPPM)

CONDITIONS: MeOH; 20°C for 20 hrs.; 50 atm H_2; substrate/catalyst molar ratio of 100:1

Ligand	% Optical Yield	Configuration	Ligand	% Optical Yield	Configuration
BPPM	71.1	S	NPPM	70.5	S
BZPPM	83.5	S	INPPM	71.1	S
PCPPM	69.9	S	BZPPM	62.8*	S

*C_6H_6/MeOH (2:1) solvent

REFERENCE: K. Achiwa, Tetrahedron Lett., (17), 1475 (1978).

REACTION TYPE: Hydrogenation of an acrylic diacid.

CATALYST: Rh(I) complex of BPPM; $[RhCl(1,5\text{-}COD)]_2$ or $[Rh(1,5\text{-}COD)(acac)]$ + $HClO_4$ precursors

LIGAND:

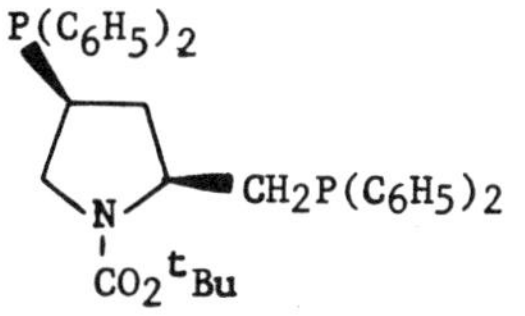

BPPM

SUBSTRATE:

$CH_2=C(CH_2COOH)\text{-}COOH$

CONDITIONS: C_6H_6/MeOH (1:3); 20°C for 20 hrs.; 20 atm H_2; substrate/catalyst molar ratio of 200:1

Catalyst	% ee	Catalyst	% ee
BPPM + $[Rh(COD)Cl]_2$	78.7	BPPM + $[Rh(COD)Cl]_2$*	90.2
$[(BBPM)Rh(COD)]^+ClO_4^-$	84.3	$[(BPPM)Rh(COD)]^+ClO_4^-$*	92.0

*NEt_3 added

REFERENCE: I. Ojima, T. Kogure, K. Achiwa, Chem. Lett., 567 (1978).

REACTION TYPE: Hydrogenation of an acrylic diacid.

CATALYST: Rh(I) complex of BPPM and 3 of its derivatives: [Rh(1,5-COD)(acac)] + $HClO_4$ or $[RhCl(1,5-COD)]_2$ precursors

LIGANDS:

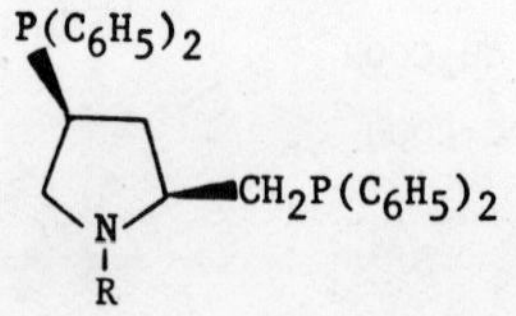

3a $R=(CH_3)_3CCO$ (PPPM-Rh) or (PPPM-Rh^+) depending on precursor
3b $R=C_6H_5CO$ (BZPPM-Rh) or (BZPPM-Rh^+) "
3c R=HCO (FPPM-Rh) or (FPPM-Rh^+) "
3d $R=(CH_3)_3COCO$ (BPPM-Rh) or (BPPM-Rh^+)

SUBSTRATE:

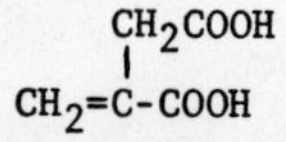

CONDITIONS: MeOH; 20°C for 20 hrs.; 50 atm H_2, substrate/catalyst molar ratio of 100:1

Ligand	% Optical Yield	Configuration	Ligand	% Optical Yield	Configuration
PPPM-Rh	84.7	S	FPPM-Rh	78.2	S
PPPM-Rh	84.1*	S	FPPM-Rh	91.8*	S
PPPM-Rh^+	82.3	S	FPPM-Rh^+	75.2	S
PPPM-Rh^+	87.1*	S	FPPM-Rh^+	94.2*	S
BZPPM-Rh	83.5	S	BPPM-Rh	71.1	S
BZPPM-Rh	80.6*	S	BPPM-Rh	91.2*	S
BZPPM-Rh^+	82.3	S	BPPM-Rh^+	71.7	S
BZPPM-Rh^+	88.9*	S	BPPM-Rh^+	93.6*	S

*NEt_3 added

REFERENCE: K. Achiwa, Chem. Lett., 561 (1978).

REACTION TYPE: Hydrogenation of substituted acrylic acids.

CATALYST: Polymer-supported Rh(I) complex of (2S,4S)-4-diphenylphosphino-2-diphenylphosphinomethylpyrrolidine; [Rh(1,5-COD)(acac)] + 70% $HClO_4$ precursor

LIGAND:

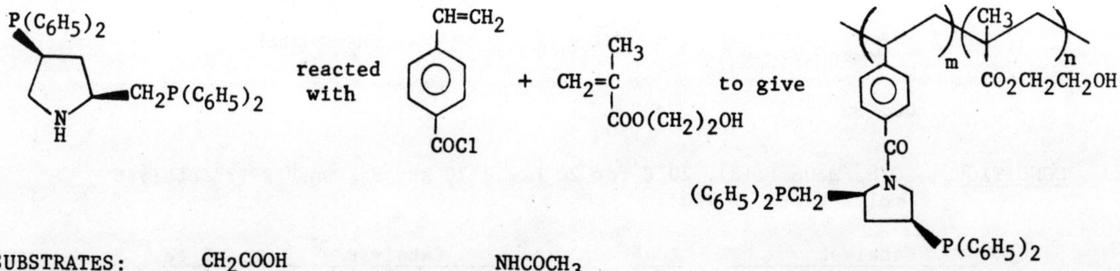

SUBSTRATES:

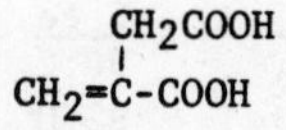

9

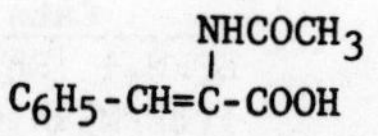

11

CONDITIONS: EtOH; 20°C for 45 hrs.; 50 atm H_2; substrate/catalyst molar ratio of 100:1; NEt_3 added

Substrate	% Optical Yield	Configuration
9	82.3[a,b]	S
11	70.0[c]	R

a) The yield with a comparable homogeneous catalyst (BZPPM ligand) was 88.9%
b) The yield with recovered catalyst was 77.6%
c) The yield with recovered catalyst was 68.0%

REFERENCE: K. Achiwa, Chem. Lett., 905 (1978).

REACTION TYPE: Hydrogenation of substituted acrylic acids.

CATALYST: Rh(I) complex of a series of N-(N'-substituted carbamoyl)-4-diphenyl-
                phosphino-2-diphenylphosphinomethylpyrrolidines (CAPP); $[RhCl(1,5-COD)]_2$
                (I) or $[Rh(ClO_4)[NBD]_2]$ (II) (NBD = norbornadiene) precursors

LIGANDS:

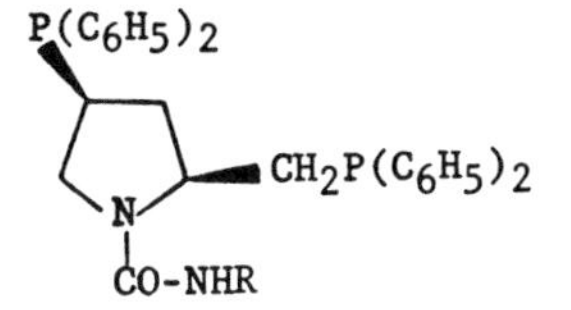

$P(C_6H_5)_2$

$CH_2P(C_6H_5)_2$

N

CO-NHR

CAPP

a $R=C_6H_5$	**e** $R=p-NO_2C_6H_4$
b $R=p-ClC_6H_4$	**f** $R=CH_3$
c $R=p-BrC_6H_4$	**g** $R=allyl$
d $R=3,4-Cl_2C_6H_3$	**h** $R=cyclohexyl$

SUBSTRATES:

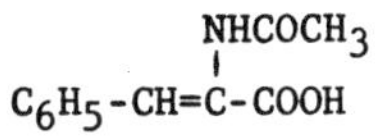

$C_6H_5-CH=C(NHCOCH_3)-COOH$
1

$C_6H_5-CH=C(NHCOCH_3)-COOCH_3$
2

$CH_2=C(CH_2COOH)-COOH$
3

CONDITIONS: EtOH for **1**, **2** and C_6H_6/MeOH (1:3) for **3**; 25°C; 1 atm H_2; substrate/catalyst
               molar ratio of 100:1 for **1**, **2** and 200:1 for **3**

Substrate 1			Substrate 2			Substrate 3		
Ligand	cp*	% ee	Ligand	cp*	% ee	Ligand	cp*	% ee
a	I	95.4	a	I	95.6	a	I	95.4
a	II	95.4	a	II	95.1	b	I	95.3
b	I	96.1	b	I	95.6	c	I	93.5
b	II	95.4	b	II	92.3	d	I	94.0
c	I	97.4	c	I	95.2	e	I	95.4
c	II	95.3	c	II	93.8	f	I	93.8
d	I	97.9	d	I	90.9	g	I	93.5
d	II	95.3	d	II	91.9	h	I	94.4
e	I	94.3	e	I	94.8			
e	II	95.7	e	II	95.3			
f	I	94.5	f	I	92.5			
f	II	93.2	f	II	91.1			
g	I	90.6	g	I	91.3			
g	II	92.5	g	II	90.2			
h	I	92.8	h	I	90.2	*catalyst precursor		
h	II	93.2	h	II	90.7			

REFERENCE: I. Ojima, N. Yoda, Tetrahedron Lett., (21), 1051 (1980).

REACTION TYPE: Hydrogenation of α-acylaminoacrylic acids.

CATALYST: Rh(I) complex of 1,2-bis(anisylphenylphosphino)ethane;
                $[RhCl(1,5-COD)]_2$ precursor

LIGAND:

$(CH_2)_2$

P

CH_3O

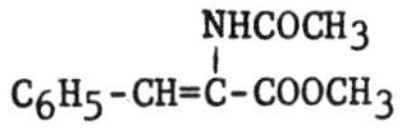

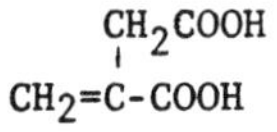

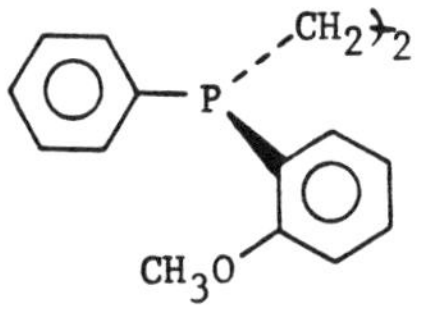

DIPAMP

SUBSTRATES:

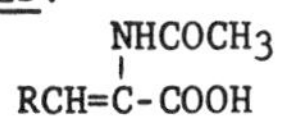

$RCH=C(NHCOCH_3)-COOH$

4a $R = C_6H_5$

4b $R = 4-(AcO)-3-(OCH_3)C_6H_3$

4c $R = 3-(1-acetyl-indolyl)-$

CONDITIONS: (as noted)

Table I. Asymmetric Reduction of α-Acetamidoacrylic Acids[a]

Substrate	Solvent	Temp, °C	Abs press, atm	Reaction time, hr	%[c,d] ee
4a	88% i-PrOH	25	3.5	3	92.8
4a	88% i-PrOH	50	3.5	0.8	93.6
4a	88% i-PrOH	25	27	0.8	91.8
4a	50% MeOH[e]	25	4	4	95.7
4a	50% MeOH[e]	50	4	1.3	95.2
4a	50% MeOH[e]	25	27	1.0	95.5
4b	MeOH[b]	50	3.5	1	89.4
4b	MeOH	50	3.5	1.5	89.5
4b	MeOH	25	3.5	4	90.9
4b	88% i-PrOH	50	3.5	0.7	94.0
4c	MeOH	50	4.0	0.75	93.5

[a] All hydrogenations were run with 0.05% metal levels based on substrate and at concentrations of 2×10^{-4} M. [b] In this run, an in situ catalyst was employed while, in all other examples, the crystalline complex [Rh(COD)(bisphosphine)]$^+$ BF$_4^-$ was used. [c] Enantiomeric excess. [d] All rotations were measured without isolation by diluting to volume and comparing with a blank, taking for pure 5a $\{[\alpha]^{20}D + 47.5°$ (c 1.0, 95% EtOH)$\}$, 5b $\{[\alpha]^{20}D + 40.8°$ (c 1.0, MeOH)$\}$, and 5c $\{[\alpha]^{20}D + 35.1°$ (c 0.5, MeOH)$\}$. In the case of the basic solutions, an additional 0.55 equiv of NaOH was added before dilution to volume. In no case was the catalyst contribution in the blank more than 2%. [e] Run as sodium carboxylate with 0.95 equiv of NaOH.

REFERENCE: W.S. Knowles, M.J. Sabacky, B.D. Vineyard, D.J. Weinkauff, J. Am. Chem. Soc.,
            97, 2567 (1975).

REACTION TYPE: Hydrogenation of α-acylaminoacrylic acids and derivatives.

CATALYST: Rh(I) complex of DIPAMP; $[RhCl(1,5\text{-}COD)]_2 + NaBF_4$ precursor

LIGAND:

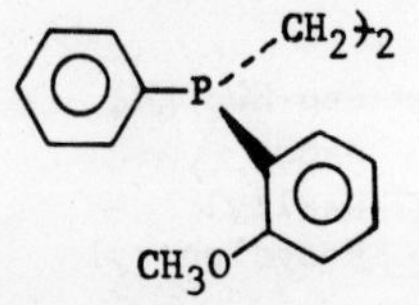

DIPAMP

SUBSTRATES:*

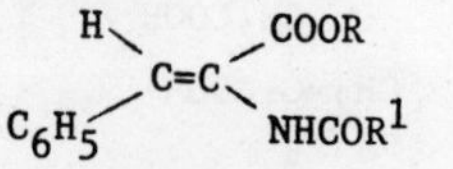

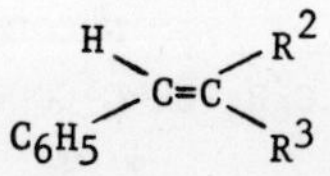

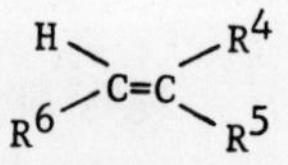

7 R=H, $R^1=CH_3$
8 $R=R^1=CH_3$
9 R=H, $R^1=C_6H_5$

10 R^2=CN, $R^3=NHCOC_6H_5$
11 R^2=COOEt, R^3=NHCOOEt
12 R^2=COOEt, R^3=NHC(S)OEt

13 R^4=COOH, $R^5=NHCOCH_2Cl$, R^6=H
14 $R^4=CONH_2$, $R^5=NHCOC_6H_5$, R^6=i-Pr

CONDITIONS: MeOH or EtOH; 50°C; 3 atm H_2; substrate/catalyst molar ratio of (200-2300):1

Substrate	% ee	Configuration
7	94	S
8	96	S
9	93	S
10	89	S

Substrate	% ee	Configuration
11	89	S
12	62	S
13	95	S
14	95	S

*Only Z-isomers; compounds with the Z-configuration are reduced with higher stereoselectivities. (H.B. Kagan, N. Langlois, T. Dang, J. Organomet. Chem., 90, 353 (1975)).

REFERENCE: B.D. Vineyard, W.S. Knowles, M.G. Sabacky, G.L. Bachman, D.J. Weinkauff, J. Am. Chem. Soc., 99, 5946 (1977).

REACTION TYPE: Hydrogenation of acrylic diacids and derivatives.

CATALYST: Rh(I) complex of DIPAMP: $[RhCl(1,5\text{-}COD)]_2 + NaBF_4$ precursor

LIGAND:

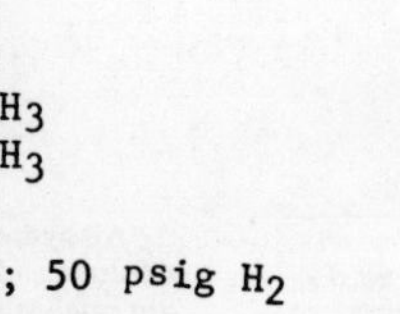

DIPAMP

SUBSTRATES:

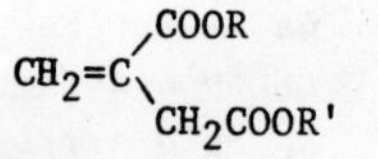

2 R=R'=H
3 R=Na, R'=Na
4 $R=CH_3$, $R'=CH_3$
5 R=H, $R'=CH_3$
6 $R=CH_3$, R=H

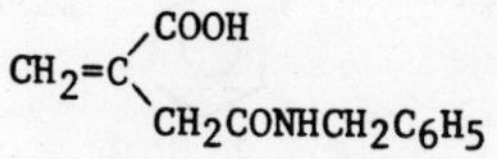

7

CONDITIONS: MeOH or EtOH; 50°C; 50 psig H_2

Substrate	% ee	Configuration
2	38	R
3	78	R
4	88	R

Substrate	% ee	Configuration
5	55	R
6	88	R
7	90	R

REFERENCE: W.C. Christopfel, B.D. Vineyard, J. Am. Chem. Soc., 101, 4406 (1979).

REACTION TYPE: Hydrogenation of geminal-substituted vinyl acetates.

CATALYST: Rh(I) complex of (R,R)-DIPAMP; $[RhCl(1,5\text{-}COD)]_2$ + $NaBF_4$ precursor

LIGAND:

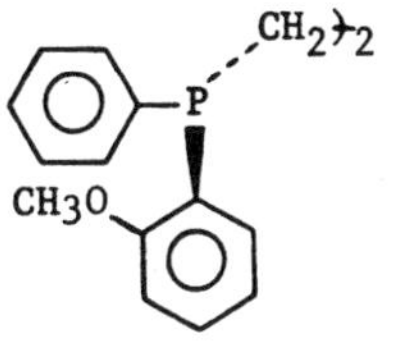

DIPAMP

SUBSTRATES:

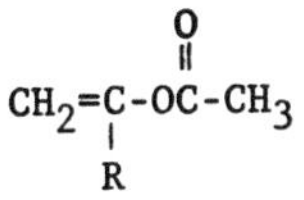

I R=CF_3 II R=p-$(NO_2)C_6H_4$ III R=C_6H_5 IV R=p-$(CH_3O)C_6H_4$ V R=COOEt

CONDITIONS: MeOH solvent unless otherwise noted; 50°C for time as noted; 50 psig H_2

Substrate	Reaction time (hrs)	%ee	Configuration
I	overnight	77	S
II	0.75	65	-
III*	1.0	55	-
IV	1.25	51	-
V*	0.4	89	S

*EtOH solvent

REFERENCE: K.E. Koenig, G.L. Bachman, B.D. Vineyard, J. Org. Chem., 45, 2362 (1980).

REACTION TYPE: Hydrogenation of an α-acetamidoacrylic acid and its ester derivative.

CATALYST: Rh(I) complex of N,N'-bis(α-methylbenzyl)-N,N'-bis(diphenylphosphino)-ethylene diamine; $[RhCl(C_2H_4)_2]_2$ precursor

LIGAND:

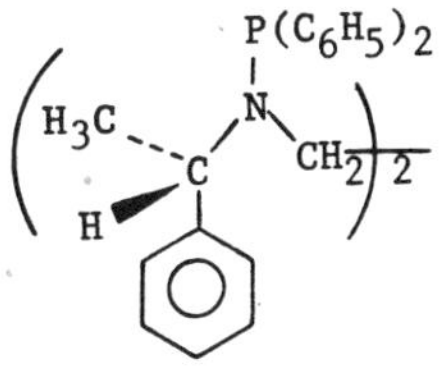

SUBSTRATES:

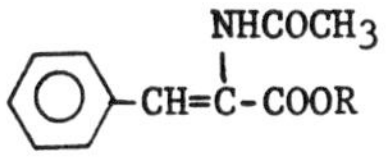

IVa R=H
IVb R=CH_3

CONDITIONS: MeOH solvent unless otherwise noted; 25°C; substrate/catalyst molar ratio of 100-500:1

Substrate	% ee	Configuration	Substrate	% ee	Configuration
IVb	66.2	R	IVb*	66.8	R
IVa	79.8	R	IVa*	81.7	R
IVb*	82.5**	R			

*The catalyst was further reacted with $AgBF_4$ in order to form a cationic complex

**C_6H_6 solvent

REFERENCE: G. Pracejus, H. Pracejus, Tetrahedron Lett., (39), 3497 (1977).

REACTION TYPE: Hydrogenation of α-acylaminoacrylic acids.

CATALYST: Rh(I) complex of N,N'-bis(R(+)α-methylbenzyl)-N,N'-bis(diphenylphosphino)-ethylene diamine or the S(-) isomer; [RhCl(1,5-COD)]$_2$ precursor

LIGAND:

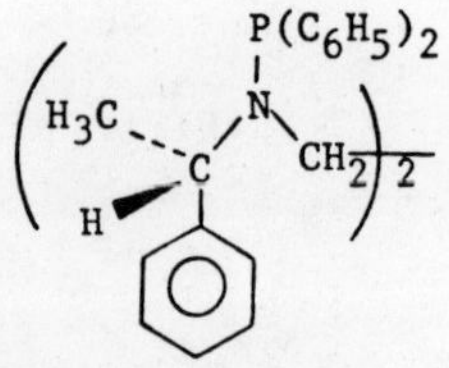

PNNP

SUPPORT:

Hectorite clay
Bentonite clay
Nontronite clay
Halloysite clay

SUBSTRATES:

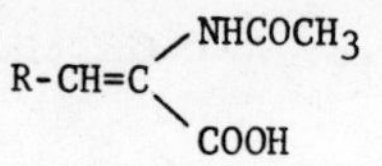

I R=H
II R=C_6H_5
III R=[4-(AcO)-3-(OCH_3)C_6H_3]

CONDITIONS: EtOH; room temperature; atmospheric pressure; substrate/catalyst molar ratio of 100:1

Substrate	Support	% ee: 1st cycle	2nd cycle	3rd cycle	4th cycle	5th cycle
I	None	72-75				
I	Hectorite	72	72	75	70	69
I	Bentonite	68	68	66	70	72
I	Nontronite	61	68	70	70	72
I	Halloysite	55	64	67	60	64
II	Hectorite	49	38	24*	-	-
III	Hectorite	72	58	47*	-	-

*Decrease probably due to selective absorption of the reduction product onto the support.

REFERENCE: M. Mazzei, W. Marconi, M. Riocci, J. Mol. Catal., 9, 381 (1980).

REACTION TYPE: Hydrogenation of α-acylaminoacrylic acids.

CATALYST: Rh(I) complex of (R)-1,2-bis(diphenylphosphino)propane; Rh(ClO_4)[NBD]$_2$ precursor

LIGAND:

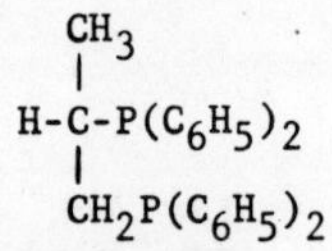

(R)-PROPHOS

SUBSTRATES:

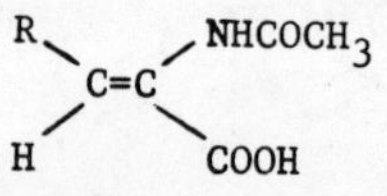

I R=H
II R=C_6H_5
III R=i-Pr
IV R=p-HOC_6H_4
V R=p-$AcOC_6H_4$
VI R=4-(AcO)-3-(OCH_3)C_6H_3

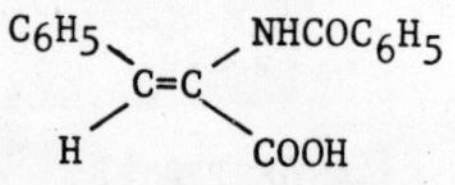

VII

CONDITIONS: 95% EtOH; 25°C; 1 atm H_2; substrate/catalyst molar ratio of 250:1

Substrate	% Optical Yield	Configuration	Substrate	% Optical Yield	Configuration
I	90	S	V	89	S
II	90	S	VI	87	S
III	87	S	VII	91	S
IV	89	S			

REFERENCE: M.D. Fryzuk, B. Bosnich, J. Am. Chem. Soc., 100, 5491 (1978).

REACTION TYPE: Hydrogenation of α-acylaminoacrylic acids.

CATALYST: Rh(I) complex of (2S, 3S)-bis(diphenylphosphino)butane; $Rh(ClO_4)[NBD]_2$ precursor

LIGAND:

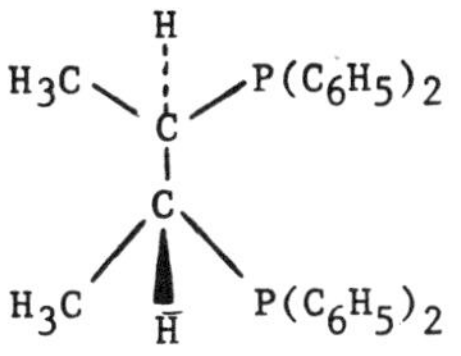

(S,S)-CHIRAPHOS

SUBSTRATES:

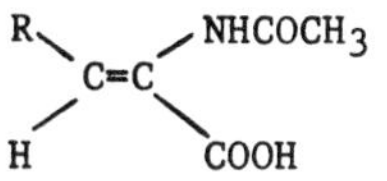

I R=H
II $R=C_6H_5$
III R=i-Pr
IV $R=p\text{-}HOC_6H_4$
V $R=p\text{-}AcOC_6H_4$
VI $R=4\text{-}(AcO)\text{-}3\text{-}(OCH_3)C_6H_3$

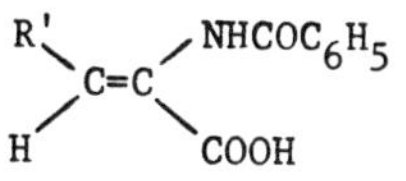

VII $R'=C_6H_5$
VIII R'=i-Pr

CONDITIONS: EtOH; 25°C; 1 atm H_2; substrate/catalyst ratio of 100:1

Substrate	% Optical Yield	Configuration
I	91	R
II	89	R
III	93	R
IV	88	R
V	88	R
VI	83	R
VII	95	R
VIII	72	R

REFERENCE: M.D. Fryzuk, B. Bosnich, J. Am. Chem. Soc., 99, 6262 (1977).

REACTION TYPE: Hydrogenation of α-acylaminoacrylic acids.

CATALYST: Rh(I) complex of (S,S)-CHIRAPHOS, (R)-PROPHOS, and (2S,4S)-bis(diphenylphosphino)pentane[(S,S)-SKEWPHOS]; $Rh(ClO_4)[NBD]_2$ precursor

LIGAND:

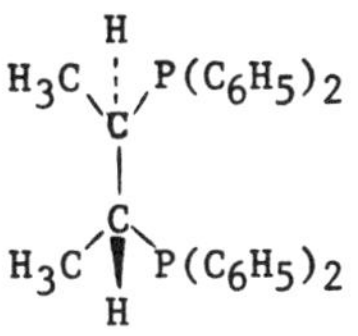

(S,S)-CHIRAPHOS

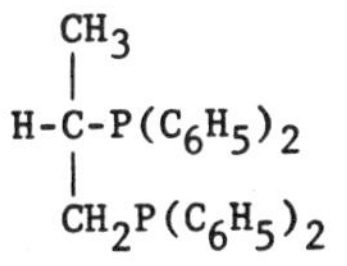

(R)-PROPHOS

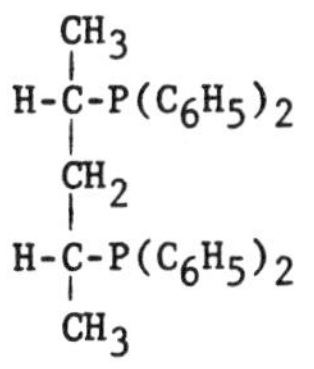

(S,S)-SKEWPHOS

SUBSTRATES:

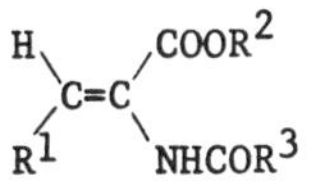

I $R^1=H$, $R^2=H$, $R^3=CH_3$
II $R^1=C_6H_5$, $R^2=H$, $R^3=C_6H_5$
III $R^1=C_6H_5$, $R^2=H$, $R^3=CH_3$
IV $R^1=C_6H_5$, $R^2=C_2H_5$, $R^3=C_6H_5$
V R^1=i-Pr, $R^2=H$, $R^3=CH_3$
VI R^1=i-Pr, $R^2=H$, $R^3=C_6H_5$
VII $R^1=4\text{-}(AcO)C_6H_3$, $R^2=H$, $R^3=CH_3$
VIII $R^1=4\text{-}(AcO)\text{-}3\text{-}(OCH_3)C_6H_3$, $R^2=H$, $R^3=CH_3$

CONDITIONS: EtOH (unless otherwise noted); 25°C; 1 atm H_2; substrate/catalyst ratio of 100:1

	CHIRAPHOS		PROPHOS		SKEWPHOS	
Substrate	% Opt. Yield	Config'n*	% Opt. Yield	Config'n	% Opt. Yield	Config'n
I	92 (88)**	R	90 (87)**	S	98*** (95)**	R
II	95 (99)	R	91 (93)	S	80 (90)	R
III	89 (74)	R	90 (91)	S	92 (93)	R
IV	- (83)	R	87 (88)	S	60 (76)	R
V	93 (100)	R	87 (87)	S	23 (17)	R
VI	72 (87)	R	- -		14 (8)	S
VII	88 (74)	R	89 92	S	84 (90)	R
VIII	83 (80)	R	87 89	S	92 (93)	R

* Configuration independent of solvent
** THF solvent for all values in parenthesis
*** 95% EtOH

REFERENCE: B. Bosnich, N.K. Roberts, unpublished data (1981). (We thank Prof. Bosnich for communicating his results to us prior to publication.)

REACTION TYPE: Hydrogenation of α-acylaminoacrylic acids.

CATALYST: Rh(I) complex of (2R,3R)-CHIRAPHOS; $Rh(ClO_4)[NBD]_2$ precursor

LIGAND:

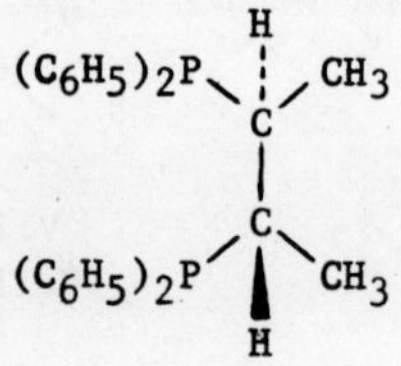

4

SUBSTRATES: $R^1\text{-CH=C(NHCOR}^2\text{)-COOH}$

I $R^1 = H$, $R^2 = CH_3$
II $R^1 = C_6H_5$, $R^2 = C_6H_5$
III $R^1 = C_6H_5$, $R^2 = CH_3$
IV $R^1 = i\text{-Pr}$, $R^2 = CH_3$
V $R^1 = 4\text{-HOC}_6H_4$, $R^2 = CH_3$
VI $R^1 = 4\text{-(HO)-3-(OCH}_3)C_6H_3$, $R^2 = C_6H_5$
VII $R^1 = 4\text{-(AcO)-3-(OCH}_3)C_6H_3$, $R^2 = CH_3$

CONDITIONS: EtOH; 1-4 bar H_2; substrate/catalyst molar ratio of 100:1

Substrate	% Optical Yield	Configuration	Substrate	% Optical Yield	Configuration
I	91	S	V	88	S
II	94	S	VI	98	S
III	88	S	VII	83	S
IV	93	S			

REFERENCE: J. Köttner, G. Greber, Chem. Ber., 113, 2323 (1980).

REACTION TYPE: Hydrogenation of a substituted α-acetamidoacrylic acid.

CATALYST: Rh(I) complex of (-)-1,2-bis(diphenylphosphino)norbornene; $[RhCl(1,5\text{-COD})]_2$ precursor

LIGAND:

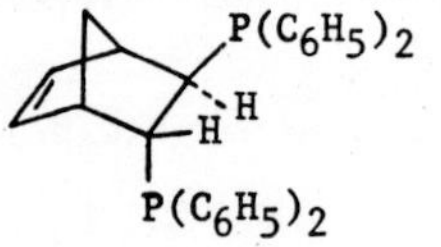

(-)-NORPHOS

SUBSTRATE: $C_6H_5\text{-CH=C(NHCOCH}_3\text{)-COOH}$

1

CONDITIONS: EtOH; 25°C for 10 hrs.

Substrate	% Optical Yield	Configuration
1	96%	S

REFERENCE: H. Brunner, W. Pieronczyk, Angew. Chem. Int. Ed. Engl., 18, 620 (1979).

REACTION TYPE: Hydrogenation of α-acylaminoacrylic acids and ester derivatives.

CATALYST: Rh(I) complex of 1-(Neomenthylphenylphosphino)-2-(diphenylphosphino)-ethane; $[RhCl(NBD)]_2$ precursor

LIGAND:

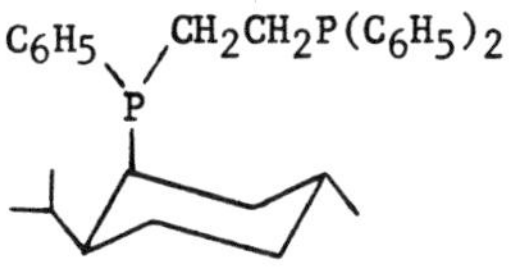

C_6H_5 $CH_2CH_2P(C_6H_5)_2$

SUBSTRATES:

$$C_6H_5 \quad C=C \quad NHCOR$$
$$H \qquad\qquad COOR_1$$

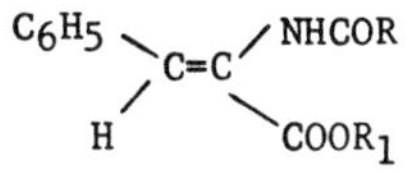

A R=CH$_3$, R$_1$=H
B R=CH$_3$, R$_1$=CH$_3$
C R=C$_6$H$_5$, R$_1$=H

CONDITIONS: MeOH/C$_6$H$_6$ (1:1, v/v); 25°C for at least 1 day; 70 bars H$_2$; substrate/catalyst molar ratio of 100:1

Substrate	% Optical Yield	Configuration
A	60	S
B	58	S
C	85	S

REFERENCE: R.B. King, J. Bakos, C.D. Hoff, L. Markó, J. Org. Chem., 44, 3095 (1979).

REACTION TYPE: Hydrogenation of α-acylaminoacrylic acids and ester derivatives.

CATALYST: Rh(I) complex of (S)-(+)-1,2-bis(diphenylphosphino)-1-phenylethane; preformed $[(phosphine)Rh(NBD)](ClO_4)$ (method A) or $[RhCl(NBD)]_2$ precursor (method B)

LIGAND:

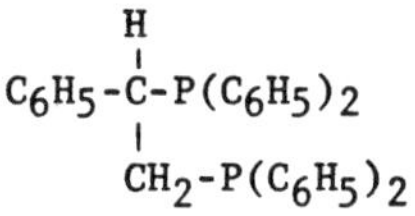

$$\overset{H}{\underset{|}{C_6H_5-C-P(C_6H_5)_2}}$$
$$CH_2-P(C_6H_5)_2$$

SUBSTRATES:

$$\overset{NHCOR^2}{\underset{|}{C_6H_5-CH=C-COOR^1}} \quad (Z - isomer\ only)$$

I   R^1 = H, R^2 = CH$_3$ III R^1 = H, R^2 = C$_6$H$_5$
II R^1 = CH$_3$, R^2 = CH$_3$ IV   R^1 = C$_2$H$_5$, R^2 = C$_6$H$_5$

CONDITIONS: (using preformed catalyst) MeOH; 30°C; 1 atm H$_2$
(using precursor catalyst) C$_6$H$_6$/MeOH (1:1, v/v); room temperature, overnight; 70 bars H$_2$; substrate/catalyst ratio of 100:1

Substrate	% Optical Yield (method A)	% Optical Yield (method B)	Configuration[*]
I	78	82	R
II	85	76	R
III	84	76	R
IV	86	88	R

[*]Configuration independent of method

REFERENCE: R.B. King, J. Bakos, C.D. Hoff, L. Markó, J. Org. Chem., 44, 1729 (1979).

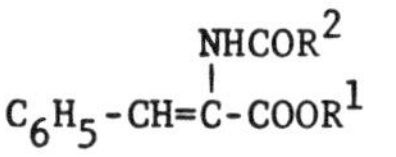

REACTION TYPE: Hydrogenation of α-acylaminoacrylic acids and ester derivatives.

CATALYST: Rh(I) complex of (R)-1,2-bis(diphenylphosphino)-1-cyclohexylethane
[(R)-CYCPHOS]; [RhCl(NBD)]$_2$ + AgPF$_6$ precursor

LIGAND:

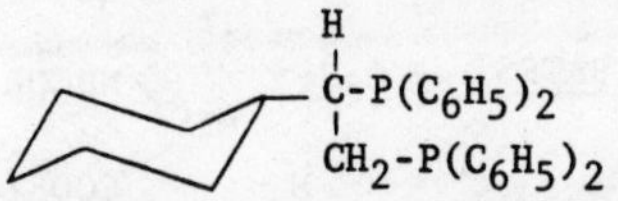

$$\begin{array}{c} H \\ | \\ C-P(C_6H_5)_2 \\ | \\ CH_2-P(C_6H_5)_2 \end{array} \quad (R)\text{-CYCPHOS}$$

SUBSTRATES:

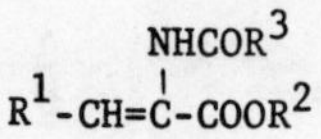

$$\begin{array}{c} NHCOR^3 \\ | \\ R^1-CH=C-COOR^2 \end{array} \quad (Z\text{ - isomer only})$$

I R^1 = i-Bu, R^2 = H, R^3 = C_6H_5	VI R^1 = C_6H_5, R^2 = H, R^3 = CH_3
II R^1 = i-Bu, R^2 = CH_3, R^3 = C_6H_5	VII R^1 = 4-HOC_6H_4, R^2 = H, R^3 = C_6H_5
III R^1 = i-Pr, R^2 = H, R^3 = C_6H_5	VIII R^1 = 4-HOC_6H_4, R^2 = H, R^3 = CH_3
IV R^1 = C_6H_5, R^2 = H, R^3 = C_6H_5	IX R^1 = β-indolyl, R^2 = H, R^3 = CH_3
V R^1 = C_6H_5, R^2 = Et, R^3 = C_6H_5	X R^1 = H, R^2 = H, R^3 = CH_3

CONDITIONS: solvent as noted; 25°C; 1 atm H$_2$; substrate/catalyst ratio of 125:1

Substrate	% Optical Yield (solvent)				Configuration*
I	90 (THF)	94 (MeOH)	95 (EtOAc)	91 (CH_2Cl_2)	S
II		86 (MeOH)	84 (EtOAc)	90 (CH_2Cl_2)	S
III	89 (THF)	90 (MeOH)	94 (EtOAc)		S
IV	94 (THF)	90 (MeOH)	93 (EtOAc)		S
V	90 (THF)	88 (MeOH)	87 (EtOAc)		S
VI	83 (THF)	84 (MeOH)	91 (EtOAc)		S
VII	98 (THF)		96 (EtOAc)		S
VIII	90 (THF)	80 (MeOH)	88 (EtOAc)		S
IX		81 (MeOH)	83 (EtOAc)	87 (CH_2Cl_2)	S
X	87 (THF)	93 (MeOH)	96 (EtOAc)		S

*Configuration of product is the same regardless of solvent

REFERENCE: D.P. Riley, R.E. Shumate, J. Org. Chem., 45, 5187 (1980).

REACTION TYPE: Hydrogenation of α-acylaminoacrylic acids.

CATALYST: Rh(I) complex of 2,2'-bis(diphenylphosphino)-1,1'-binaphthyl (BINAP);
preformed catalyst by reaction of Rh(ClO$_4$)[(BINAP)(NBD)] with H$_2$ in MeOH

LIGAND:

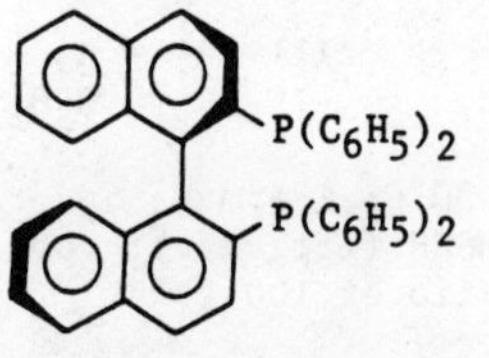

(R)-(+)-BINAP   (S)-(-)-BINAP

SUBSTRATES:

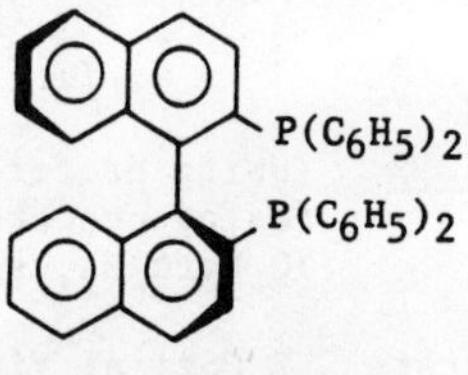

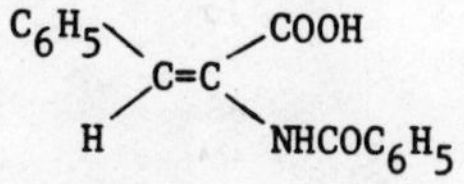

$$\begin{array}{c} C_6H_5 \\ \diagdown \\ \quad C=C \\ \diagup \quad \diagdown \\ H \qquad \begin{array}{c} COOH \\ NHCOC_6H_5 \end{array} \end{array}$$

I

$$\begin{array}{c} H \\ \diagdown \\ \quad C=C \\ \diagup \quad \diagdown \\ C_6H_5 \qquad \begin{array}{c} COOR \\ NHCOR' \end{array} \end{array}$$

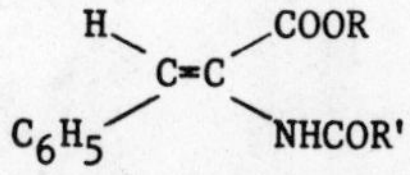

II   R=CH_3, R'=C_6H_5
III R=H, R'=CH_3

CONDITIONS: EtOH(or THF for E substrates); room temperature for 48 hrs; 3-4 atm H$_2$

SUBSTRATE	LIGAND	OPTICAL PURITY,%	CONFIGURATION
I	(S)-(-)-BINAP	87	S
II	(R)-(+)-BINAP	92	S
III	(S)-(-)-BINAP	84	R

REFERENCE: A. Miyashita, A. Yasuda, H. Takaya, K. Toriumi, T.Ito, T. Souchi, R. Noyori,
J. Am. Chem. Soc., 102, 7932 (1980).

REACTION TYPE: Hydrogenation of α-acylaminoacrylic acids.

CATALYST: Rh(I) complex of (1R,2R)-bis(N-diphenylphosphinomethylamino)-cyclohexane; [RhCl(1,5-COD)]$_2$ precursor

LIGAND: SUBSTRATES:

$$R_1\diagdown \quad \diagup NHCOR_2$$
$$C=C$$
$$H \diagup \quad \diagdown COOH$$

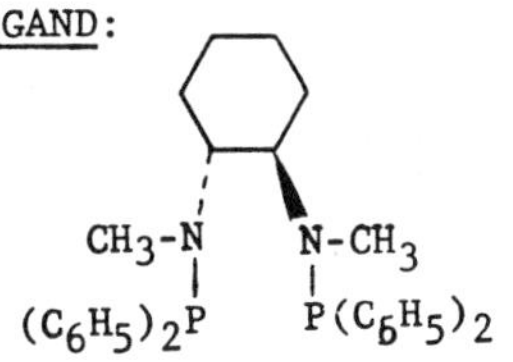

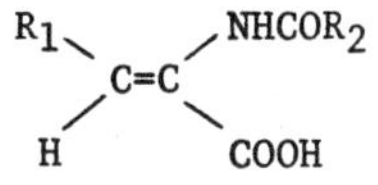

I $R_1=C_6H_5$, $R_2=CH_3$
II $R_1=C_6H_5$, $R_2=C_6H_5$
III $R_1=i\text{-}Pr$, $R_2=C_6H_5$

CONDITIONS: EtOH; room temperature for 2-4 hrs.; 1 atm H$_2$; substrate/catalyst molar ratio of 100:1

Substrate	% Optical Purity	Configuration
I	73	S
II	85	S
III	93	S

REFERENCE: K. Hanaki, K. Kashiwabara, J. Fujita, Chem. Lett., 489 (1978).

REACTION TYPE: Hydrogenation of α-acylaminoacrylic acids and amides.

CATALYST: Rh(I) complex of bis(diphenylphosphinamino)cyclohexane and the N,N'-dimethyl derivative; [Rh(1,5-COD)(acac)]$^+$HClO$_4$ precursor

LIGANDS:

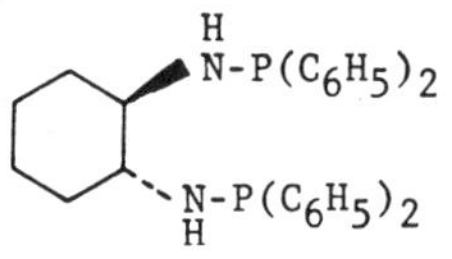

(R,R) - 1   (S,S) - 1   (R,R) - 2

SUBSTRATES:

$$C_6H_5-CH=C-COR'$$
$$\overset{\displaystyle NHCOR}{|}$$

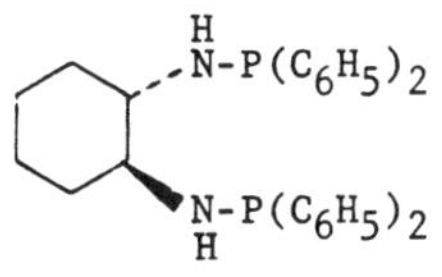

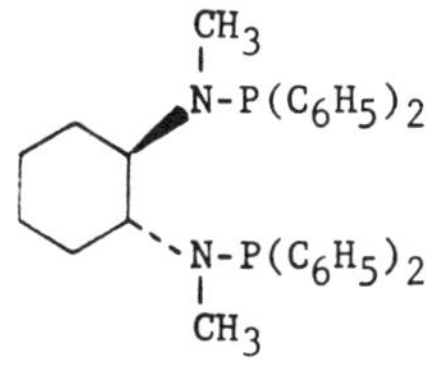

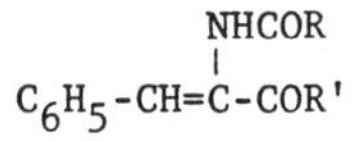

3a R=CH$_3$, R'=OH
3b R=CH$_3$, R'=NH$_2$
3c R=C$_6$H$_5$, R'=OH
3d R=C$_6$H$_5$, R'=NH$_2$

CONDITIONS: Solvent as noted; room temperature; 8 kg/cm^2 H$_2$ pressure

Substrate	Ligand	Solvent	% Optical Yield	Configuration
3a	(R,R)-1	EtOH	41	R
3a	(S,S)-1	EtOH	41	S
3a	(R,R)-2	EtOH	89	S
3a	(R,R)-1	EtOH-C$_6$H$_6$(1:1)	70	R
3a	(S,S)-1	EtOH-C$_6$H$_6$(1:1)	72	S
3b	(R,R)-1	EtOH-C$_6$H$_6$(1:1)	92	R
3b	(S,S)-1	EtOH-C$_6$H$_6$(1:1)	92	S
3c	(R,R)-1	EtOH	43	R
3c	(S,S)-1	EtOH	43	S
3c	(R,R)-2	EtOH	92	S
3c	(R,R)-1	EtOH-C$_6$H$_6$(1:1)	62	R
3c	(S,S)-1	EtOH-C$_6$H$_6$(1:1)	60	S
3d	(S,S)-1	EtOH-C$_6$H$_6$(1:1)	70	S

REFERENCE: K. Onuma, T. Ito, A. Nakamura, Tetrahedron Lett., (34), 3163 (1979).

REACTION TYPE: Hydrogenation of α-acylaminoacrylic acids and amides.

CATALYST: Rh(I) complex of bis(diphenylphosphinamino)cyclohexane, its N,N'-dimethyl derivative, and bis(diphenylphosphinamino)butane; [Rh(COD)(acac)] + $HClO_4$ precursor

LIGANDS:

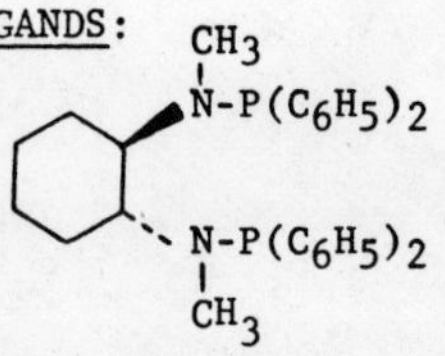

(R,R)-1

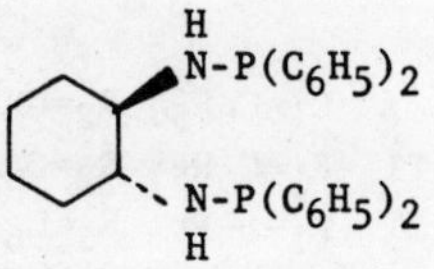

(R,R)-2

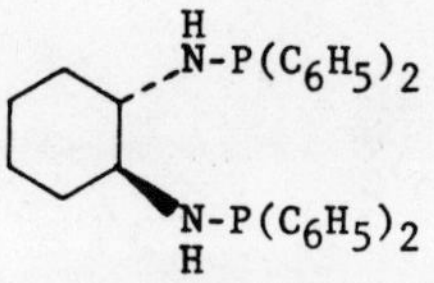

(S,S)-2

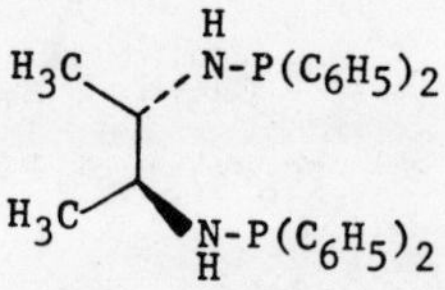

(S,S)-3

SUBSTRATES:

NHCOR
|
C_6H_5-CH=C-COR'

4a R=CH_3 R'=OH
4b R=CH_3 R'=NH_2
4c R=C_6H_5 R'=OH
4d R=C_6H_5 R'=NH_2

CONDITIONS: Solvent or mixed solvent (1:1, v/v) as noted; room temperature; 8 kg/cm^2 H_2 pressure

Substrate	Ligand	Solvent	% Optical Yield	Configuration
4a	(S,S)-2	MeOH	30	S
4a	(R,R)-2	EtOH	41	R
4a	(S,S)-2	EtOH	41	S
4a	(S,S)-3	EtOH	45	S
4a	(R,R)-1	EtOH	89	S
4a	(S,S)-2	2-propanol	71	S
4a	(S,S)-3	2-propanol	80	S
4a	(S,S)-2	MeOH/C_6H_6	50	S
4a	(R,R)-2	EtOH/C_6H_6	70	R
4a	(S,S)-2	EtOH C_6H_5	72	S
4a	(S,S)-3	EtOH/C_6H_6	62	S
4a	(S,S)-2	i-PrOH/C_6H_6	63	S
4a	(S,S)-3	i-PrOH/C_6H_6	94	S
4b	(R,R)-2	EtOH/C_6H_6	92	R
4b	(S,S)-2	EtOH/C_6H_6	92	S
4b	(S,S)-3	EtOH/C_6H_6	94	S
4c	(R,R)-2	EtOH	43	R
4c	(S,S)-2	EtOH	43	S
4c	(S,S)-3	EtOH	32	S
4c	(R,R)-1	EtOH	92	S
4c	(S,S)-2	i-PrOH	70	S
4c	(S,S)-3	i-PrOH	80	S
4c	(R,R)-2	EtOH/C_6H_6	62	R
4c	(S,S)-2	EtOH/C_6H_6	60	S
4c	(S,S)-3	EtOH/C_6H_6	69	S
4c	(S,S)-2	i-PrOH/C_6H_6	48	S
4c	(S,S)-3	i-PrOH/C_6H_6	93	S
4d	(S,S)-2	EtOH/C_6H_6	70	S
4d	(S,S)-3	EtOH/C_6H_6	80	S

REFERENCE: K. Onuma, T. Ito, A. Nakamura, Chem. Lett., 905 (1979).

REACTION TYPE: Hydrogenation of α-acetamidoacrylic acid derivatives (esters).

CATALYST: Rh(I) complex of [(-)1,1'-Bi-2-naphthylbis(diphenylphosphinite)] (III); $[Rh(cyclooctene)_2Cl]_2$ precursor

LIGAND:

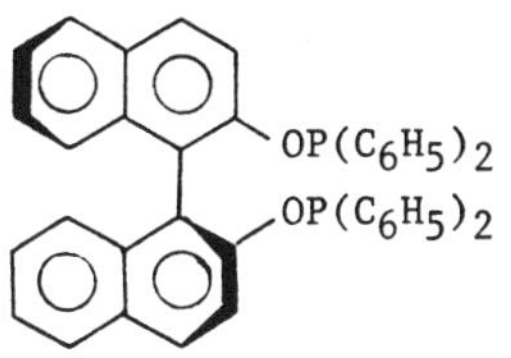

(-)-III

SUBSTRATES:

NHCOCH₃ on the α-carbon: $R-CH=C(NHCOCH_3)-COOCH_3$

A R=C_6H_5
B R=H

CONDITIONS: acetone/toluene (1:1); 0°C for 24-68.5 hrs.; 91-97 atm H_2; substrate/catalyst ratio of 50:1

Substrate	% Optical Yield
A	76
B	76

REFERENCE: R.H. Grubbs, R.A. DeVries, Tetrahedron Lett., (22), 1879 (1977).

REACTION TYPE: Hydrogenation of α-acylaminoacrylic acids.

CATALYST: Rh(I) complex of d-trans-1,2-bis(diphenylphosphinoxy)cyclohexane and d-trans-1,2-bis(diphenylphosphinoxy)cyclopentane; $[Rh(1,5-hexadiene)Cl]_2$ precursor

LIGANDS:

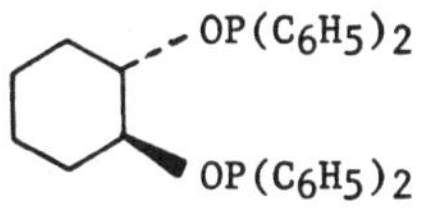

d-trans-BDPCH

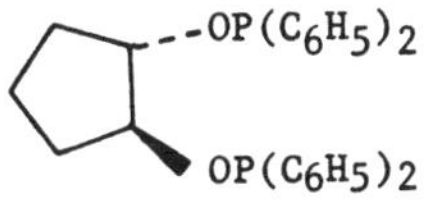

d-trans-BDPCP

SUBSTRATES:

$R-CH=C(NHCOCH_3)-COOH$

I R=C_6H_5
II R=H

CONDITIONS: no solvent noted; temperature as noted; 50 atm H_2

Substrate	Ligand	Temperature	% Optical Yield	Configuration
I	BDPCH	0	68.5	S
II	BDPCH	-20	78.9	S
I	BDPCP	0	12	S
II	BDPCP	-20	0	-

REFERENCE: T. Hayashi, M. Tanaka, I. Ogata, Tetrahedron Lett., (3), 295 (1977).

REACTION TYPE: Hydrogenation of α-acetamidoacrylic acids and esters.

CATALYST: Rh(I) complex of a D-glucose derivative: methyl-2,3-bis-O-diphenylphos-
phino-4,6-O-benzylidene-α-D-glucopyranoside; [RhCl(NBD)]$_2$ + AgPF$_6$ precursor

LIGAND:

(2) α-POOP

SUBSTRATES:

$$\underset{R'CH=C-COOR''}{\overset{NHCOCH_3}{|}}$$

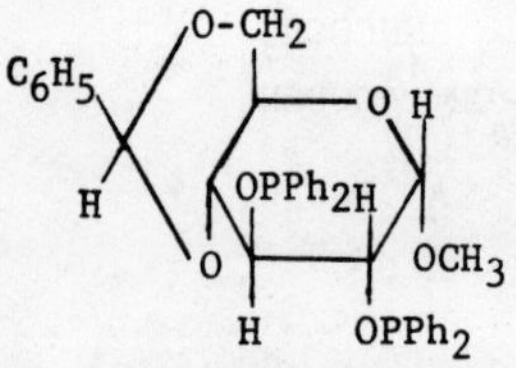

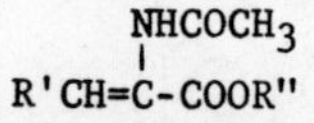

4a   R'=H, R''=H
4b   R'=C$_6$H$_5$, R''=H
4c   R'=H, R''=CH$_3$
4d   R'=C$_6$H$_5$, R'=CH$_3$

CONDITIONS: EtOH; temperature as noted for time as noted; 1 atm H$_2$; substrate/catalyst
molar ratio of 100:1

Sub-strate	Temp. (°C)/ time (min.)	% ee	Config-uration	Sub-strate	Temp. (°C)/ time (min.)	% ee	Config-uration
4a	30°/20 min.	68	S	4c	30°/10 min.	53	S
4a	0°/30 min.	74	S	4c	0°/30 min.	78	S
4a	-20°/60 min.	80	S	4d	30°/30 min.	60	S
4b	30°/60 min.	61	S	4d	0°/180 min.	65	S
4b	0°/90 min.	75	S				

REFERENCE: W.R. Cullen, Y. Sugi, Tetrahedron Lett., (19), 1635 (1978).

REACTION TYPE: Hydrogenation of α-acetamidoacrylic acids and esters.

CATALYST: Rh(I) complex of a D-glucose derivative: methyl-2,3-bis-O-diphenylphos-
phino-4,6-O-benzylidene-β-D-glucopyranoside; [RhCl(NBD)]$_2$ + AgPF$_6$ precursor

LIGAND:

β-POOP

SUBSTRATES:

$$\underset{R-CH=C-COOR'}{\overset{NHCOCH_3}{|}}$$

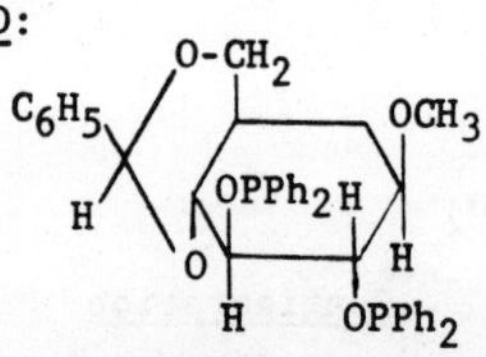

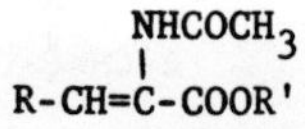

2a   R=H, R'=H
2b   R=C$_6$H$_5$, R'=H
2c   R=H, R'=CH$_3$
2d   R=C$_6$H$_5$, R'=CH$_3$

CONDITIONS: EtOH; temperature as noted for time as noted; 1 atm H$_2$; substrate/catalyst
molar ratio of 200:1

Substrate	temp./time	% ee	Config-uration	Substrate	temp./time	% ee	Config-uration
2a	30°/6 min.	90	S	2c	30°/5 min.	84	S
2a	0°/10 min.	90	S	2c	0°/10 min.	88	S
2b	30°/8 min.	91	S	2d	30°/25 min.	80	S
2b	0°/30 min.	90	S	2d	0°/70 min.	79	S

REFERENCE: Y. Sugi, W.R. Cullen, Chem. Lett., 39 (1979).

REACTION TYPE: Hydrogenation of an α-acylaminoacrylic acid.

CATALYST: Rh(I) complexes of BPPM, (-)DIOP, and DIPAMP; $[RhCl(1,5\text{-}COD)]_2$ or $[Rh(1,5\text{-}COD)(acac)] + HClO_4$ precursors

LIGANDS:

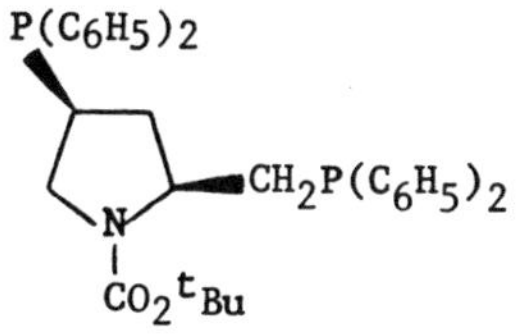

BPPM

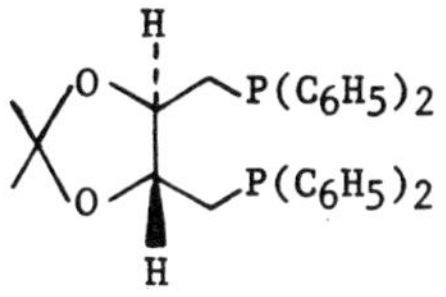

DIOP

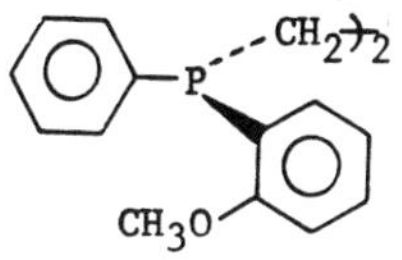

DIPAMP

SUBSTRATE:

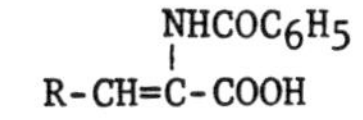

1 $R=C_6H_5$

CONDITIONS: EtOH; 25°C for 3-15 hrs.; H_2 pressure as noted; substrate/catalyst molar ratio of 100:1

Ligand	Catalyst Precursor	% ee at 1 atm H_2	% ee at 5 atm H_2	% ee at 20 atm H_2	% ee at 50 atm H_2	% ee at 100 atm H_2
BPPM	$Rh(COD)(acac)+HClO_4$	83.8 (R)**	62.3 (R)	21.2 (R)	4.7 (S)	8.4 (S)
BPPM*	$Rh(COD)(acac)+HClO_4$	93.3 (R)	83.5 (R)	78.7 (R)	66.2 (R)	64.2 (R)
BPPM	$[RhCl(COD)]_2$	84.0 (R)	67.6 (R)	12.9 (R)	8.6 (S)	14.4 (S)
BPPM*	$[RhCl(COD)]_2$	91.8 (R)	81.9 (R)	75.5 (R)	66.6 (R)	63.2 (R)
(-)DIOP	$Rh(COD)(acac)+HClO_4$	55.2 (R)	8.4 (R)	0.5 (S)	4.9 (S)	
(-)DIOP*	$Rh(COD)(acac)+HClO_4$	-	41.1 (R)	33.1 (R)	32.2 (R)	
(-)DIOP	$[RhCl(COD)]_2$	60.5 (R)	38.8 (R)	16.5 (R)	9.1 (R)	
(-)DIOP*	$[RhCl(COD)]_2$	61.8 (R)	49.4 (R)	48.1 (R)	46.8 (R)	
DIPAMP	$Rh(COD)(acac)+HClO_4$		63.6 (S)		29.9 (S)	
DIPAMP	$Rh(COD)(acac)+HClO_4$		88.1 (S)		83.8 (S)	
DIPAMP	$[RhCl(COD)]_2$		85.0 (S)		66.2 (S)	
DIPAMP	$[RhCl(COD)]_2$		88.6 (S)		86.7 (S)	

*NEt_3 added

**Configuration

REFERENCE: I. Ojima, T. Kogure, N. Yoda, Chem. Lett., 495 (1979).

REACTION TYPE: Hydrogenation of α-acylaminoacrylic acid and ester derivatives.

CATALYST: Rh(I) complexes of phosphine ligands; $[RhCl(1,5\text{-}COD)]_2$ precursor

LIGANDS:

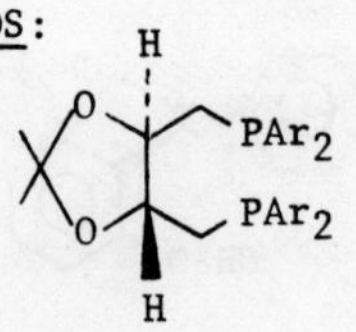

16a Ar=C_6H_5
16b Ar=3-$CH_3C_6H_4$
16c Ar=3,5-$(CH_3)_2C_6H_3$
16d Ar=3,4-$(CH_3)_2C_6H_3$
16e Ar=4-$CH_3C_6H_4$
16f Ar=3-$CH_3OC_6H_4$
16g Ar=3-ClC_6H_4
16h Ar=2-$CH_3OC_6H_4$

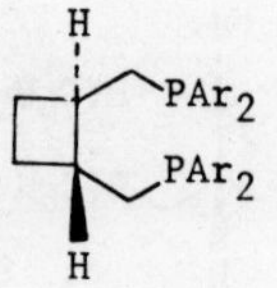

17a Ar=C_6H_5
17b Ar=3-$CH_3C_6H_4$

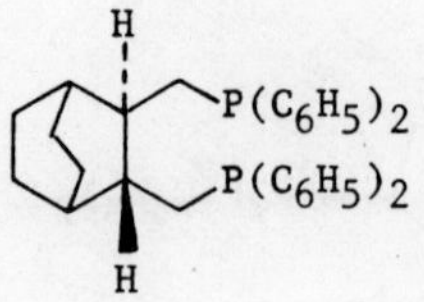

R,R-18

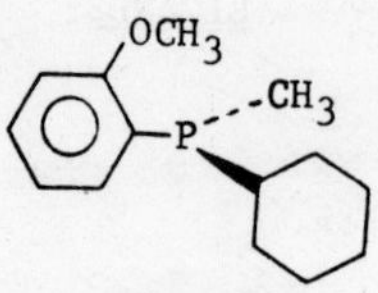

R-19 (ACMP)

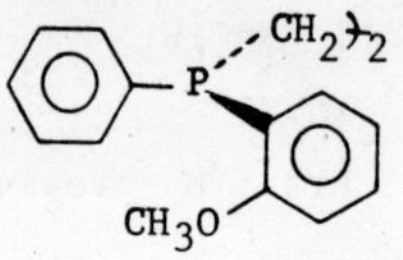

R,R-20 (DIPAMP)

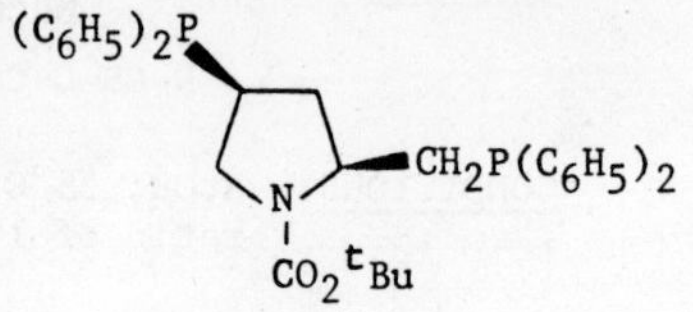

S,S-21 (BPPM)

SUBSTRATES:

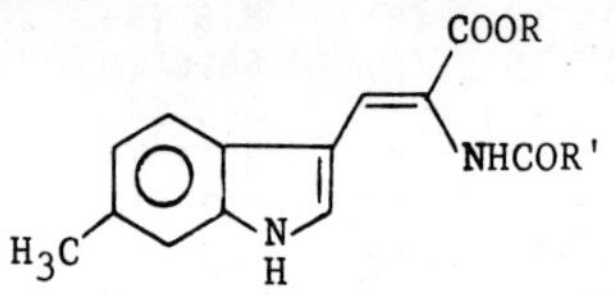

8a R'=CH_3, R=CH_3
8b R'=CH_2Cl, R=CH_3
8c R'=H, R=CH_3
8d R'=CH_3, R=C_2H_5
9 R'=CH_3, R=H

CONDITIONS: Purified MeOH ;23°C;40 psi initial H_2 pressure; substrate/catalyst weight ratios of (100-3000):1

Substrate	Ligand	% ee	Configuration	Substrate	Ligand	% ee	Configuration
8b	16b	72	R	9	16e	71.6	R
8c	16b	67	R	9	16f	72.2	R
8d	16b	70	R	9	17a	77.6	R
9	16b	82	R	9	18	85.6	R
8a (55°C)	20	95	S	9 (50°C)	19	67	S
8c (50°C/	20	92	S	9 (65°C)	20	91.2	S
100 psi)				9	21	90	R
8d (50°C)	20	96	S	8d	16b	70.4	R
9 (65°C)	20	91	S	8d	16c	70.8	R
9	16a	73.2	R	8d	16f	64.9	R
9	16b	83	R	8d	18	72	R
9	16c	86	R	8d (50°C)	20	96.2	S
9	16d	77.8	R	8d	21	87	R

REFERENCE: U. Hengartner, D. Valentine,Jr., R.K. Johnson, M.E. Larscheid, F. Pigott, F. Scheidl, J.W. Scott, R.C. Sun, J.M. Townsend, T.H. Williams, J. Org. Chem., 44, 3741 (1979).

REACTION TYPE: Hydrogenation of substituted acrylic acids

CATALYST: Rh(I) complex of the bis(phosphinite) IDOPHINITE (6) and the bis(phosphines) GLUCOPHOS (8) and IDOPHOS (3); $[Rh(COD)BF_4]_2$ precursor

LIGANDS:

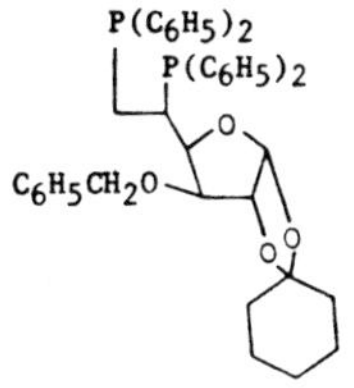

IDOPHOS (3)

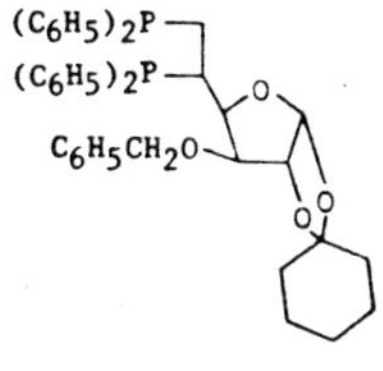

GLUCOPHOS (8)

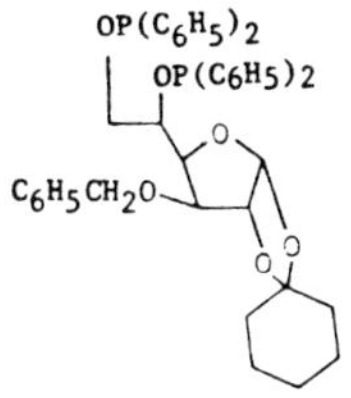

IDOPHINITE (6)

SUBSTRATES:

R^1-CH=C(R^2)-COOH

I $R^1 = C_6H_5$ $R^2 = CH_3$

II R^1 = 4-(AcO)-3-(OCH_3)C_6H_3, R^2 = $NHCOCH_3$

CONDITIONS: THF; room temperature for 1 hr; 1 atm H_2; substrate/catalyst molar ratio of 100:1; NEt_3 added

Substrate	Ligand	% ee	Configuration
I	6	48	S
I	8	61	R
II	3	67	S
II	6	65	S
II	8	37	R

REFERENCE: T.H. Johnson, G. Rangarajan, J. Org. Chem., 45, 62 (1980).

REACTION TYPE: Hydrogenation of a β-keto acid derivative (ester).

CATALYST: Asymmetrically modified Raney Ni

LIGAND: Tartaric acid as the modifying agent in the presence of various inorganic salts

2 tartaric acid + NaBr
5 tartaric acid + NaF
6 tartaric acid + NaCl
11 tartaric acid + $NiBr_2$

SUBSTRATE:

CH_3-C(=O)-CH_2-$COOCH_3$

CONDITIONS: (of hydrogenation) Methyl propionate solvent; 100°C for 1 hr.; 90 kg/cm^2 H_2

Ligand	% Optical Yield	Ligand	% Optical Yield
2	83.1	6	72.1
5	60.8	11	62.6

REFERENCE: T. Harada, Y. Izumi, Chem. Lett., 1195 (1978).

REACTION TYPE: Hydrogenation of α-keto acids via transamination to yield optically active acids.

CATALYST: Pd/C; Pd(OH)$_2$/C

LIGAND: Reaction of chiral $\underline{A}$ with $\underline{B}$ yields the optically active amino acid $\underline{C}$

$$C_6H_5\overset{H}{\underset{CH_3}{\overset{*|}{\underset{|}{C}}}}-NH_2 \quad + \quad R\overset{O}{\overset{||}{C}}-COOH \quad \xrightarrow[\text{2) Pd(OH)$_2$/H$_2$}]{\text{1) Pd/H$_2$}} \quad R\overset{NH_2}{\underset{H}{\overset{*|}{\underset{|}{C}}}}-COOH$$

$$\underline{A} \qquad\qquad \underline{B} \qquad\qquad\qquad\qquad\qquad \underline{C}$$

SUBSTRATES:

$\underline{B-1}$	R=CH$_3$	$\underline{B-3}$	R=Et
$\underline{B-2}$	R=CH$_3$ (benzyl ester)	$\underline{B-4}$	R=i-Pr

CONDITIONS: EtOH; 30°C/10 hrs.; 50 psi H$_2$; substrate/amine molar ratio of 2:1

Substrate	Ligand	% ee		Substrate	Ligand	% ee	
$\underline{B-1}$	(L)-$\underline{A}$	90.7	(L)-$\underline{C}$	$\underline{B-3}$	(L)-$\underline{A}$	81.4	(L)-$\underline{C}$
$\underline{B-2}$	(L)-$\underline{A}$	87.0	(L)-$\underline{C}$	$\underline{B-4}$	(D)-$\underline{A}$	64.2	(D)-$\underline{C}$

REFERENCE: R.G. Hiskey, R.C. Northrop, J. Am. Chem. Soc., $\underline{83}$, 4798 (1961).

REACTION TYPE: Hydrogenation of cyclic dipeptides to give L-amino acids upon hydrolysis.

CATALYST: Pd black

LIGAND: Synthesis of chiral $\underline{4}$ from $\underline{2}$ + an aldehyde, followed by hydrogenation and hydrolysis

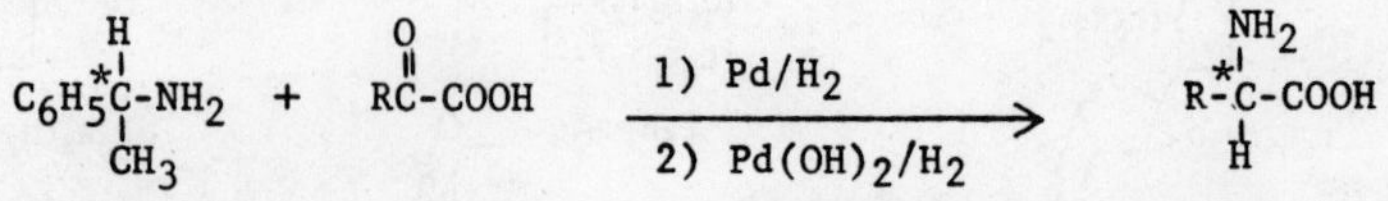

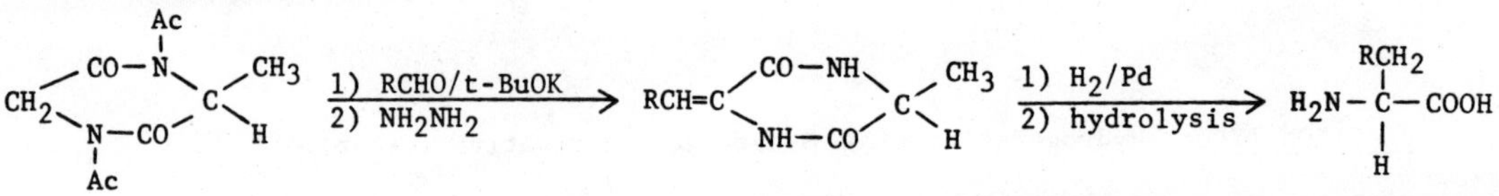

$$\underset{\underline{2}}{\text{(structure)}} \quad \xrightarrow[\text{2) NH$_2$NH$_2$}]{\text{1) RCHO/t-BuOK}} \quad \underset{\underline{4}}{\text{(structure)}} \quad \xrightarrow[\text{2) hydrolysis}]{\text{1) H$_2$/Pd}} \quad \underset{\underline{6}}{H_2N-\overset{RCH_2}{\underset{H}{\overset{|}{\underset{|}{C}}}}-COOH}$$

SUBSTRATES:

4-1	R=CH$_3$	4-26	R=C$_6$H$_5$CH$_2$CH$_2$
4-7	R=i-Pr	4-29	R=3-indolyl
4-19	R=C$_6$H$_5$		

CONDITIONS: MeOH; 25°C for 1-2 hrs.; 1 atm H$_2$

Substrate	% Chiral Induction*		Substrate	% Chiral Induction*
4-1	99		4-26	98
4-7	98		4-29	71
4-19	88			

*defined as % new L-amino acid minus % new D-amino acid

REFERENCE: T. Kanmera, S. Lee, H. Aoyagi, N. Izumiya, Tetrahedron Lett., (46), 4483 (1979).

REACTION TYPE: Synthesis of an optically active amino acid by the addition of an amine to a C-C double bond containing a chiral ligand.

CATALYST: No transition metal

LIGAND: Addition of amine 2 to chiral I (prepared by the addition of the chiral amine to the corresponding anhydride) followed by hydrolysis and debenzylation yields a chiral amino acid

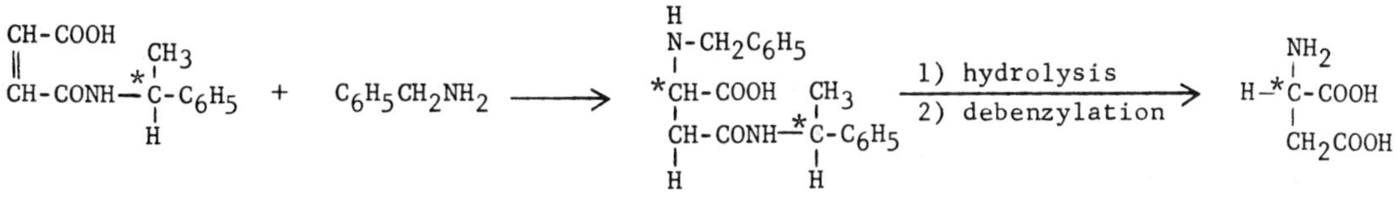

I 2

SUBSTRATE: I

CONDITIONS: (of addition) H_2O; reflux for 3 hrs.
(of hydrolysis) 48% HBr; reflux for 6 hrs.

Substrate	% Optical Yield
I	60

REFERENCE: Y. Liwschitz, A. Singerman, J. Chem. Soc. (C), 1200 (1966).

REACTION TYPE: Alkylation of a chiral oxazoline to give a chiral alkanoic acid upon hydrolysis.

CATALYST: No transition metal

LIGAND: No ligand; the chiral oxazoline induces chirality at the prochiral center

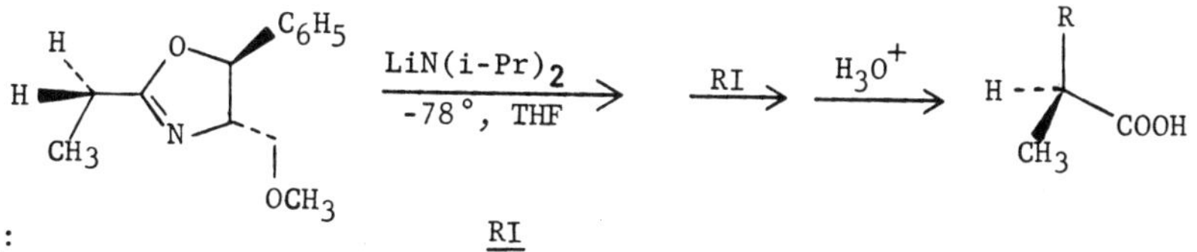

SUBSTRATES:

	RI
I	R=Et
II	R=n-Pr
III	R=n-Bu

CONDITIONS: (of alkylation reaction) THF; low temperature

Substrate	% Optical Yield	Configuration*
I	76	S
II	78	S
III	75	S

*From (4S,5S)-oxazoline

REFERENCE: A.I. Meyers, G. Knaus, K. Kamata, J. Am. Chem. Soc., 96, 268 (1974).

REACTION TYPE: Alkylation of a chiral oxazoline to give a chiral dialkylacetic acid upon hydrolysis.

CATALYST: No transition metal

LIGAND: No ligand; the chiral oxazoline induces chirality at the prochiral center

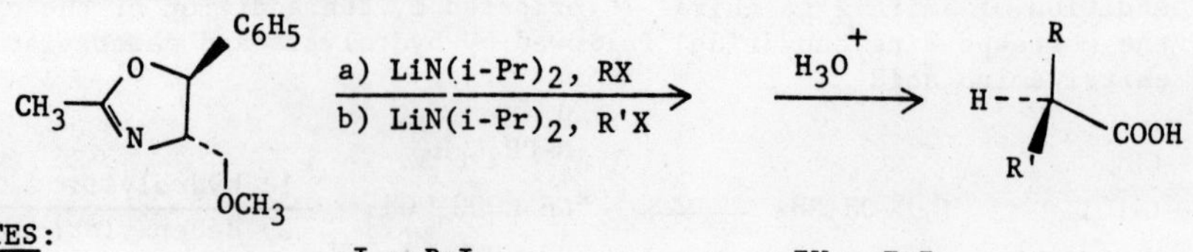

SUBSTRATES:

I = BuI
II = $C_6H_5CH_2Cl$
III = n-PrI
IV = EtI
V = Me_2SO_4

CONDITIONS: (of alkylation reactions) THF; -78°C.

Substrate RX	Substrate R'X	% Enantiomeric Purity	Configuration*
I	II	70	S
II	I	73	R
III	V	61	R
IV	V	70	R
II	V	63	R

*from (4S,5S)-oxazoline

REFERENCE: A.I. Meyers, G. Knaus, J. Am. Chem. Soc., 96, 6508 (1974).

REACTION TYPE: Alkylation of a chiral oxazoline to give a chiral 3-substituted alkanoic acid upon hydrolysis

CATALYST: No transition metal

LIGAND: No ligand; the chiral oxazoline induces chirality at the prochiral center

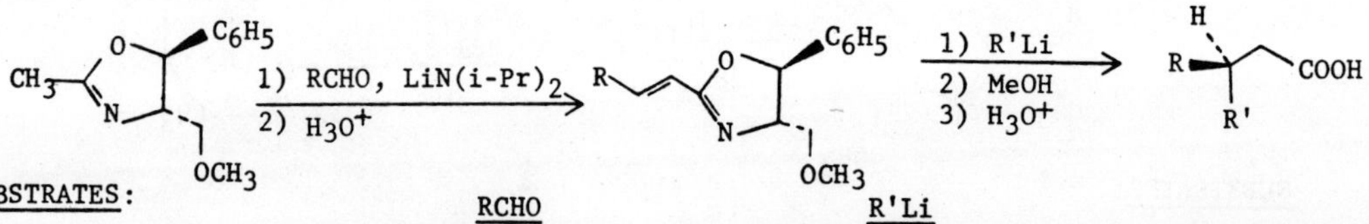

SUBSTRATES:

RCHO		R'Li	
I	R=CH_3	IV	R'=Et
II	R=Et	V	R'=n-Bu
III	R=C_6H_5	VI	R'=C_6H_5

CONDITIONS: (of both alkylation reactions) THF; -78°C

Substrate RCHO	Substrate R'Li	% Optical Purity	Configuration*
I	IV	92	R
I	V	91	R
I	VI	98	S
II	V	61	R
II	VI	92	S
III	IV	97	R
III	V	>95	R

*From (4S,5S)-Oxazoline

REFERENCE: A.I. Meyers, C.E. Whitten, J. Am. Chem. Soc., 97, 6266 (1975).

REACTION TYPE: Alkylation of a chiral oxazoline to give a chiral 5-methoxy-3-substituted acid upon hydrolysis.

CATALYST: No transition metal

LIGAND: No ligand; the chiral oxazoline induces chirality at the prochiral center

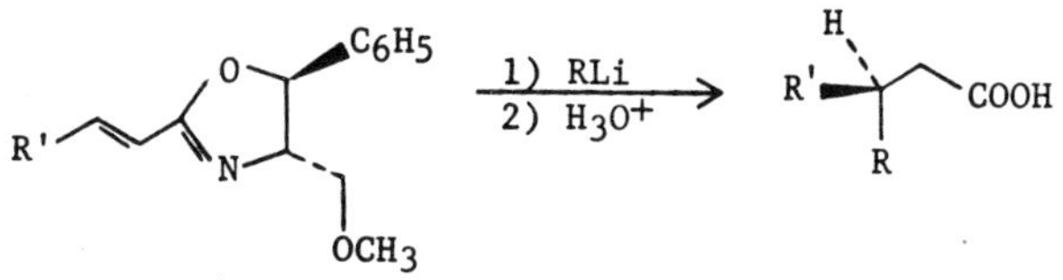

SUBSTRATES:

	R'		RLi
4	$MeOCH_2CH_2$	I	EtLi
5	2-(MeO)C_6H_4	II	n-BuLi
		III	C_6H_5Li

CONDITIONS: (of alkylation reaction) THF; -78°C

Substrate R'	RLi	% ee	Configuration	Substrate R'	RLi	% ee	Configuration
4	I	85	S	5	I	75	R
4	II	81	S	5	II	81	R
4	III	89	S	5	III	85	S

REFERENCE: A.I. Meyers, C.E. Whitten, Tetrahedron Lett., (23), 1947 (1976).

REACTION TYPE: Alkylation of chiral oxazolines to give chiral R and S α-alkylalkanoic acids.

CATALYST: No transition metal

LIGAND: No ligand; the chiral oxazoline induces chirality at the prochiral center

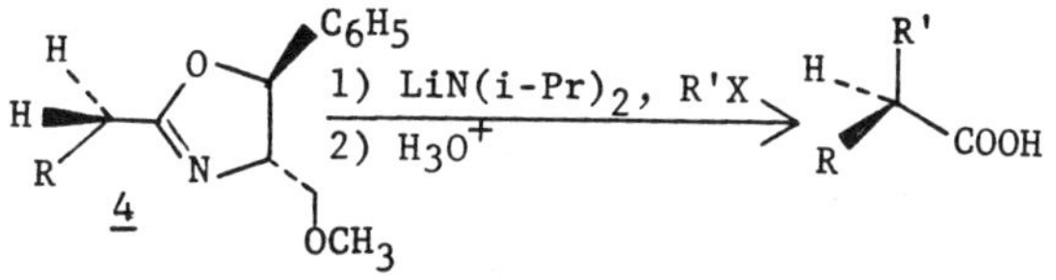

SUBSTRATES:

R				R'X			
4a	R=H	4e	R=n-Bu	I	EtI	IV	n-BuI
4b	R=Me	4f	R=$C_6H_5CH_2$	II	Me_2SO_4	V	$C_6H_5CH_2Cl$
4c	R=Et	4g	R=C_6H_5	III	n-PrI	VI	i-PrI
4d	R=n-Pr						

CONDITIONS: (of alkylation reaction) THF; -98° to -63°C.

Substrate R	R'X	% Optical Purity	Configuration	Substrate R	R'X	% Optical Purity	Configuration
4b	III	72	S	4f	II	78	R
4b	I	78	S	4c	V	85	S
4d	II	72	R	4f	I	73	R
4c	II	79	R	4e	V	82	S
4b	IV	75	S	4f	IV	86	R
4e	II	70	R	4g	III	56	R
4b	V	74	S	4g	VI	65	R

REFERENCE: A.I. Meyers, G. Knaus, K. Kamata, M.E. Ford, J. Am. Chem. Soc., 98, 567 (1976).

REACTION TYPE: Synthesis of optically active α-hydroxy acids from α,β-unsaturated acids via an asymmetric halolactonization reaction.

CATALYST: No transition metal

LIGAND: Addition of the chiral 4 to the substrate unsaturated acid yields chiral product after bromolactonization, debromination, and hydrolysis.

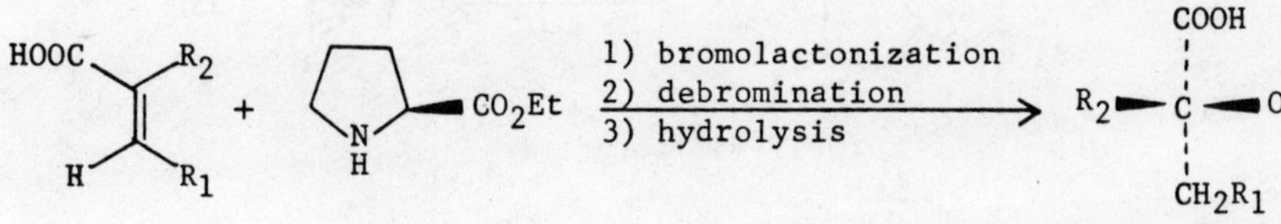

1 4 (R)-9

SUBSTRATES: 1a $R_1=R_2=CH_3$
1b $R_1=C_6H_5$, $R_2=CH_3$

CONDITIONS: (of bromolactonization) Reaction of the addition product from 1a + 4a with N-bromosuccinimide in DMF; room temperature for 20 hrs.
(of debromination) Tri-n-butyltin hydride in benzene; 90-100°C for 15 hrs.

Substrate	% Optical yield of 9	Configuration
1a	89%	R
1b	98%	R

REFERENCE: S. Tershima, S.-S. Jew, Tetrahedron Lett., (11), 1005 (1977).

REACTION TYPE: Synthesis of optically active α-hydroxy acids from α,β-unsaturated acids via an asymmetric halolactonization reaction.

CATALYST: No transition metal

LIGAND: Addition of the chiral 9 to the substrate unsaturated acid yields chiral product after bromolactonization, debromination, and hydrolysis.

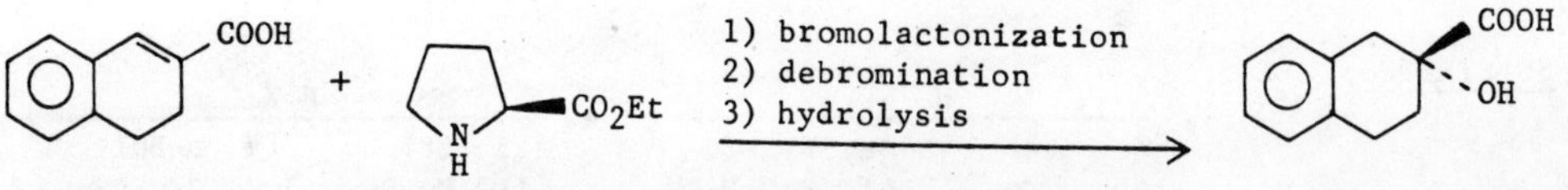

7 9 (R)-8

SUBSTRATE: 7

CONDITIONS: (of bromolactonization) Reaction of the potassium salt of the addition product from 7 + 9 (after ester hydrolysis) with NBS in DMF; -20° for 2 hrs., then room temperature for 48 hrs.

(of debromination): Tri-n-butyltin hydride and azobisisobutyronitrile in bromobenzene; 65°C for 9 hrs.

Substrate	% Optical Yield of 8	Configuration
7	92	R

REFERENCE: S. Terashima, S.-S. Jew, K. Koga, Tetrahedron Lett., (51), 4507 (1977).

REACTION TYPE: Synthesis of amino acids via asymmetric hydrocyanation of Schiff bases.

CATALYST: No transition metal

LIGAND: Addition of chiral 2a to the substrate aldehyde yields a Schiff base; hydrocyanation, ester and nitrile hydrolysis, decarboxylation, and amide hydrolysis gives the chiral product.

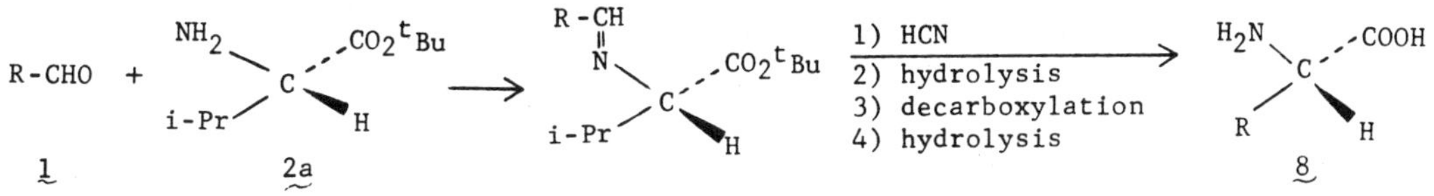

SUBSTRATE: 1, $R=C_6H_5$

CONDITIONS: (of hydrocyanation) MeOH solution of 1 + 2a; -23°C for 3 hrs.; HCN/substrate molar ratio of 6:1

Substrate	% Optical Yield*
1	63

*measured on the precursor amide

REFERENCE: S. Yamada, S. Hashimoto, Chem. Lett., 921 (1976).

REACTION TYPE: Synthesis of optically active α-alkyl-α-aminocarboxylic acids by alkylation of chiral 2-imidazolin-5-ones.

CATALYST: No transition metal

LIGAND: Addition of chiral 2 to the substrate isocyanoalkanoate 1 yields a chiral 2-imidazolin-5-one after metallation (8); chiral amino acid 11 is obtained after alkylation with 9 and hydrolysis

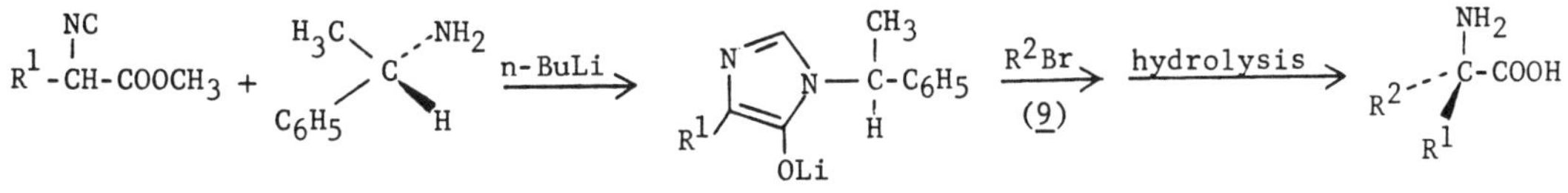

(1) (S)-(2) (8) (11)

SUBSTRATES: 1' $R^1=CH_3$; 1" $R^1=C_6H_5CH_2$

9a $R^2=C_6H_5CH_2$
9d R^2=(1-naphthyl)methyl
9e R^2=(2-naphthyl)methyl
9f R^2=(2-thienyl)methyl
9g R^2=(3-benzothienyl)methyl
9h R^2=(2-bromo-3-benzofuranyl)methyl
9t $R^2=(4\text{-}BrC_6H_4)CH_2$

CONDITIONS: (of alkylation) THF; -70° to -60°C., then warm to room temperature;neutralize
(of hydrolysis) KOH in $EtOH/H_2O$ (2:1, v/v).

Substrates		% Optical Yield	Configuration
1'	9a	>95	S
1'	9d	>95	S
1'	9e	>95	S
1'	9f	>95	S
1'	9g	>95	S
1'	9h	>95	S
1"	9t	100	S

REFERENCE: U. Schöllkopf, H.H. Hausberg, I. Hoppe, M. Segal, U. Reiter, Angew. Chem. Int. Ed. Engl., 17, 117 (1978).

REACTION TYPE: Synthesis of optically active α-alkyl-α-aminocarboxylic acids by alkylation of a chiral dihydropyrazine.

CATALYST: No transition metal

LIGAND: Synthesis of chiral 3 allows for the formation of chiral amino acid esters 7 via alkylation with 5 and subsequent hydrolysis

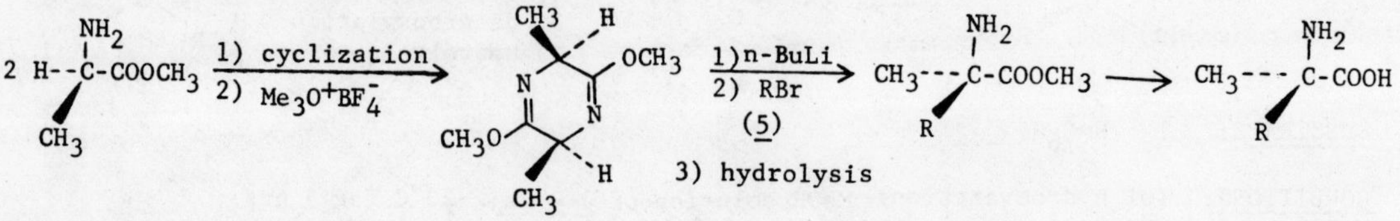

3

7

SUBSTRATES:

- 5a $R=C_6H_5CH_2$
- 5b $R=[3.4-(CH_3O)_2C_6H_3]CH_2$
- 5c $R=(2\text{-naphthyl})CH_2$
- 5d $R=(2\text{-quinolyl})CH_2$
- 5e $R=(3\text{-pyridyl})CH_2$
- 5f R=allyl
- 5g R=i-Pr
- 5h $R=(C_6H_5)_2C(OH)$

CONDITIONS: (of alkylation) THF; -70°C for 2-10 hrs., warm to room temperature and hydrolyze

Substrate	% ee	Configuration
5a	~93	R
5b	~90	R
5c	~90	R
5d	~93	R

Substrate	% ee	Configuration
5e	~ 90	R
5f	~ 90	R
5g	~ 92*	R
5h	>95*	R

*% asymmetric induction; slightly higher than % ee because 3 is not 100% optically pure

REFERENCE: U. Schöllkopf, W. Hartwig, U. Groth, Angew. Chem. Int. Ed. Engl., 18, 863 (1979).

SECTION 7

REFERENCE LIST

REFERENCE LIST

Reference Number

1 J. Read and A.M. McMath, J. Chem. Soc., 2723 (1932).
1a W.J. Pope and J. Read, J. Chem. Soc., 105, 811 (1914).
2 H.J. Backer and H.W. Mook, J. Chem. Soc., 2125 (1928).
3 G. Bellucci, G. Berti, A. Borraccini and F. Macchia, Tetrahedron, 25, 2979 (1969).
4 A.M. McMath and J. Read, J. Chem. Soc., 537 (1927).
5 H.J. Backer and H.W. Mook, Rec. Trav. Chim., 47, 464 (1928).
6 H.J. Backer and W.G. Burgers, J. Chem. Soc., 127, 233 (1925).
6a J. Read and A.M. McMath, J. Chem. Soc., 2192 (1926).
7 E. Fischer and O. Warburg, Liebigs Ann., 340, 123 (1905).
8 K. Freudenberg, Chem. Ber., 47, 2027 (1914).
9 S. Tsunoo, Chem. Ber., 68, 1341 (1935).
10 G. Gal, J.M. Chemerda, D.F. Reinhold and R.M. Purick, J. Org. Chem., 42, 142 (1977).
11 E. Hannerz, Chem. Ber., 59B, 1367 (1926).
12 K. Freudenberg and L. Markert, Chem. Ber., 60, 2447 (1927).
13 C. Neuberg and M. Silbermann, Chem. Ber., 37, 339 (1904).
14 H.J. Backer and W. Van Dam, Rec. Trav. Chim., 48, 1287 (1929).
15 A.P.N. Franchimont and H.J. Backer, Rec. Trav. Chim., 39, 751 (1920).
16 H.J. Backer and R.D. Mulder, Rec. Trav. Chim., 62, 53 (1943).
17 H.J. Backer and C.H.K. Mulder, Rec. Trav. Chim., 55, 594 (1936).
18 W. Langenbeck and O. Herbst, Chem. Ber., 86, 1524 (1953).
18a G. Amiard, R. Heymes and L. Velluz, U. S. Patent 2,991,307 (1961).
18b M.S. Dunn, M.P. Stoddard, L.B. Rubin and R.C. Bovie, J. Biol. Chem., 151, 241 (1943).
18c T. Kato and Y. Tsuchiya, Agr. Biol. Chem., 26, 467 (1962).
18d K. Vogler and P. Lanz, Helv. Chim. Acta, 49, 1348 (1966).
18e K. Witkiewicz, F. Rulko and Z. Chabudzinski, Rocz. Chem., 48, 651 (1974).
18f G. Gal, J.M. Chemerda, D.F. Reinhold and R.M. Purick, J. Org. Chem., 42, 142 (1977).
18g K. Murakami, N. Katsuta, K. Takano, Y. Yamamoto, T. Kagegawa, K. Saigo and H. Nohira, Nippon Kagaku Kaishi, 765 (1979).
18h F.B. Kipping and W.J. Pope, J. Chem. Soc., 494 (1926).
18i D.F. Holmes and R. Adams, J. Am. Chem. Soc., 56, 2093 (1934).
18j I. Chibata, S. Yamada, M. Yamamoto and M. Wada, Experientia, 24, 638 (1968).
18k L.R. Overby and A.W. Ingersoll, J. Am. Chem. Soc., 82, 2067 (1960).
18-1 F.P. Dwyer, B. Halpern and K.R. Turnbull, Aust. J. Chem., 16, 510 (1963).
18m J.M. Gillingham, U. S. Patent 3,028,395 (1962).
18n C.G. Baker and H.A. Sober, J. Am. Chem. Soc., 75, 4058 (1953).
19 L.H. Werner, A. Wettstein and K. Miescher, Helv. Chim. Acta, 30, 432 (1947).
19a G. Losse and G. Moschall, J. Prakt. Chem., 7, 38 (1958).
19b P. Rambacher and S. Mäke, German Patent 2,045,998 (1974).
20 E. Wunsch and G. Fürst, Z. Physiol. Chem., 329, 109 (1962).
20a A. Stoll and Th. Petrzilka, Helv. Chim. Acta, 35, 589 (1952).
20b G. Losse, H-J. Hebel and C. Kastner, J. Prakt. Chem., 8, 339 (1959).
20c G. Losse and M. Augustin, Chem. Ber., 91, 157 (1958).
20d G. Amiard, R. Heymes and L. Velluz, U. S. Patent 2.991.307 (1961).
20e G. Amiard, R. Heymes and L. Velluz, U. S. Patent 2,921,959 (1960).
20f B.F. Tullar, U. S. Patent 3,056,799 (1962).
20g T. Perlotto and M. Vignolo, Farmaco, Ed. Sci., 21, 30 (1966).
20h K. Oki, K. Suzuki, S. Tuchida, T. Saito and H. Kotake, Bull. Chem. Soc. Japan, 43, 2554 (1970).
20i J.M. Gillingham, U. S. Patent 3,028,395 (1962).
20j C.G. Baker and H.A. Sober, J. Am. Chem. Soc., 75, 4058 (1953).
21 Z. Grzonka and B. Liberek, Tetrahedron, 27, 1783 (1971).
22 B.G. Christensen, W.J. Leanza and T.R. Beattie, British Patent 1,204,448 (1970).
23 P.A. Levene and A. Schormüller, J. Biol. Chem., 106, 595 (1934).
24 E. Felder, D. Pitré and S. Boveri, Hoppe-Seyler's Z. Physiol Chem. 351, 943 (1970).
24a S.M. Birnbaum, R.J. Koegel, S-C. J. Fu and J.P. Greenstein, J. Biol. Chem. 198, 335 (1952).
25 A. McKenzie, J. Chem. Soc., 101, 1196 (1912).
26 B. Holmberg, Svensk Kem. Tidsk, 24, 105 (1912).
27 J. Oh-hashi and K. Harada, Bull. Chem. Soc. Japan, 40, 2977 (1967).
28 R. Kuhn and T. Wagner-Jauregg, Chem. Ber., 61B, 481 (1928).
29 R. Kuhn and R. Zell, Chem. Ber., 59, 2514 (1926).
30 A. McKenzie and H.J. Plenderleith, J. Chem. Soc., 1090 (1923).
30a D. Borrmann and R. Wegler, Chem. Ber., 100, 1575 (1967).
31 R.A. Darrall, F. Smith, M. Stacey and J.C. Tatlow, J. Chem. Soc., 2329 (1951).
32 C.E. Glassick and W.E. Adcock, Ind. Eng. Chem. Prod. Res. Develop., 3, 14 (1964).
33 G. Claeson, Arkiv Kemi, 30, 277 (1968).
34 K. Harada and J. Oh-hashi, Bull. Chem. Soc. Japan, 39, 2311 (1966).
34a D.J. Aberhart and L.J. Lin, J. Chem. Soc., Perkin 1, 2320 (1974)
34b E.J. Corey, E.J. Trybulski, L.S. Melvin,Jr., K.C. Nicolaou, J.A. Secrist, R. Lett, P.W. Sheldrake, J.R. Falck, D.J. Brunelle, M.F. Haslanger, S. Kim, and S-e Yoo, J. Am. Chem. Soc., 100, 4618 (1978).
35 M-O. Hedblom, Arkiv Kemi, 31, 489 (1969).
35a M. Gerecke, E.A.H. Friedheim and A. Brossi, Helv. Chim. Acta, 44, 955 (1961).
36 A. McKenzie, H.J. Plenderleith and N. Walker, J. Chem. Soc., 123, 2875 (1923).
36a F.W. Bachelor and G.A. Miana, Can. J. Chem., 45, 79 (1967).
36b H.D. Dakin, J. Biol. Chem., 59, 7 (1924).
36c J. Nishikawa, T. Ishizaki, F. Nakayama, H. Kawa, K. Saigo and H. Nohira, Nippon Kagaku Kaishi, 754 (1979).
37 R.B. Woodward and W.E. Doering, J. Am. Chem. Soc., 67, 860 (1945).

Reference
Number

37a W.T. Haskins and C.S. Hudson, J. Am. Chem. Soc., 61, 1266 (1939).
38 H.J. Backer and J.M. van der Zanden, Rec. Trav. Chim., 46, 473 (1927).
39 H.J. Backer and J.M. van der Zanden, Rec. Trav. Chim., 50, 645 (1931).
40 R. Ahlberg, J. Prakt. Chem., 135, 335 (1932).
40a P.A. Levene and M. Kuna, J. Biol. Chem., 141, 391 (1941).
40b G. Belucci, F. Marioni and A. Marsili, Tetrahedron, 25, 4167 (1969).
41 A.T. Bottini, V. Dev and M. Stewart, J. Org. Chem., 28, 156 (1963).
42 H. Scheibler and J. Magasanik, Chem. Ber., 48, 1810 (1915).
43 P. Friis, P. Helboe and P.O. Larsen, Acta Chem. Scand., B28, 317 (1974).
44 R.M. Rodebaugh and N.H. Cromwell, J. Heterocycl. Chem., 6, 993 (1969).
45 K. Harada, Bull Chem. Soc. Japan, 37, 1383 (1964).
45a E. Fischer, Chem. Ber., 32, 2451 (1899).
45b A. Yamamoto and H. Tsukamoto, Chem. Pharm. Bull., 13, 1131 (1965).
45c G. Losse and G. Moschall, J. Prakt. Chem., 7, 38 (1958).
45d B.F. Tullar, U. S. Patent 3,056,799 (1962).
45e K. Harada and S.W. Fox, Nature, 194, 768 (1962).
45f K. Harada, Nature, 206, 1354 (1965).
46 Y. Liwschitz, Y.E. Pfefferman and A. Singerman, J. Chem. Soc. (C), 2104 (1967).
46a H. Okai, N. Imamura and N. Izumiya, Bull. Chem. Soc. Japan, 40, 2154 (1967).
47 H. Okai, N. Imamura and N. Izumiya, Bull. Chem. Soc. Japan, 40, 2154 (1967).
47a Y. Liwschitz, A. Singerman and Y. Wiesel, Isr. J. Chem., 6, 647 (1968).
48 H.J. Backer and W. van Dam, Rec. Trav. Chim., 49, 482 (1930).
49 E. Fogassy, M. Acs and J. Gressay, Periodica Polytechnica, 20, 179 (1976).
49a G. Adembri and M. Ghelardoni, Gazz. Chim. Ital., 89, 1763 (1959).
50 J.F. Biernat and S. Ludwicka, Pol. J. Chem., 46, 1151 (1972).
51 A. Kjaer, B.W. Christensen and S.E. Hansen, Acta Chem. Scand., 13, 144 (1959).
51a P.A. Levene and H.L. Haller, J. Biol. Chem., 74, 343 (1927).
52 H.T. Clarke, J. Org. Chem., 24, 1610 (1959).
53 N.K. Kochetkov, A.M. Likhosherstov and V.N. Kulakov, Tetrahedron, 25, 2313 (1969).
54 J.W.E. Glattfield and F.V. Sander, J. Am. Chem. Soc., 43, 2675 (1921).
55 J.W.E. Glattfeld and G.E. Miller, J. Am. Chem. Soc., 42, 2314 (1920).
56 F.W. Bachelor and G.A. Miana, Can. J. Chem., 47, 4089 (1969).
57 F.W. Bachelor and G.A. Miana, Can. J. Chem., 47, 4089 (1969).
58 H.J. Backer and J.H. De Boer, Rec. Trav. Chim., 43, 297 (1924).
59 H.J. Backer and A. Bloemen, Rec. Trav. Chim., 45, 110 (1926).
60 H.J. Backer and N. Benninga, Rec. Trav. Chim., 55, 605 (1936).
61 H.J. Backer and R.D. Mulder, Rec. Trav. Chim., 62, 53 (1943).
62 H.J. Backer and N. Benninga, Rec. Trav. Chim., 55, 605 (1936).
63 H.J. Backer and N. Benninga, Rec. Trav. Chim., 55, 605 (1936).
64 H.J. Backer and C.H.K. Mulder, Rec. Trav. Chim., 55, 594 (1936).
65 E. Fischer and A. Mouneyrat, Chem. Ber., 42, 2383 (1909).
65a G. Amiard, R. Heymes and L. Velluz, U. S. Patent 2,991,307 (1961).
65b G. Triem, Chem. Ber., 71, 1522 (1938).
65c K. Murakami, N. Katsuta, K. Takano, Y. Yamamoto, T. Kakegawa, K. Saigo and H. Nohira, Nippon Kagaku Kaishi, 765 (1979).
65d C. Fujii, M. Yasui and Y. Ishimathu, U. S. Patent 3,979,457 (1976).
66 E. Fischer and H. Scheibler, Liebigs Ann. Chem., 383, 337 (1911).
67 K. Balenovic and N. Bregant, Tetrahedron, 5, 44 (1959).
67a Y. Kakimoto and M.D. Armstrong, J. Biol. Chem., 236, 3283 (1961).
68 D. Keglević and B. Ladesic, Croat. Chem. Acta, 31, 57 (1959).
69 K. Vogler and P. Lanz, Helv. Chim. Acta, 42, 209 (1959).
69a A.J. Zambito, W.L. Peretz and E.E. Howe, J. Am. Chem. Soc., 71, 2541 (1949).
69b M. Brenner, K. Rüfenacht and E. Sailer, Helv. Chim. Acta, 34, 2102 (1951).
69c B. F. Tullar, U. S. Patent 3,056,799 (1962).
69d G. Amiard, R. Heymes and L. Velluz, U.S. Patent 2,991,307 (1961).
69e G. Amiard, Bull. Soc. Chim. Fr., 447 (1956).
69f L. Velluz and G. Amiard, Bull. Soc. Chim. Fr., 903 (1953).
70 H. Arold, J. Prakt. Chem., 24, 23 (1964).
71 S. Weiss and J.A. Stekol, J. Am. Chem. Soc., 73, 2497 (1951).
71a M.D. Armstrong, J. Am. Chem. Soc., 70, 1756 (1948).
72 B.F. Tullar, U.S. Patent 3,056,799 (1962).
72a B.F. Tullar, U.S. Patent 3,056,799 (1962).
73 S. Lindstedt and G. Lindstedt, Arkiv Kemi, 22, 93 (1962).
73a M. Tomita and Y. Sendju, Z. Physiol. Chem., 169, 263 (1927).
74 K. Okawa, K. Hori, K. Hirose and Y. Nakagawa, Bull. Chem. Soc. Japan, 42, 2720 (1969).
75 H.J. Backer and C. C. Bolt, Rec. Trav. Chim., 54, 68 (1935).
76 W.J. Pope and J.B. Whitworth, Chem. Ind. (London), 49, 748 (1930).
77 W.C. Agosta, J. Am. Chem. Soc., 86, 2638 (1964).
78 A.M. Hoinowski and D.F. Hinkley, U.S. Patent 3,636,093 (1972).
79 D. Dugat, M. Verny and R. Vessiere, Tetrahedron, 27, 1715 (1971).
80 W. von E. Doering and K. Sachdev, J. Am. Chem. Soc., 96, 1168 (1974).
80a S. Inamasu, M. Horiike and Y. Inouye, Bull. Chem. Soc. Japan, 42, 1393 (1969).
81 J-F. Tocanne and C. Asselineau, Bull. Soc. Chim. France, 3346 (1965).
82 L. Schotte, Arkiv Kemi 9, 429 (1957).
83 M-O. Hedblom, Arkiv Kemi, 31, 489 (1969).
84 S-H.K. Suh and G. Hite, J. Pharm. Sci. 60, 930 (1971).
85 U.O. Hengartner, U. S. Patent 4,111,951 (1978).
86 T. Kato and Y. Tsuchiya, Agr. Biol. Chem., 26, 467 (1962).
87 D.J. Aberhart and L.J. Lin, J. Chem. Soc. Perkin 1, 2320 (1974).
88 B. Chion, J. Lajzerowicz, D. Bordeaux, A. Collet and J. Jacques, J. Phys. Chem., 82, 2682 (1978).
89 N. Takamura, S. Terashima, K. Achiwa and S. Yamada, Chem. Pharm. Bull., 15, 1776 (1967).
90 H. Iwasaki, T. Kamiya, O. Oka and J. Ueyanagi, Chem. Pharm. Bull., 17, 866 (1969).
91 G.T. Pearce, W.E. Gore and R.M. Silverstein, J. Org. Chem., 41, 2797 (1976).
92 R.G. Bergman, J. Am. Chem. Soc., 91, 7405 (1969).
93 R.G. Bergman, J. Am. Chem. Soc., 91, 7405 (1969).
94 T. Kaneko, K. Wakabayashi and H. Katsura, Bull. Chem. Soc. Japan, 35, 1149 (1962).

Reference Number

95 H. Minato, Chem. Pharm. Bull., 9, 625 (1961).
96 G. Claeson and H-G. Jonsson, Arkiv Kemi, 26, 247 (1966).
97 G. Claeson and H-G. Jonsson, Arkiv Kemi, 28, 167 (1967).
98 G. Claeson, Arkiv Kemi, 30, 511 (1969).
99 G. Claeson, Arkiv Kemi, 30, 511 (1969).
100 G. Nakaminami, M. Nakagawa, (late) Sachiko Shioi, Y. Sugiyama, S. Isemura and M. Shibuya, Tetrahedron Lett., 3983 (1967).
101 R.K. Hill and W.R. Schearer, J. Org. Chem., 27, 921 (1962).
102 T. Kaneko, K. Wakabayashi and H. Katsura, Bull. Chem. Soc. Japan, 35, 1149 (1962).
103 G. Losse and H. Raue, Chem. Ber., 101, 1532 (1968).
104 M.S. Rabinovich and G.N. Kulikova, Zhur. Obsch. Khim., 35, 237 (1965).
105 S. Tatsumi, M. Imaida and Y. Izumi, Bull. Chem. Soc. Japan, 39, 1818 (1966).
106 S. Tatsumi, M. Imaida and Y. Izumi, Bull. Chem. Soc. Japan, 39, 1818 (1966).
107 E.B. Abbot, E.A. Kidney and A. McKenzie, Chem. Ber., 71, 1210 (1938).
107a H.A. Barker, Biochem. Prep., 9, 25 (1962).
108 T. Purdie, J. Chem. Soc., 67, 944 (1895).
109 S. Tatsumi, Y. Izumi, M. Imaida, Y. Fukuda and S. Akabori, Bull. Chem. Soc. Japan, 39, 602 (1966).
110 S. Tatsumi, Y. Izumi, M. Imaida, Y. Fukuda and S. Akabori, Bull. Chem. Soc. Japan, 39, 602 (1966).
111 H.J. Backer and J. Buining, Rec. Trav. Chim., 47, 1000 (1928).
112 P.A. Levene, T. Mori, and L.A. Mikeska, J. Biol. Chem., 75, 337 (1927).
113 P.A. Levine, T. Mori, and L.A. Mikeska, J. Biol. Chem., 75, 337 (1927).
113a H. Auterhoff and W. Lang, Arch. Pharm. (Weinheim), 303, 49 (1970).
113b Y.A. Ovchinnikov, V.T. Ivanov and A.A. Kirgushkin, Izv. Akad. Nauk SSSR, 2046 (1962).
114 O. Kovacs, M. Halmos and G. Bernath, Acta Phys. Chem., 3, 118 (1957).
114a G. Amiard, R. Heymes and L. Velluz, U. S. Patent 2,794,025 (1957).
114b K. Vogler and P. Lanz, Helv. Chim. Acta. 49. 1348 (1966).
114c E. Fischer and G. Zemplen, Chem. Ber., 42, 2989 (1909).
114d S. Yamada, C. Hongo and I. Chibata, Agric. Biol. Chem., 41, 2413 (1977).
114e D. Hamer and J.P. Greenstein, J. Biol. Chem., 193, 81 (1951).
115 N. Takamura, S. Terashima, K. Achiwa and S. Yamada, Chem. Pharm. Bull., 15, 1776 (1967).
116 S. Black and N.G. Wright, J. Biol. Chem., 213, 39 (1955).
117 R. Adams and D. Fles, J. Am. Chem. Soc., 81, 4946 (1959).
118 British Patent 785,012 (1957).
118a O. Kovacs, M. Halmos and G. Bernath, Acta Univ. Szeg., Acta Phys. Chem., 3, 118 (1957).
119 G. Hillman and A. Elies, Z. Physiol. Chem., 283, 31 (1948).
119a E. Fischer, Chem. Ber., 32, 2451 (1899).
119b F.H. Radke, R.B. Fearing and S.W. Fox, J. Am. Chem. Soc., 76, 2801 (1954).
119c I. Sollin, U. S. Patent 2,945,879 (1960).
119d T. Kato and Y. Tsuchiya, Agr. Biol. Chem., 26, 473 (1962).
119e J.M. Gillingham, U. S. Patent 3,028,395 (1962).
119f F.P. Dwyer, B. Halpern and K.R. Turnbull, Aust. J. Chem., 16, 727 (1963).
120 A. Miyako, Chem. Pharm. Bull., 8, 1074 (1960).
121 K. Oki, K. Suzuki, S. Tuchida, T. Saito and H. Kotake, Bull. Chem. Soc. Japan, 43, 2554 (1970).
122 K. Oki, K. Suzuki, S. Tuchida, T. Saito and H. Kotake, Bull. Chem. Soc. Japan, 43, 2554 (1970).
123 P.A. Stadler and A. Hofmann, Helv. Chim. Acta, 45, 2005 (1962).
124 W. Theilacker and G. Wendtland, Liebig's Ann. Chem., 570, 33 (1950).
125 P. Pfeiffer and E. Heinrich, J. Prakt. Chem., 146, 105 (1936).
126 Y.K. Lee and T. Kaneko, Bull. Chem. Soc. Japan, 46, 3494 (1973).
127 Y.K. Lee and T. Kaneko, Bull. Chem. Soc. Japan, 46, 3494 (1973).
128 H.J. Backer and W. van Dam, Rec. Trav. Chim., 49, 482 (1930).
129 G. Adembri and M. Ghelardoni, Gazz. Chim. Ital., 89, 1763 (1959).
130 K. Harada, Nature, 206, 1354 (1965).
131 O. Schutz and W. Marckwald, Chem. Ber., 29, 52 (1896).
131a G. Odham, Arkiv Kemi, 20, 507 (1962).
131b K. Freudenberg and W. Lwowski, Liebigs Ann. Chem., 592, 76 (1955).
132 P.A. Levene, T. Mori, and L.A. Mikeska, J. Biol. Chem., 75, 337 (1927).
133 L.A. Shchukina, R.G. Vdovina, Y.B. Shvetsov and A.V. Karpova, Izv. Akad Nauk SSSR, 310 (1962).
134 A. Tai and M. Imaida, Bull. Chem. Soc. Japan, 51, 1114 (1978).
135 A. Tai and M. Imaida, Bull. Chem. Soc. Japan, 51, 1114 (1978).
136 D.H.G. Crout and D. Whitehouse, J. Chem. Soc., Perkin 1, 544 (1977).
137 R. Brettle and N. Polgar, J. Chem. Soc., 664 (1959).
138 F. Kogl, H. Duisberg and H. Erxleben, Liebigs Ann. Chem., 489, 156 (1931).
139 J.J. Sjolander, K. Folkers, E.A. Adelberg and E.L. Tatum, J. Am. Chem. Soc., 76, 1085 (1954).
140 H.J. Backer and M. Toxopeus, Rec. Trav. Chim., 45, 890 (1926).
141 H.J. Backer and D. van der Veen, Rec. Trav. Chim., 55, 887 (1936).
142 H.J. Backer and D. van der Veen, Rec. Trav. Chim., 55, 887 (1936).
143 H.J. Backer and C.H.K. Mulder, Rec. Trav. Chim., 55, 594 (1936).
144 P. Alaupovic, Croat. Chem. Acta, 29, 131 (1957).
144a G. Amiard, R. Heymes and L. Velluz, U. S. Patent 2,991,307 (1961).
144b K. Witkiewicz, F. Rulko and Z. Chabudzinski, Rocz. Chem., 48, 651 (1974).
144c G. Losse, R. Wagner, P. Neuland and J. Rateitschak, Chem. Ber., 91, 2410 (1958).
144d N.F. Albertson, J. Am. Chem. Soc., 73, 452 (1951).
145 E. Fischer and R. Groh, Liebigs Ann. Chem., 383, 363 (1911).
145a D.R. Pilipauskas and K.D. Kopple, Tetrahedron, 32, 2245 (1976).
146 R. Adams and D. Fles, J. Am. Chem. Soc., 81, 4946 (1959).
147 E. Fischer and R. von Gravenitz, Liebig's Ann. Chem., 406, 1 (1914).
148 E. Fischer, Chem. Ber., 39, 2320 (1906).
148a W. Langenbeck and O. Herbst, Chem. Ber., 86, 1524 (1953).
148b G. Losse, H-J. Hebel and C. Kastner, J. Prakt. Chem., 8, 339 (1959).

Reference Number

148c G. Losse and G. Müller, J. Prakt. Chem., 9, 145 (1959).
148d T. Kato and Y. Tsuchiya, Agr. Biol. Chem., 26, 467 (1962).
148e G. Amiard, R. Heymes and L. Velluz, U. S. Patent 2,991,307 (1961).
148f B.F. Tullar, U. S. Patent 3,056,799 (1962).
148g K. Oki, K. Suzuki, S. Tuchida, T. Saito and H. Kotake, Bull. Chem. Soc. Japan, 43, 2554 (1970).
148h J.M. Gillingham, U. S. Patent 3,028,395 (1962).
148i L.R. Overby and A.W. Ingersoll, J. Am. Chem. Soc., 73, 3363 (1951).
148j D.F. Holmes and R. Adams, J. Am. Chem. Soc., 56, 2093 (1934).
148k K.A.J. Wretlind, Acta Chem. Scand., 6, 611 (1952).
149 French Patent 1,389,391 (1965).
149a C.G. Baker, S-C.J. Fu, S.M. Birnbaum, H.A. Sober and J.P. Greenstein, J. Am. Chem. Soc., 74, 4701 (1952).
150 W. Windus and C.S. Marvel, J. Am. Chem. Soc., 53, 3490 (1931).
150a H. Baganz, H. Baganz and E. Vorwerk, Chem. Ber., 86, 1242 (1953).
150b K. Oki, K. Suzuki, S. Tuchida, T. Saito and H. Kotake, Bull. Chem. Soc. Japan, 43, 2554 (1970).
150c J.M. Gillingham, U. S. Patent 3,028,395 (1962).
150d B.F. Tullar, U. S. Patent 3,056,799 (1962).
150e T. Kato and Y. Tsuchiya, Agr. Biol. Chem., 26, 467 (1962).
150f G.P. Wheeler and A.W. Ingersoll, J. Am. Chem. Soc., 73, 4604 (1951).
150g G.P. Wheeler and A.W. Ingersoll, J. Am. Chem. Soc., 73, 4604 (1951).
150h G. Losse, R. Wagner, P. Neuland and J. Rateitschak, Chem. Ber., 91, 2410 (1958).
150i K. Vogler and F. Hunziker, Helv. Chim. Acta, 30, 2013 (1947).
150j M. Brenner and V. Kocher, Helv. Chim. Acta, 32, 333 (1949).
151 G. Zdansky, Arkiv Kemi, 29, 437 (1968).
152 J. Oh-hashi and K. Harada, Bull. Chem. Soc. Japan, 30, 2287 (1966).
152a A. Stoll and Th. Petrzilka, Helv. Chim. Acta, 35, 589 (1952).
153 E. Galantay, A. Szabo and J. Fried, J. Org. Chem., 28, 98 (1963).
154 Z. Grzonka and B. Liberek, Tetrahedron, 27, 1783 (1971).
155 H.J. Backer and C. C. Bolt, Rec. Trav. Chim., 54, 68 (1935).
156 British Patent 585,413 (1947).
156a French Patent 2,148,050 (1973).
157 G. Losse and M. Augustin, Chem. Ber., 91, 2418 (1958).
158 G.I. Tesser, R.J.F. Nivard and M. Gruber, Rec. Trav. Chim., 81, 713 (1962).
159 T. Tanabe, S. Yajima and M. Imaida, Bull. Chem. Soc. Japan, 41, 2178 (1968).
160 S. Gronowitz, I. Sjögren, L. Wernstedt and B. Sjöberg, Arkiv Kemi, 23, 129 (1964).
161 S. Gronowitz, Arkiv Kemi, 13, 87 (1958).
162 S. Gronowitz, Arkiv Kemi, 13, 231 (1958).
163 J.J. Gajewski, J. Am. Chem. Soc., 93, 4450 (1971).
163a F. Feist, Liebegs Ann. Chem., 436, 125 (1924).
164 H.B. Hill and F.W. Russe, Chem. Ber., 37, 2538 (1904).
165 E. Buchner and R. von der Heide, Chem. Ber., 38, 3112 (1905).
166 C.W. Perry, A. Brossi, K.H. Deitcher, W. Tautz and S. Teitel, Synthesis, 492 (1977).
166a R.W. Guthrie, J.G. Hamilton, R.W. Kierstead, O.N. Miller and A.C. Sullivan, U. S. Patent 3,810,931 (1974).
167 C.W. Perry, A. Brossi, K.H. Deitcher, W. Tautz and S. Teitel, Synthesis, 492 (1977).
168 S. Gronowitz, I. Sjögren, L. Wernstedt and B. Sjöberg, Arkiv Kemi, 23, 129 (1964).
169 B. Holmberg and E. Müller, Chem. Ber. 58, 1601 (1925).
170 N. Takamura, S. Teyashima, K. Achiwa and S. Yamada, Chem. Pharm. Bull., 15, 1776 (1967).
171 Y. Seto, K. Torii, K. Bori, K. Inabata, S. Kuwata and H. Watanabe, Bull. Chem. Soc. Japan, 47, 151 (1974).
172 W. Runge, G. Kresze and E. Ruch, Liebigs Ann. Chem., 1361 (1975).
173 M. Arai and R.J. Crawford, Can. J. Chem., 50, 2158 (1972).
174 M. Kinoshita and S. Umezawa, Bull. Chem. Soc. Japan, 32, 223 (1959).
175 M. Okada, H. Sumitomo and I. Tajima, J. Am. Chem. Soc., 101, 4013 (1979).
176 L.J. Goldsworthy, J. Chem. Soc., 124, 2012 (1924).
176a F.B. Kipping and J.J. Wren, J. Chem. Soc., 3246 (1957).
176b C.G. Overberger and Y. Shimokawa, Macromolecule, 4, 718 (1971).
177 K. Mori, Tetrahedron, 31, 1381 (1975).
177a R. Adams and F.B. Hauserman, J. Am. Chem. Soc., 74, 694 (1952).
178 M.E. Maurit, R.P. Shternberg, A.M. Pakhomov, G.I. Basilevskaya, G.V. Smirnova and N.A. Preobrazhenskii, Zh. Obsh. Khim., 30, 2256 (1960).
179 O. Cervinka and L. Hub, Coll. Czech. Chem. Comm., 33, 2927 (1968).
180 Y. Kato and T. Wakabayashi, Synth. Comm., 7, 125 (1977).
181 A. Fredga, J. Prakt. Chem., 150, 124 (1938).
182 E. Jonsson, Acta Chem. Scand., 19, 2247 (1965).
183 A. Fredga, Arkiv Kemi Mineral Geol., 12A, No. 27 (1938).
184 M-O. Hedblom, Swed. J. Agric. Res., 1, 43 (1971).
185 M-O. Hedblom, Arkiv Kemi, 31, 489 (1969).
186 A. Fredga, J. Prakt. Chem., 130, 180 (1931).
187 A. Fredga, Arkiv Kemi, Mineral Geol. 11B, No. 15 (1933).
188 J.W.C. Crawford, J. Chem. Soc., 4280 (1965).
189 J. Kenyon and W.A. Ross, J. Chem. Soc., 3407 (1951).
190 E. Hardegger and H. Ott, Helv. Chim. Acta, 38, 312 (1955).
191 W. Marki, M. Oppliger, P. Thanei and R. Schwyzer, Helv. Chim. Acta, 60, 798 (1977).
192 F.L. Pyman, J. Chem. Soc., 99, 1386 (1911).
192a R. Duschinsky, Chem. Ind. (London), 10 (1934).
193 M. Claesen, G. Laridon and H. Vanderhaeghe, Bull. Soc. Chim. Belges, 77, 579 (1968).
194 H. Lackner, Chem. Ber., 104, 3653 (1971).
195 H. Völter and G. Helmchen, Tetrahedron Lett., 1251 (1978).
196 S. Stallberg-Stenhagen, Arkiv Kemi Mineral Geol., 23A, No. 15 (1947).
196a G. Stallberg, Acta Chem. Scand., 11, 1430 (1957).
197 E.J. Corey and T. Hase, Tetrahedron Lett., 335 (1979).
198 R.B. Bradbury and S. Masamune, J. Am. Chem. Soc., 81, 5201 (1959).
199 E.T. Stiller, S.A. Harris, J. Finkelstein, J.C. Keresztesy and K. Folkers, J. Am. Chem. Soc., 62, 1785 (1940).

Reference
Number

199a A. Grussner, M. Gatzi-Fichter and T. Reichstein, Helv. Chim. Acta, 23, 1276 (1941).
199b E.S. Zhdanovich, G.S. Kozlova, T.D. Marieva, T.V. Mel'nikova and N.A. Preobrazhenskii, Zhur. Org. Khim., 4, 1359 (1968).
199c F. Kagan, R.V. Heinzelman, D.I. Weisblat and W. Greiner, J. Am. Chem. Soc., 79, 3545 (1957).
199d J. Paust, S. Pfohl, W. Reif and W. Schmidt, Liebigs Ann. Chem., 1024 (1978).
199e J. Paust, S. Pfohl, W. Reif and W. Schmidt, Liebegs Ann. Chem., 1024 (1978).
200 K. Mori, T. Takigawa and T. Matsuo, Tetrahedron, 35, 933 (1979).
201 H. Wollweber, H. Horstmann and K. Meng, Eur. J. Med. Chem., 11, 159 (1976).
201a H.V. Pohl and H. Wollweber, Eur. J. Med. Chem., 11, 163 (1976).
202 A. Fredga and M. Tenow, Arkiv Kemi, Mineral Geol., 17B, No. 3 (1943).
203 A. Fredga, Svensk. Kem. Tids., 54, 26 (1942).
204 B. Holmberg, Chem. Ber., 59, 1558 (1926).
205 L.A. Paquette and J.P. Freeman, J. Org. Chem., 35, 2249 (1970).
205a K. Serck-Hanssen, Arkiv Kemi, 19, 83 (1961).
206 E. Berner and R. Leonardsen, Liebigs Ann. Chem., 538, 1 (1939).
206a A. Fredga, Arkiv Kemi Mineral Geol., 24A, No. 32 (1947).
207 E. Berner and R. Leonardsen, Liebigs Ann. Chem., 538, 1 (1939).
207a H. Wren and J. Crawford, J. Chem. Soc., 230 (1936).
207b G. Bettoni, C. Cellucci and F. Berardi, J. Heterocyclic Chem., 17, 603 (1980).
208 G.E. McCasland and S. Proskow, J. Am. Chem. Soc., 78, 5646 (1956).
208a A. Werner and M. Basyrin, Chem. Ber., 46, 3229 (1913).
209 A. Fredga, Svensk Kem. Tids., 46, 10 (1934).
210 D.J. Cram and T.A. Whitney, J. Am. Chem. Soc., 89, 4651 (1967).
211 A. Fredga, Arkiv Kemi Mineral Geol., 12A, No. 13 (1937).
212 M-O. Hedblom, Arkiv Kemi, 31, 489 (1969).
213 A. Fredga, Uppsala Universitets Årsskrift 1935:5. "Studien Über Selen-Dikarbonsäure und Diselen-Di-Karbonsäuren."
214 A. Fredga, Arkiv Kemi Mineral Geol., 17A, No. 17 (1943).
215 A. Fredga, Uppsala Universitets Årsskrift 1935:5. "Studien Uber Selen-Dikarbonsäure und Diselen-Di-Karbonsäuren."
216 K. Freudenberg, W.F. Bruce and E. Gauf, Liebigs Ann. Chem., 510, 206 (1934).
217 T. Posternak and J.-Ph. Susz, Helv. Chim. Acta, 39, 2032 (1956).
218 M. Muroi, Y. Inouye and M. Ohno, Bull. Chem. Soc. Japan, 42, 2948 (1969).
218a S. Tatsumi, Y. Izumi, M. Imaida, Y. Fukuda and S. Akabori, Bull. Chem. Soc. Japan, 39, 602 (1966).
219 H. Wren and K.H. Hughes, J. Chem. Soc., 125, 1739 (1924).
220 H.J. Backer and W. Meijer, Rec. Trav. Chim., 46, 212 (1927).
221 C. Niemann and K.P. Link. J. Biol. Chem., 106, 773 (1934).
222 P.A. Levene, T. Mori, and L.A. Mikeska, J. Biol. Chem., 75, 337 (1927).
223 E. Fischer and H. Carl, Chem. Ber., 39, 3996 (1906).
223a P.A. Levene, T. Mori, and L.A. Mikeska, J. Biol. Chem., 75, 337 (1927).
224 W.G. Galetto and W. Gaffield, J. Chem. Soc., 2437 (1969).
225 A. Ichihara, K. Shiraishi and S. Sakamura, Tetrahedron Lett., 269 (1977).
226 K. Shiraishi, A. Ichihara and S. Sakamura, Agr. Biol. Chem., 41, 2497 (1977).
227 C.G. Overberger, K.-H. David and J.A. Moore, Macromolecules, 5, 368 (1972).
228 C.G. Overberger, K.-H. David and J.A. Moore, Macromolecules, 5, 368 (1972).
229 R.J. Hemingway, J. Pharm. Pharmac., 20, 87 (1968).
230 A. Stoll and E. Seebeck, Helv. Chim. Acta, 34, 481 (1951).
231 M. Matell, Acta Chem. Scand., 14, 677 (1960).
232 D. Pitre and S. Boveri, Farmaco, Ed. Sci., 26, 733 (1971).
233 E. Fischer and F. Brauns, Chem. Ber., 47, 3181 (1914).
234 P. Block, Jr., J. Org. Chem., 30, 1307 (1965).
235 H.C. Beyerman and P. Boekee, Rec. Trav. Chim., 78, 648 (1959).
236 M. Matell, Acta Chem. Scand., 14, 677 (1960).
237 M. Claesen, A. Vlietinck and H. Vanderhaeghe, Bull. Soc. Chim. Belges, 77, 587 (1968
237a M.S. Rabinovich, M.F. Shostakovskii and E.V. Preobrazhenskaya, Zhur. Obsch. Khim., 30, 71 (1960).
237b M.S. Rabinovich, M.F. Shostakovskii, and E.V. Preobrazhenskaya, Zhur. Obsch. Khim., 30, 71 (1960).
237c S. Wolfe and M.G. Jokinen, Can. J. Chem., 57, 1388 (1979).
238 H.J. Backer and D. van der Veen, Rec. Trav. Chim., 55, 887 (1936).
239 G. Losse, G. Seltmann and H. Tischer, Z. Physiol. Chem., 314, 224 (1959).
240 L. Hollander and V. du Vigneaud, J. Biol. Chem., 94, 243 (1931-32).
241 P.A. Levene and R.E. Marker, J. Biol. Chem., 98, 1 (1932).
242 F. Kögl and H. Erxleben, Z. Physiol. Chem., 235, 181 (1935).
242a C. Neuberg and B. Rewald, Z. Physiol. Chem., 9, 403 (1908).
243 P.A. Levene and R.E. Marker, J. Biol. Chem., 111, 299 (1935).
244 P.A. Levene, T. Mori, and L.A. Mikeska, J. Biol. Chem., 75, 337 (1927).
245 P.A. Levene, T. Mori, and L.A. Mikeska, J. Biol. Chem., 75, 337 (1927).
246 J.P. Vigneron, M. Dhaenens and A. Horeau, Tetrahedron, 33, 507 (1977).
246a G. Buchi, L. Crombie, P.J. Godin, J.S. Kaltenbronn, L.S. Siddalingaiah and D.A. Whiting, J. Chem. Soc., 2843 (1961).
246b H. Scheibler and A.S. Wheeler, Chem. Ber., 44, 2684 (1911).
247 F.M. Dean, J.C. Roberts and A. Robertson, J. Chem. Soc., 1432 (1954).
248 T. Tanabe, S. Yajima and M. Imaida, Bull. Chem. Soc. Japan, 41, 2178 (1968).
249 J.S. Brooks and G.A. Morrison, J. Chem. Soc. Perkin 1, 2114 (1974).
250 R. Brettle and N. Polgar, J. Chem. Soc., 1620 (1956).
251 L.S. Bergel'son, E.V. Dyatlovitskaya, M. Tichy and V.V. Voronkova, Izv. Akad. Nauk SSSR., 1612 (1962).
251a D.H.G. Crout and D. Whitehouse, J. Chem. Soc., Ferkin 1, 544 (1977).
251b F.B. Armstrong, U.S. Muller, J. B. Reary, D. Whitehouse and D.H.G. Crout, Biochim. Biophys. Acta, 498, 282 (1977).
252 L.D. Bergel'son, E.V. Dyatlovitskaya, M. Tichy and V.V. Voronkova, Izv. Akad. Nauk SSSR., 1612 (1962).

Reference Number

253 E. Fischer and R. Hagenbach, Chem. Ber., 34, 3764 (1901).
253a E. Abderhalden, C. Froehlich and D. Fuchs, Hoppe Seyler's Z. Physiol. Chem., 86, 454 (1913).
253b W.A.H. Huffman and A.W. Ingersoll, J. Am. Chem. Soc., 73, 3366 (1951).
253c K. Witkiewicz, F. Rulko and Z. Chabudzinski, Rocz. Chem., 48, 651 (1974).
253d G. Losse, R. Wagner, P. Neuland and J. Rateitschak, Chem. Ber., 91, 2410 (1958).
253e G. Losse, R. Wagner, P. Neuland and J. Rateitschak, Chem. Ber., 91, 2410 (1958).
254 E. Fischer and O. Warburg, Chem. Ber., 38, 3997 (1905).
254a G. Losse and H. Jeschkeit, Chem. Ber., 90, 1275 (1957).
254b G. Losse, H-J. Hebel and C. Kastner, J. Prakt. Chem., 8, 339 (1959).
254c G. Amiard, R. Heymes and L. Velluz, U. S. Patent 2,991,307 (1961).
254d K. Oki, K. Suzuki, S. Tuchida, T. Saito and H. Kotake, Bull. Chem. Soc. Japan, 43, 2554 (1970).
254e W.A.H. Huffman and A.W. Ingersoll, J. Am. Chem. Soc., 73, 3366 (1951).
254f K. Witkiewicz, F. Rulko and Z. Chabudzinski, Rocz. Chem., 48, 651 (1974).
254g G. Triem, Chem. Ber., 71, 1522 (1938).
255 W.A.H. Huffman and A.W. Ingersoll, J. Am. Chem. Soc., 73, 3366 (1951).
255a K. Vogler and P. Lans, Helv. Chim. Acta, 49, 1348 (1966).
255b K. Oki, K. Suzuki, S. Tuchida, T. Saito and H. Kotake, Bull. Chem. Soc. Japan, 43, 2554 (1970).
255c B.F. Tullar, U.S. Patent 3,056,799 (1962).
256 W.A.H. Huffman and A.W. Ingersoll, J. Am. Chem. Soc., 73, 3366 (1951).
257 E. Abderhalden, W. Faust and E. Haase, Hoppe Seyler's Z. Physiol. Chem., 228, 187 (1934).
257a D.A. Jaeger, M.D. Broadhurst and D.J. Cram, J. Am. Chem. Soc., 101, 717 (1979).
257b H. Pracejus and S. Winter, Chem. Ber., 97, 3173 (1964).
257c T. Miyazawa, K. Takashima, Y. Mitsuda, T. Yamada, S. Kuwata and H. Watanabe, Bull. Chem. Soc. Japan, 52, 1539 (1979).
258 Y.A. Ovchinnikov, V. I. Ivanov and A.A. Kiryuskin, Izv. Akad. Nauk SSSR., 2046 (1962).
258a Y.A. Ovchinnikov, V.I. Ivanov and A.A. Kiryuskin, Izv. Akad. Nauk SSSR., 2046 (1962).
258b Y.A. Ovchinnikov, V.I. Ivanov and A.A. Kiryuskin, Izv. Akad. Nauk SSSR., 2046 (1962).
259 B.A. Kern and R.H. Reitz, Agric. Biol. Chem., 42, 1275 (1978).
260 Z. Grzonka and B. Liberek, Tetrahedron, 27, 1783 (1971).
261 H.J. Backer and C.C. Bolt, Rec. Trav. Chim., 54, 68 (1935).
262 F.J. Kearley and A.W. Ingersoll, J. Am. Chem. Soc., 73, 5783 (1951).
262a F.J. Kearley and A.W. Ingersoll, J. Am. Chem. Soc., 73, 5783 (1951).
262b T.T. Yee, J.A. Cahill and J.A. Meyers III, U.S. Patent 3,651,138 (1972).
262c R.D. Emmick, U.S. Patent 2,556,907 (1951).
262d U. S. Patent 3,773,786 (1973).
262e C.P. Berg, J. Biol. Chem., 115, 9 (1936).
262f S. Watanabe and K. Suga, Isr. J. Chem., 7, 483 (1969).
262g N. Sato, T. Uzuki, K. Toi and T. Akashi, Agr. Biol. Chem., 33, 1107 (1969).
262h G.H. Suverkropp, U. S. Patent 3,932,491 (1976).
263 P. Bey, C. Danzin, V. Van Dorsselaer, P. Mamont, M. Jung and C. Tardif, J. Med. Chem., 21, 50 (1978).
264 J. Knabe and W. Furst, Arch. Pharm. (Weinheim) 312, 86 (1979).
265 J.C. Sheehan and Y.S. Lo, J. Med. Chem., 17, 371 (1974).
266 C. Martius and G. Schorre, Liebigs Ann. Chem., 570, 140 (1950).
267 J. Nishikawa, T. Ishizaki, F. Nakayama, H. Kawa, K. Saigo and H. Nohira, Nippon Kagaku Kaishi, 754 (1979).
268 T. Raznikiewicz, Acta Chem. Scand., 18, 467 (1961).
268a T. Raznikiewicz, Acta Chem. Scand., 16, 1097 (1962).
269 T. Raznikiewicz, Arkiv Kemi, 18, 467 (1961).
270 C.G. Overberger and Y. Shimokawa, Macromolecules, 4, 718 (1971).
271 I. Fleming, J. Chem. Soc. (C), 2765 (1968).
272 L. Schotte, Arkiv Kemi, 9, 407 (1956).
273 M. Hoffmann, Polish J. Chem., 52, 851 (1978).
274 W. Runge, G. Kresze and E. Ruch, Liebigs Ann. Chem., 1361 (1975).
275 W. Runge, G. Kresze and E. Ruch, Liebigs Ann. Chem., 1361 (1975).
276 L. Crombie, P.A. Jenkins and J. Roblin, J. Chem. Soc. Perkin 1, 1090 (1975).
277 R.W. Lang and H-J. Hansen, Helv. Chim. Acta, 62, 1025 (1979).
278 K. Mislow and I.V. Steinberg, J. Am. Chem. Soc., 77, 3807 (1955).
279 W. von E. Doering and K. Sachdev, J. Am. Chem. Soc., 97, 5512 (1975).
280 W. von E. Doering, M. Franck-Neumann, D. Hasselmann and R.L. Kaye, J. Am. Chem. Soc., 94, 3833 (1972).
280a S.J. Goldberg and F-L. Lam, J. Org. Chem., 31, 241 (1966).
280b From the Ph.D. Thesis (1972) of P.W. Marr, University of Toronto, Toronto, Canada.
281 R.K. Hill and A.G. Edwards, Tetrahedron, 21, 1501 (1965).
282 A.B. Arendaruk, E.I. Budovsky, B.P. Gommikh. M. Ya. Karpeisky, L.I. Kudryashov, A.P. Skoldinov, N.V. Smirnova, A.Ya. Khorlin and N.K. Kochetkov, Zhur. Obsch. Khim., 27, 1312 (1957).
283 K. Chilina, U. Thomas, A.F. Tucci, K.D. McMichael and C.M. Stevens, Biochemistry, 8, 2846 (1969).
284 Y. Inouye, S. Inamasu, M. Horiike, M. Ohno and H.M. Walborsky, Tetrahedron, 24, 2907 (1968).
285 A. Fredga and A. Sikström, Arkiv Kemi, 8, 433 (1955).
286 A. Campbell and H.N. Rydon, J. Chem. Soc., 3002 (1953).
287 L.J. Goldsworthy and W.H. Perkin, J. Chem. Soc., 105, 2639 (1914).
287a A. Collet, M.-J. Brienne and J. Jacques, Bull. Soc. Chim. France, 336 (1972).
288 C.G. Overberger and Y. Shimokawa, Macromolecules, 4, 718 (1971).
289 M.E. Maurit, R.P. Shternberg, A.M. Pakhomov, G.I. Basilevskaya, G.V. Smirnova, and N.A. Preobrazhenskii, Zh. Obsh. Khim., 30, 2256 (1960).
290 M.E. Maurit, R.P. Shternberg, A.M. Pakhomov, G.I. Basilevskaya, G.V. Smirnova, and N.A. Preobrazhenskii, Zh. Obsh. Khim., 30, 2256 (1960).

Reference Number

291 M. Matsui, T. Ohno, S. Kitamura and M. Toyao, Bull. Chem. Soc. Japan, 25, 210 (1952).
292 J.E. Némorin, E. Jonsson and A. Fredga, Arkiv Kemi, 30, 403 (1969).
293 A. Fredga and K. Styrman, Arkiv Kemi, 14, 461 (1959).
294 L. Schotte, Arkiv Kemi, 9, 413 (1957).
295 A. Fredga and A. Björn, Arkiv Kemi, 23, 91 (1964).
296 E. E. Smissman, J. T. Suh, M. Oxman and R. Daniels, J. Am. Chem. Soc., 84, 1040 (1962).
296a R. Grewe and S. Kersten, Chem. Ber., 100, 2546 (1967).
297 K. Freudenberg and W. Hohmann, Liebigs Ann. Chem., 584, 54 (1953).
298 J.E. Baldwin, D.H.R. Barton and J. Sutherland, J. Chem. Soc., 1787 (1965).
299 J. Knabe and W. Koch, Arch. Pharm. (Weinheim), 305, 757 (1972).
300 T.C. Butler, J. Pharm. Exp. Ther., 113, 178 (1955).
301 E. Hardegger and H. Ott, Helv. Chim. Acta, 38, 312 (1955).
302 C.G. Overberger, J.H. Kozlowski and E. Radlmann, J. Poly. Sci. A1,10, 2265 (1972).
303 A. Fredga, Svensk. Kem. Tids., 53, 221 (1941).
304 M.S. Newman and H. Junjappa, J. Org. Chem., 36, 2606 (1971).
305 R.G. Kostyanovsky, V.F. Rudchenko, O.A. D'yachenko, I.I. Chervin, A.B. Zolotoi and L.O. Atovmyan, Tetrahedron, 35, 213 (1979).
306 B. Ackermark, Acta Chem. Scand., 16, 599 (1962).
307 R. Sandberg, Acta Chem. Scand., 16, 1124 (1962).
307a J. Kenyon and M.C.R. Symons, J. Chem. Soc., 3580 (1953).
308 F.I. Carroll, G.N. Mitchell, J.T. Blackwell, A. Sobti and R. Meck, J. Org. Chem., 39, 3890 (1974).
309 J.B. Kay and J.B. Robinson, J. Chem. Soc. (C), 248 (1969).
310 J. Sanchez Real and J. Pascual, Anales Real Soc. Espan. Fis. y. Qum. (Madrid)., 49B, 445 (1953).
311 M. Nakazaki, K. Naemura and S. Nakahara, J. Org. Chem., 44, 2438 (1979).
311a D.S. Noyce and D.B. Denney, J. Am. Chem. Soc., 74, 5912 (1952).
312 R.P. Zelinski, N.G. Peterson and H.R. Wallner, J. Am. Chem. Soc., 74, 1504 (1952).
313 A. Fredga and M. Tenow, Arkiv Kemi, Mineral. Geol., 16B, No. 9 (1942).
314 E. Berner and R. Leonardsen, Liebigs Ann. Chem., 538, 1 (1939).
315 P.W. Clutterback, H. Raistrick and F. Reuter, Biochem. J., 31, 987 (1937).
315a G. Bettoni, C. Cellucci and F. Berardi, J. Heterocyclic Chem., 17, 603 (1980).
316 J.V. Braun and W. Reinhardt, Chem. Ber., 62, 2585 (1929).
317 S. Ställberg-Stenhagen, Arkiv Kemi Mineral. Geol. 25A, No. 10 (1947).
318 G. Losse and H. Raue, Chem. Ber., 101, 1532 (1968).
319 E. Berner and R. Leonardsen, Tids. Kjem., 64 (1943).
320 E. Berner and R. Leonardsen, Liebigs Ann. Chem., 538, 1 (1939).
321 E. Berner and R. Leonardsen, Liebigs Ann. Chem., 538, 1 (1939).
322 M. Matell, Arkiv Kemi, 3, 129 (1951).
323 A. Fredga, Arkiv Kemi Mineral. Geol. 12A, No. 15 (1937).
324 D.S. Noyce and J.H. Canfield, J. Am. Chem. Soc., 76, 3630 (1954).
325 A. Lardon and T. Reichstein, Helv. Chim. Acta, 32, 1613 (1949).
326 K. Freudenberg, W.F. Bruce and E. Gauf, Liebigs Ann. Chem., 510, 206 (1934).
327 R. Grewe, W. Lorenzen and L. Vining, Chem. Ber., 87, 793 (1954).
328 H. Nohira, K. Ehara and A. Miyashita, Bull. Chem. Soc. Japan, 43, 2230 (1970).
329 G. Losse, G. Seltmann and H. Tischer, Z. Physiol. Chem., 314, 224 (1959).
330 J. van Heijenoort and E. Bricas, Bull. Soc. Chim. Fr., 2828 (1968).
331 P.A. Leven^ and R.E. Marker, J. Biol. Chem., 98, 1 (1932).
331a P.A. Levene and L.W. Bass, J. Biol. Chem., 70, 211 (1926).
332 S. Pucci, P. Pino and E. Strino, Gazz. Chim. Ital., 98, 421 (1968).
332a P.A. Levene and R.E. Marker, J. Biol. Chem., 111, 299 (1935).
333 F.I. Carroll and R. Meck, J. Org. Chem., 34, 2676 (1969).
334 P.A. Levene, A. Rothen, G.M. Meyer and M. Kuna, J. Biol. Chem., 115, 401 (1936).
335 M. Farina, E.M. Peronaci, Chim. Ind. (Milan), 48, 602 (1966).
336 F.M. Hauser, M.L. Coleman, R.C. Huffman, F.I. Carroll, J. Org. Chem., 39, 3426 (1974
337 J.W. Lewis and N. Polgar, J. Chem. Soc., 102 (1958).
338 N.K. Kochetkov, A.M. Likhosherstov and V.N. Kulakov, Tetrahedron, 25, 2313 (1969).
339 N.K. Kochetkov, A.M. Likhosherstov and V.N. Kulakov, Tetrahedron, 25, 2313 (1969).
340 A.K. Mills and A.E. Wilder Smith, Helv. Chim. Acta, 43, 1915 (1960).
340a E. Abderhalden and S. Glaubach, Fermentforschung, 6, 348 (1922).
341 C.G. Overberger and G.M. Parker, J. Polymer Sci., A1, 6, 513 (1968).
342 H. Kotake, T. Saito and K. Okubo, Bull. Chem. Soc. Japan, 42, 1367 (1969).
342a K. Okubo and Y. Izumi, Bull. Chem. Soc. Japan, 42, 1541 (1970).
343 H. Kotake, T. Saito and K. Okubo, Bull. Chem. Soc. Japan, 42, 1367 (1969).
344 D. M. Müller and E. Strack, Hoppe-Seyler's Z. Physiol. Chem., 353, 618 (1972).
345 M.H. Maguire and G. Shaw, J. Chem. Soc., 2713 (1957).
346 N.S. Zefirov, A.F. Davydova and Y.K. Yur'ev, Zh. Obsch. Khim., 35, 817 (1965).
347 J.R.E. Hoover, G.L. Dunn, D.R. Jakas, L.L. Lam, J.J. Taggart, J.R. Guarini, and L. Phillips, J. Med. Chem., 17, 34 (1974).
348 J.R.E. Hoover, G.L. Dunn, D.R. Jakas, L.L. Lam, J.J. Taggart, J.R. Guarini, and L. Phillips, J. Med. Chem., 17, 34 (1974).
349 J.R.E. Hoover, G.L. Dunn, D.R. Jakas, L.L. Lam, J.J. Taggart, J.R. Guarini, and L. Phillips, J. Med. Chem., 17, 34 (1974).
350 Personal communication from Prof. H. Morawetz, Polytechnic Institute of Brooklyn, Brooklyn, New York.
350a A. McKenzie and N. Walker, J. Chem. Soc., 107, 1685 (1915).
350b A. McKenzie and I.H. Smith, J. Chem. Soc., 125, 1582 (1924).
351 A. Collet and J. Jacques, Bull. Soc. Chim. France, 3330 (1973).
352 A. Collet and J. Jacques, Bull. Soc. Chim. France, 3330 (1973).
353 A. Collet and J. Jacques, Bull. Soc. Chim. France, 3330 (1973).
354 A. McKenzie and G.W. Clough, J. Chem. Soc., 93, 811 (1908).
354a A. McKenzie and I.A. Smith, J. Chem. Soc., 123, 1962 (1923).
355 A. Collet and J. Jacques, Bull. Soc. Chim. France, 3330 (1973).
356 A. Collet and J. Jacques, Bull. Soc. Chim. France, 3330 (1973).
357 A. Collet and J. Jacques, Bull. Soc. Chim. France, 3330 (1973).
357a J.R.E. Hoover, G.L. Dunn, D.R. Jakas, L.L. Lam, J.J. Taggart, J.R. Guarini and L. Phillips, J. Med. Chem., 17, 34 (1974).

Reference
Number

358 E. Bellasio, A. Trani and A. Sardi, Farmaco, Ed. Sci., 27, 582 (1972).
359 A. Collet and J. Jacques, Bull. Soc. Chim. France, 3330 (1973).
360 A. Collet and J. Jacques, Bull. Soc. Chim. France, 3330 (1973).
361 A. Collet and J. Jacques, Bull. Soc. Chim. France, 3330 (1973).
362 A. McKenzie and P.A. Stewart, J. Chem. Soc., 104 (1935).
363 A. Fredga and E. Andersson, Arkiv Kemi, Mineral. Geol., 14B, No. 18 (1940).
364 A. Fredga and E. Andersson, Arkiv Kemi, Mineral. Geol., 14B, No. 38 (1941).
364a J.R.E. Hoover, G.L. Dunn, D.R. Jakas, L.L. Lam, J.J. Taggart, J.R. Guarini, and L. Phillips, J. Med. Chem., 17, 34 (1974).
365 A. La Manna, M. Grassi and L. Arpesella, Farmaco, Ed. Sci., 10, 571 (1955).
366 A.L. Palomo, German Patent (Offen.) 1,966,221 (1971).
366a G. Bison, H. Schübel and P. Janssen, German Patent (Offen.) 2,127,991 (1972).
367 C.T. Holdrege, U. S. Patent 3,479,339 (1969).
368 N.S. Zefirov, A.F. Davydova and Y.K. Yur'ev, Zhur. Obsch. Khim., 35, 1373 (1965).
369 J. Knabe and W. Fürst, Arch. Pharm. (Weinheim), 312, 86 (1979).
370 J. Knabe and W. Fürst, Arch. Pharm. (Weinheim), 312, 86 (1979).
371 W.A. Bonner, J. Org. Chem., 33, 1831 (1968).
372 R. Roger, J. Chem. Soc., 1544 (1935).
372a J.L. Norula and J. Kenyon, Current Sci. (India), 32, 260 (1963).
373 K. Pettersson, Arkiv Kemi, 7, 39 (1954).
374 S. Gronowitz, Arkiv Kemi 11, 361 (1957).
375 J. Brust, Rec. Trav. Chim., 47, 153 (1928).
376 H.J. Backer and C.H.K. Mulder, Rec. Trav. Chim., 55, 594 (1936).
377 M. Yasumoto, A. Moriyama, N. Unemi, S. Hashimoto, and T. Suzue, J. Med. Chem., 20, 1592 (1977).
378 E. Fischer and Weichhold, Chem. Ber., 41, 1286 (1908).
378a M. Betti and M. Mayer, Chem. Ber., 41, 2071 (1908).
378b G.L. Clark and G.R. Yohe, J. Am. Chem. Soc., 51, 2796 (1929).
378c S. Berlingozzi, G. Adembri and G.Bucci, Gazz. Chim. Ital., 84, 383 (1954).
378d D.R. Palmer, British Patent 1,314,739 (1973).
378e D.F. Holmes and R. Adams, J. Am. Chem. Soc., 56, 2093 (1934).
378f K. Murakami, N. Katsuta, K. Takano, Y. Yamamoto, T. Kakegawa, K. Saigo and H. Nohira, Nippon Kagaku Kaishi, 765 (1979).
378g S.G. Traynor, B.J. Kane, M.F. Betkouski and L.M. Hirschy, J. Org. Chem., 44, 1557 (1979).
379 British Patent 1,395,826 (1975).
379a T. Shirai, Y. Tashiro and S. Aoki, German Offen. 2,449,492 (1975).
379b A.A.W. Long, J.H.C. Nayler, U. S. Patent 3,674,776 (1972).
379c S. Yamada, C. Hongo, R. Yoshioka and I. Chibata, Agric. Biol. Chem., 43, 395 (1979)
379d S. Yamada, C. Hongo and I. Chibata, Agric. Biol. Chem., 42, 1521 (1978).
380 C.W. Porter and H.K. Ihrig, J. Am. Chem. Soc., 45, 1990 (1923).
381 L.N. Veselova and E.S. Chaman, Zhur. Obsch. Khim., 42, 1123 (1972).
382 K. Naemura and M. Nakazaki, Bull. Chem. Soc. Japan, 46, 888 (1973).
383 J.A. Berson, J.S. Walia, A. Remanick, S. Suzuki, P-Reynolds-Warnhoff and D. Willner, J. Am. Chem. Soc., 83, 3986 (1961).
384 J.A. Berson and R.G. Bergman, J. Am. Chem. Soc., 89, 2569 (1967).
385 E.J. Corey and B.B. Snider, J. Org. Chem., 39, 256 (1974).
386 K. Mori, Tetrahedron, 34, 915 (1978).
387 J. Dixon, B. Lythgoe, I.A. Siddiqui and J. Tideswell, J. Chem. Soc. (C), 1301 (1971).
388 From the Ph.D. Thesis of F.A. Mikulkski, Princeton University (1965).
388a W.C.M.C. Kokke and F.A. Varkevisser, J. Org. Chem., 39, 1535 (1974).
389 W.H. Mills and G.H. Keats, J. Chem. Soc., 1373 (1935).
390 V.M. Potapov, A.P. Terent'ev and V.M. Dem'yanovich, Zhur. Obsch. Khim., 29, 953 (1959).
391 W. Runge, G. Kresze and E. Ruch, Liebigs Ann. Chem., 1361 (1975).
392 J.H. Wotiz and R.J. Palchak, J. Am. Chem. Soc., 73, 1971 (1951).
393 C.D. Poulter, O.J. Muscio and R.J. Goodfellow, J. Org. Chem., 40, 139 (1975).
394 W. von E. Doering and K. Sachdev, J. Am. Chem. Soc., 96, 1168 (1974).
395 J-P. Grosclaude, H-U. Gonzenbach. J-C. Perlberger and K. Schaffner, Helv. Chim. Acta, 59, 2919 (1976).
396 R. Sandberg, Arkiv Kemi, 17, 327 (1961).
397 W.H. Perkin, J. Chem. Soc., 2129 (1910).
398 From the Ph.D. Thesis of P.W. Marr, University of Toronto, Toronto, Canada (1972).
399 J.A. Berson and D.A. Ben-Efraim, J. Am. Chem. Soc., 81, 4083 (1959).
400 T. Matsumoto, T. Okabe and K. Fukui, Chem. Letters, 773 (1973).
401 S.K. Ranganathan, J. Indian Chem. Soc., 13, 419 (1936).
402 H.N. Rydon, J. Chem. Soc., 829 (1936).
403 H.N. Rydon, J. Chem. Soc., 829 (1936).
404 H.N. Rydon, J. Chem. Soc.,1340 (1937).
405 H.N. Rydon, J. Chem. Soc., 1340 (1937).
406 R. Trave and L. Garanti, Gazz. Chim. Ital., 90, 612 (1960).
407 J.J. Gajewski, J. Am. Chem. Soc., 97, 3457 (1975).
408 A. Fredga and R. Sandberg, Suomen Kemi, B31, 42 (1958).
409 M.E. Maurit, R.P. Shternberg, A.M. Pakhomov, G.I. Basilevskaya, G-V. Smirnova and N.A. Preobrazhenskii, Zh. Obsh. Khim., 30, 2256 (1960).
410 D.E. Applequist and N.D. Werner, J. Org. Chem., 28, 48 (1963).
410a W.L.F. Armarego and T. Kobayashi, J. Chem. Soc. (C), 1635 (1969).
410b J.W. Barrett and R.P. Linstead, J. Chem. Soc., 1069 (1935).
410c E. Berner and O. Steffensen, Acta Chem. Scand., 8, 64 (1954).
411 J. Böeseken and A.E.J. Peek, Rec. Trav. Chim., 44, 841 (1925).
412 R.M. Lukes, G.I. Poos and L.H. Sarett, J. Am. Chem. Soc., 74, 1401 (1953).
413 K. Serck-Hanssen, Arkiv Kemi, 10, 135 (1957).
414 S. Tatsumi, M. Imaida and Y. Izumi, Bull. Chem. Soc. Japan, 39, 2543 (1966).
415 J. Knabe and N. Franz, Arch. Pharm. (Weinheim), 308, 313 (1975).
416 H.S. Tager and H.N. Christensen, J. Am. Chem. Soc., 94, 968 (1972).

Reference
Number

417 H S. Tager and H.N. Christensen, J. Am. Chem. Soc., 94, 968 (1972).
418 H. Pracejus and G. Kohl, Liebigs Ann. Chem., 722, 1 (1969).
419 MM.G. Vavon and P. Peignier, Bull. Soc. Chim. Fr., 45, 293 (1929).
420 J. Hoogmartens, P.J. Claes and H. Vanderhaeghe, J. Org. Chem., 39, 425 (1974).
421 J. Hoogmartens, P.J. Claes and H. Vanderhaeghe, J. Org. Chem., 39, 425 (1974).
422 A. Wohl and R. Maag, Chem. Ber., 42, 627 (1909).
423 A. Wohl and R. Maag, Chem. Ber., 42, 627 (1909).
424 T. Wieland and H. Wehrt, Chem. Ber., 92, 2106 (1959).
425 E. Abderhalden and A. Schmitz, Biochem. Z., 214, 158 (1929).
426 D.S. Acker and W.J. Wayne, J. Am. Chem. Soc., 79, 6483 (1957).
427 J.M. Walbrick, J.W. Wilson,Jr., and W.M. Jones, J. Am. Chem. Soc., 90, 2895 (1968)
428 A. Heymes, M. Dvolaitzky and J. Jacques, Bull. Soc. Chim. Fr., 2898 (1968).
429 D.S. Acker and W.J. Wayne, J. Am. Chem. Soc., 79, 6483 (1957).
430 W. Adam and N. Duran, J. Am. Chem. Soc., 99, 2729 (1977).
431 C.E. Wood and M.A. Comley, J. Chem. Soc., 125, 2630 (1924).
432 D. Pini, D. Lupinacci, and L. Porri, Gazz. Chim. Ital., 104, 1295 (1974).
433 A. Fredga, Arkiv Kemi Mineral. Geol., 23B, No. 2 (1946).
434 W.A. Noyes and L.P. Kyriakides, J. Am. Chem. Soc., 32, 1057 (1910).
435 E. Berner and R. Leonardsen, Liebigs Ann. Chem., 538, 1 (1934).
435a K. Nagarajan, Ch. Weissmann, H. Schmid and P. Karrer, Helv. Chim. Acta, 46, 1212 (1963).
436 A. Fredga and U. Sahlberg, Arkiv Kemi Mineral. Geol., 18A, No. 16 (1944).
437a M.R. Cox, G.A. Ellestad, A.J. Hannaford, I.R. Wallwork, W.B. Whalley and B. Sjöberg, J. Chem. Soc., 7257 (1965).
437.1 J. Kenyon and W.A. Ross, J. Chem. Soc., 3407 (1951).
B. Sjöberg, J. Chem. Soc., 7257 (1965).
438 MM. G. Vavon and P. Feignier, Bull. Soc. Chim. Fr., 45, 293 (1929).
439 Studien über Selen-di-karbonsäuren und Diselen-di-karbonsäuren (1935) by Prof. Arne Fredga.
440 Studien über Selen-di-karbonsäuren und Diselen-di-karbonsäuren (1935) by Prof. Arne Fredga.
441 K. Freudenberg, W.F. Bruce and E. Gauf, Liebigs Ann. Chem., 510, 206 (1934).
442 R. Ahlberg, Chem. Ber., 61B, 811 (1928).
443 J.H. Hunt and D. McHale, J. Chem. Soc., 2073 (1957).
443a D. Rudman, A. Meister and J.P. Greenstein, J. Am. Chem. Soc., 74, 551 (1952).
444 E. Fischer, A. Rohde and F. Brauns, Liebigs Ann. Chem., 402, 364 (1914).
445 S. Hase, R. Kiyoi and S. Sakakibara, Bull. Chem. Soc. Japan, 41, 1266 (1968).
445a S. Hase, R. Kiyoi and S. Sakakibara, Bull. Chem. Soc. Japan, 41, 1266 (1968).
446 P.A. Levene and M. Kuna, J. Biol. Chem., 140, 255 (1941).
447 P. Levene and R.E. Marker, J. Biol. Chem., 95, 1 (1932).
448 P.A. Levene, A. Rothen, G.M. Meyer and M. Kuna, J. Biol. Chem., 115, 401 (1936).
449 P.A. Levene and R.E. Marker, J. Biol. Chem., 91, 687 (1931).
449a J. Kenyon and B.C. Platt, J. Chem. Soc., 633 (1939).
450 P.A. Levene and R.E. Marker, J. Biol. Chem., 95, 1 (1932).
451 F.S. Prout, B. Burachinsky, W.T. Brannen,Jr. and H.L. Young, J. Org. Chem., 25, 835 (1960).
452 H. Kotake, T. Saito and K. Okubo, Bull. Chem. Soc. Japan, 42, 1367 (1969).
453 H. Kotake, T. Saito and K. Okubo, Bull. Chem. Soc. Japan, 42, 1367 (1969).
454 A. Fredga and T. Raznikiewicz, Arkiv Kemi, 14, 11 (1959).
455 M.S. Smith, R.L. Wain and F. Wightman, Ann. Appl. Biology, 39, 295 (1952).
455a From the Ph.D. Dissertation of Magnus Matell, Uppsala, Sweden (1953).
456 A. Fredga and G. Ekstedt, Arkiv Kemi, 23, 123 (1964).
457 M. Matell, Arkiv Kemi, 9, 157 (1955).
458 C. Aaron, D. Dull, J.L. Schmiegel, D. Jaeger, Y. Ohashi, and H.S. Mosher, J. Org. Chem., 32, 2797 (1967).
459 J.A. Dale, D.L. Dull and H.S. Mosher, J. Org. Chem., 34, 2543 (1969).
460 J.R.E. Hoover, G.L. Dunn, D.R. Jakas, L.L. Lam, J.J. Taggart, J.R. Guarini and L. Phillips, J. Med. Chem., 17, 34 (1974).
461 J.R.E. Hoover, G.L. Dunn, D.R. Jakas, L.L. Lam, J.J. Taggart, J.R. Guarini and L. Phillips, J. Med. Chem., 17, 34 (1974).
462 S. Senoh, Y. Maeno, S. Imamoto, A. Komamine, S. Hattori, K. Yamashita and M. Matsui, Bull. Chem. Soc. Japan, 40, 379 (1967).
463 A. Fredga, E. Gamstedt and L. Ekermo, Arkiv Kemi, 29, 515 (1968).
464 A. Fredga, E. Gamstedt and L. Ekermo, Arkiv Kemi, 29, 515 (1968).
465 C. Fedtke and R.R. Schmidt, Z. Naturforsch., 31, 252 (1976).
466 A. Fredga, Croat. Chem. Acta, 29, 313 (1957).
467 S.T. Collins and F.E. Smith, J. Sci. Food. Agric., 3, 248 (1952).
467a M. Matell, Arkiv Kemi, 4, 473 (1952).
468 A. Fredga, Croat. Chem. Acta, 29, 313 (1957).
469 M. Matell, Arkiv Kemi, 4, 473 (1952).
470 A. Fredga, Croat. Chem. Acta, 29, 313 (1957).
471 A. Fredga, Croat. Chem. Acta, 29, 313 (1957).
472 A. Fredga, Arkiv Kemi, 11, 23 (1957).
473 A. Fredga, Acta Chem. Scand., 9, 719 (1955).
474 K. Harada and Y. Nakajima, Bull. Chem. Soc. Japan, 47, 2911 (1974).
475 K. Harada, J. Org. Chem., 31, 1407 (1960).
476 A. Fredga and C.V.C. Sarmiento, Arkiv Kemi, 7, 387 (1954).
476a D.M. Bowen, J.I. DeGraw,Jr., V.R. Shah and W.A. Bonner, J. Med. Chem., 6, 315 (1963).
477 D.G. Neilson, U. Zakir and C.M. Scrimgeour, J. Chem. Soc. (C), 898 (1971).
478 E. Fischer and H. Carl, Chem. Ber., 39, 3996 (1906).
479 A. Collet and J. Jacques, Bull. Soc. Chim. France, 3857 (1972).
480 A. Collet and J. Jacques, Bull. Soc. Chim. France, 3857 (1972).
481 A. Collet and J. Jacques, Bull. Soc. Chim. France, 3857 (1972).
482 A. Fredga and M. Andersson, Arkiv Kemi, 25, 223 (1966).
483 A. Fredga and M. Andersson, Arkiv Kemi, 21, 555 (1964).

Reference Number

484 A. Fredga, Arkiv Kemi, 18, 501 (1962).
485 A. McKenzie and R.C. Strathern, J. Chem. Soc., 127, 82 (1925).
486 A. Collet and J. Jacques, Bull. Soc. Chim. France, 3857 (1972).
487 A. Collet and J. Jacques, Bull. Soc. Chim. France, 3857 (1972).
488 A. Collet and J. Jacques, Bull. Soc. Chim. France, 3857 (1972).
489 A. Fredga, A-M. Weidler and C. Grönwall, Arkiv Kemi, 17, 265 (1961).
490 A. Fredga, A-M. Weidler and C. Grönwall, Arkiv Kemi, 17, 265 (1961).
491 M. Matell, Arkiv Kemi, 7, 437 (1954).
491a D.T. Witiak, T. C-L. Ho, R.E. Hackney and W.E. Connor, J. Med. Chem., 11, 1086 (1968).
492 A. Collet, Bull. Soc. Chim. France, 215 (1975).
493 A. Collet, Bull. Soc. Chim. France, 215 (1975).
494 A. Collet, Bull. Soc. Chim. France, 215 (1975).
495 A. Collet, Bull. Soc. Chim. France, 215 (1975).
496 A. Collet, Bull. Soc. Chim. France, 215 (1975).
497 A. Collet, Bull. Soc. Chim. France, 215 (1975).
498 A. Collet and J. Jacques, Bull. Soc. Chim. France, 3857 (1972).
499 A. Collet and J. Jacques, Bull. Soc. Chim. France, 3857 (1972).
500 A. Collet and J. Jacques, Bull. Soc. Chim. France, 3857 (1972).
501 A. Fredga, Arkiv Kemi, 25, 87 (1965).
502 A. Fredga, Arkiv Kemi, 25, 87 (1965).
503 A. Fredga, Arkiv Kemi, 25, 87 (1965).
504 M.K. Hargreaves and M.A. Khan, J. Chem. Soc. Perkin 2, 1204 (1973).
505 F. Nerdel and H. Harter, Liebigs Ann. Chem., 621, 22 (1959).
506 A. Fredga, Arkiv Kemi, 7, 241 (1954).
506a F. Nerdel and H. Würgan, Liebigs Ann. Chem., 621, 34 (1959).
506b E. Miller and R. Illgen, Liebigs Ann. Chem., 521, 72 (1936).
506c F. Nerdel and L. Fischer, Chem. Ber., 87, 217 (1954).
507 P. Friis and A. Kjaer, Acta Chem. Scand., 17, 2391 (1963).
508 N.A. Krit, G.A. Ravdel and L.A. Shchukina, Zh. Obsch. Khim., 38, 1015 (1968).
509 A. Fredga, Acta Chem. Scand., 23, 2216 (1969).
510 E. Fourneau and G. Sandulesco, Bull. Soc. Chim. Fr., 33, 459 (1923).
511 A. Kjaer and P.O. Larsen, Acta Chem. Scand., 17, 2397 (1963).
512 S. Senoh, Y. Maeno and S. Imamoto, A. Komamine, S. Hattori, K. Yamashita and M. Matsui, Bull. Chem. Soc. Japan, 40, 379 (1967).
513 S. Senoh, Y. Maeno and S. Imamoto, A. Komamine, S. Hattori, K. Yamashita and M. Matsui, Bull. Chem. Soc. Japan, 40, 379 (1967).
514 P. Pratesi, A. La Manna, A. Campiglio and V. Ghislandi, J. Chem. Soc., 2069 (1958).
515 H. Gustafsson, Acta Chem. Scand., B29, 177 (1975).
516 D. Pitré and E.B. Grabitz, Hoppe-Seyler's Z. Physiol. Chem., 333, 105 (1963).
517 R. Schwyzer and E. Surbeck-Wegmann, Helv. Chim. Acta, 43, 1073 (1960).
518 J.A. Berson, J. Am. Chem. Soc., 76, 5748 (1954).
519 H.J. Backer and H.G. Kemper, Rec. Trav. Chim., 57, 761 (1938).
520 J.H. Tong, C. Petitclerc, A. D'Iorio and N.L. Benoiton, Can. J. Biochem., 49, 877 (1971).
521 J.H. Tong, C. Petitclerc, A. D'Iorio and N.L. Benoiton, Can. J. Biochem., 49, 877 (1971).
522 F. Bergel and J.A. Stock, U. S. Patent 3,032,585 (1962).
523 C.L. Arcus and J. Kenyon, J. Chem. Soc., 916 (1939).
523a A. Fredga, Arkiv Kemi, 7, 241 (1954).
523b S.I. Goldberg and F-L. Lam, J. Org. Chem., 31, 2336 (1966).
523c K. Pettersson, Arkiv Kemi, 10, 283 (1956).
523d R. Roger and D.G. Neilson, J. Chem. Soc., 627 (1960).
524 L. Lamberg and I. Hedlund, Arkiv Kemi, Mineral. Geol., 12A, No. 12 (1937).
525 A. McKenzie and J.K. Wood, J. Chem. Soc., 828 (1919).
525a G. Fodor, J. Rakoczi and Gy. Csepreghy, Acta Chim. Hung., 28, 409 (1961).
526 A. McKenzie and H.B.P. Humphries, J. Chem. Soc., 97, 121 (1910).
526a S.G. Cohen and S.Y. Weinstein, J. Am. Chem. Soc., 80, 725 (1964).
527 H. Wren and E. Wright, J. Chem. Soc., 119, 798 (1921).
528 J.R.E. Hoover, G.L. Dunn, D.R. Jakas, L.L. Lam, J.J. Taggart, J.R. Guarini and L. Phillips, J. Med. Chem., 17, 34 (1974).
529 J.R.E. Hoover, G.L. Dunn, D.R. Jakas, L.L. Lam, J.J. Taggart, J.R. Guarini and L. Phillips, J. Med. Chem., 17, 34 (1974).
530 J.R.E. Hoover, G.L. Dunn, D.R. Jakas, L.L. Lam, J.J. Taggart, J.R. Guarini and L. Phillips, J. Med. Chem., 17, 34 (1974).
531 M. Bougault, Ann. Chim., 25, 483 (1902).
532 L. Smith, J. Prakt. Chem., 84, 731 (1911).
532a A. McKenzie and G.W. Clough, J. Chem. Soc., 1016 (1910).
533 D.J.C. Pirie and I.A. Smith, J. Chem. Soc., 338 (1932).
533a D.G. Neilson and D.A.V. Peters, J. Chem. Soc., 1519 (1962).
534 W.J. Gottstein and L.C. Cheney, J. Org. Chem., 30, 2072 (1965).
534a A. Fredga and M. Matell, Arkiv Kemi, 4, 325 (1952).
535 T.R. Emerson, D.F. Ewing, W. Klyne, D.G. Neilson, D.A.V. Peters, L.H. Roach and R.J. Swan, J. Chem. Soc., 4007 (1965).
536 D.G. Neilson, U. Zakir and C.M. Scrimgeour, J. Chem. Soc. (C), 898 (1971).
536a J.R.E. Hoover, G.L. Dunn, D.R. Jakas, L.L. Lam, J.J. Taggart, J.R. Guarini and L. Phillips, J. Med. Chem., 17, 34 (1974).
537 J.R.E. Hoover, G.L. Dunn, D.R. Jakas, L.L. Lam, J.J. Taggart, J.R. Guarini and L. Phillips, J. Med. Chem., 17, 34 (1974).
537a D.G. Neilson, U. Zakir and C.M. Scrimgeour, J. Chem. Soc. (C), 898 (1971).
537b A. McKenzie and D.J.C. Pirie, Chem. Ber., 69, 861 (1936).
538 K.N.F. Shaw, M.D. Armstrong and A. McMillan, J. Org. Chem., 21, 1149 (1956).
539 A. La Manna, G. Pagani, P. Pratesi and M.L. Ricciardi, Farmaco, Ed. Sci., 19, 506 (1964).
540 A. Collet, Bull. Soc. Chim. Fr., 215 (1975).
541 A. Collet, Bull. Soc. Chim. Fr., 215 (1975).

Reference
Number

542 R.E. Pincock, M-M. Tong and K.R. Wilson, J. Am. Chem. Soc., 93, 1669 (1971).
543 A. Fredga and O. Palm, Arkiv Kemi, Mineral. Geol., 26A, No. 26 (1949).
544 S. Gronowitz and S. Larsson, Arkiv Kemi, 8, 567 (1955).
545 M.D. Armstrong, A. McMillan and K.N.F. Shaw, Biochem. Biophys. Acta, 25, 422 (1957).
546 C.H.K. Mulder, Rec. Trav. Chim., 51, 174 (1932).
547 C.H.K. Mulder, Rec. Trav. Chim., 50, 719 (1931).
548 C.H.K. Mulder, Rec. Trav. Chim.,50, 719 (1931).
549 E. Fischer and W. Schoeller, Liebigs Ann. Chem., 357, 1 (1907).
549a W. Langenbeck and O. Herbst, Chem. Ber., 86, 1524 (1953).
549b G. Losse, H-J. Hebel and C. Kastner, J. Prakt. Chem., 8, 339 (1959).
549c G. Losse, G. Müller, J. Prakt. Chem., 9, 145 (1959).
549d L.R. Overby and A.W. Ingersoll, J. Am. Chem. Soc., 82, 2067 (1960).
549e E. Fischer and A. Mouneyrat, Chem. Ber., 42, 2383 (1909).
549f H. Geipel, J. Prakt. Chem., 9, 104 (1959).
549g J.M. Gillingham, U. S. Patent 3,028,395 (1962).
549h K. Oki, K. Suzuki, S. Tuchida, T. Saito and H. Kotaka, Bull. Chem. Soc. Japan, 43, 2554 (1970).
549i F.H. Radke, R.B. Fearing and S.W. Fox, J. Am. Chem. Soc., 76, 2801 (1954).
549j L.R. Overby and A.W. Ingersoll, J. Am. Chem. Soc., 73, 3363 (1951).
549k B. Halpern, A.M. Sargeson and K.R. Turnbull, Chem. Ind. (London), 1399 (1963).
549-1 T. Kato and Y. Tsuchiya, Agr. Biol. Chem., 26, 467 (1962).
549m T. Sokolowska, Pol. J. Chem., 40, 1895 (1966).
549n S. Berlingozzi, G. Adembri and G. Bucci, Gazz. Chim. Ital., 84, 383 (1954).
549o I.A. Halmos, U. S. Patent 4,151,198 (1979).
549p W. Klötzer, Monatsh. Chem., 87, 346 (1956).
549q H.T. Huang and C. Niemann, J. Am. Chem. Soc., 73, 475 (1951).
549r K.A. Wretlind, J. Biol. Chem., 186, 221 (1950).
549s C.G. Baker and H.A. Sober, J. Am. Chem. Soc., 75, 4058 (1953).
550 E. Testa, Farmaco, Ed. Sci., 19, 895 (1964).
551 S.G. Cohen and S.Y. Weinstein, J. Am. Chem. Soc., 80, 725 (1964).
552 D.J. Cram, L.K. Gaston and H. Jäger, J. Am. Chem. Soc., 83, 2183 (1961).
553 M. Matell, Acta Chem. Scand., 7, 228 (1953).
553a P.S. Portoghese, J. Med. Chem., 8, 147 (1965).
554 J.H. Tong, C. Petitclerc, A. D'Iorio and N. Leo Benoiton, Can. J. Biochem., 49, 877 (1971).
555 R.R. Sealock, M.E. and R.S. Schweet, J. Am. Chem. Soc., 73, 5386 (1951).
555a J.H. Tong, C. Petitclerc, A. D'Iorio and N.L. Benoiton, Can. J. Biochem., 49, 877 (1971).
556 E. Fischer, Chem. Ber., 32, 3638 (1900).
556a R.R. Sealock, J. Biol. Chem., 166, 1 (1946).
556b G. Losse, H-J. Hebel and C. Kastner, J. Prakt. Chem., 8, 339 (1959).
556c J. M. Gillingham, U. S. Patent 3,028,395 (1962).
556d G. Losse, J. Prakt. Chem., 7, 141 (1959).
556e G. Triem, Chem. Ber., 71, 1522 (1938).
557 British Patent 1,450,596 (1976).
557a L.B. Crast, Jr., U. S. Patent 3,489,746 (1970).
558 British Patent 695,741 (1953).
559 J.R.E. Hoover, G.L. Dunn, D.R. Jakas, L.L. Lam, J.J. Taggart, J.R. Guarini, and L. Phillips, J. Med. Chem., 17, 34 (1974).
560 A. Neuberger, Biochem. J., 43, 599 (1948).
561 German Patent 1,963,992 (1973).
561a G. Losse, A. Barth and W. Langenbeck, Chem. Ber., 94, 2271 (1961).
561b A. Kaiser, M. Scheer, W. Häusermann and L. Marti, U. S. Patent 3,969,397 (1976).
561c S. Yamada, M. Yamamoto and I. Chibata, Chem. Ind. (London), 528 (1973).
562 H.J. Backer and H. Mulder, Rec. Trav. Chim., 53, 1120 (1934).
563 C.S. Gibson and B. Levin, J. Chem. Soc., 2754 (1929).
564 Z. Grzonka and B. Liberek, Tetrahedron, 27, 1783 (1971).
565 C.S. Gibson, J.D.A. Johnson and B. Levin, J. Chem. Soc., 479 (1929).
566 E. Fogassy, M. Acs and I. Hermecz, Periodica Polytechnica, 20, 263 (1976).
567 J.A. Berson, J.S. Walia, A. Remanick, S. Suzuki, P. Reynolds-Warnhoff and D. Willner, J. Am. Chem. Soc., 83, 3986 (1961).
568 O. Cervinka and O. Kriz, Coll. Czech. Chem. Comm., 33, 2342 (1968).
569 M. Nakazaki, K. Naemura and N. Arashiba, J. Org. Chem., 43, 888 (1978).
570 M-O. Hedblom and K. Olsson, Arkiv Kemi, 32, 309 (1970).
571 M. Nakazaki, K. Naemura and H. Kadowaki, J. Org. Chem., 41, 3728 (1976).
572 J. Dixon, B. Lythgoe, I.A. Siddiqui and J. Tideswell, J. Chem. Soc. (C), 1301 (1971).
573 B. Akermark, Arkiv Kemi, 27, 11 (1967).
574 H.M. Walborsky, L. Barash and T.C. Davis, Tetrahedron, 19, 2333 (1963).
574a B. Åkermark, Acta Chem. Scand., 21, 589 (1967).
575 H.J. Backer and H.B.J. Schurink, Rec. Trav. Chim., 50, 921 (1931).
575a H. Wynberg and J.P.M. Houbiers, J. Org. Chem., 36, 835 (1971).
576 P.R. Bruck, R.D. Clark, R.S. Davidson, W.H.H. Günther, P.S. Littlewood and B. Lythgoe, J. Chem. Soc., 2529 (1967).
577 H. Gerlach, Helv. Chim. Acta, 49, 1291 (1966).
578 E. Fischer and W. Brieger, Chem. Ber., 48, 1517 (1915).
579 J.H. Wotiz and R.J. Palchak, J. Am. Chem. Soc., 73, 1971 (1951).
580 J. Owen and J.L. Simonsen, J. Chem. Soc., 1223 (1933).
581 J. Owen and J.L. Simonsen, J. Chem. Soc., 1223 (1933).
582 T.L. Dawson and G.R. Ramage, J. Chem. Soc., 3523 (1950).
583 T.L Dawson and G.R. Ramage, J. Chem. Soc., 3523 (1950).
584 A. Campbell and H.N. Rydon, J. Chem. Soc., 3002 (1953).
585 J.W. Barrett and R.P. Linstead, J. Chem. Soc., 1069 (1935).
586 H. Conroy and E. Cohen, J. Org. Chem., 23, 616 (1958).

Reference Number

587 S.K. Ranganathan, Current Sci., 6, 277 (1937).
588 D.C. Ayres and R.A. Raphael, J. Chem. Soc., 1779 (1958).
589 E. Fischer and E. Flatau, Chem. Ber., 42, 2981 (1909).
590 W.M. McLamore, W.D. Celmer, V.V. Bogert, F.C. Pennington, B.A. Sobin and I.A. Solomons, J. Am. Chem. Soc., 75, 105 (1953).
591 F. Bergel, N.C. Hindley, A.L. Morrison and A.R. Moss, Chem. Ber., 85, 711 (1952).
592 S.G. Cohen and E. Khedouri, J. Am. Chem. Soc., 83, 1093 (1961).
593 K. Flohr, R.M. Paton and E.T. Kaiser, J. Am. Chem. Soc., 97, 1209 (1975).
594 W.V.E. Doering and K.B. Wiberg, J. Am. Chem. Soc., 72, 2608 (1950).
595 A. Maccioni, Boll. Chim. Farm., 23, 41 (1965).
596 H.L. Goering and F.H. McCarron, J. Am. Chem. Soc., 80, 2287 (1958).
597 T.L. Jacobs, R. Reed and E. Pacovska, J. Am. Chem. Soc., 73, 4505 (1951).
598 G. Blaeson and H-G. Jonsson, Arkiv Kemi, 31, 83 (1969).
599 J.v. Braun and G. Werner, Chem. Ber., 62, 1050 (1929).
600 A. Fredga and H. Ostman, Acta Chem. Scand., 10, 703 (1956).
601 E. Berner and L.H. Landmark, Acta Chem. Scand., 7, 1347 (1953).
602 S. Ställberg-Stenhagen, Arkiv Kemi, 3, 249 (1951).
603 A. Fredga, Arkiv Kemi, 6, 277 (1953).
604 M.R. Cox, H.P. Koch, and W.B. Whalley, J. Chem. Soc., Perkin 1, 174 (1973).
605 D. Rudman, A. Meister and J.P. Greenstein, J. Am. Chem. Soc., 74, 551 (1952).
606 E.T. Stiller and P.F. Wiley, J. Am. Chem. Soc., 63, 1237 (1941).
606a E.T. Stiller and P.F. Wiley, J. Am. Chem. Soc., 63, 1237 (1941).
606b R. Kuhn and T. Wieland, Chem. Ber., 73, 971 (1940).
607 P.A. Levene and R.E. Marker, J. Biol. Chem., 95, 1 (1932).
608 P.A. Levene and R.E. Marker, J. Biol. Chem., 95, 1 (1932).
609 F. Kögl and A.G. Boer, Rec. Trav. Chim., 54, 779 (1935).
610 R. Ikan, A. Markus and E.D. Bergman, J. Org. Chem., 36, 3944 (1971).
611 E. Fischer, J. Holzapfel and H.v. Gwinner, Chem. Ber., 45, 247 (1912).
612 M. Bianchi, P. Frediani, L. Lardicci and F. Piacenti, Gazz. Chim. Ital., 104, 273 (1974).
613 F.S. Prout, B. Burachinsky, W.T. Brannen, Jr. and H.L. Young, J. Org. Chem., 25, 835 (1960).
614 W. v.E. Doering and K.B. Wiberg, J. Am. Chem. Soc., 72, 2608 (1950).
615 R. Håkansson and E. Wiklund, Arkiv Kemi, 31, 101 (1969).
616 E. Wiklund and R. Håkansson, Chemica Scripta, 6, 137 (1974).
617 A. Almqvist and R. Håkansson, Chemica Scripta, 11, 186 (1977).
618 S. Gronowitz, Arkiv Kemi, 23, 307 (1965).
619 S. Gronowitz and P. Gustafson, Arkiv Kemi, 20, 289 (1962).
620 C. Dell'Erba, D. Spinelli, G. Garbarino and G. Leandri, J. Heterocyclic Chem., 5, 45 (1968).
621 E. Wiklund and R. Håkansson, Chemica Scripta, 6, 137 (1974).
622 E. Wiklund and R. Håkansson, Chemica Scripta, 6, 76 (1974).
623 E.K.G. Schmidt, Angew. Chem. Internat. Edit., 12, 777 (1973).
624 L.R. Pohl and W.F. Trager, J. Med. Chem., 16, 475 (1973).
625 K. Shinga, S. Hagishita and M. Nakagawa, Tetrahedron Lett., 4371 (1967).
626 P. Ahlberg, Chemica Scripta, 3, 183 (1973).
627 M. Naps and I.B. Johns, J. Am. Chem. Soc., 62, 2450 (1940).
628 J.A. Dale, D.L. Dull and H.S. Mosher, J. Org. Chem., 34, 2543 (1969).
629 J. Knabe and D. Strauss, Arch. Pharm. (Weinheim), 305, 54 (1972).
630 W.H. Mills, H.V. Parker and R. W. Prowse, J. Chem. Soc., 105, 1537 (1914).
631 F. Nerdel and H. Rachel, Chem. Ber., 89, 671 (1956).
632 D.B. Reisner, B.J. Ludwig, F.J. Steifel, S. Gister, M. Meyer, L.S. Powell and R.D. Sofia, Arzneim Forsch.,27, 760 (1977).
633 M. Matell, Arkiv Kemi, 6, 365 (1953).
634 E. Gamstedt, Arkiv Kemi,32, 151 (1970).
635 E. Gamstedt, Arkiv Kemi, 32, 151 (1970).
636 A. Fredga and E. Gamstedt, Arkiv Kemi, 28, 109 (1967).
637 H. Gustafsson, Arkiv Kemi, 31, 415 (1969).
638 A. Fredga, Acta Chem. Scand., B31, 869 (1977).
639 E.J. Corey, R.J. McCaully and H.S. Sachdev, J. Am. Chem. Soc., 92, 2476 (1970).
640 W.M. Colles and C.S. Gibson, J. Chem. Soc., 279 (1931).
641 W.M. Colles and C.S. Gibson, J. Chem. Soc., 99 (1928).
642 C.G. Overberger and Y. Shimokawa, Macromolecules, 4, 718 (1971).
643 A. Fredga, Chem. Ber., 89, 322 (1956).
643a From the M.Sc. Thesis of H.M. Schwartz, University of Toronto, Toronto, Canada (1975,
644 M. Ishihara, K. Yonetani, T. Shibai and Y. Tanaka, Int. Congr. Essent. Oils [Pap.] 7th 1977 (Pub. 1979) 7, 266.
645 J. M. Domagala and R. D. Bach, J. Org. Chem., 44, 3168 (1979).
646 F. Nerdel and H. Rachel, Chem. Ber., 89, 671 (1956).
647 W.C. Agosta, J. Am. Chem. Soc., 86, 2638 (1964).
648 W.C. Agosta, J. Am. Chem. Soc., 86, 2638 (1964).
649 H. Wren and H. Williams, J. Chem. Soc., 109, 572 (1916).
650 P. Fitger, Dissertation, University of Lund, Sweden (1924).
651 D.J. Cram and T. A. Whitney, J. Am. Chem. Soc., 89, 4651 (1967).
652 P.C. Guha and S.K. Ranganathan, Chem. Ber., 72, 1379 (1939).
653 A. Fredga and K-I. Sandstrom, Arkiv Kemi, 23, 245 (1965).
654 A. Fredga, A. Kjellqvist and E. Tornqvist, Arkiv Kemi, 32, 301 (1970).
655 A. Fredga, A. Kjellqvist and E. Tornqvist, Arkiv Kemi, 32, 301 (1970).
656 A. Fredga, E. Thimon and K. Rosberg, Arkiv Kemi, 32, 369 (1970).
657 M. Matell, Arkiv Kemi, 6, 365 (1953).
658 E. Fourneau and G. Sandulesco, Bull. Soc. Chim. Fr., 41, 450 (1927).
659 P. Crooij and J. Eliaers, J. Chem. Soc. (C), 559 (1969).
660 J.A. Berson, J. Am. Chem. Soc., 76, 4069 (1954).
661 A. Butenandt, and R. Weichert, Z. Physiol. Chem., 281, 122 (1944).
662 Personal communication from Dr. Koichi Niimura, The University of Tokyo, Japan.
663 K. Pettersson, Arkiv Kemi,10, 283 (1956).
663a Ph. Gold-Aubert, Helv. Chim. Acta, 41, 1512 (1958).

Reference Number

663b R. Weidmann and A. Horeau, Bull. Soc. Chim. Fr., 117 (1967).
664 A. Weidler and G. Bergson, Acta Chem. Scand., 18, 1484 (1964).
664a H.E. Smith, B.G. Padilla, J.R. Neergard and F-M. Chen, J. Am. Chem. Soc., 100, 6035 (1978).
664b V. Folli, D. Iarossi, F. Montanari and G. Torre, J. Chem. Soc. (C), 1317 (1968).
665 A.M. Schrecker, J. Org. Chem., 22, 33 (1957).
665a D.F. DeTar and C. Weis, J. Am. Chem. Soc., 79, 3045 (1957).
665b U. S. Patent 3,758,559 (1973).
666 B. Holmberg, Arkiv Kemi Mineral. Geol., 13A, No. 8 (1939).
667 A. Fredga and M. Andersson, Arkiv Kemi, 25, 223 (1966).
668 A. Fredga and M. Andersson, Arkiv Kemi, 21, 555 (1964).
669 A. Fredga and R. Backstrom, Arkiv Kemi, 25, 455 (1966).
670 M. Matell, Arkiv Kemi, 6, 251 (1953).
670a British Patent 1,030,389 (1966).
671 D. Biquard, Ann. Chim. Phys., 20, 97 (1933).
672 H. Thierfelder and E. Schempp, Z. Physiol. Chem., 114, 94 (1921).
673 M. Guetté, J. Capillon and J.-P. Guetté, Tetrahedron, 29, 3659 (1973).
673a J. A. Reid and E. E. Turner, J. Chem. Soc., 3694 (1950).
674 J. Canceill, J. Gabard and J. Jacques, Bull. Soc. Chim. France, 231 (1968).
674a T. Matsumoto, I. Tanaka and K. Fukui, Bull. Chem. Soc. Japan, 44, 3378 (1971).
675 J.M. Domagala and R.D. Bach, J. Org. Chem., 44, 2429 (1979).
675a G. Cignarella, E. Occelli, G. Maffii and E. Testa, J. Med. Chem., 6, 29 (1963).
676 A. McKenzie and A. Ritchie, Chem. Ber., 70, 23 (1937).
677 E.W. Christie, A. McKenzie and A. Ritchie, J. Chem. Soc., 153 (1935).
678 D.J. Collins and J.J. Hobbs, Austr. J. Chem., 23, 119 (1970).
679 L. Angiolini, P. Costa Bizzarri and M. Tramontini, Tetrahedron, 25, 4211 (1969).
679a D.J. Cram and K.R. Kopecky, J. Am. Chem. Soc., 81, 2748 (1959).
680 A. Fredga, I. Kiriks and C. Lundstrom, Arkiv Kemi, 25, 249 (1966).
681 A. Fredga, I. Kiriks and C. Lundstrom, Arkiv Kemi, 25, 249 (1966).
682 A. Fredga and I. Avalaht, Arkiv Kemi, 24, 425 (1965).
683 E.W. Christie, A. McKenzie and A. Ritchie, J. Chem. Soc., 153 (1935).
684 A. Weissberger and E. Dym, Liebigs Ann. Chem., 502, 74 (1933).
685 M.G. Peter, G. Snatzke, F. Snatzke, K.N. Nagarajan and H. Schmid, Helv. Chim. Acta, 57, 32 (1974).
686 A. La Manna, Farmaco, Ed. Sci., 15, 9 (1960).
687 C.M Bean, J. Kenyon and H. Phillips, J. Chem. Soc., 303 (1936).
688 M. Matsui, Y. Yamada and M. Nonoyama, Agr. Biol. Chem., 26, 351 (1962).
689 M. Matsui, Y. Yamada and M. Nonoyama, Agr. Biol. Chem., 26, 351 (1962).
690 J. Knabe and H. Junginger, Pharmazie, 7, 443 (1972).
691 J. Knabe and D. Strauss, Arch. Pharm. (Weinheim), 305, 54 (1972).
692 M.P. Paradisi and A. Romeo, J. Chem. Soc., Perkin 1, 596 (1977).
693 V. du Vigneaud and O.J. Irish, J. Biol. Chem., 122, 349 (1937-38).
694 M. Sobocinska, G. Kupryszewski and M.M. Zobaczewa, Rocz. Chem., 48, 461 (1974).
695 F. W. Bollinger, J. Med. Chem., 14, 373 (1971).
695a S. Terashima, K. Achiwa and S. Yamada, Chem. Pharm. Bull., 14, 1138 (1966).
696 J.A. Garbarino, J. Sierra and R. Tapia, J. Chem. Soc., Perkin 1, 1866 (1973).
697 W.v.E. Doering and V.Z. Pasternak, J. Am. Chem. Soc., 72, 143 (1950).
698 M.D. Armstrong and J.D. Lewis, J. Org. Chem., 17, 618 (1952).
699 D. Pitre, S. Boveri and N. Buser, Farmaco, Ed. Sci., 23, 244 (1968).
700 G. Büyük and E. Hardegger, Helv. Chim. Acta, 58, 682 (1975).
701 E.W. Tristram, J. Ten Broeke, D.F. Reinhold, M. Sletzinger, and D.E. Williams, J. Org. Chem., 29, 2053 (1964).
701a E.W. Tristram, J. Ten Broeke, D.F. Reinhold, M. Sletzinger, and D.E. Williams, J. Org. Chem., 29, 2053 (1964).
701b S. Yamada, C. Hongo, M. Yamamoto and I. Chibata, Agr. Biol. Chem., 40, 1425 (1976).
702 A. Kaiser, M. Scheer, W. Häusermann and L. Marti, U. S. Patent 3,969,397 (1976).
703 H.J. Backer and A. Bloemen, Rec. Trav. Chim., 45, 110 (1926).
704 H.J. Backer and J.H. De Boer, Rec. Trav. Chim., 43, 420 (1924).
705 C.S. Gibson and J.L. Simonsen, J. Chem. Soc., 798 (1915).
706 F. Kienzle, G.W. Holland, J.L. Jernow, S. Kwoh and P. Rosen, J. Org. Chem., 3440 (1973).
707 R.G. Vdovina, A.V. Karpova and E.S. Chaman, Zh. Obsch. Khim., 37, 1007 (1967).
708 Z. Grzonka and B. Liberek, Tetrahedron, 27, 1783 (1971).
709 C.S. Gibson and B. Levin, J. Chem. Soc., 2754 (1929).
710 W.J. Pope and J. Read, J. Chem. Soc., 97, 2199 (1910).
711 H. Gustafsson, Arkiv Kemi, 29, 587 (1968).
712 K. Undheim and G.A. Ulsaker, Acta Chem. Scand., 27, 1059 (1973).
713 M. Tichy and J. Sicher, Coll. Czech. Chem. Comm., 37, 3106 (1972).
714 H. Numan, C.B. Troostwijk, J.H. Wieringa and H. Wynberg, Tetrahedron Lett., 1761 (1977).
715 K. Adachi, K. Naemura and M. Nakazaki, Tetrahedron Lett., 5467 (1968).
716 Y. Inouye and M. Ohno, Agr. Biol. Chem., 21, 265 (1957).
717 J.M. Gardlik, L.K. Johnson, L.A. Paquette, B.A. Solheim, J.P. Springer and J. Clardy, J. Am. Chem. Soc., 101, 1615 (1979).
718 Personal communication from Prof. Leo A. Paquette, Ohio State University, Columbus, Ohio.
719 H.L. Slates, Z.S. Zelawski, D. Taub and N.L. Wendler, Tetrahedron, 30, 819 (1974).
720 J.D. Edwards, Jr. and T. Matsumoto, J. Org. Chem., 32, 1837 (1967).
721 R.A. Cutler, R.J. Stenger and C.M. Suter, J. Am. Chem. Soc., 74, 5475 (1952).
722 J.D. Edwards,Jr., T. Hase and N. Ichikawa, J. Heterocyclic Chem., 4, 487 (1967).
723 J.D. Edwards, Jr., T. Hase and N. Ichikawa, J. Heterocyclic Chem., 4, 487 (1967).
724 E. Berner, Acta Chem. Scand., 10, 268 (1956).
725 S. Kiyooka, T. Hase and J.D. Edwards, Jr., Chem. Lett., 963 (1973).
726 W. Oppolzer and H. Andres, Tetrahedron Lett., 3397 (1978).
727 D.E. Wolf, R. Mozingo, S.A. Harris, R.C. Anderson and K. Folkers, J. Am. Chem. Soc., 67, 2100 (1945).

Reference Number

727a D.E. Wolf, R. Mozingo, S.A. Harris, R.C. Anderson and K. Folkers, J. Am. Chem. Soc., 67, 2100 (1945).
727b D.E. Wolf, R. Mozingo, S.A. Harris, R.C. Anderson and K. Folkers, J. Am. Chem. Soc., 67, 2100 (1945).
728 I.G.M. Campbell and S.H. Harper, J. Sci. Food Agric., 3, 189 (1952).
728a K. Okada, K. Fujimoto, Y. Okuno and M. Matsui, Agr. Biol. Chem., 37, 2235 (1973).
728b M. Matsui and F. Horiuchi, Agr. Biol. Chem., 35, 1984 (1971).
729 I.G.M. Campbell and S.H. Harper, J. Sci. Food Agric., 3, 189 (1952).
729a M. Matsui and F. Horiuchi, Agr. Biol. Chem., 35, 1984 (1971).
729b F. Horiuchi and M. Matsui, Agr. Biol. Chem., 37, 1713 (1973).
729c German Patent 2,300,325 (1975).
730 M. Delepine and A. Willemart, Compt. Rend., 211, 153 (1940).
731 M. Janczewski and T. Bartnik, Polish J. Chem., 36, 1243 (1962).
732 A. Fredga and M. Matell, Bull. Soc. Chim. Belges., 62, 47 (1953).
733 W. Hückel, M. Sachs, J. Yantschulewitsch and F. Nerdel, Liebigs Ann. Chem., 518, 155 (1935).
734 F. Gautschi, O. Jeger, V. Prelog and R.B. Woodward, Helv. Chim. Acta, 38, 296 (1955).
735 J.D. Edwards,Jr., T. Hase, C. Hignite and T. Matsumoto, J. Org. Chem., 31, 2282 (1966).
736 J.D. Edwards,Jr. and T. Matsumoto, J. Org. Chem., 32, 2561 (1967).
737 A. Fredga, Chemica Scripta, 2, 47 (1972).
738 J. Vasilevskis, J.A. Gualtieri, S.D. Hutchings, R.C. West, J.W. Scott, D.R. Parrish, F.T. Bizzaro, G.F. Field, J. Am. Chem. Soc., 100, 7423 (1978).
739 P.A. Levene and R.E. Marker, J. Biol. Chem., 97, 563 (1932).
740 R.D. Westland, M.L. Mouk, J.L. Holmes, R.A. Cooley,Jr., J.S. Hong and M.M. Grenan, J. Med. Chem., 15, 968 (1972).
741 F.C. Copp and J.L. Simonsen, J. Chem. Soc., 415 (1940).
742 H. Wren and H. Burns, J. Chem. Soc., 117, 266 (1920).
742a J. Timmermans and J. van der Haegen, Bull. Soc. Chim. Belges., 42, 448 (1933).
743 M. Tichy, P. Malon, I. Fric and K. Blaha, Coll. Czech. Chem. Comm., 42, 3591 (1977).
744 L. Ahlquist, J. Asselineau, C. Asselineau, K. Serck-Hanssen, S. Stallberg-Stenhagen and E. Stenhagen, Arkiv Kemi, 14, 171 (1958).
745 A.R. Battersby, S.W. Breuer and S. Garratt, J. Chem. Soc. (C), 2467 (1968).
746 L. Eberson, Acta Chem. Scand., 13, 40 (1959).
747 D.H.R. Barton, L.D.S. Godinho and J.K. Sutherland, J. Chem. Soc., 1779 (1965).
748 E. Fischer, J. Holzapfel and H. v. Gwinner, Chem. Ber., 45, 247 (1912).
749 F.S. Prout, B. Burachinsky, W. T. Brannen,Jr. and H.L. Young, J. Org. Chem., 25, 835 (1960).
750 C. Asselineau and J. Asselineau, Bull. Soc. Chim. France, 1992 (1967).
751 W. Tochtermann, C. Franke and D. Schäfer, Chem. Ber., 101, 3122 (1968).
752 E.W. Yankee, B. Spencer, N.E. Howe and D.J. Cram, J. Am. Chem. Soc., 95, 4220 (1973).
753 E.W. Yankee, B. Spencer, N.E. Howe and D.J. Cram, J. Am. Chem. Soc., 95, 4220 (1973).
754 L.A. Paquette, W.B. Farnham and S.V. Ley, J. Am. Chem. Soc., 97, 7273 (1975).
755 L. Crombie, P.A. Jenkins and J. Roblin, J. Chem. Soc., Perkin 1, 1090 (1975).
756 W. Runge, G. Kresze and E. Ruch, Liebigs Ann. Chem., 1361 (1975).
757 B. Sjöberg, Arkiv Kemi, 12, 565 (1958).
758 B. Sjöberg, Arkiv Kemi, 11, 439 (1957).
759 K. Pettersson, Arkiv Kemi, 7, 339 (1954).
760 W.M. Jones, J. Am. Chem. Soc., 81, 5153 (1959).
761 C.W. Perry, A. Brossi, K.H. Deitcher, W. Tautz and S. Teitel, Synthesis, 492 (1977).
762 B. Loev, E. Macko and I.M. Fried, J. Med. Chem., 12, 854 (1969).
762a J. Knabe and D. Strauss, Arch. Pharm. (Weinheim), 305, 54 (1972).
763 D.J. Cram and P. Haberfield, J. Am. Chem. Soc., 83, 2354 (1961).
764 J. Kenyon and W.A. Ross, J. Chem. Soc., 3407 (1951).
765 B. Sjöberg, Arkiv Kemi, 12, 251 (1957).
766 K. Ichihara and H. Nakata, Z. Physiol. Chem., 243, 244 (1936).
767 D.B. Reisner, B.J. Ludwig, F.J. Steifel, S. Gister, M.Meyer, L.S. Powell and R.D. Sofia, Arzneim. Forsch., 27, 760 (1977).
768 C.M. Svahn and N.A. Jonsson, Acta Chem. Scand., B32, 137 (1978).
769 D. Pitré and S. Boveri, J. Med. Chem., 11, 406 (1968).
770 H. Sobotka, M.F. Holzman and J. Kahn, J. Am. Chem. Soc., 54, 4697 (1932).
771 A.C. Shabica and M. Tishler, J. Am. Chem. Soc., 71, 3251 (1949).
771a C.P. Berg, J. Biol. Chem., 100, 79 (1933).
771b L.R. Overby and A.W. Ingersoll, J. Am. Chem. Soc., 82, 2067 (1960).
771c G. Losse, J. Prakt. Chem., 7, 141 (1959).
771d J.N.Coker,W.L.Kohlhase,M.Fields,A.O.Rogers,M.A.Stevens,J.Org.Chem.,27, 850(1962).
771e T. Kato and Y. Tsuchiya, Agr. Biol. Chem., 26, 467 (1962).
771f J.M. Gillingham, U. S. Patent 3,028,395 (1962).
771g G. Amiard, R. Heymes and L. Velluz, U. S. Patent 2,797,226 (1957).
771h G. Amiard, R. Heymes and L. Velluz, U. S. Patent 2,797,226 (1957).
771i L. Velluz, G. Amiard and R. Heymes, Bull. Soc. Chim. France, 38 (1954).
771j British Patent 842,839 (1960).
771k M. Brenner, E. Sailer and E. Kocher, Helv. Chim. Acta, 31, 1908 (1948).
772 M. Kotake, T. Sakan and T. Miwa, Chem. Ber., 85, 690 (1952).
773 A.J. Morris and M.D. Armstrong, J. Org. Chem., 22, 306 (1957).
774 H. Rinderknecht, Helv. Chim. Acta, 47, 2403 (1964).
775 F. Bergel, M.C.E. Burnop and J.A. Stock, J. Chem. Soc., 1223 (1955).
776 H. Veldstra and C. van de Westeringh, Rec. Trav. Chim., 70, 1113 (1951).
776a A. Fredga and L. Westman, Arkiv Kemi, 7, 193 (1954).
777 C.H. DePuy, F.W. Breitbeil and K.R. DeBruin, J. Am. Chem. Soc., 88, 3347 (1966).
777a P.H. Mazzocchi and R.S. Lustig, J. Am. Chem. Soc., 97, 3714 (1975).
778 From the M. Sc. Thesis of H.M. Schwartz, University of Toronto, Toronto, Canada (1975).
779 A. Neville, J. Chem. Soc., 89, 383 (1906).
780 L. Westman, Arkiv Kemi, 12, 161 (1957).

Reference
Number

780a H. Veldstra and C. van de Westeringh, Rec. Trav. Chim., 70, 1113 (1951).
781 A. Schoofs, J-P. Guetté and A. Horeau, Compt. Rendus, 274, 1527 (1972).
782 A. Fredga, Arkiv Kemi Mineral. Geol., 24B, No. 15 (1947).
783 L. Westman, Arkiv Kemi, 11, 431 (1957).
783a K. Kawazu, T. Fujita and T. Mitsui, J. Am. Chem. Soc., 81, 932 (1959).
784 A. Fredga, Arkiv Kemi Mineral. Geol., 26B, No. 11 (1948).
785 H. Des Abbayes and R. Dabard, Tetrahedron, 31, 2111 (1975).
786 L. Novak, J.O. Jilek, B. Kakac, I. Ernest and M. Protiva, Coll. Czech. Chem. Comm., 25, 2196 (1960).
786a L. Novak and M. Protiva, Coll. Czech. Chem. Comm., 27, 2702 (1962).
787 G. Muller, G. Nominé and J. Warnant, U. S. Patent 2,952,682 (1960).
788 E. Sélégny and M. Vert, Bull. Soc. Chim. France, 2549 (1968).
789 M. Naps and I.B. Johns, J. Am. Chem. Soc., 62, 2450 (1940).
790 G.R. Clemo, W.A. Cummings and R. Raper, J. Chem. Soc., 1923 (1949).
791 M. Miyakado, N. Ohno, Y. Okuno, M. Hirano, K. Fujimoto and H. Yoshioka, Agr. Biol. Chem., 39, 267 (1975).
792 M. Miyakado, N. Ohno, Y. Okuno, M. Hirano, K. Fujimoto and H. Yoshioka, Agr. Biol. Chem., 39, 267 (1975).
793 M. Miyakado, N. Ohno, Y. Okuno, M. Hirano, K. Fujimoto and H. Yoshioka, Agr. Biol. Chem., 39, 267 (1975).
794 M.S. Matta and M.F. Rohde, J. Am. Chem. Soc., 94, 8573 (1972).
795 F. Morlacchi, V. Losacco and V. Tortorella, Gazz. Chim. Ital., 105, 349 (1975).
796 H. Mizuno, S. Terashima and S. Yamada, Chem. Pharm. Bull., 19, 227 (1971).
797 C. Alberti, B. Camerino and A. Vercellone, Gazz. Chim. Ital., 83, 930 (1953).
797a C. Alberti, B. Camerino and A. Vercellone, Gazz. Chim. Ital., 83, 930 (1953).
798 Y. Liwschitz, A.I. Vincze and E. Nemes, Bull. Res. Council Isr., 9A, 49 (1960).
799 A. Schouteeten, Y. Christidis, G. Mattioda, M.J. Brienne and J. Jacques, Bull. Soc. Chim. Belges, 88, 897 (1979).
800 J. Kenyon and K. Thaker, J. Chem. Soc., 2531 (1957).
801 J. Kenyon and K. Thaker, J. Chem. Soc., 2531 (1957).
802 H.J. Backer and M. Toxopeus, Rec. Trav. Chim., 45, 890 (1926).
803 K. Pettersson and G. Willdeck, Arkiv Kemi, 9, 333 (1956).
804 From the Ph.D. Thesis of M.B. Bochner, Princeton University, Princeton, N.J. (1962).
805 P.A. Levene, L.A. Mikeska and K. Passoth, J. Biol. Chem., 88, 27 (1930).
805a T. Fujita, K. Kawazu and T. Mitsui, Agri. Biol. Chem., 30, 1277 (1966).
806 C.Aaron, D. Dull, J.L. Schmiegel, D. Jaeger, Y. Ohashi, and H.S. Mosher, J. Org. Chem., 32, 2797 (1967).
807 G. Sörlin and G. Bergson, Arkiv Kemi, 29, 593 (1968).
808 C. Rüchardt and H. Trautwein, Chem. Ber., 98, 2478 (1965).
808a R.K. Hill and G.R. Newkome, Tetrahedron, 25, 1249 (1969).
809 C.S. Marvel, R.L. Frank and E. Prill, J. Am. Chem. Soc., 65, 1647 (1943).
810 C-E. Hagberg and S. Allenmark, Chemica Scripta, 5, 13 (1974).
811 A. Fredga and K. Olsson, Arkiv Kemi, 30, 409 (1969).
812 A. Fredga and K-I. Sandström, Arkiv Kemi, 23, 245 (1965).
813 A. Fredga and F. Plénat, Arkiv Kemi, 24, 577 (1965).
814 A. Fredga and K. Olsson, Arkiv Kemi, 30, 409 (1969).
815 A. Fredga and U. Löfroth, Arkiv Kemi, 23, 239 (1965).
815a A. Fredga and E. Gamstedt, Arkiv Kemi, 28, 211 (1967).
816 J.A. Reid and E.E. Turner, J. Chem. Soc., 3219 (1951).
817 M. Guetté, J. Capillon and J-P. Guetté, Tetrahedron, 29, 3659 (1973).
818 M. Matell, Arkiv Kemi, 1, 455 (1949).
819 R. Fusco and E. Testa, Farmaco, Ed. Sci., 12, 823 (1957).
820 E.R. Atkinson, D.D. McRitchie, L.F. Shoer, L.S. Harris, S. Archer, M.D. Aceto, J. Pearl and F.P. Luduena, J. Med. Chem., 20, 1612 (1977).
821 M. Fileti, J. Prakt. Chem., 46, 560 (1892).
821a E.R. Atkinson, D.D. McRitchie, L.F. Shoer, L.S. Harris, S. Archer, M.D. Aceto, J. Pearl and F.P. Luduena, J. Med. Chem., 20, 1612 (1977).
822 D.S. Noyce, L. Gortler, M.J. Jorgenson, F.B. Kirby and E.C. McGoran, J. Am. Chem. Soc., 87, 4329 (1965).
823 M. Matell, Arkiv Kemi, 8, 79 (1955).
824 T.J. Leitereg and D.J. Cram, J. Am. Chem. Soc., 90, 4019 (1968).
825 J.W. Clark-Lewis and R.W. Jemison, Austr. J. Chem., 18, 1791 (1965).
826 C.Aaron, D.Dull, J.L. Schmiegel, D. Jaeger, Y. Ohashi, and H.S. Mosher, J. Org. Chem., 32, 2797 (1967).
827 E.R. Atkinson, D.D. McRitchie, L.F. Shoer, L.S. Harris, S. Archer, M.D. Aceto, J. Pearl and F.P. Luduena, J. Med. Chem. 20, 1612 (1977).
828 D.S. Noyce, L. Gortler, M.J. Jorgensen, F.B. Kirby and E.C. McGoran, J. Am. Chem. Soc., 87, 4329 (1965).
829 A. Collet and J. Jacques, Tetrahedron Lett., 1265 (1978).
830 J.E. Taylor and F.H. Verhoek, J. Am. Chem. Soc., 81, 4537 (1959).
831 J. Knabe and K. Philipson, Arch. Pharm., 299, 231 (1966).
832 J.F. Klebe and H. Finkbeiner, J. Am. Chem. Soc., 90, 7255 (1968).
833 From the Ph.D. Dissertation of Dr. D. Strauss, Universität des Saarlandes, West Germany (1969).
834 K. Eichenberger and C. Egli, U. S. Patent 3,862,329 (1975).
835 G. Schmidt and H. Rosenkranz, Liebigs Ann. Chem., 124 (1975).
836 R.G. Vdovina, A.V. Karpova and E.S. Chaman, Zh. Obsch. Khim., 37, 1007 (1967).
837 J. Knabe and K. Philipson, Arch. Pharm., 299, 231 (1966).
838 H. Gustafsson, H. Ericsson and S. Lindquist, Acta Chem. Scand., B28, 1069 (1974).
839 M. Matsui and Y. Yamada, Agr. Biol. Chem., 27, 373 (1963).
840 French Patent 1,496,817 (1967).
841 J. Knabe and W. Geismar, Arch. Pharm. (Weinheim), 301, 682 (1968).
842 F.I. Carroll and R. Meck, J. Org. Chem., 34, 2676 (1969).
843 L. Crombie, J. Crossley and D.A. Mitchard, J. Chem. Soc., 4957 (1963).
844 C.C.J. Culvenor and T.A. Geissman, J. Am. Chem. Soc., 83, 1647 (1961).
845 H.H. Inhoffen, S. Schütz, P. Rossberg, O. Berges, K-H. Nordsiek, H. Penio and E. Höroldt, Chem. Ber., 91, 2626 (1958).

Reference Number

846 J. Knabe and H. Junginger, Pharmazie, 7, 443 (1972).
847 P.A. Levene and R.E. Marker, J. Biol. Chem., 97, 563 (1932).
848 M.S. Silver and T. Sone, J. Am. Chem. Soc., 90, 6193 (1968).
849 B. Eliasson, G. Odham and B. Pettersson, Acta Chem. Scand., 25, 2217 (1971).
850 C. Beard, C. Djerassi, J. Sicher, F. Šipoš and M. Tichý, Tetrahedron 19, 919 (1963)
851 R. Håkansson and A. Svensson, Chemica Scripta, 7, 186 (1975).
852 R. Håkansson and A. Svensson, Chemica Scripta, 7, 186 (1975).
853 S. Gronowitz and H. Frostling, Acta Chem. Scand., 16, 1127 (1962).
854 A. Almqvist and R. Håkansson, Chem. Scripta, 11, 180 (1977).
855 L.J. Owen and F. F. Nord, J. Org. Chem., 16, 1864 (1951).
856 G. Ege and W. Planer, Angew. Chem. Int. Ed., 758 (1969).
857 From the Ph.D. Thesis of H.U. Kuffner, University of Vienna, Austria (1972).
858 A. Fredga, Arkiv Kemi, 12, 547 (1958).
859 A. McKenzie and W.S. Dennler, Chem. Ber., 60, 220 (1927).
860 E.R. Atkinson, D.D. McRitchie, L.F. Shoer, L.S. Harris, S. Archer, M.D. Aceto, J. Pearl and F.P. Luduena, J. Med. Chem., 20, 1612 (1977).
860a From the Ph.D. Thesis of B.W.J. Ellenbroek, Catholic University of Nijmegen, Rotterdam, The Netherlands (1964).
861 E. Wiklund and R. Håkansson, Chemica Scripta, 6, 174 (1974).
862 E. Wiklund and R. Håkansson, Chemica Scripta, 6, 174 (1974).
863 R. Adams and C.W. Theobald, J. Am. Chem. Soc., 65, 2383 (1943).
864 R. Adams and R.S. Ludington, J. Am. Chem. Soc., 67, 794 (1945).
865 R. Adams and W.J. Gross, J. Am. Chem. Soc., 64, 1786 (1942).
866 K. Shinga, S. Hagishita and M. Nakagawa, Tetrahedron Lett., 4371 (1967).
867 W. Runge, G. Kresze and E. Ruch, Liebigs Ann. Chem., 1361 (1975).
868 G. Kresze, W. Runge and E. Ruch, Liebigs Ann. Chem., 756, 112 (1972).
869 W. Runge, G. Kresze and E. Ruch, Liebigs Ann. Chem., 1361 (1975).
870 E. Wiklund and R. Håkansson, Chemica Scripta, 6, 174 (1974).
871 E. Wiklung and R. Håkansson, Chemica Scripta, 6, 174 (1974).
872 R.D. Haworth and F.H. Slinger, J. Chem. Soc., 1321 (1940).
873 T.M. Lyssy, J. Org. Chem., 27, 5 (1962).
874 M. Nakazaki, K. Naemura, Y. Sugano and Y. Kataoka, J. Org. Chem., 45, 3232 (1980).
875 R. Adams and N.K. Sundholm, J. Am. Chem. Soc., 70, 2667 (1948).
876 R. Adams and J.R. Gordon, J. Am. Chem. Soc., 72, 2454 (1950).
877 J. Knabe and H. Junginger, Pharmazie, 7, 443 (1972).
878 G. Otani and S. Yamada, Chem. Pharm. Bull., 21, 2119 (1973).
879 A. Fredga and L-B. Agenäs, Arkiv Kemi, 15, 327 (1960).
880 M.R. Harnden and N.D. Wright, J. Chem. Soc., Perk. 1, 1012 (1977).
881 H. Nakamoto, M Aburatani and M. Inagaki, J. Med. Chem., 14, 1021 (1971).
881a S. Yamada, T. Fujii and T. Shioiri, Chem. Pharm. Bull., 10, 680 (1962).
882 W.H. Mills and B.C. Saunders, J. Chem. Soc., 537 (1931).
883 H.E. Smith and J.M. Luck, J. Org. Chem., 23, 837 (1958).
884 From the M.Sc. Thesis of H.M. Schwartz, University of Toronto, Toronto, Can. (1975
885 M.S. Newman and J. Linsk, J. Org. Chem., 14, 480 (1949).
886 I am indebted to Prof. D.W. Jones, Dep't of Organic Chemistry, University of Leeds, Great Britain, for this procedure.
887 Personal communication from Prof. A. de Meijere, University of Gottingen, Gottingen, West Germany
888 E.R. Atkinson, D.D. McRitchie, L.F. Shoer, L.S. Harris, S. Archer, M.D. Aceto, J. Pearl and F.P. Luduena, J. Med. Chem. 20, 1612 (1977).
889 L. Westman, Arkiv Kemi, 12, 167 (1958).
890 J. Porath, Arkiv Kemi Mineral. Geol., 26B, No. 16 (1948).
891 M. Miyakado, N. Ohno, Y. Okuno, M. Hirano, K. Fujimoto and H. Yoshioka, Agr. Biol. Chem., 39, 267 (1975).
892 French Patent 1,481,978 (1967).
893 D.J. Cram and A. Ratajczak, J. Am. Chem. Soc., 90, 2198 (1968).
894 W.S. Briggs, M. Suchy and C. Djerassi, Tetrahedron Lett., 1097 (1968).
895 H.R. Almond,Jr., D.T. Manning and C. Niemann, Biochemistry, 1, 243 (1962).
895a S. Terashima, K. Achiwa and S. Yamada, Chem. Pharm. Bull., 14, 1138 (1966).
896 H.R. Almond,Jr., D.T. Manning and C. Niemann, Biochemistry, 1, 243 (1962).
897 P.M.G. Bavin, J. Med. Chem., 9, 52 (1966).
898 R. Adams, D.C. Blomstrom and K.V.T. Sundstrom, J. Am. Chem. Soc., 76, 5478 (1954).
899 J. Knabe and R. Krauter, Arch. Pharm., 298, 1 (1965).
900 K. Pettersson and G. Willdeck, Arkiv Kemi, 9, 333 (1956).
901 P.A. Levene and R.E. Marker, J. Biol. Chem., 93, 749 (1931).
902 C. Fuganti and P. Grasselli, J. Chem. Soc. Chem. Comm., 995 (1979).
903 G. Sörlin and G. Bergson, Arkiv Kemi, 29, 593 (1968).
904 D.J. Cram, J. Am. Chem. Soc., 74, 2152 (1952).
905 M. Miyakado, N. Ohno, Y. Okuno, M. Hirano, K. Fujimoto and H. Yoshioka, Agr. Biol. Chem., 39, 267 (1975).
906 C. Aaron, D. Dull, J.L. Schmiegel, D. Jaeger, Y. Ohashi and H.S. Mosher, J. Org. Chem., 32, 2797 (1967).
906a H. Kuritani, S. Imajo, K. Shingu and M. Nakagawa, Tetrahedron Lett., 1697 (1979).
907 J.H. Dopper, B. Greijdanus, D. Oudman and H. Wynberg, Tetrahedron Lett., 4297 (1975).
908 L.A. Petrova, N.N. Bel'tsova, G.A. Tsvetkova and A.I. Klimov, Zh. Obsch. Khim., 41, 2276 (1971).
909 M. Miyakado, N. Ohno, Y. Okuno, M. Hirano, K. Fujimoto and H. Yoshioka, Agr. Biol. Chem., 39, 267 (1975).
910 M. Matell, Arkiv Kemi, 6, 375 (1953).
911 R.L. Coffin, W.W. Cox, R.G. Carlson and R.S. Givens, J. Am. Chem. Soc., 101, 3261 (1979).
912 M. Ohno, M. Okamoto and N. Kawabe, U. S. Patent 3.793,347 (1974).
913 E.R. Atkinson, D.D. McRitchie, L.F. Shoer, L.S. Harris, S. Archer, M.D. Aceto, J. Pearl and F.P. Luduena, J. Med. Chem., 20, 1612 (1977).

Reference
Number

914 A.M. Schrecker, J. Org. Chem., 22, 33 (1957).
915 H. Hamill and M.A. McKervey, Chem. Commun., 864 (1969).
916 L.H. Werner, A. Wettstein and K. Miescher, Helv. Chim. Acta, 30, 432 (1947).
917 French Patent 1,389,391 (1965).
918 British Patent 936,074 (1963).
918a French Patent 1,389,391 (1965).
919 E. Walton, A.F. Wagner, F.W. Bachelor, L.H. Peterson, F.W. Holly and K. Folkers, J. Am. Chem. Soc., 77, 5144 (1955).
920 P.A. Levene and R.E. Marker, J. Biol. Chem., 97, 563 (1932).
921 J.M. Walbrick, J.W. Wilson, Jr., and W.M. Jones, J. Am. Chem. Soc., 90, 2895 (1968)
922 L. Eberson, Acta Chem. Scand., 13, 40 (1959).
923 W. Bleazard and E. Rothstein, J. Chem. Soc., 3789 (1958).
924 H.A. Stearns and R. Adams, J. Am. Chem. Soc., 52, 2070 (1930).
925 O.T. Schmidt, R. Eckert, E. Günther and H. Fiesser, Liebegs Ann. Chem., 706, 204 (1967).
926 A. Fredga and T. Svensson, Arkiv Kemi, 25, 81 (1965).
927 M. Janczewski and K. Kut, Rocz. Chem., 42, 1159 (1968).
928 M. Matell and S. Larsson, Arkiv Kemi, 5, 379 (1953).
929 P.M. Pope and D. Woodcock, J. Chem. Soc., 577 (1955).
930 A. Khawam and E.V. Brown, J. Am. Chem. Soc., 74, 5603 (1952).
931 L. Berger and A.J. Corraz, U. S. Patent 3,868,387 (1975).
932 A. Fredga, Arkiv Kemi, 8, 463 (1955).
933 B. Sjöberg, Arkiv Kemi, 9, 295 (1956).
934 K. Pettersson, Arkiv Kemi, 7, 279 (1954).
935 K. Pettersson, Arkiv Kemi, 7, 279 (1954).
936 M. Matell, Arkiv Kemi, 5, 187 (1953).
937 B. Sjöberg, Arkiv Kemi, 15, 397 (1960)
938 E. Fourneau and Balaceano, Bull. Soc. Chim. Fr., 37, 1602 (1925).
939 M.S. Smith and R.L. Wain, Proc. Roy. Soc., 139B, 118 (1951).
940 R.G. Wilkinson, T.L. Fields and J. H. Boothe, J. Org. Chem., 26, 637 (1961).
941 W.M. Colles and C.S. Gibson, J. Chem. Soc., 124, 2505 (1924).
942 W.M. Colles and C.S. Gibson, J. Chem. Soc., 124, 2505 (1924).
943 R. Adams and M.W. Miller, J. Am. Chem. Soc., 62, 53 (1940).
944 R. Adams and W.J. Gross, J. Am. Chem. Soc., 64, 1786 (1942).
945 K. Shingu, S. Hagishita and M. Nakagawa, Tetrahedron Lett., 4371 (1967).
946 G. Kresze, W. Runge and E. Ruch, Liebigs Ann. Chem., 756, 112 (1972).
947 G. Kresze, W. Runge and E. Ruch, Liebigs Ann. Chem., 756, 112 (1972).
948 S. Yakei, Y. Inouye, M. Ohno and S. Takei, Agr. Biol. Chem., 26, 362 (1962).
949 D.H. Johnson, A. Robertson and W.B. Whalley, J. Chem. Soc., 2971 (1950).
950 R. Adams and C.W. Theobald, J. Am. Chem. Soc., 65, 2383 (1943).
951 R. Branchini, G. Casini, M. Ferappi and S. Gulinelli, Farmaco, Ed. Sci., 15, 734 (1960).
952 M.S. Matta and M.F. Rohde, J. Am. Chem. Soc., 94, 8573 (1972).
953 R. Adams and N.K. Sundholm, J. Am. Chem. Soc., 70, 2667 (1948).
954 R. Adams and J.R. Gordon, J. Am. Chem. Soc., 72, 2454 (1950).
955 R. Adams and N.K. Sundholm, J. Am. Chem. Soc., 70, 2667 (1948).
956 R. Adams and N.J. Leonard, J. Am. Chem. Soc., 66, 257 (1944).
957 R. Adams and N.K. Sundholm, J. Am. Chem. Soc., 70, 2667 (1948).
958 From the Ph.D. Thesis of J. Robbins, University of California, Berkeley, California
959 From the Ph.D. Thesis of J. Robbins, University of California, Berkeley, California
960 J. Brugidou, H. Christol, J.M. Fabre, L. Giral and R. Sales, Bull. Soc. Chim. France, 2906 (1974).
961 From the M.Sc. Thesis of H.M. Schwartz, University of Toronto, Toronto, Canada (1975).
962 J. Nishikawa, T. Ishizaki, F. Nakayawa, H. Kawa, K. Saigo and M. Nohira, Nippon Kagaku Kaishi, 754 (1979).
963 H. Keberle, W. Riess and K. Hoffmann, Arch. Int. Pharmacodyn., 163, 117 (1962).
964 B. Sjöberg and S. Sjöberg, Arkiv Kemi, 22, 447 (1964).
965 G. Nominé, G. Amiard and V. Torelli, Bull. Soc. Chim. Fr., 3664 (1968).
966 A. Hofmann and P. Stadler, U. S. Patent 3,294,835 (1966).
966a R. Barner and M. Schmid, Helv. Chim. Acta, 62, 2384 (1979).
966b A. Hofmann and P. Stadler, Swiss Patent 454,826 (1968).
967 W. Heller and C. Tamm, Helv. Chim. Acta, 57, 1766 (1974).
968 T. Matsumoto, K. Hidaka, T. Nakayama and K. Fukui, Bull. Chem. Soc. Japan, 45, 1501 (1972).
969 R. Grewe and S. Kersten, Chem. Ber., 100, 2546 (1967).
970 M. Matell, Arkiv Kemi, 9, 157 (1955).
971 C.W. Ryan, U. S. Patent 3,705,900 (1972).
972 J.B. Conant and G.H. Carlson, J. Am. Chem. Soc., 54, 4056 (1932).
973 K. Pettersson and G. Willdeck, Arkiv Kemi, 9, 333 (1956).
974 J. Almy and D.J. Cram, J. Am. Chem. Soc., 91, 4459 (1969).
975 A. Fredga, T. Unge and R. Håkansson, Chemica Scripta, 4, 123 (1973).
976 M. Andersson, Arkiv Kemi, 26, 335 (1967).
977 M. Andersson, Arkiv Kemi, 26, 335 (1967).
978 H.E. Zimmerman, T.P. Gannett and G.E. Keck, J. Org. Chem., 44, 1982 (1979).
979 T. Matsumoto, K. Fukui and J.D. Edwards, Jr., Chemistry Letters, 283 (1973).
980 G. Stork and F.H. Clarke, Jr., J. Am. Chem. Soc., 83, 3114 (1961).
981 F. Kögl and H. Erxleben, Z. Physiol. Chem., 235, 181 (1935).
982 P.A. Levene and R.E. Marker, J. Biol. Chem., 98, 1 (1932).
983 M.M. Shemyakin, Y.A. Orchinnikov, V.T. Ivanov and P.V. Kostetskii, Zh. Obsch. Khim., 37, 2617 (1967).
984 J. White and R. Adams, J. Am. Chem. Soc., 54, 2104 (1932).
985 L.H. Boch, W.W. Moyer and R. Adams, J. Am. Chem. Soc., 52, 2054 (1930).
986 E.A. Atkinson and H.J. Lawler, J. Am. Chem. Soc., 62, 1704 (1940).

Reference
Number

987 E.R. Atkinson, Organic Preparations and Procedures, 3, 71 (1971).
988 M. Rieger and F.H. Westheimer, J. Am. Chem. Soc., 72, 28 (1950).
989 F. Bell and P.H. Robinson, J. Chem. Soc., 2234 (1927).
989a R. Kuhn and O. Albrecht, Liebigs Ann. Chem., 458, 221 (1927).
990 G.H. Christie, C.W. James and J. Kenner, J. Chem. Soc., 123, 1948 (1923).
991 W. Stanley, E. McMahon and R. Adams, J. Am. Chem. Soc., 55, 706 (1933).
992 M. Rieger and F.H. Westheimer, J. Am. Chem. Soc., 72, 28 (1950).
993 G.H. Christie, A. Holderness and J. Kenner, J. Chem. Soc., 671 (1926).
994 R. Kuhn and O. Albrecht, Liebigs Ann. Chem., 465, 282 (1928).
995 R. Kuhn and O. Albrecht, Liebigs Ann. Chem., 465, 282 (1928).
996 F. Bell and P.H. Robinson, J. Chem. Soc., 2234 (1927).
996a P. Berntsson and R.E. Carter, Acta Chem. Scand., 22, 2141 (1968).
997 A.M. van Arendonk, B.C. Becker and R. Adams, J. Am. Chem. Soc., 55, 4230 (1933).
998 M.S. Leslie and E. E. Turner, J. Chem. Soc., 1758 (1930).
999 F.E. Ray and E. Kreiser, J. Am. Chem. Soc., 69, 3068 (1947).
1000 T. Svensson, Arkiv Kemi, 26, 27 (1966).
1001 J. Canceill and J. Jacques, Bull. Soc. Chim. Fr., 2727 (1973).
1002 J. Canceill and J. Jacques, Bull. Soc. Chim. Fr., 2727 (1973).
1003 J. Canceill and J. Jacques, Bull. Soc. Chim. Fr., 2727 (1973).
1004 O.T. Schmidt and K. Demmler, Liebigs Ann. Chem., 586, 179 (1954).
1005 K. Takeda, S. Hagishita, M. Sugiura, K. Kitahonoki, I. Ban, S. Miyazaki and K. Kuriyama, Tetrahedron, 26, 1435 (1970).
1006 W. Bleazard and E. Rothstein, J. Chem. Soc., 3789 (1958).
1007 R. Adams and L.O. Binder, J. Am. Chem. Soc., 63, 2773 (1941).
1008 R. Adams and J.B. Hale, J. Am. Chem. Soc., 61, 2825 (1939).
1009 D.F. Detar and J.C. Howard, J. Am. Chem. Soc., 77, 4393 (1955).
1009a R. Adams and J.B. Hale, J. Am. Chem. Soc., 61, 2825 (1939).
1009b R.W. Stoughton and R. Adams, J. Am. Chem. Soc., 52, 5263 (1930).
1010 A. Guarnieri, S. Burnelli, A. Andreani, I. Busacci, A.M. Barbaro and M. Gaiardi, Farmaco, Ed. Sci., 33, 761 (1978).
1011 M-J. Brienne and J. Jacques, Bull. Soc. Chim. Fr., 2647 (1974).
1012 M-J. Brienne and J. Jacques, Bull. Soc. Chim. Fr., 2647 (1974).
1013 A. McKenzie and S.C. Bate, J. Chem. Soc., 107, 1681 (1915).
1014 J.H.C. Nayler, British Patent 1,267,936 (1972).
1015 L.H. Bock and R. Adams, J. Am. Chem. Soc., 53, 374 (1931).
1016 J. Meisenheimer, W. Theilacker and O. Beisswenger, Liebigs Ann. Chem., 495, 249 (1932).
1017 B.R.Baker, F.J.McEvoy, R.E. Schaub, J.P.Joseph,J.H.Williams,J.Org.Chem.,18,178 (195
1018 G.N. Jean, J. Org. Chem., 21, 419 (1956).
1019 A. Khawam and E.V. Brown, J. Am. Chem. Soc., 74, 5603 (1952).
1020 H. Mechtler and K. Schlögl, Monatsh. Chem., 97, 754 (1966).
1021 M. Matell, Arkiv Kemi, 5, 187 (1953).
1022 B. Sjöberg, Arkiv Kemi, 12, 573 (1958).
1023 M. Matell, Arkiv Kemi, 6, 251 (1953).
1024 M. Matell, Arkiv Kemi, 6, 251 (1953).
1025 M. Janczewski and T. Bartnik, Polish J. Chem., 42, 1253 (1968).
1026 M. Janczewski and T. Bartnik, Polish J. Chem., 42, 1253 (1968).
1027 P. Wirth, G.E.M. Dannenberg, V. Schmied-Kowarzik, P. Weinhold and D. Gudel, German Patent (Offen.) 2,319,245 (1973).
1028 British Patent 1,426,186 (1976).
1029 E.E. Pedersen and K.A. Jensen, Acta Chem. Scand., 2, 651 (1948).
1030 A.P. Stoll and R. Süess, Helv. Chim. Acta, 57, 2487 (1974).
1031 U. Folli, D. Iarossi, F. Montanari and G. Torre, J. Chem. Soc. (C), 1317 (1968).
1032 U. Folli, D. Iarossi, F. Montanari and G. Torre, J. Chem. Soc., (C), 1317 (1968).
1033 S. Gronowitz and R. Beselin, Arkiv Kemi, 21, 349 (1963).
1034 R. Håkansson, Chemica Scripta, 3, 177 (1973).
1035 E. Wiklund and R. Håkansson, Chemica Scripta, 3, 220 (1973).
1036 S. Gronowitz and T. Frejd, Acta Chem. Scand., 26, 2279 (1972).
1037 H. Stetter and O.E. Bander, Chem. Ber., 88, 1535 (1955).
1038 A. Ratajczak and B. Misterkiewicz, J. Organomet. Chem., 91, 73 (1975).
1039 C. Chang and R. Adams, J. Am. Chem. Soc., 53, 2353 (1931).
1040 K. Shingu, S. Hagishita and M. Nakagawa, Tetrahedron Ltt., 4371 (1967).
1041 G. Kresze, W. Runge and E. Ruch, Liebigs Ann. Chem., 756, 112 (1972).
1042 H.E. Smith and T.C. Willis, Tetrahedron, 26, 107 (1970).
1043 Personal communication from Prof. A. de Meijere, Universiting of Göttingen, Göttingen, West Germany
1044 J. Diamond and N.J. Santora, U. S. Patent 3,821,267 (1974).
1045 H. Nohira and H. Miura, Nippon Kagaku Kaishi, 1122 (1975).
1046 W.L.F. Armarego and T. Kobayashi, J. Chem. Soc. (C), 1597 (1970).
1047 R. Stoermer and H.J. Steinbeck, Chem. Ber., 65, 413 (1932).
1048 R.K. Hill, T.H. Chan and J.A. Joule, Tetrahedron, 21, 147 (1965).
1049 G. Jollès, G. Poiget, J. Robert, B. Terlain and J-P. Thomas, Bull. Soc. Chim. Fr., 2252 (1965).
1050 M. Claesen, A. Vlietinck and H. Vanderhaeghe, Bull. Soc. Chim. Belges, 77, 587 (1968).
1051 R. Adams and L.J. Dankert, J. Am. Chem. Soc., 62, 2191 (1940).
1052 J. Borck, J. Dahm, V. Kopp, J. Kramer, G. Shorre, J.W.H. Hovy and E. Schorscher, U. S. Patent 3,669,956 (1972).
1053 R.B. Barlow, F.M. Franks and J.D.M. Pearson, J. Med. Chem., 16, 439 (1973).
1054 R.B. Barlow, F.M. Franks and J. D. M. Pearson, J. Med. Chem., 16, 439 (1973).
1054a French Patent 1,329,640 (1963).
1054b E.R. Atkinson, D.D. McRitchie, L.F. Shoer, L.S. Harris, S. Archer, M.D. Aceto, J. Pearl and F.P. Luduena, J. Med. Chem., 20, 1612 (1977).
1055 W. Schlientz, R. Brunner, P.A. Stadler, A.J. Frey, H. Ott and A. Hofmann, Helv. Chim. Acta, 47, 1921 (1964).

Reference Number

1056 T. Matsumoto, K. Hidaka, T. Nakayama and K. Fukui, Chemistry Letters, 1 (1972).
1057 J.H. Poupaert, R. Cavalier, M.H. Cleasen and P.A. Dumont, J. Med. Chem., 18, 1268 (1975).
1058 H. Pracejus and S. Winter, Chem. Ber., 97, 3173 (1964).
1059 R. Adams and H.W. Stewart, J. Am. Chem. Soc., 63, 2859 (1941).
1060 H. Kinoshita, M. Shintani, T. Saito and H. Kotake, Bull. Chem. Soc. Japan, 44, 286 (1971).
1061 W.T. Hoeve and H. Wynberg, J. Org. Chem., 45, 2754 (1980).
1062 M. Ikawa, J.B. Koepfli, S.G. Mudd and C. Niemann, J. Am. Chem. Soc., 75, 1035 (1953).
1063 F.E. Roberts, Jr., French Patent 1,538,286 (1968).
1064 H. Parekh, A.R. Parikh and K.A. Thaker, J. Indian Chem. Soc., 50, 802 (1973).
1065 J.H. Poupaert, J. Adline, M.H. Claesen, P. De Laey and P.A. Dumont, J. Med. Chem., 22, 1140 (1979).
1066 K. Undheim, P. Hamberg and B. Sjöberg, Acta Chem. Scand., 19, 317 (1965).
1067 H. Parekh, A.R. Parikh and K.A. Thaker, J. Indian Chem. Soc., 50, 802 (1973).
1068 H. Parekh, A.R. Parikh and K.A. Thaker, J. Inst. Chemists (India), 45, 115 (1973).
1069 H. Parekh, A.R. Parikh and K.A. Thaker, J. Inst. Chemists (India), 45, 115 (1973).
1070 J.H. Poupaert, R. Cavalier, M.H. Claesen and P.A. Dumont, J. Med. Chem., 18, 1268 (1975).
1071 D.J. Cram and L. Gosser, J. Am. Chem. Soc., 86, 5445 (1964).
1072 D.J. Cram, W.T. Ford and L. Gosser, J. Am. Chem. Soc., 90, 2598 (1968).
1073 M. Janczewski and R. Kutyla, Pol. J. Chem., 1463 (1979).
1074 D. Aziz and J.G. Breckenridge, Can. J. Res., 28B, 26 (1950).
1075 R. Adams and L.O. Binder, J. Am. Chem. Soc., 63, 2773 (1941).
1076 T. Tamegai, T. Tanaka, T. Kaneko, S. Ozaki, M. Ohmae and K. Kawabe, J. Liquid Chromatog., 2, 551 (1979).
1077 C.R. Harington, Biochem. J., 22, 1429 (1928).
1078 R. Adams and H.M. Teeter, J. Am. Chem. Soc., 62, 2188 (1940).
1079 M. Nakajima, J. Oda and H.Fukami, Agr. Biol. Chem., 27, 695 (1963).
1080 J.R. Carson (McNeil Laboratories, Inc.), U. S. Patent 3,752,826 (1973).
1081 K. Pettersson, Arkiv Kemi, 7, 339 (1954).
1081a M.B. Watson and G.W. Youngson, J. Chem. Soc. (C), 258 (1968).
1081b H. Rupe and W. Kerkovins, Chem. Ber., 45, 1398 (1912).
1082 A. McKenzie and S.T. Widdows, J. Chem. Soc., 702 (1915).
1083 M. Janczewski and W. Podkoscielny, Polish J. Chem., 39, 201 (1965).
1084 M. Janczewski and W. Podkoscienlny, Polish J. Chem., 34, 1505 (1960).
1085 W.A. Bonner, J. Am. Chem. Soc., 74, 1034 (1952).
1086 W.A. Bonner, J. Org. Chem., 32, 2497 (1967).
1087 K. Mislow and M. Siegel, J. Am. Chem. Soc., 74, 1060 (1952).
1088 E.W. Christie, A. McKenzie and A. Ritchie, J. Chem. Soc., 153 (1935).
1089 W.S. Marshall, U. S. Patent 3,600,437 (1971).
1090 R.P. Zelinski, B.W. Turnquest and E.C. Martin, J. Am. Chem. Soc., 73, 5521 (1951).
1091 A.G. Davies, F.M. Ebeid and J. Kenyon, J. Chem. Soc., 3154 (1957).
1092 F.B. Kipping, J. Chem. Soc., 18 (1935).
1093 K. Takeda, S. Hagishita, M. Sugiura, K. Kitahonoki, I. Ban, S. Miyazaki and K. Kuriyama, Tetrahedron, 26, 1435 (1970).
1094 K. Takeda, S. Hagishita, M. Sugiura, K. Kitahonoki, I. Ban, S. Miyazaki and K. Kuriyama, Tetrahedron, 26, 1435 (1970).
1095 H. Dahn, J.A. Garbarino and C.O'Murchu, Helv. Chim. Acta, 53, 1370 (1970).
1096 T.R. Lewis, M.G. Pratt, E.D. Homiller, B.F. Tullar and S. Archer, J. Am. Chem. Soc., 71, 3749 (1949).
1097 From the Ph.D. Thesis of D.F. Zinkel, University of Wisconsin, Madison, Wis. (1961)
1098 A. Khawam and E.V. Brown, J. Am. Chem. Soc., 74, 5603 (1952).
1099 E.J. Cragoe,Jr.,E.M. Schultz, J.D. Schneeberg, G.E. Stokker, O.W. Woltersdorf,Jr., G.M. Fanelli,Jr., L.S. Watson, J. Med. Chem., 18, 225 (1975).
1100 M. Matell, Arkiv Kemi, 8, 79 (1955).
1101 C.G. Overberger and G.M. Parker, J. Polymer Sci.,Al, 6, 513 (1968).
1102 P.F. Juby, T.W. Hudyma, U. S. Patent 3,696,111 (1972).
1103 British Patent 1,283,367 (1969).
1104 E.J. Corey, S.M. Albonico, U. Koelliker, T.M. Schaaf and R-K. Varma, J. Am. Chem. Soc., 93, 1491 (1971).
1105 H. Vorbruggen, U. Mende, H. Dahl, German Offen. 2,215,197 (1973).
1106 L.-F. Tietze, Angew. Chem. Internat. Edit., 12, 757 (1973).
1107 M. Rosenberger, A.J. Duggan, R. Borer, R. Müller and G. Saucy, Helv. Chim. Acta, 55, 2663 (1972).
1108 R. Adams and H.W. Stewart, J. Am. Chem. Soc., 63, 2859 (1941).
1109 M. Nakazaki, K. Yamamoto, M. Ito and S. Tanaka, J. Org. Chem., 42, 3468 (1977).
1110 B. Calas and L. Giral, Bull. Soc. Chim. Fr., 2629 (1971).
1111 Y. Abe, T. Harukawa, H. Ishikawa, T. Miki, M. Sumi and T. Toga, U. S. Patent 2,862,953 (1958).
1112 R.R. Crenshaw, T. A. Jenks, G.M. Luke and G. Bialy, J. Med. Chem., 17, 1258 (1974).
1113 A. Lüttringhaus and H. Gralheer, Liebigs Ann. Chem., 557, 108 (1947).
1114 J.W. Scott, F.T. Bizzaro, D.R. Parish and G. Saucy, Helv. Chim. Acta, 59, 290 (1976).
1115 P.A. Stadler, St. Guttmann. H. Hauth, R.L. Huguenin, E. Sandrin, G. Wersin, H. Willems and A. Hofmann, Helv. Chim. Acta, 52, 1549 (1969).
1116 C.-H. Wong, M-F. Ho and K-T. Wang, J. Org. Chem., 43, 3604 (1978).
1117 M. Nakazaki and K. Naemura, Bull. Chem. Soc. Japan, 42, 3366 (1969).
1118 Y. Abe, T. Harukawa, H. Ishikawa, T. Miki, M. Sumi and T. Toga, J. Am. Chem. Soc., 78, 1416 (1956).
1119 J-C. Bonnafous, J-C. Mani, J-C. Mani, J-L. Olivé and M. Mousseron-Canet, Tetrahedron Lett., 1119 (1973).
1120 D.J. Cram and A.S. Wingrove, J. Am. Chem. Soc., 85, 1100 (1963).
1121 R. Kuhn and H.J. Knackmuss, Chem. Ber., 96, 980 (1963).
1122 A. McKenzie and N. Walker, J. Chem. Soc., 646 (1928).
1123 J.W. Cornforth, J. Chem. Soc., Perkin 1, 2004 (1976).

Reference
Number

1124 M.K. Eberle, L. Brzechffa, G.G. Kahle, S. Talati and H-P. Weber, J. Org. Chem., 45, 3143 (1980).
1125 J. Nickl, W. Engel, A. Eckenfels, E.Seeger and G. Engelhardt, U. S. Patent 3,655,743 (1972).
1126 S. Sako, Bull. Chem. Soc. Japan, 9, 393 (1934).
1127 D.W. Slocum and K. Mislow, J. Org. Chem., 30, 2152 (1965).
1127a H. Mix, Liebigs Ann. Chem., 592, 146 (1955).
1128 M. Janczewski and K. Kurys, Rocz. Chem., 47, 661 (1973).
1129 W.E. Truce and D.D. Emrick, J. Am. Chem. Soc., 78, 6130 (1956).
1130 D. Taub, C.H. Kuo, H.L. Slates and N.L. Wendler, Tetrahedron, 19, 1 (1963).
1131 H.M. Walborsky, L. Barash, A.E. Young and F.J. Impastato, J. Am. Chem. Soc., 83, 2517 (1961).
1132 H.M. Walborsky and A.E. Young, J. Am. Chem. Soc., 86, 3288 (1964).
1133 J. Nickl, W. Engel, A. Eckenfels, E. Seeger and G. Engelhardt, U. S. Patent 3,655,743 (1972).
1134 H.M. Walborsky, L.E. Allen, H.-J. Traenckner and E.J. Powers, J. Org. Chem., 36, 2937 (1971).
1135 J. Nickl, W. Engel, A. Eckenfels, E. Seeger and G. Engelhardt, U. S. Patent 3,655,743 (1972).
1136 T-Y. Shen, C.P. Dorn,Jr. and J.P. Li, U. S. Patent 3,899,506 (1975).
1137 G. Helmchen and V. Prelog, Helv. Chim. Acta, 55, 2599 (1972).
1138 G.M. Kelkar, N.L. Pholnikar and B.V. Bhide, J. Ind. Chem. Soc., 24, 297 (1947).
1139 H.M. Walborsky and F.M. Hornyak, J. Am. Chem. Soc., 77, 6026 (1955).
1140 I.A. D'yakonov, M.I. Komendantov, F. Gui-siya and G.L. Korichev, Zh. Obsch. Khim., 32, 928 (1962).
1141 M. Janczewski and T. Matynia, Rocz. Chem., 40, 2029 (1966).
1142 J. Nickl, W. Engel, A. Eckenfels, E. Seeger and G. Engelhardt, U. S. Patent 3,655,743 (1972).
1143 S. Rendic, T. Alebic-Kolbah, F. Kajfez and V. Sunjic, Farmaco, Ed. Sci., 35, 51 (1980).
1144 C.L. Bickel, J. Am. Chem. Soc., 60, 927 (1938).
1145 H. Wren and G.L. Miller, J. Chem. Soc., 157 (1935).
1146 F. Bell, J. Chem. Soc., 835 (1934).
1147 G. Nomine and J. Cerede, French Patent 1,205,651 (1960).
1147a G. Nomine and J. Cerede, French Patent 1,205,651 (1960).
1148 Studien über Selen-di-karbonsauren und Diselen-di-karbonsauren (1935) by Professor Arne Fredga, Uppsala, Sweden
1149 Studien über Selen-di-karbonsauren und Diselen-di-karbonsauren (1935) by Professor Arne Fredga, Uppsala, Sweden
1150 W. Stanley, E. McMahon and R. Adams, J. Am. Chem. Soc., 55, 706 (1933).
1151 H.R. Burjorjee, Kamakshi, B.K. Menon and D.H. Peacock, Proc. Ind. Acad. Sci., Sect. 1A, 407 (1934).
1152 H.R. Burjorjee, Kamakshi, B.K. Menon and D.H. Peacock, Proc. Ind. Acad. Sci., Sect. 1A, 407 (1934).
1153 H.R. Burjorjee, Kamakshi, B.K. Menon and D.H. Peacock, Proc. Ind. Acad. Sci., Sect. 1A, 407 (1934).
1154 H.R. Burjorjee, Kamakshi, B.K. Menon and D.H. Peacock, Proc. Ind. Acad. Sci., Sect. 1A, 407 (1934).
1155 A. Brossi, M. Baumann and F. Burkhardt, Helv. Chim. Acta, 45, 1292 (1962).
1156 W. Stühmer and H-H. Frey, Arch. Pharm. (Weinheim), 286, 26 (1953).
1157 W.J. Gottstein and L.C. Cheney, J. Org. Chem., 30, 2072 (1965).
1158 K. Undheim, P. Hamberg and B. Sjöberg, Acta Chem. Scand., 19, 317 (1965).
1159 R. Adams and J.R. Gordon, J. Am. Chem. Soc., 72, 2458 (1950).
1160 R. Adams and A. A. Albert, J. Am. Chem. Soc., 64, 1475 (1942).
1161 E.J. Cragoe,Jr., E.M. Schultz, J.D. Schneeberg, G.E. Stokker, O.W. Woltersdorf,Jr., G.M. Fanelli, Jr., L.S. Watson, J. Med. Chem., 18, 225 (1975).
1162 R. Adams and J.R. Gordon, J. Am. Chem. Soc., 72, 2458 (1950).
1163 W. Bleazard and E. Rothstein, J. Chem. Soc., 3789 (1958).
1164 M. Kawana and S. Emoto, Bull. Chem. Soc. Japan, 39, 910 (1966).
1165 W.A. Bonner and R.A.Grimm, J. Org. Chem., 32, 3022 (1967).
1166 A. Guarneri, S. Burnelli, A. Andreani, I. Busacci, A.M. Barbaro and M. Gaiardi, Farmaco, Ed. Sci., 33, 761 (1978).
1167 A. Guarneri, S. Burnelli, A. Andreani, I. Busacci, A.M. Barbaro and M. Gaiardi, Farmaco, Ed. Sci., 33, 761 (1978).
1168 A. Guarnieri, G. Scapini, S. Burnelli and A. Andreani, Farmaco, Ed. Sci., 32, 324 (1977).
1169 A. Guarnieri, G. Scapini, S. Burnelli and A. Andreani, Farmaco, Ed. Sci., 32, 324 (1977).
1170 A. Guarnieri, S. Burnelli, L. Varoli, A.M. Barbaro and M. Gaidardi, Farmaco, Ed. Sci., 33, 992 (1978).
1171 A. Guarnieri, S. Burnelli, A. Andreani, I. Busacci, A.M. Barbaro and M. Gaiardi, Farmaco, Ed. Sci., 33, 761 (1978).
1172 A. Corbellini and M. Angeletti, Atti. acad. Lincei., 15, 968 (1932).
1173 K. Sisido, K. Kumazawa and H. Nozaki, J. Am. Chem. Soc., 82, 125 (1960).
1174 K. Sisido, K. Kumazawa and H. Nozaki, J. Am. Chem. Soc., 82, 125 (1960).
1175 F.B. Kipping, J. Chem. Soc., 1506 (1933).
1176 M. Okigawa, Y. Kawahara, Y. Fujita, N. Hasaka and N. Kawano, Tetrahedron Lett., 47 (1979).
1177 R. Adams and A. A. Albert, J. Am. Chem. Soc., 64, 1475 (1942).
1178 H.R. Almond,Jr., D.T. Manning and C. Niemann, Biochemistry 1, 243 (1962).
1179 A. Stoll, J. Rutschmann and W. Schlientz, Helv. Chim. Acta, 33, 375 (1950).
1180 J.C. Sheehan and K.R. Henery-Logan, J. Am. Chem. Soc., 81, 3089 (1959).
1181 H. Kuritani, S. Imajo, K. Shingu and M. Nakagawa, Tetrahedron Lett., 1697 (1979).
1182 M. Matell, Arkiv Kemi, 6, 375 (1953).
1183 W.L.F. Armarego and E.E. Turner, J. Chem. Soc., 3668 (1956).
1184 P.F. Juby, W.R. Goodwin, T.W. Hudyma and R.A. Partyka, J. Med. Chem., 15, 1297 (1972).

Reference Number

1184a C. Noguchi, S. Kishimoto, I. Minamida and M. Obayashi, Chem. Pharm. Bull., 22, 529 (1974).
1185 B. Gautheron and J-C. Leblanc, Bull Soc. Chim. Fr., 3629 (1971).
1186 J.L.A. Webb, J. Org. Chem., 18, 1413 (1953).
1187 Y.G. Perron, J.L. Douglas, U. S. Patent 3,696,145 (1972).
1187a P.F. Juby, W.R. Goodwin, T.W. Hudyma and R.A. Partyka, J. Med. Chem., 15, 1297 (1972).
1188 K. Wiesner, L. Poon, I. Jirkovsky and M. Fishman, Can. J. Chem., 47, 433 (1969).
1189 A. Lüttringhaus and G. Eyring, Liebigs Ann. Chem., 604, 111 (1957).
1190 H.E. Stavely and M. Berestecki, J. Am. Chem. Soc., 73, 3448 (1951).
1191 R.L. Clarke and S.J. Daum, J. Med. Chem., 13, 320 (1970).
1192 From the Ph.D. Thesis of R. Becker, Technical University of Hannover, West Germany (1975).
1193 D.F. Ewing and C.Y. Hopkins, Can. J. Chem., 45, 1259 (1967).
1194 J.F. McGhie, W.A. Ross, J.W. Spence, F.J. James and A. Joseph, Chem. Ind. (London), 1074 (1972).
1195 J.F. McGhie, W.A. Ross, J.W. Spence, F.J. James and A. Joseph, Chem. Ind. (London), 463 (1972).
1196 W.H. Mills and C.R. Nodder, J. Chem. Soc., 1407 (1920).
1197 E.S. Wallis and W. W. Moyer, J. Am. Chem. Soc., 55, 2598 (1933).
1198 M.S. Lesslie and E.E. Turner, J. Chem. Soc., 1188 (1931).
1198a F. Bell and G.A. Dinsmore, J. Chem. Soc., 3691 (1950).
1199 S. Hagishita and K. Kuriyama, Tetrahedron, 28, 1435 (1972).
1200 S. Hagishita and K. Kuriyama, Tetrahedron, 28, 1435 (1972).
1201 H.F. Gram, B.J. Berridge,Jr., E.M. Acton and L. Goodman, J. Med. Chem., 6, 85 (1963).
1202 F. Bergel, J.C.E. Burnop and J.A. Stock, J. Chem. Soc., 1223 (1955).
1203 A. Ebnöther, E. Jucker and A. Stoll, Helv. Chim. Acta, 48, 1237 (1965).
1204 S. Hagishita and K. Kuriyama, J. Chem. Soc. Perkin Trans. 2, 59 (1978).
1205 T. Aono, S. Kishimoto, Y. Araki and S. Noguchi, Chem. Pharm. Bull., 26, 1776 (1978).
1206 H.E. Zimmerman, S. S. Hixson and E.F. McBridge, J. Am. Chem. Soc., 92, 2000 (1970).
1207 H.E. Zimmerman, S. S. Hixson and E.F. McBridge, J. Am. Chem. Soc., 92, 2000 (1970).
1208 H.E. Zimmerman, S. S. Hixson and E.F. McBridge, J. Am. Chem. Soc., 92, 2000 (1970).
1209 E.W. Yankee, F.D. Badea, N.E. Howe and D.J. Cram. J. Am. Chem. Soc., 95, 4210 (1973).
1210 H. Leuchs, E. Conrad and H.v. Katinszky, Chem. Ber., 55, 2131 (1922).
1211 J. Paul and K. Schlögl, Monatsh. Chem., 104, 274 (1973).
1212 J. Paul and K. Schlögl, Monatsh. Chem., 104, 274 (1973).
1213 M-J. Luche-Ronteix, S. Bory, M. Dvolaitzky, R. Lett and A. Marquet, Bull. Soc. Chim. Fr., 2564 (1970).
1214 E. Szarvasi, L. Fontaine and C. Letourneur, Bull. Soc. Chim. Fr., 3113 (1964).
1215 T. Aono, S. Kishimoto, Y. Araki and S. Noguchi, Chem. Pharm. Bull. 26, 1776 (1978).
1216 J.H. Brewster and R.T. Prudence, J. Am. Chem. Soc., 95, 1217 (1973).
1217 R.K. Hill and D.A. Cullison, J. Am. Chem. Soc., 95, 1229 (1973).
1218 J. Ackrell, Y. Antonio, F. Franco, R. Landeros, A. Leon, J.M. Muchowski, M.L. Maddox, P.H. Nelson, W.H. Rooks, A.P. Roszkowski and M.B. Wallach, J. Med. Chem., 21, 1035 (1978).
1219 H. Keller, C. Krieger, E. Langer and H. Lehner, Liebigs Ann. Chem., 1296 (1977).
1220 T. Kametani, K. Kigasawa, M. Huragi, H. Ishimaru, S. Haga and K. Shirayama, J. Heterocyclic Chem., 15, 369 (1978).
1221 U. S. Patent 3,714,242 (1973).
1222 H.M. Walborsky, L. Barash, A.E. Young and F.J. Impastato, J. Am. Chem. Soc., 83, 2517 (1961).
1223 D.T. Hefelfinger and D.J. Cram, J. Am. Chem. Soc., 93, 4767 (1971).
1223a B. Kainradl, E. Langer, H. Lehner and K. Schlögl, Liebigs Ann. Chem., 766, 16 (1972).
1224 H. Falk, P. Reich-Rohrwig and K. Schlögl, Tetrahedron, 26, 511 (1970).
1225 M.H. Delton and D.J. Cram, J. Am. Chem. Soc., 92, 7623 (1970).
1226 M. Janczewski and E. Pawlowska, Rocz. Chem., 47, 665 (1973).
1227 M. Janczewski and T. Matynia, Rocz. Chem., 40, 2029 (1966).
1228 H.M. Walborsky, L.E. Allen, H.-J. Traenckner and E.J. Powers, J. Org. Chem., 36, 2937 (1971).
1229 A. Robertson, W.B. Whalley and J. Yates, J. Chem. Soc., 3117 (1950).
1230 British Patent 1,209,669.
1231 M.S. Leslie and U.J.H. Mayer, J. Chem. Soc., 1401 (1962).
1232 T. Petrzilka and Ch. Fehr, Helv. Chim. Acta, 56, 1218 (1973).
1233 T.J. Schwan and H.A. Burch, J. Pharm. Sci., 61, 1506 (1972).
1234 R. Adams and J.R. Gordon, J. Am. Chem. Soc., 72, 2458 (1950).
1236 E.J. Cragoe,Jr., E.M. Schultz, J.D. Schneeberg, G.E. Stokker, O.W. Woltersdorf, Jr., G.M. Fanelli,Jr., L.S. Watson, J. Med. Chem., 18, 225 (1975).
1237 R. Adams and M.J. Gortatowski, J. Am. Chem. Soc., 79, 5525 (1957).
1238 R. Adams and M.J. Gortatowski, J. Am. Chem. Soc., 79, 5525 (1957).
1239 M.S. Leslie and U.J.H. Mayer, J. Chem. Soc., 611 (1961).
1240 J.H. Dopper, B. Greijdanas and H. Wynberg, J. Am. Chem. Soc., 97, 216 (1975).
1241 A. Guarnieri, S. Burnelli, L. Varoli, A.M. Barbaro and M. Gaiardi, Farmaco, Ed. Sci., 33, 992 (1978).
1242 A. Lüttringhaus and H. Gralheer, Liebigs Ann. Chem., 550, 67 (1942).
1243 T. Kamiya, M. Hashimoto, O. Nakaguchi and T. Oku, Tetrahedron, 35, 323 (1979).
1244 H. Plieninger and J. Ruppert, Liebigs Ann. Chem., 736, 43 (1970).
1245 A.T. Blomquist, R.E. Stahl, Y.C. Meinwald and B.H. Smith, J. Org. Chem., 26, 1687 (1961).
1245a H. Eberhardt and K. Schlögl, Liebigs Ann. Chem., 760, 157 (1972).
1246 L.J. Chinn and H.L. Dryden, Jr., J. Org. Chem., 26, 3904 (1961).
1247 H.S. Aaron and C.P. Ferguson, J. Org. Chem., 33, 684 (1968).
1248 H.S. Aaron and C.P. Ferguson, J. Org. Chem., 33, 684 (1968).
1249 K. Mislow and H.D. Perlmutter, J. Am. Chem. Soc., 84, 3591 (1962).
1250 M-J. Brienne and J. Jacques, Bull. Soc. Chim. Fr., 190 (1973).

Reference
Number

1251 M-J. Brienne and J. Jacques, Bull. Soc. Chim. Fr., 190 (1973).
1252 H. Tatemitsu, F. Ogura and M. Nakagawa, Bull. Chem. Soc. Japan, 46, 915 (1973).
1253 S. Hagishita and K. Kuriyama, J. Chem. Soc. Perkin 2, 59 (1978).
1254 A.G. Brook, J. Am. Chem. Soc., 85, 3051 (1963).
1255 J.P. Dunn, D.M. Green, P.H. Nelson, W.H. Rooks,II, A. Tomolonis, and K.G. Untch, J. Med. Chem., 20, 1557 (1977).
1256 M-J. Brienne and J. Jacques, Bull. Soc. Chim. Fr., 190 (1973).
1256a S. Hagishita and K. Kuriyama, Tetrahedron, 28, 1435 (1972).
1257 S. Hagishita and K. Kuriyama, Tetrahedron, 28, 1435 (1972).
1258 Gj.Stefanovic, Lj.Lorenc, R.I. Mamuzic and M.Lj.Mihailovic,Tetrahedron 6, 304 (1959).
1259 R. Kuhn and F. Zumstein, Chem. Ber., 58, 1429 (1925).
1260 T. Aono, S. Kishimoto, Y. Araki and S. Noguchi, Chem. Pharm. Bull., 26, 1776 (1978).
1261 M-J. Luche-Ronteix, S. Bory, M. Dvolaitzky, R. Lett and A. Marquet, Bull. Soc. Chim. Fr., 2564 (1970).
1262 B.D. West and K.P. Link, J. Heterocyclic Chem., 2, 93 (1965).
1263 T. Sato, S. Akabori, M. Kainosho and K. Hata, Bull. Chem. Soc. Japan, 41, 218 (1968).
1264 R. Stoermer, Chem. Ber., 56, 1683 (1923).
1265 R. Stoermer, Chem. Ber., 56, 1683 (1923).
1266 R. Stoermer and F. Bacher, Chem. Ber., 55, 1874 (1922).
1267 R. Stoermer and F. Bacher, Chem. Ber., 55, 1860 (1922).
1268 R. Stoermer and F. Scholtz, Chem. Ber., 54, 85 (1921).
1269 L.V. Dvorken, R.B. Smyth and K. Mislow, J. Am. Chem. Soc., 80, 486 (1958).
1270 L.V. Dvorken, R.B. Smyth and K. Mislow, J. Am. Chem. Soc., 80, 486 (1958).
1271 R.K. Summerbell, B.S. Sokolski, J.P. Bays, D.J. Godfrey and A.S. Hussey, J. Org. Chem., 32, 946 (1967).
1272 F.M. Dean. P. Halewood, S. Mongkolsuk, A. Robertson and W.B. Whalley, J. Chem. Soc., 1250 (1953).
1273 F.M. Dean, P. Halewood, S. Mongkolsuk, A. Robertson and W.B. Whalley, J. Chem. Soc., 1250 (1953).
1274 E.J. Cragoe,Jr., A.M. Pietruszkiewicz and C.M. Robb, J. Org. Chem., 23, 971 (1958).
1275 W. Klötzer, Monatsh. Chem., 87, 346 (1956).
1276 D.R. Galpin, E.M. Kandeel and A.R. Martin, J. Pharm. Sci., 67, 1367 (1978).
1277 D.R. Galpin, E.M. Kandeel and A.R. Martin, J. Pharm. Sci., 67, 1367 (1978).
1278 M. Janczewski and T. Matynia, Rocz. Chem., 40, 2029 (1966).
1279 K. Mislow, S. Hyden and H. Schaefer, J. Am. Chem. Soc., 84, 1449 (1962).
1280 R. Andrisano, A.S. Angeloni, P. De Maria and M. Tramontini, J. Chem. Soc., C, 2307 (1967).
1281 M.P. Oommen and I. Vogel, J. Chem. Soc., 2148 (1930).
1282 R. Buchan and M.B. Watson, J. Chem. Soc., 2465 (1968).
1283 H.E. Zimmerman and D.S. Crumrine, J. Am. Chem. Soc., 94, 498 (1972).
1284 S. Gronowitz and J.E. Skramstead, Arkiv Kemi, 28, 115 (1967).
1285 M. Okigawa, Y. Kawahara, Y. Fujita, N. Hasaka and N. Kawano, Tetrahedron Lett., 47 (1979).
1286 L.A. Petrova, N.N. Bel'tsova, G.A. Tsvetkova and A.I. Klimov, Zh. Obshch. Khim., 41, 2276 (1971).
1287 L.A. Petrova, N.J. Bel'tsova, G.A. Tsvetkova and A.I. Klimov, Zh. Obshch. Khim., 41, 2276 (1971).
1288 A. Guarneri, S. Burnelli, L. Varoli, A.M. Barbaro and M. Gaiardi, Farmaco, Ed. Sci., 33, 992 (1978).
1289 A. Guarneri, S. Burnelli, L. Varoli, A.M. Barbaro and M. Gaiardi, Farmaco, Ed. Sci., 33, 992 (1978).
1290 D.J. Collins and J.J. Hobbs, Aust. J. Chem., 23, 1605 (1970).
1291 R. Adams and J.S. Dix, J. Am. Chem. Soc., 80, 4579 (1958).
1292 J. Schawartz, German Patent 1,154,805 (1963).
1293 J. Jacques and A. Horeau, Bull. Soc. Chim. Fr., 301 (1949).
1294 S. Gronowitz and J.E. Skramstad, Arkiv Kemi, 28, 115 (1967).
1295 G.I. Kiprianov and L.M. Kutsenko, Zh. Obsch. Khim., 34, 3928 (1964).
1296 M. Nakazaki, K. Yamamoto and M. Ito, Chem. Commun., 433 (1972).
1297 M. Nakazaki, K. Yamamoto, M. Ito and S. Tanaka, J. Org. Chem., 42, 3468 (1977).
1298 K.-A. Karlsson and I. Pascher, Chem. Phys. Lipids, 12, 65 (1974).
1299 J.F. McGhie, W.A. Ross, J.W. Spence, F.J. James and A. Joseph, Chem. Ind. (London), 463 (1972).
1300 W.I. Patterson and R. Adams, J. Am. Chem. Soc., 55, 1069 (1933).
1301 C.R. Wheeler and W.F. Trager, J. Med. Chem., 22, 1122 (1979).
1302 R. Adams and R.H. Mattson, J. Am. Chem. Soc., 76, 4925 (1954).
1303 R. Adams and R.H. Mattson, J. Am. Chem. Soc., 76, 4925 (1954).
1304 R. Adams and K.V.Y. Sundstrom, J. Am. Chem. Soc., 76, 5474 (1954).
1305 K. Sisido, K. Kumazawa and H. Nozaki, J. Am. Chem. Soc., 82, 125 (1960).
1306 B.D. West, S. Preis, C.H. Schroeder and K.P. Link, J. Am. Chem. Soc., 83, 2676 (1961).
1307 H. Falk, C. Krasna and K. Schlögl, Monatsh. Chem., 100, 254 (1969).
1308 M. Shibasaki, M. Matsubara, J. Ohnogi and K. Shibata, U. S. Patent 3,775,413 (1973).
1309 M.S. Newman and A.S. Hussey, J. Am. Chem. Soc., 69, 3023 (1947).
1310 B.D. West, S. Preis, C.H. Schroeder and K.P. Link, J. Am. Chem. Soc., 83, 2676 (1961).
1311 E.J. Cragoe,Jr. and A.M. Pietruszkiewicz, J. Org. Chem., 22, 1338 (1957).
1312 E.J. Cragoe,Jr. and A.M. Pietruszkiewicz, J. Org. Chem., 22, 1338 (1957).
1313 E.J. Cragoe, Jr. and A.M. Pietruszkiewicz, J. Org. Chem., 22, 1338 (1957).
1314 H.E. Zimmerman, J.D. Robbins, R.D. McKelvey, C.J. Samuel and L.R. Sousa, J. Am. Chem. Soc., 96, 4630 (1974).
1315 H.E. Zimmerman, J.D. Robbins, R.D. McKelvey, C.J. Samuel and L.R. Sousa, J. Am. Chem. Soc., 96, 4630 (1974).
1316 H.E. Zimmerman, J.D. Robbins, R.D. McKelvey, C.J. Samuel and L.R. Sousa, J. Am. Chem. Soc., 96, 4630 (1974).

Reference Number

1317 M. Janczewski and E. Pawlowska, Rocz. Chem., 47, 665 (1973).
1318 R. Rometsch and K. Miescher, Helv. Chim. Acta, 29, 1231 (1946).
1319 D.J. Collins and J.J. Hobbs, Aust. J. Chem., 23, 1605 (1970).
1320 R. Adams and A. Ferretti, J. Am. Chem. Soc., 83, 2559 (1961).
1321 G. Helmchen and V. Prelog, Helv. Chim. Acta, 55, 2612 (1972).
1322 M. Farina and G. Audisio, Tetrahedron, 26, 1839 (1970).
1323 S. Murahashi, Sci. Papers Inst. Phys. Chem. Research (Tokyo), 17, 297 (1932).
1324 W. Tochtermann and K. Stecher, Tetrahedron Lett., 3847 (1967).
1325 S. Murahashi, Sci. Papers Inst. Phys. Chem. Research (Tokyo), 17, 297 (1932).
1326 M. Janczewski and L. Bilczuk, Rocz. Chem., 39, 1927 (1965).
1327 J.E. Batterbee, R.S. Burden, L. Crombie and D.A. Whiting, J. Chem. Soc. (C), 2470 (1969).
1328 R.B. Woodward, M.P. Cava, W.D. Ollis, A. Hunger, H.U. Daeniker and K. Schenker, Tetrahedron, 19, 247 (1963).
1329 J. Paul and K. Schlögl, Monatsh. Chem., 104, 274 (1973).
1330 H. Neudeck and K. Schlögl, Chem. Ber., 110, 2624 (1977).
1331 M-J. Brienne and J. Jacques, Bull. Soc. Chim. Fr., 190 (1973).
1332 S. Hagishita and K. Kuriyama, Tetrahedron, 28, 1435 (1972).
1333 J.H. Hunt, J. Chem. Soc., 1926 (1957).
1334 D.W. Hill and R. Adams, J. Am. Chem. Soc., 53, 3453 (1931).
1335 British Patent 957,900 (1964).
1336 R. Stoermer and H. Starck, Chem. Ber., 70, 479 (1937).
1337 H. Falk, P. Reich-Rohrwig and K. Schlögl, Tetrahedron, 26, 511 (1970).
1338 D.J. Cram, W.J. Wechter and R.W. Kierstead, J. Am. Chem. Soc., 80, 3126 (1958).
1339 R.L. Dreibelbis, H.N. Khatri and H.M. Walborsky, J. Org. Chem., 40, 2074 (1975).
1340 A.L. Wilds and R.E. Sutton, J. Org. Chem., 16, 1371 (1951).
1341 R.D. Haworth and F.H. Slinger, J. Chem. Soc., 1098 (1940).
1342 O.T. Schmidt and K. Demmler, Liebigs Ann. Chem., 576, 85 (1952).
1343 E. Schleusener and C.H. Eugster, Helv. Chim. Acta, 55, 986 (1972).
1344 R. Adams and A. Ferretti, J. Am. Chem. Soc., 83, 2559 (1961).
1345 R. Adams and A. Ferretti, J. Am. Chem. Soc., 83, 2559 (1961).
1346 A.E. Knauf and R. Adams, J. Am. Chem. Soc., 55, 4704 (1933).
1347 D.F. Ewing and C.Y. Hopkins, Can. J. Chem., 45, 1259 (1967).
1348 Y. Sakata, F. Ogura and M. Nakagawa, Bull. Chem. Soc. Japan, 46, 611 (1973).
1349 M. Hashimoto, Y. Shimizu, F. Ogura and M. Nakagawa, Bull. Chem. Soc. Japan, 47, 1761 (1974).
1350 M. Hashimoto, Y. Shimizu, F. Ogura and M. Nakagawa, Bull. Chem. Soc. Japan, 47, 1761 (1974).
1351 Y. Sakata, F. Ogura and M. Nakagawa, Bull. Chem. Soc. Japan, 46, 611 (1973).
1352 J. Meisenheimer and O. Beisswenger, Chem. Ber., 65, 32 (1932).
1353 W. Tochtermann, H. Kuppers and C. Franke, Chem. Ber., 101, 3808 (1968).
1354 M.S. Newman and W.B. Wheatley, J. Am. Chem. Soc., 70, 1913 (1948).
1355 M.S. Leslie and U.J.H. Mayer, J. Chem. Soc., 1401 (1962).
1356 G. Traverso, Farmaco, Ed. Sci., 16, 457 (1961).
1357 British Patent 957,900 (1964).
1358 British Patent 957,900 (1964).
1359 K.V. Narayanan, R. Selvarajan and S. Swaminathan, J. Chem. Soc. (C), 540 (1968).
1360 S.D. Mikhno, N.S. Kulachkina and V.M. Berezovskii, Zhur. Org. Khim., 6, 81 (1970).
1361 M.S. Leslie and U.J.H. Mayer, J. Chem. Soc., 611 (1961).
1362 R. Adams and J.S. Dix, J. Am. Chem. Soc., 80, 4579 (1958).
1363 T.Y. Jen, G.A. Hughes and H. Smith, J. Am. Chem. Soc., 89, 4551 (1967).
1364 M Kuritani, Y. Sakata, F. Ogura and M. Nakagawa, Bull. Chem. Soc. Japan, 46, 605 (1975).
1365 D.M. Hall and E.E. Turner, J. Chem. Soc., 1242 (1955).
1365a R. Kuhn and O. Albrecht, Liebigs Ann. Chem., 465, 282 (1928).
1366 W.M. Stanley, J. Am. Chem. Soc., 53, 3104 (1931).
1366a A. Corbellini, Atti. Acad. Lincei, 13, 702 (1931).
1367 F. Bell and W.H.D. Morgan, J. Chem. Soc., 1716 (1954).
1368 K. Weil and W. Kuhn, Helv. Chim. Acta, 27, 1648 (1944).
1369 M.M. Harris, R.Z. Mazengo and A.S. Cooke, J. Chem. Soc. (C), 2575 (1967).
1370 Y. Sakata, F. Ogura and M. Nakagawa, Bull. Chem. Soc. Japan, 46, 611 (1973).
1371 Y. Sakata, F. Ogura and M. Nakagawa, Bull. Chem. Soc. Japan, 46, 611 (1973).
1372 H. Goudet, Helv. Chim. Acta, 14, 379 (1931).
1373 A. McKenzie and N. Walker, J. Chem. Soc., 646 (1928).
1374 M.S. Newman and R.M. Wise, J. Am. Chem. Soc., 78, 450 (1956).
1375 S. Hagishita and K. Kuriyama, Tetrahedron, 28, 1435 (1972).
1376 S. Hagishita and K. Kuriyama, Tetrahedron, 28, 1435 (1972).
1377 H. Wren and R.E. Burrows, J. Chem. Soc., 125, 1934 (1924).
1378 S.M. Wong, H.P. Fischer and D.J. Cram, J. Am. Chem. Soc., 94, 2235 (1971).
1379 F.B. Kipping, J. Chem. Soc., 18 (1935).
1380 W.J. Gensler, C.M. Samour, S-Y. Wang and F. Johnson, J. Am. Chem. Soc., 82, 1714 (1960).
1381 C. Chang and R. Adams, J. Am. Chem. Soc., 56, 2089 (1934).
1382 R. Adams and N. Kornblum, J. Am. Chem. Soc., 63, 188 (1941).
1383 M.S. Leslie and U.J.H. Mayer, J. Chem. Soc., 611 (1961).
1384 N.Cohen, J.W. Scott, F.T. Bizzaro, R.J. Lopresti, W.F. Eichel and G. Saucy, Helv. Chim. Acta, 61, 837 (1978).
1385 M. Nakatani, T. Kamikawa, T. Hase and T. Kubota, Bull. Chem. Soc. Japan, 50, 945 (1977).
1386 L.R. Row, P. Satyanarayana and G.S.R. Subba Rao, Tetrahedron, 23, 1915 (1967).
1387 J. DeWit and H. Wynberg, Tetrahedron, 28, 4617 (1972).
1388 H. Wren and R.E. Burrows, J. Chem. Soc., 125, 1934 (1924).
1389 M.-J. Brienne, C. Ouannes and J. Jacques, Bull. Soc. Chim. Fr., 613 (1967).
1390 D.F. Dickel, G. DeStevens, U. S. Patent 3,786,085 (1974).
1391 E. Schreier, Helv. Chim. Acta, 46, 75 (1963).

Reference
Number

1392 W.J. Cole, C.H. Gray and D.C. Nicholson, J. Chem. Soc., 4085 (1965).
1393 M. Crawford, R.A.M. MacKinnon and V.R. Supanekar, J. Chem. Soc., 2807 (1959).
1394 J. Meisenheimer and O. Beissenwenger, Chem. Ber., 65, 32 (1932).
1395 H.E. Harris, M.M. Harris, R.Z. Mazengo and S. Singh, J. Chem. Soc. Perkin 2, 1059 (1974).
1396 R. Adams and K.B. Brower, J. Am. Chem. Soc., 78, 663 (1956).
1397 R. Adams and K.B. Brower, J. Am. Chem. Soc., 78, 663 (1956).
1398 R. Adams and N. Kornblum, J. Am. Chem. Soc., 63, 188 (1941).
1399 D. Gust, G.H. Senkler,Jr. and K. Mislow, Chem. Comm., 1345 (1972).
1400 A. Sonoda, F. Ogura and M. Nakagawa, Bull. Chem. Soc. Japan, 35, 853 (1961).
1401 R. Adams and K.B. Brower, J. Am. Chem. Soc., 78, 663 (1956).
1402 H.J. Backer and H.G. Kemper, Rec. Trav. Chim., 57, 1249 (1938).
1403 R. Adams and J.J. Tjepkema, J. Am. Chem. Soc., 70, 4204 (1948).
1404 R. Adams and K.R. Brower, J. Am. Chem. Soc., 78, 663 (1956).
1405 R. Adams and K.B. Brower, J. Am. Chem. Soc., 78, 663 (1956).
1406 M. Gerecke, J.-P. Zimmermann and W. Aschwanden, Helv. Chim. Acta, 53, 991 (1970).
1407 J. Schmidlin, G. Anner, J.-R. Billeter, K. Heusler, H. Ueberwasser, P. Wieland and A. Wettstein, Helv. Chim. Acta, 40, 2291 (1957).
1408 E.H Woodruff and R. Adams, J. Am. Chem. Soc., 54, 1977 (1932).
1409 A. Corbellini and C. Pizzi, Atti Acad. Lincei, 15, 287 (1932).
1410 H. Wren and E. Wright, J. Chem. Soc., 136 (1929).
1411 H. Wren and E. Wright, J. Chem. Soc., 136 (1929).
1412 F. Bell, J. Chem. Soc., 1527 (1952).
1412a D.M. Hall and J.M. Insole, J. Chem. Soc., 2326 (1964).
1413 E.P. Kohler, J.T. Walker, M. Tishler, J. Am. Chem. Soc., 57, 1743 (1935).
1414 F. Bell and D.H. Waring, J. Chem. Soc., 2689 (1949).
1415 M. Nakamura, M. Oki and H. Nakanishi, Tetrahedron, 30, 543 (1974).
1416 R. Kuhn and O. Albrecht, Liebigs Ann. Chem. 464, 91 (1928).
1417 F. Bell and W.H.D. Morgan, J. Chem. Soc., 1963 (1950).
1418 F. Bell and W.H.D. Morgan, J. Chem. Soc., 1963 (1950).
1419 F. Bell and D.H. Waring, J. Chem. Soc., 1579 (1949).
1419a K. Lauer, R. Oda and M. Miyawaki, J. Prakt. Chem., 148, 310 (1937).
1420 F. Bell and D.H. Waring, J. Chem. Soc., 2689 (1949).
1421 S. Goldschmidt, R. Riedle and A. Reichardt, Liebigs Ann. Chem., 604, 121 (1957).
1422 G. Haas and V. Prelog, Helv. Chim. Acta, 52, 1202 (1969).
1423 G. Haas and V. Prelog, Helv. Chim. Acta, 52, 1202 (1969).
1424 O.T. Schmidt and K. Demmler, Liebigs Ann. Chem., 586, 179 (1954).

ADDENDUM

Reference
Number

1425 From the Ph.D. Dissertation of Dr. Gunther Burger, University of Karlsruhe, West Germany (1979).
1426 J.W.E. Glattfield and J.W. Chittum, J. Am. Chem. Soc., 55, 3663 (1933).
1427 J.W.E. Glattfield and L.R. Forbich, J. Am. Chem. Soc., 56, 1209 (1934).
1428 T. Inui and T. Kaneko, Nippon Kagaku Zasshi, 82, 1078 (1961).
1429 T. Inui and T. Kaneko, Nippon Kagaku Zasshi, 82, 1078 (1961).
1430 B. Ringdahl and J.C. Craig, Acta Chem. Scand., B34, 731 (1980).
1431 J.E. Baldwin, L.I. Kruse and J-K. Cha, J. Am. Chem. Soc., 103, 942 (1981).
1432 P. Loew and W.S. Johnson, J. Am. Chem. Soc., 93, 3765 (1971).
1433 J.C. Clark and J. Elks, U.S. Patent 3,976,680 (1976).
1434 H. Kawa and N. Ishikawa, Chemistry Lett., 843 (1980).
1435 C.W. Perry and S. Teitel, U.S. Patent 3,965,129 (1976).
1436 J.C. Clark and J. Elks, U. S. Patent 3,976,680 (1976).
1437 R.W. Lang and H-J. Hansen, Helv. Chim. Acta, 62, 1025 (1979).
1438 J. Knabe and N. Franz, Arch. Pharm., 309, 173 (1976).
1439 J. Knabe and J. Plisch, Tetrahedron Lett., 745 (1973).
1440 S.M. Miller, U.S. Patent 4,161,600 (1979).
1441 W. Marki, M. Oppliger, P. Thanei and R. Schwyzer, Hlev. Chim. Acta, 60, 798 (1977).
1442 J.M. Walbrick, J.W. Wilson, Jr. and W.M. Jones, J. Am. Chem. Soc., 90, 2895 (1968).
1443 S. Bauer and S. Orszagh, Czech. Patent 88,066 (1958).
1444 J.P. Greenstein, S.M. Birnbaum and M.C. Otey, J. Am. Chem. Soc., 75, 1994 (1953).
1445 E.J. Corey and J. Mann, J. Am. Chem. Soc., 95, 6832 (1973).
1446 A. Numata, T. Suzuki, K. Ohno and S. Uyeo, Yakugaku Zasshi, 88, 1298 (1968).
1447 K. Mori and H. Ueda, Tetrahedron Lett., 22, 461 (1981).
1448 K. Mori and H. Iwasawa, Tetrahedron, 36, 2209 (1980).
1449 A.L. Paloma, Afinidad, 28, 141 (1971).
1450 J.C. Clark and J. Elks, U. S. Patent 3,976,680 (1976).
1451 P.A. Grieco, W. Owens, C-L.J. Wang, E. Williams, W. Schillinger, K. Hirotsu and J. Clardy, J. Med. Chem., 23, 1072 (1980).
1452 W.H.J. Boesten, U.S. Patent 3,971,700 (1976).
1453 I.T. Barnish, P.E. Cross, J.C. Danilewicz, R.P. Dickinson, and D.A. Stopher, J. Med. Chem., 24, 399 (1981).
1454 P.E. Burt, M. Elliot, A.W. Farnham, N.F. Janes, P.H. Needham and D.A. Pulman, Pestic. Sci., 5, 791 (1974).
1455 P.E. Burt, M. Elliot, A.W. Farnham, N.F. Janes, P.H. Needham and D.A. Pulman, Pestic. Sci., 5, 791 (1974).
1456 T. Leigh, European Patent 10874 (1979).
1457 H. King and A.D. Palmer, J. Chem. Soc., 121, 2577 (1922).
1457a H. King and A.D. Palmer, J. Chem. Soc., 121, 2577 (1922).
1457b H. King and A.D. Palmer, J. Chem. Soc., 121, 2577 (1922).
1458 T. Araga, T. Saito and H. Kotake, Nippon Kagaku Zasshi, 86, 111 (1965).
1459 German Patent 2749203 (1977).

Reference Number

1460 J.C. Clark and J. Elks, U. S. Patent 3,976,680 (1976).
1461 I.T. Barnish, P.E. Cross, J.C. Danilewicz, R.P. Dickinson and D.A. Stopher, J. Med. Chem., 24, 399 (1981).
1462 B. Hegedus and A. Krasso, U. S. Patent 3920728 (1975).
1463 B. Hegedus and A. Krasso, U. S. Patent 3920728 (1975).
1464 J. Knabe and N. Franz, Arch. Pharm. 309, 173 (1976).
1465 J. Knabe and N. Franz, Arch. Pharm. 309, 173 (1976).
1466 W.M. Duffin and S. Wilkinson, British Patent 585,413 (1947).
1467 I. Iwai and Y. Kura, Yakugaku Zasshi, 80, 1193 (1960).
1468 C.F. Huebner, U. S. Patent 3759927 (1973).
1469 E.H.W. Bohme, R.E. Bambury, R.J. Baumann, R.C. Erickson, B.L. Harrison, P.F. Hoffman, F.J. McCarty, R.A. Schnettler, M.J. Vaal, and D.L. Wenstrup, J. Med. Chem., 23, 405 (1980).
1470 T-T. Chu and C.S. Marvel, J. Am. Chem. Soc., 55, 2841 (1933).
1471 D. Seyferth and Y.M. Cheng, J. Am. Chem. Soc., 95, 6763 (1973).
1472 E. Takagi, Yakugaku Zasshi, 71, 658 (1951).
1473 Procedure kindly supplied by Dr. Kiyoshi Sakai, Sankyo Company, Ltd., Tokyo, Japan.
1474 D.J. Bennett, G.R. Ramage and J.C. Simonsen, J. Chem. Soc., 418 (1940).
1475 H. Yoshioka, A. Higo, H. Hirai and N. Itaya, U.S. Patent 3922286 (1975).
1476 E.W. Yankee and D.J. Cram, J. Am. Chem. Soc., 92, 6329 (1970).
1477 J.P.M. Houbiers, European Patent Appl. 81200234.3 (1981).
1477a J.P.M. Houbiers, European Patent Appl. 8833 (1979).
1478 G. Losse, Chem. Ber., 87, 1279 (1954).
1479 R. Bucourt, M. Vignau and J. Raynal, French Patent 1496817 (1967).
1480 T. Tohyama and M. Onda, Yakugaku Zasshi, 84, 372 (1964).
1481 M. Bianchi, F. Barzaghi and F. Bonacina, Farmaco, Ed. Sci., 21, 121 (1966).
1482 A.H. Beckett, G. Kirk and R. Thomas, J. Chem. Soc., 1386 (1962).
1483 H.C. Winter, J. Am. Chem. Soc., 62, 3266 (1940).
1484 P. Karrer and H. Schneider, Helv. Chim. Acta, 13, 1281 (1930).
1485 J. Rudinger and H. Czurbova, Coll. Czech. Chem. Comm., 19, 386 (1954).
1486 Procedure obtained through the kindness of Dr. M.G. Groen, Organon International BV Oss, Holland.
1487 C.G. Overberger and D.A. Labianca, J. Org. Chem., 35, 1762 (1970).
1488 R. Adams and J.B. Hale, J. Am. Chem. Soc., 61, 2825 (1939).
1489 M. Nakazaki and K. Naemura, J. Org. Chem., 46, 106 (1981).
1490 N. Bodor, R. Woods, C. Raper, P. Kearney and J.J. Kaminski, J. Med. Chem., 23, 474 (1980).
1491 H. Nakamoto, M. Aburatani and M. Inagaki, J. Med. Chem., 14, 1021 (1971).
1492 D.G. Musson, D. Karashima, H. Rubiero, L.L. Melmon, A. Cheng and N. Castagnoli, Jr., J. Med. Chem., 23, 1318 (1980).
1493 G.H. Christie and J. Kenner, J. Chem. Soc., 123, 779 (1923).
1493a R. Kuhn and O. Albrecht, Liebigs Ann., 458, 221 (1927).
1493b D.L. Hammick, E.H. Reynolds and G. Sixsmith, J. Chem. Soc., 98 (1939).
1494 N.W. Searle and R. Adams, J. Am. Chem. Soc., 55, 1649 (1933).
1495 E. Felder, D. Pitré and H. Zutter, U.K. Pat. Appl. GB 2025968A (1980).
1496 J. Goto, M. Hasegawa, S. Nakamura, K. Shimada and T. Nambara, Chem. Pharm. Bull., 25, 847 (1977).
1497 W.T. Hoeve and H. Wynberg, J. Org. Chem., 45, 2754 (1980).
1498 H.J. Nestler and H. Bieringer, Z. Naturforsch. 35b, 366 (1980).
1499 H. Nahm and W. Siedel, Chem. Ber., 96, 1 (1963).
1500 K. Yamashita, E. Nagano and T. Oritani, Agric. Biol. Chem., 44, 1441 (1980).
1501 E.C. Kleiderer and R. Adams, J. Am. Chem. Soc., 55, 716 (1933).
1502 N. Kawano, M. Okigawa, N. Hasaka, I. Kouno, Y. Kawahara and Y. Fujita, J. Org. Chem., 46, 389 (1981).
1503 N. Blazevic, M. Zinic, T. Kovac, V. Sunjic and F. Kajfez, Acta Pharm. Jugoslav., 25, 155 (1975).
1504 G. Comisso, M. Mihalic, F. Kajfez and V. Sunjic, Gazz. Chim. Ital., 110, 123 (1980).
1505 N. Kawano, M. Okigawa, N. Hasaka, I. Kouno, Y. Kawahara and Y. Fujita, J. Org. Chem., 46, 389 (1981).
1506 E. Wyrzykiewicz, M. Kielczewski and J. Bartz, Zeszyty Nauk Uniw. Poznaniu Mat., Fiz., Chem. 29 (1965); Chem. Ab. 65, 3781^{c} (1966).
1507 N. Kawano, M. Okigawa, N. Hasaka, I. Kouno, Y. Kawahara and Y. Fujita, J. Org. Chem., 46, 389 (1981).
1508 W.J. Gensler and H.N. Schlein, J. Am. Chem. Soc., 78, 169 (1956).
1509 V. Boekelheide and E. Sturm, J. Am. Chem. Soc., 91, 902 (1969).
1510 T-T. Chu and C.S. Marvel, J. Am. Chem. Soc., 55, 2841 (1933).
1511 T-T. Chu and C.S. Marvel, J. Am. Chem. Soc., 55, 2841 (1933).
1512 W. Marki, M. Oppliger, P. Thanei and R. Schwyzer, Helv. Chim. Acta, 60, 798 (1977).
1512a N.T. Boggs,3rd., B. Goldsmith, R.E. Gawley, K.A. Koehler and R.G. Hiskey, J. Org. Chem., 44, 2262 (1979).
1513 E.J. Corey and J. Moinet, J. Am. Chem. Soc., 95, 6831 (1973).
1514 C. Koukotas and L.H. Schwartz, J. Chem. Soc. Chem. Comm., 1400 (1969).